GRIGNARD REACTIONS *of* NONMETALLIC SUBSTANCES

M. S. KHARASCH
Professor of Chemistry
The University of Chicago

OTTO REINMUTH
Research Associate
The University of Chicago

CONSTABLE AND COMPANY, LTD.
10 ORANGE STREET, LONDON W.C.2

PRINTED IN THE UNITED STATES OF AMERICA

Preface

It is reported that Sir William Osler used to open certain of his lectures to medical classes at The Johns Hopkins with the statement that he who knows syphilis knows medicine, for its symptoms can simulate those of any disease in the catalog. With but little more poetic license than the good doctor permitted himself, it might be said that he who knows and understands the Grignard reactions has a fair grasp of organic chemistry, for most fundamental processes have prototypes or analogs in phenomena observable in Grignard systems.

In view of the extent and variety of the subject matter, none but the most arrogantly self-complacent of authors could contemplate the task of summarizing, critically evaluating, and to some extent correlating the labors of a half-century except in a spirit of deep humility and with some sense of inadequacy. In extenuation of our own temerity we (the present authors) plead an intense interest in the subject matter, a fair acquaintance with the literature relating to it, considerable contemplation and some experimental study of its problems, a conviction that the general need of a work of the kind here presented has been great and continues to grow, and a belief that no one better qualified for the task seems at all likely to undertake it.

Early in our exploratory compilations of data and attempts at organization of subject matter we discovered that no exhaustive treatise (even if it were achievable with the facilities at our command) could be confined to a one-volume work producible at a cost within the means of the average prospective individual purchaser. Reluctantly but resolutely, therefore, we excluded from our plans consideration of the reactions of Grignard reagents with other metallic compounds, as well as consideration of the Grignard reagents other than those which behave as though the magnesium were directly linked to carbon.

As the work progressed, the necessity for further selection within the field thus delimited became apparent. Historical resumés have been relentlessly condensed; hypotheses that seem to have had no survival value have received no more than bare mention, and have in some cases been ignored altogether. Reports that we regard as trivial or grossly inaccurate have been relegated to merciful obscurity, and mention of articles, however interesting or significant, that did not fit into the outline finally adopted has been omitted.

In a work of this scope it is scarcely conceivable that there have been no errors of judgment in evaluation of periodical reports; probably there have been omissions by reason of oversight. Regarding these we solicit the reader's indulgence, and invite his correction.

The time-element, also, has imposed certain limitations upon the present work. In general, the major tabulations of data do not extend beyond the material covered by *Chemical Abstracts* of June, 1950. Insofar as possible we have attempted to include in the book discussion of, or at least reference to, theoretically significant articles and relevant reviews up to the time of going to press. When it has been possible to do so in manuscript we have incorporated additional data so disclosed in the appropriate tabulations.

After the Introduction and the group of chapters (II–V) dealing with the preparations and properties of the Grignard reagents, division of subject matter into chapters has been made on the basis of co-reactants, or groups of closely related co-reactants. The exact sequence of chapters adopted has no fundamental significance so far as we are aware. On the whole it seemed expedient to give high priority to reactions of great general interest (as indicated by the volume of relevant material), and to those of greatest theoretical maturity. This may serve as explanation of the fact that certain blocs of chapters which the reader might be inclined to regard as closely related have been broken by interpolations.

In the interests of space conservation any completely developed theoretical concept in one chapter is referred to in other chapters to the subject matter of which it is pertinent. Of relatively few chapters, therefore can it be said that they are complete and independent expositions of the subject matter that they purport to treat.

The method of presentation necessarily varies somewhat from chapter to chapter, depending upon the quantity, quality, and theoretical significance of the relevant data available. Whenever possible a chapter content includes: a brief historical resumé, a definition of the so-called "normal" reaction (or reactions) and some consideration of probable mechanisms, descriptions of some exemplary preparative procedures, definitions and theoretical discussions of various so-called "abnormal" reactions, and a tabulation (or tabulations) of literature data. Chapter VI (Aldehydes and Ketones) perhaps best exemplifies the "full treatment."

Despite the chastenings of experience we have not hesitated to propose working hypotheses, or to theorize speculatively, whenever it seemed to us that to do so might prove constructive. We regard as constructive such hypotheses and theories as serve to interrelate otherwise isolated phenomena, or as embody implications that suggest profitable lines of experimental investigation.

As regards some segments of the field, a more confident and a more confidence-inspiring effort at generalization and co-ordination may be attempted when the "factual" foundation has been more firmly established. In so far as the relatively rapid, essentially ionic, addition reactions are concerned, the qualitative facts may generally be taken to be substantially as reported and generally accepted. In oxidation-reduction reactions (especially those involving "non-reducing" Grignard reagents), however, the "facts" for Grignard reagents prepared from ordinary magnesium may be quite different from those for reagents prepared from sublimed magnesium of high purity. In some cases we have been able to cite experimental evidence to this effect, in others we have voiced our misgivings, and in yet others we have left it to the discernment of the reader to recognize areas of uncertainty in "factual" data.

Although we have exercised all due diligence, we are fully aware that the major tabulations of data are by no means exhaustive. No method of literature indexing at present in use would serve to discover all Grignard reactions reported. Perhaps half the entries in these tabulations have been located through references in articles to which we were directed by literature abstracts. Almost daily, up to the time of going to press, we have discovered new sources of data, and have made new interpolations in the tables. Nevertheless, we are reasonably confident that the tabulations are *comprehensive* in the sense that no significant reported phenomenon has escaped notice.

Throughout the planning and execution of this work the authors have borne in mind the imperative that information must be easily and quickly accessible to the user who employs it primarily as a ready reference compendium. The table of contents is, we hope, adapted to this end. In preparation of the General Index every effort has been made to anticipate the reader's point of view in the selection of key topics. To avoid the imposition of an unbearable burden upon the General Index, tabulations of data, insofar as possible, are self-indexed.

For example, most major tabulations of Grignard reactions are self-indexed according to the empirical formulae of the Grignard co-reactants. Conventional orderings of symbols in empirical formulae have been somewhat modified to suit individual cases. In general the ordering of symbols is: carbon; hydrogen; characteristic element (or elements), other than carbon and hydrogen, of the functional group; all other elements in alphabetical order. The ordering of the esters (RCO_2R') is based primarily upon the empirical formulae of the acid anions (RCO_2^-), and secondarily upon the empirical formulae of the radicals (R′) of the alcohols (R′OH). The ordering of the amides (RCONR′R″) is based primarily upon the empirical formulae of the acyl radicals (RCO), and secondarily upon the empirical formulae of the amido radicals (NR′R″). The ordering of the acyl halides (RCOX) is similarly based primarily upon the empirical formulae of the acyl radicals (RCO), and secondarily upon the halogen (X) present. Functional halogens (as in RX, RCOX, RMgX) are arranged in the order: Cl, Br, I. Non-functional halogens take their places in the conventional alphabetical ordering. For a given co-reactant, the Grignard reagents are ordered in accord with the principles outlined.

In general, although some exceptions have been made, polyfunctional Grignard co-reactants with one functional group reacting appear in one table only; those with more than one functional group reacting appear in more than one table.

Because the method of arrangement and indexing adopted provides no ready means for location of information relating to individual Grignard reagents, we have felt it obligatory to include, as an appendix, an Index of Grignard Reagents. With respect to a given Grignard reagent, this appendix undertakes to answer for the reader four questions. (1) Has preparation of the reagent been reported? (2) Is there a detailed description, or reference to a detailed description, of its preparation in the text? (3) Is there textual mention of unique or significant properties of the reagent? (4) With what types of co-reactants has the reagent been treated?

In the preparation of certain portions of our manuscript we have had the benefit of consultation with several of our colleagues whose information, advice, and criticism we gratefully acknowledge. In this respect we are especially indebted to: Dr. Walter Nudenberg, Dr. Wilbert H. Urry, Dr. G. Willard Wheland, and Dr. Frank H. Westheimer. We, our publishers, and their printers also owe an irreparable debt of gratitude to Mrs. Eleanor Saluski, whose indefatigable and ever-cheerful labors produced a typescript of unsurpassed cleanliness and accuracy.

M. S. KHARASCH
OTTO REINMUTH

Contents

Tables

GRIGNARD REACTIONS *of* NONMETALLIC SUBSTANCES

CHAPTER I

Historical Introduction[1]

The preparation of organomagnesium compounds antedated that of the Grignard reagents (organomagnesium halides) by some forty years. Hallwachs and Schafarik[2] produced at least traces of diethylmagnesium by heating ethyl iodide with magnesium particles in a sealed tube. Although they did not isolate the compound, they noted its reactivity toward atmospheric oxygen and water.

Cahours[3] reported the production of dimethylmagnesium and diethylmagnesium in a similar manner, and described the preparation and isolation of the latter. The description of the compound as a liquid and the analytical data recorded indicate considerable contamination with residual ethyl iodide. The material was, however, sufficiently pure to exhibit the spontaneous inflammability in air characteristic of it.

Löhr[4] prepared dimethyl-, diethyl- and dipropylmagnesium by action of the respective iodides on magnesium, and correctly described the substances as solids. In order to decide the question whether the solid residue remaining after the distillation of excess methyl iodide consists of methylmagnesium iodide or a mixture of dimethylmagnesium and magnesium iodide, Löhr prepared the organomagnesium compound by a method that admitted the presence of no iodides, namely,

$$Mg + (CH_3)_2Hg \longrightarrow (CH_3)_2Mg + Hg$$

and concluded that the organic product of the reaction of methyl iodide with magnesium (in addition to gaseous hydrocarbon) is dimethylmagnesium.

---

[1] See also: "Les Prix Nobel en 1912," P. A. Norstedt & Soner, Stockholm, *1913*, pp. 18–24, 56–9; Schmidlin, *Chem.-Ztg.*, *36*, 1449–51 (1912); "Notice sur la vie et les travaux de Victor Grignard," Courtot, *Bull. soc. chim.*, [5], *3*, 433–72 (1936); "Victor Grignard," Gilman, *Proc. Am. Chem. Soc.*, *59*, 17–19 (1937); "Genèse et évolution de la découverte des composés organo-magnésiens mixtes," Locquin, *Bull. soc. chim.*, [5], *17*, 896–906 (1950); "Commémoration du cinquantenaire de la réaction de Victor Grignard," Karrer, *Bull. soc. chim.*, [5], *17*, 907–9 (1950); "Historique et aspects particuliers de la réaction de Victor Grignard," Colonge, *Bull. soc. chim.*, [5], *17*, 910–8 (1950); "Fifty years of the Grignard reaction," Rheinboldt, *J. Chem. Education*, *27*, 476–88 (1950).

[2] Hallwachs and Schafarik, *Ann.*, *109*, 206–9 (1859).

[3] Cahours, *Ann. chim.*, [3], *58*, 5–82 (1860); *Ann.*, *114*, 227–55 (1860).

[4] Löhr, *Ann.*, *261*, 48–87 (1891).

He noted the solubility of the organomagnesium compounds in dry benzene and ether, confirmed their violent reactivity toward water, and remarked their inflammability, not only in air and oxygen, but in carbon dioxide.

Hermann Fleck[5] of Philadelphia, continuing the researches of Löhr in the laboratory of Lothar Meyer at the University of Tübingen, prepared dimethyl- and diethylmagnesium from magnesium amalgam and the respective alkyl iodides, and further investigated their properties. He showed that the reaction between diethylmagnesium and water may be represented as

$$(C_2H_5)Mg + 2\,H_2O \longrightarrow 2\,C_2H_6 + Mg(OH)_2$$

and that dimethylmagnesium reacts with acetyl chloride to form a product which, upon treatment with water, yields *t*-butyl alcohol. Strangely enough, he reported that treatment of diethylmagnesium with acetyl chloride leads, not to the formation of 2-ethyl-2-butanol, as might be expected, but of *t*-butyl alcohol.

Finding iodobenzene unreactive toward magnesium amalgam, Fleck prepared diphenylmagnesium by the interaction of magnesium and diphenylmercury. He characterized the reactions with water and oxygen, respectively, as follows:

$$(C_6H_5)_2Mg + 2\,H_2O \longrightarrow Mg(OH)_2 + 2\,C_6H_6$$

$$(C_6H_5)_2Mg + O_2 \longrightarrow Mg(OC_6H_5)_2 \xrightarrow{H_2O} Mg(OH_2) + 2\,C_6H_5OH$$

In the hope of obtaining phenylmagnesium bromide, analogous to the known phenylzinc bromide and phenylmercuric bromide, Fleck treated diphenylmagnesium with bromine, but because of the unfortunate use of an excess of bromine, was led to the conclusion that the reaction takes the course

$$(C_6H_5)_2Mg + 2\,Br_2 \longrightarrow MgBr_2 + 2\,C_6H_5Br$$

and that no stable compound of the formula C_6H_5MgBr is thus formed.

It has since been demonstrated with a high degree of probability by Gilman and Brown[6] that, sometime in the course of this experiment, Fleck must unwittingly have had phenylmagnesium bromide in hand.

Fleck's further attempt to prepare phenylmagnesium chloride by the reaction

$$(C_6H_5)_2Mg + PCl_3 \longrightarrow C_6H_5MgCl + C_6H_5PCl_2$$

also came to naught. Apparently the reaction took the course

$$(C_6H_5)_2Mg + PCl_3 \longrightarrow MgCl_2 + (C_6H_5)_2PCl$$

---

[5] Fleck, *Ann.*, *276*, 129–47 (1893).

[6] Gilman and Brown, *J. Am. Chem. Soc.*, *52*, 1181–5 (1930).

Fleck, however, effected one other reaction that was, in a sense prophetic of one of the now well-known Grignard reactions, namely:

$$(C_6H_5)_2Mg + C_6H_5CHCl_2 \longrightarrow (C_6H_5)_3CH + MgCl_2$$

The immediate predecessor of the Grignard reactions was the Barbier synthesis, which, in turn, stemmed from the Wagner-Saytzeff synthesis.

Rieth and Beilstein[7] had shown that diethylzinc reacts with aldehydes and with acetone to give readily hydrolyzable compounds, although they did not correctly characterize their products.

Wagner and Saytzeff[8] improved the technique by generating the zinc compound (from alkyl iodide and zinc) in the presence of a carbonyl compound and by subsequently hydrolyzing the resultant complexes to obtain alcohols of predetermined structure. The method was then applied by Saytzeff and many others, especially to the preparation of tertiary alcohols from ketones. The method, however, had decided disadvantages in that the yields in general were of the order of twenty to thirty percent and that the applicability was limited. (Methyl ketones, for example, were not amenable to such treatment.)

Barbier[9] conceived the happy idea that an improvement might be effected by substituting the more reactive magnesium for zinc. Operating with natural dimethylheptenone, methyl iodide, and magnesium in ether, he brought about a vigorous reaction which he characterized as follows:

$$(CH_3)_2C{=}CHCH_2CH_2COCH_3 + CH_3I + Mg \longrightarrow (CH_3)_2C{=}CHCH_2CH_2C(CH_3)_2OMgI$$

Subsequent hydrolysis yielded the desired carbinol:

$$(CH_3)_2C{=}CHCH_2CH_2C(CH_3)_2OMgI + H_2O \longrightarrow (CH_3)_2C{=}CHCH_2CH_2C(CH_3)_2OH + MgIOH$$

The Barbier synthesis, although in some respects an improvement over the Wagner-Saytzeff synthesis, also had its defects, for in some cases, it gave negative results, and in many cases, results of very uneven quality.

When Victor Grignard (1871–1935) took up graduate work in chemistry at the University of Lyon under the direction of Barbier, the latter suggested that he continue the study of magnesium. Grignard soon reached what appeared to be an impasse in the further development of the Barbier synthesis. He reasoned that the effective intermediate in reactions of this kind must be a compound of the general formula RMgX, and believed that a new line of attack might be opened by generating this intermediate and then causing it to react with a carbonyl compound. Barbier, however, did not approve the idea, and it was abandoned temporarily.

---

[7] Rieth and Beilstein, *Ann.*, *126*, 241–7 (1863).

[8] Wagner and Saytzeff, *Ann.*, *175*, 351–74 (1875).

[9] Barbier, *Compt. rend.*, *128*, 110–1 (1898); *J. Chem. Soc.*, 76,*I*, 323 (1899).

When a change in his appointment afforded Grignard somewhat greater independence of action, he made some preliminary experiments along this line on his own initiative. He was soon able to demonstrate to Barbier by means of test-tube experiments that alkyl halides do react readily with magnesium in the presence of ethyl ether to produce ether-soluble reagents (presumably of the general formula RMgX) which will in turn react with carbonyl compounds with results superior in many cases to those obtained in the Barbier synthesis. Despite his earlier skepticism, Barbier broad-mindedly commended Grignard upon the making of an important scientific discovery, and encouraged him to exploit it. Grignard's first description of the new reagents and of some of their properties and reactions appeared in 1900.[10]

A summary of Grignard's early papers and of his doctoral dissertation is to be found in the *Annales de chimie et de physique*.[11]

General progress in the field was reviewed by Grignard in 1913,[12] and again in 1926.[13]

West and Gilman[14] have prepared a bibliography of the literature relating to Grignard reagents and their reactions, covering the years 1900 through 1921.

A monograph covering the first quarter-century of the development of Grignard reagent chemistry has been prepared by Courtot,[15] one of Grignard's early collaborators.

The preparative uses of Grignard reagents have been summarized by Runge[16] in part I of volume XVI of Schmidt's "Chemie in Enzeldarstellung."

---

[10] Grignard, *Compt. rend.*, *130*, 1322 (1900); *Chem. Zentr.*, *1900,II*, 33.

[11] Grignard, *Ann. chim.*, [7], *24*, 433–90 (1901).

[12] Grignard, *Bull. soc. chim.*, [4], *13*, No. 11, Conference I–XXXVII (1913).

[13] Grignard, *Bull. soc. chim.*, [4], *39*, 1285–1321 (1926).

[14] West and Gilman, "A Bibliography of the Grignard Reaction, 1900–1921," Reprint and Circular Series of the National Research Council, No. 24, *1922*.

[15] Courtot, "Le magnesium en chimie organique," Nancy, *1926*, 351 pp.

[16] Runge, "Organomagnesiumverbindungen," part I of "Organometallverbindungen," volume XVI of "Chemie in Einzeldarstellungen," edited by Julius Schmidt, Stuttgart, *1932* (photolithoprint reproduction, Edwards Brothers, Inc., Ann Arbor, *1943*) 328 pp.

CHAPTER II

The Preparation of Grignard Reagents

Grignard's[1] method for the preparation of organomagnesium halides may be summarized as follows. One gram-atom of magnesium turnings (*ca.* 3.0 × 0.6 mm.) of 99.2–99.4 percent purity (the chief recognized impurity being iron) is placed in a well-dried, one-liter, two-necked, round-bottomed flask, fitted with a dropping funnel and a reflux condenser. One gram-molecular weight of the desired halide (say methyl iodide) is dissolved in an equal volume of anhydrous ethyl ether, and about 40–50 ml. of the solution is added to the magnesium. Almost immediately there appears at various points on the surface of the magnesium a brownish (in the case of iodides) or white (in the case of bromides) turbidity, accompanied by a very feeble effervescence. As the reaction accelerates, a white flocculation appears and the ether undergoes lively ebullition. A total of 250–300 g. of anhydrous ether is then added in two or three portions, with simultaneous cooling of the flask by means of a stream of cold air. The ebullition moderates, the flocculation (momentarily augmented) disappears almost immediately, the solution regains complete clarity, and the reaction is resumed with renewed vigor. The dropwise addition of the remainder of the ether-halide solution follows, and reaction is eventually completed by a half-hour reflux on the water-bath. There should then remain in the flask only a very fluid, nearly colorless liquid carrying a little iron in suspension.

This method Grignard found applicable to methyl, isopropyl, tertiary butyl, and secondary hexyl iodides, as well as to ethyl, propyl, isobutyl, isoamyl, and benzyl bromides.

In its principal essentials, this is substantially the method still employed in the production of the more readily available Grignard reagents for preparative purposes. Various modifications in apparatus and in details of operation have been suggested by observations and special studies on the effects of such factors as (1) the quality and quantity of metallic magnesium, (2) the presence of "activators" or "inhibitors," (3) the purity of halide, (4) the degree of ether dilution, (5) the rate of halide addition, and (6) the efficiency of stirring or other agitation on the ease of initiation of reaction, the rate of reaction, and the yield of Grignard reagent obtained.

---

[1] Grignard, *Ann. chim.*, [7], *24*, 433–90 (1901).

QUALITY AND QUANTITY OF MAGNESIUM

Although the presence of metallic impurities in the magnesium used may occasionally contribute to ease of initiation of reaction in cases of relatively unreactive halides, it is in general desirable to employ magnesium of the highest degree of purity attainable, in consideration both of the yield of Grignard reagent and the avoidance of "abnormal" side-reactions in subsequent utilization of the reagent.[2] Parenthetically, the specific nature of the impurities present is considerably more significant than the total quantity.

The yields of some Grignard reagents are not too greatly affected by the use of an inferior quality of magnesium. This is decidedly not true, however, in the cases of halides that have a pronounced tendency to undergo the Wurtz* or disproportionation reactions. Cusa and Kipping[3] found, for example, that a European magnesium, supposedly containing less then 1 percent of impurities, consistently gave Grignard reagent yields of 35 percent with cyclohexyl bromide and 50 percent with cyclohexyl chloride. When an American magnesium (containing 0.50 percent aluminum, 0.10 percent silica, 0.05 percent iron, 0.05 percent manganese, and 0.05 percent copper) was substituted, the respective yields were 92 percent and 96 percent, confirming previous reports of American workers.[4]

In view of the fact that reaction must necessarily take place at the metallic surface, the degree of division of the magnesium is obviously significant. In general, it may be expected that, *ceteris paribus*, the greater the surface present, the more readily a reaction may be initiated and the more rapidly it will proceed. However, other things seldom being equal, it is also true that extension of surface affords opportunity for undesirable surface contamination, and it has often been found in practice that very finely divided commercial magnesiums prove less reactive than magnesiums of ostensibly the same grade furnished in larger par-

---

[2] (*a*) Kharasch, Kleiger, Martin, and Mayo, *J. Am. Chem. Soc.*, 63, 2305–7 (1941); (*b*) Gilman, Zoellner, Selby, and Boatner, *Rec. trav. chim.*, *54*, 584–94 (1935); (*c*) Reid and Ubbelohde, *J. Chem. Soc.*, *1948*, 1597–601.

*As in common usage, the term "Wurtz reaction" is here loosely employed to signify a reaction of the general stoichiometric type

$$2\ RX + 2\ M^{I} \longrightarrow 2\ M^{I}X + R_2$$

or

$$2\ RX + M^{II} \longrightarrow M^{II}X_2 + R_2$$

without implication as to mechanism. The corresponding "disproportionation reaction" involving magnesium may be indicated by the stoichiometric equation:

$$2\ RX + Mg \longrightarrow MgX_2 + R_{(+H)} + R_{(-H)}$$

[3] Cusa and Kipping, *J. Soc. Chem. Ind.*, *53*, 213–4T (1934).

[4] Gilman and McCracken, *J. Am. Chem. Soc.*, *45*, 2462–6 (1923); Gray and Marvel, *ibid.*, *47*, 2796–802 (1925); Gilman and Zoellner, *ibid.*, *53*, 1945–8 (1931). See also: Gilman and Catlin, *Organic Syntheses*, Coll. Vol. I, 2nd ed., pp. 188–90, *1941*.

ticle sizes. Moreover, although a high rate of the desired reaction might be considered desirable on the ground that it discourages undesired side-reactions, it is not always an unmixed blessing.

Aside from the obvious practical necessity of avoiding too-violent ebullition of the ether medium, induced by over-rapid progress of an exothermal reaction, it is found in practice that too high a reaction rate materially reduces the yield of the Grignard reagent. This fact may probably be attributed to local concentration effects and local superheating. The principal competing reactions that operate (when high-grade magnesium is used) to reduce Grignard reagent yields are:

$$2\,RX + Mg \longrightarrow R_2 + MgX_2$$

$$2\,RX + Mg \longrightarrow R_{(+H)} + R_{(-H)} + MgX_2$$

$$RMgX + RX \longrightarrow R_{(+H)} + R_{(-H)} + MgX_2$$

and

$$RMgX + RX \longrightarrow R_2 + MgX_2$$

In general these reactions require (or at least are favored by) higher temperatures than the Grignard reagent formation reaction, and, in general, they are favored by relatively high halide (RX) concentrations.

It may be concluded, therefore, that in the preparation of Grignard reagents from the more reactive halides (see Relative Reactivities of Halides, p. 20) no advantage accrues to the use of the easily-contaminated finely divided magnesiums, and, further, that unless precautions are taken (by suitable dilution, adjustment of rate of addition of the halide, efficient agitation, and moderative cooling) to minimize local concentration and heat effects, actual disadvantage may be incurred. In an investigation of the optimum conditions for the preparation of ethylmagnesium iodide in which three size-grades of "a standard quality of American-made magnesium" turnings were used, Gilman and Meyers[5] found no significant differences in yields (94–95 percent), provided sufficient time were allowed for complete reaction in each case.

When the less reactive halides are involved, the use of *thoroughly cleansed* finely divided magnesium is advantageous, if only from the standpoint of time economy.

A British patent[6] describes a method and apparatus for continually cutting chips from a metal from which an organometallic halide is to be prepared, and supplying organic halide to the chip surfaces while they are being formed so that reaction occurs on the clean, nascent chip surfaces. A similar application of "mechanical activation" is discussed by Shaw.[7]

---

[5] Gilman and Meyers, *J. Am. Chem. Soc.*, *45*, 159–65 (1923).

[6] Stevens, British Patent 571,539, Aug. 29, 1945; *Chem. Abstr.*, *41*, P1696 (1947).

[7] Shaw, *J. Applied Mechanics*, *15*, No. 1, 37–44 (1948); *Chem. Abstr.*, *42*, 2843 (1948).

The observation of Gaddum and French[8] that electrolytically deposited* magnesium is extraordinarily reactive may or may not have a bearing on this point. They report that magnesium deposited by the electrolysis of an ethereal Grignard reagent solution reacts vigorously with cold water, violently with ethereal ethyl bromide, and readily with chlorobenzene. A freshly-deposited magnesium surface of this sort would be free of oxide and hydroxide contamination, and would, presumably, include many points of unsaturation. These qualities in themselves might well be sufficient to account for the degree of reactivity observed. However, it would be unwise to ignore the possibility that such deposits may include traces of halogen (*i.e.*, Mg_xMgX) which would certainly have an activating effect insofar as reactions with organic halides are concerned.

Although a small excess (5-10 percent) of magnesium is usually employed, there is, in general, no advantage to be gained by the use of a large excess of the metal. In the study just cited, for example, Gilman and Meyers[5] found no appreciable change in yield when a 25 percent excess of magnesium was used. Even in the exceptional special cases in which the use of a large excess of magnesium has been recommended, as in the Gilman[2b,9] preparations of allylmagnesium bromide (sixfold excess), and allylmagnesium chloride (threefold excess), it is doubtful that such an excess is at all necessary or advantageous when proper adjustment of other reaction factors is made.[10]

ACTIVATORS AND INHIBITORS

Grignard[11] found iodine a useful activator in initiating reaction between magnesium and aryl halides such as bromobenzene and the bromotoluenes.

Baeyer[12] pre-activated his magnesium with iodine, and found magnesium so activated effective in the preparation of Grignard reagents from iodoanilines and iododimethylanilines which had previously resisted reaction with magnesium, even in the presence of iodine.[13] Baeyer's method consists in heating a 10-g. portion of magnesium filings in a long-necked 150-ml. flask over a free flame. Vigorous agitation is maintained during the portionwise addition of 5 g. of iodine, each small portion being permitted to disappear before the next is added. The temperature must be

[8] Gaddum and French, *J. Am. Chem. Soc.*, *49*, 1295-9 (1927).

*The study cited dealt with the electrolysis of ethereal solutions of phenylmagnesium bromide, benzylmagnesium bromide, and benzylmagnesium chloride; the specific source of the electrolytic magnesium tested is not stated.

[9] Gilman and McGlumphey, *Bull. soc. chim.*, [4], *43*, 1322-8 (1928).

[10] *Cf.* the preparation of allylmagnesium chloride by Kharasch and Fuchs, *J. Org. Chem.*, *9*, 359-72 (1944).

[11] Tissier and Grignard, *Compt. rend.*, *132*, 1182-4 (1901).

[12] Baeyer, *Ber.*, *38*, 2759-65 (1905).

[13] Baeyer and Villiger, *Ber.*, *36*, 2774-96 (1903).

high, but not so high that the mass begins to fuse. For the quantities of materials designated, the time required is from one-quarter to one-half hour. The activated magnesium forms a matte-gray powder which turns brown on aging, and which must be carefully protected from moisture.

It is now generally recommended that Baeyer-activated magnesium be used only in relatively small quantities to initiate reaction, which then will usually proceed with ordinary magnesium.

A simplified preparation of activated magnesium is described by Gilman and Kirby.[14] Sodium-dried ether (5 ml.) is added dropwise to a well-stirred mixture of 5 g. of magnesium turnings or 30–80 mesh magnesium powder, 100 ml. of sodium-dried benzene and 2.5 g. of iodine. When the color of iodine has completely disappeared, the solvent is distilled with the aid of an oil-bath, the solid residue finally being maintained at 150–160° for about ten minutes. The activated magnesium may be transferred to a dry rubber-stoppered bottle. Reactivation before use is recommended, and may be effected by heating in a test-tube until gas evolution ceases and a color of iodine appears. Usually about 0.2 g. of activator is sufficient to initiate reaction.

Various explanations of the effectiveness of iodine as an activator have been offered. Zelinsky,[15] who believed that iodine does not react with magnesium in benzene, attributed its activating properties to the local heat effects involved in formation of an ether complex.

$$2\,(C_2H_5)_2O + Mg + I_2 \longrightarrow \begin{matrix} C_2H_5 & & Mg & & C_2H_5 \\ & O & & O & \\ C_2H_5 & & I\ \ I & & C_2H_5 \end{matrix}$$

Tingle and Gorsline[16] offered the more plausible explanation that the activating agency is a "magnesium subiodide" (Mg_2I_2), though their formulation of the subsequent reaction mechanism would probably be received with general skepticism today.

Gomberg and Bachmann[17] also attribute activation to magnesious iodide (·MgI), and formulate the following free-radical mechanism:

$$RX + \cdot MgI \longrightarrow XMgI + R\cdot$$

$$XMgI + Mg \longrightarrow \cdot MgX + \cdot MgI$$

$$R\cdot + \cdot MgX \longrightarrow RMgX$$

They report, "We find that the addition of a small amount of magnesium iodide solution activates the metal just as well as does free iodine, so the doctrine of 'etching' is untenable. In this manner, we found it pos-

---

[14] Gilman and Kirby, *Rec. trav. chim.*, *54*, 577–83 (1935).

[15] Zelinsky, *J. Russ. Phys.-Chem. Soc.*, *35*, 399–404 (1903); *Chem. Zentr.*, *1903,II*, 277.

[16] Tingle and Gorsline, *Am. Chem. J.*, 37, 483–94 (1907).

[17] Gomberg and Bachmann, *J. Am. Chem. Soc.*, *49*, 236–57 (1927).

sible to bring about activation in some of the most resistant cases, such as *p*-bromobiphenyl, and apparently even with *p*-iododimethylaniline...."

Gilman and Vanderwal[18] found that magnesium bromide etherate shortens the time necessary for initiation of reaction between *n*-butyl bromide and magnesium. (From a practical standpoint, of course, this reaction requires no activation.)

Gilman and Zoellner[19] have investigated the effects on yields of various amounts of iodine used for activation purposes in the preparation of Grignard reagents from *n*-butyl bromide and *t*-butyl chloride. With no iodine at all and with 0.0125 atom equivalent of iodine per 0.05 mole equivalent of halide, the yields were about the same (*ca.* 96 percent for *n*-butylmagnesium bromide; *ca.* 83 percent for *t*-butylmagnesium chloride). With 1.0 atom equivalent of iodine per 0.05 mole equivalent of halide the corresponding yields were *ca.* 96 percent and *ca.* 80 percent, respectively. In general, intermediate quantities of iodine gave lower yields. They conclude that, except in very small or very large proportional quantities, iodine (*i.e.*, MgI_2) tends to reduce yields.

Among the numerous other activators that have been recommended are bromine, a readily reactive alkyl halide (such as ethyl bromide), a small amount of preformed Grignard reagent (such as ethylmagnesium bromide), hydrogen halides, various metallic halides, and various magnesium alloys. Probably the first four, at least, all owe their effectiveness in part at least to the introduction of small quantities of magnesious halide.

Taboury[20] recommended the use of bromine to facilitate the initiation of sluggish halide-magnesium reactions. His procedure is described as follows. Magnesium turnings (amount not specified) are placed in a suitably equipped flask. Then a small amount of ether-halide solution is introduced, followed by 1 ml. of bromine. Reaction begins within a few minutes. Ether-halide solution is added in small portions. Reaction is completed by thirty minutes reflux. This method brought α-naphthyl bromide, which required an hour and three-quarters reflux for initiation of reaction in the absence of bromine, into prompt reaction.

The efficacy of bromine as an activator has been confirmed by Gilman *et al.*,[21] who found that the fumes from a glass stopper often constituted a sufficient quantity.

Activation by ethyl bromide or by ethylmagnesium bromide is exemplified in the method of Ehrlich and Sachs.[22] They report: "When magnesium powder is covered with ether, and a little ethyl bromide is added, vigorous reaction soon sets in. The system is cooled, and most of the liquid

---

[18] Gilman and Vanderwal, *Rec. trav. chim.*, *48*, 160–2 (1929).
[19] Gilman and Zoellner, *J. Am. Chem. Soc.*, *53*, 1583–6 (1931).
[20] Taboury, *Ann. chim.*, [8], *15*, 5–66 (1908).
[21] Gilman, Peterson, and Schulze, *Rec. trav. chim.*, *47*, 19–27 (1928).
[22] Ehrlich and Sachs, *Ber.*, *36*, 4296–9 (1903).

is decanted. An ether solution of bromodimethylaniline is then added with gentle warming, and reaction takes place readily, although not with quantitative yield." When magnesium powder or ribbon is added to bromodimethylaniline in ether solution, there is no appreciable reaction after a day's heating, even though iodine be added. The method of Ehrlich and Sachs probably has the double merit of supplying an activator and cleansing the metal surface.

Zelinsky (*loc. cit.*[15]) found methyl iodide an effective activator in the preparation of Grignard reagents from naphthenic chlorides. In a study of the effectiveness of various activators in initiating reaction between magnesium and β-bromostyrene, Gilman *et al.* (*loc. cit.*[21]) found methylene iodide, ethyl iodide, and β-bromoethyl ether effective in varying degrees. None of the organic halides they tested performed so satisfactorily as a small amount of previously prepared Grignard reagent (suitably, ethylmagnesium bromide).

Andrianov and Gribanova[23] recommend the use of a small amount of ethyl orthosilicate [$(C_2H_5O)_4Si$] as an activator, and claim good results even in the absence of ethyl ether. In a sample procedure, a few drops of the silicate is added to 12 g. of metallic magnesium; about half the calculated quantity of organic halide is introduced dropwise. The remainder of the organic halide, dissolved in four or five parts [volumes?] of toluene or xylene is then added. The yields claimed for several organomagnesium halides prepared in this way are as follows: ethylmagnesium bromide (96 percent); isobutylmagnesium chloride (51 percent); isoamylmagnesium bromide (58 percent); *n*-hexylmagnesium bromide (60 percent); *n*-octylmagnesium bromide (35 percent); phenylmagnesium bromide (23-25 percent).

Hesse[24] mentions having attempted activation of reaction between magnesium and pinene hydrochloride with aluminum chloride with poor results. However, in this case, iodine and ethyl bromide also proved unsatisfactory, best results being obtained with a modification of the method of Ehrlich and Sachs (*loc. cit.*[22]). Hufferd[25] reports that aluminum bromide, freshly prepared from aluminum and bromine, can often be used to initiate a Grignard preparation, but adds that the reagent has not been tried with any of the more difficult preparations. Gilman *et al.* (*loc. cit.*[21]) found zinc bromide, zinc iodide, mercuric iodide, cupric chloride, and gold chloride effective in varying degrees, but mercurous iodide, cupric bromide, ferrous and ferric chlorides, palladium chloride and potassium chloroplatinate ineffective.

---

[23] Andrianov and Gribanova, *J. Gen. Chem.* (U.S.S.R.), *8*, 552-6 (1938); *Chem. Abstr.*, *32*, 7892 (1938).
[24] Hesse, *Ber.*, *39*, 1127-55 (1906).
[25] Hufferd, *J. Am. Chem. Soc.*, *49*, 1845-6 (1927).

Hurd and Webb,[26] acting on privately communicated advice from Henry Gilman, tried a copper-magnesium alloy containing 12.75 percent copper in the preparation of Grignard reagents from α-bromo-β,β-diarylethylenes. They were thus able (with the aid of iodine and ethyl bromide activation) to reduce the time of preparation of the phenyl-α-naphthyl compound from a half-week with similarly activated magnesium turnings to a half-day with the alloy. They also state that the yield for the phenyl-*p*-tolyl compound was increased from 5 percent with magnesium to 51 percent with magnesium-copper alloy.

Gilman *et al.* (*loc. cit.*[21]) tried a number of magnesium alloys in the preparation of Grignard reagents from *n*-butyl chloride and styryl bromide. In each case, a small crystal of iodine was added at the beginning of the preparation. Among those tested, they list the following in the order of decreasing effectiveness: 12.75 percent copper, 2 percent copper, 50 percent copper, 50 percent tin, (ordinary magnesium turnings), 10 percent lead, 4.03 percent manganese, 1.83 percent manganese. They recommend an activator "conveniently and readily prepared, in less than ten minutes, by heating in an evacuated flask an alloy of magnesium containing 12.75 percent copper with about 20 percent by weight of iodine." The new "catalyst" is said to be "distinctly superior to Baeyer's activated magnesium."

Best results, in general, are claimed for the use of 0.25–0.50 g. of iodine-activated alloy with ordinary magnesium turnings and a 15–20 percent ether-halide solution.

When copper-magnesium alloy or the iodine-activated alloy is used as the sole source of magnesium in the preparation of Grignard reagents, the yield is usually materially lowered. In a study by Gilman and Zoellner,[27] "the powdered alloy, as such (2.0, 3.0, or 5.0 g.), or activated (1.5 or 2.0 g.), was covered with 5 ml. of ether; then twenty drops of the pure RX compound and a crystal of iodine....was added. The mixture was heated for ten minutes by means of a water-bath at 45°. Then the remainder of the halide (a total of 0.05 mole), mixed with 25 ml. of ether, was added over a period of thirty minutes with stirring. After all the halide had been added, the reaction mixture was stirred for an additional ten minutes." In Table II-I, representative yield values selected from those recorded by Gilman and Zoellner are set forth.*

In comparative studies by Johnson and Adkins[28] of the yields obtained from a 12 percent copper-88 percent magnesium alloy and from ordinary

[26] Hurd and Webb, *J. Am. Chem. Soc.*, *49*, 546–59 (1927).

[27] Gilman and Zoellner, *J. Am. Chem. Soc.*, *53*, 1581–3 (1931).

* It will be obvious to the experienced reader, without comment from the present authors, that the implied precision and reproducibility of the data in this and many of the succeeding tabulations of this chapter are spurious. In recording such data the authors endorse only the general qualitative trends indicated.

[28] Johnson and Adkins, *J. Am. Chem. Soc.*, *53*, 1520–3 (1931); *54*, 1943–7 (1932).

TABLE II-I

YIELDS (%) OF ORGANOMAGNESIUM HALIDES FROM MAGNESIUM, MAGNESIUM-COPPER ALLOY, AND IODINE-ACTIVATED MAGNESIUM-COPPER ALLOY

Halide	Cu-Mg	Cu-Mg-I_2	Mg
n-C_4H_9Br	55.4–55.8	62.8	94.0
$C_6H_5CH_2Cl$	89.5	72.6	93.1
C_6H_5Br	82.3–83.9	79.0	94.7
4-$CH_3C_6H_4Br$	92.0	78.8	86.9

magnesium turnings, respectively, in reaction with sixteen different halides, the results were qualitatively confirmative of those of Gilman and Zoellner. The greatest difference in yields was obtained with allyl bromide: 72.3 ± 0.2 percent for magnesium and 5.7 ± 2.0 percent for the alloy.

In a heterogeneous reaction like that between an organic halide and metallic magnesium, it is, of course, difficult to distinguish between purely mechanical inhibition, which prevents effective contact between the ether-halide solution and the metal, and specific anticatalytic activity. The effect of a greasy film on the metal is certainly, and the effect of an oxide film is probably, of the purely mechanical type. Any contaminant which can react with the metallic magnesium, the organic halide, the solvent, or the Grignard reagent first produced to form or deposit an adherent, impervious coating on the metal will retard or prevent reaction. Some of the less ether-soluble Grignard reagents themselves tend to form such a coating. Many, though possibly not all, inhibiting effects can be accounted for in this way.

Bischoff[29] has reported that phenetole and various ketones and esters, and Ahrens and Stapler[30] that various aldehydes inhibit reaction between ethylene bromide and magnesium. Reychler[31] found chloroform a marked inhibitor of reaction between magnesium and methyl iodide, ethyl iodide, ethyl bromide, or bromobenzene. He also reported that acetone, ethyl acetate, carbon tetrachloride and bromoform display inhibitory effects.

Freundler and Damond,[32] experiencing the impossibility of preparing some Grignard reagents in ether contaminated with carbon disulfide, purposely used traces of that inhibitor to moderate the reaction of n-butyl bromide with magnesium (which they considered over-vigorous), and claimed to have obtained higher yields in that way. Most present-day workers would prefer other methods of controlling a vigorous reaction.

Gilman and Vanderwal (*loc. cit.*[18]) investigated the effects of various possible contaminants as inhibitors of reaction between n-butyl bromide and magnesium. The standard of comparison adopted was the time re-

[29] Bischoff, *Ber.*, 38, 2078–83 (1905).
[30] Ahrens and Stapler, *Ber.*, 38, 3260–7 (1905).
[31] Reychler, *Bull. soc. chim.*, [3], 35, 803–11 (1906).
[32] Freundler and Damond, *Bull. soc. chim.*, [3], 35, 106–11 (1906).

quired for 2 ml. of *n*-butyl bromide and 0.5 g. of magnesium turnings in 5 ml. of sodium-dried ether to yield a positive color test for Grignard reagent with Michler's ketone[33] (on the average, about seven and one-quarter minutes). Powdered glass and mercury (which might be introduced through the breakage of a mercury seal) were found to be without effect. Seasoned rubber (from an aged rubber stopper) or fresh rubber (cut from the inside of a new rubber stopper) were likewise without effect, but scrapings from the outside of a new rubber stopper were inhibitory. Gilman and Vanderwal attribute the inhibition to organic sulfur compounds, which are, they say, in general, inhibitors.[34] Dry air was without effect, but saturation of the ether with dry oxygen increased the induction period to eleven minutes. Carbon dioxide had a slight, and hydrogen chloride a more pronounced retarding effect.

Although nearly all experienced workers agree that operation in a thoroughly dried system is desirable, there appears to be some difference of opinion as to whether or not moisture actually inhibits Grignard reagent formation. On the basis of the test just described, Gilman and Vanderwal (*loc. cit.*[18]) conclude that it does. They found that the induction period of seven and one-quarter minutes for sodium-dried ether was increased to twenty minutes for commercial "anhydrous" ether. When 4.5 ml. of dried ether and 0.5 ml. of saturated ether was used, the period was thirty-three minutes, and with 2.5 ml. each of dried and saturated ether, about two hours.

It should be noted, however, that the times recorded are not the times necessary for the production of a small amount of Grignard reagent, but rather the times necessary for the production of a small excess of Grignard reagent over that sufficient to react with all the water present.*

From the results of a study of the influence of water in the synthesis of certain arylmagnesium bromides Jezierski[35] concluded that "water present in reagents checks the spontaneous course of the Grignard reaction; when the water is removed, the reaction starts instantly." He believed that the inhibitory influence of water is a "physical phenomenon."

Although they make no specific statement regarding induction times, Schmalfuss and Wetzel[36] maintain that moisture does not interfere with the preparation and subsequent reactions of Grignard reagents, provided due allowance is made for destruction of the Grignard reagent by water. They claim a 98 percent yield of methyldiphenylmethanol from benzo-

[33] Gilman and Schulze, *J. Am. Chem. Soc.*, *47*, 2002–5 (1925).

[34] *Cf.* however, Hepworth, *J. Chem. Soc.*, *119*, 1249–56 (1921).

*Concerning the limitations of this test, see Chapter III, Estimation and Detection of Grignard Reagents.

[35] Jezierski, *Roczniki Chem.*, *18*, 567–73 (1938); *Chem. Abstr.*, *33*, 4213 (1939).

[36] Schmalfuss and Wetzel, *J. prakt. Chem.*, [2], *109*, 158–60 (1925); Schmalfuss, *ibid.*, [2], *113*, 46–7 (1926).

phenone, operating in moist ether. They prepared phenyldimethylmethanol from methylmagnesium chloride and ethyl benzoate in 37 percent yield in dry ether and 38 percent yield in moist ether. The corresponding yields of phenyldiethylmethanol from ethylmagnesium bromide and benzoic acid reported were 53 percent and 64 percent.

In a relatively early study, Meyer and Tögel[37] investigated the effects of the addition of varying amounts of water to the reaction system in the course of the preparation of benzoic acid by Grignardization of bromobenzene and carbonation of the resultant phenylmagnesium bromide. In each of a series of ten experiments the Grignard reagent was prepared from 15.7 g. (0.1 mole) of bromobenzene and 2.4 g. (0.1 g.-atom) of magnesium in 50 ml. of ethyl ether. They report that when water was added to the various reaction systems in amounts varying from one to ten drops (1 drop = 0.0625 g.) the amounts of byproduct biphenyl formed increased from 1.95 to 63.5 percent, and the yields of benzoic acid obtained on subsequent carbonation decreased from 82.0 to 24.2 percent.

Attempts in the laboratories of the University of Chicago to verify the findings of Meyer and Tögel have failed.[38] With the reagent quantities specified the amount of biphenyl formed was substantially constant (8-13 percent), and was independent of the amount of water present. Among the various factors investigated the only one that materially affected the formation of biphenyl was variation of the quantity of ether present. (More concentrated halide solutions formed more biphenyl.) The source of the discrepancy is not apparent, but it is perhaps a relevant commentary on the work of Meyer and Tögel that they also claimed to have prepared biphenyl in 53-64 percent yields by means of the reaction:

$$C_6H_5OH + C_6H_5MgBr \longrightarrow (C_6H_5-)_2 + MgBrOH$$

In a study of Wurtz product * formation and solvent coupling in the preparation of benzylmagnesium chloride and phenylmagnesium bromide in hydrocarbon solvents it was found that the yields of Wurtz and coupling products were independent of the (relatively small) amounts of water added during the reactions,[39] and it was at first supposed that the formation of these products was attributable to free-radical reactions induced by "catalytic" quantities of water in the presence of metallic magnesium. It was subsequently found, however, that substantially the same yields of these products are formed under rigorously anhydrous conditions.[38]

[37] Meyer and Tögel, *Ann.*, *347*, 55-92 (1906).

[38] Kane (with Kharasch), Dissertation, University of Chicago, *1941*.

*The term "Wurtz product" is here loosely used to indicate a product of the type R_2 derived from an organic halide RX by the action of a metal. In the case of benzyl chloride such a product might arise in part from the Grignard reaction:

$$C_6H_5CH_2Cl + C_6H_5CH_2MgCl \longrightarrow (C_6H_5CH_2-)_2 + MgCl_2$$

In the case of bromobenzene it must be otherwise formed.

[39] Kharasch, Goldberg, and Mayo, *J. Am. Chem. Soc.*, *60*, 2004 (1938).

PURITY OF HALIDE

A good grade of commercial halide is often found satisfactory for the preparation of the corresponding Grignard reagent, especially in the cases of readily prepared reagents such as *n*-butylmagnesium bromide and phenylmagnesium bromide. However, in general, the desirability of a high degree of purity in the halide is emphasized. It is recommended, for example, that benzyl chloride be freshly distilled.[40]

Several investigators have reported difficulty in preparing α-naphthylmethylmagnesium halides in good yields.[41] Gilman and Kirby[42] emphasize the necessity for the use of halide of high purity. They found α-naphthylmethyl chloride prepared by direct chlorination of the corresponding hydrocarbon unsatisfactory, but obtained estimated yields of about 80 percent with chloride prepared by treatment of the carbinol with thionyl chloride.

Miller and Bachman[43] reported that 9-bromoanthracene did not react appreciably with magnesium and ether even in a sealed tube at 200°. Bachmann and Kloetzel,[44] however, report yields as high as 86 percent. They specify the use of a good grade (99.7 percent) of finely divided, thoroughly cleansed magnesium with a bromide melting at 100° or higher. Bromide melting below 100° is said to be unsuitable, and ordinary magnesium turnings reacted to the extent of only 55 percent in twenty-four hours.

RELATIVE QUANTITY OF ETHER

No thorough investigation of the optimum proportions of ether to be used in the preparation of Grignard reagents has been made. Doubtless these depend in varying degrees upon a number of interrelated experimental conditions, such as: the reactivity of the halide, the tendency of the halide to undergo the Wurtz or disproportionation reactions, the tendency of the halide to react with its own Grignard reagent, the solubility of the Grignard reagent, the rate of addition of the halide, the efficiency of stirring, etc. In view of the fact that high concentrations and higher temperatures tend to favor side-reactions, there is probably for each group of more or less closely related halides a range of ether dilutions below which yields tend to drop off rapidly, and above which any gain in yield is offset by the additional cost and labor involved in handling larger quantities of ether.

---

[40] Gilman and Catlin, *Organic Syntheses*, Coll. Vol. I, 2nd ed., pp. 471–3, *1941*; Adkins and Zartman, *ibid.*, Coll. Vol. II, pp. 606–7, *1943*.

[41] Weitzenbock and Lieb, *Monatsh.*, 33, 549–65 (1912); Mayer and Sieglitz, *Ber.*, *55B*, 1835–59 (1922); Conant, Small, and Sloan, *J. Am. Chem. Soc.*, *48*, 1743–57 (1926).

[42] Gilman and Kirby, *J. Am. Chem. Soc.*, *51*, 3475–8 (1929).

[43] Miller and Bachman, *J. Am. Chem. Soc.*, 57, 766–71 (1935).

[44] Bachmann and Kloetzel, *J. Org. Chem.*, 3, 55–61 (1938).

In a study in which ether-halide solutions were added slowly, with efficient stirring, to ether-covered magnesium, activated by a small crystal of iodine, Gilman and McCracken[45] noted some rather striking variations in yield with variations in degree of dilution in the cases of *n*-butyl bromide, bromobenzene and benzyl chloride. Data, selected from their tabulation, are presented in Table II-II.*

TABLE II-II

EFFECTS OF ETHER DILUTION OF HALIDE ON GRIGNARD REAGENT YIELDS

Halide	Et_2O/RX (moles)	Yield RMgX (%)
n-C_4H_9Br	0.4	52.1
	0.5	71.2
	1.0	92.0
C_6H_5Br	1.0	52.6
	2.0	68.1
	3.0	72.6
	4.0	91.8
	5.0	94.5
	6.0	94.3
$C_6H_5CH_2Cl$	1.0	38.6
	2.0	80.6
	3.0	86.7
	4.0	88.7
	10.0	93.3

The molar ratios of ether to halide recommended by Gilman and McCracken are: *n*-butyl bromide, 1.3 : 1.5; bromobenzene, 4 : 5; benzyl chloride, 6 : 7.

In their study of the optimum conditions for the preparation of ethylmagnesium iodide, Gilman and Meyers (*loc. cit.*[5]) apparently did not investigate in detail the effect of ether dilution upon yields, but found an ether-halide molar ratio of approximately 8 : 1 satisfactory (94–95 percent yield). Incidentally, they found that use of half the ether to cover the magnesium and the other half to dilute the halide gave results superior to those obtained by the method originally employed by Grignard (*loc. cit.*[1]).

In a report on a similar study of the preparation of *t*-butylmagnesium chloride, Gilman and Zoellner[46] recommend an ether-halide molar ratio of seven or eight to one.

Gilman and McGlumphey (*loc. cit.*[9]) report that, in the preparation of allylmagnesium bromide, a 7.5 : 1 ether-halide molar ratio gives yields superior to those obtained with 6 : 1 or 5 : 1 ratios.

[45] Gilman and McCracken, *Rec. trav. chim.*, 46, 463–72 (1927).

*In recording these data the present authors do not endorse their implied precision and reproducibility; the general qualitative trend indicated is accepted as significant.

[46] Gilman and Zoellner, *J. Am. Chem. Soc.*, 50, 425–8 (1928).

For the corresponding chloride, Kharasch and Fuchs (*loc. cit.*[10]) found an ether-halide ratio of approximately 3 : 1 quite satisfactory, although the Grignard reagent is relatively insoluble and is thus prepared in suspension. The two preparations, of course, are not strictly comparable, for, aside from the different characteristics of the two halides and their respective Grignard reagents, Kharasch and Fuchs operated at ice-bath temperatures, whereas Gilman and McGlumphey did not resort to cooling.

In general, when no previous data are available, and when there is no reason to suspect the halide employed of markedly abnormal behavior, it may be regarded as a safe rule to allow sufficient ether to cover the metallic magnesium plus sufficient to dilute the halide to give a solution containing 25–30 percent of halide by volume.

Gilman and Vanderwal[47] have investigated the effect of relative ether-halide concentrations on time of reaction initiation for four halides: *n*-butyl bromide, *n*-butyl chloride, bromobenzene, and benzyl chloride. One-half gram of magnesium turnings was activated with 5 drops of 25 percent ether-iodine solution (except in the case of *n*-butyl bromide, which required no activation). Seven milliliters of an ether-halide solution was then added. The time necessary for appearance of a Grignard reagent color test (Gilman and Schulze, *loc. cit.*[33]) was noted. In each case, the time-concentration curve passed through a minimum. The "optimal" halide concentrations by volume were: *n*-butyl bromide, *ca.* 55 percent; *n*-butyl chloride, *ca.* 70 percent; bromobenzene 25–30 percent; benzyl chloride 25–30 percent.

RATE OF ADDITION OF HALIDE

Like the degree of dilution of the halide, the rate of addition of the halide solution must be regarded as one of several interdependent factors. In general, however, relatively slow addition is to be recommended for iodides, most bromides, and a few of the more reactive chlorides.

Efficient agitation, high dilution, and, in some cases, cooling of the reaction mixture may be employed to minimize the time required for a comparatively large-scale preparation, but there is usually a limit below which unprofitable sacrifices in yield are made.

A rough indication of the effect of rate of halide addition on Grignard reagent yields in small-scale runs is afforded by data taken from two studies by Gilman *et al.*[48] and presented in Table II-III.* In the orthodox preparations (*Slow Add'n*) 0.054 gram-atom of magnesium was placed in

---

[47] Gilman and Vanderwal, *Bull. soc. chim.*, [4], *45*, 641–4 (1929).

[48] Gilman, Zoellner, and Dickey, *J. Am. Chem. Soc.*, *51*, 1576–83, 1583–7 (1929).

* In recording these data the present authors do not endorse their implied precision and reproducibility; the general qualitative trend indicated is accepted as significant.

TABLE II-III

EFFECT OF RATE OF HALIDE ADDITION ON GRIGNARD REAGENT YIELDS

Halide	Average yield (%)		Halide	Average yield (%)	
	Slow Add'n	Rapid Add'n		Slow Add'n	Rapid Add'n
C_2H_5Br	93.1	86.6	n-$C_7H_{15}Br$	88.8	72.9
n-C_3H_7Br	91.7	82.5	n-$C_8H_{17}Br$	88.4	73.3
i-C_3H_7Br	84.0	70.5	n-C_4H_9Cl	91.2	90.6
n-C_4H_9Br	94.0	79.2	n-C_4H_9I	85.6	67.8
i-C_4H_9Br	87.2	76.7	$C_6H_5CH_2Cl$	93.1	92.9
s-C_4H_9Br	77.7	61.6	C_6H_5Br	94.7	89.8
t-C_4H_9Br	25.1	17.8	2-$CH_3C_6H_4Br$	92.7	88.3
n-$C_5H_{11}Br$	88.6	73.2	3-$CH_3C_6H_4Br$	88.0	81.3
i-$C_5H_{11}Br$	88.0	70.2	4-$CH_3C_6H_4Br$	86.9	83.3
s-$C_5H_{11}Br$	66.8	49.2	1-$C_{10}H_7Br$	94.8	91.7
t-$C_5H_{11}Br$	23.7	19.1	2-$C_{10}H_7Br$	83.8	81.3
n-$C_6H_{13}Br$	92.0	77.2			

an oven-dried flask, together with 6.5 ml. of dried ether, 0.04 g. of iodine and 0.2 ml. of halide. Reaction was initiated by reflux at 45°. The remainder of a total of 0.05 mole of halide, dissolved in the remainder of a total of 30 ml. of ether, was then added gradually, with stirring, over a period of thirty to thirty-five minutes. Completion of reaction was effected by five to ten minutes reflux, in the cases of the alkyl halides, or fifteen to thirty minutes reflux, in the cases of the aryl halides. In the other study (*Rapid Add'n*) the conditions were the same except that after initiation of reaction the remainder of the ether-halide solution was added all at once.

In an extension of the studies just summarized, Gilman *et al.* (*loc. cit.*[48]) investigated the behavior of a considerable number of alkyl and aralkyl chlorides. In general, there was little or no significant difference in yields of organomagnesium chlorides between the slow-addition and rapid-addition experiments.

In the preparation of ethylmagnesium iodide, Gilman and Meyers (*loc. cit.*[5]) found that, up to forty-five minutes, the yield increased with increase in time of addition of the halide solution (9.5 g. of ethyl iodide in 25 ml. of ether).

For the preparation of *t*-butylmagnesium chloride, a rate of addition of the halide-ether solution of about 90 drops or 1.4 ml. per minute is recommended,[46] and it is stated that the slower the addition the higher the yield.[49]

AGITATION OF THE REACTION MIXTURE

In view of the probable inducement of undesirable side reactions by local superheating or local concentration effects, efficient stirring should

[49] Puntambeker and Zoellner, *Organic Syntheses*, Coll. Vol. I, 2nd ed., pp. 524-6, *1941*.

be regarded as a routine requirement in all Grignard reagent preparations. In the preparation of ethylmagnesium iodide, Gilman and Meyers (*loc. cit.*[33]) found that efficient stirring materially enhanced the yield. In preparations of suspensions of relatively insoluble Grignard reagents such as, for example allylmagnesium chloride (Kharasch and Fuchs, *loc. cit.*[10]) or 9-anthrylmagnesium bromide (Bachmann and Kloetzel, *loc. cit.*[44]), vigorous stirring is not only desirable, but imperative.

RELATIVE REACTIVITIES OF HALIDES

It is generally known that, on the basis of (1) ease of initiation of reaction with magnesium (as judged by the necessity for the use of activators), (2) length of time necessary for reaction with magnesium to become detectable, and (3) rate of disappearance of magnesium after reaction begins, the organic halides stand in the order of decreasing reactivity: RI > RBr > RCl, when the organic radical R remains the same throughout. This, of course, implies nothing about relative yields of the respective Grignard reagents or of the yields of products that may be obtained in subsequent reactions of the Grignard reagents. On the whole, however, it is evident that relatively high reactivity with respect to the criteria mentioned is usually accompanied by relatively high reactivity in side-reactions. Therefore, it is true in general that, of the Grignard reagents, RMgX, conveniently preparable, the one prepared from the least reactive halide is likely to be obtained in highest yield and to perform most satisfactorily in subsequent reactions.

As regards variations in halide activity when the halogen X remains the same, but the radical R is varied, it may be said that, despite a few apparent exceptions (scarcely surprising in the case of a heterogeneous reaction), the general rule is that halides (RX) in which the radical R is weakly electronegative, are more reactive toward magnesium in the presence of ethyl ether than halides in which the radical R is moderately or strongly electronegative.*

However, it cannot be too strongly emphasized that steric effects, relative product solubilities, relative diffusibilities, and even more obscure factors may lead to individual exceptions to the general tendencies described in the foregoing generalizations.

Rudd and Turner[50] have studied the relative reactivities of several pairs of halides toward magnesium by means of competitive reactions. Magnesium (0.025 gram atom), activated with 1.5 mg. of iodine, was allowed to react completely with a mixture of 0.025 mole each of halides I and II in 50 ml. of ether. The solution was then analyzed for halide ions.

---

*Concerning relative electronegativities of organic radicals, see: Kharasch and Reinmuth, *J. Chem. Education*, *5*, 404–18 (1928); 8, 1703–48 (1931); Kharasch, Reinmuth, and Mayo, *ibid.*, *11*, 82–96 (1934); *13*, 7–19 (1936).

[50] Rudd and Turner, *J. Chem. Soc.*, *1928*, 686–91.

TABLE II-IV

RELATIVE REACTIVITIES OF HALIDE PAIRS TOWARD MAGNESIUM

Halide Pair	Halide Ions in Sol'n (% Total)		
	Cl^-	Br^-	I^-
C_2H_5Cl-C_2H_5Br	24	76	—
n-C_3H_7Cl-*n*-C_3H_7Br	19	81	—
n-C_4H_9Cl-*n*-C_4H_9Br	9	91	—
$C_6H_5CH_2Cl$-*n*-C_4H_9Br	27	73	—
CH_3Cl-CH_3I	27	—	73
C_2H_5Cl-C_2H_5I	29	—	71
n-C_3H_7Cl-*n*-C_3H_7I	44	—	56
n-C_4H_9Cl-*n*-C_4H_9I	46	—	54
CH_3Br-CH_3I	—	71	29
C_2H_5Br-C_2H_5I	—	46	54
n-C_3H_7Br-*n*-C_3H_7I	—	57	43
n-C_4H_9Br-*n*-C_4H_9I	—	27	73
C_6H_5Br-C_6H_5I	—	52	48
2-$CH_3C_6H_4Br$-2-$CH_3C_6H_4I$	—	94	6
3-$CH_3C_6H_4Br$-3-$CH_3C_6H_4I$	—	88	12
4-$CH_3C_6H_4Br$-4-$CH_3C_6H_4I$	—	84	16

No account was taken of possible side-reactions. The data are recorded in Table II-IV.*

Strangely enough, Rudd and Turner report that a mixture of methyl chloride and methyl bromide did not react. Gilman and Vanderwal[51] investigated this halide pair under slightly different conditions. Five grams of magnesium, activated with a trace of iodine was covered with 75 g. of ether. A mixture of the gaseous halides, with the chloride in excess, was led into the ether until the magnesium had completely disappeared. Subsequent analysis revealed a bromide-chloride ratio of approximately 5:1.

In a study somewhat similar to that of Rudd and Turner, St. John and St. John[52] allowed 0.5 mole each of two halides to compete in reaction with 0.5 mole of magnesium. The halide pairs were so chosen that the Grignard reagent formed from one member of each pair could be determined by gas analysis. Total Grignard reagent formation was determined by acid titration. The percentage yields of Grignard reagents from the respective halide pairs were as follows: *n*-butyl bromide 33, bromobenzene

* In view of the demonstrated effect of the presence of a relatively reactive halide upon the apparent reactivity toward magnesium of a relatively unreactive halide (see Grignard Reagent Preparation by "Entrainment" p. 38), the quantitative significance of data obtained from such competitive reactions is highly questionable. In the opinion of the present authors, however, the qualitative differences indicated are real and significant.

[51] Gilman and Vanderwal, *Bull. soc. chim.*, [4], 45, 135–7 (1929).

[52] St. John and St. John, *Rec. trav. chim.*, 55, 585–8 (1936).

67; ethyl bromide 47, 1-naphthyl bromide 53; *n*-butyl bromide 46, benzyl chloride 54.

The comparative yields from the first two pairs of halides are rather striking in view of the results of other methods of comparing relative halide reactivities. St. John and St. John conclude that the presence of one halide affects the reactivity of the other (a possibility also suggested by Rudd and Turner). However, here again, there was no attempt to evaluate the products of side-reactions, which might throw a different light on the results.

In a further study of the relative reactivities of halides toward magnesium, Gilman and Vanderwal[53] treated 0.5 g. of magnesium turnings with 0.0187 mole of halide in 5 ml. of dry ether. Aliquot samples were withdrawn at definite intervals and submitted to a color test for a Grignard reagent (Gilman and Schulze, *loc. cit.*[33]). The times observed are recorded in Table II-V.

TABLE II-V

RELATIVE REACTIVITIES OF HALIDES TOWARD MAGNESIUM

Halide	Time for G.R. Test	Halide	Time for G.R. Test
CH_3I	3.5 min.	*n*-$C_6H_{13}I$	27.5 min.
C_2H_5I	4.5 min.	*n*-$C_7H_{15}Br$	12.5 min.
n-C_3H_7Br	7.5 min.	*n*-$C_8H_{17}Br$	16.3 min.
n-C_3H_7I	6.4 min.	$(CH_2)_5CHBr$	25.0 min.
n-C_4H_9Br	7.5 min.	$C_6H_5CH_2Cl$	25.0 min.
n-C_4H_9I	7.6 min.	C_6H_5Br	32.0 min.
i-C_4H_9Br	5.4 min.	2-$C_{10}H_7Br$	Several hours
s-C_4H_9Br	3.5 min.		

Under these conditions *n*-butyl chloride and 1-naphthyl bromide give no test in several years; cyclohexyl chloride, no test in two years; *p*-dibromobenzene, no test in one year. The *t*-butyl bromide could not be compared with the other butyl bromides, for, under these conditions, although it reacts with magnesium, it does not form a Grignard reagent.

Several of the aromatic halides were tested under similar conditions, but with the addition of ten drops of 5 percent ether-iodine solution as activator. The times observed were: *p*-dibromobenzene, 15.0 min.; *p*-bromotoluene, 16.5 min.; *m*-bromotoluene, 20.5 min.; *o*-bromotoluene, 23.0 min.; 2-naphthyl bromide, 21.2 min.; 1-bromonaphthalene, 25.8 min.

SOME ILLUSTRATIVE PREPARATIONS IN THE CLASSICAL MANNER

Apparatus. The container of choice for Grignard reagent preparations is a round-bottomed, three-necked flask of the standard-taper ground-glass-joint type. It should be fitted with an efficient mechanical stirrer, a condenser, and a dropping funnel. The dropping funnel may be replaced by various other attachments or by a ground-glass plug as occasion demands.

[53] Gilman and Vanderwal, *Bull. soc. chim.*, [4], *45*, 344–9 (1929).

The stirrer shaft may be provided with a mercury seal as a guard against atmospheric contamination. The authors prefer a seal of the Trubore type. Stirrers of this type are available in all-glass construction. Equally satisfactory models have been machined from brass in the University of Chicago shops. The authors have found a stirrer blade of the plate-glass crescent type the most satisfactory for general purposes.

Generally speaking, any fairly efficient reflux condenser will give adequate service. In warm, humid weather, however, a condenser of the interior-coolant type which is not subject to external sweating has obvious advantages. The open end of the condenser should be protected with calcium chloride and soda-lime tubes in series, or with a trap.

For the average occasional preparation no further protection against atmospheric contamination is necessary. In all quantitative studies, however, and when large numbers of preparations are being made, particularly in humid weather, it is advantageous to operate in an inert atmosphere, preferably nitrogen. Tank nitrogen may be used with no treatment other than a passage through a drying (calcium chloride) tower. The authors prefer to remove traces of oxygen by passage over heated copper granules. A Pyrex tube, packed with copper granules and externally heated with a Nichrome coil controlled by a variable transformer, has proved satisfactory. Satisfactory nitrogen-purification trains are also described by Fieser[54] and by Kohler *et al.*[55]

To insure complete dryness the authors place in the flask the magnesium to be used, and admit deoxygenated, dried nitrogen to the apparatus through a special plug which replaces the dropping funnel. When most of the air has been swept from the apparatus the flask is thoroughly flamed with a cool Bunsen flame to drive off adsorbed moisture, passage of nitrogen being continued throughout.

For all quantitative studies and for preparations in which the presence of residual metallic magnesium is objectionable, filtration of the Grignard solution through a sintered-glass disc or a glass-wool plug is effected with the aid of nitrogen pressure. When filtration is unnecessary and when the normal order of addition is used, subsequent reactions are carried out in the original flask.

The "cyclic reactor." A "cyclic reactor," especially useful for the preparation in good yields of Grignard reagents that react readily with the halides from which they are prepared is described by Rowlands *et al.*[55.1] as follows.

"We have obtained gratifying results by a system which attains high dilution by continuously recycling a moderate initial amount of solvent

---

[54] Fieser, *J. Am. Chem. Soc.*, *46*, 2639–47 (1924).

[55] Kohler, Stone, and Fuson, *J. Am. Chem. Soc.*, *49*, 3181–8 (1927).

[55.1] Rowlands, Greenlee, and Boord, *Abstracts of Papers*, 117th Meeting, A.C.S., Philadelphia, Pa., April 9–13, 1950, p. 8-L.

(usually ether). The halide is slowly added to the solvent stream as it enters the top of a vertical tube packed with amalgamated magnesium turnings. The Grignard reagent formed is swept into and accumulated in a heated flask while the solvent is refluxed back into the reaction tube. A 'hump' in the return line to the flask insures that the magnesium is covered with solvent at all times; the amalgamation is essential.

"Using this device we have consistently obtained yields of 85-95 percent from allyl bromide and 80-87 percent from crotyl bromide. Benzyl bromide gave a 96 percent yield and benzhydryl bromide 25 percent. With our apparatus Newman and Wotiz[55.2] got 98 percent yield from *n*-butylpropargyl bromide."

Gaertner[55.3] has also made use of this device for the preparation of various thenylmagnesium chlorides. The best percentage yields obtained by Gaertner in the "cyclic reactor" and the percentage yields obtained by conventional methods (in parentheses) were: 2-thenylmagnesium chloride, 98.0 (7.3); 2-thianaphthenylmethylmagnesium chloride, 93.0 (61.0); 3-thianaphthenylmethylmagnesium chloride, 99.0 (36.0).

Reagents. For general purposes magnesium turnings of the highest grade of purity obtainable (sublimed metal) are recommended. When it appears advisable to use more finely divided magnesium the turnings may be reduced to the desired size in a mill or even in a hand mortar.

For many routine preparations ordinary commercial anhydrous ether is entirely satisfactory. For quantitative studies, and for some special preparations, sodium-dried ether is indicated. It is claimed[56] that commercial ethers may be dried sufficiently for use as Grignard reaction solvents by adding an amount of silicon tetrachloride equivalent to the amount of water present and separating by filtration the precipitated silicic acid. Dehydration and general purification of ether by distillation from methylmagnesium iodide (any readily available Grignard reagent should serve as well) has also been recommended.[57]

By personal communication from Mr. George V. D. Tiers of the University of Chicago the authors are apprised of a method of solvent purification (particularly dehydration and deoxygenation) which they have not seen described elsewhere. The method appears to be rather generally applicable to ethers (*e.g.*, ethyl ether, tetrahydrofuran, glycol and polyglycol diethers), tertiary amines (*e.g.*, triethylamine, *N*-methylmorpholine), and aromatic hydrocarbons (*e.g.*, benzene, toluene).

[55.2] Newman and Wotiz, *J. Am. Chem. Soc.*, *71*, 1292-7 (1949). See also: Wotiz, *ibid.*, *72*, 1639-42 (1950); Wotiz and Palchak, *ibid.*, *73*, 1971-2 (1951); Wotiz, Matthews, and Lieb, *ibid.*, *73*, 5503-4 (1951).

[55.3] Gaertner, (*a*) *J. Am. Chem. Soc.*, *73*, 3934-7 (1951); (*b*) *ibid.*, *74*, 766-7 (1952); (*c*) *ibid.*, *74*, 2185-8 (1952).

[56] Buchanan and Simpson, U. S. Patent 2,446,408, Aug. 3, 1948; *Chem. Abstr.*, *42*, P8208 (1948).

[57] Mackle, *Proc. Roy. Irish Acad.*, *52B*, 49-56 (1948); *Chem. Abstr.*, *43*, 3780 (1949).

Solvent batches of any convenient size may be processed; for illustrative purposes the procedure is outlined as follows. To one litre of good-quality commercial ethyl ether, dried over anhydrous potassium hydroxide, in a reflux apparatus protected against access of moisture, is added 3–5 g. of benzophenone. The resultant solution is brought to reflux, and small particles of freshly-cut metallic sodium are added at intervals.

For obvious reasons the purification process is of indefinite length, and may require as much as two days. A solution of desirable purity is characterized by a persistent intense deep-blue coloration. A yellowish or greenish coloration indicates the necessity for the addition of more benzophenone (followed by further sodium addition). The purified solvent may be distilled, if desired, in a stream of dried nitrogen, but this precaution is unnecessary except for extremely oxygen-sensitive solvents (*e.g.*, isopropyl ether).

Although many commercial halides are of excellent purity and may be used without preliminary treatment in routine preparations, it is, in general, desirable that the halide be at least redistilled. Benzyl chloride, for example, should always be freshly distilled. A few halides give satisfactory results only when special standards of purity are met.

General method for preparation of organomagnesium halides. The method of Gilman *et al.* (*loc. cit.*[48]), outlined in connection with the discussion of the effect of rate of halide addition upon yields of Grignard reagents, may be regarded as a general, though probably not an optimal, method for the preparation of organomagnesium halides. It is applicable to *n*-alkyl bromides, many secondary alkyl bromides and the more reactive aryl bromides. Some indication of the yields to be expected is to be derived from the "slow addition" column of Table II-III.

Using this method with *n*-alkyl bromides, and treating the resultant Grignard reagents with allyl bromide, Wilkinson[58] obtained the indicated overall percentage yields of the following 1-alkenes: pentene, 94; hexene, 77; heptene, 90; octene, 89; nonene, 85.

Yields of twenty-one Grignard reagents prepared by a similar general method are reported by Gilman and McCracken.[59]

Methylmagnesium chloride.[60] One hundred grams of magnesium turnings in a suitably equipped flask surrounded by an ice-salt bath are covered with anhydrous ether. The chilled ether is saturated with commercial methyl chloride which has been passed through a calcium chloride tower. The cooling bath is then removed, and the mixture is allowed to come to

[58] Wilkinson, *J. Chem. Soc.*, *1931*, 3057–62.

[59] Gilman and McCracken, *J. Am. Chem. Soc.*, *45*, 2462–6 (1923).

[60] (*a*) Marvel and Moon, *J. Am. Chem. Soc.*, *62*, 45–9 (1940). See also: (*b*) Houben, *Ber.*, *39*, 1736–53 (1906); (*c*) Houben, Boedler, and Fischer, *Ber.*, *69B*, 1766–88 (1936); (*d*) Schmalfuss, *J. prakt. Chem.*, *108*, 88–90 (1924); (*e*) Gilman, Zoellner, Selby, and Boatner, *Rec. trav. chim.*, *54*, 584–94 (1935); (*f*) Coburn, *Organic Syntheses*, *27*, 65–7 (1947).

room temperature. If reaction does not begin, the cooling and saturation are repeated. Once reaction has been initiated 500 ml. of anhydrous ether is added, and methyl chloride is slowly passed into the mixture until all the magnesium has disappeared. A grayish precipitate of methylmagnesium chloride separates during the reaction. If ether loss becomes excessive more ether is added during the course of the reaction.

By treatment of a methylmagnesium chloride suspension, prepared as described, with *o*-bromobenzaldehyde, Marvel and Moon obtained an 87 percent yield of the expected secondary alcohol. By treatment of a suspension prepared in a similar manner with benzophenone, Schmalfuss obtained a 98 percent yield of the expected tertiary alcohol. In a preparation by Houben *et al.*,[60c] a variation of this method showed a 99.7 percent yield of Grignard reagent (on the basis of the magnesium consumed) by acid titration.

Ethylmagnesium chloride[61] may be prepared in essentially the same manner as methylmagnesium chloride. Houben *et al.*[60c] report a 98.6 percent yield by acid titration.

General method for the preparation of alkylmagnesium chlorides.[62] A general method, applied to the preparation of ethyl-, *n*-propyl-, isopropyl-, *n*-butyl-, isobutyl-, *s*-butyl-, and *t*-butylmagnesium chlorides, is described by Huston and Langham essentially as follows. Magnesium turnings (54.7 g., 2.25 moles are placed in a two-liter flask equipped with a mercury-sealed stirrer, an inlet tube for nitrogen, a reflux condenser, and a dropping funnel. After the system has been swept with dry nitrogen, 4–5 g. of alkyl chloride, dissolved in 100 ml. of anhydrous ethyl ether, is added. Initiation of reaction is facilitated by the addition of a small amount of ethyl bromide dissolved in 100 ml. of ethyl ether. The remainder of 2 moles of alkyl chloride, dissolved in 800 ml. of ethyl ether, is added from the dropping funnel at a rate to maintain moderate refluxing. (In the case of *t*-butyl chloride the rate of addition is exceptionally slow.) After completion of the chloride addition, a slow stream of nitrogen is introduced, and stirring is continued for two hours. Reaction is completed by overnight standing.

Although it is stated that Grignard reagent samples were evaluated by acid titration of aliquot portions, no values are reported.

Tertiary alkylmagnesium chlorides.[63] In a suitably equipped flask are placed a few small crystals of iodine and 98 g. of freshly turned mag-

[61] Kyriakides, *J. Am. Chem. Soc.*, *36*, 657–63 (1914).

[62] Huston and Langham, *J. Org. Chem.*, *12*, 90–5 (1947).

[63] (*a*) Whitmore and Badertsher, *J. Am. Chem. Soc.*, *55*, 1559–67 (1933). See also: (*b*) Whitmore and Houk, *ibid.*, *54*, 3714–8 (1932); (*c*) Greenwood, Whitmore, and Crooks, *ibid.*, *60*, 2028–30 (1938); (*d*) Gilman and Zoellner, *ibid.*, *50*, 425–8 (1928); *Rec. trav. chim.*, *47*, 1058–63 (1928); (*e*) Puntambeker and Zoellner, *Organic Syntheses*, Coll. Vol. I, 2nd ed., pp. 524–6, *1941*; (*f*) Rheinboldt, Mott, and Motzkus, *J. prakt. Chem.*, *134*, 257–81 (1933).

nesium. The bottom of the flask is heated with a small flame until the iodine begins to vaporize, and is then allowed to cool. Thirty milliliters of a solution of four moles of the tertiary halide in 500 ml. of dry ether is added. If reaction does not begin under these conditions a few drops of ethyl bromide or *n*-butyl bromide is added. After reaction has started and progressed for a few minutes, 200 ml. of dry ether is added to the reaction mixture. Four hundred seventy-five milliliters of ether-chloride solution is then added, with efficient stirring, at a rate not faster than one drop per second. Even slower addition is advisable in the case of the higher tertiary chlorides. After the first portion of the chloride has been added the remainder of the solution is diluted with an additional 300 ml. of dry ether and is added at the same rate with continued stirring. The mixture is permitted to reflux during the ether-chloride addition, no external cooling being applied. Heating after completion of the chloride addition is unnecessary; stirring, however, is continued for one hour.

Whitmore and Badertsher claim the indicated percentage yields (as determined by acid titration) of the following *t*-alkylmagnesium chlorides: $t\text{-}C_4H_9MgCl$, 80.0; $t\text{-}C_5H_{11}MgCl$, 73.6; $n\text{-}C_4H_9(CH_3)_2CMgCl$, 79.0; $n\text{-}C_5H_{11}(CH_3)_2CMgCl$, 59.9; $CH_3(C_2H_5)_2CMgCl$, 70.4; $CH_3(C_2H_5)(n\text{-}C_3H_7)CMgCl$, 77.7; $CH_3(C_2H_5)(n\text{-}C_4H_9)CMgCl$, 70.0; $(C_2H_5)_3CMgCl$, 58.3. Substantially the same method was used for $t\text{-}C_4H_9MgCl$ by Whitmore and Houk, who claim an 85 percent yield (by titration), and by Greenwood *et al.*, who claim yields of 75–85 percent (by titration). Rheinboldt *et al.* used a method differing only in detail for 1–2 mole lots of $t\text{-}C_4H_9MgCl$, and claim yields of Grignard reagent as high as 90 percent. According to Gilman and Zoellner, who used a similar method for $t\text{-}C_4H_9MgCl$, large runs give better yields than small ones, and 200-mesh magnesium powder gives better yields than fine magnesium turnings. Upon carbonation of a solution of $t\text{-}C_4H_9MgCl$ prepared by a similar method, Puntambeker and Zoellner obtained trimethylacetic acid in 61–63 percent yields from magnesium turnings, and in 69–70 percent yields from magnesium powder.

Allylmagnesium chloride.[64] Magnesium turnings (80 g.) and dry ether (400 ml.) are placed in a suitably equipped flask, which is cooled in an ice-bath. The mixture is vigorously stirred, and allyl chloride (230 g.) in dry ether (400 ml.) solution is added from a dropping funnel at such a rate that little or no gas evolution takes place. Formation of the Grignard reagent begins almost immediately, and is usually complete within ten hours. The allyl Grignard reagent so prepared is a white crystalline solid which forms a smooth suspension in ether.

The chloride reacts in suspension to give better yields of products than can be obtained by the use of clear solutions of the corresponding bromide. Treatment of α-chloro-β-diethylaminoethane with an excess of

[64] Kharasch and Fuchs, *J. Org. Chem.*, 9, 359–72 (1944).

allylmagnesium chloride suspension gave an 85 percent yield of the expected unsaturated amine (on the basis of the chloroalkylamine expended).

β-Methallylmagnesium chloride.[64] This compound may be prepared in the same manner as allylmagnesium chloride.

Cyclohexylmagnesium chloride.[65] In a suitably equipped 1-liter flask 26.7 g. (1.1 g.-atom) of magnesium is covered with about 100 ml. of anhydrous ether, and 15 ml. of pure cyclohexyl chloride and a crystal of iodine are added. Heat is then applied until five to ten minutes after the iodine color has disappeared. An additional 125 ml. of ether is added, stirring is begun, and the remainder of a total of 118.5 g. (121 ml., 1.0 mole) of cyclohexyl chloride, dissolved in 225 ml. of ether, is added with moderate rapidity (0.5–0.75 hr.), with cooling if necessary. (In the preparation of cyclohexylmagnesium bromide the addition of the ether-halide solution must be much slower.) Stirring and refluxing are continued for fifteen to twenty minutes after completion of the addition.

Grignard reagent yields of about 92 percent (by titration) are claimed. Carbonation leads to the expected carboxylic acid in about 93 percent yield (on the basis of Grignard reagent present) or 85 percent overall. (Cyclohexylmagnesium bromide is obtained in about 80 percent yield, with subsequent carbonation leading to a 66 percent overall yield of the carboxylic acid.)

Cinnamylmagnesium chloride.[66] Cinnamyl chloride (m. 7–8°) prepared from cinnamyl alcohol (m. 32–33°) by the action of thionyl chloride in chloroform-pyridine solution was used. Reaction is initiated by the addition of 20 drops of pure, freshly distilled chloride to 15 g. of 30–60 mesh magnesium covered with 25 ml. of dry ether. A solution of 30.5 g. of chloride in 275 ml. of ether is then added very slowly (2.25 hrs.) with vigorous stirring.

Titration yields of 83–87 percent are reported. Carbonation leads to α-phenyl-α-vinylacetic acid in 62–66 percent yields.

Phenylmagnesium bromide.[67] Magnesium turnings (20 g.), bromobenzene (3–5 g.) and dry ether (150 ml.) are combined. One gram of iodine-activated magnesium is added, and the mixture is stirred until reaction begins. The remainder of a total of 78.5 g. of bromobenzene, dissolved in 200 ml. of ether, is then added in the course of a half-hour.

---

[65] (*a*) Gilman and Zoellner, *J. Am. Chem. Soc.*, 53, 1945–8 (1931). See also: (*b*) Gilman and Catlan, *Organic Syntheses*, Coll. Vol. I, 2nd ed., pp. 188–90, *1941*.

[66] Gilman and Harris, (*a*) *Rec. trav. chim.*, 50, 1052–5 (1931); (*b*) *J. Am. Chem. Soc.*, 53, 3541–6 (1931); (*c*) Young, Ballou, and Nozaki, *J. Am. Chem. Soc.*, 61, 12–15 (1939); (*d*) Campbell and Young, *J. Am. Chem. Soc.*, 69, 688–90 (1947).

[67] (*a*) Hershberg, *Helv. Chim. Acta*, 17, 351–8 (1934). See also: (*b*) Allen and Converse, *Organic Syntheses*, Coll. Vol. I, 2nd ed., pp. 226–7, *1941*; (*c*) Gilman, St. John, and St. John, *Rec. trav. chim.*, 48, 593–6 (1929).

By treatment of a Grignard solution so prepared with allyl bromide, Hershberg obtained an 82 percent overall yield of allylbenzene. Allen and Converse report an overall yield of about 75 percent of the expected carbinol upon treatment of a Grignard solution prepared by a similar method with ethyl acetate. Using a similar method, Gilman *et al.* claim Grignard reagent yields of 96–98 percent (by acid titration).

Mesitylmagnesium bromide.[68] In a suitably equipped 3-liter flask is placed 48 g. of fine magnesium turnings, 100 g. of bromomesitylene and 150 g. of ether. Reaction is initiated by the addition of a little iodine or Gilman's iodine-activated copper-magnesium alloy. Stirring is begun, and a solution of 298 g. of bromide in 600 g. of ether is added at a rate to maintain brisk refluxing. After the addition is completed refluxing is continued until nearly all the magnesium has disappeared.

Isodurene is obtained in 52–60 percent yields by treatment of a Grignard solution so prepared with dimethyl sulfate.

9-Phenanthrylmagnesium bromide.[69] A mixture of 6.45 g. of 9-bromophenanthrene, 0.65 g. of magnesium, 0.05 g. of iodine, 15 ml. of ether and 15 ml. of benzene is refluxed under nitrogen for four to five hours, at the end of which time 95–98 percent of the theoretical amount of magnesium should have reacted.

Bachmann describes the treatment of Grignard solutions so prepared with some fifteen co-reactants. Among the percentage yields of "normal" products reported are: CO_2, 70; C_6H_5CHO, 72; $(C_6H_5)_2CO$, 76.

9-Anthrylmagnesium bromide.[70] For use in the preparation of this Grignard reagent pure (99.7 percent), cleaned magnesium ribbon was pulverized in a Wiley mill, washed twice with acetone, and dried. (Ordinary magnesium turnings reacted to the extent of only 55 percent in twenty-four hours.) The purity of the halide is also important; 9-bromoanthracene melting below 100° is not suitable. Of the several methods tried by Bachmann and Kloetzel the following gave the best yield of Grignard reagent (86 percent by acid titration).

A mixture of 2.57 g. of 9-bromoanthracene, 0.50 g. of magnesium powder, 5 drops of ethyl bromide and 20 ml. of ether is refluxed for twenty-four hours, with frequent agitation during the first few hours.

Styrylmagnesium bromide.[71] A mixture of 7.32 g. of 30–80 mesh magnesium, 30 drops of styryl bromide, 0.08 g. of iodine and 20 ml. of ether is refluxed for about fifteen minutes to initiate reaction. When reaction

[68] (*a*) Smith and MacDougall, *J. Am. Chem. Soc.*, *51*, 3001–8 (1929); (*b*) Smith, *Organic Syntheses*, Coll. Vol. II, pp. 360–2, *1943*.

[69] (*a*) Bachmann, *J. Am. Chem. Soc.*, *56*, 1363–7 (1934). See also: (*b*) Pschorr, *Ber.*, *30*, 3128–9 (1906).

[70] Bachmann and Kloetzel, *J. Org. Chem.*, *3*, 55–61 (1938).

[71] Gilman, Zoellner, Selby, and Boatner, *Rec. trav. chim.*, *54*, 584–94 (1935).

TABLE II-VI

SOME GRIGNARD REAGENT PREPARATIONS IN THE CLASSICAL MANNER

Halide, RX	Yield G.R., RMgX (%)	Co-reactant	Yield, "Normal" Product (%)	Ref.
C_2H_5Br	...	$(C_2H_5O)_2CO$	82–88	*15*
i-C_3H_5Br	...	CH_3CHO	53–54	*4*
n-C_4H_9Br	...	$O{=\!=}(CH_2)_2$	60–62	*5*
n-C_4H_9Br	...	$HCO_2C_2H_5$	83–85	*3*
n-C_4H_9Br	87–91	...	...	*10*
i-C_4H_9Br	74	...	...	*21*
s-C_4H_9Cl	...	CO_2	76–86	*7*
n-$C_5H_{11}Br$	...	$(C_2H_5O)_3CH$	45–50	*2*
t-$C_4H_9CH_2Cl$	89	$(i\text{-}C_3H_7)_2CO$	4*	*19*
$(CH_2)_5CHBr$	*ca.* 80	$H_2C{=\!=}CHCH_2Br$	60–64	*14*
$CH_3(n\text{-}C_4H_9)CHBr$	...	H_2O	50–53	*16*
4-BrC_6H_4Br	...	H_2O	70†	*17*
$(CH_3)_3SiOSi(CH_3)_2CH_2Cl$	80	...	...	*22*
2-$F_3CC_6H_4Br$	98	CO_2	86	*12*
4-$F_3CC_6H_4Br$	...	CO_2	90	*12*
$C_6H_5CH_2Cl$	91	...	...	*10*
$C_6H_5CH_2Cl$	...	$(C_2H_5)_2SO$	70–75	*6*
$C_6H_5CH_2Cl$	...	$(C_6H_5)_2CO$	54–59‡	*1*
$C_6H_5CH_2Cl$	93	...	...	*11*
4-$CH_3C_6H_4Br$	...	$CH_3COC_2H_5$	71	*18*
4-$CH_3OC_6H_4CH_2Cl$	90	...	...	*23*
1-$C_{10}H_7Br$	96	...	...	*10*
1-$C_{10}H_7Br$	...	CO_2	68–70	*9*
1-$C_{10}H_7Br$	...	$(C_2H_5O)_2CO$	68–73	*20*
1-$C_{10}H_7CH_2Cl$	*ca.* 80	CO_2	59	*7*
1-$C_{10}H_7CH_2Cl$	88–92	H_2O	80	*24*
4-$(C_2H_5)_3SiC_6H_4Br$	...	H_2O	83	*25*
4-$C_6H_5CH_2OC_6H_4CH_2Cl$	90	...	...	*23*
n-$C_{18}H_{37}MgBr$	85	...	...	*26*
$(C_6H_5)_2C{=\!=}C(C_6H_5)Br$	...	CO_2	89	*13*

* The ketone undergoes enolization to the extent of 90 percent.

† The Wurtz product, (4-BrC_6H_4—$)_2$, was formed to the extent of 10.0 percent; benzene, from 4-$BrMgC_6H_4MgBr$, to the extent of 12.8 percent, was also recovered.

‡ The product isolated in this case is the olefin (*i.e.*, the dehydrate of the "normal" addition product).

REFERENCES FOR TABLE II-VI

(*1*) Adkins and Zartman, *Organic Syntheses*, Col. Vol. II, pp. 606–7, *1943*.
(*2*) Bachmann, *Organic Syntheses*, Coll. Vol. II, pp. 323–5, *1943*.
(*3*) Coleman and Craig, *Organic Syntheses*, Coll. Vol. II, pp. 179–81, *1943*.
(*4*) Drake and Cook, *Organic Syntheses*, Coll. Vol. II, pp. 406–7, *1943*.
(*5*) Dreger, *Organic Syntheses*, Coll. Vol. I, 2nd ed., pp. 306–8, *1941*.
(*6*) Gilman and Catlin, *Organic Syntheses*, Coll. Vol. I, 2nd ed., pp. 471–3, *1941*
(*7*) Gilman and Kirby, *J. Am. Chem. Soc.*, 57, 3475–8 (1929).
(*8*) Gilman and Kirby, *Organic Syntheses*, Coll. Vol. I, 2nd ed., pp. 361–4, *1941*.

(9) Gilman, St. John, and Schulze, *Organic Syntheses*, Coll. Vol. II, pp. 425–7, *1941*.
(10) Gilman, St. John, and St. John, *Rec. trav. chim.*, *48*, 593–6 (1929).
(11) Gilman, Zoellner, and Dickey, *J. Am. Chem. Soc.*, *51*, 1576–83, 1583–7 (1929).
(12) Jones, *J. Am. Chem. Soc.*, *69*, 2346–50 (1947).
(13) Koelsch, *J. Am. Chem. Soc.*, *54*, 2045–8 (1932).
(14) Lespieau and Bourguel, *Organic Syntheses*, Coll. Vol. I, 2nd ed., pp. 186–7, *1941*.
(15) Moyer and Marvel, *Organic Syntheses*, Coll. Vol. II, pp. 602–4, *1943*.
(16) Noller, *Organic Syntheses*, Coll. Vol. II, pp. 478–80, *1943*.
(17) Quelet, *Bull. soc. chim.*, [4], *41*, 933–6 (1927).
(18) Rupe and Burgin, *Ber.*, *44*, 1218–25 (1911).
(19) Whitmore and George, *J. Am. Chem. Soc.*, *64*, 1239–42 (1942).
(20) Whitmore and Loder, *Organic Syntheses*, Coll. Vol. II, pp. 282–3, *1943*.
(21) Whitmore and Lux, *J. Am. Chem. Soc.*, *54*, 3448–54 (1932).
(22) Roedel, *J. Am. Chem. Soc.*, *71*, 269–72 (1949).
(23) Van Campen, Meisner, and Parmerter, *J. Am. Chem. Soc.*, *70*, 2296–7 (1948).
(24) Grummitt and Buck, *J. Am. Chem. Soc.*, *65*, 295–6 (1943).
(25) Grüttner and Krause, *Ber.*, *50*, 1559–68 (1917).
(26) Jones, *J. Am. Chem. Soc.*, *69*, 2350–4 (1947).

begins 40 ml. of ether is added. Then a solution of 18.3 g. of bromide in 47 ml. of ether is added over the course of an hour, with refluxing and stirring. Refluxing and stirring are continued for fifteen minutes after completion of the addition.

A 90 percent yield of Grignard reagent (by acid titration) is reported. The magnesium used in this study was of 99.8 percent purity, containing 0.15 percent copper, 0.06 percent iron, and 0.02 percent silica. Various other samples of magnesium turnings gave yields of 68–78 percent, depending upon the source.

Triphenylmethylmagnesium bromide.[72] The bromide is preferred for preparation of the Grignard reagent because, unlike the chloride,[73] it does not require iodine activation. A mixture of 16.2 g. of triphenylmethyl bromide, 1.34 g. (0.12 g. excess) of magnesium ribbon, 25 ml. of ether and 50 ml. of benzene is heated on a steam bath. The solution is protected against oxygen and against light. The reaction is apparently completed in less than an hour. The solution is filtered through sintered glass.

Acid titration and hydrocarbon isolated upon hydrolysis indicate a Grignard reagent yield of 95–97 percent. Carbonation leads to nearly quantitative yields of triphenylacetic acid.

Other Grignard reagent preparations. Some references to other Grignard reagent preparations described in more or less detail in the literature are assembled in Table II-VI.

[72] Gomberg and Bachmann, *J. Am. Chem. Soc.*, *52*, 2455–61 (1930).
[73] Schmidlin, *Ber.*, *39*, 628–36 (1906).

Because of the relatively lower yields of Grignard reagents attainable and the susceptibility of the Grignard reagents to side-reactions, iodides are not recommended for preparative purposes, and no examples are included in the foregoing illustrative preparations. In a study by Houben *et al.* (*loc. cit.*[60c]), in which methods of preparation were varied somewhat according to the halide concerned, relative yields of several normal and iso alkylmagnesium chlorides, bromides, and iodides, were determined by titration on the basis of the magnesium (99.8 percent) consumed, (Table II-VII).*

TABLE II-VII

RELATIVE YIELDS OF SOME NORMAL AND ISO ALKYLMAGNESIUM HALIDES

R (in RX)	Yields (%) of RMgX		
	Chlorides	Bromides	Iodides
CH_3	99.7	98.9	100.0
C_2H_5	98.6	97.0	96.4
n-C_3H_7	98.2	92.5	91.8
i-C_3H_7	93.9	83.5	57.5
n-C_4H_9	98.5	88.5	85.0
i-C_4H_9	98.9	82.3	79.6
i-C_5H_{11}	96.3	79.1	75.1
n-C_6H_{13}	97.2	86.8	79.9
n-C_7H_{15}	97.5	88.1	79.0
n-C_8H_{17}	96.2	86.8	81.7
n-$C_{10}H_{21}$	96.0	86.8	78.0
i-$C_{11}H_{23}$	89.7	62.1	42.9
n-$C_{16}H_{33}$	96.0	81.4	79.7

SOME LIMITATIONS OF THE CLASSICAL METHOD

From the rather meagre experimental evidence available it would appear that, in general, the *gem*-dihalides are poor prospects for Grignard reagent preparation. Emschwiller[74] claims to have prepared methylenemagnesium bromide [$H_2C(MgBr)_2$] and iodide [$H_2C(MgI)_2$] from methylene bromide and iodide, respectively, asserting that methane is liberated upon hydrolysis of the reaction mixture. Chang and Chao-Lun Tseng[75] report confirmation of Emschwiller's results in so far as methylene iodide is concerned, but add that the maximum yield is 10 percent, and that the supposed Grignard reagent does not react with acetone, benzophenone, Michler's ketone, or carbon dioxide.

---

* In recording these data the present authors do not endorse their implied precision and reproducibility; the general qualitative trend indicated is accepted as significant.

[74] Emschwiller, *Compt. rend.*, *183*, 665–7 (1926); *Chem. Abstr.*, *21*, 563 (1927).

[75] Chang and Chao-Lun Tseng, *Trans. Sci. Soc. China*, 7, 243–51 (1932), *Chem. Abstr.*, *26*, 5544 (1932).

According to Chao-Lun Tseng,[76] pure anhydrous chloroform, bromoform, or carbon tetrachloride do not react with magnesium in ethyl ether. Addition of iodine, methyl iodide, or ethyl iodide had no "catalytic" effect. Preliminary experiments showed that carbon tetrabromide reacts vigorously with magnesium.

According to Henne,[77] neither dichlorodifluoromethane, chlorodifluoromethane, nor bromodifluoromethane react with molten sodium, the implication being that they are similarly inert toward magnesium.

Chang and Chao-Lun Tseng[78] report that neither benzylidene chloride ($C_6H_5CHCl_2$) nor benzylidyne chloride ($C_6H_5CCl_3$) react with magnesium in the absence of a "catalyst." Addition of ethylmagnesium iodide initiates reaction which leads to the formation of a yellow amorphous product (apparently a mixture of hydrocarbons of high molecular weight).

In general the *vic*-dihalides are also poor risks in Grignard reagent preparation. Tissier and Grignard[79] found that, with magnesium, ethylene bromide undergoes an internal Wurtz reaction to yield ethylene and magnesium bromide.* The "crystalline products" obtained by Ahrens and Stapler[80] from magnesium, ethylene bromide, and aromatic aldehydes were doubtless Werner complexes of the approximate average composition $RCHO \cdot MgBr_2 \cdot O(C_2H_5)_2$. On distillation they yielded the respective aldehydes and ethyl ether. Bischoff[81] was similarly unsuccessful in attempts to prepare ethylenemagnesium bromide ($BrMgCH_2CH_2MgBr$) from ethyl bromide. Courtot[82] treated 2,3-dimethyl-3,4-dibromobutene with magnesium and obtained 2,3-dimethylbutadiene (biïsopropenyl).

By a combination of the internal Wurtz and the Grignardization reactions, von Braun *et al.*[83] have prepared several unsaturated Grignard reagents from tribromides, *e.g.*,

---

[76] Chao-Lun Tseng, *Natl. Central. Univ. Sci. Repts.*, Ser. A, *1*, No. 2, 1–4 (1931); *Chem. Abstr.*, *26*, 2166 (1932); *Trans. Sci. Soc. China*, 7, 233–7 (1932); *Chem. Abstr.*, *26*, 5544 (1932).

[77] Henne, *J. Am. Chem. Soc.*, *60*, 2275–6 (1938).

[78] Chang and Chao-Lun Tseng, *Trans. Sci. Soc. China*, 7, 239–42 (1932); *Chem. Abstr.*, *26*, 5544 (1932).

[79] Tissier and Grignard, *Compt. rend.*, *132*, 835 (1901); *Chem. Zentr.*, *1901,I*, 999.

* Incidentally this reaction constitutes the basis of a method for the preparation of small quantities of anhydrous ethereal magnesium bromide more convenient in some respects than the classical method of Zelinsky, *J. Russ. Phys.-Chem. Soc.*, *35*, 399–404 (1903); *J. Chem. Soc.*, *84,I*, 802 (1903), and Menschutkin, *Z. anorg. chem.*, *49*, 34–45 (1906).

[80] Ahrens and Stapler, *Ber.*, *38*, 1296–8, 3259–67 (1905).

[81] Bischoff, *Ber.*, *38*, 2078–83 (1905).

[82] Courtot, *Bull. soc. chim.*, [3], *35*, 969–88 (1906).

[83] (*a*) von Braun and Sobecki, *Ber.*, *44*, 1039–48 (1911); (*b*) von Braun and Deutsch, *Ber.*, *44*, 3699–706 (1911); (*c*) von Braun and Kohler, *Ber.*, *51*, 79–96 (1918); (*d*) von Braun and Kirschbaum, *Ber.*, *52B*, 1713–6 (1919).

$$BrCH_2CHBr(CH_2)_2Br + 2\,Mg \longrightarrow H_2C{=}CH(CH_2)_2MgBr + MgBr_2$$

$$BrCH_2CHBr(CH_2)_3Br + 2\,Mg \longrightarrow H_2C{=}CH(CH_2)_3MgBr + MgBr_2$$

$$CH_3CHBrCHBr(CH_2)_2Br + 2\,Mg \longrightarrow CH_3CH{=}CH(CH_2)_2MgBr + MgBr_2$$

Somewhat more surprising is the report by Henne (*loc. cit.*[77]) that 1,1-difluoro-2-iodoethane reacts with magnesium to yield fluoroethylene together with a mixture of magnesium fluoride and iodide, and that 1,1-difluoro-2-bromoethane does not react with magnesium at all. Brice *et al.*[84] have found that heptafluorobromopropane reacts with magnesium to form a Grignard reagent which liberates heptafluoropropane upon hydrolysis, but emphasize the necessity of maintaining rigorously anhydrous conditions during the Grignardization.

More recently Haszeldine[84.1] reports that both the purity of the magnesium used and the nature of the reaction solvent employed exert a profound influence on success in the preparation of a Grignard reagent from heptafluoroïodopropane.

Adjacency less than vicinal of the halogen atoms in a dihalide may also interfere with Grignardization. Bischoff (*loc. cit.*[81]) was unsuccessful in the attempt to prepare trimethylenemagnesium bromide [$BrMg(CH_2)_3MgBr$] from trimethylene bromide. Zelinsky and Gutt,[85] who treated trimethylene bromide with magnesium in ether, and then carbonated the resultant reaction mixture, isolated cyclopropane and propene, together with a 20 percent yield of suberic acid [$HO_2C(CH_2)_6CO_2H$].

Exceptions might be expected, however, as in cases in which the 3-halogen atom of a 1,3-dihalide is relatively unreactive. Lespieau and Deluchat[86] found that, although, under the conditions employed by them, treatment of 2,4-dibromo-1-butene with magnesium yielded chiefly the Wurtz product (2,7-dibromo-1,7-octadiene), some Grignard reagent [$H_2C{=}CBr(CH_2)_2MgBr$] was formed, for treatment of the reaction mixture with methyl chloromethyl ether produced a small amount of 2-bromo-5-methoxy-1-butene. Similarly, although Henne and Whaley[87] had reported that 1,1,1-trifluoro-3-chloropropane reacts neither with ethylmagnesium bromide nor magnesium, McBee and Truchan,[88] by maintaining rigorously anhydrous conditions, were able to prepare a Grignard reagent which, upon oxidation, yielded 39.5 percent of the expected alcohol, and, upon carbonation, yielded 42.5 percent of the expected acid.

---

[84] Brice, Pearlson, and Simons, *J. Am. Chem. Soc.*, *68*, 968–9 (1946).

[84.1] Haszeldine, *J. Chem. Soc.*, *1952*, 3423–8.

[85] Zelinsky and Gutt, *Ber.*, *40*, 3049–50 (1907).

[86] Lespieau and Deluchat, *Compt. rend.*, *183*, 889–91 (1926); *Chem. Zentr.*, *1927*,*I*, 260.

[87] Henne and Whaley, *J. Am. Chem. Soc.*, *64*, 1157–9 (1942).

[88] McBee and Truchan, *J. Am. Chem. Soc.*, *70*, 2910–1 (1948).

$$F_3CCH_2CH_2Cl \xrightarrow{Mg} F_3CCH_2CH_2MgCl \xrightarrow{O_2} \xrightarrow{H_3O^+} F_3CCH_2CH_2OH$$

$$F_3CCH_2CH_2Cl \xrightarrow{Mg} F_3CCH_2CH_2MgCl \xrightarrow{CO_2} \xrightarrow{H_3O^+} F_3CCH_2CH_2CO_2H$$

According to von Braun and Sobecki,[89] treatment of ethereal tetramethylene bromide with magnesium and subsequent carbonation of the reaction mixture yields cyclobutane, a very small amount of cyclopentanone, and sebacic [$HO_2C(CH_2)_8CO_2H$] and 1,12-dodecanedicarboxylic acids.

Schmitt[90] claims to have prepared dehydrosqualene,

$$[(CH_3)_2C=CH(CH_2)_2C(CH_3)=CHCH=CHC(CH_3)=CHCH_2-]_2$$

by a Barbier-type reaction involving metallic magnesium, tetramethylene bromide, and pseudoionone (ψ-ionone),

$$CH_3COCH=CHCH=C(CH_3)(CH_2)_2CH=C(CH_3)_2$$

No statement is made concerning the yield.

Pentamethylene and the higher polymethylene halides give fairly satisfactory yields of the dimagnesium compounds, although most workers report considerable Wurtz reaction.[91] Cycloalkane formation appears to be negligible.

As regards their reactions with magnesium the β- and γ-halo ethers have something in common with the analogous dihalides, for it appears that the phenoxy group, at least, may sometimes play the part of a pseudohalogen. Grignard[92] observed, for example, that β-bromophenetole reacts with magnesium principally to form ethylene and the bromomagnesium salt of phenol, together with a little 1,4-diphenoxybutane. In so far as it proceeds (until halted by occlusion of the magnesium surface), the reaction of β-ethoxyisoheptyl bromide with magnesium is similar.[93]

$$i\text{-}C_5H_{11}CH(OC_2H_5)CH_2Br + Mg \longrightarrow i\text{-}C_5H_{11}CH=CH_2 + MgBrOC_2H_5$$

The behavior of γ-iodopropoxybenzene is analogous to that of trimethylene bromide in that reaction with magnesium leads chiefly to cyclopro-

[89] von Braun and Sobecki, *Ber.*, *44*, 1918–31 (1911).

[90] Schmitt, *Ann.*, *547*, 115–22 (1941).

[91] See, *e.g.*: Grignard and Vignon, *Compt. rend.*, *144*, 1358–60 (1907); *Chem. Abstr.*, *1*, 2553 (1907); von Braun and Sobecki, *Ber.*, *44*, 1039–48, 1918–31 (1911); Hilpert and Grüttner, *Ber.*, *47*, 177–85 (1914); Dionneau, *Ann. chim.*, [9], 3, 194–268 (1915); Grüttner and Wiernik, *Ber.*, *48*, 1473–86 (1915); Grüttner and Krause, *Ber.*, *49*, 2666–75 (1916); Lespieau, *Compt. rend.*, *187*, 605–7 (1928); *Chem. Abstr.*, *23*, 817 (1929); *Bull. soc. chim.*, [4], *43*, 1189–93 (1928); Müller and Schutz, *Ber.*, *71B*, 689–91 (1938); Lukeš and Bláha, *Chem. Listy*, *46*, 683–4 (1952); *Chem. Abstr.*, *47*, 8013 (1953).

[92] Grignard, *Compt. rend.*, *138*, 1048–50 (1904); *J. Chem. Soc.*, *86*,*I*, 494 (1904).

[93] Swallen and Boord, *J. Am. Chem. Soc.*, *52*, 651–60 (1930).

pane and iodomagnesium phenoxide, together with a little 1,6-diphenoxyhexane.[94] Apparently the analogous bromo ether behaves similarly.[95]

According to Gaertner,[95.1] the reaction of magnesium with 2-chloromethylbenzofuran is analogous to that with β-bromophenetole, for the only identifiable product appears to be *o*-allenylphenol.

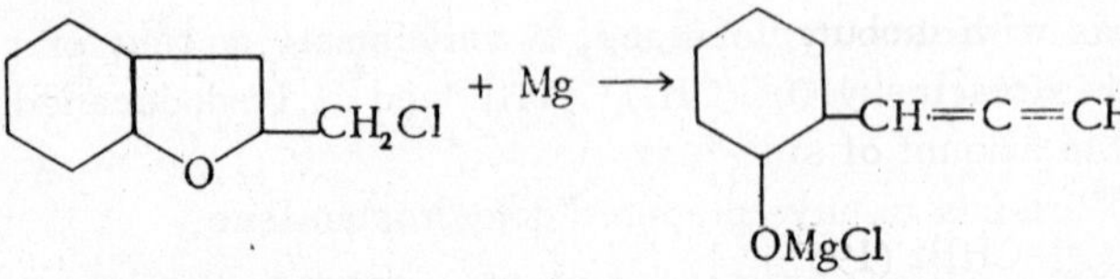

$$\text{(2-chloromethylbenzofuran, } CH_2Cl) + Mg \longrightarrow \text{(o-MgClO-}C_6H_4\text{)}-CH{=}C{=}CH_2$$

Probably a similar ether cleavage prevents preparation of a Grignard reagent from furfuryl chloride.[95.1, 95.2]

On the basis of the rather limited evidence available it would appear that the alkoxy groups are somewhat less inclined than the phenoxy group to behave as pseudohalogens, for successful preparations of Grignard reagents are reported in the cases of 1-bromo-3-methoxypropane (Erlenmeyer and Marbet, *loc. cit.*[95]), 1-iodo-3-methoxypropane,[96a] 1-bromo-3-amoxypropane,[96b] and 1-iodo-3-amoxypropane.[96a]

Halo ethers of the type $RO(CH_2)_nX$ in which n is greater than three are also reported as reacting normally with magnesium to form Grignard reagents.[96a,b,97]

It is said of β-chloroethyl ether $[(ClCH_2CH_2)_2O]$ that it shows no tendency to form a Grignard reagent, and of the corresponding diïodo compound that its reaction with magnesium yields no isolable product.[98]

Austerweil[99] claimed to have prepared isoprene by the improbable reaction sequence:

$$H_2C{=}CHBr \xrightarrow{Mg} H_2C{=}CHMgBr \xrightarrow{ClC(CH_3){=}CH_2} H_2C{=}CHC(CH_3){=}CH_2$$

It would appear much more likely, however, that if the experimental procedure described yields isoprene at all, it does so through a Wurtz-type reaction. Austerweil's product also included butadiene and 2,3-dimethylbutadiene (biïsopropenyl). According to Krestinsky,[100] vinyl bromide reacts with magnesium to yield a mixture of ethylene and acetylene.

---

[94] Paul, *Compt. rend.*, *192*, 964–5 (1931); *Chem. Zentr.*, *1931*,*I*, 3667.

[95] Erlenmeyer and Marbet, *Helv. Chim. Acta*, *29*, 1946–9 (1946).

[95.1] Gaertner, *J. Am. Chem. Soc.*, 73, 4400–4 (1951). See also Chapter V.

[95.2] Gilman and Hewlett, *Rec. trav. chim.*, *51*, 93–7 (1932).

[96] Hamonet, (*a*) *Compt. rend.*, *138*, 975–7 (1904); *Chem. Zentr.*, *1904*,*I*, 1400; (*b*) *Bull. soc. chim.*, [3], 33, 528–33 (1905).

[97] von Braun, Deutsch, and Smatloch, *Ber.*, *45*, 1246–63 (1912).

[98] Gibson and Johnson, *J. Chem. Soc.*, *1930*, 2525–30.

[99] Austerweil, German Patent 245,180, March 4, 1912; Friedländer, *10*, 1027–8 (1913); *Chem. Zentr.*, *1912*,*I*, 1267.

[100] Krestinsky, *Ber.*, *55B*, 2770–4 (1922).

From the results of iodine titration, Kirrman[101] obtained very little evidence of the Grignardization of either 1-bromo- or 2-bromo-1-heptene. Carbonation of the reaction mixtures apparently gave rise to some acidic products, but no pure acids were isolated.

Apparently, however, the substituted vinyl halides are somewhat more amenable to Grignardization than is vinyl bromide itself, for successful preparations with isobutenyl bromide and α-methylisobutenyl bromide are reported by Krestinsky (*loc. cit.*[100]). There is, however, evidence of a considerable amount of side-reaction, as the following examples[102] show.

(1) $(CH_3)_2C{=}CHBr$ (195 g.) + Mg (37 g.) + CH_3CHO (100 g.) $\longrightarrow$
i-C_4H_8 (8 l.) + C_2H_5OH (12 g.) + $(CH_3)_2C{=}CHCH(OH)CH_3$ (20 g.) +
$(CH_3)_2C{=}CHCH(O_2CCH_3)CH_3$ + $(CH_3)_2C{=}CHCH{=}CH_2$

(2) $(CH_3)_2C{=}CHBr$ (165 g.) + Mg (29 g.) + i-C_3H_7CHO (88 g.) $\longrightarrow$
i-C_4H_8 + i-C_4H_9OH (8 g.) + $(CH_3)_2C{=}CHCH(OH)$-i-C_3H_7 (22 g.) +
$(CH_3)_2C{=}CHCH{=}C(CH_3)_2$ + other products

The biïsobutenyl of example 2 might reasonably be attributed, in part at least, to Wurtz reaction, but it would seem that the 4-methyl-1,3-pentadiene of example 1 must be the dehydrate of the "normal" product.

Tiffeneau[103] treated styryl bromide with magnesium, and, after hydrolysis of the reaction mixture, isolated styrene, bistyryl, and phenylacetylene. Carbonation and subsequent acidification of a similar reaction mixture yielded both cinnamic and phenylpropiolic acids. The Grignard reagent from which the phenylpropiolic acid must have been derived is attributed to the reactions:

$$2\ C_6H_5CH{=}CHBr + Mg \longrightarrow C_6H_5CH{=}CH_2 + C_6H_5C{\equiv}CH + MgBr_2$$

$$C_6H_5C{\equiv}CH + C_6H_5CH{=}CHMgBr \longrightarrow C_6H_5C{\equiv}CMgBr + C_6H_5CH{=}CH_2$$

Tiffeneau (*loc. cit.*[103]) was also successful in preparing a Grignard reagent from β-methylstyryl bromide. The preparations and reactions of other vinyl Grignard reagents have been described by (*inter alios*): Ziegler and Ochs,[104] Hurd and Webb,[105] Koelsch,[106] Smith and Sprung,[107] and Tsatsas.[108]

---

[101] Kirrmann, *Compt. rend.*, *184*, 1178–9 (1927); *Chem. Zentr.*, *1927,II*, 236.

[102] Krestinsky, (*a*) *Ber.*, *55B*, 2754–62 (1922); (*b*) *ibid.*, *55B*, 2762–70 (1922).

[103] Tiffeneau, *Compt. rend.*, *135*, 1346–8 (1902); *J. Chem. Soc.*, *84,I*, 241 (1903). See also: Meyer and Schuster, *Ber.*, *55B*, 815–9 (1922); Rupe and Proske, *Ber.*, *43*, 1231–4 (1910).

[104] Ziegler and Ochs, *Ber.*, *55B*, 2257–77 (1922).

[105] Hurd and Webb, *J. Am. Chem. Soc.*, *49*, 546–59 (1927).

[106] Koelsch, (*a*) *J. Am. Chem. Soc.*, *54*, 2045–8 (1932); (*b*) *ibid.*, *54*, 2487–93 (1932); (*c*) *ibid.*, *54*, 3384–9 (1932).

[107] Smith and Sprung, *J. Am. Chem. Soc.*, *65*, 1276–83 (1943).

[108] Tsatsas, *Compt. rend.*, *220*, 662–4 (1945); *Chem. Abstr.*, *40*, 4699 (1946); *Ann. chim.*, [12], *1*, 342–94 (1946).

Reported attempts to prepare organomagnesium fluorides have been uniformly unsuccessful. Swarts[109] found that amyl fluoride reacts very slowly with iodine-activated magnesium. After one hundred hours reflux in ethyl ether the identified products were decane and magnesium fluoride. According to Gilman and Heck,[110] a small amount of biphenyl is formed when fluorobenzene is heated with magnesium for two hundred hours at 300°. When fluorobenzene is sealed in a tube with iodine-activated magnesium-copper alloy, the mixture gives no color test with Michler's ketone at the end of six months; at the end of eighteen months the color test is positive. Bernstein *et al.*[111] made various attempts to prepare a Grignard reagent from benzyl fluoride, including one in which the halide was sealed in a tube with ethyl ether and heated at 100° for ten days. The only product obtained was a little bibenzyl.

Among other halides that have been reported as resisting Grignardization are: 2-bromofluorene, 3-bromoacenaphthene;[112] 2-iodothiazole;[113] 1-chloro-1,1-diphenylethane;[114] and 4-bromododecane.[115] Conceivably some, at least, of these might yield to sufficiently adroit manipulation.

GRIGNARD REAGENT PREPARATION BY "ENTRAINMENT"

The method of "entrainment," or continuous activation was introduced by Grignard[116] to effect the preparation of organomagnesium halides from organic halides that do not yield to the ordinary methods of activation, or that give very poor yields under ordinary conditions. It consists essentially in the treatment of an excess of metallic magnesium with an ethereal solution of a mixture of halides comprising one equivalent of the halide corresponding to the desired Grignard reagent and one or more equivalents of a halide that reacts readily with magnesium (suitably ethyl bromide).

From Grignard's original note (*loc. cit.*[116]), a note by Clément,[117] who collaborated in the original work, and a later note by Grignard,[118] one might gather that carbonation of a Grignard solution of pentamethylphenylmagnesium bromide, prepared with the aid of one equivalent of ethyl bromide, leads to an 80–82 percent overall yield of pentamethyl-

---

[109] Swarts, *Bull. soc. chim. Belg.*, *30*, 302–15 (1921).

[110] Gilman and Heck, *J. Am. Chem. Soc.*, *53*, 377–8 (1931).

[111] Bernstein, Roth, and Miller, *J. Am. Chem. Soc.*, *70*, 2310–4 (1948).

[112] Miller and Bachman, *J. Am. Chem. Soc.*, *57*, 766–71 (1935).

[113] Travagli, *Gazz. chim. ital.*, *78*, 592–9 (1948); *Chem. Abstr.*, *43*, 2615 (1949).

[114] Brown, Mighton, and Senkus, *J. Org. Chem.*, *3*, 62–75 (1938).

[115] Petrov and Ol'dekop, *J. Gen. Chem.* (U.S.S.R.), *18*, 859–64 (1948); *Chem. Abstr.*, *43*, 107 (1949).

[116] Grignard, *Compt. rend.*, *198*, 625–8 (1934).

[117] Clément, *Compt. rend.*, *198*, 665–7 (1934).

[118] Grignard, *Compt. rend.*, *198*, 2217–20 (1934).

benzoic acid. However, an expanded article by Clement,[119] together with an article by Savard and Hösögüt,[120] makes it appear that this yield must have been based on the amount of pentamethylphenylmagnesium bromide present (40–60 percent on the basis of the bromide expended), leading to an overall 36–49 percent yield of acid.

The yields of other organomagnesium halides, prepared with the aid of other collaborators, and reported in Grignard's original note, as determined by hydrolysis, appear to be more in line with reasonable expectation.

$$\underset{(1\ \text{equiv.})}{3,4\text{-}(CH_3O)_2C_6H_3Br} + \underset{(2\ \text{equiv.})}{C_2H_5Br} + \underset{(\text{excess})}{Mg} \longrightarrow 3,4\text{-}(CH_3O)_2C_6H_3MgBr \xrightarrow{H_2O} \underset{(24\text{–}25\%)}{1,2\text{-}(CH_3O)_2C_6H_4}$$

$$\underset{(1\ \text{equiv.})}{4\text{-}BrC_6H_4MgBr} + \underset{(2\ \text{equiv.})}{C_2H_5Br} + \underset{(\text{excess})}{Mg} \longrightarrow 1,4\text{-}(BrMg)_2C_6H_4 \xrightarrow{H_2O} \underset{(40\%)}{C_6H_6}$$

$$\underset{(1\ \text{equiv.})}{4\text{-}BrC_6H_4CH_2MgBr} + \underset{(2\ \text{equiv.})}{C_2H_5Br} + \underset{(\text{excess})}{Mg} \longrightarrow 4\text{-}BrMgC_6H_4CH_2MgBr \xrightarrow{H_2O} \underset{(35\%)}{CH_3C_6H_5}$$

According to Clément (*loc. cit.*[117]), optimum results in the ethyl bromide "entrainment" preparation of pentamethylphenylmagnesium bromide are obtained by the use of at least one equivalent of ethyl bromide per equivalent of pentamethylbromobenzene in a dilution of about one liter of ether per mole of bromide mixture, and with the use of magnesium in about 25 percent excess.

In his later article Clément (*loc. cit.*[119]) reports that, in the preparation of pentamethylphenylmagnesium bromide with the aid of ethyl bromide, yields vary from 40–60 percent depending upon the experimental conditions (concentration of ethereal solution, temperature of reaction, rate of introduction of "entrainer"). Yields also vary with the "entrainer" used, attaining 80–90 percent with methyl bromide. Clément found that replacement of ethyl bromide with ethyl iodide did not materially affect the yield. He also used allyl bromide and allyl iodide successfully.

The principal competitor of Grignard reagent formation appears to be an unsymmetrical Wurtz reaction.* According to one example reported by

[119] Clément, *Ann. chim.*, [11], *13*, 243–316 (1940).

[120] Savard and Hösögüt, *Rev. faculté sci. univ. Istanbul*, [N.S.], *3*, 164–73 (1938); *Chem. Abstr.*, *32*, 5795 (1938).

* It may be noted that, in general, Grignard reactions of the type

$$RMgX + ArX \longrightarrow ArR + MgX_2$$

do not take place, and that, as a rule, Grignard reactions of the type

$$ArMgX + C_2H_5X \longrightarrow ArC_2H_5 + MgX_2$$

give poor, if any, yields under the usual conditions of Grignard reagent preparation.

Clément (*loc. cit.*[119]),

$$\underset{(0.2\ \text{mole})}{(CH_3)_5C_6Br} + \underset{(0.2\ \text{mole})}{C_2H_5Br} + \underset{(10\ \text{g.})}{Mg} \xrightarrow{H_2O} \underset{(40\%)}{(CH_3)_5C_6H} + \underset{(54\%)}{(CH_3)_5C_6C_2H_5}$$

When methyl bromide (or iodide) is used under similar conditions the Wurtz reaction takes place to the extent of only 10–20 percent.

The foregoing example of Clément falls in line with several given by Savard and Hösögüt (*loc. cit.*[120]), of which the following may serve as illustrative:

$$\underset{(0.2\ \text{mole})}{(CH_3)_5C_6Br} + \underset{(0.2\ \text{mole})}{C_2H_5Br} + \underset{(10\ \text{g.})}{Mg} \xrightarrow{CO_2}$$

$$\underset{(2\ \text{g.})}{(CH_3)_5C_6Br} + \underset{(17\ \text{g.})}{(CH_3)_5C_6C_2H_5} + \underset{(15\ \text{g.})}{(CH_3)_5C_6CO_2H}$$

The preparative procedures reported vary somewhat in detail, but the following description by Mann and Watson[121] is fairly representative. "A round-bottomed flask of 1-liter capacity was fitted with a reflux water-condenser, stirrer, dropping-funnel, and an inlet-tube through which a current of nitrogen could be passed throughout the experiment; the necks of this condenser and dropping-funnel were closed with calcium chloride tubes. Magnesium turnings (15 g.) were placed in the flask, and a solution of ethyl bromide (1 ml., 0.02 mole) in ether (50 ml.) [was] added. A crystal of iodine was also added to initiate the reaction. When the ether was boiling, the stirrer was started, and a solution of pure, dry 2-bromopyridine (28.8 ml., 0.49 mole) and ethyl bromide (10.5 ml., 0.23 mole) in ether (250 ml.) was run in at such a rate that gentle boiling continued. The addition required seventy-five minutes, and the formation of the Grignard reagent was then completed by refluxing the mixture for a further two hours."

References to several other exemplary preparations are assembled in Table II-VIII.

Urion[122] has suggested that the "entrainment" method of preparation constitutes an example of functional exchange of the type RMgBr + R′Br ⟶ R′MgBr + RBr. In support of his hypothesis, Urion combined approximately equimolecular quantities of cyclohexyl bromide and ethylmagnesium bromide, allowed the mixture to stand for twenty-four hours, and obtained, upon hydrolysis, a 12 percent yield of cyclohexane. Removal of ether by distillation from a mixture similarly prepared was reported to increase the yield of cyclohexane to 40 percent. An equimolecular mixture of 4-bromophenylmagnesium bromide and ethylmagnesium bromide from which the ether had been partially removed by distillation yielded, upon hydrolysis, 15 percent of benzene.

---

[121] Mann and Watson, *J. Org. Chem.*, *13*, 502–31 (1948).

[122] Urion, *Compt. rend.*, *198*, 1244–6 (1934).

TABLE II-VIII

SOME REPRESENTATIVE GRIGNARD REAGENT PREPARATIONS BY THE METHOD OF "ENTRAINMENT"

Halide, RX (corresponding to RMgX)	"Entrainer," R′X′	Co-reactant	Yield, "Normal" Product (%)	Ref.
2-Bromopyridine	C_2H_5Br	$AsCl_3$	*ca.* 80 (crude)	*3*
2-Bromopyridine	C_2H_5Br	PCl_3	33	*3*
2-Bromopyridine	C_2H_5Br	C_6H_5CHO	49	*11*
2-Bromopyridine	C_2H_5Br	$4\text{-}BrC_6H_4(C_6H_5)PCl$	(?)*	*3*
2-Bromopyridine	C_2H_5Br	$C_6H_5AsCl_2$	10	*10*
2-Bromopyridine	C_2H_5Br	$C_6H_5PCl_2$	(?)*	*10*
2-Bromopyridine	C_2H_5Br	$(C_6H_5)_2AsCl$	4	*10*
2-Bromopyridine	C_2H_5Br	$(C_6H_5)_2PCl$	20	*10*
3-Bromopyridine	C_2H_5Br	$4\text{-}BrC_6H_4(C_6H_5)PCl$	(?)*	*3*
Chlorobenzene	C_2H_5Br	CO_2	39	*7*
2,5-Dimethyl-3-iodothiophene	C_2H_5Br	CO_2	40	*15*
1-Bromo-2-methoxymethylbenzene	C_2H_5Br	$(CH_2)_2O$	53	*6*
1-Bromo-3,4-dimethoxybenzene	C_2H_5Br	H_2O	18	*7*
4-Bromodimethylaniline	C_2H_5Br	$4\text{-}BrC_6H_4(C_6H_5)PCl$	37 †	*3*
$C_8H_{17}Cl$ ‡	C_2H_5Br	CO_2	34	*16*
1-Bromomethyl-2-β-bromoethylbenzene	C_2H_5Br	CO_2	(?) §	*6*
4-Bromohemimellithene ¶	C_2H_5Br	$(CH_2)_2O$	(?)*	*14*
1-Bromo-2-ethoxymethylbenzene	C_2H_5Br	$(CH_2)_2O$	35	*5*
$1\text{-}C_{10}H_7Cl$	C_2H_5Br	CO_2	16	*7*
$1\text{-}C_{10}H_7Cl$	C_2H_5Br	H_2O	46	*7*

* The "normal" product was obtained, but the yield is not stated.

† Fifteen to twenty percent of the halide used was recovered as dimethylaniline.

‡ The halide employed is "diisobutylene hydrochloride"; the acid recovered is neopentyldimethylacetic, $t\text{-}C_4H_9CH_2C(CH_3)_2CO_2H$.

§ Thirteen and nine-tenths grams of the dibromide yielded 1.4 g. of a white solid, $C_{20}H_{22}O_4$, and 3.9 g. of *o*-ethylphenylacetic acid, $2\text{-}C_2H_5C_6H_4CH_2CO_2H$.

¶ 1-Bromo-2,3,4-trimethylbenzene.

TABLE II-VIII (Continued)

Halide, RX (corresponding to RMgX)	"Entrainer," R′X′	Co-reactant	Yield, "Normal" Product (%)	Ref.
1-Methoxymethyl-2-β-chloroethylbenzene	C_2H_5Br	CO_2	58	*6*
Duryl bromide ‖	C_2H_5Br	3,4,5-$(CH_3O)_3C_6H_2COCl$	16	*4*
1-Bromo-4-methylnaphthalene	CH_3I	$(CH_2)_5CO$	50**	*1*
2-Bromo-6-methoxynaphthalene	CH_3I	$CH_3CO(CH_2)_2CO_2C_2H_5$	(?)*	*12*
2-Bromo-6-methoxynaphthalene	C_2H_5Br	1-Methyl-2-piperidone	15	*9*
2-Bromo-6-methoxynaphthalene	C_2H_5Br	CO_2	50	*21*
2-Bromo-6-methoxynaphthalene	C_2H_5Br	CO_2	33	*22*
1-Iodo-6-methoxynaphthalene	C_2H_5	HCHO	80	*2*
Bromopentamethylbenzene	C_2H_5Br	$HCO_2C_2H_5$	9††	*8*
1-Bromo-2,4,5-trimethyl-3,6-dimethoxybenzene	C_2H_5Br	CO_2	71	*17*
1-Bromo-2,4,5-trimethyl-3,6-dimethoxybenzene	C_2H_5Br	$(CH_2)_2O$	62	*17*
3-Iodoacenaphthene	C_2H_5Br	$(CH_2)_2O$	55	*18*
1-Bromo-3,4-dimethylnaphthalene	CH_3I	$(CH_2)_5CO$	64**	*1*
2,2,5,7,8-Pentamethyl-6-bromochroman	C_2H_5Br	O_2	8	*13*
9-Bromo-10-phenylanthracene	C_2H_5Br	CO_2	40	*19*
9,10-Di-(*p*-bromophenyl)-anthracene	CH_3I	CO_2	(?)*	*20*

‖1-Bromo-2,3,5,6-tetramethylbenzene.

** The product isolated is the hydrocarbon (*i.e.*, the dehydrate of the "normal" addition product).

††About 13 percent of dipentamethylphenylmethane was also isolated.

REFERENCES FOR TABLE II-VIII

(*1*) Bergmann and Szmuszkowicz, *J. Am. Chem. Soc.*, *69*, 1367–70 (1947).
(*2*) Billeter and Miescher, *Helv. Chim. Acta*, *29*, 859–71 (1946).
(*3*) Davies and Mann, *J. Chem. Soc.*, *1944*, 276–83.
(*4*) Fuson and Gaertner, *J. Org. Chem.*, *13*, 496–501 (1948).
(*5*) Holliman and Mann, *J. Chem. Soc.*, *1942*, 737–41.
(*6*) Holliman and Mann, *J. Chem. Soc.*, *1947*, 1634–42.
(*7*) Jezierski, *Roczniki Chem.*, *20*, 47–53 (1946); *Chem. Abstr.*, *42*, 1910 (1948).
(*8*) Lapkin, *J. Gen. Chem.* (U.S.S.R.), *16*, 729–34 (1946); *Chem. Abstr.*, *41*, 1218 (1947).
(*9*) Lee, Ziering, Berger, and Heineman, *Jubilee Vol. Emil Barell*, *1946*, 264–305; *Chem. Abstr.*, *41*, 6246 (1947).
(*10*) Mann and Watson, *J. Org. Chem.*, *13*, 502–31 (1948).
(*11*) Overhoff and Proost, *Rec. trav. chim.*, *57*, 179–84 (1938).
(*12*) Robinson and Slater, *J. Chem. Soc.*, *1941*, 376–85.
(*13*) Smith, U. S. Patent 2,397,212, Jan. 7, 1943; *Chem. Abstr.*, P3573 (1946).
(*14*) Smith and Agre, *J. Am. Chem. Soc.*, *60*, 648–52 (1938).
(*15*) Steinkopf, Poulsson, and Herdey, *Ann.*, *536*, 128–34 (1938).
(*16*) Whitmore, Wheeler, and Surmatis, *J. Am. Chem. Soc.*, *63*, 3237 (1941).
(*17*) Smith, Wawzonek, and Miller, *J. Org. Chem.*, *6*, 229–35 (1941); Smith and Miller, *J. Am. Chem. Soc.*, *64*, 440–5 (1942).
(*18*) Cook, Haslewood, and Robinson, *J. Chem. Soc.*, *1935*, 667–71.
(*19*) Dufraisse, Velluz, and Velluz, *Bull. soc. chim.*, [5], *4*, 1260–4 (1937).
(*20*) Dufraisse and Margoulis-Molho, *Bull. soc. chim.*, [5], *7*, 930–3 (1940).
(*21*) Fries and Schimmelschmidt, *Ber.*, *58B*, 2835–45 (1925).
(*22*) Hudson, *J. Chem. Soc.*, *1946*, 76–8.

However, an earlier study by Gilman and Jones,[123] a note by Grignard (*loc. cit.*[118]), and a more recent study by Kharasch and Fuchs[124] rather conclusively disprove the generality of functional exchange of the type envisioned by Urion, and cast some doubt on the specific examples cited by him.

Gilman and Jones (*loc. cit.*[123]) submitted to three-hour reflux ether-benzene or ether-toluene solutions of equimolecular mixtures of bromobenzene and benzylmagnesium chloride, of benzyl chloride and phenylmagnesium bromide, of bromobenzene and triphenylmethylmagnesium chloride, of triphenylmethyl chloride and phenylmagnesium bromide, and of triphenylmethyl chloride and benzylmagnesium chloride, respectively. Upon conclusion of the reflux, the solutions were cooled and carbonated. In no case was any carboxylic acid other than that corresponding to the Grignard reagent originally present isolated.

As Grignard (*loc. cit.*[118]) has pointed out, the yield of benzene (15 percent), from the dimagnesium Grignard compound of *p*-dibromobenzene, obtained by Urion does not differ greatly from the yield (12.8 percent) obtained by Quelet[125] through the treatment of an excess of magnesium with

[123] Gilman and Jones, *J. Am. Chem. Soc.*, *51*, 2840–3 (1929).
[124] Kharasch and Fuchs, *J. Org. Chem.*, *10*, 292–7 (1945).
[125] Quelet, *Bull. soc. chim.*, [4], *41*, 933–6 (1927).

p-dibromobenzene in the conventional manner. Grignard further showed that the yields of 3,4-dimethoxyphenylmagnesium bromide, of pentamethylphenylmagnesium bromide and of the dimagnesium Grignard compounds of *p*-dibromobenzene and *p*-bromobenzyl bromide obtainable by the method of "entrainment" are all materially greater than the corresponding yields obtainable by one or more of three variations of Urion's method.

It has been found in the laboratories of the University of Chicago[124] that a mixture of ethylmagnesium bromide and cyclohexyl bromide, on heating, evolves ethane, ethylene, cyclohexane and cyclohexene. It is possible that in his second experiment, Urion failed to detect ethane and ethylene and mistook a mixture of cyclohexane (b. 81.4°) and cyclohexene (b. 83°) for cyclohexane.

Kharasch and Fuchs (*loc. cit.*[124]) could detect no functional exchange between *n*-butylmagnesium bromide and bromobenzene, *n*-butylmagnesium bromide and *p*-bromoanisole, *n*-butylmagnesium bromide and triphenylvinyl bromide, methylmagnesium bromide and *p*-biphenylyl bromide, methylmagnesium bromide and 9-chlorofluorene, or phenylmagnesium bromide and *n*-butyl bromide, although some of these and other Grignard-halide pairs did undergo exchange when cobaltous chloride was added to the mixture.

On the whole the available evidence suggests that functional exchange (*q.v.*) is probably in most cases a free-radical reaction that may be initiated by the presence of certain metallic impurities in the magnesium used, by the presence of magnesious halides, or by one of several other reaction factors that could give rise to free radicals.

Grignard's[118] interpretation of the efficacy of the "entrainment" method of preparation assumes the formation of a relatively ether-soluble complex of the type $C_2H_5MgBr \cdot RMgBr \cdot n(C_2H_5)_2O$. In view of the fact that magnesium bromide has been shown to be much more soluble in ethereal *n*-butylmagnesium bromide solutions than in ether,[126] it does not appear altogether implausible that a relatively ether-insoluble Grignard reagent might be more ether-soluble in the presence of a relatively ether-soluble Grignard reagent. Whatever the detailed mechanics of the process there is no doubt that many of the Grignard reagents preparable by the "entrainment" method are relatively ether-insoluble and might be expected to form an impervious coating on a magnesium surface, and that the overall effect of the presence of the auxiliary halide ("entrainer") is a continuous cleansing of the surface.

There is, however, another aspect of the phenomenon that should not be entirely overlooked. There would seem to be some reason to believe that the Grignard reagent formation reaction is, in a sense, self-activating. A possible explanation of this effect (if it be real) is that even a comparatively clean magnesium surface has relatively few points of unsatura-

[126] Doering and Noller, *J. Am. Chem. Soc.*, *61*, 3436 (1939).

tion at which reaction with an organic halide may take place. Reaction at any one of these points, and diffusion into solution of the Grignard reagent formed, probably increases the number of points of unsaturation and so facilitates further reaction. Such an effect might be expected to be especially significant in the cases of such relatively unreactive halides as chlorobenzene and 1-chloronaphthalene.

PREPARATION OF GRIGNARD REAGENTS IN SOLVENTS OTHER THAN ETHYL ETHER[127]

Ethers other than ethyl ether. Unsuccessful in attempts to prepare organomagnesium halides in "neutral" solvents such as benzene or ligroïn, Grignard (*loc. cit.*[1]) attributed peculiar significance to the constitution of ethyl ether as a reaction medium and investigated the suitability of other ethers, specifically, methyl isoamyl ether and anisole, which he pronounced satisfactory.

Tschugaeff[128] suggested the use of ethereal methylmagnesium iodide as a reagent for the quantitative evaluation of hydroxyl groups in organic compounds by measurement of the volume of methane evolved in the reaction:

$$CH_3MgI + ROH \longrightarrow ROMgI + CH_4$$

The variability of the vapor pressure of ethyl ether with temperature, however, introduced considerable errors into the method as originally proposed. These Hibbert and Sudborough[129] sought to eliminate by substituting amyl ether for ethyl ether as a solvent. To 6.09 g. of magnesium covered with 100 ml. of thoroughly dried amyl ether, they introduced 35.5 g. of methyl iodide dissolved in 20 ml. of dry amyl ether. Reaction was initiated by gentle warming on a sand-bath and was then allowed to proceed spontaneously, being completed ultimately by a half-hour of heating. The solution was then decanted from residual magnesium and made up to 200 ml. with dry amyl ether.

Senier *et al.*[130] made use of mixtures of ethyl ether with less volatile ethers, such as anisole and phenetole, in their investigation of acridine-Grignard reagent addition products.

In a series of studies, in which he generalized the Tschugaeff method for the determination of "active" hydrogen, Zerewitinoff[131] followed the

[127] Early work in this field has been reviewed by Gilman and McCracken, *Rec. trav. chim.*, *46*, 463–72 (1927).

[128] Tschugaeff, *Ber.*, *35*, 3912–4 (1902).

[129] Hibbert and Sudborough, *Proc. Chem. Soc.*, *19*, 285–6 (1903); *J. Chem. Soc.*, *85*, 933–8 (1904).

[130] Senier, Austin, and Clarke, *J. Chem. Soc.*, 87, 1469–74 (1905).

[131] Zerewitinoff, *Ber.*, *40*, 2023–31 (1907); *41*, 2233–43, 2244–5 (1908); *43*, 3490–5 (1910); *45*, 2384–9 (1912); *47*, 1659, 2417–23 (1914); *Z. anal. Chem.*, *50*, 680–91 (1911); *Chem. Abstr.*, 6, 203 (1912); *Z. anal. Chem.*, *52*, 729–37 (1914); *Chem. Abstr.*, 8, 2074 (1914).

lead of Hibbert and Sudborough in adopting amyl ether as a solvent. His amyl ether solutions were prepared by combining 9.6 g. of magnesium with 35.5 g. of methyl iodide and a few iodine crystals in 100 ml. of sodium-dried amyl ether. Reaction began spontaneously and was encouraged, if necessary, by gentle warming, being completed eventually by one to two hours heating on a boiling water-bath.

Sudborough and Hibbert[132] have also used phenetole as a solvent in "active" hydrogen determinations. To 6.09 g. of magnesium in 120 ml. of phenetole, they added a solution of 35.5 g. of methyl iodide in 20 ml. of phenetole. The mixture was warmed for forty-five minutes on a sand-bath, and was finally boiled for thirty minutes to expel residual methyl iodide.

Other references to the use of high-boiling ethers in Tschugaeff-Zerewitinoff determinations may be found in Chapter XVIII.

Bourgom,[133] who prepared n-butylmagnesium bromide in methylal $[(CH_3O)_2CH_2]$, found that the reaction tended to slow down and eventually stop (due to Grignard reagent insolubility) when a ratio of two moles of bromide to 500 ml. of methylal was used, but proceeded satisfactorily with one mole of bromide to 500 ml. of methylal.

Because of the difficulty of separating 1-pentene (b. 40°) from ethyl ether, Kirrmann[134] used n-propyl ether (b. 91°) in carrying out the reaction

$$C_2H_5MgBr + BrCH_2CH{=}CH_2 \longrightarrow n\text{-}C_3H_7CH{=}CH_2$$

obtaining a 94 percent yield of the olefin.

In an investigation of the oxygen-induced luminescence of Grignard reagent solutions, Evans and Diepenhorst[135] prepared over ninety Grignard reagents in a variety of solvents, including some seventeen ethers. No details of their preparations are described, save that they were carried out in sealed Pyrex tubes, with iodine and n-butyl bromide as the principal activators employed.

Fuson[136] attempted to evade the difficulties introduced by ethyl ether vapor into measurement of the volume of gases evolved in coupling reactions by employing isoamyl ether as a reaction medium, but reported that the reaction

$$C_6H_5CH_2Cl + CH_3MgI \longrightarrow (C_6H_5CH_2\text{—})_2 + C_2H_6$$

does not take place in the latter solvent.

In the belief that n-butyl ether might profitably be substituted for the lower-boiling, more volatile and more inflammable ethyl ether in many

---

[132] Sudborough and Hibbert, *J. Chem. Soc.*, *95*, 477–80 (1909); Hibbert, *ibid.*, *101*, 328–41 (1912).

[133] Bourgom, *Bull. soc. chim. Belg.*, 33, 101–15 (1924).

[134] Kirrmann, *Bull. soc. chim.*, [4], 39, 988–91 (1926).

[135] Evans and Diepenhorst, *J. Am. Chem. Soc.*, *48*, 715–23 (1926).

[136] Fuson, *J. Am. Chem. Soc.*, *48*, 2681–9 (1926).

Grignard reactions, Marvel *et al.*,[137] prepared several Grignard reagents in the former solvent and estimated the percentage yields by titration.

The preparations are described substantially as follows. In a flask were placed about 40 ml. of *n*-butyl ether, 1.5 g. of magnesium turnings and a crystal of iodine. The theoretical equivalent of halide, dissolved in enough *n*-butyl ether to make a total volume of 30 ml. was placed in a separatory funnel. A small amount of the halide solution was added, and reaction was initiated by warming. The temperature necessary varied somewhat with the individual halide. When reaction had begun, the remainder of the halide solution was added, with stirring, at a rate that allowed reaction to proceed smoothly. After completion of the addition, stirring was continued until the mixture had cooled to room temperature. Minimum and maximum yields obtained in multiple experiments are recorded in Table II-IX.

TABLE II-IX

PREPARATION OF GRIGNARD REAGENTS IN *n*-BUTYL ETHER

Halide	Yield RMgBr (%)	Halide	Yield RMgBr (%)
C_2H_5Br	91–93	C_6H_5Br	70–77
n-C_3H_7Br	89–90	$(CH_2)_5CHBr$	80–83
i-C_3H_7Br	79–80	*n*-$C_7H_{15}Br$	73–81
n-C_4H_9Br	86–87	$C_6H_5CH_2CH_2Br$	68–71
i-C_4H_9Br	82–86	1-$C_{10}H_7Br$	63–71
s-C_4H_9Br	68–72		

Whitmore *et al.*[138] describe the preparation of a *n*-butyl ether solution of *t*-butylmagnesium chloride as follows. "Dry *n*-butyl ether (25 ml.) and 5 ml. of pure *n*-propyl bromide were added to 4 moles of magnesium turnings in the usual apparatus to initiate the reaction. When the reaction started 1 liter of the dry ether containing 5 ml. of *n*-propyl bromide was added. The addition of this relatively large amount of *n*-propyl bromide was necessary to ensure continued reaction. *t*-Butyl chloride (370 g., 4 moles) in 1700 ml. of the ether was added over a period of twenty-four hours; stirring was continued for eighteen hours. The flask was cooled in a stream of running water at 16–18°. The yield was 73%."

Young *et al.*[139] have also made use of *n*-butyl ether in the preparation of butenylmagnesium bromide solutions. They observe that, as compared with ethyl ether, butyl ether preparations of organomagnesium halides of this type require higher molar dilutions and more efficient stirring because of the greater tendency toward reaction in the sense:

$$RMgX + RX \longrightarrow R_2 + MgX_2$$

[137] Marvel, Blomquist, and Vaughn, *J. Am. Chem. Soc.*, *50*, 2810–2 (1928).

[138] Whitmore, Whitaker, Mosher, Breivik, Wheeler, Miner, Sutherland, Wagner, Clapper, Lewis, Lux, and Popkin, *J. Am. Chem. Soc.*, *63*, 643–54 (1941).

[139] Young, Prater, and Winstein, *J. Am. Chem. Soc.*, *55*, 4908–11 (1933).

They recommend a solvent-halide ratio of 38:1 for allyl bromide and of 76:1 for crotyl bromide.

In the experiment which gave the maximum (99 percent) yield of Grignard reagent, 0.42 gram-atom of freshly cut 20-30 mesh (99.5 percent) magnesium turnings was covered with butyl ether. Allyl bromide (0.035 mole), dissolved in the remainder of a total of 1.33 mole of butyl ether was then added gradually, with highly efficient stirring, over a period of three hours.

The optimum crotyl bromide preparation, which gave a quantitative yield of Grignard reagent, was conducted in the same manner, save that twice the relative quantity of butyl ether was used.

Preparations of butenylmagnesium bromide in *n*-propyl ether and in a mixture of 90 percent isopropyl ether and 10 percent ethyl ether are also described.[140]

A French patent[141] protects the use of methyl amyl, methyl cyclohexyl and methyl benzyl ethers in the preparation of β-substituted ethyl alcohols from ethylene chlorohydrin. In one example described, 14.4 parts of magnesium turnings, 0.1 part of iodine and 25 parts of a solution comprising 94 parts of bromobenzene in 376 parts of methyl amyl ether are combined and warmed to 50° to initiate reaction. The mixture is then cooled to 15-20°, and the remainder of the halide solution is added. When all the metal has disappeared, the resultant Grignard solution is treated with 16 parts of ethylene chlorohydrin with warming. A 95 percent yield of phenethyl alcohol is claimed.

Rathman and Leighty[142] have investigated isopropyl ether as a possible substitute for ethyl ether as a solvent for Grignard reactions, and are inclined to regard it as unsatisfactory. . However, from the abstract available, it is not apparent whether or not any attempt was made to eliminate peroxides (for which isopropyl ether is notoriously infamous), nor is it evident that anything approximating optimum reaction conditions was attained.

Hillyer[143] claims that treatment with potassium permanganate and sodium fails to remove all peroxide from isopropyl ether, and that the product is unsuitable for Grignard reagent preparation, but that isopropyl ether purified with chromic oxide "proved very satisfactory for a Grignard reaction."

---

[140] Young, Lane, Loshokoff, and Winstein, *J. Am. Chem. Soc.*, *59*, 2441-3 (1937).

[141] I. G. Farbenindustrie Akt.-Ges., French Patent, 682,142, May 23, 1930; *Chem. Zentr.*, *1930*, *II*, 3082.

[142] Rathman and Leighty, *Trans. Illinois State Acad. Sci.*, *24*, 312-5 (1931); *Chem. Abstr.*, *26*, 2167 (1932).

[143] Hillyer, U. S. Patent 2,380,524, July 31, 1945; *Chem. Abstr.*, *39*, P5465 (1945).

Tarbell and Paulson[144] have prepared phenylmagnesium bromide in (+)-2-methoxybutane with a view to the possibility of effecting an induced asymmetric synthesis by treating the Grignard reagent with acetaldehyde. (Incidentally, the product obtained was the racemic secondary alcohol.)

Carlin and Smith[145] have found that, although 1,3-dioxane behaves similarly to 1,4-dioxane as a precipitant of RMgX and MgX_2, 4-methyl-1,3-dioxane is suitable for use as a solvent in the preparation and reaction of Grignard reagents. Using a procedure somewhat similar to that employed by Marvel *et al.* (*loc. cit.*[137]) in the preparation of *n*-butyl ether Grignard solutions, they prepared several Grignard reagents in the yields indicated in Table II-X. No ether cleavage was detected.

TABLE II-X

PREPARATION OF GRIGNARD REAGENTS IN 4-METHYL-1,3-DIOXANE

Halide	Yield RMgX (%)	Halide	Yield RMgX (%)
C_2H_5Br	92–93	*t*-C_4H_9Cl	63
n-C_3H_7Br	90–92	$(CH_2)_5CHBr$	86–87
i-C_3H_7Br	81–88	*n*-$C_7H_{15}Br$	88–89
n-C_4H_9Br	92–93	C_6H_5Br	81–86
i-C_4H_9Br	88–89	$C_6H_5CH{=}CHBr$	58–62
s-C_4H_9Br	83–86	1-$C_{10}H_7Br$	76

The lower alkyl halides reacted spontaneously; cyclohexyl and *n*-heptyl bromides required brief heating to initiate reaction; solutions of the aromatic bromides and β-bromostyrene required continuous boiling.

Tertiary amines. Tschelinzeff,[146] remarked the similarity between the reactions of Grignard reagents with many oxygen compounds, on the one hand, and their nitrogen analogs, on the other hand, *e.g.*, water and ammonia, alcohols and amines (primary and secondary), ketones and nitriles, esters and amides. From this he reasoned that the nitrogen analog of an ether (*i.e.*, a tertiary amine) might well play the same rôle as an ether in the preparation of a Grignard reagent. For an experimental test of his hypothesis, he selected dimethylaniline, and, in two moles of the solvent, treated one gram-atom of magnesium (activated with a crystal of iodine) with one mole of ethyl iodide. The resultant Grignard solution reacted with benzaldehyde to give a 62 percent yield of ethylphenylmethanol, and with acetophenone to give a 50–60 percent yield of methylethylphenylmethanol, together with 12.5–15.0 percent of the corresponding dehydration product.

Betti and Lucchi[147] have prepared methylmagnesium iodide and phenylmagnesium bromide in *N*,*N*-dimethylbornylamine (details of method, and yields obtained, not stated in the available abstract).

[144] Tarbell and Paulson, *J. Am. Chem. Soc.*, *64*, 2842–4 (1942).

[145] Carlin and Smith, *J. Am. Chem. Soc.*, *69*, 2007–8 (1947).

[146] Tschelinzeff, *Ber.*, *37*, 2081–5 (1904).

[147] Betti and Lucchi, *Boll. sci. facolta chim. ind., Bologna*, *1940*, No. 1–2, 2–5; *Chem. Abstr.*, *34*, 2354 (1940).

By private communication from Dr. W. G. Brown (The University of Chicago), the authors are advised that the *N*-alkylmorpholines, which have proved excellent media for lithium aluminum hydride reactions, are also highly satisfactory both for the preparation and subsequent reactions of Grignard reagents.

Hydrocarbons. As has already been noted, Grignard (*loc. cit.*[1]) reported failure in attempts to prepare organomagnesium halides in "neutral" solvents such as benzene and ligroïn.

Malmgren[148] obtained no reaction between magnesium and α-camphoryl bromide at water-bath temperature; vigorous reaction set in at 120°, but produced only tar. He also obtained no reaction in boiling benzene, but found that reaction proceeded smoothly in boiling toluene or xylene. Reaction also took place in ethyl ether. In each case, however, there was considerable Wurtz reaction as well as Grignard reagent formation.

Tschelinzeff[149] attempted the preparation of Grignard reagents from a series of iodides (not specified) in benzene, both thiophene-free and thiophene-contaminated, but noted no perceptible reaction after forty-eight hours at the boiling point. In xylene, he was able to prepare Grignard reagents from ethyl, *n*-propyl, *n*-butyl and *n*-amyl iodides without the use of a "catalyst."

When a few drops of a tertiary amine (suitably dimethylaniline) was added, such preparations could be carried out in benzene, toluene, xylene, hexane, petroleum ether, benzine, and terpenoid hydrocarbons. Reaction often began spontaneously, but could always be initiated by warming to 30-40°, or by adding a crystal of iodine. Moderative cooling to control the reaction was sometimes desirable. Reaction was ultimately completed by steam-bath warming. In one experiment described, 0.2 mole of ethyl iodide, 0.2 gram-atom of magnesium, and 0.01 mole of dimethylaniline were combined in benzene. Treatment of the resultant Grignard reagent solution with 0.2 mole of benzaldehyde gave ethylphenylmethanol in 78 percent yield.

Similar tertiary amine-promoted Grignard reagent preparations in hydrocarbon solvents are described by Tschelinzeff,[150] by Stadnikoff[151] and by Hess and Rheinboldt.[152]

Tingle and Gorsline[153] were able to prepare Grignard reagents in ligroïn (b. 36°) by the addition of relatively small amounts of ethyl ether, quinoline or pyridine. In one experiment they combined 7.8 g. of ethyl

[148] Malmgren, *Ber.*, *36*, 2608-42 (1903).

[149] Tschelinzeff, *Ber.*, *37*, 4534-40 (1904).

[150] Tschelinzeff, *Ber.*, *38*, 3664-73 (1905).

[151] Stadnikoff, *Ber.*, *44*, 1157-60 (1911); *J. prakt. Chem.*, [2], *88*, 1-20 (1913); Stadnikoff and Kusmina-Aron, *ibid.*, [2], *88*, 20-5 (1913).

[152] Hess and Rheinboldt, *Ber.*, *54B*, 2043-55 (1921).

[153] Tingle and Gorsline, *Am. Chem. J.*, *37*, 483-94 (1907).

iodide, 1.22 g. of magnesium, 500 ml. of ligroïn and 30 ml. of quinoline. There was no evident reaction at room temperature, but the magnesium disappeared upon twenty minutes boiling.

It may be noted, parenthetically, that at higher temperatures, quinoline apparently reacts with Grignard reagents. Thus, when Oddo[154] heated an iodine-activated mixture of 6 g. of magnesium, 40 g. of bromobenzene, 50 ml. of toluene and 32 g. of quinoline in an oil bath at 140°, and then hydrolyzed the reaction mixture, he was able to isolate α-phenylquinoline from the hydrolysis product.

Pickard and Kenyon[155] boiled a mixture of 250 ml. of dry, thiophene-free benzene, 1.5 g. of methyl iodide, and 0.3 g. of magnesium powder for several hours without being able to detect any reaction. They then added 3.0 g. of tribenzylphosphine oxide. After a short time the clear liquid became cloudy, and magnesium began to dissolve. After seven hours reflux the solution was filtered hot. On cooling, small, colorless prismatic needles separated. The analysis was consistent with the formulation $2\ (C_6H_5CH_2)_3PO \cdot CH_3MgI$.

A comparative study of the effectiveness of various ethers and their sulfur analogs in facilitating Grignard reagent formation in benzene solution has been made by Hepworth.[156] The method used consisted in introducing 1 g. of the substance to be investigated, 0.3 g. of magnesium and 2 g. of methyl iodide into 50 ml. of dry benzene, and submitting the mixture to reflux on a water-bath. The following conclusions were drawn. In general, oxygen compounds are much more effective than their sulfur analogs. Open-chain compounds are more effective than the related heterocycles: *e.g.*, ethyl *n*-propyl ether is more effective than pentamethylene oxide; ethyl *n*-propyl sulfide is more effective than pentamethylene sulfide. 1,4-Dithiane and 1,4-dioxane are more active than pentamethylene sulfide and oxide, respectively, but much less active than the corresponding open-chain sulfide and ether respectively. 1,4-Thioxane is more effective than 1,4-dithiane, being almost the equal of 1,4-dioxane. Ethyl selenide and methyl telluride are about equal to ethyl sulfide. Phenyl sulfoxide and isoamyl sulfoxide are effective, and form Grignard reagent complexes. Methyl sulfone and phenyl sulfone are ineffective. The rate of reaction does not depend upon the basicity of the "catalyst."

Gilman and McCracken[157] have reviewed earlier work on the preparation of Grignard reagents in solvents other than ethyl ether, and have investigated the effect on Grignard reagent yields of various hydrocarbon-ethyl ether mixtures. They conclude that, in general, the use of a mixed solvent results in a drop in yield of about 10 percent below that obtained

[154] Oddo, *Atti acad. Lincei*, [5], *16*, *I*, 538–45 (1907); *Chem. Zentr.*, *1907,II*, 73.

[155] Pickard and Kenyon, *J. Chem. Soc.*, *89*, 262–73 (1906).

[156] Hepworth, *J. Chem. Soc.*, *119*, 1249–56 (1921).

[157] Gilman and McCracken, *Rec. trav. chim.*, *46*, 463–72 (1927).

with the optimum ethyl ether concentration. They recommend that, when the use of a mixed solvent is desirable in subsequent reaction, the Grignard reagent be prepared in a minimal quantity of ethyl ether and that the hydrocarbon then be added.

The preparation of alkylmagnesium halides in benzene, without the aid of activators or "catalysts," has been studied by Schlenk.[158] One-tenth mole of alkyl halide, 5 g. of sandpapered magnesium ribbon and 100 ml. of benzene were sealed in a glass tube and mechanically shaken for two months. The yield of Grignard reagent was estimated by acid titration, and the amount of Wurtz product was calculated with the aid of a supplementary halide-ion determination. Results are recorded in Table II-XI.

TABLE II-XI

REACTION OF MAGNESIUM WITH ALKYL HALIDES IN BENZENE

Halide	Yield RMgX (%)	Yield Wurtz Product (%)
CH_3I	0	...
C_2H_5I	11.2	10.8
n-C_3H_7I	1.0	4.0
n-C_4H_9I	96.0	4.0
n-$C_7H_{15}I$	3.0	3.0
n-$C_8H_{17}I$	96.0	4.0
C_2H_5Br	2.0	5.0
n-C_4H_9Br	38.0	...
n-C_4H_9Cl	55.0	...

Schlenk also investigated a considerable number of iodine-activated Barbier-type reactions of esters and ketones in benzene.

Unable to prepare 2,4,6-triphenylphenylmagnesium bromide in ethyl ether (possibly because of its low solubility in that medium), Kohler and Blanchard[159] had resort to the following procedure. "To a solution of 20 g. of the bromo compound in 22 g. of boiling xylene were added 5 g. of magnesium, 4 ml. of a dilute ethereal ethylmagnesium bromide solution and 10 drops of ethyl bromide. The mixture was boiled and stirred vigorously until the reaction started. More bromo compound was then added at fifteen-minute intervals, along with benzene and ether, until 70 g. of the bromo compound, 150 ml. of benzene, and 50 ml. of ether had been added. After continued boiling for two and one-half hours, most of the magnesium had dissolved." Subsequent carbonation of the Grignard reagent so prepared yielded 53.5 g. (84.1 percent) of 2,4,6-triphenylbenzoic acid.

Barrè and Repentigny[160] describe the preparation of several Grignard reagents in hydrocarbon solvents with dimethylaniline as "catalyst."

[158] Schlenk, *Ber.*, *64B*, 739–43 (1931).
[159] Kohler and Blanchard, *J. Am. Chem. Soc.*, 57, 367–71 (1935).
[160] Barre and Repentigny, *Can. J. Research*, 27B, 716–20 (1949).

(Diethyl-, di-*n*-propyl-, and di-*n*-butylaniline are said to perform less satisfactorily.) Their data are summarized in Table II-XII; yields were determined by acid titration (see Chapter III, Estimation and Detection of Grignard Reagents).

TABLE II-XII
PREPARATIONS OF SEVERAL GRIGNARD REAGENTS IN HYDROCARBON SOLVENTS WITH THE AID OF DIMETHYLANILINE

Halide	Solvent	Grams Amine	Hours Reflux	Temp. (°C)	Yield (%)
C_2H_5I	C_6H_6	0.05	5–7	80	82
C_2H_5I	$CH_3C_6H_5$	0.05	5–7	80	82
C_2H_5Br	C_6H_6	0.33	4–7	80	96
C_2H_5Br	Ligroïn*	1.00	4–7	90–100	94
n-C_4H_9Cl	C_6H_6	1.25	11–18	80	90–96
n-C_4H_9Cl	Ligroïn*	1.25	11–18	90–100	92
s-C_4H_9Cl	C_6H_6	1.25	14	80	86
i-$C_5H_{11}Cl$	C_6H_6	1.25	14	80	80
C_6H_5Br	C_6H_6	1.25	14	80	81
$C_6H_5CH_2Cl$ †	C_6H_6	1.25	14	80	20–30

* B.p., 80–100°.
† Benzyl chloride quaternizes to some extent; neither allyl bromide nor *t*-butyl chloride give appreciable yields of Grignard reagent.

Kuznetsov[161] has prepared *n*-propyl-, isobutyl-, and isoamylmagnesium iodides in xylene with the aid of a few drops of dimethylaniline.

According to Neogi,[162] Grignard reagents may be prepared in "neutral solvents" with the aid of "catalytic quantities" of triethylsulfonium iodide [$(C_2H_5)_3SI$]. Methyl, ethyl, *n*-propyl, isobutyl, and isoamyl iodides are mentioned as yielding Grignard reagents by this method.

Oddo[163] has reported several Barbier-type syntheses with alkyl iodides, benzene, magnesium, and aldehydes.

Schorigin *et al.*[164] describe unsuccessful attempts to prepare *n*-butyl- and isoamylmagnesium chlorides in toluene with iodine-activated magnesium.

PREPARATION OF GRIGNARD REAGENTS WITHOUT SOLVENT (OTHER THAN EXCESS HALIDE)

Contrary to the opinion of some early investigators, who held that the formation of an ether-halide complex of the type

[161] Kuznetsov, *J. Gen. Chem.* (U.S.S.R.), *12*, 631–7 (1942); *Chem. Abstr.*, *38*, 1494 (1944).

[162] Neogi, *Proc. Asiatic Soc. Bengal, Proc. 8th Indian Sci. Cong.*, *17*, cxxxi (1921); *Chem. Abstr.*, *17*, 3478 (1923).

[163] Oddo, *Gazz. chim. ital.*, *41*,*I*, 273–94 (1911); *Chem. Abstr.*, *5*, 2639 (1911).

[164] Schorigin, Issagulianz, and Gussewa, *Ber.*, *66B*, 1426–31 (1933).

$$\begin{matrix} R & & C_2H_5 \\ & O & \\ X & & C_2H_5 \end{matrix}$$

was a necessary prerequisite to reaction with magnesium to form a Grignard reagent, it was shown by Spencer and Stokes[165] that many Grignard reagents may be prepared merely by heating the halide with magnesium. There is always an appreciable proportion of Wurtz product, and usually, when disproportionation is possible, of disproportionation products as well.

Spencer and Stokes found that iodobenzene gave a product which, upon hydrolysis yielded 44 percent of benzene and 54 percent of biphenyl. Bromobenzene behaved similarly, although it reacted less readily with magnesium. Other similar reactions carried out by Spencer and Stokes were:

$$p\text{-}CH_3C_6H_4I \xrightarrow{Mg} \xrightarrow{H_2O} CH_3C_6H_5\ (87\%)$$

$$o\text{-}CH_3C_6H_4Br \xrightarrow{Mg} \xrightarrow{H_2O} CH_3C_6H_5\ (87\%)$$

$$m\text{-}H_2NC_6H_4Br \xrightarrow{Mg} \xrightarrow{H_2O} H_2NC_6H_5\ (90\%)$$

$$o\text{-}H_2NC_6H_4Cl \xrightarrow{Mg} \xrightarrow{H_2O} H_2NC_6H_5\ (\text{"good yield"})$$

$$p\text{-}HOC_6H_4Br \xrightarrow{Mg} \xrightarrow{H_2O} HOC_6H_5\ (40\text{–}50\%)$$

$$1\text{-}C_{10}H_7Br \xrightarrow{Mg} \xrightarrow{H_2O} C_{10}H_8\ (72\%)$$

Bromoacenaphthene and bromosuccinic acid also reacted in this way, but the method did not appear to be applicable to benzylidene chloride, *p*-chlorophenol, *o*-chlorophenol, 1-chloronaphthalene, *p*-chlorotoluene, methyl iodide, methylene iodide, trimethylene iodide or isopropyl iodide.

The study described was extended by Spencer and Crewdson:[166]

$$i\text{-}C_5H_{11}I \xrightarrow{Mg} \xrightarrow{H_2O} i\text{-}C_5H_{12}\ (62\%)$$

$$s\text{-}C_8H_{17}I \xrightarrow{Mg} \xrightarrow{H_2O} C_8H_{18}\ (84\%)$$

$$i\text{-}C_5H_{11}Br \xrightarrow{Mg} \xrightarrow{H_2O} i\text{-}C_5H_{12}\ (\text{"a little"}) + (i\text{-}C_5H_{11}\text{—})_2\ (67\%)$$

$$H_3CO_2CCH_2Br \xrightarrow{Mg} \xrightarrow{H_2O} \text{recovered } BrCH_2CO_2CH_3\ (41\%) + CH_3CO_2CH_3$$

$$(34\%, \text{ on basis of bromoacetate consumed}) + (\text{—}CH_2CO_2CH_3)_2\ (48\%)$$

Chlorobenzene heated in a sealed tube with magnesium for six hours at 270°, then cooled and treated with water yielded 60 percent of benzene. Methyl iodide, ethyl bromide, ethyl chloride and isobutyl chloride, heated with magnesium in sealed tubes at *ca.* 250° for six to eight hours yielded

[165] Spencer and Stokes, *J. Chem. Soc.*, 93, 68–72 (1908).
[166] Spencer and Crewdson, *J. Chem. Soc.*, 93, 1821–6 (1908).

some Grignard reagent, together with varying quantities of Wurtz products, unsaturated gases, and hydrogen.

Gilman and Brown[167] report that when 11.2 g. (0.1 mole) of chlorobenzene and 3.6 g. (0.15 g.-atom) of magnesium were sealed in an evacuated bomb-tube and heated at 150–160° for three hours, and the light-brown, powdery product was washed with benzene and dissolved in 1:1 ether-benzene solution and titrated, the result indicated an 84 percent yield of Grignard reagent. (There was no reaction at 140°; at temperatures higher than that employed there was charring.)

Shorigin *et al.*[168] prepared the Grignard reagent from chlorobenzene without the aid of solvents. They used an iron autoclave, equipped with a mechanical stirrer, operated under 2.5 atmospheres pressure for three to three and one-half hours at 160–165°. The best yield of Grignard reagent (calculated as C_6H_5MgCl), evaluated by dilute sulfuric acid titration, was 70 percent on the basis of the chlorobenzene consumed (59 percent on the basis of the magnesium consumed), obtained when the reactants were combined in the ratio of 4 moles of chlorobenzene per gram-atom of magnesium. The byproducts were biphenyl and a little terphenyl. The amount of biphenyl formed depended on the relative proportions of the reactants: 1.5 Mg + 1 C_6H_5Cl, 8 percent; 1.2 Mg + 1 C_6H_5Cl, 14 percent; 1.0 Mg + 1 C_6H_5Cl, 16 percent.

Unsuccessful attempts to prepare *n*-butyl-, isoamyl-, and *n*-octylmagnesium chlorides by refluxing magnesium in the respective alkyl chlorides are also reported.[169]

According to Weissenborn,[170] phenylmagnesium chloride or its homologs may be prepared by boiling chlorobenzene or its homologs with magnesium or an alloy of magnesium in the presence of an activator, such as cuprous chloride, aluminum bromide, or iodine. In an amendment to the original patent, Weissenborn[171] claims that the activator may be omitted if the magnesium is thoroughly clean.

Andrianov and Gribanova[172] advocate the use of ethyl orthosilicate $(C_2H_5O)_4Si$ as an activator or "catalyst." According to them, alkyl or aryl halides react with magnesium in the presence of a little ester to give

[167] Gilman and Brown, *J. Am. Chem. Soc.*, *52*, 3330–2 (1930).

[168] (*a*) Shorigin, Issaguljanz, Gusşewa, Ossipowa, and Poljakowa, *Ber.*, *64B*, 2584–90 (1931); (*b*) Shorigin and Issaguljanz, *Trans. VI Mendeleev Congr. Theoret. Applied Chem. 1932*, *2*, Pt. 1, 973–80 (1935); *Chem. Zentr.*, *1936*, *II*, 2345; *Chem. Abstr.*, *30*, 4157 (1936).

[169] Schorigin, Issagulianz, and Gussewa, *Ber.*, *66B*, 1426–31 (1933).

[170] Weissenborn, German Patent 660,075, May 17, 1938; *Chem. Abstr.*, *32*, P5857 (1938).

[171] Weissenborn, German Patent, 697,420, Sept. 19, 1940; *Chem. Abstr.*, *35*, P6600 (1941).

[172] Andrianov and Gribanova, *J. Gen. Chem.* (U.S.S.R.), *8*, 552–6 (1938); *Chem. Abstr.*, *32*, 7892 (1938).

"good" yields of the corresponding Grignard reagents. The exothermic reaction proceeds in the absence of ether and is completed without external heating, or by digesting at 40–50° for an hour and a half.

It is said that equally good results are obtained when to 12 g. of magnesium and a few drops of ethyl orthosilicate, one-half of the halide is introduced dropwise directly, and the other half dissolved in 4–5 parts of toluene or xylene. In this way, the following Grignard reagents were prepared in the indicated percentage yields: C_2H_5MgBr, 96; *i*-C_4H_9MgCl, 51; *i*-$C_5H_{11}MgBr$, 58.5; *n*-$C_6H_{13}MgBr$, 60; *n*-$C_8H_{17}MgBr$, 35; C_6H_5MgBr, 23–25.

Manske and Ledingham[173] have prepared phenylmagnesium chloride by refluxing magnesium in an excess of chlorobenzene, with the aid of iodine activation when necessary. About ten hours is required for complete dissolution of 72 g. (3.0 g.-atoms) of magnesium in 1000 g. (8.9 moles) of chlorobenzene. When a batch of Grignard reagent so prepared was treated with 99 g. (2.25 moles) of ethylene oxide the yield of phenethyl alcohol obtained was 185 g. (*ca.* 1.5 mole)—about 50.5 percent on the basis of magnesium expended, or 67.4 percent on the basis of ethylene oxide used. Of especial interest is their report that small amounts of 4-biphenylethanol and 4-terphenyl-4-ethanol were also isolated.

Similarly prepared phenylmagnesium chloride, when carbonated, yielded benzoic, 4-biphenylcarboxylic, and 4-terphenyl-4-carboxylic acids.

As might be expected, biphenyl and terphenyl were present in both cases.

MECHANISM AND KINETICS OF GRIGNARD REAGENT FORMATION

The earlier contributions to this subject were purely speculative and may now be either disregarded as contrary to known facts or reinterpreted in the light of fuller knowledge. Although comparatively few studies have been directed primarily toward the solution of the problems involved, the accumulation of incidental evidence permits the presentation of a credible, though somewhat incomplete description of the process of organomagnesium halide formation.

Mindful of the facts that most organic halides appear remarkably unreactive toward magnesium in inert media such as benzene, and that reaction in such media may often be "catalyzed" by the addition of relatively small quantities of ether or tertiary amines, Tschelinzeff[174] advanced the hypothesis that the actual reactant with magnesium is an oxonium or quaternary ammonium salt. To this proposal, Grignard[175] offered the objection that, as compared to alkyl halides, quaternary ammonium halides are conspicuously inert toward magnesium. Meisenheimer

[173] Manske and Ledingham, *Can. J. Research*, 27, 158–60 (1949).
[174] Tschelinzeff, *Ber.*, 37, 4534–40 (1904).
[175] Grignard, *Bull. soc. chim.*, [4], *1*, 256–62 (1907).

and Casper[176] pointed out, further, that, although the formation of phenylmagnesium iodide in inert solvents is "catalyzed" by tertiary amines, iodobenzene does not form quaternary ammonium salts. They also added the further objection that the interaction of magnesium with an organic halide in the presence of an ether or a tertiary amine yields only the Grignard reagent corresponding to the original organic halide—never a mixture of Grignard reagents, as might reasonably be expected if the true organic reactant were an oxonium or quaternary ammonium salt. To this, if further argument be necessary, may be added the now known facts that ethereal solutions of organic halides in general, display none of the characteristic properties of oxonium salt solutions, and that some Grignard reagents, at least, may be prepared, though with relative difficulty, in inert solvents or without benefit of solvent other than excess halide.

In the light of present knowledge the most plausible hypothesis concerning the function of such agents as ethers and tertiary amines in Grignard reagent formation is that they are not catalysts in the generally accepted sense of the term. They merely make possible the continuation of a reaction they have had no part in initiating by facilitating removal of the product of reaction from the surface of the magnesium, which would otherwise be occluded and inactivated.

In a preliminary study on the kinetics of Grignard reagent formation, Kilpatrick and Simons[177] concluded that reaction between ethereal ethyl bromide and magnesium is initiated only at points of contact (magnesium-glass or magnesium-magnesium). The use of iodine as an "activator" reduces the induction period, but does not alter the rate of reaction otherwise. After the induction period, the rate of reaction is proportional to the ethyl bromide concentration and to the magnesium surface exposed.

In an extension of this study, Gzemski and Kilpatrick[178] made use of an improved modification of the apparatus originally employed. A freshly polished, or etched, magnesium cylinder served as the source of metal. Vertically aligned, it was rotated at high speed in contact with two vertically aligned shoes which were adjusted so that no actual abrasion of the magnesium took place. Under constant temperature control ($25 \pm 0.05°$) reproducible rates were thus obtained. The nature of the contact material did not greatly affect the rate of reaction as measured by the rate of dissolution of magnesium, but did in some cases affect the yield of Grignard reagent. (Copper and aluminum shoes both gave lower yields than glass shoes.) Gzemski and Kilpatrick conclude that the essential function of the contact is to facilitate the rupture of any coating originally present on the magnesium and then to prevent contamination of the surface with products. They found that, when the magnesium surface remains

---

[176] Meisenheimer and Casper, *Ber.*, *54B*, 1655–65 (1921).
[177] Kilpatrick and Simons, *J. Org. Chem.*, *2*, 459–69 (1938).
[178] Gzemski and Kilpatrick, *J. Org. Chem.*, *5*, 264–75 (1940).

constant in extent, increased halide concentration increases the rate of reaction as measured by the rate of metal dissolution, but decreases the ratio of active Grignard reagent to magnesium halide in the reaction product. This observation is in accord with those of Gilman *et al.*[179] on the effects of ether dilution and rate of halide addition on Grignard reagent yields.

Their observation on the effect of iodine is also consistent with the conclusion that can be drawn from earlier work on "activators" (see Activators and Inhibitors, p. 8). In general, "activators" facilitate the preparation of Grignard reagents by materially shortening the induction period. It appears to be a reasonable hypothesis that they do so either by cleansing the magnesium surface or by introducing free radicals (through the agency of magnesious halides) or by a combination of both effects.

Kondyrew[180] first observed that when externally connected platinum and magnesium electrodes are immersed in an ethereal ethyl bromide solution, magnesium dissolves and a potential is set up. Brun,[181] who studied this effect in more detail, found the potential so produced to be characteristic of the individual halide and of its concentration. What is much more pertinent to the present discussion, however, he measured the actual passage of current between the electrodes and found it to be extremely small. For example, during the dissolution of 2.25 g. of magnesium in an ethyl bromide solution, less than 0.1 coulomb of current passed, as compared with the 18,093 coulombs calculable for the dissolution of a like amount of metal in an ordinary electrical cell. The conclusion that Grignard reagent formation is essentially a non-ionic reaction appears inescapable.

The suggestion made by Gomberg and Bachmann[182] to account for iodine or magnesium iodide activation of magnesium, and subsequently adopted by Gilman *et al.*,[183] namely, that organomagnesium halide formation is a radical reaction in which magnesious halides participate is consistent with the known facts. Gomberg and Bachmann believe, as did Grignard,[184] that when no activator is present, reaction is initiated through the agency of small amounts of magnesium halide arising from the Wurtz reaction. This, of course, begs the question of the nature of the Wurtz reaction and its relationship to the Grignard reaction. If this view be accepted, their scheme should be amended to include the corresponding disproportionation reactions:

[179] (*a*) Gilman and McCracken, *Rec. trav. chim.*, *46*, 463–72 (1927); (*b*) Gilman, Zoellner, and Dickey, *J. Am. Chem. Soc.*, *51*, 1576–83, 1583–7 (1929).

[180] Kondyrew, *Ber.*, *58B*, 459–63 (1925).

[181] Brun, *J. chim. phys.*, 36, 147–59 (1939).

[182] Gomberg and Bachmann, *J. Am. Chem. Soc.*, *49*, 236–57 (1927).

[183] (*a*) Gilman and Fothergill, *J. Am. Chem. Soc.*, *50*, 3334–41 (1928); (*b*) Gilman and Kirby, *ibid.*, *51*, 1571–6 (1929).

[184] Grignard, *Bull. soc. chim.*, [4], *1*, 256–62 (1907).

(1a) $2\ RX + Mg \longrightarrow MgX_2 + R_2$

(1b) $2\ RX + Mg \longrightarrow MgX_2 + R_{(+H)} + R_{(-H)}$

(2) $MgX_2 + Mg \rightleftharpoons 2\ {\cdot}MgX$

(3) $RX + {\cdot}MgX \longrightarrow MgX_2 + R{\cdot}$

(4) $R{\cdot} + {\cdot}MgX \longrightarrow RMgX$

There would appear to be no compelling reason to regard these radicals as "free" in the sense that they occur in significant numbers in the body of the solution. The processes described might very well take place at the solid-liquid interface.

Most of the commonly encountered by-products of the preparation of Grignard reagents can also be accounted for on the basis of radicals, and it is notable that they are in general the same as those produced by the electrolytic discharge of Grignard anions. These are the so-called Wurtz products, the disproportionation products, and the products that may be attributed to the attack of free radicals upon the solvent.

The mechanism of the sodium Wurtz-Fittig reaction has been the subject of extensive study and discussion,[185] and convincing arguments can be made out for a free-radical process on the one hand or an interaction between arylsodium and an organic halide on the other. Probably both processes take place, depending upon the reactants and the experimental conditions.

With metallic magnesium, which has a higher discharge potential than sodium, the free-radical mechanism might well be expected to predominate. As a matter of fact, it is well known that appreciable quantities of biphenyl are always produced in the preparation of phenylmagnesium halides, whereas the reaction

$$C_6H_5MgBr + BrC_6H_5 \longrightarrow (C_6H_5—)_2 + MgBr_2$$

does not take place. Indeed, the allyl halides are among the relatively few conspicuous exceptions to the rule that, under the conditions ordinarily employed in the preparation of Grignard reagents, organic halides do not react with their own Grignard reagents.

The disproportionation reactions which take place at the surface of the metal are closely akin to the Wurtz reaction and probably go through a free-radical mechanism also. The more reactive free radicals like methyl (and undoubtedly the aryl radicals) attack the solvent to some extent and couple to some extent. The less reactive free radicals, such as the benzyl, which cannot disproportionate, couple or attack the solvent. Radicals, such as the ethyl and the *t*-butyl disproportionate almost completely with traces only of coupling products, if any. For the alkyl radicals that are not too highly branched, the tendency toward coupling in-

[185] *Cf.*, *e.g.*, Bachmann and Clark, *J. Am. Chem. Soc.*, *49*, 2089–98 (1927).

creases and the tendency toward disproportionation decreases with increasing molecular weight.

Disproportionation may also take place in solution by interaction between the halide and its Grignard reagent, but this reaction usually requires higher temperatures than does the formation of the Grignard reagent.

$$C_2H_5MgBr + C_2H_5Br \longrightarrow MgBr_2 + C_2H_6 + C_2H_4 \text{ (Späth[186])}$$

$$t\text{-}C_4H_9MgCl + t\text{-}C_4H_9Cl \longrightarrow MgCl_2 + i\text{-}C_4H_{10} + i\text{-}C_4H_8 \text{ (Bouvault[187])}$$

Studies of the gaseous byproducts evolved in the preparation of alkylmagnesium halides have been made by Tschelinzeff,[188] by Jolibois,[189] by Job *et al.*,[190] and by Gilman and Fothergill (*loc. cit.*[183a]).

Granting that the electrical effects previously discussed exclude an ionic reaction mechanism for Grignard reagent formation, further evidence of a radical mechanism is to be seen in the structural peculiarities of the Grignard reagents prepared from such allylic halides as cinnamyl chloride[191] and crotyl- and α-methallyl bromides.[192] The corresponding free radicals are resonant structures which may be described by the canonical forms:

$$C_6H_5CH{=}CHCH_2\cdot \longleftrightarrow \cdot CH(C_6H_5)CH{=}CH_2$$

$$CH_3CH{=}CHCH_2\cdot \longleftrightarrow \cdot CH(CH_3)CH{=}CH_2$$

The Grignard reagent from cinnamyl chloride reacts chiefly as though it had the structure $CH_2{=}CH(C_6H_5)CHMgCl$; that from crotyl bromide, from α-methallyl bromide, or from mixtures thereof in various proportions, as though it were a mixture of

$$CH_3CH{=}CHCH_2MgBr \text{ and } CH_3(CH_2{=}CH)CHMgBr$$

These phenomena are discussed in more detail in Chapter XVII, Allylic Rearrangements in Grignard Reactions.

It may also be noted that optically active halides of the types RR′C*HX and RR′R″C*X react with magnesium to give optically inactive Grignard reagents, which in turn react with co-reactants to give optically inactive products.[193]

---

[186] Späth, *Monatsh.*, *34*, 1965–2014 (1913).

[187] Bouvault, *Compt. rend.*, *138*, 1108–10 (1904); *J. Chem. Soc.*, *86,I*, 546 (1904). See also: Madelung and Volker, *J. prakt. Chem.*, [2], *115*, 24–44 (1927); Gilman and Zoellner, *J. Am. Chem. Soc.*, *50*, 425–8 (1928).

[188] Tschelinzeff, *J. Russ. Phys.-Chem. Soc.*, *36*, 549–54 (1904); *J. Chem. Soc.*, *86,I*, 641 (1904).

[189] Jolibois, *Compt. rend.*, *155*, 213–5 (1912); *Chem. Abstr.*, *6*, 2740 (1912).

[190] Job, Reich, and Dubien, *Bull. soc. chim.*, [4], *37*, 976–7 (1925).

[191] Gilman and Harris, *J. Am. Chem. Soc.*, *53*, 3541–6 (1931).

[192] Young, Winstein, and Prater, *J. Am. Chem. Soc.*, *58*, 289–91 (1936).

[193] See, *e.g.*: Porter, *J. Am. Chem. Soc.*, *57*, 1436 (1935).

A proposed reaction scheme. In order to take as full account as possible of the qualitative and quantitative observations herewith reviewed, and at the same time to provide a basis for elucidation of the various side-reactions that occur during Grignard reagent formation, the authors propose a modification of the reaction scheme of Gomberg and Bachmann (*loc. cit.*[182]). Although admittedly speculative, the concept offered appears to constitute a useful working hypothesis in that it is consistent with all the well-established facts and that it affords a basis of correlation for a considerable mass of empirical data.

It seems probable that a clean, fresh, mechanically-created surface of metallic magnesium includes many points of unsaturation * which may be regarded as centers of exceptional reactivity. Even brief exposure to ordinary atmospheres undoubtedly destroys many such centers by chemical action; probably others disappear upon aging in inert atmospheres by a process akin to annealing. These ideas would seem to account sufficiently for the extraordinary efficacy of the method of "mechanical activation" previously discussed.

It is, perhaps, wiser to avoid diagrammatic representations as tending to suggest physical pictures that may be subject to too-literal interpretation. For purposes of entering into illustrative detail, however, a particle of metallic magnesium with its points of surface unsaturation may be represented by the symbol $(Mg)_x(Mg\cdot)_{2y}$, in which, of course, $x >> 2y$. The initial reaction of a clean, partially unsaturated surface of magnesium with an organic halide may be represented by equation 1.

$$(1) \quad (Mg)_x(Mg\cdot)_{2y} + RX \longrightarrow [(Mg)_x(Mg\cdot)_{2y-1}(MgX) + R\cdot] \longrightarrow (Mg)_{x-2}(Mg\cdot)_{2y}(MgX)(MgR)$$

Subsequent reaction steps that might lead to Grignard reagent formation may be represented by equations 2, 3, and 4.

$$(2) \quad (Mg)_{x-2}(Mg\cdot)_{2y}(MgX)(MgR) + RX \longrightarrow (Mg)_{x-4}(Mg\cdot)_{2y+2} + 2\ RMgX$$

$$(3) \quad (Mg)_{x-2}(Mg\cdot)_{2y}(MgX)(MgR) + RX \longrightarrow (Mg)_{x-4}(Mg\cdot)_{2y+2} + MgX_2 + R_2Mg$$

$$(4) \quad (Mg)_{x-2}(Mg\cdot)_{2y}(MgX)(MgR) + RX \longrightarrow (Mg)_{x-5}(Mg\cdot)_{2y+2}(MgX)(MgR) + RMgX$$

Possibly adjacent MgX and MgR groups may react in the sense of equation 5.

$$(5) \quad (Mg)_{x-2}(Mg\cdot)_{2y}(MgX)(MgR) \longrightarrow (Mg)_{x-3}(Mg\cdot)_{2y+2} + RMgX$$

* For the sake of simplicity, points of unsaturation are represented in the equations that follow as actual free valences. No doubt lattice distortions resulting in elongated or otherwise strained intermetallic bonds also constitute centers of exceptional reactivity, at least in so far as the more reactive halides are concerned.

Another reaction not leading directly to Grignard reagent formation, but which might ultimately do so, or which might, on the other hand, lead to Wurtz product formation is suggested in equation 6.

$$(6)\quad (Mg)_{x-2}(Mg^{\bullet})_{2y}(MgX)(MgR) + RX \longrightarrow (Mg)_{x-5}(Mg^{\bullet})_{2y+2}(MgR)_2 + MgX_2$$

The tendency for the reactivity of the surface* to increase as reaction progresses is probably exaggerated in equations 2–5 as written, for it seems likely that at least some adjacent centers of unsaturation would undergo mutual saturation before being subjected to further halide attack. However, a net effect in the qualitative sense indicated would explain in part at least: (*a*) the inductive period observed at the beginning of the halide-magnesium reaction; (*b*) the tendency of the reaction rate to increase as reaction proceeds; (*c*) the efficacy of relatively reactive halides (*e.g.*, ethyl bromide) as magnesium activators; and (*d*) in part, at least, the efficacy of the "entrainment" method of preparation.

The process of halogen activation probably involves both the attack of molecular halogen upon preëxistent reactive centers (equation 7) and the attack of atomic halogen upon the saturated metallic surface (equation 8).

$$(7)\quad (Mg)_x(Mg^{\bullet})_{2y} + X_2 \longrightarrow [(Mg_x)(Mg^{\bullet})_{2y-1}(MgX) + X^{\bullet}] \longrightarrow (Mg)_{x-2}(Mg^{\bullet})_{2y}(MgX)_2$$

$$(8)\quad (Mg)_x(Mg^{\bullet})_{2y} + X^{\bullet} \longrightarrow (Mg)_{x-2}(Mg^{\bullet})_{2y+1}(MgX)$$

Magnesium halide activation is probably initiated at points of unsaturation only (equation 9).

$$(9)\quad (Mg)_x(Mg^{\bullet})_{2y} + MgX_2 \longrightarrow [(Mg)_x(Mg^{\bullet})_{2y-1}(MgX) + {}^{\bullet}MgX] \longrightarrow (Mg)_{x-2}(Mg^{\bullet})_{2y}(MgX)_2$$

The commonly accepted idea that a small amount of preformed Grignard reagent solution serves as an activator may have no basis beyond the fact that such a solution would contain a certain amount of magnesium halide, partly as a consequence of Wurtz or disproportionation side-reactions occurring during its formation, and partly as a consequence of the Schlenk equilibrium (see Chapter IV, Constitution and Dissociation of the Grignard Reagent). However, it would be quite possible to write an equation analogous to equation 9 in which MgX_2 is replaced by RMgX or R_2Mg.

*Centers of exceptional reactivity (or, more briefly, reactive centers) may be taken to include actual points of unsaturation ($Mg^{\bullet}$) and surface-adherent halogen atoms (MgX) and organic radicals (MgR). Reactivity (toward organic halides) is presumed to decrease in the order: $(Mg^{\bullet}) > (MgX) > (MgR) >> (Mg)_x$. Surface reactivity may increase either through an increase in the number of reactive centers (equation 4) or an increase in the reactivity of a constant number of reactive centers (equations 2 and 3).

The Wurtz and disproportionation reactions. Concerning the Wurtz reaction, present knowledge of the behavior of free radicals in solution enables us to discount certain proposed mechanisms as either improbable or incapable of general application. In the cases of such highly reactive free radicals as the phenyl, or even the methyl, the notion that they could survive long enough in the presence of any of the usual Grignard solvents to undergo the reaction

$$2\,R\cdot \longrightarrow R_2$$

to an appreciable extent is absurd. Surface-attached radicals, however, probably have a considerable degree of surface mobility (through simultaneous bond scission and bond formation) and it seems altogether probable that two adjacent radicals might form a dimer through a reaction which might be represented as in equations 10a, b.

(10a) $(Mg)_{x-5}(Mg\cdot)_{2y+2}(MgR)_2 \longrightarrow (Mg)_{x-5}(Mg\cdot)_{2y+4} + R_2$

(10b) $(Mg)_{x-5}(Mg\cdot)_{2y+2}(MgR)_2 \longrightarrow (Mg)_{x-3}(Mg\cdot)_{2y+2} + R_2$

The net energy change would certainly favor such reactions. An increase in the temperature of the reaction system might be expected both to increase the surface mobility of radicals and to contribute to any energy of activation that might be required for the dimerization—an effect consistent with the empirical observation that, in general, higher reaction temperatures favor Wurtz product formation.

Another probable source of Wurtz product that should not be ignored may be represented as in equations 11a, b.

(11a) $(Mg)_{x-5}(Mg\cdot)_{2y+2}(MgR)_2 + RMgX \longrightarrow$
$[(Mg)_{x-5}(Mg\cdot)_{2y+3}(MgR) + \cdot MgX + R_2] \longrightarrow$
$(Mg)_{x-6}(Mg\cdot)_{2y+4}(MgX)(MgR) + R_2$

(11b) $(Mg)_{x-2}(Mg\cdot)_{2y}(MgX)(MgR) + RMgX \longrightarrow$
$[(Mg)_{x-2}(Mg\cdot)_{2y+1}(MgX) + \cdot MgX + R_2] \longrightarrow$
$(Mg)_{x-3}(Mg\cdot)_{2y+2}(MgX)_2 + R_2$

The disproportionation reactions are very closely allied to the Wurtz reaction, and whether one or the other occurs is determined principally by the nature of the radical involved. For alkyl radicals (other than methyl) equations 10 and 11 may be rewritten with the substitution of $R_{(+H)} + R_{(-H)}$ for R_2.

Reactions involving the solvent. Whether or not free radicals ever actually escape into the body of the solution in significant quantities is a question that can scarcely be answered with any assurance. However, it is altogether conceivable that under favorable experimental conditions they do, in which case it may be said that their ultimate fate depends on both the nature of the free radical concerned and the nature of the solvent medium.

Solvents containing relatively labile hydrogen atoms are attacked by the more reactive (*i.e.*, in general, the more "electronegative"[194]) radicals, including, *e.g.*, methyl and phenyl.

$$R\cdot + SolvH \longrightarrow RH + Solv\cdot \quad (12)$$

In such solvents the less reactive radicals (*i.e.*, those incapable of abstracting hydrogen atoms from the solvent) may be expected to accumulate in the system until their reactions with each other or with the Grignard reagent assume significant proportions. In the cases of radicals structurally incapable of disproportionation the Wurtz product is formed (equations 13 and 14).

$$2\,R\cdot \longrightarrow R_2 \quad (13)$$

$$R\cdot + RMgX \longrightarrow R_2 + \cdot MgX \quad (14)$$

In the cases of radicals structurally capable of disproportionation, that reaction may be expected to take place exclusively with alkyl radicals of low molecular weight, and predominantly with alkyl radicals of higher molecular weight (equations 15 and 16).

$$2\,R\cdot \longrightarrow R_{(+H)} + R_{(-H)} \quad (15)$$

$$R\cdot + RMgX \longrightarrow R_{(+H)} + R_{(-H)} + \cdot MgX \quad (16)$$

Aromatic solvents appear to react additively with radicals of all types. Thus, the reaction of benzyl chloride with magnesium in benzene produces (in addition to the Grignard reagent) both bibenzyl (the Wurtz product) and diphenylmethane; bromobenzene with magnesium in toluene produces both biphenyl and 4-methylbiphenyl.[195] When Manske and Ledingham[196] carbonated phenylmagnesium chloride solutions obtained by the reaction of magnesium with excess chlorobenzene, they were able to isolate (in addition to benzoic acid) small amounts of 4-biphenylcarboxylic and 4-terphenyl-4-carboxylic acids. Similarly, treatment of such solutions with ethylene oxide yielded (in addition to phenethyl alcohol) small amounts of 4-biphenylethanol and 4-terphenyl-4-ethanol.

Presumably the first step in such additive reactions must be a process like that described in equation 17.

---

[194] Concerning relative electronegativities of organic radicals, see: Kharasch and Reinmuth, *J. Chem. Education*, *5*, 404–18 (1928); *8*, 1703–48 (1931); Kharasch, Reinmuth, and Mayo, *ibid.*, *11*, 82–96 (1934); *13*, 7–19 (1936).

[195] Kharasch, Goldberg, and Mayo, *J. Am. Chem. Soc.*, *60*, 2004 (1938). Although water was added to the reaction systems described in this report, it has since been shown by Kane, Dissertation, University of Chicago, *1941*, that the water does not enter into the reactions under discussion.

[196] Manske and Ledingham, *Can. J. Research*, *27*, 158–60 (1949).

(17) 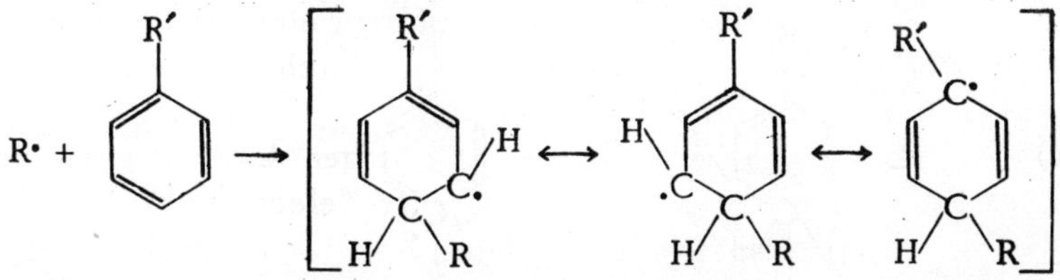 R· + [aromatic ring with R′] → [resonance structures of the addition intermediate]

The fate of the excess (and undoubtedly extremely labile) hydrogen atom in the addition intermediate is as yet unknown. On the whole, a spontaneous dissociation of the type illustrated in equation 18 appears highly improbable.

(18) 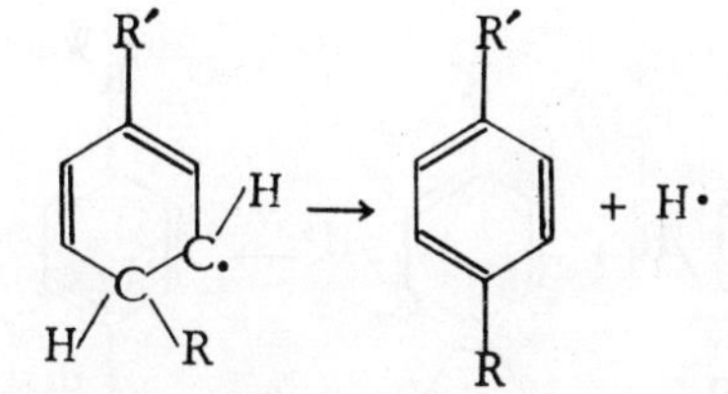 [intermediate] → [R′–C₆H₄–R] + H·

However, transfer to any available hydrogen acceptor should be effected very readily indeed (equation 19).

(19) 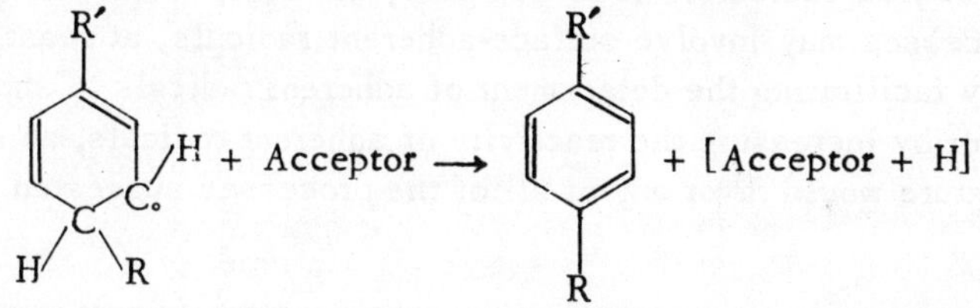 [intermediate] + Acceptor → [R′–C₆H₄–R] + [Acceptor + H]

Credible transfers of this type are illustrated in equations 19a, b, c.

(19a) 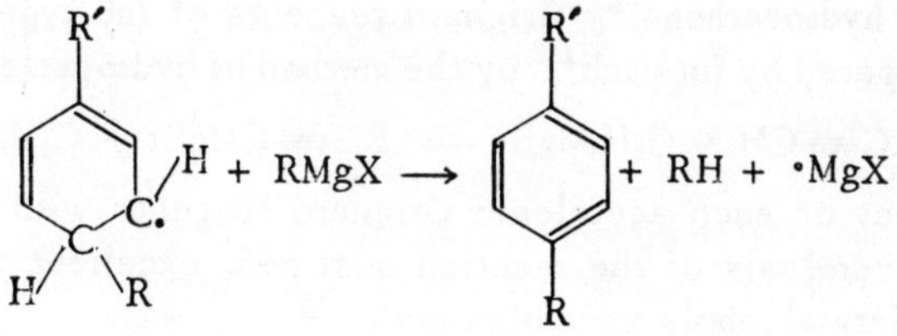 [intermediate] + RMgX → [R′–C₆H₄–R] + RH + ·MgX

(19b) 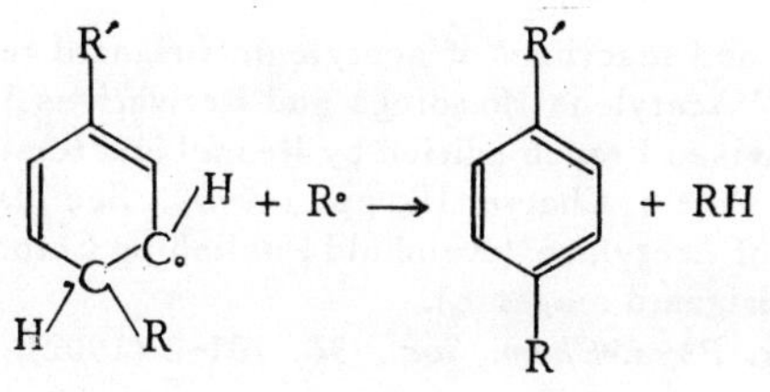 [intermediate] + R· → [R′–C₆H₄–R] + RH

(19c) 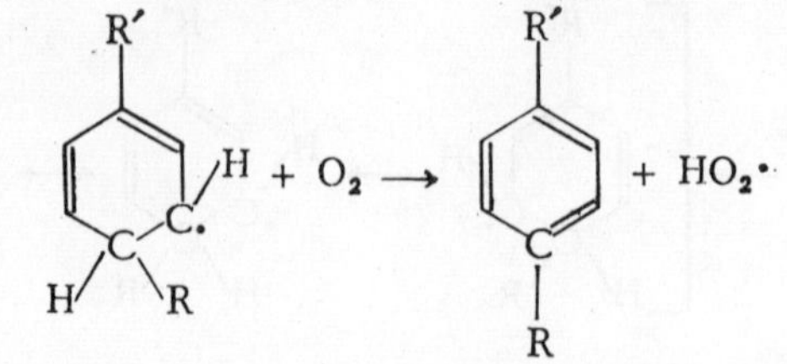 R′, H, C·, C, H, R + O_2 ⟶ R′, C, R + $HO_2\cdot$

A disproportionation of the type suggested in equation 20 is not regarded as implausible *per se*, but as unlikely because of the high probability that reaction with some hydrogen acceptor would intervene to circumvent it.

(20) 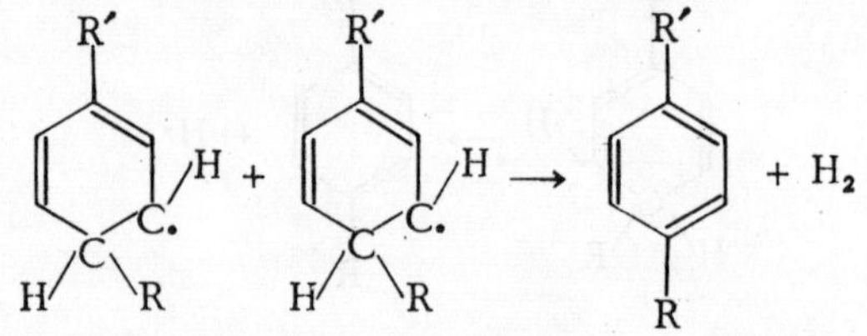 R′, H, C·, C, H, R + R′, H, C·, C, H, R ⟶ R′, R + H_2

The reactions just discussed (equations 12–20) have been represented as those of *free* radicals. It is possible, however, that some or all of these processes may involve surface-adherent radicals, at least in part. Whether by facilitating the detachment of adherent radicals to supply *free* radicals, or by increasing the reactivity of adherent radicals, an increase in temperature would favor any or all of the processes suggested.

HYDROGEN DISPLACEMENT METHODS OF GRIGNARD REAGENT PREPARATION

Acetylenic hydrocarbons.* Grignard reagents of the type $RC{\equiv}CMgX$ were first prepared by Iotsitch[197] by the method of hydrogen displacement.

$$RC{\equiv}CH + C_2H_5MgBr \longrightarrow RC{\equiv}CMgBr + C_2H_6$$

Upon treatment of such acetylenic Grignard reagents with ketones and subsequent hydrolysis of the reaction mixtures, excellent yields of the expected tertiary alcohols were obtained:

---

* The preparations and reactions of acetylenic Grignard reagents have been reviewed by Piganiol, "Acetylene Homologs and Derivatives," English translation from the second revised French edition by Hessel and Rust, Mapleton House, Brooklyn, N. Y., *1950*, Part 4, Chapter III, pp. 249–69. See also: Nieuwland and Vogt, "The Chemistry of Acetylene" Reinhold Publishing Corporation, New York, *1945* (Subject Index—Grignard reagents).

[197] Iotsitch, *J. Russ. Phys.-Chem. Soc.*, *34*, 101–2 (1902); *Bull. soc. chim.*, [3], *28*, 922 (1902).

$$C_6H_5C\equiv CMgBr + (CH_3)_2CO \longrightarrow C_6H_5C\equiv C(CH_3)_2COH \quad (95\%);$$

$$C_6H_5C\equiv CMgBr + \begin{array}{c} CH_2 \\ H_2C \quad\; CH{-}CH_3 \\ | \qquad\quad | \\ H_2C \qquad CH_2 \\ C \\ \| \\ O \end{array} \longrightarrow \begin{array}{c} CH_2 \\ H_2C \quad\; CH{-}CH_3 \\ | \qquad\quad | \\ H_2C \qquad CH_2 \\ C \\ HO \qquad C\equiv CC_6H_5 \end{array} \quad (97\%);$$

$$n\text{-}C_5H_{11}C\equiv CMgBr + (CH_3)_2CO \longrightarrow n\text{-}C_5H_{11}\ C\equiv C(CH_3)COH \quad (80\%).$$

Iotsitch[198] obtained the expected products from phenylethynylmagnesium bromide and ethyl acetate, chloral, and 2,2,3-trichlorobutanal, respectively.

Meyer and Streuli[199] report that 1-octadecyne does not react with methylmagnesium bromide in boiling ethyl ether, but that reaction does take place in boiling *n*-butyl ether and can be followed quantitatively by measurement of the methane evolved. The resultant acetylenic Grignard reagent is said to be unreactive toward benzaldehyde, benzoyl chloride and methyl benzoate, but reacts normally with carbon dioxide (25 percent yield), the dinitrile of thapsic acid (85 percent yield), and with eicosane-3,18-dione (88 percent yield).

Kroeger and Nieuwland,[200] however, apparently experienced no difficulty in preparing *n*-heptynyl-, *n*-hexynyl-, or phenylethynylmagnesium halides from ethyl ethereal solutions of methylmagnesium iodide, ethylmagnesium bromide, or ethylmagnesium chloride. For the preparation of the bromides (from ethylmagnesium bromide) they describe their procedure as follows. "The calculated quantity of acetylenic hydrocarbon was dissolved in ether and added to the prepared Grignard [reagent], after which the solution was refluxed until no more ethane was evolved. In the case of quarter-mole runs, this required a half-hour for phenylacetylene and about two hours for alkylacetylenes."

According to them, the ethynylmagnesium chlorides are considerably less ether-soluble than the corresponding bromides or iodides or than ethylmagnesium chloride. When 0.5 mole of 1-heptyne, 1-hexyne, or phenylacetylene reacts with 0.5 mole of ethylmagnesium chloride in 250 ml. of ethyl ether, part of the acetylenic Grignard reagent is precipitated as a white solid.

The dimagnesium Grignard reagent of acetylene itself was also prepared by Iotsitch[201] by the passage of acetylene into an ethereal solution

---

[198] Iotsitch, *J. Russ. Phys.-Chem. Soc.*, *34*, 241–2 (1902); *Bull. soc. chim.*, [3], *30*, 209 (1903).

[199] Meyer and Streuli, *Helv. Chim. Acta*, *20*, 1179–83 (1937).

[200] Kroeger and Nieuwland, *J. Am. Chem. Soc.*, *58*, 1861–3 (1936).

[201] Iotsitch, *J. Russ. Phys.-Chem. Soc.*, *34*, 242–4 (1902); *Bull. soc. chim.*, [3], *30*, 210 (1903).

of ethylmagnesium bromide, and was found to react normally with carbon dioxide, ketones, and aldehydes.

According to Kleinfeller[202] the dimagnesium Grignard reagent of acetylene ($BrMgC{\equiv}CMgBr$ or the corresponding diïodide), when prepared in ether solution is an ether-insoluble, ether-free oil that undergoes characteristic Grignard reactions. On long standing (three to four weeks) it becomes a crystalline solid which still reacts with water to liberate acetylene, but which no longer reacts like a Grignard reagent with the usual organic or inorganic reactants. The change is described as

$$BrMgC{\equiv}CMgBr \rightleftharpoons MgBr_2 + C_2Mg\,,$$

which Kleinfeller regards as a special case of the Schlenk equilibrium,[203]

$$2\,RMgX \rightleftharpoons R_2Mg + MgX_2\,,$$

which in this instance lies completely to the right.

An analogous observation has been made by Durand,[204] who cautiously heated ethynylenemagnesium iodide to the point of incipient carbonization. When the cooled mass was extracted with ether, magnesium iodide was removed, and a white, porous, amorphous, iodine-free residue remained. This, when treated with water, liberated acetylene. The reaction postulated is:

$$({\equiv}CMgI)_2 \xrightarrow{\Delta} C_2Mg + MgI_2.$$

A method advocated as convenient for the preparation of large quantities of ethynylenemagnesium bromide [$({\equiv}CMgBr)_2$] is described by Kleinfeller[205] essentially as follows. Dry acetylene is led into ethereal ethylmagnesium bromide until ethane evolution ceases and the acetylenic Grignard reagent forms a film-covered dark, heavy layer. It is expedient to conserve gas by employing a series of interconnected absorption vessels. For a series of five flasks, each containing ethylmagnesium bromide from 36.3 g. of ethyl bromide, about forty-eight hours is required for complete conversion.

Oddo[206] claimed to have prepared the monomagnesium Grignard reagent of acetylene by saturating an ethereal solution of phenylmagnesium bromide with acetylene. Iotsitch[207] was unable to confirm the presence of the monomagnesium compound under the conditions apparently described in the abstract of Oddo's paper, but did obtain a mixture of propargyl al-

---

[202] Kleinfeller, *Ber.*, *62B*, 2736–8 (1929).

[203] Schlenk and Schlenk, *Ber.*, *62B*, 920–4 (1929). See Chapter IV, Constitution and Dissociation of the Grignard Reagent.

[204] Durand, *Bull. soc. chim.*, [4], *35*, 944–5 (1924).

[205] Kleinfeller, *J. prakt. Chem.*, [2], *119*, 66–73 (1928).

[206] Oddo, *Gazz. chim. ital.*, [2], *34*, 429–36 (1904); *Bull. soc. chim.*, [3], *36*, 682 (1906).

[207] Iotsitch, *J. Russ. Phys.-Chem. Soc.*, 38, 252–3 (1906); *Bull. soc. chim.*, [4], *4*, 981 (1908).

cohol and the acetylenic glycol when he passed a current of acetylene through the reaction flask during the five hours necessary for completion of the reaction between trioxymethylene and the dimagnesium compound. Analogous results were obtained with 3-methylcyclohexanone and menthone.

By saturating an ethereal solution of phenylmagnesium bromide with acetylene, then decomposing the resultant acetylenic Grignard compounds with water, and measuring the volume of acetylene evolved, Salkind and Rosenfeld[208] estimated that the yield of monomagnesium compound so obtained could not exceed 36 percent. When passage of acetylene through the solution was continued for thirty hours, the indicated yield of monomagnesium compound was about 51 percent. Under the same conditions, except that brisk refluxing of the ethereal solution was maintained throughout, the indicated yield of monomagnesium compound approximated 100 percent.

Lespieau[209] prepared an acetylenic Grignard reagent which he believed to consist principally of the dimagnesium compound by passing ether-saturated acetylene into a dilute ethereal solution of ethylmagnesium bromide for forty to eighty hours. Dropwise addition of a calculated 0.3 equivalent of aldehyde or ketone dissolved in a threefold volume of ether resulted in yields up to 25 percent of alcohols (as distinguished from glycols). Lespieau attributed alcohol formation to partial reaction in the sense:

$$BrMgC{\equiv}CMgBr \xrightarrow{RCHO} BrMgC{\equiv}CCHROMgBr \xrightarrow{H_2O} HC{\equiv}CCHROH$$

Krestinski and Marjin[210] saturated an ice-salt-cooled ethereal solution of the dimagnesium Grignard compound with acetylene, added isobutyraldehyde and allowed the mixture to stand overnight. They attribute the alcohol obtained [$HC{\equiv}CCH(i\text{-}C_3H_7)OH$] to the equilibrium:

$$BrMgC{\equiv}CMgBr + HC{\equiv}CH \rightleftharpoons 2\ HC{\equiv}CMgBr$$

According to Grignard *et al.*,[211] a yield of 95 percent of the dimagnesium Grignard reagent may be obtained by saturating an ethereal solution of ethylmagnesium bromide, prepared in the usual manner, with acetylene. When such a solution is further treated with acetylene under an excess pressure of a half atmosphere at 45° for about four hours, an 85 percent yield of the monomagnesium compound is obtained. Carbonation leads to propiolic acid in about 78 percent yield. Treatment of a similar solution

---

[208] Salkind and Rosenfeld, *Ber.*, *57B*, 1690–2 (1924).

[209] Lespieau, *Bull. soc. chim.*, [4], *39*, 991–4 (1926).

[210] Krestinski and Marjin, *Ber.*, *60B*, 1866–9 (1927).

[211] Grignard, Lapayre, and Tchéoufaki, *Compt. rend.*, *187*, 517–20 (1928). See also: Tchéoufaki, *Contr. Inst. Chem. Nat. Acad. Peiping*, *1*, 127–52 (1934); *Chem. Zentr.*, *1937,II*, 2982.

of dimagnesium compound with acetylene under one-half atmosphere excess pressure at −10° for about three-quarters hour gives a nearly quantitative yield of monomagnesium compound which, in turn, reacts with allyl bromide to give allylacetylene in 75 percent yield.

Kleinfeller and Lohmann[212] have reviewed earlier work on the monomagnesium compound and have made a kinetic study of the reactions involved. They conclude that the entire process may be described by the concurrent and mutually independent reactions *A* and the successive reactions *B*, *C* and *D*.

(*A*) $HC{\equiv}CH + C_2H_5MgBr \longrightarrow HC{\equiv}CMgBr + C_2H_6$

$HC{\equiv}CH + 2\ C_2H_5MgBr \longrightarrow BrMgC{\equiv}CMgBr + 2\ C_2H_6$

(*B*) $HC{\equiv}CH + 2\ C_2H_5MgBr \longrightarrow BrMgC{\equiv}CMgBr + 2\ C_2H_6$

$HC{\equiv}CH + BrMgC{\equiv}CMgBr \longrightarrow 2\ HC{\equiv}CMgBr$

(*C*) $HC{\equiv}CH + C_2H_5MgBr \longrightarrow HC{\equiv}CMgBr + C_2H_6$

$HC{\equiv}CMgBr + C_2H_5MgBr \longrightarrow BrMgC{\equiv}CMgBr + C_2H_6$

(*D*) $HC{\equiv}CH + C_2H_5MgBr \longrightarrow HC{\equiv}CMgBr + C_2H_6$

$2\ HC{\equiv}CMgBr \longrightarrow BrMgC{\equiv}CMgBr + HC{\equiv}CH$

That acetylenic Grignard reagents may be prepared by halogen replacement as well as by hydrogen replacement has been demonstrated by Iotsitch,[213] who treated bromoacetylene with ethylmagnesium bromide and obtained a Grignard reagent which yielded acetylenedicarboxylic acid upon carbonation and subsequent acid hydrolysis.

$$HC{\equiv}CBr + 2\ C_2H_5MgBr \longrightarrow ({\equiv}CMgBr)_2 + C_2H_6 + C_2H_5Br$$

$$({\equiv}CMgBr)_2 \xrightarrow{2\ CO_2} ({\equiv}CCO_2MgBr)_2 \xrightarrow{HA} ({\equiv}CCO_2H)_2 + MgBr_2 + MgA_2$$

Treatment of a Grignard reagent so prepared with acetone resulted in a 60 percent yield of the expected glycol; with "methylcyclohexanone" a 75 percent yield of glycol was obtained. Diïodoacetylene also yielded ethynylenemagnesium bromide when treated with ethylmagnesium bromide.

Similar halogen displacement has been observed by Kharasch *et al.*[214]

$$\underset{(0.097\ \text{mole})}{C_6H_5C{\equiv}CBr} + \underset{(0.16\ \text{mole})}{CH_3MgBr} \xrightarrow{H_3O^+} \underset{(89\%)}{C_6H_5C{\equiv}CH} + CH_3Br$$

$$\underset{(0.097\ \text{mole})}{C_6H_5C{\equiv}CBr} + \underset{(0.16\ \text{mole})}{CH_3MgBr} \xrightarrow{CO_2} \underset{(7.2\ \text{g.},\ 55\%)}{C_6H_5C{\equiv}CCO_2H} + \underset{(1.9\ \text{g.},\ 21\%)}{C_6H_5C{\equiv}CH}$$

These halogen replacement reactions are undoubtedly more closely related to the analogous hydrogen replacements than to the free-radical functional exchanges (*q.v.*, Chapter XVI.)

---

[212] Kleinfeller and Lohmann, *Ber.*, *71B*, 2608–13 (1938).
[213] Iotsitch, *J. Russ. Phys.-Chem. Soc.*, 36, 1545–51 (1904); *Bull. soc. chim.*, [3], 36, 177 (1906).
[214] Kharasch, Lambert, and Urry, *J. Org. Chem.*, *10*, 298–306 (1945).

Non-acetylenic hydrocarbons and their derivatives*

Cyclopentadiene, indene, and fluorene. Grignard and Courtot[215] found that cyclopentadiene, indene, and fluorene all react with ordinary Grignard reagents in a manner similar to that of the 1-alkynes.

Cyclopentadiene reacts slowly with ethylmagnesium bromide in boiling ether, reaction being incomplete for one-mole quantities at the end of twelve hours. If the ether be partially replaced by thiophene-free benzene, reaction is complete in five or six hours at 60°. Many cyclopentadiene derivatives have, like cyclopentadiene itself, a strong tendency to dimerize. Thus the acid obtained (in *ca.* 60 percent yield) by carbonation of cyclopentadienylmagnesium bromide is the dimeric acid, probably

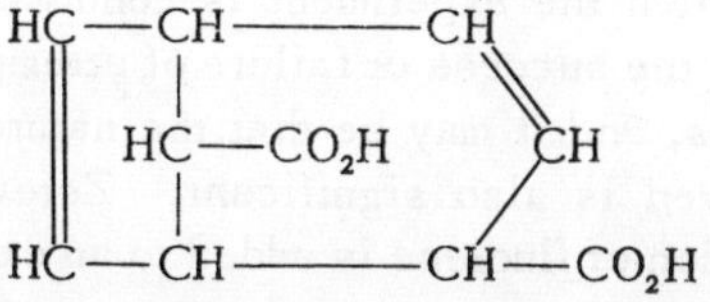

```
HC—CH————CH
‖    |      \\
‖   HC—CO₂H   CH
‖    |       /
HC—CH————CH—CO₂H
```

Indene requires a somewhat higher temperature (90-100°) for reaction with ethylmagnesium bromide. In toluene solution at 100°, reaction is substantially complete (for one-mole quantities) in about ten hours. Treatment of α-indenylmagnesium bromide with iodine leads, not to α-indenyl iodide, but to α,α′-biindenyl, possibly because of the great reactivity of the iodide toward Grignard reagents, although this course of reaction is not unique,[216] and may have another mechanism.

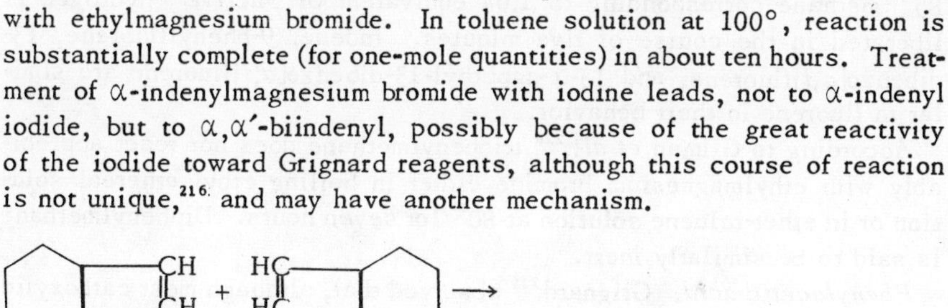

```
[C6H4]—CH=CH—CH(I)  +  [C6H4]—CH=CH—CH(MgBr)  ⟶

[C6H4]—CH=CH—CH——CH—CH=CH—[C6H4]  + MgBrI
```

Cyanogen bromide yields the *alpha* bromide, but cyanogen chloride leads to α-cyanoindene. Carbonation leads to the α-carboxylic acid in 86 percent yield.

---

* Although this section is concerned primarily with reactions of trué hydrocarbons, the classification is intended to include other displacements of carbon-linked hydrogen.

[215] Grignard and Courtot, (*a*) *Compt. rend.*, *152*, 272-4 (1911); *Chem. Zentr.*, *1911,I*, 885; (*b*) *Compt. rend.*, *152*, 1493-5 (1911); *Chem. Zentr.*, *1911,II*, 148; (*c*) *Compt. rend.*, *158*, 1763-6 (1914); *Chem. Zentr.*, *1914,II*, 397; (*d*) *Compt. rend.*, *160*, 500-4 (1915); *Chem. Zentr.*, *1915,II*, 406; (*e*) Courtot, *Ann. chim.*, [9], *4*, 58-136, 157-224 (1915).

[216] See: Datta and Mitter, *J. Am. Chem. Soc.*, *41*, 287-92 (1919).

9-Fluorenylmagnesium bromide was prepared from fluorene and ethylmagnesium bromide held at 135-140° in xylene solution for twelve hours. A yield of 65 percent of the expected tertiary alcohol is claimed by Courtot[215b] upon treatment of the Grignard reagent with benzophenone. Miller and Bachman[217] reported inability to repeat Courtot's preparation of fluorenylmagnesium bromide in satisfactory yields and add that "invariably about 65 percent of the original fluorene was recovered unchanged and the amount of ethane evolved corresponded to only 32 percent reaction." Young and Roberts[218] report that neither fluorene nor quinaldine show any evidence of the presence of "active" hydrogen during several hours reflux with ethyl ethereal butenylmagnesium bromide. However, the temperature at which the experiment is conducted is unquestionably an important factor in the success or failure of attempts to displace hydrogen from hydrocarbons, and it may be that the nature of the specific Grignard reagent employed is also significant. Zerewitinoff[219] found that when a pyridine solution of fluorene is added to an excess of amyl ethereal methylmagnesium iodide at room temperature no reaction takes place; at 85° methane corresponding to 1.04 equivalent of "active" hydrogen is liberated in the course of five minutes. Indene, 9-phenylfluorene, 13-dibenzo[*a*,*i*]fluorene, and 13-α-naphthyl-13-dibenzo[*a*,*i*]fluorene are similar to fluorene in their behavior.

According to Gilman *et al.*,[220] triphenylmethane does not react appreciably with ethylmagnesium bromide either in boiling ethyl ethereal solution or in ether-toluene solution at 80° for seven hours. Diphenylmethane is said to be similarly inert.

Phenylacetic acid. Grignard[221] observed that, although most carboxylic acids react with an excess of organomagnesium halide to form a tertiary alcohol, phenylacetic acid constitutes an exception in that the second molecule of Grignard reagent enters into a double displacement reaction in which one of the *alpha* hydrogen atoms of the acid is involved.

$$C_6H_5CH_2CO_2H + 2\ RMgX \longrightarrow C_6H_5CH(MgX)CO_2MgX + 2\ RH$$

Incidentally, Klages[222] reports that the corresponding ethyl ester reacts "normally" with methyl- or ethylmagnesium iodide to yield the expected tertiary alcohol. "Normal" reactions of the ethyl ester with phenylmagnesium bromide,[223] benzylmagnesium chloride[223, 224] and benzylmag-

---

[217] Miller and Bachman, *J. Am. Chem. Soc.*, *57*, 766-71 (1935).

[218] Young and Roberts, *J. Am. Chem. Soc.*, *68*, 1472-5 (1946).

[219] Zerewitinoff, *Ber.*, *45*, 2384-9 (1912).

[220] (*a*) Gilman and Peterson, *Rec. trav. chim.*, *48*, 247-50 (1929); (*b*) Gilman and Leermakers, *ibid.*, *48*, 577-9 (1929).

[221] Grignard, *Bull. soc. chim.*, [3], *31*, 751-7 (1904).

[222] Klages, *Ber.*, *37*, 1721-6 (1904).

[223] Klages and Heilmann, *Ber.*, *37*, 1447-57 (1904).

[224] Austin and Johnson, *J. Am. Chem. Soc.*, *54*, 647-60 (1932).

nesium bromide[225] have also been reported. Conant and Blatt,[226] however, have found that the ester reacts with isopropylmagnesium bromide to give a 94 percent yield of α-phenylphenylactoacetic ester

$$[C_6H_5CH_2COCH(C_6H_5)CO_2C_2H_5],$$

together with "saturated gas" (undoubtedly propane). Reaction with isopropylmagnesium chloride is similar.[227] These Claisen (or acetoacetic ester-type) condensations are unquestionably consequences of ester enolization and reaction of the enolate with more ester.

Schlenk *et al.*[228] maintain (and with reason, in the opinion of the present authors) that the reaction of a salt of phenylacetic acid with a Grignard reagent is essentially an enolization. The resultant enolate is by no means unique in behaving like a true Grignard reagent; the enolate of acetomesitylene furnishes a similar example,[229] though one not so extensively investigated. The behavior of the enolates of the methyl and ethyl dineopentylcarbinyl ketones is also illustrative.[230]

Ivanoff *et al.*[231] have carried out many normal Grignard reactions with reagents of the types $C_6H_5CH(MgBr)CO_2MgCl$ and $C_6H_5CH(MgBr)CO_2Na$. Ivanoff and Spassoff[231a] report, for example, a 62.5 percent yield of phenylmalonic acid by treatment of a salt of phenylacetic acid with ethylmagnesium bromide, followed by carbonation and hydrolysis.

*Sulfones.** Although Hepworth and Clapham[231.1] had reported that phenyl benzyl sulfone is recovered, apparently unchanged, after high-temperature treatment with methylmagnesium iodide and hydrolysis of the reaction mixture, Kohler and Potter[231.2] found that phenethyl *p*-tolyl sulfone and β,β-diphenylethyl *p*-tolyl sulfone have at least one "active" hydrogen atom each, displaceable at 50–75°. Methyl *p*-tolyl sulfone liberates methane slowly from methylmagnesium iodide at room temperature, and has at least two "active" hydrogen atoms, for its halomagnesium derivative yields dibenzoylmethyl *p*-tolyl sulfone upon treatment with benzoyl chloride. Kohler and Potter[231.3] also obtained from bis-(*p*-tolylsulfonyl)-

---

[225] Sachs and Loevy, *Ber.*, *36*, 3236 (1903).

[226] Conant and Blatt, *J. Am. Chem. Soc.*, *51*, 1227–36 (1929).

[227] Ivanoff and Spassoff, *Bull. soc. chim.*, [4], *49*, 375–7 (1931).

[228] Schlenk, Hilleman, and Rodloff, *Ann.*, *487*, 135–54 (1931).

[229] Fuson, Fugate, and Fisher, *J. Am. Chem. Soc.*, *61*, 2362–5 (1939).

[230] (*a*) Whitmore and Randall, *J. Am. Chem. Soc.*, *64*, 1242–6 (1942); (*b*) Whitmore and Lester, *J. Am. Chem. Soc.*, *64*, 1247–51, 1251–3 (1942).

[231] Ivanoff and Spassoff, (*a*) *Bull. soc. chim.*, [4], *49*, 19–23 (1931); (*b*) [4], *49*, 371–5 (1931); (*c*) [4], *49*, 375–7 (1931); (*d*) [4], *49*, 377–9 (1931); (*e*) Ivanoff, Mihova, and Christova, *ibid.*, [4], *51*, 1321–5 (1932); (*f*) Ivanoff and Nicoloff, *ibid.*, [4], *51*, 1325–31, 1331–7 (1932).

* See also Chapter XXI, Sulfones.

[231.1] Hepworth and Clapham, *J. Chem. Soc.*, *119*, 1188–98 (1921).

[231.2] Kohler and Potter, *J. Am. Chem. Soc.*, *57*, 1316–21 (1935).

[231.3] Kohler and Potter, *J. Am. Chem. Soc.*, *58*, 2166–30 (1936).

methane by hydrogen displacement a bromomagnesium derivative which, upon treatment with benzoyl chloride, yielded α,α-bis-(*p*-tolylsulfonyl)-acetophenone. Gilman and Webb,[231.4] obtained an acidic gum by successive treatment of ethyl phenyl sulfone with ethylmagnesium bromide and carbon dioxide. Field[231.5] has treated methyl phenyl sulfone successively with ethylmagnesium bromide and benzaldehyde, obtaining 1-phenyl-2-phenylsulfonylethanol.

Undoubtedly the halomagnesium derivatives arising from sulfone hydrogen displacement are analogous to the enolates capable of functioning as true Grignard reagents.

Aromatic ethers. In view of the relatively few cases and the rather meagre yields so far reported, the replacement of an *ortho* hydrogen atom of an aromatic ether by an —MgX group can scarcely be said to rank as a general preparative method for Grignard reagents. Certainly the hydrogen atoms so displaced are not of the type ordinarily designated as "active." Probably the reactions involved represent, as Challenger and Miller[232] suggest, one of the possible types of thermal decomposition of oxonium complexes. (See Ether Cleavage by Grignard Reagents, Chapter XVI).

In an example described by Challenger and Miller (*loc. cit.*[232]), 2 g. of magnesium was allowed to react with 9 g. of ethyl bromide in 120 ml. of ethyl ether; 25 g. of phenetole was then added, the ethyl ether was removed by distillation, and the residue was heated under reflux at 200° for five hours. Treatment of the resultant solution with mercuric bromide yielded 24 percent of *o*-bromomercuriphenetole.

Similar treatment of anisole at 180° for eight hours, and subsequent mercuration yielded 9-11 percent of *o*-bromomercurianisole. Substitution of isopropylmagnesium chloride for ethylmagnesium bromide in an analogous treatment of anisole led to a 3 percent yield of the *o*-mercuri compound.

In an example described by Gilman and Haubein,[233] a filtered ethylmagnesium bromide solution, prepared from 0.4 mole of ethyl bromide, was combined with a solution of 0.1 mole of dibenzofuran in 50 ml. of ether; the ether was removed by distillation, and the residue was heated at 165° for six hours. Subsequent carbonation led to a 5 percent yield of the 4-carboxylic acid.

2-Methylbenzothiazole. Courtot and Tchelitcheff[234] report that when 2-methylbenzothiazole is treated with ethylmagnesium bromide an "ac-

---

[231.4] Gilman and Webb, *J. Am. Chem. Soc.*, *71*, 4062-6 (1949).

[231.5] Field, *J. Am. Chem. Soc.*, *74*, 3919-21 (1952).

[232] Challenger and Miller, *J. Chem. Soc.*, *1938*, 894-9.

[233] Gilman and Haubein, *J. Am. Chem. Soc.*, *67*, 1033-4 (1945).

[234] Courtot and Tchelitcheff, *Compt. rend.*, *217*, 201-3 (1943); *Chem. Abstr.*, 38, 5502 (1944).

tive" hydrogen atom of the methyl group is displaced, with formation of a Grignard reagent that, upon carbonation, yields 2-benzothiazoleacetic acid. Treatment of the reagent with acetone or benzophenone yields the expected tertiary alcohol.

Thiophthene. Treatment of thiophthene with ethylmagnesium bromide in dimethylaniline, and subsequent carbonation of the reaction mixture is reported to yield "thiophthenecarboxylic acid" (m.p., 247°).[235]

Nitrogen heterocycles with "active" hydrogen. Oddo[236] discovered that methylmagnesium iodide reacts with pyrrole in ether solution to form a pyrrylmagnesium iodide which may be precipitated from ether as a pyridine complex $(C_5H_5N)_2 \cdot C_4H_4NMgI$. By carbonation of an ethereal solution of pyrrylmagnesium iodide, he obtained the α-carboxylic acid in 25–30 percent yield. Somewhat better yields (*ca.* 40 percent) have since been reported by others.[237]

Oddo further reported that pyrrylmagnesium iodide reacts with chloroformic ester[238a] to form the α-carbethoxy derivative, and with acyl chlorides[238b] to form the *alpha* ketones in yields of 50–60 percent for the aliphatic acyl chlorides, and as great as 80 percent for the aromatic acyl chlorides.

In general, the pyrrylmagnesium halides react as though they had the constitution

```
HC —— CH
||     ||
HC     C——MgX
  \   /
    N
    H
```

This, of course, is only one of the chemical peculiarities of pyrrole which have led to the assumption that it is tautomeric with the α- and β-pyrrolenines,[239] whose formal resemblance to cyclopentadiene is obvious.

```
HC ══ CH          HC —— CH          H2C —— CH
|      |          ||     ||          |      ||
HC     CH2   ⇌    HC     CH    ⇌    HC     CH
  \\  /             \   /             \\  /
    N                 N                 N
                      H
```

---

[235] Challenger, Clapham, and Emmott, *J. Inst. Petroleum*, *34*, 922–9 (1948); *Chem. Abstr.*, *43*, 4666 (1949).

[236] Oddo, *Gazz. chim. ital.*, *39,I*, 649–59 (1909); *Chem. Zentr.*, *1909,II*, 914.

[237] (*a*) Gilman and Pickens, *J. Am. Chem. Soc.*, *47*, 245–54 (1925); (*b*) McCay and Schmidt, *ibid.*, *48*, 1933–9 (1926).

[238] Oddo, (*a*) *Gazz. chim. ital.*, *40,II*, 353–67 (1910); *Chem. Zentr.*, *1911,I*, 322; (*b*) *Ber.*, *43*, 1012–21 (1910).

[239] See: Fischer and Orth, "Die Chemie des Pyrrole," Band I, Leipzig, *1934*, p. 7.

Nenitzescu[240] has argued that because the pyrrylmagnesium halides give positive color reactions with Michler's ketone they should be formulated as carbon-linked Grignard reagents. (Nitrogen-linked Grignard reagents, including the indolyl, react negatively to this test.)

Gilman and Heck,[241] however, point out that in the presence of acetic acid and iodine, which are used to develop the Michler's ketone color test, pyrrole produces a bluish coloration which might be mistaken for a positive Grignard reagent color test.

The arguments, pro and con, are equally beside the point, for if a pyrridylmagnesium halide, regardless of its constitution, is capable of reacting with a carbonyl group to establish a carbon-to-carbon bond (as there is ample evidence that it is) there is no reason why it should not react with Michler's ketone to form the leuco base of the triphenylmethane dye upon which the color test is based.

Gilman prefers the nitrogen-linked Grignard reagent formulation and maintains that the known reactions of a pyrrylmagnesium halide so formulated are entirely analogous to the comparable reactions of the sodium enolate of acetoacetic ester. He bases his argument chiefly on the fact that pyrrole, like indole, skatole, and carbazole, shows only one active hydrogen atom when submitted to Zerewitinoff analysis,[242] and contends that a rearrangement of the type

```
HC——CH            HC——CH
||    ||     →    ||    ||
HC    CH          HC    C—MgX
  \  //             \  /
   N                 N
   |                 H
  MgX
```

should lead to the indication of at least two active hydrogen atoms. This argument, however, loses a good deal of whatever cogency it may possess when the Grignard reagent is formulated as an α-pyrrolenine derivative.

```
HC══CH
|    |
HC   CH—MgX
 \\  /
   N
```

The reactions of a pyrrylmagnesium halide might be adequately accounted for by formulation as a mixture of derivatives of the three hypothetical tautomeric forms, with the α-pyrrolenine derivative in marked preponderance, or of considerably greater reactivity than the other forms.

Alternatively the Grignard reagent might be formulated as an ionic,

---

[240] Nenitzescu, *Bull. soc. chim. Romania, 11*, 130–4 (1930); *Chem. Abstr., 24*, 2458 (1930).

[241] Gilman and Heck, *J. Am. Chem. Soc., 52*, 4949–54 (1930).

[242] Oddo, *Ber., 44*, 2048–52 (1911). See also: Gilman and Heck, *loc. cit.*[241]

though not necessarily highly dissociated compound $[(C_4H_4N)^-(MgBr)^+]$, with a resonant anion in which, for reasons perhaps not altogether obvious, the *alpha* position is that favored for electrophilic attack.

```
HC—— CH           HC══CH
‖     |            |    |
HC    CH   ⟷   ⊖HC    CH   ⟷
  \  /             \  //
   N                N
   ⊖

   HC══ CH          ⊖HC—— CH          HC—— CH⊖
   |     |            |     ‖           ‖     |
   HC    CH⊖   ⟷     HC    CH    ⟷    HC    CH
     \  /              \\  /              \  //
      N                 N                  N
```

Oddo[243] has suggested a "mesohydric" formulation for pyrrole and a corresponding formulation for the Grignard reagents, which he believes accounts satisfactorily for their behavior.

```
HC ═══════ CH
‖            :
‖    H···    :
‖    :       :
HC   :     · CH
  \  ·     //
     N
```

In any event, the reaction of a pyrrylmagnesium halide as a nitrogen-linked Grignard reagent, with subsequent rearrangement of the product would seem to be definitely ruled out, for some cases at least, by the high temperature necessary to effect such a rearrangement. de Jong,[244] for example, confirmed the preparation of 2-ethylpyrrole from pyrrylmagnesium bromide and ethyl bromide in ether solution by Hess *et al.*,[245] but had to employ a temperature of about 650° to effect the rearrangement of *N*-ethylpyrrole to 2-ethylpyrrole.

Hess[245] has explained the double substitution reactions sometimes observed, like, for instance, that with allyl bromide,

```
                                  HC—— CH
              H2C═CHCH2Br         ‖     ‖
C4H4NMgBr  ─────────────→         HC    C—CH2CH═CH2
                                    \  /
                                     N
                                     H
                                                HC—— CH
                                  +             ‖     ‖
                                     H2C═CHCH2—C    C—CH2CH═CH2
                                                  \  /
                                                   N
                                                   H
```

243 Oddo, *Gazz. chim. ital.*, *64*, 584–94 (1934); *Chem. Zentr.*, *1935,I*, 393.
244 de Jong, *Rec. trav. chim.*, *48*, 1029–30 (1929).
245 Hess, Wissing, and Suchier, *Ber.*, *48*, 1865–84 (1915).

as resulting from interaction of the original pyrryl Grignard reagent with some of the product first formed, and has supported his interpretation by treating pyrrylmagnesium bromide with 2-allylpyrrole and then carbonating the resultant product to obtain 5-allylpyrrole-2-carboxylic acid.

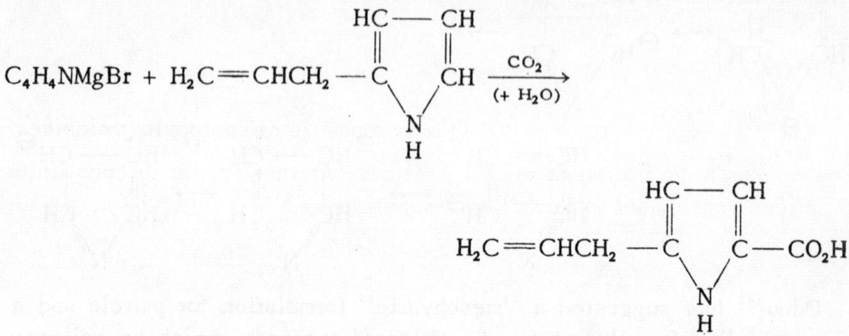

$$C_4H_4NMgBr + H_2C{=}CHCH_2{-}\underset{\text{NH}}{C{=}CH{-}CH{=}CH} \xrightarrow[(+\ H_2O)]{CO_2} H_2C{=}CHCH_2{-}\underset{\text{NH}}{C{=}CH{-}CH{=}C}{-}CO_2H$$

According to Oddo and Perotti,[246] the pyrryl Grignard reagent reacts with acetophenone to form, chiefly, the di-α-pyrrylmethane, with very little of the carbinol ordinarily to be expected. This observation suggests that the pyrryl reagent is capable of undergoing the rather unusual reaction:

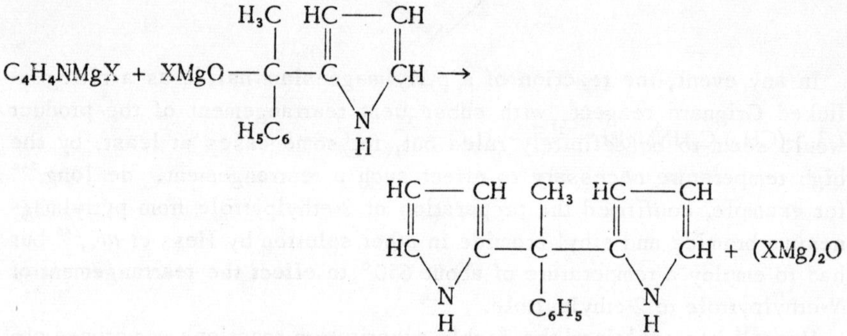

$$C_4H_4NMgX + XMgO{-}\underset{H_5C_6}{\overset{H_3C}{C}}{-}\underset{\text{NH}}{C{=}CH{-}CH{=}CH} \rightarrow \underset{\text{NH}}{HC{=}CH{-}CH{=}C}{-}\underset{C_6H_5}{\overset{CH_3}{C}}{-}\underset{\text{NH}}{C{=}CH{-}CH{=}CH} + (XMg)_2O$$

The mono-*alpha*-alkylated pyrroles form Grignard reagents which react with the introduction of substituents at the previously unsubstituted *alpha* position.[247]

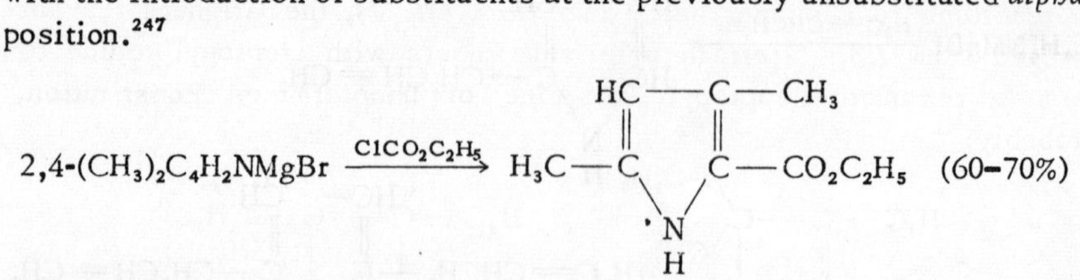

$$2,4\text{-}(CH_3)_2C_4H_2NMgBr \xrightarrow{ClCO_2C_2H_5} H_3C{-}\underset{\text{NH}}{C{=}CH{-}C(CH_3){=}C}{-}CO_2C_2H_5 \quad (60\text{–}70\%)$$

---

[246] Oddo and Perotti, *Gazz. chim. ital.*, *60*, 13–21 (1930); *Chem. Zentr.*, *1930,I*, 3051; *Chem. Abstr.*, *24*, 3875 (1930).

[247] Fischer, Weiss, and Schubert, *Ber.*, *56B*, 1194–202 (1932); Fischer, *Organic Syntheses*, Coll. Vol. II, pp. 198–200, *1943*. See also: Fischer, Baumann, and Riedl, *Ann.*, *475*, 205–41 (1921).

Reaction of a Grignard reagent prepared from an α,α'-dialkylpyrrole results in substitution at one of the *beta* positions.[248]

```
                                   HC —— C-i-C3H7
                                   ‖      ‖
2,5-(CH3)2C4H2NMgBr --i-C3H7I--> H3C—C      C—CH3
                                      \    /
                                        N
                                        H
```

+ two isomeric diïsopropylpyrrolenines

Previous substitution at a *beta* position does not appear to constitute a serious impediment to further *beta*-substitution.[249]

```
                                            /CH3
                                     HC —— C
                                     ‖      | \C2H5
2,5-(CH3)2-3-C2H5C4HNMgBr --CH3I--> H3C—C     C—CH3
                                        \   //
                                          N

                                   H3C—C —— C—C2H5
                                        ‖    ‖
                                 + H3C—C      C—CH3
                                        \    /
                                          N
                                          H
```

```
                                         /CH3
                                  HC —— C
                                  ‖      | \C2H5
2,3,5-(CH3)3C4HNMgBr --C2H5Br--> H3C—C     C—CH3
                                     \   //
                                       N

                                   HC —— C—CH3
                                   ‖      ‖
                            + H3C—C        C—CH3
                                   \     /
                                      N
                                      |
                                     C2H5
```

According to Plancher and Tanzi (*loc. cit.*[248]), the Grignard reagent derived from 2,3,4,5-tetramethylpyrrole reacts with isopropyl iodide to form a tetramethylisopropylpyrrolenine of undetermined constitution, probably:

```
               /i-C3H7
H3C—C —— C                      H3C—C ══ C—CH3
    ‖      | \CH3                   |      | /CH3
H3C—C      C—CH3        or      H3C—C      C
     \   //                          \\   / \i-C3H7
       N                               N
```

---

[248] Plancher and Tanzi, *Atti accad. Lincei*, [5], *23*, II, 412–7 (1914); *Chem. Zentr.*, *1915,I*, 743; *Chem. Abstr.*, *9*, 1477 (1915).

[249] Hess, Wissing, and Suchier, *Ber.*, *48*, 1865–84 (1915).

Offhand prediction might lead to the expectation that *N*-substituted pyrroles would prove unreactive toward Grignard reagents, for they neither possess the "active" >NH grouping nor can they be formulated as pyrrolenines. As a matter of fact, however, Hess and Wissing[250] have found that *N*-methylpyrrole reacts so vigorously with ethylmagnesium bromide in ethereal solution that the reaction must be moderated by cooling. This phenomenon is probably satisfactorily explicable as the result of decomposition, with rearrangement, of an unstable tertiary amine-Grignard reagent complex. This interpretation is analogous to that advanced to account for the formation of an aromatic Grignard reagent by interaction of an aromatic ether with ethylmagnesium bromide, but with the difference that, whereas the one process takes place spontaneously, the other is only partial under "forced conditions."

The *N*-methylpyrrylmagnesium bromide so formed reacts with the usual Grignard reagent co-reactants to form α-substituted *N*-methylpyrroles.

```
HC——CH                                        HC——CH
||  ||                RCOCl                   ||  ||
HC   C—MgBr   ——————————————————————→         HC   C—COR
  \ /         (R = CH3,C2H5,C6H5)               \ /
   N                                             N
   |                                             |
   CH3                                           CH3

HC——CH                        HC——CH
||  ||         ClCO2C2H5      ||  ||
HC   C—MgBr   ——————————→     HC   C—CO2C2H5
  \ /                           \ /
   N                             N
   |                             |
   CH3                           CH3
                                                 HC——CH
                                                 ||  ||
                                  + H5C2O2C—C     C—CO2C2H5
                                              \ /
                                               N
                                               |
                                               CH3

HC——CH                 HC——CH
||  ||        Cl2      ||  ||
HC   C—MgBr  ————→     HC   C—Cl
  \ /                    \ /
   N                      N
   |                      |
   CH3                    CH3
```

Other examples of the reactions of pyrryl- and substituted pyrrylmagnesium halides will be found in the appropriate tabulations.

Oddo[251] discovered that indole, like pyrrole, reacts with one equivalent

---

[250] Hess and Wissing, *Ber.*, *47*, 1416–28 (1914).

[251] Oddo, *Gazz. chim. ital.*, *41*, I, 221–34 (1911); *Chem. Zentr.*, *1911*,*I*, 1852.

of ethylmagnesium iodide to liberate ethane and to form a Grignard reagent that can be precipitated from ether solution in the form of a pyridine complex, $(C_5H_5N)_2 \cdot C_8H_6NMgI$.

The constitutions of the products formed by interaction of indolylmagnesium halides with the usual Grignard reagent co-reactants appear to vary (1) with the nature of the co-reactant and (2) with the experimental conditions.

Oddo (*loc. cit.*[251]) reports that treatment of indolylmagnesium iodide with methyl iodide under "forced conditions" for fifteen hours yields skatole (the *beta* derivative), whereas twelve hours reflux in ether solution yields a mixture of *N*-methylindole and *N*-methylskatole.

Oddo and Sessa[252] found that the addition of acetyl chloride to a cooled ethereal solution of indolylmagnesium iodide yielded a mixture of the *beta* ketone and the *N*,β-diacetyl derivative. Propionyl chloride behaved similarly. Under the same conditions, *n*-butyryl chloride and benzoyl chloride gave the respective *beta* ketones. When allowed to react more energetically, benzoyl chloride gave the *N*,β-disubstitution product. Carbon dioxide and chloroformic ester were reported as yielding the *N* and the *alpha* derivatives, respectively, but this appears highly improbable in the light of the general behavior of indolylmagnesium halides and of the subsequent studies of Majima and Kotake.[253] In an attempt to repeat the experiment of Oddo and Sessa, Majima and Kotake [253b] treated an ice-salt-cooled solution of indolylmagnesium iodide with one equivalent of chloroformic ester. The mixture was then allowed to stand at room temperature for a time, and was finally heated on the steam bath for an hour. The product was a mixture of the β-carboxylic and *N*,β-dicarboxylic esters. The use of two equivalents of chloroformic ester and warming for two and a half hours on the steam-bath led to the *N*,β-dicarboxylic ester. One equivalent of chloroformic ester added at ice-bath temperature and stirred for an additional hour with ice-cooling gave the β-carboxylic ester in 78 percent yield.

Carbon dioxide is also reported[253a] as yielding the β-carboxylic acid.

According to Majima and Kotake,[253a, 254] anisole is a superior solvent for the preparation and subsequent reaction with carbonyl compounds of indolyl Grignard reagents. That this rather surprising observation cannot be attributed to the relatively high boiling point of anisole is indicated by the following summary of the description of one of their experiments. Magnesium turnings (2.4 g.) in 10 ml. of anisole were activated with a very small particle of iodine; then 16 g. (*ca.* 2 equivalents) of ethyl iodide was added dropwise with stirring. After completion of the reaction, an ice-salt bath was applied, and 5.9 g. of indole in 7–8 ml. of

---

[252] Oddo and Sessa, *Gazz. chim. ital.*, *41*, I, 234–48 (1911); *Chem. Zentr.*, *1911*,*I*, 1853.

[253] Majima and Kotake, (*a*) *Ber.*, *55B*, 3865–72 (1922); (*b*) *63B*, 2237–45 (1930).

[254] Majima and Kotake, *Ber.*, *55B*, 3859–65 (1922).

anisole was added gradually with vigorous stirring. In the cold 1.1–1.2 l. of ethane is evolved. When the reaction is carried out in ethyl ether, no gas is evolved in the cold; the reaction begins at room temperature and can be completed only by warming. Treatment of an anisole solution of indolylmagnesium iodide, prepared as described, with ethyl formate under cooling, gives the aldehyde in 40 percent yield. "Phenetole is also a satisfactory solvent for the foregoing series of reactions (though with smaller yield), but the aldehyde is not obtained in ethyl ether or *n*-amyl ether."

The final statement is apparently contradicted by Putochin.[255] A summary of his account follows. Magnesium turnings (1.2 g.), activated with a little iodine, were covered with 10 ml. of benzene, and 1 ml. of ethyl ether was added. Ethyl iodide (8.5 g.) is then added dropwise with stirring. Reaction begins on warming to 70° on a water-bath, and is complete in two to three hours. The solution is cooled with snow, and 3 g. of indole in 8 ml. of benzene is added gradually with vigorous shaking. Ethane (*ca.* 600 ml.) is evolved. Intensive cooling with a snow-salt mixture during dropwise addition of 10 ml. of ethyl formate leads to *N*-formylindole (2.5 g.). Similar results are obtained in ethyl ether or *n*-amyl ether. Warming during the ester addition gives the *beta* aldehyde; *results are similar in ethyl ether or n-amyl ether.*

Other reactions of indolylmagnesium halides are described by: Majima and Shigematsu,[256] Majima, Shigematsu, and Rokkaku,[257] Majima and Hoshino,[258] and Mingoia.[259]

As might be expected, the Grignard reagents derived from 2-methylindole behave like the indolylmagnesium halides themselves, the *beta* (3) position being the one favored for the introduction of substituents. Representative reactions are reported by: Oddo,[260] Madelung and Tencer,[261] Majima *et al.* (*loc. cit.*[258]), Mingoia (*loc. cit.*[259]), Oddo and Tognacchini,[262] Oddo and Perotti,[263] Hoshino,[264] Hoshino and Tamura,[265] and by Sanna and Chessa.[266]

---

[255] Putochin, *Ber.*, *59B*, 1987–98 (1926).

[256] Majima and Shigematsu, *Ber.*, *57B*, 1449–53 (1924).

[257] Majima, Shigematsu, and Rokkaku, *Ber.*, *57B*, 1453–6 (1924).

[258] Majima and Hoshino, *Ber.*, *58B*, 2042–6 (1925).

[259] Mingoia, *Gazz. chim. ital.*, *56*, 772–81 (1926); *Chem. Zentr.*, *1927,I*, 2309.

[260] Oddo, *Gazz. chim. ital.*, *43*, II, 190–211 (1913); *Chem. Zentr.*, *1913,II*, 1402.

[261] Madelung and Tencer, *Ber.*, *48*, 949–53 (1915).

[262] Oddo and Tognacchini, *Gazz. chim. ital.*, *53*, 271–5 (1923); *Chem. Zentr.*, *1923,III*, 925; *Chem. Abstr.*, *17*, 2883 (1923).

[263] Oddo and Perotti, *Gazz. chim. ital.*, *60*, 13–21 (1930); *Chem. Zentr.*, *1930,I*, 3051; *Chem. Abstr.*, *24*, 3875 (1930).

[264] Hoshino, *Ann.*, *500*, 35–42 (1932).

[265] Hoshino and Tamura, *Ann.*, *500*, 42–52 (1932).

[266] Sanna and Chessa, *Gazz. chim. ital.*, *58*, 121–7 (1928); *Chem. Zentr.*, *1928,I*, 2505; *Chem. Abstr.*, *22*, 2562 (1928).

The Grignard reagents derived from skatole (3-methylindole) are reported to react to give *N*-substituted skatoles (Oddo[267]),

$$\beta\text{-}CH_3C_8H_5NMgBr \xrightarrow{CO_2}$$ C—CH_3, CH, N, CO_2H

$$\beta\text{-}CH_3C_8H_5NMgBr \xrightarrow{ClCO_2C_2H_5}$$ C—CH_3, CH, N, $CO_2C_2H_5$

α-substituted skatoles (Oddo, *loc. cit.*[267]),

$$\beta\text{-}CH_3C_8H_5NMgX \xrightarrow{CH_3COCl}$$

C—CH_3, C—$COCH_3$, N, H + C—CH_3, CH, N, $COCH_3$

and indolenine derivatives (Hoshino, *loc. cit.*[264]),

$$\beta\text{-}CH_3C_8H_5NMgI \xrightarrow{CH_3I}$$ CH_3, C, CH_3, N=CH

The α,β-disubstituted indolylmagnesium halides react to give both α,β,N-trisubstituted indoles and indolenine derivatives, according to Hoshino (*loc. cit.*[264]),

$$\alpha,\beta\text{-}(CH_3)_2C_8H_4NMgI \xrightarrow{CH_3I}$$ CH_3, C, CH_3, N=C—CH_3

$$\alpha\text{-}CH_3\text{-}\beta\text{-}C_6H_5CH_2C_8H_4NMgI \xrightarrow{C_6H_5CH_2Cl}$$

C—$CH_2C_6H_5$, C—CH_3, N, $CH_2C_6H_5$ + $CH_2C_6H_5$, C, $CH_2C_6H_5$, N=C—CH_3

and Hoshino and Tamura (*loc. cit.*[265]).

---

[267] Oddo, *Gazz. chim. ital.*, *42*, I, 361–75 (1912); *Chem. Zentr.*, *1912*,*II*, 193.

α,β-$(CH_3)_2C_8H_4NMgI \xrightarrow{ClCH_2CN}$ 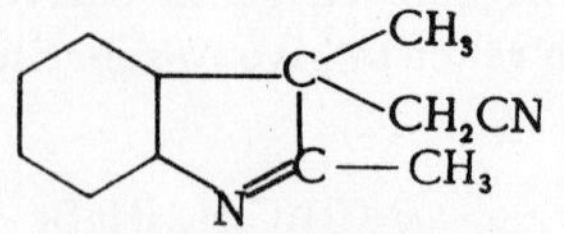

Other examples of the reactions of indolyl- and substituted indolylmagnesium halides will be found in the appropriate tabulations.

Imidazole (glyoxaline) reacts with ethylmagnesium halides, liberating one equivalent of ethane, and forming imidazolyl Grignard reagents,[268] which react somewhat like the pyrryl Grignard reagents, though they are apparently less reactive. Imidazolylmagnesium halide reacts with benzoyl chloride to give a benzoylated imidazole believed to be the *mu* (2) derivative.[269]

$C_3H_3N_2MgX + C_6H_5COCl \rightarrow$ 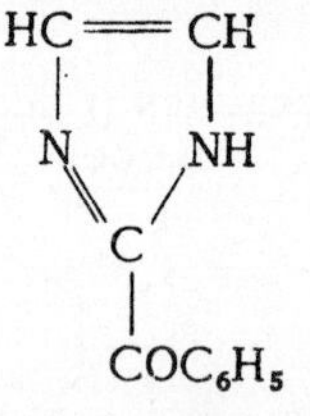

Imidazolylmagnesium bromide, with ether removed, treated on the water-bath for twenty hours with an excess of methyl iodide yields the *N*,*μ*-(1,2-) dimethyl derivative.[270] The reaction with ethyl iodide is similar. Other reactions reported by Oddo and Mingoia (*loc. cit.*[270]) are as follows:

$C_3H_2N_2MgBr \xrightarrow{ClCO_2C_2H_5} C_6H_8O_2N_2$, probably 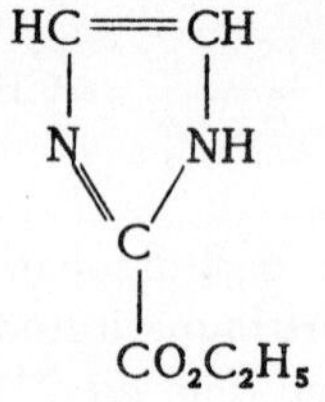

$C_3H_2N_2MgBr \xrightarrow{COCl_2}$ 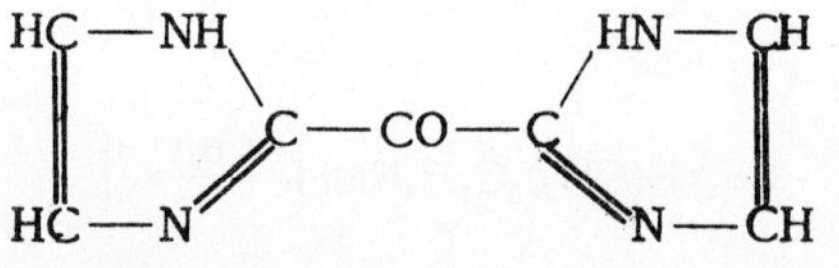

$$C_3H_2N_2MgBr \xrightarrow{ClCOCO_2C_2H_5} (C_2H_5O_2CCONHCH{=})_2$$

$$C_3H_2N_2MgBr \xrightarrow{ClCOCH_2CO_2C_2H_5} (C_2H_5O_2CCH_2CONHCH{=})_2$$

Oddo and Mingoia (*loc. cit.*[270]) did not obtain a stable acid upon treatment of imidazolylmagnesium bromide with carbon dioxide, imidazole be-

[268] Oddo and Mingoia, *Gazz. chim. ital.*, 56, 958–60 (1926); *Chem. Abstr.*, 21, 1263 (1927).

[269] Oddo and Mingoia, *Gazz. chim. ital.*, 58, 573–84 (1928); *Chem. Abstr.*, 23, 1638 (1929).

[270] Oddo and Mingoia, *Gazz. chim. ital.*, 58, 584–97 (1928); *Chem. Abstr.*, 23, 1638 (1929).

ing recovered. Analogous results were obtained with acetyl chloride, ethyl acetate and acetic anhydride. To account for this rather surprising unreactivity, they suggest a "mesohydric" structure for imidazole, with a corresponding structure for the Grignard reagent.

```
HC ══════ CH
|   .H.    |
N:.     .:N
   ·.C.·
     H
```

In a later paper, Oddo and Ingraffia[271] report that an imidazolylmagnesium halide treated with acetyl chloride in a sealed tube at 55–60° for two hours yielded the μ-acetyl derivative. They suggest that an unstable acetate, readily hydrolyzed by water, is first formed and then rearranges on heating to the stable form.

```
HC ──── N.                 HC ──── N.
‖   Ac:      :CH   Δ→      ‖   H:      :CAc
HC ──── N'                 HC ──── N'
```

Mingoia[272] finds that pyrazole, like its isomer, imidazole, reacts with ethylmagnesium bromide, liberating one equivalent of ethane and forming a new Grignard reagent. Some of the reactions of pyrazolylmagnesium bromide reported by Mingoia are as follows:

```
                 C6H5COCl        HC ── CH
C3H3N2MgBr  ──────────────→      ‖     ‖
                                 HC    N
                                   \  /
                                    N
                                    |
                                  COC6H5

                 COCl2      HC═N               N═CH
C3H3N2MgBr  ─────────→      |    \            /   |
                            |     N ─ CO ─ N      |
                            |    /            \   |
                            HC═CH              CH═CH

                 ClCO2C2H5       HC ── CH
C3H3N2MgBr  ──────────────→      ‖     ‖
                                 HC    N
                                   \  /
                                    N
                                    |
                                 CO2C2H5
```

---

[271] Oddo and Ingraffia, *Gazz. chim. ital.*, *61*, 446–9 (1931); *Chem. Abstr.*, *26*, 452 (1932).

[272] Mingoia, *Gazz. chim. ital.*, *61*, 449–58 (1931); *Chem. Abstr.*, *26*, 453 (1932).

When an ethereal solution of the Grignard reagent was treated with acetyl chloride, or acetic anhydride, pyrazole was recovered almost quantitatively. In a sealed-tube reaction at 60° for four hours, acetyl chloride did yield a little of the *N*-acetyl derivative.

Carbazole behaves like a typical secondary amine in that it reacts with ordinary Grignard reagents such as methylmagnesium iodide and ethylmagnesium bromide, liberating one equivalent of gaseous hydrocarbon, and forming nitrogen-linked Grignard reagents, which in turn react with carbon dioxide, chloroformic ester and carboxylic acid chlorides to form the usual *N*-derivatives.[273]

(carbazolyl)N–MgI $\xrightarrow{CO_2}$ (carbazolyl)N–CO_2H

(carbazolyl)N–MgI $\xrightarrow{ClCO_2C_2H_5}$ (carbazolyl)N–$CO_2C_2H_5$

(carbazolyl)N–MgX $\xrightarrow{RCOCl\,*}$ (carbazolyl)N–COR

Carbazolylmagnesium iodide is reported to react with carbon dioxide in the absence of solvent at 250–270° to yield a carbon-linked carboxylic acid, probably the *ortho* (1) derivative,[273a, b] but this is doubtless an example of a well-known type of thermal rearrangement.

GRIGNARD REAGENTS FROM FREE RADICALS

In the course of a discussion of the mechanism of Grignard reagent formation, Gilman and Fothergill[274] announced, without supplying any details, that "it is possible to prepare triphenylmethylmagnesium iodide from triphenylmethyl and magnesious iodide (·MgI)."

---

[273] Oddo, (*a*) *Gazz. chim. ital.*, *41*, I, 255–72 (1911); *Chem. Zentr.*, *1911*,*I*, 1854; (*b*) *Mim. accad. Lincei*, [v], *14*, 510–623 (1923); *Chem. Abstr.*, *19*, 2492 (1925); (*c*) Sanna and Chessa, *Gazz. chim. ital.*, *58*, 121–7 (1928); *Chem. Zentr.*, *1928*,*I*, 2505; *Chem. Abstr.*, *22*, 2562 (1928).

* R = CH_3, C_2H_5, C_6H_5, $C_2H_5OCH_2$.

[274] Gilman and Fothergill, *J. Am. Chem. Soc.*, *51*, 3149–57 (1929).

In the meantime, while investigating the possibility of the reduction of triphenylmethanol to triphenylmethyl by means of magnesium bromide and metallic magnesium, Gomberg and Bachmann[275] found that, although the proposed interaction does produce triphenylmethyl (in addition to triphenylmethane), it is not in fact a simple reduction. In the course of their elucidation of the mechanism of the reaction, they found that when two equivalents of triphenylmethyl in 2:1 benzene-ethyl ether solution are heated for several hours on a steam-bath with one equivalent of magnesium bromide and a slight excess over one equivalent of metallic magnesium, triphenylmethylmagnesium bromide is produced in *ca.* 93 percent yield. They further noted that when triphenylmethyl bromide in 2:1 benzene-ethyl ether solution is treated with metallic magnesium, no Grignard reagent is detectable until more than half the magnesium present has reacted, although an ultimate yield of 96–97 percent is obtained. The series of reactions proposed to account for the phenomena observed is as follows:

$$(C_6H_5)_3COH + MgBr_2 \longrightarrow (C_6H_5)_3CBr + MgBrOH$$

$$(C_6H_5)_3CBr + \tfrac{1}{2}Mg \longrightarrow (C_6H_5)_3C\cdot + \tfrac{1}{2}MgBr_2$$

$$(C_6H_5)_3C\cdot + \tfrac{1}{2}MgBr_2 + \tfrac{1}{2}Mg \longrightarrow (C_6H_5)_3CMgBr$$

Magnesium iodide may be substituted for magnesium bromide with similar results.

Bachmann[276] reports that phenyl-*o*-biphenylenemethyl behaves similarly to triphenylmethyl when treated with magnesium bromide (or iodide) and metallic magnesium, although the reaction is slower.

In an extension of the earlier studies, Bachmann[277] showed that only a small amount of magnesium iodide is necessary to bring about reaction between magnesium and triphenylmethyl, and suggests that the product is probably an equilibrium mixture of bistriphenylmethylmagnesium, triphenylmethylmagnesium iodide, and magnesium iodide.

$$\underset{(13.4\text{ g.})}{(C_6H_5)_3C\cdot} + \underset{(0.77\text{ g.})}{Mg} + \underset{(3.0\text{ g.})}{MgI_2} \xrightarrow{H_2O} \underset{(92\%)}{(C_6H_5)_3CH}$$

ADDITION OF GRIGNARD REAGENTS TO OLEFINS

Blaise[278] investigated qualitatively the possibility of the formation of addition compounds through the reaction of Grignard reagents with unsaturated hydrocarbons ("hexylene," "caprylene," phenylacetylene) with negative results. Since then various attempts to account for the formation of certain products of the reactions of Grignard reagents with un-

[275] Gomberg and Bachmann, *J. Am. Chem. Soc.*, *52*, 2455–61 (1930).
[276] Bachmann, *J. Am. Chem. Soc.*, *52*, 3287–90 (1930).
[277] Bachmann, *J. Am. Chem. Soc.*, *52*, 4412–3 (1930).
[278] Blaise, *Compt. rend.*, *132*, 38–41 (1901); *J. Chem. Soc.*, *80*,*I*, 133 (1901).

saturated compounds[279] by the assumption of Grignard reagent addition at a carbon-to-carbon double bond have been rather thoroughly discredited by Gilman and co-workers,[280] who have also attempted the condensation of Grignard reagents with some thirty or more unsaturated hydrocarbons (olefinic, conjugated diolefinic, allenic, and acetylenic) without success. Other similar experiments with negative results have been reported by Wieland and Krause[281] and by Kinney and Larsen.[282]

More recently, however, Fuson,[283] noting the reported reactivity of di-*o*-biphenyleneethylene (9,9′-bifluorenylidene) toward various carbonyl co-reactants,[284] and its ability to condense with phenyllithium to form 1-phenyl-1,2-di-*o*-biphenyleneethane,[285] recognized the possibility that condensation of this highly-conjugated olefin with a Grignard reagent might be effected, and reasoned that the chances of success would probably be greatest with one of the more reactive[286] Grignard reagents. Condensation with *t*-butylmagnesium chloride (68 percent yield) was effected by eighteen hours reflux in benzene-ether solution. Similar condensations with benzylmagnesium chloride (57.6 percent yield) and *p*-chlorobenzylmagnesium chloride (12.5 percent yield) were brought about by reflux (*ca.* sixteen hours) in ether solution. The benzyl addition products were shown to be Grignard reagents by their further reaction with benzyl chlorides.

$$C_{12}H_8{=}C(CH_2C_6H_5)C({=}C_{12}H_8)MgCl + C_6H_5CH_2Cl \longrightarrow [C_6H_5CH_2(C_{12}H_8{=})C{-}]_2$$

$$C_{12}H_8{=}C(CH_2C_6H_4)C({=}C_{12}H_8)MgCl + 4\text{-}ClC_6H_5CH_2Cl \longrightarrow C_{12}H_8{=}C(CH_2C_6H_4)C({=}C_{12}H_8)CH_2C_6H_5\text{-}4\text{-}Cl$$

$$C_{12}H_8{=}C(CH_2C_6H_4\text{-}4\text{-}Cl)C({=}C_{12}H_8)MgCl + C_6H_5CH_2Cl \longrightarrow C_{12}H_8{=}C(CH_2C_6H_4\text{-}4\text{-}Cl)C({=}C_{12}H_8)CH_2C_6H_5$$

---

279 Staudinger, *Ann.*, *356*, 51–123 (1907); Rupe and Burgin, *Ber.*, *43*, 423–9 (1926); Rupe, *Ann.*, *402*, 149–86 (1913); Lespieau, *Bull. soc. chim.*, [4], *29*, 528–35 (1921); Staudinger, Kreis, and Shilt, *Helv. Chim. Acta*, *5*, 743–56 (1922).

280 Gilman and Heckert, *J. Am. Chem. Soc.*, *42*, 1010–4 (1920); Gilman and Crawford, *ibid.*, *45*, 554–8 (1923); Gilman and Shumaker, *ibid.*, *47*, 514–5 (1925); Gilman and Petersen, *ibid.*, *48*, 423–9 (1926); Gilman and Harris, *ibid.*, *49*, 1825–8 (1927); Gilman, Kirby, Fothergill, and Harris, *Proc. Iowa Acad. Sci.*, *54*, 221–2 (1928); *Chem. Abstr.*, *22*, 4504 (1928); Gilman and McGlumphey, *Rec. trav. chim.*, *47*, 418–22 (1928); Gilman and Harris, *ibid.*, *49*, 762–5 (1930); Gilman and Schulz, *J. Am. Chem. Soc.*, *52*, 3588–90 (1930); Gilman and Kirby, *ibid.*, *54*, 345–55 (1932).

281 Wieland and Krause, *Ann.*, *443*, 129–41 (1925).

282 Kinney and Larsen, *J. Am. Chem. Soc.*, *57*, 1054–6 (1935).

283 Fuson and Porter, *J. Am. Chem. Soc.*, *70*, 895–7 (1948).

284 Pinck and Hilbert, *J. Am. Chem. Soc.*, *57*, 2398–402 (1935); *68*, 2014–6 (1946).

285 Ziegler and Schäfer, *Ann.*, *511*, 101–9 (1934).

286 As regards carbonyl double-bond addition; see, *e.g.*, Kharasch and Weinhouse, *J. Org. Chem.*, *1*, 209–30 (1936).

Attempted condensations of the olefin with methylmagnesium iodide and phenylmagnesium bromide were unsuccessful.

Extension of this study by Fuson *et al.*[287] has shown that *t*-butylmagnesium, benzylmagnesium, and *p*-chlorobenzylmagnesium chlorides undergo 1,4-addition to 1,4-di-*o*-biphenylene-1,3-butadiene.

$$C_{12}H_8{=}C{=}CHCH{=}C{=}C_{12}H_8 + RMgX \longrightarrow C_{12}H_8{=}CRCH{=}CHC(MgX){=}C_{12}H_8$$

It is of incidental interest that, in contrast to the reactive Grignard reagents, phenyllithium appears to undergo a double 1,2-addition.

$$C_{12}H_8{=}C{=}CHCH{=}C{=}C_{12}H_8 + 2\ C_6H_5Li \longrightarrow C_{12}H_8{=}CLiCH(C_6H_5)CH(C_6H_5)CLi{=}C_{12}H_8$$

s-Butylmagnesium, phenylmagnesium, and phenethylmagnesium bromides did not react with this hydrocarbon under the conditions employed. With the vinylog, 1,6-di-*o*-biphenylene-1,3,5-hexatriene, *t*-butylmagnesium and benzylmagnesium chlorides condensed additively in a 1,6 manner.

$$C_{12}H_8{=}C{=}CHCH{=}CHCH{=}C{=}C_{12}H_8 + RMgX \longrightarrow C_{12}H_8{=}CRCH{=}CHCH{=}CHC(MgX){=}C_{12}H_8$$

Although Wieland and Krause (*loc. cit.*[281]) had reported negative results for methylmagnesium iodide and phenylmagnesium bromide, Fuson and Mumford[288] found that *t*-butylmagnesium chloride reacts additively with dibenzofulvene (9-methylenefluorene), yielding, upon subsequent hydrolysis, 9-neopentylfluorene.

$$C_{12}H_8{=}C{=}CH_2 \xrightarrow{t\text{-BuMgCl}} \xrightarrow{H_2O} C_{12}H_8{=}CHCH_2\text{-}t\text{-}C_4H_9$$

They also found that 2,3-diphenylbenzofulvene undergoes an analogous reaction to yield 1-neopentyl-2,3-diphenylindene.

[Structures: 2,3-diphenylbenzofulvene (indene ring with C_6H_5 at C-2 and C-3, $=CH_2$ at C-1) → 1-neopentyl-2,3-diphenylindene (C-1 bearing H and CH_2-*t*-C_4H_9)]

According to Fuson and York,[289] 1,2,3,4-tetraphenylfulvene reacts with

---

[287] Fuson, Dewald, and Gaertner, *J. Org. Chem.*, *16*, 21–32 (1951).
[288] Fuson and Mumford, *J. Org. Chem.*, *17*, 255–61 (1952).
[289] Fuson and York, *J. Org. Chem.*, *18*, 570–4 (1953).

t-butylmagnesium and benzylmagnesium chlorides to form adducts of the type illustrated in the following equation.

$$\begin{array}{c} H_5C_6 \text{—}\!\!\!\!\!\!\;\; \;\; -C_6H_5 \\ H_5C_6 \text{—} \quad -C_6H_5 \\ C \\ \| \\ CH_2 \end{array} \xrightarrow{RMgCl} \begin{array}{c} H_5C_6 \quad -C_6H_5 \\ H_5C_6 \quad -C_6H_5 \\ C \\ RH_2C \diagup \;\; \diagdown MgCl \end{array}$$

GRIGNARD REAGENTS FROM ORGANOLITHIUM COMPOUNDS

Gilman[290] calls attention to the fact that the prompt conversion of organolithium compounds to the corresponding Grignard reagents by means of magnesium bromide or iodide may be of preparative value for the synthesis of Grignard reagents otherwise obtained with difficulty. He cites by way of example *p*-dimethylaminophenylmagnesium bromide which is prepared from the bromide and magnesium with difficulty and in poor yields. The corresponding lithium compound, obtainable in 96 percent yield is said to be readily convertible to the Grignard reagent by treatment with magnesium iodide.

GRIGNARD REAGENTS FROM ORGANOMERCURI COMPOUNDS

Nesmeyanov and Pecherskaya[291] report that when *o*-chloromercuriphenol (5.0 g.) is treated with ethylmagnesium bromide (4.0 g.) it forms a Grignard reagent which, upon further treatment with benzophenone (2.8 g.), forms *o*-hydroxytriphenylmethanol in 25 percent yield. Ninety percent of the theoretical quantity of ethylmercuric chloride was recovered. Treatment of a similarly prepared Grignard reagent with carbon dioxide yielded salicylic acid (20 percent).

The same investigators[292] had previously reviewed the work of Abelmann[293] and of Grignard and Abelmann[294] on the reaction of α-chloromercuriacetophenone with ethylmagnesium bromide and had announced that the true product of the reaction is an enolate of acetophenone [$C_6H_5C(OMgBr){=}CH_2$] which reacts with carbon dioxide to form the bromomagnesium salt of benzoylacetic acid ($C_6H_5COCH_2CO_2MgBr$).

GRIGNARD REAGENTS FROM ALKYL SULFATES

Suter and Gerhart[295] report that ethyl sulfate reacts readily with magnesium in dry ethyl ether solution to give a slightly soluble Grignard-

---

[290] Gilman and Swiss, *J. Am. Chem. Soc.*, 62, 1847–9 (1940).

[291] Nesmeyanov and Pecherskaya, *Bull. acad. sci. U.R.S.S., Classe sci. chim.*, *1943*, 317–8; *Chem. Abstr.*, 38, 5492 (1944).

[292] Nesmeyanov and Pecherskaya, *Bull. acad. sci. U.R.S.S., Classe sci. chim.*, *1941*, 67–74; *Chem. Zentr.*, *1942,I*, 2389; *Chem. Abstr.*, 37, 3416 (1943).

[293] Abelmann, *Ber.*, 47, 2931–5 (1914).

[294] Grignard and Abelmann, *Bull. soc. chim.*, [4], *19*, 18–25 (1916).

[295] Suter and Gerhart, *J. Am. Chem. Soc.*, 55, 3496 (1933).

type reagent that is said to give a "good" yield of ethylphenylcarbinol on treatment with benzaldehyde. *n*-Butyl sulfate reacts similarly with magnesium, and the product yields butane upon hydrolysis.

They also report[296] that *n*-butylmagnesium bromide reacts with *n*-butylmagnesium sulfate to form *n*-butyl bromide and a Grignard-type reagent which was at first formulated as $n\text{-}C_4H_9MgOSO_2\text{-}n\text{-}C_4H_9$. Further study has shown, however, that only a small percentage of the basic magnesium is present in the precipitate formed in the reaction. If any large amount of *n*-butylmagnesium *n*-butyl sulfate is formed in the reaction it must disproportionate in the sense:

$$2\, n\text{-}C_4H_9MgOSO_2\text{-}n\text{-}C_4H_9 \longrightarrow (n\text{-}C_4H_9)_2Mg + (n\text{-}C_4H_9O_2SO)_2Mg$$

Optimum conditions for the preparation of di-*n*-butylmagnesium from magnesium and *n*-butyl sulfate are described as follows. "A mixture of 1.26 g. of magnesium (0.05 mole plus 5 percent excess) and 1.27 g. (0.01 g.-atom) of iodine was covered with 60 ml. of ether in a graduated flask and warmed slightly until the iodine was converted into magnesium iodide. To the mixture was added, over a period of three hours, 10.5 g. (0.05 mole) of *n*-butyl sulfate, and refluxing [was] continued for an additional hour. Titration of the filtered reaction mixture indicated a 78-80 percent yield of di-*n*-butylmagnesium."

Use of the same procedure with methyl sulfate gave only a 28 percent yield of dimethylmagnesium, probably because of reaction of the dimethylmagnesium formed with excess ester (see Alkyl Sulfates, Chapter XXI). The gas evolved was a mixture of ethane (96.1 percent) and methane, the amount of ethane corresponding to approximately 50 percent of the theoretical.

[296] Suter and Gerhart, *J. Am. Chem. Soc.*, 57, 107-9 (1935).

CHAPTER III

Estimation and Detection of Grignard Reagents

ESTIMATION

Boudroux[1] reported that the addition of powdered iodine to ethereal solutions of organomagnesium bromides or chlorides gives yields of the order of 80 percent of the corresponding organic iodides, according to the equation:

$$RMgX + I_2 \rightarrow RI + MgXI$$

Notwithstanding the fact that Boudroux's report scarcely indicated a quantitative reaction, Jolibois[2] adopted it as the basis for a method of Grignard reagent evaluation which consisted essentially in titrating an aliquot portion of the reagent with a standard solution of iodine, the persistence of iodine color being accepted as an indication of the completion of the titration.

This method was also used by Leroide[3] for the evaluation of *n*-propylmagnesium chloride and bromide solutions.

The iodine-Grignard reagent reaction was investigated in somewhat more detail by Datta and Mitter[4], who found that the conditions of reaction have a marked influence on the products and yields obtained. They reported, in part, that when solid iodine is added gradually to an ethereal solution of phenylmagnesium bromide, there are obtained iodobenzene in 25 to 30 percent yield and benzene in 30 to 40 percent yield, together with a small quantity of biphenyl, but that, when phenylmagnesium bromide solution is added to ethereal iodine solution, iodobenzene is formed in 90 percent yield. They also found that ethylmagnesium iodide, when treated with iodine, gives only a small yield of ethyl iodide.

In view of the byproducts reported for phenylmagnesium bromide, it is obvious that side-reaction is not adequately described by the equation:

$$2\ RMgX + I_2 \rightarrow R_2 + 2\ MgXI$$[5]

When the collateral evidence is taken into account, it appears possible

---

[1]Boudroux, *Compt. rend.*, *135*, 1350–1 (1902); *J. Chem. Soc.*, *84,I*, 221 (1903).

[2]Jolibois, *Compt. rend.*, *155*, 213–5 (1912); *Chem. Abstr.*, *6*, 2740 (1912).

[3]Leroide, *Ann. chim.*, [9], *16*, 354–410 (1921).

[4]Datta and Mitter, *J. Am. Chem. Soc.*, *41*, 287–92 (1919).

[5]See: Gilman, Wilkinson, Fishel, and Meyers, *J. Am. Chem. Soc.*, *45*, 150–8 (1923).

that reaction leading to both the desired product and the byproducts is initiated by some such process as:

$$RMgX + I\cdot \longrightarrow R\cdot + MgXI$$

In the presence of an excess of iodine, the reaction might then be expected to proceed predominantly as follows:

$$R\cdot + I_2 \longrightarrow RI + I\cdot$$

whereas, in the absence or scarcity of iodine, the free radicals liberated might be expected to attack the solvent or the Grignard reagent, or to dimerize, or to disproportionate in accordance with their respective natures (see Mechanism and Kinetics of Grignard Reagent Formation, Chapter II).

It would be difficult to account for the relatively high yield of benzene reported on any basis other than the attack of free phenyl radicals upon the solvent (assuming that reasonable precautions against moisture were taken, and that the persistence of iodine coloration does in fact indicate total consumption of the Grignard reagent*). Biphenyl (aside from that formed in the preparation of the Grignard reagent) might be due in part to reaction of phenyl radicals with the Grignard reagent and in part to attack of phenyl radicals on benzene.

Whatever the exact nature of the desired and side-reactions, the stoichiometrical fact remains that the latter require only half as much iodine per mole of Grignard reagent as the former. To the extent that the liberated free radicals attacked the solvent (ethyl ether), however, the error might be compensated, at least in part, for acetaldehyde (a postulated product) reacts readily with iodine, presumably according to the equation:

$$I_2 + CH_3CHO \longrightarrow CH_2ICHO + HI$$ [6]

Gilman *et al.* (*loc. cit.*[5]) have reviewed the possibilities of Grignard reagent determination and have discarded the iodimetric method on the ground that the reaction upon which it is based is not quantitative.

Their attempts to find a quantitative co-reactant that would yield a product that could be determined gravimetrically were unsuccessful. Phenyl isocyanate proved unsatisfactory and other compounds (not specified) even more so.

They investigated an "indirect" method of analysis which involved evaluation of the amount of magnesium consumed in Grignard reagent formation and in side-reactions by determination of loss in weight, and evaluation of the amount of organic halide consumed by Volhard determination of halide ion produced. Although the results were fairly consistent with those of the gas analysis method which they adopted as standard, they felt that the method, which necessitated filtration, either

---

*Total consumption of the reagent was assumed, but not demonstrated, in the study cited.

[6]Chautard, *Ann. chim.*, [6], *16*, 145–200 (1889).

admitted of too great errors by reason of moisture and oxygen contamination, or demanded too exacting a technique for convenience and rapidity.

The gas analysis method, considered standard, was an adaptation of the Zerewitinoff[7] method for the determination of active hydrogen. It consisted of measuring the amount of gas evolved when a Grignard reagent is hydrolyzed. Obviously this method is restricted in scope to Grignard reagents yielding, upon hydrolysis, hydrocarbons that are gases at ordinary temperatures.

The acid titration method finally adopted is based upon the fact that hydrolysis of the active constituents of the Grignard reagent (R_2Mg, RMgX) produces "basic magnesium" $Mg(OH)_2$, MgXOH, whereas the inert magnesium halide is unaffected. The principle potential sources of error are the production of "basic magnesium" by the direct attack of water on magnesium, or by the destruction of a portion of the Grignard reagent by moisture, and the production of $(RO)_2Mg$ and ROMgX by atmospheric oxygen. Carbon dioxide would give products yielding equivalent quantities of acid and base upon hydrolysis, as Gilman *et al.* suggest, only if reaction stopped at the RCO_2MgX stage, which seems highly improbable in the presence of a huge excess of Grignard reagent. Nevertheless, the standard precautions in preparation and handling would minimize such errors.

The procedure followed was to add 50 ml. of distilled water to a 20-ml. aliquot portion of Grignard reagent solution and then to add an estimated 20 ml. excess of standard acid (H_2SO_4, *ca.* 0.25 *N*). Back-titration was effected with standard sodium hydroxide solution with the aid of methyl orange as indicator.

Results obtained by this method ran uniformly about 4 percent higher than those obtained by the gas analysis method.

Job *et al.*[8] have objected to the acceptance of the gas analysis method as a standard of reference, and have maintained that, when proper technique is used, the iodimetric method is the most accurate available. Their criticism of the gas analysis method is based principally upon the claim that the gas evolved upon hydrolysis of ethylmagnesium bromide always contains a considerable proportion of ethylene.

The procedure advocated by Job and Reich employs an estimated twofold excess of a solution of *ca.* 50 g. per l. of dry iodine in anhydrous ether. To this is added a 1- to 2-ml. sample of the Grignard solution and then 200–300 ml. of aqueous acetic acid solution. The excess of iodine is titrated with 0.1 *N* sodium thiosulfate solution. It is unnecessary that the iodine solution be standardized if an iodine blank is titrated with each sample.

---

[7] Zerewitinoff, *Ber.*, *40*, 2023–31 (1907).

[8] Job and Reich, *Bull. soc. chim.*, [4], 33, 1414–33 (1923); Job, Reich, and Dubien, *ibid.*, [4], 37, 976–7 (1925).

Gilman and Meyers[9] undertook a comparison of the gas-analysis and acid-titration methods with the modified iodimetric method of Job and Reich. They reported inability to duplicate the results of Job and Reich as regards the degree of discrepancy between the gas analysis and acid titration methods on the one hand and the iodimetric method on the other. Their report indicated that, on the average, acid titration gives results about 5 percent higher than gas analysis, whereas iodine titration gives results about 10 percent lower.

In a subsequent report, Gilman *et al,*[10] recommend that the acid-Grignard mixture be heated for about fifteen minutes before back-titration. Phenolphthalein is also preferred to methyl orange as indicator, not only because it gives a more readily recognizable end-point, but because it gives somewhat lower results, thus bringing the acidimetric determinations within about 1 percent of the gas-analysis determination.

Whatever the merits of the iodimetric-acidimetric controversy, organic chemists appear to have accepted the acidimetric method rather generally, possibly because of the extreme simplicity of its technique and the consistency of its results. Incidentally, smaller aliquot portions of Grignard solution and lower concentrations of standard acid and base than those originally employed by Gilman *et al.* have been found entirely satisfactory.

DETECTION

As early as 1904, Sachs and Sachs[11] suggested that Michler's ketone, $[p\text{-}(CH_3)_2NC_6H_4]_2CO$, should constitute an ideal test reagent for phenylmagnesium bromide because of the facility with which these compounds interact to form Malachite green,

$$\left[\begin{matrix} C_6H_5 \\ p\text{-}(CH_3)_2NC_6H_4 \end{matrix} \Big\rangle C{=}\langle C_6H_4 \rangle{=}N(CH_3)_2 \right]^+ Cl^-$$

For more than two decades, however, no successful attempt was made to discover a general detector for Grignard reagents. Gilman and Schulze[12] then announced that Michler's ketone itself could serve as such a detector.

They describe the test procedure as follows: "One-half to 1 ml. of the solution to be tested is treated, at room temperature, with an equal volume of a 1 percent solution of Michler's ketone in dry benzene. The reaction product is then hydrolyzed by the slow addition of 1 ml. of water, during which the test-tube is gently agitated to moderate the vigor of the reaction. The subsequent addition of several drops of a 0.2 per-

[9]Gilman and Meyers, *Rec. trav. chim.*, *45*, 314–9 (1926).
[10]Gilman, Zoellner, and Dickey, *J. Am. Chem. Soc.*, *51*, 1576–83 (1929).
[11]Sachs and Sachs, *Ber.*, *37*, 3088–92 (1904).
[12]Gilman and Schulze, *J. Am. Chem. Soc.*, *47*, 2002–5 (1925).

cent solution of iodine in glacial acetic acid develops a characteristic greenish-blue color when Grignard reagent is present."

Some twenty-five Grignard reagents were tested, and of these, only one ($C_6H_5C \equiv CMgBr$) gave a comparatively weak, though still positive test. In general only the true Grignard reagents, in which magnesium is attached directly to carbon, give positive tests. Grignard-type reagents containing the groupings —OMgX, —NMgX, —SMgX or —AsMgX are negative. Some enolates, notably that of acetomesitylene, which gives a positive test, may, however, be exceptions.[13] In general, organometallic compounds other than Grignard reagents which can add to the carbonyl group (C_6H_5CaI, C_6H_5BaI, C_2H_5Na, 4-$CH_3C_6H_4Na$) gave positive tests, whereas those incapable of reacting additively with the carbonyl group C_2H_5ZnI, $(C_2H_5)_2Zn$, $(C_2H_5)_2Hg$, (4-$CH_3C_6H_4)_2Hg$, 4-$CH_3C_6H_4HgI$, $(C_2H_5)_4Pb$ gave negative tests. Benzene, dimethylaniline, pyridine, and quinoline do not interfere. Gilman and Heck[14] later found that pyrrole, acetic acid, and iodine give a blue coloration that might be mistaken for a positive test.

The sensitivity of the test was investigated with ethylmagnesium bromide, which was found to be detectable at a concentration of 0.037 *M*.

One limitation of the test should be noted: it cannot always be relied upon to indicate the complete utilization of a Grignard reagent in a reaction, particularly in a reaction with a relatively reactive co-reactant. In a study of the relative reactivities of aldehydes and ketones, Kharasch and Cooper[15] found that Michler's ketone sometimes gave a negative test when the presence of large quantities of Grignard reagent could be demonstrated by treating the solution with ethereal mercuric chloride and subsequently isolating the organomercuric chloride corresponding to the Grignard reagent.

To investigate the sensitivity of the color test in the presence of a compound that condenses relatively rapidly with the Grignard reagent, the following procedure was adopted.[15] To each of a series of test-tubes was added 0.5 ml. of a 1 percent solution of Michler's ketone in dry benzene and a measured amount of a 1 percent solution of pure benzaldehyde in dry benzene; 0.5 ml. of ethereal phenylmagnesium bromide solution (*ca.* 1.5 *N*) was then added. The contents were then treated with 1 ml. of water and, finally with five drops of a 0.2 percent solution of iodine in glacial acetic acid. The appearance of a greenish coloration was considered a positive test. The results are summarized in Table III-I.[15] The color test would probably prove sensitive in the presence of relatively high concentrations of Grignard co-reactants less reactive than Michler's ketone, or of about the same degree of reactivity. However,

[13]Gilman and Jones, *J. Am. Chem. Soc.*, *63*, 1162–3 (1941).

[14]Gilman and Heck, *J. Am. Chem. Soc.*, *52*, 4949–54 (1930).

[15]Cooper, Doctoral dissertation, University of Chicago, 1937; Kharasch and Cooper, *J. Org. Chem.*, *10*, 46–54 (1945).

TABLE III-I

SENSITIVITY OF THE MICHLER'S KETONE TEST FOR PHENYLMAGNESIUM BROMIDE IN THE PRESENCE OF BENZALDEHYDE[15]

Michler's ketone (g.) / Benzaldehyde (g.)	Test
∞	+
50 : 1	+
25 : 1	+
10 : 1	+
5 : 1	+
5 : 2	+
5 : 3	+
1 : 1	+
1 : 2	+ (faint)
1 : 3	–
1 : 4	–
1 : 5	–
1 : 10	–
1 : 20	–
1 : 50	–

when more reactive substances are present, resort must be had to an alternative method, such as treatment with ethereal mercuric chloride.

Two supplementary color tests have been developed by Gilman and coworkers. The first,[16] designated as Color Test II, is positive for organolithium compounds but negative for Grignard reagents. It may be applied by adding 0.5–1.0 ml. of organometallic solution to an equal volume of a 15 percent solution of *p*-bromodimethylaniline in dry benzene. Then 1.0 ml. of a 15 percent solution of benzophenone in dry benzene is added, and after a few seconds the mixture is hydrolyzed with water and acidified with hydrochloric acid. A red coloration in the water layer is a positive test for a "reactive" organolithium compound.

$$RLi + 4\text{-}(CH_3)_2NC_6H_4Br \longrightarrow 4\text{-}(CH_3)_2NC_6H_4Li + RBr$$

$$4\text{-}(CH_3)_2NC_6H_4Li + (C_6H_5)_2CO \xrightarrow[HCl]{H_2O} \left[(C_6H_5)_2C{=}C_6H_4{=}N(CH_3)_2\right]^+Cl^- \quad \text{(red)}$$

The second,[17] designated as Color Test III, may be used to distinguish between the "more reactive"* arylmagnesium halides, on the one hand, and the alkyl- and "less reactive" arylmagnesium halides, on the other.

[16] Gilman and Swiss, *J. Am. Chem. Soc.*, *62*, 1847-9 (1940).

[17] Gilman and Yablunky, *J. Am. Chem. Soc.*, 63, 839–44 (1941).

*Apparently, the order of reactivity implied here is that toward benzonitrile [See: Gilman, St. John, St. John, and Lichtenwalter, *Rec. trav. chim.*, *55*, 577–85 (1936); Gilman, "Organic Chemistry," John Wiley & Sons, Inc., New York, 2nd ed., *1943*, Vol. I, pp. 518–9].

It may be applied by adding 1.0 ml. of the organometallic solution to 1.0 ml. of an approximately 1.0 percent solution of triphenylbismuth dichloride in dry benzene. With aryllithium and most arylmagnesium compounds a deep purple color appears instantaneously. This test was found to be positive for diphenylmagnesium and for phenyl-, *o*-tolyl-, *p*-tolyl-, α-naphthyl-, and *p*-chlorobenzylmagnesium bromides; it is negative for ethyl-, *n*-propyl-, *n*-butyl-, and mesitylmagnesium bromides. The nature of the colored compounds formed in positive tests is not certainly known.

CHAPTER IV

Constitution and Dissociation of Grignard Reagents

SOLVENT ASSOCIATION

The constitution of the Grignard reagent, particularly in ethereal solution, has been the subject of a great deal of experimental study, and of speculation and controversy *ad libitum*. Early contributions in the field have been reviewed by (*inter alios*): Thorp and Kamm,[1] Grignard,[2] Meisenheimer and Casper,[3] Terentjew,[4] Courtot,[5] Gilman and Fothergill,[6] Runge[7] and Jolibois and Kullmann.[7.1] Because much of the material involved can now be of little more than antiquarian interest, a brief historical resumê rather than an exhaustive review is here presented.

The analyses of Grignard[8] and of Blaise[9] had shown that, when an ethereal solution of an organomagnesium halide (CH_3MgI, C_2H_5MgBr, C_2H_5MgI) is evaporated, and the residue is dried under reduced pressure, one molecule of ether per molecule of organomagnesium halide is retained with great tenacity, being removed only partially after several hours at temperatures as high as 150°. Grignard[8] originally suggested that in such residues ether plays a rôle analogous to that of water of crystallization.

In a discussion of oxonium compounds and the potential quadrivalency of oxygen, Baeyer and Villiger[10] cited these data, and proposed for methylmagnesium iodide from ethyl ethereal solution the formulation

$$\begin{matrix} H_5C_2 & & MgCH_3 \\ & O & \\ H_5C_2 & & I \end{matrix}$$

---

[1]Thorp and Kamm, *J. Am. Chem. Soc.*, *36*, 1022–8 (1914).

[2]Grignard, (*a*) *Bull. soc. chim.*, [4], *13*, Conference I–XXXVIII (1913); (*b*) [4], *39*, 1285–321 (1926).

[3]Meisenheimer and Casper, *Ber.*, *54B*, 1655–65 (1921).

[4]Terenjew, *Z. anorg. Chem.*, *156*, 73–84 (1926).

[5]Courtot, "Le Magnesium en Chimie Organique," Nancy, *1926*, pp. 32–44.

[6]Gilman and Fothergill, *J. Am. Chem. Soc.*, *51*, 3149–57 (1929).

[7]Runge, "Organometalverbindung. I Teil: Organomagnesiumverbindungen," Stuttgart, *1932*, pp. 5–7.

[7.1]Jolibois and Kullmann, *Bull. soc. chim.*, [5], *17*, 919–32 (1950).

[8]Grignard, *Ann. chim.*, [7], *24*, 433–90 (1901).

[9]Blaise, *Compt. rend.*, *132*, 839–41 (1901); *Chem. Zentr.*, *1901*, *I*, 1000.

[10]Baeyer and Villiger, *Ber.*, *35*, 1201–12 (1902).

Grignard[11] accepted in principle the concept of an ethereal organomagnesium halide as an oxonium compound, but preferred, as more consistent with the mode of scission of such compounds in chemical reactions, the formulation

$$\begin{matrix} H_5C_2 & & MgI \\ & O & \\ H_5C_2 & & CH_3 \end{matrix}$$

It would be a necessary implication of Grignard's hypothesis that the unsymmetrical etherate of a Grignard reagent with an organic radical foreign to the ether be preparable in three different ways, and that, of the three conceivable modes of subsequent reaction of the etherate, the preferred one might or might not yield a non-ethereal product corresponding to the alkyl halide employed in the preparation of the Grignard reagent

$$\begin{matrix} RX + R'OR'' \searrow & & \nearrow RH + R'OR'' + MgXOH \\ R'X + ROR'' \xrightarrow{Mg} & \begin{matrix} R & & R'' \\ & O & \\ R' & & MgX \end{matrix} & \xrightarrow{(H_2O)} R'H + ROR'' + MgXOH \\ R''X + ROR' \nearrow & & \searrow R''H + R'OR'' + MgXOH \end{matrix}$$

Stadnikoff,[12] working for the most part with readily-cloven ethers,* such as ethyl triphenylmethyl, propyl benzhydryl, and butyl benzhydryl, supposed that he had accumulated evidence in favor of the oxonium intermediate hypothesis by effecting such reactions as:

$$n\text{-}C_4H_9OCH(C_6H_5)_2 + n\text{-}C_3H_7I + Mg \xrightarrow{(H_2O)} C_3H_8\ (12.5\%)$$
$$+ [(C_6H_5)_2CH—]_2\ (14.5\%) + (C_6H_5)_2CH\text{-}n\text{-}C_3H_7\ (35.0\%)$$
$$+ \text{recovered } n\text{-}C_4H_9OCH(C_6H_5)_2$$

Gorskiĭ[13] and Tschellinzeff[14] correctly characterized these reactions as involving ether cleavages of the type:

$$RMgX + R'OR'' \longrightarrow R'OMgX + RR''$$

Thorp and Kamm[15] demonstrated conclusively that the etherates derived from ethyl ether, bromobenzene, and magnesium, on the one hand, and phenetole, ethyl bromide, and magnesium, on the other, are not identical.

---

[11]Grignard, *Compt. rend.*, *136*, 1260–2 (1903); *J. Chem. Soc.*, *84,I*, 552 (1903); *Bull. soc. chim.*, [3], *29*, 944–8 (1903).

[12]Stadnikoff, *J. Russ. Phys.-Chem. Soc.*, *43*, 1244–57 (1911); *44*, 1219–47, 1256–64 (1912); *Chem. Abstr.*, *6*, 1434 (1912); *7*, 983, 984 (1913); *Ber.*, *44*, 1157–60 (1911); *46*, 2496–503 (1913); *J. prakt. Chem.*, [2], *88*, 1–20 (1913).

*See: Chapter XV, Reactions of Grignard Reagents with Ethers, Acetals, and Ketals.

[13]Gorskiĭ *J. Russ. Phys.-Chem. Soc.*, *44*, 581–6 (1912); *45*, 163–6 (1913); *J. Chem. Soc.*, *102,I*, 622 (1912); *104,I*, 462 (1913).

[14]Tschellinzeff and Pavloff, *J. Russ. Phys.-Chem. Soc.*, *45*, 289–300 (1913); *J. Chem. Soc.*, *104,I*, 461 (1913).

[15]Thorp and Kamm, *J. Am. Chem. Soc.*, *36*, 1022–8 (1914).

$$(C_2H_5)_2O + C_6H_5Br + Mg \xrightarrow{H_2O} C_6H_6 \quad (60\%)$$

$$C_2H_5OC_6H_5 + C_2H_5Br + Mg \xrightarrow{H_2O} C_2H_6 \quad (99.7\%)$$

$$(C_2H_5)_2O + C_6H_5Br + Mg \xrightarrow{CO_2} \xrightarrow{H_3O^+} C_6H_5CO_2H \quad (50\%)$$

$$C_2H_5OC_6H_5 + C_2H_5Br + Mg \xrightarrow{CO_2} \xrightarrow{H_3O^+} C_2H_5CO_2H*$$

Zelinsky[16] prepared a "dietherate" of magnesium iodide and "trietherates" of magnesium bromide and magnesium iodide, from which two molecules of ether could be rather readily removed to produce the more stable "monoetherate." Blaise[17] isolated a crystalline compound, resulting from the reaction of ethereal iodine with magnesium, which he believed to be the "dietherate" of magnesium iodide, and for which he proposed the formulation

$$(C_2H_5)_2O\overset{I\ \ I}{\langle\ \ \rangle}O(C_2H_5)_2 \quad (\text{ring: } O-I-I-O \text{ bridged by } Mg)$$

Tschelinzeff[18] prepared organomagnesium halides (C_2H_5MgI, n-C_3H_7MgI, i-C_4H_9MgI, i-$C_5H_{11}MgI$) in benzene and benzine solutions with the aid of a few drops of dimethylaniline "catalyst," and measured the heat evolved upon the addition of an equivalent of ethyl ether. On the ground that the heat effect does not vary much for the Grignard reagents or the solvents investigated, he preferred to regard the "monoetherates" as Werner[19] complexes rather than as oxonium salts, and he suggested the formulation

$$\left(\begin{matrix} H_5C_2 \\ H_5C_2 \end{matrix}\Big\rangle O \ldots MgR\right)X$$

In a continuation of this study, Tschelinzeff[20] isolated and analyzed the "dietherates" of isopropyl- and isoamylmagnesium iodides, and determined that the thermal increments for addition of the first and second equivalents of ether were approximately equal. For the "dietherates"

*Propionic acid was not specifically identified as such, but it was shown that the readily-distillable acid obtained included no traces of either benzoic or halogen acids.

[16]Zelinsky, *J. Russ. Phys.-Chem.*, *35*, 399–404 (1903); *J. Chem. Soc.*, *84,I*, 802.

[17]Blaise, *Compt. rend.*, *139*, 1211–3 (1904); *J. Chem. Soc.*, *88,I*, 111 (1905).

[18]Tschelinzeff, *Ber.*, *37*, 2081–92, 4534–40 (1904); *38*, 3664–73 (1905); *39*, 773–9 (1906).

[19]*Cf.* Werner, *Ann.*, *322*, 261–351 (1902).

[20]Tschelinzeff, *Ber.*, *39*, 773–9 (1906).

he employed the formulation

$$\begin{array}{l} H_5C_2\diagdown\quad\diagup MgR \\ \qquad\quad O \qquad\quad \diagup C_2H_5 \\ H_5C_2\diagup\quad\diagdown I:O \\ \qquad\qquad\qquad\quad \diagdown C_2H_5 \end{array}$$

Investigating the heats of hydrolysis of several "isomeric" ether-Grignard reagent complexes ($RMgX \cdot 2\,R'OR''$), Tschelinzeff[21] found the differences to be of the order of the experimental error—a fact which he regarded as constituting a further argument in favor of a Werner complex formulation as opposed to an oxonium salt formulation.

Zerewitinoff[22] reported that methylmagnesium iodide forms a crystalline monoetherate with amyl ether.

GRIGNARD REAGENT ASSOCIATION

In the meantime Abegg[23] made two suggestions to which chemists apparently paid little attention at the time, but which were subsequently reproposed, and which, in principle, are now universally accepted. He assigned a polar constitution to the Grignard reagent and described the hydrolysis reaction by the equation

$$H^+OH^- + R^-[MgX]^+ = R^-H^+ + [MgX]^+\ OH^-$$

He also mentioned the possibility of a disproportionation reaction in the sense

$$2\,RMgX = MgX_2 + MgR_2$$

and (in a footnote) remarked: "Es wäre wichtig festzustellen, ob hier nicht ein Gleichgewicht erreicht werden kann."

Jolibois[24] reported that, whereas the diethylmagnesium of Lohr[25] is virtually insoluble in ethyl ether, it dissolves readily in an ethereal solution of magnesium iodide to give a solution which has various of the properties of an ethylmagnesium iodide solution prepared in the usual way. He further reported that under certain specified conditions such a solution may be electrolyzed with the deposition of magnesium at the cathode and without apparent gas evolution. On these grounds, he suggested that the Grignard reagent should be represented as $Mg(C_2H_5)_2 \cdot MgI_2$.

Grignard (*loc. cit.*[22]) admitted that molecular-weight determinations on organomagnesium halides in ether solution seemed to indicate a molecule twice the size indicated by the simple formula RMgX, but pointed out that the same is true of magnesium iodide, and maintained that such

---

[21]Tschelinzeff, *Compt. rend.*, *144*, 88–90 (1907); *Chem. Abstr.*, *1*, 1122 (1907).
[22]Zerewitinoff, *Ber.*, *41*, 2244–5 (1908).
[23]Abegg, *Ber.*, *38*, 4112–6 (1905).
[24]Jolibois, *Compt. rend.*, *155*, 353–5 (1912); *Chem. Abstr.*, *6*, 2741 (1912).
[25]Lohr, *Ann.*, *261*, 48–87 (1891).

determinations could in no wise distinguish between $R_2Mg{\cdot}MgX_2$ and $(RMgX)_2$.

Meisenheimer and Casper[26] presented various arguments against the formulation of Grignard reagents as oxonium salts and proposed that the "dietherates," which they regarded as the usual components of Grignard solutions at ordinary temperatures, be formulated as complexes of the type

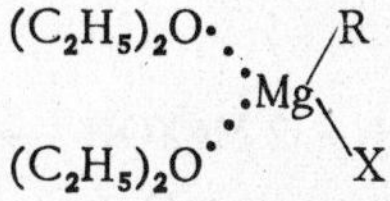

$$\begin{matrix} (C_2H_5)_2O\cdot\cdot & & R \\ & :Mg & \\ (C_2H_5)_2O\cdot & & X \end{matrix}$$

Terentjew (*loc. cit.*[4]) confirmed for methylmagnesium iodide in ethereal solution the "double" molecular weight observed by Grignard, and suggested the formulation $Mg[I_2{\cdot}Mg{\cdot}(CH_3)_2{\cdot}2\ (C_2H_5)O]$, or, more specifically,

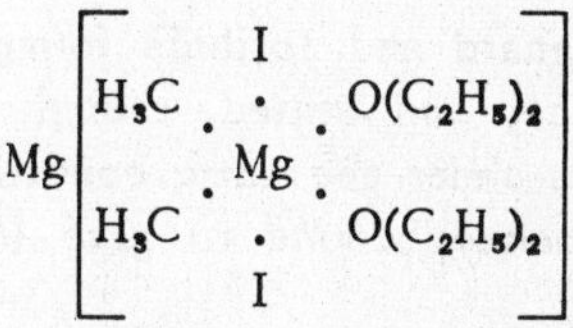

$$Mg\left[\begin{matrix} & I & \\ H_3C & \cdot & O(C_2H_5)_2 \\ & Mg & \\ H_3C & \cdot & O(C_2H_5)_2 \\ & I & \end{matrix}\right]$$

Job and Dubien[27] proposed the somewhat similar, though less specific formulation

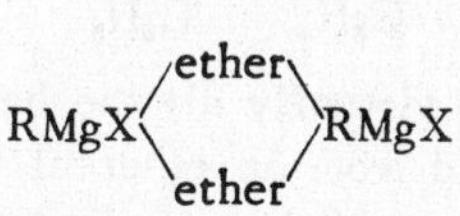

$$RMgX\begin{matrix} \text{ether} \\ \\ \text{ether} \end{matrix}RMgX$$

Meisenheimer and Schlichenmaier[28] repeated and extended Terentjew's study of the molecular weight of methylmagnesium iodide in ethyl ether and reported that the apparent molecular weight varies with the concentration of the solution. They regarded their monomolecular formulation as satisfactory, and attributed higher apparent molecular weights to "molecular association."

Various chemical expedients were invoked for the purpose of effecting a choice between the "symmetrical" formulation of Jolibois ($R_2Mg{\cdot}MgX_2$) and the "unsymmetrical" formulation of Grignard (RMgX) or its bimolecular equivalent [$(RMgX)_2$]. All proved inconclusive, and, in the light of present knowledge, much of the discussion seems trivial. A few examples should serve as illustrative.

Job and Dubien[29] believed that measurement of the rate of gas evolution when a large excess of magnesium is treated with ethereal ethyl

[26]Meisenheimer and Casper, *Ber.*, *54B*, 1655–65 (1921).
[27]Job and Dubien, *Compt. rend.*, *184*, 155–7 (1927).
[28]Meisenheimer and Schlichenmaier, *Ber.*, *61B*, 720–9 (1928).
[29]Job and Dubien, *Bull. soc. chim.*. [4], *39*, 383 (1926).

bromide at the boiling point of ether could establish a reaction order and hence permit a choice between RMgBr and $R_2Mg{\cdot}MgBr_2$.

Ivanoff[30] argued that magnesium bromide should be ether-extractable from $(C_2H_5CO_2)_2Mg{\cdot}MgBr_2$ but not from $C_2H_5CO_2MgBr$.

The question whether a Grignard reagent is hydrolyzed according to the equation:

$$R_2Mg{\cdot}MgX_2 + 2\,H_2O \longrightarrow 2\,RH + Mg(OH)_2 + MgX_2$$

or according to the equation:

$$2\,RMgX + 2\,H_2O \longrightarrow 2\,RH + 2\,MgXOH \longrightarrow 2\,RH + Mg(OH_2) + MgX_2$$

was debated by Kierzek[31] and Mingoia[32].

THE SCHLENK EQUILIBRIUM

Schlenk and Schlenk[33] commented upon the futility of attempting to decide between the Grignard and Jolibois formulations on the basis of purely chemical evidence, and stated, though without presentation of experimental detail, that under the same conditions, "phenylmagnesium bromide" reacts with benzophenone to give $[(C_6H_5)_3CO]_2Mg$, but with fluorenone to give

$$\begin{array}{l} C_6H_4\diagdown\ \ \diagup OMgBr \\ \ \ |\qquad\ \ C \\ C_6H_4\diagup\ \ \diagdown C_6H_5 \end{array}$$

They found, however, that virtually all the halogen and part of the magnesium may be precipitated from an ethereal Grignard reagent (C_2H_5MgI, C_6H_5MgBr) solution by the addition of dioxane. They interpreted this fact, in what still seems the only plausible manner, as indicating that the Grignard reagent exists in a state of equilibrium, which, reduced to its simplest terms, may be represented by:

$$2\,RMgX \rightleftharpoons R_2Mg + MgX_2$$

or

$$R_2Mg{\cdot}MgX_2 \rightleftharpoons R_2Mg + MgX_2$$

The equilibrium point of the former equation should, they argued, be independent of concentration; that of the latter should vary with concentration. Schlenk and Schlenk found no change in the apparent equilibrium point upon eightfold dilution of a "concentrated" ethylmagnesium iodide solution with ether.

---

[30]Ivanoff, *Compt. rend.*, *185*, 505–7 (1927); *cf.* comment by Grignard, *ibid.*, *185*, 507–9 (1927).

[31]Kierzek, *Bull. soc. chim.*, [4], *41*, 759, 1299–1308 (1927); *cf.* comment by Grignard, *ibid.*, [4], *41*, 759–60 (1927).

[32]Mingoia, *Gazz. chim. ital.*, *58*, 532–41 (1928).

[33]Schlenk and Schlenk, *Ber.*, *62B*, 920–4 (1929).

They also investigated the rate at which equilibrium is attained, and found it very rapid, if not instantaneous, in the case of phenylmagnesium bromide, but relatively slow in the case of ethylmagnesium iodide. Cope,[34] however, reports rapid attainment of equilibrium for ethylmagnesium iodide and ethylmagnesium bromide as well as phenylmagnesium bromide.

Upon the assumption that the true equilibrium point may be ascertained in the manner described, Schlenk[35] made the determinations recorded in the upper part of Table IV-I. Further determinations by Cope[36] are recorded in the lower part of Table IV-I. Additional values are reported by Noller and Hilmer,[37] by Johnson and Adkins[38] and by Bartlett and Barry.[39] That the values are reasonably reproducible is indicated by the concordant figures for phenylmagnesium bromide and iodide.

TABLE IV-I

DISPROPORTIONATION EQUILIBRIA (?) OF GRIGNARD REAGENTS IN ETHYL ETHER SOLUTION

RX	RMgX (%)	R_2Mg (%)	MgX_2 (%)
CH_3I	87.0	6.5	6.5
C_2H_5I	43.0	28.5	28.5
C_2H_5Br	41.0	29.5	29.5
C_2H_5Cl	15.0	42.5	42.5
n-C_3H_7I	24.0	38.0	38.0
n-C_3H_7Br	24.0	38.0	38.0
n-C_3H_7Cl	17.0	41.5	41.5
C_6H_5I	38.0	31.0	31.0
C_6H_5Br	30.0	35.0	35.0
C_6H_5I	39.0	30.5	30.5
C_6H_5Br	28.5	35.75	35.75
2,4-$(CH_3)_2C_6H_3Br$	44.0	28.0	28.0
2,4-$(CH_3)_2C_6H_3I$	55.0	22.5	22.5
2,4,6-$(CH_3)_3C_6H_2Br$	64.0	18.0	18.0

Cope (*loc. cit.*[34]) has found that the equilibrium point, as measured in this way, varies with temperature and with the solvent. For phenylmagnesium bromide 0.2178 N in magnesium, the percentage of $(C_6H_5)_2Mg$ rises from 31.0 at $-15°$ to 35.0 at 35°. At 20°, the percentage is 12.0 in n-butyl ether as compared to 33.5 in ethyl ether. For methylmagnesium iodide at 20°, the percentages are 0.1 in n-butyl ether and 1.0 in ben-

[34]Cope, *J. Am. Chem. Soc.*, *57*, 2238–40 (1933).
[35]Schlenk, *Ber.*, *64B*, 734–6 (1931).
[36]Cope, *J. Am. Chem. Soc.*, *56*, 1578–81 (1934).
[37]Noller and Hilmer, *J. Am. Chem. Soc.*, *54*, 2503–6 (1932).
[38]Johnson and Adkins, *J. Am. Chem. Soc.*, *54*, 1943–7 (1932).
[39]Bartlett and Barry, *J. Am. Chem. Soc.*, *56*, 2683–5 (1934).

zene, which may be compared to Schlenk's figure of 6.5 in ethyl ether at room temperature.

Cope[40] also showed that pyridine may be used as a precipitant, although it does not effect as complete halogen removal as does dioxane. The indicated $(C_6H_5)_2Mg$ perçentages for phenylmagnesium bromide solutions under comparable conditions are 34.0–34.5 for pyridine and 30.0–32.0 for dioxane. Isoquinoline proved unsatisfactory as a precipitant.

Subsequent studies by Noller *et al.*[41] have thrown doubt on the reliability of the dioxane-precipitation method as a means of establishing the actual state of equilibrium in a Grignard solution. Cope (*loc. cit.*[34]) had already noted that the diphenylmagnesium content of an ethereal solution increases with time when the solution is allowed to stand in contact with the dioxane precipitate from the original phenylmagnesium bromide solution. Noller and White[41a] found that the same phenomenon occurred when solutions of ethyl-, isobutyl-, *t*-butyl- and phenylmagnesium bromides were subjected to dioxane precipitation, and the resultant mixtures were then shaken for several hours. Ethylmagnesium bromide was studied in greatest detail, and to some solutions were added excess magnesium bromide or diethylmagnesium in varying amounts. Under these conditions, naturally enough, satisfactory equilibrium data were not obtained, although the amount of ethyl radical remaining in the precipitate increased in a general way with the amount of bromine present. With shaking, all the precipitates tended to approach a constant composition, regardless of the composition of the original solution.

The question that arises, of course, is whether the increase in R_2Mg content of the ethereal solution on standing or shaking with the dioxane precipitate is due to leaching of occluded or coprecipitated R_2Mg or to gradual disproportionation of precipitated RMgX. Noller and White believe the change is too great to be accounted for by mere occlusion. In solutions dilute enough for the solute to be approximately monomolecular, coprecipitation should be negligible. The fact that Cope[34,40] found that the ethereal solutions always contain detectable traces, though analytically insignificant quantities, of halogen makes it seem not too improbable that further disproportionation of the solid phase may take place on prolonged contact with the solution.

As a matter of practical interest, however, yields of diorganomagnesium compounds prepared by the method of Schlenk[42] may be materially enhanced by shaking the dioxane precipitate with the solution for periods of four to ten hours (Noller and White, *loc. cit.*[41a]).

---

[40]Cope, *J. Am. Chem. Soc.*, *60*, 2215–7 (1938).

[41](a) Noller and White, *J. Am. Chem. Soc.*, *59*, 1354–6 (1937); (b) Noller and Raney, *ibid.*, *62*, 1749–51 (1940).

[42]Schlenk, *Ber.*, *64B*, 736–9 (1931).

Kullman's[43] observations are, in part, confirmatory of those of Noller and White (*loc. cit.*[41a]). According to Kullman, the addition to an ethereal ethylmagnesium bromide solution of sufficient dioxane to effect complete bromide precipitation leaves only 55–60 percent of the ethyl groups in solution in the form of diethylmagnesium. With time the diethylmagnesium content of the solution increases, the percentage of ether-soluble ethyl groups reaching 70–75 percent in twenty-four hours. Addition of the same amount of dioxane in three or four portions, with about twenty-four hours intervening between each addition and the next, results in bromide precipitation which leaves 93–97 percent of the ethyl groups in ethereal solution in the form of diethylmagnesium.

Recalling Rheinboldt's[44] preparation of crystalline magnesium iodide dioxanate ($MgI_2 \cdot 2\ C_4H_8O_2$) by the addition of dioxane to an ethereal solution of magnesium iodide, and of the corresponding bromide and chloride dioxanates by more convenient methods, Kullman postulates that $(C_2H_5)_2Mg \cdot C_4H_8O_2$ is ether-soluble, that $Br_2Mg \cdot 2\ C_4H_8O_2$ is ether-insoluble, and that the amount of dioxane necessary for complete bromide precipitation is three molecular equivalents for each two gram-equivalents of magnesium present. He concludes that no ethylmagnesium bromide is precipitated as such.

Basing their argument on the relative rates and heats of reaction of solutions of methylmagnesium iodide and dimethylmagnesium, respectively, in butyl ether with acetone and with ethyl acetate, Aston and Bernhard[45] conclude that a butyl ether solution of methylmagnesium iodide contains almost no free dimethylmagnesium. In further support of this conclusion they cite the ready inflammability of dialkylmagnesium solutions and the comparative stability of the corresponding alkylmagnesium halide solutions. They suggest that the Grignard reagent equilibrium be formulated as:

$$2\ RMgX \rightleftharpoons [R_2Mg \cdot MgX_2] \rightleftharpoons R_2Mg + MgX_2$$

On the basis of their own and Menschutkin's[46] determinations of the freezing points of ethereal magnesium iodide solutions, and of their own measurements of the freezing points of ethereal methylmagnesium iodide solutions, Stewart and Ubbelohde[47] propose the equilibrium:

$$n\ MgI_2 + CH_3MgI + m\ Et_2O \rightleftharpoons n\ MgI_2 \cdot CH_3MgI \cdot m\ Et_2O$$

in which n has a probable value of 2. They tentatively formulate the

---

[43] Kullman, *Compt. rend.*, *231*, 866–8 (1950).

[44] Rheinboldt, Luyken, and Schmittmann, *J. prakt. Chem.*, [2], *149*, 30–54 (1937).

[45] Aston and Bernhard, *Nature*, *165*, 485 (1950).

[46] Menschutkin, *Z. anorg. Chem.*, *49*, 34–45 (1906).

[47] Stewart and Ubbelohde, *J. Chem. Soc.*, *1949*, 2649–56.

complex as:

$$m\ Et_2O\cdot Mg^{++}\left[\begin{array}{ccccc} H_3C\cdot & & \cdot I\cdot & & \cdot I \\ & :Mg: & & :Mg: & \\ I & & I & & I \end{array}\right]^{--}$$

In so far as these arguments need be taken seriously at all, they merely labor the obvious and generally-recognized point that the Schlenk equation constitutes an over-simplified statement.

In view of the limited solubility of magnesium chloride etherate in ether (*ca.* 0.001 mole per 1000 g. of solution),[48] one might anticipate that organomagnesium chloride solutions would deposit magnesium chloride etherate, and that the disproportionation equilibrium would be shifted far toward the right. Indeed, this phenomenon has been reported by Schlenk and Schlenk (*loc. cit.*[33]) as occurring in benzylmagnesium chloride solutions after several days standing. They attributed the delayed precipitation to supersaturation. Cope[34] has also found that methylmagnesium chloride solutions deposit magnesium chloride; in this case, the deposition is immediate rather than delayed, but the disproportionation nevertheless remains relatively slight. Noller and Raney have investigated *n*-butylmagnesium chloride solutions under conditions which preclude the possibility of supersaturation (*i.e.*, by shaking with anhydrous magnesium chloride). Under these conditions, a little magnesium chloride is precipitated (3–10 percent of the total chlorine content), whereas the dioxane-precipitation method indicates that about 88 percent of the basic magnesium present is in the form of $(n\text{-}C_4H_9)_2Mg$. One must conclude either that the precipitation gives a grossly inaccurate picture of the disproportionation equilibrium or that magnesium chloride etherate is more soluble in the Grignard solution than in ether. In view of the fact that magnesium bromide etherate has been shown to be much more soluble in *n*-butylmagnesium bromide solution than in ether,[49] the latter seems the more credible conclusion.

A later note by Noller and Castro[50] indicates that the question may not be merely one of complex solubilities. They found that chloride precipitation from *n*-butylmagnesium chloride is greatly accelerated and increased by oxygen contamination. Indeed, with the most careful precautions to exclude oxygen there is virtually no chloride precipitation in one hundred sixty days. They postulate that ROMgX would carry down some $MgCl_2$ and be converted eventually to $ROMgX\cdot 2\ MgCl_2$. However, in the case of benzylmagnesium chloride, they were unable to prevent chloride precipitation even by the most careful precautions against oxygen contamination.

---

[48] Noller and Raney, *J. Am. Chem. Soc.*, *62*, 1749–51 (1940).
[49] Doering and Noller, *J. Am. Chem. Soc.*, *61*, 3436 (1939).
[50] Noller and Castro, *J. Am. Chem. Soc.*, *64*, 2509–10 (1942).

"Equilibrium" determinations similar to those of Noller and Raney (*loc. cit.*[48]) have been made by Coleman and Brooks[51] on butyl ether solutions of ethylmagnesium and butylmagnesium chlorides.

ELECTROLYTIC PROPERTIES OF GRIGNARD REAGENT SOLUTIONS

Jolibois'[24] observation that ethereal solutions of ethylmagnesium bromide are electrically conducting was confirmed by Nelson and Evans.[52] Subsequent studies of the conductivities of ethereal ethylmagnesium bromide and iodide and of propyl- and isopropylmagnesium iodides have been made by Kondyrew *et al.*[53] In general, the conductivities increase with rising temperature. For the ethyl Grignard reagents, the conductivities pass through a maximum with increasing concentration.

Kondyrew[53a] also noted that when externally connected magnesium and platinum electrodes are immersed in an ethereal ethyl bromide solution magnesium is dissolved and a potential is set up (0.76 volt under the experimental conditions employed).

Studies on the electrolysis of Grignard reagents have been made by Gaddum and French[54] (phenylmagnesium bromide, benzylmagnesium chloride), by Rodebush and Peterson[55] (ethylmagnesium bromide), by French and Drane[56] (isoamylmagnesium chloride), and by Duval[57] (phenylmagnesium bromide).

In view of its apparent molecular weight and its electrolytic characteristics, Duval suggests that ethereal phenylmagnesium bromide be formulated as $[MgPh_2Br_2(Et_2O)_2]Mg$. Decombe and Duval[58] believe that in such a complex, the anionic magnesium should be replaceable by a less reactive metal such as zinc. By the action of methyl iodide on magnesium-zinc alloy in ethyl ether and in ethyl acetate, they have prepared crystalline compounds which they formulate as $[ZnMe_2I_2(Et_2O)_2]Mg$ and $[ZnMe_2I_2(AcOEt)_2]Mg$, respectively, and which give analyses consistent with those formulae. Upon hydrolysis, the compounds yield methane, zinc iodide and magnesium hydroxide. Upon electrolysis, magnesium is deposited on the cathode and zinc is transported toward the anode.

---

[51]Coleman and Brooks, *J. Am. Chem. Soc.*, *68*, 1620–1 (1946).

[52]Nelson and Evans, *J. Am. Chem. Soc.*, *39*, 82–3 (1917).

[53](a) Kondyrew, *Ber.*, *58B*, 459–63 (1925); (b) Kondyrew and Manojew, *ibid.*, *58B*, 464–7 (1925); (c) Kondyrew, *ibid.*, *61B*, 208–12 (1928); *J. Russ. Phys.-Chem. Soc.*, *60*, 545–51 (1928); *Chem. Abstr.*, *23*, 1321 (1929); (d) Kondyrew and Ssusi, *Ber.*, *62B*, 1856–61 (1929); (e) Kondyrew and Zhel'vis, *J. Gen. Chem.* (U.S.S.R.), *4*, 203–8 (1934); *Chem. Abstr.*, *29*, 25 (1935).

[54]Gaddum and French, *J. Am. Chem. Soc.*, *49*, 1295–9 (1927).

[55]Rodebush and Peterson, *J. Am. Chem. Soc.*, *51*, 638–9 (1929).

[56]French and Drane, *J. Am. Chem. Soc.*, *52*, 4904–6 (1930).

[57]Duval, *Compt. rend.*, *202*, 1184–6 (1936).

[58]Decombe and Duval, *Compt. rend.*, *206*, 1024–6; *Chem. Abstr.*, *32*, 4940 (1938).

These authors believe that it should be possible to replace cationic magnesium with a more active metal such as calcium, forming compounds which they would formulate as $[MgR_2X_2(Et_2O)_2]Ca$.

For the most detailed and informative studies in the electrolytic field, we are indebted to Evans and his co-workers.[59]

The data most pertinent to the question of the constitution of the Grignard reagent may be summarized as follows.

1. Magnesium is deposited on the cathode; hydrocarbons and sometimes hydrogen and secondary organic products are liberated in the anode portion of the cell.

2. All concentration losses of solute constituents occur in the cathode portion. The anode portion shows a gain in all solute constituents at all times, even after losing an equivalent amount of R by electrolysis.

3. The relative amounts of R and X gained by the anode portion are not constant, but depend upon the ratio of R to X in the original solution. When the MgX_2 concentration is low, R_2Mg or RMgX is transported to the anode; when the MgX_2 concentration is high, MgX_2 is transported to the anode.

4. The net migration of magnesium to the anode portion shows that it is present in the anion as well as in the cation.

5. There is always a net gain of MgX_2 in the solution.

6. Current efficiency is high at low concentrations of the Grignard solution, but falls off with increasing concentration (for CH_3MgBr, 100 percent at 0.27 *N*; 48 percent at 2.58 *N*).

Ionization of Grignard reagents. From these observations and previously ascertained facts concerning the properties of Grignard solutions (already summarized in the foregoing resumé), Evans and Pearson (*loc. cit.*[59h]) have evolved a satisfactory description of the nature of the Grignard solution and the electrolysis process which may be paraphrased as follows.

In a suitable medium, the components of the Schlenk equilibrium are capable of ionization in the senses indicated by the following over-simplified* scheme:

---

[59](a) Evans and Lee, *J. Am. Chem. Soc.*, *56*, 654–7 (1934); (b) Evans, Lee, and Lee, *ibid.*, *57*, 489–90 (1935); Evans and Field, *ibid.*, *58*, (c) 720–4, (d) 2284–6 (1936); (e) Evans and Braithwaite, *ibid.*, *61*, 898–900 (1939); (f) Evans, Braithwaite, and Field, *ibid.*, *62*, 534–6 (1940); (g) Evans, Pearson, and Braithwaite, *ibid.*, *63*, 2574–6 (1941); (h) Evans and Pearson, *ibid.*, *64*, 2865–71 (1942).

*In part the simplification is equivalent to indicating the ionization of hydrogen chloride in an aqueous medium as

$$HCl \rightleftharpoons H^+ + Cl^-$$

rather than

$$HCl + H_2O \rightleftharpoons H_3O^+ + Cl^-$$

(1a) $RMgX \rightleftharpoons R^- + MgX^+$, or (in special cases)

(1b) $RMgX \rightleftharpoons X^- + RMg^+$

(2) $R_2Mg \rightleftharpoons R^- + RMg^+$

(3) $MgX_2 \rightleftharpoons X^- + MgX^+$

The formation of Mg^{++} ions in ethyl ether solution is regarded as highly improbable, partly because of the very low dielectric constant of the solvent.

The anions, with one or more unshared electron pairs, are bases and hence are not attracted to the electrodotic solvent molecules, but rather to the electrophilic solute molecules. The smallest possible anions present in very dilute Grignard solutions may therefore be represented as belonging to the species:

$$\left[\begin{array}{c} R \\ \cdot\cdot \\ R : Mg : OEt_2 \\ \cdot\cdot \\ X \end{array}\right]^- \quad \left[\begin{array}{c} R \\ \cdot\cdot \\ R : Mg : OEt_2 \\ \cdot\cdot \\ R \end{array}\right]^- \quad \left[\begin{array}{c} X \\ \cdot\cdot \\ R : Mg : OEt_2 \\ \cdot\cdot \\ X \end{array}\right]^- \quad \left[\begin{array}{c} X \\ \cdot\cdot \\ X : Mg : OEt_2 \\ \cdot\cdot \\ X \end{array}\right]^-$$

The repulsion of like charges would, of course, prevent mutual association between members of this class, but not between members of this class and positively charged or neutral electron acceptors. The more concentrated the solution, the higher will be the degree of association, and the larger the composite anion. Conceivable modes of secondary association might be represented by:

$$\left[\begin{array}{ccccccc} & R & & & & R & \\ & \cdot\cdot & & \cdot\cdot & & \cdot\cdot & \\ Et_2O : & Mg & : & X & : & Mg & : OEt_2 \\ & \cdot\cdot & & \cdot\cdot & & \cdot\cdot & \\ & R & & : X : & & & \\ & & & \cdot\cdot & & & \end{array}\right]^- \quad \left[\begin{array}{ccccccc} & R & & Et & & R & \\ & \cdot\cdot & & \cdot\cdot & & \cdot\cdot & \\ R : & Mg & : & O & : & Mg & : OEt_2 \\ & \cdot\cdot & & \cdot\cdot & & \cdot\cdot & \\ & : X : & & Et & : & X : & \\ & \cdot\cdot & & & & \cdot\cdot & \end{array}\right]^-$$

The anions, however large, remain fairly mobile because of their limited attraction for the solvent (one molecule of ether, or less, per atom of magnesium).

The cations, on the other hand, with their great electron deficiency, are highly acidic in the Lewis sense, and are undoubtedly relatively highly solvated by the basic solvent, with a consequent lowering of mobility despite their (probably) smaller average size.

$$\left[\begin{array}{ccc} & \cdot\cdot & \\ & : X : & \\ & \cdot\cdot & \\ Et_2O : & Mg & : Et_2O \\ & \cdot\cdot & \\ & OEt_2 & \end{array}\right]^+ \quad \left[\begin{array}{ccccccc} & & & & & \cdot\cdot & \\ & Et_2O & & & & : X : & \\ & \cdot\cdot & & \cdot\cdot & & \cdot\cdot & \\ Et_2O : & Mg & : & X & : & Mg & : OEt_2 \\ & \cdot\cdot & & \cdot\cdot & & \cdot\cdot & \\ & Et_2O & & & & R & \end{array}\right]^+$$

It need scarcely be emphasized that in solvents of low dielectric constant, like ethyl ether, the tendency toward the association of ion-pairs must be very great, and, concordantly, that the actual degree of ionic dissociation must be very small.

Electrolytic discharge of ions. Electrolytic reactions at the anode and cathode, respectively, may be represented in simplified style as follows:

$$R_2MgX^- \longrightarrow R\cdot + RMgX + \epsilon^-$$

$$R_3Mg^- \longrightarrow R\cdot + R_2Mg + \epsilon^-$$

$$RMgX_2^- \longrightarrow R\cdot + MgX_2 + \epsilon^-$$

$$2\,MgX^+ + 2\,\epsilon^- \longrightarrow 2\,MgX\cdot \longrightarrow Mg + MgX_2$$

The ultimate fate of the radicals liberated at the anode varies with the nature of the individual radical.

The non-gaseous organic products of the electrolysis of phenylmagnesium bromide have been reported as benzene,[57] biphenyl,[54,59g] terphenyl, higher "polymer," and styrene.[59g]

For methylmagnesium iodide or bromide in ethyl ether, the corresponding products are methane, ethane, ethylene and isobutylene.[59a,c] The relative amounts of the products vary with solution concentration and current density. In *n*-butyl ether the products are methane, ethane, butane, butenes, butyl alcohol, and 2-pentanol[59d].

The ethylmagnesium halides yield ethane and ethylene in nearly equimolecular proportions, together with a little hydrogen.[59a]

n-Propylmagnesium bromide yields propane, propylene, hexane, ethylene, hydrogen, ethanol, propanol, methylpropylcarbinol, and diethylcarbinol.[59a]

Isopropylmagnesium bromide yields propane, propylene, ethylene, hydrogen, ethanol, isopropyl alcohol, and traces of 2,4-dimethylbutane.[59e]

t-Butylmagnesium bromide yields chiefly isobutane and isobutylene.[59f]

n-Butyl-, isobutyl-, *s*-butyl-, and *n*-hexylmagnesium bromides yield the radical coupling products (R_2) exclusively.[59f]

It is therefore evident that three courses of action are open to radicals liberated at the anode:

(1) attack upon the solvent, *e.g.*,

$$R\cdot + H_3CCH_2OCH_2CH_3 \longrightarrow RH + H_3C(CH_3CH_2O)CH\cdot$$

(2) coupling,

$$2\,R\cdot \longrightarrow R_2$$

and (3) disproportionation,

$$2\,R\cdot \longrightarrow R_{(+H)} + R_{(-H)} \quad \text{or} \quad 2\,R\cdot \longrightarrow 2\,R_{(-H)} + H_2$$

For the more reactive (in general, the more "electronegative"*) free radicals, the tendency to attack the solvent is strong. Indeed, it is doubtful that any of the diphenyl formed in the electrolysis of phenylmagnesium bromide is the result of simple radical coupling, other than that which takes place at the electrode surface. Some of it may be formed by the attack of phenyl radicals upon benzene already formed by attack upon the solvent, or by attack upon the Grignard reagent. Certainly terphenyl and higher "polymers" must have an origin other than simple coupling.

For the somewhat less, but still moderately, active methyl radical, the tendency to attack the solvent is still rather strong, though the liberation of ethane from butyl ether solution and the increase in proportion of ethane liberated at higher concentrations and higher current densities in ethyl ether solution suggest that coupling takes place concurrently, at least at the electrode surface.

For the slightly less active but much less stable ethyl radical, disproportionation is almost total.

The propyl radical, less active than the ethyl radical, but more stable, couples to the extent of about 50 percent, disproportionates to a somewhat less extent, and attacks the solvent slightly.

The isopropyl and *t*-butyl radicals, both relatively unstable, undergo disproportionation chiefly.

The relatively unreactive, but relatively stable, *n*-butyl, isobutyl, *s*-butyl, and *n*-hexyl radicals couple almost quantitatively (as does the benzyl radical).

Some of the secondary reactions postulated by Evans *et al.* as consequent upon radical attack upon the solvent may be described as follows:

$$CH_3(C_2H_5O)CH\cdot \longrightarrow C_2H_5\cdot + CH_3CHO$$

$$CH_3CHO + RMgX \longrightarrow CH_3CHROMgX \xrightarrow{H_2O} CH_3CHROH$$

$$CH_3CHROH \xrightarrow{-H_2O} RCH{=}CH_2$$

$$n\text{-}C_3H_7(n\text{-}C_4H_9O)CH\cdot \longrightarrow n\text{-}C_4H_9\cdot + n\text{-}C_3H_7CHO$$

$$n\text{-}C_3H_7CHO + RMgX \longrightarrow n\text{-}C_3H_7CHROMgX \xrightarrow{H_2O} n\text{-}C_3H_7CHROH$$

$$C_2H_5(n\text{-}C_4H_9OCH_2)CH\cdot \longrightarrow n\text{-}C_4H_9O\cdot + CH_2{=}CHC_2H_5$$

$$n\text{-}C_4H_9O\cdot + \cdot MgX \longrightarrow n\text{-}C_4H_9OMgX \xrightarrow{H_2O} n\text{-}C_4H_9OH$$

The behavior of radicals liberated by electrolytic neutralization of

*Concerning the relative "electronegativities" of organic radicals see: Kharasch and Reinmuth, *J. Chem. Education*, *5*, 404–18 (1928); 8, 1703–48 (1931); Kharasch, Reinmuth, and Mayo, *ibid.*, *11*, 82–96 (1934); *13*, 7–19 (1936).

anions is, in general, similar to that observed by Kharasch *et al.*[60] for free radicals generated by the attack of cobaltous chloride on Grignard reagents.

In certain special cases, as has already been suggested, dissociation of the Grignard reagent may take place in the sense $RMgX \rightleftharpoons X^- + RMg^+$. There appears to be some reason to suppose that this may occasionally be true of $C_6H_5C{\equiv}CMgI$[59b]. The anodic electrolysis process and sequelae may then be described as follows:

$$RMgX_2^- \longrightarrow X\cdot + RMgX + \epsilon^-$$

$$R_2MgX^- \longrightarrow X\cdot + R_2Mg + \epsilon^-$$

$$MgX_3^- \longrightarrow X\cdot + MgX_2 + \epsilon^-$$

$$2\,X\cdot \longrightarrow X_2$$

$$RMgX + X_2 \longrightarrow RX + MgX_2$$

$$RX + Mg\ (\text{cathode}) \longrightarrow RMgX$$

Evans (*loc. cit.*)[59b] found that the decomposition potential varies with the individual Grignard reagent. For molar solution, the average decomposition voltages observed were: C_6H_5MgBr, 2.17; CH_3MgBr, 1.94; n-C_3H_7MgBr, 1.42; n-C_4H_9MgBr, 1.32; C_2H_5MgBr, 1.28; s-C_4H_9MgBr, 1.24; i-C_3H_7, 1.07; t-C_4H_9MgBr, 0.97; $H_2C{=}CHCH_2MgBr$, 0.86. Although there are minor deviations (scarcely surprising in view of the complexity of relatively concentrated solutions, and the possibility of polarization effects), the trend is unmistakably from relatively high voltages for relatively "electronegative" radicals to low voltages for weakly electronegative radicals.

NON-IONIC DISSOCIATION OF GRIGNARD REAGENTS

In some "normal" reactions of Grignard reagents (as, *e.g.*, those with azo compounds, *q.v.*), and in many so-called "abnormal" reactions (see, *e.g.*, Chapters V and VI) there is obviously homopolar scission of the organometallic bond of the Grignard reagent. In such cases, however, it is usually unnecessary to assume a dissociation equilibrium of the kind suggested by Alexander,[61]

$$RMgX \rightleftharpoons R\cdot + \cdot MgX$$

as a prerequisite to reaction. "Forced" (*i.e.*, high-temperature) reactions,

[60] See, *e.g.*: Kharasch and Fields, *J. Am. Chem. Soc.*, *63*, 2316–20 (1941); Kharasch and Kleimann, *ibid.*, *65*, 491–3 (1943); Kharasch, Lewis, and Reynolds, *ibid.*, *65*, 493 (1943); Kharasch, Nudenberg, and Archer, *65*, 495–8 (1943); Kharasch, Lewis, and Reynolds, *ibid.*, *65*, 498–500 (1943).

[61] Alexander, "Principles of Ionic Organic Reactions," John Wiley & Sons, Inc., New York, *1950*, p. 188; *cf.* Chapter V, this monograph.

or those of such atypical reagents as the triphenylmethylmagnesium halides may occasionally involve such dissociations, but in general it appears much more probable that the reactions either (1) proceed by a mechanism that does not involve the actual release of free radicals into the solution, or (2) are initiated by an induced dissociation:

$$RMgX + AB \longrightarrow R\cdot + MgXB + A\cdot$$

CHAPTER V

Some Radical Reactions of Grignard Reagents

HOMOLYTIC DISSOCIATION

Although the majority of the so-called "normal" Grignard reagent reactions appear to be essentially ionic in nature,* some reactions, especially among those commonly regarded as "abnormal," are most readily explicable upon the basis of the hypothesis that the R-MgX bond undergoes homolytic scission. Such reactions may result in the liberation of free radicals in the reaction system, but the existence of *free* radicals is by no means an essential feature of a radical reaction (*i.e.*, a reaction involving homolytic scission of the R-MgX bond). It is therefore unnecessary, in general, to assume an equilibrium of the type proposed by Alexander,[1]

$$R\cdot + \cdot MgX \rightleftharpoons RMgX \rightleftharpoons R^- + MgX^+$$

$$\updownarrow$$

$$\tfrac{1}{2}\, R_2Mg + \tfrac{1}{2}\, MgX_2$$

although such equilibria may occur in special cases (as, *e.g.*, those of the triarylmethylmagnesium halides).

It is probable that in some "forced" (*i.e.*, high-temperature) reactions dissociation of the Grignard reagent in the sense

$$RMgX \longrightarrow R\cdot + \cdot MgX$$

occurs, but in general no equilibrium is attained in such cases because of the reactivity of the radicals R· toward each other† or toward other components of the reaction system (*e.g.*, Et_2O and RMgX).

It appears highly probable, however, that, in general, the homolytic dissociation of the R-MgX bond in Grignard reactions is an induced

*This statement should not be interpreted as implying that actual dissociation of the reagent into ions is a necessary prelude to reaction. It is sufficient to postulate that heterolytic scission of the R-MgX bond occurs in the course of the reaction.

[1]Alexander, "Principles of Ionic Organic Reactions," John Wiley & Sons, Inc., New York, *1950*, p. 188.

†The commonest reactions of radicals with each other are (irreversible) dimerization,

$$2\, R\cdot \longrightarrow R_2$$

and disproportionation,

$$2\, R\cdot \longrightarrow R_{(+H)} + R_{(-H)}$$

phenomenon requiring the participation of a co-reactant. Such induced homolytic dissociations may give rise to the liberation of *free* radicals by, *inter alia*, processes like those represented in equations 1 and 2.

$$\text{(1)} \quad RMgX + AB \rightarrow R\cdot + \cdot A + MgBX$$

$$\text{(2)} \quad RMgX + A'B' \rightarrow R\cdot + \cdot A'B'MgX$$

In some radical reactions it appears extremely improbable that any *free* radicals are ever released. The reduction of an azo compound by an arylmagnesium halide is a case in point (see Chapter XIX, Azo Compounds). Although present knowledge of such reactions is inadequate to support any assured statement regarding reaction mechanism, the reaction products invite tentative consideration of some such scheme as the following.

$$(ArN=)_2 + 2\,Ar'MgX \longrightarrow Ar-\overset{\cdot\cdot}{N}=\overset{\cdot\cdot}{N}-Ar \text{ (with } X-Mg(Ar') \text{ and } Mg(Ar')-X \text{ coordinated to N)}$$

$$\downarrow$$

$$Ar-N \cdots N-Ar \text{ (} X-Mg \text{ and } Mg-X \text{ on N; } Ar' \cdots Ar' \text{)}$$

$$\leftarrow \quad Ar-N-N-Ar \text{ (} X-Mg \text{ and } Mg-X \text{ on N)} \quad + \quad Ar'-Ar'$$

$$\downarrow (H_2O)$$

$$(ArNH-)_2 + Ar'_2 + Mg(OH)_2 + MgX_2$$

ACTION OF SOME METALLIC HALIDES ON GRIGNARD REAGENTS

Any attempt at a comprehensive review of the reactions of Grignard reagents with metallic halides would extend beyond the projected scope of the present work. Nevertheless, the use of various metallic halides by numerous investigators either as (*a*) supposed catalysts of "normal" Grignard reactions, or as (*b*) initiators or facilitators of "abnormal" Grignard reactions compels some attention to this subject.

Unfortunately, present knowledge of the reactions of Grignard reagents with metallic compounds is by no means satisfactorily extensive or exact. Save for minor extensions, the brief statement of Gilman and Lichtenwalter[2] summarizes about all that is presently known with any degree of certainty.

"In general, metallic halides react with Grignard reagents to give organometallic compounds which are less reactive than the RMgX compounds:

$$C_6H_5MgX + MX_2 \rightarrow C_6H_5MX \; [\text{or } (C_6H_5)_2M] + MgX_2$$

However, there are some metallic halides which react with Grignard reagents to give only a coupling product:

---

[2]Gilman and Lichtenwalter, *J. Am. Chem. Soc.*, *61*, 957–9 (1939).

$$C_6H_5MgX + MX_2 \longrightarrow C_6H_5C_6H_5 + MgX_2 + MX \text{ [or M]}$$

A third, and intermediate, class of metallic halides reacts with RMgX compounds to give highly thermally unstable organometallic compounds which decompose readily to the coupling product and metal:

$$(C_6H_5)_2M \longrightarrow C_6H_5C_6H_5 + M''$$

With reactions that lead to the preparation of relatively stable organometallic compounds the present work is not concerned. Regarding reactions in which thermally unstable organometallic compounds play a part certain points that have been little stressed, or that have been ignored or overlooked altogether, in literature discussions are worthy of passing comment.

Unstable Intermediate Organometallic Compounds. It appears to have been fairly credibly established that organosilver compounds (arising from the interaction of Grignard reagents with silver halides) and organocopper compounds (arising from the interaction of Grignard reagents with cuprous halides, or with cupric halides, which readily undergo Grignard reduction to cuprous compounds) exist, and are relatively stable at low temperatures.[2,3] Considerable evidence has also been adduced by Hein *et al.*[4] to indicate that organochromium compounds may be similarly prepared at low temperatures.

Although some investigators have postulated, and others have implied, that the dimerization (*i.e.*, "coupling") of the Grignard reagent radical arising through the decomposition of a thermally unstable organometallic intermediate is a free-radical process, the preponderance of the evidence is strongly to the contrary. The fact that phenylsilver decomposes in ethereal solution to give good yields of biphenyl, with no evidence of attack upon the solvent, would preclude the possibility that any appreciable quantity of *free* phenyl radicals is released into the reaction system.[5] It must be concluded, therefore, that such thermal decompositions are essentially radical reactions of second (or higher) order, with respect to the organometallic intermediate, in which no *free* radicals participate.*

$$2x\ RAg \longrightarrow x\ R_2 + 2x\ Ag$$

---

[3] For contributory evidence and leading references see: Gilman and Parker, *J. Am. Chem. Soc.*, *46*, 2823–7 (1924); Gilman and Straley, *Rec. trav. chim.*, *55*, 821–34 (1936); Gilman and Lichtenwalter, *loc. cit.*[2]

[4] Hein, *Ber.*, *54B*, 1905–38, 2708–27, 2727–44 (1921); Hein and Schwartzkopf, *ibid.*, *57B*, 8–14 (1924); Hein and Spaete, *ibid.*, *57B*, 899–908 (1924).

[5] See, *e.g.*: Bickley and Gardner, *J. Org. Chem.*, *5*, 126–32 (1940).

*The fact that the radicals of alkyl Grignard reagents undergo disproportionation as well as dimerization in such reactions does not constitute a cogent argument for the presence of *free* radicals in the system. There would appear to be no valid reason why disproportionation might not take place by a bi- or polymolecular process analogous to that which gives rise to dimerization.

$$2\ AgR' \longrightarrow R'_{(+H)} + R'_{(-H)} + Ag$$

The addition-polymerization reactions initiated by Ziegler *et al.*[6] in butadiene-phenylmagnesium bromide systems with the aid of silver bromide or cupric chloride, and in styrene-propylmagnesium bromide systems with the aid of silver bromide, are compatible with this conclusion if it be postulated that good radical acceptors (as both butadiene and styrene have been shown to be) are capable of inducing homolytic scission of a relatively unstable organometallic bond.

$$RCH{=\!=}CH_2 + R'Ag \rightarrow [RCH{-\!-}CH_2R']\cdot + Ag$$

Granted the probability of such induced dissociations (for which there would seem to be ample precedent), the scheme might be extended to include the participation of ready hydrogen donors. It is thus possible to account credibly for the formation of 3,3′-bicyclohexenyl in cyclohexene-butylmagnesium bromide-cupric chloride systems, mentioned, but not described in detail, by Ziegler *et al. (loc. cit.*[6]*).*

$$C_6H_{10} + BuCu \rightarrow C_6H_9\cdot + BuH + Cu$$
$$2\ C_6H_9\cdot \rightarrow C_6H_9C_6H_9$$

We so make use of the working hypothesis that induced radical reactions may generate derived *free* radicals by either additive or subtractive processes.

Incidentally, the reactions of aurous chloride carbonyl with arylmagnesium halides probably involve unstable organogold compounds. The yields of biaryls obtained with aurous chloride carbonyl are, in general, better than those attainable with silver halides, that with phenylmagnesium bromide being quantitative within the limits of experimental error.[7]

$$C_6H_5MgBr + AuClCO \rightarrow C_6H_5Au + CO$$
$$2\ C_6H_5Au \rightarrow C_6H_5C_6H_5 + 2\ Au$$

It should be noted, however, that assumption of the validity of the foregoing dimerization schemes does not necessarily preclude the possibility of the occurrence of the following competitive processes:

$$RM + RMgX \rightarrow R_2 + M + \cdot MgX$$

Reactions of Group VIII (Fe, Co, Ni) Halides. The fact that halides of iron, cobalt, and nickel undergo with Grignard reagents overall reactions formally resembling those of the silver and cuprous halides[8] suggests that reaction mechanisms for the group VIII metallic halides may be analogous to those for the IB halides, and that the hypothetical organometallic intermediates of the one class may differ from the demonstrated organometallic intermediates of the other class primarily in degree of stability.

---

[6] Ziegler, Eimers, Hechelhammer, and Wilms, *Ann.*, *567,* 43–96 (1950).
[7] Kharasch and Isbell, *J. Am. Chem. Soc.*, *52,* 2919–27 (1930).
[8] *Cf.* Gilman and Lichtenwalter, *loc. cit.*[2]

The existence of organoiron compounds has been postulated, and some circumstantial evidence purporting to support the postulation has been presented.[9] However, with one conspicuous exception, no such compounds have as yet been isolated, and the evidence for their existence, such as it is, may be otherwise interpreted.[10]

The biscyclopentadienyliron obtained by Kealy and Pauson (*loc. cit.*[10]) in the attempt to prepare biscyclopentadienyl by effecting a "coupling" reaction between cyclopentadienylmagnesium bromide and ferric chloride is unique in its stability with respect to thermal decomposition and to the action of water, acid, and alkali. On the basis of various physical measurements and of the aromaticity of the compound, as evidenced by its ability to undergo the Friedel-Crafts reaction with acyl halides, Woodward *et al.*[11] deduce the complete equivalency of the methylidyne (CH) groups, and propose the following structure, as well as the name *ferrocene*.

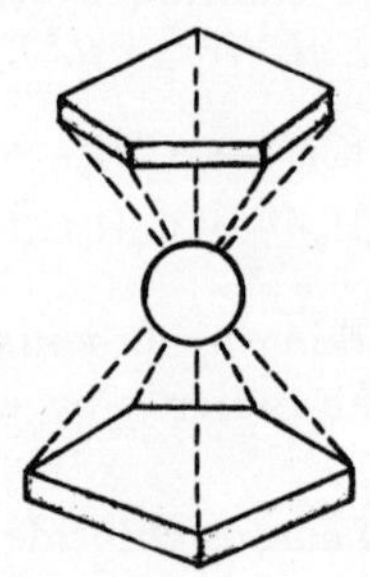

According to Champetier (*loc. cit.*[9]), the overall reaction of phenylmagnesium bromide with ferric chloride,

$$6\ C_6H_5MgBr + 2\ FeCl_3 \longrightarrow 3\ C_6H_5C_6H_5 + 2\ Fe + 3\ MgBr_2 + 3\ MgCl_2$$

takes place in two stages which may be represented stoichiometrically as follows:

$$(1)\quad 2\ C_6H_5MgBr + 2\ FeCl_3 \longrightarrow C_6H_5C_6H_5 + 2\ FeCl_2 + MgBr_2 + MgCl_2$$

$$(2)\quad 2\ C_6H_5MgBr + FeCl_2 \longrightarrow C_6H_5C_6H_5 + Fe + MgBr_2 + MgCl_2$$

It is, of course, possible to postulate for the first stage of this oxidation-reduction a process analogous to that proposed for those involving silver and cuprous halides.

$$(1a)\quad C_6H_5MgBr + FeCl_3 \longrightarrow C_6H_5FeCl_2 + MgBrCl$$

$$(1b)\quad 2\ C_6H_5FeCl_2 \longrightarrow C_6H_5C_6H_5 + 2\ FeCl_2$$

---

[9]See, *e.g.*, Champetier, *Bull. soc. chim.*, [4], *47*, 1131–7 (1930); Krause and von Grosse, "Die Chemie der metal-organischen Verbindung," Berlin, *1937*, pp. 784–6.

[10]See, *e.g.*, Kealy and Pauson, *Nature*, *168*, 1039–40 (1951).

[11]Wilkinson, Rosenblum, Whiting, and Woodward, *J. Am. Chem. Soc.*, *74*, 2125–6 (1952); Woodward, Rosenblum, and Whiting, *ibid.*, *74*, 3458–9 (1952).

The second stage of the oxidation-reduction might be hypothetically represented in various ways, of which the following are illustrative.

(2a) $C_6H_5MgBr + FeCl_2 \rightarrow C_6H_5FeCl + MgClBr$

(2b) $2\ C_6H_5FeCl \rightarrow C_6H_5C_6H_5 + Fe + FeCl_2$

(2aa) $2\ C_6H_5MgBr + FeCl_2 \rightarrow (C_6H_5)_2Fe + MgBr_2 + MgCl_2$

(2bb) $(C_6H_5)_2Fe \rightarrow C_6H_5C_6H_5 + Fe$

The statement of Oddo,[12] unaccompanied by supporting detail, to the effect that alkylmagnesium halides differ from the corresponding aryl reagents in their behavior toward ferric chloride in that the principal organic product is an alkyl chloride rather than a bialkyl, invites further investigation. The reaction is formulated by Oddo as follows:

$$RMgBr + Fe_2Cl_6 \rightarrow RCl + 2\ FeCl_2 + MgBrCl$$

Confident interpretation of the reactions of any of the group VIII halides with Grignard reagents must await more intensive (and extensive) study with the aid of techniques more refined than those hitherto applied to investigations in this field.

The reactions of nickel chloride ($NiCl_2$) with Grignard reagents have received somewhat less attention than those of the iron chlorides. At present writing the gross picture for nickel chloride would appear to resemble that for cobaltous chloride more closely than that for ferrous chloride, although it is conceivable that all these reactions differ from one another in degree rather than in kind.

Under the circumstances it would be idle to speculate upon the courses of reactions in which it is reported that a system comprising ethereal phenylmagnesium bromide and nickel chloride absorbs ethylene,[13] or that a system comprising ethereal phenylmagnesium bromide and ferric chloride absorbs several molecular equivalents of acetylene.[14] As rather sketchily described, these reactions have the appearance of processes involving radical transfer, though not necessarily of processes involving *free* radicals.

Polya and Ingles[15] have added ethereal Grignard reagent solutions to ethereal solutions of cobaltous bromide and cobaltous iodide, obtaining dark-colored precipitates which were separated and then extracted with benzene. The benzene-extraction residues contained no metallic cobalt. Precipitates obtained by dilution of the benzene extracts with ligroïn

---

[12] Oddo, *Gazz. chim. ital.*, *44,II,* 268–78 (1914); *Chem. Abstr.*, *9,* 795 (1915); *Chem. Zentr.*, *1915,I,* 743.

[13] Job and Reich, *Compt. rend.*, *179,* 330–2 (1924); *Chem. Abstr.*, *19,* 236 (1925).

[14] Job and Champetier, *Compt. rend.*, *189,* 1089–91 (1929); *Chem. Abstr.*, *24,* 1616 (1930); *Bull. soc. chim.*, [4], *47,* 279–89 (1930).

[15] Polya and Ingles, *Nature*, *164,* 447 (1949); Ingles and Polya, *J. Chem. Soc.*, *1949,* 2280–2.

were analyzed. Polya and Ingles correlate their analytical data with such empirical formulations as $(1\text{-}C_{10}H_7)_3CoI$, $(1\text{-}C_{10}H_7)_2CoI_2$, $(2\text{-}C_{10}H_7)COBr_2$, $C_6H_5CoBr_3 \cdot C_6H_6$, $CH_3CoI_3 \cdot (C_6H_6)_2$, $C_3H_7CoI_3 \cdot C_6H_6$, etc., and interpret their findings as indicative of the existence of organocobalt compounds. It should be noted, however, that the ligroïn precipitates analyzed are not identical with those originally formed, for the analytical samples are virtually insoluble in benzene.

It may also be noted in passing that arguments for the existence of monovalent cobalt, based primarily on analytical data, have been advanced.[16]

At the present writing, however, it must be admitted that the principal argument in favor of the transitory existence of organocobalt compounds or cobaltous subhalides is the utility of the working hypothesis based thereupon. Because a considerable number of induced Grignard reactions effected with the aid of cobaltous halides may be rather plausibly interpreted in terms of that working hypothesis a separate section is devoted to the topic.

SOME REACTIONS INDUCED BY COBALTOUS HALIDES*

The overall "coupling" reactions described in the preceding sections, and documented in Table V-I, may be regarded as oxidation-reduction reactions in which the Grignard reagent (or, more specifically, the organic group of the Grignard reagent) plays the rôle of reductant. This generalization may be expressed in formal equations such as the following:

$$2\,R^{\delta-}MgX^{\delta+} + M^{\delta+}X'^{\delta-} \longrightarrow R^0R^0 + 2\,M^0 + 2\,X'^{\delta-}MgX^{\delta+}$$

$$2\,R^{\delta-}MgX^{\delta+} + 2\,M^{\delta3+}X_3'^{\delta-} \longrightarrow R^0R^0 + 2\,M^{\delta2+}X_2'^{\delta-} + 2\,X'^{\delta-}MgX^{\delta+}$$

Similarly, the oxidation-reduction aspect of the "normal" condensation of a Grignard reagent with an organic halide may be emphasized in the formal equation:

$$R^{\delta-}MgX^{\delta+} + R'^{\delta+}X'^{\delta-} \longrightarrow R^0R'^0 + X'^{\delta-}MgX^{\delta+}$$

It is interesting that various metallic halides (notably cobaltous halides) may be impressed into service as go-betweens in effecting fundamentally analogous Grignard oxidation-reduction processes which proceed extremely slowly, if at all, under ordinary reaction conditions. The working hypothesis adopted by the present authors to elucidate such relayed, or induced, oxidation-reduction processes may be illustrated for one type of example by the following formal equations:

---

[16] For references see: Mellor, "A Comprehensive Treatise on Inorganic and Theoretical Chemistry," Longmans, Green and Co., New York, Vol. XIV, *1935*, p. 525.

*See also: Chapter XVI, Induced "Coupling" Reactions.

(1) $R^{\delta -}MgX^{\delta +} + Co^{\delta 2+}X_2'^{\delta -} \rightarrow R^0CoX'^0 + X'^{\delta -}MgX^{\delta +}$

(2a) $2\ R^0CoX'^0 \rightarrow R^0R^0 + 2\ \cdot CoX'^0$

(2b) $2\ R^0CoX'^0 \rightarrow R_{(+H)} + R_{(-H)} + 2\ \cdot CoX'^0$

(2c) $R^0CoX'^0 \rightarrow \cdot R + \cdot CoX'$

(3) $R'^{\delta +}X''^{\delta -} + \cdot CoX'^0 \rightarrow \cdot R'^0 + X''^{\delta -}CoX'^{\delta +}$

Whereas these equations admittedly depict a mental construct justified primarily by its utility, it is of minor importance whether the expression $2\ \cdot CoX'^0$ be accepted literally, whether it be interpreted as indicative of a potential equilibrium,

$$2\ \cdot CoX'^0 \rightleftharpoons X'CoCoX'$$

or whether it be regarded as equivalent to a relatively unstable dimer highly susceptible to induced homolytic dissociation.

In fairness to the reader, and in justice to Wilds and McCormack[17] it should be noted that these investigators have proposed an alternative reaction scheme, postulating an unstable diorganocobalt compound as an ephemeral intermediate, and a highly reactive (colloidal) form of metallic cobalt as the active reducing agent. As applied to reactions involving ethylmagnesium bromide and cobaltous chloride, the proposal of Wilds and McCormack may be expressed as follows:

$$2\ C_2H_5MgBr + CoCl_2 \rightarrow MgBr_2 + MgCl_2 + [(C_2H_5)_2Co]$$
$$[(C_2H_5)_2Co] \rightarrow C_2H_4 + C_2H_6 + Co$$

Aside from pride of parenthood (by no means a negligible consideration), the present authors prefer the scheme originally proposed, chiefly on the ground that the position of cobalt in the periodic system and in the electromotive series raises grave *a priori* doubt that it is (in whatever physical state) a sufficiently active metal to participate in some of the Wurtz-type and ketyl-formation reactions that must be attributed to it. In this connection it may be noted that in a reaction involving phenylmagnesium bromide and bromobenzene, in which cobaltous chloride to the amount of a few mole percent was highly effective, pyrophoric metallic cobalt, even in equivalent quantities, was found to have no effect whatever.[18] This observation is, of course, irrelevant if the colloidal metallic cobalt of Wilds and McCormack is, in fact, significantly more active than pyrophoric cobalt.

Other reactions in which the present authors doubt that cobalt is a sufficiently active metal to serve as the effective reducing agent are the reductions of azobenzene and hydrazobenzene to aniline by a Grignard reagent in the presence of cobaltous chloride (unpublished work, University of Chicago). It seems more probable that reductive cleavage of the

[17] Wilds and McCormack, *J. Org. Chem.*, *14*, 45–55 (1949).
[18] Kharasch and Fields, *J. Am. Chem. Soc.*, *63*, 2316–20 (1941).

nitrogen-to-nitrogen bond takes place as follows:

$$[C_6H_5(XMg)N—]_2 + \cdot CoCl \rightarrow C_6H_5(XMg)N\cdot + C_6H_5(XMg)NCoCl$$

So far as existing *direct* evidence is concerned, the reader need feel no compulsion to reject one proposed scheme in favor of the other. In the ensuing discussion, however, the present authors will continue to use the scheme preferred by them.

Behavior of Free Radicals in Solution. The ultimate fate of the free radical $\cdot R'^{0}$ (of Equation 3) is determined primarily by the nature of the free radical itself, and secondarily by the nature of the reaction medium. In general, the more reactive (*i.e.*, the more "electronegative"[19]) free radicals may be expected to react with some component of the reaction system. In the simplest cases for Grignard systems such reactions are usually abstractive (of labile hydrogen atoms, or of radicals).

(4) $\cdot R' + H_2C(OC_2H_5)CH_3 \rightarrow R'H + \cdot HC(OC_2H_5)CH_3$

(5) $\cdot R' + RMgX \rightarrow R'H + R_{(-H)} + \cdot MgX$

(6) $\cdot R' + RMgX \rightarrow R'R + \cdot MgX$

If to the reaction system there is added (either by concurrent reaction processes, or by intention) a more complaisant hydrogen donor than ethyl ether, or if the ethereal solvent is replaced in whole or in large part, by another hydrogen donor, labile hydrogen atom abstraction in the sense of equation 4a may take place.

(4a) $\cdot R' + RH \rightarrow R'H + \cdot R$

Examples of the latter type of reaction are to be found in the formation of bi-α-cumyl (α,α′-dimethylbibenzyl, 2,3-dimethyl-2,3-diphenylbutane) when an alkylmagnesium bromide, an alkyl bromide, and cobaltous chloride interact in the presence of cumene (isopropylbenzene.)[20]

Free radicals less reactive (*i.e.*, less "electronegative") than the methyl do not appear to react extensively with ethyl ether or with most Grignard reagents at the boiling point of an ethereal Grignard reaction system. In the absence of a more liberal hydrogen donor (than ethyl ether), such radicals, if structurally incapable of disproportionation, usually dimerize.

(7) $2 \cdot R' \rightarrow R_2'$

Of the free radicals structurally capable of disproportionation, the lower primary aliphatic radicals disproportionate predominantly,[21] al-

[19] Concerning relative "electronegativities" of organic radicals, see: Kharasch and Reinmuth, *J. Chem. Education*, *5*, 404–18 (1928); *8*, 1703–48 (1931); Kharasch, Reinmuth, and Mayo, *ibid.*, *11*, 82–96 (1934); *13*, 7–19 (1936).

[20] Kharasch and Urry, *J. Org. Chem.*, *13*, 101–9 (1948).

[21] See, *e.g.*, Kharasch, Lewis, and Reynolds, *J. Am. Chem. Soc.*, *65*, 493–5 (1943).

though this would not appear at first glance to be the thermodynamically favored course of reaction.* Some, at least, of the secondary radicals (*e.g.*, *s*-butyl, cyclohexyl)[22] disproportionate in part and dimerize in part. By extension from the results of peroxide-induced free-radical reactions, and from unpublished results of Grignard free-radical studies in the laboratories of the University of Chicago, it may be expected that the higher aliphatic radicals (say, above hexyl) will also disproportionate in part and dimerize in part. Relatively unreactive resonance-stabilized free radicals (such as the benzyl) may, in general, be expected to dimerize completely. Examples are to be found in the α-cumyl (α,α-dimethylbenzyl) radical (see Kharasch and Urry, *loc. cit.*[20]) and the α-ethyl-*p*-methoxybenzyl radical.[23]

It should be noted, however, that although resonance-stabilization may be a sufficient, it is by no means a necessary condition for radical dimerization, as witness the dimerizations of cyclohexyl and bornyl free radicals (Kharasch, Engelmann, and Urry, *loc. cit.*[22]).

Although the phenomenon, presumably, is relatively rare, account must also be taken of the possibility of free-radical rearrangement. It has been shown in studies of peroxide-induced free-radical reactions that the simpler alkyl radicals (specifically, propyl and isopropyl[24]) do not rearrange. However, there is also evidence strongly suggestive that more complicated heteroëlementary radicals may undergo rearrangement.[25]

$$RCH{=}CH_2 + \cdot SO_2Cl \longrightarrow R(ClO_2SCH_2)CH\cdot \longrightarrow RCHClCH_2SO_2\cdot$$

The first example, so far as the present authors are aware, of the rearrangement of a hydrocarbon radical in a Grignard free-radical reaction was observed when phenylmagnesium bromide was treated with a catalytic quantity of cobaltous chloride and *ca.* one equivalent of neophyl chloride (1-chloro-2,2-dimethyl-3-phenylpropane).[26] The products of the reaction (in addition to biphenyl) are cumene (isopropylbenzene), β-methallylbenzene, 2-methylpropenylbenzene, and a mixture of isomeric neophyl dimers [$(C_{10}H_{13}—)_2$]. It appears, therefore, that, either prior to or simultaneously with disproportionation (and dimerization) some rearrangement of the neophyl radical must occur.

---

*For example, it may be calculated, without resort to assumptions concerning the heat of vaporization of carbon, that ΔH_0° for the reaction $2\ C_2H_5\cdot \longrightarrow C_2H_6 + C_2H_4$ is of the order of −62 kcal./mole, whereas ΔH_0° for the reaction $2\ C_2H_5\cdot \longrightarrow n\text{-}C_4H_{10}$ is of the order of −83 kcal./mole.

[22]See, *e.g.*, Kharasch, Engelmann, and Urry, *J. Am. Chem. Soc.*, *66*, 365–7 (1944).

[23]Kharasch and Kleiman, *J. Am. Chem. Soc.*, *65*, 491–3 (1943).

[24]Kharasch, Kane, and Brown, *J. Am. Chem. Soc.*, *63*, 526–8 (1941).

[25]Kharasch and Zavist, *J. Am. Chem. Soc.*, *73*, 964–7 (1951).

[26]Urry and Kharasch, *J. Am. Chem. Soc.*, *66*, 1438–40 (1944).

$$C_6H_5CH_2(CH_3)_2C\cdot \rightarrow C_6H_5CH_2CH(CH_3)_2 + C_6H_5CH_2C(CH_3){=}CH_2 + C_6H_5CH{=}C(CH_3)_2$$

Examples of rearrangements involving hydrogen migrations are to be found in the disproportionations of the γ-phenylpropyl and *n*-butyl radicals. The principal unsaturated products of these reactions are, respectively, *trans*-β-methylstyrene (rather than allylbenzene) and *trans*-2-butene (rather than 1-butene).[27]

Although it does not involve a true radical rearrangement, an example of the so-called allylic rearrangement (see Chapter XVII) is to be found in the cobaltous chloride-induced coupling of the free radical derived from cinnamyl chloride. When cinnamyl chloride is treated with methylmagnesium bromide the "normal" condensation product, 1-butenylbenzene, is obtained in *ca.* 89 percent yield. When, however, *ca.* 5 mole percent of cobaltous chloride is added to the reaction system, the yield of "normal" product is reduced to *ca.* 12 percent, and the "coupling" products, 1,6-diphenyl-1,5-hexadiene (*ca.* 30 percent) and 1,4-diphenyl-1,5-hexadiene (*ca.* 40 percent), are obtained in yields aggregating approximately 70 percent (Kharasch *et. al, loc. cit.*[27]).

$$2\,[C_6H_5CH{=}CHCH_2\cdot \leftrightarrow H_2C{=}CH(C_6H_5)CH\cdot] \rightarrow (C_6H_5CH{=}CHCH_2{-})_2 + C_6H_5CH{=}CHCH_2CH(C_6H_5)CH{=}CH_2$$

Incidentally, nickel chloride ($NiCl_2$) and chromic chloride ($CrCl_3$) appear to be about as effective as cobaltous chloride in the induction of this reaction; manganous chloride ($MnCl_2$) and ferric chloride ($FeCl_3$) are similarly, but much less, effective.

From the results of numerous studies of photochemical and peroxide-induced free-radical reactions it may be further deduced that when suitable radical acceptors are present in Grignard reaction systems there is the possibility that any free radicals generated may react, at least in part, additively, *e.g.:*

$$RCH{=}CH_2 + \cdot R' \rightarrow R(R'CH_2)CH\cdot$$

Coupling of Acyl Radicals. It is, perhaps, worthy of explicit mention that, whereas coupling (or disproportionation) of the organic group of a Grignard reagent through the agency of a cobaltous halide requires a stoichiometrically equivalent quantity of the halide, addition to the reaction system of an organic halide converts the process to a chain reaction in which the original cobaltous halide or its equivalent is continually regenerated, and thus functions as a true catalyst. That the catalyst is gradually consumed by side reactions (probably chiefly through reduction to metallic cobalt) is beside the point.

Acyl, as well as alkyl, cycloalkyl, aralkyl, and aryl halides, are susceptible to halogen abstraction by cobaltous subhalides. For example,

---

[27] Kharasch, Lambert, and Urry, *J. Org. Chem.*, *10*, 298–306 (1945).

when 0.31 mole of benzoyl chloride was treated with an ethereal solution of 0.35 mole of phenylmagnesium bromide containing 2 mole percent of cobaltous chloride, the products (in addition to biphenyl, benzoic acid, ethyl benzoate, and benzophenone) were α-benzoylbenzhydrol, tetraphenylethylene oxide, and α-β-dibenzoxystilbene.[28] For the latter three products benzil, formed by the dimerization of benzoyl radicals, is obviously the substrate.

$$C_6H_5COCOC_6H_5 \xrightarrow{C_6H_5MgBr} \xrightarrow{H_3O^+} HO(C_6H_5)_2CCOC_6H_5$$

$$C_6H_5COCOC_6H_5 \xrightarrow{2\ C_6H_5MgBr} \xrightarrow{H_3O^+} (C_6H_5)_2C\underset{O}{\diagdown\!\diagup}C(C_6H_5)_2$$

$$C_6H_5COCOC_6H_5 \xrightarrow{2\ \cdot MX} \xrightarrow{C_6H_5COCl} [C_6H_5(C_6H_5CO_2)C{=}]_2$$

Similar coupling of the mesitoyl radical when mesitoyl chloride is treated with methyl- or phenylmagnesium bromide in the presence of catalytic quantities of cobaltous chloride has been reported[29] (see Chapter IX, Coupling).

Metallic Subhalide Reduction of Ketones. The one-electron reduction of a ketone to the corresponding pinacol by a metallic subhalide (see Chapter VI, Magnesious Halide Reduction) may also be effected by means of a chain reaction through the agency of a cobaltous halide.* For example, methylmagnesium bromide reacts "normally" with benzophenone to give a nearly quantitative (*ca.* 95 percent) yield of 1,1-diphenylethanol (α-methylbenzhydrol). When, however, about 2 mole percent of cobaltous chloride is present in the reaction system the yield of "normal" addition product drops to about 2 percent, and benzopinacol is obtained in *ca.* 93 percent yield.[30]

In such reactions the regeneration of cobaltous halide might conceivably take place in either of two ways:

(1) $MgX_2 + \cdot CoCl \longrightarrow \cdot MgX + CoClX$

or

(2a) $[R'_2(ClCoO)C{-}] + 2\ RMgX \longrightarrow [R'_2(XMgO)C{-}]_2 + 2\ RCoCl$

or

(2b) $2\ RCoCl \longrightarrow R_2 + 2\ \cdot CoCl$

(2c) $2\ RCoCl \longrightarrow 2\ R\cdot + 2\ \cdot CoCl$

The ketyl radical dimerization, therefore, is best described by the generalized equation:

$$2\ R'_2CO + 2\ \cdot MX \longrightarrow 2\ R'_2(XMO)C\cdot \longrightarrow [R'_2(XMO)C{-}]_2$$

---

[28] Kharasch, Nudenberg, and Archer, *J. Am. Chem. Soc.*, 65, 495-8 (1943).

[29] Kharasch, Morrison, and Urry, *J. Am. Chem. Soc.*, 66, 368-71 (1944).

*Incidentally, ferric chloride is similarly, though less, effective in such reactions.

[30] Kharasch and Lambert, *J. Am. Chem. Soc.*, 63, 2315-6 (1941).

It has been shown by Fuson and Hornberger[31] that the dimerization of the ketyl radical derived from a "highly hindered" ketone (specifically, benzoylmesitylene) takes an unusual course, yielding, in this instance, mesityl 2′-(mesitylhydroxymethyl)-2-biphenylyl ketone,

$$2,4,6\text{-}(CH_3)C_6H_2COC_6H_4\text{-}2\text{-}[C_6H_4\text{-}2\text{-}CH(OH)C_6H_2\text{-}2,4,6\text{-}(CH_3)_3],$$

rather than the expected pinacol (see Chapter VI, Magnesious Halide Reduction, and Chapter IX, "Coupling").

Hydrogen Cleavage of Ethers. Whereas the ordinary Grignard reagent cleavage of an ether in the absence of metallic (other than magnesium) halides appears to be an essentially ionic solvolytic reaction (see Chapter XV, Cleavages of Acyclic Ethers), the cleavage of an ether by a potentially reducing Grignard reagent (*i.e.*, one having a labile *beta* hydrogen atom) in the presence of a stoichiometrically equivalent quantity of a suitable metallic halide has rather the appearance of a hydrogenolysis. The two types of reactions may be described, respectively, by the equations:

$$ROR' \xrightarrow{R''MgX} ROMgX + R'R''$$

$$ROR' \xrightarrow[+\ MX_2']{R''MgX} ROMgX + R'H + R''_{(-H)}$$

For example, when phenyl benzyl ether is treated at room temperature with four molecular equivalents of *n*-butylmagnesium bromide in the presence of two molecular equivalents of cobaltous chloride, phenol is obtained in 86 percent yield; the other products are toluene and butene.[32] In such reactions nickel chloride and ferric chloride are similarly, though somewhat less, effective.

Reactions of ω-Haloalkyl Phenyl Ethers. Available data on the cobaltous bromide-induced reactions of ω-haloalkyl phenyl ethers with Grignard reagents[33] are not strictly comparable with those of the study just cited,[32] for they involve for the most part phenylmagnesium bromide (a non-reducing Grignard reagent) and isopropylmagnesium bromide (a fair reducing agent) rather than *n*-butylmagnesium bromide (a moderately good reducing agent). In any case, however, it would appear that these reactions should be regarded as special cases of the alkyl halide type of reaction rather than typical ether cleavages. Although details of reaction mechanism are still obscure, the primary point of attack would seem to be the *omega* halogen atom.

$$C_6H_5O(CH_2)_nX + \cdot CoBr \rightarrow C_6H_5O(CH_2)_n\cdot + CoBrX$$

Without any further implications as to reaction mechanisms, the products isolated in a series of such reactions may be indicated as follows:

---

[31] Fuson and Hornberger, *J. Org. Chem.*, *16*, 631–6 (1951).
[32] Kharasch and Huang, *J. Org. Chem.*, *17*, 669–77 (1952).
[33] Kharasch, Stampa, and Nudenberg, unpublished work.

$$C_6H_5O(CH_2)_2\cdot \longrightarrow C_6H_5OH\ (58\text{–}90\%) + C_2H_4\ (65\text{–}81\%) + C_6H_5O(CH_2)_2H\ (0\text{–}4\%)$$

$$C_6H_5O(CH_2)_3\cdot \longrightarrow C_6H_5OH\ (59\text{–}70\%) + (CH_2)_3\ (70\text{–}71\%) + C_6H_5O(CH_2)_3H\ (18\text{–}27\%) + [C_6H_5O(CH_2)_3\text{—}]_2\ (\text{trace})$$

$$C_6H_5O(CH_2)_4\cdot \longrightarrow C_6H_5OH\ (0\text{–}8\%) + C_6H_5O(CH_2)_4H\ (66\text{–}76\%) + C_6H_5O(CH_2)_2CH{=}CH_2\ (8\text{–}9\%) + [C_6H_5O(CH_2)_4\text{—}]_2\ (\text{trace})$$

$$C_6H_5O(CH_2)_5\cdot \longrightarrow C_6H_5O(CH_2)_5H\ (61\%) + C_6H_5O(CH_2)_3CH{=}CH_2\ (26\%) + [C_6H_5O(CH_2)_5\text{—}]_2\ (\text{trace})$$

$$C_6H_5O(CH_2)_6\cdot \longrightarrow C_6H_5OH\ (0\text{–}7\%) + C_6H_5O(CH_2)_6H\ (40\text{–}60\%) + C_6H_5O(CH_2)_4CH{=}CH_2\ (4\text{–}7\%) + [C_6H_5O(CH_2)_6\text{—}]_2\ (18\text{–}25\%)$$

The variation in fate of $C_6H_5O(CH_2)_n\cdot$ radicals with variation in n is noteworthy. When n is two or three the principal course of reaction involves dissociation (either induced or spontaneous).

When n is four or five there appears to be some disproportionation, but the marked excess of saturated ether over unsaturated ether suggests either attack upon some relatively liberal hydrogen donor in the reaction system or a considerable amount of induced functional exchange in the sense,

$$C_6H_5O(CH_2)_nX + RMgX' \longrightarrow C_6H_5O(CH_2)_nMgX' + RX$$

or both. Whereas it appears highly improbable (in view of the behavior of alkyl radicals other than methyl) that such radicals are sufficiently reactive to attack ethyl ether, the most probable candidate for hydrogen donor, other than the $C_6H_5O(CH_2)_n\cdot$ radical itself, would appear to be the original haloalkyl phenyl ether.

$$C_6H_5O(CH_2)_n\cdot + C_6H_5O(CH_2)_nX \longrightarrow C_6H_5O(CH_2)_nH + C_6H_5O[X(CH_2)_{n-1}]CH\cdot$$

Moreover, it cannot be taken for granted that all the unsaturated ether formed is the product of simple radical disproportionation.

$$2\ C_6H_5O(CH_2)_n\cdot \longrightarrow C_6H_5O(CH_2)_nH + C_6H_5O(CH_2)_{n-2}CH{=}CH_2$$

When n is six there is still predominant formation of saturated and unsaturated ethers (with saturated ether in excess) together with considerable apparent dimerization. It seems probable that the coupling product is attributable principally to simple radical combination.

$$2\ C_6H_5O(CH_2)_6\cdot \longrightarrow [C_6H_5O(CH_2)_6\text{—}]_2$$

In this connection it may be noted, for what the observation is worth, that when 1-bromohexane was treated with methylmagnesium bromide and cobaltous bromide, (save for traces of nonane) only hexane and hexene were formed; no dodecane could be detected (Kharasch, Stampa, and Nudenberg, *loc. cit.*[33]). So far as the present authors are aware, the reaction of *n*-hexylmagnesium bromide with 1-bromohexane has not been carefully studied.

Similar results have been obtained with 1-bromoöctane. The more stable secondary radical derived from 2-bromoöctane, however, does undergo appreciable dimerization. Possibly the phenoxy group in $C_6H_5O(CH_2)_6\cdot$ has a stabilizing effect.

Functional Exchange.* Aside from reductive enolizations of α-halo ketones *(q.v.)*, giving rise to enolates that behave like Grignard reagents, and halogen displacements of 1-bromoethynes and some heterocyclic halides (analogous to hydrogen displacements), evidence of uncatalyzed functional exchange in the sense

$$RMgX + R'X' \rightarrow RX' + R'MgX$$

is dubious, to say the least.

It is possible, however, by operating at low temperature (–5 to 0°), and by carbonating the resultant reaction mixture, to demonstrate for some RMgX-R′X′ pairs an appreciable degree of exchange (as evidenced by $R'CO_2H$ isolation) when a small amount (*ca.* 1 mole percent) of cobaltous chloride is present in the reaction system.[34] Ferric chloride appears to be similarly, though perhaps somewhat less, effective. For example:

$$n\text{-}C_4H_9MgBr + C_6H_5Br + CoCl_2\ (1\%) \xrightarrow{CO_2} C_6H_5CO_2H\ (7\%)$$

$$CH_3MgBr + \text{9-Chlorofluorene} + CoCl_2\ (1\%) \xrightarrow{CO_2} \text{9-Fluorenecarboxylic acid (10\%)}$$

$$CH_3MgBr + \text{9-Bromophenanthrene} + CoCl_2\ (1\%) \xrightarrow{CO_2} \text{9-Phenanthrenecarboxylic acid (3\%)}$$

$$C_6H_5MgBr + n\text{-}C_4H_9Br + CoCl_2\ (1\%) \xrightarrow{CO_2} n\text{-}C_4H_9CO_2H\ (3\%)$$

$$CH_3MgBr + (C_6H_5)_2C{=}CBrC_6H_5 + CoCl_2\ (3\%) \xrightarrow{CO_2} (C_6H_5)_2C{=}C(CO_2H)C_6H_5\ (32\%)$$

$$CH_3MgBr + (C_6H_5)_2C{=}CBrC_6H_5 + FeCl_3\ (3\%) \xrightarrow{CO_2} (C_6H_5)_2C{=}C(CO_2H)C_6H_5\ (13\%)$$

Save that such exchanges are not the simple metathetical processes that the definitive equations heretofore employed might seem to imply, little can be said with certainty about the reaction mechanisms involved. Conceivably a free-radical attack on the Grignard reagent in the sense

$$R'\cdot + RMgX \rightarrow R'MgX + R\cdot$$

takes place.

Supplementary Bibliography. Some studies of the effects of cobaltous and other metallic halides on the courses of Grignard reactions not specifically cited in the foregoing discussion are as follows:

*See also Chapter XVI, Functional Exchange.

[34] Kharasch and Fuchs, *J. Org. Chem.*, *10*, 292–7 (1945).

Kharasch, Kleiger, Martin, and Mayo, *J. Am. Chem. Soc.*, *63*, 2305–7 (1941);
Kharasch and Tawney, *J. Am. Chem. Soc.*, *63*, 2308–15 (1941);
Kharasch and Sayles, *J. Am. Chem. Soc.*, *64*, 2972–5 (1942);
Kharasch and Reynolds, *J. Am. Chem. Soc.*, *65*, 501–4 (1943);
Kharasch and Fuchs, *J. Am. Chem. Soc.*, *65*, 504–7 (1943);
Kharasch, Sayles, and Fields, *J. Am. Chem. Soc.*, *66*, 481–2 (1944);
Kharasch and Tawney, *J. Am. Chem. Soc.*, *67*, 128–30 (1945).

UNCATALYZED "COUPLING" REACTIONS*

Numerous reactions in which a susceptible organic halide (suitably an arylated methyl halide), treated with a homolytically dissociable Grignard reagent (suitably methylmagnesium iodide), yields a product attributable to dimerization of the free radical derived from the organic halide have been reported (see Tables XVI-I and IX-II), notably by Fuson *et al.*[35] That homolytic dissociation of the Grignard reagent in such reactions is not a unimolecular thermal process of the type $RMgX \longrightarrow R\cdot + \cdot MgX$ is strongly suggested by at least two considerations. (1) Analytical studies by Grignard[36] and by Blaise[37] indicate that ethereal Grignard reagents such as methyl- or ethylmagnesium iodide may be heated (for purposes of desolvation) for considerable periods of time to temperatures as high as 150° without significant decomposition, whereas many "coupling" reactions take place at the boiling point of an ethyl ethereal solution (*ca.* 40°). (2) The occurrence of "coupling" depends, not upon the nature of the Grignard reagent alone, but to a great extent upon the nature of the organic halide also, being especially favored in the cases of halides capable of yielding resonance-stabilized free radicals. The present authors conclude, therefore, that in such reactions free radicals are generated by the mutually induced homolytic dissociations of the Grignard reagent *and* the organic halide.

$$RX + R'MgX' \longrightarrow R\cdot + MgXX' + R'\cdot$$

It is of incidental interest in this connection that relayed or indirect coupling may be effected without the intervention of a metallic halide when ethyl-, *n*-propyl-, or isopropylmagnesium bromide is heated, together with the corresponding alkyl bromide, in cumene to about 100° (the "coupling" product being bi-α-cumyl). Methylmagnesium bromide is too

---

*See also: Chapter XVI, "Coupling" Reactions; Chapter IX, Other "Abnormal" Reactions.

[35] (*a*) Fuson, *J. Am. Chem. Soc.*, *48*, 830–6 (1926); Fuson and Ross, *ibid.*, *55*, 720–3 (1933); Ellingboe and Fuson, *ibid.*, *55*, 2960–6 (1933); Fuson, Denton, and Kneisley, *ibid.*, *63*, 2652–3 (1941); Fuson, Chadwick, and Ward, *ibid.*, *68*, 389–93 (1946); Fuson, Kneisley, Rabjohn, and Ward, *ibid.*, *68*, 533 (1946), Fuson, Denton, and Best, *J. Org. Chem.*, *8*, 64–72 (1943); (*b*) Fuson and Corse, *J. Am. Chem. Soc.*, *60*, 2063–6 (1938).

[36] Grignard, *Ann. chim.*, [7], *24*, 433–90 (1901).

[37] Blaise, *Compt. rend.*, *132*, 839–41 (1901); *Chem. Zentr.*, *1901*, *I*, 1000.

stable to effect "coupling" under such conditions (Kharasch and Urry, *loc. cit.*[20]).

In general it may be expected that the order of susceptibility to homolytic scission among organomagnesium halides will be: iodides > bromides > chlorides. As regards the organic group of the Grignard reagent, low "electronegativity" is more conducive to homolytic dissociation than high "electronegativity," with resonance stabilization of the radical being an especially predisposing factor.

TABLE V-I

SOME REACTIONS OF GROUP IB AND GROUP VIII HALIDES WITH GRIGNARD REAGENTS

Metallic Halide	Grignard Reagent(s)	Product(s)	Ref.
AgCl	C_6H_5MgBr	$C_6H_5Ag \xrightarrow{\Delta} C_6H_5C_6H_5$ (27.5%) + Ag	1
AgCl	$ArMgBr$*	$ArAg \xrightarrow{\Delta} Ar_2$ + Ag	1
AgBr (1.0 mole)	CH_3MgBr (0.5 mole) + C_6H_5MgBr (0.5 mole)	$CH_3C_6H_5$ (4.0 g., 0.044 mole) + $C_6H_5C_6H_5$ (17.0 g., 0.110 mole)	2
AgBr (1.0 mole)	CH_3MgBr (0.5 mole) + $C_6H_5CH_2MgCl$ (0.5 mole)	$C_2H_5C_6H_5$ (1.0 g., 0.010 mole) + $C_6H_5CH_2CH_2C_6H_5$ (29.0 g., 0.160 mole)	2
AgBr (1.0 mole)	C_2H_5MgBr (0.5 mole) + C_6H_5MgBr (0.5 mole)	$C_2H_5C_6H_5$ (10.0 g., 0.095 mole) + $C_6H_5C_6H_5$ (13.0 g., 0.085 mole)	2
AgBr (1.0 mole)	C_2H_5MgBr (0.5 mole) + $C_6H_5CH_2MgCl$ (0.5 mole)	n-$C_3H_7C_6H_5$ (3.0 g., 0.060 mole) + $C_6H_5CH_2CH_2C_6H_5$ (29.0 g., 0.160 mole)	2
AgBr (2.0 moles)	n-C_3H_7MgBr (1.0 mole) + C_6H_5MgBr (1.0 mole)	n-$C_3H_7C_6H_5$ (46.0 g., 0.384 mole) + $C_6H_5C_6H_5$ (27.0 g., 0.180 mole) + C_6H_{14} (1.0 g., 0.012 mole)	2
AgBr (1.0 mole)	n-C_3H_7MgBr (0.5 mole) + $C_6H_5CH_2MgCl$ (0.5 mole)	n-$C_4H_9C_6H_5$ (1.3 g., 0.020 mole) + $C_6H_5CH_2CH_2C_6H_5$ (28.0 g., 0.155 mole)	2
AgBr (2.0 moles)	i-C_3H_7MgBr (1.0 mole) + C_6H_5MgBr (1.0 mole)	i-$C_3H_7C_6H_5$ (13.5 g., 0.110 mole) + $C_6H_5C_6H_5$ (42.0 g., 0.270 mole) + C_6H_{14} (1.0 g., 0.010 mole)	2
AgBr (1.0 mole)	i-C_3H_7MgBr (0.5 mole) + $C_6H_5CH_2MgCl$ (0.5 mole)	i-$C_4H_9C_6H_5$ (28.0 g., 0.210 mole) + $C_6H_5CH_2CH_2C_6H_5$ (10.0 g., 0.055 mole)	2
AgBr (0.5 mole)	n-C_4H_9MgCl (0.5 mole C_4H_9Cl)	C_8H_{18} (10.8 g., 37.8%)	3
AgBr (1.0 mole)	n-C_4H_9MgBr (1.0 mole C_4H_9Br)	C_8H_{18} (24 g., 42%)	4
AgBr (0.5 mole)	n-C_4H_9MgBr (0.5 mole C_4H_9Br)	C_8H_{18} (18.4 g., 64.4%)	3
AgBr (2.0 moles)	n-C_4H_9MgBr (1.0 mole) + C_6H_5MgBr (1.0 mole)	n-$C_4H_9C_6H_5$ (51.0 g., 0.381 mole) + $C_6H_5C_6H_5$ (31.0 g., 0.200 mole) + C_8H_{18} (7.0 g., 0.062 mole)	2,3

*Ar = 2,5-$(CH_3)_2C_6H_3$, 1-$C_{10}H_7$, 4-$C_6H_5OC_6H_4$. Although no details are given, the reactions are said to be similar to that of C_6H_5MgBr.

TABLE V-I (Continued)

Metallic Halide	Grignard Reagent(s)	Product(s)	Ref.
AgBr (0.5 mole)	n-C_4H_9MgI (0.5 mole C_4H_9I)	C_8H_{18} (10.4 g., 36.4%)	3
AgBr (1.0 mole)	i-C_4H_9MgBr (1.0 mole)	C_8H_{18} (20.0 g., 37.5%) + gas	5
AgBr (1.0 mole)	i-C_4H_9MgBr (0.5 mole) + C_6H_5MgBr (0.5 mole)	i-$C_4H_9C_6H_5$ (23.0 g., 0.170 mole) + $C_6H_5C_6H_5$ (16.5 g., 0.107 mole) + C_8H_{18} (0.7 g., 0.006 mole)	2
AgBr (1.0 mole)	s-C_4H_9MgBr (1.0 mole)	C_8H_{18} (7.5 g., 13.0%) + gas	5
AgBr (2.0 moles)	s-C_4H_9MgBr (1.0 mole) + C_6H_5MgBr (1.0 mole)	s-$C_4H_9C_6H_5$ (9.5 g., 0.070 mole) + $C_6H_5C_6H_5$ (58.5 g., 0.370 mole) + C_8H_{18} (6.0 g., 0.050 mole)	2
AgBr (0.5 mole)	t-C_4H_9MgCl (0.5 mole)	C_8H_{18} (5.5 g., 19.4%)	6
AgBr (0.5 mole)	t-C_4H_9MgBr (0.25 mole) + C_6H_5MgBr (0.25 mole)	$C_6H_5C_6H_5$ (13.0 g., 0.085 mole) + C_8H_{18} (2.0 g., 0.018 mole)	2
AgBr	C_6H_5MgBr	C_6H_5Ag (60%) $\xrightarrow{-18^\circ}$ $C_6H_5C_6H_5$ + Ag	7
AgBr (1.0 mole)	C_6H_5MgBr (1.0 mole C_6H_5Br)	$C_6H_5C_6H_5$ (51 g., 66%)	4
AgBr (0.5 mole)	C_6H_5MgBr (0.5 mole C_6H_5Br)	$C_6H_5C_6H_5$ (25.0 g., 64.8%)	3
AgBr	C_6H_5MgBr + 4-$CH_3OC_6H_4MgBr$	$C_6H_5C_6H_5$ (22.0–48.0%) + 4-$CH_3OC_6H_4C_6H_5$ (4.7–8.2%) + 4-$CH_3OC_6H_4C_6H_4$-4-OCH_3 (3.8–19.4%)	8
AgBr (0.4 mole)	n-$C_4H_9C{\equiv}CMgBr$ (0.4 mole C_6H_{10})	n-$C_4H_9C{\equiv}CAg$ (46 g., 62%)	*10*
AgBr (1.0 mole)	$(CH_2)_5CHMgBr$ (1.0 mole $C_6H_{11}Br$)	$(CH_2)_5CHCH(CH_2)_5$ (25 g., 40%)	4
AgBr (0.25 mole)	n-$C_6H_{13}MgBr$ (0.25 mole $C_6H_{13}Br$)	$C_{12}H_{26}$ (15.3 g., 82.9%) + C_6H_{14} and C_6H_{12} (aggr. 1.2 g., *ca.* 6.7%)	9
AgBr (1.0 mole)	$C_6H_5CH_2MgCl$ (1.0 mole C_7H_7Cl)	$C_6H_5CH_2CH_2C_6H_5$ (65 g., 71%)	4
AgBr (0.05 mole)	4-$CH_3C_6H_4MgBr$ (0.05 mole C_7H_7Br)	4-$CH_3C_6H_4C_6H_4$-4-CH_3 (3.3 g., 72%)	4
AgBr (0.35 mole)	4-$CH_3OC_6H_4MgBr$ (0.35 mole C_7H_7BrO)	4-$CH_3OC_6H_4C_6H_4$-4-OCH_3 (17.5 g., 48%)	4
CuI	C_2H_5MgI	C_2H_4 + C_2H_6 + Cu	7,*11*

TABLE V-I (Continued)

Metallic Halide	Grignard Reagent(s)	Product(s)	Ref.
CuI	n-C_3H_7MgX	$C_3H_6 + C_3H_8$	*11*
CuI	C_6H_5MgI	C_6H_5Cu (60%)	*7*
CuX*	C_2H_5MgX'	$C_2H_4 + C_2H_6$	*11*
CuX*	n-C_3H_7MgX'	$C_3H_6 + C_3H_8$	*11*
$CuCl_2$ (20.3 g.)	i-$C_5H_{11}MgBr$ (22.7 g. $C_5H_{11}Br$)	$C_{10}H_{22}$ (4–5 g., *ca.* 60%)	*12*
$CuCl_2$	t-C_4H_9MgCl	*No* C_8H_{18}	*6*
$CuCl_2$ (27.0 g.)	C_6H_5MgBr (31.4 g. C_6H_5)	$C_6H_5C_6H_5$ (13.1 g., 90%)	*12*
$CuCl_2$ (13.5 g.)	$C_6H_5CH_2MgCl$ (12.6 g. C_7H_7Cl)	$C_6H_5CH_2CH_2C_6H_5$ (7 g., 83.5%)	*12*
$CuCl_2$ (51.3 g.)	2-$CH_3C_6H_4MgBr$ (60.0 g.)	2-$CH_3C_6H_4C_6H_4$-2-CH_3 (30%)	*19*
$CuCl_2$ (27.0 g.)	4-$CH_3C_6H_4MgBr$ (34.2 g. C_7H_7Br)	4-$CH_3C_6H_4C_6H_4$-4-CH_3 (15.3 g., 84%)	*12*
$CuCl_2$	$C_6H_5CH{=}CHMgBr$ (1 equiv.)	$C_6H_5CH{=}CHCH{=}CHC_6H_5$ (17.6%)†	*13*
$CuCl_2$ (13.5 g.)	$C_6H_5CH{=}CHMgBr$ (18.3 g. C_8H_7Br)	$C_6H_5CH{=}CHCH{=}CHC_6H_5$ (3–4 g., 40–45%)	*12*
$CuCl_2$ (13.5 g.)	1-$C_{10}H_7MgBr$ (20.7 g. $C_{10}H_7Br$)	1-$C_{10}H_7$-1-$C_{10}H_7$ (10.0 g., 80%)	*12*
$CuBr_2$	C_2H_5MgX	$C_2H_4 + C_2H_6$	*11*
$CuBr_2$	n-C_3H_7MgX	$C_3H_6 + C_3H_8$	*11*
$CuBr_2$ (0.4 mole)	$C_6H_5C{\equiv}CMgBr$ (0.4 mole C_8H_6)	$C_6H_5C{\equiv}CC{\equiv}CC_6H_5$ (29 g., 72%)	*10*
$FeCl_2$	C_2H_5MgX	$C_2H_4 + C_2H_6$	*11*
$FeCl_2$	n-C_3H_7MgX	$C_3H_6 + C_3H_8$	*11*
$FeCl_2$ (0.01 mole)	C_6H_5MgI (0.03 mole)	$C_6H_5C_6H_5$ (98%)	*14*
$FeCl_3$	C_2H_5MgBr	$C_2H_4 + C_2H_6$	*11*
2 $FeCl_3$	Alk-MgBr	Alk-Cl + 2 $FeCl_2$ + MgBrCl	*17*

*X = Cl, Br, I, CN, CNS.

†A check experiment showed that dimer (Wurtz product) to the extent of 10 percent is formed in the preparation of the Grignard reagent.

TABLE V-I (Continued)

Metallic Halide	Grignard Reagent(s)	Product(s)	Ref.
2 $FeCl_3$	2 C_6H_5MgBr	$C_6H_5C_6H_5$ + 2 $FeCl_2$	*15*
2 $FeCl_3$	6 C_6H_5MgBr	3 $C_6H_5C_6H_5$ + 2 Fe	*15*
$FeCl_3$ (8.1 g.)	C_6H_5MgBr (23.8 g. C_6H_5Br)	$C_6H_5C_6H_5$ (3.4 g.) + resin (2.4 g.) + $FeCl_2$	*16*
$FeCl_3$	C_6H_5MgBr	$C_6H_5C_6H_5$	*11*
$FeCl_3$	$CH_3C_6H_4MgBr$	$CH_3C_6H_4C_6H_4CH_3$	*11*
$CoCl_2$	C_2H_5MgX	C_2H_4 + C_2H_6	*11*
$CoCl_2$	*n*-C_3H_7MgBr	C_3H_6 + C_3H_8	*11*
$CoCl_2$ (0.03 mole)	C_6H_5MgBr (0.11 mole)	$C_6H_5C_6H_5$ (64%)	*18*
$CoBr_2$ (0.01 mole)	C_6H_5MgI (0.03 mole)	$C_6H_5C_6H_5$ (98%)	*14*
$CoBr_2$	2,4,6-$(CH_3)_3C_6H_2MgBr$	[2,4,6-$(CH_3)_3C_6H_2$—]$_2$ (20%)	*14*
$NiCl_2$	C_2H_5MgX	C_2H_4 + C_2H_6	*11*
$NiCl_2$	*n*-C_3H_7MgX	C_3H_6 + C_3H_8	*11*
$NiBr_2$ (0.03 mole)	C_6H_5MgI (0.095 mole)	$C_6H_5C_6H_5$ (100%)	*14*

REFERENCES FOR TABLE V-I

(*1*) Krause and Wendt, *Ber.*, *56B*, 2064–6 (1923).
(*2*) Joseph and Gardner, *J. Org. Chem.*, *5*, 61–7 (1940).
(*3*) Bickley and Gardner, *J. Org. Chem.*, *5*, 126–32 (1940).
(*4*) Gardner and Borgstrom, *J. Am. Chem. Soc.*, *51*, 3375–7 (1929).
(*5*) Gardner and Joseph, *J. Am. Chem. Soc.*, *61*, 2551–2 (1939).
(*6*) Whitmore, Stehman, and Herdon, *J. Am. Chem. Soc.*, *55*, 3807–9 (1933).
(*7*) Reich, *Compt. rend.*, *177*, 322–4 (1923); *Chem. Zentr.*, *1923,III*, 1010.
(*8*) Gardner, Joseph, and Gollub, *J. Am. Chem. Soc.*, *59*, 2583–4 (1939).
(*9*) Gardner and Snyder, *J. Am. Chem. Soc.*, *62*, 2879–80 (1940).
(*10*) Danehy and Nieuwland, *J. Am. Chem. Soc.*, *58*, 1609–10 (1936).
(*11*) Kondyrew and Fomin, *J. Russ. Phys.-Chem. Soc.*, *47*, 190–8 (1915); *Chem. Zentr.*, *1916,I*, 832.
(*12*) Sakellarios and Kyrimis, *Ber.*, *57B*, 322–6 (1924).
(*13*) Gilman and Parker, *J. Am. Chem. Soc.*, *46*, 2823–7 (1924).
(*14*) Gilman and Lichtenwalter, *J. Am. Chem. Soc.*, *61*, 957–9 (1939).
(*15*) Champetier, *Bull. soc. chim.*, [4], *47*, 1131–7 (1930).
(*16*) Bennett and Turner, *J. Chem. Soc.*, *105*, 1057–62 (1914).
(*17*) Oddo, *Gazz. chim. ital.*, *44,II*, 268–78 (1914); *Chem. Abstr.*, *9*, 795 (1915); *Chem. Zentr.*, *1915,I*, 743.
(*18*) Kharasch and Fields, *J. Am. Chem. Soc.*, *63*, 2316–20 (1941).
(*19*) Turner, *J. Proc. Royal Soc. N.S. Wales*, *54*, 37–9 (1920); *Chem. Abstr.*, *15*, 669 (1921).

CHAPTER VI

Reactions of Grignard Reagents with Aldehydes, Ketones, and Ketenes

THE "NORMAL" ADDITION REACTIONS

Probably in part for historical reasons, and in part because of their general utility as preparative methods, the addition reactions at the carbonyl double bond have come to be regarded as the "normal" reactions of Grignard reagents with aldehydes and ketones. These additions are polar in the sense that the cationoid (electrophilic) portion of the Grignard reagent becomes attached to the relatively negative oxygen atom, whereas the anionoid (nucleophilic, electrodotic) portion of the reagent becomes attached to the relatively positive carbon atom. Although Grignard reagent solutions are now known to be much more complex systems than the simple formulations originally employed by Grignard might seem to imply (see Chapter IV, Constitution and Dissociation of Grignard Reagents), those simple formulations are altogether adequate to describe their stoichiometrical behavior.

$$HCHO + RMgX \longrightarrow RCH_2OMgX \xrightarrow{H_2O} RCH_2OH + MgXOH$$

$$RCHO + R'MgX \longrightarrow RR'CHOMgX \xrightarrow{H_2O} RR'CHOH + MgXOH$$

$$RCOR' + R''MgX \longrightarrow RR'R''COMgX \xrightarrow{H_2O} RR'R''COH + MgXOH$$

Although these additions are polar, that they are not necessarily ionic in the sense that ionic *dissociation* of the Grignard reagent is a prerequisite to their occurrence is suggested by the fact that they may be conducted in such inert, nonionizing solvents as benzene and toluene.

Of the details of reaction mechanism, little can be said with assurance. Various investigators, among them Straus[1], Grignard[2], von Braun *et al.*[3], Meisenheimer[4], and Hess *et al.*[5], have suggested that the first step in the

[1]Straus, *Ann.*, *393*, 235–337 (1912) (footnote, p. 241).

[2]Grignard, *Bull. soc. chim.*, [4], *13*, Conference, I-XXXVII (1913).

[3](*a*) von Braun, Heider, and Miller, *Ber.*, *50*, 1637–51 (1917); (*b*) von Braun and Kirschbaum, *ibid.*, *52B*, 1725–30 (1919).

[4]Meisenheimer and Casper, *Ber.*, *54B*, 1655–65 (1921); Meisenheimer, *Ann.*, *442*, 180–210 (1925).

[5]Hess and Rheinboldt, *Ber.*, *54B*, 2043–55 (1921); Hess and Wustrow, *Ann.*, *437*, 256–73 (1924); Rheinboldt and Roleff, *J. prakt. Chem.*, [2], *109*, 175–90 (1925).

reaction of a Grignard reagent with a carbonyl compound is the formation of a complex of one sort or another.

von Braun's complex, like Grignard's, is patterned after the ether oxonium complex of Grignard[6], and a subsequent rearrangement to the alkoxide form in the case of addition reactions is assumed.

$$\begin{matrix} R \\ H \end{matrix}\!\!>\!C{=}O\!:\!\begin{matrix} \cdot MgBr \\ \cdot R' \end{matrix} \longrightarrow \begin{matrix} R \\ H \end{matrix}\!\!>\!C\!<\!\begin{matrix} OMgBr \\ R' \end{matrix}$$

Neither concept can be satisfactorily represented in electronic notation.

Meisenheimer's complex is of the Werner type with a coördination number of four for magnesium; rearrangement in the course of addition is postulated.

$$\begin{matrix} (C_2H_5)_2O\cdot \\ (C_2H_5)_2O\cdot \end{matrix}\!:\!Mg\!<\!\begin{matrix} CH_3 \\ I \end{matrix} \xrightarrow{(CH_3)_2CO} \begin{matrix} (C_2H_5)_2O\cdot \\ (CH_3)_2CO\cdot \end{matrix}\!:\!Mg\!<\!\begin{matrix} CH_3 \\ I \end{matrix} \longrightarrow \begin{matrix} (C_2H_5)_2O\cdot \\ (CH_3)_3CO \end{matrix}\!>\!Mg\!<\!\begin{matrix} \cdot O(C_2H_5)_2 \\ I \end{matrix}$$

Hess's complex is of a type not very clearly defined, and no rearrangement prior to hydrolysis is postulated, save in the case of reduction.

$$\begin{matrix} R \\ R' \end{matrix}\!\!>\!C{=}O \xrightarrow{C_2H_5MgBr} \begin{matrix} R \\ R' \end{matrix}\!\!>\!C{=}O\ldots Mg\!<\!\begin{matrix} Br \\ C_2H_5 \end{matrix} \begin{cases} \xrightarrow{H_2O} \begin{matrix} R \\ R' \end{matrix}\!\!>\!C\!<\!\begin{matrix} OH \\ C_2H_5 \end{matrix} \\ \xrightarrow{\Delta} \begin{matrix} R \\ R' \end{matrix}\!\!>\!C{=}O\ldots Mg\!<\!\begin{matrix} Br \\ H \end{matrix} + C_2H_4 \end{cases}$$

On the whole, Meisenheimer's description of the complex accords best with modern chemical concepts and with the known properties of Grignard reagents, although there is now good reason to doubt that addition is effected by so simple a process as monomolecular complex rearrangement.

Klages[7] believed that he had isolated such a complex when he added acetomesitylene [2,4,6-$(CH_3)_3C_6H_2COCH_3$] to two equivalents of ethereal ethylmagnesium iodide and obtained a white crystalline precipitate which gave an elementary analysis which he accepted as consistent with the formulation $(CH_3)_3C_6H_2COCH_3 \cdot C_2H_5MgI \cdot (C_2H_5)_2O$. Even after five hours heating at 100°, treatment of the precipitate with water regenerated acetomesitylene. However, it has since been shown by Kohler *et al.*[8] that treatment of a xylene solution of acetomesitylene with excess methyl-

[6]Grignard, *Bull. soc., chim.*, [3], *29*, 944–8 (1903).
[7]Klages, *Ber.*, *35*, 2633–46 (1902).
[8]Kohler, Stone, and Fuson, *J. Am. Chem. Soc.*, *49*, 3181–8 (1927).

magnesium iodide in isoamyl ether solution results in the evolution of methane and the quantitative formation of an enolate, according to the equation:

$$2,4,6\text{-}(CH_3)_3C_6H_2COCH_3 + CH_3MgI \longrightarrow [2,4,6\text{-}(CH_3)_3C_6H_2COCH_2]^-[MgI]^+ + CH_4$$

Klages' product, therefore, is almost certainly that suggested by Kohler and Baltzly[9], $[(CH_3)_3C_6H_2COCH_2]^-[MgI]^+ \cdot (C_2H_5)_2O$, probably contaminated with a little excess ether.

Indirect evidence of intermediate Grignard reagent complex formation with camphor (1,7,7-trimethylbicyclo[2.2.1]heptan-2-one), a relatively unreactive cyclic ketone, is reported by Bredt-Savelsburg[10], who has observed that camphor does not sublime from Grignard reagent mixtures as it does from ordinary mechanical mixtures. That this phenomenon is not attributable to enolate formation is indicated by the extreme slowness with which camphor is enolized by Grignard reagents (see Enolate Formation by Grignard Reagents, p. 166).

More positive evidence of Grignard reagent-carbonyl group complex formation involves the relatively unreactive non-enolizable cyclic ketone fenchone (1,3,3-trimethylbicyclo[2.2.1]heptan-2-one). Leroide[11] reports that this ketone combines with phenyl-, *o*-tolyl-, and *p*-tolylmagnesium bromides to give products insoluble in ether-toluene solution. By prolonged heating in large quantities of solvent these are slowly converted to the corresponding alcoholates. A 7 percent yield of the phenyl tertiary alcohol was obtained in this way. The more reactive[12] benzylmagnesium chloride formed the alcoholate directly to give a 45 percent yield of the tertiary alcohol.

Nesmeyanov and Sazanova[13] have confirmed the observation that phenylmagnesium bromide forms an ether-insoluble product with fenchone. According to them, this product gives no Gilman color test with Michler's ketone (see Chapter III, Estimation and Detection of Grignard Reagents), an indication that the complex is remarkably stable. Partial analysis revealed a magnesium-bromide ratio of 1.0:1.4, an indication that the $MgBr_2$ and C_6H_5MgBr complexes are less soluble than the $(C_6H_5)_2Mg$ complex (see Chapter IV, Constitution and Dissociation of Grignard Reagents). This might account for their failure to isolate benzene when fenchone is regenerated by hydrolysis of the precipitate.

---

[9] Kohler and Baltzly, *J. Am. Chem. Soc.*, *54*, 4015–26 (1932).

[10] Bredt-Savelsburg, *J. prakt. Chem.*, [2], *107*, 65–85 (1924).

[11] Leroide, *Compt. rend.*, *148*, 1611–3 (1909); *Chem. Zentr.*, *1909*, *II*, 358.

[12] Concerning relative reactivities of Grignard reagents toward carbonyl groups see: Kharasch and Weinhouse, *J. Org. Chem.*, *1*, 209–30 (1936).

[13] Nesmeyanov and Sazanova, *Bull. acad. sci. U.R.S.S.*, *Classe sci. chim.*, *1941*, 499–519; *Chem. Abstr.*, 37, 2723 (1943).

Kohler[14] reports that in cold ethereal solution ethylmagnesium bromide forms with diphenylbenzalacetophenone [$C_6H_5COC(C_6H_5){=}C(C_6H_5)_2$] a combination that is in part precipitated. Upon hydrolysis the ketone is recovered quantitatively. Obviously, enolization is not involved. Prolonged boiling of the ethereal suspension brings about true reaction which results in at least 30 percent yield of the carbinol (or its dehydration product). According to Kohler and Nygaard[15] neither methylmagnesium iodide nor phenylmagnesium bromide react with diphenylbenzalacetophenone in ethereal solution, even under prolonged reflux, but reaction can be brought about by operating at somewhat higher temperatures in benzene.

von Braun *et al.*[16] report that, with acetone, butanone, and acetophenone, the Grignard reagent prepared from *N*-methyl-*N*-β-bromoethylaniline forms ether-insoluble complexes from which the ketones may be recovered by hydrolysis. With the more reactive butyraldehyde, however, normal reaction takes place.

Complexes of methylmagnesium iodide with acetobromoglucose ($C_{14}H_{19}O_9Br \cdot 2\ CH_3MgI$), pentaäcetylglucose ($C_{16}H_{22}O_{11} \cdot 2\ CH_3MgI$), tetraacetylglucose ($C_{14}H_{20}O_{10} \cdot 2\ CH_3MgI$), and tetraäcetyl α-methyl glucoside ($C_{15}H_{22}O_{10} \cdot 2\ CH_3MgI$) have also been reported by Fischer and Hess[17].

Pfeiffer and Blank[18] (who, incidentally, accepted Klages' acetomesitylene "complex" at face value) have advanced the hypothesis that alcoholate formation is effected, not by monomolecular rearrangement of the Grignard reagent-carbonyl group complex, but by interaction of the complex with a second molecule of Grignard reagent. They reported that the addition of one equivalent of an ethereal ethylmagnesium bromide solution to an ethereal benzophenone solution (concentrations not stated) gave rise to a "dirty" white precipitate which quickly coalesced into an oily, ether-insoluble subsident layer. The oily product was regarded as unsuitable for analysis but was found to regenerate most of the benzophenone originally present when treated with water. When the experiment was repeated with two or three equivalents of ethylmagnesium bromide the alcoholate [$C_2H_5(C_6H_5)_2COMgBr$] was formed.

For the remainder of their study Pfeiffer and Blank unfortunately chose ketones that could yield only equivocal results, namely: *p*-aminobenzophenone, *p*-dimethylaminobenzophenone, and Michler's ketone [*p*,*p*'-bis(dimethylamino)benzophenone]. It is well-known that most primary aromatic amines behave toward Grignard reagents at room (or lower) temperature as though they contained one "active" hydrogen atom (see

[14] Kohler, *Am. Chem. J.*, *38*, 511–61 (1907).
[15] Kohler and Nygaard, *J. Am. Chem. Soc.*, *52*, 4128–39 (1936).
[16] von Braun, Heider, and Miller, *Ber.*, *50*, 1637–51 (1917).
[17] Fischer and Hess, *Ber.*, *45*, 912–5 (1912).
[18] Pfeiffer and Blank, *J. prakt. Chem.*, [2], *153*, 242–56 (1939).

Chapter XVIII) and that tertiary amines form Grignard reagent complexes which are, in general, more stable and less ether-soluble than the corresponding "etherates" (see Chapter II, Preparation of Grignard Reagents in Solvents Other than Ethyl Ether).

The validity of the benzophenone experiment of Pfeiffer and Blank (*loc. cit.*[18]) has been questioned by Nesmeyanov and Sazanova (*loc. cit.*[13]), who state that the precipitate formed when an ethereal solution of benzophenone is added dropwise to one equivalent of ethereal ethylmagnesium bromide is the alcoholate. However, the differences in the two experimental techniques employed are altogether adequate to account for the differences in observed results. If the reaction scheme proposed by Pfeiffer and Blank is indeed the correct one, use of the "normal" order of reactant addition (which insures that the major portion of the reaction take place in the presence of an excess of Grignard reagent) should lead to alcoholate formation.

The reaction mechanism proposed by Pfeiffer and Blank is also the one favored by Swain[19], who has studied the kinetics of the nitrile-Grignard reagent reaction (see Chapter X, Reactions of Grignard Reagents with Nitriles and Other Cyano Compounds). The second-order nature of the latter reaction, considered in conjunction with the relative reactivities of nitriles toward phenylmagnesium bromide[20] and the relative reactivities of various Grignard reagents with benzonitrile, and with the relative migration tendencies of organic radicals in the pinacol rearrangement, leads Swain to conclude that the rate-determining step is probably an intramolecular rearrangement of a Werner complex. In the ketone reactions the radical order of reactivity of Grignard reagents toward benzophenone[21] is the reverse of the order of reactivity toward benzonitrile. The reactions must therefore have different mechanisms, and, since the direct reaction of ketone with Grignard reagent seems to be excluded, the reaction of Grignard reagent with activated complex appears most probable.

It may be remarked in passing (though entirely without prejudice) that this is one of several instances in which the concept of a quasi six-membered ring may be invoked to suggest for Grignard reactions a mechanism consistent with the observed facts.

```
       R″                       .R″.                      R″
 R\    \               R\   .·   :                 R\    /
   >C   Mg—X             >C      Mg—X                >C        Mg—X
 R′/ ||        →       R′/ :     :          →      R′/ |         |
    O    R″               O.  .R″                      O         R″
     :  /                   ··                          \
     Mg                     Mg                           Mg
     |                      |                            |
     X                      X                            X
```

[19]Swain, *J. Am. Chem. Soc.*, *69*, 2396–9 (1947).
[20]Gilman and Lichtenwalter, *Rec. trav. chim.*, *55*, 588–90 (1936).
[21]Kharasch and Weinhouse, *J. Org. Chem.*, *1*, 209–30 (1936).

PREPARATIVE PROCEDURES

Grignard's[22] method of conducting reactions between organomagnesium halides and aldehydes, ketones, or esters was essentially the same in all cases. To one equivalent of ethereal Grignard reagent solution in a water-cooled flask, equipped with a reflux condenser, was added dropwise one molecular equivalent of aldehyde or ketone, or one-half molecular equivalent of ester, dissolved in its own volume of anhydrous ethyl ether. If the product proved to be soluble in ether, reaction was then completed by several hours gentle reflux on a water-bath. If the product proved to be a crystalline precipitate or a viscous subsident layer, Grignard preferred, rather than risk local superheating, to allow the reaction mixture to stand for a day at laboratory temperature.

The product was then hydrolyzed by portionwise addition of cracked ice to the reaction mixture, and precipitated magnesium hydroxide was dissolved by the addition of a little hydrochloric acid or a dilute solution of acetic acid. The ethereal layer was then separated, washed successively with sodium bicarbonate and sodium bisulfite solutions, and eventually distilled, with the aid of reduced pressure if necessary. In cases in which the alcoholic product was appreciably soluble in water, the aqueous layer was subjected to steam distillation, and the distillate was "salted" with potassium carbonate.

For the more readily reactive ether-soluble carbonyl compounds, reacting with the chosen Grignard reagent to yield relatively stable (as regards dehydration) alcohols, Grignard's procedure requires little modification. Efficient mechanical stirring during the addition operation, and, in cases in which the product is ether-insoluble, throughout the entire reaction period is desirable. Ice or ice-salt cooling is both more efficient and more convenient than cooling with running water.

If the carbonyl compound is both ether-insoluble and relatively unreactive, it may be added to the Grignard reagent solution dropwise (if a liquid) or portionwise in the form of a fine powder (if a solid). For the sake of convenience, solids may be powdered and suspended in ether, or, better, dissolved in some suitable solvent such as benzene, toluene, or xylene. If the carbonyl compound, though ether-insoluble, is relatively reactive, suspension or solution (preferably the latter) is indicated.

For very unreactive carbonyl compounds, it is often desirable, and sometimes necessary, either to add to the ethereal solution or suspension a higher-boiling solvent (*e.g.*, benzene, toluene, or a high-boiling ether) or to replace the ethyl ether in whole or in part with such a solvent. This is usually best accomplished by employing the high-boiling liquid as a solvent or suspension medium for the addition of the carbonyl compound

[22]Grignard, *Ann. chim.*, [7], *24*, 433–90 (1901).

and then, if desirable, removing part or all of the ethyl ether by distillation. In cases where it is necessary to resort to such tactics, however, it must be anticipated that the isolable product may be an olefin (the result of dehydration of the primary reaction product), especially if the primary product is the halomagnesium alcoholate of a readily dehydrated alcohol.

While it seems highly probable that some "dehydrations" take place prior to hydrolysis by a thermally-induced decomposition of the type

$$RR'C(OMgX)CHR''R''' \rightarrow RR'C{=}CR''R''' + MgXOH$$

many are unquestionably attributable to the method of recovery of the product.

Other considerations permitting, dehydration may be prevented or minimized by: (1) conducting the Grignard reaction at a relatively low temperature; (2) avoiding excess acidity in the hydrolysis operation (as by employing iced saturated ammonium chloride solution as a hydrolyzing agent); (3) removing all traces of acid from the hydrolysis product (as by thorough washing with sodium bicarbonate solution); and (4) conducting the final distillation at very low pressure (preferably a fraction of a millimeter of mercury).

Because there is usually no objection to the presence of an excess of Grignard reagent, whereas the presence of an excess of carbonyl compound may be disadvantageous,* the "normal" order of addition (*i.e.*, the addition of carbonyl compound to the Grignard reagent) is almost invariably employed for preparative purposes in the case of aldehydes and ketones. When the concentration of the Grignard solution is known through analysis, a slight measured excess is usually employed. Because Grignard reagent yields are always somewhat, and often considerably, less than quantitative, due allowance must be made for this fact if it is known or suspected that an excess of carbonyl compound may prove disadvantageous.

Formaldehyde (generated by thermal depolymerization of one of its polymers) may be bubbled into a Grignard reagent solution or led over its surface (preferably in a stream of dry nitrogen). Alternatively, the solid polymer may be added to the Grignard reagent solution, and the mixture may then be submitted to prolonged reflux.

Citations to a few illustrative preparations described in some detail in the literature are assembled in Table VI-I. Others may be located by reference to the appropriate reaction tabulations.

---

*As, for example, in the case of the oxidation of the Grignard reaction product by benzaldehyde (see Alkoxide Reduction, p. 158).

TABLE VI-I

SOME ILLUSTRATIVE PREPARATIVE REACTIONS OF GRIGNARD REAGENTS WITH ALDEHYDES AND KETONES

(Yield refers to "normal" product.)

Reactants	Mode of Add'n	Reaction Time	Hydrolytic Agent	Yield (%)	Ref.
HCHO (from 38 g. paraform) + s-C_4H_9MgBr (150 g. C_4H_9Br)	Gas + N_2 into ice-salt-cooled G.r.	HCHO absorb'n + 5 min. (odor)	Ice	67	*1*
HCHO (from 50 g. paraform) + $(CH_2)_5CHMgCl$ (118.5 g. $C_6H_{11}Cl$)	Gas + N_2 over G.r. at room temp.	*Ca.* 1.75 hr.	Ice + 30% H_2SO_4	64–69	*2*
"Trioxymethylene" (30 g.) + n-$C_{18}H_{37}MgCl$ (144.4 g. $C_{18}H_{37}Cl$)	Single add'n solid to G.r.	6–8 hrs. reflux	30% H_2SO_4 (ice-cooling)	59	*3*
Polyoxymethylene (1 equiv) + n-$C_5H_{11}MgBr$ (in i-Am_2O)	Single add'n solid to cooled G.r.	1 hr. at 150°	Ice + aqu. HCl	47	*4*
CH_3CHO (44 g.) + C_2H_5MgBr (115 g. C_2H_5Br)	Grad'l add'n Et_2O-RCHO to ice-cooled G.r.	Add'n time + 0.5 hr.	H_2O + dil. aqu. HCl	80	*5*
CH_3CHO (from 30 g. paraldehyde) + C_2H_5MgBr (680 g. C_2H_5Br)	Gas + N_2 into G.r.	12 hrs.	Ice + NH_4Cl	67	*1*
$CH_3CH{=}CHCHO$ + n-C_3H_7MgBr ("large excess")	Add'n RCHO to G.r. at −28 to −22°	Overnight at 25°	Iced aqu. H_2SO_4	78	*6*
C_6H_5CHO (15.9 g.) + $(CH_3)_2N(CH_2)_3MgCl$ (30 g. $C_5H_{12}ClN$)	Portionwise add'n Et_2O-RCHO to G.r.	12 hrs. reflux	Ice + aqu. HCl	70	7
4-$CH_3OC_6H_4CHO$ (28 g.) + C_6H_5MgBr (40 g. C_6H_5Br	Dropwise add'n RCHO to ice-cooled G.r.	24 hrs. at 0°	Cold dil. aqu. HAc	90	8

TABLE VI-I (Continued)

Reactants	Mode of Add'n	Reaction Time	Hydrolytic Agent	Yield (%)	Ref.
9-Anthraldehyde (30 g.) + CH_3MgI (21.5 g. CH_3I)	Add'n C_6H_6-RCHO to G.r.	0.5 hr. reflux	Aqu. NH_4Cl	92	*9*
$(CH_3)_2CO$ (6 moles) + *n*-C_4H_9MgBr (6.5 moles C_4H_9Br)	Slow add'n Et_2O-R_2CO to G.r.	Overnight at room temp.	H_2O + ice + 10% aqu. HCl	92	*10*
HON=$CHCOC_6H_5$ (15 g.) + C_6H_5MgBr (80 g. C_6H_5Br)	Portionwise add'n powdered RCOR′ to G.r.	1 hr. reflux	Ice + 10% aqu. H_2SO_4	75	*11*
$(C_6H_5)_2CO$ (18.2 g.) + H_2C=$CHCH_2MgBr$ (100 ml. 1.32 *N*)	Dropwise add'n C_6H_6-R_2CO to G.r. at 10–20°	Add'n time	10% aqu. H_2SO_4	72	*12*
C_6H_5CO-1-$C_{10}H_7$ (0.10 mole) + *n*-C_3H_7MgBr (0.12 mole C_3H_7Br)	Portionwise add'n C_6H_6-RCOR′ to ice-cooled G.r.	24 hrs.	Ice + NH_4Cl	65	*13*
2-Methylcyclohexanone (6 moles) + CH_3MgI (7 moles)	Slow add'n Et_2O-RCOR′ to ice-cooled G.r.	Add'n time (8 hrs.) + warming to room temp.	Ice + aqu. HCl	67	*14*
7-Methyl-α-tetralone + *i*-C_3H_7MgBr (1.25 equiv. Mg)	Slow add'n Et_2O-RCOR′ to ice-cooled G.r.	Warming to room temp.; 5–10 min. reflux	Ice + NH_4Cl	70	*15*

REFERENCES FOR TABLE VI-I.

(1) Wood and Scarf, *J. Soc. Chem. Ind.*, *42*, 13–15T (1923).
(2) Gilman and Catlin, *Organic Syntheses*, Coll. Vol. I, 2nd ed., 188–90 (1941).
(3) Turkiewicz, *Ber.*, *72B*, 1060–3 (1939).
(4) Veibel, Lundqvist, Anderson, and Frederiksen, *Bull. soc. chim.*, [5], *6*, 990–8 (1939).
(5) Clarke, *J. Am. Chem. Soc.*, *30*, 1144–52 (1908).
(6) Stevens, *J. Am. Chem. Soc.*, *57*, 1112–7 (1935).
(7) Marxer, *Helv. Chim. Acta*, *24*, 209–15E (1941).
(8) Bachmann, *J. Am. Chem. Soc.*, *55*, 2135–9 (1933).
(9) Fieser and Hartwell, *J. Am. Chem. Soc.*, *60*, 2555–9 (1938).
(10) Edgar, Calingaert, and Marker, *J. Am. Chem. Soc.*, *51*, 1483–91 (1929).
(11) Orékhoff and Tiffeneau, *Bull. soc. chim.*, [4], *41*, 839–43 (1927).
(12) Kharasch and Weinhouse, *J. Org. Chem.*, *1*, 209–30 (1934).
(13) Blicke and Powers, *J. Am. Chem. Soc.*, *51*, 3378–83 (1929).
(14) Signaigo and Cramer, *J. Am. Chem. Soc.*, *55*, 3326–32 (1933).
(15) Barnett and Sanders, *J. Chem. Soc.*, *1933*, 434–7.

GRIGNARD REDUCTIONS OF ALDEHYDES AND KETONES

Three types of Grignard reduction of carbonyl compounds have been observed. In the first, a Grignard reagent of the type RR′CHCR″R‴MgX (in which, R, R′, R″, and R‴ may be H) serves as the reducing agent:

$$R''''CHO + RR'CHCR''R'''MgX \rightarrow R''''CH_2OMgX + RR'C{=}CR''R'''$$

$$R''''COR''''' + RR'CHCR''R'''MgX \rightarrow R''''R'''''CHOMgX + RR'C{=}CR''R'''$$

In the second, an alkoxide of the type RR′CHOMgX is the reducing agent:

$$R''CHO + RR'CHOMgX \rightarrow R''CH_2OMgX + RCOR'$$

$$R''COR''' + RR'CHOMgX \rightarrow R''R'''CHOMgX + RCOR'$$

In the third, reduction is effected by magnesious halide (·MgBr or ·MgI):

$$2\ RCHO + 2{\cdot}MgX \rightarrow 2\ R(XMgO)CH{\cdot} \xrightarrow{H_2O} [R(HO)CH—]_2 + 2\ MgXOH$$

$$2\ RCOR' + 2{\cdot}MgX \rightarrow 2\ RR'(XMgO)C{\cdot} \xrightarrow{H_2O} [RR'(HO)C—]_2 + 2\ MgXOH$$

The first two are hydrogenation reductions; the third involves electron transfer only.

Reduction by the Grignard reagent. The true Grignard reagent reduction was first observed by Grignard himself, and was reported in his doctoral dissertation and in his classical paper on the preparation and reactions of organomagnesium halides[23]. From the reaction between isoamylmagnesium bromide and benzaldehyde, he obtained as byproducts, in addition to a 56 percent yield of the expected secondary alcohol, small amounts of benzyl alcohol and biïsoamyl. (The biïsoamyl was undoubtedly the

[23]Grignard, *Ann. chim.*, [7], *24*, 433–90 (1901).

product of a Wurtz side-reaction occurring during the preparation of the Grignard reagent.)

Similar reductions of chloral were observed by Iotsitch[24], who also noted the simultaneous evolution of olefin.*

$$CCl_3CHO + C_2H_5MgBr \longrightarrow CCl_3CH_2OH\ (50\%) + CCl_3(C_2H_5)CHOH\ (15\%) + C_2H_4$$

$$CCl_3CHO + i\text{-}C_5H_{11}MgBr \longrightarrow CCl_3CH_2OH\ (60\%) + CCl_3(i\text{-}C_5H_{11})CHOH\ (10\%) + C_5H_{10}$$

Whitmore *et al.*[25] have reported a nearly quantitative aldehyde reduction by *t*-amylmagnesium chloride.

$$CH_3(t\text{-}C_4H_9)\ (t\text{-}C_4H_9CH_2)CCHO + t\text{-}C_5H_{11}MgCl \longrightarrow CH_3(t\text{-}C_4H_9)\ (t\text{-}C_4H_9CH_2)CCH_2OH\ (90\%)$$

The analogous reduction of ketones, with simultaneous olefin liberation, was observed by Sabatier and Mailhe[26].

$$(CH_2)_5CO + n\text{-}C_3H_7MgI \longrightarrow (CH_2)_5CHOH\ (50\%) + (CH_2)_5C(n\text{-}C_3H_7)OH\ (25\%) + C_3H_6$$

$$(CH_2)_5CO + i\text{-}C_4H_9MgI \longrightarrow (CH_2)_5CHOH + (CH_2)_5C(i\text{-}C_4H_9)OH\ (10\%) + i\text{-}C_4H_8$$

$$(CH_2)_5CO + i\text{-}C_5H_{11}MgI \longrightarrow (CH_2)_5CHOH\ (20\%) + (CH_2)_5C(i\text{-}C_5H_{11})OH + C_5H_{10}$$

$$(CH_2)_5CO + (CH_2)_5CHMgCl \longrightarrow (CH_2)_5CHOH + (CH_2)_5C[CH(CH_2)_5]OH + C_6H_{10}$$

$$(C_6H_5)_2CO + (CH_2)_5CHMgCl \longrightarrow (C_6H_5)_2CHOH + C_6H_{10}$$

---

[24]Iotsitch, *J. Russ. Phys.-Chem. Soc.*, *36*, 443–6 (1904); *Bull. soc. chim.*, [3], *34*, 329 (1905). See also: Hébert, *Bull. soc. chim.*, [4], *27*, 45–55 (1920); Dean and Wolf, *J. Am. Chem. Soc.*, *58*, 332–3 (1936); Kharasch, Kleiger, Martin, and Mayo, *ibid.*, *63*, 2305–7 (1941); Gilman and Abbot, *J. Org. Chem.*, *8*, 224–9 (1943); Floutz, *J. Am. Chem. Soc.*, *65*, 2255 (1943).

*Too much theoretical significance should not be ascribed to the quantitative aspects of early studies described here, or in analogous discussions hereafter. Investigations at the University of Chicago [*e.g.*, Kharasch, Kleiger, and Mayo, *J. Am. Chem. Soc.*, *63*, 2305–7 (1941)] indicate that quantitative, and in some cases qualitative, relationships may be materially affected by relatively small quantities of metallic impurities present in the magnesium employed for the preparation of the Grignard reagent.

[25]Whitmore, Whitaker, Mosher, Breivik, Wheeler, Miner, Sutherland, Wagner, Clapper, Lewis, Lux, and Popkin, *J. Am. Chem. Soc.*, *63*, 643–54 (1941).

[26]Sabatier and Mailhe, (*a*) *Compt. rend.*, *139*, 343–6 (1904); *J. Chem. Soc.*, *86*, *I*, 809 (1904); *Chem. Zentr.*, *1904*, *II*, 704; (*b*) *Ann. chim.*, [8], *10*, 527–74 (1907).

Early observations were summarized by Sabatier and Mailhe[27] essentially as follows. "Secondary reactions of this type occur as a rule only to a slight extent when the Grignard reaction is applied to aliphatic or aromatic aldehydes, chloral being the most notable exception. With ketones, and especially cyclic ketones, on the contrary, the secondary reaction assumes greater importance. The nature of the alkyl group in the alkylmagnesium halide used also exerts some influence on the extent to which the secondary reaction takes place; thus isobutyl favors its occurrence, whilst primary alkyl groups as a rule show this tendency to a much less extent, and aromatic groups do not exhibit it at all. Magnesium haloid derivatives of secondary alkyl groups always furnish the secondary reaction to a greater or less extent."

Hess and Wustrow[28] reported the isolation of the primary addition products of ethylmagnesium bromide, isobutylmagnesium bromide, and isobutylmagnesium chloride with cinnamaldehyde, and stated that on heating, they lost in weight an amount corresponding to one equivalent of olefin. Meisenheimer[29] was unable to confirm these results, and also called attention to the fact that Hess and Wustrow had actually isolated from the reaction of isobutylmagnesium chloride with cinnamaldehyde only about 8.5 percent of the amount of isobutylene bromide corresponding to the amount of cinnamic alcohol obtained. In his own experiments on the reduction of benzaldehyde with ethylmagnesium and isobutylmagnesium bromides, Meisenheimer did not succeed in isolating the theoretically equivalent quantities of olefin. Blicke and Powers[30] isolated approximately 23 percent of the total amount of alkyl radical as propylene bromide from a reaction of *n*-propylmagnesium bromide with benzophenone which resulted in 50 percent reduction of the ketone to benzhydrol. Using a technique better adapted to the quantitative isolation of products, Noller *et al.*[31], were able to show that in the reaction of isobutylmagnesium bromide with benzophenone, the amount of isobutylene evolved corresponds exactly to the amount of benzhydrol produced. They further demonstrated that not more than 0.1 percent of the hydrocarbon evolved can be isobutane.

Whitmore and George[32] have also shown that in the reaction between isopropylmagnesium bromide and diïsopropyl ketone, within reasonable limits of experimental error, the amount of propylene evolved corresponds to the amount of secondary alcohol produced, and the amount of propane to the amount of enolization.

---

[27]Sabatier and Mailhe, *Compt. rend.*, *141*, 298–301 (1905); *J. Chem. Soc.*, *88*, *I*, 706 (1905).

[28]Hess and Wustrow, *Ann.*, *437*, 256–73 (1924).

[29]Meisenheimer, *Ann.*, *442*, 180–210 (1925).

[30]Blicke and Powers, *J. Am. Chem. Soc.*, *51*, 3378–83 (1929).

[31]Noller, Grebe, and Knox, *J. Am. Chem. Soc.*, *54*, 4690–6 (1932).

[32]Whitmore and George, *J. Am. Chem. Soc.*, *64*, 1239–42 (1942).

It now appears fairly evident that failure to isolate equivalent quantities of reduction product and olefin in reactions of this type is attributable either to: (1) inadequate method, (2) faulty technique, or (3) especially in the case of aldehydes, to the presence of excess carbonyl compound, leading to some reduction of the alkoxide type (*q.v.*).

Meisenheimer's formulation of the reactions between benzaldehyde and ethylmagnesium bromide is, of course, little more than a record of the observed products.

$$C_2H_5MgBr + C_6H_5CHO \longrightarrow C_6H_5CHO\ldots MgBrC_2H_5 \begin{cases} \nearrow C_6H_5CH(C_2H_5)OMgBr \\ \searrow C_6H_5CH_2OMgBr + C_2H_4 \end{cases}$$

The somewhat similar formulation of Hess *et al.*[33] for aldehydes, and of Rheinboldt and Roleff[34] for ketones includes a concept that might or might not be significant.

$$\begin{matrix} R \\ R' \end{matrix}\!\!>CO\ldots Mg\!<\!\begin{matrix} X \\ C_2H_5 \end{matrix} \longrightarrow \begin{matrix} R \\ R' \end{matrix}\!\!>CO\ldots Mg\!<\!\begin{matrix} X \\ H \end{matrix} + C_2H_4$$

About the only direct experimental evidence advanced in support of an intermediate complex of the kind suggested by Hess and Rheinboldt is the observation of Noller *et al.* (*loc. cit.*[31]) that when isobutylmagnesium bromide and benzophenone react in *n*-butyl ether solution there is immediate evolution of isobutylene, but no permanent precipitation of $(C_6H_5)_2CHOMgBr$, notwithstanding the fact that the alkoxide is soluble in *n*-butyl ether to the extent of only 0.006 g. per ml. That the solubility of the intermediate is not a supersaturation effect was shown by addition of solid $(C_6H_5)_2CHOMgBr$ to the solution. However, the possibility of formation of a relatively soluble complex of $(C_6H_5)_2CHOMgBr$ with excess Grignard reagent or with magnesium bromide is not precluded.[35] There is also the possibility that the reduction product is largely in the form of $[(C_6H_5)_2CHO]_2Mg$, which is relatively ether-soluble.[36]

Whether or not such compounds as halomagnesium hydrides actually exist, either independently or as complex components, remains an open question, although bromomagnesium hydride (HMgBr) as a reducing agent has been made the subject of patent claims.[37]

---

[33] Hess and Rheinboldt, *Ber.*, *54B*, 2043–55 (1921); Hess and Wustrow, (*loc. cit.*[28]).

[34] Rheinboldt and Roleff, *J. prakt. Chem.*, [2], *109*, 175–90 (1925).

[35] Doering and Noller, *J. Am. Chem. Soc.*, *61*, 3436 (1939), found that $MgBr_2 \cdot 2 Et_2O$ is markedly more soluble in an ethereal solution of *n*-butylmagnesium bromide than in ethyl ether.

[36] See: Noller, *J. Am. Chem. Soc.*, *53*, 635–43 (1931).

[37] Milas, U. S. Patent 2,432,921, June 20, 1944; *Chem. Abstr.*, *42*, P2278 (1948).

Clapp and Woodward[38] report that, when pyrolyzed *in vacuo* at 220°, ethylmagnesium bromide evolves pure ethylene. "By treatment of the [solid] pyrolysis product in suspension in an ether-benzene mixture of benzophenone it has been possible to obtain a 66 percent yield of benzhydrol." The pyrolysis product of methylmagnesium iodide, on the other hand, did not prove an effective reducing agent for benzophenone. These observations, however, have little or no direct bearing on the reduction mechanism proposed by Hess, Rheinboldt *et al.* (*loc. cit.*[33, 34]).

Jolibois,[39] had earlier studied the pyrolysis of ethylmagnesium iodide at 175°, and summarized his observations and conclusions in the equation:

$$2\ C_2H_5MgI \xrightarrow{\Delta} 2\ C_2H_4 + (2\ HMgI) \longrightarrow 2\ C_2H_4 + H_2Mg + MgI_2$$

He reported that ether extraction of the solid residue removes magnesium iodide, leaving magnesium hydride, which liberates hydrogen at 280°.

However attractive the notion of a hydride as the effective agent in Grignard reductions may appear to some theorists, it suffers the lethal defect that it neither provides nor admits of a reasonable explanation of asymmetric reductions (to be discussed hereafter).

Blicke and Powers (*loc. cit.*[30]) have proposed that reaction between a Grignard reagent and an aldehyde or ketone is initiated by homolytic scission of the Grignard reagent with free-radical formation.

$$RR'CO + R''MgX \longrightarrow RR'C(OMgX)\cdot + R''\cdot$$

They assume that one or more of the following reactions may then take place:

(1) $RR'C(OMgX)\cdot + R''\cdot \longrightarrow RR'R''COMgX$ (normal addition)

(2) $RR'C(OMgX)\cdot + R''\cdot \longrightarrow RR'CHOMgX + R''_{(-H)}$ (reduction)

(3) $2\ RR'C(OMgX)\cdot \longrightarrow [RR'C(OMgX)—]_2$ (pinacol formation)

(4) $2\ R''\cdot \longrightarrow R''_2$

To the dimerization reaction of equation 4, of course, should be added the alternatives of free-radical disproportionation (5) and attack upon the solvent (6).

(5) $2\ R''\cdot \longrightarrow R''H + R''_{(-H)}$

(6) $R''\cdot + (C_2H_5)_2O \longrightarrow R''H + C_2H_5O(CH_3)CH\cdot$

The evidence against such a reaction mechanism is largely negative, yet it is, in the aggregate, rather convincing. Many interactions between Grignard reagents and carbonyl compounds lead to nearly quantitative yields of the normal addition products. This is not a very probable outcome of the initial reaction step postulated. The ketyls [RR'C(OMgX)·]

[38] Clapp and Woodward, *J. Am. Chem. Soc.*, *60*, 1019-20 (1938).

[39] Jolibois, *Compt. rend.*, *155*, 353-5 (1912); *Chem. Abstr.*, 6, 2741 (1912).

are in general highly colored, yet many Grignard additions and reductions take place with little or no perceptible color development. The presence of ketyl radicals should always lead to the formation of some pinacol, yet pinacol formation has never been demonstrated (save for triarylmethylmagnesium halides) where it is also certain that metallic magnesium has been rigorously excluded.[40] The presence of free organic radicals corresponding to the Grignard reagent (R″·) should always lead to some disproportionation, dimerization, or attack upon the solvent. In the case of isobutylmagnesium bromide and benzophenone, at least, it has been shown that the amount of isobutylene evolved corresponds quantitatively to the amount of benzhydrol produced (Noller *et al.*, *loc. cit.*[31]). In no case where a dimer has been reported, has it been shown that the amount differs materially from that which might be expected to result from the Wurtz side-reaction in the preparation of the Grignard reagent.

A slightly different free-radical mechanism, but one open to similar objections, has been proposed by Lagerev[41], and accepted by Temp and Gibalevich[42].

On the basis of the reactions of several Grignard reagents with a relatively small number of aldehydes and ketones, some of which reactions were undoubtedly complicated by enolization and condensation, Conant *et al.*[43] conclude that the reducing tendency of an alkyl Grignard reagent increases with the size and complexity of the alkyl group. That so simple a generalization is inadequate to cover the subject, however, is shown by the fact that neither *t*-butylmagnesium bromide[44] nor chloride[45] reduce benzophenone appreciably, whereas *n*-butylmagnesium bromide gives *ca.* 59 percent reduction[44,45].

Whitmore and George (*loc. cit.*[32]), have sought to relate the reducing tendency of alkyl Grignard reagents to the nature and number of *beta* hydrogen atoms in the alkyl radical; tertiary, secondary, and primary hydrogens are decreasingly effective. However, this generalization also requires some modification, for *t*-butylmagnesium bromide (with nine primary *beta* hydrogen atoms) is no more effective in the reduction of benzophenone than ethylmagnesium bromide (with only three primary *beta* hydrogen atoms).

Noller and Hilmer (*loc. cit.*[44]) investigated the hypothesis, somewhat similar in principle, that the reducing tendency of an alkylmagnesium bromide might be related to the ease of dehydrobromination of the cor-

---

[40]See, *e.g.*, Gilman and Fothergill, *J. Am. Chem. Soc.*, *51*, 3149–57 (1929).

[41]Lagerev, *J. Gen. Chem.* (U.S.S.R.), 6, 1766–8 (1936); *Chem. Abstr.*, *31*, 4308 (1937).

[42]Temp and Gibalevich, *Trudy Uzbekskogo Gosudarst. Univ., Sbornik Rabot Khim.*, *15*, 95–7 (1939); *Chem. Abstr.*, *35*, 4367 (1941).

[43]Conant and Blatt, *J. Am. Chem. Soc.*, *51*, 1227–36 (1929); Conant, Webb, and Mendum, *ibid.*, *51*, 1246–55 (1929).

[44]Noller and Hilmer, *J. Am. Chem. Soc.*, *54*, 2503–6 (1932).

[45]Kharasch and Weinhouse, *J. Org. Chem.*, *1*, 209–30 (1936).

responding alkyl bromide in pyridine, but were unable to establish any direct correlation between these properties.

Kharasch and Weinhouse (*loc. cit.*[45]) have pointed out that the reductions of aromatic ketones, such as benzophenone, are competitive with the normal addition reaction. (In the cases of many aliphatic and aliphatic-aromatic ketones, reaction may be further complicated by enolization and condensation.) Even in the simplest case, therefore—the reactions of benzophenone with a series of alkylmagnesium halides—the amount of reduction product formed is not a direct measure of the reducing tendency of the Grignard reagent. By means of competitive reactions, it was shown that the reactivity of the Grignard reagent with respect to the normal addition reaction increases markedly as the "electronegativity" of the organic radical of the Grignard reagent decreases.[46] In general the reducing power of the Grignard reagent also tends to increase (but less rapidly) with decreasing "electronegativity" of the organic radical of the Grignard reagent.* The necessary consequence is that in the case of Grignard reagents with sufficiently weakly electronegative radicals, high potential reducing power may be partially or completely masked by still greater reactivity with respect to the normal addition reaction. Table VI-II, in which the organic radicals are listed in the order of decreasing "electronegativity," is illustrative.

It should be noted in passing that the relative rates of reactions involving "hindered" ketones or very bulky Grignard reagents, or both, may be markedly affected by steric factors.

TABLE VI-II

REDUCTION OF BENZOPHENONE BY ALKYLMAGNESIUM HALIDES

R (in RMgX)	βH atoms	Reduction (%)
C_2H_5	3 prim.	2.0
n-C_3H_7	2 sec.	58.0
n-C_4H_9	2 sec.	59.0
i-C_4H_9	1 tert.	91.0
i-C_5H_{11}	2 sec.	30.0
$(CH_2)_5CH$	4 sec.	7.0
$(CH_2)_4CH$	4 sec.	94.0
s-C_4H_9	3 prim., 2 sec.	40.0
i-C_3H_7	6 prim.	13.0
$C_6H_5(CH_2)_2$	2 sec.	33.0
$C_6H_5(CH_2)_3$	2 sec.	20.0
t-C_4H_9	9 prim.	0.0

[46]Concerning relative electronegativities of organic radicals, see: Kharasch and Reinmuth, *J. Chem. Education*, *5*, 404–18 (1928); *8*, 1703–48 (1931); Kharasch, Reinmuth, and Mayo, *ibid.*, *11*, 82–96 (1934); *13*, 7–19 (1936).

*More specifically, the primary *beta* hydrogen atoms of the *t*-butyl group are potentially more labile (with respect to the reduction reaction under discussion) than the primary *beta* hydrogen atoms of the ethyl group; the secondary *beta* hydrogen atoms of the phenethyl group are potentially more labile than the secondary *beta* hydrogen atoms of the propyl group.

Other studies of the reducing action of Grignard reagents have been made by Stas[47], by Grignard and Delarue[48], and by Blatt and Stone.[49] Numerous examples of side-reaction reductions are recorded in the appropriate tabulations.

Concerning the actual mechanism of the Grignard reagent reduction Whitmore[50] has offered a suggestion involving the concept of a quasi six-membered ring transition state.

```
        H              .H.             H
R'\    |  /     R'\ .  ·  . /    R'\   /
   C   C<   →      C     C<  →     C   C<
R/ ‖   |     R/  :     :     R/  |   ‖
   O   C<          O·.   .C<       O   C<
   ..  /           ..  /            \
      Mg              Mg              Mg
      |               |               |
      X               X               X
```

This scheme has several attractive features: (*a*) it does not conflict with any of the observed facts relating to Grignard reagent reductions of the type under discussion; (*b*) it accounts, in part, for the fact that a labile *beta* hydrogen atom is essential to such reductions; (*c*) it furnishes a possible basis for the elucidation of asymmetric reductions; and, (*d*) it embodies a fundamental concept that can be extended, not only to elucidation of other so-called "abnormal" reactions, but to that of the "normal" addition reaction as well.

In a study of various reactions of bornyl- and isobornylmagnesium chlorides,* Rivière[51] had found that the former reacts with esters (ethyl carbonate, ethyl formate, ethyl chloroformate) to give "normal" products almost exclusively, whereas the latter behaves predominantly as a reducing agent. Since these reagents are optically active stereoisomers it became a matter of considerable interest to ascertain whether or not the reduction of an unsymmetrical ketone with isobornylmagnesium chloride would yield an optically active secondary alcohol. With Vavon and

---

[47]Stas, *Bull. soc. chim. Belg.*, *34*, 188–90 (1925); *35*, 379–86 (1926).

[48]Grignard and Delarue, *Bull. soc. chim.*, [4], *47*, 237 (1930).

[49]Blatt and Stone, *J. Am. Chem. Soc.*, *54*, 1495–9 (1932).

[50]Frank C. Whitmore, paper presented before the Atlantic City meeting of the American Chemical Society, April, 1943, as quoted by Mosher and LaCombe, *J. Am. Chem. Soc.*, *72*, 3994–9 (1950).

* The Grignard reagent obtained in 60–70 percent yields by the treatment of ethereal pinene hydrochloride with magnesium apparently consists of an equimolecular mixture of bornyl- and isobornylmagnesium chlorides. The "isomerized" Grignard reagent obtained by heating such a mixture in xylene at 140° for three hours is substantially pure bornylmagnesium chloride. The residual Grignard reagent remaining after partial (*ca.* 65 percent) carbonation of the Grignard reagent mixture derived from pinene hydrochloride is substantially pure isobornylmagnesium chloride.

[51]Rivière, *Ann. chim.*, [12], *1*, 157–231 (1946).

Angelo,[52] Riviére found that acetophenone does indeed undergo asymmetric reduction with isobornylmagnesium chloride. The results obtained in a subsequent extension of the study[53] to a total of six ketones of the $RCOC_6H_5$ type are summarized in Table VI-III.

TABLE VI-III

REDUCTION OF UNSYMMETRICAL KETONES WITH ISOBORNYLMAGNESIUM CHLORIDE

$RCOC_6H_5$	Yield (%) of $RCH(OH)C_6H_5$	Optical Activity of Product	Optical Activity of Pure (+)-$RCH(OH)C_6H_5$
$CH_3COC_6H_5$	55	$[\alpha]_{578}$ 20.10°	$[\alpha]_{578}$ 54.86°
$C_2H_5COC_6H_5$	50	$[\alpha]_D$ 10.60°	$[\alpha]_D$ 55.54°
n-$C_3H_7COC_6H_5$	50	$[\alpha]_D$ 26.70°	$[\alpha]_D$ 57.21°
i-$C_3H_7COC_6H_5$	80	$[\alpha]_D$ 26.40°	$[\alpha]_D$ 47.66°
n-$C_4H_9COC_6H_5$	44	$[\alpha]_D$ 21.10°	$[\alpha]_D$ 40.83°
s-$C_4H_9COC_6H_5$	90	$[\alpha]_D$ 25.90°	$[\alpha]_D$ 36.00°

Mosher and La Combe[54] have investigated the action of "dextrorotatory" 2-methylbutylmagnesium chloride* on pinacolin under a variety of experimental conditions, and have obtained 9.0–35.6 percent yields of pinacolyl alcohol ranging in optical activity from $[\alpha]_D^{20}$ + 0.42 to $[\alpha]_D^{20}$ + 0.70, indicating that the reduction products contain the dextro isomer in 13.0–16.1 percent excess.†

$$CH_3CO\text{-}t\text{-}C_4H_9 + (+)\text{-}CH_3(C_2H_5)CHCH_2MgCl \longrightarrow$$
$$[H_2C{=}C(O)\text{-}t\text{-}C_4H_9]^- MgCl^+ \ (11.1\text{–}39.5\%) + \text{tertiary alcohol and/or}$$
$$\text{ketol } (8.1\text{–}37.9\%) + H_2C{=}C(CH_3)C_2H_5 \ (6{,}2\text{–}31.2\%) + \text{DL- and}$$
$$(+)\text{-}CH_3(t\text{-}C_4H_9)CHOH \ (9.0\text{–}35.6\%)$$

Whereas it appears improbable that any vague inductive effect of an optically asymmetric reaction medium would suffice to instigate a partially asymmetric synthesis of any kind,‡ it seems reasonable to seek an

[52]Vavon, Riviére, and Angelo, *Compt. rend.*, *222*, 959–61 (1946); *Chem. Abstr.*, *40*, 4365 (1946).

[53]Vavon and Angelo, *Compt. rend.*, *224*, 1435–7 (1947); *Chem. Abstr.*, *41*, 6221 (1947).

[54]Mosher and LaCombe, *J. Am. Chem. Soc.*, *72*, 3994–9 (1950).

* Prepared from (+)-$CH_3(C_2H_5)CHCH_2Cl$ of 94–96% optical purity.

† The pure optical isomer, (+)-$CH_3(t\text{-}C_4H_9)CHOH$, has a specific rotation $[\alpha]_D^{20}$ + 7.71.

‡ In this connection it may be noted that Tarbell and Paulson, *J. Am. Chem. Soc.*, *64*, 2842–4 (1942), treated phenylmagnesium bromide, prepared in (+)-2-methoxybutane, with acetaldehyde and obtained 60–68 percent yields of the racemic addition product, DL-$CH_3(C_6H_5)CHOH$. Cohen and Wright, *Abstracts of Papers,* 121st Meeting, A.C.S., Buffalo, N. Y., March 23–27, 1952, p. 32K, operating in (+)-2,3-dimethoxybutane, or in benzene or toluene to which at least one molecular equivalent of the optically active ether had been added, obtained

explanation of the phenomenon in an intermediate reaction complex capable of existing in two stereoisomeric forms, one of which is presumably somewhat favored over the other by steric effects. Mosher and La Combe (*loc. cit.*[54]) have offered such an interpretation based on the concept of a quasi six-membered ring intermediate. Unfortunately, none of the commercially-available model sets is especially well adapted to the illustration of this thesis, and planar diagrams are perhaps even less satisfactory. However, the general sense of the argument may be conveyed by the following formulae (**A, B**).

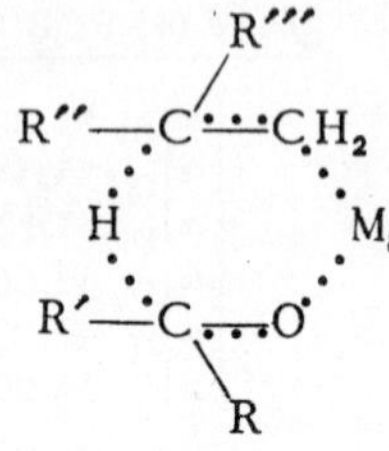

$$\begin{array}{ccc} & R''' & \\ R''-C & \cdots & CH_2 \\ H & & Mg-X \\ R'-C & \cdots & O \\ & R & \end{array} \qquad \begin{array}{ccc} & R' & \\ R-C & \cdots & O \\ H & & Mg-X \\ R''-C & \cdots & CH_2 \\ & R''' & \end{array}$$

(A) 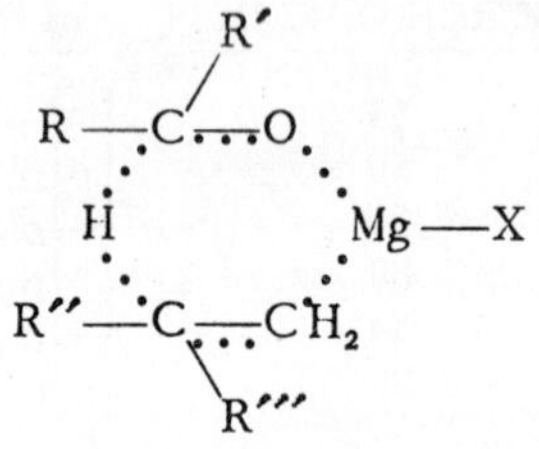 **(B)**

Mosher and La Combe[55] assume further that one member of the postulated six-membered ring of the transition state must be an asymmetric center, and believe that the symmetrical reduction of pinacolin by (+)-3-methylpentylmagnesium chloride supports this view.

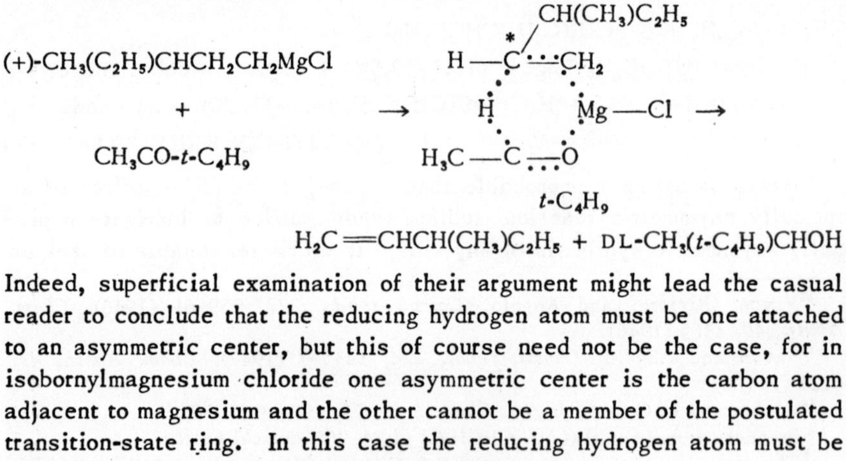

$$\begin{array}{c} (+)\text{-}CH_3(C_2H_5)CHCH_2CH_2MgCl \\ + \\ CH_3CO\text{-}t\text{-}C_4H_9 \end{array} \rightarrow \begin{array}{ccc} & CH(CH_3)C_2H_5 & \\ H-\overset{*}{C} & \cdots & CH_2 \\ H & & Mg-Cl \\ H_3C-C & \cdots & O \\ & t\text{-}C_4H_9 & \end{array} \rightarrow$$

$$H_2C{=}CHCH(CH_3)C_2H_5 + \text{DL-}CH_3(t\text{-}C_4H_9)CHOH$$

Indeed, superficial examination of their argument might lead the casual reader to conclude that the reducing hydrogen atom must be one attached to an asymmetric center, but this of course need not be the case, for in isobornylmagnesium chloride one asymmetric center is the carbon atom adjacent to magnesium and the other cannot be a member of the postulated transition-state ring. In this case the reducing hydrogen atom must be one of two attached to an inactive *beta* carbon atom.

---

products with a small but significant (1–2 percent) degree of activity when a Grignard reagent prepared from inactive *s*-butyl chloride was treated with benzaldehyde or other co-reactants. In such cases, however, optically active ethers or amines [see Betti and Lucchi, *Boll. sci. facolta chim. ind., Bologna, 1940*, No. 1–2, 2–5; *Chem. Abstr.*, *34*, 2354 (1940)] constitute somewhat more than an asymmetric environment, for they are capable of entering into the transition-state intermediate through complex formation with the Grignard reagent.

[55] Mosher and La Combe, *J. Am. Chem. Soc.*, 72, 4991–4 (1950).

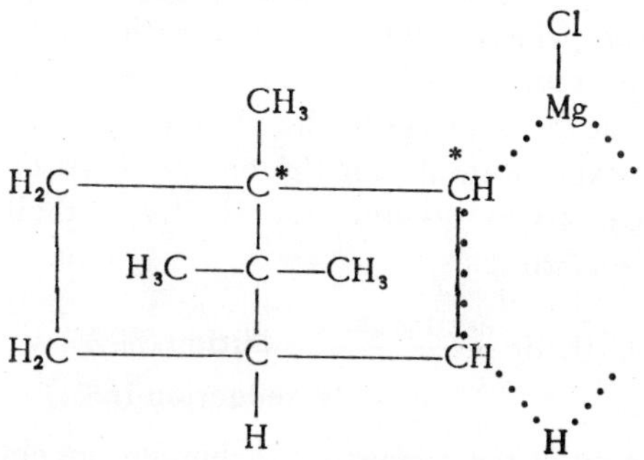

Cl
|
CH$_3$ Mg
H_2C — C^* — $\overset{*}{CH}$
H_3C—C—CH_3
H_2C — C — CH
H H

The fundamental necessity of the hypothesis is, of course, that the postulated transition state shall be capable of two stereoisomeric forms (A′, B′), one of which is sterically favored over the other. It may well be that no acyclic Grignard reagent other than one with the reducing hydrogen atom attached to an asymmetric carbon atom can enter into a transition state fulfilling the stated conditions; if so, however, the fact may be regarded as, in a sense, coincidental.

Possibility of suppressing Grignard reagent reduction. The respective mechanisms tentatively proposed to account for "normal" addition of a Grignard reagent at a carbonyl double bond and for the Grignard reagent reduction of a carbonyl group suggest the possibility of suppressing the latter in favor of the former. To this end labilization of the carbonyl double bond might be effected by complex formation with an organometallic compound incapable of either reduction or rapid "normal" 1,2 carbonyl addition [*e.g.*: $(C_6H_5)_2Cd$, C_6H_5ZnX, $(CH_3)_2Hg$, MgX_2]. "Normal" addition of a reducing Grignard reagent might then take place by reaction of the reagent with a previously-formed complex—providing that complete exchange in the senses

$$RR'CO\!:\!MgX_2 + R''MgX' \rightleftharpoons RR'CO\!:\!MgR''X' + MgX_2$$

or

$$RR'CO\!:\!MgX_2 + R''MgX' \rightleftharpoons RR'CO\!:\!MgR''X + MgXX'$$

is not too rapid in comparison with addition.

For example:

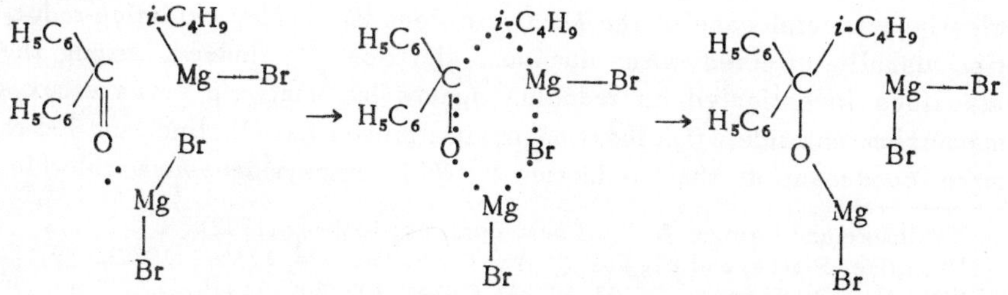

$(H_5C_6)_2C{=}O$ + i-C_4H_9—Mg—Br + Br—Mg—Br → [$(H_5C_6)_2C{\cdots}O{\cdots}$Mg(Br) / i-$C_4H_9{\cdots}$Mg—Br transition complex] → $(H_5C_6)_2C(i\text{-}C_4H_9)$—O—Mg—Br + Mg(Br)—Br

Since the first draft of this discussion was written, Swain[56] has published a note presenting the same idea, and reporting that in the case of

[56] Swain and Boyles, *J. Am. Chem. Soc.*, 73, 870–2 (1951).

the reaction of *n*-propylmagnesium bromide with diïsopropyl ketone, at least, the suggested technique is indeed capable of enhancing the yield of addition product at the expense of the yield of reduction product.

Employing the experimental conditions of Whitmore and George[57], Swain obtained quantitative results very similar to theirs, which may be summarized in the equation:

$$(i\text{-}C_3H_7)_2CO : Mg(n\text{-}C_3H_7)Br \xrightarrow{n\text{-}C_3H_7MgBr} \text{Addition (30\%)} + \text{reduction (63\%)} + \text{enolization (3\%)}$$

Employing a variation of the suggested technique, he obtained the following results:

$$(i\text{-}C_3H_7)_2CO : MgBr_2 \xrightarrow{n\text{-}C_3H_7MgBr} \text{Addition (65\%)} + \text{reduction (26\%)} + \text{enolization (1\%)}$$

In terms of the working hypothesis investigated it may be said (ignoring the relatively insignificant complication introduced by enolization) that the amount of reduction observed in the second experiment (26 percent) is roughly indicative of the amount of complex exchange that took place during the reaction period. Such exchange could be minimized by saturation of the Grignard reagent solution with magnesium bromide prior to its combination with the ketone-halide complex solution (or suspension).

A similar suppression of reduction with consequent facilitation of addition has been reported by McBee *et al.*[57.1] in the case of the reaction of ethylmagnesium iodide with pentafluoropropionaldehyde:

$$C_2F_5CHO + C_2H_5MgI \longrightarrow \text{Addition (34\%)} + \text{reduction (56\%)};$$

$$C_2F_5CHO : MgBr_2 + C_2H_5MgI \longrightarrow \text{Addition (58\%)} + \text{reduction (36\%)}.$$

Alkoxide reduction. Marshall[58] claims to have been the first to observe that in reactions with a Grignard reagent, an excess of aldehyde operates as an oxidizing agent. He found, for example that when phenylmagnesium bromide is treated with two equivalents of benzaldehyde, the products are benzyl alcohol and benzophenone, together with a small amount of material which he designated as symmetrical tetraphenylethane. This is clearly a special case of the Meerwein-Ponndorf-Verley oxidation-reduction usually effected with aluminum alkoxides.[59] Indeed, among the alkoxides investigated as reducing agents by Meerwein[60] was ethoxymagnesium chloride. (Diethoxymagnesium proved too alkaline, and led to more condensation than reduction.) With ethoxymagnesium chloride,

[57]Whitmore and George, *J. Am. Chem. Soc.*, *64*, 1239–42 (1942).

[57.1]McBee, Pierce, and Higgins, *J. Am. Chem. Soc.*, *74*, 1736–7 (1952).

[58]Marshall, *J. Chem. Soc.*, *105*, 527–34 (1914); *107*, 509–23 (1915).

[59]See: A. L. Wilds, "Reduction with Aluminum Alkoxides," Chapter 5, Vol. II of "Organic Reactions," edited by Roger Adams, John Wiley & Sons, Inc., New York, *1944*, pp. 178–223.

[60]Meerwein and Schmidt, *Ann.*, *444*, 221–38 (1925).

reduction products of the following aldehydes were obtained in the indicated percentage yields: cinnamaldehyde (*ca.* 80), benzaldehyde (76), anisaldehyde (75), *p*-nitrobenzaldehyde (70), crotonaldehyde (60), citronellal (70–80). From the cinnamaldehyde reaction, 51 percent of the theoretical quantity of acetaldehyde was isolated.

$$C_2H_5OMgCl + C_6H_5CH{=}CHCHO \rightarrow C_6H_5CH{=}CHCH_2OMgCl + CH_3CHO$$

Meisenheimer,[61] who had apparently overlooked Marshall's work, used an excess of benzaldehyde in some experiments in a study of the reducing action of Grignard reagents. In a later study[62] he investigated the residues which were always formed in considerable amount when ethylmagnesium bromide was allowed to react with an excess of benzaldehyde, and succeeded in isolating and identifying propiophenone. He recognized and pointed out the relationship of this work to that of Meerwein and and Schmidt (*loc. cit.*[60]).

$$C_2H_5(C_6H_5)CHOMgBr + C_6H_5CHO \rightarrow C_2H_5COC_6H_5 + C_6H_5CH_2OMgBr$$

Shankland and Gomberg[63] have investigated the reducing action of several alkoxymagnesium iodides on a variety of aldehydes and ketones. In general, these reactions appear to be rather rapid. For example, at the boiling point of ether, the diïodomagnesium derivative of dihydrobenzoïn effects a 95.3 percent reduction of benzaldehyde (as measured by the yield of benzoïn) in fifteen minutes. (In general, yields of alcohols isolable are about 10 percent lower than benzoïn yields.)

$$C_6H_5CH(OMgI)CH(OMgI)C_6H_5 + C_6H_5CHO \rightarrow C_6H_5CH(OMgI)COC_6H_5 + C_6H_5CH_2OMgI$$

Bradsher[64] has used a similar reaction as a method of ketone preparation.

$$\underset{\text{(from 56 g. iodide)}}{2\text{-}C_6H_5C_6H_4MgI} + \underset{\text{(22 ml.)}}{C_6H_5CHO} \xrightarrow[\text{in } C_6H_6]{\text{22 hrs. reflux}} \underset{\text{(35.8 g., 69.5\%)}}{2\text{-}C_6H_5C_6H_4COC_6H_5}$$

Gray and Fuson[65] describe a reaction which is probably best explained as a Meerwein oxidation-reduction combined with a condensation.

$$2,4,6\text{-}(CH_3)_3C_6H_2COCHO + 2,4,6\text{-}(CH_3)_3C_6H_2MgBr \rightarrow [2,4,5\text{-}(CH_3)_3C_6H_2CO\text{—}]_2 + [2,4,6\text{-}(CH_3)_3C_6H_2COCH(OH)\text{—}]_2$$

The overall reaction may be broken down into the following steps:*

$$MesCOCHO + MesMgBr \rightarrow MesCOCH(OMgBr)Mes$$

$$MesCOCHO + MesCOCH(OMgBr)Mes \rightarrow [MesCO\text{—}]_2 + MesCOCH_2OMgBr$$

$$MesCOCHO + MesCOCH_2OMgBr \rightarrow MesCOCH(OMgBr)CH(OH)COMes$$

[61] Meisenheimer, *Ann.*, *442*, 180–210 (1925).
[62] Meisenheimer, *Ann.*, *446*, 76–86 (1926).
[63] Shankland and Gomberg, *J. Am. Chem. Soc.*, *52*, 4973–8 (1930).
[64] Bradsher, *J. Am. Chem. Soc.*, *66*, 45–6 (1944).
[65] Gray and Fuson, *J. Am. Chem. Soc.*, *56*, 739–41 (1934).
*Mes = mesityl = $2,4,6\text{-}(CH_3)_3C_6H_2$—.

Paradoxically enough, oxygen contamination of a Grignard reagent which is in itself incapable of effecting reduction may lead to a Meerwein reduction. This is probably the cause of the small amount of reduction product observed by Kharasch and Weinhouse (*loc. cit.*[45]) in the treatment of benzophenone with allylmagnesium bromide, and by Gilman and and Abbott[66] in the treatment of chloral with benzylmagnesium chloride.

$$H_2C{=}CHCH_2MgBr + \tfrac{1}{2}\,O_2 \rightarrow H_2C{=}CHCH_2OMgBr^{*}$$

$$(C_6H_5)_2CO + H_2C{=}CHCH_2OMgBr \rightarrow H_2C{=}CHCHO + (C_6H_5)_2CHOMgBr$$

$$C_6H_5CH_2MgCl + \tfrac{1}{2}\,O_2 \rightarrow C_6H_5CH_2OMgCl^{\dagger}$$

$$Cl_3CCHO + C_6H_5CH_2OMgCl \rightarrow C_6H_5CHO + Cl_3CCH_2OMgBr$$

For the alkoxide reductions, as for the Grignard reagent reductions, a transition state involving a quasi six-membered ring may be postulated.

```
      H                       .H.                     H
 R\    \   /R''       R\  .'     '.  /R''     R\    /      /R''
   >C   C<      →       >C         C<      →    >C      C<
 R'/ ||  | \R'''      R'/ :         : \R'''   R'/ |     || \R'''
    O    O              O.         .O            O      O
    .   /                 '.     .'               \
   .  Mg                     Mg                    Mg
      |                      |                     |
      X                      X                     X
```

At this writing no report of an asymmetric reduction of this kind effected with the aid of an optically active halomagnesium alkoxide has come to the attention of the present authors. However, partially asymmetric reactions have been reported in the closely analogous cases of carbonyl reductions with optically active potassium and aluminum alkoxides.[67,68,69]

Magnesious halide reduction. Schmidlin[70] observed that the reaction of triphenylmethylmagnesium chloride with benzophenone in the presence of excess magnesium powder leads to the production of benzpinacol rather than of the expected pentaphenylethanol. It has since been shown by Gilman and Fothergill[71] that, in the cases of triphenylmethylmagnesium bromide and chloride, the presence of metallic magnesium is unnecessary to pinacol formation.

---

[66] Gilman and Abbot, *J. Org. Chem.*, 8, 224–9 (1943).

* These equations represent stoichiometrical relationships only. Concerning the oxygenation of Grignard reagents see: Chapter XX, Reactions of Grignard Reagents with Oxygen, etc.

[67] Doering and Aschner, Abstracts of Papers, 112th meeting of the American Chemical Society, New York, September, 1947, p. 21L.

[68] Doering and Young, *J. Am. Chem. Soc.*, 72, 631 (1950).

[69] Jackman, Mills, and Shannon, *J. Am. Chem. Soc.*, 72, 4814–5 (1950).

[70] Schmidlin, *Ber.*, 39, 4198–204 (1906).

[71] Gilman and Fothergill, *J. Am. Chem. Soc.*, 51, 3149–57 (1929).

The nature of this reaction has been clarified by the work of Gomberg *et al.*,[72] who showed that similar reductions of aromatic ketones may be effected with magnesium-magnesium iodide or magnesium-magnesium bromide, but not with magnesium-magnesium chloride, mixtures. Neither magnesium alone nor magnesium halide alone is effective. The reaction solutions are intensely colored, and do not obey Beer's law.

The reactions are explained as a consequence of the ability of magnesium bromide (or iodide), in contact with metallic magnesium to behave as though it were in equilibrium with the magnesious halide.

$$MgX_2 + Mg \rightleftharpoons 2\cdot MgX$$

$$2\,(C_6H_5)_2CO + 2\cdot MgX \longrightarrow 2\,XMgO(C_6H_5)_2C\cdot$$

$$2\,XMgO(C_6H_5)_2C\cdot \rightleftharpoons [XMgO(C_6H_5)_2C—]_2 \xrightarrow{H_2O} [HO(C_6H_5)_2C—]_2 + MgX_2 + Mg(OH)_2$$

The intense coloration is attributed to the ketyl radical $[XMgO(C_6H_5)_2C\cdot]$.

By such means Schönberg and Moubasher[73] have succeeded in reducing 1,2,3-indantrione to hydrintanin.

1,2,3-Indantrione (1.0 g.) $\xrightarrow{\cdot MgI}\ \xrightarrow{H_2O}$ [dimer of 2-hydroxy-1,3-indandione hydrate unit: C(=O)–C(OH)– / C(OH)(OH)]$_2$ (0.6 g.)

An interesting variation on the usual theme of pinacol formation in the case of an α,β-unsaturated "hindered" ketone is reported by Fuson *et al.*[74,*]

$$\underset{(11.68\ g.)}{MesCOC(Mes){=}CH_2} \xrightarrow[I_2\ (9.80\ g.)]{Mg\ (1.92\ g.)} \xrightarrow{(+H_2O)} \underset{(94\%)}{[MesC(OH){=}C(Mes)CH_2—]_2}$$

A different, though formally analogous, dimerization has been observed by Fuson and Hornberger.[75]

$$\underset{(60.0\ g.)}{MesCOC_6H_5} \xrightarrow[I_2\ (22.0\ g.)]{Mg\ (30.0\ g.)} MesCH(OH)–C_6H_4–C_6H_4–COMes$$

(I) (6.35 g., 10.5%)

---

[72](*a*) Gomberg and Bachmann, *J. Am. Chem. Soc.*, *49*, 236–57 (1927); (*b*) Gomberg, Bailar, and Van Natta, *Rec. trav. chim.*, *48*, 847–51 (1929); (*c*) Gomberg and Shankland, *J. Am. Chem. Soc.*, *51*, 306–9 (1929); (*d*) Gomberg and Bailar, *J. Am. Chem. Soc.*, *51*, 2229–38 (1929).

[73]Schönberg and Moubasher, *J. Chem. Soc.*, *1949*, 212–4.

[74]Fuson, Byers, and Rachlin, *J. Am. Chem. Soc.*, *64*, 2891–3 (1942).

* Mes = mesityl = $2,4,6\text{-}(CH_3)_3C_6H_2—$.

[75]Fuson and Hornberger, *J. Org. Chem.*, *16*, 631–6 (1951).

Possibly the resonant ketyl radicals combine to form the equivalent of a dihydride of the product here represented, and two extremely labile hydrogen atoms (or the equivalent) are eventually removed by a suitable hydrogen acceptor, as, *e.g.*, atmospheric oxygen. In view of the low yield reported, even the possibility of a Meerwein oxidation-reduction cannot be rejected.

However, it is conceivable that this reaction actually has more in common with the 1,4-additions of Grignard reagents to conjugated carbonyl systems (*q.v.*) than with the generally accepted ketyl dimerization scheme formulated to elucidate the ordinary magnesious halide reductions of ketones.* It has been shown by Gomberg and Bachmann[76] that at least some free radicals are capable of combining with magnesious halide to form Grignard reagents (see Grignard Reagents from Free Radicals, Chapter II). A scheme embodying the concept of Grignard reagent formation and 1,4-addition to a conjugated carbonyl system might be outlined as follows:

$$MesCOC_6H_5 \xrightarrow{\cdot MgX} \left[Mes\text{—}\dot{C}(OMgX)\text{—}C_6H_5 \longleftrightarrow Mes\text{—}C(OMgX){=}C_6H_5(\dot{C}\text{—}H) \right] \xrightarrow{\cdot MgX}$$

XMgO
Mes—CH—(ring)—MgX (ortho)

$$\xrightarrow{MesCOC_6H_5}$$

XMgO
Mes—CH—(ring), ring C(H)—(ring)=C(OMgX)—Mes

$$\xrightarrow[\text{[+ Ox]}]{2\ H_2O}$$

$MesCH(OH)$—(ring)—(ring)—$COMes$ $+ Mg(OH)_2 + MgX_2 + OxH_2$

(I)

---

*Incidentally, as will become apparent in the succeeding discussion, it would be possible to interpret the ordinary pinacol production as involving the formation of a Grignard reagent from a ketyl free radical and the 1,2-addition of the Grignard reagent so derived to the carbonyl double bond of the ketone, although there seems no good reason to do so.

[76]Gomberg and Bachmann, *J. Am. Chem. Soc.*, *52*, 2455–61 (1930).

In its essentials (though with minor modifications) this is the scheme proposed by Fuson and Hornberger[77] to account for similar reductive couplings involving methoxyl group displacement* (see also 1,4-Additions Involving Cleavage, p. 231).

$MesCOC_6H_5$ + $MesCOC_6H_4$-2-OCH_3 $\xrightarrow[I_2]{Mg}$ MesCH(OH)–C_6H_4–C_6H_4–COMes (28%) + CH_3OH

$DurCOC_6H_5$ + $MesCOC_6H_4$-2-OCH_3 $\xrightarrow[I_2]{Mg}$ DurCH(OH)–C_6H_4–C_6H_4–COMes (25%) + CH_3OH

$MesCOC_6H_5$ + $DurCOC_6H_4$-2-OCH_3 $\xrightarrow[I_2]{Mg}$ MesCH(OH)–C_6H_4–C_6H_4–CODur (24%) + CH_3OH

$DurCOC_6H_5$ + $DurCOC_6H_4$-2-OCH_3 $\xrightarrow[I_2]{Mg}$ DurCH(OH)–C_6H_4–C_6H_4–CODur (23%) + CH_3OH

$MesCOC_6H_4$-2-OCH_3 + $MesCOC_6H_4$-2-OCH_3 $\xrightarrow[I_2]{Mg}$ 9,10-Mes,Mes-phenanthrene (10.5%) + H–C(Mes)–C(Mes)–OH (biphenyl-bridged, with OCH_3) (?) (22%)

[77]Fuson and Hornberger, *J. Org. Chem.*, *16*, 637–42 (1951).
*Dur = duryl = 2,3,5,6-$(CH_3)_4C_6H$—.

Although attractive enough in itself, the reaction scheme proposed by Fuson and Hornberger (*loc. cit.*[77]) does not seem readily adaptable to elucidation of the formation of mesityl 2′-(mesitylhydroxymethyl)-2-biphenylyl ketone (**I**), observed, though (apparently erroneously) reported as pinacol formation, by Kharasch *et al.*[78] in the reaction of phenylmagnesium bromide with mesitoyl chloride in the presence of cobaltous chloride (see Chapter IX, Coupling). In the reaction cited there would appear to be no reasonable hypothesis of ketone "dimer" formation alternative to postulation of mutual combination of free radicals of type **II**, in which M signifies a metal (Co or Mg), and X signifies a halogen (Cl or Br).

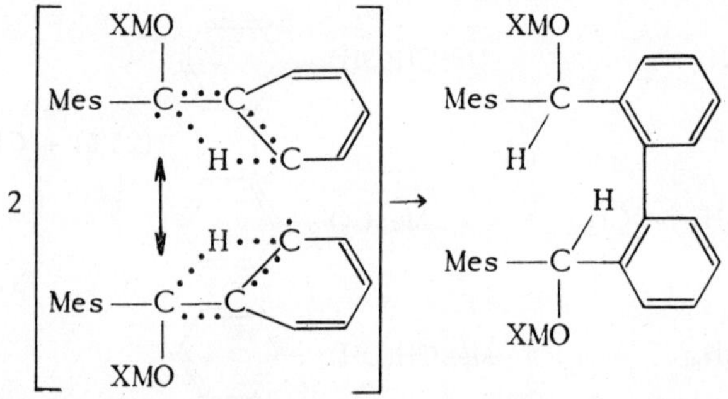

(**II**)

Some aldehydes also undergo magnesious halide reductions, as in the case of 2,4-dimethylbenzaldehyde, reported by Fuson and Ward.[79]

$$2,4\text{-}(CH_3)_2C_6H_3CHO \xrightarrow{Mg\ +\ MgI_2} \xrightarrow{(+H_2O)} [2,4\text{-}(CH_3)_2C_6H_3(HO)CH—]_2$$

As might be expected, and as was observed by Law[80] in the alkaline electrolytic reductions of *p*-tolualdehyde, and 2,4-dimethyl- and 3,5-dimethylbenzaldehydes, the product is obtained in two stereoisomeric forms—presumably the meso and the racemic.

In the presence of an excess of aldehyde the magnesious halide reduction may be combined with a Meerwein oxidation-reduction, as in a case reported by Gomberg and Bachmann.[81] The second step of the reaction appears to be very rapid as compared to the first.

$$2\ C_6H_5CHO \xrightarrow{Mg\ +\ MgI_2} [C_6H_5(IMgO)CH—]_2$$

$$[C_6H_5(IMgO)CH—]_2 \xrightarrow{C_6H_5CHO} C_6H_5COCH(OMgI)C_6H_5 + C_6H_5CH_2OMgI$$

[78]Kharasch, Morrison, and Urry, *J. Am. Chem. Soc.*, *66*, 368–71 (1944).
[79]Fuson and Ward, *J. Am. Chem. Soc.*, *68*, 521–2 (1946).
[80]Law, *J. Chem. Soc.*, *91*, 748–60 (1907).
[81]Gomberg and Bachmann, *J. Am. Chem. Soc.*, *52*, 4967–72 (1930).

The magnesious halide reduction of a benzil leads to benzoïn enolate formation.[82, 83]

$$(RCO—)_2 + 2 \cdot MgX \longrightarrow [R(XMgO)C=]_2$$

$$\xrightarrow{H_2O} RCOCH(OH)R + MgX_2 + Mg(OH)_2$$

According to Gomberg and Van Natta (*loc. cit.*[82b]), similar reductions are effected by magnesium iodide alone in the absence of metallic magnesium. This phenomenon is attributed to the equilibrium:

$$(RCO—)_2 + 2\ MgI_2 \rightleftharpoons [R(IMgO)C=]_2 + I_2$$

In several experiments free iodine ranging in amount from 16 to 50 percent of the theoretical was determined by titration.

Although Gomberg's interpretation of the magnesium iodide reduction reaction is by no means implausible, the observation of Stewart and Ubbelohde[84] that oxygen-free solutions of magnesium iodide in ether become brown and cloudy on exposure to daylight appears relevant to the point under consideration. This observation would seem to constitute sufficient evidence for the dissociation:

$$MgI_2 \xrightarrow{h\nu} \cdot MgI + I \cdot$$

A comparison between the behaviors of the dark and illuminated reduction systems would be of some interest.

In the light of the studies of Gomberg and his co-workers, it appears fairly evident that in the reductions effected by Grignard reagents with extremely weak electronegative organic radicals (specifically, triarylmethylmagnesium halides), magnesious halide is the essential reducing agent.

$$2\ (C_6H_5)_3CMgBr + 2\ (C_6H_5)_2CO \longrightarrow 2\ BrMgO(C_6H_5)_2C \cdot + 2\ (C_6H_5)_3C \cdot$$

In the cases in which pinacol formation has been reported as resulting from the action of alkyl- or arylmagnesium halides on aromatic ketones,[85] there can be little doubt that the active reducing agent is magnesious halide arising from the interaction of residual magnesium with magnesium halide formed as a product of a Wurtz side-reaction or resulting from the Schlenk equilibrium. Mere siphoning of the Grignard solution may not be relied upon to insure the removal of finely suspended magnesium, and even a glass-wool plug is sometimes an insufficient safeguard.

---

[82](*a*) Gomberg and Bachmann, *J. Am. Chem. Soc.*, *49*, 2584–92 (1927); (*b*) Gomberg and Van Natta, *J. Am. Chem. Soc.*, *51*, 2238–45 (1929).

[83]Fuson and Corse, *J. Am. Chem. Soc.*, *61*, 975 (1939).

[84]Stewart and Ubbelohde, *J. Chem. Soc.*, *1949*, 2649–56.

[85]See, *e.g.*: Barnett, Cook, and Nixon, *J. Chem. Soc.*, *1927*, 505–12; Davies, Dixon, and Jones, *ibid.*, *1930*, 1916–21; Arbuzov and Arbuzova, *J. Gen. Chem.* (U.S.S.R.), *2*, 388–96 (1932); *Chem. Abstr.*, *27*, 974 (1933); *British Chem. Abstr.*, *1932A*, 1250; *Chem. Zentr.*, *1933*, *I*, 2940.

Gilman and Fothergill (*loc. cit.*[71]) have shown that, in the presence of free magnesium, one of the products of reaction of benzophenone with alkylmagnesium iodides and bromides (but not chlorides) is benzpinacol. When free magnesium was carefully excluded, no pinacol formation could be detected.

That metallic impurities in the magnesium employed in the preparation of the Grignard reagent may, however, occasionally play a part in such reactions is suggested by various observations of Kharasch and co-workers.[86] For example, isobutylmagnesium bromide ordinarily reacts with benzophenone to give high yields (of the order of 90 percent) of benzhydrol, the Grignard reagent reduction product. When about 2 mole percent of manganous chloride is present in the reaction system, however, benzhydrol formation becomes negligible, and benzpinacol is formed to the extent of 90 percent or more. Chromous and ferric chlorides have similar, but less pronounced, effects.[86a] With methylmagnesium bromide, benzophenone undergoes "normal" addition to give the tertiary alcohol in a yield of the order of 95 percent. When about 2 mole percent of cobaltous chloride is present in the reaction system the yield of tertiary alcohol is diminished to about 2 percent, and benzpinacol is formed in about 93 percent yield. Ferric chloride has a similar, but less pronounced effect.[86c] With methylmagnesium bromide, isophorone (3,5,5-trimethyl-2-cyclohexen-1-one) forms the "normal" 1,2-addition product in *ca.* 91 percent yield; in the presence of 1 mole percent of cobaltous chloride yields of pinacol range from 67.0 to 78.5 percent.[86b]

ENOLATE FORMATION BY GRIGNARD REAGENTS

Grignard[87] observed that when methylmagnesium iodide reacts with ethyl ethylacetoacetate, considerable amounts of methane are evolved and correspondingly large quantities of the keto ester are recovered (the yield of the expected hydroxy ester being rather small). He correctly ascribed this phenomenon to "enolization" (*i.e.*, to enolate formation).

Zelinsky[88] found that, although acetylacetone reacts readily with methylmagnesium iodide, the expected glycol is obtained in negligible quantities. He drew the conclusion, now known to be unjustified, that acetylacetone is a "pseudoketone," existing largely in the enolic form.

In an early study of the applicability of Tschugaeff's[89] suggested method for the quantitative evaluation of hydroxyl groups in organic substances, Hibbert and Sudborough[90] included acetoacetic ester and found

---

[86](*a*) Kharasch, Kleiger, Martin, and Mayo, *J. Am. Chem. Soc.*, *63*, 2305–7 (1941); (*b*) Kharasch and Tawney, *J. Am. Chem. Soc.*, *63*, 2308–15 (1941); (*c*) Kharasch and Lambert, *J. Am. Chem. Soc.*, *63*, 2315–6 (1941).

[87]Grignard, *Compt. rend.*, *134*, 849–51 (1902); *J. Chem. Soc.*, 82, *I*, 420.

[88]Zelinsky, *Ber.*, *35*, 2138–40 (1902).

[89]Tschugaeff, *Ber.*, *35*, 3912–4 (1902).

[90]Hibbert and Sudborough, *J. Chem. Soc.*, *85*, 933–8 (1904).

that, with methylmagnesium iodide in amyl ether, about 90 percent of the amount of methane equivalent to one hydroxyl group is liberated.

Zerewitinoff,[91] in the second of his classical series of studies on the determination of "active" hydrogen in organic compounds, included, among other enolizable compounds, acetylacetone, benzoylacetone, and acetoacetic ester. He found that, when treated with methylmagnesium iodide in amyl ether at 100°, they all gave rise to methane evolution equivalent to one "active" hydrogen atom per molecule. (At 20° the yield of methane was somewhat less.)

Dupont[92] reported that 2,2,5,5-tetramethyltetrahydrofuran-3-one "reacts as an enol" with ethyl-, *n*-propyl-, isobutyl-, phenyl- and *p*-tolylmagnesium bromides. With methyl-, ethynyl- and benzylmagnesium bromides, it yields the expected alcohols. 2,5-Dimethyl-2,5-diethyltetrahydrofuran-3-one is said to "react quantitatively as the enol."

Bhagvat and Sudborough[93] examined a number of aldehydes, ketones, and keto esters by the method of Zerewitinoff and announced that, whereas most aldehydes and ketones react "normally" (*i.e.*, additively), *beta* ketonic esters and *alpha, gamma* diketones yield large volumes of gas.

Ethylzinc iodide was recommended by Job and Reich[94] as a suitable reagent for the study of enols by the Zerewitinoff method on the ground that it does not react additively with carbonyl or ester groups. That it does not react solely with the enolic form, however, is evidenced by their observation that it "enolizes" acetoacetic ester slowly, but malonic ester and acetylacetone quite rapidly.

Using camphor, a very unreactive and slowly enolizable ketone, as test material, Bredt-Savelsburg[95] found that the rate of enolization is dependent upon the temperature, upon the particular Grignard reagent employed, and upon the solvent. The low rate of enolization of camphor is illustrated in the data of Table VI-IV. Other illustrative data are

TABLE VI-IV

RATE OF ENOLIZATION OF CAMPHOR BY METHYLMAGNESIUM IODIDE IN ETHYL ETHER SOLUTION AT 20°

Time (hrs.)	Enolization (%)
0.5	13.0
5.0	14.1
10.0	14.9
25.0	30.4
40.0	44.7

[91]Zerewitinoff, *Ber.*, *41*, 2233–43 (1908).

[92]Dupont, *Compt. rend.*, *154*, 519–21 (1912); *Chem. Zentr.*, *1912*, *I*, 1318.

[93]Bhagvat and Sudborough, *Proc. Asiatic. Soc. Bengal*, *15*, cxxvi (1919); *Chem. Abstr.*, *14*, 1674 (1920).

[94]Job and Reich, *Bull. soc. chim.*, [4], *33*, 1414–33 (1923).

[95]Bredt-Savelsburg, *J. prakt. chem.*, [2], *107*, 65–85 (1924).

assembled in Table VI-V. The effect of temperature is illustrated by the enolization of camphor by methylmagnesium iodide in ethyl ether to the extent of 6.8 percent at 0° and of 14.8 percent at 20° in the course of ten hours.

TABLE VI-V

EFFECT OF SOLVENT AND OF NATURE OF GRIGNARD REAGENT UPON RATE OF ENOLIZATION OF CAMPHOR AT ROOM TEMPERATURE

RMgX	Solvent	Time (hrs.)	Enolization (%)
CH_3MgI	Am_2O	36	*ca.* 3.6
CH_3MgI	C_6H_6	30	32.5
CH_3MgI	Et_2O	40	44.7
CH_3MgI	Et_2O	10	14.8
CH_3MgBr	Et_2O	10	24.0
CH_3MgCl	Et_2O	10	28.2
C_2H_5MgI	Et_2O	43	14.0
C_6H_5MgBr	Am_2O	24	21.0
1-$C_{10}H_7MgBr$	Et_2O	24	25.0

Grignard and Savard[96] investigated the action of some twenty-two Grignard reagents on pulegone (2-methyl-5-isopropylidenecyclohexanone) at 40°. Because it was not demonstrated that the gases evolved were due solely to enolization (rather than to a combination of enolization and reduction), their tabulation of data is here reproduced in part only in Table VI-VI.

TABLE VI-VI

ENOLIZATION OF PULEGONE BY VARIOUS NON-REDUCING GRIGNARD REAGENTS IN ETHYL ETHER AT 40°

Grignard Reagent	Enolization (%)
CH_3MgI	26
CH_3MgBr	33
C_6H_5MgI	35
C_6H_5MgBr	41
$C_6H_5CH_2MgI$	39
$C_6H_5CH_2MgBr$	44

In order to study the competition between the "normal" addition and the enolization reactions, Kohler *et al.*,[97] devised a modification of the Zerewitinoff apparatus, commonly called the "Grignard machine," which facilitates measurement, not only of the amount of methane evolved, but of the amount of methylmagnesium iodide consumed. Their data are summarized in Table VI-VII. In all cases, reactants were heated to completion of reaction (Grignard reagent in excess).

---

[96]Grignard and Savard, *Bull. soc. chim. Belg.*, 36, 97–107 (1927).

[97]Kohler, Stone, and Fuson, *J. Am. Chem. Soc.*, 49, 3181–8 (1927); Kohler and Richtmyer, *J. Am. Chem. Soc.*, 52, 3736–8 (1930).

TABLE VI-VII

REACTION OF METHYLMAGNESIUM IODIDE WITH VARIOUS KETONES IN ISOAMYL ETHER (QUANTITIES IN MILLIMOLES)

Ketone	Am't. Ketone	Am't. Gas Evolved	Am't. G. R. Consumed
$(C_6H_5)_2CO$	1.77	0.03	1.74
$(C_6H_5CO)_2$	0.97	0.09	1.95
$C_6H_5COCH(OH)C_6H_5$	1.08	1.10	2.15
$(C_6H_5CO)_2CH_2$	0.50	0.53	1.04
$(C_6H_5CO)_2CHCH_3$	0.50	0.08	1.05
$(C_6H_5CO)_2CHBr$	0.50	0.03	1.02
$CH_3COC_6H_5$	2.28	0.33	2.27
$CH_3COC_6H_5$	2.31	0.36	2.30
$C_6H_5COCH_2C_6H_5$	1.76	0.10	1.79
$C_6H_5COCH(C_6H_5)_2$	1.15	0.16	1.16
$CH_3COC_6H_2$-2,4,6-$(CH_3)_2$	0.95	0.94	0.92

Grignard and Blanchon[98] investigated the "enolization" of cyclohexanone by isopropylmagnesium bromide in ethyl ether, and believed that they had isolated the enolate and even the enol. This, however, was contradicted by Kohler and Thompson,[99] who repeated the experiment and obtained cyclohexanol (68 percent) and 2-cyclohexylidenecyclohexanone (26 percent). Their comment, however, somewhat overstepped the facts in the case. "Grignard reagents containing secondary and tertiary hydrocarbon residues frequently act as condensing and reducing agents, but we can find no evidence that they are more effective than others in inducing enolization, and we also fail to find any evidence that any Grignard reagents can convert mono ketones into enolates unless the hindrance to addition is prohibitive."

Apparently Kohler and Thompson either did not at that time recognize the relationship between enolization and condensation or expressed their true meaning ambiguously.

In the paper just cited, Grignard and Blanchon also reported the "enolization" of di-*n*-butyl ketone by a series of aliphatic Grignard reagents. As no attempt was made to distinguish between gases evolved through enolization and gases arising from reduction, their data are not here reproduced. The non-reducing methylmagnesium iodide and bromide effected 7.5 percent and 6.9 percent enolization, respectively, in ethyl ether solution at 13–14°.

The necessity of using a non-reducing Grignard reagent (preferably methylmagnesium bromide or chloride), or of otherwise taking account of reduction, in investigations of this kind is illustrated by the studies of Blatt and Stone[100] (Table VI-VIII) and of Whitmore and George[101] (Table VI-IX).

---

[98] Grignard and Blanchon, *Bull. soc. chim.*, [4], *49*, 23–42 (1931).
[99] Kohler and Thompson, *J. Am. Chem. Soc.*, *55*, 3822–33 (1933).
[100] Blatt and Stone, *J. Am. Chem. Soc.*, *54*, 1495–9 (1932).
[101] Whitmore and George, *J. Am. Chem. Soc.*, *64*, 1239–42 (1942).

TABLE VI-VIII

REACTIONS OF *n*-PROPYL AND ISOPROPYLMAGNESIUM BROMIDES WITH VARIOUS *n*-PROPYL AND ISOPROPYL KETONES

Ketone	RMgX	Add'n (%)	Red'n (%)	Enol'n (%)	Total (%)
$(n\text{-}C_3H_7)_2CO$	$n\text{-}C_3H_7MgBr$	54	24	...	78
$(n\text{-}C_3H_7)_2CO$	$i\text{-}C_3H_7MgBr$	44	5	15	64*
$n\text{-}C_3H_7CO\text{-}i\text{-}C_3H_7$	$n\text{-}C_3H_7MgBr$	63	17	...	80
$n\text{-}C_3H_7CO\text{-}i\text{-}C_3H_7$	$i\text{-}C_3H_7MgBr$	17	49	...	66
$(i\text{-}C_3H_7)_2CO$	$n\text{-}C_3H_7MgBr$	43	34	...	77
$(i\text{-}C_3H_7)_2CO$	$i\text{-}C_3H_7MgBr$	0	80	...	80

*Considerable condensation.

TABLE VI-IX

REACTIONS OF VARIOUS GRIGNARD REAGENTS WITH DIISOPROPYL KETONE

RMgX	Add'n (%)	Red'n (%)	Enol'n (%)	Total (%)
CH_3MgBr	95	0	0	95
C_2H_5MgBr	77	21	2	100
$n\text{-}C_3H_7MgBr$	36	60	2	98
$i\text{-}C_3H_7MgBr$	0	65	29	94
$i\text{-}C_4H_9MgBr$	8	78	11	97
$t\text{-}C_4H_9CH_2MgCl$	4	0	90	94
$t\text{-}C_4H_9MgX$	...	65	...	...

In view of the facts that enolate formation is commonly recognized as competitive with normal addition, and that the latter reaction appears to be subject to marked steric inhibition, whereas the former, in general, is not (as witness the behavior of the mesityl ketones), Whitmore and Lester[102] have studied the interactions of some dineopentylmethyl ketones with several Grignard reagents. Methyl dineopentylmethyl ketone was enolized quantitatively by isopropyl-, isobutyl-, and *t*-butylmagnesium halides. Ethyl dineopentylmethyl ketone reacted similarly with *t*-butylmagnesium chloride. That enolization may, in special cases, be sterically inhibited is suggested by their finding that the phenyl, *o*-tolyl, and *p*-tolyl dineopentylmethyl ketones underwent quantitative addition when treated with methylmagnesium bromide in the "Grignard machine." Presumably the only labile *alpha* hydrogen atom present in these ketones is sterically hindered by the two neopentyl groups.

The results of some "Grignard machine" studies by Whitmore *et al.*[103,104,105] and Kadesch[106] on the competition between the enolization and addition reactions of methylmagnesium halides with ketones are

[102] Whitmore and Lester, *J. Am. Chem. Soc.*, *64*, 1247–51 (1942).
[103] Whitmore and Randall, *J. Am. Chem. Soc.*, *64*, 1242–6 (1942).
[104] Whitmore and Block, *J. Am. Chem. Soc.*, *64*, 1619–21 (1942).
[105] Whitmore and Lewis, *J. Am. Chem. Soc.*, *64*, 2964–6 (1942).
[106] Kadesch, *J. Am. Chem. Soc.*, *66*, 1207–13 (1944).

TABLE VI-X

COMPETITIVE ENOLIZATION AND ADDITION REACTIONS OF METHYLMAGNESIUM HALIDES WITH KETONES

Ketone	Enol'n (%)	Add'n (%)	Reference
CH_3COCH_2-*t*-C_4H_9	0	100	W. and L.[105]
$CH_3COCH(CH_3)_2$	0	100	W. and B.[104]
$CH_3COC(CH_3)_3$	5	86	W. and L.[105]
			W. and B.[104]
CH_3CO-*s*-C_4H_9	32	...	W. and B.[104]
$C_2H_5COCH(CH_3)_2$	0	100	W. and B.[104]
$CH_3COC(CH_3)_2C_2H_5$	14	74	W. and L.[105]
$C_2H_5COC(CH_3)_3$	9	86	W. and B.[104]
$CH_3COC_6H_5$	9	76	K.[106]
$CH_3COC(C_2H_5)_2CH_3$	84	0	W. and L.[105]
$CH_3COCH(CH_3)$-*t*-C_4H_9	48	47	W. and B.[104]
n-C_3H_7CO-*s*-C_4H_9	53	40	W. and B.[104]
i-C_3H_7CO-*t*-C_4H_9	0	49	W. and B.[104]
1-Indanone	12	97	K.[106]
$CH_3COC_6H_4$-2-CH_3	14	58	K.[106]
$CH_3COC(C_2H_5)_3$	94	0	W. and L.[105]
$C_2H_5COCH(CH_3)$-*t*-C_4H_9	62	33	W. and B.[104]
1-Tetralone	17	57	K.[106]
$CH_3COC_6H_3$-2,4-$(CH_3)_2$	19	55	K.[106]
$H_2C{=}CHCOC(C_2H_5)_3$	0	58	W. and L.[105]
t-$C_4H_9COCH(C_2H_5)_2$	5	19	W. and B.[104]
$HOCH_2CH_2COC(C_2H_5)_3$	58	27	W. and L.[105]
CH_3CO-1-$C_{10}H_7$	6	74	K.[106]
CH_3CO-2-$C_{10}H_7$	15	117	K.[106]
4,7-Dimethyl-1-indanone	21	67	K.[106]
5,7-Dimethyl-1-indanone	16	66	K.[106]
Benzosuberone*	25	61	K.[106]
$CH_3COC_6H_2$-2,4,6-$(CH_3)_3$	73	...	K.[106]
1-Acetyl-2-methylnaphthalene	102	0	K.[106]
5,8-Dimethyl-1-tetralone	17	60	K.[106]
CH_3COC_6H-2,3,5,6-$(CH_3)_4$	81	0	K.[106]
i-$C_4H_9COC(C_2H_5)_3$	85	0	W. and L.[105]
6,9-Dimethylbenzosuberone†	101	0	K.[106]
4-Methyl-7-isopropyl-1-indanone	22	51	K.[106]
$CH_3COC(CH_3)$(*t*-C_4H_9)CH_2-*t*-C_4H_9	94	0	W. and R.[103]
$C_2H_5COC(CH_3)$(*t*-C_4H_9)CH_2-*t*-C_4H_9	57	0	W. and R.[103]
i-$C_3H_7COC(CH_3)$(*t*-C_4H_9)CH_2-*t*-C_4H_9	25	0	W. and R.[103]

*5-Oxobenzosuberan; 5-oxo-5,6,8,9-tetrahydro-7*H*-cycloheptabenzene.
†1,4-Dimethyl-5-oxobenzosuberan.

assembled in Table VI-X. Whereas the halide used and other experimental details vary from study to study, the data of the various studies are not strictly comparable one with another.

A similar "Grignard machine" study of the reactions of methylmagnesium iodide with various more or less "hindered" ketones, by Smith and Guss[107] is summarized in Table VI-XI.

[107]Smith and Guss, *J. Am. Chem. Soc.*, 59, 804–6 (1937).

TABLE VI-XI

COMPETITIVE ENOLIZATION AND ADDITION REACTIONS OF METHYLMAGNESIUM IODIDE WITH SEVERAL ACETYL AND DIACETYL METHYLATED BENZENES

Ketone	"Active" H	Addition
Acetophenone	0.025	1.025
Aceto-*m*-xylene	0.05	1.02
Acetomesitylene	1.03	0.00
5-Acetopseudocumene	0.25	0.79
Acetodurene	0.97	0.04
Acetoïsodurene	0.94	0.07
Acetoprehnitene	0.75	0.27
Acetopentamethylbenzene	0.93	0.01
Diaceto-*m*-xylene	0.16	1.82
Diacetomesitylene	1.82	0.26
Diacetopseudocumene	1.66	0.44
Diacetodurene	1.62	0.54
Diacetoïsodurene	1.72	0.48
Diacetoprehnitene	1.68	0.46

The enolization of various cyclic diketones has been investigated by Koelsch *et al.*[108]

That the Grignard reagent does not simply react with enol present, but that it actually converts ketone to enolate is readily seen by comparison

TABLE VI-XII

ENOL CONTENT OF SEVERAL KETONES AS ESTIMATED BY C_2H_5ZnI REACTION

Ketone	% Enol
$(CH_3)_2CO$	0
$(n\text{-}C_3H_7)_2CO$	0
$(n\text{-}C_4H_9)_2CO$	0
$(C_6H_5CH_2)_2CO$	0
$CH_3COC_6H_5$	0
$(CH_2)_4CO$	0
$(CH_2)_5CO$	8.2
4-Methylcyclohexanone	6.3
Menthone*	0
Carvone†	0
Thujone‡	0
$[(CH_3)_2C{=}CH]_2CO$	6.3

*3-Methyl-6-isopropylcyclohexanone.
†2-Methyl-5-isopropenyl-2-cyclohexen-1-one.
‡2-Methyl-5-isopropylbicyclo[3.1.0]hexan-3-one.

[108] (*a*) Koelsch, *J. Am. Chem. Soc.*, 58, 1321–4 (1936); (*b*) Koelsch and Geissman, *J. Org. Chem.*, 3, 480–8 (1939); (*c*) Koelsch and Wawzonek, *ibid.*, 6, 684–9 (1941).

of Grignard enolization data with percentage enol content determined by one of the standard methods.[109]

On the assumption, not completely justified, that enolization by ethylzinc iodide is very slow as compared with the reaction of that reagent with the enol form of a ketone, Grignard and Blanchon (*loc. cit.*[98]) employed the method of Job and Reich (*loc. cit.*[94]) to determine the enol content of several ketones. Their data are presented in Table VI-XII.

TABLE VI-XIII

ENOL CONTENT OF SEVERAL KETONES AS ESTIMATED BY MEYER'S BROMINATION METHOD

Ketone	% Enol
$CH_3COCH_2CO_2CH_3$	4.1
$CH_3COCH_2CO_2C_2H_5$	7.7
$CH_3COCH(CH_3)CO_2CH_3$	3.2
$CH_3COCHBrCO_2C_2H_5$	4.0
$C_6H_5COCH_2CO_2C_2H_5$	31.9
$C_6H_5COCH_2CO_2CH_3$	16.3
$(H_5C_2O_2CCH_2)_2CO$	16.8
$(CH_3CO)_2CH_2$	80.4
$CH_3COCH_2COC_6H_5$	98.6
$(C_6H_5CO)CH_2$	102.0

TABLE VI-XIV

ENOL CONTENT OF SEVERAL KETONES AS ESTIMATED BY SCHWARZENBACH'S MODIFICATION OF MEYER'S BROMINATION METHOD

Ketone	% Enol
$(CH_3CO)_2CH_2$	15.5
$(CH_3CO)_2CHBr$	8.1
$(CH_3CO)_2CHCH_3$	2.8
$CH_3COCH_2CO_2C_2H_5$	0.38
2-Acetylcyclohexanone	29.1
2-Acetylcyclopentanone	15.1
1,3-Indandione	1.6
2-Methyl-1,3-indandione	1.03
Dimedon*	95.3
1,2-Cyclohexanedione	100
3-Methyl-1,2-cyclohexanedione	100
1,2-Cyclopentanedione	100
3-Methyl-1,2-cyclopentanedione	100
α-Oxo-β-methylbutyrolactone	100
$(CH_3)_2CO$	2.5×10^{-4}
$(CH_3CO)_2$	5.6×10^{-3}
$(CH_2)_4CO$	4.8×10^{-3}
$(CH_2)_5CO$	2×10^{-2}

*5,5-Dimethyl-1,3-cyclohexanedione.

[109]For references to methods of determining enol content, see: Schwarzenbach and Felder, *Helv. Chim. Acta,* 27, 1044–60 (1944). See also: Knorr, *Ber.*, 44, 2772–8 (1911).

Several determinations by the classical bromination method of Meyer[110] are recorded in Table VI-XIII.

Schwarzenbach *et al.*[111] have elaborated and refined the technique of Meyer to devise a method that is probably the most reliable of the generally applicable methods at present available. Some of their data are collected in Table VI-XIV.

Probable mechanism of Grignard reagent enolate formation. Practically nothing has been demonstrated directly concerning the mechanism of the Grignard reagent enolate formation, doubtless because of its relatively complicated nature. However, the general acid-base-catalyzed enolization of ketones, particularly acetone, has been thoroughly studied and is well understood.[112]

The so-called acid-catalyzed enolization in aqueous solution involves two processes: (1) the association of a proton, supplied by any acid present, but predominantly by H_3O^+, with the oxygen of the ketone carbonyl group to form an intermediate ion; (2) the abstraction from an *alpha* carbon atom of the intermediate ion of a proton by any base present, but predominantly by H_2O. Hammett has formulated these processes as follows:

$$KH + H_3O^+ \rightarrow IH_2^+ + H_2O$$
$$IH_2^+ + H_2O \rightarrow EH + H_3O^+$$

in which KH represents the ketone, IH_2^+ the intermediate ion, and EH the enol. Of the processes represented, the latter is regarded as the rate-determining step.

The Grignard enolate formation differs from the aqueous "acid-catalyzed" enolization in several important respects, yet, if it be conceded that the transformation may be acid-base-catalyzed in the Lewis as well as in the Brønsted-Lowry sense, a striking parallelism exists. In the Lewis sense, the molecular and ionic species RMgX, R_2Mg, MgX_2, MgX^+, and RMg^+, all of which are present in variously associated and solvated forms in an ethereal Grignard reagent solution, are all acids. Presumably any and all of these might serve as catalyst for the first

---

[110]Meyer, *Ann.*, *380*, 212–42 (1911).

[111]Schwarzenbach and Felder, *Helv. Chim. Acta*, *27*, 1044–60 (1944); Schwarzenbach and Willwer, *Helv. Chim. Acta*, *30*, 656–8, 659–63, 663–9, 669–74 (1947).

[112](*a*) Dawson *et al.*, *J. Chem. Soc.*, *1926*, 2282–96, 2872–8, 3166–73; *1927*, 213–22, 458–66, 756–61; *1928*, 543–51, 1239–48, 1248–57, 2844–53; *1929*, 1217–29, 1884–95, 2530–9; *1930*, 79–85, 2180–9; *1931*, 2658–65; *1932*, 2612–20; (*b*) Pedersen, *J. Phys. Chem.*, *38*, 581–99 (1934); *Trans. Faraday Soc.*, *34*, 237–44 (1938); (*c*) Reitz, *Z. physik. Chem.*, *179A*, 119–34 (1937); (*d*) Zucker and Hammett, *J. Am. Chem. Soc.*, *61*, 2779–84, 2785–90, 2791–8 (1939). For an excellent discussion of concerted displacement reactions, including enolizations, consult: Swain, *J. Am. Chem. Soc.*, 72, 4578–83 (1950).

stage* of the transformation by forming an intermediate complex through the oxygen of the ketone carbonyl group. Pursuing the parallelism farther, the bases present, or potentially available for participation in the second stage of the transformation, are R^-, X^-, and Et_2O. It is highly doubtful that the halide ion, X^-, is sufficiently basic to play any significant part. The more basic ether might conceivably abstract a proton and subsequently yield it to the very strongly basic organic ion, R^-, but this, on the whole, appears unlikely because it involves the transfer of a proton from carbon to oxygen. At all events, the reaction by-product isolated in quantitative yield is RH.

Selecting, for the sake of simplicity, one of the possible acid catalysts and the most probable of the basic reactants, the transformation may be represented as follows:

$$(1) \quad R'COCHR''R''' + MgX^+ \rightleftharpoons [R'C(OMgX)CHR''R''']^+$$

$$(2) \quad [R'C(OMgX)CHR''R''']^+ + R^- \rightarrow R'C(OMgX){=}CR''R''' + RH$$

This is essentially the scheme proposed by Arnold *et al.*[113]

Because the reaction $R^- + H^+ \rightarrow RH$ is irreversible, R^-, and its source, RMgX, become participants in the reaction and hence are not "catalysts" in the commonly accepted definition of the term. Nevertheless, the likeness of this irreversible enolate formation to "acid-catalyzed" enolization is obvious.

There remains to be considered as a possible mechanism of reaction a process (or series of processes) essentially that suggested by Bredt-Savelsburg[114], and accepted by Grignard[115] himself, namely the association of a molecule of ketone with a molecule of Grignard reagent to form an intermediate complex, and the subsequent decomposition of the complex to yield enolate and hydrocarbon.

$$RMgX + R'COCHR''R''' \rightarrow [R'C(OMgXR)CHR''R'''] \rightarrow R'C(OMgX){=}CR''R''' + RH$$

Actually, there is no significant difference between the two mechanisms proposed, for if we attempt to represent either of them in greater detail, we arrive at a sequence somewhat like the following:

$$RMgX + R'COCHR''R''' \rightarrow [R'C(OMgXR)CHR''R'''] \rightarrow [R'C(OMgX)CHR''R''']^+R^- \rightarrow R'C(OMgX){=}CR''R''' + RH$$

---

* The reaction is divided into "first" and "second" stages for the sake of convenience in discussion; it may well be, and probably is, of the concerted displacement type.

[113] Arnold, Bank, and Liggett, *J. Am. Chem. Soc.*, *63*, 3444-6 (1941).

[114] Bredt-Savelsburg, *J. prakt. Chem.*, [2], *107*, 65-85 (1924).

[115] Grignard and Savard, *Bull. soc. chim. Belg.*, *36*, 97-107 (1927); Grignard and Blanchon, *Bull. soc. chim.*, [4], *49*, 23-42 (1931).

Although ionic formulae are convenient adjuncts to the elucidation of the ideas here proposed, actual dissociation of the ions represented is not necessarily implied. Neither is there any compulsion to assume that the fundamental processes specified in equations 1 and 2 are consecutive rather than simultaneous. A conceivable mechanism embodying the concept of a quasi six-membered ring transition state might be represented as follows:

```
     R″  R‴               R″  R‴                R″  R‴
      \  /                 \  /                  \  /
       C                    C                     C
      / \                  /·  ·                 //
R′—C     H          R′—C·     H          R′—C      H
   ‖           →         ⋮       ⋮     →       |       |
   O    R               O       R             O       R
  ·    /                 ·     ·                \
   · Mg                   · Mg ·                  Mg
      |                      |                     |
      X                      X                     X
```

This is essentially the scheme proposed by Lutz and Kibler.[116]

It should be emphasized, of course, that, for the sake of convenience, all these equations are over-simplified (see Chapter IV, Constitution and Dissociation of the Grignard Reagent).

It may not be amiss, either, to call to the reader's attention the fact that in supposedly quantitative studies the amount of Grignard enolization observable may be markedly affected by metallic impurities (notably iron) present in the magnesium used for reagent preparation. For example, it has been observed at the University of Chicago[116.1] that, whereas methylmagnesium bromide prepared from sublimed magnesium undergoes rapid "normal" addition to isophorone (3,3,5-trimethyl-2-cyclohexen-1-one) without detectable enolization (*i.e.*, methane evolution), the presence of as little as one mole percent of ferric bromide leads to the production of a reaction mixture which, upon treatment with benzoyl chloride, yields appreciable quantities of the enol benzoate.

GRIGNARD CONDENSATIONS OF ALDEHYDES AND KETONES

Grignard[117] himself noted that the interaction of acetone and isoamylmagnesium bromide leads to the formation, not only of the expected tertiary alcohol (in 46 percent yield), but also of small amounts of mesityl oxide [$(CH_3)_2C{=}CHCOCH_3$] and phorone [$(CH_3)_2C{=}CHCOCH{=}C(CH_3)_2$].

Carre[118] reported that, from the treatment of *o*-methylbenzylmagnesium bromide with acetone, he obtained only meagre (*ca.* 1 percent) yields of

---

[116] Lutz and Kibler, *J. Am. Chem. Soc.*, *62*, 360–72 (1940).

[116.1] Kharasch and Tawney, *J. Am. Chem. Soc.*, *63*, 2308–15 (1941); Kharasch, Rowe, and Ordas, unpublished work.

[117] Grignard, *Ann. chim.*, [7], *24*, 433–90 (1901).

[118] Carré, *Bull. soc. chim.*, [4], *5*, 486–9 (1909).

the tertiary alcohol, together with considerable amounts of condensation products, principally phorone.

Upon treatment of isopropylmagnesium iodide with cyclopentanone, Meisenheimer[119] obtained a 16 percent yield of the "normal" product, but found the principal product to be 2-cyclopentylidenecyclopentanone.

From butanone and isopropylmagnesium bromide, Pariselle and Simon[120] obtained the expected tertiary alcohol and 5-methyl-4-hepten-3-one in approximately equivalent amounts (*ca.* 25 percent).

According to Grignard and Escourru[121], the *beta* isomer

$$[CH_3COCH_2CH_2CH{=}C(CH_3)_2]$$

of the natural methylheptenone mixture reacts with isopropyl-, *n*-butyl-, and isoamylmagnesium halides to form the corresponding tertiary alcohols in varying yields. In most cases, a ketonic byproduct with analysis corresponding to the empirical formula $C_{12}H_{26}O$ is also obtained. This is believed to be the dehydrated ketol,

$$(CH_3)_2C{=}CHCH_2CH_2C(CH_3){=}C(COCH_3)CH_2CH{=}C(CH_3)_2$$

From the treatment of 3-pentanone with *t*-butylmagnesium chloride, and of pinacolone (CH_3CO-*t*-C_4H_9) with isopropylmagnesium bromide or *t*-butylmagnesium chloride, Conant and Blatt[122] obtained condensation products not specifically characterized.

Tolstopyatov[123] found that, with methylmagnesium bromide or iodide, pinacolin yields about 90 percent of the "normal" product, about 6 percent of the ketol, and somewhat less of the dehydrated ketol,

$$t\text{-}C_4H_9COCH{=}C(CH_3)\text{-}t\text{-}C_4H_9$$

According to Esafov[124], mesityl oxide $[CH_3COCH{=}C(CH_3)_2]$ yields with ethylmagnesium bromide very little of the "normal" product, the principal reaction being the formation of high-boiling condensation products. With both mesityl oxide and furfurylideneacetone, phenylmagnesium bromide yields high-boiling condensation products only.

Whitmore *et al.*[125] report that methyl isopropyl ketone yields with *t*-butylmagnesium chloride [in addition to 46 percent recovered ketone (from the enolate), 29 percent secondary alcohol (from ketone reduction), isobutylene, and isobutane] 18 percent of the ketol. With isoamylmagnesium chloride, the products isolated were recovered ketone (2.4 percent),

---

[119]Meisenheimer, *Ann.*, *405*, 129–75 (1914).

[120]Pariselle and Simon, *Compt. rend.*, *173*, 86–9 (1921).

[121]Grignard and Escourru, *Compt. rend.*, *176*, 1860–3 (1923).

[122]Conant and Blatt, *J. Am. Chem. Soc.*, *51*, 1227–36 (1929).

[123]Tolstopyatov, *J. Russ. Phys.-Chem. Soc.*, *62*, 1813–28 (1930); *Chem. Abstr.*, *25*, 3959 (1931); *Chem. Zentr.*, *1931*, *I*, 2738.

[124]Esafov, *J. Gen. Chem.* (U.S.S.R.), *9*, 467–70 (1939); *Chem. Abstr.*, *33*, 9282 (1939).

[125]Whitmore, Whitaker, Breivik, Wheeler, Miner, and Sutherland, *J. Am. Chem. Soc.*, *63*, 643–54 (1941).

secondary alcohol (49.0 percent), and ketol dehydration product (35.6 percent).

From pinacolone and *t*-butylmagnesium chloride, Hickinbottom and Schlüchterer[126] obtained, in addition to secondary alcohol, the ketol and its dehydration product.

In general, whether the ketol or its dehydration product is obtained depends upon the method of recovery. Often, it is more convenient to isolate the dehydration product.

Relatively little lucid discussion of the condensation side-reaction has appeared in the periodical literature, possibly for the reason that many workers have regarded the fundamental facts as too obvious to justify elaboration.

Grignard undoubtedly recognized these reactions as typical "base-catalyzed" ketolizations, and he demonstrated, with Dubien,[127] and with Fluchaire[128] that aldehyde aldolization, ketone ketolization, and cross-condensation between aldehydes and ketones may be brought about by a variety of ROMgX compounds. (See also the work of Grignard and Colonge[129] on similar condensations effected with the aid of RNHMgX and RR′NMgX compounds.)

Tolstopyatov (*loc. cit.*[123]) suggested that, in the interaction between methylmagnesium halide and pinacolone, the condensing agent is $t\text{-}C_4H_9(CH_3)_2COMgX$.

Ivanoff and Spassoff,[130] who detected among the products of reaction of ethyl acetate with isopropylmagnesium chloride, the ketol of the ketone which would presumably be formed in the first stage of reaction of the ester with the Grignard reagent, accounted for its presence as follows:*

$$CH_3CO_2C_2H_5 + i\text{-}C_3H_7MgCl \rightarrow CH_3(ClMgO)C(OC_2H_5)\text{-}i\text{-}C_3H_7$$
$$\rightarrow CH_3CO\text{-}i\text{-}C_3H_7 + C_2H_5OMgCl$$

$$CH_3CO_2C_2H_5 + i\text{-}C_3H_7MgCl \rightarrow H_2C{=}C(OMgCl)\text{-}i\text{-}C_3H_7 + C_3H_8$$

$$2\ CH_3CO\text{-}i\text{-}C_3H_7 \xrightarrow[H_2C{=}C(OMgCl)\text{-}i\text{-}C_3H_7]{C_2H_5OMgCl} CH_3(i\text{-}C_3H_7)C(OH)CH_2CO\text{-}i\text{-}C_3H_7$$

In a sequel[131] to the paper cited, they expressed the opinion that the most probable ketolization agents are the halomagnesium salts of the enol and of the ketol which are found in the reaction medium, and reasoned that a good enolizing reagent is indirectly a good condensing agent. On

[126]Hickinbottom and Schlüchterer, *Nature*, *155*, 19 (1945).

[127]Grignard and Dubien, *Compt. rend.*, *177*, 299–302 (1923).

[128]Grignard and Fluchaire, *Ann. chim.*, [10], *9*, 5–54 (1928).

[129](*a*) Grignard and Colonge, *Compt. rend.*, *194*, 929–33 (1932); (*b*) Colonge, *ibid.*, *196*, 1414–6 (1933); (*c*) Colonge, *Bull. soc. chim.*, [5], *1*, 1101–14 (1934).

[130]Ivanoff and Spassoff, *Bull. soc. chim.*, [5], 2, 816–24 (1935).

* See discussion of apparent ester enolization, Chapter VIII.

[131]Ivanoff and Spassoff, *Bull. soc. chim.*, [5], 2, 1435–8 (1935).

this basis, they planned the ketolization study the results of which are summarized in Table VI-XV.

TABLE VI-XV

KETOLIZATION THROUGH THE AGENCY OF GRIGNARD REAGENTS

Ketone	Grignard Reagent	Yield of Ketol (%)
CH_3CO-*i*-C_3H_7	*i*-C_3H_7MgCl	70
	s-C_4H_9MgBr	37
	t-C_4H_9MgCl	50
CH_3CO-*t*-C_4H_9	*i*-C_3H_7MgCl	43
	s-C_4H_9MgBr	45
	t-C_4H_9MgCl	48
$(CH_2)_4CO$	*i*-C_3H_7MgCl	36
	s-C_4H_9MgCl	42
$(CH_2)_5CO$	*i*-C_3H_7MgCl	15

On the basis of a rather superficial survey of the literature (if one may judge by their bibliography), Hickinbottom and Schlüchterer (*loc. cit.*[126]) offer the following contribution. "The experimental data at present available leads [*sic*] to the conclusion that alkylmagnesium halides with highly branched chains not only bring about reduction of the ketone, but also promote condensation. The structure of the ketone is also an important factor; those with an available hydrogen adjacent to the carbonyl and a slow rate of reaction toward Grignard reagents condense more readily. If they react with Grignard reagents which do not cause reduction, such as the arylmagnesium halides, the formation of the condensation is still more favored."

According to the commonly accepted present-day view, the essential step in self-ketolization is the addition of an enolate ion to the carbon member of the carbonyl double bond of a molecule of the corresponding keto form.

$$\left[\begin{array}{c} RR'C{=}\overset{\displaystyle O^{}}{\overset{|}{C}}{-}R'' \\ \updownarrow \\ RR'C{-}\underset{\displaystyle O}{\underset{\|}{C}}{-}R'' \end{array}\right]^{-} \xrightarrow{R''COCHRR'} \left[\begin{array}{c} RR'C{-}\overset{\displaystyle O}{\overset{\|}{C}}{-}R'' \\ | \\ R''{-}\underset{\displaystyle O}{\underset{|}{C}}{-}CHRR' \end{array}\right]^{-} \xrightarrow{H^+} \begin{array}{c} RR'C{-}\overset{\displaystyle O}{\overset{\|}{C}}{-}R \\ | \\ R''{-}\underset{\displaystyle OH}{\underset{|}{C}}{-}CHRR' \end{array}$$

Necessarily, therefore, only enolizable ketones may be expected to self-ketolize, and the enolate may be regarded as a reactant rather than a "ketolization agent." It further follows that enolization may itself become a competing reaction, for ketones which enolize extremely readily, or which undergo addition with difficulty (*e.g.*, actomesitylene), cannot be expected to ketolize appreciably for lack of the necessary reactive keto molecules. Note, however, that cross-condensation is not necessarily precluded. This is doubtless one reason why the enolate of acetomesitylene is said to react with benzaldehyde like a "true Grignard reagent of the formula $C_9H_{11}COCH_2MgBr$."[132]

Whether the participant enolate ions arise through the agency of some "base," such as NaOH, ROMgX or RR′NMgX, through direct attack of the Grignard reagent upon an enol, or through Grignard enolization of a ketone, is immaterial.

Whenever any appreciable amount of enolate is present, the keto form remaining is subject to several competing reactions, among them: (1) further enolization; (2) condensation with enolate ions; (3) "normal" Grignard reagent addition; and, in cases where the Grignard reagent is also a reducing agent, (4) reduction. In the first two of these reactions, the nature of the ketone itself is the primary determinant of rates; in the latter two, the natures of both ketone and Grignard reagent are significant. To predict the total outcome of any given situation complicated by so many rates of competing reactions, which, in turn, are determined by more or less independent properties of each of two reactants, by means of concise generalizations is manifestly impossible. Nevertheless, given a specific Grignard reagent-ketone pair, the experienced operator may make qualitative predictions with considerable confidence.

Reports of aldehyde condensations have been rarer than reports of ketone condensations, in part, perhaps, because of the greater average reactivity of aldehyde carbonyl groups with respect to "normal" Grignard reagent addition.

Faworsky[133] reported, without revealing any experimental details, that, in the preparation of isopropyl-*t*-butylmethanol from isobutyraldehyde and *t*-butylmagnesium chloride, he obtained yields of about 25 percent of the secondary alcohol, 50 percent of isobutyl alcohol, and 25 percent of 2,2,4-trimethylpentane-1,3-diol (the reduction product of the aldol). Under the conditions employed by them, Conant and Blatt (*loc. cit.*[122]), however, were unable to detect any glycol among the products of this reaction.

Vanine[134] reported that the products of interaction of isobutylmagnesium bromide and *n*-heptaldehyde are the secondary alcohol, "aldehyde polymer," and an alcohol of the empirical formula $C_{12}H_{26}O$.

Occasionally, an aldehyde participates in a secondary condensation. For example, Marshall[135] found, among the products of reaction of excess benzaldehyde and methylmagnesium iodide, phenyl styryl ketone (which he incorrectly characterized as "methyldeoxybenzoïn").

---

[132]Fuson, Fugate, and Fisher, *J. Am. Chem. Soc.*, *61*, 2362–5 (1939).

[133]Faworsky, *J. prakt. Chem.*, [2], 88, 641–98 (1913).

[134]Vanine, *J. Russ. Phys.-Chem. Soc.*, *47*, 1094–1101 (1915); *Bull. soc. chim.*, [4], *20*, 495 (1916).

[135]Marshall, *J. Chem. Soc.*, *105*, 527–34 (1914); *107*, 509–23 (1915).

$$C_6H_5CHO + [H_2C{=}C(O){-}C_6H_5]^- \rightarrow [C_6H_5CHOCH_2COC_6H_5]^- \xrightarrow{H^+}$$

$$C_6H_5CH(OH)CH_2COC_6H_5 \xrightarrow{-H_2O} C_6H_5CH{=}CHCOC_6H_5$$

The α,β-dimesitoylethylene glycol of Gray and Fuson[136] is probably also the result of a secondary condensation.

$$C_9H_{11}COCHO + C_9H_{11}COCOMgBr \rightarrow C_9H_{11}COCH(OH)CH(OMgBr)COC_9H_{11}$$

A different type of "condensation" has been reported by Franke and Kuhn.[137]

$$HOCH_2(CH_3)_2CCHO\ (51\ g.) + CH_3MgI \rightarrow HOCH_2(CH_3)_2CCO_2CH_2C(CH_3)_2CH_2OH\ (30\ g.)$$

This represents a special case of the Tichtchenko[138] reaction, which may be regarded as a variation of the Cannizzaro reaction. In their study of the action of ROMgX compounds on aldehydes, Grignard and Fluchaire (*loc. cit.*[128]) found that aldolization is usually accompanied by the Cannizzaro-Tichtchenko oxidation-reduction-condensation.

α-HALO KETONES AND ALDEHYDES*

Saturated α-halo ketones undergo with Grignard reagents (one equivalent) four types of reactions, namely: (1) normal addition at the carbonyl double bond to give a tertiary alcoholate; (2) replacement of the *alpha* halogen atom by the organic radical of the Grignard reagent; (3) formation of the enolate of the corresponding non-halogenated ketone; and (4) formation of the enolate of the α-halogenated ketone.

$$(1)\quad RCHXCOR' + R''MgX' \longrightarrow RCHXC(OMgX')R'R'' \xrightarrow{H_2O} RCHXC(OH)R'R'' + MgX'OH$$

$$(2)\quad RCHXCOR' + R''MgX' \longrightarrow RR''CHCOR' + MgX'X$$

$$(3)\quad RCHXCOR' + R''MgX' \longrightarrow RCH{=}C(OMgX')R' + R''X \xrightarrow{H_2O} RCH_2COR' + R''X + MgX'OH$$

$$(4)\quad RCHXCOR' + R''MgX' \longrightarrow RCX{=}C(OMgX')R' + R''H \xrightarrow{H_2O} RCHXCOR' + R''H + MgX'OH$$

---

[136] Gray and Fuson, *J. Am. Chem. Soc.*, *56*, 739–41 (1934).

[137] Franke and Kuhn, *Monatsh.*, *25*, 865–70 (1904).

[138] Tichtchenko, *J. Russ. Phys.-Chem. Soc.*, 38, 355–419, 482–520 (1906); *Bull. soc. chim.*, [4], *4*, 982, 1121 (1908).

*The reactions of organomagnesium derivatives with α-chlorocyclanones have been reviewed by Tiffeneau, *Bull. soc. chim.*, [5], *12*, 621–7 (1945).

"Normal" addition. The first of these reactions takes place when there is little hindrance, steric or otherwise, to normal addition, and when the halomagnesium halohydrinate so formed is stable under the reaction conditions imposed. Examples have been reported by Fourneau,[139] by Fourneau and Tiffeneau,[140] by Kyriakides,[141] by Pastereau and Bernard,[142] by Bartlett and Rosenwald,[143] by Tiffeneau and Tchoubar,[144] and by Kohler and Tishler.[145]

$$ClCH_2COCH_3 \xrightarrow[\text{(or } CH_3MgBr)]{CH_3MgI} ClCH_2(CH_3)_2COH\ (20\%) + (CH_3)_2CHCH(OH)CH_3 \quad \text{(Ref. } \mathit{139, 140})$$

$$ClCH_2COCH_3 \xrightarrow{C_2H_5MgBr} ClCH_2(CH_3)(C_2H_5)COH\ (72\%) + CH_3(C_2H_5)CHCH(OH)C_2H_5 \quad \text{(Ref. } \mathit{139, 140, 141})$$

$$ClCH_2COCH_3 \xrightarrow{C_6H_5MgBr} ClCH_2(CH_3)(C_6H_5)COH \quad \text{(Ref. } \mathit{139})$$

$$ClCH_2COC_2H_5 \xrightarrow{C_2H_5MgBr} ClCH_2(C_2H_5)_2COH + (C_2H_5)_2CHCH(OH)C_2H_5 \quad \text{(Ref. } \mathit{140})$$

$$CH_3COCHClC(CH_3)_2OH \xrightarrow{CH_3MgI} [HO(CH_3)_2C]_2\dot{C}HCl \quad \text{(Ref. } \mathit{142})$$

$$\text{2-chlorocyclohexanone} \xrightarrow[\text{(or } CH_3MgBr)]{CH_3MgI} \text{2-chloro-1-methylcyclohexanol} \quad \text{(Ref. } \mathit{144,145})$$

$$C_6H_5COCHBrCH(C_6H_5)_2 \xrightarrow{C_6H_5C{\equiv}CMgBr} C_6H_5(C_6H_5C{\equiv}C)[(C_6H_5)_2CHCHBr]COH \quad \text{(Ref. } \mathit{134})$$

Halogen-radical exchange. Reactions in which the *alpha* halogen atom of a ketone is replaced by the organic radical of the Grignard reagent have been reported by Bouveault and Chereau,[146] by Tiffeneau,[147] by Vavon

[139] Fourneau, *Compt. rend.*, *134*, 774–5 (1902); *Chem. Zentr.*, *1902*, *I*, 1092.

[140] Fourneau and Tiffeneau, *Compt. rend.*, *145*, 437–9 (1907); *Chem. Zentr.*, *1907*, *II*, 1320.

[141] Kyriakides, *J. Am. Chem. Soc.*, *36*, 657–63 (1914).

[142] Pastereau and Bernard, *Compt. rend.*, *174*, 1555–7 (1922); *Chem. Abstr.*, *16*, 2842 (1922).

[143] Bartlett and Rosenwald, *J. Am. Chem. Soc.*, *56*, 1990–4 (1934).

[144] Tiffeneau and Tchoubar, *Compt. rend.*, *198*, 941–3 (1934).

[145] Kohler and Tishler, *J. Am. Chem. Soc.*, *57*, 217–24 (1935).

[146] Bouveault and Chereau, *Compt. rend.*, *142*, 1086–7 (1906); *Chem. Zentr.*, *1906*, *II*, 125.

[147] Tiffeneau, *Ann. chim.*, [8], *10*, 322–78 (1907).

and Mitchovitch,[148] by Vavon and Perlin-Borrel,[149] by Tiffeneau and Tchoubar,[144] by McKenzie, Roger, and McKay,[150] by Richard,[151] by Roger and McGregor,[152] by Mitchovitch,[153] and by Sackur.[154] A similar replacement of the *alpha* halogen atom of an aldehyde is reported by Tchoubar and Sackur.[155]

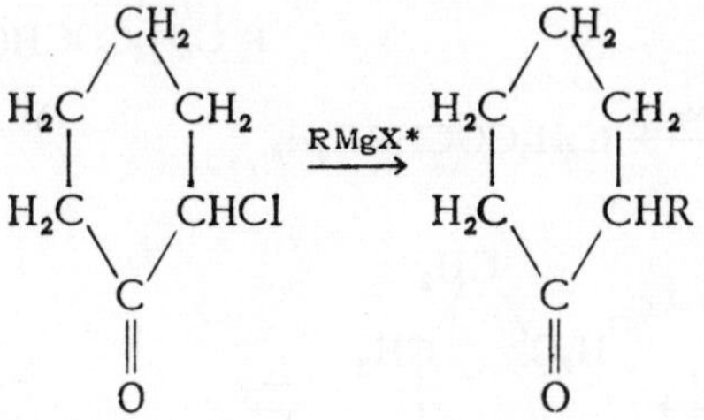

(Ref. *146*)

$$ClCH_2COCH_3 \xrightarrow{C_6H_5MgBr} ClCH_2(CH_3)(C_6H_5)COMgBr$$

$$\xrightarrow{130\text{–}140^\circ} CH_3COCH_2C_6H_5 + MgBrCl \qquad \text{(Ref. } \mathit{147}\text{)}$$

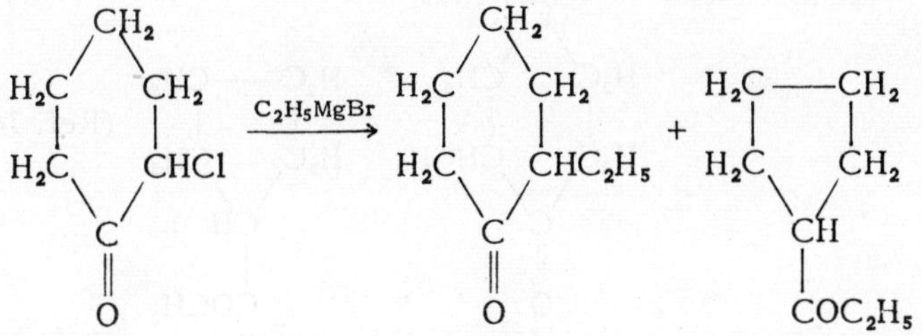

(Ref. *148*)

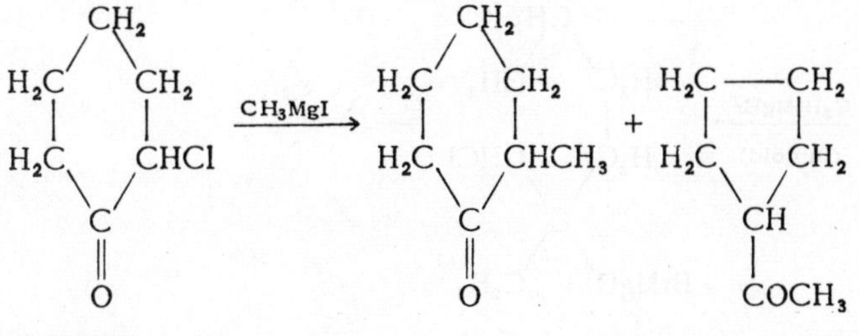

(Ref. *149*)

---

[148] Vavon and Mitchovitch, *Bull. soc. chim.*, [4], *45*, 961–72 (1929).
[149] Vavon and Perlin-Borrel, *Bull. soc. chim.*, [4], *51*, 994 (1932).
[150] McKenzie, Roger, and McKay, *J. Chem. Soc.*, *1932*, 2597–604.
[151] Richard, *Compt. rend.*, *198*, 1242–4 (1934).
[152] Roger and McGregor, *J. Chem. Soc.*, *1934*, 1850–3.
[153] Mitchovitch, *Compt. rend.*, *200*, 1601–3 (1935).
[154] Sackur, *Compt. rend.*, *208*, 1092–4 (1939); *Chem. Abstr.*, *33*, 9296 (1939); *Chem. Zentr.*, *1940*, *I*, 859.
[155] Tchoubar and Sackur, *Compt. rend.*, *207*, 1105–6 (1938); *Chem. Abstr.*, *33*, 2111 (1939).

*R = CH_3, C_2H_5, i-C_3H_7.

$$C_6H_5COCHClC_6H_5 \xrightarrow{4\text{-}CH_3C_6H_4MgBr} C_6H_5COCH(C_6H_5)C_6H_4\text{-}4\text{-}CH_3 \quad \text{(Ref. } \textit{150}\text{)}$$

$$C_6H_5COCHClC_6H_5 \xrightarrow{2\ C_6H_5MgBr} (C_6H_5)_2C(OH)CH(C_6H_5)_2 \quad \text{(Ref. } \textit{151}\text{)}$$

$$C_6H_5COCHClC_6H_5 \xrightarrow{C_6H_5MgBr} (C_6H_5)_2C(OH)CH(C_6H_5)_2 + C_6H_5COCH(C_6H_5)_2 \quad \text{(Ref. } \textit{152}\text{)}$$

$$C_6H_5COCHClC_6H_5 \xrightarrow{RMgBr^{*}} C_6H_5COCHRC_6H_5 \quad \text{(Ref. } \textit{152}\text{)}$$

$$\begin{array}{ccc} & CH_2 & \\ H_2C & & CH_2 \\ H_2C & & CHCl \\ & C & \\ & \| & \\ & O & \end{array} \xrightarrow[\text{(In cold)}]{CH_3MgI} \begin{array}{ccc} & CH_2 & \\ H_2C & & CH_2 \\ H_2C & & CHCl \\ & C & \\ IMgO & & CH_3 \end{array} \xrightarrow{\Delta}$$

$$\begin{array}{ccc} & CH_2 & \\ H_2C & & CH_2 \\ H_2C & & CHCH_3 \\ & C & \\ & \| & \\ & O & \end{array} + \begin{array}{ccc} H_2C & - & CH_2 \\ H_2C & & CH_2 \\ & CH & \\ & | & \\ & COCH_3 & \end{array} \quad \text{(Ref. } \textit{144}\text{)}$$

$$\begin{array}{ccc} & CH_2 & \\ H_2C & & CH_2 \\ H_2C & & CHCl \\ & C & \\ & \| & \\ & O & \end{array} \xrightarrow[\text{(In cold)}]{C_2H_5MgBr} \begin{array}{ccc} & CH_2 & \\ H_2C & & CH_2 \\ H_2C & & CHCl \\ & C & \\ BrMgO & & C_2H_5 \end{array} \xrightarrow{\Delta}$$

$$\begin{array}{ccc} & CH_2 & \\ H_2C & & CH_2 \\ H_2C & & CHC_2H_5 \\ & C & \\ & \| & \\ & O & \end{array} + \begin{array}{ccc} H_2C & - & CH_2 \\ H_2C & & CH_2 \\ & CH & \\ & | & \\ & COC_2H_5 & \end{array} \quad \text{(Ref. } \textit{144}\text{)}$$

---

*R = 2-$CH_3C_6H_4$, 3-$CH_3C_6H_4$.

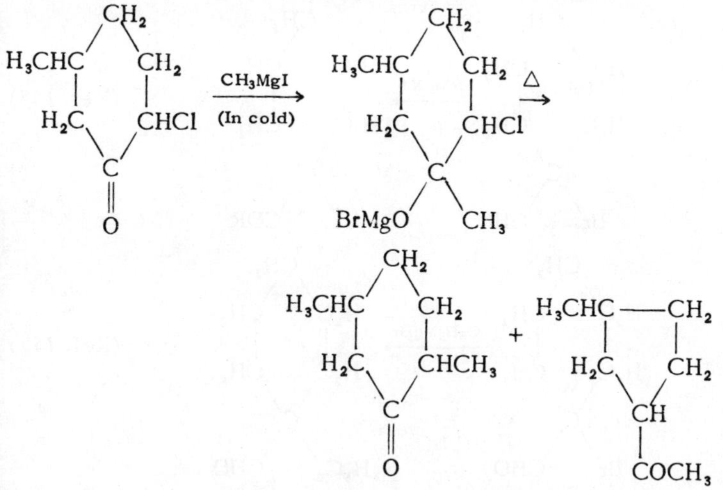

CH_2
H_3CHC CH_2
H_2C $CHCl$
C
O

$\xrightarrow[\text{(In cold)}]{CH_3MgI}$

CH_2
H_3CHC CH_2
H_2C $CHCl$
C
BrMgO CH_3

$\xrightarrow{\Delta}$

CH_2
H_3CHC CH_2
H_2C $CHCH_3$
C
O

\+

H_3CHC — CH_2
H_2C CH_2
CH
$COCH_3$

(Ref. *144*)

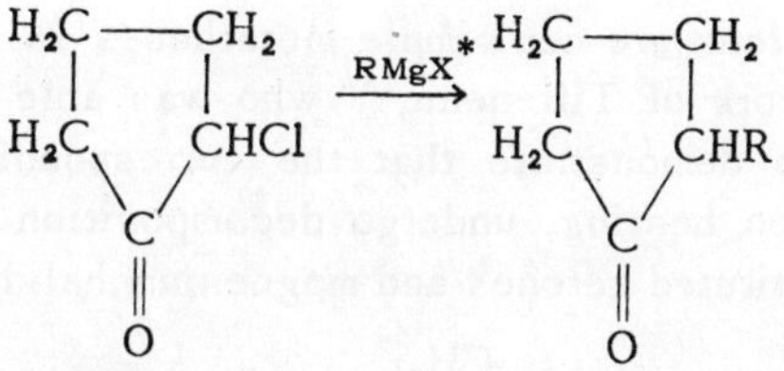

H_2C — CH_2
H_2C $CHCl$
C
O

$\xrightarrow{RMgX^*}$

H_2C — CH_2
H_2C CHR
C
O

(Ref. *153*)

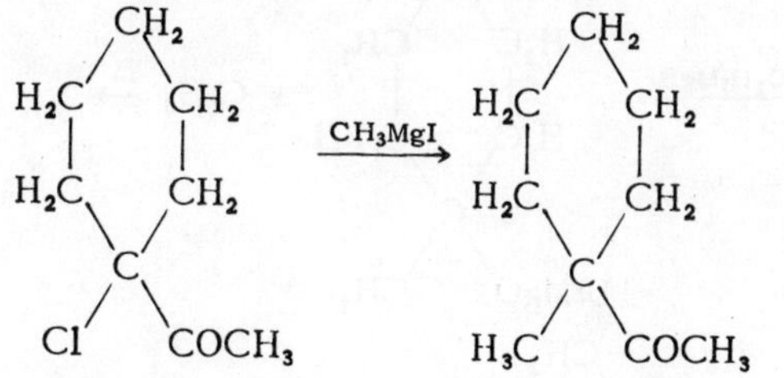

CH_2
H_2C CH_2
H_2C CH_2
C
Cl $COCH_3$

$\xrightarrow{CH_3MgI}$

CH_2
H_2C CH_2
H_2C CH_2
C
H_3C $COCH_3$

(Ref. *154*)

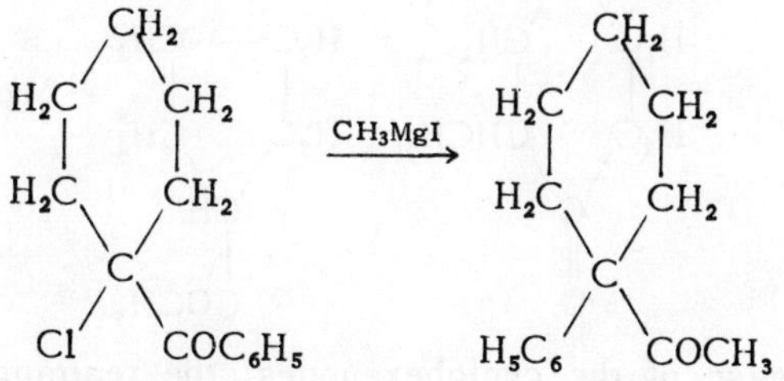

CH_2
H_2C CH_2
H_2C CH_2
C
Cl COC_6H_5

$\xrightarrow{CH_3MgI}$

CH_2
H_2C CH_2
H_2C CH_2
C
H_5C_6 $COCH_3$

(Ref. *154*)

CH_2
H_2C CH_2
H_2C CH_2
C
Cl $COCH_3$

$\xrightarrow{C_6H_5MgBr}$

CH_2
H_2C CH_2
H_2C CH_2
C
H_5C_6 $COCH_3$

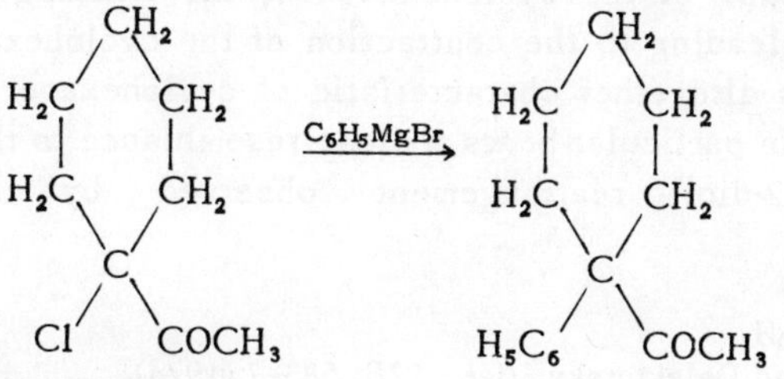

(Ref. *154*)

---

*R = CH_3, C_2H_5, $i\text{-}C_3H_7$, C_6H_5.

```
        CH2                         CH2
       /   \                       /   \
   H2C       CH2    RMgX*      H2C       CH2
    |         |   -------->     |         |                (Ref. 155)
   H2C       CH2               H2C       CH2
       \   /                       \   /
         C                           C
       /   \                       /   \
    Br       CHO                 H       COR

        CH2                         CH2
       /   \                       /   \
   H2C       CH2   C6H5MgBr    H2C       CH2
    |         |   -------->     |         |                (Ref. 155)
   H2C       CH2               H2C       CH2
       \   /                       \   /
         C                           C
       /   \                       /   \
    Br       CHO              H5C6       CHO
```

That these reactions are not simple metatheses is convincingly demonstrated by the work of Tiffeneau,[147] who was able to isolate several halohydrins and to demonstrate that the corresponding halomagnesium halohydrinates, upon heating, undergo decomposition and rearrangement to yield the α-substituted ketones and magnesium halide.

```
        CH2                          CH2
       /   \                        /   \
   H2C       CH2   C2H5MgBr     H2C       CH2
    |         |    -------->     |         |      + C2H6  --Δ-->
   H2C       CHCl               H2C       CHCl
       \   /                        \   /
         C                            C
       /   \                        /   \
    HO       CH3               BrMgO      CH3

        CH2
       /   \
   H2C       CH2         H2C —— CH2
    |         |     +     |       |     + MgBrCl   (Ref. 147)
   H2C       CHCH3       H2C      CH2
       \   /                 \   /
         C                    CH
         ‖                     |
         O                    COCH3
```

That, in the case of the cyclohexanones, the rearrangement takes, in part, a course leading to the contraction of the cyclohexane to a cyclopentane ring is altogether characteristic of cyclohexane systems. This rearrangement in particular bears a close resemblance to the 1,2-dimethylcyclohexane-1,2-diol rearrangement observed by Nametkin and Delektorsky.[156]

---

*R = CH_3, C_2H_5.

[156] Nametkin and Delektorsky, *Ber.*, *57B*, 583-7 (1924).

```
       CH2
      /   \
  H2C      CH2                            H2C ——CH2
   |        |  CH3         Δ               |      |
  H2C       C<       ——————————————→     H2C     CH2
      \   /    OH    (or dil. H2SO4)          \  /
        C                                      C
      /   \                                  /   \
   H3C     OH                             H3C     COCH3
```

Of especial interest is Sackur's[154] demonstration that 1-chloro-1-acetylcyclohexane, when treated with phenylmagnesium bromide, and 1-chloro-1-benzoylcyclohexane, when treated with methylmagnesium iodide, both yield 1-acetyl-1-phenylcyclohexanone—an illustration of the relative migration tendencies of aryl and alkyl groups in rearrangements of this kind, and, incidentally, a phenomenon that could not conceivably result from simple metathesis.

All these rearrangements are strikingly similar to those of the well-known pinacol-pinacolone type.[157]

```
        CH2                           CH2
       /   \                         /   \
    H2C     CH2                   H2C     CH2
     |       |          →          |       |          + MgBr2
    H2C     CH2                   H2C     CH2
       \   /                         \   /
         C    H                        C
       /   \ /                       /   \
     Br     C                   H5C6      C—H
           / \                            ‖
      BrMgO   C6H5                        O

    H5C2   H                 H5C2       H
        \  |                     \      |
 H5C2—C—C—C6H5   →    H5C2—C—C=O + H2O     (Ref. 158)
        /   \                    /
      HO     OH              H5C6

        CH2                           CH2
       /   \                         /   \
    H2C     CH2                   H2C     CH2
     |       |          →          |       |          + MgBr2
    H2C     CH2                   H2C     CH2
       \   /                         \   /
         C    H                        C
       /   \ /                       /   \
     Br     C                       H     C—C2H5
           / \                            ‖
      BrMgO   C2H5                        O
```

[157] See, *e.g.*: Porter, "Molecular Rearrangements," The Chemical Catalog Co., Inc., New York, *1928*, Chapter III; Wallis, Chapter 12, Vol. I of "Organic Chemistry," edited by Gilman, John Wiley and Sons, New York, 2nd ed., *1943*.

[158] Tiffeneau and Lévy, *Bull. soc. chim.*, [4], 33, 735–79 (1923).

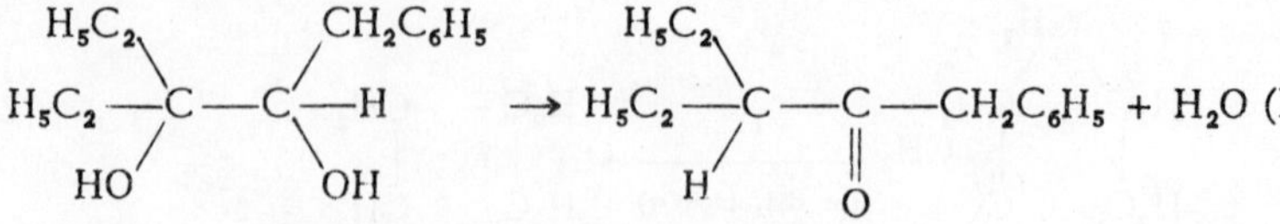

$$(H_5C_2)_2C(OH)\text{—}CH(OH)CH_2C_6H_5 \rightarrow (H_5C_2)_2CH\text{—}CO\text{—}CH_2C_6H_5 + H_2O \quad \text{(Ref. } \mathit{159}\text{)}$$

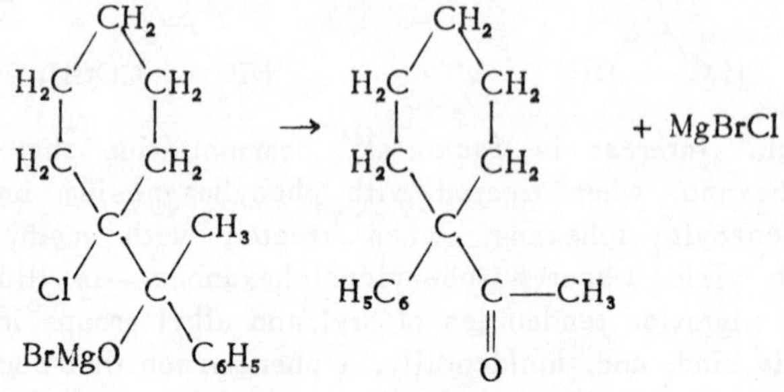

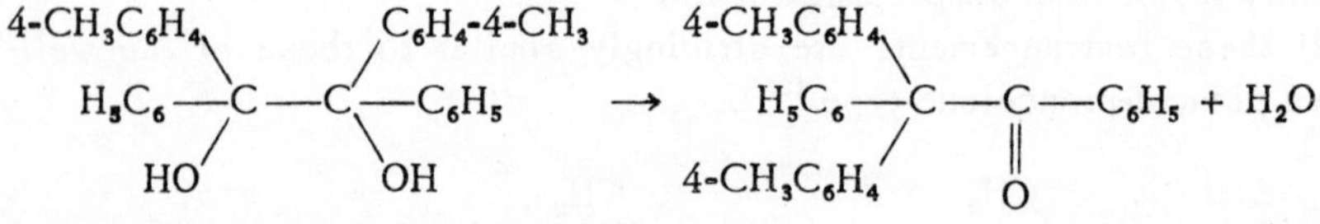

$$\text{1-chloro-1-methylcyclohexyl—}C(OMgBr)(C_6H_5)\text{—}CH_3 \;(\text{ring: } CH_2, H_2C, CH_2, H_2C, CH_2, C(CH_3)(Cl)) \rightarrow \text{1-phenylcyclohexyl—}C(=O)\text{—}CH_3 + MgBrCl$$

$$(4\text{-}CH_3C_6H_4)(H_5C_6)C(OH)\text{—}C(OH)(C_6H_4\text{-}4\text{-}CH_3)C_6H_5 \rightarrow (4\text{-}CH_3C_6H_4)_2(H_5C_6)C\text{—}C(=O)\text{—}C_6H_5 + H_2O$$

(Ref. *160*)

Newman and Booth[161] have reported that treatment of 2-chloro-4-methylcyclohexanone with phenylmagnesium bromide leads to a mixture of 2-phenyl-4-methylcyclohexanone and 2-phenyl-5-methylcyclohexanone, with the former apparently predominating. However, since this reaction involved prolonged refluxing in xylene solution, opportunities for rearrangement suggest caution in drawing conclusions from it.

A reaction in which halogen replacement with rearrangement takes place, together with addition at the carbonyl double bond, has been reported by Foldi and Demjén.[162]

$$\underset{(170\text{ g.})}{4\text{-}CH_3OC_6H_4COCHClC_6H_4\text{-}4\text{-}OCH_3} \xrightarrow[\text{(from 138 g. } C_2H_5Br)]{2\ C_2H_5MgBr} \underset{(72\text{ g.})}{(4\text{-}CH_3OC_6H_4)_2CHC(C_2H_5)_2OH}$$

An interesting variation occurs in the behavior of the α-bromo aldehyde studied by Tchoubar and Sackur (*loc. cit.*[155]). In this case, the intermediate halomagnesium bromohydrinates are evidently relatively unstable, for it proved impossible to isolate the bromohydrins even when operations were conducted at 0°. When alkyl (methyl, ethyl) Grignard reagents were employed, migration of a hydrogen atom occurred, resulting in formation

---

[159] Lévy, *Bull. soc. chim.*, [4], 33, 1655–66 (1923).
[160] Bachmann and Moser, *J. Am. Chem. Soc.*, *54*, 1124–33 (1932).
[161] Newman and Booth, *J. Org. Chem.*, *12*, 737–9 (1947).
[162] Foldi and Demjén, *Ber.*, *74B*, 930–4 (1941).

of the ketones, whereas, when an aryl (phenyl) Grignard reagent was used, the aryl group migrated, forming an α-arylated aldehyde.

That the α-halogen replacement reactions of α-halo ketones thus far discussed probably do not take place through an epoxide intermediate is indicated by an experiment of Sackur's[154] in which he isomerized α-phenyl-α-cyclohexylideneëthane oxide by heating it in the presence of zinc chloride or kieselguhr. The product, which he tentatively identified as 2-methyl-2-phenylcycloheptanone* is, in any case, definitely different from that obtained in the Grignard reactions.

Henry,[163] however, has reported a reaction that appears most satisfactorily explicable on the basis of the epoxide intermediate which he himself postulated.†

$$ClCH_2COCH_3 \xrightarrow{CH_3MgBr} (CH_3)_2C(OMgBr)CH_2Cl \rightarrow [(CH_3)_2C\underset{O}{\diagdown\!\diagup}CH_2 \rightleftharpoons (CH_3)_2CHCHO]$$

$$\xrightarrow{CH_3MgBr} (CH_3)_2CHCH(OH)CH_3$$

Similar reactions of methylmagnesium bromide and iodide with bromoacetone are reported by Huston *et al.*[164] The byproducts isolated by Fourneau and Tiffeneau (*loc. cit.*[140]) from their chloroacetone and 1-chloro-2-butanone reactions would appear to have had a similar origin.

In an article more recent than any of those here cited, Geissman and Akawie[165] present an interesting and instructive discussion of the two types of rearrangements (pinacol-pinacolone and oxide-intermediate) considered in the foregoing summary.

The types of reaction already discussed occur when the reacting carbonyl compound and Grignard reagent are of such nature that addition of the Grignard reagent at the carbonyl double bond takes place rather readily. The reduction (*i.e.*, dehalogenation) and enolization reactions occur only when addition at the carbonyl double bond takes place with difficulty or is sterically inhibited.

Dehalogenation (reductive enolization). The earliest recorded examples of the reduction reaction that have come to the attention of the present authors are the reactions of α-bromocamphor reported by Malmgren.[166]

**Chemical Abstracts* erroneously reports 2-methyl-2-phenylcyclopentanone.

[163] Henry, *Compt. rend.*, *145*, 21–25 (1907); *Chem. Zentr.*, *1907, II*, 889; *Chem. Abstr.*, *1*, 2682 (1907).

†It is, of course, possible that the halohydrinate isomerizes directly to the aldehyde without passing through an intermediate epoxide (see Halohydrins, Chapter XVI).

[164] Huston, Jackson, and Spero, *J. Am. Chem. Soc.*, *63*, 1459–60 (1941).

[165] Geissman and Akawie, *J. Am. Chem. Soc.*, *73*, 1993–8 (1951).

[166] Malmgren, *Ber.*, *36*, 2608–42 (1903).

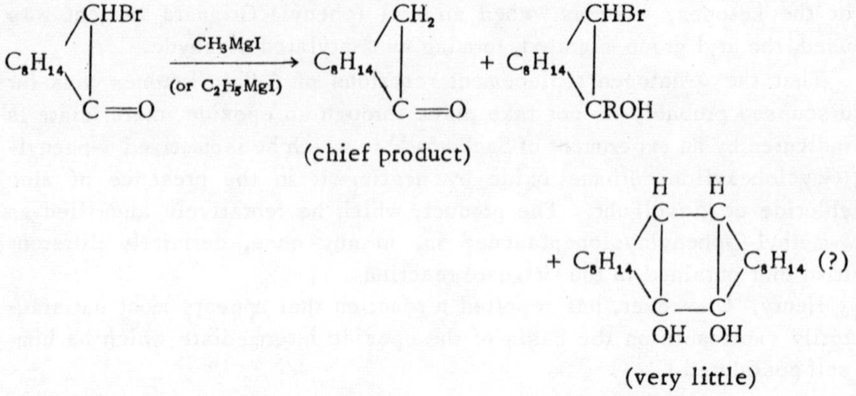

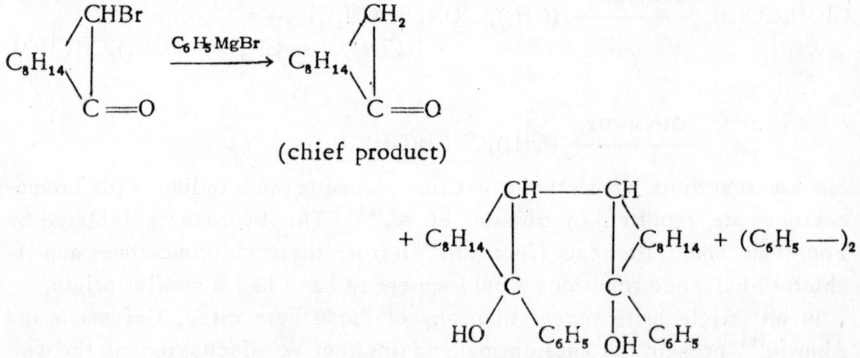

$$C_8H_{14}\left\langle\begin{matrix} CHBr \\ | \\ C{=}O \end{matrix}\right. \xrightarrow[\text{(or } C_2H_5MgI)]{CH_3MgI} C_8H_{14}\left\langle\begin{matrix} CH_2 \\ | \\ C{=}O \end{matrix}\right. + C_8H_{14}\left\langle\begin{matrix} CHBr \\ | \\ CROH \end{matrix}\right.$$

(chief product)

$$+\ C_8H_{14}\left\langle\begin{matrix} \overset{H}{C} - \overset{H}{C} \\ | \quad\quad | \\ \underset{OH}{C} - \underset{OH}{C} \end{matrix}\right\rangle C_8H_{14}\ (?)$$

(very little)

$$C_8H_{14}\left\langle\begin{matrix} CHBr \\ | \\ C{=}O \end{matrix}\right. \xrightarrow{C_6H_5MgBr} C_8H_{14}\left\langle\begin{matrix} CH_2 \\ | \\ C{=}O \end{matrix}\right.$$

(chief product)

$$+\ C_8H_{14}\left\langle\begin{matrix} CH - CH \\ | \quad\quad | \\ C \quad\quad C \\ HO\ \ C_6H_5 \quad OH\ \ C_6H_5 \end{matrix}\right\rangle C_8H_{14} + (C_6H_5 -)_2$$

In the light of present knowledge, the constitution assigned by Malmgren to the minor product of the alkyl Grignard reagent reactions appears highly improbable. There can be little doubt that the substance isolated by Malmgren was, in reality, the coupling product (see Grignard Reagent Coupling, Chapter XIV).

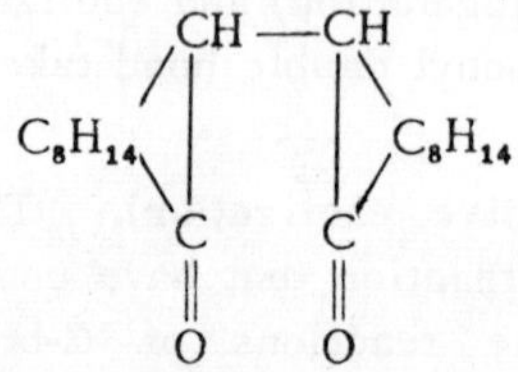

$$C_8H_{14}\left\langle\begin{matrix} CH - CH \\ | \quad\quad | \\ \underset{O}{\overset{\|}{C}} \quad\quad \underset{O}{\overset{\|}{C}} \end{matrix}\right\rangle C_8H_{14}$$

The biphenyl detected among the products of the phenylmagnesium bromide reaction doubtless arises in part from the Wurtz side-reaction in the preparation of the Grignard reagent and in part from the coupling reaction.

Kohler and Johnstin[167] treated 1-bromo-1-benzoyl-2,2-diphenylethane with a large excess of phenylmagnesium bromide and obtained an enolate which, upon treatment with water, yielded the unbrominated ketone. Benzoylation of the enolate yielded a product which, because of its ease

[167]Kohler and Johnstin, *Am. Chem. J.*, 33, 35–45 (1905).

of hydrolysis, they formulated as a benzoic ester. At that time, Kohler also believed that the products of the Grignard reaction (in addition to the enolate) are biphenyl and magnesium bromide.

Umnowa[168] found that when α,α′-dibromoisobutyrone reacts with two molecules of methylmagnesium iodide or bromide, one bromine atom is replaced by a methyl group while the other is displaced in such a way that upon hydrolysis of the product, it is replaced by a hydrogen atom. She described the reaction as follows:

$$[(CH_3)_2CBr]_2CO \xrightarrow{2\,CH_3MgI} MgBrI + CH_3I + (CH_3)_3CCOC(CH_3)_2MgBr$$
$$\xrightarrow{H_2O} (CH_3)_3CCOCH(CH_3)_2 + MgBrOH$$

The reaction with phenylmagnesium bromide is similar.[169]

By prolonged (sixty hours) heating with an excess of methyl Grignard reagent, she believed that she was able to bring about the reaction of a third molecule of the Grignard reagent.

$$[(CH_3)_2CBr]_2CO \xrightarrow{3\,CH_3MgBr} (CH_3)_3CC(CH_3)(OMgBr)C(CH_3)_2MgBr$$
$$\xrightarrow{CO_2} (CH_3)_3CC(CH_3)(OMgBr)C(CH_3)_2CO_2MgBr$$
$$\xrightarrow{H_2O} (CH_3)_2CC(CH_3)(OH)C(CH_3)_2CO_2H$$

Carbonation of the initial product also yields a carboxylic acid.

$$C_6H_5(CH_3)_2COC(CH_3)_2MgBr \xrightarrow{CO_2} C_6H_5(CH_3)_2COC(CH_3)_2CO_2MgBr$$
$$\xrightarrow{H_2O} C_6H_5(CH_3)_2COC(CH_3)_2CO_2H$$

For these reasons, she formulated the product of reaction of two molecules of Grignard reagent with one molecule of the dibromo ketone as a Grignard reagent rather than as an enolate.

Löwenbein and Schuster[170] recognized the product of the interaction of phenylmagnesium bromide with α-bromo-α,α-diphenylacetophenone as an enolate, but they represented the reaction as consuming two equivalents of the Grignard reagent, and believed that biphenyl is one of its products.

$$(C_6H_5)_2CBrCOC_6H_5 + C_6H_5MgBr \longrightarrow$$
$$C_6H_5CO(C_6H_5)_2C\cdot + MgBr_2 + C_6H_5\cdot$$
$$\downarrow \qquad\qquad\qquad \downarrow$$
$$(C_6H_5)_2C{=}C(C_6H_5)O\cdot \qquad (C_6H_5{-})_2$$
$$\downarrow [C_6H_5MgBr]$$
$$(C_6H_5)_2C{=}C(C_6H_5)OMgBr + C_6H_5\cdot$$
$$\downarrow [H_2O] \qquad\qquad \downarrow$$
$$(C_6H_5)_2CHCOC_6H_5 + MgBrOH \; (C_6H_5{-})_2$$

168Umnowa, *J. Russ. Phys.-Chem. Soc.*, *44*, 1395–1406 (1912); *Chem. Zentr.*, *1913,I*, 1402; *Chem. Abstr.*, 7, 987 (1913).

169Umnowa, *J. Russ. Phys.-Chem. Soc.*, *45*, 881–4 (1913); *Chem. Abstr.*, 7, 3601 (1913).

170Löwenbein and Schuster, *Ann.*, *481*, 106–19 (1930).

Kohler and Tishler[171] studied the reaction of phenylmagnesium bromide with α-bromo-α,β,β-triphenylpropiophenone with special attention to the structure of the reaction product. Upon hydrolysis of the Grignard complex, they obtained a relatively stable enol which was converted by means of atmospheric oxygen to a known "enol peroxide."[172]

$$(C_6H_5)_2CHCBr(C_6H_5)COC_6H_5 \xrightarrow{C_6H_5MgBr} (C_6H_5)_2CHC(C_6H_5){=}C(C_6H_5)OMgBr + C_6H_5Br$$

$$\downarrow [H_2O]$$

$$(C_6H_5)_2CHC(C_6H_5)C(C_6H_5)OH^* \xleftarrow{O_2} (C_6H_5)_2CHC(C_6H_5){=}C(C_6H_5)OMgBr$$

(with the two C atoms of the first formula joined through an O—O bridge)

The fate of the hydrocarbon residue of the Grignard reagent was established beyond question by employing the corresponding α-iodo ketone. The iodobenzene formed was isolated and identified as the iodochloride. Kohler and Tishler could detect only the amount of biphenyl usually arising from the Wurtz side-reaction in the preparation of a phenylmagnesium halide.

$$(C_6H_5)_2CHCI(C_6H_5)COC_6H_5 \xrightarrow{C_6H_5MgBr} (C_6H_5)_2CHC(C_6H_5){=}C(C_6H_5)OMgBr + C_6H_5I$$

Further confirmation of the course of such reactions has been supplied by Fuson *et al.*[173] and by Howk and McElvain.[174]

$$2,4,6\text{-}(CH_3)_3\text{-}3,5\text{-}Br_2C_6COCH_2Br + n\text{-}C_4H_9MgBr \xrightarrow{H_2O} CH_3COC_9H_9Br_2\ (75.0\%) + n\text{-}C_4H_9Br\ (57.6\%)$$

$$2,4,6\text{-}(CH_3)_3\text{-}3,5\text{-}Br_2C_6COCH_2Br + n\text{-}C_5H_{11}MgBr \xrightarrow{H_2O} CH_3COC_9H_9Br_2\ (81.8\%) + n\text{-}C_5H_{11}Br\ (63.5\%)$$

$$2,4,6\text{-}(CH_3)_3\text{-}3,5\text{-}Br_2C_6COCH_2Br + 4\text{-}CH_3C_6H_4MgBr \xrightarrow{H_2O} CH_3COC_9H_9Br_2\ (71.5\%) + 4\text{-}CH_3C_6H_4Br\ (68.4\%)$$

$$2,4,6\text{-}(CH_3)_3\text{-}3,5\text{-}Br_2C_6COCH_2Br + C_6H_5MgBr \xrightarrow{H_2O} CH_3COC_9H_9Br_2\ (65.8\%) + C_6H_5Br\ (72.0\%)$$

---

[171] Kohler and Tishler, *J. Am. Chem. Soc.*, *54*, 1594–600 (1932).

[172] Kohler, *Am. Chem. J.*, *36*, 177–95 (1906).

*Kohler's formulation of his "enol peroxides" is undoubtedly erroneous. Rigaudy, *Compt. rend.*, *226*, 1993–5 (1948), has pointed out the probable instability of a 2-carbon 2-oxygen four-membered ring, has cited the similarity in properties between Kohler's "enol peroxides" and known hydroperoxides, and has shown that the ultraviolet absorption spectrum of one of Kohler's "enol peroxides" bears evidence of the presence of a carbonyl group and is closely similar to those of analogous ketones but quite different from that of an analogous carbinol. The more probable formulation in this instance would seem to be $(C_6H_5)_2CHC(OOH)(C_6H_5)COC_6H_5$.

[173] Fisher, Snyder, and Fuson, *J. Am. Chem. Soc.*, *54*, 3665–74 (1932).

[174] Howk and McElvain, *J. Am. Chem. Soc.*, *55*, 3372–80 (1933).

$$C_6H_5COCBr(CH_3)CO_2C_2H_5 + C_6H_5MgBr \rightarrow C_6H_5C(OMgBr){=}C(CH_3)CO_2C_2H_5\ (85\%) + C_6H_5Br\ (81\%) + [C_2H_5O_2C(C_6H_5CO)CH{-}]_2 + (C_6H_5{-})_2 + MgBr_2$$

A similar dehalogenation reaction, in which there is, however, a simultaneous rearrangement of double bonds within the molecule, has been reported by Allen and Gates.[175]

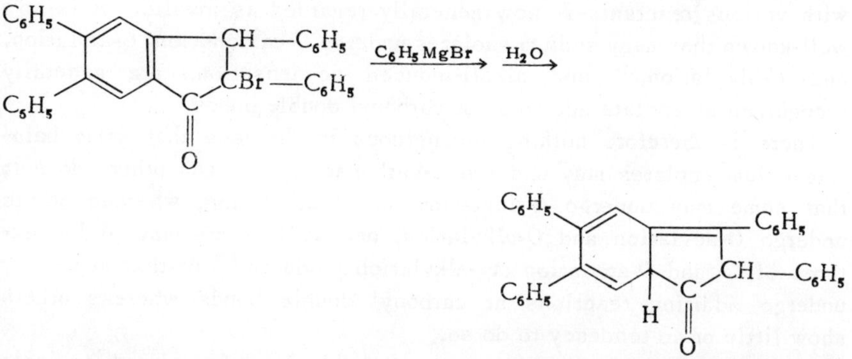

5,6-Diphenyl-2-bromo-2,3-diphenyl-1-indanone (ring with $CH{-}C_6H_5$, $CBr{-}C_6H_5$, $C{=}O$) $\xrightarrow{C_6H_5MgBr}$ $\xrightarrow{H_2O}$ product with ring C_6H_5, $CH{-}C_6H_5$, $C{=}O$, H

Probable mechanism of α-halo ketone dehalogenation. Whereas the halomagnesium compounds arising from the dehalogenation of α-halo ketones by Grignard reagents are, in general, identical in chemical properties with the enolates derived by treatment of the corresponding non-halogenated ketones with Grignard reagents, it seems altogether logical to formulate them as enolates. A rather interesting study by Kohler *et al.*[176] may be cited in illustration.*

(1) $C_6H_5CH{=}CHCO{-}Mes + C_6H_5MgBr \rightarrow [(C_6H_5)_2CHCH{=}CO{-}Mes]^- MgBr^+$ (A)

(2) $(C_6H_5)_2CHCH_2CO{-}Mes + C_2H_5MgBr \rightarrow [(C_6H_5)_2CHCH{=}CO{-}Mes]^- MgBr^+$ (B) $+ C_2H_6$

(3) $(C_6H_5)_2CHCHBrCO{-}Mes + C_2H_5MgBr \rightarrow [(C_6H_5)_2CHCH{=}CO{-}Mes]^- MgBr^+$ (B) $+ C_2H_5Br$

In appearance, in solubility, and in many chemical properties the products of reaction 1 (A) and of reactions 2 and 3 (B) appear to be identical. However, treatment of A with benzoyl chloride produces (in at least 96 percent yield) a benzoate melting at 161°, whereas similar treatment of B produces a benzoate melting at 148°. The two benzoates are evidently stereoisomers.

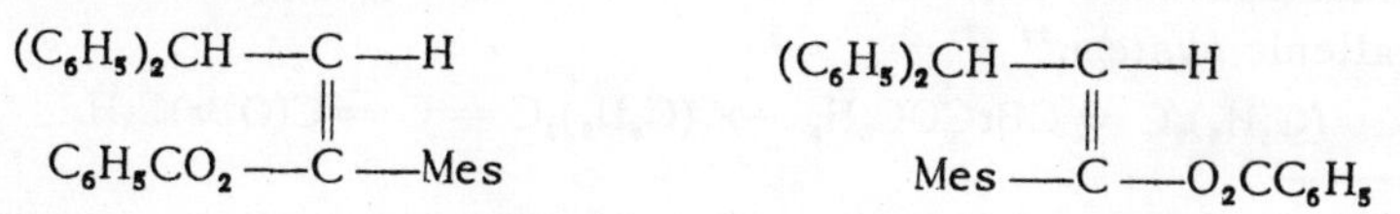

$(C_6H_5)_2CH{-}C{-}H$ / $C_6H_5CO_2{-}C{-}Mes$ (C=C) $(C_6H_5)_2CH{-}C{-}H$ / $Mes{-}C{-}O_2CC_6H_5$ (C=C)

[175] Allen and Gates, *J. Am. Chem. Soc.*, 64, 2127-30 (1942).
[176] Kohler, Tishler, and Potter, *J. Am. Chem. Soc.*, 57, 2517-21 (1935).
*Mes = mesityl = 2,4,6-$(CH_3)_3C_6H_2$—

Similar stereoisomers have been observed by Michael and Ross[177] in the products arising from the treatment of sodium enolates with chlorocarbonic ester.

The argument that halomagnesium compounds of the type under consideration should be formulated either as true Grignard reagents or as enolates depending upon the nature of the products formed in reactions with various reactants is now generally regarded as invalid. It is now well-known that many sodium enolates undergo *C*-carbonation, *C*-arylation, and *C*-alkylation,[178] and alkali-induced condensations are generally recognized as enolate additions at carbonyl double bonds.

There is therefore nothing incongruous in the idea that some halomagnesium enolates may undergo *C*-carbonation, whereas others do not; that some may undergo *C*-acylation and *C*-alkylation, whereas others undergo *O*-acylation and *O*-alkylation, and still others may yield mixtures of *C*- and *O*-acylation or -alkylation products;[179] or that some may undergo addition reactions at carbonyl double bonds whereas others show little or no tendency to do so.

Such halomagnesium enolates are probably best formulated as ionic compounds with resonant anions.

$$\left[R{-}\underset{\underset{R'}{|}}{C}{=}\overset{\overset{O}{|}}{C}{-}R'' \leftrightarrow R{-}\underset{\underset{R'}{|}}{C}{-}\overset{\overset{O}{\|}}{C}{-}R'' \right]^{-} MgX^{+}$$

The products formed upon treatment of the enolates with various reagents are probably influenced, to some extent at least, by the relative contributions of the respective electronic forms to the character of the resonant ion, but may, in some cases, be determined primarily by steric factors.

Howk and McElvain (*loc. cit.*[174]) have suggested that the Grignard reagent dehalogenation of α-halo ketones, with halomagnesium enolate formation, is preceded by rearrangement of the α-halo ketone to form an enol hypohalite.

$$RR'CXCOR'' \rightarrow RR'C{=}C(OX)R''$$

As Kohler and Tishler (*loc. cit.*[171]) have pointed out, "even if one were disposed to believe in the possibility of such a shift of the halogen atom, it would seem incredible in compounds like α-bromo-β-phenylbenzalacetophenone where it would involve rearrangement of a conjugated to an allenic system."

$$(C_6H_5)_2C{=}CBrCOC_6H_5 \rightarrow (C_6H_5)_2C{=}C{=}C(OBr)C_6H_5$$

---

[177] Michael and Ross, *J. Am. Chem. Soc.*, 53, 2394–414 (1931).

[178] See, *e.g.*, Schlenk, Hilleman, and Rodloff, *Ann.*, 487, 135–54 (1931).

[179] See, *e.g.*, Kohler and Peterson, *J. Am. Chem. Soc.*, 55, 1073–82 (1933); Kohler and Potter, *ibid.*, 58, 2166–70 (1936).

Schönberg and Moubasher[180] attribute the conversion of α-bromo ketones to the corresponding unbrominated ketones, by heating with Grignard reagents and hydrolizing the resultant product, to the magnesium halide present rather than to the Grignard reagent itself. They were able to show that, in some cases at least, the conversion may be effected by magnesium iodide or magnesium bromide.

$$C_6H_5COCBr(C_6H_5)_2 + MgI_2 \xrightarrow[\text{in } Et_2O]{\text{6 hrs. reflux}} \xrightarrow{H_2O} C_6H_5COCH(C_6H_5)_2$$

$$C_6H_5COCBr(C_6H_5)_2 + MgBr_2 \xrightarrow[\text{in } Et_2O]{\text{9 hrs. reflux}} \xrightarrow{H_2O} \text{Recovered bromo ketone}$$

$$C_6H_5COCBr(C_6H_5)_2 + MgBr_2 \xrightarrow[\text{in anisole}]{\text{9 hrs. at } 85^\circ} \xrightarrow{H_2O} C_6H_5COCH(C_6H_5)_2$$

However, their work demonstrates only that the conversion may be effected in some cases by the halides. There is no evidence that it is not effected as readily, or even more readily, by Grignard reagents.

On the whole, there would seem to be no serious objection to postulating for enolate formation of this kind a mechanism very similar to that for enolate formation from the corresponding unhalogenated ketones.

$$\begin{aligned} RCOCHR'R'' + R'''MgX &\rightarrow [RC(OMgXR''')CHR'R''] \\ &\rightarrow [RCO(OMgX)CHR'R'']^+R'''^- \\ &\rightarrow RC(OMgX){=}CR'R'' + R'''H \\ RCOCBrR'R'' + R'''MgX &\rightarrow [RC(OMgXR''')CBrR'R''] \\ &\rightarrow [RCO(OMgX)CBrR'R'']^+R'''^- \\ &\rightarrow RC(OMgX){=}CR'R'' + R'''Br \end{aligned}$$

Such a postulate implies that the *alpha* halogen atom displays some disposition to react as "positive" halogen, although the actual presence of free positive halogen ions need not be assumed. On this basis the different behaviors of bromoacetomesitylene and chloroacetomesitylene[181] are readily understandable, for bromine would certainly assume the rôle of "positive" halogen more readily than would chlorine.

$$\begin{aligned} BrCH_2CO\text{—}Mes + C_2H_5MgBr &\rightarrow H_2C{=}C(OMgBr)Mes + C_2H_5Br \\ &\xrightarrow{H_2O} CH_3CO\text{—}Mes\ (65.4\%) \\ ClCH_2CO\text{—}Mes + C_2H_5MgBr &\rightarrow CHCl{=}C(OMgBr)Mes + C_2H_6 \\ &\xrightarrow{H_2O} ClCH_2CO\text{—}Mes\ (100\%) \end{aligned}$$

As in the case of the ordinary ketone enolizations already discussed, these reactions may, of course, be formulated as concerted displacements involving quasi six-membered ring transition states.

[180] Schönberg and Moubasher, *J. Chem. Soc.*, *1944*, 462–3.
[181] Fisher, Snyder, and Fuson, *J. Am. Chem. Soc.*, *54*, 3665–74 (1932).

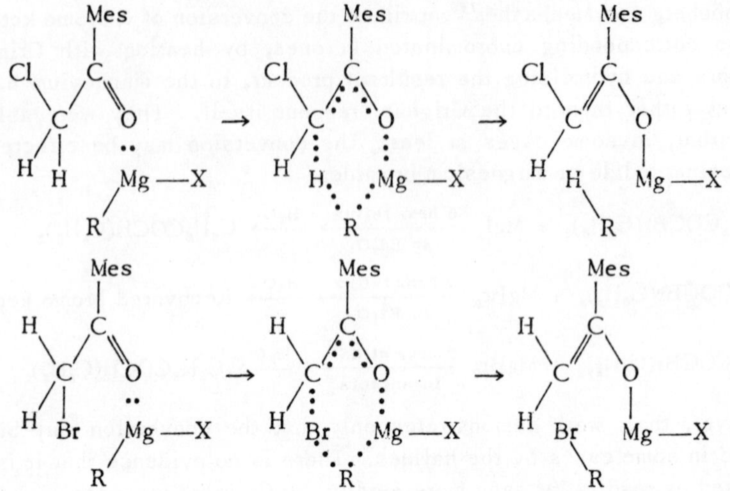

Mes Mes Mes
Cl C Cl C Cl C
C O → C O → C O
H H Mg—X H H. .Mg—X H H Mg—X
R R R

Mes Mes Mes
H C H C H C
C O → C O → C O
H Br Mg—X H Br Mg—X H Br Mg—X
R R R

This is essentially the scheme proposed by Lutz *et al.*[182] for "reductive enolization."

GRIGNARD REAGENT ADDITION TO CONJUGATED CARBONYL SYSTEMS

In terms of the conventional system of numbering for α,β-unsaturated aldehydes and ketones,

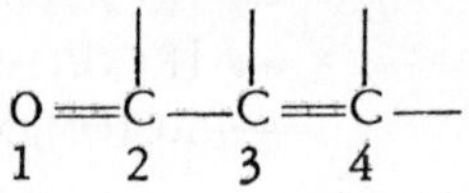

$$\underset{1}{O}{=}\underset{2}{C}{-}\underset{3}{C}{=}\underset{4}{C}{-}$$

most aldehydes and many ketones react additively with Grignard reagents to give, predominantly or exclusively, the "normal" 1,2-addition product. Many ketones, however, give, predominantly or exclusively, the 1,4-addition product. Grignard[183] himself reported the 1,4-addition of methylmagnesium iodide to α-ethylideneacetoacetic ester.

$$CH_3COC(CO_2C_2H_5){=}CHCH_3 \xrightarrow{CH_3MgI} CH_3C(OMgI){=}C(CO_2C_2H_5)CH(CH_3)_2$$

$$\xrightarrow{H_2O} CH_3COCH(CO_2C_2H_5)CH(CH_3)_2 + MgIOH$$

Since then many examples of 1,4-addition of Grignard reagents to conjugated carbonyl systems have been reported, and various investigators, notably Kohler and his students, have studied the factors influencing the order of addition in reactions of this kind.

Despite the seeming wealth of data collected in Table VI-XVI the amount of detailed and thoroughly reliable information available is en-

[182] Lutz and Kibler, *J. Am. Chem. Soc.*, *62*, 360–72 (1940); Lutz and Reveley, *ibid.*, *63*, 3180–9 (1941).

[183] Grignard, *Ann. chim.*, [7], *24*, 433–90 (1901).

tirely too meagre to justify the formulation of any broad generalizations concerning the factors affecting the order of addition of Grignard reagents to conjugated carbonyl systems. In far too many instances only the "expected" product, the major product, or the most readily isolated product has been reported, and that not always quantitatively. In such cases it is only when the yield is relatively high (above 50 percent) that the data may be regarded as having diagnostic significance. Even in supposedly quantitative studies, methods of product separation employed have not always been adequate, as has been pointed out by Alexander and Coraor.[184]

Byproducts in general have been almost universally ignored, and little or no attention has been paid to the nature of theoretically significant condensation products. Condensation products probably arise from two principal sources: (*a*) ketol (or aldol) condensations, and (*b*) diene polymerizations.

The initial product of the 1,4-addition of a Grignard reagent to an α,β-unsaturated ketone is, of course, an enolate, and, when the enolate and the original ketone are of such nature that 1,2-addition of the enolate at the carbonyl double bond of the ketone may take place, ketolization occurs.

$$RCOCR'{=}CR''R''' + R''''MgX \rightarrow [RCO{=}CR'CR''R'''R'''']^{-}MgX^{+}$$

$$RCOCR'{=}CR''R''' + [RCO{=}CR'CR''R'''R'''']^{-}MgX^{+} \rightarrow RCOCR'(CR''R'''R'''')CR(OMgX)CR'{=}CR''R'''$$

It is altogether conceivable that in cases of ketones with relatively reactive carbonyl double bonds practically all the initial 1,4-addition product formed may be consumed in subsequent ketol condensations, and the only product reported may be that of the competing, though not necessarily predominant, 1,2-addition reaction.

When the unsaturated ketone has one or more "active" hydrogen atoms attached to the non-olefinic carbon atom adjacent to the carbonyl group, enolization in the ordinary sense is also possible and may give rise to ketolization.

The products of "normal" 1,2-addition at the carbonyl double bond often undergo further unsaturation, either during the Grignard reaction or in the processes of hydrolysis and recovery, forming conjugated dienes which polymerize more or less readily.

Furthermore, alkyl or aralkyl Grignard reagents may effect reduction of unsaturated aldehydes and ketones as they do with the corresponding saturated compounds (see Grignard Reductions of Aldehydes and Ketones, p. 147). The only material isolated by Lutz and Reveley[185] as a result

[184] Alexander and Coraor, *J. Am. Chem. Soc.*, 73, 2721-3 (1951).
[185] Lutz and Reveley, *J. Am. Chem. Soc.*, 63, 3178-80 (1941).

TABLE VI-XVI

ADDITION OF GRIGNARD REAGENTS TO CONJUGATED CARBONYL SYSTEMS OF THE TYPE $RCOCR^1{=}CR^2R^3$

R	R^1	R^2	R^3	R^4MgX	1,2-Add'n (%)	1,4-Add'n (%)	Cond'n* (%)	Ref.†
H	H	H	H	CH_3MgBr	52	...	...	VI-XVII: 20,68, 72,272, 361
H	H	H	H	CH_3MgBr	73	...	...	48
H	H	H	H	CH_3MgBr	80	...	...	258
H	H	H	H	CH_3MgI	52	...	...	334,20, 66,72, 198,361
H	H	H	H	$(\equiv CMgBr)_2$	29‡	...	*ca.* 54	394,81,420
H	H	H	H	$(\equiv CMgBr)_2$	36§	...	...	393,391
H	H	H	H	C_2H_5MgBr	57¶	...	...	70,67,72
H	H	H	H	C_2H_5MgBr	65	...	...	272,33
H	H	H	H	C_2H_5MgBr	67	...	*ca.* 11	185
H	H	H	H	$H_2C{=}CHCH_2MgBr$	35–40	...	...	258
H	H	H	H	n-C_3H_7MgBr	41	...	...	68,72

*In cases where the α,β-unsaturated carbonyl compound itself is incapable of enolization, condensation can take place only through the enolate formed by 1,4-addition.

†To avoid duplication and conserve space a separate listing of references for this table is omitted. For the aldehydes (R = H), the reference numbers are those of Table VI-XVII; for the ketones (R ≠ H), those of Table VI-XVIII. In general, the yields recorded are those reported in the first reference listed; other references may be regarded as supplementary.

‡The addition product reported is $[\equiv CCH(OH)CH{=}CH_2]_2$.

§The principal addition product reported is $HC\equiv C(H_2C{=}CH)CHOH$.

¶It is reported that the maximum yield of addition product (57.4%) was obtained with a ratio of 1.85 mole of Grignard reagent to 1.00 mole of aldehyde; a smaller excess of Grignard reagent or an excess of aldehyde gave lower yields.

TABLE VI-XVI (Continued)

R	R¹	R²	R³	R⁴MgX	1,2-Add'n (%)	1,4-Add'n (%)	Cond'n (%)	Ref.
H	H	H	H	n-C_3H_7MgBr	60	...	...	*272,33, 249*
H	H	H	H	i-C_3H_7MgBr	15	...	...	*33*
H	H	H	H	Butenyl-MgBr*	<25	...	...	*258*
H	H	H	H	n-C_4H_9MgBr	35	...	...	*68,72*
H	H	H	H	n-C_4H_9MgBr	45	...	...	*272,33*
H	H	H	H	i-C_4H_9MgBr	+	...	...	*33*
H	H	H	H	$CH_3O(CH_2)_3MgCl$	46	...	...	*409*
H	H	H	H	n-$C_5H_{11}MgBr$	46	...	...	*118*
H	H	H	H	i-$C_5H_{11}MgBr$	59	...	...	*72*
H	H	H	H	C_6H_5MgBr	52	0	...	*179,41, 185,238*
H	H	H	H	C_6H_3MgBr	75	...	...	*69*
H	H	H	H	n-$C_6H_{13}MgBr$	94	...	...	*72*
H	H	H	H	$C_6H_5CH_2MgX$†	*ca.* 5	...	...	*69; cf. 61*
H	H	H	H	2-$CH_3C_6H_4MgBr$	55	...	...	*69*
H	H	H	H	4-$CH_3C_6H_4MgBr$	57	...	...	*69,41*
H	H	H	H	$(C_2H_5O)_2CHC\equiv CMgBr$	+	...	...	*423*
H	H	H	H	$C_6H_5(CH_2)_2MgBr$	>57	...	...	*69*
H	H	H	H	$C_6H_5(CH_2)_3MgBr$	57	...	...	*69*
H	Br	H	H	CH_3MgI	+‡	...	...	*199*
H	Br	H	H	$(\equiv CMgBr)_2$	+§	...	...	*391*

*Ou Kiun-Houo (VI–XVI: *258*) reported this reaction as involving crotylmagnesium bromide; *cf.*, however, Chapter XVII, Allylic Rearrangements in Grignard Reactions. The product reported is $H_2C{=}CH[H_2C{=}CHCH(CH_3)]CHOH$.

†X = Cl, Br.

‡The yield is reported as "good."

§The product reported is $HC\equiv C(H_2C{=}CBr)CHOH$.

TABLE VI-XVI (Continued)

R	R^1	R^2	R^3	R^4MgX	1,2-Add'n (%)	1,4-Add'n (%)	Cond'n (%)	Ref.
H	CH_3	H	H	$(\equiv CMgBr)_2$	52	...	...	*65*
H	H	CH_3	H	CH_3MgCl	81–86	...	...	*53*
H	H	CH_3	H	CH_3MgBr	30	...	...	*240,146, 343*
H	H	CH_3	H	CH_3MgI	90	...	...	*194,59, 121,281*
H	H	CH_3	H	$(\equiv CMgBr)_2$	*ca.* 36*	...	...	*397,81, 420*
H	H	CH_3	H	$(\equiv CMgBr)_2$	29†	...	...	*393,395*
H	H	CH_3	H	C_2H_5MgBr	65	...	...	*280,146, 281,343*
H	H	CH_3	H	C_2H_5MgBr	70.3	0.1	11.4	*309,272*
H	H	CH_3	H	C_2H_5MgBr	90	...	...	*194*
H	H	CH_3	H	$H_2C{=}CHCH_2MgBr$	+	trace	...	*309*
H	H	CH_3	H	$H_2C{=}CHCH_2MgBr$	*ca.* 80	...	...	*136,82, 181,258, 264*
H	H	CH_3	H	$n\text{-}C_3H_7MgCl$	74	...	...	*6*
H	H	CH_3	H	$n\text{-}C_3H_7MgBr$	46	...	...	*240,146, 280,281, 343*
H	H	CH_3	H	$n\text{-}C_3H_7MgBr$	78.3	trace	7.6	*309*
H	H	CH_3	H	$i\text{-}C_3H_7MgBr$	*ca.* 30	...	...	*281,343, 350*
H	H	CH_3	H	$i\text{-}C_3H_7MgBr$	46.5	0.3	34.1	*309*

*The addition product reported is $[\equiv CCH(OH)CH{=}CHCH_3]_2$.

†The addition product reported is $HC\equiv C(CH_3CH{=}CH)CHOH$.

TABLE VI-XVI (Continued)

R	R¹	R²	R³	R⁴MgX	1,2-Add'n (%)	1,4-Add'n (%)	Cond'n (%)	Ref.
H	H	CH_3	H	$H_2C{=}CHC{\equiv}CMgBr$	36.3	...	...	*406*
H	H	CH_3	H	n-C_4H_9MgBr	51	...	...	*204*
H	H	CH_3	H	i-C_4H_9MgBr	14.8–18.6*	...	21–28	*138*
H	H	CH_3	H	i-C_4H_9MgBr	*ca.* 30	...	...	*281,343*
H	H	CH_3	H	i-C_4H_9MgI	2†	...	60	*138*
H	H	CH_3	H	s-C_4H_9MgBr	42.2‡	...	...	*138*
H	H	CH_3	H	s-C_4H_9MgBr	15.3§	...	+	*138*
H	H	CH_3	H	t-C_4H_9MgCl	3.4	...	...	*240*
H	H	CH_3	H	t-C_4H_9MgCl	30.6	20.3	39.3	*308,309*
H	H	CH_3	H	t-C_4H_9MgBr	3.0	10.8	55.4	*309*
H	H	CH_3	H	$H_2C{=}C(CH_3)C{\equiv}CMgBr$	43.2	...	...	*406*
H	H	CH_3	H	i-$C_5H_{11}MgBr$	45	...	...	*121,343*
H	H	CH_3	H	t-$C_5H_{11}MgCl$	16.3	22.6	45.7	*309*
H	H	CH_3	H	C_6H_5MgBr	70	...	...	*40,61*
H	H	CH_3	H	C_6H_5MgBr	*ca.* 90	0.1	7.1	*309*
H	H	CH_3	H	$CH_3CH{=}C(CH_3)C{\equiv}CMgBr$	80.0	...	...	*407*
H	H	CH_3	H	n-$C_4H_9C{\equiv}CMgBr$	+	...	...	*127*
H	H	CH_3	H	$(CH_2)_5CHC{\equiv}CMgBr$	52	...	...	*126*
H	H	CH_3	H	1-$C_{10}H_7MgBr$	+	...	...	*301*
H	H	CH_3	H	$CH_3CH{=}CHCH(OMgBr)C{\equiv}CMgBr$	40	...	...	*398*
H	H	$H_2C{=}CH$	H	CH_3MgBr	75	...	...	*364*
H	H	$H_2C{=}CH$	H	$H_2C{=}CHCH_2MgBr$	90	...	...	*365*

*Yields of reduction product ($CH_3CH{=}CHCH_2OH$) from a trace to 20% are also reported.

†A 10% yield of crude reduction product ($CH_3CH{=}CHCH_2OH$) is also reported.

‡Reaction at 0°.

§Twenty-four hours at room temperature.

TABLE VI-XVI (Continued)

R	R[1]	R[2]	R[3]	R[4]MgX	1,2-Add'n (%)	1,4-Add'n (%)	Cond'n (%)	Ref.
H	H	n-C_3H_7	H	n-C_3H_7MgBr	75	...	...	*72*
H	H	$CH_3(CH{=}CH)_2$	H	$(\equiv CMgBr)_2$*	20.4	...	...	*400*
H	H	$CH_3(CH{=}CH)_2$	H	$RC\equiv CMgBr$†	26.8	...	...	*126*
H	H	C_6H_5	H	CH_3MgBr	+	...	...	*178,243*
H	H	C_6H_5	H	CH_3MgI	62	...	...	*380,40, 61,295; cf. 219*
H	H	C_6H_5	H	$(\equiv CMgBr)_2$	+‡	...	...	*149,81*
H	H	C_6H_5	H	C_2H_5MgBr	67	...	...	*173,138, 229*
H	H	C_6H_5	H	C_2H_5MgI	+§	...	...	*219*
H	H	C_6H_5	H	n-C_4H_9MgBr	36.5¶	...	...	*267*
H	H	C_6H_5	H	i-C_4H_9MgBr	+‖	...	...	*229,138*
H	H	C_6H_5	H	t-$C_5H_{11}MgCl$	...	10	...	*358*
H	H	C_6H_5	H	4-BrC_6H_4MgBr	+	...	...	*360*
H	H	C_6H_5	H	4-ClC_6H_4MgI	*ca.* 88	...	...	*41*
H	H	C_6H_5	H	C_6H_5MgBr	51	...	...	*252,200*
H	H	C_6H_5	H	C_6H_5MgBr	63	...	...	*44,184*
H	H	C_6H_5	H	4-$CH_3C_6H_4MgBr$	39	...	...	*41*

*The addition product reported is $[\equiv CCH(OH)(CH{=}CH)_3CH_3]_2$.

†R = 1-cyclohexenyl.

‡The addition product reported is $[\equiv CCH(OH)CH{=}CHC_6H_5]_2$.

§The products isolated obviously result from a Meerwein oxidation-reduction;

$$C_2H_5(C_6H_5CH{=}CH)CHOMgI + C_6H_5CH{=}CHCHO \longrightarrow C_2H_5COCH{=}CHC_6H_5 + C_6H_5CH{=}CHCH_2OMgI.$$

¶A *ca.* 15% yield of reduction product ($C_6H_5CH{=}CHCH_2OH$) is also reported.

‖The product is reported as obtained "in satisfactory yield and purity."

TABLE VI-XVI (Continued)

R	R^1	R^2	R^3	R^4MgX	1,2-Add'n (%)	1,4-Add'n (%)	Cond'n (%)	Ref.
H	H	C_6H_5	H	$4\text{-}CH_3OC_6H_4MgBr$	16	0	...	*360*
H	H	C_6H_5	H	$(C_2H_5)_2N(CH_2)_3MgCl$	+	...	...	*233*
H	H	C_6H_5	H	$C_6H_5CH(CO_2Na)MgCl$*	75	...	...	*158*
H	H	$RCH{=}CHC(CH_3){=}CH$†	H	$C_2H_5OC{\equiv}CMgBr$	+	...	...	*384*
H	Br	C_6H_5	H	CH_3MgI	+	...	...	*295*
H	Br	C_6H_5	H	C_6H_5MgBr	+	...	...	*184*
H	CH_3	CH_3	H	CH_3MgI	+	...	...	*350*
H	CH_3	CH_3	H	$RMgBr$‡	+	...	...	*1*
H	CH_3	C_2H_5	H	CH_3MgI	65	...	...	*121*
H	CH_3	C_2H_5	H	C_2H_5MgBr	88	...	...	*30,343*
H	CH_3	C_2H_5	H	$n\text{-}C_3H_7MgCl$	83	...	...	*30,343*
H	CH_3	C_2H_5	H	$i\text{-}C_4H_9MgBr$	67.5	...	...	*30*
H	CH_3	C_2H_5	H	$i\text{-}C_5H_{11}MgBr$	80	...	...	*30*
H	CH_3	C_6H_5	H	CH_3MgI	+	...	...	*425*
H	CH_3	RCH_2†§	H	$({\equiv}CMgBr)_2$	*ca.* 40¶	...	...	*147*
H	CH_3	RCH_2†§	H	$BrMgOCH_2CH{=}CHC{\equiv}CMgBr$	+	...	...	*404*
H	CH_3	RCH_2†§	H	$BrMgOCH_2CH(CH_3)C{\equiv}CMgBr$	81	...	...	*402,141*
H	CH_3	RCH_2†§	H	$n\text{-}C_4H_9C{\equiv}CMgBr$	92	...	...	*403*
H	CH_3	RCH_2†§	H	$CH_3OCH_2CH{=}C(CH_3)C{\equiv}CMgBr$	+	...	...	*157*

*In the opinion of Schlenk, Hilleman, and Rodloff, *Ann.*, *487*, 135–54 (1931), this "Grignard reagent" should be formulated as an enolate.

†R = 2,6,6-trimethyl-1-cyclohexenyl.

‡R = CH_3, C_2H_5, $i\text{-}C_5H_{11}$.

§This is the so-called "β-ionone C_{14} aldehyde" (VI-XVII: *402, 403*).

¶The addition product reported is $[{\equiv}CCH(OH)C(CH_3){=}CHCH_2R]_2$.

TABLE VI-XVI (Continued)

R	R^1	R^3	R^3	R^4MgX	1,2-Add'n (%)	1,4-Add'n (%)	Cond'n (%)	Ref.
H	CH_3	RCH_2[*][†]	H	$CH_3OCH(CH_3)CH{=}CHC{\equiv}CMgBr$	94	...	...	*403*
H	CH_3	RCH_2[*][†]	H	$n\text{-}C_4H_9OCH_2CH{=}C(CH_3)\text{-}C{\equiv}CMgBr$	*ca.* 80	...	...	*157*
H	CH_3	RCH_2[*][†]	H	$C_6H_5OCH_2CH{=}C(CH_3)\text{-}C{\equiv}CMgBr$	*ca.* 28	...	...	*157*
H	H	CH_3	CH_3	$C_{10}H_{19}MgBr$[‡]	+	...	...	*239*
H	H	CH_3	$(CH_3)_2C{=}CH(CH_2)_2$	RMgX[§]	+	...	...	*9*
H	H	CH_3	$(CH_3)_2C{=}CH(CH_2)_2$	$CH_3CH{=}C(CH_3)C{\equiv}CMgBr$	72.9	...	...	*407*
H	H	CH_3	$(CH_3)_2C{=}CH(CH_2)_2$	$(C_2H_5)_2N(CH_2)_3MgCl$	+	...	...	*233*
H	Br	Br	CO_2H	CH_3MgI	$\leqq 50$[¶]	...	...	*302*
H	Br	Br	CO_2H	C_2H_5MgBr	$\leqq 50$[¶]	...	...	*302*
H	Cl	Cl	CO_2H	CH_3MgI	+[¶]	...	...	*302*
H	Cl	Cl	CO_2H	C_2H_5MgBr	+[¶]	...	...	*302*
CH_3	H	H	H	$n\text{-}C_4H_9C{\equiv}CMgBr$	51	...	...	VI-XVIII: *83*
CH_3	H	H	H	$R'C{\equiv}CMgBr$[‖]	45-50	...	...	*84*
C_6H_5	H	H	H	CH_3MgI	0	+	...	*256*
C_6H_5	H	H	H	Butenyl-MgBr	...	...	+	*255*
C_6H_5	H	H	H	C_6H_5MgBr	0	+	...	*256*
CH_3	H	Cl	H	CH_3MgBr	48	...	...	*629*
CH_3	H	Cl	H	$H_2C{=}CHCH_2MgBr$	85	...	...	*629*

[*] R = 2,6,6-trimethyl-1-cyclohexenyl.

[†] This is the so-called "β-ionone C_{14} aldehyde" (VI-XVII: *402*, *403*).

[‡] From 1-bromo-2-(4-methyl-3-cyclohexen-1-yl)propane.

[§] R = CH_3, C_2H_5, $i\text{-}C_4H_9$, C_6H_5.

[¶] The product reported is a lactone, *i.e.*, a 3,4-dihalo-5-alkyldihydrofuran-2-one.

[‖] R′ = 1-cyclohexenyl.

TABLE VI-XVI (Continued)

R	R[1]	R[2]	R[3]	R^4MgX	1,2-Add'n (%)	1,4-Add'n (%)	Cond'n (%)	Ref.
CH_3	H	Cl	H	n-$C_4H_9C\equiv CMgBr$	95	...	...	*629*
CH_3	H	CH_3	H	CH_3MgBr	72.4	20.1	...	*111*
CH_3	H	CH_3	H	CH_3MgI	80.0	1.2	...	*10,108, 109,110*
CH_3	H	CH_3	H	C_2H_5MgBr	+	...	...	*109,110*
CH_3	H	CH_3	H	C_2H_5MgBr	41.4	38.6	...	*112*
CH_3	H	CH_3	H	C_2H_5MgBr	+	71.4	...	*111*
CH_3	H	CH_3	H	C_2H_5MgBr	$\leqq 47.6x$*	$52.4x$*	...	*622*
CH_3	H	CH_3	H	i-C_3H_7MgBr	$\leqq 34.5x$*	$65.5x$*	...	*622*
CH_3	H	CH_3	H	i-C_4H_9MgCl	+	...	...	*109,110*
CH_3	H	CH_3	H	t-C_4H_9MgCl	16.7	54.0	...	*112*
CH_3	H	CH_3	H	t-C_4H_9MgCl	$\leqq 38.3x$*	$61.7x$*	...	*622*
CH_3	H	CH_3	H	i-$C_5H_{11}MgBr$	+	...	...	*109,110*
CH_3	H	CH_3	H	C_6H_5MgBr	+	37	...	*111*
CH_3	H	CH_3	H	n-$C_4H_9C\equiv CMgBr$	49.4	...	...	*83*
CH_3	H	C_2H_5	H	C_2H_5MgBr	$\leqq 56.9x$*	$43.1x$*	...	*622*
CH_3	H	C_2H_5	H	i-C_3H_7MgBr	$\leqq 43.5x$*	$56.5x$*	...	*622*
CH_3	H	C_2H_5	H	t-C_4H_9MgCl	$\leqq 52.0x$*	$48.0x$*	...	*622*
CH_3	H	$CH_3CH=CH$	H	$RC\equiv CMgBr$†	56	...	...	*182,630*
CH_3	H	n-C_3H_7	H	CH_3MgI	75	0	+	*183,184*
CH_3	H	n-C_3H_7	H	C_2H_5MgBr	65	...	...	*183*
CH_3	H	n-C_3H_7	H	C_2H_5MgBr	46.0	30.7	...	*185*
CH_3	H	n-C_3H_7	H	C_2H_5MgBr	+‡	+‡	...	*186*

*For the series of reactions studied, x is said to range from 0.86 to 1.00.

†R = 1-cyclohexenyl.

‡The ratio of 1,2-addition product to 1,4-addition product is reported to be about 3.1 : 1.0; the unsaturated ketone is the *trans* isomer.

TABLE VI-XVI (Continued)

R	R^1	R^2	R^3	R^4MgX	1,2-Add'n (%)	1,4-Add'n (%)	Cnd'n (%)	Ref.
CH_3	H	n-C_3H_7	H	C_2H_5MgBr	≦48.0 x*	52.0 x*	...	*622*
CH_3	H	n-C_3H_7	H	n-C_3H_7MgBr	55	...	...	*183*
CH_3	H	n-C_3H_7	H	i-C_3H_7MgBr	+†	+†	...	*186*
CH_3	H	n-C_3H_7	H	i-C_3H_7MgBr	≦37.0 x*	63.0 x*	...	*622*
CH_3	H	n-C_3H_7	H	n-C_4H_9MgBr	45	...	...	*183*
CH_3	H	n-C_3H_7	H	i-C_4H_9MgBr	38	...	...	*183*
CH_3	H	n-C_3H_7	H	t-C_4H_9MgCl	+‡	+‡	...	*186*
CH_3	H	n-C_3H_7	H	t-C_4H_9MgCl	≦40.1 x*	59.9 x*	...	*622*
CH_3	H	n-C_3H_7	H	i-$C_5H_{11}MgBr$	30	...	...	*183*
CH_3	H	n-C_3H_7	H	C_6H_5MgBr	20	...	...	*183,184*
CH_3	H	α-C_4H_3O§	H	C_2H_5MgBr	...	50	+	*599*
CH_3	H	α-C_4H_3O§	H	n-C_3H_7MgBr	...	50	...	*599*
CH_3	H	α-C_4H_3O§	H	i-C_3H_7MgBr	...	61	...	*599*
CH_3	H	α-C_4H_3O§	H	i-C_4H_9MgBr	...	+	...	*599*
CH_3	H	α-C_4H_3O§	H	i-$C_5H_{11}MgI$	...	44	...	*224*
CH_3	H	α-C_4H_3O§	H	C_6H_5MgBr	...	...	+	*140*
CH_3	H	C_6H_5	H	CH_3MgI	+	...	...	*206*
CH_3	H	C_6H_5	H	C_2H_5MgI	37.2	56.5	6.3	*111*
CH_3	H	C_6H_5	H	C_2H_5MgI	+¶	...	...	*206*

* For the series of reactions studied, x is said to range from 0.86 to 1.00.

† The ratio of 1,2-addition product to 1,4-addition product is reported to be about 1.2 : 1.0; the unsaturated ketone is the *trans* isomer.

‡ The ratio of 1,2-addition product to 1,4-addition product is reported to be about 1.9 : 1.0; the unsaturated ketone is the *trans* isomer.

§ The ketone is furfurylideneacetone; α-C_4H_3O = 2-furyl.

¶ The yield of diene (dehydration product) is reported as "good."

TABLE VI-XVI (Continued)

R	R^1	R^2	R^3	R^4MgX	1,2-Add'n (%)	1,4-Add'n (%)	Cond'n (%)	Ref.
CH_3	H	C_6H_5	H	$H_2C{=}CHCH_2MgBr$	31	...	...	*599*
CH_3	H	C_6H_5	H	$C_2H_5OC{\equiv}CMgBr$	80	...	...	*43*
CH_3	H	C_6H_5	H	t-C_4H_9MgCl	27	15	+	*276*
CH_3	H	C_6H_5	H	i-$C_5H_{11}MgBr$	...	52*	...	*277*
CH_3	H	C_6H_5	H	C_6H_5MgI	+	4.9	...	*111*
CH_3	H	C_6H_5	H	$(CH_2)_5CHMgBr$	trace	64.4	...	*278*
CH_3	H	n-C_6H_{13}	H	CH_3MgI	16	...	...	*294*
CH_3	H	n-C_6H_{13}	H	C_2H_5MgBr	+	...	...	*294*
CH_3	H	n-C_6H_{13}	H	i-$C_5H_{11}MgBr$	+	...	...	*294*
CH_3	H	2-HOC_6H_4	H	CH_3MgI	...	18.2	...	*273*
CH_3	H	4-$CH_3OC_6H_4$	H	C_2H_5MgBr	+	61.2	...	*111*
CH_3	H	4-$CH_3OC_6H_4$	H	$(CH_2)_5CHMgBr$	+	70.2	...	*278*
CH_3	H	$C_6H_5CH{=}CH$	H	$C_6H_5CH_2MgCl$	+†	...	...	*329*
CH_3	H	Mes‡	H	RMgX	+	+	...	*401*
CH_3	H	ψ-C_9H_{15}§	H	$(—CH_2CH_2MgBr)_2$	+	...	...	*634*
CH_3	H	ψ-C_9H_{15}§	H	$CH_3O(CH_2)_3MgBr$	53.5	...	...	*409*
CH_3	H	ψ-C_9H_{15}§	H	$C_2H_5O(CH_2)_3MgBr$	52	...	...	*409*
CH_3	H	ψ-C_9H_{15}§	H	$C_6H_5O(CH_2)_3MgBr$	49	...	...	*409*
CH_3	H	α-C_9H_{15}¶	H	$H_2C{=}CHCH_2MgBr$	*ca.* 65	...	...	*635*
CH_3	H	α-C_9H_{15}¶	H	$CH_3CH{=}C(CH_3)CH{=}CHCH_2$-MgBr	+	...	...	*95*
CH_3	H	β-C_9H_{15}‖	H	$H_2C{=}CHC{\equiv}CMgBr$	59	...	...	*636, 637*

* The abstract reports a 6-octanone, but this is obviously a misprint.

† The yield of diene is described as "poor."

‡ Mes = mesityl = 2,4,6-$(CH_3)_3C_6H_2$—.

§ The ketone is pseudoionone; ψ-C_9H_{15} = $(CH_3)_2C{=}CHCH_2CH_2C(CH_3){=}CH$.

¶ The ketone is α-ionone; α-C_9H_{15} = 2,4,4-trimethylcyclohexen-3-yl.

‖ The ketone is β-ionone; β-C_9H_{15} = 1,3,3-trimethylcyclohexen-2-yl.

TABLE VI-XVI (Continued)

R	R^1	R^2	R^3	R^4MgX	1,2-Add'n (%)	1,4-Add'n (%)	Cond'n (%)	Ref.
CH_3	H	β-C_9H_{15}*	H	$C_2H_5OC\equiv CMgBr$	73	...	...	233,487
CH_3	H	β-C_9H_{15}*	H	$(=CHCH_2MgBr)_2$	+	...	...	638
CH_3	H	β-C_9H_{15}*	H	$H_2C=C(CH_3)C\equiv CMgBr$	48	...	...	636
CH_3	H	β-C_9H_{15}*	H	$CH_3CH=C(CH_3)C\equiv CMgBr$	52	...	...	636
CH_3	H	β-C_9H_{15}*	H	$(C_2H_5O)_2CHCH_2MgBr$	64	...	...	639
C_2H_5	H	CH_3	H	C_2H_5MgBr	$\leqq 32.3x$†	$67.7x$†	...	622
C_2H_5	H	CH_3	H	i-C_3H_7MgBr	$\leqq 19.8x$†	$80.2x$†	...	622
C_2H_5	H	CH_3	H	t-C_4H_9MgCl	$\leqq 33.7x$†	$66.3x$†	...	622
C_2H_5	H	n-C_3H_7	H	C_2H_5MgBr	38.6	...	...	184
C_2H_5	H	C_6H_5	H	C_2H_5MgBr	+	71.0	...	111
C_2H_5	H	C_6H_5	H	i-C_4H_9MgBr	+	58.9	...	111
C_2H_5	H	C_6H_5	H	C_6H_5MgBr	+	40.0	...	111
C_2H_5	H	C_6H_5	H	$(CH_2)_5CHMgBr$	+	70.4	...	278
n-C_3H_7	H	$(C_2H_5)_2N$	H	C_2H_5MgBr	...	+‡	...	153
i-C_3H_7	H	C_6H_5	H	C_2H_5MgBr	0	90.2	...	111
i-C_3H_7	H	C_6H_5	H	C_6H_5MgBr	*ca.* 9	86.6	...	111
t-C_4H_9	H	C_6H_5	H	C_2H_5MgBr	0	98.1	...	111
t-C_4H_9	H	C_6H_5	H	C_6H_5MgBr	0	96.9	...	111
4-BrC_6H_4	H	α-C_4H_3O§	H	C_2H_5MgBr	...	95.0	...	346
4-BrC_6H_4	H	α-C_4H_3O§	H	n-C_3H_7MgBr	...	80.0	...	346
4-BrC_6H_4	H	α-C_4H_3O§	H	C_6H_5MgBr	...	85.0	...	346
4-BrC_6H_4	H	C_6H_5	H	$(CH_2)_4CHMgBr$	...	48.0	...	452

* The ketone is β-ionone; β-C_9H_{15} = 1,3,3-trimethylcyclohexen-2-yl.

† For the series of reactions studied, x is said to range from 0.86 to 1.00.

‡ This reaction is accompanied by cleavage; the product is n-$C_3H_7COCH=CHR$, where R is the organic radical of the Grignard reagent (RMgX).

§ The ketone is furfurylidene-p-bromoacetophenone; α-C_4H_3O = 2-furyl.

TABLE VI-XVI (Continued)

R	R[1]	R[2]	R[3]	R^4MgX	1,2-Add'n (%)	1,4-Add'n (%)	Cond'n (%)	Ref.
$4\text{-}BrC_6H_4$	H	C_6H_5	H	$4\text{-}BrC_6H_4MgBr$	...	38.6	...	*453*
$4\text{-}BrC_6H_4$	H	$4\text{-}BrC_6H_4CO$	H	C_6H_5MgBr	...	53.0	...	*488*
$4\text{-}BrC_6H_4$	H	$C_6H_5CH{=}CH$	H	$C_6H_5CH_2MgCl$	...	+	...	*506*
$4\text{-}ClC_6H_4$	H	$\alpha\text{-}C_4H_3O$*	H	C_2H_5MgBr	...	95.0	...	*346*
$4\text{-}ClC_6H_4$	H	$\alpha\text{-}C_4H_3O$*	H	$n\text{-}C_3H_7MgBr$	...	72.0	...	*347*
$4\text{-}ClC_6H_4$	H	$\alpha\text{-}C_4H_3O$*	H	C_6H_5MgBr	...	94.0	...	*347*
$4\text{-}ClC_6H_4$	H	C_6H_5	H	C_6H_5MgBr	...	66.9	...	*453*
C_6H_5	H	CCl_3	H	C_6H_5MgBr	...	93.0	...	*111*
C_6H_5	H	CO_2H	H	C_2H_5MgBr	...	+	...	*274*
C_6H_5	H	CO_2H	H	C_6H_5MgBr	...	22.5	...	*274*
C_6H_5	H	CO_2H	H	$4\text{-}CH_3OC_6H_4MgBr$	...	22.0	...	*274*
C_6H_5	H	CH_3	H	CH_3MgI	0	+	...	*256*
C_6H_5	H	CH_3	H	C_6H_5MgBr	0	+	...	*256*
C_6H_5	H	$(CH_3)_2N$	H	C_2H_5MgBr	...	+†	...	*153*
C_6H_5	H	$(CH_3)_2N$	H	C_6H_5MgBr	...	+†	...	*153*
C_6H_5	H	$\alpha\text{-}C_4H_3O$‡	H	RMgX§	...	+	...	*624*
C_6H_5	H	C_6H_5	H	CH_3MgBr	...	55–56	37–39	*611*
C_6H_5	H	C_6H_5	H	CH_3MgI	+¶	+	...	*108*
C_6H_5	H	C_6H_5	H	C_2H_5MgBr	...	58.2	+	*449,464*
C_6H_5	H	C_6H_5	H	C_2H_5MgBr	trace	95.8	...	*111,147*
C_6H_5	H	C_6H_5	H	C_2H_5MgBr	27.1	35.1	...	*454*

* The ketone is furfurylidene-*p*-chloroacetophenone; $\alpha\text{-}C_4H_3O$ = 2-furyl.

† This addition is accompanied by cleavage; the product is $C_6H_5COCH{=}CHR$, where R is the organic radical of the Grignard reagent (RMgX).

‡ The ketone is α-furfurylideneacetophenone; $\alpha\text{-}C_4H_3O$ = 2-furyl.

§ RMgX = CH_3MgI, C_2H_5MgBr, C_6H_5MgBr.

¶ Major product.

TABLE VI-XVI (Continued)

R	R^1	R^2	R^3	R^4MgX	1,2-Add'n (%)	1,4-Add'n (%)	Cond'n (%)	Ref.
C_6H_5	H	C_6H_5	H	C_2H_5MgBr	*ca.* 40	*ca.* 60	...	*611*
C_6H_5	H	C_6H_5	H	$H_2C{=}CHCH_2MgBr$	18.7	...	...	*599*
C_6H_5	H	C_6H_5	H	C_6H_5MgBr	+	...	...	*455*
C_6H_5	H	C_6H_5	H	C_6H_5MgBr	3.6	85.2	...	*111,147, 449,464, 569,611*
C_6H_5	H	C_6H_5	H	$(CH_2)_5CHMgBr$	*ca.* 5	*ca.* 95	...	*278*
C_6H_5	H	C_6H_5	H	$4\text{-}CH_3C_6H_4MgBr$	...	+	...	*449*
C_6H_5	H	C_6H_5	H	$4\text{-}CH_3OC_6H_4MgBr$	...	+	...	*449*
C_6H_5	H	C_6H_5	H	$4\text{-}(CH_3)_2NC_6H_4MgI$	...	71.0	...	*465*
C_6H_5	H	C_6H_5	H	$1\text{-}C_{10}H_7MgBr$	...	+	...	*275*
C_6H_5	H	$2\text{-}HOC_6H_4$	H	C_6H_5MgBr	...	80.0*	...	*438*
C_6H_5	H	$2\text{-}HOC_6H_4$	H	$4\text{-}CH_3C_6H_4MgBr$	...	61.0†	...	*438*
C_6H_5	H	$C_6H_5SO_2$	H	C_6H_5MgBr	+	...	...	*653*
C_6H_5	H	$(CH_2)_5CH$	H	C_2H_5MgBr	...	+	...	*278*
C_6H_5	H	$(CH_2)_5CH$	H	C_6H_5MgBr	trace	+	...	*278*
C_6H_5	H	$4\text{-}CH_3OC_6H_4$	H	C_2H_5MgBr	+	93.2	...	*111*
C_6H_5	H	$4\text{-}CH_3OC_6H_4$	H	C_6H_5MgBr	1.6	95.7	...	*111*
C_6H_5	H	$3,4\text{-}CH_2O_2C_6H_3$	H	CH_3MgI	...	39.3	+	*449*
C_6H_5	H	$3,4\text{-}CH_2O_2C_6H_3$	H	C_2H_5MgBr	...	+	...	*449*
C_6H_5	H	$3,4\text{-}CH_2O_2C_6H_3$	H	C_6H_5MgBr	...	+	...	*449*
C_6H_5	H	C_6H_5CO	H	C_6H_5MgBr	...	60–65	...	*488,641*
C_6H_5	H	$C_6H_5CH{=}CH$	H	C_2H_5MgBr	...	+	...	*507*
C_6H_5	H	$C_6H_5CH{=}CH$	H	C_6H_5MgBr	...	73.1	...	*507*

* The product reported is 2,4-diphenyl-2-chromanol.

† The product reported is 2-phenyl-4-*p*-tolyl-2-chromanol.

TABLE VI-XVI (Continued)

R	R^1	R^2	R^3	R^4MgX	1,2-Add'n (%)	1,4-Add'n (%)	Cond'n (%)	Ref.
C_6H_5	H	$C_6H_5CH=CH$	H	$C_6H_5CH_2MgCl$	...	+	...	*507*
C_6H_5	H	$4\text{-}(CH_3)_2NC_6H_4$	H	C_6H_5MgBr	...	66.0	...	*465*
$(CH_2)_5CH$	H	C_6H_5	H	C_2H_5MgBr	0	+	...	*278*
$(CH_2)_5CH$	H	C_6H_5	H	C_6H_5MgBr	trace	+	...	*278*
$4\text{-}CH_3C_6H_4$	H	CO_2H	H	C_6H_5MgBr	...	27.2	...	*274*
$4\text{-}CH_3C_6H_4$	H	$\alpha\text{-}C_4H_3O$*	H	CH_3MgI	...	50.0	...	*346*
$4\text{-}CH_3C_6H_4$	H	$\alpha\text{-}C_4H_3O$*	H	C_2H_5MgBr	...	70.0	...	*346*
$4\text{-}CH_3C_6H_4$	H	$\alpha\text{-}C_4H_3O$*	H	$i\text{-}C_3H_7MgBr$	...	80.0	...	*346*
$4\text{-}CH_3C_6H_4$	H	$\alpha\text{-}C_4H_3O$*	H	$i\text{-}C_4H_9MgBr$	...	70.0	...	*346*
$4\text{-}CH_3C_6H_4$	H	$\alpha\text{-}C_4H_3O$*	H	C_6H_5MgBr	...	80.0	...	*346*
$4\text{-}CH_3C_6H_4$	H	$2\text{-}HOC_6H_4$	H	C_6H_5MgBr	...	+†	...	*438*
$4\text{-}CH_3OC_6H_4$	H	$\alpha\text{-}C_4H_3O$‡	H	C_2H_5MgBr	...	73.3	...	*347*
$4\text{-}CH_3OC_6H_4$	H	$\alpha\text{-}C_4H_3O$‡	H	$n\text{-}C_3H_7MgBr$	...	67.0	...	*347*
$4\text{-}CH_3OC_6H_4$	H	C_6H_5	H	C_2H_5MgBr	trace	94.4	...	*111*
$4\text{-}CH_3OC_6H_4$	H	C_6H_5	H	C_6H_5MgBr	trace	96.2	...	*111*
$4\text{-}CH_3OC_6H_4$	H	$4\text{-}CH_3OC_6H_4$	H	CH_3MgI	...	45.0	...	*513*
$4\text{-}CH_3OC_6H_4$	H	$4\text{-}CH_3OC_6H_4$	H	C_2H_5MgBr	...	80.0	...	*513*
$4\text{-}CH_3OC_6H_4$	H	$4\text{-}CH_3OC_6H_4$	H	$n\text{-}C_3H_7MgBr$	...	80.0	...	*513*
$4\text{-}CH_3OC_6H_4$	H	$4\text{-}CH_3OC_6H_4$	H	$i\text{-}C_3H_7MgBr$	...	75.0	...	*513,514*
$4\text{-}CH_3OC_6H_4$	H	$4\text{-}CH_3OC_6H_4$	H	$n\text{-}C_4H_9MgBr$	...	70.0	...	*513*
$4\text{-}CH_3OC_6H_4$	H	$4\text{-}CH_3OC_6H_4$	H	$n\text{-}C_5H_{11}MgBr$	...	75.0	...	*513*
$4\text{-}CH_3OC_6H_4$	H	$4\text{-}CH_3OC_6H_4$	H	C_6H_5MgBr	...	75.0	...	*513*
$4\text{-}CH_3OC_6H_4$	H	$4\text{-}CH_3OC_6H_4$	H	$(CH_2)_5CHMgCl$	...	85.0	...	*514*

* The ketone is α-furfurylidene-*p*-methylacetophenone; $\alpha\text{-}C_4H_3O$ = 2-furyl.

† The product reported is 2-*p*-tolyl-4-phenyl-2-chromanol.

‡ The ketone is α-furfurylidene-*p*-methoxyacetophenone; $\alpha\text{-}C_4H_3O$ = 2-furyl.

TABLE VI-XVI (Continued)

R	R^1	R^2	R^3	R^4MgX	1,2-Add'n (%)	1,4-Add'n (%)	Cond'n (%)	Ref.
4-$CH_3OC_6H_4$	H	4-$CH_3OC_6H_4$	H	$C_6H_5CH_2MgCl$	...	70.0	...	*513*
4-$CH_3OC_6H_4$	H	4-$CH_3OC_6H_4$	H	4-$CH_3OC_6H_4MgBr$	...	70.0	...	*513*
4-$CH_3OC_6H_4$	H	$C_6H_5CH{=}CH$	H	$C_6H_5CH_2MgCl$	...	+	...	*506*
$C_6H_5CH{=}CH$	H	C_6H_5	H	C_2H_5MgBr	...	90.4	...	*111*
$C_6H_5CH{=}CH$	H	C_6H_5	H	*t*-C_4H_9MgCl	...	76.1	...	*276*
$C_6H_5CH{=}CH$	H	C_6H_5	H	C_6H_5MgBr	...	78.8	...	*111*
$C_6H_5CH{=}CH$	H	C_6H_5	H	$C_6H_5C{\equiv}CMgBr$	?	...	...	*367*
Mes*	H	CH_3	H	Mes-MgBr*	...	70.0	...	*393*
Mes*	H	$CH_3CH{=}CH$	H	C_6H_5MgBr	...	81	...	*640*
Mes*	H	C_6H_5	H	RMgX	0	+	...	*401*
Mes*	H	C_6H_5	H	C_6H_5MgBr	...	94	...	*111,539*
Mes*	H	C_6H_5	H	Mes-MgBr*	...	+	...	*393*
Mes*	H	Mes*	H	RMgX	0	+	...	*401*
Mes*	H	Mes*	H	CH_3MgI	...	+†	...	*393*
Mes*	H	Mes*	H	C_6H_5MgBr	...	+	...	*393*
Mes*	H	Mes*	H	Mes-MgBr*	...	46.0	...	*393*
Mes*	H	MesCO*	H	*t*-C_4H_9MgCl	...	50	...	*576*
Mes*	H	MesCO*	H	C_6H_5MgBr	...	59–60	...	*488*
Dur‡	H	$CH_3CH{=}CH$	H	C_6H_5MgBr	...	73	...	*640*
$C_2H_5(C_6H_5)CHCH_2$	H	C_6H_5	H	C_2H_5MgBr	0	*ca.* 100	...	*111*
$C_2H_5(C_6H_5)CHCH_2$	H	C_6H_5	H	C_6H_5MgBr	*ca.* 7	90.4	...	*111*
$(C_6H_5)_2CHCH_2$	H	C_6H_5	H	C_2H_5MgBr	0	100 (?)§	...	*111*

* Mes = mesityl = 2,4,6-$(CH_3)_3C_6H_2$—.
† The yield is reported as "high."
‡ Dur = duryl = 2,3,5,6-$(CH_3)_4C_6H$—.
§ The reported yield (in grams) may be a misprint; it constitutes somewhat more than 100% of the theoretically possible yield.

TABLE VI-XVI (Continued)

R	R¹	R²	R³	R⁴MgX	1,2-Add'n (%)	1,4-Add'n (%)	Cond'n (%)	Ref.
$(C_6H_5)_2CHCH_2$	H	C_6H_5	H	C_6H_5MgBr	trace	46.4	...	*111*
CH_3	H	CH_3	CH_3	CH_3MgBr	+*	...	...	*137,604*
CH_3	H	CH_3	CH_3	CH_3MgI	+	...	...	*61*
CH_3	H	CH_3	CH_3	CH_3MgI	24.3	...	...	*138,139*
CH_3	H	CH_3	CH_3	CH_3MgI	87.0	...	...	*613*
CH_3	H	CH_3	CH_3	$(\equiv CMgI)_2$	+	...	...	*125*
CH_3	H	CH_3	CH_3	C_2H_5MgBr	+	...	...	*111,140, 604*
CH_3	H	CH_3	CH_3	C_2H_5MgBr	50.9†	...	...	*141*
CH_3	H	CH_3	CH_3	C_2H_5MgBr	17.3‡	...	...	*141*
CH_3	H	CH_3	CH_3	C_2H_5MgI	+	...	...	*232*
CH_3	H	CH_3	CH_3	$H_2C=CHCH_2MgBr$	*ca.* 91	...	...	*25,142, 143*
CH_3	H	CH_3	CH_3	$H_2C=CHCH_2MgBr$	75	...	...	*599*
CH_3	H	CH_3	CH_3	*n*-C_3H_7MgBr	+	...	...	*232,604*
CH_3	H	CH_3	CH_3	*i*-C_3H_7MgBr	+	...	...	*144,604*
CH_3	H	CH_3	CH_3	$H_2C=CHC\equiv CMgBr$	40.0	...	...	*40*
CH_3	H	CH_3	CH_3	*n*-C_4H_9MgBr	+	...	...	*604*
CH_3	H	CH_3	CH_3	*n*-C_4H_9MgI	+	...	...	*232*
CH_3	H	CH_3	CH_3	*i*-C_4H_9MgBr	+	...	...	*604*
CH_3	H	CH_3	CH_3	*t*-C_4H_9MgCl	46	0	...	*112,144*

* The total yield of addition product on the basis of reacting ketone is not stated. From Raman spectra data, Dupont and Menut (*137*) conclude that mesityl oxide comprises about 80% $CH_3COCH=C(CH_3)_2$ and about 20% $CH_3COCH_2C(CH_3)=CH_2$. The addition product isolated was estimated to consist of 75–80% $(CH_3)_2C=CHC(CH_3)_2OH$ and 20–25% $H_2C=C(CH_3)CH_2C(CH_3)_2OH$

† Reaction at $-10°$.

‡ Reaction at $15°$.

TABLE VI-XVI (Continued)

R	R^1	R^2	R^3	R^4MgX	1,2-Add'n (%)	1,4-Add'n (%)	Cond'n (%)	Ref.
CH_3	H	CH_3	CH_3	n-$C_5H_{11}MgBr$	+	...	...	*604*
CH_3	H	CH_3	CH_3	i-$C_5H_{11}MgBr$	+	...	...	*604,145*
CH_3	H	CH_3	CH_3	t-$C_5H_{11}MgCl$	8.3	16.2	+	*305*
CH_3	H	CH_3	CH_3	C_6H_5MgBr	40.1	...	+	*146,140, 147*
CH_3	H	CH_3	CH_3	n-$C_4H_9C{\equiv}CMgBr$	78.9	...	...	*83*
CH_3	H	CH_3	CH_3	$C_6H_5CH_2MgCl$	+	...	...	*148*
CH_3	H	CH_3	CH_3	$C_6H_5CH(CO_2Na)MgCl$*	+†	...	...	*149*
CH_3	H	CH_3	CH_3	9-Fluorenyl-MgBr	30	...	...	*626*
CH_3	H	α-C_4H_3O‡	$CO_2C_2H_5$	n-C_3H_7MgBr	...	55	...	*308*
CH_3	H	α-C_4H_3O‡	$CO_2C_2H_5$	C_6H_5MgBr	...	52	...	*308*
C_2H_5	H	CH_3	C_2H_5	C_2H_5MgBr	31.5§	...	...	*239*
C_2H_5	H	CH_3	C_2H_5	C_2H_5MgBr	52.9¶	...	...	*184*
C_2H_5	H	CH_3	C_2H_5	i-$C_5H_{11}MgBr$	+	...	...	*239*
$CH_3OCH_2CH_2$	H	CH_3	CH_3	CH_3MgI	31.4	...	...	*245*
$(CH_3)_2C{=}CH$	H	CH_3	CH_3	CH_3MgI	2.5	...	...	*138*
$(CH_3)_2C{=}CH$	H	CH_3	CH_3	$C_6H_5CH_2MgCl$	+	...	...	*148*
t-C_4H_9	H	CH_3	t-C_4H_9	C_2H_5MgBr	70.0	...	...	*150*
C_6H_5	H	CH_3	CH_3	C_6H_5MgBr	0	+	...	*256*
C_6H_5	H	CH_3	C_6H_5	C_2H_5MgBr	...	44.1	...	*111*
C_6H_5	H	CH_3	C_6H_5	C_6H_5MgBr	...	37.4	...	*111*

*In the opinion of Schlenk, Hilleman, and Rodloff, *Ann.*, 487, 135–54 (1931), this "Grignard reagent" should be formulated as an enolate.

†The yield is reported as "good."

‡α-C_4H_3O = 2-furyl.

§Reaction at room temperature.

¶Reaction at $-14°$.

TABLE VI-XVI (Continued)

R	R^1	R^2	R^3	R^4MgX	1,2-Add'n (%)	1,4-Add'n (%)	Cond'n (%)	Ref.
C_6H_5	H	CH_3	C_6H_5	$C_6H_5CH(CO_2Na)MgCl$*	...	+	+	*149*
C_6H_5	H	C_2H_5O	C_6H_5	C_2H_5MgBr	+	+	...	*147*
C_6H_5	H	C_2H_5O	C_6H_5	C_2H_5MgBr†	+	...	...	*147*
C_6H_5	H	C_2H_5O	C_6H_5	C_6H_5MgBr‡	+	+	...	*147*
C_6H_5	H	C_6H_5	C_6H_5	C_2H_5MgBr	+	15.0	...	*111*
C_6H_5	H	C_6H_5	C_6H_5	C_6H_5MgBr	+	0	...	*111,455*
C_6H_5	H	C_6H_5	$C_6H_5SO_2$	C_6H_5MgBr	+	...	...	*654*
C_6H_5	H	C_6H_5	C_6H_5CO	C_6H_5MgBr	...	*ca.* 80	...	*602*
Mes§	H	CH_3	C_6H_5	CH_3MgI	...	+	...	*538*
Mes§	H	CH_3	C_6H_5	C_6H_5MgBr	...	82.7¶	...	*538*
Mes§	H	t-C_4H_9	MesCO§	C_6H_5MgBr	...	31‖	...	*590*
Mes§	H	t-C_4H_9	MesCO§	C_6H_5MgBr	...	70**	...	*590*
Mes§	H	C_6H_5	C_6H_5	CH_3MgI	...	82.0	...	*538*
Mes§	H	C_6H_5	C_6H_5	C_2H_5MgBr	...	+	...	*538*
Mes§	H	C_6H_5	C_6H_5	C_6H_5MgBr	...	60.0	...	*538*
Mes§	H	C_6H_5	MesCO§	t-C_4H_9MgCl	...	+	...	*590*
C_6H_5	Mes§	H	H	C_6H_5MgBr	0	0	...	*500*

* In the opinion of Schlenk, Hilleman, and Rodloff, *Ann.*, *487*, 135–54 (1931), this "Grignard reagent" should be formulated as an enolate.

† Concentrated Grignard reagent solution.

‡ Dilute Grignard reagent solution.

§ Mes = mesityl = 2,4,6-$(CH_3)_3C_6H_2$—.

¶ On basis of ketone unrecovered.

‖ Addition of ketone to Grignard reagent solution at room temperature, ten minutes standing.

** Addition of ketone to Grignard reagent solution at 0°; fifteen minutes standing.

TABLE VI-XVI (Continued)

R	R¹	R²	R³	R⁴MgX	1,2-Add'n (%)	1,4-Add'n (%)	Cond'n (%)	Ref.
Mes*	Mes*	H	H	CH_3MgI	...	+	...	*575*
Mes*	Mes*	H	H	C_6H_5MgBr	...	+	...	*575*
Idur†	Mes*	H	H	C_6H_5MgBr	...	+	...	*575*
Dur‡	Mes*	H	H	CH_3MgI	...	+	...	*575*
CH_3	Br	C_6H_5	H	C_6H_5MgBr	...	92.8	...	*272*
CH_3	CH_3	CH_3	H	CH_3MgI	70.0	...	...	*150*
CH_3	CH_3	CH_3	H	n-C_4H_9MgBr	+§	+§	...	*150*
CH_3	CH_3	$(CH_3)_2N$	H	CH_3MgI	...	+¶	...	*153*
CH_3	CH_3	$(CH_3)_2N$	H	C_2H_5MgBr	...	+¶	...	*153*
CH_3	CH_3	n-C_3H_7	H	C_2H_5MgBr	+	+	...	*150*
CH_3	n-C_3H_7	C_2H_5	H	C_2H_5MgBr	41.2	29.4	...	*185*
CH_3	$CO_2C_2H_5$	CH_3	H	CH_3MgI	...	+	...	*151*
CH_3	$CO_2C_2H_5$	α-C_4H_3O‖	H	C_2H_5MgI	...	59.4	...	*308*
C_6H_5	Br	C_6H_5	H	C_6H_5MgBr	...	95.6	...	*275*
C_6H_5	Br	C_6H_5	H	4-$CH_3C_6H_4MgBr$	...	91.0	...	*603*
C_6H_5	CH_3	C_2H_5	H	C_6H_5MgBr	...	+	...	*147*
C_6H_5	CH_3	C_6H_5	H	CH_3MgI	91.0	...	...	*490*
C_6H_5	CH_3	C_6H_5	H	C_2H_5MgBr	...	+	...	*147*
C_6H_5	CH_3	C_6H_5	H	C_6H_5MgBr	...	+	...	*569*

* Mes = mesityl = 2,4,6-$(CH_3)_3C_6H_2$—.

† Idur = isoduryl = 2,3,4,6-$(CH_3)_4C_6H$—.

‡ Dur = duryl = 2,3,5,6-$(CH_3)_4C_6H$—.

§ The ratio of 1,2- to 1,4-addition product is reported to be about 77:23.

¶ This reaction involves cleavage; the product isolated is $CH_3COC(CH_3){=}CHR$, in which R represents the organic radical of the Grignard reagent (RMgX).

‖ α-C_4H_3O = 2-furyl.

TABLE VI-XVI (Continued)

R	R^1	R^2	R^3	R^4MgX	1,2-Add'n (%)	1,4-Add'n (%)	Cond'n (%)	Ref.
C_6H_5	$(CH_2)_5N$	C_6H_5	H	C_6H_5MgBr	...	61.0	...	*559*
C_6H_5	C_6H_5	C_6H_5	H	CH_3MgI	54–63	...	...	*591*
C_6H_5	C_6H_5	C_6H_5	H	C_2H_5MgBr	...	100*	...	*645*
C_6H_5	C_6H_5	C_6H_5	H	C_6H_5MgBr	...	95.8	...	*591*
C_6H_5	C_6H_5	C_6H_5	H	$C_6H_5CH_2MgCl$	...	25.7	...	*435*
$4\text{-}CH_3OC_6H_4$	CH_3	$4\text{-}CH_3OC_6H_4$	H	CH_3MgI	+†	trace	...	*518*
$4\text{-}CH_3OC_6H_4$	CH_3	$4\text{-}CH_3OC_6H_4$	H	C_2H_5MgBr	...	*ca.* 80	...	*518*
$4\text{-}CH_3OC_6H_4$	CH_3	$4\text{-}CH_3OC_6H_4$	H	$n\text{-}C_3H_7MgBr$	...	*ca.* 80	...	*518*
$4\text{-}CH_3OC_6H_4$	C_2H_5	$4\text{-}CH_3OC_6H_4$	H	CH_3MgI	+†	trace	...	*518*
$4\text{-}CH_3OC_6H_4$	C_2H_5	$4\text{-}CH_3OC_6H_4$	H	C_2H_5MgBr	...	*ca.* 80	...	*518*
$4\text{-}CH_3OC_6H_4$	C_2H_5	$4\text{-}CH_3OC_6H_4$	H	$n\text{-}C_3H_7MgBr$	...	*ca.* 80	...	*518*
$4\text{-}CH_3OC_6H_4$	$n\text{-}C_3H_7$	$4\text{-}CH_3OC_6H_4$	H	CH_3MgI	+†	trace	...	*518*
$4\text{-}CH_3OC_6H_4$	$n\text{-}C_3H_7$	$4\text{-}CH_3OC_6H_4$	H	C_2H_5MgBr	...	*ca.* 80	...	*518*
$4\text{-}CH_3OC_6H_4$	$n\text{-}C_3H_7$	$4\text{-}CH_3OC_6H_4$	H	$n\text{-}C_3H_7MgBr$	...	*ca.* 80	...	*518*
Mes‡	CH_3	Mes‡	H	Mes-MgBr‡	...	46.0	...	*393*
Mes‡	$n\text{-}C_4H_9$	Mes‡	H	C_6H_5MgBr	...	+	...	*590*
CH_3	CH_3	CH_3	C_2H_5	CH_3MgI	63.0	...	...	*150*
CH_3	CH_3	CH_3	C_2H_5	C_2H_5MgBr	60.0	...	...	*150*
CH_3	CH_3	CH_3	C_2H_5	$n\text{-}C_3H_7MgBr$	38.0	...	...	*150*
CH_3	CH_3	CH_3	C_2H_5	$n\text{-}C_4H_9MgBr$	38.0	...	...	*150*
C_6H_5	CH_3	CH_3	CO_2H	C_6H_5MgBr	...	85.5	...	*332*

* Either isomer of the unsaturated ketone (m., respectively, 88–89° or 102°) gives the same yield of saturated ketone in the same ratio of isomeric forms (m., respectively, 92° and 170°). The reported yields (in grams) are somewhat more than 100 percent of the theoretical.

† The principal products appear to be indenes, which could arise only from 1,2-addition.

‡ Mes = mesityl = 2,4,6-$(CH_3)_3C_6H_2$—.

TABLE VI-XVI (Continued)

R	R^1	R^2	R^3	R^4MgX	1,2-Add'n (%)	1,4-Add'n (%)	Cond'n (%)	Ref.
C_6H_5	C_4H_8NO*	C_4H_8NO*	C_6H_5	CH_3MgI	2.4	...	...	*544*
C_6H_5	C_6H_5	C_6H_5	C_6H_5	CH_3MgI	54–63	...	...	*591*
C_6H_5	C_6H_5	C_6H_5	C_6H_5	C_6H_5MgBr	31.9	37.3†	...	*591*
C_6H_5	C_6H_5	C_6H_5	C_6H_5O	C_6H_5MgBr	70–90	...	...	*602*

* C_4H_8NO = 4-morpholino.

† This 1,4-addition involves the aromatic nucleus rather than the olefinic double bond.

of the interaction of *t*-butylmagnesium chloride with 1-phenyl-1,2-dimesitoylethylene was the reduction product 1-phenyl-1,2-dimesitoylethane.

$$\text{MesCOC}(C_6H_5)\!=\!\text{CHCOMes} \xrightarrow{t\text{-}C_4H_9\text{MgCl}}$$

$$\text{MesCH(OMgCl)C}(C_6H_5)\!=\!\text{CHCH(OMgCl)Mes} \xrightarrow{H_2O}$$

$$\text{MesCOCH}(C_6H_5)CH_2\text{COMes}$$

Facilitation of 1,4- at the expense of 1,2-addition. Due consideration should also be given to the fact that many of the earlier studies in this field necessarily employed metallic magnesium of a relatively low degree of purity. Although no exhaustive study of this subject has been made, the work of Kharasch and Tawney[186] has shown that the presence of metallic impurities may materially affect the ratios of 1,2- and 1,4-addition products. It was found, for example, that, when treated with methylmagnesium bromide prepared from highly purified magnesium,* isophorone yielded 90.8 percent of 1,2-addition products (carbinol and diene), with no 1,4-addition product detectable. The inclusion of as little as one mole percent of cuprous chloride† in the reaction mixture reduced the yield of 1,2-addition product (diene) to 6.9 percent and induced an 82.5 percent yield of 1,4-addition product. Metallic copper had a similar, though much less pronounced effect.

Isophorone (3,5,5-trimethylcyclohex-2-en-1-one: H_2C, $(H_3C)_2C$, $C{-}CH_3$, CH, $C{=}O$)

$\xrightarrow{CH_3MgBr}$ carbinol (HO, CH_3) (42.6%) + diene (HC, CH, $C{-}CH_3$) (48.2%)

$\xrightarrow[+\ CuBr]{CH_3MgBr}$ 3,3,5,5-tetramethylcyclohexanone ($C(CH_3)_2$, CH_2, $C{=}O$) (82.5%) + diene (6.9%)

---

[186]Kharasch and Tawney, *J. Am. Chem. Soc.*, 63, 2308–15 (1941).

*Radio grade Mazlo rolled ribbon (99.98 percent Mg), supplied by the Aluminum Company of America. The impurities were stated to be 0.01–0.015 percent combined iron and aluminum, together with silicon and traces of copper and nickel.

†In the presence of an excess of Grignard reagent a cupric halide would, of course, have the same effect, for it would be reduced immediately to the cuprous salt.

Ferric, nickelous, and cobaltous chlorides gave rise to other reactions which materially reduced the amount of, or completely superseded, the addition reactions.

Similar inductions of 1,4-additions with the aid of cuprous halides have been reported by Birch and Robinson[187] (carvone + CH_3MgI + CuBr), by Ruzicka *et al.*[188] (3-methyl-2-cyclohexen-1-one + CH_3MgI + CuCl), and by Stoll and Commarmont[189] (2-cyclopentadecen-1-one + CH_3MgBr + $CuCl_2$).

The possibility of inducing 1,4-addition at will suggests a new method for the introduction of angular methyl groups into polycyclic compounds, although this possibility may be limited by structural rigidity. In the relatively simple model experiment involving 4,4a,5,6,7,8-hexahydro-2(3*H*)-naphthalenone, methylmagnesium iodide, and cuprous bromide, Birch and Robinson (*loc. cit.*[187]) obtained a 60 percent yield of *cis*-8a-methyloctahydro-2(1*H*)-naphthalenone.

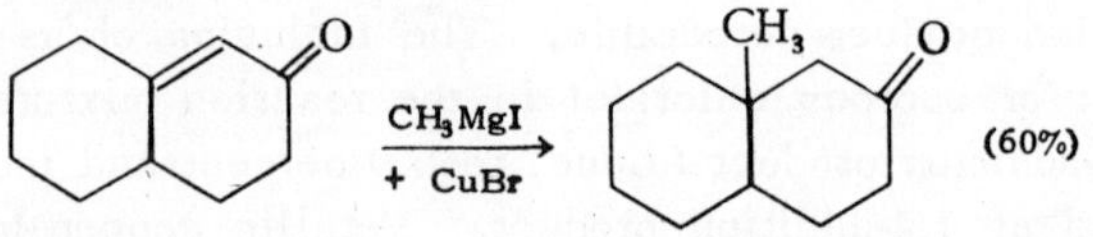

CH_3MgI + CuBr → (60%)

With 17-isopropyl-6,7,8,14,16,17-hexahydro-15-cyclopenta [*a*] phenanthren-11(9*H*)-one, methylmagnesium bromide or iodide, and cuprous chloride or bromide, however, they were unsuccessful in introducing an angular methyl group at carbon atom 13, and isolated only the dehydrate of the 1,2-addition product.[190]

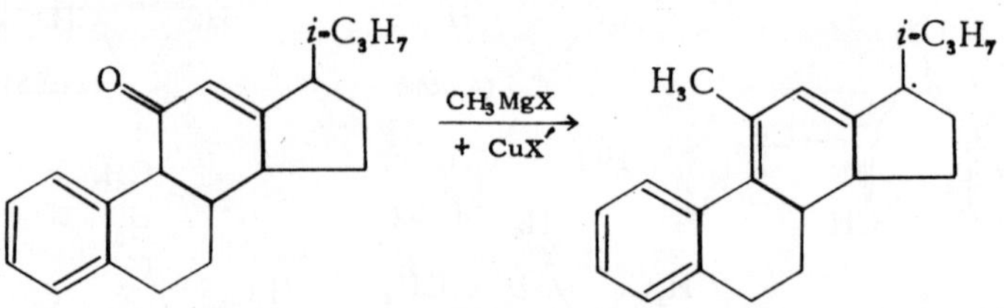

CH_3MgX + CuX′ →

The rationale of the cuprous halide induction of 1,4-addition can scarcely be said to have been unequivocally established, but the available evidence affords a basis for a reasonable working hypothesis. On the premise that 1,2- and 1,4-addition are (potentially, at least) competing reactions it would appear that the function of the cuprous halide might be either to facilitate 1,4-addition or to inhibit 1,2-addition. The Birch and Robinson experiments suggest the probability that the former

---

[187] Birch and Robinson, *J. Chem. Soc.*, *1943*, 501–2.
[188] Büchi, Jeger, and Ruzicka, *Helv. Chim. Acta*, *31*, 241–8 (1948).
[189] Stoll and Commarmont, *Helv. Chim. Acta*, *31*, 554–5 (1948).
[190] Birch and Robinson, *J. Chem. Soc.*, *1944*, 503–6.

is the case. Taken in conjunction with the well-known tendency of cuprous halides to form complexes with olefinic compounds,[191] this probability lends credibility to the hypothesis that complex formation labilizes the carbon-to-carbon double bond in a manner that facilitates 1,4-addition.

Possibility of suppressing 1,2-addition. It seems logical to suppose that a similar end-result could be achieved by the suppression of 1,2-addition, as by the employment of a diorganocadmium reagent in place of the Grignard reagent. The 1,2-addition of a diorganocadmium compound to a carbonyl double bond either does not take place at all, or takes place so slowly as to be negligible in comparison with a competing reaction (see section on Preparation of Ketones, Chapter IX). That cadmium compounds are probably capable of 1,4-addition to α,β-unsaturated ketones is indicated by their analogous 1,4-addition in good yield to esters of the type $RCH{=}C(CO_2C_2H_5)_2$.[192] In especially refractory cases it might be found profitable both to suppress 1,2-addition (as by the use of a cadmium or zinc reagent) and to facilitate 1,4-addition (as by the aid of a cuprous halide).

Since the first draft of this discussion was written it has been reported by Wittig *et al.*[193] that, although diphenylcadmium reacts very slowly with benzylideneacetophenone at room temperature, it undergoes nearly quantitative 1,4-addition in eight hours at 100°. Gilman and Kirby[194] had previously reported 1,4-addition of diphenylzinc to benzylideneacetophenone in 91 percent yield.

Probable Mechanism of 1,4-Addition. There is little (or no) direct evidence on which to base a theory of the mechanism of the 1,4-addition of a Grignard reagent to an α,β-unsaturated carbonyl compound. In view, however, of the apparently satisfactory applicability of the concept of a quasi six-membered ring transition state to the elucidation of other Grignard reactions,* there is strong temptation to extend the notion somewhat farther. A speculation that appears fairly plausible in that it conflicts with none of the presently known facts may be diagrammatically presented as follows:

---

[191]For leading references see: Keller, *Chem. Revs.*, *28*, 229–67 (1941); Gilliland, Bliss, and Kip, *J. Am. Chem. Soc.*, *63*, 2088–90 (1941); Kepner and Andrews, *J. Org. Chem.*, *13*, 208–13 (1948); Keefer, Andrews, and Kepner, *J. Am. Chem. Soc.*, *71*, 2381–3 (1949).

[192]Riegel, Siegel, and Lilienfeld, *J. Am. Chem. Soc.*, *68*, 984–5 (1946).

[193]Wittig, Meyer, and Lange, *Ann.*, *571*, 167–201 (1951).

[194]Gilman and Kirby, *J. Am. Chem. Soc.*, *63*, 2046–8 (1941).

*For example, the "normal" 1,2-addition at a carbonyl double bond, the Grignard reagent reduction of a carbonyl compound, the Meerwein reduction of a carbonyl compound by a halomagnesium alkoxide, and the Grignard enolization of a carbonyl compound.

```
        R¹                        R¹                          R¹
        |                         |                           |
        C                        .C.                          C
      /   \   R²               .'   \   R²                  //  \   R²
R—C       C/            R—C       C/              R—C        C/
   ||       \R³  →          ⋮       ⋮ \R³  →          |        |\R³
   O     R⁴                 O    R⁴                   O      R⁴
    ·· /                     \  .·                     \    /
     Mg                        Mg                        Mg
     |                         |                         |
     X                         X                         X
```

$$R(XMgO)C{=}CR^1CR^2R^3R^4 \xrightarrow{H_2O} RCOCR^1CR^2R^3R^4$$

or

$$R(XMgO)C{=}CR^1CR^2R^3R^4 \xrightarrow{H_2O} R(HO)C{=}CR^1CR^2R^3R^4$$

The product of a 1,4-addition of this kind is, of course, an enolate; whether the vinyl alcohol (*i.e.*, the enol) or the ketone is obtained on hydrolysis depends on the nature of the individual compound.

It may not be amiss to remind the reader that enolates derived by the 1,4-addition of Grignard reagents to α,β-unsaturated ketones appear to be stereoisomers of the structurally identical enolates derived by Grignard enolization of the related saturated ketones. An observation to this effect by Kohler *et al.* (*loc. cit.*[176]) has already been cited in connection with the discussion of reductive enolization of α-halo ketones (*q.v.*). Lutz and Kibler[195] report a similar observation which may be summarized as follows:*

$$(MesCOCH{=})_2 + MesMgBr \longrightarrow \text{Enolate} \xrightarrow{I} MesCOCH(Mes)CHICOMes, \text{ m. } 213^\circ$$

$$MesCOCH(Mes)CH_2COMes + RMgBr \longrightarrow \text{Enolate} \xrightarrow{I} MesCOCH(Mes)CHICOMes, \text{ m. } 178^\circ$$

Essentially the mechanism suggested above has been proposed by Lutz and Reveley.[196] To this Alexander and Coraor[197] offer the objection that it cannot be a general one in that it does not appear to them to be applicable to the conjugate additions of 2-cyclohexen-1-one. "It is clear, however," they write, "that the cyclic, intramolecular process cannot be the only route leading to conjugate addition, for it has been reported that 2-cyclohexen-1-one undergoes conjugate addition with Grignard reagents, yet the distance between the carbonyl oxygen and the β-carbon atom of

---

[195] Lutz and Kibler, *J. Am. Chem. Soc.*, *62*, 360–72 (1940).

*Mes = mesityl = $2,4,6\text{-}(CH_3)_3C_6H_2$—; R = CH_3, C_2H_5, C_6H_5.

[196] Lutz and Reveley, *J. Am. Chem. Soc.*, *63*, 3180–9 (1941).

[197] Alexander and Coraor, *J. Am. Chem. Soc.*, *73*, 2721–3 (1951).

this compound appears to be too great to permit the formation of a complex such as [the quasi six-membered ring transition state] suggested."

Alexander and Coraor have further compared the 1,4-additions of ethyl, isopropyl, and *t*-butyl Grignard reagents to 2-cyclohexen-1-one and its open-chain analogs, 3-penten-2-one, 3-hexen-2-one, 4-hexen-3-one, and 3-hepten-2-one. Except for ethylmagnesium bromide, they found the relative proportions of 1,4-addition to 2-cyclohexen-1-one comparable to those of the 1,4-additions to its open-chain analogs. To them, "these results suggest that a possible path of reaction involving a cyclic intramolecular transition state is relatively unimportant."

In the opinion of the present authors this argument implicitly attributes to the ketone-Grignard reagent complex a rigidity which it probably does not in fact possess. Undoubtedly Werner complex formation with the Grignard reagent would materially alter the character of the carbonyl double bond, and might reasonably be expected to enhance considerably its angular flexibility; probably some of this labilizing effect would be transmitted to the conjugated carbon-to-carbon double bond. If that bond were further labilized by complex formation, as with a cuprous halide, the entire structure might conceivably attain a flexibility comparable to that of, say, an organomagnesium derivative of cyclohexanol. According to the Sachse-Mohr theory, such a derivative could assume, at least momentarily, a configuration like that of the model projected in the following diagram.

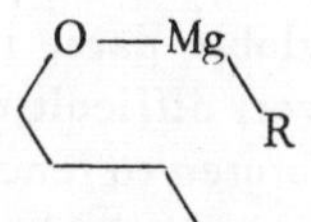

Possible suppression of 1,4- in favor of 1,2-addition.* The working hypotheses tentatively proposed to account respectively for 1,4- and 1,2-additions suggest that it might be possible to suppress the former in favor of the latter by an experimental device analogous to that proposed for the suppression of Grignard reagent reduction in favor of "normal" addition.

If it were possible to form the initial Werner complex (I) with a metallic compound incapable of 1,4-addition (suitably MgX_2), and then to treat that complex with a Grignard reagent, 1,2-addition might be favored at the expense of 1,4-addition provided that complex exchange in the senses already defined were not too rapid.

---

*The practically equivalent facilitation of 1,2- at the expense of 1,4-addition might also be invoked by the use of the organo compound of a more "active" metal, as, *e.g.*, lithium or potassium, [see Gilman and Kirby, (*loc. cit.*[194])], although the possible introduction of new complications into the reaction precludes confident prediction of improved results in syntheses.

$$R{-}C(=O){-}C(R^1){=}C(R^2)(R^3)\cdots X{-}Mg{-}X \;\; \xrightarrow{R^4MgX'} \;\; \cdots \;\; \rightarrow \;\; R^1{-}C(=C R^2R^3){-}C(R)(R^4){-}O{-}Mg{-}X \;\; Mg{-}X' \;\; X$$

(I).

Such exchange might be minimized by saturating the Grignard reagent solution with magnesium halide (which is considerably more soluble in Grignard reagent solutions than in pure ether).

For highly "hindered" ketones (such as mesityl or duryl) 1,2-addition might still be very slow in comparison with complex exchange (and, therefore, in comparison with 1,4-addition). In intermediate cases, however, it should be possible to effect a material increase in the ratio of 1,2- to 1,4-addition.

Constitutional factors affecting order of addition. It would appear highly probable on *a priori* theoretical grounds that the nature of the unsaturated carbonyl compound should be the primary factor determining the order of addition, and the available data, insofar as they are decisive, support that view. It is, however, difficult to formulate any broad generalizations relating structural features to reactive behavior.

Kohler and Heritage[198] attempted a limited correlation of this sort, saying: "... the reaction between substances of this type [C=C—C=O] and organic magnesium compounds varies in a remarkable way with the atoms or groups in combination with the carbon atom of the carbonyl group. The reaction is always one of direct addition, but in the case of aldehydes and of those ketones that contain the group —CH=CH—C(CH_3)=O the magnesium compound combines exclusively with the carbonyl group, while only 1,4-addition takes place when the ketone contains the group —CH=CH—C(C_6H_5)=O." The reactions of benzalacetone ($CH_3COCH=CHC_6H_5$) and of various of its derivatives have since been shown by Kohler and his students, as well as by others, to constitute glaring exceptions to one part of the foregoing statement, and the work of Stevens[199] on α,β-unsaturated aldehydes and of Kohler and others on benzalacetophenone suggest that the remainder be somewhat modified (see Table VI-XVI).

---

[198] Kohler and Heritage, *Am. Chem. J.*, 33, 21–35 (1905).
[199] Stevens, *J. Am. Chem. Soc.*, 57, 1112–7 (1935).

Colonge[200] has offered a somewhat broader, but still empirical, summarization of the reported facts. With substitution of the conventional system of numbering for that employed by Colonge, his statement may be freely translated as follows.

"(*a*). If carbon atom number 4 of the conjugated system carries a second hydrocarbon substituent [*i.e.*, two substituents] there is no [1,4] addition of the Grignard reagent, but normal reaction at the carbonyl group [1,2-addition].

"(*b*). The presence of a substituent on carbon atom number 3 and the absence of a second substituent [*i.e.*, the presence of only one substituent] on carbon atom number 4 favors [1,4] addition to the conjugated system.

"(*c*). When there is a substituent on carbon atom number 3 and a second substituent [*i.e.*, two substituents] on carbon atom number 4, only normal [1,2] addition at the ketonic function is observed.

"(*d*). In the aliphatic series, under the most favorable conditions, addition to the conjugated system [1,4 addition] is never as important as normal addition to the carbonyl group [1,2 addition]."

The rules stated by Chelintsev and Till[201] are merely a partial paraphrase of those of Colonge.

In view of the fact that 1,2- and 1,4-additions may be regarded as competitive with each other (as well as with various side-reactions), the reactivity of the carbonyl group might reasonably be expected to play an important part in determining the order of addition. In α,β-unsaturated carbonyl compounds ($RCOCR^1{=}CR^2R^3$) the atom or radical R would naturally have a pronounced effect on the reactivity of the carbonyl group. The question then arises, whether this effect is predominantly steric or predominantly electronic.

If the effect be predominantly electronic the facts that aldehydes (R = H) are in general more reactive toward Grignard reagents than are ketones, and that methyl ketones ($R = CH_3$) are in general more reactive than aryl ketones [$R = C_6H_5$, 2,4,6-$(CH_3)_3C_6H_2$, etc.] would suggest that, the remainder of the molecule remaining substantially the same, the reactivity of the carbonyl group should increase as the "electronegativity" of R decreases,[202] and that 1,2-addition should be correspondingly favored.* Unfortunately no data are available for comparison of the behavior of

---

[200] Colonge, *Bull. soc. chim.*, [5], *2*, 754–61 (1935).

[201] Chelintsev and Till, *Uchenye Zapiski Saratov Gosudarst. Univ. N. G. Chernyshevskogo, Khim.*, *15*, No. 4, 24–31 (1940); *Chem. Abstr.*, *35*, 6953 (1941).

[202] Concerning the relative electronegativities of organic radicals see: Kharasch and Reinmuth, *J. Chem. Education*, (*a*) *5*, 404–18 (1928); (*b*) *8*, 1703–48 (1931); Kharasch, Reinmuth, and Mayo, *ibid.*, (*c*) *11*, 82–96 (1934); (*d*) *13*, 7–19 (1936).

*These conclusions appear to be fully substantiated by the relative reactivity studies of Hibbert, *J. Chem. Soc.*, *101*, 341–4 (1912), and Lewis and Wright, *J. Am. Chem. Soc.*, *74*, 1257–9 (1952).

3-pentene-2-one ($CH_3COCH{=}CHCH_3$) and 5,5-dimethyl-2-hexen-4-one (t-$C_4H_9COCH{=}CHCH_3$). With both benzalacetone ($CH_3COCH{=}CHC_6H_5$) and benzalpinacolin (t-$C_4H_9COCH{=}CHC_6H_5$) 1,4-addition appears to predominate.

If, on the other hand, the effect be predominantly steric, one must conclude that the bulkier the group R the less the reactivity of the carbonyl group, the greater the inhibition of 1,2-addition, and to the extent that suppression of one competing reaction affects the issue, the greater the tendency to 1,4-addition.

There remains the possibility that steric and electronic influences are effective in similar degree, in which case they may reinforce each other, as when R = mesityl [2,4,6-$(CH_3)_3C_6H_2$], or operate in opposition to each other, as when R = t-butyl. The available information justifies no conclusions.

As regards 1,2-addition, the electronic effect of a substituent on carbon atom number 3 (R^1), either activating or deactivating, might be expected to be relatively minor, whereas the steric effect (which could be inhibitory only) might be considerable. As regards 1,4-addition, involving the union of a negative ion with an olefinic carbon atom, R^1 might exert an inhibitory steric effect and, depending upon its nature, an activating or deactivating electronic effect. Regarding the net outcome the experimental evidence is fragmentary and conflicting, Colonge's rule notwithstanding.

As regards 1,2-addition, substitution on carbon atom number 4 (R^2,R^3) might be expected to exert a relatively minor electronic effect (either activating or deactivating) and a negligible (inhibitory) steric effect. As regards 1,4-addition, both electronic effects (either activating or deactivating, depending upon the nature of the substituents) and steric (inhibitory) effects are to be expected. On the basis of the available evidence (inadequate, it is true), the steric effect would appear to predominate. Mesityl oxide [$CH_3COCH{=}C(CH_3)_2$] appears to undergo 1,2-addition chiefly, whereas with benzalacetone ($CH_3COCH{=}CHC_6H_5$) 1,4-addition appears to predominate. The activating electronic effect of two methyl groups attached to an olefinic carbon atom is nearly, though probably not quite altogether, equal to that of one phenyl group. The inhibiting steric effect is undoubtedly greater.

The results of a comparative study of the reactions of various organometallic compounds with benzalacetophenone by Gilman and Kirby[203] are summarized in part as follows. "With benzalacetophenone the less reactive phenylmetallic compounds of beryllium, magnesium, zinc, and manganese show predominantly, if not exclusively, 1,4-addition. The highly reactive compounds of potassium and calcium show 1,2-addition. The organometallic compounds of intermediate activity (sodium and lithium) show both 1,2- and 1,4-addition."

[203] Gilman and Kirby, *J. Am. Chem. Soc.*, 63, 2046–8 (1941).

This suggests that for some α,β-unsaturated carbonyl compounds at least the nature of the Grignard reagent employed might affect to some extent the order of addition. For compounds which show both 1,2- and 1,4-addition it might be expected that the more reactive[204] of two Grignard reagents would undergo the higher ratio of 1,2- to 1,4-addition. In the only relevant study reported,[205] the ratio of 1,4- to 1,2-addition for a series of unsaturated ketones appeared to be higher for the somewhat more reactive ethylmagnesium bromide than for phenylmagnesium bromide. However, in view of the facts that all byproducts were ignored, and that only the ratios of 1,4- to 1,2-addition products actually isolated were determined, this study can scarcely be regarded as critical.

On the whole, despite the apparent wealth of experimental data (see Table VI-XVI), knowledge of the factors determining the order of addition of Grignard reagents to conjugated carbonyl systems is unsatisfactorily meager.

The reaction mechanisms proposed as working hypotheses describe 1,2-addition as trimolecular (involving one molecule of carbonyl compound and two molecules of Grignard reagent), whereas 1,4-addition is assumed to be bimolecular (involving one molecule each of carbonyl compound and Grignard reagent). This suggests that the concentration of Grignard reagent employed might affect the relative proportions of 1,2- and 1,4-addition products formed. To the best knowledge of the present authors no systematic investigation on this point has been undertaken, but Reynolds[206] has reported that treatment of the ethyl enol ether of dibenzoylmethane [$C_6H_5COCH{=}C(OC_2H_5)C_6H_5$] with a "concentrated" solution of phenylmagnesium bromide yields the 1,2-addition product only, whereas the use of a "dilute" Grignard reagent solution leads to the formation of both 1,2- and 1,4-addition products.

The proposal previously made as to the possibility of suppressing 1,4- in favor of 1,2-addition implies that the magnesium halide content of a Grignard reagent solution might affect the relative proportions of 1,2- and 1,4-addition products formed in reactions with conjugated carbonyl systems. Because the excess magnesium halide content of a specific Grignard reagent may vary within wide limits depending upon the method of preparation and the quality of the magnesium used, because the tendency to Wurtz byproduct formation in Grignard reagent preparation varies considerably from halide to halide, and because the Schlenk equilibrium point appears to vary from Grignard reagent to Grignard reagent, it would seem desirable to approach the question of the effects of constitution on the direction of addition to conjugated carbonyl systems by way of the

---

[204]Concerning relative reactivities of Grignard reagents with respect to "normal" (*i.e.*, 1,2-) addition to a carbonyl group see: Kharasch and Weinhouse, *J. Org. Chem.*, *1*, 209–30 (1936).

[205]Kohler, *Am. Chem. J.*, *38*, 511–61 (1907).

[206]Reynolds, *Am. Chem. J.*, *44*, 305–31 (1910).

diorganomagnesium compounds. (Supplementary studies with reagents of varying, but definitely known, halide contents would also be of interest.)

That there may be a considerable difference in the temperature gradients of the 1,2- and 1,4-addition reactions is suggested by the report of Lutz Reveley[207] that 1-*t*-butyl-1,2-dimesitoylethylene reacts with mesitylmagnesium bromide at room temperature to give 31 percent of 1,4-addition product, whereas the yield at 0° was 70 percent. Temperature control is therefore indicated unless preliminary experiments show it to be unnecessary.

Obviously, it would be wise to avoid unnecessary complications by employing non-reducing Grignard reagents. A possible series that would include a considerable range of radical electronegativities, as well as radical sizes might comprise mesityl, phenyl, methyl, neopentyl, and benzyl reagents. For comparative purposes it would be desirable that all reactions be run at the highest attainable common Grignard reagent concentration and at some considerably lower common concentration, or with "normal" and "inverse" order of addition.

One careful quantitative study of the reactions of such a series of diorganomagnesium compounds with a series of twelve or fifteen intelligently selected ketones would contribute more to understanding of the subject than have all the reported observations of the past half-century.

Among the 1,2-additions not listed in Table VI-XVI are those of methylmagnesium iodide and phenylmagnesium bromide to ω-acetylcamphene, reported by Lipp and Quadevlieg.[208] The products isolated were the dienes.

```
            H                                      H
            C                                      C
         /  |  \                                /  |  \
     H2C    |   C(CH3)2                     H2C    |   C(CH3)2
      |    CH2 |               RMgX          |    CH2 |
     H2C    |   C=CHCOCH3     ------>       H2C    |   C=CHCR=CH2
         \  |  /                                \  |  /
            C                                      C
            H
```

Of special interest are the reactions of diphenylbenzalacetophenone, as reported by Kohler and Nygaard.[209] This ketone does not react with Grignard reagents in ethyl ether solution even under prolonged reflux. In benzene, at higher temperatures, methylmagnesium iodide gives 1,2-addition products, whereas phenylmagnesium bromide gives, in part, 1,2-addition products, and, in part, a 1,4-addition product. It is remarkable that, although there is an olefinic double bond conjugated with the carbonyl group, the 1,4-addition involves the aromatic ring.

---

[207] Lutz and Reveley, *J. Am. Chem. Soc.*, *63*, 3178–80 (1941).

[208] Lipp and Quaedvlieg, *Ber.*, *62B*, 2311–22 (1929).

[209] Kohler and Nygaard, *J. Am. Chem. Soc.*, *52*, 4128–39 (1930). See also: Kharasch and Sayles, *J. Am. Chem. Soc.*, *64*, 2972–4 (1942).

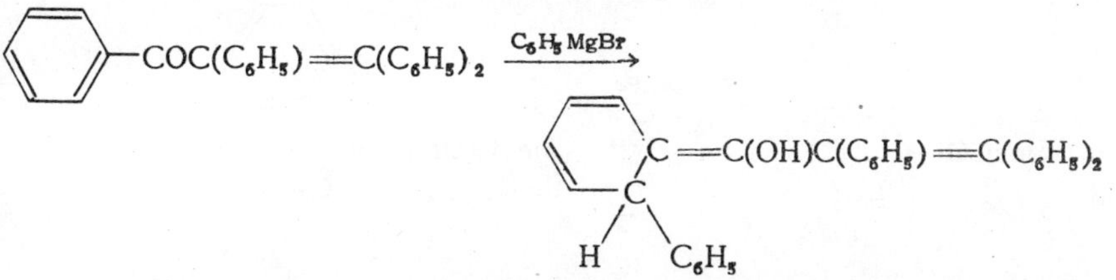

$$C_6H_5COC(C_6H_5)\!=\!C(C_6H_5)_2 \xrightarrow{C_6H_5MgBr} \text{(cyclohexadienyl, 6-H, 6-}C_6H_5\text{)}C\!=\!C(OH)C(C_6H_5)\!=\!C(C_6H_5)_2$$

It would be interesting to know whether or not cuprous halide labilization of the olefinic double would suffice to alter the direction of addition in this case. (If desired, 1,2-addition could be suppressed by use of the cadmium reagent.) Unquestionably 4,4-diphenyl substitution is sterically inimical to the olefinic 1,4-addition, but that it does not constitute an insuperable barrier thereto is demonstrated by the behavior of benzhydrylideneacetomesitylene, as reported by Kohler and Barnes.[210]

$$MesCOCH\!=\!C(C_6H_5)_2 \xrightarrow{C_6H_5MgBr} MesC(OH)\!=\!CHC(C_6H_5)_3$$

Fuson *et al.*[211] have also reported 1,4-additions involving aromatic rings, in cases, however, in which there is no olefinic double bond in conjugation with the carbonyl group.

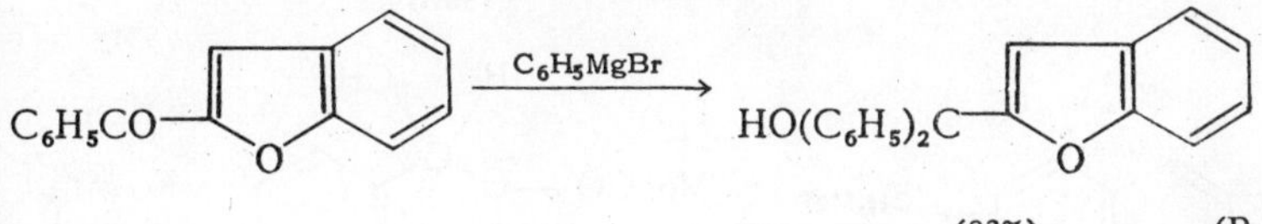

$$C_6H_5CO\text{-(2-benzofuryl)} \xrightarrow{C_6H_5MgBr} HO(C_6H_5)_2C\text{-(2-benzofuryl)}$$

(83%) (Ref. *211a*)

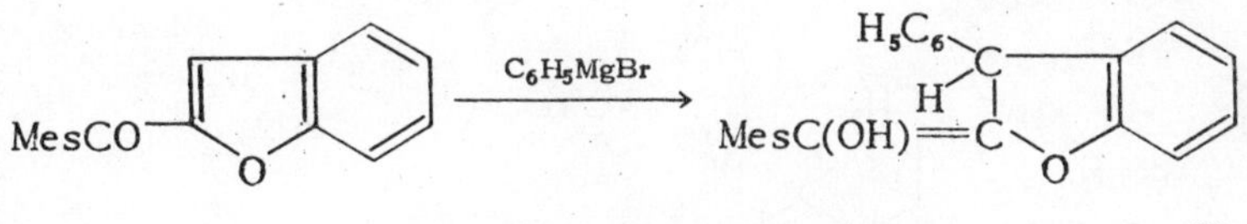

$$MesCO\text{-(2-benzofuryl)} \xrightarrow{C_6H_5MgBr} MesC(OH)\!=\!C\text{-(2,3-dihydrobenzofuran, 3-H, 3-}C_6H_5\text{)}$$

(Ref. *211a*)

$$MesCO\text{-}C_6H_5 \xrightarrow{C_6H_5MgBr} MesCO\text{-}C_6H_4\text{-}C_6H_5 \text{ (ortho)}$$

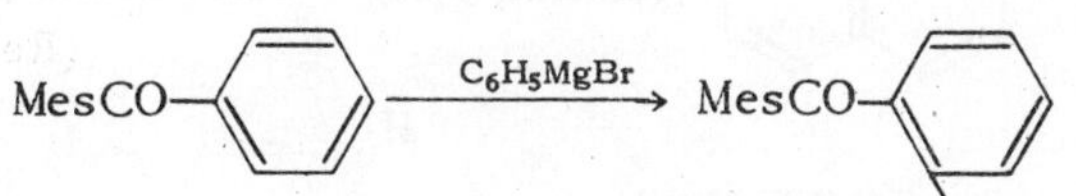

(18%)*

$+ C_{22}H_{22}O_2$ (m. 245–246°) $+ (C_6H_5\text{—})_2$ + tar. (Ref. *211b*)

---

[210] Kohler and Barnes, *J. Am. Chem. Soc.*, *55*, 690–5 (1933).

[211] (*a*) Fuson, Kaiser, and Speck, *J. Org. Chem.*, *6*, 845–51 (1941); (*b*) Fuson, Armstrong, and Speck, *J. Org. Chem.*, *7*, 297–302 (1942); (*c*) Fuson, McKusick, and Spangler, *J. Am. Chem. Soc.*, *67*, 597–601 (1945); (*d*) Fuson and Gaertner, *J. Org. Chem.*, *13*, 496–501 (1948).

*Presumably by atmospheric oxidation of the dihydro derivative originally formed.

MesCO–(1-naphthyl) $\xrightarrow{C_6H_5MgBr}$ MesC(OH)═C (H)(C)(C_6H_5)

$\xrightarrow{O_2}$ HO–(naphthalene, C_6H_5) + $MesCO_2H$ + tar (Ref. *211b*)

MesCO–(1-naphthyl) $\xrightarrow{CH_3MgI}$ MesCO–C(H)–C(H)(CH_3) (58%) (Ref. *211c*)

MesCO–(2-naphthyl) $\xrightarrow{CH_3MgI}$ MesCO–C(H)–C(H)(CH_3)

+ MesCO–(1-CH_3-2-naphthyl) (totaling 57%) + unidentified products (Ref. *211c*)

MesCO–C_6H_4–OCH_3 $\xrightarrow{C_6H_5CH_2MgCl}$ MesCO–C(H)–OCH_3, C(H)($CH_2C_6H_5$) (20%)) (Ref. *211d*)

DurCO–C_6H_4–OCH_3 $\xrightarrow{C_6H_5CH_2MgCl}$ DurCO–C(H)–OCH_3, C(H)($CH_2C_6H_5$) (2.2%) (Ref. *211d*)

The general subject of organometallic reagent 1,4-addition to conjugated systems containing aromatic double bonds has been reviewed by Gaertner.[211.1]

Cleavage reactions involving 1,4-addition. Various cleavage reactions which formally involve 1,4-addition have been reported. Among these are the amine cleavages studied by Benary.[212,*]

$$RCOCH{=}CHNR'_2 + R''MgX \rightarrow [RC(OMgX){=}CHCHR''NR'_2] \xrightarrow{H_2O} RCOCH{=}CHR'' + MgXOH + NHR'_2$$

Lutz and Reveley[213] report cleavages of furan rings, effected by treatment of 3-mesitoylfurans with excess methylmagnesium iodide. They formulate the reactions as follows:

```
H5C6 —C ——C —COMes              [ H5C6 —C ——C ═C(Mes)(OMgI)  ]
      ‖     ‖          CH3MgI    [       ‖     |              ]   CH3MgI
Mes —C     C —CH3     ——————→    [ Mes —C     C(CH3)(CH3)     ]   ——————→
      \   /                      [       \   /                ]
        O                        [         O                  ]

      Mes —C —OMgI                       Mes —CO
           ‖                                  |
H5C6 —C —C —C(CH3)3      HCl      H5C6 —C —CHC(CH3)3
      ‖                 ——————→          ‖
Mes —C —OMgI                      Mes —C —OH
```

```
  HC ——C —COMes                 [  HC ——C ═C(Mes)(OMgI)  ]
   ‖     ‖           CH3MgI     [   ‖     |              ]   CH3MgI
Mes —C    C —CH3    ——————→     [ Mes —C    C(CH3)(CH3)  ]   ——————→
      \  /                      [       \  /             ]
        O                       [         O              ]

  Mes —C —OMgI                  Mes —CO
       ‖                             |
  HC —C —C(CH3)2      HCl       HC —CHC(CH3)3
   ‖                ——————→      ‖
Mes —C —OMgI               Mes —C —OH
```

[211.1] Gaertner, *Chem. Revs.*, *45*, 493–521 (1949).

[212] Benary, *Ber.*, *64B*, 2543–5 (1931).

* $R = n\text{-}C_3H_7$, C_6H_5; $R' = CH_3$, C_2H_5; $R'' = CH_3$, C_2H_5, C_6H_5; $X = Br, I$.

[213] Lutz and Reveley, *J. Am. Chem. Soc.*, *63*, 3178–80, 3180–9 (1941).

Aromatic ether cleavages that differ from those ordinarily observed (see Ether Cleavage by Grignard Reagents, Chapter XV), in that demethoxylation rather than demethylation occurs, are reported by Fuson *et al.*[214]

MesCO—(3-OCH_3-phenyl) $\xrightarrow[(30°)]{C_6H_5MgBr}$ MesCO—(3-C_6H_5-phenyl) (35%)

MesCO—(2-OCH_3-phenyl) $\xrightarrow[(60°)]{C_6H_5MgBr}$ MesCO—(2,6-di-C_6H_5-phenyl) (20%)

MesCO—(2-OCH_3-4-CH_3-phenyl) $\xrightarrow[(30°)]{C_6H_5MgBr}$ MesCO—(2-C_6H_5-4-CH_3-phenyl) (18%)

MesCO—(2-OCH_3-4-CH_3-phenyl) $\xrightarrow[(60°)]{C_6H_5MgBr}$ MesCO—(2-C_6H_5-5-C_6H_5-4-CH_3-phenyl) (20%)

MesCO—(2-OCH_3-1-naphthyl) $\xrightarrow{RMgX^*}$ MesCO—(2-R-1-naphthyl)

[214](*a*) Fuson and Speck, *J. Am. Chem. Soc.*, *64*, 2446–8 (1942); (*b*) Fuson and Hornberger, *J. Org. Chem.*, *16*, 631–6 (1951); (*c*) Fuson and Hornberger, *J. Org. Chem.*, *16*, 637–42 (1951); (*d*) Fuson and Shealy, *J. Org. Chem.*, *16*, 643–7 (1951).

*RMgX = CH_3MgI (56%), C_2H_5MgBr (80%), *n*-C_4H_9MgBr (55%), C_6H_5MgBr (59%), 1-$C_{10}H_7MgBr$ (76%).

Instances of 1,4-addition involving an unsaturated *alpha* side-chain of a cyclic ketone are also known. Those of furfurylidenementhone and furfurylidenecamphor, reported, respectively, by Boedtker *et al.*[215] and by Wolff,[216] are illustrative.

```
            CH2                                         CH2
           /   \                                       /   \
       H2C       CH—CH3          RMgX*             H2C       CH—CH3
        |        |              ------>             |        |
i-C3H7—HC        C=CHC4H3O                 i-C3H7—HC         CH—CHRC4H3O
           \   /                                       \   /
             C                                           C
             ||                                          ||
             O                                           O
```

```
          C=CHC4H3O                           CH—CHRC4H3O
         /|              RMgX†               /|
   C8H14  |             ------>        C8H14  |
         \|                                  \|
          C=O                                 C=O
```

According to Maxim *et al.*[217] the 1,4-addition of Grignard reagents to 2-furfurylidene- and 2-benzylidenepulegone involves the isopropylidene double bond.

```
           CH3                                    CH3
           |                                      |
           CH                                     CH
          /  \                                   /  \
       H2C    C=CHC4H3O       RMgX‡          H2C    C=CHC4H3O
        |     |              ------>          |     |
       H2C    C=O                            H2C    C=O
          \  /                                  \  /
           C                                     CH
           ||                                    |
           C                                H3C—C—CH3
          /  \                                   |
       CH3    CH3                                R
```

[215]Boedtker, Wiger, and Aagaard, *J. pharm. chim.*, 6, 193–204 (1927); *Chem. Abstr.*, *22*, 584 (1928); *Chem. Zentr.*, *1927,II*, 2189.

[216]Wolff, *Compt. rend.*, *172*, 1357–60 (1921); *Chem. Zentr.*, *1921,III*, 828; *Ann. chim.*, [9], *20*, 82–130 (1923).

*R = CH_3, C_2H_5, n-C_3H_7, i-C_3H_7, n-C_4H_9, i-C_4H_9, i-C_5H_{11}, C_6H_5.

†R = C_6H_5, $C_6H_5CH_2$, 4-$CH_3C_6H_4$, 4-$CH_3OC_6H_4$.

[217]Maxim, Zugravescu, and Teodorescu, *Bull. soc. chim.*, [5], 7, 382–93 (1940); *Chem. Abstr.*, 36, 2851 (1942).

‡R = C_2H_5, n-C_3H_7, i-C_4H_9, C_6H_5, $C_6H_5CH_2$.

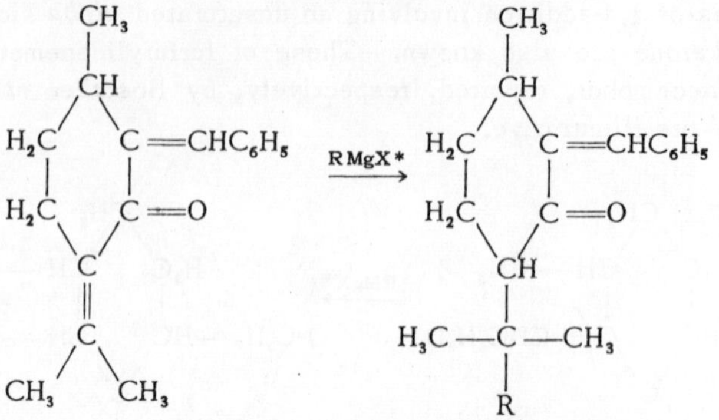

$$\text{3-methyl-6-isopropylidene-2-benzylidenecyclohexanone} \xrightarrow{\text{RMgX}^*} \text{product with } (CH_3)_2CR \text{ at C-6}$$

$$\begin{array}{c} CH_3CH\!<\!\begin{array}{l} CH_2-CH_2 \\ C(=CHC_6H_5)-C(=O) \end{array}\!\!>\!C=C(CH_3)_2 \end{array} \xrightarrow{\text{RMgX}^*} \begin{array}{c} CH_3CH\!<\!\begin{array}{l} CH_2-CH_2 \\ C(=CHC_6H_5)-C(=O) \end{array}\!\!>\!CH-C(CH_3)_2R \end{array}$$

This was scarcely to be expected in view of the behavior of furfurylideneacetone, benzalacetone, and mesitylene oxide (see Table VI-XVI).

Other 1,4-additions involving unsaturated *alpha* side-chains of cyclic ketones have been reported by Doeuvre[218] (pulegone), Kohler[219] (2,6-dibenzylidene-3-methylcyclohexanone), and Haller and Bauer[220] (α-benzylidenecamphor).

Both 1,2- and 1,4-additions, as well as mixtures of products, are reported for α,β-unsaturated single-ring cyclic ketones. On the basis of the available data no simple rules seem applicable to prediction of the order of addition.

Little is known concerning the behavior of compounds in which the carbon atoms *alpha* and *beta* to the carbonyl group are mutually triply bonded. Kohler (*loc. cit.*[205]) reported only 1,2-addition of phenylmagnesium bromide to phenylbenzoylacetylene. Fuson and Meek,[221] however, have found that the additions of methylmagnesium iodide, phenylmagnesium bromide, or mesitylmagnesium bromide to phenylmesitoylacetylene or mesitylmesitoylacetylene are predominantly, if not exclusively, 1,4.

1,6- (or "Transannular 1,4-") addition. Baeyer and Villiger[222] suggested, without proof of structure, that the addition of methylmagnesium iodide to fuchsone takes place in the 1,6 positions. This has since been confirmed by Julian and Gist,[223] who also found that naphthofuchsone undergoes 1,6-addition, whereas anthrafuchsone (benzhydrylideneanthrone) reacts "normally" (*i.e.*, 1,2).

---

*R = C_2H_5, n-C_3H_7, i-C_4H_9, C_6H_5, $C_6H_5CH_2$.

[218] Doeuvre, *Bull. soc. chim.*, [5], *6*, 1067–9 (1939).

[219] Kohler, *Am. Chem. J.*, *37*, 369–92 (1907).

[220] Haller and Bauer, *Compt. rend.*, *142*, 971–6 (1906); *Chem. Zentr.*, *1906*, *I*, 1827.

[221] Fuson and Meek, *J. Org. Chem.*, *10*, 551–61 (1945).

[222] Baeyer and Villiger, *Ber.*, *36*, 2774–96 (1903).

[223] Julian and Gist, *J. Am. Chem. Soc.*, *57*, 2030–2 (1934).

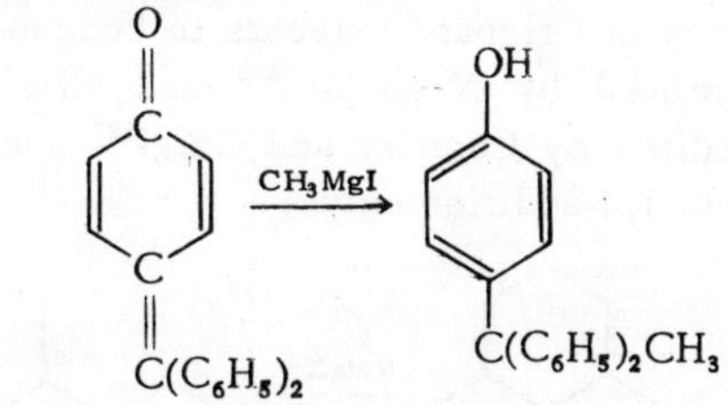

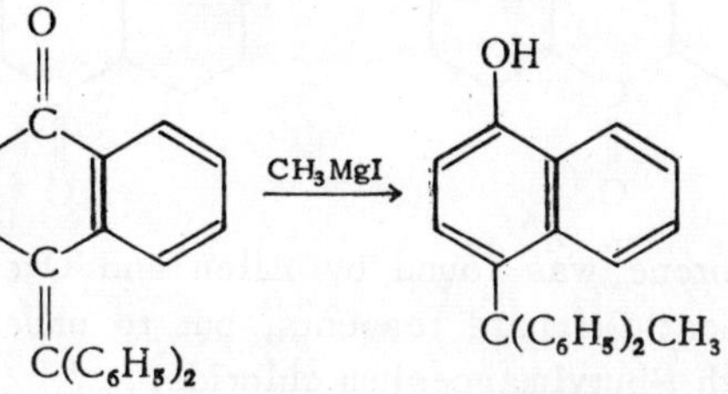

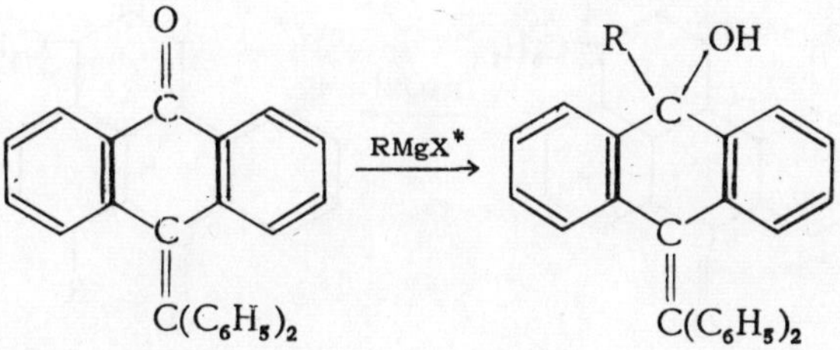

$$C(C_6H_5)_2\text{-quinone methide} \xrightarrow{CH_3MgI} \text{HO-}C_6H_4\text{-}C(C_6H_5)_2CH_3$$

$$\xrightarrow{CH_3MgI}$$

$$\xrightarrow{RMgX^*}$$

Methylene- and benzylideneanthrone, however, are reported to undergo 1,6-addition.[224]

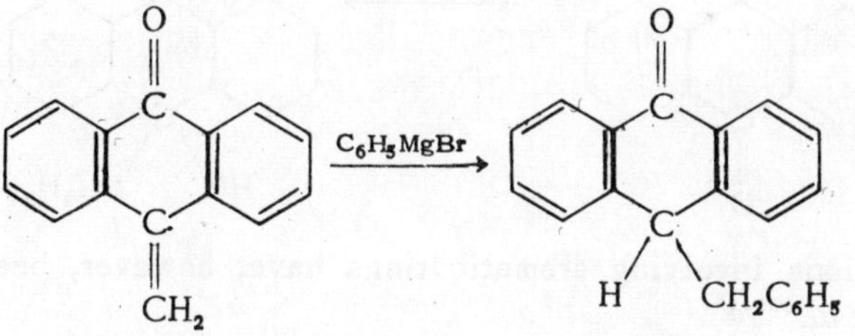

$$\xrightarrow{C_6H_5MgBr}$$ (Ref. *224b*)

$$\xrightarrow{C_6H_5MgBr}$$

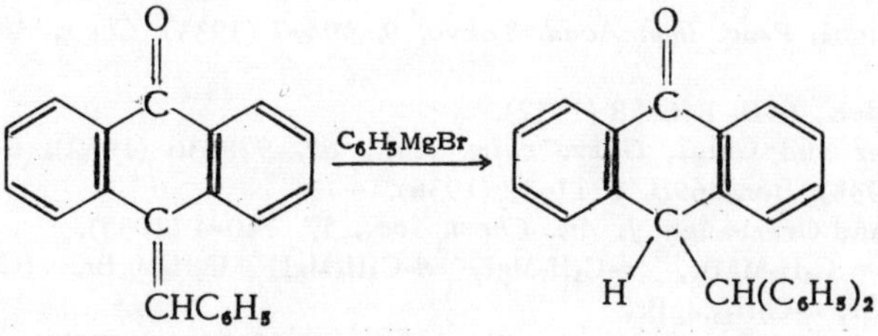

*RMgX = CH_3MgI, C_6H_5MgBr.

[224](*a*) Julian and Magnani, *J. Am. Chem. Soc.*, 56, 2174–7 (1934); (*b*) Julian and Cole, *J. Am. Chem. Soc.*, 57, 1607–11 (1935).

The 1,6-additions of Grignard reagents to benzanthrone (7-benz[*de*]anthracen-7-one) claimed by Nakanishi[225] and Clar[226] have been rather thoroughly discredited by Charrier and Ghigi[227] and by Allen and Overbaugh,[228] who found 1,4-addition only.

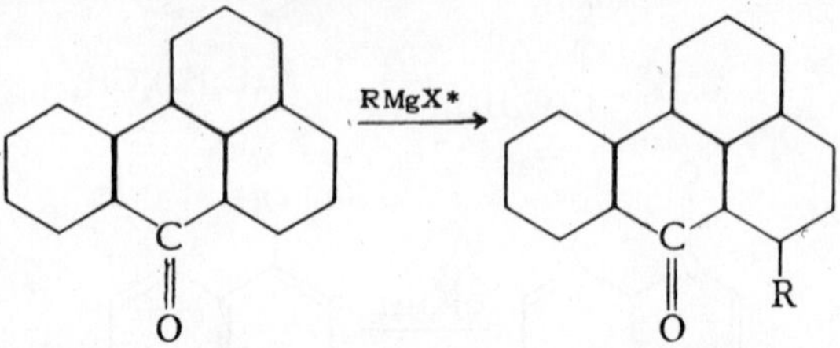

RMgX* →

3-Phenylbenzanthrone was found by Allen and Overbaugh[229] to behave similarly with most Grignard reagents, but to undergo "normal" (*i.e.*, 1,2-) addition with *t*-butylmagnesium chloride.

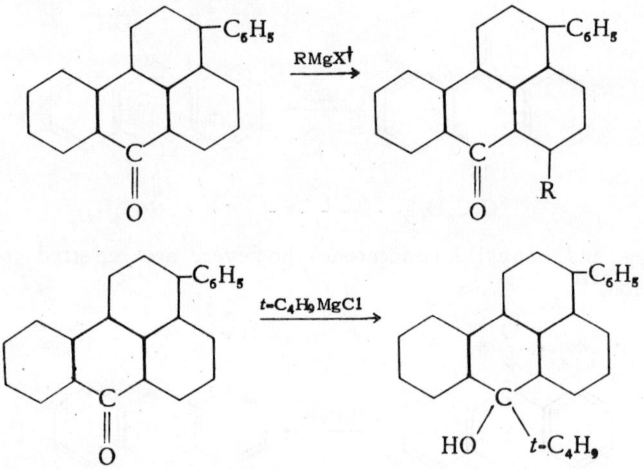

C_6H_5 RMgX† →

t-C_4H_9MgCl → HO t-C_4H_9

1,6-Additions involving aromatic rings have, however, been observed by Fuson *et al.*[230,‡]

[225] Nakanishi, *Proc. Imp. Acad. Tokyo*, *9*, 394–7 (1933); *Chem. Abstr.*, *28*, 762 (1934).

[226] Clar, *Ber.*, *65B*, 846–58 (1932).

[227] Charrier and Ghigi, *Gazz. chim. ital.*, *62*, 928–36 (1932); *Chem. Abstr.*, *27*, 1344 (1933); *Ber.*, *69B*, 2211–32 (1936).

[228] Allen and Overbaugh, *J. Am. Chem. Soc.*, *57*, 740–4 (1935).

*RMgX = C_2H_5MgBr, n-C_3H_7MgI, n-C_4H_9MgI, C_6H_5MgBr, $(CH_2)_5CHMgCl$, $C_6H_5CH_2MgCl$, n-$C_7H_{15}MgBr$.

[229] Allen and Overbaugh, *J. Am. Chem. Soc.*, *57*, 1322–5 (1935).

†R = C_2H_5, n-C_4H_9, $(CH_2)_5CH$, C_6H_5, $C_6H_5CH_2$, $C_6H_5CH{=}CH$.

[230] (*a*) Fuson and McKusick, *J. Am. Chem. Soc.*, *65*, 60–4 (1943); (*b*) Fuson and Gaertner, *J. Org. Chem.*, *13*, 496–501 (1948); (*c*) Fuson and Tull, *J. Am. Chem. Soc.*, *71*, 2542–6 (1949).

‡Dur = duryl = 2,3,5,6-$(CH_3)_4C_6H$—; Mes = mesityl = 2,4,6-$(CH_3)_3C_6H_2$—.

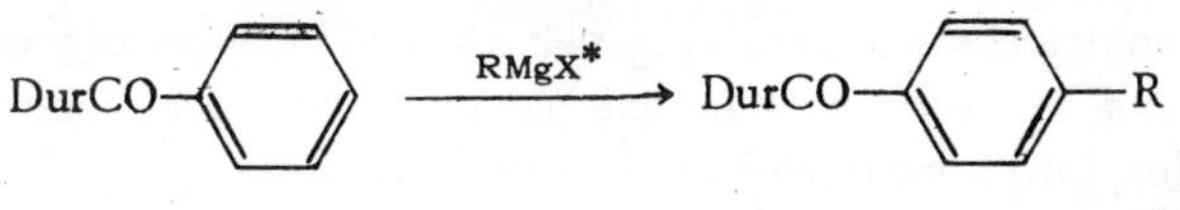

DurCO–C_6H_5 —RMgX*→ DurCO–C_6H_4–R

(Ref. *230 a,c*)

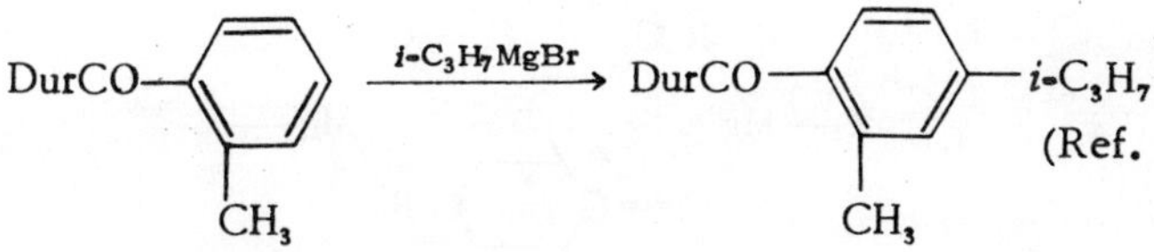

DurCO–(CH$_3$-substituted ring) —i-C_3H_7MgBr→ DurCO–(CH$_3$-substituted ring)–i-C_3H_7

(Ref. *230c*)

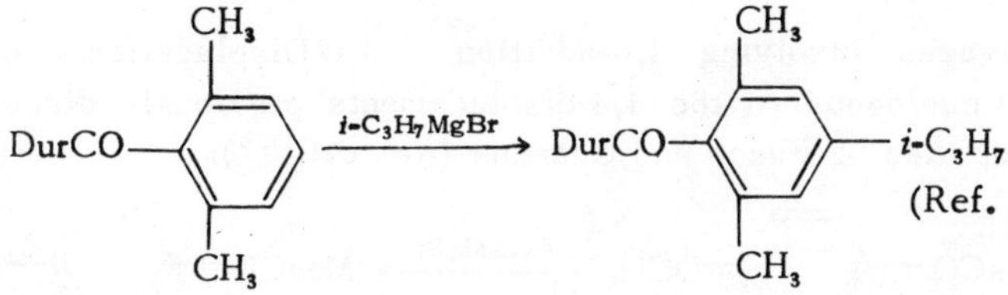

DurCO–(ring bearing two CH$_3$) —i-C_3H_7MgBr→ DurCO–(ring bearing two CH$_3$)–i-C_3H_7

(Ref. *230c*)

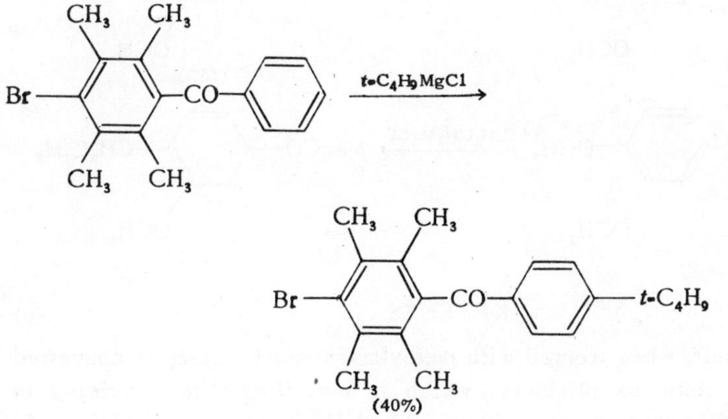

Br–(ring bearing four CH$_3$)–CO–C_6H_5 —t-C_4H_9MgCl→

Br–(ring bearing four CH$_3$)–CO–C_6H_4–t-C_4H_9 (Ref. *230c*)

(40%)

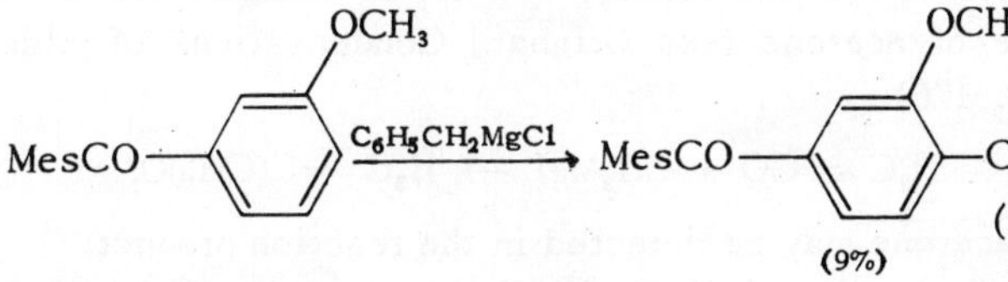

MesCO–(OCH$_3$-substituted ring) —$C_6H_5CH_2MgCl$→ MesCO–(OCH$_3$-substituted ring)–$CH_2C_6H_5$

(9%)

(Ref. *230a*)

With regard to the 1,6-additions of Julian *et al.* (*loc. cit.*[223, 224]), it is, perhaps, possible to conceive of a cycloid transition state (albeit somewhat strained) analogous to the quasi six-membered ring proposed to account for the 1,4-additions. With regard to those reported by Fuson *et al.* (*loc. cit.*[230]), however, the impediment to an extension of the 1,4-addition hypothesis appears more serious. In the latter case at least (and perhaps in both) it may be necessary to postulate a different mech-

---

*RMgX = i-C_3H_7MgBr (38%)[230c]; s-C_4H_9MgBr (63%)[230c]; t-C_4H_9MgCl (33%)[230a]; $(CH_2)_5CHMgCl$ (38%)[230c]; $C_6H_5CH_2MgCl$ (20%)[230a].

anism. A transition state involving two carbonyl complexes would seem a concept less far-fetched than one necessitating the constraint of a single complex into a monstrously distorted cycloid.

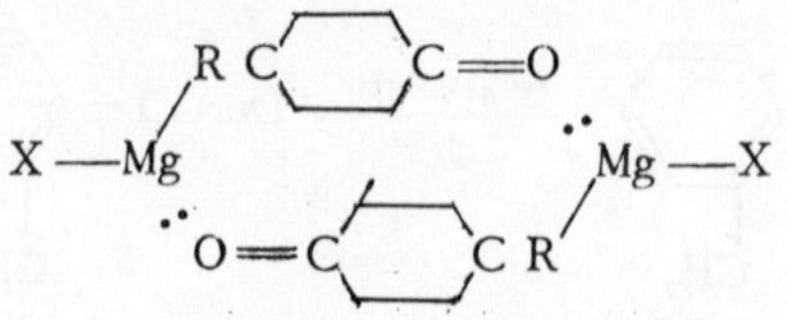

R C⟨ ⟩C=O, X—Mg, Mg—X, O=C⟨ ⟩C R

Cleavages involving 1,6-addition. 1,6-Displacements of methoxy groups analogous to the 1,4-displacements previously discussed have been reported by Fuson and Gaertner (*loc. cit.*[230b]).

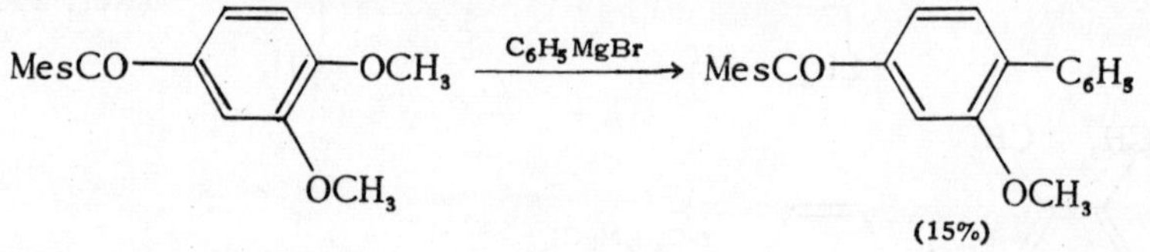

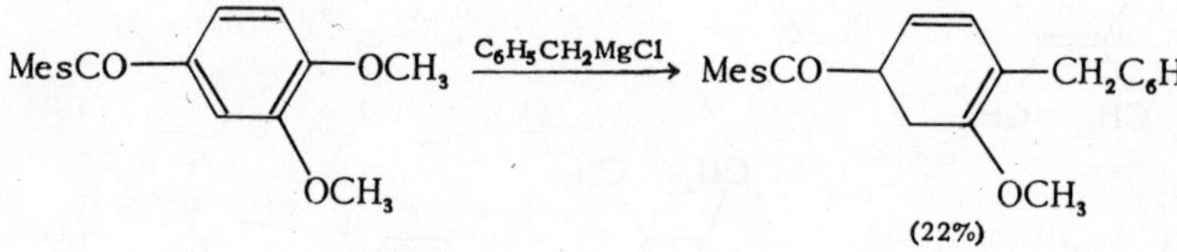

$$\text{MesCO}-C_6H_3(OCH_3)-OCH_3 \xrightarrow{C_6H_5MgBr} \text{MesCO}-C_6H_3(OCH_3)-C_6H_5 \quad (15\%)$$

$$\text{MesCO}-C_6H_3(OCH_3)-OCH_3 \xrightarrow{C_6H_5CH_2MgCl} \text{MesCO}-C_6H_4(OCH_3)-CH_2C_6H_5 \quad (22\%)$$

KETENES

Ketene itself, when treated with methylmagnesium iodide, is converted chiefly into resinous products, which is not altogether surprising in view of the fact that the primary product of Grignard reagent addition is the enolate of acetone (see Grignard Condensations of Aldehydes and Ketones, p. 176).

$$H_2C{=}CO + CH_3MgI \rightarrow H_2C{=}C(CH_3)OMgI$$

Traces of acetone may be detected in the reaction product.[231]

Aromatic ketenes react "normally" (*i.e.*, by 1,2-addition at the carbonyl double bond) with non-reducing Grignard reagents to form enolates, from which the enols, or corresponding ketones, are obtained by hydrolysis.

$$(C_6H_5)_2C{=}CO \xrightarrow{C_6H_5MgBr} (C_6H_5)_2C{=}C(OMgBr)C_6H_5 \xrightarrow{H_2O} (C_6H_5)_2C{=}C(OH)C_6H_5 \quad \text{(Ref. } 232, 233\text{)}$$

[231] Deakin and Wilsmore, *J. Chem. Soc.*, 97, 1968–78 (1910).
[232] Staudinger, *Ann.*, 356, 51–123 (1907).
[233] Gilman and Heckert, *J. Am. Chem. Soc.*, 42, 1010–4 (1920).

$$\mathrm{Mes(C_6H_5)C{=}CO \xrightarrow{CH_3MgI} Mes(C_6H_5)C{=}C(OMgBr)CH_3 \xrightarrow{H_2O} Mes(C_6H_5)CHCOCH_3} \quad \text{(Ref. 234)}$$

$$\mathrm{Mes(C_6H_5)C{=}CO \xrightarrow{MesMgBr} Mes(C_6H_5)C{=}C(OMgBr)Mes \xrightarrow{H_2O} Mes(C_6H_5)C{=}C(OH)Mes} \quad \text{(Ref. 235)}$$

$$\mathrm{(C_6H_5)_2C{=}CO \xrightarrow{C_6H_5C{\equiv}CMgBr} (C_6H_5)_2C{=}C(OMgBr)C{\equiv}CC_6H_5 \xrightarrow{H_2O} (C_6H_5)_2CHCOC{\equiv}CC_6H_5} \quad \text{(Ref. 236)}$$

$$\mathrm{MesCH{=}CO \xrightarrow{MesMgBr} MesCH{=}C(OMgBr)Mes \xrightarrow{H_2O} MesCHCOMes} \quad \text{(Ref. 237)}$$

Diaryl ketenes with at least one mesityl or duryl group are reduced by reducing Grignard reagents to the corresponding vinyl alcohols.

$$\mathrm{Mes(C_6H_5)C{=}CO \xrightarrow{(CH_2)_5CHMgCl} Mes(C_6H_5)C{=}CHOH} \quad \text{(Ref. 238)}$$

$$\mathrm{Dur(C_6H_5)C{=}CO \xrightarrow{\mathit{t}\text{-}C_4H_9MgBr} Dur(C_6H_5)C{=}CHOH} \quad \text{(Ref. 238)}$$

Other examples of the reactions of ketenes with Grignard reagents are to be found in Table VI-XVIII.

---

[234] Fuson, Armstrong, Chadwick, and Kneisley, *J. Am. Chem. Soc.*, 67, 386–93 (1946).
[235] Fuson, Armstrong, Kneisley, and Shenk, *J. Am. Chem. Soc.*, 66, 1464–6 (1944).
[236] Smith and Hoehn, *J. Am. Chem. Soc.*, 63, 1176–8 (1941).
[237] Fuson, Armstrong, and Shenk, *J. Am. Chem. Soc.*, 66, 964–7 (1944).
[238] Fuson, Foster, Shenk, and Maynert, *J. Am. Chem. Soc.*, 57, 1937–9 (1945).

TABLE VI-XVII

REACTIONS OF GRIGNARD REAGENTS WITH ALDEHYDES

Aldehyde	RMgX	Product(s)	Ref.
CH_2O			
HCHO	C_2H_5MgBr	n-C_3H_7OH (poor yield); $CH_2(OC_2H_5)_2$	*372*
HCHO (from 50 g. paraform)	$H_2C{=}CHC{\equiv}CMgBr$ (65 g. C_4H_4)	$H_2C{=}CHC{\equiv}CCH_2OH$ (65%)	*245*
HCHO	2-Furyl-MgI	Furfuryl alcohol (31%)	*109*
HCHO	Pyrryl-MgX	A pyrrolic ether, $C_{22}H_{14}O_2N_2$; tar and other unidentified products	*236*
HCHO	Butenyl-MgBr*	$H_2C{=}CHCH(CH_3)CH_2OH$ (*ca.* 50%); octadienes; *no* $CH_3CH{=}CHCH_2CH_2OH$	*283*
HCHO (from 38 g. paraform)	s-C_4H_9MgBr (150 g. C_4H_9Br)	s-$C_4H_9CH_2OH$ (64.5 g., 67%)	*363*
HCHO	t-C_4H_9MgCl	t-$C_4H_9CH_2OH$ (42–50%)	*55*
HCHO (from 7.5 g. paraform)	3-Furfuryl-MgCl (14.3 g. C_5H_5ClO)	3-Methyl-2-furfuryl alcohol (4.6 g., 33.4%)	*451*
HCHO (from 50 g. paraform)	2-Thenyl-MgCl (0.242 mole)	2-Methyl-3-thenyl alcohol (15.1 g., 49%)	*443*
HCHO (*ca.* 1 equiv.)	n-$C_3H_7C{\equiv}CMgBr$ (2 moles)	n-$C_3H_7C{\equiv}CCH_2OH$ (140 g., 71%)	*450*
HCHO (from 45 g. paraform)	$(CH_2)_4CHMgBr$ (149 g. C_5H_9Br)	$(CH_2)_4CHCH_2OH$ (62–64%)	*251*
HCHO (from 80 g., 2.67 moles paraform)	(+)-$CH_3(C_2H_5)CHCH_2MgCl$† (207 g., 1.93 mole $C_5H_{11}Cl$)	(+)-$CH_3(C_2H_5)CHCH_2CH_2OH$ (101.9 g., 52%)	*388*
HCHO (from 65 g. paraform)	$CH_3(n$-$C_3H_7)CHMgBr$ (302 g. $C_5H_{11}Br$)	$CH_3(n$-$C_3H_7)CHCH_2OH$ (108 g., 53%)	*363*
HCHO	t-$C_5H_{11}MgCl$	t-$C_5H_{11}CH_2OH$ (40–47%)	*55*
HCHO (from 50.0 g. paraform)	$CH_3OCH_2CH(CH_3)CH_2MgCl$ (122.5 g., 1.0 mole $C_5H_{11}ClO$)	$CH_3OCH_2CH(CH_3)CH_2CH_2OH$ (79.0 g., (67%)	*425*
HCHO	4-BrC_6H_4MgBr	4-$BrC_6H_4CH_2OH$ (61%)	*373*
HCHO (from 1.5–2.0 equiv. "trioxymethylene")	C_6H_5MgBr	$C_6H_5CH_2OH$ (70%)	*372*

* From 80% $CH_3CH{=}CHCH_2Br$, 20% $H_2C{=}CHCHBrCH_3$.

† From (+)-1-chloro-2-methylbutane, $[\alpha]_D^{20}$ + 1.26.

TABLE VI-XVII (Continued)

Aldehyde	RMgX	Product(s)	Ref.
CH_2O (*cont.*)			
HCHO (*ca.* 1 equiv.)	n-$C_4H_9C{\equiv}CMgBr$ (82 g. C_6H_{10})	n-$C_4H_9C{\equiv}CCH_2OH$ (92 g., 82%)	*450,19*
HCHO	$(CH_2)_5CHMgCl$	$(CH_2)_5CHCH_2OH$ (64–69%)	*108,265*
HCHO	$(CH_2)_5CHMgBr$	$(CH_2)_5CHCH_2OH$ (61–65%)	*3,426*
HCHO	$CH_3(i$-$C_4H_9)CHMgBr$	i-$C_4H_9CH(CH_3)CH_2OH$ (30%)	*47*
HCHO	3-$F_3CC_6H_4MgBr$	3-$F_3CC_6H_4CH_2OH$ (38%)	*427*
HCHO (20 g., 0.66 mole)	$C_6H_5CH_2MgCl$ (0.85 mole)	2-$CH_3C_6H_4CH_2OH$ (35 g., 40%)	*454*
HCHO	$(CH_2)_5CHCH_2MgBr$	$(CH_2)_5CHCH_2CH_2OH$ (46%)	*111*
HCHO	$CH_3(n$-$C_3H_7)CH(CH_2)_2MgBr$	$CH_3(n$-$C_3H_7)CH(CH_2)_3OH$	*204*
HCHO	$(C_2H_5)_3CMgCl$	$(C_2H_5)_3CCH_2OH$ (10%)	*351,352*
HCHO	$CH_3(C_2H_5)(n$-$C_3H_7)CMgCl$	$CH_3(C_2H_5)(n$-$C_3H_7)CCH_2OH$ (30%)	*351*
HCHO	$(C_2H_5)_2N(CH_2)_3Cl$ + Mg	$(C_2H_5)_2N(CH_2)_3CH_2OH$	*233*
HCHO	$C_6H_5C{\equiv}CMgBr$ (12 g. C_8H_6)	$C_6H_5C{\equiv}CCH_2OH$ (4 g.)	*389*
HCHO	Indolyl-MgX	β-Indolylmethanol; β-indolylmethyl ether	*236*
HCHO	n-$C_6H_{13}C{\equiv}CMgBr$	n-$C_6H_{13}C{\equiv}CCH_2OH$ (83%)	*389*
HCHO	$(CH_2)_5CHCH_2CH_2MgBr$	$(CH_2)_5CH(CH_2)_3OH$ (79%)	*426*
HCHO	3,3-Dimethylcyclohexyl-MgBr (143.3 g. $C_8H_{15}Br$)	3,3-Dimethylcyclohexylmethanol (71.0 g., 67%)	*374*
HCHO	n-$C_5H_{11}(CH_3)_2CMgCl$	n-$C_5H_{11}(CH_3)_2CCH_2OH$ (40.7%)	*351*
HCHO	$CH_3(n$-$C_3H_7)CH(CH_2)_3MgBr$	$CH_3(n$-$C_3H_7)CH(CH_2)_4OH$ (58%)	*46*
HCHO	$CH_3(C_2H_5)(n$-$C_4H_9)CMgCl$	$CH_3(C_2H_5)(n$-$C_4H_9)CCH_2OH$ (31%)	*351*
HCHO (from 10 g. paraform)	2-Thianaphthenylmethyl-MgCl (0.0167 mole)	2-Methyl-3-thianaphthenylmethanol (1.05 g., 35%)	*444*
HCHO (from 40 g. paraform)	3-Thianaphthenylmethyl-MgCl (45 g. C_9H_7ClS)	2-(3-Thianaphthenyl)ethanol; 2-Methyl-3-thianaphthenylmethanol (1.3 g., 18%); 2-(2-hydroxymethyl-3-thianaphthenyl)ethanol (?)	*445*

TABLE VI-XVII (Continued)

Aldehyde	RMgX	Product(s)	Ref.
CH_2O (*cont.*)			
HCHO	2-Methylindolyl-MgX	α-Methyl-β-indolylmethanol	236
HCHO	$C_6H_5(CH_2)_3MgBr$	$C_6H_5(CH_2)_4OH$	34
HCHO	$CH_3COC(C_2H_5)_3 + C_2H_5MgBr$	$(C_2H_5)_3CCOCH_2CH_2OH$* (34%)	354
HCHO (from 25 g. "trioxymethylene")	$1\text{-}C_{10}H_7MgBr$ (64 g. $C_{10}H_7Br$)	$1\text{-}C_{10}H_7CH_2OH$ (58%)	372
HCHO	$(CH_2)_5CH(CH_2)_4MgBr$	$(CH_2)_5CH(CH_2)_5OH$ (58%)	426
HCHO	$1\text{-}C_{10}H_7CH_2MgCl$	$(1\text{-}C_{10}H_7CH_2-)_2$ (6.4%); $1\text{-}CH_3\text{-}2\text{-}HOCH_2C_{10}H_6$; unidentified product	110
HCHO	$1\text{-}C_{10}H_7CH_2MgCl$ (18 g. $C_{11}H_9Cl$)	$1\text{-}C_{10}H_7CH_2CH_2OH$ (8 g.)	448
HCHO	$2\text{-}C_{10}H_7CH_2MgCl$	$2\text{-}C_{10}H_7CH_2CH_2OH$	448
HCHO	$2\text{-}C_{10}H_7CH_2MgBr$	$2\text{-}C_{10}H_7CH_2CH_2OH$; $1\text{-}HOCH_2\text{-}2\text{-}CH_3C_{10}H_6$ (?)	305
HCHO	$4\text{-}CH_3C_{10}H_6\text{-}1\text{-}MgBr$	$1\text{-}HOCH_2\text{-}4\text{-}CH_3C_{10}H_6$ (40–50%)	373
HCHO (from 123 g. paraform)	$6\text{-}CH_3OC_{10}H_6\text{-}1\text{-}MgI$ (555 g. $C_{11}H_9IO$)	$1\text{-}HOCH_2\text{-}6\text{-}CH_3OC_{10}H_6$ (300 g., 80%)	29
HCHO	$C_2H_5(C_6H_5)CH(CH_2)_2MgBr$	$C_2H_5(C_6H_5)CH(CH_2)_3OH$	203
HCHO	$L\text{-}C_2H_5(C_6H_5)CH(CH_2)_2MgBr$	$L\text{-}C_2H_5(C_6H_5)CH(CH_2)_3OH$	203
HCHO	$(CH_3)_5C_6MgBr$	$(CH_3)_5C_6CH_2OH$	51
HCHO	9-Phenanthryl-MgBr	9-Phenanthrylmethanol (50%)	11
HCHO	$n\text{-}C_{16}H_{33}MgBr$	$n\text{-}C_{17}H_{35}OH$ (53%)	347
HCHO	$n\text{-}C_{17}H_{35}MgBr$	$n\text{-}C_{18}H_{37}OH$ (64%)	347
HCHO (excess)	$(C_6H_5)_2C{=}C(C_6H_5)MgBr$ (5.00 g. $C_{20}H_{15}Br$)	$(C_6H_5)_2C{=}C(C_6H_5)CH_2OH$ (2.05 g.)	182
$(CH_2O)_x$			
"Trioxymethylene"	$(\equiv CMgBr)_2$	$(\equiv CCH_2OH)_2$	81,154
"Trioxymethylene"	$HC\equiv CMgBr$	$HC\equiv CCH_2OH$	154

*Enolate addition.

TABLE VI-XVII (Continued)

Aldehyde	RMgX	Product(s)	Ref.
$(CH_2O)_x$ *(cont.)*			
"Trioxymethylene" (30 g.)	$H_2C{=}CHCH_2Br$ (121 g.) + Mg (24 g.)	$H_2C{=}CHCH_2CH_2OH$ (26%)	*166,258; cf. 261*
"Trioxymethylene"	$H_2C{=}CHC{\equiv}CMgBr$	No reaction	*244*
Paraformaldehyde (10 g.)	Butenyl-MgBr (62 g. C_4H_7Br)	$H_2C{=}CHCH(CH_3)CH_2OH$ (15 g., 38%)	*439*
"Trioxymethylene"	n-C_4H_9MgCl	n-$C_5H_{11}OH$ (64%)	*386*
"Trioxymethylene"	n-C_4H_9MgBr	n-$C_5H_{11}OH$ (70%); $(n$-$C_5H_{11}O)_2CH_2$	*34*
"Trioxymethylene"	n-C_4H_9MgBr	n-$C_5H_{11}OH$ (47%)	*254*
"Trioxymethylene"	i-C_4H_9MgBr	i-$C_5H_{11}OH$ (50%)	*321*
"Trioxymethylene"	s-C_4H_9MgBr	$CH_3(C_2H_5)CHCH_2OH$ (59%)	*254*
"Trioxymethylene"	t-C_4H_9MgCl	t-$C_4H_9CH_2OH$	*59*
"Polyoxymethylene" (1.2–1.3 excess)	t-C_4H_9MgCl	t-$C_4H_9CH_2OH$ (40%)	*336*
"Trioxymethylene" (42 g.)	$(CH_2)_4CHMgCl$ (94 g. C_5H_9Cl)	$(CH_2)_4CHCH_2OH$ (40 g., 40%); $[(CH_2)_4CH{-}]_2$ (*ca.* 8 g., 12.5%); $[(CH_2)_4CHO]_2CH_2$ (45 g., 40.5%)	*328,371*
"Polyoxymethylene"	n-$C_5H_{11}MgBr$	n-$C_6H_{13}OH$ (47%)	*336*
"Trioxymethylene"	$CH_3(n$-$C_3H_7)CHMgBr$	$CH_3(n$-$C_3H_7)CHCH_2OH$ (70%)	*254*
"Trioxymethylene" (60 g.)	C_6H_5MgBr (157 g. C_6H_5Br)	$C_6H_5CH_2Br$ (35 g.); $(C_6H_5{-})_2$ (10 g.); C_6H_5CHO (20 g. bisulfite comp'd.)	*219*
"Trioxymethylene"	$(CH_2)_5CHMgCl$	$(CH_2)_5CHCH_2OH$	*288*
Paraformaldehyde (100 g.)	$(CH_2)_5CHMgBr$ (163 g. $C_6H_{11}Br$)	$(CH_2)_5CHCH_2OH$ (70 g., 60%)	*221*
"Trioxymethylene"	$CH_3(i$-$C_4H_9)CHMgBr$	$CH_3(i$-$C_4H_9)CHCH_2OH$ (*ca.* 8%); "secondary products" (chiefly)	*327*
"Trioxymethylene" (23 g.)	1-Cyclohexenylmethyl-MgCl (20 g. $C_7H_{11}Cl$)	$C_6H_9CH_2CH_2OH$ (40%)	*448*
"Trioxymethylene" (18 g.)	$(CH_2)_5CHCH_2MgI$ (134 g. $C_7H_{13}I$)	$(CH_2)_5CHCH_2CH_2OH$ (30 g.)	*371*
"Trioxymethylene"	$(CH_2)_6CHMgI$	$(CH_2)_6CHCH_2OH$	*284*
"Trioxymethylene"	Indolyl-MgX	β-Indolylmethanol	*236*

TABLE VI-XVII (Continued)

Aldehyde	RMgX	Product(s)	Ref.
$(CH_2O)_x$ *(cont.)*			
"Trioxymethylene" (24 g.)	$2\text{-}CH_3C_6H_4CH_2MgBr$ (40 g. C_8H_9Br)	$2\text{-}CH_3C_6H_4CH_2CH_2OH$ (1.5%); $2,3\text{-}(CH_3)_2C_6H_3CH_2OH$ (28.5%)	*448*
"Trioxymethylene" (20 g.)	$3\text{-}CH_3C_6H_4CH_2MgBr$ (185 g. C_8H_9Br)	$3\text{-}CH_3C_6H_4CH_2CH_2OH$ (8–10 g.)	*441*
"Trioxymethylene"	$4\text{-}CH_3C_6H_4CH_2MgBr$	$4\text{-}CH_3C_6H_4CH_2CH_2OH$ (7.5%); $2,5\text{-}(CH_3)_2C_6H_3CH_2OH$ (22.5%)	*448*
"Trioxymethylene"	$CH_3(C_6H_5)CHMgBr$	$CH_3(C_6H_5)CHCH_2OH$	*448*
"Trioxymethylene"	$(CH_3)_2C{=}CH(CH_2)_2CH(CH_3)MgBr$	$(CH_3)_2C{=}CH(CH_2)_2CH(CH_3)CH_2OH$ (15%)	*76*
"Trioxymethylene"	1-Indenyl-MgBr	α-Benzofulvanol	*122*
"Trioxymethylene"	2-Methylindolyl-MgX	α-Methyl-β-indolylmethanol; α-Methyl-β-indolylmethyl ether	*236*
"Trioxymethylene"	$C_6H_5(CH_2)_3MgBr$	$C_6H_5(CH_2)_4OH$ (54–59%); $n\text{-}C_3H_7C_6H_5$; $[C_6H_5(CH_2)_3-]_2$	*344*
"Trioxymethylene"	$3,5\text{-}(CH_3)_2C_6H_3CH_2MgBr$	$2,4,6\text{-}(CH_3)_3C_6H_2CH_2OH$; $[2,4,6\text{-}(CH_3)_3C_6H_2CH_2]_2O$	*442*
"Trioxymethylene" (30 g.)	$2,4,6\text{-}(CH_3)_3C_6H_2MgBr$ (250 g. $C_9H_{11}Br$)	$2,4,6\text{-}(CH_3)_3C_6H_2CH_2OH$ (4 g.)	*442*
"Trioxymethylene"	$(CH_3)_2C{=}CH(CH_2)_2CH(CH_3)CH_2MgBr$	$(CH_3)_2C{=}CH(CH_2)_2CH(CH_3)CH_2CH_2OH$ (41%)	*76*
"Trioxymethylene"	$4\text{-}i\text{-}C_3H_7C_6H_4CH_2MgCl$	$4\text{-}i\text{-}C_3H_7C_6H_4CH_2CH_2OH$ (31%)	*27*
"Trioxymethylene"	$C_6H_5O(CH_2)_5MgI$	$C_6H_5O(CH_2)_5CH_2OH$	*345*
"Trioxymethylene" (35 g.)	$n\text{-}C_{12}H_{25}MgCl$ (120 g. $C_{12}H_{25}Cl$)	$n\text{-}C_{13}H_{27}OH$ (70 g., 60%); $(n\text{-}C_{13}H_{27}O)_2CH_2$ (15 g., 14%); $C_{24}H_{50}$; olefins (16 g.)	*328*
"Trioxymethylene"	$(C_6H_5)_2C{=}CHMgBr$ + Mg	$(C_6H_5)_2C{=}CHCH_2OH$ (21%); $[(C_6H_5)_2C{=}CH-]_2$	*373*
Paraformaldehyde (2.84 g., 0.094 mole)	$n\text{-}C_{14}H_{29}MgBr$ (15.5 g., 0.057 mole $C_{14}H_{29}Br$)	$n\text{-}C_{15}H_{31}OH$ (2.2 g., 17.2%)	*62*

TABLE VI-XVII (Continued)

Aldehyde	RMgX	Product(s)	Ref.
$(CH_2O)_x$ (*cont.*)			
"Trioxymethylene" (30 g.)	n-$C_{18}H_{37}MgCl$ (144 g. $C_{18}H_{37}Cl$)	$C_{18}H_{36}$ + $C_{18}H_{38}$ (20 g., 16%); n-$C_{19}H_{39}OH$ (84 g., 59%); $(n$-$C_{19}H_{39}O)_2CH_2$ (28 g., 22%)	*328*
C_2HOBr_3			
Br_3CCHO	$(\equiv CMgI)_2$	$[\equiv CCH(OH)CBr_3]_2$	*155*
C_2HOCl_3			
CCl_3CHO	CH_3MgBr	$CCl_3(CH_3)CHOH$ (40%); CCl_3CH_2OH; tar	*172,405*
CCl_3CHO	CH_3MgI	$CCl_3(CH_3)CHOH$ (40%)	*385,132,362, 379,405*
CCl_3CHO	$(\equiv CMgBr)_2$	$[\equiv CCH(OH)CCl_3]_2$	*149,81,419*
CCl_3CHO	C_2H_5MgBr	$CCl_3(C_2H_5)CHOH$ (10–15%); CCl_3CH_2OH (50–60%)	*153*
CCl_3CHO (37 g.)	C_2H_5MgBr (32 g. C_2H_5Br)	$CCl_3(C_2H_5)CHOH$ (13–14 g.)	*142*
CCl_3CHO	C_2H_5MgBr	CCl_3CH_2OH (54%); tar*	*107*
CCl_3CHO	C_2H_5MgI	$CCl_3(C_2H_5)CHOH$ (16%)	*379*
CCl_3CHO	$H_2C{=}CHCH_2Cl$ + Mg	$CCl_3(H_2C{=}CHCH_2)CHOH$	*390*
CCl_3CHO (37 g.)	n-C_3H_7MgBr (34 g. C_3H_7Br)	$CCl_3(n$-$C_3H_7)CHOH$ (10–11 g.)	*142*
CCl_3CHO (74 g.)	i-C_3H_7MgBr (68 g. C_3H_7Br)	$CCl_3(i$-$C_3H_7)CHOH$ (30–32 g.)	*142*
CCl_3CHO (0.25 mole)	2-Thienyl-MgBr (0.25 mole C_4H_3BrS)	$CCl_3(\alpha$-$C_4H_3S)CHOH$ (36 g., 62%)	*97*
CCl_3CHO (74 g.)	n-C_4H_9MgBr (70 g. C_4H_9Br)	$CCl_3(n$-$C_4H_9)CHOH$ (35–37 g.)	*143*
CCl_3CHO (0.25 mole)	n-$C_5H_{11}MgBr$ (0.25 mole $C_5H_{11}Br$)	CCl_3CH_2OH (19–23%); C_5H_{10} (23–27 g. $C_5H_{10}Br_2$)†	*95*

* In a total of seventeen runs, including experiments in which C_2H_5MgCl and C_2H_5MgI were used, and employing temperatures varying from −75° to 34° and reaction times of fifteen minutes to twenty-four hours, no significant deviations from the results above recorded were observed.

† "Normal" or "inverse" addition.

TABLE VI-XVII (Continued)

Aldehyde	RMgX	Product(s)	Ref.
C_2HOCl_3 (*cont.*)			
CCl_3CHO	$4\text{-}BrC_6H_4MgBr$	$CCl_3(4\text{-}BrC_6H_4)CHOH$ (29%)	*379*,*152*
CCl_3CHO	C_6H_5MgBr	$CCl_3(C_6H_5)CHOH$	*379*
CCl_3CHO	C_6H_5MgX	$CCl_3(C_6H_5)CHOH$ (*ca.* 70%)	*94*
CCl_3CHO	$HBrC{=}CH(CH_2)_2C{\equiv}CMgBr$	$CCl_3[HBrC{=}CH(CH_2)_2C{\equiv}C]CHOH$ (90%)	*151*
CCl_3CHO (0.2 mole)	$(CH_2)_5CHMgBr$ (0.2 mole $C_6H_{11}Br$)	CCl_3CH_2OH (12.5 g.); C_6H_{10} (14.5 g. $C_6H_{10}Br_2$); $[(CH_2)_5CH—]_2$ (1 g.)*	*94*,*379*
CCl_3CHO (0.25 mole)	$n\text{-}C_6H_{13}MgBr$ (0.25 mole $C_6H_{13}Br$)	CCl_3CH_2OH (21.0–22.5 g.); C_6H_{12} (27.0–28.0 g. $C_6H_{12}Br_2$); tar (4.2–4.5 g.)†	95
CCl_3CHO (0.25 mole)	$n\text{-}C_6H_{13}MgBr$ (0.25 mole $C_6H_{13}Br$)	CCl_3CH_2OH (26.0 g.); C_6H_{12} (33.5 g. $C_6H_{12}Br_2$); tar (2.0 g.)‡	95
CCl_3CHO (37 g.)	$C_6H_5CH_2MgCl$ (35 g. C_7H_7Cl)	$CCl_3(C_6H_5CH_2)CHOH$ (10–11 g.)	*142*
CCl_3CHO	$C_6H_5CH_2MgCl$	$CCl_3(C_6H_5CH_2)CHOH$ (26%); CCl_3CH_2OH (1.06%);§ tar	*107*,*379*
CCl_3CHO	$2\text{-}CH_3C_6H_4MgX$	$CCl_3(2\text{-}CH_3C_6H_4)CHOH$ (*ca.* 70%)	*94*
CCl_3CHO	$2\text{-}CH_3C_6H_4MgBr$	$CCl_3(2\text{-}CH_3C_6H_4)CHOH$ (80%)	*417*
CCl_3CHO	$4\text{-}CH_3C_6H_4MgBr$	$CCl_3(4\text{-}CH_3C_6H_4)CHOH$ (50%)	*417*
CCl_3CHO	$C_6H_5C{\equiv}CMgBr$	$Cl_3C(C_6H_5C{\equiv}C)CHOH$ (75%)	*148*
CCl_3CHO (0.25 mole)	$C_6H_5(CH_2)_2MgBr$ (0.25 mole C_8H_9Br)	CCl_3CH_2OH (12–16 g.); $C_6H_5CH{=}CH_2$ (6 g.); $[C_6H_5(CH_2)_2—]_2$ (1–2 g.)	*64*
CCl_3CHO	$2,5\text{-}(CH_3)_2C_6H_3MgBr$	$CCl_3[2,5\text{-}(CH_3)_2C_6H_3]CHOH$ (53%)	*297*
CCl_3CHO (0.25 mole)	$C_6H_5(CH_2)_3MgBr$ (0.25 mole $C_9H_{11}Br$)	CCl_3CH_2OH (13–18 g.); $C_6H_5CH_2CH{=}CH_2$ (12 g.); $[C_6H_5(CH_2)_3—]_2$ (3–7 g.)	*64*

* "Normal" addition; the same products were obtained in somewhat higher yields when "inverse" addition was employed.

† "Normal" addition.

‡ "Inverse" addition.

§ Probably attributable to atmospheric oxygen contamination of the Grignard reagent (see *textual* discussion of alkoxide reduction p. 158).

TABLE VI-XVII (Continued)

Aldehyde	RMgX	Product(s)	Ref.
C_2HOCl_3 (*cont.*)			
CCl_3CHO (0.25 mole)	$C_6H_5(CH_2)_4MgBr$ (0.25 mole $C_{10}H_{13}Br$)	CCl_3CH_2OH (16–18 g.); $C_6H_5(CH_2)_2CH{=}CH_2$ (29–34 g. as bromide); $[C_6H_5(CH_2)_4{-}]_2$ (3 g.)	*64*
C_2HOF_3			
CF_3CHO (0.2–0.3 mole)	CH_3MgI (0.4–0.6 mole)	$CF_3(CH_3)CHOH$ (67.0%)	*436*
CF_3CHO (0.2–0.3 mole)	C_2H_5MgI (0.4–0.6 mole)	$CF_3(C_2H_5)CHOH$ (60.0%); CF_3CH_2OH (20.0%)	*436*
CF_3CHO (0.2–0.3 mole)	i-C_3H_7MgBr (0.4–0.6 mole)	CF_3CH_2OH (87.0%)	*436*
CF_3CHO (0.2–0.3 mole)	t-C_4H_9MgCl (0.4–0.6 mole)	$CF_3(t\text{-}C_4H_9)CHOH$ (7.0%); CF_3CH_2OH (84.0%)	*436*
CF_3CHO (0.2–0.3 mole)	C_6H_5MgBr (0.4–0.6 mole)	$CF_3(C_6H_5)CHOH$ (88.0%)	*436*
CF_3CHO (0.2–0.3 mole)	$C_6H_5CH_2MgBr$ (0.4–0.6 mole)	$CF_3(C_6H_5CH_2)CHOH$ (81.0%)	*436*
$C_2H_2OCl_2$			
$CHCl_2CHO$	CH_3MgBr	$CHCl_2(CH_3)CHOH$ (57.4%)	*362*
C_2H_3OCl			
$ClCH_2CHO$	$({\equiv}CMgBr)_2$	$ClCH_2(HC{\equiv}C)CHOH$	*391*
$ClCH_2CHO$	$H_2C{=}CHCH_2MgBr$	$ClCH_2(H_2C{=}CHCH_2)CHOH$ (40%)	*26*
$ClCH_2CHO$ (40 g.)	4-BrC_6H_4MgBr (118 g. $C_6H_4Br_2$)	$ClCH_2(4\text{-}BrC_6H_4)CHOH$ (40%)	*26*
C_2H_4O			
CH_3CHO	CH_3MgI	$(CH_3)_2CHOH$ (67%)	*121*
CH_3CHO	$({\equiv}CMgBr)_2$	$[{\equiv}CCH(CH_3)OH]_2$ (<70%)	*370,150,418*
CH_3CHO	$({\equiv}CMgBr)_2$	$CH_3(HC{\equiv}C)CHOH$ (20–23%)	*392*
CH_3CHO (0.25 mole) + $(C_6H_5)_2CO$ (0.50 mole)	$({\equiv}CMgBr)_2$	$CH_3CH(OH)C{\equiv}CC(C_6H_5)_2OH$ (17 g., 27%); $[{\equiv}CC(C_6H_5)_2OH]$ (61 g.)	*294*

TABLE VI-XVII (Continued)

Aldehyde	RMgX	Product(s)	Ref.
C_2H_4O (*cont.*)			
CH_3CHO (44 g.)	C_2H_5MgBr (115 g. C_2H_5Br)	$CH_3(C_2H_5)CHOH$ (80%)	*49*
CH_3CHO (from 300 g. paraldehyde)	C_2H_5MgBr (680 g. C_2H_5Br)	$CH_3(C_2H_5)CHOH$ (275 g., 67%)	*363,375*
CH_3CHO	$HC \equiv CCH_2MgBr$	$CH_3(HC \equiv CCH_2)CHOH$ (50%)	*449*
CH_3CHO	$H_2C = CHCH_2MgCl$	$CH_3(H_2C = CHCH_2)CHOH$ (57%)	*424*
CH_3CHO	$H_2C = CHCH_2MgBr$	$CH_3(H_2C = CHCH_2)CHOH$ (with 2 equiv. CH_3CHO, 40%; 1.5 equiv. CH_3CHO, 44–45%; 1.2 equiv. CH_3CHO, 49.5%)	*258*
CH_3CHO	$H_2C = CHCH_2Br$ + Mg	$CH_3(H_2C = CHCH_2)CHOH$ (12–20%)	*262*
CH_3CHO	$H_2C = CHCH_2Br$ + Mg	$CH_3(H_2C = CHCH_2)CHOH$ (55%)	*311*
CH_3CHO	n-C_3H_7MgBr	$CH_3(n$-$C_3H_7)CHOH$ (50%)	*169,341,375*
CH_3CHO (from 300 g. paraldehyde)	n-C_3H_7MgBr (from 768 g. bromide)	$CH_3(n$-$C_3H_7)CHOH$ (76%)*	*363*
CH_3CHO	i-C_3H_7MgBr	$CH_3(i$-$C_3H_7)CHOH$ (53–54%)	*80,255*
CH_3CHO	$H_2C = CHC \equiv CMgBr$	$CH_3(H_2C = CHC \equiv C)CHOH$ (57%)	*244*
CH_3CHO	Pyrryl-MgBr	1,1-Di-2-pyrrylethane; 1-(2-pyrryl)-1-(2-pyrrilidene)ethane	*256*
CH_3CHO	$H_2C = C(CH_3)CH_2MgCl$	$CH_3[H_2C = C(CH_3)CH_2]CHOH$ (65%)	*312*
CH_3CHO (50 g.)	$H_2C = C(CH_3)CH_2Cl$ (90 g.) + Mg (24 g.)	$CH_3[H_2C = C(CH_3)CH_2]CHOH$ (*ca.* 20 g. crude)	*171*
CH_3CHO	Butenyl-MgBr†	$CH_3[H_2C = CHCH(CH_3)]CHOH$ (<25%)	*258*
CH_3CHO	Butenyl-MgBr‡	$CH_3[H_2C = CHCH(CH_3)]CHOH$ (*ca.* 84%); octadienes. [*No* $CH_3(CH_3CH = CHCH_2)CHOH$]	*283*
CH_3CHO (100 g.)	$(CH_3)_2C = CHMgBr$ (195 g. C_4H_7Br)	$CH_3[(CH_3)_2C = CH]CHOH$ (20 g.); $(CH_3)_2C = CH_2$; C_2H_5OH	*189*

* Aldehyde vapor led into Grignard reagent solution in stream of nitrogen.

† From crotyl bromide ($CH_3CH = CHCH_2Br$).

‡ From 80% $CH_3CH = CHCH_2Br$, 20% $H_2C = CHCHBrCH_3$.

TABLE VI-XVII (Continued)

Aldehyde	RMgX	Product(s)	Ref.
C_2H_4O (*cont.*)			
CH_3CHO	n-C_4H_9MgBr	$CH_3(n$-$C_4H_9)CHOH$ (54%)	*333,58,254, 341*
CH_3CHO	n-C_4H_9MgI	$CH_3(n$-$C_4H_9)CHOH$ (*ca.* 10%)	*375*
CH_3CHO	i-C_4H_9MgCl	$CH_3(i$-$C_4H_9)CHOH$	*114*
CH_3CHO	i-C_4H_9MgBr	$CH_3(i$-$C_4H_9)CHOH$ (49%)	*47,327,375*
CH_3CHO	$(CH_3)_3SiCH_2MgCl$	$CH_3[(CH_3)_3SiCH_2]CHOH$	*357*
CH_3CHO (33 g.)	$H_2C{=}C(CH_3)C{\equiv}CMgBr$ (from 84 g. C_2H_5Br)	$CH_3[H_2C{=}C(CH_3)C{\equiv}C]CHOH$ (56 g.)	*244*
CH_3CHO	$(CH_3)_2C{=}C(CH_3)MgBr$	$CH_3[(CH_3)_2C{=}C(CH_3)]CHOH$	*191*
CH_3CHO	$(CH_2)_4CHMgCl$	$CH_3[(CH_2)_4CH]CHOH$ (33%)	*429,85*
CH_3CHO	$(CH_2)_4CHMgBr$	$CH_3[(CH_2)_4CH]CHOH$	*428*
CH_3CHO	n-$C_5H_{11}MgBr$	$CH_3(n$-$C_5H_{11})CHOH$	*135*
CH_3CHO	i-$C_5H_{11}MgBr$	$CH_3(i$-$C_5H_{11})CHOH$ (60–85%)*	*326*
CH_3CHO	$CH_3(C_2H_5)CHCH_2MgBr$	$CH_3[CH_3(C_2H_5)CHCH_2]CHOH$	*63*
CH_3CHO	t-$C_5H_{11}MgCl$	$CH_3(t$-$C_5H_{11})CHOH$ (36%)	*84*
CH_3CHO	t-$C_5H_{11}MgBr$	$CH_3(t$-$C_5H_{11})CHOH$	*355*
CH_3CHO	4-BrC_6H_4MgBr	$CH_3(4$-$BrC_6H_4)CHOH$ (75%)	*277,152*
CH_3CHO (80 g., 1.365 mole)	3-ClC_6H_4MgBr (229 g., 1.2 mole C_6H_4BrCl)	$CH_3(3$-$ClC_6H_4)CHOH$ (154.5–164.5 g., 82.5–88.0%)	*259*
CH_3CHO (56.5 g.)	4-FC_6H_4MgBr (209.8 g. C_6H_4BrF)	$CH_3(4$-$FC_6H_4)CHOH$ (110.5 g., 66%)	*15*
CH_3CHO	C_6H_5MgBr	$CH_3(C_6H_5)CHOH$ (<93%)	*105*
CH_3CHO (45 g.)	C_6H_5MgBr (75 g. C_6H_5Br)	$CH_3COC_6H_5$ (*ca.* 60*x*%); $CH_3(C_6H_5)CHBr$	*446,447*
CH_3CHO	C_6H_5MgBr	$CH_3(C_6H_5)CHOH$ (optically active, 1.33°; after 24 hrs., 0.33°)†	*28*

* Tuot (*326*) reports the yields for a series of carbinol preparations as varying from 60–85%.

† Grignard reagent prepared in *N,N*-dimethylbornylamine; condensed with aldehyde in benzene.

TABLE VI-XVII (Continued)

Aldehyde	RMgX	Product(s)	Ref.
C_2H_4O (*cont.*)			
CH_3CHO	C_6H_5MgBr	$C_6H_5CH(CH_3)OH$ (60–88%); (optically inactive)*	*313*
CH_3CHO	$(CH_2)_5CHMgCl$	$CH_3[(CH_2)_5CH]CHOH$ ("yield excellent")	*35*
CH_3CHO	$(CH_2)_5CHMgBr$	$CH_3[(CH_2)_5CH]CHOH$	*385,440*
CH_3CHO	2-Br-4-$F_3CC_6H_3MgBr$	CH_3(2-Br-4-$F_3CC_6H_3$)CHOH	*15*
CH_3CHO (9.5 g.)	3-F_3C-4-FC_6H_3MgBr (42.0 g. $C_7H_3BrF_4$)	CH_3(3-F_3C-4-FC_6H_3)CHOH (22.0 g., 61%)	*15*
CH_3CHO	3-$F_3CC_6H_4MgBr$	CH_3(3-$F_3CC_6H_4$)CHOH (83%)	*259*
CH_3CHO	$C_6H_5CH_2MgCl$	$CH_3(C_6H_5CH_2)CHOH$ (65.6%)	*356,305,195*
CH_3CHO (*ca.* 0.3 mole)	$C_6H_5CH_2MgCl$ (*ca.* 0.4 mole)	$CH_3(C_6H_5CH_2)CHOH$ (32%); 2-$CH_3CH(OH)C_6H_4CH_2CH(OH)CH_3$ (29%)	*454*
CH_3CHO	3-$CH_3C_6H_4MgBr$	CH_3(3-$CH_3C_6H_4$)CHOH (71%)	*259*
CH_3CHO	4-$CH_3C_6H_4MgBr$	CH_3(4-$CH_3C_6H_4$)CHOH	*205*
CH_3CHO	*n*-$C_5H_{11}C\equiv CMgBr$ (25 g. *n*-$C_5H_{11}C\equiv CH$)	CH_3(*n*-$C_5H_{11}C\equiv C$)CHOH (12 g., crude)	*237*
CH_3CHO	$(C_2H_5O)_2CHC\equiv CMgBr$	$CH_3[(C_2H_5O)_2CHC\equiv C]CHOH$	*115,423*
CH_3CHO	$(CH_2)_5CHCH_2MgI$	$CH_3[(CH_2)_5CHCH_2]CHOH$ (40%)	*101*
CH_3CHO	2-Methylcyclohexyl-MgBr	1-Methyl-2-ethylidenecyclohexane	*241*
CH_3CHO	*n*-$C_7H_{15}MgBr$	CH_3(*n*-C_7H_{15})CHOH (80–85%)	*332*
CH_3CHO	*n*-$C_7H_{15}MgI$	CH_3(*n*-C_7H_{15})CHOH ("very little")	*375*
CH_3CHO	CH_3(*n*-C_5H_{11})CHMgBr	$CH_3[CH_3$(*n*-C_5H_{11})CH]CHOH (60%)	*2*
CH_3CHO (20 g.)	$C_6H_5C\equiv CMgBr$ (22 g. $C_6H_5\equiv CH$)	$CH_3(C_6H_5C\equiv C)CHOH$ (15 g.); recovered $C_6H_5C\equiv CH$ (7 g.)	*237,44,279*
CH_3CHO	2-$ClC_6H_4CH(CO_2MgCl)MgCl$ †	CH_3[2-$ClC_6H_4CH(CO_2H)$]CHOH (69%)	*158*

* Grignard reagent prepared in (+)-2-methoxybutane.

† In the opinion of Schlenk, Hilleman, and Rodloff, *Ann.*, *487*, 135–54 (1931), this "Grignard reagent" should be formulated as an enolate.

TABLE VI-XVII (Continued)

Aldehyde	RMgX	Product(s)	Ref.
C_2H_4O (*cont.*)			
CH_3CHO	$C_6H_5OC{\equiv}CMgBr$	$CH_3(C_6H_5OC{\equiv}C)CHOH$ (28%; 64%, crude); C_6H_5OH* (9%)	*160*
CH_3CHO †	Indolyl-MgBr	$[CH_3(\beta\text{-}C_8H_6N)CH]_2O$	*256*
CH_3CHO	Indolyl-MgBr	1,1-Bis-β-indolylethane	*376*
CH_3CHO	$C_6H_5(CH_2)_2MgBr$	$CH_3(C_6H_5CH_2CH_2)CHOH$ (85%)	*39,31*
CH_3CHO	$3\text{-}CH_3C_6H_4CH_2MgBr$	$CH_3(3\text{-}CH_3C_6H_4CH_2)CHOH$	*441*
CH_3CHO	$(CH_2)_5CHC{\equiv}CMgBr$	$CH_3[(CH_2)_5CHC{\equiv}C]CHOH$	*116*
CH_3CHO (excess)	$C_6H_5(CH_2)_3MgBr$	$CH_3[C_6H_5(CH_2)_3]CHOH$ (75%)	*438*
CH_3CHO (19.8 g.)	$(CH_3)_2C{=}CH(CH_2)_2CH(CH_3)MgBr$ (86 g. $C_8H_{15}Br$)	$CH_3[(CH_3)_2C{=}CH(CH_2)_2CH(CH_3)]CHOH$ (30 g.); $(CH_3)_2C{=}CH(CH_2)_2CH(CH_3)COCH_3$ (10 g.); $C_8H_{16} + C_8H_{14}$ (5 g.); high-boiling residue (7 g.)	*77*
CH_3CHO (220 g.)	$n\text{-}C_8H_{17}MgBr$ (970 g. $C_8H_{17}Br$)	$CH_3(n\text{-}C_8H_{17})CHOH$ (634 g., 80%)	*274*
CH_3CHO	$n\text{-}C_8H_{17}MgI$	$CH_3(n\text{-}C_8H_{17})CHOH$ ("very little")	*375*
CH_3CHO	$CH_3(n\text{-}C_6H_{13})CHMgBr$	$CH_3[CH_3(n\text{-}C_6H_{13})CH]CHOH$	*117*
CH_3CHO	1-Indenyl-MgBr	Methyl-1-indenylmethanol (71%)	*60*
CH_3CHO †	2-Methylindolyl-MgBr	$[CH_3(C_9H_8N)CH]_2O$	*256*
CH_3CHO	2-Methylindolyl-MgBr	1,1-Bis-(α-methyl-β-indolyl)ethane	*376*
CH_3CHO	$C_6H_5CH{=}CHCH_2MgCl$	$CH_3[H_2C{=}CHCH(C_6H_5)]CHOH$; $(C_6H_5CH{=}CHCH_2{-})_2$; $C_6H_5CH{=}CHCH_3$	*258*
CH_3CHO (75 g., 1.7 mole)	$3\text{-}s\text{-}C_4H_9C_6H_4MgBr$ (321 g., 7.505 mole $C_{10}H_{13}Br$)	$CH_3(3\text{-}s\text{-}C_4H_9C_6H_4)CHOH$ (150 g., 0.843 mole, 56%)	*220*
CH_3O	$3\text{-}t\text{-}C_4H_9C_6H_4MgBr$	$CH_3(3\text{-}t\text{-}C_4H_9C_6H_4)CHOH$ (56%)	*259*

* Attributed to cleavage of the $C_6H_5OC{\equiv}C^-$ ion.

† Paraldehyde reacts similarly but is less reactive.

TABLE VI-XVII (Continued)

Aldehyde	RMgX	Product(s)	Ref.
C_2H_4O (*cont.*)			
CH_3CHO	$(CH_3)_5C_6MgBr$	$CH_3[(CH_3)_5C_6]CHOH$ (5%)	*51,52*
CH_3CHO	$(CH_3)_5C_6Br + CH_3I + Mg$	$(CH_3)_6C_6$ (small am't); $(CH_3)_5C_6H$ (small am't); $(CH_3)_5C_6CHO$ (?) (20%)	*296*
CH_3CHO (120 g., 2.73 moles)	$4-(CH_2)_5CHC_6H_4MgBr$ (574 g., 2.4 moles $C_{12}H_{15}Br$)	$CH_3[4-(CH_2)_5CHC_6H_4]CHOH$ (80 g., 18%); $[4-(CH_2)_5CHC_6H_4-]_2$ (20 g., 2.6%); "polymeric residue"	*220*
CH_3CHO (0.2 mole)	$4-(C_2H_5)_3SiC_6H_4MgBr$ (0.1 mole $C_{12}H_{19}BrSi$)	$CH_3[4-(C_2H_5)_3SiC_6H_4]CHOH$ ("satisfactory yield")	*125*
CH_3CHO	9-Phenanthryl-MgBr	Methyl-9-phenanthrylmethanol (75%)	*11*
CH_3CHO	$(C_6H_5)_2C{=}CHMgBr$	$CH_3[(C_6H_5)_2C{=}CH]CHOH$	*373*
CH_3CHO (20 ml.)	$C_{16}H_{33}MgBr$* (41 g., 0.135 mole $C_{16}H_{33}Br$)	6,10,14-Trimethylpentadecanol (25.5 g., 70%)	*303*
CH_3CHO	$(C_6H_5)_3CMgCl$	"Passive"	*299*
CH_3CHO (0.077 mole)	3-Cholesteryl-MgCl (9.2 g., 0.023 mole $C_{27}H_{45}Cl$)	"Methyl-3-cholesterylcarbinol"	*18*
$(C_2H_4O)_x$			
Paraldehyde	$C_2H_5I + Mg$	$CH_3(C_2H_5)CHOH$	*416*
Paraldehyde	C_6H_5MgBr	DL-$CH_3(C_6H_5)CHOH$† (60%)	*313*
C_3HOF_5			
C_2F_5CHO (0.2–0.3 mole)	CH_3MgI (0.4–0.6 mole)	$CH_3(C_2F_5)CHOH$ (87.0%)	*436*
C_2F_5CHO (0.2–0.3 mole)	C_2H_5MgI (0.4–0.6 mole)	$C_2F_5(C_2H_5)CHOH$ (33.6%); $C_2F_5CH_2OH$ (55.5%)	*436*
$C_2F_5CHO : MgBr_2$ (0.2–0.3 mole)	C_2H_5MgI (0.4–0.6 mole)	$C_2F_5(C_2H_5)CHOH$ (58.0%) $C_2F_5CH_2OH$ (36.4%)	*436*

* i-$C_6H_{13}CH(CH_3)(CH_2)_3CH(CH_3)(CH_2)_3MgBr$.

† Grignard reagent prepared in *N,N*-dimethylbornylamine; paraldehyde added; one hour at 110–120°.

TABLE VI-XVII (Continued)

Aldehyde	RMgX	Product(s)	Ref.
C_3HOF_5 (*cont.*)			
C_2F_5CHO (0.2–0.3 mole)	i-C_3H_7MgBr (0.4–0.6 mole)	$C_2F_5CH_2OH$ (90.0%)	*436*
C_2F_5CHO (0.2–0.3 mole)	t-C_4H_9MgCl (0.4–0.6 mole)	$C_2F_5(t\text{-}C_4H_9)CHOH$ (14.3%) $C_2F_5CH_2OH$ (76.2%)	*436*
C_2F_5CHO (0.2–0.3 mole)	C_6H_5MgBr (0.4–0.6 mole)	$C_2F_5(C_6H_5)CHOH$ (86.0%)	*436*
C_2F_5CHO (0.2–0.3 mole)	$C_6H_5CH_2MgCl$ (0.4–0.6 mole)	$C_2F_5(C_6H_5CH_2)CHOH$ (83.0%)	*436*
C_3H_3OBr			
$H_2C{=}CBrCHO$	CH_3MgI	$CH_3(H_2C{=}CBr)CHOH$ ("good yield")	*199*
$H_2C{=}CBrCHO$	$({\equiv}CMgBr)_2$	$HC{\equiv}C(H_2C{=}CBr)CHOH$	*391*
$C_3H_3OBr_3$			
$BrCH_2CBr_2CHO$	$({\equiv}CMgBr)_2$	$HC{\equiv}C(H_2C{=}CBr)CHOH$	*391*
C_3H_4O			
$H_2C{=}CHCHO$ (+ hydroquinone)	CH_3MgBr	$CH_3(H_2C{=}CH)CHOH$ (52%)*	*20,272*
$H_2C{=}CHCHO$ (112 g.)	CH_3MgBr (200 g. CH_3Br)	$CH_3(H_2C{=}CH)CHOH$ (73%)	*48*
$H_2C{=}CHCHO$	CH_3MgBr	$CH_3(H_2C{=}CH)CHOH$ (80% on basis of acrolein; 64% on basis of Mg; 58% on basis of bromide)	*258*
$H_2C{=}CHCHO$ (+ 1 g. hydroquinone per mole)	CH_3MgX†	$CH_3(H_2C{=}CH)CHOH$ (52%)*	*20,68,72,361*
$H_2C{=}CHCHO$ (110 g.) (+ hydroquinone)	CH_3MgI (284 g. CH_3I)	$CH_3(H_2C{=}CH)CHOH$ (52%)	*334,66,198, 361*
$H_2C{=}CHCHO$	$({\equiv}CMgBr)_2$	$[{\equiv}CCH(OH)CH{=}CH_2]_2$	*81,420*

* Without hydroquinone stabilization the yield of alcohol was *ca.* 25%.
† X = Br, I.

TABLE VI-XVII (Continued)

Aldehyde	RMgX	Product(s)	Ref.
C_3H_4O (*cont.*)			
$H_2C{=}CHCHO$	$({\equiv}CMgBr)_2$	$HC{\equiv}C(H_2C{=}CH)CHOH$	*391*
$H_2C{=}CHCHO$ (25 g.)	$({\equiv}CMgBr)_2$ (50 g. Mg)	$HC{\equiv}C(H_2C{=}CH)CHOH$ (11 g.); $[{\equiv}CCH(OH)CH{=}CH_2]_2$ (*ca.* 2 g.)	*393*
$H_2C{=}CHCHO$ (28 g.)	$({\equiv}CMgBr)_2$ (12 g. Mg)	$[{\equiv}CCH(OH)CH{=}CH_2]_2$ (10 g.); $(H_2C{=}CHCHO)_x$ (15 g.)	*394*
$H_2C{=}CHCHO$ (100 g.)	C_2H_5MgBr (80 g. Mg)	$H_2C{=}CH(C_2H_5)CHOH$ (122 g.); colored residue (20 g.)	*185*
$H_2C{=}CHCHO$	C_2H_5MgBr	$H_2C{=}CH(C_2H_5)CHOH$ (65%)	*272,33*
$H_2C{=}CHCHO$ (1.00 mole)	C_2H_5MgBr (1.85 mole)	$H_2C{=}CH(C_2H_5)CHOH$ (57.4%)*	*70,67,72*
$H_2C{=}CHCHO$	$H_2C{=}CHCH_2MgBr$	$H_2C{=}CH_2(CH_2{=}CHCH_2)CHOH$ (35–40%)	*258*
$H_2C{=}CHCHO$	n-C_3H_7MgBr	$H_2C{=}CH(n$-$C_3H_7)CHOH$ (60%)	*272,33,249*
$H_2C{=}CHCHO$	n-C_3H_7MgBr	$H_2C{=}CH(n$-$C_3H_7)CHOH$ (41%)	*68,72*
$H_2C{=}CHCHO$	i-C_3H_7MgBr	$H_2C{=}CH(i$-$C_3H_7)CHOH$ (15%)	*33*
$H_2C{=}CHCHO$	Butenyl-MgBr †	$H_2C{=}CH[H_2C{=}CHCH(CH_3)]CHOH$ (<25%)	*258*
$H_2C{=}CHCHO$	n-C_4H_9MgBr	$H_2C{=}CH(n$-$C_4H_9)CHOH$ (45%)	*272,33*
$H_2C{=}CHCHO$	n-C_4H_9MgBr	$H_2C{=}CH(n$-$C_4H_9)CHOH$ (35%)	*68,72*
$H_2C{=}CHCHO$	i-C_4H_9MgBr	$H_2C{=}CH(i$-$C_4H_9)CHOH$	*33*
$H_2C{=}CHCHO$ (56.0 g., 1 mole)	$CH_3O(CH_2)_3MgCl$ (108.6 g. C_4H_9ClO)	$H_2C{=}CH[CH_3O(CH_2)_3]CHOH$ (60.0 g., 46%)	*409*
$H_2C{=}CHCHO$	n-$C_5H_{11}MgBr$	$H_2C{=}CH(n$-$C_5H_{11})CHOH$ (46%)	*118*
$H_2C{=}CHCHO$	i-$C_5H_{11}MgBr$	$H_2C{=}CH(i$-$C_5H_{11})CHOH$ (59%)	*72*
$H_2C{=}CHCHO$ (40 g.)	C_6H_5MgBr	$H_2C{=}CH(C_6H_5)CHOH$ (50 g.)	*179,41,69, 185,238*
$H_2C{=}CHCHO$	n-$C_6H_{13}MgBr$	$H_2C{=}CH(n$-$C_6H_{13})CHOH$ (94%)	*72*

* Maximum yield; smaller excess of Grignard reagent or excess of aldehyde gave lower yields.

† From crotyl bromide ($CH_3CH{=}CHCH_2Br$); see Chapter XVII, Allylic Rearrangements in Grignard Reactions.

TABLE VI-XVII (Continued)

Aldehyde	RMgX	Product(s)	Ref.
C_3H_4O (*cont.*)			
$H_2C{=}CHCHO$	$C_6H_5CH_2MgX$*	$H_2C{=}CH(C_6H_5CH_2)CHOH$ (*ca.* 5%)	*69; cf. 61*
$H_2C{=}CHCHO$	2-$CH_3C_6H_4MgBr$	$H_2C{=}CH(2\text{-}CH_3C_6H_4)CHOH$ (55%)	*69*
$H_2C{=}CHCHO$ (14 g.)	4-$CH_3C_6H_4MgBr$ (43 g. C_7H_7Br	$H_2C{=}CH(4\text{-}CH_3C_6H_4)CHOH$ (20 g.); $(4\text{-}CH_3C_6H_4{-})_2$	*41*
$H_2C{=}CHCHO$	4-$CH_3C_6H_4MgBr$	$H_2C{=}CH(4\text{-}CH_3C_6H_4)CHOH$ (57%)	*69*
$H_2C{=}CHCHO$	$(C_2H_5O)_2CHC{\equiv}CMgBr$	$H_2C{=}CH[(CH_2H_5O)_2CHC{\equiv}C]CHOH$	*423*
$H_2C{=}CHCHO$	$C_6H_5(CH_2)_2MgBr$	$H_2C{=}CH[C_6H_5(CH_2)_2]CHOH$ (>57%)	*69*
$H_2C{=}CHCHO$	$C_6H_5(CH_2)_3MgBr$	$H_2C{=}CH[C_6H_5(CH_2)_3]CHOH$ (57%)	*69*
$C_3H_4OCl_2$			
$ClCH_2CHClCHO$	$({\equiv}CMgBr)_2$	$HC{\equiv}C(ClCH_2CHCl)CHOH$	*391*
C_3H_5OCl			
$ClCH_2CH_2CHO$	CH_3MgI	$CH_3(ClCH_2CH_2)CHOH$	*98,86*
$ClCH_2CH_2CHO$	$({\equiv}CMgBr)_2$	$HC{\equiv}C(ClCH_2CH_2)CHOH$	*391*
$ClCH_2CH_2CHO$	C_2H_5MgBr	$ClCH_2CH_2(C_2H_5)CHOH$	*98*
$ClCH_2CH_2CHO$	n-C_3H_7MgBr	$ClCH_2CH_2(n\text{-}C_3H_7)CHOH$	*98,16*
$ClCH_2CH_2CHO$	i-$C_5H_{11}MgBr$	$ClCH_2CH_2(i\text{-}C_5H_{11})CHOH$	*98*
$ClCH_2CH_2CHO$ (8.3 g., 0.09 mole)	4-$ClC_{10}H_6$-1-MgI (28.9 g., 0.1 mole $C_{10}H_6ICl$)	$ClCH_2CH_2(4\text{-}Cl\text{-}1\text{-}C_{10}H_6)CHOH$	*161*
$ClCH_2CH_2CHO$	4-$CH_3OC_{10}H_6$-1-$MgBr$	$ClCH_2CH_2(4\text{-}CH_3O\text{-}1\text{-}C_{10}H_6)CHOH$	*161*
C_3H_6O			
C_2H_5CHO	$({\equiv}CMgBr)_2$	$[{\equiv}CCH(OH)C_2H_5]_2$ (<70%)	*370*
C_2H_5CHO	$({\equiv}CMgBr)_2$	$HC{\equiv}C(C_2H_5)CHOH$	*392*
C_2H_5CHO (58.0 g., 1.0 mole)	$H_2C{=}CHCH_2MgCl$ (40.0 g. Mg)	$C_2H_5(H_2C{=}CHCH_2)CHOH$ (78.2 g., 0.782 mole, 78%)	*411*

*X = Br, Cl.

TABLE VI-XVII (Continued)

Aldehyde	RMgX	Product(s)	Ref.
C_3H_6O (*cont.*)			
C_2H_5CHO	$H_2C{=}CHCH_2MgBr$	$C_2H_5(H_2C{=}CHCH_2)CHOH$ (62%, crude; 52%, purified)	*136,258*
C_2H_5CHO	Butenyl-MgBr*	$C_2H_5[CH_2{=}CHCH(CH_3)]CHOH$ (25%)	*258*
C_2H_5CHO	s-C_4H_9MgCl	$C_2H_5(s$-$C_4H_9)CHOH$ (65%)	*83*
C_2H_5CHO (1.65 mole)	t-C_4H_9MgCl (5 moles C_4H_9Cl)	$C_2H_5(t$-$C_4H_9)CHOH$ (60%)	*84*
C_2H_5CHO	t-C_4H_9MgCl	$C_2H_5(t$-$C_4H_9)CHOH$ (26%)	*359,385*
C_2H_5CHO (116 g.)	$CH_3O(CH_2)_3MgCl$ (202 g. C_4H_9ClO)	$C_2H_5[CH_3O(CH_2)_3]CHOH$	*87*
C_2H_5CHO	$(CH_2)_4CHMgBr$	$C_2H_5[(CH_2)_4CH]CHOH$ (19.5%)	*85*
C_2H_5CHO (60 g.)	4-BrC_6H_4MgBr	$C_2H_5(4$-$BrC_6H_4)CHOH$ (95–100 g.)	*277*
C_2H_5CHO	C_6H_5MgBr	$C_2H_5(C_6H_5)CHOH$	*247*
C_2H_5CHO	n-$C_6H_{13}MgI$	$C_2H_5(n$-$C_6H_{13})CHOH$ (*ca.* 50%)	*106*
C_2H_5CHO (128 g.)	3-$F_3CC_6H_4MgBr$ (450 g. $C_7H_4BrF_3$)	$C_2H_5(3$-$F_3CC_6H_4)CHOH$ (300 g., 73%)	*15*
C_2H_5CHO	2-$CH_3C_6H_4MgBr$	$C_2H_5(2$-$CH_3C_6H_4)CHOH$	*206*
C_2H_5CHO	3-$CH_3C_6H_4MgBr$	$C_2H_5(3$-$CH_3C_6H_4)CHOH$	*206*
C_2H_5CHO (0.50 mole)	$C_6H_5CH_2MgCl$ (0.57 mole)	$C_2H_5(C_6H_5CH_2)CHOH$ (35%); 2-$C_2H_5CH(OH)C_6H_4CH_2CH(OH)C_2H_5$ (62%)	*454*
C_2H_5CHO	$C_6H_5C{\equiv}CMgX$	$C_2H_5(C_6H_5C{\equiv}C)CHOH$ (52%)	*215*
C_2H_5CHO	$(CH_3)_2C{=}CH(CH_2)_2CH(CH_3)MgBr$	$C_2H_5[(CH_3)_2C{=}CH(CH_2)_2CH(CH_3)]CHOH$	*77*
C_2H_5CHO	1-Indenyl-MgBr	Ethyl-1-indenylmethanol (61%)	*60*
C_2H_5CHO (16 g.)	4-$CH_3CH{=}CHC_6H_4MgBr$	$C_2H_5(4$-$CH_3CH{=}CHC_6H_4)CHOH$ (10 g.)	*278*
C_2H_5CHO (25.7 g.)	2-$C_6H_5C_6H_4MgBr$ (51.5 g. $C_{12}H_9Br$)	$C_2H_5(2$-$C_6H_5C_6H_4)CHOH$ (25.0 g., 60%)	*430*
C_2H_5CHO (0.2 mole)	4-$(C_2H_5)_3SiC_6H_4MgBr$ (0.1 mole $C_{12}H_{19}BrSi$)	$C_2H_5[4$-$(C_2H_5)_3SiC_6H_4]CHOH$ ("very poor yield")	*125*

* From crotyl bromide ($CH_3CH{=}CHCH_2Br$).

TABLE VI-XVII (Continued)

Aldehyde	RMgX	Product(s)	Ref.
C_4HOF_7			
n-C_3F_7CHO (0.2–0.3 mole)	C_2H_5MgI (0.4–0.6 mole)	$C_2H_5(n\text{-}C_3F_7)CHOH$ (19.0%); n-$C_3F_7CH_2OH$ (61.0%)	*436*
$C_4H_2O_3Br_2$			
$HO_2CCBr{=}CBrCHO$ (10.4 g.)	CH_3MgI (26.5 g.)	3,4-Dibromo-5-methyldihydrofuran-2-one ("not over 50%")	*302*
$HO_2CCBr{=}CBrCHO$	C_2H_5MgBr	3,4-Dibromo-5-ethyldihydrofuran-2-one ("not over 50%")	*302*
$C_4H_2O_3Cl_2$			
$HO_2CCCl{=}CClCHO$	CH_3MgI	3,4-Dichloro-5-methyldihydrofuran-2-one	*302*
$HO_2CCCl{=}CClCHO$	C_2H_5MgBr	3,4-Dichloro-5-ethyldihydrofuran-2-one	*302*
$C_4H_5OCl_3$			
$CH_3CHClCCl_2CHO$ (0.25 mole)	2-Thienyl-MgBr (0.25 mole C_4H_3BrS)	$CH_3CHClCCl_2(\alpha\text{-}C_4H_3S)CHOH$ (48 g., 74%)	*97*
$CH_3CHClCCl_2CHO$ (0.25 mole)	C_6H_5MgBr (0.25 mole C_6H_5Br)	$CH_3CHClCCl_2(C_6H_5)CHOH$ (45 g., 71.1%); $CH_3CHClCCl_2CHO \cdot H_2O$ (5 g.); $(C_6H_5—)_2$ (1.3 g.); residue (2.0 g.)	*96*
$CH_3CHClCCl_2CHO$ (0.25 mole)	$(CH_2)_5CHMgBr$ (0.25 mole $C_6H_{11}Br$)	$CH_3CHClCCl_2CHO \cdot H_2O$ (8.5–9.0 g.); $CH_3CHClCCl_2CH_2OH$ (22.5–23.0 g.); C_6H_{10} (26.0–27.5 g. $C_6H_{10}Br_2$); tar (3.0–4.0 g.)	*96*
$CH_3CHClCCl_2CHO$ (0.25 mole)	n-$C_6H_{13}MgBr$ (0.25 mole $C_6H_{13}Br$)	$CH_3CHClCCl_2CHO \cdot H_2O$ (6.0–7.0 g.); $CH_3CHClCCl_2CH_2OH$ (27.0–28.5 g.); C_6H_{12} (31.5–33.0 g. $C_6H_{12}Br_2$); tar (2.5–4.0 g.)	*96*
$CH_3CHClCCl_2CHO$ (0.25 mole)	$C_6H_5CH_2MgCl$ (0.25 mole C_6H_7Cl)	$CH_3CHClCCl_2CHO \cdot H_2O$ (15.5 g.); $(C_6H_5CH_2—)_2$ (13.7 g.); tar (14.0 g.)	*96*

TABLE VI-XVII (Continued)

Aldehyde	RMgX	Product(s)	Ref.
$C_4H_5OCl_3$ (*cont.*)			
$CH_3CHClCCl_2CHO$	$C_6H_5C{\equiv}CMgBr$	$CH_3CHClCCl_2(C_6H_5C{\equiv}C)CHOH$ (70%)	*148*
$CH_3CHClCCl_2CHO$ (0.25 mole)	$C_6H_5(CH_2)_2MgBr$ (0.25 mole C_8H_9Br)	$CH_3CHClCCl_2CHO{\cdot}H_2O$ (5.0–6.0 g.); $CH_3CHClCCl_2CH_2OH$ (21.5–22.5 g.); C_8H_8 (32.0–33.0 g. $C_8H_8Br_2$); tar (6.5–7.0 g.)	*96*
C_4H_6O			
$CH_3CH{=}CHCHO$ (142 g., 2.02 moles)	CH_3MgCl (61 g. Mg)	$CH_3(CH_3CH{=}CH)CHOH$ (81–86%)	*53*
$CH_3CH{=}CHCHO$	CH_3MgBr	$CH_3(CH_3CH{=}CH)CHOH$ (30%)	*240,146,343*
$CH_3CH{=}CHCHO$	CH_3MgI	$CH_3(CH_3CH{=}CH)CHOH$	*121,59,281*
$CH_3CH{=}CHCHO$	CH_3MgI	$CH_3(CH_3CH{=}CH)CHOH$ (90%)	*194*
$CH_3CH{=}CHCHO$ (25 g.)	$({\equiv}CMgBr)_2$ (50 g. Mg)	$HC{\equiv}C(CH_3CH{=}CH)CHOH$ (10 g.)*	*393,395*
$CH_3CH{=}CHCHO$ (35 g.)	$({\equiv}CMgBr)_2$ (12 g. Mg)	$[{\equiv}CCH(OH)CH{=}CHCH_3]_2$ (30 g., crude)	*397,81,420*
$CH_3CH{=}CHCHO$	C_2H_5MgBr	$C_2H_5(CH_3CH{=}CH)CHOH$ (65%)	*280,146,281, 343*
$CH_3CH{=}CHCHO$	C_2H_5MgBr (excess)	$C_2H_5(CH_3CH{=}CH)CHOH$ (70.3%); $CH_3(C_2H_5)CHCH_2CHO$ (0.1%); "complex products" (11.4%)	*309,272*
$CH_3CH{=}CHCHO$	C_2H_5MgBr	$C_2H_5(CH_3CH{=}CH)CHOH$ (90%)	*194*
$CH_3CH{=}CHCHO$	$H_2C{=}CHCH_2MgBr$	$CH_3CH{=}CH(H_2C{=}CHCH_2)CHOH$ (82%, crude)	*136,82,181, 258,264*
$CH_3CH{=}CHCHO$	$H_2C{=}CHCH_2MgBr$ (excess)	$H_2C{=}CHCH_2(CH_3CH{=}CH)CHOH$; $CH_3(H_2C{=}CHCH_2)CHCH_2CHO$ (trace)	*309*
$CH_3CH{=}CHCHO$	n-C_3H_7MgCl	$CH_3CH{=}CH(n\text{-}C_3H_7)CHOH$ (74%)	*6*
$CH_3CH{=}CHCHO$	n-C_3H_7MgBr	$CH_3CH{=}CH(n\text{-}C_3H_7)CHOH$ (46%)	*240,146,280, 281,343*

* Hydrolysis with NH_4Cl; acid isomerizes the product (see: Jones and McCombie, *J. Chem. Soc.*, *1943*, 261–4).

TABLE VI-XVII (Continued)

Aldehyde	RMgX	Product(s)	Ref.
C_4H_6O (*cont.*)			
$CH_3CH{=}CHCHO$	*n*-C_3H_7MgBr (excess)	$CH_3CH{=}CH$(*n*-C_3H_7)$CHOH$ (78.3%); CH_3(*n*-C_3H_7)$CHCH_2CHO$ (trace); "complex products" (7.6%)	*309*
$CH_3CH{=}CHCHO$	*i*-C_3H_7MgBr	$CH_3CH{=}CH$(*i*-C_3H_7)$CHOH$ (*ca.* 30%)	*281,343,350*
$CH_3CH{=}CHCHO$	*i*-C_3H_7MgBr (excess)	$CH_3CH{=}CH$(*i*-C_3H_7)$CHOH$ (46.5%); CH_3(*i*-C_3H_7)$CHCH_2CHO$ (0.3%); "complex products" (34.1%)	*309*
$CH_3CH{=}CHCHO$ (19 g.)	$H_2C{=}CHC{\equiv}CMgBr$ (23 g. C_4H_4)	$CH_3CH{=}CH(H_2C{=}CHC{\equiv}C)CHOH$ (12 g.)	*406*
$CH_3CH{=}CHCHO$	*n*-C_4H_9MgBr	$CH_3CH{=}CH$(*n*-C_4H_9)$CHOH$ (51%)	*240*
$CH_3CH{=}CHCHO$	*i*-C_4H_9MgBr	$CH_3CH{=}CH$(*i*-C_4H_9)$CHOH$ (*ca.* 30%)	*281,343*
$CH_3CH{=}CHCHO$ (10 g.)	*i*-C_4H_9MgBr (22 g. C_4H_9Br)	$CH_3CH{=}CH$(*i*-C_4H_9)$CHOH$ (3.4 g., crude); $CH_3CH{=}CHCH_2OH$ (trace); residue (2.1 g.); slow C_4H_8-evolution*	*138,281*
$CH_3CH{=}CHCHO$ (10 g.)	*i*-C_4H_9MgBr (22 g. C_4H_9Br)	$CH_3CH{=}CH$(*i*-C_4H_9)$CHOH$ (2.7 g., crude); $CH_3CH{=}CHCH_2OH$ (2.0 g., crude); residue (2.8 g.); C_4H_8 †	*138*
$CH_3CH{=}CHCHO$ (10 g.)	*i*-C_4H_9MgI (29 g. C_4H_9I)	$CH_3CH{=}CH$(*i*-C_4H_9)$CHOH$ (0.5 g., pure); $CH_3CH{=}CHCH_2OH$ (1.0 g., crude); residue (6.0 g.); C_4H_8	*138*
$CH_3CH{=}CHCHO$ (10 g.)	*s*-C_4H_9MgBr (22 g. C_4H_9Br)	$CH_3CH{=}CH$(*s*-C_4H_9)$CHOH$ (9 g. pure); *no* olefin; *no* $CH_3CH{=}CHCH_2OH$ ‡	*138*

* One and one-half hour at room temperature.

† One hour reflux Hess and Wustrow (*138*) report other similar experiments in various solvents and at various temperatures.

‡ Reaction at 0°.

TABLE VI-XVII (Continued)

Aldehyde	RMgX	Product(s)	Ref.
C_4H_6O (*cont.*)			
$CH_3CH{=}CHCHO$ (10 g.)	s-C_4H_9MgBr (22 g. C_4H_9Br)	$CH_3CH{=}CH(s\text{-}C_4H_9)CHOH$ (2.8 g., crude); $CH_3CH{=}CHCH_2OH$ (1.1 g., crude); residue (1.6 g.); slow C_4H_8-evolution*	*138*
$CH_3CH{=}CHCHO$ (10 g.)	s-C_4H_9MgBr (22 g. C_4H_9Br)	$CH_3CH{=}CHCH_2OH$ (0.6 g., crude); $(CH_3CH{=}CHCH_2)_2O$; other high-boiling products; C_4H_8 (*ca.* 1.1 l.)†	*138*
$CH_3CH{=}CHCHO$	t-C_4H_9MgCl	$CH_3CH{=}CH(t\text{-}C_4H_9)CHOH$ (3.4%)	*240*
$CH_3CH{=}CHCHO$ (20 g.)	t-C_4H_9MgCl (75 g. C_4H_9Cl)	$CH_3CH{=}CH(t\text{-}C_4H_9)CHOH$ (30.6%); $CH_3(t\text{-}C_4H_9)CHCH_2CHO$ (20.3%); "complex products" (39.3%)	*308,309*
$CH_3CH{=}CHCHO$	t-C_4H_9MgBr	$CH_3CH{=}CH(t\text{-}C_4H_9)CHOH$ (3%); $CH_3(t\text{-}C_4H_9)CHCH_2CHO$ (10.8%); "complex products" (55.4%)	*309*
$CH_3CH{=}CHCHO$ (63 g.)	$H_2C{=}C(CH_3)C{\equiv}CMgBr$ (67 g. C_5H_6)	$CH_3CH{=}CH[H_2C{=}C(CH_3)C{\equiv}C]CHOH$ (58 g.)	*406*
$CH_3CH{=}CHCHO$	i-$C_5H_{11}MgBr$	$CH_3CH{=}CH(i\text{-}C_5H_{11})CHOH$ (45%)	*121,343*
$CH_3CH{=}CHCHO$ (28 g.)	t-$C_5H_{11}MgCl$ (86 g. $C_5H_{11}Cl$)	$CH_3CH{=}CH(t\text{-}C_5H_{11})CHOH$ (16.3%); $CH_3(t\text{-}C_5H_{11})CHCH_2CHO$ (22.6%); "complex products" (45.7%)	*309*
$CH_3CH{=}CHCHO$	C_6H_5MgBr (excess)	$CH_3CH{=}CH(C_6H_5)CHOH$ (*ca.* 90%); $CH_3(C_6H_5)CHCH_2CHO$ (0.1%); "complex products" (7.1%)	*309*
$CH_3CH{=}CHCHO$ (35 g.)	C_6H_5MgBr (94 g. C_6H_5Br)	$CH_3CH{=}CH(C_6H_5)CHOH$ (51 g., 70%)	*40,61*
$CH_3CH{=}CHCHO$ (18 g.)	$CH_3CH{=}C(CH_3)C{\equiv}CMgBr$ (20 g. C_6H_8)	$CH_3CH{=}CH[CH_3CH{=}C(CH_3)C{\equiv}C]CHOH$ (31 g., 80%)	*407*

* Twenty-four hours at room temperature.
† Removal of ether; one hour at 110°.

TABLE VI-XVII (Continued)

Aldehyde	RMgX	Product(s)	Ref.
C_4H_6O (*cont.*)			
$CH_3CH{=}CHCHO$ (8.8 g.)	$CH_3CH{=}CHCH(OMgBr)C{\equiv}CMgBr$ (12.0 g. C_6H_8O)	$[{\equiv}CCH(OH)CH{=}CHCH_3]_2$ (9.8 g., 40%)	*398*
$CH_3CH{=}CHCHO$	$n\text{-}C_4H_9C{\equiv}CMgBr$	$CH_3CH{=}CH(n\text{-}C_4H_9C{\equiv}C)CHOH$	*127*
$CH_3CH{=}CHCHO$ (17.5 g.)	$(CH_2)_5CHC{\equiv}CMgBr$ (31 g. C_8H_{12})	$CH_3CH{=}CH[(CH_2)_5CHC{\equiv}C]CHOH$ (52%)	*126*
$CH_3CH{=}CHCHO$	$1\text{-}C_{10}H_7MgBr$	$CH_3CH{=}CH(1\text{-}C_{10}H_7)CHOH$	*301*
$H_2C{=}C(CH_3)CHO$ (70 g., 1 mole)	$({\equiv}CMgBr)_2$ (24 g. Mg)	$[{\equiv}CCH(OH)C(CH_3){=}CH_2]_2$ (42.9 g., 52%)	*65*
$H_2C{=}C(CH_3)CHO$ (3.10 g.)	$(CH_3)_2C{=}CHCH_2CH_2MgBr$ (7.35 g. $C_6H_{11}Br$)	$H_2C{=}C(CH_3)[(CH_3)_2C{=}CHCH_2CH_2]CHOH$ + olefin (aggregating 2.35 g. of which 78% was alcohol)	*431*
$H_2C{=}C(CH_3)CHO$ (3.1 g.)	$i\text{-}C_6H_{13}MgBr$ (6.0 g. $C_6H_{13}Br$)	$H_2C{=}C(CH_3)(i\text{-}C_6H_{13})CHOH$ + olefin (equiv. to 86% alcohol)	*431*
C_4H_7OBr			
$CH_3CHBrCH_2CHO$	$n\text{-}C_3H_7MgBr$	$n\text{-}C_3H_7(CH_3CHBrCH_2)CHOH$	*200*
C_4H_7OCl			
$(CH_3)_2CClCHO$	CH_3MgBr	$i\text{-}C_3H_7(CH_3)_2COH$ (53%)	*133,134*
C_4H_8O			
$n\text{-}C_3H_7CHO$	$({\equiv}CMgBr)_2$	$HC{\equiv}C(n\text{-}C_3H_7)CHOH$ (20–23%)	*392*
$n\text{-}C_3H_7CHO$ (216.2 g.)	$({\equiv}CMgBr)_2$ (1.54 mole)	$[{\equiv}CCH(OH)\text{-}n\text{-}C_3H_7]_2$ (213.0 g., 41.8%)	*399*
$n\text{-}C_3H_7CHO$	$({\equiv}CMgBr)_2$	$[{\equiv}CCH(OH)\text{-}n\text{-}C_3H_7]_2$ (70.2%)	*370*
$n\text{-}C_3H_7CHO$	$HC{\equiv}CH$ + 2 C_2H_5MgBr	$[{\equiv}CCH(OH)\text{-}n\text{-}C_3H_7]_2$ (38%)	*268*
$n\text{-}C_3H_7CHO$	C_2H_5MgBr	$C_2H_5(n\text{-}C_3H_7)CHOH$	*266*
$n\text{-}C_3H_7CHO$	$H_2C{=}CHCH_2MgBr$	$H_2C{=}CHCH_2(n\text{-}C_3H_7)CHOH$ (66%, crude; 57% purified)	*136,56,167, 181*

TABLE VI-XVII (Continued)

Aldehyde	RMgX	Product(s)	Ref.
C_4H_8O (*cont.*)			
n-C_3H_7CHO	n-C_3H_7MgBr	$(n$-$C_3H_7)_2CHOH$ (60–85%)*	*326*
n-C_3H_7CHO	i-C_4H_9MgBr	n-$C_3H_7(i$-$C_4H_9)CHOH$ (60–85%)*	*326*
n-C_3H_7CHO (48.0 g.)	i-C_4H_9MgBr (142.7 g. C_4H_9Br)	n-$C_3H_7(i$-$C_4H_9)CHOH$ (32.0%, crude); n-C_4H_9OH (51.7%, crude); C_4H_8	*267*
n-C_3H_7CHO	s-C_4H_9MgCl	n-$C_3H_7(s$-$C_4H_9)CHOH$ (62%)	*83*
n-C_3H_7CHO (4.0 g.)	$BrMgOCH_2CH{=}CHC{\equiv}CMgBr$ (4.5 g. C_5H_6O)	n-$C_3H_7CH(OH)C{\equiv}CCH{=}CHCH_2OH$ (2.5 g., 30%)	*394*
n-C_3H_7CHO	$(CH_2)_4CHMgBr$	n-$C_3H_7[(CH_2)_4CH]CHOH$	*85*
n-C_3H_7CHO	n-$C_5H_{11}MgBr$	n-$C_3H_7(n$-$C_5H_{11})CHOH$ (33%)	*271*
n-C_3H_7CHO	4-BrC_6H_4MgBr	n-$C_3H_7(4$-$BrC_6H_4)CHOH$ (48%)	*277*
n-C_3H_7CHO (27.4 g.)	$CH_3CH{=}C(CH_3)C{\equiv}CMgBr$ (31.0 g. C_6H_8)	n-$C_3H_7[CH_3CH{=}C(CH_3)C{\equiv}C]CHOH$ (37.0 g., 60%)	*407*
n-C_3H_7CHO (*ca.* 0.3 mole)	$C_6H_5CH_2MgCl$ (*ca.* 0.4 mole)	n-$C_3H_7(C_6H_5CH_2)CHOH$ (40%); 2-n-$C_3H_7CH(OH)C_6H_4CH_2CH(OH)$-$n$-$C_3H_7$ (33%)	*454*
n-C_3H_7CHO	$C_6H_5C{\equiv}CMgX$	n-$C_3H_7(C_6H_5C{\equiv}C)CHOH$ (83%)	*215*
n-C_3H_7CHO (9.0 g.)	$CH_3CH{=}CHCH(OMgBr)C{\equiv}CMgBr$ (12.5 g. C_6H_8O)	n-$C_3H_7CH(OH)C{\equiv}CCH(OH)CH{=}CHCH_3$ (12.0 g., 55%)	*398*
n-C_3H_7CHO	$C_6H_5CH(CO_2Na)MgCl$ †	n-$C_3H_7CH(OH)CH(C_6H_5)CO_2H$	*158*
n-C_3H_7CHO (30 g.)	n-$C_9H_{19}MgBr$ (123 g. $C_9H_{19}Br$)	n-$C_3H_7(n$-$C_9H_{19})CHOH$ (60 g.)	*269*
n-C_3H_7CHO (60 g.)	n-$C_{10}H_{21}MgBr$ (270 g. $C_{10}H_{21}Br$)	n-$C_3H_7(n$-$C_{10}H_{21})CHOH$ (117 g.)	*269*
n-C_3H_7CHO	2-$C_6H_5C_6H_4MgI$	n-$C_3H_7(2$-$C_6H_5C_6H_4)CHOH$ (>96%) ‡	38

* Tuot (*326*) reports the yields for a series of carbinol preparations as ranging from 60% to 85%.

† In the opinion of Schlenk, Hilleman, and Rodloff, *Ann.*, *487*, 135–54 (1931), this "Grignard reagent" should be formulated as an enolate.

‡ The figure recorded represents overall yield of olefin obtained upon subsequent dehydration.

TABLE VI-XVII (Continued)

Aldehyde	RMgX	Product(s)	Ref.
C_4H_8O (*cont.*)			
n-C_3H_7CHO (0.2 mole)	4-$(C_2H_5)_3SiC_6H_4MgBr$ (0.1 mole $C_{12}H_{19}BrSi$)	n-$C_3H_7[4$-$(C_2H_5)_3SiC_6H_4]CHOH$ ("very poor yield")	*125*
n-C_3H_7CHO (17 g.)	n-$C_3H_7(n$-$C_8H_{17})CHMgI$ (90 g. $C_{12}H_{25}I$)	n-$C_3H_7[n$-$C_3H_7(n$-$C_8H_{17})CH]CHOH$ (10.5 g.)	*269*
i-C_3H_7CHO (36 g.)	$(\equiv CMgBr)_2$ (12 g. Mg)	$[\equiv CCH(OH)$-i-$C_3H_7]_2$ (two isomers, totaling 27%)	*65,149*
i-C_3H_7CHO (33 g.)	C_2H_5MgBr (56 g. C_2H_5Br)	$C_2H_5(i$-$C_3H_7)CHOH$ (28 g., 68%)	*255,385*
i-C_3H_7CHO (72 g.)	$H_2C{=}CHC{\equiv}CMgBr$ (from 110 g. C_2H_5Br)	i-$C_3H_7(CH_2{=}CHC{\equiv}C)CHOH$ (56 g.)	*244*
i-C_3H_7CHO	n-C_3H_7MgBr	n-$C_3H_7(i$-$C_3H_7)CHOH$	*242*
i-C_3H_7CHO	i-C_3H_7MgBr	$(i$-$C_3H_7)_2CHOH$; i-C_4H_9OH	*385*
i-C_3H_7CHO (264 g.)	$(CH_3)_2C{=}CHMgBr$ (500 g. C_4H_7Br)	i-$C_3H_7[(CH_3)_2C{=}CH]CHOH$ (102 g.); i-C_4H_9OH; i-C_4H_8	*190*
i-C_3H_7CHO	n-C_4H_9MgBr	i-$C_3H_7(n$-$C_4H_9)CHOH$; i-C_4H_9OH	*242*
i-C_3H_7CHO	i-C_4H_9MgBr	i-$C_3H_7(i$-$C_4H_9)CHOH$	*232,385*
i-C_3H_7CHO (54 g., 0.75 mole)	s-C_4H_9MgBr (102 g., 0.75 mole C_4H_9Br)	Recovered aldehyde (22%); i-C_4H_9OH (37%); i-$C_3H_7(s$-$C_4H_9)CHOH$ (31%, crude); butenes in following proportions: 1-butene (34%); *cis*-2-butene (8%); *trans*-2-butene (58%)	*367*
i-C_3H_7CHO	t-C_4H_9MgCl	i-$C_3H_7(t$-$C_4H_9)CHOH$ (25%); i-$C_3H_7CH(OH)C(CH_3)_2CHO$ (*ca.* 25%); i-C_4H_9OH (*ca.* 50%)	*385*
i-C_3H_7CHO	t-C_4H_9MgCl	i-$C_3H_7(t$-$C_4H_9)CHOH$ (35%); i-C_4H_9OH (35%); solid, m. p. 51–52° (7.5%); $(t$-C_4H_9—$)_2$ (1.5%)	*353*
i-C_3H_7CHO	i-$C_5H_{11}MgBr$	i-$C_3H_7(i$-$C_5H_{11})CHOH$ (60–85%)*	*326,232*

* Tuot (*326*) reports the yields for a series of carbinols as ranging from 60% to 85%.

TABLE VI-XVII (Continued)

Aldehyde	RMgX	Product(s)	Ref.
C_4H_8O (*cont.*)			
i-C_3H_7CHO (107 g., 1.48 mole)	t-C_4H_9MgCl (1.47 mole)	i-C_4H_9OH (84%)	*358*
i-C_3H_7CHO	$CH_3(C_2H_5)(BrMgO)CC\equiv CMgBr$	i-$C_3H_7[CH_3(C_2H_5)C(OH)C\equiv C]CHOH$ (55%)	*211*
i-C_3H_7CHO	$(CH_2)_5CHMgBr$	$(CH_2)_5CH(OH)$-i-C_3H_7	*385*
i-C_3H_7CHO	i-$C_6H_{13}MgBr$	i-$C_3H_7(i$-$C_6H_{13})CHOH$	*232*
i-C_3H_7CHO (*ca.* 0.3 mole)	$C_6H_5CH_2MgCl$ (*ca.* 0.4 mole)	i-$C_3H_7(C_6H_5CH_2)CHOH$ (75%); 2-i-$C_3H_7CH(OH)C_6H_4CH_2CH(OH)$-$i$-$C_3H_7$ (13%)	*454,31*
i-C_3H_7CHO	4-$CH_3C_6H_4MgBr$	i-$C_3H_7(4$-$CH_3C_6H_4)CHOH$ (53%)	*377*
i-C_3H_7CHO	$C_6H_5CH(CO_2Na)MgCl$*	i-$C_3H_7CH(OH)CH(CO_2H)C_6H_5$, mixture of A (m.p. 139–140°) and B (m.p. 171–172°) isomers (77%)	
i-C_3H_7CHO	$C_6H_5(CH_2)_2MgBr$	i-$C_3H_7(C_6H_5CH_2CH_2)CHOH$ (59.5%)	*32*
i-C_3H_7CHO (0.2 mole)	4-$(C_2H_5)_3SiC_6H_4MgBr$ (0.1 mole $C_{12}H_{19}BrSi$)	i-$C_3H_7[4$-$(C_2H_5)_3SiC_6H_4]CHOH$ ("very poor yield")	*125*
$C_4H_8O_2$			
$CH_3CH(OH)CH_2CHO$ (1 mole)	CH_3MgI (2.25 mole)	$CH_3[CH_3CH(OH)CH_2]CHOH$ (6 g.)	*100*
$CH_3CH(OH)CH_2CHO$	C_2H_5MgBr (2.25 equiv.)	$C_2H_5[CH_3CH(OH)CH_2]CHOH$	*200*
$CH_3CH(OH)CH_2CHO$	C_2H_5MgI (2.25 equiv.)	$C_2H_5[CH_3OH(OH)CH_2]CHOH$	*100*
$CH_3CH(OH)CH_2CHO$	C_6H_5MgI (2.25 equiv.)	$CH_3CH(OH)CH_2CH(C_6H_5)OH$; dehydr'n product	*100*
C_5H_4OS			
2-Thiophenecarboxaldehyde (112 g., 1.0 mole)	$H_2C{=}CHCH_2MgBr$ (145 g., 1.2 mole C_3H_5Br)	$H_2C{=}CHCH_2(\alpha$-$C_4H_3S)CHOH$ (95 g., 61%)	*412*

* In the opinion of Schlenk, Hilleman, and Rodloff, *Ann.*, *487*, 135–54 (1931), this "Grignard reagent" should be formulated as an enolate.

TABLE VI-XVII (Continued)

Aldehyde	RMgX	Product(s)	Ref.
$C_5H_4O_2$			
Furfural	CH_3MgX	1-α-Furylethanol	*331*
Furfural	C_2H_5MgBr	1-α-Furyl-1-propanol; $C_2H_5CH{=}CHCH_2COCH(C_2H_5)OH$	*193*
Furfural	$H_2C{=}CHC{\equiv}CMgBr$	1-α-Furylpent-4-en-2-yn-1-ol	*244*
Furfural	$H_2C{=}CHCH_2Br$ + Mg	1-α-Furylbut-3-en-1-ol (78%)	*306*
Furfural	n-C_3H_7MgBr	1-α-Furyl-1-butanol	*164*
Furfural	n-C_3H_7MgX	1-α-Furyl-1-butanol, n-$C_3H_7CH{=}CHCH_2COCH(n$-$C_3H_7)OH$	*193*
Furfural	i-C_4H_9MgX	1-α-Furyl-3-methyl-1-butanol; i-$C_4H_9CH{=}CHCH_2COCH(i$-$C_4H_9)OH$	*193*
Furfural	t-C_4H_9MgX	1-α-Furyl-2,2-dimethyl-1-propanol	*331*
Furfural	i-$C_5H_{11}MgBr$	1-α-Furyl-4-methyl-1-pentanol (43%)	*121*
Furfural	$C_6H_5CH_2MgBr$	1-α-Furyl-2-phenylethanol (32%)	*218*
Furfural	$(C_2H_5)_2N(CH_2)_3MgCl$	1-α-Furyl-4-diethylamino-1-butanol	*224*
Furfural	$(C_2H_5)_2N(CH_2)_3Cl$ + Mg	1-α-Furyl-4-diethylamino-1-butanol	*233*
Furfural (12 g.)	$C_6H_5CH(CO_2Na)MgCl$*	α-Phenyl-β-(α-furyl)lactic acid (23 g.)	*158*
Furfural (7.0 g.)	1-$C_{10}H_7MgBr$ (20.7 g. $C_{10}H_7Br$)	α-Furyl-α-naphthylmethanol	*331*
C_5H_6O			
$H_2C{=}CHCH{=}CHCHO$ (33.5 g., 0.41 mole)	CH_3MgBr (58.0 g. CH_3Br)	$CH_3(H_2C{=}CHCH{=}CH)CHOH$ (30.0 g., 75%)	*364*
$H_2C{=}CHCH{=}CHCHO$ (41 g.)	$H_2C{=}CHCH_2MgBr$ (80 g. C_3H_5Br)	"Octatrienol" (55 g., 90%)	*365*
C_5H_8O			
$CH_3CH{=}C(CH_3)CHO$	CH_3MgBr	$CH_3[CH_3CH{=}C(CH_3)]CHOH$	*1*

*In the opinion of Schlenk, Hilleman, and Rodloff, *Ann.*, *487*, 135–54 (1931), this "Grignard reagent" should be formulated as an enolate.

TABLE VI-XVII (Continued)

Aldehyde	RMgX	Product(s)	Ref.
C_5H_8O (*cont.*)			
$CH_3CH{=}C(CH_3)CHO$	CH_3MgI	$CH_3[CH_3CH{=}C(CH_3)]CHOH$	*350*
$CH_3CH{=}C(CH_3)CHO$	C_2H_5MgBr	$C_2H_5[CH_3CH{=}C(CH_3)]CHOH$	*1*
$CH_3CH{=}C(CH_3)CHO$	$i\text{-}C_5H_{11}MgBr$	$i\text{-}C_5H_{11}[CH_3CH{=}C(CH_3)]CHOH$	*1*
$(CH_3)_2CH{=}CHCHO$ (5 g.)	$C_{10}H_{19}MgBr$*	$(CH_3)_2CH{=}CH(C_{10}H_{19})CHOH$ (yielding 0.4 g. zingiberene on dehydr'n)	*239*
C_5H_9OBr			
$n\text{-}C_3H_7CHBrCHO$	C_2H_5MgBr	C_9H_{18}	*174*
$C_5H_{10}O$			
$n\text{-}C_4H_9CHO$	$n\text{-}C_3H_7MgBr$	$n\text{-}C_3H_7(n\text{-}C_4H_9)CHOH$ (60–85%)†	*326*
$n\text{-}C_4H_9CHO$	$i\text{-}C_3H_7MgBr$	$i\text{-}C_3H_7(n\text{-}C_4H_9)CHOH$ (60–85%)†	*326*
$n\text{-}C_4H_9CHO$	$n\text{-}C_4H_9MgBr$	$(n\text{-}C_4H_9)_2CHOH$ (65%)	*213*
$n\text{-}C_4H_9CHO$	$i\text{-}C_4H_9MgBr$	$n\text{-}C_4H_9(i\text{-}C_4H_9)CHOH$ (60–85%)†	*326*
$n\text{-}C_4H_9CHO$	$(CH_2)_4CHMgBr$	$n\text{-}C_4H_9[(CH_2)_4CH]CHOH$ (18%)	*85*
$n\text{-}C_4H_9CHO$	$i\text{-}C_5H_{11}MgBr$	$n\text{-}C_4H_9(i\text{-}C_5H_{11})CHOH$ (60–85%)†	*326*
$n\text{-}C_4H_9CHO$ (22 g.)	$n\text{-}C_5H_{11}C{\equiv}CMgBr$	$n\text{-}C_4H_9(n\text{-}C_5H_{11}C{\equiv}C)CHOH$ (8 g.)	*237*
$n\text{-}C_4H_9CHO$	$2\text{-}C_6H_5C_6H_4MgI$	$n\text{-}C_4H_9(2\text{-}C_6H_5C_6H_4)CHOH$ ($>42\%$)‡	*38*
$i\text{-}C_4H_9CHO$	$({\equiv}CMgBr)_2$	$[{\equiv}CCH(OH)\text{-}i\text{-}C_4H_9]_2$	*420*
$i\text{-}C_4H_9CHO$	C_2H_5MgBr	$C_2H_5(i\text{-}C_4H_9)CHOH$	*266*
$i\text{-}C_4H_9CHO$	$n\text{-}C_3H_7MgBr$	$n\text{-}C_3H_7(i\text{-}C_4H_9)CHOH$; $i\text{-}C_5H_{11}OH$	*242*
$i\text{-}C_4H_9CHO$	$n\text{-}C_3H_7MgI$	$n\text{-}C_3H_7(i\text{-}C_4H_9)CHOH$ ("very good yield")	*50*
$i\text{-}C_4H_9CHO$	$i\text{-}C_3H_7MgBr$	$i\text{-}C_3H_7(i\text{-}C_4H_9)CHOH$ (60–85%)†	*326*
$i\text{-}C_4H_9CHO$	$n\text{-}C_4H_9CMgBr$	$n\text{-}C_4H_9(i\text{-}C_4H_9)CHOH$	*213*
$i\text{-}C_4H_9CHO$	$i\text{-}C_4H_9MgBr$	$(i\text{-}C_4H_9)_2CHOH$ (55%)	*121*
$i\text{-}C_4H_9CHO$	$i\text{-}C_4H_9MgBr$	$(i\text{-}C_4H_9)_2CHOH$ (60–85%)†	*326*

* From 5 g. 1-bromo-2-(4-methyl-3-cyclohexen-1-yl)propane.

† Tuot (*326*) reports the yields for a series of carbinol preparations as ranging from 60% to 85%.

‡ Figure recorded represents overall yield of olefin obtained upon subsequent dehydration.

TABLE VI-XVII (Continued)

Aldehyde	RMgX	Product(s)	Ref.
$C_5H_{10}O$ (*cont.*)			
i-C_4H_9CHO	i-$C_5H_{11}MgBr$	i-C_4H_9(i-C_5H_{11})CHOH (60–85%)*	*326*
i-C_4H_9CHO	$(CH_2)_5CHMgCl$	i-$C_4H_9[(CH_2)_5CH]$CHOH ("high yield")	*388*
i-C_4H_9CHO	n-$C_6H_{13}MgX$	i-C_4H_9(n-C_6H_{13})CHOH (73%)	*349*
i-C_4H_9CHO	$C_6H_5CH_2Cl$ + Mg	i-$C_4H_9(C_6H_5CH_2)$CHOH (35.1%)	*270*
i-C_4H_9CHO (28 g.)	n-$C_8H_{17}MgBr$ (89 g. $C_8H_{17}Br$)	i-$C_5H_{11}OH$; C_8H_{16}	*267*
i-C_4H_9CHO	$CH_3(C_6H_5)N(CH_2)_3MgX$	i-$C_4H_9[CH_3(C_6H_5)N(CH_2)_3]$CHOH; $[CH_3(C_6H_5)N(CH_2)_3-]_2$	*346*
i-C_4H_9CHO	2-$C_6H_5C_6H_4MgI$	i-C_4H_9(2-$C_6H_5C_6H_4$)CHOH (>73%)†	*38*
s-C_4H_9CHO	C_2H_5MgBr	C_2H_5(s-C_4H_9)CHOH	*99*
s-C_4H_9CHO (8 g., 0.09 mole)	n-C_4H_9MgBr (0.1 mole)	n-C_4H_9(s-C_4H_9)CHOH (3.8 g., 38%)	*368*
t-C_4H_9CHO (0.12 mole)	n-C_3H_7MgBr	n-C_3H_7(t-C_4H_9)CHOH (0.06 mole); t-$C_4H_9CH_2OH$ (trace)	*55*
t-C_4H_5 CHO (0.12 mole)	i-C_3H_7MgCl	i-C_3H_7(t-C_4H_9)CHOH (0.04 mole); t-$C_4H_9CH_2OH$ (0.01 mole)	*55*
t-C_4H_9CHO (0.2 mole)	t-C_4H_9MgCl	t-$C_4H_9CH_2OH$ (0.13 mole)	*55*
$C_5H_{10}O_2$			
$HOCH_2(CH_3)_2CCHO$ (25 g.)	CH_3MgI (88 g. CH_3I)	$CH_3[HOCH_2(CH_3)_2C]$CHOH (6 g.); CH_4	*100*
$HOCH_2(CH_3)_2CCHO$ (15.8 g.)	C_2H_5MgI (49.0 g. C_2H_5I)	$C_2H_5[HOCH_2(CH_3)_2C]$CHOH (6.0 g., crude)	*100*
$HOCH_2(CH_3)_2CCHO$ (15 g.)	C_6H_5MgBr (100 g. C_6H_5Br)	$C_6H_5[HOCH_2(CH_3)_2C]$CHOH (11 g.)	*100*
C_6H_5ON			
2-Pyridinecarboxaldehyde	C_2H_5MgBr	1-α-Pyridyl-1-propanol (63%)	*197*

* Tuot (*326*) reports the yields for a series of carbinol preparations as ranging from 60% to 85%.

† Figure recorded represents overall yield of olefin obtained upon subsequent dehydration.

TABLE VI-XVII (Continued)

Aldehyde	RMgX	Product(s)	Ref.
C_6H_5ON (*cont.*)			
3-Pyridinecarboxaldehyde	$(C_2H_5)_2N(CH_2)_3Cl$ + Mg	1-β-Pyridyl-4-diethylamino-1-butanol	233
$C_6H_6O_2$			
5-Methyl-2-furaldehyde	*i*-C_3H_7MgX	1-(5-Methyl-2-furyl)-1-butanol	330
C_6H_8O			
1-Cyclopentenecarboxaldehyde	CH_3MgBr (*ca.* 1.3 equiv.)	1-(1-Cyclopentenyl)ethanol (85–90%)	329
1-Cyclopentenecarboxaldehyde	C_2H_5MgBr (*ca.* 1.3 equiv.)	1-(1-Cyclopentenyl)-1-propanol (85–90%)	329
1-Cyclopentenecarboxaldehyde	*n*-C_3H_7MgBr (*ca.* 1.3 equiv.)	1-(1-Cyclopentenyl)-1-butanol (85–90%)	329
$CH_3(CH{=}CH)_2CHO$ (22 g.)	$(\equiv CMgBr)_2$ (6 g. Mg)	$[\equiv CCH(OH)(CH{=}CH)_2CH_3]_2$ (12 g., 42%)	400
$CH_3(CH{=}CH)_2CHO$ (38 g.)	1-Cyclohexenylethynyl-MgBr (42 g. C_8H_{10})	1-(1-Cyclohexen-1-yl)-4,6-octadien-1-yn-3-ol (36 g.)	126
$C_6H_{10}O$			
n-$C_3H_7CH{=}CHCHO$	*n*-C_3H_7MgBr	*n*-C_3H_7(*n*-$C_3H_7CH{=}CH$)CHOH (75%)	72
$C_2H_5CH{=}C(CH_3)CHO$	CH_3MgI	$CH_3[C_2H_5CH{=}C(CH_3)]CHOH$ (65%)	121
$C_2H_5CH{=}C(CH_3)CHO$	C_2H_5MgBr	$C_2H_5[C_2H_5CH{=}C(CH_3)]CHOH$ (88%)	30,343
$C_2H_5CH{=}C(CH_3)CHO$	*n*-C_3H_7MgCl	*n*-$C_3H_7[C_2H_5CH{=}C(CH_3)]CHOH$ (83%)	30,343
$C_2H_5CH{=}C(CH_3)CHO$	*i*-C_4H_9MgBr	*i*-$C_4H_9[C_2H_5CH{=}C(CH_3)]CHOH$ (67.5%)	30
$C_2H_5CH{=}C(CH_3)CHO$	*i*-$C_5H_{11}MgBr$	*i*-$C_5H_{11}[C_2H_5CH{=}C(CH_3)]CHOH$ (80%)	30
$(CH_2)_4CHCHO$	*n*-C_4H_9MgCl	*n*-$C_4H_9[(CH_2)_4CH]CHOH$ (60%)	335
$(CH_2)_4CHCHO$	$C_6H_5CH_2CH_2MgBr$	$(CH_2)_4CH(C_6H_5CH_2CH_2)CHOH$ ("excellent yield")	413
$C_6H_{12}O$			
n-$C_5H_{11}CHO$	*n*-$C_{10}H_{21}MgBr$	*n*-C_5H_{11}(*n*-$C_{10}H_{21}$)CHOH (60%)	8

TABLE VI-XVII (Continued)

Aldehyde	RMgX	Product(s)	Ref.
$C_6H_{12}O$ (*cont.*)			
n-$C_5H_{11}CHO$	2-$C_6H_5C_6H_4MgI$	n-$C_5H_{11}(2$-$C_6H_5C_6H_4)CHOH$ (> 59%)*	*38*
i-$C_5H_{11}CHO$	$(CH_2)_5CHMgCl$	i-$C_5H_{11}[(CH_2)_5CH]CHOH$	*288*
$CH_3(n$-$C_3H_7)CHCHO$	n-$C_5H_{11}MgBr$	n-$C_5H_{11}[CH_3(n$-$C_3H_7)CH]CHOH$	*173*
$(C_2H_5)_2CHCHO$ (3.5 g., 0.25 mole)	t-C_4H_9MgCl (0.31 mole)	$(C_2H_5)_2CHCH_2OH$ (4.8 g.); t-$C_4H_9[(C_2H_5)_2CH]CHOH$ (24.0 g.)	*358*
$(C_2H_5)_2CHCHO$ (0.4 mole)	t-$C_5H_{11}MgCl$ (0.5 mole)	$(C_2H_5)_2CHCH_2OH$ (67%); t-$C_5H_{11}[(C_2H_5)_2CH]CHOH$ (21%)	*358*
t-$C_5H_{11}CHO$ (0.10 mole)	n-C_3H_7MgBr	n-$C_3H_7(t$-$C_5H_{11})CHOH$ (0.045 mole); t-$C_5H_{11}CH_2OH$ (0.015 mole)	*55*
t-$C_5H_{11}CHO$ (0.09 mole)	i-C_3H_7MgBr	i-$C_3H_7(t$-$C_5H_{11})CHOH$ (0.024 mole); t-$C_5H_{11}CH_2OH$ (0.030 mole)	*55*
t-$C_5H_{11}CHO$ (0.5 mole)	t-C_4H_9MgCl (0.11 mole Mg)	t-$C_5H_{11}CH_2OH$ (0.03 mole)	*55*
$C_6H_{12}O_2$			
$C_2H_5CH(OH)CH(CH_3)CHO$ (1 mole)	CH_3MgI (2.5 moles CH_3I)	$C_2H_5CH(OH)CH(CH_3)CH(CH_3)OH$	*100*
$C_2H_5CH(OH)CH(CH_3)CHO$	C_2H_5MgI	$C_2H_5CH(OH)CH(CH_3)CH(C_2H_5)OH$ (70%)	*100*
$C_2H_5CH(OH)CH(CH_3)CHO$ (1 mole)	C_6H_5MgI (2.5 moles C_6H_5I)	$C_2H_5CH(OH)CH(CH_3)CH(C_6H_5)OH$	*100*
$C_6H_{12}O_3$			
$(C_2H_5O)_2CHCHO$	CH_3MgI	$CH_3[(C_2H_5O)_2CH]CHOH$ (71%)	*92*
C_7HOCl_5			
C_6Cl_5CHO (14 g.)	CH_3MgI (9 g. CH_3I	$CH_3(C_6Cl_5)CHOH$ (7.3 g.); recovered aldehyde (3.6 g.)	*210*
C_6Cl_5CHO (5 g.)	C_6H_5MgBr (4 g. C_6H_5Br)	$C_6Cl_5(C_6H_5)CHOH$	*210*

* Figure recorded represents overall yield of olefin obtained upon subsequent dehydration.

TABLE VI-XVII (Continued)

Aldehyde	RMgX	Product(s)	Ref.
$C_7H_4OCl_2$ (*cont.*)			
2,3-$Cl_2C_6H_3CHO$	CH_3MgI	CH_3(2,3-$Cl_2C_6H_3$)CHOH (76%)	259
2,4-$Cl_2C_6H_3CHO$	CH_3MgI	CH_3(2,4-$Cl_2C_6H_3$)CHOH (62%)	259
2,5-$Cl_2C_6H_3CHO$ (110 g.)	CH_3MgBr	CH_3(2,5-$Cl_2C_6H_3$)CHOH (110 g., 83%)	401
2,6-$Cl_2C_6H_3CHO$	CH_3MgI	CH_3(2,6-$Cl_2C_6H_3$)CHOH (89%)	259
3,4-$Cl_2C_6H_3CHO$	CH_3MgI	CH_3(3,4-$Cl_2C_6H_3$)CHOH (73%)	259
3,5-$Cl_2C_6H_3CHO$	CH_3MgI	CH_3(3,5-$Cl_2C_6H_3$)CHOH (69%)	259
C_7H_5OBr			
2-BrC_6H_4CHO	CH_3MgI	CH_3(2-BrC_6H_4)CHOH (73%)	259
3-BrC_6H_4CHO	CH_3MgI	CH_3(3-BrC_6H_4)CHOH (74%)	259
4-BrC_6H_4CHO	CH_3MgI	CH_3(4-BrC_6H_4)CHOH (64%)	259
4-BrC_6H_4CHO	CH_3MgI	CH_3(4-BrC_6H_4)CHOH (95%)	277
4-BrC_6H_4CHO	CH_3MgBr	CH_3(4-BrC_6H_4)CHOH	373
4-BrC_6H_4CHO	C_2H_5MgBr	C_2H_5(4-BrC_6H_4)CHOH (90%)	277
4-BrC_6H_4CHO	*n*-C_3H_7MgBr	*n*-C_3H_7(4-BrC_6H_4)CHOH (90%)	276,277
4-BrC_6H_4CHO	C_6H_5MgBr	4-BrC_6H_4(C_6H_5)CHOH ("good yield")	253
C_7H_5OCl			
2-ClC_6H_4CHO (140.0 g.)	CH_3MgBr (26.7 g. Mg)	CH_3(2-ClC_6H_4)CHOH (119.0 g., 76%)	401
2-ClC_6H_4CHO	CH_3MgI	CH_3(2-ClC_6H_4)CHOH (69%)	259
2-ClC_6H_4CHO	$C_6H_5CH_2MgCl$	2-ClC_6H_4($C_6H_5CH_2$)CHOH (30%)	25
2-ClC_6H_4CHO	8-$CH_3C_{10}H_6$-1-MgBr	2-ClC_6H_4[8-CH_3-1-$C_{10}H_6$]CHOH (44%)	90
3-ClC_6H_4CHO (142 g.)	CH_3MgBr	CH_3(3-ClC_6H_4)CHOH (118 g., 76%)	401
3-ClC_6H_4CHO	$C_6H_5(CH_2)_2MgBr$	3-ClC_6H_4[$C_6H_5(CH_2)_2$]CHOH (64%)	39
4-ClC_6H_4CHO (141 g.)	CH_3MgBr	CH_3(4-ClC_6H_4)CHOH (134 g., 86%)	401
4-ClC_6H_4CHO	CH_3MgI	CH_3(4-ClC_6H_4)CHOH (59%)	259

TABLE VI-XVII (Continued)

Aldehyde	RMgX	Product(s)	Ref.
C_7H_5OCl (*cont.*)			
4-ClC_6H_4CHO	$C_6H_5CH(CO_2Na)MgCl$*	4-$ClC_6H_4CH(OH)CH(C_6H_5)CO_2H$ (40%); 4-$ClC_6H_4CO_2H$; $C_6H_5CO_2H$	*158*
C_7H_5OF			
2-FC_6H_4CHO (99 g.)	CH_3MgBr	CH_3(2-FC_6H_4)CHOH (87 g., 78%)	*401*
3-FC_6H_4CHO (99 g.)	CH_3MgBr	CH_3(3-FC_6H_4)CHOH (83 g., 74%)	*401*
4-FC_6H_4CHO (99 g.)	CH_3MgBr	CH_3(4-FC_6H_4)CHOH (94 g., 84%)	*401*
$C_7H_5O_3N$			
2-$O_2NC_6H_4CHO$	2-$CH_3C_6H_4MgBr$	2-$O_2NC_6H_4$(2-$CH_3C_6H_4$)CHOH	*255*
3-$O_2NC_6H_4CHO$	*n*-C_4H_9MgBr	Tar	*248*
3-$O_2NC_6H_4CHO$ (47 g., 0.312 mole)	C_6H_5MgBr (0.196 mole)	C_6H_5(3-$O_2NC_6H_4$)CHOH (77%)	*248*
C_7H_6O			
C_6H_5CHO	CH_3MgI	$CH_3(C_6H_5)CHOH$ (*ca.* 78%)	*121,119,375*
C_6H_5CHO	CH_3MgI	$CH_3(C_6H_5)CHOH$ (93%)	*105*
C_6H_5CHO (excess)	CH_3MgI	$CH_3COC_6H_5$; $C_6H_5COCH{=}CHC_6H_5$; $(C_6H_5CO)_2CH_2$	*447,446*
C_6H_5CHO	CH_3MgI	$CH_3(C_6H_5)CHOH$ (6 g.) (optically active, 0.30°; after 24 hrs., 0.18°)†	*28*
C_6H_5CHO	CH_3MgI	DL-$CH_3(C_6H_5)CHOH$‡ (60–68%)	*313*
C_6H_5CHO	$(\equiv CMgBr)_2$	$HC\equiv C(C_6H_5)CHOH$ (20–23%)	*392,391*

* In the opinion of Schlenk, Hilleman, and Rodloff, *Ann.*, *487*, 135–54 (1931), this "Grignard reagent" should be formulated as an enolate.

† Grignard reagent prepared in *N*,*N*-dimethylbornylamine. The present authors question the optical activity of the product.

‡ Grignard reagent prepared in (+)-2-methoxybutane.

TABLE VI-XVII (Continued)

Aldehyde	RMgX	Product(s)	Ref.
C_7H_6O (*cont.*)			
C_6H_5CHO (20 g.) + $(C_6H_5)_2CO$ (30 g.)	$(\equiv CMgBr)_2$ (0.5 mole)	$[\equiv CC(C_6H_5)_2OH]_2$; $[\equiv CCH(OH)C_6H_5]_2$; 2 isomers;* $HO(C_6H_5)_2CC\equiv CCH(C_6H_5)OH$*	*294*
C_6H_5CHO	$(\equiv CMgBr)_2$	$[\equiv CCH(OH)C_6H_5]_2$ (<70%)	*370,151,327, 81,139, 419,422*
C_6H_5CHO	C_2H_5MgBr	$C_2H_5(C_6H_5)CHOH$ (*ca.* 78%)	*121,105,119, 137,247, 254,341, 375*
C_6H_5CHO	C_2H_5MgBr	$C_2H_5(C_6H_5)CHOH$; $C_6H_5CH_2OH$; residue†	*229*
C_6H_5CHO	C_2H_5MgI	$C_2H_5(C_6H_5)CHOH$; $C_6H_5CH_2OH$; residue†	*229,137,257*
C_6H_5CHO (79 g., 1.5 equiv.)	C_2H_5MgI (78 g. C_2H_5I)	$C_6H_5CH_2OH$ (*ca.* 16 g.); $C_2H_5(C_6H_5)CHOH$; $C_2H_5COC_6H_5$; $(C_6H_5CO)_2CHCH_3$ (16 g., crude)	*447*
C_6H_5CHO	C_2H_5I + Mg	$C_2H_5(C_6H_5)CHOH$ (chief product); $C_6H_5CH=CHCH_3$; $[C_2H_5(C_6H_5)CH]_2O$	*416*
C_6H_5CHO	$H_2C=CHCH_2Br$ + Mg	$H_2C=CHCH_2(C_6H_5)CHOH$	*180,161*
C_6H_5CHO	n-C_3H_7MgBr	n-$C_3H_7(C_6H_5)CHOH$ (80%)	*105,119,121, 254,341*
C_6H_5CHO (1.5 equiv.)	n-C_3H_7MgI (68 g. C_3H_7I)	$(C_6H_5CO)_2CHC_2H_5$ (23 g., crude)	*447*
C_6H_5CHO	n-C_3H_7MgI	n-$C_3H_7(C_6H_5)CHOH$ (*ca.* quant.)	*177,257*
C_6H_5CHO	n-C_3H_7I + Mg	n-$C_3H_7(C_6H_5)CHOH$ (chief product); $C_6H_5CH=CHC_2H_5$; $[n$-$C_3H_7(C_6H_5)CH]_2O$	*416*

* Isolated as the corresponding 3,4-dibromo-2,5-dihydrofurans.

† Meisenheimer (*229*) reports results for experiments conducted under a wide variety of conditions.

TABLE VI-XVII (Continued)

Aldehyde	RMgX	Product(s)	Ref.
C_7H_6O (*cont.*)			
C_6H_5CHO	$i\text{-}C_3H_7MgBr$	$i\text{-}C_3H_7(C_6H_5)CHOH$	*385*
C_6H_5CHO	$i\text{-}C_3H_7MgI$	$i\text{-}C_3H_7(C_6H_5)CHOH$	*121*
C_6H_5CHO (1.5 equiv.)	$i\text{-}C_3H_7MgI$	Rec. C_6H_5CHO; $i\text{-}C_3H_7COC_6H_5$; $i\text{-}C_3H_7(C_6H_5)CHOH$	*447,446*
C_6H_5CHO	$H_2C{=}CHC{\equiv}CMgX$	$H_2C{=}CHC{\equiv}C(C_6H_5)CHOH$ (73%)	*369*
C_6H_5CHO	Butenyl-MgBr*	$H_2C{=}CHCH(CH_3)CH(C_6H_5)OH$ (<25%)	*258*
C_6H_5CHO	$(CH_3)_2C{=}CHMgBr$	$(CH_3)_2C{=}CHCH(C_6H_5)OH$	*191*
C_6H_5CHO	$n\text{-}C_4H_9MgCl$	$n\text{-}C_4H_9(C_6H_5)CHOH$ (66%)	*386*
C_6H_5CHO	$n\text{-}C_4H_9MgBr$	$n\text{-}C_4H_9(C_6H_5)CHOH$	*341*
C_6H_5CHO (0.2 mole)	$i\text{-}C_4H_9MgBr$ (0.2 mole C_4H_9Br)	Recovered C_6H_5CHO (20–27%); $i\text{-}C_4H_9(C_6H_5)CHOH$ (21 g.); residue (0.5 g.); $C_6H_5CH_2OH$ (12%); $(CH_3)_2C{=}CH_2$	*229,120*
C_6H_5CHO (38.6 g.)	$s\text{-}C_4H_9MgBr$ (50.0 g. C_4H_9Br)	$s\text{-}C_4H_9(C_6H_5)CHOH$ (60%)	*432*
C_6H_5CHO (53 g., 0.5 mole)	$t\text{-}C_4H_9MgCl$ (92.5 g., 1 mole C_4H_9Cl)	$t\text{-}C_4H_9(C_6H_5)CHOH$ (55–61%)	*323*
C_6H_5CHO (20 g.)	2,6-Pyridylidene-$(MgBr)_2$	2,6-Bis(phenylhydroxymethyl)pyridine (4 g., crude); 2-(phenylhydroxymethyl)pyridine (1 g.)	*273*
C_6H_5CHO (16 g.)	2-Pyridyl-MgBr (16 g. C_5H_4BrN)	Phenyl-2-pyridylmethanol (9 g., 49%)	*260*
C_6H_5CHO	$(CH_2)_4CHMgBr$	$(CH_2)_4CH(C_6H_5)CHOH$ (7%)	*85*
C_6H_5CHO	$(CH_2)_4CHMgCl$	$(CH_2)_4CH(C_6H_5)CHOH$; "1,3-dibenzylidenecyclopentanone"	*192*
C_6H_5CHO	$i\text{-}C_5H_{11}MgBr$	$i\text{-}C_5H_{11}(C_6H_5)CHOH$ (56%)	*121*
C_6H_5CHO (106 g.)	$s\text{-}C_4H_9CH_2MgBr$ (151 g. $C_5H_{11}Br$)	$s\text{-}C_4H_9CH_2(C_6H_5)CHOH$ (40 g.)	*63*
C_6H_5CHO (15.9 g.)	$(CH_3)_2N(CH_2)_3MgCl$ (30 g. $C_5H_{12}ClN$)	$(CH_3)_2N(CH_2)_3CH(C_6H_5)OH$ (70%)	*224*
C_6H_5CHO	$(CH_3)_2N(CH_2)_3Cl$ + Mg	$(CH_3)_2N(CH_2)_3CH(C_6H_5)OH$	*233*
C_6H_5CHO	$4\text{-}BrC_6H_4MgBr$	$4\text{-}BrC_6H_4(C_6H_5)CHOH$	*234*
C_6H_5CHO	$4\text{-}ClC_6H_4MgI$	$4\text{-}ClC_6H_4(C_6H_5)CHOH$	*234*

* From crotyl bromide ($CH_3CH{=}CHCH_2Br$).

TABLE VI-XVII (Continued)

Aldehyde	RMgX	Product(s)	Ref.
C_7H_6O (*cont.*)			
C_6H_5CHO	3-FC_6H_4MgBr	3-$FC_6H_4(C_6H_5)CHOH$ (47%)	*14*
C_6H_5CHO	4-FC_6H_4MgBr	4-$FC_6H_5(C_6H_5)CHOH$ (58%)	*14,378*
C_6H_5CHO (1.0 equiv.)	C_6H_5MgBr	$(C_6H_5)_2CHOH$ (55%)	*447,289,290*
C_6H_5CHO (50 g.)	C_6H_5MgBr (24 g. Mg + 75 g. C_6H_5Br)	$[(C_6H_5)_2CH—]_2$ (30 g.); $(C_6H_5)_2CHOH$	*447*
C_6H_5CHO (106 g., 2.0 equiv.)	C_6H_5MgBr (75 g. C_6H_5Br)	Rec. C_6H_5CHO; $C_6H_5CH_2OH$; $(C_6H_5)_2CO$; $[(C_6H_5)_2CH—]_2$	*446,447*
C_6H_5CHO (13.0 g.)	$CH_3CH=CHCH(OMgBr)C\equiv CMgBr$ (12.0 g. C_6H_8O)	$C_6H_5CH(OH)C\equiv CCH(OH)CH=CHCH_3$ (10.5 g., 40%)	*398*
C_6H_5CHO	n-$C_4H_9C\equiv CMgBr$	$C_6H_5(n$-$C_4H_9C\equiv C)CHOH$ (62%)	*44*
C_6H_5CHO	$(CH_2)_5CHMgCl$	$C_6H_5[(CH_2)_5CH]CHOH$	*388*
C_6H_5CHO (6.5 g.)	$(CH_2)_5CHMgBr$ (10.0 g. $C_6H_{11}Br$)	$C_6H_5[(CH_2)_5CH]CHOH$ (70%)	*342,288,440*
C_6H_5CHO	$C_6H_5CH_2MgCl$	$C_6H_5(C_6H_5CH_2)CHOH$* (95%)	*298,128,305, 324,327*
C_6H_5CHO (0.38 mole)	$C_6H_5CH_2MgCl$ (0.40 mole)	$C_6H_5(C_6H_5CH_2)CHOH$ (64.0 g., 0.32 mole); 1,3-diphenylisochroman (1.8 g.)†	*453*
C_6H_5CHO (0.38 mole)	$C_6H_5CH_2MgCl$ (0.40 mole)	$C_6H_5(C_6H_5CH_2)CHOH$ (33.9 g., 0.17 mole); 1,3-diphenylisochroman (20.3 g., 0.067 mole)‡	*453*
C_6H_5CHO (excess)	$C_6H_5CH_2MgBr$	$C_6H_5(C_6H_5CO)_2CH$; $C_6H_5COCH_2C_6H_5$; $C_6H_5(C_6H_5CH_2)CHOH$	*447*
C_6H_5CHO	2-$CH_3C_6H_4MgBr$	C_6H_5(2-$CH_3C_6H_4)CHOH$	*325,253*
C_6H_5CHO	3-$CH_3C_6H_4MgBr$	C_6H_5(3-$CH_3C_6H_5)CHOH$	*253*
C_6H_5CHO	4-$CH_3C_6H_4MgI$ (excess)	C_6H_5(4-$CH_3C_6H_4)CHOH$	*447*

* Concerning "abnormal" products obtained under other experimental conditions see: Schmidlin and Garcia-Banûs, (*298*); Garcia-Banûs, *Anales. soc. españ. fís. quím.*, *26*, 372–98 (1928); *Chem. Abstr.*, *23*, 2178–80 (1929).

† Normal addition.

‡ Inverse addition.

TABLE VI-XVII (Continued)

Aldehyde	RMgX	Product(s)	Ref.
C_7H_6O (*cont.*)			
C_6H_5CHO	$4\text{-}CH_3C_6H_4MgI$ (0.5 equiv.)	$C_6H_5CH_2OH$; $C_6H_5COC_6H_4\text{-}4\text{-}CH_3$	*447*
C_6H_5CHO	$3\text{-}CH_3OC_6H_4MgBr$	$C_6H_5(3\text{-}CH_3OC_6H_4)CHOH$ (55%)	*14*
C_6H_5CHO (12.7 g.)	$C_6H_5SO_2CH_2MgBr$ (15.0 g. $C_7H_8O_2S$)	$C_6H_5(C_6H_5SO_2CH_2)CHOH$ (22.7 g., 90% crude; 18.5 g., 73% pure)	*437*
C_6H_5CHO	$(CH_2)_5CHCH_2MgI$	$C_6H_5[(CH_2)_2CHCH_2]CHOH$ (36%)	*339*
C_6H_5CHO	$(CH_2)_5CHCH_2MgBr$	$C_6H_5[(CH_2)_5CHCH_2]CHOH$ (60%)	*265*
C_6H_5CHO	$(C_2H_5)_2N(CH_2)_3MgCl$	$C_6H_5[(C_2H_5)_2N(CH_2)_3]CHOH$ (67%)	*224*
C_6H_5CHO	$(C_2H_5)_2N(CH_2)_3Cl + Mg$	$C_6H_5[(C_2H_5)_2N(CH_2)_3]CHOH$	*233*
C_6H_5CHO	$C_6H_5C \equiv CMgBr$	$C_6H_5(C_6H_5C \equiv C)CHOH$	*44*
C_6H_5CHO	$C_6H_5CH(CO_2Na)MgCl$*	$C_6H_5CH(OH)CH(CO_2H)C_6H_5$ (60%)	*158*
C_6H_5CHO	$C_6H_5(CH_2)_2MgBr$ (10 g. C_8H_9Br)	$C_6H_5[C_6H_5(CH_2)_2]CHOH$ (80 g.)	*39*
C_6H_5CHO (5 ml.)	$2,3\text{-}(CH_3)_2C_6H_3MgBr$	$C_6H_5[2,3\text{-}(CH_3)_2C_6H_3]CHOH$ (44%)	*124*
C_6H_5CHO	$3,5\text{-}(CH_3)_2C_6H_3MgBr$	$C_6H_5[3,5\text{-}(CH_3)_2C_6H_3]CHOH$ (50%)	*124*
C_6H_5CHO	$(CH_2)_5N(CH_2)_3MgCl$	$C_6H_5[(CH_2)_5N(CH_2)_3]CHOH$ (63%)	*224*
C_6H_5CHO	$(CH_2)_5N(CH_2)_3Cl + Mg$	$C_6H_5[(CH_2)_5N(CH_2)_3]CHOH$	*233*
C_6H_5CHO	1-Indenyl-MgBr	Phenyl-1-indenylmethanol	*60*
C_6H_5CHO	$(C_2H_5)_2N(CH_2)_5MgCl$	$(C_2H_5)_2N(CH_2)_5CH(C_6H_5)OH$	*224*
C_6H_5CHO	$(C_2H_5)_2N(CH_2)_5Cl + Mg$	$(C_2H_5)_2N(CH_2)_5CH(C_6H_5)OH$	*233*
C_6H_5CHO	$(CH_3)_5C_6Br + C_2H_5Br + Mg$	$(CH_3)_5C_6H$; "bis(pentamethylbenzhydrol)"	*296*
C_6H_5CHO	$(n\text{-}C_4H_9)_2N(CH_2)_3MgCl$	$(n\text{-}C_4H_9)_2N(CH_2)_3CH(C_6H_5)OH$ (69%)	*224*
C_6H_5CHO	$(n\text{-}C_4H_9)_2N(CH_2)_3Cl + Mg$	$(n\text{-}C_4H_9)_2N(CH_2)_3CH(C_6H_5)OH$	*233*
C_6H_5CHO (16 g.)	$2\text{-}C_6H_5C_6H_4MgI$ (4 g. Mg)	$C_6H_5(2\text{-}C_6H_5C_6H_4)CHOH$ (21 g.)	*183*
C_6H_5CHO (2^+ equiv.)	$2\text{-}C_6H_5C_6H_4MgI$	$2\text{-}C_6H_5C_6H_4COC_6H_5$ (69.5%)	*37*
C_6H_5CHO	9-Phenanthryl-MgBr	Phenyl-9-phenanthrylmethanol (72%)	*11*

* In the opinion of Schlenk, Hilleman, and Rodloff, *Ann.*, *487*, 135–54 (1931), this "Grignard reagent" should be formulated as an enolate.

TABLE VI-XVII (Continued)

Aldehyde	RMgX	Product(s)	Ref.
C_7H_6O (*cont.*)			
C_6H_5CHO	$(C_6H_5)_3CMgCl$	$C_6H_5[(C_6H_5)_3C]CHOH$; $C_6H_5CH(OH)C_6H_4$-4-$CH(C_6H_5)_2$ (proportions depending on expt'l conditions.)	*298*,**324*
C_6H_5CHO (1.6 g.)	$(C_6H_5)_2C=C(C_6H_5)MgBr$ (5.0 g. $C_{20}H_{15}Br$)	$C_6H_5[(C_6H_5)_2C=C(C_6H_5)]CHOH$	*182*
C_6H_5CHO	2,4,6-$(C_6H_5)_3C_6H_2MgBr$ (excess †)	C_6H_5[2,4,6-$(C_6H_5)_3C_6H_2$]CHOH	*186*
$C_7H_6O_2$			
2-HOC_6H_4CHO	1-Indenyl-MgBr (2 equiv.)	2-Hydroxyphenyl-1-indenylmethanol (62%)	*60*
3-HOC_6H_4CHO	*n*-$C_5H_{11}MgI$	*n*-C_5H_{11}(3-HOC_6H_4)CHOH (97%)	*228*
4-HOC_6H_4CHO	$C_6H_5CH(CO_2Na)MgCl$ ‡	4-$HOC_6H_4CH(OH)CH(C_6H_5)CO_2H$ (15.5%); 4-$HOC_6H_4CH=CHC_6H_5$(29.6%)	*158*
$C_7H_{11}OBr$			
2-Bromocyclohexanecarboxaldehyde	CH_3MgI	$CH_3COCH(CH_2)_5$	*315*
2-Bromocyclohexanecarboxaldehyde	C_2H_5MgBr	$C_2H_5COCH(CH_2)_5$	*315*
2-Bromocyclohexanecarboxaldehyde	C_6H_5MgBr	2-Phenylcyclohexanecarboxaldehyde §	*315*
$C_7H_{12}O$			
$(CH_2)_5CHCHO$	$C_6H_5CH_2MgCl$	$(CH_2)_5CH(C_6H_5CH_2)CHOH$ (76%)	*339*

* Earlier references are listed by Schmidlin and Garcia-Banùs (*298*).

† To avoid benzaldehyde oxidation of product to ketone.

‡ In the opinion of Schlenk, Hilleman, and Rodloff, *Ann.*, *487*, 135-54 (1931), this "Grignard reagent" should be formulated as an enolate.

§ Due to rearrangement of (and elimination from) initially formed unstable halohydrin.

TABLE VI-XVII (Continued)

Aldehyde	RMgX	Product(s)	Ref.
$C_7H_{13}OBr$			
n-$C_5H_{11}CHBrCHO$	CH_3MgI	$CH_3(n$-$C_5H_{11}CHBr)CHOH$ ("poor yield"); CH_3CO-n-C_6H_{13}; n-$C_6H_{13}(CH_3)_2COH$; C_9H_{18}	*174*
$C_7H_{14}O$			
n-$C_6H_{13}CHO$	$(\equiv CMgBr)_2$	$[\equiv CCH(OH)$-n-$C_6H_{13}]_2$	*81*
n-$C_6H_{13}CHO$	$(\equiv CMgI)_2$	$[\equiv CCH(OH)$-n-$C_6H_{13}]_2$; $HC\equiv C(n$-$C_6H_{13})CHOH$	*155*
n-$C_6H_{13}CHO$	C_2H_5MgBr	$C_2H_5(n$-$C_6H_{13})CHOH$ (60–85%)*	*326,375*
n-$C_6H_{13}CHO$	$H_2C=CHCH_2Br$ + Mg	$H_2C=CHCH_2(n$-$C_6H_{13})CHOH$ (48%)	*165*
n-$C_6H_{13}CHO$	n-C_3H_7MgCl	n-$C_3H_7(n$-$C_6H_{13})CHOH$ (74%)	*169*
n-$C_6H_{13}CHO$ (8.0 moles)	i-C_3H_7MgBr (8.8 moles C_3H_7Br)	i-$C_3H_7(n$-$C_6H_{13})CHOH$ (66%)	*43,269*
n-$C_6H_{13}CHO$	n-C_4H_9MgX	n-$C_4H_9(n$-$C_6H_{13})CHOH$	*104*
n-$C_6H_{13}CHO$ (280 g.)	n-C_4H_9MgI (458 g. C_4H_9I)	n-$C_4H_9(n$-$C_6H_{13})CHOH$ (110 g.)	*42*
n-$C_6H_{13}CHO$	$(CH_2)_4CHMgBr$	$(CH_2)_4CH(n$-$C_6H_{13})CHOH$ (11%)	*85*
n-$C_6H_{13}CHO$	n-$C_5H_{11}MgX$	n-$C_5H_{11}(n$-$C_6H_{13})CHOH$	*104*
n-$C_6H_{13}CHO$ (100 g.)	i-$C_5H_{11}MgBr$ (180 g. $C_5H_{11}Br$)	i-$C_5H_{11}(n$-$C_6H_{13})CHOH$ (102 g.)	*269*
n-$C_6H_{13}CHO$	C_6H_5MgBr	$C_6H_5(n$-$C_6H_{13})CHOH$	*54*
n-$C_6H_{13}CHO$	n-$C_6H_{13}MgX$	$(n$-$C_6H_{13})_2CHOH$	*104*
n-$C_6H_{13}CHO$ (*ca.* 0.3 mole)	$C_6H_5CH_2MgCl$ (*ca.* 0.4 mole)	n-$C_6H_{13}(C_6H_5CH_2)CHOH$ (55%); 2-n-$C_6H_{13}CH(OH)C_6H_4CH_2CH(OH)$-$n$-$C_6H_{13}$ (14%)	*454*
n-$C_6H_{13}CHO$	n-$C_7H_{15}MgX$	n-$C_6H_{13}(n$-$C_7H_{15})CHOH$	*104*
n-$C_6H_{13}CHO$	$C_6H_5C\equiv CMgBr$	n-$C_6H_{13}(C_6H_5C\equiv C)CHOH$ (75%)	*214*
n-$C_6H_{13}CHO$	$C_6H_5CH(CO_2Na)MgCl$ †	n-$C_6H_{13}CH(OH)CH(C_6H_5)CO_2H$	*158*

* Tuot (*326*) reports the yields for a series of preparations as ranging from 60% to 85%.

† In the opinion of Schlenk, Hilleman, and Rodloff, *Ann.*, *487*, 135–54 (1931), this "Grignard reagent" should be formulated as an enolate.

TABLE VI-XVII (Continued)

Aldehyde	RMgX	Product(s)	Ref.
$C_7H_{14}O$ (*cont.*)			
n-$C_6H_{13}CHO$	$C_6H_5(CH_2)_2CH(CH_3)CH_2MgBr$	n-$C_6H_{13}[C_6H_5(CH_2)_2CH(CH_3)CH_2]CHOH$	*202*
n-$C_6H_{13}CHO$	2-$C_6H_5C_6H_4MgI$	n-C_6H_{13}(2-$C_6H_5C_6H_4$)CHOH (>50%)*	*38*
$C_7H_{15}ON$			
$(CH_3)_2NCH_2(CH_3)_2CCHO$	C_2H_5MgI (2 equiv.)	$C_2H_5[(CH_3)_2NCH_2(CH_3)_2C]CHOH$ ("good yield")†	*226*
$(CH_3)_2NCH_2(CH_3)_2CCHO$	n-C_4H_9MgBr (2 equiv.)	n-$C_4H_9[(CH_3)_2NCH_2(CH_3)_2C]CHOH$ ("good yield")†	*226*
$(CH_3)_2NCH_2(CH_3)_2CCHO$	C_6H_5MgBr (2 equiv.)	$C_6H_5[(CH_3)_2NCH_2(CH_3)_2C]CHOH$ ("good yield")†	*226*
$C_8H_6O_2$			
C_6H_4-1,2-$(CHO)_2$ (100 g.)	RMgBr‡ (100 g. Mg)	C_6H_4-1,2-$(CHROH)_2$‡	*74*
C_6H_4-1,2-$(CHO)_2$ (6.7 g.)	CH_3MgI (24.9 g. CH_3I)	C_6H_4-1,2-$[CH(OH)CH_3]_2$	*246*
C_6H_4-1,2-$(CHO)_2$	C_2H_5MgI (3.5 equiv.)	C_6H_4-1,2-$[CH(OH)C_2H_5]_2$	*246*
C_6H_4-1,2-$(CHO)_2$	C_6H_5MgI	1,3-Diphenylphthalan	*246*
C_6H_4-1,3-$(CHO)_2$ (100 g.)	RMgBr‡ (100 g. Mg)	C_6H_4-1,3-$(CHROH)_2$‡	*74*
C_6H_4-1,3-$(CHO)_2$ (50 g., 0.37 mole)	CH_3MgI (313 g., 2.1 moles CH_3I)	C_6H_4-1,3-$[CH(OH)CH_3]_2$ (25 g., 40%, crude)	*163*
C_6H_4-1,4-$(CHO)_2$ (100 g.)	RMgBr‡ (100 g. Mg)	C_6H_4-1,4-$(CHROH)_2$‡	*74*
C_6H_5COCHO	C_6H_5MgBr	$(C_6H_5)_2C(OH)CH(C_6H_5)OH$ (4 g., crude)	*212*
"Dimeric crotonaldehyde"§	CH_3MgX (1.25 equiv.)	$CH_3(C_7H_{11}O)CHOH$ (>50%)	*79*

* Figure recorded represents overall yield of olefin obtained upon subsequent dehydration.

† Yields stated to be "good, in general," for series of reactions studied.

‡ R = CH_3, C_2H_5, C_6H_5.

§ Delepine (73) assigns to "dimeric crotonaldehyde" the constitution of 4,6-dimethyl-5-oxacyclohexene-1-carboxaldehyde.

TABLE VI-XVII (Continued)

Aldehyde	RMgX	Product(s)	Ref.
$C_8H_6O_2$ (*cont.*)			
"Dimeric crotonaldehyde"*	C_2H_5MgI (1.25 equiv.)	$C_2H_5(C_7H_{11}O)CHOH$ (>50%)	79,73
"Dimeric crotonaldehyde"*	$i\text{-}C_3H_7MgX$ (1.25 equiv.)	$i\text{-}C_3H_7(C_7H_{11}O)CHOH$ (>50%)	79
"Dimeric crotonaldehyde"*	$i\text{-}C_4H_9MgX$	$i\text{-}C_4H_9(C_7H_{11}O)CHOH$ (>50%)	79
"Dimeric crotonaldehyde"*	$i\text{-}C_5H_{11}MgX$	$i\text{-}C_5H_{11}(C_7H_{11}O)CHOH$ (>50%)	79
$C_8H_6O_2Cl_2$			
$2\text{-}CH_3O\text{-}3,5\text{-}Cl_2C_6H_2CHO$ (5.000 g.)	9-Phenanthryl-MgBr (0.645 g. $C_{14}H_9Br$)	$2\text{-}CH_3O\text{-}3,5\text{-}Cl_2C_6H_2(9\text{-}C_{14}H_9)CHOH$ (3.6 g., 37%)	314
$C_8H_6O_3$			
$3,4\text{-}CH_2O_2{=}C_6H_3CHO$	CH_3MgI	$CH_3(3,4\text{-}CH_2O_2{=}C_6H_3)CHOH$; $3,4\text{-}CH_2O_2{=}C_6H_3CH{=}CH_2$; $3,4\text{-}CH_2O_2{=}C_6H_3COCH_3$; $(3,4\text{-}CH_2O_2{=}C_6H_3CH{=}CH\text{—})_x$	216,176
$3,4\text{-}CH_2O_2{=}C_6H_3CHO$	C_2H_5MgI	$C_2H_5(3,4\text{-}CH_2O_2{=}C_6H_3)CHOH$	216
$3,4\text{-}CH_2O_2{=}C_6H_3CHO$ (60.0 g.)	$H_2C{=}CHCH_2Cl$ (65.0 g.) + Mg (17.0 g.)	$H_2C{=}CHCH_2(3,4\text{-}CH_2O_2{=}C_6H_3)CHOH$ (54.4 g.)	414
$3,4\text{-}CH_2O_2{=}C_6H_3CHO$	$H_2C{=}CHCH_2Br$ + Mg	$H_2C{=}CHCH_2(3,4\text{-}CH_2O_2{=}C_6H_3)CHOH$	188
$3,4\text{-}CH_2O_2{=}C_6H_3CHO$	$n\text{-}C_3H_7MgI$ (2 equiv.)	$n\text{-}C_3H_7(3,4\text{-}CH_2O_2{=}C_6H_3)CHOH$	217
$3,4\text{-}CH_2O_2{=}C_6H_3CHO$	$i\text{-}C_3H_7MgBr$	$i\text{-}C_3H_7(3,4\text{-}CH_2O_2{=}C_6H_3)CHOH$	317
$3,4\text{-}CH_2O_2{=}C_6H_3CHO$	$(CH_3)_2N(CH_2)_3MgCl$	$(CH_3)_2N(CH_2)_3(3,4\text{-}CH_2O_2{=}C_6H_3)CHOH$	224
$3,4\text{-}CH_2O_2{=}C_6H_3CHO$	$(CH_3)_2N(CH_2)_3Cl$ + Mg	$(CH_3)_2N(CH_2)_3(3,4\text{-}CH_2O_2{=}C_6H_3)CHOH$	233
$3,4\text{-}CH_2O_2{=}C_6H_3CHO$ (47.5 g.)	$C_6H_5CH_2MgCl$ (40.0 g. C_7H_7Cl)	$3,4\text{-}CH_2O_2{=}C_6H_3CH{=}CHC_6H_5$ (18 g.)	131
$3,4\text{-}CH_2O_2{=}C_6H_3CHO$	$C_6H_5CH_2MgCl$ (2 equiv.)	$C_6H_5CH_2(3,4\text{-}CH_2O_2{=}C_6H_3)CHOH$ (90%)	317
$3,4\text{-}CH_2O_2{=}C_6H_3CHO$	$(C_2H_5)_2N(CH_2)_3MgCl$	$3,4\text{-}CH_2O_2{=}C_6H_3[(C_2H_5)_2N(CH_2)_3]CHOH$	224

*Delepine (73) assigns to "dimeric crotonaldehyde" the constitution of 4,6-dimethyl-5-oxacyclohexene-1-carboxaldehyde.

TABLE VI-XVII (Continued)

Aldehyde	RMgX	Product(s)	Ref.
$C_8H_6O_3$ (*cont.*)			
3,4-CH_2O_2=C_6H_3CHO	$(C_2H_5)_2N(CH_2)_3Cl$ + Mg	3,4-CH_2O_2=$C_6H_3[(C_2H_5)_2N(CH_2)_3]CHOH$	*233*
3,4-CH_2O_2=C_6H_3CHO	$C_6H_5CH(CO_2Na)MgCl$*	3,4-CH_2O_2=$C_6H_3CH(OH)CH(C_6H_5)CO_2H$ (23%)	*158*
3,4-CH_2O_2=C_6H_3CHO	$(CH_2)_5N(CH_2)_3MgCl$	3,4-CH_2O_2=$C_6H_3[(CH_2)_5N(CH_2)_3]CHOH$	*224*
3,4-CH_2O_2=C_6H_3CHO	$(CH_2)_5N(CH_2)_3Cl$ + Mg	3,4-CH_2O_2=$C_6H_3[(CH_2)_2N(CH_2)_3]CHOH$	*233*
3,4-CH_2O_2=C_6H_3CHO	1-Indenyl-MgBr	3,4-Methylenedioxyphenyl-1-indenylmethanol	*60*
$C_8H_7O_3$			
2-$HO_2CC_6H_4CHO$	CH_3MgI (4 equiv.)	3-Methylphthalide	*302*
2-$HO_2CC_6H_4CHO$	C_2H_5MgI (31.2 g. C_2H_5I)	3-Ethylphthalide (9 g.)	*231*
2-$HO_2CC_6H_4CHO$	C_6H_5MgI (4 equiv.)	3-Phenylphthalide	*231*
C_8H_8O			
$C_6H_5CH_2CHO$	2-ClC_6H_4MgI	2-$ClC_6H_4(C_6H_5CH_2)CHOH$ (70%)	*25*
$C_6H_5CH_2CHO$	$(CH_2)_5CHMgCl$	$(CH_2)_5CH(C_6H_5CH_2)CHOH$ (61%)	*265*
$C_6H_5CH_2CHO$ (21.4 g.)	2-$C_6H_5C_6H_4MgI$ (50.0 g. $C_{12}H_9I$)	$C_6H_5CH_2(2\text{-}C_6H_5C_6H_4)CHOH$ (9.5 g., 19%)	*430*
$C_6H_5CH_2CHO$ (12.5 g.)	9-Phenanthryl-MgBr (25.7 ml. $C_{14}H_9Br$)	1-(9-Phenanthryl)-2-phenylethanol (16.0 g.)	*22*
4-$CH_3C_6H_4CHO$	$(\equiv CMgBr)_2$	$[\equiv CCH(OH)C_6H_4\text{-}4\text{-}CH_3]_2$	*421,422*
4-$CH_3C_6H_4CHO$	C_2H_5I + Mg	$C_2H_5(4\text{-}CH_3C_6H_4)CHOH$; $(C_8H_8O)_2$; 4-$CH_3C_6H_4CH_2OH$	*416*
4-$CH_3C_6H_4CHO$	*i*-C_3H_7MgBr	*i*-$C_3H_7(4\text{-}CH_3C_6H_4)CHOH$ (41%)	*377*
$C_8H_8O_2$			
2-$CH_3OC_6H_4CHO$	CH_3MgI	$CH_3(2\text{-}CH_3OC_6H_4)CHOH$ (80%)	*176,222,275, 307*

* In the opinion of Schlenk, Hilleman, and Rodloff, *Ann.*, *487*, 135–54 (1931), this "Grignard reagent" should be formulated as an enolate.

TABLE VI-XVII (Continued)

Aldehyde	RMgX	Product(s)	Ref.
$C_8H_8O_2$ (*cont.*)			
2-$CH_3OC_6H_4CHO$	CH_3MgBr	CH_3(2-$CH_3OC_6H_4$)CHOH	*130*
2-$CH_3OC_6H_4CHO$	*i*-C_3H_7MgBr	*i*-C_3H_7(2-$CH_3OC_6H_4$)CHOH (93–94%)	*209*
2-$CH_3OC_6H_4CHO$	C_6H_5MgX*	C_6H_5(2-$CH_3OC_6H_4$)CHOH (95–97%)	*310*
2-$CH_3OC_6H_4CHO$	$C_6H_5CH(CO_2Na)MgCl$ †	2-$CH_3OC_6H_4CH(OH)CH(C_6H_5)CO_2H$ (95.8%)	*158*
3-$CH_3OC_6H_4CHO$	CH_3MgI (excess)	CH_3(3-$CH_3OC_6H_4$)CHOH	*176,307*
3-$CH_3OC_6H_4CHO$	*i*-C_3H_7MgBr	*i*-C_3H_7(3-$CH_3OC_6H_4$)CHOH (93–94%)	*209*
3-$CH_3OC_6H_4CHO$	*n*-C_4H_9MgCl	*n*-C_4H_9(3-$CH_3OC_6H_4$)CHOH (92%, crude)	*4*
4-$CH_3OC_6H_4CHO$	CH_3MgBr (excess)	CH_3(4-$CH_3OC_6H_4$)CHOH	*130*
4-$CH_3OC_6H_4CHO$	CH_3MgI (excess)	CH_3(4-$CH_3OC_6H_4$)CHOH	*176,307*
4-$CH_3OC_6H_4CHO$	$(\equiv CMgBr)_2$	$[\equiv CCH(OH)C_6H_4$-4-$OCH_3]_2$	*421,422*
4-$CH_3OC_6H_4CHO$	$(\equiv CMgI)_2$	$[\equiv CCH(OH)C_6H_4$-4-$OCH_3]_2$	*155*
4-$CH_3OC_6H_4CHO$	C_2H_5MgX*	C_2H_5(4-$CH_3OC_6H_4$)CHOH; 4-$CH_3OC_6H_4CH{=}CHCH_3$	*129*
4-$CH_3OC_6H_4CHO$	C_2H_5MgBr	4-$CH_3OC_6H_4CH{=}CHCH_3$; (4-$CH_3OC_6H_4CH{=}CHCH_3)_2$	*366*
4-$CH_3OC_6H_4CHO$	C_2H_5MgI	C_2H_5(4-$CH_3OC_6H_4$)CHOH	*293*
4-$CH_3OC_6H_4CHO$	*s*-C_4H_9MgBr (1.5 equiv.)	*s*-C_4H_9(4-$CH_3OC_6H_4$)CHOH	*348*
4-$CH_3OC_6H_4CHO$	*n*-$C_5H_{11}MgBr$	*n*-C_5H_{11}(4-$CH_3OC_6H_4$)CHOH	*63*
4-$CH_3OC_6H_4CHO$	4-BrC_6H_4MgBr	4-BrC_6H_4(4-$CH_3OC_6H_4$)CHOH	*234*
4-$CH_3OC_6H_4CHO$	4-ClC_6H_4MgI	4-ClC_6H_4(4-$CH_3OC_6H_4$)CHOH	*234*
4-$CH_3OC_6H_4CHO$ (28 g.)	C_6H_5MgBr (40 g. C_6H_5Br)	C_6H_5(4-$CH_3OC_6H_4$)CHOH (40 g., 90%)	*10; cf. 187*
4-$CH_3OC_6H_4CHO$	$(CH_2)_5CHMgBr$	$(CH_2)_5CH$(4-$CH_3OC_6H_4$)CHOH	*300*
4-$CH_3OC_6H_4CHO$	3-$CH_3C_6H_4MgBr$	3-$CH_3C_6H_4$(4-$CH_3OC_6H_4$)CHOH (55%)	*13*
4-$CH_3OC_6H_4CHO$	$(C_2H_5)_2N(CH_2)_3MgCl$	$(C_2H_5)_2N(CH_2)_3$(4-$CH_3OC_6H_4$)CHOH	*224*
4-$CH_3OC_6H_4CHO$	$(C_2H_5)_2N(CH_2)_3Cl$ + Mg	$(C_2H_5)_2N(CH_2)_3$(4-$CH_3OC_6H_4$)CHOH	*233,304*

* X = Br, I.

† In the opinion of Schlenk, Hilleman, and Rodloff, *Ann.*, *487*, 135–54 (1931), this "Grignard reagent" should be formulated as an enolate.

TABLE VI-XVII (Continued)

Aldehyde	RMgX	Product(s)	Ref.
$C_8H_8O_2$ (*cont.*)			
4-$CH_3OC_6H_4CHO$	$C_6H_5CH(CO_2Na)MgCl$*	4-$CH_3OC_6H_4CH(OH)CH(C_6H_5)CO_2H$ (95.8%)	*158*
4-$CH_3OC_6H_4CHO$	$(CH_2)_5N(CH_2)_3MgCl$	4-$CH_3OC_6H_4[(CH_2)_5N(CH_2)_3]CHOH$ (74%)	*224*
4-$CH_3OC_6H_4CHO$	$(CH_2)_5N(CH_2)_3Cl$ + Mg	4-$CH_3OC_6H_4[(CH_2)_5N(CH_2)_3]CHOH$	*233*
4-$CH_3OC_6H_4CHO$	1-Indenyl-MgBr	Anisyl-1-indenylmethanol (75%)	*60*
4-$CH_3OC_6H_4CHO$	1-$C_{10}H_7MgBr$	4-$CH_3OC_6H_4(1\text{-}C_{10}H_7)CHOH$ (74%)	*301*
$C_8H_8O_3$			
2-CH_3O-3-HOC_6H_3CHO	C_2H_5MgBr	2-CH_3O-3-$HOC_6H_3CH{=}CHCH_3$ (20%)	*78*
2-CH_3O-3-HOC_6H_3CHO	C_2H_5MgI	$C_2H_5(2\text{-}CH_3O\text{-}3\text{-}HOC_6H_3)CHOH$ (90%); 2-CH_3O-3-$HOC_6H_3CH{=}CHCH_3$ (10%) (Total yield not stated)	*78*
3-CH_3O-4-HOC_6H_3CHO	$C_6H_5CH(CO_2Na)MgCl$*	3-CH_3O-4-$HOC_6H_3CH(OH)CH(C_6H_5)CO_2H$ (22%); 3-CH_3O-4-$HOC_6H_3CH{=}CHC_6H_5$	*158*
$C_8H_{10}O$			
$CH_3(CH{=}CH)_3CHO$ (31 g.)	$({\equiv}CMgBr)_2$ (6 g. Mg)	$[{\equiv}CCH(OH)(CH{=}CH)_3CH_3]_2$ (7 g.)	*400*
$CH_3(CH{=}CH)_3CHO$ (12 g.)	1-Cyclohexenylethynyl-MgBr (10 g. C_8H_{10}	1-(1-Cyclohexenyl)deca-4,6,8-trien-1-yn-3-ol (6.1 g.)	*126*
$\Delta^{4,6}$-Dihydro-*o*-tolualdehyde (50 g.)	CH_3MgI (71 g. CH_3I)	1-CH_3-2-$C_2H_5C_6H_4$ (71%, crude)	*123*
$\Delta^{4,6}$-Dihydro-*o*-tolualdehyde	C_2H_5MgI	1-CH_3-2-*n*-$C_3H_7C_6H_4$ (68%, crude)	*123*
$C_8H_{16}O$			
n-$C_7H_{15}CHO$	CH_3MgI	$CH_3(n\text{-}C_7H_{15})CHOH$	*375*
n-$C_7H_{15}CHO$	$HC{\equiv}CH$ + 2 C_2H_5MgBr	$[{\equiv}CCH(OH)\text{-}n\text{-}C_7H_{15}]_2$ (42%)	*268*

* In the opinion of Schlenk, Hilleman, and Rodloff, *Ann.*, *487*, 135–54 (1931), this "Grignard reagent" should be formulated as an enolate.

TABLE VI-XVII (Continued)

Aldehyde	RMgX	Product(s)	Ref.
$C_8H_{16}O$ (*cont.*)			
$n\text{-}C_7H_{15}CHO$	$n\text{-}C_8H_{17}MgCl$	$n\text{-}C_7H_{15}(n\text{-}C_8H_{17})CHOH$ (67%)	*8*
$C_2H_5(n\text{-}C_4H_9)CHCHO$ (*ca.* 0.3 mole)	$C_6H_5CH_2MgCl$ (*ca.* 0.4 mole)	$C_6H_5CH_2[C_2H_5(n\text{-}C_4H_9)CH]CHOH$ (66%); $2\text{-}C_2H_5(n\text{-}C_4H_9)CHCH(OH)—C_6H_4CH_2CH(OH)CH(C_2H_5)\text{-}n\text{-}C_4H_9$ (6%)	*454*
C_9H_6O			
$C_6H_5C{\equiv}CCHO$ (13 g.)	CH_3MgI	$CH_3(C_6H_5C{\equiv}C)CHOH$ (7.5 g.); recovered aldehyde (*ca.* 1.0 g.)	*36*
$C_6H_5C{\equiv}CCHO$ (13 g.)	C_2H_5MgBr	$C_2H_5(C_6H_5C{\equiv}C)CHOH$ (9.5 g.)	*36*
$C_6H_5C{\equiv}CCHO$ (13 g.)	$n\text{-}C_3H_7MgI$	$n\text{-}C_3H_7(C_6H_5C{\equiv}C)CHOH$ (7.5 g.)	*36*
$C_6H_5C{\equiv}CCHO$ (13 g.)	$i\text{-}C_4H_9MgI$	$i\text{-}C_4H_9(C_6H_5C{\equiv}C)CHOH$ (5.5 g.)	*36*
$C_6H_5C{\equiv}CCHO$ (13 g.)	C_6H_5MgBr	$C_6H_5(C_6H_5C{\equiv}C)CHOH$ (7.0 g.)	*36*
C_9H_7OBr			
$C_6H_5CH{=}CBrCHO$	CH_3MgI	$CH_3(C_6H_5CH{=}CBr)CHOH$	*295*
$C_6H_5CH{=}CBrCHO$	C_6H_5MgBr	$C_6H_5(C_6H_5CH{=}CBr)CHOH$	*184*
C_9H_8O			
$C_6H_5CH{=}CHCHO$	CH_3MgBr	$CH_3(C_6H_5CH{=}CH)CHOH$	*243,178*
$C_6H_5CH{=}CHCHO$ (26 g.)	CH_3MgI (32 g. CH_3I)	$CH_3(C_6H_5CH{=}CH)CHOH$ (18 g.)	*380,40,61, 295*
$C_6H_5CH{=}CHCHO$	CH_3MgI (0.5 equiv.)	$CH_3COCH{=}CHC_6H_5$; $C_6H_5CH{=}CHCH_2OH$; $C_6H_5CH{=}CHCO_2H$; recovered aldehyde	*219*
$C_6H_5CH{=}CHCHO$	$({\equiv}MgBr)_2$	$[{\equiv}CCH(OH)CH{=}CHC_6H_5]_2$	*149,81*
$C_6H_5CH{=}CHCHO$ (30 g.)	C_2H_5MgBr (33 g. C_2H_5Br)	$C_2H_5(C_6H_5CH{=}CH)CHOH$ (24.5 g.)	*173,138,229*
$C_6H_5CH{=}CHCHO$	C_2H_5MgI (0.5 equiv.)	$C_2H_5COCH{=}CHC_6H_5$; $C_6H_5CH{=}CHCH_2OH$	*219*
$C_6H_5CH{=}CHCHO$ (32 g.)	$n\text{-}C_4H_9MgBr$ (67 g. C_4H_9Br)	$n\text{-}C_4H_9(C_6H_5CH{=}CH)CHOH$ (17 g.); $C_6H_5CH{=}CHCH_2OH$ (5 g.)	*267*

TABLE VI-XVII (Continued)

Aldehyde	RMgX	Product(s)	Ref.
C_9H_8O (*cont.*)			
$C_6H_5CH{=}CHCHO$ (9.5 g.)	i-C_4H_9MgCl (8.5 g. C_4H_9Cl)	Recovered aldehyde (30%)	*229*
$C_6H_5CH{=}CHCHO$ (9.5 g.)	i-C_4H_9MgBr (13.7 g. C_4H_9Br)	Recovered aldehyde (12%); i-$C_4H_9(C_6H_5CH{=}CH)CHOH$ ("in satisfactory yield and purity"); *no* $C_6H_5CH{=}CHCH_2OH$	*229,138*
$C_6H_5CH{=}CHCHO$ (64 g., 0.485 mole	t-$C_5H_{11}MgCl$ (0.79 mole)	t-$C_5H_{11}(C_6H_5)CHCH_2CHO$; *no* $C_6H_5CH{=}CHCH_2OH$	*358*
$C_6H_5CH{=}CHCHO$	4-BrC_6H_4MgBr	4-$BrC_6H_4(C_6H_5CH{=}CH)CHOH$ (m.p., 100°); unidentified oil	*360*
$C_6H_5CH{=}CHCHO$ (33 g.)	4-ClC_6H_4MgI (60 g. C_6H_4ClI)	4-$ClC_6H_4(C_6H_5CH{=}CH)CHOH$; $C_6H_5(4$-$ClC_6H_4CH{=}CH)CHOH$ (total yield, 54 g., crude)	*41*
$C_6H_5CH{=}CHCHO$ (25 g.)	C_6H_5MgBr (47 g. C_6H_5Br)	$C_6H_5(C_6H_5CH{=}CH)CHOH$ (21 g.)	*252,200*
$C_6H_5CH{=}CHCHO$	C_6H_5MgBr	*trans*-$C_6H_5(C_6H_5CH{=}CH)CHOH$ (63%)	*44,184*
$C_6H_5CH{=}CHCHO$ (33 g.)	4-$CH_3C_6H_4MgBr$ (43 g. C_7H_7Br)	4-$CH_3C_6H_4(C_6H_5CH{=}CH)CHOH$ (22 g.)	*41*
$C_6H_5CH{=}CHCHO$	4-$CH_3OC_6H_4MgBr$	4-$CH_3OC_6H_4(C_6H_5CH{=}CH)CHOH$ (m.p., 106–107°) (16%); no sat'd aldehyde (1,4-addition) detected	*360*
$C_6H_5CH{=}CHCHO$	$(C_2H_5)_2N(CH_2)_3Cl$ + Mg	$(C_2H_5)_2N(CH_2)_3CH(OH)CH{=}CHC_6H_5$	*233*
$C_6H_5CH{=}CHCHO$	$C_6H_5CH(CO_2Na)MgCl$*	$C_6H_5CH{=}CH_2CH(OH)CH(C_6H_5)CO_2H$ (75%)	*158*
$C_9H_{10}O$			
$CH_3(C_6H_5)CHCHO$	t-C_4H_9MgCl	t-$C_4H_9[CH_3(C_6H_5)CH]CHOH$; $CH_3(C_6H_5)CHCH_2OH$	*381*

* In the opinion of Schlenk, Hilleman, and Rodloff, *Ann.*, *487*, 135–54 (1931), this "Grignard reagent" should be formulated as an enolate.

TABLE VI-XVII (Continued)

Aldehyde	RMgX	Product(s)	Ref.
$C_9H_{10}O$ (*cont.*)			
$CH_3(C_6H_5)CHCHO$	C_6H_5MgBr	$C_6H_5[CH_3(C_6H_5)CH]CHOH$, α form (65%)	*433,170,316*
$C_6H_5(CH_2)_2CHO$	CH_3MgI	$CH_3(C_6H_5CH_2CH_2)CHOH$	*31*
3,5-$(CH_3)_2C_6H_3CHO$ (320 g., 2.83 moles)	CH_3MgI	$CH_3[3,5\text{-}(CH_3)_2C_6H_3]CHOH$ (338.5 g., 80%)	*223*
$C_9H_{10}O_2$			
4-$C_2H_5OC_6H_4CHO$ (60 g.)	C_2H_5MgI (125 g. C_2H_5I)	4-$C_2H_5OC_6H_4CH{=}CHCH_3$ (32 g.); higher-boiling products	*21*
$C_9H_{10}O_3$			
2,3-$(CH_3O)_2C_6H_3CHO$	CH_3MgI	$CH_3[2,3\text{-}(CH_3O)_2C_6H_3]CHOH$ (93%)	*263*
2,3-$(CH_3O)_2C_6H_3CHO$	C_2H_5MgBr	$C_2H_5[2,3\text{-}(CH_3O)_2C_6H_3]CHOH$	*78*
2,3-$(CH_3O)_2C_6H_3CHO$ (24.9 g.)	C_6H_5MgBr (15.7 g. C_6H_5Br)	$C_6H_5[2,3\text{-}(CH_3O)_2C_6H_3]CHOH$	*17*
2,3-$(CH_3O)_2C_6H_3CHO$ (16.6 g.)	4-$CH_3OC_6H_4MgBr$ (12.5 g. C_7H_7BrO)	4-$CH_3OC_6H_4[2,3\text{-}(CH_3O)_2C_6H_3]CHOH$	*17*
3,4-$(CH_3O)_2C_6H_3CHO$ (400 g., 2.41 moles)	CH_3MgI (344 g., 2.42 moles CH_3I)	3,4-$(CH_3O)_2C_6H_3CH{=}CH_2$(281 g., 18%)	*434*
3,4-$(CH_3O)_2C_6H_3CHO$ (33 g.)	C_2H_5MgBr	$C_2H_5[3,4\text{-}(CH_3O)_2C_6H_3]CHOH$ (16 g.); recovered aldehyde (10 g.)	*21*
3,4-$(CH_3O)_2C_6H_3CHO$ (66.4 g.)	$H_2C{=}CHCH_2Cl$ (64.8 g.) + Mg (17.0 g.)	$H_2C{=}CHCH_2[3,4\text{-}(CH_3O)_2C_6H_3]CHOH$ (72.7 g., 87%)	*414*
3,4-$(CH_3O)_2C_6H_3CHO$	$(C_2H_5)_2N(CH_2)_3MgCl$	$(C_2H_5)_2N(CH_2)_3[3,4\text{-}(CH_3O)_2C_6H_3]CHOH$ (10–15%)	*224*
3,4-$(CH_3O)_2C_6H_3CHO$	$(C_2H_5)_2N(CH_2)_3Cl$ + Mg	$(C_2H_5)_2N(CH_2)_3[3,4\text{-}(CH_3O)_2C_6H_3]CHOH$	*233*
$C_9H_{11}ON$			
4-$(CH_3)_2NC_6H_4CHO$	CH_3MgI	$CH_3[4\text{-}(CH_3)_2NC_6H_4]CHOH$ (75%)	*291*
4-$(CH_3)_2NC_6H_4CHO$	C_2H_5MgBr	$C_2H_5[4\text{-}(CH_3)_2NC_6H_4]CHOH$ (74%)	*291*
4-$(CH_3)_2NC_6H_4CHO$	4-BrC_6H_4MgBr	4-$BrC_6H_4[4\text{-}(CH_3)_2NC_6H_4]CHOH$	*234*
4-$(CH_3)_2NC_6H_4CHO$	4-ClC_6H_4MgBr	4-$ClC_6H_4[4\text{-}(CH_3)_2NC_6H_4]CHOH$	*234*

TABLE VI-XVII (Continued)

Aldehyde	RMgX	Product(s)	Ref.
$C_9H_{11}ON$ (*cont.*)			
4-$(CH_3)_2NC_6H_4CHO$	C_6H_5MgBr	$C_6H_5[4\text{-}(CH_3)_2NC_6H_4]CHOH$	*292*
4-$(CH_3)_2NC_6H_4CHO$	$C_6H_5CH_2MgCl$	$C_6H_5CH_2[4\text{-}(CH_3)_2NC_6H_4]CHOH$ (86%)	*291*
4-$(CH_3)_2NC_6H_4CHO$	$(C_2H_5)_2N(CH_2)_3Cl$ + Mg	$(C_2H_5)_2N(CH_2)_3[4\text{-}(CH_3)_2NC_6H_4]CHOH$	*233*
4-$(CH_3)_2NC_6H_4CHO$	1-$C_{10}H_7MgBr$	1-$C_{10}H_7[4\text{-}(CH_3)_2NC_6H_4]CHOH$ (90%, crude)	*291*
$C_9H_{16}O$			
$(CH_3)_2C{=}CH(CH_2)_2CH(CH_3)CHO$	CH_3MgI	$CH_3[(CH_3)_2C{=}CH(CH_2)_2CH(CH_3)]CHOH$ (60%)	77
$C_9H_{19}ON$			
$(C_2H_5)_2NCH_2(CH_3)_2CCHO$	C_6H_5MgBr (2 equiv.)	$C_6H_5[(C_2H_5)_2NCH_2(CH_3)_2C]CHOH$ ("good yield")*	*226*
$(C_2H_5)_2NCH_2(CH_3)_2CCHO$ (23.6 g., 0.15 mole)	4-$CH_3OC_{10}H_6$-1-MgBr (47.4 g., 0.2 mole $C_{11}H_9BrO$)	$(C_2H_5)_2NCH_2(CH_3)_2C(4\text{-}CH_3O\text{-}1\text{-}C_{10}H_6)CHOH$ (37.8 g., 72% crude hydrochloride)	*161*
$C_{10}H_7ON$			
Quinaldehyde †	CH_3MgI	1-α-Quinolylethanol	*145*
Quinaldehyde †	C_2H_5MgBr	1-α-Quinolyl-1-propanol	*145*
Quinaldehyde †	C_6H_5MgBr	Phenyl-α-quinolylmethanol (60%)	*145*
$C_{10}H_{10}O$			
$C_6H_5CH{=}C(CH_3)CHO$	CH_3MgI	$CH_3[C_6H_5CH{=}C(CH_3)]CHOH$	*425*
$C_{10}H_{10}O_2$			
$C_6H_5COCH(CH_3)CHO$ ‡	C_2H_5MgBr	$C_6H_5COCH(CH_3)CH(OH)C_2H_5$	*407*

* Yields stated to be "good, in general," for series of reactions studied.

† 2-Quinolinecarboxaldehyde.

‡ The reactions recorded are reported by Reynolds (407) as those of $C_6H_5COC(CH_3){=}CHOH$.

TABLE VI-XVII (Continued)

Aldehyde	RMgX	Product(s)	Ref.
$C_{10}H_{10}O_2$ (*cont.*)			
$C_6H_5COCH(CH_3)CHO$*	C_6H_5MgBr	$C_6H_5COC(CH_3){=}CHC_6H_5$	*407*
$C_{10}H_{10}O_5$			
$2,5\text{-}(CH_3O)_2\text{-}3,4\text{-}CH_2O_2{=}C_6HCHO$	CH_3MgI	$CH_3[2,5\text{-}(CH_3O)_2\text{-}3,4\text{-}CH_2O_2{=}C_6H]CHOH$ †	*88*
$2,5\text{-}(CH_3O)_2\text{-}3,4\text{-}CH_2O_2{=}C_6HCHO$	C_2H_5MgI	$C_2H_5[2,5\text{-}(CH_3O)_2\text{-}3,4\text{-}CH_2O_2{=}C_6H]CHOH$ †	*88*
$2,5\text{-}(CH_3O)_2\text{-}3,4\text{-}CH_2O_2{=}C_6HCHO$	C_6H_5MgI	$C_6H_5[2,5\text{-}(CH_3O)_2\text{-}3,4\text{-}CH_2O_2{=}C_6H]CHOH$ †	*88*
$2\text{-}HO_2C\text{-}3,4\text{-}(CH_3O)_2C_6H_2CHO$	CH_3MgI (3 equiv.)	α-Methylmeconine ‡	*302*
$2\text{-}HO_2C\text{-}3,4\text{-}(CH_3O)_2C_6H_2CHO$ (7.8 g.)	C_2H_5MgI (23.4 g. C_2H_5I)	α-Ethylmeconine § (7.6 g., 96%)	*230*
$2\text{-}HO_2C\text{-}3,4\text{-}(CH_3O)_2C_6H_2CHO$ (7.8 g.)	$n\text{-}C_3H_7MgI$ (25.4 g. C_3H_7I)	α-*n*-Propylmeconine ¶ (6.5 g., 70%)	*230*
$2\text{-}HO_2C\text{-}3,4\text{-}(CH_3O)_2C_6H_2CHO$ (5.2 g.)	C_6H_5MgI (20.4 g. C_6H_5I)	α-Phenylmeconine ‖	*230*
$C_{10}H_{12}O$			
$C_2H_5(C_6H_5)CHCHO$	C_6H_5MgBr	$C_6H_5[C_2H_5(C_6H_5)CH]CHOH$, α form (55%)	*433,170*
$C_6H_5(CH_3)_2CCHO$ (32 g.)	C_6H_5MgBr (1.5 equiv.)	$C_6H_5[C_6H_5(CH_3)_2C]CHOH$ (16 g.)	*207*
$i\text{-}C_3H_7C_6H_4CHO$	$(n\text{-}C_4H_9)_2N(CH_2)_3Cl$ + Mg	$(n\text{-}C_4H_9)_2N(CH_2)_3(i\text{-}C_3H_7C_6H_4)CHOH$	*233*
$2,4,6\text{-}(CH_3)_3C_6H_2CHO$ (44.4 g.)	$C_6H_5CH_2MgCl$ (49.2 g. C_7H_7Cl)	$C_6H_5CH_2[2,4,6\text{-}(CH_3)_3C_6H_2]CHOH$ (52.1 g., crude)	*102*

* The reactions recorded are reported by Reynolds (*407*) as those of $C_6H_5COC(CH_3){=}CHOH$.

† A benzene-aldehyde suspension was added to the well-cooled Grignard reagent solution; inadequate cooling yields the corresponding ether.

‡ 3-Methyl-6,7-dimethoxyphthalide.

§ 3-Ethyl-6,7-dimethoxyphthalide.

¶ 3-*n*-Propyl-6,7-dimethoxyphthalide.

‖ 3-Phenyl-6,7-dimethoxyphthalide.

TABLE VI-XVII (Continued)

Aldehyde	RMgX	Product(s)	Ref.
$C_{10}H_{12}O$ (*cont.*)			
2,4,6-$(CH_3)_3C_6H_2CHO$	2,4,6-$(CH_3)_3C_6H_2CH_2MgCl$	2,4,6-$(CH_3)_3C_6H_2$[2,4,6-$(CH_3)_3C_6H_2CH_2$]CHOH; [2,4,6-$(CH_3)_3C_6H_2CH_2$—]$_2$	*102*
$C_{10}H_{12}O_4$			
3,4,5-$(CH_3O)_3C_6H_2CHO$	CH_3MgI	CH_3[3,4,5-$(CH_3O)_3C_6H_2$]CHOH (65%)	227
3,4,5-$(CH_3O)_3C_6H_2CHO$	C_2H_5MgI	C_2H_5[3,4,5-$(CH_3O)_3C_6H_2$]CHOH (60%)	227
$C_{10}H_{13}O_3N$			
2,4-Dimethyl-5-carbethoxy-3-pyrrolecarboxaldehyde	CH_3MgI	1-(2,4-Dimethyl-5-carbethoxy-3-pyrryl)ethanol (80%)	*93*
$C_{10}H_{16}O$			
$(CH_3)_2C{=}CH(CH_2)_2C(CH_3){=}CHCHO$	CH_3MgX	$CH_3[(CH_3)_2C{=}CH(CH_2)_2C(CH_3){=}CH]CHOH$	*9*
$(CH_3)_2C{=}CH(CH_2)_2C(CH_3){=}CHCHO$	C_2H_5MgX	$C_2H_5[(CH_3)_2C{=}CH(CH_2)_2C(CH_3){=}CH]CHOH$	*9*
$(CH_3)_2C{=}CH(CH_2)_2C(CH_3){=}CHCHO$	*i*-C_4H_9MgX	*i*-$C_4H_9[(CH_3)_2C{=}CH(CH_2)_2C(CH_3){=}CH]CHOH$	*9*
$(CH_3)_2C{=}CH(CH_2)_2C(CH_3){=}CHCHO$	C_6H_5MgX	$C_6H_5[(CH_3)_2C{=}CH(CH_2)_2C(CH_3){=}CH]CHOH$	*9*
$(CH_3)_2C{=}CH(CH_2)_2C(CH_3){=}CHCHO$ (27.4 g.)	$CH_3CH{=}C(CH_3)C{\equiv}CMgBr$ (14.7 g. C_6H_8)	$(CH_3)_2C{=}CH(CH_2)_2C(CH_3){=}CH[CH_3CH{=}C(CH_3)C{\equiv}C]CHOH$ (30.5 g.)	*407*
$(CH_3)_2C{=}CH(CH_2)_2C(CH_3){=}CHCHO$	$(C_2H_5)_2N(CH_2)_3Cl$ + Mg	$(C_2H_5)_2N(CH_2)_3[(CH_3)_2C{=}CH(CH_2)_2C(CH_3){=}CH]CHOH$	233
3-Camphenilanecarboxaldehyde	C_6H_5MgBr	Phenyl-3-(2,2-dimethyl-norcamphanyl)methanol	*5*
3-Camphenilanecarboxaldehyde	$C_6H_5CH_2MgCl$	Benzyl-3-(2,2-dimethyl-norcamphanyl)methanol	*5*

TABLE VI-XVII (Continued)

Aldehyde	RMgX	Product(s)	Ref.
$C_{10}H_{16}O$ (*cont.*)			
3-Camphenilanecarboxaldehyde	1-$C_{10}H_7MgBr$	"Carbinol not isolable in pure form"	*5*
α-Campholenaldehyde*	CH_3MgI	1-(2,2,3-Trimethylcyclopent-3-enyl)propan-2-ol	*282*
α-Campholenaldehyde*	1-$C_{10}H_7MgBr$	"Carbinol not isolable in pure form"	*5*
$C_{10}H_{16}O_3$			
1,2,2-Trimethyl-3-carboxycyclopentane-1-carboxaldehyde	C_2H_5MgBr	β-Ethyl-β-campholide† (yield "poorer than for Me ester"; *i.e.*, $<37\%$)	*337*
$C_{10}H_{18}O$			
$(CH_3)_2C{=}CH(CH_2)_2CH(CH_3)CH_2CHO$	CH_3MgI	$CH_3[(CH_3)_2C{=}CH(CH_2)_2CH(CH_3)CH_2]CHOH$ (60%)	*77,287*
$(CH_3)_2C{=}CH(CH_2)_2CH(CH_3)CH_2CHO$	CH_3MgBr	$CH_3[(CH_3)_2C{=}CH(CH_2)_2CH(CH_3)CH_2]CHOH$ (quant.)	*285*
$(CH_3)_2C{=}CH(CH_2)_2CH(CH_3)CH_2CHO$	C_2H_5MgBr	$C_2H_5[(CH_3)_2C{=}CH(CH_2)_2CH(CH_3)CH_2]CHOH$	*285,121*
$(CH_3)_2C{=}CH(CH_2)_2CH(CH_3)CH_2CHO$	$H_2C{=}CHCH_2Br$ + Mg	$H_2C{=}CHCH_2[(CH_3)_2C{=}CH(CH_2)_2CH(CH_3)CH_2]CHOH$; $(H_2C{=}CHCH_2-)_2$	*285*
$(CH_3)_2C{=}CH(CH_2)_2CH(CH_3)CH_2CHO$	*n*-C_3H_7MgBr	*n*-$C_3H_7[(CH_3)_2C{=}CH(CH_2)_2CH(CH_3)CH_2]CHOH$ (quant.)	*285*
$(CH_3)_2C{=}CH(CH_2)_2CH(CH_3)CH_2CHO$	*n*-C_4H_9MgBr	*n*-$C_4H_9[(CH_3)_2C{=}CH(CH_2)_2CH(CH_3)CH_2]CHOH$	*113*
$(CH_3)_2C{=}CH(CH_2)_2CH(CH_3)CH_2CHO$ (35 g.)	$(CH_2)_5CHMgBr$ (50 g. $C_6H_{11}Br$)	$(CH_2)_5CH[CH_3)_2C{=}CH(CH_2)_2CH(CH_3)CH_2]CHOH$ (35–40 g.); $(CH_2)_6$; $[(CH_2)_5CH-]_2$	*285*

* 2,2,3-Trimethyl-3-cyclopentene-1-acetaldehyde.
† 4-Ethyl-5,8,8-trimethyl-3-oxabicyclo[3.2.1]octan-2-one.

TABLE VI-XVII (Continued)

Aldehyde	RMgX	Product(s)	Ref.
$C_{10}H_{18}O$ (*cont.*)			
$(CH_3)_2C{=}CH(CH_2)_2CH(CH_3)CH_2CHO$ (25 g.)	C_6H_5MgBr (31.4 g. C_6H_5Br)	$C_6H_5[(CH_3)_2C{=}CH(CH_2)_2CH(CH_3)CH_2]CHOH$ (25 g.)	*285*
$(CH_3)_2C{=}CH(CH_2)_2CH(CH_3)CH_2CHO$	$C_6H_5CH_2MgCl$	$C_6H_5CH_2[(CH_3)_2C{=}CH(CH_2)_2CH(CH_3)CH_2]CHOH$ (20%)*	*285,113*
$(CH_3)_2C{=}CH(CH_2)_2CH(CH_3)CH_2CHO$ (52.0 g., 0.338 mole)	$C_6H_5CH_2MgCl$ (0.663 mole C_7H_7Cl)	$C_6H_5CH_2[(CH_3)_2C{=}CH(CH_2)_2CH(CH_3)CH_2]CHOH$ (40.5 g.); $C_6H_5CH_2OH$; $C_6H_5CH_3$; isopulegol†; 1-$RCH_2(HO)CH$-2-$RCH_2(HO)CHCH_2C_6H_4$‡ (21.5 g. crude)	*452*
$(CH_3)_2C{=}CH(CH_2)_2CH(CH_3)CH_2CHO$	$C_6H_5C{\equiv}CMgBr$	$C_6H_5C{\equiv}C[(CH_3)_2C{=}CH(CH_2)_2CH(CH_3)CH_2]CHOH$	*286*
$(CH_3)_2C{=}CH(CH_2)_2CH(CH_3)CH_2CHO$	$C_6H_5(CH_2)_2MgBr$	$C_6H_5(CH_2)_2[(CH_3)_2C{=}CH(CH_2)_2CH(CH_3)CH_2]CHOH$ (70%)	*285*
$C_{10}H_{18}O_3$			
$H_3CO_2C(CH_2)_7CHO$ (37.2 g.)	n-C_4H_9MgBr (27.4 g. C_4H_9Br)	n-$C_4H_9[H_3CO_2C(CH_2)_7]CHOH$ (18.5 g., 38%)	*250*
$H_3CO_2C(CH_2)_7CHO$ (80 g.)	$(CH_2)_5CHMgBr$	$(CH_2)_5CH[H_3CO_2C(CH_2)_7]CHOH$ (25 g., 23%)	*426*
$H_3CO_2C(CH_2)_7CHO$	$(CH_2)_5CH(CH_2)_2MgBr$	$(CH_2)_5CH(CH_2)_2[H_3CO_2C(CH_2)_7]CHOH$ (26%)	*140*
$H_3CO_2C(CH_2)_7CHO$ (30 g.)	n-$C_9H_{19}MgBr$ (1 equiv.)	n-$C_9H_{19}[H_3CO_2C(CH_2)_7]CHOH$ (17 g.)	*322*
$C_{10}H_{20}O$			
n-$C_9H_{19}CHO$	n-$C_6H_{13}MgBr$	n-$C_6H_{13}(n$-$C_9H_{19})CHOH$ (70%)	*8*
n-$C_9H_{19}CHO$	$(C_2H_5)_2N(CH_2)_3Cl$ + Mg	n-$C_9H_{19}[(C_2H_5)_2N(CH_2)_3]CHOH$	*233*

* Yield still poorer with $C_6H_5CH_2MgBr$.

† $\Delta^{8(9)}$-*p*-Menthenol-3; 5-methyl-2-isopropenylcyclohexanol.

‡ R = $(CH_3)_2C{=}CH(CH_2)_2CH(CH_3)$—.

TABLE VI-XVII (Continued)

Aldehyde	RMgX	Product(s)	Ref.
$C_{10}H_{20}O$ (*cont.*)			
n-$C_9H_{19}CHO$	$(n\text{-}C_4H_9)_2N(CH_2)_3Cl$ + Mg	n-$C_9H_{19}[(n\text{-}C_4H_9)_2N(CH_2)_3]CHOH$	*233*
$C_{11}H_8O$			
1-$C_{10}H_7CHO$ (28.9 g.)	$H_2C{=}CHCH_2Cl$ (27.4 ml.) + Mg (6.05 g.)	$H_2C{=}CHCH_2(1\text{-}C_{10}H_7)CHOH$ (31.3 g., 94%)	*414,415*
1-$C_{10}H_7CHO$	$(C_2H_5)_2N(CH_2)_3MgCl$	1-$C_{10}H_7[(C_2H_5)_2N(CH_2)_3]CHOH$	*224*
1-$C_{10}H_7CHO$	$(C_2H_5)_2N(CH_2)_3Cl$ + Mg	1-$C_{10}H_7[(C_2H_5)_2N(CH_2)_3]CHOH$	*233*
2-$C_{10}H_7CHO$	C_6H_5MgBr	$C_6H_5(2\text{-}C_{10}H_7)CHOH$ (86%)	*14*
2-$C_{10}H_7CHO$ (11 g.)	9-Phenanthryl-MgBr (18 g. $C_{14}H_9Br$)	$[2\text{-}C_{10}H_7CH_2{-}]_2$	*23*
$C_{11}H_9O_2N$			
1-Methyl-2-oxo-1,2-dihydro-cinchoninaldehyde* (2.0 g., 0.01 mole)	C_6H_5MgBr (4.0 g. C_6H_5Br)	1-Methyl-4-α-hydroxybenzylcarbostyril (0.9 g., 32%)	*57*
$C_{11}H_{12}O_2$			
2,4,6-$(CH_3)_3C_6H_2COCHO$ (17.6 g.)	C_6H_5MgBr (31.4 g. C_6H_5Br)	2,4,6-$(CH_3)_3C_6H_2COCOC_6H_5$ (6.43 g.)	*382*
2,4,6-$(CH_3)_3C_6H_2COCHO$	2,4,6-$(CH_3)_3C_6H_2MgBr$	$[2,4,6\text{-}(CH_3)_3C_6H_2COCH(OH){-}]_2$; $[2,4,6\text{-}(CH_3)_3C_6H_2CO{-}]_2$	*382*
$C_{11}H_{16}ON_2$			
2,4,-$[(CH_3)_2N]_2C_6H_3CHO$	C_2H_5MgBr (3 equiv.)	$C_2H_5\{2,4\text{-}[(CH_3)_2N]_2C_6H_3\}CHOH$	*383*

* 1-Methyl-4-formyl-2(1*H*)-quinolinone.

TABLE VI-XVII (Continued)

Aldehyde	RMgX	Product(s)	Ref.
$C_{11}H_{18}O_3$			
1,2,2-Trimethyl-3-carbomethoxy-cyclopentane-1-carboxaldehyde	CH_3MgI (4 equiv.)	β-Methyl-β-campholide* (62%); 1,2,2-trimethyl-1-(1-hydroxyethyl)-3-(2-hydroxy-2-propyl)cyclopentane; 1,2,4,4,8,8-hexamethyl-3-oxabicyclo[3.2.1]octane; 1,2,2-trimethyl-1-(1-hydroxyethyl)-3-isopropenylcyclopentane; 1,2,2- trimethyl-1-vinyl-3-isopropenylcyclopentane	338
1,2,2-Trimethyl-3-carbomethoxy-cyclopentane-1-carboxaldehyde	C_2H_5MgBr	β-Ethyl-β-campholide† (37–40%); 1,2,2-trimethyl-1-propenyl-3-(Δ^2-3-pentenyl)cyclopentane; 1,8,8-trimethyl-2,4,4-triethyl-3-oxabicyclo[3.2.1]octane; 1,2,2-trimethyl-1-(1-hydroxypropyl)-3-(Δ^2-3-pentenyl)cyclopentane; 1,2,2-trimethyl-1-(1-hydroxypropyl)-3-(3-hydroxy-3-pentyl)cyclopentane	337,338
1,2,2-Trimethyl-3-carbomethoxy-cyclopentane-1-carboxaldehyde	n-C_3H_7MgBr	β-n-Propyl-β-campholide (3%); probably some β-campholide	337
1,2,2-Trimethyl-3-carbomethoxy-cyclopentane-1-carboxaldehyde	n-C_4H_9MgBr	β-n-Butyl-β-campholide; β-campholide	337
1,2,2-Trimethyl-3-carbomethoxy-cyclopentane-1-carboxaldehyde	C_6H_5MgBr (2 equiv.)	β-Phenyl-β-campholide	337
1,2,2-Trimethyl-3-carbomethoxy-cyclopentane-1-carboxaldehyde	$C_6H_5CH_2MgCl$	β-Benzyl-β-campholide	337

* 4,5,8,8-Tetramethyl-3-oxabicyclo[3.2.1]octan-2-one.
† 4-Ethyl-5,8,8-trimethyl-3-oxabicyclo[3.2.1]octan-2-one.

TABLE VI-XVII (Continued)

Aldehyde	RMgX	Product(s)	Ref.
$C_{11}H_{20}O_3$			
$H_5C_2O_2C(CH_2)_7CHO$	n-C_3H_7MgI	n-$C_3H_7CH(OH)(CH_2)_7CO_2C_2H_5$	7
$H_3CO_2C(CH_2)_8CHO$	$(CH_2)_4CHCH_2MgBr$	$(CH_2)_4CHCH_2CH(OH)(CH_2)_8CO_2CH_3$	*251*
$H_3CO_2C(CH_2)_8CHO$ (48.0 g.)	$(CH_2)_5CHMgBr$	$(CH_2)_5CH[H_3CO_2C(CH_2)_8]CHOH$ (15.4 g., 23%)	*426*
$H_3CO_2C(CH_2)_8CHO$ (47 g.)	$(CH_2)_5CHCH_2CH_2MgBr$	$(CH_2)_5CHCH_2CH_2[H_3CO_2C(CH_2)_8]CHOH$ (10 g., 14%)	*426*
$H_3CO_2C(CH_2)_8CHO$ (45 g.)	n-$C_8H_{17}MgBr$ (1 equiv.)	n-$C_8H_{17}CH(OH)(CH_2)_8CO_2CH_3$ (25 g.)	*322*
$C_{11}H_{23}ON$			
$(n$-$C_3H_7)_2NCH_2(CH_3)_2CCHO$	4-$CH_3OC_{10}H_6$-1-MgBr	4-CH_3O-1-$C_{10}H_6[(n$-$C_3H_7)_2NCH_2(CH_3)_2C]CHOH$	*159*
$C_{12}H_{20}O_3$			
1,2,2-Trimethyl-3-carbethoxy-cyclopentane-1-carboxaldehyde	C_2H_5MgBr	β-Ethyl-β-campholide	*337*
$C_{12}H_{22}O_3$			
$H_5C_2O_2C(CH_2)_8CHO$ (96 g., 0.45 mole)	t-$C_4H_9CH_2CH_2MgCl$ (61 g., 0.5 mole $C_6H_{13}Cl$)	t-$C_4H_9CH_2CH_2[H_5C_2O_2C(CH_2)_8]CHOH$ (70%)	*435*
$H_5C_2O_2C(CH_2)_8CHO$ (96 g., 0.45 mole)	t-$C_4H_9(CH_2)_4MgCl$ (75 g., 0.5 mole $C_8H_{17}Cl$)	t-$C_4H_9(CH_2)_4[H_5C_2O_2C(CH_2)_8]CHOH$ (63%)	*435*
$H_3CO_2C(CH_2)_9CHO$ (16 g.)	n-$C_7H_{15}MgBr$ (1 equiv.)	n-$C_7H_{15}[H_3CO_2C(CH_2)_9]CHOH$ (10 g.)	*322*
$C_{12}H_{24}O$			
n-$C_{11}H_{23}CHO$	n-C_4H_9MgCl	n-$C_4H_9(n$-$C_{11}H_{23})CHOH$ (58%)	8
$CH_3(t$-$C_4H_9)(t$-$C_4H_9CH_2)CCHO$ (36.8 g., 0.2 mole)	t-$C_5H_{11}MgCl$ (0.4 mole)	$CH_3(t$-$C_4H_9)(t$-$C_4H_9CH_2)CCH_2OH$ (90%)	358
$C_{13}H_{12}O_2$			
2-Ethoxy-1-naphthalene-carboxaldehyde (20 g.)	9-Phenanthryl-MgBr	2-Ethoxy-1-naphthyl-9-phenanthryl-methanol (22 g., 58%)	*24*

TABLE VI-XVII (Continued)

Aldehyde	RMgX	Product(s)	Ref.
$C_{13}H_{24}O_3$			
$H_3CO_2C(CH_2)_{10}CHO$ (38 g.)	n-$C_6H_{13}MgBr$ (1 equiv.)	n-$C_6H_{13}CH(OH)(CH_2)_{10}CO_2CH_3$ (13 g.)	*322*
$C_{13}H_{27}ON$			
$(n\text{-}C_4H_9)_2NCH_2(CH_3)_2CCHO$	4-$CH_3OC_{10}H_6$-1-MgBr	4-CH_3O-1-$C_{10}H_6[(n\text{-}C_4H_9)_2NCH_2(CH_3)_2C]CHOH$	*161*
$C_{14}H_{12}O$			
$(C_6H_5)_2CHCHO$ (98 g.)	4-$CH_3OC_6H_4MgBr$ (140 g. C_7H_7BrO)	4-$CH_3OC_6H_4[(C_6H_5)_2CH]CHOH$ (150 g.)	*196*
$C_{14}H_{12}O_2$			
3-$C_6H_5CH_2OC_6H_4CHO$	$(C_2H_5)_2N(CH_2)_3Cl$ + Mg	$(C_2H_5)_2N(CH_2)_3CH(OH)C_6H_4$-3-$CH_2OC_6H_5$	233
4-$C_6H_5CH_2OC_6H_4CHO$	$(C_2H_5)_2N(CH_2)_3Cl$ + Mg	$(C_2H_5)_2N(CH_2)_3CH(OH)C_6H_4$-4-$CH_2OC_6H_5$	233
$C_{14}H_{22}O$			
$RCH{=}CHCH(CH_3)CHO$* (10.8 g.)	$C_2H_5OCH_2CH{=}C(CH_3)C{\equiv}CMgBr$ (6.5 g. $C_8H_{12}O$)	$RCH{=}CHCH(CH_3)CH(OH)C{\equiv}CC(CH_3){=}CHCH_2OC_2H_5$*	235
$RCH_2CH{=}C(CH_3)CHO$*† (17 g.)	$({\equiv}CMgBr)_2$ (27 g. C_2H_5Br)	$[{\equiv}CCH(OH)C(CH_3){=}CHCH_2R]_2$* (11 g., crude)	*147*
$RCH_2CH{=}C(CH_3)CHO$*†	$BrMgOCH_2CH{=}CHC{\equiv}CMgBr$	$RCH_2CH{=}C(CH_3)CH(OH)C{\equiv}CCH{=}CHCH_2OH$	*404*
$RCH_2CH{=}C(CH_3)CHO$*† (72.0 g.)	$BrMgOCH_2CH{=}C(CH_3)C{\equiv}CMgBr$ (39.6 g. C_6H_8O)	$RCH_2CH{=}C(CH_3)CH(OH)C{\equiv}CC(CH_3){=}CHCH_2OH$* (85.0 g., 81%)	*402,141*
$RCH_2CH{=}C(CH_3)CHO$*† (3.5 g.)	n-$C_4H_9C{\equiv}CMgBr$ (5.0 g. C_6H_{10})	$RCH_2CH{=}C(CH_3)CH(OH)C{\equiv}C$-$n$-$C_4H_9$* (4.5 g., 92%)	*403*

* R = 2,6,6-Trimethyl-1-cyclohexenyl.
† This is the so-called "β-ionone C_{14} aldehyde" (*402,403*).

TABLE VI-XVII (Continued)

Aldehyde	RMgX	Product(s)	Ref.
$C_{14}H_{22}O$ (*cont.*)			
$RCH_2CH{=}C(CH_3)CHO$*†	$CH_3OCH_2CH{=}C(CH_3)C{\equiv}CMgBr$	$RCH_2CH{=}C(CH_3)CH(OH)C{\equiv}CC(CH_3){=}CHCH_2OCH_3$*	*157*
$RCH_2CH{=}C(CH_3)CHO$*† (5.15 g.)	$CH_3OCH(CH_3)CH{=}CHC{\equiv}CMgBr$ (6 g. $C_7H_{10}O$)	$RCH_2CH{=}C(CH_3)CH(OH)C{\equiv}CCH{=}CHCH(CH_3)OCH_3$* (5.7 g., 94% on basis of aldehyde consumed); recovered aldehyde (1.2 g., 23%)	*403*
$RCH_2CH{=}C(CH_3)CHO$*† (30.0 g.)	n-$C_4H_9OCH_2CH{=}C(CH_3)C{\equiv}CMgBr$ (31.0 g. $C_{10}H_{16}O$)	$RCH_2CH{=}C(CH_3)CH(OH)C{\equiv}CC(CH_3){=}CHCH_2O$-$n$-$C_4H_9$* (41.5 g.)	*157*
$RCH_2CH{=}C(CH_3)CHO$*† (39.3 g.)	$C_6H_5OCH_2CH{=}C(CH_3)C{\equiv}CMgBr$ (36.6 g. $C_{12}H_{12}O$)	$RCH_2CH{=}C(CH_3)CH(OH)C{\equiv}CC(CH_3){=}CHCH_2OC_6H_5$* (20.0 g.)	*157*
$C_{14}H_{26}O_3$			
$H_5C_2O_2C(CH_2)_{10}CHO$ (50 g., 0.2 mole)	t-$C_4H_9(CH_2)_4MgCl$ (30 g., 0.2 mole $C_8H_{17}Cl$)	t-$C_4H_9(CH_2)_4[H_5C_2O_2C(CH_2)_{10}]CHOH$ (57 g.)	*435*
$H_3CO_2C(CH_2)_{11}CHO$	$(CH_2)_4CHMgBr$	$(CH_2)_4CHCH(OH)(CH_2)_{11}CO_2CH_3$; $H_3CO_2C(CH_2)_{11}CH_2OH$; $[H_3CO_2C(CH_2)_{11}CH(OH){-}]_2$	*251*
$H_3CO_2C(CH_2)_{11}CHO$ (41 g.)	n-$C_5H_{11}MgBr$	n-$C_5H_{11}CH(OH)(CH_2)_{11}CO_2CH_3$ (10 g.)	*322*
$H_3CO_2C(CH_2)_{11}CHO$ (72.6 g.)	$(CH_2)_5CHMgBr$ (1 equiv.)	$(CH_2)_5CHCH(OH)(CH_2)_{11}CO_2CH_3$ (13.5 g.)	*140*
$C_{15}H_{10}O$			
2-Phenanthrenecarboxaldehyde	C_6H_5MgBr	Phenyl-2-phenanthrylmethanol (80%)	*12*
3-Phenanthrenecarboxaldehyde	C_6H_5MgBr	Phenyl-3-phenanthrylmethanol (64%)	*12*
9-Phenanthrenecarboxaldehyde (20 g.)	1-$C_{10}H_7MgBr$ (20 g. $C_{10}H_7Br$)	1-Naphthyl-9-phenanthrylmethanol	*23*

*R = 2,6,6-Trimethyl-1-cyclohexenyl.

†This is the so-called "β-ionone C_{14} aldehyde" (*402, 403*).

TABLE VI-XVII (Continued)

Aldehyde	RMgX	Product(s)	Ref.
$C_{15}H_{10}O$ (*cont.*)			
9-Phenanthrenecarboxaldehyde (11 g.)	2-$CH_3C_{10}H_6$-1-MgBr (11 g. $C_{11}H_9Br$)	2-Methyl-1-naphthyl-9-phenanthrylmethanol	*24*
9-Anthraldehyde (30 g.)	CH_3MgI (21.5 g. CH_3I)	1-(9-Anthracyl)ethanol (29.6 g., 92%)	*89*
9-Anthraldehyde (5.0 g.)	C_6H_5MgBr	Phenyl-9-anthracylmethanol (3.3 g.)	*165*
$C_{15}H_{12}O_4$			
3-CH_3O-4-$C_6H_5CO_2C_6H_3CHO$	CH_3MgI	CH_3(3-CH_3O-4-$C_6H_5CO_2C_6H_3$)CHOH (85%)	*91*
3-CH_3O-4-$C_6H_5CO_2C_6H_3CHO$	*n*-C_3H_7MgI	*n*-C_3H_7(3-CH_3O-4-$C_6H_5CO_2C_6H_3$)CHOH (31.5%)	*144*
3-CH_3O-4-$C_6H_5CO_2C_6H_3CHO$	*n*-C_4H_9MgI	*n*-C_4H_9(3-CH_3O-4-$C_6H_5CO_2C_6H_3$)CHOH (48%)	*144*
3-CH_3O-4-$C_6H_5CO_2C_6H_3CHO$	*n*-$C_5H_{11}MgI$	*n*-C_5H_{11}(3-CH_3O-4-$C_6H_5CO_2C_6H_3$)CHOH (48%)	*144*
$C_{15}H_{14}O$			
$CH_3(C_6H_5)_2CCHO$ (14 g.)	CH_3MgI (1.25 equiv.)	$CH_3[CH_3(C_6H_5)_2C]CHOH$ (11 g.)	*207*
$CH_3(C_6H_5)_2CCHO$ (21 g.)	C_6H_5MgBr (1.25 equiv.)	$C_6H_5[CH_3(C_6H_5)_2C]CHOH$ (17 g.)	*207*
$C_6H_5(C_6H_5CH_2)CHCHO$	C_6H_5MgBr	$C_6H_5[C_6H_5(C_6H_5CH_2)CH]CHOH$, α form	*433*
DL-$C_6H_5(C_6H_5CH_2)CHCHO$	C_6H_5MgBr	α-DL-$C_6H_5[C_6H_5(C_6H_5CH_2)CH]CHOH$, m. 92°	*318*
$C_{15}H_{31}ON$			
$(n\text{-}C_5H_{11})_2NCH_2(CH_3)_2CCHO$	4-$CH_3OC_{10}H_6$-1-MgBr	4-CH_3O-1-$C_{10}H_6[(n\text{-}C_5H_{11})_2NCH_2(CH_3)_2C]CHOH$	*161*
$C_{16}H_{16}O$			
$C_2H_5(C_6H_5)_2CCHO$	CH_3MgI (1.25 equiv.)	$CH_3[C_2H_5(C_6H_5)_2C]CHOH$	*207*

TABLE VI-XVII (Continued)

Aldehyde	RMgX	Product(s)	Ref.
$C_{16}H_{16}O$ (*cont.*)			
$(C_6H_5CH_2)_2CHCHO$	$4\text{-}CH_3OC_6H_4MgBr$	$4\text{-}CH_3OC_6H_4[(C_6H_5CH_2)_2CH]CHOH$	*319*
$C_{16}H_{24}O$			
$2,4,6\text{-}(i\text{-}C_3H_7)_3C_6H_2CHO$ (69.6 g.)	$C_6H_5CH_2MgCl$	$C_6H_5CH_2[2,4,6\text{-}(i\text{-}C_3H_7)_3C_6H_2]CHOH$ (75 g., crude)	*102*
$C_{17}H_{13}O_2$			
2-Phenyl-6-methoxyquinoline-4-carboxaldehyde (5.0 g., 0.019 mole)	$(C_2H_5)_2N(CH_2)_3MgCl$ (8.5 g., 0.057 mole $C_7H_{16}ClN$)	α-(3-Diethylaminopropyl)-2-phenyl-6-methoxy-4-quinolinemethanol (isolated as hydrochloride, 8.3 g., 97%)	*112*
2-Phenyl-6-methoxyquinoline-4-carboxaldehyde (5.0 g., 0.019 mole)	$(n\text{-}C_4H_9)_2N(CH_2)_3MgCl$ (11.7 g., 0.057 mole $C_{11}H_{24}ClN$)	α-(3-Di-*n*-butylaminopropyl)-2-phenyl-6-methoxy-4-quinolinemethanol (isolated as hydrochloride, 5.0 g., 52%)	*112*
$C_{17}H_{15}O_5$			
$(-)\text{-}C_6H_5CO_2CH_2CH(O_2CC_6H_5)CHO$	C_6H_5MgBr	$C_6H_5CO_2CH_2CH(O_2CC_6H_5)CH(C_6H_5)OH$, α(−) form	*320*
$C_{17}H_{18}O$			
$CH_3(C_6H_5CH_2)_2CCHO$	CH_3MgI	$CH_3[CH_3(C_6H_5CH_2)_2C]CHOH$	*208*
$C_6H_5[2,4,6\text{-}(CH_3)_3C_6H_2]CHCHO$ (0.5 g.)	C_6H_5MgBr (0.505 g. C_6H_5Br)	$C_6H_5[2,4,6\text{-}(CH_3)_3C_6H_2]CHCH(C_6H_5)OH$	*103*
$C_{17}H_{22}O_3$			
Benzyl 1-formyl-1,2,2-trimethylcyclopentane-3-carboxylate	C_2H_5MgBr	β-Ethyl-β-campholide* (25%)	*337*

* 4-Ethyl-5,8,8-trimethyl-3-oxabicyclo[3.2.1]octan-2-one.

TABLE VI-XVII (Continued)

Aldehyde	RMgX	Product(s)	Ref.
$C_{17}H_{24}O$			
$RCH{=}CHC(CH_3){=}CHCH{=}CHCHO$*	$C_2H_5OC{\equiv}CMgBr$	$C_2H_5OC{\equiv}C[RCH{=}CHC(CH_3){=}CHCH{=}CH]CHOH$*	384
$C_{18}H_{34}O_3$			
$H_5C_2O_2C(CH_2)_{14}CHO$ (0.25 mole)	t-$C_4H_9CH_2CH_2MgCl$ (0.25 mole $C_6H_{13}Cl$)	t-$C_4H_9CH_2CH_2[H_5C_2O_2C(CH_2)_{14}]CHOH$	435
$H_5C_2O_2C(CH_2)_{14}CHO$	t-$C_4H_9(CH_2)_4MgCl$	t-$C_4H_9(CH_2)_4[H_5C_2O_2C(CH_2)_{14}]CHOH$	435
$C_{19}H_{12}O$			
7-Benz[*a*]anthracenecarboxaldehyde	CH_3MgI	1-(7-Benz[*a*]anthracyl)ethanol (56%)	89
$C_{20}H_{36}O_2$			
Citronellal aldol [$RCH_2CH(OH)CHRCHO$]† (25.0 g., 0.0815 mole)	C_6H_5MgBr (0.241 mole)	$RCH_2CH(OH)CHRCH(OH)C_6H_5$† (23.8 g.)	452
$C_{21}H_{14}O$			
10-Phenyl-9-anthraldehyde (8.3 g.)	C_6H_5MgBr (2.4 g. Mg)	9-Phenyl-10-(α-hydroxybenzyl)anthracene (3.5 g.)	165
$C_{22}H_{20}O$			
$C_6H_5(4\text{-}CH_3C_6H_4)_2CCHO$	C_6H_5MgBr (3 equiv.)	$C_6H_5[C_6H_5(4\text{-}CH_3C_6H_4)_2C]CHOH$	207
$C_{30}H_{40}O$			
β-Apo-2-carotinal (90 mg.)	C_2H_5MgBr (0.3 g. C_2H_5Br)	Corresponding secondary alcohol (39 mg.)	168

* R = 2,6,6-Trimethyl-1-cyclohexenyl.
† R = $(CH_3)_2C{=}CH(CH_2)_2CH(CH_3)$—.

REFERENCES FOR TABLE VI-XVII

(*1*) Abelmann, *Ber.*, *40*, 4589–90 (1907).
(*2*) Adams, Harfenist, and Loewe, *J. Am. Chem. Soc.*, *71*, 1624–8 (1949).
(*3*) Adams and Noller, *Organic Syntheses*, *6*, 22–5 (1926); 7, 90 (1927); 8, 124 (1928).
(*4*) Alles, Icke, and Feigen, *J. Am. Chem. Soc.*, *64*, 2031–5 (1942).
(*5*) Arbuzov, *J. Gen. Chem.* (U.S.S.R.), *9*, 249–54 (1939); *Chem. Abstr.*, *33*, 6279 (1939).
(*6*) Arcus and Kenyon, *J. Chem. Soc.*, *1938*, 312–8.
(*7*) Asano, *J. Pharm. Soc., Japan*, *1927*, No. 544, 76–7; *Chem. Zentr.*, *1927,II*, 1016.
(*8*) Asinger and Eckholdt, *Ber.*, *76B*, 579–84 (1943).
(*9*) Austerweil and Cochin, *Compt. rend.*, *151*, 440–1 (1911); *Chem. Abstr.*, *5*, 2091 (1911).
(*10*) Bachmann, *J. Am. Chem. Soc.*, *55*, 2135–9 (1933).
(*11*) Bachmann, *J. Am. Chem. Soc.*, *56*, 1363–7 (1934).
(*12*) Bachmann, *J. Am. Chem. Soc.*, *57*, 555–9 (1935).
(*13*) Bachmann and Ferguson, *J. Am. Chem. Soc.*, *56*, 2081–4 (1934).
(*14*) Bachmann, Hoffman, and Whitehead, *J. Org. Chem.*, *8*, 320–30 (1943).
(*15*) Bachman and Lewis, *J. Am. Chem. Soc.*, *69*, 2022–5 (1947).
(*16*) Backer and Bolt, *Rec. trav. chim.*, *54*, 68–72 (1935).
(*17*) Baker and Smith, *J. Chem. Soc.*, *1936*, 346–8.
(*18*) Baker and Squire, *J. Am. Chem. Soc.*, *70*, 1487–90 (1948).
(*19*) Bartlett and Rosen, *J. Am. Chem. Soc.*, *64*, 543–6 (1942).
(*20*) Baudrenghien, *Bull. soc. chim. Belg.*, *31*, 160–70 (1922).
(*21*) Béhal and Tiffeneau, *Bull. soc. chim.*, [4], 3, 301–10 (1908).
(*22*) Bergmann and Bergmann, *J. Am. Chem. Soc.*, *59*, 1443–50 (1937).
(*23*) Bergmann and Israelashivili, *J. Am. Chem. Soc.*, *68*, 1–5 (1946).
(*24*) Bergmann and Israelashivili, *J. Am. Chem. Soc.*, *68*, 354–6 (1946).
(*25*) Bergmann, Weizman, and Schapiro, *J. Org. Chem.*, *9*, 408–14 (1944).
(*26*) Bergkvist, *Svensk. Kem. Tid.*, *59*, 27–30 (1947); *Chem. Abstr.*, *41*, 5095 (1947).
(*27*) Bert, *Bull. soc. chim.*, [4], 37, 1577–91 (1925).
(*28*) Betti and Lucchi, *Boll. sci. facolta chim. ind., Bologna*, *1940*, No. 1–2, 2–5; *Chem. Abstr.*, *34*, 2354 (1940).
(*29*) Billeter and Miescher, *Helv. Chim. Acta*, *29*, 859–71 (1946).
(*30*) Bjelouss, *Ber.*, *43*, 2330–3 (1910).
(*31*) Bogert and Davidson, *J. Am. Chem. Soc.*, *56*, 185–90 (1934).
(*32*) Bogert, Davidson, and Appelbaum, *J. Am. Chem. Soc.*, *56*, 959–63 (1934).
(*33*) Bouis, *Ann. chim.*, [10], 9, 402–65 (1928).
(*34*) Bourgom, *Bull. soc. chim. Belg.*, *33*, 101–15 (1924).
(*35*) Bouveault, *Bull. soc. chim.*, [3], *29*, 1049–51 (1903).
(*36*) Brachin, *Bull. soc. chim.*, [3], *35*, 1163–79 (1906).
(*37*) Bradsher, *J. Am. Chem. Soc.*, *66*, 45–6 (1944).
(*38*) Bradsher and Amore, *J. Am. Chem. Soc.*, *63*, 493–5 (1941).
(*39*) Brewin and Turner, *J. Chem. Soc.*, *1930*, 502–4.
(*40*) Burton, *J. Chem. Soc.*, *1929*, 455–8.
(*41*) Burton and Ingold, *J. Chem. Soc.*, *1928*, 904–21.
(*42*) Byrtschenko, *J. Russ. Phys.-Chem. Soc.*, *42*, 876–9 (1910); *Chem. Zentr.*, *1910,II*, 1744.
(*43*) Calingaert and Soroos, *J. Am. Chem. Soc.*, *58*, 635–6 (1936).
(*44*) Campbell, Campbell, and McGuire, *Proc. Indiana Acad. Sci.*, *50*, 87–93 (1940); *Chem. Abstr.*, *35*, 5872 (1941).

(45) Campbell and McGuire, *Proc. Indiana Acad. Sci.*, *50*, 87–93 (1940); *Chem. Abstr.*, *35*, 5872 (1941).
(46) Cason, Adams, Bennett, and Register, *J. Am. Chem. Soc.*, *66*, 1764–7 (1944).
(47) Chu and Marvel, *J. Am. Chem. Soc.*, *53*, 4449 (1931).
(48) Claisen and Tietze, *Ber.*, *59B*, 2344–51 (1926).
(49) Clarke, *J. Am. Chem. Soc.*, *30*, 1144–52 (1908).
(50) Clarke, *J. Am. Chem. Soc.*, *31*, 107–16 (1909).
(51) Clément, *Compt. rend.*, *207*, 864–6 (1938); *Chem. Abstr.*, *33*, 7747 (1939).
(52) Clément, *Ann. chim.*, [11], *13*, 243–316 (1940).
(53) Coburn, *Organic Syntheses*, *27*, 65–7 (1947).
(54) Colacicchi, *Atti accad. Lincei*, [5], *19,II*, 600–5 (1910); *Chem. Zentr.*, *1911,I*, 382.
(55) Conant, Webb, and Mendum, *J. Am. Chem. Soc.*, *51*, 1246–55 (1929).
(56) Consden, Duveen, and Kenyon, *J. Chem. Soc.*, *1938*, 2104–6.
(57) Cook and Stamper, *J. Am. Chem. Soc.*, *69*, 1467–8 (1947).
(58) Cottle and Hollyday, *J. Org. Chem.*, *12*, 510–6 (1947).
(59) Courtot, *Bull. soc. chim.*, [3], *35*, 969–88 (1906).
(60) Courtot, *Ann. chim.*, [9], *4*, 58–136 (1915).
(61) Coyner and Ropp, *J. Am. Chem. Soc.*, *69*, 2231–2 (1947).
(62) Dauben, *J. Am. Chem. Soc.*, *70*, 1376–8 (1948).
(63) Davies, Dixon, and Jones, *J. Chem. Soc.*, *1930*, 468–73.
(64) Dean and Wolf, *J. Am. Chem. Soc.*, *58*, 332–3 (1936).
(65) Deemer, Lutwak, and Strong, *J. Am. Chem. Soc.*, *70*, 154–7 (1948).
(66) Delaby, *Bull. soc. chim.*, [4], *27*, 609–11 (1920).
(67) Delaby, *Compt. rend.*, *175*, 167–70 (1922).
(68) Delaby, *Compt. rend.*, *175*, 967–70 (1922).
(69) Delaby, *Compt. rend.*, *194*, 1248–50 (1932).
(70) Delaby, *Ann. chim.*, [9], *19*, 275–326 (1923).
(71) Delaby, *Bull. soc. chim.*, [4], *33*, 602–26 (1923).
(72) Delaby and Guillot-Allegré, *Bull. soc. chim.*, [4], *53*, 301–20 (1933).
(73) Delepine, *Compt. rend.*, *150*, 535–7 (1910); *Chem. Zentr.*, *1910,I*, 1495.
(74) Deluchat, *Ann. chim.*, [11], *1*, 181–255 (1934).
(75) Doering and Beringer, *J. Am. Chem. Soc.*, *71*, 2221–6 (1949).
(76) Doeuvre, *Bull. soc. chim.*, [4], *45*, 403–12 (1929).
(77) Doeuvre, *Bull. soc. chim.*, [4], *45*, 710–5 (1929).
(78) Douetteau, *Bull. soc. chim.*, [4], *11*, 652–6 (1912).
(79) Douris, *Compt. rend.*, *157*, 943–5 (1913); *Chem. Zentr.*, *1914,I*, 123.
(80) Drake and Cooke, *Organic Syntheses*, Coll. Vol. II, pp. 406–7 (1943).
(81) Dupont, *Ann. chim.*, [8], *30*, 485–587 (1913).
(82) Duveen and Kenyon, *Bull. soc. chim.*, [5], *5*, 704–9 (1938).
(83) Duveen and Kenyon, *Bull. soc. chim.*, [5], *5*, 1120–6 (1938).
(84) Edgar, Calingaert, and Marker, *J. Am. Chem. Soc.*, *51*, 1483–91 (1929).
(85) Edwards and Reid, *J. Am. Chem. Soc.*, *52*, 3235–41 (1930).
(86) Elderfield, Craig, Lauer, Arnold, Gensler, Head, Bembry, Mighton, Tinker, Galbreath, Holley, Goldman, Maynard, and Picus, *J. Am. Chem. Soc.*, *68*, 1516–23 (1943).
(87) Elderfield and Head, U. S. Patent 2,422,957, June 24, 1947; *Chem. Abstr.*, *41*, P6274 (1947).
(88) Fabinyi and Szeki, *Ber.*, *50*, 1335–9 (1917).
(89) Fieser and Hartwell, *J. Am. Chem. Soc.*, *60*, 2555–9 (1938).
(90) Fieser and Seligman, *J. Am. Chem. Soc.*, *61*, 136–42 (1939).
(91) Finnemore, *J. Chem. Soc.*, *93*, 1520–4 (1908).

(92) Fischer and Baer, *Helv. Chim. Acta*, *18*, 514–21 (1935).
(93) Fischer and Zeile, *Ann.*, *462*, 210–30 (1928).
(94) Floutz, *J. Am. Chem. Soc.*, *65*, 2255 (1943).
(95) Floutz, *J. Am. Chem. Soc.*, *67*, 1615–6 (1945).
(96) Floutz, *J. Am. Chem. Soc.*, *68*, 2490–1 (1946).
(97) Floutz, *J. Am. Chem. Soc.*, *71*, 2859–60 (1949).
(98) Fourneau and Ramart-Lucas, *Bull. soc. chim.*, [4], *25*, 364–70 (1919).
(99) Fourneau and Tiffeneau, *Compt. rend.*, *145*, 437–9 (1907); *Chem. Zentr.*, *1907*,*II*, 1320.
(100) Franke and Kohn, *Monatsh.*, *27*, 1097–128 (1906).
(101) Freundler, *Compt. rend.*, *142*, 343–5 (1906); *Chem. Zentr.*, *1906*,*I*, 934.
(102) Fuson, Denton, and Best, *J. Org. Chem.*, *8*, 64–72 (1943).
(103) Fuson and Tan, *J. Am. Chem. Soc.*, *70*, 602–5 (1948).
(104) Garach, *Groupement franc. dévelop. recherches aéronaut.*, *Note tech. No. 15*, 30 pp. (1944); *Chem. Abstr.*, *43*, 2156 (1949).
(105) Gauthier and Gauthier, *Bull. soc. chim.*, [4], *53*, 323–6 (1933).
(106) Gérard, *Bull. acad. roy. Belg.*, *Classe sci.*, *1906*, 790–5; *Chem. Zentr.*, *1907*,*I*, 1398.
(107) Gilman and Abbot, *J. Org. Chem.*, *8*, 224–9 (1943).
(108) Gilman and Catlin, *Organic Syntheses*, Coll. Vol. I, 1st ed., pp. 182–5 (1932); 2nd ed., pp. 188–90 (1941).
(109) Gilman and Franz, *Rec. trav. chim.*, *51*, 991–5 (1932).
(110) Gilman and Kirby, *J. Am. Chem. Soc.*, *51*, 3475–8 (1929).
(111) Gilman and Kirby, *J. Am. Chem. Soc.*, *54*, 345–55 (1932).
(112) Gilman, Marshall, and Benkeser, *J. Am. Chem. Soc.*, *68*, 1849–50 (1946).
(113) Gilman and Schulz, *J. Am. Chem. Soc.*, *52*, 3588–90 (1930).
(114) Gorski, *J. Russ. Phys.-Chem. Soc.*, *42*, 1356–8 (1910); *Chem. Zentr.*, *1911*,*I*, 635.
(115) Grard, *Compt. rend.*, *189*, 541–3 (1929).
(116) Grédy, *Compt. rend.*, *199*, 153–4 (1934); *Chem. Abstr.*, *28*, 6117 (1934).
(117) Grédy, *Bull. soc. chim.*, [5], *2*, 1038–44 (1935).
(118) Grédy, *Bull. soc. chim.*, [5], *3*, 1093–101 (1936).
(119) Grignard, *Ann. Univ. Lyon*, N.S., *6*, 1–116 (1901); *Chem. Zentr.*, *1901*,*II*, 622.
(120) Grignard, *Compt. rend.*, *130*, 1322–4 (1900); *J. Chem. Soc.*, *78*,*I*, 382 (1900).
(121) Grignard, *Ann. chim.*, [7], *24*, 433–90 (1901).
(122) Grignard and Courtot, *Compt. rend.*, *160*, 500–4 (1915); *Chem. Zentr.*, *1915*,*II*, 406.
(123) Grundmann, *Chem. Ber.*, *81*, 513–9 (1948); *Chem. Abstr.*, *43*, 5376 (1949).
(124) Grunert, Nichol, and Sandin, *J. Am. Chem. Soc.*, *69*, 2254–6 (1947).
(125) Grüttner and Cauer, *Ber.*, *51*, 1283–92 (1918).
(126) Heilbron, Jones, Lewis, Richardson, and Weedon, *J. Chem. Soc.*, *1949*, 742–6.
(127) Heilbron, Jones, and Raphael, *J. Chem. Soc.*, *1943*, 264–5.
(128) Hell, *Ber.*, *37*, 453–8 (1904).
(129) Hell and Hofmann, *Ber.*, *37*, 4188–93 (1904).
(130) Hell and Hofmann, *Ber.*, *38*, 1676–80 (1905).
(131) Hell and Wiegandt, *Ber.*, *37*, 1429–32 (1904).
(132) Henry, *Compt. rend.*, *138*, 205–6 (1904); *J. Chem. Soc.*, *86*,*I*, 279 (1904).
(133) Henry, *Compt. rend.*, *144*, 308–13 (1907); *Chem. Zentr.*, *1907*,*I*, 1102.
(134) Henry, *Bull. acad. roy. Belg.*, *Classe sci.*, *1907*, 162–89; *Chem. Zentr.*, *1907*,*II*, 445.
(135) Henry and Dewael, *Bull. acad. roy. Belg.*, *Classe sci.*, *1908*, 857–63; *Chem. Zentr.*, *1909*,*I*, 1854.

(136) Henze, Allen, and Leslie, *J. Org. Chem.*, *7*, 326–35 (1942).
(137) Hess and Rheinboldt, *Ber.*, *54B*, 2043–55 (1921).
(138) Hess and Wustrow, *Ann.*, *434*, 256–73 (1924).
(139) Salkind and Issakovitch, *J. Russ. Phys.-Chem. Soc.*, *45*, 1896–903 (1914); *Bull. soc. chim.*, [4], *16*, 546 (1914).
(140) Hiers and Adams, *J. Am. Chem. Soc.*, *48*, 1089–93 (1926).
(141) Hoffmann-LaRoche & Co. A.-G., Swiss Patent 250,374, July 1, 1948; *Chem. Abstr.*, *43*, P7959 (1949).
(142) Howard, *J. Am. Chem. Soc.*, *48*, 774–5 (1926).
(143) Howard, *J. Am. Chem. Soc.*, *49*, 1068–9 (1927).
(144) Howells, Little, and Andersen, *J. Am. Chem. Soc.*, *52*, 4076–82 (1930).
(145) Howiz and Kopke, *Ann.*, *396*, 38–52 (1913).
(146) Hurd and Cohen, *J. Am. Chem. Soc.*, *53*, 1917–22 (1931).
(147) Inhoffen, Pommer, and Bohlmann, *Ann.*, *561*, 26–31 (1948).
(148) Iotsitch, *J. Russ. Phys.-Chem. Soc.*, *34*, 241–2 (1902); *Bull. soc. chim.*, [3], *30*, 209 (1903).
(149) Iotsitch, *J. Russ. Phys.-Chem. Soc.*, *34*, 242–4 (1902); *Bull. soc. chim.*, [3], *30*, 210 (1903).
(150) Iotsitch, *J. Russ. Phys.-Chem. Soc.*, *35*, 430–1 (1903); *Bull. soc. chim.*, [3], *32*, 551, (1904).
(151) Iotsitch, *J. Russ. Phys.-Chem. Soc.*, *35*, 1269–75 (1905); *Bull. soc. chim.*, [3], *34*, 181 (1905).
(152) Iotsitch, *J. Russ. Phys.-Chem. Soc.*, *36*, 8–9 (1904); *Bull. soc. chim.*, [3], *34*, 204 (1905).
(153) Iotsitch, *J. Russ. Phys.-Chem. Soc.*, *36*, 443–6 (1904); *Bull. soc. chim.*, [3], *34*, 329 (1905).
(154) Iotsitch, *J. Russ. Phys.-Chem. Soc.*, *38*, 252–3 (1906); *Bull. soc. chim.*, [4], *4*, 981 (1908).
(155) Iotsitch, *J. Russ. Phys.-Chem. Soc.*, *38*, 656–9 (1906); *Bull. soc. chim.*, [4], *4*, 1203 (1908).
(156) Isler, Kofler, Huber, and Ronco, *Experientia*, *2*, 31 (1946); *Chem. Abstr.*, *40*, 4032 (1946).
(157) Isler, Ronco, Guex, Hindley, Huber, Dialer, and Kofler, *Helv. Chim. Acta*, *32*, 489–505 (1949).
(158) Ivanoff and Nicoloff, *Bull. soc. chim.*, [4], *51*, 1325–31 (1932).
(159) Jacobs, *J. Org. Chem.*, *11*, 223–8 (1946).
(160) Jacobs, Cramer, and Weiss, *J. Am. Chem. Soc.*, *62*, 1849–54 (1940).
(161) Jacobs, Winstein, Linden, and Seymour, *J. Org. Chem.*, *11*, 223–8 (1946).
(162) Jaworsky, *Ber.*, *42*, 435–8 (1909).
(163) Johnston and Williams, *J. Am. Chem. Soc.*, *69*, 2065 (1947).
(164) Jolkver, *Rec. trav. chim.*, *28*, 439–43 (1909).
(165) Julian, Cole, Diemer, and Schafer, *J. Am. Chem. Soc.*, *71*, 2058–61 (1949).
(166) Juvala, *Ber.*, *63B*, 1989–2009 (1930).
(167) Karasev, *J. Gen. Chem.* (U.S.S.R.), *10*, 1699–703 (1940); *Chem. Abstr.*, *35*, 3223 (1941).
(168) Karrer, Ruegger, and Geiger, *Helv. Chim. Acta*, *21*, 1171–4 (1938).
(169) Karrer, Shibata, Wettstein, and Jacubowiecz, *Helv. Chim. Acta*, *13*, 1292–1308 (1930).
(170) Kayser, *Compt. rend.*, *199*, 1424–7 (1934).
(171) Kenyon and Young, *J. Chem. Soc.*, *1938*, 1452–4.
(172) Kharasch, Kleiger, Martin, and Mayo, *J. Am. Chem. Soc.*, *63*, 2305–7 (1941).
(173) Kinney and Spliethoff, *J. Org. Chem.*, *14*, 71–8 (1949).
(174) Kirrman, *Compt. rend.*, *184*, 1463–5 (1927).

(175) Klages, *Ber.*, *35*, 2646–9 (1902).
(176) Klages, *Ber.*, *36*, 3584–97 (1903).
(177) Klages, *Ber.*, *37*, 2301–17 (1904).
(178) Klages, *Ber.*, *39*, 2587–95 (1906).
(179) Klages and Klenk, *Ber.*, *39*, 2552–5 (1906).
(180) Klimenko, *J. Russ. Phys.-Chem. Soc.*, *43*, 212–3 (1911); *Chem. Zentr.*, *1911,I*, 1852.
(181) Knorr, German Patent 544,388, Jan. 28, 1932; *Friedländer*, *18*, 180–4 (1933).
(182) Koelsch, *J. Am. Chem. Soc.*, *54*, 2045–8 (1932).
(183) Koelsch, *J. Am. Chem. Soc.*, *56*, 480–4 (1934).
(184) Kohler, *Am. Chem. J.*, *31*, 642–61 (1904).
(185) Kohler, *Am. Chem. J.*, *38*, 511–61 (1907).
(186) Kohler and Blanchard, *J. Am. Chem. Soc.*, *57*, 367–71 (1935).
(187) Kohler and Patch, *J. Am. Chem. Soc.*, *38*, 1205–16 (1916).
(188) Korjukin, *J. Russ. Phys.-Chem. Soc.*, *43*, 204–7 (1910); *Chem. Zentr.*, *1911,I*, 1852.
(189) Krestinsky, *Ber.*, *55B*, 2754–62 (1922).
(190) Krestinsky, *Ber.*, *55B*, 2762–70 (1922).
(191) Krestinsky, *Ber.*, *55B*, 2770–4 (1922).
(192) Kursanov and Solodkov, *Compt. rend. acad. sci. U.R.S.S.*, *27*, 797–800 (1940); *Chem. Abstr.*, *35*, 1770 (1941).
(193) Kuznetsov, *J. Gen. Chem.* (U.S.S.R.), *9*, 2263–8 (1939); *Chem. Abstr.*, *34*, 5052 (1940).
(194) Kyriakides, *J. Am. Chem. Soc.*, *36*, 657–63 (1914).
(195) Lagerev and Shamshurin, *J. Gen. Chem.* (U.S.S.R.), *9*, 199–202 (1939); *Chem. Abstr.*, *33*, 6258 (1939).
(196) LaGrave, *Ann. chim.*, [10], *8*, 363–446 (1927).
(197) Lautenschlager and Onsager, *Ber.*, *51*, 602–5 (1918).
(198) Lépingle, *Bull. soc. chim.*, [4], *39*, 864–73 (1926).
(199) Lespieau, *Compt. rend.*, *150*, 113–4 (1910); *Chem. Zentr.*, *1910,I*, 1001.
(200) Lespieau and Wakeman, *Bull. soc. chim.*, [4], *51*, 384–400 (1932).
(201) Levene and Haller, *J. Biol. Chem.*, *76*, 415–22 (1928).
(202) Levene and Harris, *J. Biol. Chem.*, *111*, 735–8 (1935).
(203) Levene and Marker, *J. Biol. Chem.*, *93*, 749–74 (1931).
(204) Levene and Marker, *J. Biol. Chem.*, *103*, 299–309 (1933).
(205) Levina, *J. Gen. Chem.* (U.S.S.R.), *7*, 684–7 (1937); *Chem. Abstr.*, *31*, 5772 (1937).
(206) Levina and Grinberg, *J. Gen. Chem.* (U.S.S.R.), *7*, 2306–8 (1937); *Chem. Abstr.*, *32*, 509 (1938).
(207) Lévy, *Bull. soc. chim.*, [4], *29*, 878–99 (1921).
(208) Lévy, *Bull. soc. chim.*, [4], *39*, 67–72 (1926).
(209) Lévy and Pernot, *Bull. soc. chim.*, [4], *49*, 1721–30 (1931).
(210) Lock, *Ber.*, *72B*, 300–4 (1939).
(211) Lozac'h, *Bull. soc. chim.*, [5], *8*, 519–21 (1941).
(212) Madelung and Oberwegner, *Ber.*, *65B*, 931–41 (1932).
(213) Malengreau, *Bull. acad. roy. Belg.*, *Classe Sci.*, *1906*, 802–10; *Chem. Zentr.*, *1907,I*, 1398.
(214) Malenok and Sologub, *J. Gen. Chem.* (U.S.S.R.), *10*, 150–3 (1940); *Chem. Abstr.*, *34*, 7286 (1940).
(215) Malenok and Sologub, *J. Gen. Chem.* (U.S.S.R.), *11*, 983–90 (1941); *Chem. Abstr.*, *37*, 355 (1943).
(216) Mameli, *Gazz. chim. ital.*, *34,I*, 358–74 (1904); *Chem. Zentr.*, *1904,II*, 214.

(217) Mameli and Alagra, *Atti accad. Lincei*, [5], *14,II*, 170–80 (1905); *Chem. Zentr.*, *1905,II*, 895.
(218) Marko and P'yankov, *Uchenye Zapiski Molotov. Gosudarst. Univ.*, *3*, No. 4, 9–14 (1939); *Khim. Referat. Zhur.*, *4*, No. 4, 49 (1941); *Chem. Abstr.*, *37*, 5058 (1943).
(219) Marshall, *J. Chem. Soc.*, *127*, 2184–5 (1925).
(220) Marvel, Allen, and Overberger, *J. Am. Chem. Soc.*, *68*, 1088–91 (1946).
(221) Marvel, Blomquist, and Vaughan, *J. Am. Chem. Soc.*, *50*, 2810–2 (1928).
(222) Marvel and Hein, *J. Am. Chem. Soc.*, *70*, 1895–8 (1948).
(223) Marvel, Saunders, and Overberger, *J. Am. Chem. Soc.*, *68*, 1085–8 (1946).
(224) Marxer, *Helv. Chim. Acta*, *24*, 209–15E (1941).
(225) Mascarelli and Pirona, *Atti X° congr. intern. chim.*, *3*, 249–50 (1939); *Chem. Abstr.*, *33*, 9314 (1939).
(226) Matti and Barman, *Bull. soc. chim.*, [5], *2*, 1742–4 (1935).
(227) Mauthner, *J. prakt. chem.*, [2], *92*, 194–201 (1915).
(228) McPhee and Ball, *J. Am. Chem. Soc.*, *66*, 1636–40 (1944).
(229) Meisenheimer, *Ann.*, *442*, 180–210 (1925).
(230) Mermod and Simonis, *Ber.*, *39*, 897–9 (1906).
(231) Mermod and Simonis, *Ber.*, *41*, 982–5 (1908).
(232) Michiels, *Bull. acad. roy. Belg.*, *Classe sci.*, *1912*, 10–34; *Chem. Zentr.*, *1912,I*, 1105; *Chem. Abstr.*, *6*, 1611 (1912).
(233) Miescher and Marxer, U. S. Patent 2,411,664, Nov. 26, 1946; *Chem. Abstr.*, *41*, P6276 (1947).
(234) Mihaĭlescu and Caragea, *Bull. sect. sci. acad. romaine*, *12*, No. 4/5, 7–18 (1929); *Chem. Abstr.*, *24*, 2116 (1930).
(235) Milas, U. S. Patent 2,412,465, Dec. 10, 1946; *Chem. Abstr.*, *41*, P1240 (1947).
(236) Mingoia, *Gazz. chim. ital.*, *62*, 844–54 (1932); *Chem. Abstr.*, *27*, 503 (1933).
(237) Moureu, *Bull. soc. chim.*, [3], *33*, 151–7 (1905).
(238) Moureu and Gallagher, *Bull. soc. chim.*, [4], *29*, 1009–17 (1921).
(239) Mukherjee, *J. Indian Chem. Soc.*, *25*, 155–64 (1948); *Chem. Abstr.*, *43*, 2605 (1949).
(240) Mulliken, Wakeman, and Gerry, *J. Am. Chem. Soc.*, *57*, 1605–7 (1935).
(241) Murat, *Ann. chim.*, [8], *16*, 108–26 (1909).
(242) Muset, *Bull. acad. roy. Belg.*, *Classe sci.*, *1906*, 775–89; *Chem. Abstr.*, *1*, 1969 (1907).
(243) Muskat and Herrman, *J. Am. Chem. Soc.*, *53*, 252–60 (1931).
(244) Nazarov and Elizarova, *Bull. acad. sci. U.R.S.S.*, *Classe sci. chim.*, *1940*, 189–94; *Chem. Abstr.*, *36*, 741 (1942).
(245) Nazarov and Torgov, *Bull. acad. sci. U.R.S.S.*, *Classe sci. chim.*, *1946*, 495–9; *Chem. Abstr.*, *42*, 7735 (1948).
(246) Nelken and Simonis, *Ber.*, *41*, 986–9 (1908).
(247) Nesmeyanov and Sazanova, *Bull. acad. sci. U.R.S.S.*, *Classe sci. chim.*, *1941*, 499–519; *Chem. Abstr.*, *37*, 2723 (1943).
(248) Newman and Smith, *J. Org. Chem.*, *13*, 592–8 (1948).
(249) Niemann, Benson, and Mead, *J. Org. Chem.*, *8*, 397–404 (1943).
(250) Noller and Adams, *J. Am. Chem. Soc.*, *48*, 1074–80 (1926).
(251) Noller and Adams, *J. Am. Chem. Soc.*, *48*, 1080–9 (1926).
(252) Nomura, *Bull. soc. chim.*, [4], *37*, 1245–7 (1925).
(253) Norris and Blake, *J. Am. Chem. Soc.*, *50*, 1808–12 (1928).
(254) Norris and Cortese, *J. Am. Chem. Soc.*, *49*, 2640–50 (1927).
(255) Norton and Hass, *J. Am. Chem. Soc.*, *58*, 2147–50 (1936).

(256) Oddo and Cambieri, *Gazz. chim. ital.*, *70*, 559–66 (1940); *Chem. Abstr.*, *35*, 1050 (1941).
(257) Oddo and del Rosso, *Gazz. chim. ital.*, *41,I*, 273–94 (1910); *Chem. Zentr.*, *1911,I*, 1855.
(258) Ou Kiun-Houo, *Ann. chim.*, [11], *13*, 175–241 (1940).
(259) Overberger, Saunders, Allen, and Gander, *Organic Syntheses*, *28*, 28–30 (1948).
(260) Overhoff and Proost, *Rec. trav. chim.*, *57*, 179–84 (1938).
(261) Pariselle, *Compt. rend.*, *148*, 849–51 (1909); *Chem. Zentr.*, *1909,I*, 1744.
(262) Pariselle, *Compt. rend.*, *154*, 710–2 (1912); *Chem. Zentr.*, *1912,I*, 1441.
(263) Pauly and Buttlar, *Ann.*, *383*, 230–88 (1911).
(264) Pel'kis and Pazenko, *Zapiski Inst. Khim.*, *Akad. Nauk. U.R.S.R.*, *Inst. Khim.*, 6, Nos. 3–4, 311–39 (1940); *Chem. Abstr.*, *35*, 2469 (1941).
(265) Perlmann, Davidson, and Bogert, *J. Org. Chem.*, *1*, 288–99 (1936).
(266) Petrov and Kaplan, *J. Gen. Chem.* (U.S.S.R.), *12*, 99–103 (1942); *Chem. Abstr.*, *37*, 1983 (1943).
(267) Petrov and Kaplan, *Otdel Khim. Nauk. Izvest. Akad. Nauk. S.S.S.R.*, *1947*, 295–308; *Chem. Abstr.*, *43*, 1718 (1949).
(268) Petrov and Karlik, *J. Gen. Chem.* (U.S.S.R.), *11*, 1100–3 (1941); *Chem. Abstr.*, *37*, 4049 (1942).
(269) Petrov and Ol'dekop, *J. Gen. Chem.* (U.S.S.R.), *18*, 859–64 (1948); *Chem. Abstr.*, *43*, 107 (1949).
(270) Petyunin, *Trudy Moskov. Med. Inst.*, *1940*, No. 16, 7–12; *Khim. Referat. Zhur.*, *4*, No. 9, 58 (1941); *Chem. Abstr.*, *38*, 950 (1944).
(271) Pexsters, *Bull. acad. roy. Belg.*, *Classe sci.*, *1906*, 796–802; *Chem. Zentr.*, *1907,I*, 1398.
(272) Prévost, *Ann. chim.*, [10], *10*, 147–81 (1928).
(273) Proost and Wibaut, *Rec. trav. chim.*, *59*, 971–7 (1940).
(274) Prout, Cason, and Ingersoll, *J. Am. Chem. Soc.*, *70*, 298–305 (1948).
(275) Pschorr and Einbeck, *Ber.*, *38*, 2067–77 (1905).
(276) Quelet, *Compt. rend.*, *186*, 236–8 (1928).
(277) Quelet, *Bull. soc. chim.*, [4], *45*, 75–97 (1929).
(278) Quelet, *Bull. soc. chim.*, [4], *45*, 255–74 (1929).
(279) Quelet and Golse, *Compt. rend.*, *224*, 661–3 (1947); *Chem. Abstr.*, *41*, 4779 (1947).
(280) Reif, *Ber.*, *39*, 1603–4 (1906).
(281) Reif, *Ber.*, *41*, 2739–46 (1908).
(282) Ritter and Russell, *J. Am. Chem. Soc.*, *58*, 291–3 (1936).
(283) Roberts and Young, *J. Am. Chem. Soc.*, *67*, 148–50 (1945).
(284) Rozanov, *J. Russ. Phys.-Chem. Soc.*, *61*, 2313–8 (1929); *Chem. Abstr.*, *24*, 3766 (1930).
(285) Rupe, *Ann.*, *402*, 149–86 (1914).
(286) Rupe and Rinderknecht, *Ann.*, *442*, 61–73 (1925).
(287) Rupe and Spittgerber, *Ber.*, *40*, 2813–7 (1907).
(288) Sabatier and Mailhe, *Compt. rend.*, *139*, 343–6 (1904); *J. Chem. Soc.*, *86,I*, 809 (1904); *Chem. Zentr.*, *1904,II*, 704.
(289) Sabatier and Murat, *Compt. rend.*, *157*, 1496–500 (1913); *Chem. Abstr.*, *8*, 1088 (1914).
(290) Sabatier and Murat, *Compt. rend.*, *158*, 534–7 (1914); *Chem. Abstr.*, *8*, 1751 (1914).
(291) Sachs and Sachs, *Ber.*, *38*, 511–7 (1905).
(292) Sachs and Steinert, *Ber.*, *37*, 1733–45 (1904).

(293) Sah, *J. Chinese Chem. Soc.*, *13*, 89–95 (1946); *Chem. Abstr.*, *41*, 5869 (1947).
(294) Salkind and Teterin, *Ber.*, *66B*, 321–5 (1933).
(295) Sand and Singer, *Ber.*, *35*, 3170–87 (1902).
(296) Savard and Hösögüt, *Rev. faculté sci. univ. Istanbul*, [N.S.], *3*, 164–73 (1938); *Chem. Abstr.*, *32*, 5795 (1938).
(297) Savariau, *Compt. rend.*, *146*, 297–8 (1908); *Chem. Zentr.*, *1908,I*, 1388.
(298) Schmidlin and Garcia-Banús, *Ber.*, *45*, 3193–203 (1912).
(299) Schmidlin and Hodgson, *Ber.*, *41*, 430–7 (1907).
(300) Schmidlin and von Escher, *Ber.*, *45*, 889–99 (1912).
(301) Shurakowski, *J. Russ. Phys.-Chem. Soc.*, *41*, 1687–94 (1910); *Chem. Zentr.*, *1910,I*, 1144.
(302) Simonis, Marben, and Mermod, *Ber.*, 38, 3981–5 (1905).
(303) Smith and Sprung, *J. Am. Chem. Soc.*, *65*, 1276–83 (1943).
(304) Soc. pour l'ind. chim. à Bâle; Swiss Patent 232,887, Sept. 16, 1944 (Cl. 36 *q*); *Chem. Abstr.*, *43*, P5403 (1949).
(305) Sontag, *Ann. chim.*, [11], *1*, 359–438 (1934).
(306) Ssemenzow and Konjuchow-Dobryna, *J. Russ. Phys.-Chem. Soc.*, *43*, 990–2 (1911); *Chem. Zentr.*, *1911,II*, 1923.
(307) Stedman and Stedman, *J. Chem. Soc.*, *1929*, 609–17.
(308) Stevens, *J. Am. Chem. Soc.*, *56*, 1425 (1934).
(309) Stevens, *J. Am. Chem. Soc.*, *57*, 1112–7 (1935).
(310) Stoermer and Friderici, *Ber.*, *41*, 324–43 (1908).
(311) Stohr, *Ber.*, *72B*, 1138–9 (1939).
(312) Tamele, Ott, Marple, and Hearne, *Ind. Eng. Chem.*, 33, 115–20 (1941).
(313) Tarbell and Paulson, *J. Am. Chem. Soc.*, *64*, 2842–4 (1942).
(314) Tarbell and Sato, *J. Am. Chem. Soc.*, 68, 1091–4 (1946).
(315) Tchoubar and Sackur, *Compt. rend.*, *207*, 1105–6 (1938); *Chem. Abstr.*, *33*, 2111 (1939).
(316) Tiffeneau, *Ann. chim.*, [8], *10*, 322–78 (1907).
(317) Tiffeneau and Lévy, *Bull. soc. chim.*, [4], *49*, 1738–53 (1931).
(318) Tiffeneau, Lévy, and Kayser, *Compt. rend.*, *196*, 1407–8 (1933).
(319) Tiffeneau, Lévy, and Weill, *Bull. soc. chim.*, [4], *49*, 1709–21 (1931).
(320) Tiffeneau and Neuberg, *Compt. rend.*, *198*, 2174–6 (1934).
(321) Timmermans and Hennaut-Roland, *Anales soc. españ. fis. quim.*, *27*, 460–72 (1929); *Chem. Abstr.*, *24*, 54 (1930).
(322) Tomecko and Adams, *J. Am. Chem. Soc.*, *49*, 522–30 (1927).
(323) Tsatsas, *Ann. chim.*, [12], *1*, 342–94 (1946).
(324) Tschitschibabin, *Ber.*, *42*, 3469–79 (1909).
(325) Tschitschibabin, *J. Russ. Phys.-Chem. Soc.*, *4*, 1116–7 (1910); *Chem. Zentr.*, *1910,I*, 32.
(326) Tuot, *Compt. rend.*, *202*, 1339–40 (1936).
(327) Tuot and Guyard, *Bull. soc. chim.*, [5], *14*, 1087–96 (1947).
(328) Turkiewicz, *Ber.*, *72B*, 1060–3 (1938).
(329) Urion, *Compt. rend.*, *194*, 2311–3 (1932).
(330) Ushakov and Kucherov, *J. Gen. Chem.* (U.S.S.R.), *14*, 1080–6 (1944); *Chem. Abstr.*, *40*, 7185 (1946).
(331) Ushakov and Kucherov, *J. Gen. Chem.* (U.S.S.R.), *14*, 1087–91 (1944); *Chem. Abstr.*, *40*, 7186 (1946).
(332) Van Gysegem, *Bull. acad. roy. Belg.*, *1906*, 692–706; *Chem. Zentr.*, *1907,I*, 529.
(333) van Risseghem, *Bull. soc. chim. Belg.*, *35*, 328–64 (1926).
(334) van Risseghem, *Bull. soc. chim. Belg.*, 39, 349–68 (1930).

(335) Vavon and Guédon, *Bull. soc. chim.*, [4], *47*, 901–10 (1930).
(336) Veibel, Lundqvist, Andersen, and Frederiksen, *Bull. soc. chim.*, [5], *6*, 990–8 (1939).
(337) Vène, *Ann. chim.*, [11], *10*, 194–279 (1938).
(338) Vène, *Bull. soc. chim.*, [5], *6*, 692–7 (1939).
(339) Venús-Danilova and Bol'shukhin, *J. Gen. Chem.* (U.S.S.R.), *9*, 975–84 (1939); *Chem. Abstr.*, *33*, 8595 (1939).
(340) Venús-Danilova and Brichko, *J. Gen. Chem.* (U.S.S.R.), *17*, 1549–58 (1947); *Chem. Abstr.*, *42*, 2243 (1948).
(341) Vernimmen, *Bull. soc. chim. Belg.*, *33*, 96–101 (1924).
(342) von Auwers and Treppmann, *Ber.*, *48*, 1207–25 (1915).
(343) von Auwers and Westermann, *Ber.*, *54B*, 2993–9 (1921).
(344) von Braun, *Ber.*, *44*, 2867–81 (1911).
(345) von Braun, Deutsch, and Schmatloch, *Ber.*, *45*, 1246–63 (1912).
(346) von Braun and Kirschbaum, *Ber.*, *52B*, 1725–30 (1919).
(347) Webster and Schaefer, *Proc. S. Dakota Acad. Sci.*, *19*, 124–9 (1939); *Chem. Abstr.*, *34*, 2784 (1940).
(348) Weill, *Bull. soc. chim.*, [4], *49*, 1795–806 (1931).
(349) Werner and Bogert, *J. Org. Chem.*, *3*, 578–87 (1939).
(350) Whitby and Gallay, *Can. J. Research*, *6*, 280–91 (1932); *Chem. Abstr.*, *26*, 3479 (1932).
(351) Whitmore and Badertscher, *J. Am. Chem. Soc.*, *55*, 1559–67 (1933).
(352) Whitmore and Church, *J. Am. Chem. Soc.*, *55*, 1119–24 (1933).
(353) Whitmore and Houk, *J. Am. Chem. Soc.*, *54*, 3714–8 (1932).
(354) Whitmore and Lewis, *J. Am. Chem. Soc.*, *64*, 1618–9 (1942).
(355) Whitmore and Lewis, *J. Am. Chem. Soc.*, *64*, 2964–6 (1942).
(356) Whitmore and Sloat, *J. Am. Chem. Soc.*, *64*, 2968–70 (1942).
(357) Whitmore, Sommer, Gold, and Van Strien, *J. Am. Chem. Soc.*, *69*, 1551 (1947).
(358) Whitmore, Whitaker, Mosher, Breivik, Wheeler, Miner, Sutherland, Wagner, Clapper, Lewis, Lux, and Popkin, *J. Am. Chem. Soc.*, *63*, 643–54 (1941).
(359) Wibaut, Hoog, Langedijk, Overhoff, and Smittenberg, *Rec. trav. chim.*, *58*, 329–77 (1939).
(360) Willstaedt, *Ber.*, *64B*, 2693–5 (1931).
(361) Wohl and Losanitsch, *Ber.*, *41*, 3621–2 (1908).
(362) Wohl and Roth, *Ber.*, *40*, 212–8 (1907).
(363) Wood and Scarf, *J. Soc. Chem. Ind.*, *42*, 13–15T (1923).
(364) Woods and Schwartzman, *J. Am. Chem. Soc.*, *70*, 3394–6 (1948).
(365) Woods and Schwartzman, *J. Am. Chem. Soc.*, *71*, 1396–9 (1949).
(366) Yamashita, *J. Chem. Soc. Japan*, *62*, 1216–8 (1941); *Chem. Abstr.*, *41*, 3070 (1947).
(367) Young and Roberts, *J. Am. Chem. Soc.*, *67*, 1040 (1945).
(368) Young and Roberts, *J. Am. Chem. Soc.*, *68*, 649–52 (1946).
(369) Zal'kind and Kulikov, *J. Gen. Chem.* (U.S.S.R.), *15*, 643–9 (1945); *Chem. Abstr.*, *40*, 6061 (1946).
(370) Zal'kind and Labuzov, *J. Gen. Chem.* (U.S.S.R.), *9*, 1525–32 (1939); *Chem. Abstr.*, *34*, 2788 (1940).
(371) Zelinsky, *Ber.*, *41*, 2628–9 (1908).
(372) Ziegler, *Ber.*, *54B*, 737–40 (1921).
(373) Ziegler and Tiemann, *Ber.*, *55B*, 3406–16 (1922).
(374) von Doering and Beringer, *J. Am. Chem. Soc.*, *71*, 2221–6 (1949).
(375) Pickard and Kenyon, *J. Chem. Soc.*, *99*, 45–72 (1911).
(376) Oddo and Toffoli, *Gazz. chim. ital.*, *64*, 359–63 (1934); *Chem. Abstr.*, *28*, 6436 (1934).

(377) Venus-Danilova and Brichko, *J. Gen. Chem.* (U.S.S.R.), *17*, 1849–57 (1947); *Chem. Abstr.*, *42*, 4160 (1948).
(378) Schiemann and Pillarsky, *Ber.*, *64B*, 1340–5 (1931).
(379) Hébert, *Bull. soc. chim.*, [4], *27*, 45–55 (1920).
(380) Klages, *Ber.*, *35*, 2649–52 (1902).
(381) Khaletzkiĭ, *J. Gen. Chem.* (U.S.S.R.), *6*, 1–14 (1936); *Chem. Abstr.*, *30*, 4844 (1936).
(382) Gray and Fuson, *J. Am. Chem. Soc.*, *56*, 739–41 (1934).
(383) Sachs and Appenzeller, *Ber.*, *41*, 91–108 (1908).
(384) van Dorp and Arens, *Nature*, *160*, 189 (1947).
(385) Faworsky, *J. prakt. Chem.*, [2], *88*, 641–98 (1913).
(386) Heilbron, Jones, and Weedon, *J. Chem. Soc.*, *1944*, 140–1.
(387) Heilbron, Johnson, Jones, and Raphael, *J. Chem. Soc.*, *1943*, 265–8.
(388) Mosher and La Combe, *J. Am. Chem. Soc.*, *72*, 4991–4 (1950).
(389) Guest, *J. Am. Chem. Soc.*, *47*, 860–3 (1925).
(390) Iotsitch, *J. Russ. Phys.-Chem. Soc.*, *42*, 1083 (1910); *Bull. soc. chim.*, [4], *10*, 1148 (1911).
(391) Lespieau, *Bull. soc. chim.*, [4], *39*, 991–4 (1926).
(392) Zal'kind and Gverdtsiteli, *J. Gen. Chem.* (U.S.S.R.), *9*, 971–4 (1939); *Chem. Abstr.*, *33*, 8569 (1939).
(393) Lespieau and Lombard, *Bull. soc. chim.*, [4], *39*, 369–73 (1935).
(394) Heilbron, Jones, Lacey, McCombie, and Raphael, *J. Chem. Soc.*, *1945*, 77–81.
(395) Teterin and Ivanov, *J. Gen. Chem.* (U.S.S.R.), *7*, 1629–31 (1937); *Chem. Abstr.*, *31*, 8305 (1937).
(396) Marvel and Schertz, *J. Am. Chem. Soc.*, *65*, 2054–8 (1943).
(397) Heilbron, Jones, and Raphael, *J. Chem. Soc.*, *1943*, 268–70.
(398) Cymerman, Heilbron, Johnson, and Jones, *J. Chem. Soc.*, *1944*, 144–4.
(399) Marvel and Williams, *J. Am. Chem. Soc.*, *61*, 2714–6 (1939).
(400) Heilbron, Jones, and Raphael, *J. Chem. Soc.*, *1944*, 136–9.
(401) Brooks, *J. Am. Chem. Soc.*, *66*, 1295–7 (1944).
(402) Isler, Huber, Ronco, and Kofler, *Helv. Chim. Acta*, *30*, 1911–27 (1947).
(403) Cymerman, Heilbron, Jones, and Lacey, *J. Chem. Soc.*, *1946*, 500–3.
(404) Heilbron, *J. Chem. Soc.*, *1948*, 386–93.
(405) Victoria, *Rec. trav. chim.*, *24*, 265–96 (1905).
(406) Barré and Repentigny, *Can. J. Research*, *27B*, 716–20 (1949).
(407) Reynolds, *Am. Chem. J.*, *44*, 305–31 (1910).
(408) Sabatier and Mailhe, *Ann. chim.*, [8], *10*, 527–74 (1907).
(409) Letzinger and Schnizer, *J. Org. Chem.*, *16*, 704–7 (1951).
(410) Newman, *J. Am. Chem. Soc.*, *62*, 2295–300 (1940).
(411) Freedman and Becker, *J. Org. Chem.*, *16*, 1701–11 (1951).
(412) Gmitter and Benton, *J. Am. Chem. Soc.*, *72*, 4586–9 (1950).
(413) Robinson, *J. Chem. Soc.*, *1936*, 80.
(414) Arnold and Coyner, *J. Am. Chem. Soc.*, *66*, 1543–5 (1944).
(415) Gaylord and Becker, *J. Org. Chem.*, *15*, 305–16 (1950).
(416) Oddo, *Gazz. chim. ital.*, *41*,*I*, 273–94 (1911); *Chem. Abstr.*, *5*, 2639 (1911).
(417) Iotsitch, *J. Russ. Phys.-Chem. Soc.*, *34*, 96–8 (1902); *Bull. soc. chim.*, [3], *28*, 920 (1902).
(418) Dupont, *Compt. rend.*, *149*, 1381–3 (1910); *Chem. Abstr.*, *4*, 1479 (1910).
(419) Dupont, *Compt. rend.*, *150*, 1121–3 (1910); *Chem. Abstr.*, *4*, 2096 (1910).
(420) Dupont, *Compt. rend.*, *153*, 275–7 (1911); *Chem. Abstr.*, *5*, 3408 (1911).
(421) Dupont, *Compt. rend.*, *158*, 714–6 (1914); *Chem. Zentr.*, *1914*,*I*, 1503.
(422) Dupont, *Bull. soc. chim.*, [4], *15*, 604–8 (1914).

(423) Grard, *Ann. chim.*, [10], *13*, 336–81 (1930).
(424) Yur'ev, Voronkov, Gragerov, and Ya, *J. Gen. Chem.* (U.S.S.R.), *18*, 1804–10 (1948); *Chem. Abstr.*, *43*, 3818 (1949).
(425) Elderfield, Pitt, and Wempen, *J. Am. Chem. Soc.*, *72*, 1334–45 (1950).
(426) Hiers and Adams, *J. Am. Chem. Soc.*, *48*, 2385–95 (1926).
(427) Szmant, Anzenberger, and Hartle, *J. Am. Chem. Soc.*, *72*, 1419–20 (1950).
(428) Godchot, Bedos, and Cauquil, *Bull. soc. chim.*, [4], *43*, 521–2 (1928).
(429) Plate, Shafran, and Batuev, *J. Gen. Chem.* (U.S.S.R.), *Chem. Abstr.*, *44*, 7785 (1950).
(430) Dice, Watkins, and Schuman, *J. Am. Chem. Soc.*, *72*, 1738–40 (1950).
(431) Schinz and Simon, *Helv. Chim. Acta*, *28*, 774–80 (1945).
(432) Glattfeld and Cameron, *J. Am. Chem. Soc.*, *49*, 1043–8 (1927).
(433) Kayser, *Ann. chim.*, [11], *6*, 145–248 (1936).
(434) Frank, Adams, Allen, Gander, and Smith, *J. Am. Chem. Soc.*, *68*, 1365–8 (1946).
(435) Sobotka and Stynler, *J. Am. Chem. Soc.*, *72*, 5139–43 (1950).
(436) McBee, Pierce, and Higgins, *J. Am. Chem. Soc.*, *74*, 1736–7 (1952).
(437) Field, *J. Am. Chem. Soc.*, *74*, 3919–21 (1952).
(438) Lawrence and Shelton, *Ind. Eng. Chem.*, *42*, 136–40 (1950).
(439) Inhoffen, Bohlman, and Reinefeld, *Chem. Ber.*, *82*, 313–6 (1949).
(440) Godchot and Cauquil, *Bull. soc. chim.*, [4], *43*, 520–1 (1928).
(441) Carré, *Bull. soc. chim.*, [4], *5*, 486–9 (1909).
(442) Carré, *Bull. soc. chim.*, [4], *7*, 841–6 (1910).
(443) Gaertner, *J. Am. Chem. Soc.*, *73*, 3934–7 (1951).
(444) Gaertner, *J. Am. Chem. Soc.*, *74*, 766–7 (1952).
(445) Gaertner, *J. Am. Chem. Soc.*, *74*, 2185–8 (1952).
(446) Marshall, *Proc. Chem. Soc.*, *30*, 13–4 (1914); *J. Chem. Soc.*, *105*, 527–34 (1914).
(447) Marshall, *J. Chem. Soc.*, *107*, 509–23 (1915).
(448) Mousseron and Du, *Bull. soc. chim.*, [5], *15*, 91–6 (1948).
(449) Prévost, Gaudemar, and Honigberg, *Compt. rend.*, *230*, 1186–8 (1950); *Chem. Abstr.*, *45*, 1497 (1951).
(450) Newman and Wotiz, *J. Am. Chem. Soc.*, *71*, 1292–7 (1949).
(451) Sherman and Amstutz, *J. Am. Chem. Soc.*, *72*, 2195–9 (1950).
(452) Young and Siegel, *J. Am. Chem. Soc.*, *66*, 354–8 (1944).
(453) Siegel, Coburn, and Levering, *J. Am. Chem. Soc.*, *73*, 3163–5 (1951).
(454) Siegel, Boyer, and Joy, *J. Am. Chem. Soc.*, *73*, 3237–40 (1951).

TABLE VI-XVIII

REACTIONS OF GRIGNARD REAGENTS WITH KETENES AND ACYCLIC KETONES

Ketonic Comp'd	RMgX	Product(s)	Ref.
C_2H_2O			
$H_2C{=}CO$	CH_3MgI	$(CH_3)_2CO$ (trace); brown resin	89
$H_2C{=}CO$	C_2H_5MgCl*	$CH_3COC_2H_5$ (36.6%)	1
$H_2C{=}CO$	C_2H_5MgBr	$CH_3COC_2H_5$ (trace)	2
$H_2C{=}CO$	n-C_3H_7MgBr	CH_3CO-n-C_3H_7 (34.2–35.6%)	2
$H_2C{=}CO$	n-C_4H_9MgBr	CH_3CO-n-C_4H_9 (32.7%)	2
$H_2C{=}CO$	C_6H_5MgBr	$CH_3COC_6H_5$ (30–35%)	1
$C_3H_3OCl_3$			
Cl_3CCOCH_3	CH_3MgBr	$Cl_3C(CH_3)_2COH$	3
$C_3H_3OF_3$			
CF_3COCH_3 (0.2–0.3 mole)	C_2H_5MgI (0.4–0.6 mole)	$CF_3(CH_3)(C_2H_5)COH$ (78.9%); $CF_3(CH_3)CHOH$ (13.9%)	654
$C_3H_4OCl_2$			
$(ClCH_2)_2CO$	CH_3MgBr	$CH_3(ClCH_2)_2COH$	3
$(ClCH_2)_2CO$	$H_2C{=}CHCH_2MgBr$	$H_2C{=}CHCH_2(ClCH_2)_2COH$ (36%)	4
$C_3H_4O_3$			
HO_2CCOCH_3 (20 g.)	4-$CH_3C_6H_4MgBr$ (116 g. C_7H_7Br)	DL-$HO_2C(CH_3)$(4-$CH_3C_6H_4$)COH (15 g.)	5
HO_2CCOCH_3 (11.5 g.)	4-$CH_3OC_6H_4MgBr$ (66.5 g. C_7H_7BrO)	DL-$HO_2C(CH_3)$(4-$CH_3OC_6H_4$)COH (10.3 g.)	5
C_3H_5OBr			
$BrCH_2COCH_3$	CH_3MgBr (2 equiv.)	CH_3(i-C_3H_7)CHOH (18%)	6
$BrCH_2COCH_3$	CH_3MgI (2 equiv.)	CH_3(i-C_3H_7)CHOH (12%)	6

*The use of C_2H_5MgBr is said to lead to considerable ketene dimerization.

TABLE VI-XVIII (Continued)

Ketonic Comp'd	RMgX	Product(s)	Ref.
C_3H_5OCl			
$ClCH_2COCH_3$	CH_3MgBr	$ClCH_2(CH_3)_2COH$	2
$ClCH_2COCH_3$	CH_3MgBr (2 equiv.)	$CH_3(i\text{-}C_3H_7)CHOH$	7
$ClCH_2COCH_3$	CH_3MgX*	$ClCH_2(CH_3)_2COH$; $CH_3(i\text{-}C_3H_7)CHOH$	9
$ClCH_2COCH_3$	CH_3MgI	$ClCH_2(CH_3)_2COH$ (*ca.* 20%)	8
$ClCH_2COCH_3$	$(\equiv CMgBr)_2$	$[\equiv CC(CH_3)(CH_2Cl)OH]_2$	621
$ClCH_2COCH_3$	C_2H_5MgCl	1,2-Epoxy-2-methylbutane (60%)	9
$ClCH_2COCH_3$	C_2H_5MgBr	$ClCH_2(CH_3)(C_2H_5)COH$ (72%)†	8
$ClCH_2COCH_3$	C_2H_5MgBr	$ClCH_2(CH_3)(C_2H_5)COH$; $C_2H_5(s\text{-}C_4H_9)CHOH$	9
$ClCH_2COCH_3$	C_2H_5MgBr	1,2-Epoxy-2-methylbutane (68%); $C_2H_5(s\text{-}C_4H_9)CHOH$ ("small am'ts")	10
$ClCH_2COCH_3$	$H_2C{=}CHCH_2MgBr$	$ClCH_2(CH_3)(H_2C{=}CHCH_2)COH$ (55%)	4
$ClCH_2COCH_3$	$(i\text{-}C_5H_{11})_2Mg$	$CH_3(i\text{-}C_5H_{11})(i\text{-}C_6H_{13})COH$	11
$ClCH_2COCH_3$	C_6H_5MgBr	$ClCH_2(CH_3)(C_6H_5)COH$	8
$ClCH_2COCH_3$	C_6H_5MgBr	$CH_3COCH_2C_6H_5$	12, 13
$ClCH_2COCH_3$ (32 g.)	$4\text{-}CH_3C_6H_4MgBr$ (86 g. C_7H_7Br)	$CH_3COCH_2C_6H_4\text{-}4\text{-}CH_3$ (29 g.)	14
$ClCH_2COCH_3$	$n\text{-}C_5H_{11}C{\equiv}CMgBr$	$ClCH_2(CH_3)(n\text{-}C_5H_{11}C{\equiv}C)COH$	15
$ClCH_2COCH_3$	$2\text{-}C_6H_5C_6H_4MgI$	$ClCH_2(CH_3)(2\text{-}C_6H_5C_6H_4)COH$	16
$ClCH_2COCH_3$ (115 g., 1.25 mole)	$RC{\equiv}CMgBr$‡ (1.25 mole)	$ClCH_2(CH_3)(RC{\equiv}C)COH$‡ (167 g.)	97
$C_3H_5O_2N$			
$HON{=}CHCOCH_3$ (17.5 g.)	C_2H_5MgBr (87 g. C_2H_5Br)	$HON{=}CH(CH_3)(C_2H_5)COH$ (50%); $CH_3(C_2H_5)_2COH$; $CH_3COC_2H_5$	17
$HON{=}CHCOCH_3$ (17.5 g.)	$n\text{-}C_4H_9MgBr$ (129.6 g. C_4H_9Br)	$HON{=}CH(CH_3)(n\text{-}C_4H_9)COH$ (50%); $CH_3CO\text{-}n\text{-}C_4H_9$	17

*X = Br, I.

†Claim subsequently modified by Fourneau and Tiffeneau (9).

‡R = 1-Cyclohexenyl.

TABLE VI-XVIII (Continued)

Ketonic Comp'd	RMgX	Product(s)	Ref.
$C_3H_5O_2N$ (*cont.*)			
HON$=$CHCOCH$_3$ (29 g.)	C_6H_5MgBr (210 g. C_6H_5Br)	HON$=$CH(CH$_3$)(C$_6$H$_5$)COH (36%); CH$_3$COC$_6$H$_5$	*17*
C_3H_6O			
$(CH_3)_2CO$	CH_3MgI	$(CH_3)_3COH$ (70%)	*18*
$(CH_3)_2CO$	$(\equiv CMgBr)_2$	$[\equiv CC(CH_3)_2OH]_2$ (80%)	*19,20, 21,22, 118,628*
$(CH_3)_2CO$ (10.6 g.) + $(C_6H_5)_2CO$ (54.6 g.)	$(\equiv CMgBr)_2$	$[\equiv CC(CH_3)_2OH]_2$ (2.5 g.); $[\equiv CC(C_6H_5)_2OH]_2$ (34.0 g.); $HO(CH_3)_2CC\equiv CC(C_6H_5)_2OH$	*23*
$(CH_3)_2CO$	C_2H_5MgCl	$C_2H_5(CH_3)_2COH$ (70%)	*10*
$(CH_3)_2CO$ (45 g.)	C_2H_5MgBr (81 g. C_2H_5Br)	$C_2H_5(CH_3)_2COH$ (*ca.* 25 g.)	*24*
$(CH_3)_2CO$	C_2H_5I + Mg*	$C_2H_5(CH_3)_2COH$	*609*
$(CH_3)_2CO$	$CH_3C\equiv CMgBr$	$CH_3C\equiv C(CH_3)_2COH$ (95%)	*36*
$(CH_3)_2CO$	$H_2C=CHCH_2MgBr$	$H_2C=CHCH_2(CH_3)_2COH$ (70%, crude; 53%, purified)	*25,26, 27,28, 29,30*
$(CH_3)_2CO$ (2.3 moles)	*n*-C_3H_7MgBr (2.5 moles C_3H_7Br)	*n*-$C_3H_7(CH_3)_2COH$ (159 g.)	*31,11, 32,33, 34,35*
$(CH_3)_2CO$	*n*-C_3H_7MgI	*n*-$(C_3H_7)(CH_3)_2COH$ (contam'd with I comp'ds)	*32*
$(CH_3)_2CO$	*i*-C_3H_7MgBr	*i*-$C_3H_7(CH_3)_2COH$	*37,11*
$(CH_3)_2CO$	$H_2C=CHC\equiv CMgBr$	$H_2C=CHC\equiv C(CH_3)_2OH$ (53%)	*38,39,40*
$(CH_3)_2CO$	2-Thienyl-MgI	α-$C_4H_3S(CH_3)_2COH$; α-$C_4H_3S(CH_3)C=CH_2$	*41*
$(CH_3)_2CO$	$C_2H_5C\equiv CMgBr$	$C_2H_5C\equiv C(CH_3)_2COH$	*42*

*Without solvent (other than the reactants).

TABLE VI-XVIII (Continued)

Ketonic Comp'd	RMgX	Product(s)	Ref.
C_3H_6O (*cont.*)			
$(CH_3)_2CO$ (5.8 g.)	$C_2H_5OC\equiv CMgBr$ (7.5 g. $C_2H_5OC\equiv CH$)	$C_2H_5OC\equiv C(CH_3)_2COH$ (63%)	*43*
$(CH_3)_2CO$	$(CH_2)_4CHMgBr$	$(CH_2)_4CH(CH_3)_2COH + (CH_2)_4C{=}CH_2$ (aggregating 45%)	*69*
$(CH_3)_2CO$	$H_2C{=}C(CH_3)CH_2Cl$ + Mg	$H_2C{=}C(CH_3)CH_2(CH_3)_2COH$ (59%); $[H_2C{=}C(CH_3)CH_2{-}]_2$ (37%)	*44*
$(CH_3)_2CO$	Butenyl-MgBr*	$H_2C{=}CCH(CH_3)C(CH_3)_2OH$ (*ca.* 81%); [*no* $CH_3CH{=}CHCH_2(CH_3)_2COH$]	*45*
$(CH_3)_2CO$	n-C_4H_9MgCl	n-$C_4H_9(CH_3)_2COH$ (70%)	*614*
$(CH_3)_2CO$ (6.0 moles)	n-C_4H_9MgBr (6.5 moles C_4H_9Br)	n-$C_4H_9(CH_3)_2COH$ (640 g., 92%)	*46,31,33*
$(CH_3)_2CO$	n-C_4H_9MgBr	n-$C_4H_9(CH_3)_2COH$ (73.6%); $(CH_3)_2CHOH$ (6.6%); $[HO(CH_3)_2C{-}]_2$ (5.0%); C_7H_{14} (41%); C_8H_{18} (6.0%); C_4H_8 (7.9%)	*49*
$(CH_3)_2CO$	i-C_4H_9MgBr	i-$C_4H_9(CH_3)_2COH$ (54%)	*46,34,50*
$(CH_3)_2CO$	i-C_4H_9MgI	i-$C_4H_9(CH_3)_2COH$	*51*
$(CH_3)_2CO$	s-C_4H_9MgBr	s-$C_4H_9(CH_3)_2COH$	*46,31,35*
$(CH_3)_2CO$†	t-C_4H_9MgCl	t-$C_4H_9(CH_3)_2COH$ (28%)	*46,52*
$(CH_3)_2CO$	t-C_4H_9MgI	t-$C_4H_9(CH_3)_2COH$ (traces only); $(CH_3)_2C{=}CH$	*18*
$(CH_3)_2CO$	$H_2C{=}C(CH_3)C\equiv CMgBr$	$H_2C{=}C(CH_3)C\equiv C(CH_3)_2COH$ (58%)	*40*
$(CH_3)_2CO$	n-$C_5H_{11}MgBr$	n-$C_5H_{11}(CH_3)_2COH$ (63%)	*33*
$(CH_3)_2CO$	i-$C_5H_{11}MgBr$	i-$C_5H_{11}(CH_3)_2COH$ (46%); $CH_3COCH{=}CH(CH_3)_2$; $[(CH_3)_2C{=}CH]_2CO$	*18,54,55*
$(CH_3)_2CO$	$(CH_2)_5CHMgCl$	$(CH_2)_5CH(CH_3)_2COH$	*58,59*
$(CH_3)_2CO$	$C_6H_5CH_2MgCl$	$C_6H_5CH_2(CH_3)_2COH$	*60*

*From 80% $CH_3CH{=}CHCH_2Br$, 20% $CH_3(H_2C{=}CH)CHBr$.

†Edgar *et al.* (*46*) have emphasized the necessity for the use of acetone of high purity to avoid condensation, with negligible carbinol formation.

TABLE VI-XVIII (Continued)

Ketonic Comp'd	RMgX	Product(s)	Ref.
C_3H_6O (*cont.*)			
$(CH_3)_2CO$	$C_6H_5CH_2MgBr$	$C_6H_5CH_2(CH_3)_2COH$	*18,61*
$(CH_3)_2CO$	2-,3-,or 4-$CH_3C_6H_4MgBr$	2-,3-,or 4-$CH_3C_6H_4(CH_3)_2COH$	62
$(CH_3)_2CO$	4-$CH_3C_6H_4MgBr$	4-$CH_3C_6H_4(CH_3)_2COH$	63
$(CH_3)_2CO$	$C_6H_5C{\equiv}CMgX$	$C_6H_5C{\equiv}C(CH_3)_2COH$ (95%)	64
$(CH_3)_2CO$	$C_6H_5C{\equiv}CMgBr$	$C_6H_5C{\equiv}C(CH_3)_2COH$ (55%)	65
$(CH_3)_2CO$	$C_6H_5OC{\equiv}CMgBr$	$C_6H_5OC{\equiv}C(CH_3)_2COH$ (63%); C_6H_5OH	66
$(CH_3)_2CO$	2-Benzothiazolyl-CH_2MgBr	$C_7H_4NSCH_2(CH_3)_2COH$	385
$(CH_3)_2CO$	$C_6H_5(CH_2)_2MgBr$	$C_6H_5CH_2CH_2(CH_3)_2COH$	67,68
$(CH_3)_2CO$	2-$CH_3C_6H_4CH_2MgBr$	2-$CH_3C_6H_4CH_2(CH_3)_2COH$	655
$(CH_3)_2CO$	3-$CH_3C_6H_4CH_2MgBr$ (185 g. C_8H_9Br)	3-$CH_3C_6H_4CH_2(CH_3)_2COH$ (18–20 g.)	655
$(CH_3)_2CO$	*n*-$C_8H_{17}MgBr$	*n*-$C_8H_{17}(CH_3)_2COH$	48
$(CH_3)_2CO$	1-Indenyl-MgBr	1-$C_9H_7(CH_3)_2COH$ (80%)	69
$(CH_3)_2CO$	2-Methylindolyl-MgBr	2,2-Bis-(2-methyl-3-indolyl)propane	70
$(CH_3)_2CO$	$C_6H_5(CH_2)_3MgBr$	$C_6H_5(CH_2)_3C(CH_3)_2OH$ (51%)	71
$(CH_3)_2CO$ (7.5 g.)	1-$C_{10}H_7MgBr$ (25 g. $C_{10}H_7Br$)	1-$C_{10}H_7(CH_3)_2COH$ (21.6 g.)	72
$(CH_3)_2CO$	$CH_3(C_6H_5)CH(CH_2)_2MgBr$	$CH_3(C_6H_5)CHCH_2CH_2(CH_3)_2COH$	73
$(CH_3)_2CO$	3-$CH_3C_6H_4(CH_2)_3MgBr$	3-$CH_3C_6H_4(CH_2)_3C(CH_3)_2OH$;	71
$(CH_3)_2CO$	$CH_3(C_6H_5)N(CH_2)_3MgBr$	$CH_3(C_6H_5)N(CH_2)_3C(CH_3)_2OH$; $CH_3(n\text{-}C_3H_7)(C_6H_5)N$	73
$(CH_3)_2CO$	*α*-Camphoryl-MgBr*	*α*-$C_{10}H_{15}O(CH_3)_2COH$ (75–80%)	74,75
$(CH_3)_2CO$	$(CH_3)_5C_6MgCl$	$(CH_3)_5C_6(CH_3)_2COH$	76
$(CH_3)_2CO$	$(CH_3)_5C_6MgBr$	$(CH_3)_5C_6(CH_3)_2COH$ (*ca.* 47%)	77
$(CH_3)_2CO$	$(CH_3)_5C_6MgBr$	$(CH_3)_5C_6(CH_3)_2COH$ (25%); $(CH_3)_5C_6C(CH_3){=}CH_2$	78

*It seems possible (even probable) that this "Grignard reagent" is in fact an enolate.

TABLE VI-XVIII (Continued)

Ketonic Comp'd	RMgX	Product (s)	Ref.
C_3H_6O (*cont.*)			
$(CH_3)_2CO$	2,4,5-$(CH_3)_3$-3,6-$(CH_3O)_2C_6(CH_2)_2MgCl$	2,4,5-$(CH_3)_3$-3,6-$(CH_3O)_2C_6(CH_2)_2C(CH_3)_2OH$	79,80
$(CH_3)_2CO$ (6.5 g.)	9-Phenanthryl-MgBr (25.7 ml. $C_{14}H_9Br$)	9-$C_{14}H_9(CH_3)_2COH$ (yielding 9.2 g. olefin)	617
$(CH_3)_2CO$	$(C_6H_5)_3CMgCl$	"Passive"	81
$C_3H_6O_2$			
CH_3COCH_2OH	C_2H_5MgI (2 equiv.)	$HOCH_2(CH_3)(C_2H_5)COH$ (>50%)	82
$C_4H_3OF_5$			
$CH_3COC_2F_5$ (0.2–0.3 mole)	C_2H_5MgI (0.4–0.6 mole)	$CH_3(C_2F_5)(C_2H_5)COH$ (41.6%); $CH_3(C_2F_5)CHOH$ (44.5%)	654
C_4H_5OCl			
$CH_3COCH{=}CHCl$ (20 g.)	CH_3MgBr (7 g. Mg)	$ClCH{=}CH(CH_3)_2COH$ (11 g.)	629
$CH_3COCH{=}CHCl$ (52 g.)	$H_2C{=}CHC{\equiv}CMgBr$ (52 g. C_4H_4)	$CH_3(ClCH{=}CH)(H_2C{=}CHC{\equiv}C)COH$ (67 g., 85%)	629
$CH_3COCH{=}CHCl$ (42 g.)	*n*-$C_4H_9C{\equiv}CMgBr$ (55 g. C_6H_{10})	$CH_3(ClCH{=}CH)$(*n*-$C_4H_9C{\equiv}C)COH$ (69.9 g., 95%)	629
C_4H_6O			
$CH_3COCH{=}CH_2$ (17.5 g.)	*n*-$C_4H_9C{\equiv}CMgBr$ (24.0 g. *n*-$C_4H_9C{\equiv}CH$)	$CH_3(H_2C{=}CH)$(*n*-$C_4H_9C{\equiv}C)COH$ (19.5 g.)	83
$CH_3COCH{=}CH_2$	$RC{\equiv}CMgBr$*	$CH_3(H_2C{=}CH)(RC{\equiv}C)COH$* (45–50%)	84

*R = 1-Cyclohexenyl.

TABLE VI-XVIII (Continued)

Ketonic Comp'd	RMgX	Product(s)	Ref.
$C_4H_6O_2$			
$(CH_3CO—)_2$	$(\equiv CMgBr)_2$	$HO(CH_3)(HC\equiv C)COCH_3$	*85*
$(CH_3CO—)_2$	$H_2C{=}CHCH_2Br$ + Mg	$[—C(OH)(CH_3)CH_2CH{=}CH_2]_2$ (*ca.* 10–16%)	*86*
$(CH_3CO—)_2$	$BrMg(CH_2)_5MgBr$	1,2-Dimethylcycloheptane-1,2-diol.	*87*
$(CH_3CO—)_2$ (0.1 mole)	$4\text{-}CH_3C_6H_4MgBr$ (0.25 mole)	$[HO(CH_3)(4\text{-}CH_3C_6H_4)C—]_2$, m.p. 136–137° ("small yield")	*88*
C_4H_7OCl			
$ClCH_2COC_2H_5$	C_2H_5MgBr	$ClCH_2(C_2H_5)_2COH$; $C_2H_5CH(OH)CH(C_2H_5)_2$ (?)	*9*
$ClCH_2COC_2H_5$	$n\text{-}C_5H_{11}C\equiv CMgBr$	$ClCH_2(C_2H_5)(n\text{-}C_5H_{11}C\equiv C)COH$	*15*
$CH_3COCHClCH_3$	CH_3MgBr	$CH_3CHCl(CH_3)_2COH$	*9*
$CH_3COCHClCH_3$	C_2H_5MgBr	$CH_3(CH_3CHCl)(C_2H_5)COH$	*8,9*
$C_4H_7O_2N$			
$CH_3COC({=}NOH)CH_3$ (15.2 g.)	CH_3MgI (64.0 g. CH_3I)	$(CH_3)_2C(OH)C({=}NOH)CH_3$ (57%)	*17,90*
$CH_3COC({=}NOH)CH_3$ (20.2 g.)	$n\text{-}C_4H_9MgBr$ (109.6 g. C_4H_9Br)	$CH_3(n\text{-}C_4H_9)C(OH)C({=}NOH)CH_3$ (66%)	*17*
$CH_3CO(C{=}NOH)CH_3$	$4\text{-}CH_3C_6H_4MgBr$	$CH_3(4\text{-}CH_3C_6H_4)C(OH)C({=}NOH)CH_3$ (83%)	*17*
$CH_3COC({=}NOH)CH_3$ (25.3 g.)	$n\text{-}C_8H_{17}MgBr$ (193.0 g. $C_8H_{17}Br$)	$CH_3(n\text{-}C_8H_{17})C(OH)C({=}NOH)CH_3$ (65%)	*17*
C_4H_8O			
$CH_3COC_2H_5$	$(\equiv CMgBr)_2$ (excess)	$[\equiv CC(OH)(CH_3)C_2H_5]_2$ (*ca.* quant.)	*22,21,118*
$CH_3COC_2H_5$	$(\equiv CMgBr)_2$ + $HC\equiv CMgBr$	$CH_3(HC\equiv C)(C_2H_5)COH$ (6%); $[\equiv CC(OH)(CH_3)C_2H_5]_2$ (65%)	*91*
$CH_3COC_2H_5$ (2.4 moles)	C_2H_5MgBr (2.5 moles C_2H_5Br)	$CH_3(C_2H_5)_2COH$ (67%)	*38,33,35, 47,92, 93*
$CH_3COC_2H_5$	$CH_3C\equiv CMgBr$	$CH_3(C_2H_5)(CH_3C\equiv C)COH$ (70%)	*94*

TABLE VI-XVIII (Continued)

Ketonic Comp'd	RMgX	Product(s)	Ref.
C_4H_8O (*cont.*)			
$CH_3COC_2H_5$ (156.0 g.)	$H_2C{=}CHCH_2Cl$ (200.0 g.) + Mg (62.5 g.)	$CH_3(C_2H_5)(H_2C{=}CHCH_2)COH$ (154.0 g., 52%)	*95*
$CH_3COC_2H_5$	$H_2C{=}CHCH_2MgBr$	$CH_3(C_2H_5)(H_2C{=}CHCH_2)COH$ (84%, crude)	*25,95*
$CH_3COC_2H_5$	$n\text{-}C_3H_7MgBr$	$CH_3(C_2H_5)(n\text{-}C_3H_7)COH$ (64%)	*46,55*
$CH_3COC_2H_5$	$i\text{-}C_3H_7MgCl$	$CH_3(C_2H_5)(i\text{-}C_3H_7)COH$ (28%); ketol (30%)	*96*
$CH_3COC_2H_5$	$i\text{-}C_3H_7MgBr$	$CH_3(C_2H_5)(i\text{-}C_3H_7)COH$	*93*
$CH_3COC_2H_5$	2-Thienyl-MgI	$CH_3(C_2H_5)(\alpha\text{-}C_4H_3S)COH$; dehydr'n product	*41*
$CH_3COC_2H_5$	$n\text{-}C_4H_9MgBr$	$CH_3(C_2H_5)(n\text{-}C_4H_9)COH$ (65.5%)	*38,47,98, 99*
$CH_3COC_2H_5$	$s\text{-}C_4H_9MgBr$	$CH_3(C_2H_5)(s\text{-}C_4H_9)COH$ (25%)	*38*
$CH_3COC_2H_5$	$i\text{-}C_3H_7C{\equiv}CMgBr$	$CH_3(C_2H_5)(i\text{-}C_3H_7C{\equiv}C)COH$ (76%)	*94*
$CH_3COC_2H_5$ (72 g.)	$n\text{-}C_5H_{11}MgBr$ (151 g. $C_5H_{11}Br$)	$CH_3(C_2H_5)(n\text{-}C_5H_{11})COH$ (35 g.)	*100,54,55, 101*
$CH_3COC_2H_5$	$i\text{-}C_5H_{11}MgBr$	$CH_3(C_2H_5)(i\text{-}C_5H_{11})COH$	*54*
$CH_3COC_2H_5$ (72 g.)	DL-$s\text{-}C_4H_9CH_2MgBr$ (151 g. $C_5H_{11}Br$)	$CH_3(C_2H_5)(s\text{-}C_4H_9CH_2)COH$ (25 g.)	*100*
$CH_3COC_2H_5$	$t\text{-}C_5H_{11}MgBr$	$CH_3(C_2H_5)(t\text{-}C_5H_{11})COH$	*102*
$CH_3COC_2H_5$	$CH_3CH{=}C(CH_3)C{\equiv}CMgBr$	$CH_3(C_2H_5)[CH_3CH{=}C(CH_3)C{\equiv}C]COH$ (79%)	*94*
$CH_3COC_2H_5$	$n\text{-}C_4H_9C{\equiv}CMgBr$	$CH_3(C_2H_5)(n\text{-}C_4H_9C{\equiv}C)COH$ (92%)	*103*
$CH_3COC_2H_5$	$t\text{-}C_4H_9C{\equiv}CMgBr$	$CH_3(C_2H_5)(t\text{-}C_4H_9C{\equiv}C)COH$ (58%)	*94*
$CH_3COC_2H_5$ (50 g.)	$C_6H_5CH_2MgCl$ (100 g. C_7H_7Cl)	$CH_3(C_2H_5)(C_6H_5CH_2)COH$ (83%)	*650*
$CH_3COC_2H_5$	$C_6H_5CH_2MgCl$	$CH_3(C_2H_5)(C_6H_5CH_2)COH$; $C_6H_5CH_2OH$; $(C_6H_5CH_2{-})_2$	*101,68*
$CH_3COC_2H_5$	$C_6H_5CH_2Cl$ + Mg	$CH_3(C_2H_5)(C_6H_5CH_2)COH$	*104*
$CH_3COC_2H_5$	$4\text{-}CH_3C_6H_4MgBr$ (51 g. C_7H_7Br)	$CH_3(C_2H_5)(4\text{-}CH_3C_6H_4)COH$ (35 g., crude); $(4\text{-}CH_3C_6H_4{-})_2$	*105*

TABLE VI-XVIII (Continued)

Ketonic Comp'd	RMgX	Product (s)	Ref.
C_4H_8O (*cont.*)			
$CH_3COC_2H_5$	$C_6H_5C{\equiv}CMgBr$	$CH_3(C_2H_5)(C_6H_5C{\equiv}C)COH$ (65%)	*94*
$CH_3COC_2H_5$	2,4-$(CH_3)_2C_6H_3CH_2MgCl$	$CH_3(C_2H_5)[2,4\text{-}(CH_3)_2C_6H_3CH_2]COH$ (>41%)*	*106*
$CH_3COC_2H_5$	$(CH_3)_5C_6Br + CH_3I + Mg$	$(CH_3)_6C_6$ ("a little"); $(CH_3)_5COCH_3$ (?) (40%)	*78*
$CH_3COC_2H_5$	2,4,5-$(CH_3)_3$-3,6-$(CH_3O)_2C_6(CH_2)_2MgCl$	$CH_3(C_2H_5)[2,4,5\text{-}(CH_3)_3\text{-}3,6\text{-}(CH_3O)_2C_6(CH_2)_2]COH$†	*80*
$C_5H_3OF_7$			
CH_3CO-*n*-C_3F_7 (0.2–0.3 mole)	C_2H_5MgI (0.4–0.6 mole)	$CH_3(C_2H_5)(n\text{-}C_3F_7)COH$ (18.0%); $CH_3(n\text{-}C_3F_7)CHOH$ (61.6%)	*654*
$C_5H_6O_3$			
$(CH_3CO)_2CO$	CH_3MgBr	$[HO(CH_3)_2C]_2CO$	*107*
C_5H_8O			
$CH_3COCH_2CH{=}CH_2$	CH_3MgI	$H_2C{=}CHCH_2(CH_3)_2COH$ (80%)	*134,135*
$CH_3COCH_2CH{=}CH_2$ (37 g.)	*n*-C_3H_7MgBr (63 g. C_3H_7Br)	$CH_3(H_2C{=}CHCH_2)(n\text{-}C_3H_7)COH$ (yielding 37 g. crude olefin)	*136*
$CH_3COCH{=}CHCH_3$ (35 g.)	CH_3MgBr (20 g. Mg)	$CH_3CH{=}CH(CH_3)_2COH$ (8–9 g.); CH_3CO-*i*-C_4H_9 (*ca.* 30 g.)	*111*
$CH_3COCH{=}CHCH_3$ (40 g.)	CH_3MgI (1.5 equiv.)	$CH_3CH{=}CH(CH_3)_2COH$ (80%); CH_3CO-*i*-C_4H_9 (1 g.)	*10,108, 109,110*
$CH_3COCH{=}CHCH_3$	C_2H_5MgBr	$CH_3(C_2H_5)(CH_3CH{=}CH)COH$ (41.4%); CH_3COCH-*s*-C_4H_9 (38.6%)	*112,109, 110,111*

*The figure recorded represents the overall yield of alkylated benzene obtained by dehydration of the carbinol and hydrogenation of the resultant olefin.

†Isolated, after AcOH-HBr cyclization, as 2,5,7,8-tetramethyl-2-ethyl-6-chromanol.

TABLE VI-XVIII (Continued)

Ketonic Comp'd	RMgX	Product(s)	Ref.
C_5H_8O (*cont.*)			
$CH_3COCH{=}CHCH_3$ (0.5 mole)	C_2H_5MgBr (1.0 mole C_2H_5Br)	$CH_3COCH_2CH(CH_3)C_2H_5$ (52.4 x%)*	*622*
$CH_3COCH{=}CHCH_3$ (0.5 mole)	*i*-C_3H_7MgBr (1.0 mole C_3H_7Br)	$CH_3COCH_2CH(CH_3)$-*i*-C_3H_7 (65.5 x%)*	*622*
$CH_3COCH{=}CHCH_3$	*i*-C_4H_9MgCl	$CH_3(CH_3CH{=}CH)$(*i*-C_4H_9)COH	*109,110*
$CH_3COCH{=}CHCH_3$	*t*-C_4H_9MgCl	$CH_3(CH_3CH{=}CH)$(*t*-C_4H_9)COH (16.7%); $CH_3COCH_2CH(CH_3)$-*t*-C_4H_9 (54.0%)	*112*
$CH_3COCH{=}CHCH_3$ (0.5 mole)	*t*-C_4H_9MgCl (1.0 mole C_4H_9Cl)	$CH_3COCH_2CH(CH_3)$-*t*-C_4H_9 (61.7 x%)*	*622*
$CH_3COCH{=}CHCH_3$	*i*-$C_5H_{11}MgBr$	$CH_3(CH_3CH{=}CH)$(*i*-C_5H_{11})COH	*109,110*
$CH_3COCH{=}CHCH_3$ (40 g.)	C_6H_5MgBr	$CH_3(CH_3CH{=}CH)(C_6H_5)COH$; $CH_3COCH_2CH(C_2H_5)C_6H_5$ (30 g.)	*111*
$CH_3COCH{=}CHCH_3$ (20 g.)	*n*-$C_4H_9C{\equiv}CMgBr$ (24 g. *n*-$C_4H_9C{\equiv}CH$)	$CH_3(CH_3CH{=}CH)$(*n*-$C_4H_9C{\equiv}C$)COH (19.5 g.)	*83*
$CH_3COCH(CH_2)_2$ (14 g.)	CH_3MgI	$(CH_2)_2CH(CH_3)_2COH$ (9 g.)	*113*
$CH_3COCH(CH_2)_2$	C_2H_5MgBr	$CH_3(C_2H_5)[(CH_2)_2CH]COH$	*114,115, 116*
$C_5H_8O_3$			
$CH_3COCH_2O_2CCH_3$	C_2H_5MgBr (1 equiv.)	$CH_3(C_2H_5)_2COH$; $CH_3(C_2H_5)C(OH)CH_2O_2CCH_3$; recovered keto ester (20%)	*82*
$CH_3COCO_2C_2H_5$ (13 g.)	2-$CH_3C_6H_4MgBr$ (38 g. C_7H_7Br)	CH_3(2-$CH_3C_6H_4$)$C(OH)CO_2C_2H_5$ (50%)	*119*
$CH_3COCO_2C_2H_5$ (29 g.)	4-$CH_3C_6H_4MgBr$ (42 g. C_7H_7Br)	CH_3(4-$CH_3C_6H_4$)$C(OH)CO_2C_2H_5$ (35%)	*119*
$CH_3COCO_2C_2H_5$ (29g .)	2,4,6-$(CH_3)_3C_6H_2MgBr$ (50 g. $C_9H_{11}Br$)	CH_3[2,4,6-$(CH_3)_3C_6H_2$]$C(OH)CO_2C_2H_5$ (20%)	*119*
$CH_3COCO_2C_2H_5$ (14.5 g.)	2,4,6-$(CH_3)_3C_6H_2MgBr$ (50.0 g. $C_9H_{11}Br$)	CH_3[2,4,6-$(CH_3)_3C_6H_2$]$C(OH)CO_2C_2H_5$ (50%)	*119*

*In this study only the relative yields of 1,4-addition products were evaluated. Total yields of products for the reactions studied are said to range from 86 to 100% (*i.e.*, x = 0.86–1.00).

TABLE VI-XVIII (Continued)

Ketonic Comp'd	RMgX	Product(s)	Ref.
$C_5H_8O_3$ (*cont.*)			
$CH_3COCO_2C_2H_5$ (23.2 g.)	1-$C_{10}H_7MgBr$ (41.4 g. $C_{10}H_7Br$)	$CH_3(1\text{-}C_{10}H_7)C(OH)CO_2C_2H_5$ (35%)	*119*
C_5H_9OBr			
$CH_3COCBr(CH_3)_2$	CH_3MgI	*t*-$C_4H_9(CH_3)_2COH$ (62%)	*120*
C_5H_9OCl			
$ClCH_2CH_2COC_2H_5$	C_2H_5MgBr	$ClCH_2CH_2(C_2H_5)_2COH$	*117*
$C_5H_9O_2N$			
$CH_3COC(=NOCH_3)CH_3$	CH_3MgI	$HO(CH_3)_2CC(=NOCH_3)CH_3$ (60%)	*90*
$C_5H_{10}O$			
CH_3CO-*n*-C_3H_7	$(\equiv CMgBr)_2$	$[\equiv C(CH_3)(n\text{-}C_3H_7)OH]_2$ (70-75%)	*118,21,22*
CH_3CO-*n*-C_3H_7	$H_2C=CHCH_2Br$ + Mg	$CH_3(H_2C=CHCH_2)(n\text{-}C_3H_7)COH$ (88%, crude)	*28*
CH_3CO-*n*-C_3H_7	*i*-C_3H_7MgCl	$CH_3(n\text{-}C_3H_7)(i\text{-}C_3H_7)COH$ (22%); ketol (27%)	*96*
CH_3CO-*n*-C_3H_7	*i*-C_3H_7MgBr	$CH_3(n\text{-}C_3H_7)(i\text{-}C_3H_7)COH$ (32%)	*31,121*
CH_3CO-*n*-C_3H_7	$H_2C=C(CH_3)CH_2MgCl$	$CH_3(n\text{-}C_3H_7)[H_2C=C(CH_3)CH_2]COH$; $[H_2C=C(CH_3)CH_2-]_2$	*44*
CH_3CO-*n*-C_3H_7	*n*-C_4H_9MgBr	$CH_3(n\text{-}C_3H_7)(n\text{-}C_4H_9)COH$ (68%)	*99*
CH_3CO-*n*-C_3H_7	*t*-C_4H_9MgCl	$CH_3(n\text{-}C_3H_7)(t\text{-}C_4H_9)COH$	*122*
CH_3CO-*n*-C_3H_7	*n*-$C_4H_9C\equiv CMgBr$	$CH_3(n\text{-}C_3H_7)(n\text{-}C_4H_9C\equiv C)COH$ (91%)	*103*
CH_3CO-*n*-C_3H_7 (120 g.)	$C_6H_5C\equiv CMgBr$ (143 g. $C_6H_5C\equiv CH$)	$CH_3(n\text{-}C_3H_7)(C_6H_5C\equiv C)COH$ (140 g.)	*123*
CH_3CO-*n*-C_3H_7 (0.17 mole)	$RC\equiv CMgBr$* (0.17 mole)	$CH_3(n\text{-}C_3H_7)(RC\equiv C)COH$* (17.0 g., 48%)	97

*R = 1-Cyclohexenyl.

TABLE VI-XVIII (Continued)

Ketonic Comp'd	RMgX	Product(s)	Ref.
$C_5H_{10}O$ (*cont.*)			
CH_3CO-*n*-C_3H_7	α-Camphoryl-MgBr*	CH_3(*n*-C_3H_7)(α-$C_{10}H_{15}O$)COH (75–79%)	*75*
CH_3CO-*n*-C_3H_7	2,4,5-$(CH_3)_3$-3,6-$(CH_3O)_2C_6(CH_2)_2MgCl$	CH_3(*n*-C_3H_7)[2,4,5-$(CH_3)_3$-3,6-$(CH_3O)_2C_6(CH_2)_2$]COH†	*80*
CH_3CO-*i*-C_3H_7	CH_3MgCl	Addition, 100%; enolization 0%.‡	*124*
CH_3CO-*i*-C_3H_7	C_2H_5MgBr	$CH_3(C_2H_5)$(*i*-C_3H_7)COH (59%)	*121*
CH_3CO-*i*-C_3H_7 (15 g.)	*n*-C_3H_7MgBr (21 g. C_3H_7Br)	CH_3(*n*-C_3H_7)(*i*-C_3H_7)COH (10 g.)	*126,37, 121*
CH_3CO-*i*-C_3H_7	*i*-C_3H_7MgCl	$HO(CH_3)$(*i*-C_3H_7)CCH_2CO-*i*-C_3H_7 (70%)	*127*
CH_3CO-*i*-C_3H_7	*i*-C_3H_7MgCl	CH_3(*n*-C_3H_7)(*i*-C_3H_7)COH (trace); ketol (70%)	*96*
CH_3CO-*i*-C_3H_7 (0.3 mole)	*i*-C_3H_7MgBr (0.5 mole)	$HO(CH_3)$(*i*-C_3H_7)CCH_2CO-*i*-C_3H_7 (18 g., 70%)	*127*
CH_3CO-*i*-C_3H_7	*n*-C_4H_9MgBr	CH_3(*i*-C_3H_7)(*n*-C_4H_9)COH (61%)	*121,128*
CH_3CO-*i*-C_3H_7	*s*-C_4H_9MgBr	$HO(CH_3)$(*i*-C_3H_7)CCH_2CO-*i*-C_3H_7 (37%)	*127*
CH_3CO-*i*-C_3H_7	*t*-C_4H_9MgCl	$HO(CH_3)$(*i*-C_3H_7)CCH_2CO-*i*-C_3H_7 (50%)	*127*
CH_3CO-*i*-C_3H_7	*n*-$C_5H_{11}MgBr$	CH_3(*i*-C_3H_7)(*n*-C_5H_{11})COH (60%)	*121*
CH_3CO-*i*-C_3H_7	$C_6H_5CH_2MgCl$	CH_3(*i*-C_3H_7)$(C_6H_5CH_2)$COH	*68*
$(C_2H_5)_2CO$	$(\equiv CMgBr)_2$ (excess)	$[\equiv CC(C_2H_5)_2OH]_2$ (*ca.* quant.)	*22*
$(C_2H_5)_2CO$	$(\equiv CMgI)_2$	$[\equiv CC(C_2H_5)_2OH]_2$	*125*
$(C_2H_5)_2CO$ (40 g.)	C_2H_5MgBr (12 g. Mg.)	$(C_2H_5)_3COH$ (91%)	*37,33*
$(C_2H_5)_2CO$	C_2H_5Br + Mg	$(C_2H_5)_3COH$ (60%)	*104*
$(C_2H_5)_2CO$ (43 g.)	*n*-C_3H_7MgI (90 g. C_3H_7I)	*n*-$C_3H_7(C_2H_5)_2COH$ (50 g.)	*129*
$(C_2H_5)_2CO$	*i*-C_3H_7MgCl	Carbinol (*none*); ketol (52–55%)	*96*
$(C_2H_5)_2CO$	*n*-C_4H_9MgBr	*n*-$C_4H_9(C_2H_5)_2COH$ (67%)	*128*
$(C_2H_5)_2CO$	$C_6H_5CH_2MgCl$	$C_6H_5CH_2(C_2H_5)_2COH$; $C_6H_5CH_2OH$; $(C_6H_5CH_2—)_2$	*101*
$(C_2H_5)_2CO$	1-Indenyl-MgBr	1-Indenyldiethylmethanol	*69*

*It seems possible (even probable) that this "Grignard reagent" is in fact an enolate.

†Isolated, after AcOH-HBr cyclization, as 2,5,7,8-tetramethyl-2-*n*-propyl-6-chromanol.

‡"Grignard machine" study.

TABLE VI-XVIII (Continued)

Ketonic Comp'd	RMgX	Product(s)	Ref.
$C_5H_{10}O_2$			
$CH_3COC(CH_3)_2OH$	CH_3MgI	$[-C(CH_3)_2OH]_2$	*130*
$CH_3COC(CH_3)_2OH$	$H_2C=CHCH_2MgBr$	$HO(H_2C=CCH_2)(CH_3)CC(CH_3)_2OH$ (70%, crude)	*25*
$C_2H_5COCH(OH)CH_3$	C_2H_5MgBr	$HO(C_2H_5)_2CCH(OH)CH_3$	*131*
$C_6H_4O_3S$			
2-Thienylglyoxylic acid	CH_3MgI	$HO(CH_3)(2\text{-}C_4C_3S)CCO_2H$ (82%)	*132*
2-Thienylglyoxylic acid (31.2 g.)	2-Thienyl-MgBr (98.0 g. C_4H_3SBr)	$HO(2\text{-}C_4H_3S)_2CCO_2H$ (50.5 g., crude)	*132*
2-Thienylglyoxylic acid	C_6H_5MgBr	$HO(C_6H_5)(2\text{-}C_4H_3S)CCO_2H$	*132*
2-Thienylglyoxylic acid	$(CH_2)_5CHMgBr$	$HO[(CH_2)_5CH](2\text{-}C_4H_3S)CCO_2H$	*132*
2-Thienylglyoxylic acid	$C_6H_5CH_2MgBr$	$HO(C_6H_5CH_2)(2\text{-}C_4H_3S)CCO_2H$	*132*
2-Thienylglyoxylic acid	$1\text{-}C_{10}H_7MgBr$	$HO(1\text{-}C_{10}H_7)(2\text{-}C_4H_3S)CCO_2H$	*132*
2-Thienylglyoxylic acid	$4\text{-}C_6H_5C_6H_4MgBr$	$HO(4\text{-}C_6H_5C_6H_4)(2\text{-}C_4H_3S)CCO_2H$	*132*
$C_6H_{10}O$			
$CH_3CO(CH_2)_2CH=CH_2$ (20.0 g.)	CH_3MgI (30.3 g. CH_3I)	$HO(CH_3)_2C(CH_2)_2CH=CH_2$ (20.0 g.)	*241*
$CH_3COCH=CHC_2H_5$ (0.5 mole)	C_2H_5MgBr (1.0 mole C_2H_5Br)	$CH_3COCH_2CH(C_2H_5)_2$ (43.1 x%)*	622
$CH_3COCH=CHC_2H_5$ (0.5 mole)	$i\text{-}C_3H_7MgBr$ (1.0 mole C_3H_7Br)	$CH_3COCH_2CH(C_2H_5)\text{-}i\text{-}C_3H_7$ (56.5 x%)*	622
$CH_3COCH=CHC_2H_5$ (0.5 mole)	$t\text{-}C_4H_9MgCl$ (1.0 mole C_4H_9Cl)	$CH_3COCH_2CH(C_2H_5)\text{-}t\text{-}C_4H_9$ (48.0 x%)*	622
Mesityl oxide $[CH_3COCH=C(CH_3)_2$ (*ca.* 80%) + $CH_3COCH_2C(CH_3)=CH_2$ (*ca.* 20%)]†	CH_3MgBr	$(CH_3)_2C=CHC(CH_3)_2OH$† (75–80%); $H_2C=C(CH_3)CH_2C(CH_3)_2OH$† (20–25%)	*137,604*

*In this study only the relative yields of 1,4-addition products were evaluated. Total yields of products for the reactions studied are said to range from 86 to 100% (*i.e.*, $x = 0.86–1.00$).

†These assignments of the constitutions of mesityl oxide and the carbinols are made by Dupont and Menut (*137*) on the basis of a study of their Raman spectra. The total yield of addition products on the basis of reacting ketone is not stated.

TABLE VI-XVIII (Continued)

Ketonic Comp'd	RMgX	Product(s)	Ref.
$C_6H_{10}O$ (*cont.*)			
$CH_3COCH{=}C(CH_3)_2$	CH_3MgI	$H_2C{=}C(CH_3)CH{=}C(CH_3)_2$	*61*
$CH_3COCH{=}C(CH_3)_2$	CH_3MgI	$(CH_3)_2C{=}CH(CH_3)_2COH$ (30%); $H_2C{=}C(CH_3)CH{=}C(CH_3)_2$ (57%)	*613*
$CH_3COCH{=}C(CH_3)_2$ (50.0 g.)	CH_3MgI (72.4 g. CH_3I)	$(CH_3)_2C{=}CH(CH_3)_2COH$ (17.0 g.)	*138,139*
$CH_3COCH{=}C(CH_3)_2$	$({\equiv}CMgI)_2$	$[{\equiv}CC(OH)(CH_3)CH{=}C(CH_3)_2]_2$	*125*
$CH_3COCH{=}C(CH_3)_2$ (200 g.)	C_2H_5MgBr (70 g. Mg)	$CH_3(C_2H_5)[(CH_3)_2CH{=}CH]COH$	*111,140, 604*
$CH_3COCH{=}C(CH_3)_2$	C_2H_5MgBr	$CH_3(C_2H_5)[(CH_3)_2CH{=}CH]COH$ (>50.9%); $CH_3COCH_2C(CH_3)_2C_2H_5$ (*ca.* 6.5%)*	*141*
$CH_3COCH{=}C(CH_3)_2$	C_2H_5MgBr	$H_2C{=}C(C_2H_5)CH{=}C(CH_3)_2$; higher-boiling isomer.†	*141*
$CH_3COCH{=}C(CH_3)_2$	C_2H_5MgI	$CH_3(C_2H_5)[(CH_3)_2C{=}CH]COH$	232
$CH_3COCH{=}C(CH_3)_2$	$H_2C{=}CHCH_2MgBr$	$CH_3(H_2C{=}CHCH_2)[(CH_3)_2C{=}CH]COH$ (91%, crude)	*25,142, 143*
$CH_3COCH{=}C(CH_3)_2$	$H_2C{=}CHCH_2Br$ + Mg	$CH_3(H_2C{=}CHCH_2)[(CH_3)_2C{=}CH]COH$ (75%)	*599*
$CH_3COCH{=}C(CH_3)_2$	n-C_3H_7MgBr	$CH_3(n$-$C_3H_7)[(CH_3)_2C{=}CH]COH$	*232,604*
$CH_3COCH{=}C(CH_3)_2$	i-C_3H_7MgBr	$C_9H_{17}OH$	*144*
$CH_3COCH{=}C(CH_3)_2$	i-C_3H_7MgBr	$CH_3(i$-$C_3H_7)[(CH_3)_2C{=}CH]COH$	*604*
$CH_3COCH{=}C(CH_3)_2$	$H_2C{=}CHC{\equiv}CMgBr$	$H_2C{=}CHC{\equiv}CC({=}CH_2)CH{=}C(CH_3)_2$ (40%)	*40*
$CH_3COCH{=}C(CH_3)_2$	n-C_4H_9MgBr	$CH_3(n$-$C_4H_9)[(CH_3)_2C{=}CH]COH$	*604*
$CH_3COCH{=}C(CH_3)_2$	n-C_4H_9MgI	$CH_3(n$-$C_4H_9)[(CH_3)_2C{=}CH]COH$	*232*
$CH_3COCH{=}C(CH_3)_2$	i-C_4H_9MgBr	$CH_3(i$-$C_4H_9)[(CH_3)_2C{=}CH]COH$	*604*

*Simultaneous addition of Grignard reagent and Et_2O-ketone solutions to Et_2O at $-10°$. The overall yield of diene upon dehydration of the carbinole was 50.9%.

†Simultaneous addition of Grignard reagent and Et_2O-ketone solutions to Et_2O at 15°. The total yield of crude dienes was 17.3%.

TABLE VI-XVIII (Continued)

Ketonic Comp'd	RMgX	Product(s)	Ref.
$C_6H_{10}O$ (*cont.*)			
$CH_3COCH{=}C(CH_3)_2$	$t\text{-}C_4H_9MgCl$	$CH_3[(CH_3)_2C{=}CH](t\text{-}C_4H_9)COH$ (46%); *no* 1,4 add'n.	*112,144*
$CH_3COCH{=}C(CH_3)_2$	$n\text{-}C_5H_{11}MgBr$	$CH_3(n\text{-}C_5H_{11})[(CH_3)_2C{=}CH]COH$	*604*
$CH_3COCH{=}C(CH_3)_2$	$i\text{-}C_5H_{11}MgBr$	$CH_3(i\text{-}C_5H_{11})[(CH_3)_2C{=}CH]COH$	*604*
$CH_3COCH{=}C(CH_3)_2$	$i\text{-}C_5H_{11}MgBr$	Dienes, only.	*145*
$CH_3COCH{=}C(CH_3)_2$ (318.5 g., 3.25 moles)	$t\text{-}C_5H_{11}MgCl$ (3.5 moles)	$CH_3COCH_2C(CH_3)_2\text{-}t\text{-}C_5H_{11}$ (16.2%); dienes (8.3%); recovered ketone (8.0%); condensate	*305*
$CH_3COCH{=}C(CH_3)_2$ (25 g.)	C_6H_5MgBr (38 g. C_6H_5Br)	$CH_3(C_6H_5)C{=}C{=}C(CH_3)_2$ (18 g.)	*146,140, 147*
$CH_3COCH{=}C(CH_3)_2$ (12.0 g.)	$n\text{-}C_4H_9C{\equiv}CMgBr$ (11.3 g. $n\text{-}C_4H_9C{\equiv}CH$)	$CH_3[(CH_3)_2C{=}CH](n\text{-}C_4H_9C{\equiv}C)COH$ (14.2 g.)	*83*
$CH_3COCH{=}C(CH_3)_2$	$C_6H_5CH_2MgCl$	$CH_3[(CH_3)_2C{=}CH](C_6H_5CH_2)COH$	*148*
$CH_3COCH{=}C(CH_3)_2$	$C_6H_5CH(CO_2Na)MgCl$*	$CH_3[(CH_3)_2C{=}CH][C_6H_5(HO_2C)CH]COH$ ("good yield")	*149*
$CH_3COCH{=}C(CH_3)_2$ (24.5 g.)	9-Fluorenyl-MgBr	Fluorene (27%); 4-(9-fluorenylidene)-2-methyl-2-pentene (30%)	*626*
$CH_3COC(CH_3){=}CHCH_3$	CH_3MgI	$CH_3CH{=}C(CH_3)C(CH_3)_2OH$ (70%)	*150*
$CH_3COC(CH_3){=}CHCH_3$	$n\text{-}C_4H_9MgBr$	$CH_3[CH_3CH{=}C(CH_3)](n\text{-}C_4H_9)COH$ + $CH_3COCH(CH_3)CH(CH_3)\text{-}n\text{-}C_4H_9$ (in ratio of *ca.* 77 : 23)	*150*
$C_2H_5COCH{=}CHCH_3$ (0.5 mole)	C_2H_5MgBr (1.0 mole C_2H_5Br)	$C_2H_5COCH_2CH(CH_3)C_2H_5$ (67.7 x%)†	*622*
$C_2H_5COCH{=}CHCH_3$ (0.5 mole)	$i\text{-}C_3H_7MgBr$ (1.0 mole C_3H_7Br)	$C_2H_5COCH_2CH(CH_3)\text{-}i\text{-}C_3H_7$ (80.2 x%)†	*622*

*In the opinion of Schlenk, Hilleman, and Rodloff, *Ann.*, *487*, 135–54 (1931), this "Grignard reagent" should be formulated as an enolate.

†In this study only the relative yields of 1,4-addition products were evaluated. Total yields of products for the reactions studied are said to range from 86 to 100% (*i.e.*, x = 0.86–1.00).

TABLE VI-XVIII (Continued)

Ketonic Comp'd	RMgX	Product (s)	Ref.
$C_6H_{10}O$ (*cont.*)			
$C_2H_5COCH{=}CHCH_3$ (0.5 mole)	t-C_4H_9MgCl (1.0 mole C_4H_9Cl)	$C_2H_5COCH_2CH(CH_3)$-t-C_4H_9 (66.3 x%)*	*622*
$C_2H_5COCH(CH_2)_2$	CH_3MgBr	$CH_3(C_2H_5)[(CH_2)_2CH]COH$	*114,115*
$C_2H_5COCH(CH_2)_2$	C_2H_5MgBr	$(CH_2)_2CH(C_2H_5)_2COH$	*115*
$C_2H_5COCH(CH_2)_2$	n-C_3H_7MgBr	$C_2H_5[(CH_2)_2CH](n\text{-}C_3H_7)COH$	*115*
$C_2H_5COCH(CH_2)_2$	n-C_4H_9MgBr	$C_2H_5[(CH_2)_2CH](n\text{-}C_4H_9)COH$	*115*
$C_2H_5COCH(CH_2)_2$	n-$C_5H_{11}MgBr$	$C_2H_5[(CH_2)_2CH](i\text{-}C_5H_{11})COH$	*115*
$C_6H_{10}O_2$			
$(CH_3COCH_2{-})_2$	$({\equiv}CMgBr)_2$	$HO(CH_3)(HC{\equiv}C)CH_2CH_2COCH_3$	*82*
$C_6H_{10}O_3$			
$CH_3COCH_2CO_2C_2H_5$ (65 g.)	CH_3MgI (1 equiv.)	Forms enolate, $Mg(C_6H_9O_3)_2$; 57 g. ketone recovered; CH_4	*151,152*
$C_6H_{11}OCl$			
$CH_3COCCl(CH_3)_2$	CH_3MgBr	t-C_4H_9OH; $(CH_3)C{=}CH_2$	*161*
$CH_3COCCl(CH_3)_2$	C_2H_5MgBr	$CH_3(C_2H_5)_2COH$; $(C_2H_5)_2C{=}CH_2$; $(CH_3)_2C{=}CH_2$	*161*
$CH_3COCCl(CH_3)_2$	C_6H_5MgBr	$CH_3(C_6H_5)_2COH$; $(C_6H_5)_2C{=}CH_2$; $(CH_3)_2C{=}CH_2$	*161*
$CH_3COCCl(CH_3)_2$	$(CH_2)_5CHMgBr$	$CH_3[(CH_2)_5CH]_2COH$; $[(CH_2)_5CH]_2C{=}CH_2$; $(CH_3)_2C{=}CH_2$	*161*
$C_6H_{11}ON$			
$CH_3COCH{=}CHN(CH_3)_2$	C_6H_5MgBr	$CH_3COCH{=}CHC_6H_5$	*153*

*In this study only the relative yields of 1,4-addition products were evaluated. Total yields of products for the reactions studied are said to range from 86 to 100% (*i.e.*, x = 0.86–1.00).

TABLE VI-XVIII (Continued)

Ketonic Comp'd	RMgX	Product(s)	Ref.
$C_6H_{11}O_2Cl$			
$CH_3COCHClC(CH_3)_2OH$	CH_3MgI (2 equiv.)	$[HO(CH_3)_2C]_2CHOH$ (40–60%)	154,155
$C_6H_{12}O$			
CH_3CO-n-C_4H_9	$(\equiv CMgI)_2$	$[\equiv CC(CH_3)(n\text{-}C_4H_9)OH]_2$	125
CH_3CO-n-C_4H_9	C_2H_5MgBr	$CH_3(C_2H_5)(n\text{-}C_4H_9)COH$ (*ca.* quant.)	156
CH_3CO-n-C_4H_9	C_2H_5MgI	$CH_3(C_2H_5)(n\text{-}C_4H_9)COH$	157
CH_3CO-n-C_4H_9	n-C_3H_7MgI	$CH_3(n\text{-}C_3H_7)(n\text{-}C_4H_9)COH$	158
CH_3CO-n-C_4H_9 (2.0 moles)	n-C_4H_9MgBr (4.5 moles)	$CH_3(n\text{-}C_4H_9)_2COH$; olefin (0.15 mole); $CH_3(n\text{-}C_4H_9)CHOH$ (11.8 g., 9%); recovered ketone (19.3 g.)	159
CH_3CO-n-C_4H_9 (165 g., 1.65 mole)	$(CH_2)_5C(OH)C\equiv CH$ (186 g., 1.5 mole) + C_2H_5MgBr (380 g., 3.48 moles C_2H_5Br)	1-(3-Hydroxy-3-methyl-1-heptynyl)-cyclohexanol (207–214 g., 59–61%)	160
CH_3CO-i-C_4H_9	C_2H_5MgBr	$CH_3(C_2H_5)(i\text{-}C_4H_9)COH$ (77%)	162
CH_3CO-i-C_4H_9	C_2H_5MgI	$CH_3(C_2H_5)(i\text{-}C_4H_9)COH$ (40–60%);* C_8H_{16}; C_2H_6	142
CH_3CO-i-C_4H_9	$H_2C{=}CHCH_2MgBr$	$CH_3(H_2C{=}CHCH_2)(i\text{-}C_4H_9)COH$ (83%, crude)	25,142, 143
CH_3CO-i-C_4H_9	n-C_3H_7MgBr	$CH_3(n\text{-}C_3H_7)(i\text{-}C_4H_9)COH$ (40–60%);* C_9H_{18}; C_3H_8	142
CH_3CO-i-C_4H_9 (70 g.)	n-C_3H_7MgI (171 g. CH_3I)	$H_2C{=}C(n\text{-}C_3H_7)(i\text{-}C_3H_7)$ (?)† (20 g.)	164
CH_3CO-i-C_4H_9	i-C_3H_7MgCl	Carbinol (*none*); ketol (55%)	96
CH_3CO-i-C_4H_9	i-C_3H_7MgBr	$CH_3(i\text{-}C_3H_7)(i\text{-}C_4H_9)COH$	54

*Carbinol yields of 40–60% are reported for a series of reactions studied.

†Although this product is once mentioned (evidently through a slip of the pen) as "2-methene-4-methylheptane," there is no doubt that the compound reported is that represented by the formula above. It would appear much more probable, however, that the carbinol dehydration product is $CH_3(n\text{-}C_3H_7)CHCH{=}C(CH_3)_2$ or a mixture thereof with $CH_3(i\text{-}C_3H_7)C{=}CH\text{-}n\text{-}C_3H_7$.

TABLE VI-XVIII (Continued)

Ketonic Comp'd	RMgX	Product (s)	Ref.
$C_6H_{12}O$ (*cont.*)			
CH_3CO-*i*-C_4H_9	*n*-C_4H_9MgBr	CH_3(*n*-C_4H_9)(*i*-C_4H_9)COH	*54*
CH_3CO-*i*-C_4H_9	*i*-C_4H_9MgBr	CH_3(*i*-C_4H_9)$_2$COH (40–60%)*	*142*
CH_3CO-*i*-C_4H_9	*i*-$C_5H_{11}MgBr$	CH_3(*i*-C_4H_9)(*i*-C_5H_{11})COH	*54*
CH_3CO-*i*-C_4H_9	C_6H_5MgBr	CH_3(*i*-C_4H_9)(C_6H_5)COH (40–60%);* $CH_3(C_6H_5)C{=}CH$-*i*-C_3H_7; C_6H_6	*142*
CH_3CO-*i*-C_4H_9	2,4,5-$(CH_3)_3$-3,6-$(CH_3O)_2C_6(CH_2)_2MgCl$	CH_3(*i*-C_4H_9)[2,4,5-$(CH_3)_3$-3,6-$(CH_3O)_2C_6(CH_2)_2$]COH†	*80*
CH_3CO-*s*-C_4H_9	CH_3MgCl	Addition (?%); enolization (32%)‡	*124*
CH_3CO-*t*-C_4H_9	CH_3MgCl	Addition (86%); enolization (5%)‡	*124*
CH_3CO-*t*-C_4H_9	CH_3MgBr	Addition (86%); enolization (5%)†	*168*
CH_3CO-*t*-C_4H_9	CH_3MgBr	Carbinol (?%); ketol (6%)	*96*
CH_3CO-*t*-C_4H_9 (10 g.)	CH_3MgBr (3 g. Mg)	*t*-$C_4H_9(CH_3)_2COH$ (12 g.)	*166,18*
CH_3CO-*t*-C_4H_9	CH_3MgI	*t*-$C_4H_9(CH_3)_2COH$ (90%); $HO(CH_3)$(*t*-C_4H_9)CH_2CO-*t*-C_4H_9 (6%)	*167,31*
CH_3CO-*t*-C_4H_9	$({\equiv}CMgBr)_2$	$[{\equiv}CC(CH_3)$(*t*-C_4H_9)$OH]_2$ (80%)	*118,19*
CH_3CO-*t*-C_4H_9	C_2H_5MgBr	Carbinol (?%); ketol (7.5%)	*96*
CH_3CO-*t*-C_4H_9 (50 g.)	C_2H_5MgBr (82 g. C_2H_5Br)	$CH_3(C_2H_5)$(*t*-C_4H_9)COH (34 g.)	*169,31,35, 170*
CH_3CO-*t*-C_4H_9	C_2H_5MgBr	CH_3(*t*-C_4H_9)$C{=}CHCO$-*t*-C_4H_9; $HO(CH_3)$(*t*-C_4H_9)CH_2CO-*t*-C_4H_9	*165*
CH_3CO-*t*-C_4H_9	$CH_3C{\equiv}CMgBr$	$CH_3(CH_3C{\equiv}C)$(*t*-C_4H_9)COH (50%)	*118*
CH_3CO-*t*-C_4H_9	*n*-C_3H_7MgCl	Carbinol (? %); ketol (19%)	*96*
CH_3CO-*t*-C_4H_9	*n*-C_3H_7MgCl	CH_3(*n*-C_3H_7)(*t*-C_4H_9)COH (*ca.* 25%); CH_3(*t*-C_4H_9)CHOH; C_3H_6; C_3H_8	*171*

*Carbinol yields of 40–60% are reported for a series of reactions studied.

†Isolated, after AcOH-HBr cyclization, as 2,5,7,8-tetramethyl-2-isobutyl-6-chromanol.

‡"Grignard machine" study.

TABLE VI-XVIII (Continued)

Ketonic Comp'd	RMgX	Product(s)	Ref.
$C_6H_{12}O$ (*cont.*)			
CH_3CO-*t*-C_4H_9	*i*-C_3H_7MgCl	Carbinol (? %); ketol (62%)	*96*
CH_3CO-*t*-C_4H_9	*i*-C_3H_7MgCl	$HO(CH_3)$(*t*-C_4H_9)CCH_2CO-*t*-C_4H_9 (43%)	*127*
CH_3CO-*t*-C_4H_9	*s*-C_4H_9MgBr	$HO(CH_3)$(*t*-C_4H_9)CCH_2CO-*t*-C_4H_9 (45%)	*127*
CH_3CO-*t*-C_4H_9	*t*-C_4H_9MgCl	$HO(CH_3)$(*t*-C_4H_9)CCH_2CO-*t*-C_4H_9 (48%)	*127*
CH_3CO-*t*-C_4H_9	*t*-C_4H_9MgCl	CH_3(*t*-C_4H_9)$CHOH$; CH_3(*t*-C_4H_9)$C{=}CHCO$-*t*-C_4H_9; $HO(CH_3)$(*t*-C_4H_9)CCH_2CO-*t*-C_4H_9; (*no* add'n product)	*165*
CH_3CO-*t*-C_4H_9	(+)-$CH_3(C_2H_5)CHCH_2MgCl$*	CH_3(*t*-C_4H_9)$CHOH$, $[\alpha]_D^{20}$ + 0.42 to $[\alpha]_D^{20}$ + 0.70 (9.0–35.6%); CH_3(*t*-C_4H_9)$[CH_3(C_2H_5)CHCH_2]COH$ + ketol (aggregating 8.1–37.9%); $H_2C{=}C(CH_3)C_2H_5$ (6.2–31.2%); recovered ketone (11.1–39.5%)†	*612*
CH_3CO-*t*-C_4H_9	C_6H_5MgBr	CH_3(*t*-C_4H_9)$(C_6H_5)COH$ (60%)	*172,232*
CH_3CO-*t*-C_4H_9	C_6H_5MgBr	CH_3(*t*-C_4H_9)$C{=}CHCO$-*t*-C_4H_9; $HO(CH_3)$(*t*-C_4H_9)CCH_2CO-*t*-C_4H_9	*165*
CH_3CO-*t*-C_4H_9 (55.0 g., 0.55 mole)	(+)-$CH_3(C_2H_5)CH(CH_2)_2MgCl$‡ (87.2 g., 0.72 mole $C_6H_{13}Cl$)	(+)-CH_3(*t*-C_4H_9)$CHOH$ (0.001 mole, 0.2%); $CH_3(C_2H_5)CHCH{=}CH_2$ (0.0009 mole); $CH_3(C_2H_5)_2CH$; recovered ketone (53%); add'n and/or cond'n products (*ca.* 20%)	*612*
C_2H_5CO-*n*-C_3H_7	$C_6H_5CH_2Cl$ + Mg	C_2H_5(*n*-C_3H_7)$(C_6H_5CH_2)COH$ (60%); dehydr'n product	*104*
C_2H_5CO-*i*-C_3H_7	CH_3MgCl	Addition (100%); enolization (0%)§	*124*
C_2H_5CO-*i*-C_3H_7	C_2H_5MgBr	*i*-$C_3H_7(C_2H_5)_2COH$	*37*

*Prepared from (+)-$CH_3(C_2H_5)CHCH_2Cl$ of 94–96% optical purity.

†The reaction was conducted under a variety of conditions; total yields of recovered products ranged from 66.9 to 83.5%.

‡Prepared from (+)-$CH_3(C_2H_5)CH(CH_2)_2Cl$ of 74% optical purity.

§"Grignard machine" study.

TABLE VI-XVIII (Continued)

Ketonic Comp'd	RMgX	Product(s)	Ref.
$C_6H_{12}O$ (*cont.*)			
C_2H_5CO-*i*-C_3H_7 (25 g.)	*n*-C_3H_7MgBr (10 g. Mg)	C_2H_5(*n*-C_3H_7)(*i*-C_3H_7)COH (*ca.* quant.)	37
C_2H_5CO-*i*-C_3H_7	*i*-C_3H_7MgCl	Carbinol (none); ketol (60%)	96
C_2H_5CO-*i*-C_3H_7 (25 g.)	*i*-C_3H_7MgBr (10 g. Mg)	C_2H_5(*i*-C_3H_7)$_2$COH (50%); C_2H_5(*i*-C_3H_7)CHOH (30%)	37
$C_6H_{12}O_2$			
$CH_3COCH_2C(CH_3)_2OH$	CH_3MgBr	$[HO(CH_3)_2C]_2CH_2$	*174,107*
$CH_3COCH_2C(CH_3)_2OH$	CH_3MgI (2 equiv.)	$[HO(CH_3)_2C]_2CH_2$	*177,178*
$CH_3COCH_2C(CH_3)_2OH$ (350 g.)	C_2H_5MgBr (2.25 equiv.)	$HO(CH_3)_2CCH_2C(CH_3)(C_2H_5)OH$ (160 g.)	*175,176*
$CH_3COCH_2C(CH_3)_2OH$	*n*-C_3H_7MgBr	$HO(CH_3)_2CCH_2C(CH_3)$(*n*-C_3H_7)OH	*176*
$CH_3COCH_2C(CH_3)_2OH$	*i*-C_3H_7MgBr	$HO(CH_3)_2CCH_2C(CH_3)$(*i*-C_3H_7)OH	*176*
$CH_3COCH_2C(CH_3)_2OH$	*n*-C_4H_9MgBr	$HO(CH_3)_2CCH_2C(CH_3)$(*n*-C_4H_9)OH	*176*
$CH_3COCH_2C(CH_3)_2OH$	*i*-C_4H_9MgBr	$HO(CH_3)_2CCH_2C(CH_3)$(*i*-C_4H_9)OH	*176*
$CH_3COCH_2C(CH_3)_2OH$	*n*-$C_5H_{11}MgBr$	$HO(CH_3)_2CCH_2C(CH_3)$(*n*-C_5H_{11})OH	*176*
$CH_3COCH_2C(CH_3)_2OH$	*i*-$C_5H_{11}MgBr$	$HO(CH_3)_2CCH_2C(CH_3)$(*i*-C_5H_{11})OH	*176*
$C_2H_5COCH(OH)C_2H_5$ (30 g.)	C_6H_5MgBr (130 g. C_6H_5Br)	$HO(C_2H_5)(C_6H_5)CCH(OH)C_2H_5$	*179*
$C_2H_5COCH(OH)C_2H_5$ (11.6 g.)	$(CH_2)_5CHMgBr$ (41 g., $C_6H_{11}Br$)	$HO(C_2H_5)[(CH_2)_5CH]CCH(OH)C_2H_5$ (2.2 g.)	*173*
$C_2H_5COCH(OH)C_2H_5$ (39 g.)	4-$CH_3OC_6H_4MgBr$ (180 g. C_7H_7OBr)	$HO(C_2H_5)$(4-$CH_3OC_6H_4$)$CCH(OH)C_2H_5$ (20–25 g.)	*173*
C_7H_7ON			
3-Acetopyridine	C_6H_5(1-$C_{10}H_7$)C$=$CHMgBr	C_6H_5(1-$C_{10}H_7$)C$=$CH(C_5H_4N)(CH_3)COH (30%)	*180*
C_7H_8OS			
2-Propionylthiophene	C_2H_5MgI	α-$C_4H_3S(C_2H_5)_2COH$	*181*

TABLE VI-XVIII (Continued)

Ketonic Comp'd	RMgX	Product(s)	Ref.
$C_7H_{10}O$			
$CH_3COCH{=}CHCH{=}CHCH_3$ (55 g.)	$RC{\equiv}CMgBr$* (62 g. $RC{\equiv}CH$*)	$CH_3(CH_3CH{=}CHCH{=}CH)(RC{\equiv}C)COH$* (60 g.)	*182,630*
$C_7H_{10}O_3$			
$H_5C_2O_2C(C_2H_5)C{=}CO$ (11.0 g., 0.077 mole)	C_6H_5MgBr (0.2 mole)	$C_2H_5(C_6H_5CO)C{=}C(C_6H_5)_2$ (2.5 g.); $C_2H_5(C_6H_5CO)CHCO_2C_2H_5$ (5.0 ml)†	*606*
$H_5C_2O_2C(C_2H_5)C{=}CO$ (8.5 g., 0.06 mole)	C_6H_5MgBr (0.2 mole)	$C_2H_5(C_6H_5CO)CHCO_2C_2H_5$ (6.0 g.); n-$C_3H_7COC_6H_5$ (<2.0 g.)‡	*606*
$C_7H_{10}O_5$			
$(H_5C_2O_2C)_2CO$ (29.0 g.)	2-$CH_3C_6H_4MgBr$ (28.5 g. C_7H_7Br)	2-$CH_3C_6H_4(H_5C_2O_2C)_2COH$ (30%)	*119*
$(H_5C_2O_2C)_2CO$ (43.5 g.)	2,4,6-$(CH_3)_3C_6H_2MgBr$ (50.0 g. $C_9H_{11}Br$)	2,4,6-$(CH_3)_3C_6H_2(H_5C_2O_2C)_2COH$ (25%)	*119*
$(H_5C_2O_2C)_2CO$ (43.0 g.)	1-$C_{10}H_7MgBr$ (52.0 g. $C_{10}H_7Br$)	1-$C_{10}H_7(H_5C_2O_2C)_2COH$ (40%)	*119*
$C_7H_{12}O$			
$CH_3COCH{=}CH$-n-C_3H_7	CH_3MgI	n-$C_3H_7CH{=}CH(CH_3)_2COH$ (75%); ketol ("a little")	*183*
$CH_3COCH{=}CH$-n-C_3H_7 (10.5 g.)	CH_3MgI (17.0 g. CH_3I)	n-$C_3H_7CH{=}CH(CH_3)_2COH$ (yielding 16.0% diene)	*184*
$CH_3COCH{=}CH$-n-C_3H_7 (10.5 g.)	CH_3MgI (34.0 g. CH_3I)	n-$C_3H_7CH{=}CH(CH_3)_2COH$ (yielding 29.5% diene)	*184*
$CH_3COCH{=}CH$-n-C_3H_7	C_2H_5MgBr	$CH_3(C_2H_5)(n$-$C_3H_7CH{=}CH)COH$ (65%)	*183*

*R = 1-Cyclohexenyl.

†Dropwise addition of Et_2O-ketene solution to Grignard reagent solution.

‡Dropwise addition of Grignard reagent solution to Et_2O-ketene solution; half-hour reflux.

TABLE VI-XVIII (Continued)

Ketonic Comp'd	RMgX	Product (s)	Ref.
$C_7H_{12}O$ (*cont.*)			
$CH_3COCH{=}CH\text{-}n\text{-}C_3H_7$ (37.0 g.)	C_2H_5MgBr (13.6 g. Mg)	$CH_3(C_2H_5)(n\text{-}C_3H_7CH{=}CH)COH$ (*ca.* 21.6 g.); $CH_3COCH_2CH(C_2H_5)(n\text{-}C_3H_7)$ (*ca.* 14.4 g.)	*185*
$CH_3COCH{=}CH\text{-}n\text{-}C_3H_7$ (56.0 g., 0.5 mole)	C_2H_5MgBr (24.2 g., 1.0 mole C_2H_5Br)	$CH_3COCH_2CH(C_2H_5)\text{-}i\text{-}C_3H_7$ (52.0 x%)*	*622*
trans-$CH_3COCH{=}CH\text{-}n\text{-}C_3H_7$	C_2H_5MgBr	$CH_3(C_2H_5)(n\text{-}C_3H_7CH{=}CH)COH$ (75.8 x%); $CH_3COCH_2CH(C_2H_5)n\text{-}C_3H_7$ (24.2 x%)	*186*
$CH_3COCH{=}CH\text{-}n\text{-}C_3H_7$	$n\text{-}C_3H_7MgBr$	$CH_3(n\text{-}C_3H_7)(n\text{-}C_3H_7CH{=}CH)COH$ (55%)	*183*
trans-$CH_3COCH{=}CH\text{-}n\text{-}C_3H_7$	$i\text{-}C_3H_7MgBr$	$CH_3(i\text{-}C_3H_7)(n\text{-}C_3H_7CH{=}CH)COH$ (53.7 x%); $CH_3COCH_2CH(n\text{-}C_3H_7)\text{-}i\text{-}C_3H_7$ (46.3 x%)	*186*
$CH_3COCH{=}CH\text{-}n\text{-}C_3H_7$ (0.5 mole)	$i\text{-}C_3H_7MgBr$ (1.0 mole C_3H_7Br)	$CH_3COCH_2CH(n\text{-}C_3H_7)\text{-}i\text{-}C_3H_7$ (63.0 x%)*	*622*
$CH_3COCH{=}CH\text{-}n\text{-}C_3H_7$	$n\text{-}C_4H_9MgBr$	$CH_3(n\text{-}C_4H_9)(n\text{-}C_3H_7CH{=}CH)COH$ (45%)	*183*
$CH_3COCH{=}CH\text{-}n\text{-}C_3H_7$	$i\text{-}C_4H_9MgBr$	$CH_3(i\text{-}C_4H_9)(n\text{-}C_3H_7CH{=}CH)COH$ (38%)	*183*
$CH_3COCH{=}CH\text{-}n\text{-}C_3H_7$ (0.5 mole)	$t\text{-}C_4H_9MgCl$ (1.0 mole C_4H_9Cl)	$CH_3COCH_2CH(n\text{-}C_3H_7)\text{-}t\text{-}C_4H_9$ (59.9 x%)*	*622*
trans-$CH_3COCH{=}CH\text{-}n\text{-}C_3H_7$	$t\text{-}C_4H_9MgCl$	$CH_3(t\text{-}C_4H_9)(n\text{-}C_3H_7CH{=}CH)COH$ (65.1 x%); $CH_3COCH_2CH(n\text{-}C_3H_7)\text{-}t\text{-}C_4H_9$ (34.9 x%)	*186*
$CH_3COCH{=}CH\text{-}n\text{-}C_3H_7$	$i\text{-}C_5H_{11}MgBr$	$CH_3(i\text{-}C_5H_{11})(n\text{-}C_3H_7CH{=}CH)COH$ (30%)	*183*
$CH_3COCH{=}CH\text{-}n\text{-}C_3H_7$	C_6H_5MgBr	$CH_3(n\text{-}C_3H_7CH{=}CH)(C_6H_5)COH$ (20%)	*183,184*
$(CH_2)_2CHCO\text{-}n\text{-}C_3H_7$	CH_3MgBr	$CH_3[(CH_2)_2CH](n\text{-}C_3H_7)COH$	*115*
$(CH_2)_2CHCO\text{-}n\text{-}C_3H_7$	$n\text{-}C_3H_7MgBr$	$(CH_2)_2CH(n\text{-}C_3H_7)_2COH$	*115*
$(CH_2)_2CHCO\text{-}n\text{-}C_3H_7$	$n\text{-}C_4H_9MgBr$	$(CH_2)_2CH(n\text{-}C_3H_7)(n\text{-}C_4H_9)COH$	*115*
$(CH_2)_2CHCO\text{-}n\text{-}C_3H_7$	$n\text{-}C_5H_{11}MgBr$	$(CH_2)_2CH(n\text{-}C_3H_7)(n\text{-}C_5H_{11})COH$	*115*
$(CH_2)_2CHCO\text{-}n\text{-}C_3H_7$	$n\text{-}C_6H_{13}MgBr$	$(CH_2)_2CH(n\text{-}C_3H_7)(n\text{-}C_6H_{13})COH$	*115*

*In this study only the relative yields of 1,4-addition products were evaluated. Total yields of products for the reactions studied are said to range from 86–100% (*i.e.*, x = 0.86–1.00).

TABLE VI-XVIII (Continued)

Ketonic Comp'd	RMgX	Product(s)	Ref.
$C_7H_{12}O_3$			
$CH_3CO(CH_2)_2CO_2C_2H_5$ (130.2 g.)	CH_3MgI (142.0 g. CH_3I)	γ,γ-Dimethylbutyrolactone (63.7 g., 62%)	*580*
$CH_3CO(CH_2)_2CO_2C_2H_5$	C_2H_5MgBr (1 equiv.)	γ-Hydroxy-γ-methylcaproic acid γ-lactone (35%)	*151,187*
$CH_3CO(CH_2)_2CO_2C_2H_5$	C_2H_5MgBr (3 equiv.)	$HO(CH_3)(C_2H_5)C(CH_2)_2C(C_2H_5)_2OH$ (63%)	*151,187*
$CH_3CO(CH_2)_2CO_2C_2H_5$	$CH_3C{\equiv}CMgBr$	$HO(CH_3)(CH_3C{\equiv}C)C(CH_2)_2C(C{\equiv}CCH_3)_2OH$	*608*
$CH_3CO(CH_2)_2CO_2C_2H_5$ (212.0 g.)	*n*-C_3H_7MgBr (207.0 g. C_3H_7Br)	γ-Methyl-γ-*n*-propylbutyrolactone (157.6 g., 73.3%)	*607*
$CH_3CO(CH_2)_2CO_2C_2H_5$	*n*-$C_5H_{11}MgCl$ (213 g. $C_5H_{11}Cl$)	γ-Hydroxy-γ-methylpelargonic acid γ-lactone (*ca.* 98 g.)	*189*
$CH_3CO(CH_2)_2CO_2C_2H_5$	*i*-$C_5H_{11}MgBr$ (1 equiv.)	γ-Hydroxy-γ,ζ-dimethylcaprylic acid γ-lactone	*151,187*
$CH_3CO(CH_2)_2CO_2C_2H_5$	*i*-$C_5H_{11}MgBr$ (3 equiv.)	$HO(CH_3)(i\text{-}C_5H_{11})C(CH_2)_2C(i\text{-}C_5H_{11})_2OH$	*151,187*
$CH_3CO(CH_2)_2CO_2C_2H_5$	C_6H_5MgBr (1 equiv.)	γ-Hydroxy-γ-phenylvaleric acid γ-lactone (30%)	*187*
$CH_3CO(CH_2)_2CO_2C_2H_5$ (2 moles)	*n*-$C_6H_{13}MgCl$ (2 moles $C_6H_{13}Cl$)	γ-Hydroxy-γ-methylcapric acid γ-lactone (103.2 g., 28%); recovered ketone (25.1 g.)	*188*
$CH_3CO(CH_2)_2CO_2C_2H_5$ (2 moles)	*n*-$C_6H_{13}MgBr$ (2 moles $C_6H_{13}Br$)	γ-Hydroxy-γ-methylcapric acid γ-lactone (113.0 g., 31%)	*188*
$CH_3CO(CH_2)_2CO_2C_2H_5$ (26.0 g.)	*n*-$C_{10}H_{21}MgBr$ (44.2 g. $C_{10}H_{21}Br$)	γ-Methyl-γ-*n*-decylbutyrolactone (36.4 g., 84.4%)	*607*
$C_7H_{13}ON$			
$CH_3COC(CH_3){=}CHN(CH_3)_2$	CH_3MgI (1.5 equiv.)	$CH_3COC(CH_3){=}CHCH_3$	*153*
$CH_3COC(CH_3){=}CHN(CH_3)_2$	C_2H_5MgBr (1.5 equiv.)	$CH_3COC(CH_3){=}CHC_2H_5$	*153*

TABLE VI-XVIII (Continued)

Ketonic Comp'd	RMgX	Product(s)	Ref.
$C_7H_{14}O$			
CH_3CO-*n*-C_5H_{11}	CH_3MgCl	*n*-$C_5H_{11}(CH_3)_2COH$ (61%)	*191*
CH_3CO-*n*-C_5H_{11}	$(\equiv CMgBr)_2$	$[\equiv C(CH_3)$ (*n*-$C_5H_{11})OH]_2$ (72–76%)	*631*
CH_3CO-*n*-C_5H_{11}	C_2H_5MgBr	$CH_3(C_2H_5)$(*n*-C_5H_{11})COH (76–77%)	*191,47*
CH_3CO-*n*-C_5H_{11}	$CH_3C\equiv CMgBr$	$CH_3(CH_3C\equiv C)$(*n*-C_5H_{11})COH (71%)	*94*
CH_3CO-*n*-C_5H_{11}	*n*-C_3H_7MgBr	CH_3(*n*-C_3H_7)(*n*-C_5H_{11})COH (70%)	*191,47*
CH_3CO-*n*-C_5H_{11}	*i*-C_3H_7MgCl	Carbinol (*none*); ketol (50%)	*96*
CH_3CO-*n*-C_5H_{11}	*n*-C_4H_9MgBr	CH_3(*n*-C_4H_9)(*n*-C_5H_{11})COH (68%)	*191,47*
CH_3CO-*n*-C_5H_{11}	$CH_3CH{=}C(CH_3)C\equiv CMgBr$	CH_3(*n*-C_5H_{11})$[CH_3CH{=}C(CH_3)C\equiv C]$COH (79%)	*94*
CH_3CO-*n*-C_5H_{11}	*n*-$C_4H_9C\equiv CMgBr$	CH_3(*n*-C_5H_{11})(*n*-$C_4H_9C\equiv C$)COH (87%)	*103*
CH_3CO-*n*-C_5H_{11}	$C_6H_5C\equiv CMgBr$	CH_3(*n*-C_5H_{11})$(C_6H_5C\equiv C)$COH (78%)	*94*
CH_3CO-*n*-C_5H_{11} (159.6 g., 1.4 mole)	$C_6H_5(CH_2)_5MgBr$ (319.5 g., 1.4 mole $C_{11}H_{15}Br$)	CH_3(*n*-C_5H_{11})$[C_6H_5(CH_2)_5]$COH (40.1%)	*610*
CH_3CO-*i*-C_5H_{11}	CH_3MgI (50 g. CH_3I)	*i*-$C_5H_{11}(CH_3)_2COH$ (44 g.)	*156*
CH_3CO-*i*-C_5H_{11}	C_2H_5MgBr (100 g. C_2H_5Br)	$CH_3(C_2H_5)$(*i*-C_5H_{11})COH (61 g.)	*163*
CH_3COCH_2-*s*-C_4H_9	CH_3MgI	*s*-$C_4H_9CH_2(CH_3)_2COH$ (90%)	*162*
CH_3COCH_2-*t*-C_4H_9	CH_3MgBr	Addition (100%); enolization (0%)*	*168*
CH_3COCH_2-*t*-C_4H_9 (3.1 moles)	C_2H_5MgBr (5.0 moles C_2H_5Br)	$CH_3(C_2H_5)$(*t*-$C_4H_9CH_2$)COH (359 g., crude)	*159*
CH_3COCH_2-*t*-C_4H_9 (3.0 moles)	*n*-C_3H_7MgBr (4.5 moles C_3H_7Br)	CH_3(*n*-C_3H_7)(*t*-$C_4H_9CH_2$)COH (77 g., 0.49 mole); decenes (106 g., 0.76 mole); CH_3(*t*-$C_4H_9CH_2$)CHOH (5.5%); recovered ketone	*159*
CH_3COCH_2-*t*-C_4H_9 (3.00 moles)	*n*-C_4H_9MgBr (3.17 moles)	CH_3(*n*-C_4H_9)(*t*-$C_4H_9CH_2$)COH (62.0%); CH_3(*t*-$C_4H_9CH_2$)CHOH (5.7%)	*159*
CH_3COCH_2-*t*-C_4H_9 (3.00 moles)	*n*-$C_5H_{11}MgBr$ (3.75 moles)	CH_3(*n*-C_5H_{11})(*t*-$C_4H_9CH_2$)COH (222 g., crude); dodecenes (0.63 mole); CH_3(*t*-$C_4H_9CH_2$)CHOH (3.4%)	*159*

*"Grignard machine" study.

TABLE VI-XVIII (Continued)

Ketonic Comp'd	RMgX	Product(s)	Ref.
$C_7H_{14}O$ (*cont.*)			
$CH_3COCH(CH_3)$-*n*-C_3H_7 (57 g.)	CH_3MgI (80 g. CH_3I)	CH_3(*n*-C_3H_7)$CH(CH_3)_2COH$ (54 g.)	*126*
$CH_3COCH(CH_3)$-*i*-C_3H_7 (55 g.)	CH_3MgI (0.6 mole CH_3I)	CH_3(*i*-C_3H_7)$CH(CH_3)_2COH$ (36 g., 51%)	*190*
CH_3CO-*t*-C_5H_{11}	CH_3MgCl	*t*-$C_5H_{11}(CH_3)_2COH$ (65%)	*170*
CH_3CO-*t*-C_5H_{11}	CH_3MgBr	Addition (74%); enolization (14%)*	*168*
C_2H_5CO-*t*-C_4H_9	CH_3MgCl	Addition (86%); enolization (9%)*	*168*
C_2H_5CO-*t*-C_4H_9	C_6H_5MgBr	C_2H_5(*t*-C_4H_9)$(C_6H_5)COH$ (20%)	*172,234*
(*n*-C_3H_7)$_2CO$	($\equiv CMgBr)_2$	[$\equiv CC$(*n*-C_3H_7)$_2OH]_2$ (89%)	*199,21,631*
(*n*-C_3H_7)$_2CO$ (25 g.)	C_2H_5MgBr (8 g. Mg)	C_2H_5(*n*-C_3H_7)$_2COH$ (76%)	*37*
(*n*-C_3H_7)$_2CO$	*n*-C_3H_7MgBr	(*n*-C_3H_7)$_3COH$ (35%); (*n*-C_3H_7)$_2CHOH$ (10%); C_3H_6	*193*
(*n*-C_3H_7)$_2CO$	*n*-C_3H_7MgBr	(*n*-C_3H_7)$_3COH$ (60%); (*n*-C_3H_7)$_2CHOH$ (20%)	*37*
(*n*-C_3H_7)$_2CO$ (0.5 mole)	*n*-C_3H_7MgBr (1.2 mole C_3H_7Br)	(*n*-C_3H_7)$_3COH$ (54%); (*n*-C_3H_7)$_2CHOH$ (24%)	*194*
(*n*-C_3H_7)$_2CO$	*n*-C_3H_7MgI	(*n*-C_3H_7)$_3COH$	*157*
(*n*-C_3H_7)$_2CO$	*i*-C_3H_7MgBr	*i*-C_3H_7(*n*-C_3H_7)$_2COH$	*37*
(*n*-C_3H_7)$_2CO$	*i*-C_3H_7MgBr	*i*-C_3H_7(*n*-C_3H_7)$_2COH$ (44%); (*n*-C_3H_7)$_2CHOH$ (5%); enolization (15%)	*194*
(*n*-C_3H_7)$_2CO$	2-Thienyl-MgI	*α*-C_4H_3S(*n*-C_3H_7)$_2COH$	*41*
(*n*-C_3H_7)$_2CO$	*i*-C_4H_9MgCl	*i*-C_4H_9(*n*-C_3H_7)$_2COH$ (20–25%)	*195*
(*n*-C_3H_7)$_2CO$	*i*-$C_5H_{11}MgBr$	*i*-C_5H_{11}(*n*-C_3H_7)$_2COH$	*195*
(*n*-C_3H_7)$_2CO$	C_6H_5MgBr	C_6H_5(*n*-C_3H_7)$_2COH$	*195*
(*n*-C_3H_7)$_2CO$	$(CH_2)_5CHMgCl$	$(CH_2)_5CH$(*n*-C_3H_7)$_2COH$	*195*
(*n*-C_3H_7)$_2CO$	$C_6H_5CH_2MgCl$	$C_6H_5CH_2$(*n*-C_3H_7)$_2COH$	*195*
(*n*-C_3H_7)$_2CO$	2-$ClC_6H_4CH(CO_2MgCl)MgCl$†	2-$ClC_6H_4CH(CO_2H)C$(*n*-C_3H_7)$_2OH$	*149*
(*n*-C_3H_7)$_2CO$	$C_6H_5CH(CO_2Na)MgX$†	$C_6H_5CH(CO_2H)C$(*n*-C_3H_7)$_2OH$ (88%)	*200*

*"Grignard machine" study.

†In the opinion of Schlenk, Hilleman, and Rodloff, *Ann.*, *487*, 135–54 (1931), these "Grignard reagents" should be formulated as enolates.

TABLE VI-XVIII (Continued)

Ketonic Comp'd	RMgX	Product (s)	Ref.
$C_7H_{14}O$ (*cont.*)			
$(n\text{-}C_3H_7)_2CO$	2-Methylindolyl-MgX	4,4-Bis-(2-methyl-3-indolyl)heptane	70
$n\text{-}C_3H_7CO\text{-}i\text{-}C_3H_7$	$n\text{-}C_3H_7MgBr$	$i\text{-}C_3H_7(n\text{-}C_3H_7)_2COH$ (63%); $n\text{-}C_3H_7(i\text{-}C_3H_7)CHOH$ (17%)	194
$n\text{-}C_3H_7CO\text{-}i\text{-}C_3H_7$	$i\text{-}C_3H_7MgBr$	$n\text{-}C_3H_7(i\text{-}C_3H_7)_2COH$ (17%); $n\text{-}C_3H_7(i\text{-}C_3H_7)CHOH$ (49%)	194
$(i\text{-}C_3H_7)_2CO$ (25 g.)	CH_3MgBr (10 g. Mg)	$CH_3(i\text{-}C_3H_7)_2COH$ (78%)	37,196
$(i\text{-}C_3H_7)_2CO$	$(\equiv CMgBr)_2$	$[HO(i\text{-}C_3H_7)_2C\equiv]_2$	199
$(i\text{-}C_3H_7)_2CO$	$(\equiv CMgI)_2$	$[HO(i\text{-}C_3H_7)_2C\equiv]_2$	125
$(i\text{-}C_3H_7)_2CO$	C_2H_5MgBr	$C_2H_5(i\text{-}C_3H_7)_2COH$ (77%); $(i\text{-}C_3H_7)_2CHOH$ (21%); recovered ketone (2%)*	196,37
$(i\text{-}C_3H_7)_2CO$	$n\text{-}C_3H_7MgBr$	$n\text{-}C_3H_7(i\text{-}C_3H_7)_2COH$ (35.8%); $(i\text{-}C_3H_7)_2CHOH$ (60.3%); recovered ketone (2%)*	196,37, 194,618
$(i\text{-}C_3H_7)_2CO$ + $MgBr_2$	$n\text{-}C_3H_7MgBr$	$n\text{-}C_3H_7(i\text{-}C_3H_7)_2CO$ (65%); $(i\text{-}C_3H_7)_2CHOH$ (26%); recovered ketone (3%)	618
$(i\text{-}C_3H_7)_2CO$	$i\text{-}C_3H_7MgBr$	$(i\text{-}C_3H_7)_3COH$ (*none*); $(i\text{-}C_3H_7)_2CHOH$ (65%); recovered ketone (29%)*	196,37, 193,194
$(i\text{-}C_3H_7)_2CO$	Butenyl-MgCl	$CH_3(H_2C{=}CH)CH(i\text{-}C_3H_7)_2COH$ (79.9%); $CH_3CH{=}CHCH_2(i\text{-}C_3H_7)_2COH$ (5.1%); octadienes	197
$(i\text{-}C_3H_7)_2CO$	Butenyl-MgBr	$CH_3(H_2C{=}CH)CH(i\text{-}C_3H_7)_2COH$ (75.6%); $CH_3CH{=}CHCH_2(i\text{-}C_3H_7)_2COH$ (13.4%); octadienes	197
$(i\text{-}C_3H_7)_2CO$	$i\text{-}C_4H_9MgBr$	$i\text{-}C_4H_9(i\text{-}C_3H_7)_2COH$ (7.9%); $(i\text{-}C_3H_7)_2CHOH$ (78.2%); recovered ketone (10.6%)*	196

*The amount of recovered ketone is interpreted as indicative of the extent of enolization. However, this can be correct in general only when ketolization is negligible (see Grignard Condensations of Aldehydes and Ketones, p. 176).

TABLE VI-XVIII (Continued)

Ketonic Comp'd	RMgX	Product (s)	Ref.
$C_7H_{14}O$ (*cont.*)			
$(i\text{-}C_3H_7)_2CO$	$t\text{-}C_4H_9CH_2MgCl$	$t\text{-}C_4H_9CH_2(i\text{-}C_3H_7)_2COH$ (4%); $(i\text{-}C_3H_7)_2CHOH$ (*none*); recovered ketone (90%)*	*196*
$(i\text{-}C_3H_7)_2CO$ (25 g.)	C_6H_5MgBr (10 g. Mg)	$C_6H_5(i\text{-}C_3H_7)_2COH$ (24 g.)	*37*
$(i\text{-}C_3H_7)_2CO$	$n\text{-}C_4H_9C\equiv CMgBr$	$n\text{-}C_4H_9C\equiv C(i\text{-}C_3H_7)_2COH$ (68%)	*94*
$C_7H_{14}O_2$			
$CH_3COCH_2CH(OH)n\text{-}C_2H_7$	CH_3MgI	$HO(CH_3)_2CCH_2CH(OH)\text{-}n\text{-}C_3H_7$ (90%)	*183*
$CH_3COCH_2CH(OH)n\text{-}C_3H_7$	C_2H_5MgBr	$HO(CH_3)(C_2H_5)CCH_2CH(OH)\text{-}n\text{-}C_3H_7$	*183*
$CH_3COCH_2CH(OH)\text{-}n\text{-}C_3H_7$	C_6H_5MgBr	$HO(CH_3)(C_6H_5)CCH_2CH(OH)\text{-}n\text{-}C_3H_7$	*183*
$C_2H_5OCH_2CO\text{-}n\text{-}C_3H_7$	C_2H_5MgBr	$C_2H_5(C_2H_5OCH_2)(n\text{-}C_3H_7)COH$	*198*
$C_2H_5OCH_2CO\text{-}n\text{-}C_3H_7$	$i\text{-}C_5H_{11}MgX$	$C_2H_5OCH_2(n\text{-}C_3H_7)(i\text{-}C_5H_{11})COH$	*198*
$C_7H_{14}O_3$			
$[HO(CH_3)_2C]_2CO$ (20 g.)	CH_3MgI	$[HO(CH_3)_2C]_2C(OH)CH_3$ (114 g., 64%); CH_4 (6 l.)	*620*
$C_7H_{15}ON$			
$CH_3COCH_2N(C_2H_5)_2$	$2\text{-}C_6H_5C_6H_4MgI$	$CH_3[(C_2H_5)_2NCH_2](2\text{-}C_6H_5C_6H_4)COH$	*16*
$C_8H_5OF_3$			
$F_3CCOC_6H_5$	C_6H_5MgBr	$F_3C(C_6H_5)_2COH$ (46%)	*209*
C_8H_5ON			
$NCCOC_6H_5$	C_2H_5MgBr	$C_2H_5C(=NH\cdot HCN)COC_6H_5$; $C_6H_5(C_2H_5)_2COH$	*202*
$NCCOC_6H_5$	C_6H_5MgBr	$(C_6H_5)_3COH$	*202*
$NCCOC_6H_5$	$C_6H_5CH_2MgCl$	$C_6H_5(C_6H_5CH_2)_2COH$	*202*

*The amount of recovered ketone is interpreted as indicative of the extent of enolization. However, this can be correct in general only when ketolization is negligible (see Grignard Condensations of Aldehydes and Ketones, p. 176).

TABLE VI-XVIII (Continued)

Ketonic Comp'd	RMgX	Product (s)	Ref.
$C_8H_6O_2$			
$CHOCOC_6H_5$ (5 g.)	C_6H_5MgBr (4 g. C_6H_5Br)	$C_6H_5CH(OH)C(C_6H_5)_2OH$ (4 g., crude)	*203*
C_8H_7OBr			
$CH_3COC_6H_4$-3-Br (567 g., 2.85 moles)	C_2H_5MgBr (3.2 moles)	$CH_3(3\text{-}BrC_6H_4)C{=}CH_2$ (420 g., 70%)	*210*
C_8H_7OCl			
$ClCH_2COC_6H_5$	$C_6H_5CH_2MgCl$	*No ortho*-substitution; actual product (s) not identified	*204*
$CH_3COC_6H_4$-2-Cl	4-$CH_3C_{10}H_6$-1-MgBr	$CH_3(2\text{-}ClC_6H_4)(4\text{-}CH_3C_{10}H_6\text{-}1\text{-}COH)$ (*ca.* 37%); 1-$CH_3C_{10}H_7$; recovered ketone	*205*
$CH_3COC_6H_4$-2-Cl	8-$CH_3C_{10}H_6$-1-MgBr	$CH_3(2\text{-}ClC_6H_4)(8\text{-}CH_3C_{10}H_6\text{-}1\text{-})COH$ (*ca.* 20%)	*205*
C_8H_7OI			
$CH_3COC_6H_4$-4-I	C_2H_5MgI	$CH_3(4\text{-}IC_6H_4)C{=}CHCH_3$	*206*
$C_8H_7ON_3$			
$N_3CH_2COC_6H_5$	C_6H_5MgBr (2 equiv.)	$C_6H_5NHN{=}NCH_2(C_6H_5)_2COH$ (50%)	*211*
$C_8H_7O_2N$			
$HON{=}CHCOC_6H_5$ (30.0 g.)	C_2H_5MgBr (87.2 g. C_2H_5Br)	$HON{=}CH_2(C_2H_5)(C_6H_5)COH$ (28%)	*17*
$HON{=}CHCOC_6H_5$ (50 g.)	*n*-C_4H_9MgBr (220 g. C_4H_9Br)	$HON{=}CH_2(n\text{-}C_4H_9)(C_6H_5)COH$ (90 g., crude)	*17*
$HON{=}CHCOC_6H_5$ (15 g.)	C_6H_5MgBr (80 g. C_6H_5Br)	$HON{=}CH_2(C_6H_5)_2COH$ (75%)	*207, 17, 208*
$HON{=}CHCOC_6H_5$ (30 g.)	4-$CH_3C_6H_4MgBr$ (136 g. C_7H_7Br)	$HON{=}CH_2(C_6H_5)(4\text{-}CH_3C_6H_4)COH$ (54 g., crude)	*17*
C_8H_8O			
$CH_3COC_6H_5$	CH_3MgI	$C_6H_5(CH_3)_2COH$ (65%); $CH_3(C_6H_5)C{=}CH_2$ (21%)	*18, 61, 206, 212*

TABLE VI-XVIII (Continued)

Ketonic Comp'd	RMgX	Product (s)	Ref.
C_8H_8O (*cont.*)			
$CH_3COC_6H_5$	$(\equiv CMgBr)_2$	$[\equiv CC(CH_3)(C_6H_5)OH]_2$ (*ca.* quant.)	*22,21,199*
$CH_3COC_6H_5$	$(\equiv CMgI)_2$	$[\equiv CC(CH_3)(C_6H_5)OH]_2$	*125*
$CH_3COC_6H_5$	$HC\equiv CMgBr$	$CH_3(HC\equiv C)(C_6H_5)COH$ (26%)	*214*
$CH_3COC_6H_5$	C_2H_5MgBr	$CH_3(C_2H_5)(C_6H_5)COH$	*215*
$CH_3COC_6H_5$	C_2H_5MgI	$CH_3(C_6H_5)C{=}CHCH_3$	*206*
$CH_3COC_6H_5$	$H_2C{=}CHCH_2MgBr$	$CH_3(H_2C{=}CHCH_2)(C_6H_5)COH$	*216,28*
$CH_3COC_6H_5$	n-C_3H_7MgBr	$CH_3(n$-$C_3H_7)(C_6H_5)COH$	*619*
$CH_3COC_6H_5$	n-C_3H_7MgI	$CH_3(C_6H_5)C{=}CHC_2H_5$	*206*
$CH_3COC_6H_5$	2-Thienyl-MgI	$CH_3(\alpha$-$C_4H_3S)(C_6H_5)COH$	*41*
$CH_3COC_6H_5$	Pyrryl-MgX	1,1-Bis-(2-pyrryl)-1-phenylethane; α-(2-pyrryl)-α-phenylethanol	*70*
$CH_3COC_6H_5$ (21.5 g.)	$C_2H_5OC\equiv CMgBr$ (12 g. $C_2H_5OC\equiv CH$)	$CH_3(C_2H_5OC\equiv C)(C_6H_5)COH$ (15 g.); recovered ketone (4 g.)	*233*
$CH_3COC_6H_5$	$C_2H_5OC\equiv CMgBr$	$CH_3(C_2H_5OC\equiv C)(C_6H_5)COH$ (97.7%)	*43*
$CH_3COC_6H_5$	n-C_4H_9MgBr	$CH_3(n$-$C_4H_9)(C_6H_5)COH$	*217*
$CH_3COC_6H_5$	i-C_4H_9MgI	$CH_3(i$-$C_4H_9)(C_6H_5)COH$; $CH_3(C_6H_5)C{=}CH$-i-C_3H_7; recovered ketone	*146*
$CH_3COC_6H_5$ (22 g.)	2-Pyridyl-MgBr	$CH_3(\alpha$-$C_5H_4N)(C_6H_5)COH$ (2.5 g., crude)	*218*
$CH_3COC_6H_5$ (120 g.)	n-$C_5H_{11}MgBr$ (151 g. $C_5H_{11}Br$)	$CH_3(n$-$C_5H_{11})(C_6H_5)COH$ (58 g.)	*100*
$CH_3COC_6H_5$	i-$C_5H_{11}MgI$	$CH_3(i$-$C_5H_{11})(C_6H_5)COH$; $CH_3(C_6H_5)C{=}CH$-i-C_4H_9	*146,206*
$CH_3COC_6H_5$ (1 mole)	DL-s-$C_4H_9CH_2MgBr$	$CH_3(C_2H_5)CHCH_2(C_6H_5)(CH_3)COH$ (27 g.); recovered ketone (62 g.)*	*100*
$CH_3COC_6H_5$	C_6H_5MgBr	$CH_3(C_6H_5)_2COH$ (yielding 58% olefin)	*180,213, 219*
$CH_3COC_6H_5$	$(CH_2)_5CHMgCl$	$(CH_2)_5CH(CH_3)(C_6H_5)COH$ (50%)	*59,58*

*Attributed to enolization.

TABLE VI-XVIII (Continued)

Ketonic Comp'd	RMgX	Product(s)	Ref.
C_8H_8O (*cont.*)			
$CH_3COC_6H_5$	$C_6H_5CH_2MgCl$	$CH_3(C_6H_5)(C_6H_5CH_2)COH$ (92%)	*199,220*
$CH_3COC_6H_5$	$C_6H_5CH_2Cl$ + Mg	$CH_3(C_6H_5)(C_6H_5CH_2)COH$; $CH_3(C_6H_5)C{=}CHC_6H_5$	*104*
$CH_3COC_6H_5$	4-$CH_3C_6H_4MgBr$	$CH_3(C_6H_5)(4\text{-}CH_3C_6H_4)COH$ (yielding 48–60% olefin)	*180*
$CH_3COC_6H_5$	$(C_2H_5)_2N(CH_2)_3Cl$ + Mg	$CH_3(C_6H_5)[(C_2H_5)_2N(CH_2)_3]COH$	*226*
$CH_3COC_6H_5$	$C_6H_5CH(CO_2Na)MgX$*	$CH_3(C_6H_5)[C_6H_5CH(CO_2H)]COH$ ("good yield") .	*200*
$CH_3COC_6H_5$	1-Indenyl-MgBr	$CH_3(C_6H_5)(1\text{-}C_9H_7)COH$; "some" dehydr'n product	*69*
$CH_3COC_6H_5$	2-Methylindolyl-MgX (2 equiv.)	1,1-Bis-(2-methyl-3-indolyl)-1-phenylethane	*70*
$CH_3COC_6H_5$ (20 g.)	2,4,6-$(CH_3)_3C_6H_2MgBr$ (41 g. $C_9H_{11}Br$)	2,4,6-$(CH_3)_3C_6H_2(C_6H_5)C{=}CH_2$ (3 g.); recovered ketone (12 g.); $(CH_3)_3C_6H_3$ (12 g.)	*221*
$CH_3COC_6H_5$	1-$C_{10}H_7MgBr$	$CH_3(C_6H_5)(1\text{-}C_{10}H_7)COH$ (yielding 51% olefin)	*180,227*
$CH_3COC_6H_5$	2,3,4,6-$(CH_3)_4C_6HMgBr$	2,3,4,6-$(CH_3)_4C_6H(C_6H_5)C{=}CH_2$ (10%)	*221*
$CH_3COC_6H_5$ (42 g.)	2,3,5,6-$(CH_3)_4C_6HMgBr$ (5 g. $C_{10}H_{13}Br$)	2,3,5,6-$(CH_3)_4C_6H(C_6H_5)C{=}CH_2$ (3.5 g.); enolization (80%)	*228*
$CH_3COC_6H_5$	Isobornyl-MgCl	$CH_3(C_6H_5)CHOH$, $[\alpha]_{578}$ 20.10°† (55%)	*230,229*
$CH_3COC_6H_5$	*n*-$C_{12}H_{25}MgBr$	$CH_3(C_6H_5)(n\text{-}C_{12}H_{25})COH$; $C_{22}H_{32}$	*222*
$CH_3COC_6H_5$ (12.5 g.)	9-Phenanthryl-MgBr (25.7 ml. $C_{14}H_9Br$)	9-$C_{14}H_9(CH_3)(C_6H_5)COH$ (yielding 4.5 g. olefin)	*617*
$CH_3COC_6H_5$	$(C_6H_5)_2C{=}CHMgBr$	$(C_6H_5)_2C{=}CH(C_6H_5)(CH_3)COH$	*223*
$CH_3COC_6H_5$ (288 g., 2.4 moles)	*n*-$C_{18}H_{37}MgBr$ (750 g., 2.25 moles $C_{18}H_{37}Br$)	$CH_3(C_6H_5)(n\text{-}C_{18}H_{37})COH$ (yielding 896 g. crude olefins)	*231*

*In the opinion of Schlenk, Hilleman, and Rodloff, *Ann.*, *487*, 135–54 (1931), this "Grignard reagent" should be formulated as an enolate.

†For the pure enantiomorph, $[\alpha]_{578}$ 54.86°.

TABLE VI-XVIII (Continued)

Ketonic Comp'd	RMgX	Product (s)	Ref.
$C_8H_8O_2$			
$HOCH_2COC_6H_5$ (11 g.)	CH_3MgI (25 g. CH_3I)	$HOCH_2(CH_3)(C_6H_5)COH$	*225*
$HOCH_2COC_6H_5$	C_2H_5MgX (2 equiv.)	$HOCH_2(C_2H_5)(C_6H_5)COH$ (15.4%); 2,5-diethyl-2,5-diphenyl-1,4-dioxane (29.8%)	*225*
$HOCH_2COC_6H_5$ (13.6 g.)	C_6H_5MgBr (31.4 g. C_6H_5Br)	$HOCH_2(C_6H_5)_2COH$	*225*
Furfurylideneacetone (80 g.)	C_2H_5MgBr (120 g. C_2H_5Br)	$CH_3COCH_2CH(\alpha\text{-}C_4H_3O)C_2H_5$ (50 g., 50%); high-boiling residue	*599*
Furfurylidenaacetone (50 g.)	$n\text{-}C_3H_7MgBr$ (100 g. C_3H_7Br)	$CH_3COCH_2CH(\alpha\text{-}C_4H_3O)\text{-}n\text{-}C_3H_7$ (50%)	*599*
Furfurylideneacetone (80 g.)	$i\text{-}C_3H_7MgBr$ (130 g. C_3H_7Br)	$CH_3COCH_2CH(\alpha\text{-}C_4H_3O)\text{-}i\text{-}C_3H_7$ (65 g., 61%)	*599*
Furfurylideneacetone (60 g.)	$i\text{-}C_4H_9MgBr$ (145 g. C_4H_9Br)	$CH_3COCH_2CH(\alpha\text{-}C_4H_3O)\text{-}i\text{-}C_4H_9$	*599*
Furfurylideneacetone	$i\text{-}C_5H_{11}MgI$	$CH_3COCH_2CH(\alpha\text{-}C_4H_3O)\text{-}i\text{-}C_5H_{11}$ (44%)	*224*
Furfurylideneacetone	C_6H_5MgBr	High-boiling cond'n products	*140*
C_8H_9ON			
2-Acetyl-5-methylpyridine	CH_3MgI	Dimethyl-(5-methyl-2-pyridyl)methanol	*235*
$C_8H_{10}OBrN$			
$HBr \cdot H_2NCH_2COC_6H_5$	$n\text{-}C_4H_9MgI$	$H_2NCH_2(n\text{-}C_4H_9)(C_6H_5)COH$	*236*
$HBr \cdot H_2NCH_2COC_6H_5$	$(CH_2)_5CHMgCl$	$H_2NCH_2(C_6H_5)[(CH_2)_5CH]COH$	*236*
$C_8H_{10}OClN$			
$HCl \cdot H_2NCH_2COC_6H_5$ (5 g.)	$4\text{-}CH_3C_6H_4MgBr$ (30 g. C_7H_7Br)	$H_2NCH_2(C_6H_5)(4\text{-}CH_3C_6H_4)COH$ (4.5 g.)	*238*
$C_8H_{12}O$			
$CH_3COC{\equiv}C\text{-}n\text{-}C_4H_9$ (3.5 g.)	$n\text{-}C_4H_9C{\equiv}CMgBr$ (2.7 g. $n\text{-}C_4H_9C{\equiv}CH$)	$CH_3(n\text{-}C_4H_9C{\equiv}C)_2COH$ (1.9 g.); recovered ketone (1.0 g.)	*83*
$C_8H_{12}O_3$			
$CH_3COC(CO_2C_2H_5){=}CHCH_3$	CH_3MgI (1 equiv.)	Recovered ketone; $CH_3CO\text{-}i\text{-}C_4H_9$*	*151*

*Dropwise addition of ketone to Grignard reagent solution.

TABLE VI-XVIII (Continued)

Ketonic Comp'd	RMgX	Product(s)	Ref.
$C_8H_{12}O_3$ (*cont.*)			
$CH_3COC(CO_2C_2H_5)=CHCH_3$	CH_3MgI (1 equiv.)	Condens'n products chiefly; recovered ketone; CH_3CO-i-C_4H_9 (trace)*	*151*
$C_8H_{13}OCl$			
$CH_3COCCl(CH_2)_5$	CH_3MgX	$CH_3COC(CH_3)(CH_2)_5$; *no* chlorohydrin isolable	*237*
$CH_3COCCl(CH_2)_5$	C_6H_5MgX	$CH_3COC(C_6H_5)(CH_2)_5$; *no* chlorohydrin isolable	*237*
$C_8H_{14}O$			
$CH_3CO(CH_2)_2CH=C(CH_3)_2$ (39.2 g.)	CH_3MgI (45.0 g. CH_3I)	$(CH_3)_2C=CHCH_2CH_2(CH_3)_2COH$ (44.2 g., crude)	*244, 134, 242*
$CH_3CO(CH_2)_2CH=C(CH_3)_2$ (100 g.)	CH_3I (113 g.) + Mg (20 g.)	$(CH_3)_2C=CHCH_2CH_2(CH_3)_2COH$	*243*
$CH_3CO(CH_2)_2CH=C(CH_3)_2$	C_2H_5MgBr	$CH_3(C_2H_5)[(CH_3)_2C=CHCH_2CH_2]COH$ (82%)	*242*
$CH_3CO(CH_2)_2CH=C(CH_3)_2$	n-C_3H_7MgBr	$CH_3(n\text{-}C_3H_7)[(CH_3)_2C=CHCH_2CH]COH$ (85%)	*242*
$CH_3CO(CH_2)_2CH=C(CH_3)_2$	i-C_3H_7MgBr	$CH_3(i\text{-}C_3H_7)[(CH_3)_2C=CHCH_2CH_2]COH$ ("poor yield")	*242*
$CH_3CO(CH_2)_2CH=C(CH_3)_2$ (7.5 g.)	$C_2H_5OC\equiv CMgBr$ (6.3 g. $C_2H_5OC\equiv CH$)	$CH_3(C_2H_5OC\equiv C)[(CH_3)_2C=CHCH_2CH_2]COH$ (8.5 g., 73%)	*233*
$CH_3CO(CH_2)_2CH=C(CH_3)_2$	n-C_5H_9MgBr	$CH_3(n\text{-}C_4H_9)[(CH_3)_2C=CHCH_2CH_2]COH$ (65%)	*242*
$CH_3CO(CH_2)_2CH=C(CH_3)_2$	i-$C_5H_{11}MgBr$	$CH_3(i\text{-}C_5H_{11})[(CH_3)_2C=CHCH_2CH_2]COH$ (70%)	*242*
$CH_3CO(CH_2)_2CH=C(CH_3)_2$	C_6H_5MgBr	$CH_3(C_6H_5)[(CH_3)_2C=CHCH_2CH_2]COH$ (55%)	*242*
$CH_3CO(CH_2)_2CH=C(CH_3)_2$	$C_6H_5CH_2MgCl$	$CH_3(C_6H_5CH_2)[(CH_3)_2C=CHCH_2CH_2]COH$ (45%)	*242*

*Gradual addition of Grignard reagent solution to ketone.

TABLE VI-XVIII (Continued)

Ketonic Comp'd	RMgX	Product(s)	Ref.
$C_8H_{14}O$ (*cont.*)			
$CH_3CO(CH_2)_2CH{=}C(CH_3)_2$	$C_6H_5C{\equiv}CMgBr$	$CH_3[(CH_3)_2C{=}CHCH_2CH_2](C_6H_5C{\equiv}C)COH$ (*ca.* 75%)	*36*
$CH_3COCH(CH_2)_5$	CH_3MgBr	$(CH_2)_5CH(CH_3)_2COH$ (56%)	*212*
$CH_3COC(CH_3){=}CH\text{-}n\text{-}C_3H_7$ (40 g.)	C_2H_5MgBr	$CH_3(C_2H_5)[n\text{-}C_3H_7CH{=}C(CH_3)]COH$ (15 g.); $CH_3COCH(CH_3)CH(C_2H_5)\text{-}n\text{-}C_3H_7$ (yielding 3 g., 20% semi-carbazone)	*150*
$CH_3COC(CH_3){=}C(CH_3)C_2H_5$	CH_3MgI	$CH_3(C_2H_5)C{=}(CH_3)C(CH_3)_2COH$ (63%)	*150*
$CH_3COC(CH_3){=}C(CH_3)C_2H_5$	C_2H_5MgBr	$CH_3(C_2H_5)[CH_3(C_2H_5)C{=}(CH_3)C]COH$ (60%)	*150*
$CH_3COC(CH_3){=}C(CH_3)C_2H_5$	$n\text{-}C_3H_7MgBr$	$CH_3(n\text{-}C_3H_7)[CH_3(C_2H_5)C{=}(CH_3)C]COH$ (38%)	*150*
$CH_3COC(CH_3){=}C(CH_3)C_2H_5$	$n\text{-}C_4H_9MgBr$	$CH_3(n\text{-}C_4H_9)[CH_3(C_2H_5)C{=}(CH_3)C]COH$ (38%)	*150*
$C_2H_5COCH{=}CH\text{-}n\text{-}C_3H_7$ (40 g.)	C_2H_5MgBr (60 g. C_2H_5Br)	$n\text{-}C_3H_7CH{=}CH(C_2H_5)_2COH$ (yielding 38.6% diene)	*184*
$C_2H_5COCH{=}C(CH_3)C_2H_5$ (20 g.)	C_2H_5MgBr (20 g. C_2H_5Br)	$CH_3(C_2H_5)C{=}CH(C_2H_5)_2COH$ (yielding 52.9% diene)*	*184*
$C_2H_5COCH{=}C(CH_3)C_2H_5$ (12.6 g.)	C_2H_5MgBr (11.0 g. C_2H_5Br)	$CH_3(C_2H_5)C{=}CH(C_2H_5)_2COH$ (yielding 31.5% diene)†	*239*
$C_2H_5COCH{=}C(CH_3)C_2H_5$	$i\text{-}C_5H_{11}MgBr$	$CH_3[CH_3(C_2H_5)C{=}CH](i\text{-}C_5H_{11})COH$	*239*
$(CH_2)_2CHCO\text{-}n\text{-}C_4H_9$	CH_3MgBr	$CH_3[(CH_2)_2CH](n\text{-}C_4H_9)COH$	*115*
$(CH_2)_2CHCO\text{-}n\text{-}C_4H_9$	$n\text{-}C_4H_9MgBr$	$(CH_2)_2CH(n\text{-}C_4H_9)_2COH$	*115*
$(CH_2)_2CHCO\text{-}n\text{-}C_4H_9$	$n\text{-}C_5H_{11}MgBr$	$(CH_2)_2CH(n\text{-}C_4H_9)(n\text{-}C_5H_{11})COH$	*115*
$(CH_2)_2CHCO\text{-}i\text{-}C_4H_9$	C_2H_5MgBr	$C_2H_5[(CH_2)_2CH](n\text{-}C_4H_9)COH$	*240*
$(CH_2)_2CHCO\text{-}i\text{-}C_4H_9$	$n\text{-}C_3H_7MgBr$	$(CH_2)_2CH(n\text{-}C_3H_7)(i\text{-}C_4H_9)COH$	*240*

*Slow reverse addition at -14°.

†Slow reverse addition at room temperature; sixteen hours standing.

TABLE VI-XVIII (Continued)

Ketonic Comp'd	RMgX	Product(s)	Ref.
$C_8H_{14}O_2$			
$CH_3O(CH_2)_2COCH{=}C(CH_3)_2$ (126 g.)	CH_3MgI (140 g. CH_3I)	$CH_3OCH_2CH_2C({=}CH_2)CH{=}C(CH_3)_2$ + $CH_3OCH_2CH{=}C(CH_3)CH{=}C(CH_3)_2$ (totaling 39 g.)	*245*
$(i\text{-}C_3H_7CO{-})_2$ (35.5 g.)	C_2H_5MgI (56.0 g. C_2H_5I)	$HO(C_2H_5)(i\text{-}C_3H_7)CCO\text{-}i\text{-}C_3H_7$ (30%)	*246*
$C_8H_{14}O_3$			
$CH_3COCO_2\text{-}i\text{-}C_5H_{11}$	CH_3MgI (1 equiv.)	$HO(CH_3)_2CCO_2\text{-}i\text{-}C_5H_{11}$ (25%)	*151,187*
$CH_3COCO_2\text{-}i\text{-}C_5H_{11}$	$i\text{-}C_5H_{11}MgBr$ (1 equiv.)	$HO(CH_3)(i\text{-}C_5H_{11})CCO_2\text{-}i\text{-}C_5H_{11}$ (25%)	*151,187*
$CH_3COCO_2\text{-}i\text{-}C_5H_{11}$	$1\text{-}C_{10}H_7MgBr$ (1 equiv.)	$HO(CH_3)(1\text{-}C_{10}H_7)CCO_2\text{-}i\text{-}C_5H_{11}$ (25%)	*151,187*
$CH_3COCH(C_2H_5)CO_2C_2H_5$	CH_3MgI (1 equiv.)	$HO(CH_3)_2CCH(C_2H_5)CO_2C_2H_5$ ("very little"); recovered ketone	*151,152*
$CH_3COCH(C_2H_5)CO_2C_2H_5$ (53 g.)	CH_3MgI (3 equiv.)	$[HO(CH_3)_2C]_2CHC_2H_5$ ("very poor yield"); $HO(CH_3)_2CCH(C_2H_5)CO_2C_2H_5$ ("probably a little"); recovered ketone (*ca.* 30 g.)	*151,152*
$CH_3COC(CH_3)_2CO_2C_2H_5$	CH_3MgI	$[HO(CH_3)_2C]_2C(CH_3)_2$	*247*
$C_8H_{16}O$			
$CH_3CO\text{-}n\text{-}C_6H_{13}$	CH_3MgCl	$n\text{-}C_6H_{13}(CH_3)_2COH$ (85%)	*128,248*
$CH_3CO\text{-}n\text{-}C_6H_{13}$	$({\equiv}CMgI)_2$	$[{\equiv}CC(CH_3)(n\text{-}C_6H_{13})OH]_2$	*125*
$CH_3CO\text{-}n\text{-}C_6H_{13}$ (9.4 moles)	$n\text{-}C_2H_5MgBr$ (11.0 moles C_2H_5Br)	$CH_3(C_2H_5)(n\text{-}C_6H_{13})COH$ (77%)	*249,248*
$CH_3COCH(CH_3)\text{-}t\text{-}C_4H_9$	CH_3MgCl	Addition (47%); enolization (48%)*	*124*
$CH_3COC(C_2H_5)_2CH_3$	CH_3MgBr	Addition (0%); enolization (84%)*	*168*
D(+)-$C_2H_5COCH_2CH(CH_3)C_2H_5$	CH_3MgX	$CH_3(C_2H_5)[CH_3(C_2H_5)CHCH_2]COH$	*250*
$n\text{-}C_3H_7CO\text{-}s\text{-}C_4H_9$	CH_3MgCl	Addition (40%); enolization (53%)*	*124*
$i\text{-}C_3H_7CO\text{-}i\text{-}C_4H_9$	$({\equiv}CMgBr)_2$	$[{\equiv}CC(i\text{-}C_3H_7)(i\text{-}C_4H_9)OH]_2$ (81%)	*199*
$i\text{-}C_3H_7CO\text{-}t\text{-}C_4H_9$	CH_3MgCl	Addition (49%); enolization (0%)*	*124*

*"Grignard machine" study.

TABLE VI-XVIII (Continued)

Ketonic Comp'd	RMgX	Product(s)	Ref.
$C_8H_{16}O$ (*cont.*)			
i-C_3H_7CO-t-C_4H_9 (0.29 mole)	Butenyl-MgBr (1 equiv.)	i-$C_3H_7[CH_3(H_2C{=}CH)CH](t$-$C_4H_9)COH$ (74%)	251
$C_8H_{16}O_2$			
n-$C_3H_7COCH(OH)$-n-C_3H_7 (36 g.)	C_6H_5MgBr (170 g. C_6H_5Br)	n-$C_3H_7[n$-$C_3H_7CH(OH)](C_6H_5)COH$ (*ca.* 47 g.)	252
$C_8H_{17}ON$			
$CH_3CO(CH_2)_2N(C_2H_5)_2$	RMgBr*	$(C_2H_5)_2N(CH_2)_2CR(CH_3)OH$* (15–33%)	253
$C_9H_4OBr_2S_2$			
Bis-(5-Bromo-2-thienyl) ketone	$C_6H_5CH_2MgCl$	Product dec. on dist'n	254
$C_9H_6OS_2$			
Bis-2-thienyl ketone (6 g.)	$C_6H_5CH_2MgCl$ (5 g. C_7H_7Cl)	Carbinol [yielding 4.5 g. crude $C_6H_5CH{=}C(\alpha$-$C_4H_3S)_2$	254
C_9H_8O			
$H_2C{=}CHCOC_6H_5$	CH_3MgI	n-$C_3H_7COC_6H_5$; *no* carbinol	256
$H_2C{=}CHCOC_6H_5$ (38.1 g., 0.29 mole)	Butenyl-MgBr (0.29 mole)	"Polymeric" material	255
$H_2C{=}CHCOC_6H_5$	C_6H_5MgBr	$C_6H_5(CH_2)_2COC_6H_5$; *no* carbinol	256
$C_9H_8O_2Cl_2$			
$C_2H_5COC_6H_2$-2-OH-3,5-Cl_2 (7.82 g.)	2-$C_6H_5C_6H_4MgI$ (2 ml. $C_{12}H_9I$)	C_2H_5(2-HO-3,5-$Cl_2C_6H_2$)(2-$C_6H_5C_6H_4$)COH (6.5 g., 49%)	257
$C_9H_9O_2N$			
$CH_3COC({=}NOH)C_6H_5$ (16.3 g.)	C_6H_5MgBr (63 g. C_6H_5Br)	$CH_3(C_6H_5)[C_6H_5(HON{=})C]COH$ (71%)	207

*R = C_6H_5, 1-$C_{10}H_7$, 2-$C_{10}H_7$, 4-CH_3O-1-$C_{10}H_6$, 9-Phenanthryl.

TABLE VI-XVIII (Continued)

Ketonic Comp'd	RMgX	Product(s)	Ref.
$C_9H_{10}O$			
$CH_3COCH_2C_6H_5$ (134 g.)	C_2H_5MgBr (136 g. C_2H_5Br)	$CH_3(C_2H_5)(C_6H_5CH_2)COH$	*252*
$CH_3COC_6H_4$-4-CH_3	2-Methylindolyl-MgX	1,1-Bis-(2-methyl-3-indolyl)-1-p-tolylethane	*70*
$C_2H_5COC_6H_5$	n-C_3H_7MgI	$C_2H_5(n\text{-}C_3H_7)(C_6H_5)COH$ (yielding 72% 3-phenylhexane upon dehydr'n and hydrogen'n)	*259*
$C_2H_5COC_6H_5$	$C_6H_5CH_2MgCl$	$C_2H_5(C_6H_5)(C_6H_5CH_2)COH$	*260, 199*
$C_2H_5COC_6H_5$	$C_6H_5(CH_2)_3MgCl$	$C_2H_5(C_6H_5)[C_6H_5(CH_2)_3]COH$ (64%)	*261*
$C_2H_5COC_6H_5$	Isobornyl-MgCl*	$C_2H_5(C_6H_5)CHOH$, $[\alpha]_D$ 10.60° (50%)†	*230*
$C_9H_{10}O_2$			
$CH_3COCH_2OC_6H_5$	2-$C_6H_5C_6H_4MgI$	$CH_3(C_6H_5OCH_2)(2\text{-}C_6H_5C_6H_4)COH$	*16*
$CH_3COCH(OH)C_6H_5$	CH_3MgBr	$HO(CH_3)_2CCH(OH)C_6H_5$; $CH_3[CH_3(HO)CH](C_6H_5)COH$‡	*258*
$CH_3COCH(OH)C_6H_5$ (6 g.)	C_2H_5MgBr (13 g. C_2H_5Br)	$HO(CH_3)(C_2H_5)CCH(OH)C_6H_5$ (3 g., crude)	*179*
$CH_3COCH(OH)C_6H_5$	C_6H_5MgBr	$HO(CH_3)(C_6H_5)CCH(OH)C_6H_5$	*258*
$CH_3CH(OH)COC_6H_5$	CH_3MgBr	$CH_3[CH_3(HO)CH](C_6H_5)COH$	*258*
$CH_3CH(OH)COC_6H_5$	C_6H_5MgBr	$CH_3(HO)CH(C_6H_5)_2COH$; $HO(CH_3)(C_6H_5)CCH(OH)C_6H_5$‡	*258*
$C_9H_{12}OClN$			
$CH_3CH(NH_2\cdot HCl)COC_6H_5$ (6 g.)	CH_3MgI (6 equiv.)	$CH_3[CH_3(HCl\cdot H_2N)CH](C_6H_5)COH$ (5.5 g.)	*262*
$CH_3CH(NH_2\cdot HCl)COC_6H_5$ (8 g.)	$C_6H_5CH_2MgCl$ (6 equiv.)	$CH_3(HCl\cdot H_2N)CH(C_6H_5)(C_6H_5CH_2)COH$ (8.5 g.)	*262*

*Prepared by partial (*ca.* 65%) carbonation of the Grignard reagent mixture from (+)-α-pinene hydrochloride.

†For the pure enantiomorph, $[\alpha]_D$ 55.54°.

‡The mixture of products is attributed to a ketone isomerization equilibrium presumed to be established through a ketone-Grignard reagent coördination complex.

TABLE VI-XVIII (Continued)

Ketonic Comp'd	RMgX	Product(s)	Ref.
$C_9H_{12}OClN$ (*cont.*)			
$CH_3CH(NH_2 \cdot HCl)COC_6H_5$	$4\text{-}CH_3C_6H_4MgBr$	$CH_3(H_2N)CH(C_6H_5)(4\text{-}CH_3C_6H_4)COH$	*263*
$CH_3CH(NH_2 \cdot HCl)COC_6H_5$	$4\text{-}CH_3OC_6H_4MgBr$	$CH_3(H_2N)CH(C_6H_5)(4\text{-}CH_3OC_6H_4)COH$	*263*
$CH_3CH(NH_2 \cdot HCl)COC_6H_5$ (6.0 g.)	$1\text{-}C_{10}H_7MgBr$ (35.5 g. $C_{10}H_7Br$)	$CH_3(HCl \cdot H_2N)CH(C_6H_5)(1\text{-}C_{10}H_7)COH$ (4.5 g.)	*262*
$C_9H_{12}O_2ClN$			
$HCl \cdot H_2NCH_2COC_6H_4\text{-}2\text{-}OCH_3$	C_6H_5MgBr	$H_2NCH_2(C_6H_5)(2\text{-}CH_3OC_6H_4)COH$	*264*
$HCl \cdot H_2NCH_2COC_6H_4\text{-}2\text{-}OCH_3$	$4\text{-}CH_3OC_6H_4MgBr$	$H_2NCH_2(2\text{-}CH_3OC_6H_4)(4\text{-}CH_3OC_6H_4)COH$	*264*
$HCl \cdot H_2NCH_2COC_6H_4\text{-}4\text{-}OCH_3$	C_6H_5MgBr	$H_2NCH_2(C_6H_5)(4\text{-}CH_3OC_6H_4)COH$	*264*
$C_9H_{14}O$			
$[(CH_3)_2C{=}CH]_2CO$	CH_3MgI	$CH_3[(CH_3)_2C{=}CH]_2COH$ (2.5%)	*138*
$[(CH_3)_2C{=}CH]_2CO$	$C_6H_5CH_2MgCl$	$C_6H_5CH_2[(CH_3)_2C{=}CH]_2COH$	*148*
$C_9H_{14}O_2$			
$HOCH{=}CHCO(CH_2)_2CH{=}C(CH_3)_2$	CH_3MgI	$C_{10}H_{18}O_2$ (75%) $[(CH_3)_2C{=}CH(CH_2)_3C(OH)(CH_3)CH_2CHO]$ (?)	*265*
$C_9H_{14}O_5$			
$CH_3COC(CH_3)(CO_2CH_3)CH_2CO_2CH_3$	$i\text{-}C_4H_9MgBr$	$CH_3(i\text{-}C_4H_9)[H_3CO_2CCH_2(CH_3)\text{-}(H_3CO_2C)C]COH$	*266*
$CH_3COC(CH_3)(CO_2CH_3)CH_2CO_2CH_3$	C_6H_5MgBr	$CH_3(C_6H_5)[H_3CO_2CCH_2(CH_3)(H_3CO_2C)C]COH$	*266*
$C_9H_{16}O$			
cis- or *trans*-$CH_3COC(n\text{-}C_3H_7){=}CHC_2H_5$* (0.2 mole)	C_2H_5MgBr (7.2 g. Mg)	$CH_3(C_2H_5)[C_2H_5CH{=}C(n\text{-}C_3H_7)]COH$ (14 g., crude); $CH_3COCH(n\text{-}C_3H_7)CH(C_2H_5)_2$ (10 g.)	*185*
$CH_3CO(CH_2)_2C(i\text{-}C_3H_7){=}CH_2$	CH_3MgX	$HO(CH_3)_2C(CH_2)_2C(i\text{-}C_3H_7){=}CH_2$ (80%)	*267*

*Colonge (*185*) regards as "*cis*" the isomer which forms the semicarbazone melting at 142°, and as "*trans*" the isomer that forms the semicarbazone melting at 122°.

TABLE VI-XVIII (Continued)

Ketonic Comp'd	RMgX	Product(s)	Ref.
$C_9H_{16}O$ (*cont.*)			
$CH_3CO(CH_2)_2C(i\text{-}C_3H_7)=CH_2$	$(CH_2)_5CHMgX$	$CH_3[(CH_2)_5CH][H_2C=C(i\text{-}C_3H_7)]COH$ (46.5%)	*267*
$CH_3CO(CH_2)_2C(i\text{-}C_3H_7)=CH_2$	$n\text{-}C_6H_{13}MgX$	$CH_3[H_2C=C(i\text{-}C_3H_7)](n\text{-}C_6H_{13})COH$ (69%)	*267*
$CH_3CO(CH_2)_2C(i\text{-}C_3H_7)=CH_2$	$i\text{-}C_4H_9(n\text{-}C_6H_{13})CHMgBr$	$CH_3[H_2C=C(i\text{-}C_3H_7)][i\text{-}C_4H_9(n\text{-}C_6H_{13})CH]COH$ (45%)	*267*
$t\text{-}C_4H_9CO(CH_2)_2CH=CH_2$	CH_3MgI	$CH_3[H_2C=CH(CH_2)_2](t\text{-}C_4H_9)COH$ (90%)	*134*
$C_9H_{16}O_2$			
$(CH_3CO)_2C(C_2H_5)_2$	$(\equiv CMgBr)_2$	$CH_3CO(C_2H_5)_2CC(CH_3)(C\equiv CH)OH$	*85*
$C_9H_{16}O_3$			
$CH_3COC(C_2H_5)_2CO_2CH_3$	CH_3MgI (1 equiv.)	$(C_2H_5)_2CHCOCO_2CH_3$; recovered ketone	*152*
$CH_3COC(CH_2)_4CO_2C_2H_5$ (21.5 g.)	C_2H_5MgI (23.4 g. C_2H_5I)	$CH_3(C_2H_5)[H_5C_2O_2(CH_4)_2]COH$	*269*
$CH_3CO(CH_2)_4CO_2C_2H_5$ (33 g.)	$n\text{-}C_4H_9MgBr$ (34 g. C_4H_9Br)	$CH_3(n\text{-}C_4H_9)[H_5C_2O_2(CH_2)_4]COH$ [yielding 25% $n\text{-}C_4H_9CH(CH_3)(CH_2)_4CO_2H$]	*136*
$CH_3CO(CH_2)_4CO_2C_2H_5$ (3.45 g.)	$n\text{-}C_{18}H_{37}MgBr$ (8.65 g. $C_{18}H_{37}Br$)	$CH_3[H_5C_2O_2(CH_2)_4](n\text{-}C_{18}H_{37})COH$	*269*
$C_9H_{17}ON$			
$CH_3CO(CH_2)_2N(C_2H_5)_2$	CH_3MgI	$(C_2H_5)_2N(CH_2)_2C(CH_3)_2OH$	*270*
$C_9H_{18}O$			
$CH_3CO\text{-}n\text{-}C_7H_{15}$	CH_3MgI	$n\text{-}C_7H_{15}(CH_3)_2COH$ (*ca.* quant)	*268*
$CH_3COCH(n\text{-}C_3H_7)_2$	$(n\text{-}C_3H_7)_2CHMgBr$	$CH_3CH(OH)CH(n\text{-}C_3H_7)_2$; "other secondary products"	*199*
$CH_3COC(C_2H_5)_3$	CH_3MgBr	Addition (0%); enolization (94%)*	*168*
$C_2H_5COCH(CH_3)\text{-}t\text{-}C_4H_9$	CH_3MgCl	Addition (33%); enolization (62%)*	*124*

*"Grignard machine" study.

TABLE VI-XVIII (Continued)

Ketonic Comp'd	RMgX	Product (s)	Ref.
$C_9H_{18}O$ (*cont.*)			
$C_2H_5COC(C_2H_5)_3$	C_2H_5MgBr (+ HCHO)*	$(C_2H_5)_3CCO(CH_2)_2OH$ (34%)	*192*
n-$C_3H_7COCH(CH_3)$-n-C_3H_7	n-$C_5H_{11}MgBr$	n-$C_3H_7(n$-$C_5H_{11})[CH_3(n$-$C_3H_7)CH]COH$	*11*
$(n$-$C_4H_9)_2CO$	$(\equiv CMgBr)_2$	$[\equiv CC(n$-$C_4H_9)_2OH]_2$ (83%)	*199*
$(i$-$C_4H_9)_2CO$	CH_3MgI	$CH_3(i$-$C_4H_9)_2COH$	*11*
$(i$-$C_4H_9)_2CO$	$(\equiv CMgBr)_2$	$[\equiv CC(i$-$C_4H_9)_2OH]_2$ (80%)	*21*
i-C_4H_9CO-t-C_4H_9	$(\equiv CMgI)_2$	$[\equiv CC(i$-$C_4H_9)(t$-$C_4H_9)OH]_2$	*125*
$(t$-$C_4H_9)_2CO$ (21 g.)	$H_2C{=}CHC{\equiv}CMgBr$	$H_2C{=}CHC{\equiv}C(t$-$C_4H_9)_2COH$ (14 g.)	*40*
$(t$-$C_4H_9)_2CO$	Butenyl-MgBr	$CH_3CH{=}CHCH_2(t$-$C_4H_9)_2COH$ (69%)	*251*
$C_{10}H_6O_4$			
Furil	CH_3MgI	2,3-Di-α-furyl-2,3-butadiene	*271*
Furil	C_2H_5MgI	3,4-Di-α-furyl-2,4-hexadiene	*271*
$C_{10}H_7OCl_3$			
$C_6H_5COCH{=}CHCCl_3$	C_6H_5MgBr	$C_6H_5COCH_2CH(CCl_3)C_6H_5$ (93%)	*111*
$C_{10}H_8O_3$			
$HO_2CCH{=}CHCOC_6H_5$	C_2H_5MgBr	$C_6H_5COCH_2CH(C_2H_5)CO_2H$ (?)	*274*
$HO_2CCH{=}CHCOC_6H_5$ (11 g.)	C_6H_5MgBr (40 g. C_6H_5Br)	$C_6H_5COCH_2CH(C_6H_5)CO_2H$ (22.5%)	*274*
$HO_2CCH{=}CHCOC_6H_5$	4-$CH_3OC_6H_4MgBr$	$C_6H_5COCH_2CH(C_6H_4$-4-$OCH_3)CO_2H$ (22%)	*274*
$C_{10}H_9OBr$			
$CH_3COCBr{=}CHC_6H_5$ (28 g.)	C_6H_5MgBr (33 g. C_6H_5Br)	$CH_3COCHBrCH(C_6H_5)_2$ (35 g.)	*272*
$C_{10}H_{10}O$			
$CH_3COCH{=}CHC_6H_5$ (15 g.)	CH_3MgI (32 g. CH_3I)	$H_2C{=}C(CH_3)CH{=}CHC_6H_5$	*206*
$CH_3COCH{=}CHC_6H_5$ (60 g.)	C_2H_5MgI (18 g. Mg)	$CH_3COCH_2CH(C_2H_5)C_6H_5$ (41 g., 56.6%); diene (37.2%); condensate (6.3%)	*111*

*This reaction is in effect an enolate addition to formaldehyde.

TABLE VI-XVIII (Continued)

Ketonic Comp'd	RMgX	Product(s)	Ref.
$C_{10}H_{10}O$ (*cont.*)			
$CH_3COCH{=}CHC_6H_5$	C_2H_5MgI	$CH_3CH{=}C(CH_3)CH{=}CHC_6H_5$ ("good yield")	*206*
$CH_3COCH{=}CHC_6H_5$	$H_2C{=}CHCH_2Br$ + Mg	$CH_3(H_2C{=}CHCH_2)(C_6H_5CH{=}CH)COH$ (31%)	*599*
$CH_3COCH{=}CHC_6H_5$	$C_2H_5OC{\equiv}CMgBr$	$CH_3(C_2H_5OC{\equiv}C)(C_6H_5CH{=}CH)COH$ (80%)	*43*
$CH_3COCH{=}CHC_6H_5$ (35 g.)	t-C_4H_9MgCl (12 g. Mg)	$CH_3COCH_2CH(t\text{-}C_4H_9)C_6H_5$ (*ca.* 8 g., 15%); $H_2C{=}C(t\text{-}C_4H_9)CH{=}CHC_6H_5$ (27%)	*276*
$CH_3COCH{=}CHC_6H_5$	i-$C_6H_{11}MgBr$	$CH_3COCH_2CH(i\text{-}C_5H_{11})C_6H_5$ * (52%)	*277*
$CH_3COCH{=}CHC_6H_5$ (240 g.)	C_6H_5MgI (72 g. Mg)	$CH_3COCH_2CH(C_6H_5)_2$ (18 g., 4.9%); diene	*111*
$CH_3COCH{=}CHC_6H_5$ (36.4 g.)	$(CH_2)_5CHMgBr$ (excess)	$CH_3COCH_2CH(C_6H_5)CH(CH_2)_5$ (37.2 g.); $CH_3[(CH_2)_5CH](C_6H_5CH{=}CH)COH$	*278*
$CH_3CH{=}CHCOC_6H_5$	CH_3MgI	i-$C_4H_9COC_6H_5$; *no* carbinol.	*256*
$CH_3CH{=}CHCOC_6H_5$	C_6H_5MgBr	$C_6H_5COCH_2CH(CH_3)C_6H_5$; *no* carbinol	*256*
$(CH_2)_2CHCOC_6H_5$	C_6H_5MgBr	$(CH_2)_5CH(C_6H_5)_2COH$	*279*
$C_{10}H_{10}O_2$			
$CH_3COCH{=}CHC_6H_4$-2-OH (7.5 g.)	CH_3MgI (0.1 mole)	$CH_3COCH_2CH(CH_3)C_6H_4$-2-OH (1.5 g.)	*273*
$HOCH{=}C(CH_3)COC_6H_5$ †	C_2H_5MgBr	$HO(C_2H_5)CHCH(CH_3)COC_6H_5$	*147*
$HOCH{=}C(CH_3)COC_6H_5$ †	C_6H_5MgBr	$C_6H_5CH{=}C(CH_3)COC_6H_5$	*147*
$C_{10}H_{10}O_3$			
$CH_3COCH_2O_2CC_6H_5$	C_2H_5MgBr (4 equiv.)	$HO(CH_3)(C_2H_5)CCH_2OH$; $C_6H_5(C_2H_5)_2COH$; $C_6H_5CO_2H$	*82*
$H_3CO_2CCOC_6H_4$-4-CH_3	C_6H_5MgBr	$HO_2C(C_6H_5)(4\text{-}CH_3C_6H_4)COH$	*280*
$H_5C_2O_2CCOC_6H_5$	CH_3MgI (1 equiv.)	$CH_3(H_5C_2O_2C)(C_6H_5)COH$ (60%)	*151,187*

*The abstract reports a "6-octanone," but this is obviously a misprint.

†The reactions reported could be more plausibly represented as those of $C_6H_5COCH(CH_3)CHO$ or $C_6H_5C(OH){=}C(CH_3)CHO$.

TABLE VI-XVIII (Continued)

Ketonic Comp'd	RMgX	Product(s)	Ref.
$C_{10}H_{10}O_3$ (*cont.*)			
$H_5C_2O_2CCOC_6H_5$	C_2H_5MgBr (1 equiv.)	$C_2H_5(H_5C_2O_2C)(C_6H_5)COH$ (82%)	151,187
$H_5C_2O_2CCOC_6H_5$ (100 g.)	$1-C_{10}H_7MgBr$ (137 g. $C_{10}H_7Br$)	$HO_2C(C_6H_5)(1-C_{10}H_7)COH$	280
$C_{10}H_{12}O$			
$CH_3CO(CH_2)_2C_6H_5$ (15 g.)	CH_3MgI (16 g. CH_3I)	$C_6H_5CH_2CH_2(CH_3)_2COH$ (10 g.)	146
$CH_3CO(CH_2)_2C_6H_5$ (15 g.)	C_2H_5MgI (16 g. C_2H_5I)	$CH_3(C_2H_5)(C_6H_5CH_2CH_2)COH$ (13 g.)	146
$CH_3CO(CH_2)_2C_6H_5$	$C_6H_5CH_2MgCl$	$CH_3(C_6H_5CH_2)(C_6H_5CH_2CH_2)COH$	282
$CH_3COC_6H_3$-2,4-$(CH_3)_2$*	$H_2C{=}CHCH_2Br$ + Mg	$CH_3(H_2C{=}CHCH_2)[2,4-(CH_3)_2C_6H_3]COH$ (quant.)	283
$CH_3COC_6H_3$-2,4-$(CH_3)_2$	$i-C_3H_7MgBr$	$CH_3(i-C_3H_7)[2,4-(CH_3)_2C_6H_3]COH$ (yielding 32% alkylated benzene on dehydr'n and hydrogen'n)	106
$CH_3COC_6H_3$-2,5-$(CH_3)_2$*	$H_2C{=}CHCH_2Br$ + Mg	$CH_3(H_2C{=}CHCH_2)[2,5-(CH_3)_2C_6H_3]COH$ (quant.)	283
$CH_3COC_6H_3$-3,4-$(CH_3)_2$*	$H_2C{=}CHCH_2Br$ + Mg	$CH_3(H_2C{=}CHCH_2)[3,4-(CH_3)_2C_6H_3]COH$ (96.4%)	283
$C_2H_5COC_6H_4$-4-CH_3	$H_2C{=}CHCH_2Br$ + Mg	$C_2H_5(H_2C{=}CHCH_2)(4-CH_3C_6H_4)COH$ (75%)	284
$n-C_3H_7COC_6H_5$	CH_3MgI	$CH_3(n-C_3H_7)(C_6H_5)COH$ (74%)	619
$n-C_3H_7COC_6H_5$	C_2H_5MgBr	$C_2H_5(n-C_3H_7)(C_6H_5)COH$	285
$n-C_3H_7COC_6H_5$	C_6H_5MgBr	$n-C_3H_7(C_6H_5)_2COH$	287
$n-C_3H_7COC_6H_5$	$C_6H_5CH_2MgCl$	$n-C_3H_7(C_6H_5)(C_6H_5CH_2)COH$ (94%)	199
$n-C_3H_7COC_6H_5$	$n-C_8H_{17}MgBr$	$n-C_3H_7(C_6H_5)(n-C_8H_{17})COH$	144
$n-C_3H_7COC_6H_5$	Isobornyl-MgCl†	$n-C_3H_7(C_6H_5)CHOH$, $[\alpha]_D$ 26.70° (50%)‡	230

*Identification of the carbinols, and hence of the corresponding xylyl ketones, from *Beilstein*, 6 (296), 1931.
†Prepared by partial (*ca.* 65%) carbonation of the Grignard reagent mixture from (+)-α-pinene hydrochlorides.
‡ Activity of the pure enantiomorph, $[\alpha]_D$ 57.21°.

TABLE VI-XVIII (Continued)

Ketonic Comp'd	RMgX	Product(s)	Ref.
$C_{10}H_{12}O$ (*cont.*)			
n-$C_3H_7COC_6H_5$ (1.10 mole)	n-$C_{16}H_{33}MgBr$ (1.25 mole)	n-$C_3H_7(C_6H_5)(n$-$C_{16}H_{33})COH$ (yielding 73% crude olefin)	*231*
i-$C_3H_7COC_6H_5$ (30 g.)	C_2H_5MgI (48 g. C_2H_5I)	$C_2H_5(i$-$C_3H_7)(C_6H_5)COH$ (28 g.)	*286*
i-$C_3H_7COC_6H_5$	n-C_3H_7MgBr	n-$C_3H_7(i$-$C_3H_7)(C_6H_5)COH$	*286*
i-$C_3H_7COC_6H_5$	Isobornyl-MgCl*	i-$C_3H_7(C_6H_5)CHOH$, $[\alpha]_D$ 26.40° (80%)†	*230*
$C_{10}H_{12}O_2$			
$C_2H_5COC_6H_4$-4-OCH_3 (17 g.)	$C_2H_5(4$-$CH_3OC_6H_4)CHMgCl$ (20 g. $C_{10}H_{13}ClO$)	$C_2H_5(4$-$CH_3OC_6H_4)[C_2H_5(4$-$CH_3OC_6H_4CH]COH$	*288*
$C_2H_5COC_6H_4$-4-OCH_3 (17 g.)	$C_2H_5(4$-$CH_3OC_6H_4)CHBr$ (23 g.) + Mg	$C_2H_5(4$-$CH_3OC_6H_4)[C_2H_5(4$-$CH_3OC_6H_4CH]COH$	*288*
$C_2H_5COCH(OH)C_6H_5$	CH_3MgBr	$HO(CH_3)(C_2H_5)CCH(OH)C_6H_5$ (80%)	*289,258*
$C_2H_5COCH(OH)C_6H_5$	C_2H_5MgBr	$HO(C_2H_5)_2CCH(OH)C_6H_5$ (chiefly); $HO(C_2H_5)(C_6H_5)CCH(OH)C_2H_5$	*289,258*
$C_2H_5COCH(OH)C_6H_5$	n-C_3H_7MgBr	$HO(C_2H_5)(n$-$C_3H_7)CCH(OH)C_6H_5$	*289,258*
$C_2H_5CH(OH)COC_6H_5$	CH_3MgBr	$HO(CH_3)(C_6H_5)CCH(OH)C_2H_5$ (84%)	*289,258*
$C_2H_5CH(OH)COC_6H_5$	C_2H_5MgBr	β-$HO(C_2H_5)(C_6H_5)CCH(OH)C_2H_5$	*289,258*
$C_2H_5CH(OH)COC_6H_5$	n-C_3H_7MgBr	$HO(n$-$C_3H_7)(C_6H_5)CCH(OH)C_2H_5$	*289,258*
$C_2H_5CH(OH)COC_6H_5$	C_6H_5MgBr	$HO(C_6H_5)_2CCH(OH)C_2H_5$ (chiefly); $HO(C_2H_5)(C_6H_5)CCH(OH)C_6H_5$	*289,258*
$HO(CH_3)_2CCOC_6H_5$	C_6H_5MgBr	$HO(CH_3)_2CC(C_6H_5)_2OH$	*258,292*
$HO(CH_3)_2CCOC_6H_5$	t-$C_4H_9C{\equiv}CMgBr$	$HO(CH_3)_2CC(C_6H_5)(C{\equiv}C$-$t$-$C_4H_9)OH$ (75.5%)	*290*
$C_{10}H_{12}O_3$			
$CH_3COC_6H_3$-2,5-$(OCH_3)_2$	i-C_3H_7MgBr	$CH_3(i$-$C_3H_7)[2,5$-$(CH_3O)_2C_6H_3]COH$ (90%)	*281*

*Prepared by partial (*ca.* 65%) carbonation of the Grignard reagent mixture from (+)-α-pinene hydrochlorides.

†Activity of the pure enantiomorph, $[\alpha]_D$ 47.66°.

TABLE VI-XVIII (Continued)

Ketonic Comp'd	RMgX	Product(s)	Ref.
$C_{10}H_{12}O_3$ (*cont.*)			
$CH_3COCH(OH)C_6H_4$-4-OCH_3	C_2H_5MgBr (5 equiv.)	α-$HO(CH_3)(C_2H_5)CCH(OH)C_6H_4$-4-$OCH_3$	*291*
$(CH_3O)_2CHCOC_6H_5$ (9 g.)	C_6H_5MgBr (8 g. C_6H_5Br)	$(CH_3O)_2CH(C_6H_5)_2COH$ (5 g., crude)	*203*
$C_{10}H_{13}ON$			
$CH_3COC_6H_4$-4-$N(CH_3)_2$ (14 g.)	C_6H_5(1-$C_{10}H_7$)$C{=}CHMgBr$ (32 g. $C_{18}H_{13}Br$)	CH_3[4-$(CH_3)_2NC_6H_4$][C_6H_5(1-$C_{10}H_7$)$C{=}$CH]COH	*180*
$CH_3CH(NHCH_3)COC_6H_5$ (7 g.)	C_6H_5MgBr (7 g. C_6H_5Br)	$CH_3(CH_3NH)CH(C_6H_5)_2COH$ (5.8 g.)	*293*
$C_{10}H_{14}OClN$			
$CH_3CH(NH_2{\cdot}HCl)COC_6H_4$-4-$CH_3$	C_6H_5MgBr	$CH_3(H_2N)CH(C_6H_5)$(4-$CH_3C_6H_4$)COH	*263*
$CH_3CH(NH_2{\cdot}HCl)COC_6H_4$-4-$CH_3$	4-$CH_3OC_6H_4MgBr$	$CH_3(H_2N)CH$(4-$CH_3C_6H_4$)(4-$CH_3OC_6H_4$)COH	*263*
$C_{10}H_{14}O_2ClN$			
$HCl{\cdot}H_2NCH_2COC_6H_4$-2-$OC_2H_5$	C_6H_5MgBr	$H_2NCH_2(C_6H_5)$(2-$C_2H_5OC_6H_4$)COH	*264*
$HCl{\cdot}H_2NCH_2COC_6H_4$-4-$OC_2H_5$	C_6H_5MgBr	$H_2NCH_2(C_6H_5)$(4-$C_2H_5OC_6H_4$)COH	*264*
$CH_3(HCl{\cdot}H_2N)CHCOC_6H_4$-4-$OCH_3$	C_6H_5MgBr	$CH_3(H_2N)CH(C_6H_5)$(4-$CH_3OC_6H_4$)COH	*263*
$CH_3(HCl{\cdot}H_2N)CHCOC_6H_4$-4-$OCH_3$	4-$CH_3C_6H_4MgBr$	$CH_3(H_2N)CH$(4-$CH_3C_6H_4$)(4-$CH_3OC_6H_4$)COH	*263*
$C_{10}H_{14}O_3ClN$			
$HCl{\cdot}H_2NCH_2COC_6H_3$-2,4-$(OCH_3)_2$	C_6H_5MgBr	$H_2NCH_2(C_6H_5)$[2,4-$(CH_3O)_2C_6H_3$]COH	*264*
$HCl{\cdot}H_2NCH_2COC_6H_3$-2,5-$(OCH_3)_2$	C_6H_5MgBr	$H_2NCH_2(C_6H_5)$[2,5-$(CH_3O)_2C_6H_3$]COH	*264*
$HCl{\cdot}H_2NCH_2COC_6H_3$-3,4-$(OCH_3)_2$	C_6H_5MgBr	$H_2NCH_2(C_6H_5)$[3,4-$(CH_3O)_2C_6H_3$]COH	*264*
$C_{10}H_{16}O_5$			
$CH_3COCH(CO_2C_2H_5)CH_2CO_2C_2H_5$	CH_3MgI (1 equiv.)	Enolization, chiefly; traces ethyl terebinate	*151,187*
$C_{10}H_{17}ON$			
$CH_3COC(CH_3){=}CHN(CH_2)_5$	C_2H_5MgBr	$CH_3COC(CH_3){=}CHC_2H_5$	*153*

TABLE VI-XVIII (Continued)

Ketonic Comp'd	RMgX	Product(s)	Ref.
$C_{10}H_{18}O$			
$CH_3COCH{=}CH\text{-}n\text{-}C_6H_{13}$	CH_3MgI	$H_2C{=}C(CH_3)CH{=}CH\text{-}n\text{-}C_6H_{13}$ (16%)	*294*
$CH_3COCH{=}CH\text{-}n\text{-}C_6H_{13}$	C_2H_5MgBr	$CH_3CH{=}C(CH_3)CH{=}CH\text{-}n\text{-}C_6H_{13}$; $H_2C{=}C(C_2H_5)CH{=}CH\text{-}n\text{-}C_6H_{13}$	*294*
$CH_3COCH{=}CH\text{-}n\text{-}C_6H_{13}$	$i\text{-}C_5H_{11}MgBr$	$i\text{-}C_4H_9CH{=}C(CH_3)CH{=}CH\text{-}n\text{-}C_6H_{13}$; $H_2C{=}C(i\text{-}C_5H_{11})CH{=}CH\text{-}n\text{-}C_6H_{13}$	*294*
$H_2C{=}CHCOC(C_2H_5)_3$	CH_3MgBr	Addition (58%); enolization (0%)*	*168*
$C_{10}H_{18}O_3$			
$CH_3COCH(O_2CCH_3)\text{-}n\text{-}C_5H_{11}$ (12.7 g.)	CH_3MgBr (15 g. Mg)	$t\text{-}C_4H_9OH$ ("a little"); $HO(CH_3)_2CCH(OH)\text{-}n\text{-}C_5H_{11}$ (6.5 g.)	*295*
$CH_3COC(C_2H_5)_2CO_2CH_3$ (40 g.)	CH_3MgI (1 equiv.)	$(C_2H_5)_2CHCO_2C_2H_5$ (10 g.); recovered ketone (20 g.)†	*151*
$CH_3COC(C_2H_5)_2CO_2CH_3$	CH_3MgI (3 equiv.)	Recovered ketone (*ca.* quant.)‡	*151*
$CH_3COC(C_2H_5)_2CO_2CH_3$ (30 g.)	CH_3MgI (3 equiv.)	C_8H_{16}, b.p. 115–120° (10 g.); $t\text{-}C_4H_9OH$ (?)§	*151*
$C_{10}H_{19}ON$			
$n\text{-}C_3H_7COCH{=}CHN(C_2H_5)_2$	C_2H_5MgBr (1.5 equiv.)	$n\text{-}C_3H_7COCH{=}CHC_2H_5$	*153*
$C_{10}H_{19}O_2N$			
$C_2H_5CO(CH_2)_2CON(C_2H_5)_2$	C_2H_5MgBr (excess)	$HO(C_2H_5)_2C(CH_2)_2CON(C_2H_5)_2$ (chiefly); $(C_2H_5COCH_2—)_2$ (5%); 2,2,5-triethyldihydrofuran	*296*

*"Grignard machine" study.

†Dropwise addition of Grignard reagent solution to ketone; twenty-four hours at room temperature.

‡Gradual addition of ketone to Grignard reagent solution; three days reflux.

§Gradual addition of ketone to Grignard solution; 8 hours at 100° (autoclave).

TABLE VI-XVIII (Continued)

Ketonic Comp'd	RMgX	Product(s)	Ref.
$C_{10}H_{20}O$			
$C_2H_5COCH(CH_3)$-n-C_5H_{11}	n-$C_5H_{11}MgBr$ (1.2 equiv.)	$C_2H_5(n\text{-}C_5H_{11})[CH_3(n\text{-}C_5H_{11})CH]COH$	*297*
n-C_3H_7CO-n-C_6H_{13}	$H_2C{=}CHCH_2MgCl$	$H_2C{=}CHCH_2(n\text{-}C_3H_7)(n\text{-}C_6H_{13})COH$	*298*
n-C_3H_7CO-n-C_6H_{13} (11 g.)	n-$C_5H_{11}MgBr$ (22 g. $C_5H_{11}Br$)	$n\text{-}C_3H_7(n\text{-}C_5H_{11})(n\text{-}C_6H_{13})COH$	*297,11*
n-$C_3H_7COCH_2CH(CH_3)$-n-C_3H_7	n-$C_5H_{11}MgBr$	$n\text{-}C_3H_7(n\text{-}C_5H_{11})[CH_3(n\text{-}C_3H_7)CHCH_2]COH$ (yielding olefin *ca.* quant.)	*297*
t-$C_4H_9COCH_2$-t-C_4H_9	CH_3MgI	$CH_3(t\text{-}C_4H_9)(t\text{-}C_4H_9CH_2)COH$ (51%)	*299*
t-$C_4H_9COCH(C_2H_5)_2$	CH_3MgCl	Addition (19%); enolization (5%)*	*124*
t-$C_4H_9COCH(C_2H_5)_2$ (0.5 mole)	t-C_4H_9MgCl (0.8 mole)	$t\text{-}C_4H_9[(C_2H_5)_2CH]CHOH$ (38%); recovered ketone (45%)	*305*
$C_{11}H_8OS$			
2-Benzoylthiophene	C_6H_5MgBr	$\alpha\text{-}C_4H_3S(C_6H_5)_2COH$	*272*
2-Benzoylthiophene	$1\text{-}C_{10}H_7CH_2MgCl$	$\alpha\text{-}C_4H_3S(C_6H_5)C{=}CH\text{-}1\text{-}C_{10}H_7$	*301*
$C_{11}H_9ON$			
1-Acetylisoquinoline (1.71 g.)	CH_3MgI (4.26 g. CH_3I)	2-(1-Isoquinolyl)-2-propanol (1.05 g., 56%)	*302*
1-Acetylisoquinoline (0.01 mole)	C_6H_5MgBr (0.03 mole)	1-Phenyl-1-(1-isoquinolyl)ethanol (1.92 g., 47%)	*302*
4-Acetylisoquinoline (0.0025 mole)	CH_3MgI (0.0075 mole)	2-(4-Isoquinolyl)-2-propanol (0.35 g., 75%)	*302*
4-Acetylisoquinoline (0.01 mole)	C_6H_5MgBr (0.03 mole)	1-Phenyl-1-(4-isoquinolyl)ethanol (1.74 g., 70%)	*302*
$C_{11}H_{10}O$			
$C_2H_5COC{\equiv}CC_6H_5$ (10.7 g.)	CH_3MgI (10.6 g. CH_3I)	$CH_3CH{=}C(CH_3)C{\equiv}CC_6H_5$	*300*

*"Grignard machine" study.

TABLE VI-XVIII (Continued)

Ketonic Comp'd	RMgX	Product(s)	Ref.
$C_{10}H_{11}OS_2$			
2,5-Dimethyl-3-(2-thenoyl)thiophene (5 g.)	$C_6H_5CH_2MgCl$ (5 g. C_7H_7Cl)	Carbinol (yielding 5 g. dehydrate)	*254*
$C_{11}H_{10}O_3$			
$HO_2CCH{=}CHCOC_6H_4$-4-CH_3	C_6H_5MgBr	4-$CH_3C_6H_4COCH_2CH(C_6H_5)CO_2H$ (27.2%)	*274*
$C_{11}H_{11}ON$			
2-Methyl-3-acetylpyrrocoline (1 mole)	C_2H_5MgBr (2.5 mole)	3-Methylpyrrocoline (5.8 g.); $C_{13}H_{15}N$ (22.6 g.); $C_{15}H_{21}N$ (26.6 g.)	*306,304; cf. 318*
$C_{11}H_{12}O$			
$C_2H_5COCH{=}CHC_6H_5$	C_2H_5MgBr	$C_2H_5COCH_2CH(C_2H_5)C_6H_5$ (71%); $HO(C_2H_5)_2CCH{=}CHC_6H_5$	*111*
$C_2H_5COCH{=}CHC_6H_5$ (30.0 g.)	*i*-C_4H_9MgBr	$C_2H_5COCH_2CH(i\text{-}C_4H_9)C_6H_5$ (23.5 g.); $HO(C_2H_5)(i\text{-}C_4H_9)CCH{=}CHC_6H_5$	*111*
$C_2H_5COCH{=}CHC_6H_5$ (100 g.)	C_6H_5MgBr	$C_2H_5COCH_2CH(C_6H_5)_2$ (60 g., 40%); $HO(C_2H_5)(C_6H_5)CCH{=}CHC_6H_5$	*111*
$C_2H_5COCH{=}CHC_6H_5$ (40 g.)	$(CH_2)_5CHMgBr$	$C_2H_5COCH_2CH(C_6H_5)CH(CH_2)_5$ (43 g.); $C_2H_5[(CH_2)_5CH](C_6H_5CH{=}CH)COH$	*278*
$C_6H_5COCH{=}C(CH_3)_2$	C_6H_5MgBr	$C_6H_5COCH_2C(CH_3)_2C_6H_5$; *no* carbinol	*256*
2,4,6-$(CH_3)_3C_6H_2CH{=}CO$	2,4,6-$(CH_3)_3C_6H_2MgBr$	2,4,6-$(CH_3)_3C_6H_2CH_2COC_6H_2$-2,4,6-$(CH_3)_3$	*312*
$C_{11}H_{12}O_2$			
$CH_3COC_6H_4$-4-$OCH_2CH{=}CH_2$ (17.6 g.)	C_6H_5MgBr (40 g. C_6H_5Br)	$H_2C{=}C(C_6H_5)C_6H_4$-4-OH (13.5 g., 70%)	*307*
$CH_3COCH{=}CHC_6H_4$-4-OCH_3 (60 g.)	C_2H_5MgBr	$CH_3COCH_2CH(C_2H_5)C_6H_4$-4-$OCH_3$ (43 g.)	*111*

TABLE VI-XVIII (Continued)

Ketonic Comp'd	RMgX	Product(s)	Ref.
$C_{11}H_{12}O_2$ (*cont.*)			
$CH_3COCH{=}CHC_6H_4$-4-OCH_3	$(CH_2)_5CHMgBr$ (excess)	$CH_3COCH_2CH[CH(CH_2)_5]C_6H_4$-4-$OCH_3$ (44 g.); $CH_3[(CH_2)_5CH](4\text{-}CH_3OC_6H_4CH{=}CH)COH$	*278*
$C_{11}H_{12}O_3$			
$CH_3COCH(O_2CCH_3)C_6H_5$ + $C_6H_5COCH(O_2CCH_3)CH_3$	CH_3MgBr	$HO(CH_3)_2CCH(OH)C_6H_5$; $HO(CH_3)(C_6H_5)CCH(OH)CH_3$	*313*
$C_6H_5COCH(O_2CCH_3)CH_3$	CH_3MgBr	$HO(CH_3)(C_6H_5)CCH(OH)CH_3$	*313*
$C_6H_5CO(CH_2)_2CO_2CH_3$	CH_3MgI	$HO(CH_3)(C_6H_5)C(CH_2)_2C(CH_3)_2OH$ (88%)	*314*
$C_6H_5CO(CH_2)_2CO_2CH_3$	C_6H_5MgBr	$[HO(C_6H_5)_2CCH_2{-}]_2$	*314*
2,6-$(CH_3CO)_2$-4-$CH_3C_6H_2OH$ (19.2 g.)	CH_3MgI (170.4 g. CH_3I)	2,6-Bis-(2-hydroxy-2-propyl)-4-methylphenol (14 g., 51%)	*303*
$C_{11}H_{12}O_4$			
1-Acetyl-1-carbethoxy-2-α-furylethene (25 g.)	C_2H_5MgI (45 g. C_2H_5I)	$CH_3COCH(CO_2C_2H_5)CH(C_2H_5)$-α-$C_4H_3O$ (17 g.)	*308*
1-Acetyl-2-carbethoxy-2-α-furylethene (25 g.)	*n*-C_3H_7MgBr (36 g. C_3H_7Br)	$CH_3COCH(CO_2C_2H_5)CH(n\text{-}C_3H_7)$-α-$C_4H_3O$ (16 g., 55%)	*308*
1-Acetyl-2-carbethoxy-2-α-furylethene (20 g.)	C_6H_5MgBr (42 g. C_6H_5Br)	$CH_3COCH(CO_2C_2H_5)CH(\alpha\text{-}C_4H_3O)C_6H_5$ (15 g., 52%)	*308*
1-Carbethoxy-1-α-furoylcyclopropane	C_6H_5MgBr	α-(2-Furyl)-α-(1-carbethoxy-1-cyclopropyl)benzyl alcohol	*319*
$C_{11}H_{13}ON$			
$(CH_3)_2NCH{=}CHCOC_6H_5$	C_2H_5MgBr (1.5 equiv.)	$C_2H_5CH{=}CHCOC_6H_5$	*153*
$(CH_3)_2NCH{=}CHCOC_6H_5$	C_6H_5MgBr (1.5 equiv.)	$C_6H_5COCH{=}CHC_6H_5$	*153*

TABLE VI-XVIII (Continued)

Ketonic Comp'd	RMgX	Product(s)	Ref.
$C_{11}H_{13}O_2Cl$			
CH_3COC_6H-2,4-$(CH_3)_2$-3-Cl-6-OCH_3	C_2H_5MgBr (+CO_2)	2,4-$(CH_3)_2$-3-Cl-6-$CH_3OC_6HCOCH_2CO_2H$ (45%)	*315*
$C_{11}H_{13}O_2N$			
$CH_3COC(=NOCH_2C_6H_5)CH_3$	CH_3MgI	$HO(CH_3)_2CC(=NOCH_2C_6H_5)CH_3$ (75%)	*90*
$C_{11}H_{14}O$			
$CH_3COC_6H_2$-2,4,6-$(CH_3)_3$	CH_3MgI (2 equiv.)	Recovered ketone	*206*
$CH_3COC_6H_2$-2,4,6-$(CH_3)_3$ (49.0 g., 0.3 mole)	Butenyl-MgBr (0.36 mole)	$CH_3[CH_3(H_2C=CH)CH][2,4,6$-$(CH_3)_3C_6H_2]COH$ (83%); recovered ketone (12%); butenes (<3%)	*309,316*
$CH_3COC_6H_2$-2,4,6-$(CH_3)_3$ (8.0 g., 0.05 mole)	$C_6H_5CH_2MgCl$ (9.5 g., 0.075 mole C_7H_7Cl)	$CH_3(C_6H_5CH_2)[2,4,6$-$(CH_3)_3C_6H_2]COH$ (52%); "enolization products" (38%)	*309,316*
$C_2H_5COC_6H_3$-2,4-$(CH_3)_2$	C_2H_5MgBr	2,4-$(CH_3)_2C_6H_3(C_2H_5)_2COH$ (yielding 56.5% alkylated benzene on dehydr'n and hydrogen'n)	*106*
n-$C_3H_7COC_6H_4$-4-CH_3	$H_2C=CHCH_2Br$ + Mg	$H_2C=CHCH_2(n\text{-}C_3H_7)(4\text{-}CH_3C_6H_4)COH$ (75%)	*284*
n-$C_4H_9COC_6H_5$	Isobornyl-MgCl*	*n*-$C_4H_9(C_6H_5)CHOH$, $[\alpha]_D$ 21.10° (44%)†	*230*
s-$C_4H_9COC_6H_5$	Isobornyl-MgCl	*s*-$C_4H_9(C_6H_5)CHOH$, $[\alpha]_D$ 25.9° (90%)‡	*230*
t-$C_4H_9COC_6H_3$ (60 g.)	CH_3MgI	$CH_3(t\text{-}C_4H_9)(C_6H_5)COH$ (54 g., 84%)	*234,320*
t-$C_4H_9COC_6H_5$ (70 g.)	C_2H_5MgI	$C_2H_5(t\text{-}C_4H_9)(C_6H_5)COH$ (51 g., 85%)	*234,321*
t-$C_4H_9COC_6H_5$	*n*-C_3H_7MgI	*t*-$C_4H_9(C_6H_5)CHOH$	*234,320*
t-$C_4H_9COC_6H_5$	*i*-C_3H_7MgI	*t*-$C_4H_9(C_6H_5)CHOH$	*234*
t-$C_4H_9COC_6H_5$	C_6H_5MgBr	*t*-$C_4H_9(C_6H_5)_2COH$ (70%); $CH_3COC_6H_5$; $(C_6H_5)_2CO$	*234,320*

*Prepared by partial (*ca.* 65%) carbonation of the Grignard reagent mixture from (+)-α-pinene hydrochloride.

†Activity of pure enantiomorph, $[\alpha]_D$ 40.83°.

‡Activity of pure enantiomorph, $[\alpha]_D$ 36.0°.

TABLE VI-XVIII (Continued)

Ketonic Comp'd	RMgX	Product(s)	Ref.
$C_{11}H_{14}O$ (*cont.*)			
$t\text{-}C_4H_9COC_6H_5$ (162 g.)	$t\text{-}C_4H_9C{\equiv}CMgBr$ (82 g. C_6H_{10})	$t\text{-}C_4H_9(C_6H_5)(t\text{-}C_4H_9C{\equiv}C)COH$ (200 g., 68%)	*656*
$t\text{-}C_4H_9COC_6H_5$	$C_6H_5CH_2MgCl$	$t\text{-}C_4H_9(C_6H_5)(C_6H_5CH_2)COH$ (75%); $(C_6H_5CH_2{-})_2$	*234,230*
$t\text{-}C_4H_9COC_6H_5$	$4\text{-}CH_3OC_6H_4MgBr$	$t\text{-}C_4H_9(C_6H_5)(4\text{-}CH_3OC_6H_4)COH$	*234*
$t\text{-}C_4H_9COC_6H_5$ (5.3 g.)	$C_6H_5C{\equiv}CMgBr$ (6 g. $C_6H_5C{\equiv}CH$)	$t\text{-}C_4H_9(C_6H_5)(C_6H_5C{\equiv}C)COH$ (8.8 g., 98%)	*310*
$t\text{-}C_4H_9COC_6H_5$	$4\text{-}C_2H_5C_6H_4MgBr$	$t\text{-}C_4H_9(C_6H_5)(4\text{-}C_2H_5C_6H_4)COH$	*234*
$C_{11}H_{14}ON_2$			
$CH_3COC[{=}NN(CH_3)C_6H_5]CH_3$	CH_3MgI	$HO(CH_3)_2CC[{=}NN(CH_3)C_6H_5]CH_3$ (75–80%)	*657*
$CH_3COC[{=}NN(CH_3)C_6H_5]CH_3$	C_2H_5MgI	$HO(CH_3)(C_2H_5)CC[{=}NN(CH_3)C_6H_5]CH_3$ (65%)	*657*
$CH_3COC[{=}NN(CH_3)C_6H_5]CH_3$	C_6H_5MgBr	$HO(CH_3)(C_6H_5)CC[{=}NN(CH_3)C_6H_5]CH_3$ (76%)	*657*
$C_{11}H_{14}O_2$			
$C_2H_5O(CH_2)_2COC_6H_5$ (33 g.)	C_2H_5MgBr	$C_2H_5(C_2H_5OCH_2CH_2)(C_6H_5)COH$ (22 g.)	*147*
$C_2H_5O(CH_2)_2COC_6H_5$ (32 g.)	C_6H_5MgBr	$C_2H_5OCH_2CH_2(C_6H_5)_2COH$ (30 g.)	*147*
$HO(CH_3)_2CCOC_6H_4\text{-}4\text{-}CH_3$ (18 g.)	$C_6H_5C{\equiv}CMgBr$ (31.2 g. $C_6H_5C{\equiv}CH$)	$HO(CH_3)_2CC(C_6H_4\text{-}4\text{-}CH_3)(C{\equiv}CC_6H_5)OH$ (75%)	*311*
$C_{11}H_{14}O_3$			
$CH_3COC_6H_2\text{-}2,5\text{-}(OH)_2\text{-}4\text{-}n\text{-}C_3H_7$	$i\text{-}C_3H_7MgBr$	$CH_3(i\text{-}C_3H_7)[2,5\text{-}(HO)_2\text{-}4\text{-}n\text{-}C_3H_7C_6H_2]COH$ (84%)	*281*
$C_2H_5COCH(OH)C_6H_4\text{-}4\text{-}OCH_3$	CH_3MgI (5 equiv.)	$\beta\text{-}HO(CH_3)(C_2H_5)CCH(OH)C_6H_4\text{-}4\text{-}OCH_3$	*291*
$C_2H_5COCH(OH)C_6H_4\text{-}4\text{-}OCH_3$	$n\text{-}C_3H_7MgBr$ (5 equiv.)	$\alpha\text{-}HO(C_2H_5)(n\text{-}C_3H_7)CCH(OH)C_6H_4\text{-}4\text{-}OCH_3$	*291*
$C_2H_5COCH(OH)C_6H_4\text{-}4\text{-}OCH_3$	C_6H_5MgBr	$\alpha\text{-}HO(C_2H_5)(C_6H_5)CCH(OH)C_6H_4\text{-}4\text{-}OCH_3$	*322*
$C_2H_5COCH(OH)C_6H_4\text{-}4\text{-}OCH_3$	$4\text{-}CH_3OC_6H_4MgBr$	$\alpha\text{-}HO(C_2H_5)(4\text{-}CH_3OC_6H_4)CCH(OH)C_6H_4\text{-}4\text{-}OCH_3$	*322*

TABLE VI-XVIII (Continued)

Ketonic Comp'd	RMgX	Product(s)	Ref.
$C_{11}H_{14}O_4$			
Ethyl furoyldimethylacetate	C_2H_5MgBr	$HO(C_2H_5)(\alpha\text{-}C_4H_8O)CC(CH_3)_2CO_2C_2H_5$ ("small yield")	*319*
Ethyl furoyldimethylacetate	C_6H_5MgBr	$(\alpha\text{-}C_4H_3O)CO[(C_6H_5)_2CH]C(CH_3)_2$	*319*
$C_{11}H_{22}O$			
$CH_3CO\text{-}n\text{-}C_9H_{19}$	CH_3MgI	$n\text{-}C_9H_{19}(CH_3)_2COH$ (*ca.* quant.)	*268*
$CH_3CO\text{-}n\text{-}C_9H_{19}$	$(\equiv CMgBr)_2$	$[\equiv CC(CH_3)(n\text{-}C_9H_{19})OH]_2$ (71%)	*323*
$CH_3CO\text{-}n\text{-}C_9H_{19}$ (170 g.)	$n\text{-}C_5H_{11}MgBr$ (1 equiv.)	$CH_3(n\text{-}C_5H_{11})(n\text{-}C_9H_{19})COH$ (80 ml.); recovered ketone (50 ml.); $C_{10}H_{22}$ (20 ml.)	*100*
$CH_3COCH(t\text{-}C_4H_9)_2$	$i\text{-}C_3H_7MgX$	Recovered ketone (85–90%)*	*324*
$CH_3COCH(t\text{-}C_4H_9)_2$	$i\text{-}C_4H_9MgX$	Recovered ketone (85–90%)*	*324*
$CH_3COCH(t\text{-}C_4H_9)_2$	$t\text{-}C_4H_9MgX$	Recovered ketone (85–90%)*	*324*
$C_{12}H_9ON$			
4-Benzoylpyridine	C_6H_5MgBr	$\gamma\text{-}C_5H_5N(C_6H_5)_2COH$	*325,326*
$C_{12}H_{10}O$			
$CH_3CO\text{-}1\text{-}C_{10}H_7$	CH_3MgI	$1\text{-}C_{10}H_7(CH_3)_2COH$ (*ca.* quant.).	*18,334*
$CH_3CO\text{-}1\text{-}C_{10}H_7$ (42.5 g.)	$2,4,6\text{-}(CH_3)_3C_6H_2MgBr$ (63.7 g. $C_9H_{11}Br$)	$1\text{-}C_{10}H_7[2,4,6\text{-}(CH_3)_3CH_2]C{=}CH_2$ (8.2 g.); recovered ketone (26 g., 61%); $1,3,5\text{-}(CH_3)_3C_6H_3$ (20 g.)	*327*
$CH_3CO\text{-}2\text{-}C_{10}H_7$	CH_3MgI	$2\text{-}C_{10}H_7(CH_3)_2COH$ (yielding 85% olefin)	*328,330*
$CH_3CO\text{-}2\text{-}C_{10}H_7$	C_2H_5MgBr	$CH_3(C_2H_5)(2\text{-}C_{10}H_7)COH + CH_3(2\text{-}C_{10}H_7)C{=}CHCH_3$ (yielding a total of 77% olefin)	*328*
$CH_3CO\text{-}2\text{-}C_{10}H_7$	$2\text{-}CH_3C_6H_4MgBr$ (95 g. C_7H_7Br)	$CH_3(2\text{-}CH_3C_6H_4)(2\text{-}C_{10}H_7)COH$ (yielding 83 g., 68% olefin)	*331*

*Attributed to substantially complete enolization.

TABLE VI-XVIII (Continued)

Ketonic Comp'd	RMgX	Product(s)	Ref.
$C_{12}H_{10}OS$			
2-Phenylacetylthiophene	C_2H_5MgBr (+ $NaNH_2$)	2-(Ethylphenylacetyl)thiophene	*301*
2-Phenylacetylthiophene	C_2H_5MgBr (excess) (+ $NaNH_2$)	After dehydr'n: 1,2-diethyl-1-(2-thienyl)-2-phenylethene	*301*
$C_{12}H_{12}O$			
$CH_3COCH{=}CHCH{=}CHC_6H_5$	$C_6H_5CH_2MgCl$	$C_6H_5CH{=}C(CH_3)CH{=}CHCH{=}CHC_6H_5$ ("poor yield")	329
n-$C_3H_7COC{\equiv}CC_6H_5$ (18 g.)	C_2H_5MgBr (13 g. C_2H_5Br)	$C_2H_5(n\text{-}C_3H_7)(C_6H_5C{\equiv}C)COH$	300
$C_{12}H_{12}OClN$			
$HCl{\cdot}H_2NCH_2CO$-1-$C_{10}H_7$ (12.8 g.)	1-$C_{10}H_7MgBr$* (8.5 g. Mg)	$HCl{\cdot}H_2NCH_2(1\text{-}C_{10}H_7)_2COH$ (9.5 g.)	337
$C_{12}H_{12}O_3$			
$HO_2C(CH_3)C{=}C(CH_3)COC_6H_5$ (5 g.)	C_6H_5MgBr (8.5 g. C_6H_5Br)	$C_6H_5COCH(CH_3)C(CH_3)(C_6H_5)CO_2H$ (2 forms, aggregating 5.9 g., 85.5%)	332
$C_{12}H_{14}O$			
i-$C_3H_7COCH{=}CHC_6H_5$ (60 g.)	C_2H_5MgBr	i-$C_3H_7COCH_2CH(C_2H_5)C_6H_5$ (32 g.)	*111*
i-$C_3H_7COCH{=}CHC_6H_5$ (30 g.)	C_6H_5MgBr	i-$C_3H_7COCH_2CH(C_6H_5)_2$ (37.5 g.); $HO(C_2H_5)(i\text{-}C_3H_7)CCH{=}CHC_6H_5$ (*ca.* 4 g.)	*111*
$C_2H_5CH{=}C(CH_3)COC_6H_5$	C_6H_5MgBr	$C_6H_5COCH(CH_3)CH(C_2H_5)C_6H_5$	*147*
$C_{12}H_{14}O_3$			
$CH_3COCH(O_2CCH_3)C_6H_4$-4-CH_3 (17 g.)	CH_3MgBr (6 g. Mg)	$HO(CH_3)_2CCH(OH)C_6H_4$-4-CH_3 (3.6 g.); t-C_4H_9OH	*14*
$CH_3COCH(O_2CC_6H_5)C_2H_5$	CH_3MgBr	$HO(CH_3)_2CCH(OH)C_6H_5$	*258*

*It is reported that the Grignard reagent was prepared from "β-bromonaphthalene," but this is apparently a misprint.

TABLE VI-XVIII (Continued)

Ketonic Comp'd	RMgX	Product(s)	Ref.
$C_{12}H_{14}O_3$ (*cont.*)			
$CH_3COC(CH_3)(CH_2CO_2H)C_6H_5$	CH_3MgI	$HO(CH_3)_2CC(CH_3)(CH_2CO_2H)C_6H_5$	*336*
$CH_3COC(CH_3)(CH_2CO_2H)C_6H_5$	CH_3MgI	β,γ-Dimethyl-β-phenyl-γ-hydroxyvaleric acid γ-lactone	*335*
$HO_2CCH(CH_3)CH_2COC_6H_4$-4-$CH_3$	CH_3MgI	$CH_3(4\text{-}CH_3C_6H_4)C{=}CHCH(CH_3)CO_2H$	*317*
$C_{12}H_{15}O_2Cl$			
CH_3COC_6H-2,4-$(CH_3)_2$-3-Cl-6-OC_2H_5	C_2H_5MgBr (+ CO_2)	2,4-$(CH_3)_2$-3-Cl-6-$C_2H_5OC_6HCOCH_2CO_2H$ (55%)	*315*
$C_2H_5COC_6H$-2,4-$(CH_3)_2$-3-Cl-6-OCH_3	C_2H_5MgBr (+ CO_2)	2,4-$(CH_3)_2$-3-Cl-6-$CH_3OCHCH(CH_3)CO_2H$ (50%)	*315*
$C_{12}H_{16}O$			
$CH_3COCH_2C(CH_3)_2C_6H_5$	CH_3MgI	$HO(CH_3)_2CCH_2C(CH_3)_2C_6H_5$	*68*
$CH_3COCH_2C(CH_3)_2C_6H_5$ (19.4 g.)	C_6H_5MgBr (25.3 ml. C_2H_5Br)	$CH_3(C_6H_5)C{=}CHC(CH_3)_2C_6H_5$ (8 g.)	*57*
$CH_3COC_6H_4$-4-*t*-C_4H_9	CH_3MgI (2.5 equiv.)	4-*t*-$C_4H_9C_6H_4(CH_3)_2COH$ (75–80%)	*338*
n-$C_3H_7COC_6H_3$-2,4-$(CH_3)_2$	CH_3MgI	CH_3(*n*-C_3H_7)[2,4-$(CH_3)_2C_6H_3$]COH (yielding 72% alkylated benzene upon dehydr'n and hydrogen'n)	*106*
i-$C_3H_7COC_6H_3$-2,4-$(CH_3)_2$	CH_3MgI	CH_3(*i*-C_3H_7)[2,4-$(CH_3)_2C_6H_3$]COH (yielding 64% alkylated benzene upon dehydr'n and hydrogen'n)	*106*
$C_{12}H_{16}O_2$			
$C_2H_5COC_6H_2$-2,4-$(CH_3)_2$-6-OCH_3	C_2H_5MgBr (+ CO_2)	2,4-$(CH_3)_2$-6-$CH_3OC_6H_2CH(CH_3)CO_2H$ (30%); unidentified products	*315*
$C_{12}H_{16}O_3$			
n-$C_3H_7COC_6H_3$-3,5-$(OCH_3)_2$ (21.2 g.)	CH_3MgI (14.5 g. CH_3I)	CH_3(*n*-C_3H_7)[3,5-$(CH_3O)_2C_6H_3$]COH	*333*
n-$C_3H_7COCH(OH)C_6H_4$-4-OCH_3	C_2H_5MgBr (5 equiv.)	β-$HO(C_2H_5)$(*n*-C_3H_7)$CCH(OH)C_6H_4$-4-OCH_3	*291*

TABLE VI-XVIII (Continued)

Ketonic Comp'd	RMgX	Product(s)	Ref.
$C_{12}H_{18}O$			
8-Acetylcamphene	C_6H_5MgBr	8-(α-Phenylvinyl)camphene	339
$C_{12}H_{22}O$			
$CH_3CO(CH_2)_8CH{=}CH_2$ (15 g.)	$CH_3(n\text{-}C_7H_{15})CH(CH_2)_2MgBr$	$CH_3[H_2C{=}CH(CH_2)_8][CH_3(n\text{-}C_7H_{15})CH(CH_2)_2]COH$	136
$CH_3CO(CH_2)_8CH{=}CH_2$ (25 g.)	(+)-$CH_3(i\text{-}C_6H_{13})CH(CH_2)_3MgBr$ (35 g. $C_{11}H_{23}Br$)	$CH_3[H_2C{=}CH(CH_2)_8][CH_3(i\text{-}C_6H_{13})CH(CH_2)_3]COH$	136
$CH_3CO(CH_2)_8CH{=}CH_2$ (18.5 g.)	$n\text{-}C_{12}H_{25}MgBr$ (2.4 g. Mg)	$CH_3[H_2C{=}CH(CH_2)_8](n\text{-}C_{12}H_{25})COH$ (yielding 18.7 g. diene)	136
$t\text{-}C_4H_9COCH{=}C(CH_3)\text{-}t\text{-}C_4H_9$	C_2H_5MgBr	$C_2H_5(t\text{-}C_4H_9)[CH_3(t\text{-}C_4H_9)C{=}CH]COH$ (70%)	150
$C_{12}H_{22}O_2$			
$(t\text{-}C_4H_9CO)_2CHCH_3$	CH_3MgBr	Addition (129/2%); enolization (27/2%)*	124
$C_{12}H_{24}O$			
$C_2H_5COCH(t\text{-}C_4H_9)_2$	$t\text{-}C_4H_9MgCl$	Recovered ketone (87%)†	324
$i\text{-}C_4H_9COC(C_2H_5)_3$	CH_3MgBr	Addition (0%); enolization (85%)*	168
$C_{12}H_{25}ON$			
$CH_3CO(CH_2)_2N(n\text{-}C_4H_9)_2$	RMgBr‡	$CH_3CR(OH)CH_2CH_2N(n\text{-}C_4H_9)_2$‡ (15–33%)	253
$C_{13}H_7OBr_3$			
$C_6H_5COC_6H_2\text{-}2,4,6\text{-}Br_3$ (4.5 g., 0.011 0.011 mole)	C_6H_5MgBr (6.5 g., 0.041 mole C_6H_5Br)	Tar	340

*"Grignard machine" study.

†Attributed to substantially complete enolization.

‡R = 1-$C_{10}H_7$, 4-CH_3O-1-$C_{10}H_6$, 9-phenanthryl.

TABLE VI-XVIII (Continued)

Ketonic Comp'd	RMgX	Product(s)	Ref.
$C_{13}H_8OBr_2$			
$(4\text{-}BrC_6H_4)_2CO$	$4\text{-}ClC_6H_4MgBr$	$4\text{-}ClC_6H_4(4\text{-}BrC_6H_4)_2COH$ ("low yield")	343
$(4\text{-}BrC_6H_4)_2CO$	C_6H_5MgBr	$C_6H_5(4\text{-}BrC_6H_4)_2COH$	343
$(4\text{-}BrC_6H_4)_2CO$ (10 g.)	$4\text{-}ClC_6H_4CH_2MgCl$ (12 g. $C_7H_6Cl_2$)	$4\text{-}ClC_6H_4CH_2(4\text{-}BrC_6H_4)_2COH$	387
$C_{13}H_8OCl_2$			
$(4\text{-}ClC_6H_4)_2CO$ (0.25 mole)	CH_3MgBr (0.25 mole)	$CH_3(4\text{-}ClC_6H_4)_2COH$ (59.3 g., 89%)	348,349
$(4\text{-}ClC_6H_4)_2CO$	CH_3MgI	$CH_3(4\text{-}ClC_6H_4)_2COH$	341
$(4\text{-}ClC_6H_4)_2CO$ (10 g.)	$4\text{-}ClC_6H_4CH_2MgCl$ (14 g. $C_7H_6Cl_2$)	$4\text{-}ClC_6H_4CH_2(4\text{-}ClC_6H_4)_2COH$ (*ca.* quant.)	387
$C_{13}H_8OI_2$			
$(4\text{-}IC_6H_4)_2CO$ (0.5 g.)	$4\text{-}ClC_6H_4CH_2MgCl$ (0.7 $C_7H_6Cl_2$)	$4\text{-}ClC_6H_4CH_2(4\text{-}IC_6H_4)_2COH$ (*ca.* quant.)	387
$C_{13}H_9OBr$			
$4\text{-}BrC_6H_4COC_6H_5$	$n\text{-}C_3H_7MgBr$	$4\text{-}BrC_6H_4(C_6H_5)CHOH$ (24%)*	287
$4BrC_6H_4COC_6H_5$	$C_6H_5C\equiv CMgBr$	$4\text{-}BrC_6H_4(C_6H_5)(C_6H_5C\equiv C)COH$ (85%)	344
$C_{13}H_9OCl$			
$4\text{-}ClC_6H_4COC_6H_5$	$C_6H_5CH_2MgCl$	$4\text{-}ClC_6H_4(C_6H_5)(C_6H_5CH_2)COH$	345
$4\text{-}ClC_6H_4COC_6H_5$ (10 g.)	$2,4,6\text{-}(CH_3)_3C_6H_2MgBr$ (2 g. Mg)	No apparent reaction	342
$C_{13}H_9O_2Br$			
Furfurylidene-*p*-bromoacetophenone	C_2H_5MgBr	$C_2H_5(\alpha\text{-}C_4H_3O)CHCH_2COC_6H_4\text{-}4\text{-}Br$ (95%)	346
Furfurylidene-*p*-bromoacetophenone	$n\text{-}C_3H_7MgBr$	$n\text{-}C_3H_7(\alpha\text{-}C_4H_3O)CHCH_2COC_6H_4\text{-}4\text{-}Br$ (80%)	346
Furyfurlidene-*p*-bromoacetophenone	C_6H_5MgBr	$\alpha\text{-}C_4H_5O(C_6H_5)CHCH_2COC_6H_4\text{-}4\text{-}Br$ (85%)	346

*From a study of the reducing action of Grignard reagents in which the yields of reduction products only are reported.

TABLE VI-XVIII (Continued)

Ketonic Comp'd	RMgX	Product(s)	Ref.
$C_{13}H_9O_2Cl$			
Furfurylidene-*p*-chloroacetophenone	C_2H_5MgBr	$C_2H_5(\alpha\text{-}C_4H_3O)CHCH_2COC_6H_4\text{-}4\text{-}Cl$ (95%)	346
Furfurylidene-*p*-chloroacetophenone	*n*-C_3H_7MgBr	*n*-$C_3H_7(\alpha\text{-}C_4H_3O)CHCH_2COC_6H_4\text{-}4\text{-}Cl$ (72%)	347
Furfurylidene-*p*-chloroacetophenone	C_6H_5MgBr	$\alpha\text{-}C_4H_3O(C_6H_5)CHCH_2C_6H_4\text{-}4\text{-}Cl$ (94%)	347
$C_{13}H_{10}O$			
$(C_6H_5)_2CO$	CH_3MgBr	$CH_3(C_6H_5)_2COH$ (95%)	605
$(C_6H_5)_2CO$	CH_3MgI	$CH_3(C_6H_5)_2COH$	350,287
$(C_6H_5)_2CO$	CH_3MgI	$(C_6H_5)_2C{=}CH_2$*	350
$(C_6H_5)_2CO$	$(\equiv CMgBr)_2$ (excess)	$[\equiv CC(C_6H_5)_2OH]_2$ (*ca.*, quant.)	22,21
$(C_6H_5)_2CO$ (0.3 mole) + $(CH_3)_2CO$ (0.2 mole)	$(\equiv CMgBr)_2$	$[\equiv CC(C_6H_5)_2OH]_2$ (34.0 g.); $[\equiv CC(CH_3)_2OH]_2$ (2.5 g.); $HO(CH_3)_2CC\equiv CC(C_6H_5)_2OH$	23
$(C_6H_5)_2CO$ (0.50 mole) + CH_3CHO (0.25 mole)	$(\equiv CMgBr)_2$	$[\equiv CC(C_6H_5)_2OH]_2$ (61 g.); $HO(C_6H_5)_2CC\equiv CCH(OH)CH_3$ (17 g., 27%)	23
$(C_6H_5)_2CO$ (30 g.) + C_6H_5CHO (20 g.)	$(\equiv CMgBr)_2$ (0.5 mole)	$[\equiv CC(C_6H_5)_2OH]_2$; $[\equiv CCH(C_6H_5)OH]_2$ (2 isomers);† $HO(C_6H_5)_2CC\equiv CCH(C_6H_5)OH$†	23
$(C_6H_5)_2CO$	$(\equiv CMgBr)_2$	$HC\equiv C(C_6H_5)_2COH$	632
$(C_6H_5)_2CO$	C_2H_5MgBr	$C_2H_5(C_6H_5)_2COH$ (80%)	287,199, 215,389, 611
$(C_6H_5)_2CO$ (40 g.)	C_2H_5MgBr (23.9 g. C_2H_5Br)	$(C_6H_5)_2CHOH$ (30 g.)	388
$(C_6H_5)_2CO$	C_2H_5MgI	$(C_6H_5)_2CHOH$	388
$(C_6H_5)_2CO$	C_2H_5MgI	$(C_6H_5)_2C{=}CHCH_3$‡	350

*Addition of powdered ketone to Grignard reagent solution; removal of ether; "prolonged" heating at 100°.

†Isolated as the corresponding 3,4-dibromo-2,5-dihydrofurans.

‡Addition of powdered ketone to cooled Grignard reagent solution; five hours on water-bath.

TABLE VI-XVIII (Continued)

Ketonic Comp'd	RMgX	Product(s)	Ref.
$C_{13}H_{10}O$ (*cont.*)			
$(C_6H_5)_2CO$ (18.2 g.)	$H_2C{=}CHCH_2MgBr$ (100 ml. 1.32 *N*)	$H_2C{=}CHCH_2(C_6H_5)_2COH$ (72%); $(C_6H_5)_2CHOH$*	*351,28*
$(C_6H_5)_2CO$	$H_2C{=}CHCH_2Br$ + Mg	$H_2C{=}CHCH_2(C_6H_5)_2COH$	*279*
$(C_6H_5)_2CO$ (0.10 mole)	*n*-C_3H_7MgBr (0.12 mole C_3H_7Br)	$(C_6H_5)_2CHOH$ (50%)	*287*
$(C_6H_5)_2CO$	*n*-C_3H_7MgBr	*n*-$C_3H_7(C_6H_5)_2COH$ (?)†	*353*
$(C_6H_5)_2CO$	*i*-C_3H_7MgBr	$(C_6H_5)_2CHOH$ (22%)‡	*287*
$(C_6H_5)_2CO$ (in C_6H_6) (70 g.)	*i*-C_3H_7MgBr (28.7 g. C_3H_7Br)	Recovered ketone (nearly complete); *no* $(C_6H_5)_2CHOH$; *i*-$C_3H_7C_6H_5$ (14 g.)	*388*
$(C_6H_5)_2CO$	*i*-C_3H_7MgI	*i*-$C_3H_7(C_6H_5)_2COH$	*260*
$(C_6H_5)_2CO$	$H_2C{=}CHC{\equiv}CMgBr$	$H_2C{=}CHC{\equiv}C(C_6H_5)_2COH$	*40*
$(C_6H_5)_2CO$	2-Thienyl-MgBr	α-$C_4H_3S(C_6H_5)_2COH$	*41*
$(C_6H_5)_2CO$ (18 g.)	Pyrryl-MgBr (6.7 g. C_4H_5N)	α-$C_4H_4N(C_6H_5)_2COH$	*380*
$(C_6H_5)_2CO$ (18 g.)	Pyrryl-MgBr (13.4 g. C_4H_5N)	(α-$C_4H_4N)_2C(C_6H_5)_2$	*380*
$(C_6H_5)_2CO$	Butenyl-MgBr	$CH_3(H_2C{=}CH)CH(C_6H_5)_2COH$ (chiefly)§	*251*
$(C_6H_5)_2CO$	*n*-C_4H_9MgBr	$(C_6H_5)_2CHOH$ (17–30%); $[(C_6H_5)_2CH]_2O$ (5.6%)	*217*
$(C_6H_5)_2CO$ (0.10 mole)	*n*-C_4H_9MgI (0.12 mole C_4H_9I)	$(C_6H_5)_2CHOH$ (27%)‡	*287*
$(C_6H_5)_2CO$ (127.5 g.)	*i*-C_4H_9MgBr (170.2 g. C_4H_9Br)	$(C_6H_5)_2CHOH$ (80 g.); $[HO(C_6H_5)_2C{-}]_2$; $[(C_6H_5)_2CH]_2O$; $(C_6H_5)_2C{=}CH$-*i*-C_3H_7 (45 g.)	*354*
$(C_6H_5)_2CO$	*i*-C_4H_9MgBr	$(C_6H_5)_2CHOH$ (90%)	*355,215*
$(C_6H_5)_2CO$	*i*-C_4H_9MgBr	$(C_6H_5)_2CHOH$ (74.3%); $(CH_3)_2C{=}CH_2$ (74.4%)	*356*

*Probably attributable to atmospheric oxygen contamination of the Grignard reagent (see textual discussion of alkoxide reduction).

†The product reported by Klages and Heilmann *(353)* as the tertiary alcohol is said by Blicke and Powers *(287)* to be benzhydrol.

‡From a study of the reducing action of Grignard reagents in which the yields of reduction products only are reported.

§So adjudged because the product, upon thermal decomposition, yields butenes comprising approximately 77% *trans*-2-butene and 23% *cis*-2-butene.

TABLE VI-XVIII (Continued)

Ketonic Comp'd	RMgX	Product(s)	Ref.
$C_{13}H_{10}O$ (*cont.*)			
$(C_6H_5)_2CO$	*i*-C_4H_9MgI	$(C_6H_5)_2CHOH$ (74%)*	*287*
$(C_6H_5)_2CO$	*t*-C_4H_9MgBr	$(C_6H_5)_2CHOH$ (38%)	*102,357*
$(C_6H_5)_2CO$ (30 g.)	2-Pyridyl-MgBr	α-$C_5H_5N(C_6H_5)_2COH$ (4 g.)	*218*
$(C_6H_5)_2CO$	$(CH)_5MgBr$†	$(CH)_4CH(C_6H_5)_2COH$	*358*
$(C_6H_5)_2CO$	*t*-$C_5H_{11}MgBr$	$(C_6H_5)_2CHOH$ (38%)	*102,357*
$(C_6H_5)_2CO$	4-BrC_6H_4MgBr	4-$BrC_6H_4(C_6H_5)_2COH$	*359*
$(C_6H_5)_2CO$ (2.8 g.)	2-$BrMgOC_6H_4MgBr$ (4 g. C_2H_5MgBr + 5g. 2-$ClHgC_6H_4OH$)	2-$HOC_6H_4(C_6H_5)_2COH$ (25%, based on RHgCl)	383
$(C_6H_5)_2CO$	4-ClC_6H_4MgI	4-$ClC_6H_4(C_6H_5)_2COH$	*359*
$(C_6H_5)_2CO$ (91 g.)	C_6H_5MgBr (13.5 g. Mg)	$(C_6H_5)_3COH$ (*ca.* 90%)	*381,360*
$(C_6H_5)_2CO$ (45 g.)	$CH_3CH{=}CHCH(OMgBr)C{\equiv}CMgBr$ (24 g. C_6H_8O)	$CH_3CH{=}CHCH(OH)C{\equiv}C(C_6H_5)_2COH$ (43 g.)	*633,632*
$(C_6H_5)_2CO$ (5 g.)	*t*-$C_4H_9C{\equiv}CMgBr$ (3 g. *t*-$C_4H_9C{\equiv}CH$)	*t*-$C_4H_9C{\equiv}C(C_6H_5)_2COH$ (7 g.)	*310*
$(C_6H_5)_2CO$	$(CH_2)_5CHMgCl$	$(C_6H_5)_2CHOH$; C_6H_{10}	*58,59*
$(C_6H_5)_2CO$	$(CH_2)_5CHMgCl$	$(CH_2)_5CH(C_6H_5)_2COH$ (65%)	*619*
$(C_6H_5)_2CO$ (12 g.)	4-$ClC_6H_4CH_2MgCl$ (20 g. $C_7H_6Cl_2$)	4-$ClC_6H_4CH_2(C_6H_5)_2COH$ (*ca.* quant.)	*387*
$(C_6H_5)_2CO$ (60 g.)	$C_6H_5CH_2MgCl$ (60 g. C_7H_7Cl)	$C_6H_5CH_2(C_6H_5)_2COH$ (80–85 g.)	*361,199, 362,619*
$(C_6H_5)_2CO$ (18 g.)	2-$CH_3C_6H_4MgBr$ (25 g. C_7H_7Br)	2-$CH_3C_6H_4(C_6H_5)_2COH$ (8 g.)	*364,363, 365*
$(C_6H_5)_2CO$ (12 g.)	3-$CH_3C_6H_4MgBr$ (20 g. C_7H_7Br)	3-$CH_3C_6H_4(C_6H_5)_2COH$ (8 g.)	*364*
$(C_6H_5)_2CO$ (8 g.)	4-$CH_3C_6H_4MgBr$ (10 g. C_7H_7Br)	4-$CH_3C_6H_4(C_6H_5)_2COH$ (3.25 g.)	*364,365*
$(C_6H_5)_2CO$	2-$CH_3OC_6H_4MgBr$	2-$CH_3OC_6H_4(C_6H_5)_2COH$	*619*

*From a study of the reducing action of Grignard reagents in which the yields of reduction products only are reported.

†5-Cyclopentadienylmagnesium bromide.

TABLE VI-XVIII (Continued)

Ketonic Comp'd	RMgX	Product (s)	Ref.
$C_{13}H_{10}O$ (*cont.*)			
$(C_6H_5)_2CO$	$4\text{-}CH_3OC_6H_4MgBr$	$4\text{-}CH_3OC_6H_4(C_6H_5)_2COH$ (60%)	*365*
$(C_6H_5)_2CO$	$n\text{-}C_5H_{11}C{\equiv}CMgBr$	$n\text{-}C_5H_{11}C{\equiv}C(C_6H_5)_2COH$	*65*
$(C_6H_5)_2CO$	$(C_2H_5)_2N(CH_2)_3MgCl$	$(C_2H_5)_2N(CH_2)_3C(C_6H_5)_2OH$ (66%)	*366,390*
$(C_6H_5)_2CO$ (18 g.)	$(C_2H_5)_2N(CH_2)_3Cl$ (30 g.) + Mg (4.8 g.)	$(C_2H_5)_2N(CH_2)_3C(C_6H_5)_2OH$	*226*
$(C_6H_5)_2CO$	$C_6H_5C{\equiv}CMgBr$	$C_6H_5C{\equiv}C(C_6H_5)_2COH$ (79%)	*367,664 660,663, 36*
$(C_6H_5)_2CO$	$2\text{-}ClC_6H_4CH(CO_2MgCl)MgCl$*	$2\text{-}ClC_6H_4CH(CO_2H)C(C_6H_5)_2OH$	*149*
$(C_6H_5)_2CO$ (12.2 g.)	$3\text{-}ClC_6H_4CH(CO_2MgCl)MgCl$* (8.3 g. $3\text{-}ClC_6H_4CH_2CO_2H$)	$3\text{-}ClC_6H_4CH(CO_2H)C(C_6H_5)_2OH$ (13.2 g.)	*384*
$(C_6H_5)_2CO$	2-Benzothiazolylmethyl-MgBr	$2\text{-}C_7H_4NSCH_2(C_6H_5)_2COH$	*385*
$(C_6H_5)_2CO$	$C_6H_5CH(CO_2Na)MgX$*	$C_6H_5CH(CO_2H)C(C_6H_5)_2OH$ ("good yield")	*200*
$(C_6H_5)_2CO$	$C_6H_5CH{=}CHMgBr$	$C_6H_5CH{=}CH(C_6H_5)_2COH$ (?)† (14%)	*369; cf. 370*
$(C_6H_5)_2CO$	$C_6H_5(CH_2)_2MgBr$	$C_6H_5CH_2CH_2(C_6H_5)_2COH$	*619*
$(C_6H_5)_2CO$ (40 g.)	$2\text{-}C_2H_5C_6H_4MgBr$ (42 g. C_8H_9Br)	$2\text{-}C_2H_5C_6H_4(C_6H_5)_2COH$ (32 g.)	*382*
$(C_6H_5)_2CO$	$4\text{-}(CH_3)_2NC_6H_4MgBr$	$4\text{-}(CH_3)_2NC_6H_4(C_6H_5)_2COH$	*371*
$(C_6H_5)_2CO$	$CH_3(C_2H_5)_2CC{\equiv}CMgBr$	$CH_3(C_2H_5)_2CC{\equiv}C(C_6H_5)_2COH$ (71%)	*372*
$(C_6H_5)_2CO$	$(CH_2)_5N(CH_2)_3MgCl$	$(CH_2)_5N(CH_2)_3C(C_6H_5)_2OH$	*366,226*

*In the opinion of Schlenk, Hilleman, and Rodloff, *Ann.*, *487*, 135–54 (1931); this "Grignard reagent" should be formulated as an enolate.

†The product, purified by methanol crystallization by Meyer and Scuster *(369)*, and by them ascribed the carbinol constitution formulated above, is said by Straus and Eherenstein *(370)* to be the high-melting form of the methyl ether, $(C_6H_5)_2C{=}CHCH(OCH_3)C_6H_3$. The probable course of the rearrangement is discussed.

TABLE VI-XVIII (Continued)

Ketonic Comp'd	RMgX	Product (s)	Ref.
$C_{13}H_{10}O$ (*cont.*)			
$(C_6H_5)_2CO$	1-Indenyl-MgBr	α-$C_9H_7(C_6H_5)_2COH$ (82%)	69
$(C_6H_5)_2CO$	$4\text{-}CH_3C_6H_4C{\equiv}CMgBr$	$4\text{-}CH_3C_6H_4C{\equiv}C(C_6H_5)_2COH$ (62%)	65
$(C_6H_5)_2CO$ (5.0 g.)	3-Thianaphthenylmethyl-MgCl	3-Benzhydrilidenemethylthianaphthene (1.64 g., 19%)	659
$(C_6H_5)_2CO$ (75 g.)	4-*n*-$C_3H_7C_6H_4MgBr$ (100 g. $C_9H_{11}Br$)	4-*n*-$C_3H_7C_6H_4(C_6H_5)_2COH$ (yielding 24 g. chloride)	382
$(C_6H_5)_2CO$	$2\text{-}C_2H_5OCH_2C_6H_4MgBr$	$2\text{-}C_2H_5OCH_2C_6H_4(C_6H_5)_2COH$	363
$(C_6H_5)_2CO$	$1\text{-}C_{10}H_7MgBr$	$1\text{-}C_{10}H_7(C_6H_5)_2COH$	368,365
$(C_6H_5)_2CO$ (88 g.)	4-*i*-$C_4H_9C_6H_4MgBr$ (107 g. $C_{10}H_{13}Br$)	4-*i*-$C_4H_9C_6H_4(C_6H_5)_2COH$ (yielding 26 g. chloride)	382
$(C_6H_5)_2CO$ (85 g.)	4-*s*-$C_4H_9C_6H_4MgBr$ (107 g. $C_{10}H_{13}Br$)	4-*s*-$C_4H_9C_6H_4(C_6H_5)_2COH$ (yielding 22 g. chloride)	382
$(C_6H_5)_2CO$	α-Camphoryl-MgBr*	α-$C_{10}H_{15}O(C_6H_5)_2COH$ (70%)	75
$(C_6H_5)_2CO$ (47 g.)	3-*n*-$C_5H_{11}C_6H_4MgBr$ (66 g. $C_{11}H_{15}Br$)	3-*n*-$C_5H_{11}C_6H_4(C_6H_5)_2COH$ (yielding 13 g. chloride)	382
$(C_6H_5)_2CO$ (40 g.)	4-*t*-$C_5H_{11}C_6H_4MgBr$ (57 g. $C_{11}H_{15}Br$)	4-*t*-$C_5H_{11}C_6H_4(C_6H_5)_2COH$ (yielding 11 g. chloride)	382
$(C_6H_5)_2CO$	$(n\text{-}C_4H_9)_2N(CH_2)_3MgCl$	$(n\text{-}C_4H_9)_2N(CH_2)_3C(C_6H_5)_2OH$	366,226, 390
$(C_6H_5)_2CO$	$2\text{-}C_{10}H_7C{\equiv}CMgBr$	$2\text{-}C_{10}H_7C{\equiv}C(C_6H_5)_2COH$ (50%)	65
$(C_6H_5)_2CO$ (6.1 g.)	$1\text{-}C_{10}H_7CH(CO_2MgCl)MgCl$† (4.2 g. $1\text{-}C_{10}H_7CH_2CO_2H$)	$HO_2C(1\text{-}C_{10}H_7)CH(C_6H_5)_2COH$	384
$(C_6H_5)_2CO$	$4\text{-}C_6H_5C_6H_4MgBr$	$4\text{-}C_6H_5C_6H_4(C_6H_5)_2COH$	373

*Probably this "Grignard reagent" is an enolate.

†In the opinion of Schlenk, Hilleman, and Rodloff, *Ann.*, *487*, 135–54 (1931), this "Grignard reagent" should be formulated as an enolate.

TABLE VI-XVIII (Continued)

Ketonic Comp'd	RMgX	Product(s)	Ref.
$C_{13}H_{10}O$ (*cont.*)			
$(C_6H_5)_2CO$	$4\text{-}C_6H_5C_6H_4MgI$	$4\text{-}C_6H_5C_6H_4(C_6H_5)_2COH$*	*375*
$(C_6H_5)_2CO$	5-Acenaphthenyl-MgBr	$5\text{-}C_{12}H_9(C_6H_5)_2COH$	*374*
$(C_6H_5)_2CO$	9-Fluorenyl-MgBr	$9\text{-}C_{13}H_9(C_6H_5)_2COH$	*376*
$(C_6H_5)_2CO$ (2 g.)	9-Anthryl-MgBr (2.5 g. $C_{14}H_9Br$)	$9\text{-}C_{14}H_9(C_6H_5)_2COH$ (36%)	*386*
$(C_6H_5)_2CO$	9-Phenanthryl-MgBr	$9\text{-}C_{14}H_9(C_6H_5)_2COH$ (76%)	*377*
$(C_6H_5)_2CO$	$(C_6H_5)_2C{=}CHMgBr$	$(C_6H_5)_2C{=}CH(C_6H_5)_2COH$ (75%)	*378*
$(C_6H_5)_2CO$ (2 g.)	$4\text{-}C_6H_5C_6H_4CH{=}C(C_6H_5)MgBr$ (5 g. $C_{20}H_{15}Br$)	$4\text{-}C_6H_5C_6H_4CH{=}C(C_6H_5)C(C_6H_5)_2OH$ (1.75 g.)	*379*
$(C_6H_5)_2CO$ (5 g.)	$(C_6H_5)_2C{=}C(C_6H_5)MgBr$ (10 g. $C_{20}H_{15}Br$)	$(C_6H_5)_2C{=}C(C_6H_5)C(C_6H_5)_2OH$ (3.1 g.); tetraphenylindene (2.25 g.)	*379*
$C_{13}H_{10}OBrN$			
$C_6H_5COC_6H_3\text{-}2\text{-}NH_2\text{-}5\text{-}Br$ (5 g.)	CH_3MgI (12 g. CH_3I)	$CH_3(C_6H_5)(2\text{-}H_2N\text{-}5\text{-}BrC_6H_3)COH$	*391*
$C_{13}H_{10}O_2$			
$(\alpha\text{-}C_4H_{13}O)CH{=}CHCOC_6H_5$†	RmgX‡.	$(C_4H_3O)CHRCH_2COC_6H_5$	*624*
$C_{13}H_{10}O_2ClN$			
$4\text{-}HOC_6H_4COC_6H_3\text{-}2\text{-}NH_2\text{-}5\text{-}Cl$ (10 g.)	CH_3MgI (40 g. CH_3I)	$4\text{-}HOC_6H_4(2\text{-}H_2N\text{-}5\text{-}ClC_6H_3)C{=}CH_2$ (6.7 g.)	*391*
$C_{13}H_{10}O_3$			
$C_6H_5COC_6H_3\text{-}2,4\text{-}(OH)_2$	C_6H_5MgBr	$2,4\text{-}(HO)_2C_6H_3(C_6H_5)_2COH$	*392,394, 395*

*According to Schlenk and Weickel (*375*), the yield of carbinol obtained is dependent primarily upon the quality of the iodine-activated magnesium employed in preparation of the Grignard reagent.

†Furfurylideneacetophenone.

‡RMgX = CH_3MgI, C_2H_5MgBr, C_6H_5MgBr.

TABLE VI-XVIII (Continued)

Ketonic Comp'd	RMgX	Product(s)	Ref.
$C_{13}H_{10}O_3$ (*cont.*)			
2-$HOC_6H_4COC_6H_4$-4-OH	C_6H_5MgBr	C_6H_5(2-HOC_6H_4)(4-HOC_6H_4)COH	*394*
3-$HOC_6H_4COC_6H_4$-4-OH	C_6H_5MgBr	C_6H_5(3-HOC_6H_4)(4-HOC_6H_4)COH	*394*
(3-$HOC_6H_4)_2CO$	C_6H_5MgBr	C_6H_5(3-$HOC_6H_4)_2COH$	*394*
$C_{13}H_{11}ON$			
$C_6H_5COC_6H_4$-2-NH_2 (20 g.)	CH_3MgI (60 g. CH_3I)	$CH_3(C_6H_5)$(2-$H_2NC_6H_4$)COH (*ca.* quant.)	*397,396*
$C_6H_5COC_6H_4$-2-NH_2 (14 g.)	C_2H_5MgI	$C_2H_5(C_6H_5)$(2-$H_2NC_6H_4$)COH (15.6 g.)	*398*
$C_6H_5COC_6H_4$-4-NH_2 (2.00 g.)	C_2H_5MgBr (6.72 g. C_2H_5Br)	$C_2H_5(C_6H_5)$(4-$H_2NC_6H_4$)COH	*389*
$C_6H_5COC_6H_4$-4-NH_2 (2.0 g.)	*i*-C_3H_7MgBr (7.5 g. C_3H_7Br)	*i*-$C_3H_7(C_6H_5)$(4-$N_2NC_6H_4$)COH ("a little"); recovered ketone	*389*
$C_6H_5COC_6H_4$-4-NH_2 (2.0 g.)	*n*-C_4H_9MgBr (11.2 g. C_4H_9Br)	*n*-$C_4H_9(C_6H_5)$(4-$H_2NC_6H_4$)COH	*389*
$C_{13}H_{12}O$			
1-$CH_3COC_{10}H_6$-4-CH_3	CH_3MgI	1-[$HO(CH_3)_2C$]$C_{10}H_6$-4-CH_3	*399*
$C_{13}H_{12}O_2$			
CH_3COCH_2O-2-$C_{10}H_7$	2-$C_6H_5C_6H_4MgI$	CH_3(2-$C_{10}H_7OCH_2$)(2-$C_6H_5C_6H_4$)COH	*16*
$C_{13}H_{14}O_2$			
2-*p*-Toluylcyclopentanone	C_2H_5MgBr	2-(α-*p*-Tolylpropylidene)cyclopentanone; 1-ethyl-2-*p*-toluylcyclopentene	*400*
$C_{13}H_{15}OCl$			
$C_6H_5COCCl(CH_2)_5$	CH_3MgX	$CH_3COC(C_6H_5)(CH_2)_5$; *no* chlorohydrin isolable	*237*
$C_{13}H_{16}O$			
$CH_3COCH{=}CHC_6H_2$-2,4,6-$(CH_3)_3$	RMgX	$R(CH_3)$[2,4,6-$(CH_3)_3C_6H_2CH{=}CH$]COH; $CH_3COCH_2CHRC_6H_2$-2,4,6-$(CH_3)_3$	*401*

TABLE VI-XVIII (Continued)

Ketonic Comp'd	RMgX	Product(s)	Ref.
$C_{13}H_{16}O$ (*cont.*)			
$CH_3CH{=}CHCOC_6H_2$-2,4,6-$(CH_3)_3$ (6.15 g.)	2,4,6-$(CH_3)_3C_6H_2MgBr$ (14.60 g. $C_9H_{11}Br$)	2,4,6-$(CH_3)_3C_6H_2COCH_2CH(CH_3)C_6H_2$-2,4,6-$(CH_3)_3$ (7 g.)	393
t-$C_4H_9COCH{=}CHC_6H_5$ (30 g.)	C_2H_5MgBr	*t*-$C_4H_9COCH_2CH(C_2H_5)C_6H_5$ (34 g.)	*111*
t-$C_4H_9COCH{=}CHC_6H_5$ (30 g.)	C_6H_5MgBr	*t*-$C_4H_9COCH_2CH(C_6H_5)_2$ (41 g.)	*111*
$C_{13}H_{16}O_2$			
2-Methyl-2-benzoyl-3,5-epoxypentane	C_6H_5MgBr	1,1-Diphenyl-2,2-dimethyl-4,5-epoxy-1-pentanol	*665*
$C_{13}H_{16}O_3$			
$H_3CO_2C(CH_2)_2COC_6H_3$-3,4-$(CH_3)_2$	CH_3MgI	3,4-$(CH_3)_2C_6H_3C(CH_3){=}CHCH_2CO_2CH_3$ (62%)	*402*
$H_3CO_2CCH(CH_3)CH_2COC_6H_4$-4-$CH_3$ (11.0 g.)	CH_3MgI (15.0 g. CH_3I)	4-$CH_3C_6H_4C(CH_3){=}CHCH(CH_3)CO_2H$ (9.0–9.5 g., 90–95%)	*615*
$H_5C_2O_2C(CH_2)_2COC_6H_4$-4-$CH_3$ (11.0 g.)	C_2H_5MgBr (8.0 ml. C_2H_5Br)	4-$CH_3C_6H_4C(C_2H_5){=}CHCH_2CO_2H$ (75%)	*616*
$C_{13}H_{17}O_2Cl$			
$C_2H_5COC_6H$-2,4-$(CH_3)_2$-3-Cl-6-OC_2H_5	C_2H_5MgBr (+ CO_2)	2,4-$(CH_3)_2$-3-Cl-6-$C_2H_5OC_6HCOCH(CH_3)CO_2H$ (41%)	*315*
$C_{13}H_{18}O$			
i-$C_3H_7COC_6H_2$-2,4,6-$(CH_3)_3$	Butenyl-MgBr	*i*-$C_3H_7[CH_3(H_2C{=}CH)CH][$2,4,6-$(CH_3)_3C_6H_2]COH$ (chiefly)*	*251*
C_6H_5CO-*n*-C_6H_{13}	C_6H_5MgBr	*n*-$C_6H_{13}(C_6H_5)_2COH$	*353*
$CH_3(C_2H_5)_2CCOC_6H_5$	CH_3MgI	$CH_3(C_6H_5)[CH_3(C_2H_5)_2C]COH$	*234*

*So adjudged because thermal decomposition of the product yielded 6 ± 5% of 1-butene, 24 ± 5% of *trans*-2-butene, and 70 ± 5% of *cis*-2-butene, as evaluated by absorption spectrum measurements.

TABLE VI-XVIII (Continued)

Ketonic Comp'd	RMgX	Product(s)	Ref.
$C_{13}H_{18}O$ (*cont.*)			
$CH_3(C_2H_5)_2CCOC_6H_5$	C_6H_5MgBr	$CH_3(C_2H_5)_2C(C_6H_5)_2COH$* (75%)	234
$CH_3(C_2H_5)_2CCOC_6H_5$	$C_6H_5CH_2MgCl$	$C_6H_5[CH_3(C_2H_5)_2C](C_6H_5CH_2)COH$†	234
$C_{13}H_{18}O_2$			
$C_2H_5COCH(C_2H_5)C_6H_4$-4-OCH_3	CH_3MgI	$CH_3(C_2H_5)[C_2H_5(4\text{-}CH_3OC_6H_4)CH]COH$	173
$C_2H_5COCH(C_2H_5)C_6H_4$-4-OCH_3	$CH_3O(C_2H_5)CH(CH_2)_2MgCl$	$C_2H_5[CH_3O(C_2H_5)CH(CH_2)_2][C_2H_5(4\text{-}CH_3OC_6H_4)CH]COH$	408
$(C_2H_5)_2CHCOC_6H_4$-4-OCH_3	4-$CH_3OC_6H_4MgBr$	$(C_2H_5)_2CH(4\text{-}CH_3OC_6H_4)_2COH$	404
$C_{13}H_{18}O_4$			
Ethyl furoyldiethylacetate	C_2H_5MgBr	$C_4H_3O(C_2H_5)_2COH$	319
Ethyl furoyldiethylacetate	C_6H_5MgBr	$C_4H_3O(C_6H_5)_2COH$	319
$C_{13}H_{20}O$			
Pseudoionone‡	$(-CH_2CH_2Br)_2$ + Mg	Dehydrosqualene§	634
Pseudoionone‡ (28.8 g.)	$CH_3O(CH_2)_3Br$ (25 g.) + Mg (4.4 g.)	1-Methoxy-4,8,12-trimethyltrideca-3,5,7,11-tetraene (19.9 g., 53.5%)	409
Pseudoionone‡ (96.0 g., 0.5 mole)	$C_2H_5O(CH_2)_3Br$ (100.0 g., 0.6 mole) + Mg (15.2 g., 0.625 mole)	1-Ethoxy-4,8,12-trimethyltrideca-3,5,7,11-tetraene (52%)	409
Pseudoionone‡ (15.6 g.)	$C_6H_5O(CH_2)_3Br$ (22.9 g.) + Mg (2.7 g.)	1-Benzyloxy-4,8,12-trimethyltrideca-3,5,7,11-tetraene (12.8 g., 49%)	409

*This carbinol, upon distillation at ordinary pressure, decomposes into $(C_6H_5)_2CO + CH_3CH{=}C(C_2H_5)_2$.

†This carbinol, upon distillation at ordinary pressure, decomposes into $C_6H_5COCH_2C_6H_5 + CH_3CH{=}C(C_2H_5)_2$.

‡$CH_3COCH{=}CHCH{=}C(CH_3)CH_2CH_2CH{=}C(CH_3)_2$.

§$[(CH_3)_2C{=}CH(CH_2)_2C(CH_3){=}CHCH{=}CHC(CH_3){=}CHCH_2-]_2$.

TABLE VI-XVIII (Continued)

Ketonic Comp'd	RMgX	Product (s)	Ref.
$C_{13}H_{20}O$ (*cont.*)			
α-Ionone* (35.0 g.)	$H_2C{=}CHCH_2Br$ (36.0 g.) + Mg (7.3 g.)	2,4,4-Trimethyl-3-(3-hydroxy-3-methyl-1,5-hexadienyl)cyclohexene (28.0 g., crude)	*635*
α-Ionone* (3.5 g.)	$CH_3CH{=}C(CH_3)CH{=}CHCH_2Br$ (3.0 g.) + Mg (0.5 g.)	2,4,4-Trimethyl-3-(3-hydroxy-3,7-dimethyl-1,5,7-nonatrienyl)cyclohexene	*95*
β-Ionone†	CH_3MgI	Ionene‡; CH_4	*405*
β-Ionone†	$H_2C{=}CHCH_2Br$ + Mg	"Little or no carbinol"	*635*
β-Ionone† (0.125 mole)	$H_2C{=}CHC{\equiv}CMgBr$ (0.150 mole C_4H_4)	$R(CH_3)(H_2C{=}CHC{\equiv}C)COH$§ (59%)	*636,637*
β-Ionone† (40 g.)	$C_2H_5OC{\equiv}CMgBr$ (6.3 g. $C_2H_5OC{\equiv}CH$)	$R(CH_3)(H_2C_5OC{\equiv}C)COH$§ (8.5 g., 73%)	*233,487*
β-Ionone†	$({=}CHCH_2Br)_2$ + Mg	$[R(CH_3)(HO)CCH_2CH{=}]_2$§	*638*
β-Ionone†	$H_5C_2O_2CCH_2Br$ + Mg	Ionene‡; $R(CH_3)C{=}CHCO_2C_2H_5$§	*405*
β-Ionone†	i-C_4H_9MgBr	Ionene‡; i-C_4H_{10}	*405*
β-Ionone† (0.125 mole)	$H_2C{=}C(CH_3)C{\equiv}CMgBr$ (0.150 mole C_5H_6)	$R(CH_3)[H_2C{=}C(CH_3)C{\equiv}C]COH$§ (48%)	*636*
β-Ionone† (0.125 mole)	$CH_3CH{=}C(CH_3)C{\equiv}CMgBr$ (0.150 mole C_6H_8)	$R(CH_3)[CH_3CH{=}C(CH_3)C{\equiv}C]COH$§ (52%)	*636*
β-Ionone† (20.0 g.)	$(C_2H_5O)_2CHCH_2Br$ (21.6 g.) + Mg	$R(CH_3)C{=}CHCHO$§ (14.7 g., 64%)	*639*
$C_{13}H_{20}O_2$			
5-α-Furyl-8-methyl-2-nonanone	i-$C_5H_{11}MgI$	$CH_3(i\text{-}C_5H_{11})[\alpha\text{-}C_4H_3O(i\text{-}C_5H_{11})CHCH_2]COH$ (38%)	*405*

*2,4,4-Trimethyl-3-(β-acetovinyl)cyclohexene.
†1,3,3-Trimethyl-2-(β-acetovinyl)cyclohexene.
‡1,1,6-Trimethyltetralin.
§R = β-(2,6,6-trimethyl-1-cyclohexenyl)vinyl.

TABLE VI-XVIII (Continued)

Ketonic Comp'd	RMgX	Product (s)	Ref.
$C_{13}H_{22}O$			
Geranylacetone*	$(-CH_2CH_2Br)_2$ + Mg	Squalene†	406
$[(CH_2)_5CH]_2CO$	C_6H_5MgBr	$C_6H_5[(CH_2)_5CH]_2COH$	406
$[(CH_2)_5CH]_2CO$	$(CH_2)_5CHMgCl$	$[(CH_2)_5CH]_2CHOH$; cyclohexene	59
$C_{13}H_{24}O$			
$CH_3CO(CH_2)_9CH{=}CH_2$ (9.4 g.)	$CH_3(n\text{-}C_4H_9)CH(CH_2)_5MgBr$	$CH_3[H_2C{=}CH(CH_2)_9][CH_3(n\text{-}C_4H_9)CH(CH_2)_5]COH$ (8.6 g., crude)	136
$CH_3COCH(n\text{-}C_4H_9)CH{=}CH\text{-}t\text{-}C_4H_9$ (28 g.)	$n\text{-}C_8H_{17}MgBr$ (40 g. $C_8H_{17}Br$)	$CH_3(n\text{-}C_8H_{17})[n\text{-}C_4H_9(t\text{-}C_4H_9CH{=}CH)CH]COH$ (11 g.); $CH_3[n\text{-}C_4H_9(t\text{-}C_4H_9CH{=}CH)CH]CHOH$ (9 g.); $H_2C{=}CH\text{-}n\text{-}C_6H_{13}$ (6 g.)	388
Tetrahydroïonone‡	$H_2C{=}CHC{\equiv}CMgBr$	1-(2,2,6-Trimethylcyclohexyl)-3-methylhept-4-yn-6-en-3-ol (80%)	636
Tetrahydroïonone‡ (7.40 g.)	$C_2H_5OC{\equiv}CMgBr$ (2.64 g. C_4H_6BrO)	1-Ethoxy-3-methyl-5-(2,2,6-trimethylcyclohexyl)-1-pentyn-3-ol	410
Tetrahydroïonone‡	$H_2C{=}C(CH_3)C{\equiv}CMgBr$	1-(2,2,6-Trimethylcyclohexyl)-3,6-dimethylhept-4-yn-6-en-3-ol (80%)	636
Tetrahydroïonone‡	$CH_3CH{=}C(CH_3)C{\equiv}CMgBr$	1-(2,2,6-Trimethylcyclohexyl)-3,6-dimethyloct-4-yn-6-en-3-ol (80%)	636
$C_{13}H_{24}O_3$			
$CH_3CO(CH_2)_8CO_2C_2H_5$	$n\text{-}C_{12}H_{25}MgBr$	After hydrogen'n: $n\text{-}C_{12}H_{25}CH(CH_3)(CH_2)_8CO_2H$	407

*$CH_3CO(CH_2)_2CH{=}C(CH_3)(CH_2)_2CH{=}C(CH_3)_2$.
†$[(CH_3)_2C{=}CH(CH_2)_2C(CH_3){=}CH(CH_2)_2C(CH_3){=}CHCH_2-]_2$.
‡1,1,3-Trimethyl-2-(β-acetoethyl)cyclohexane.

TABLE VI-XVIII (Continued)

Ketonic Comp'd	RMgX	Product(s)	Ref.
$C_{13}H_{24}O_3$ *(cont.)*			
$CH_3CO(CH_2)_8CO_2C_2H_5$	n-$C_{14}H_{29}MgBr$	After hydrogen'n: n-$C_{14}H_{29}CH(CH_3)(CH_2)_8CO_2H$	*407*
$CH_3CO(CH_2)_8CO_2C_2H_5$	n-$C_{14}H_{29}MgBr$	$CH_3[H_5C_2O_2C(CH_2)_8](n\text{-}C_{14}H_{29})COH$	*269*
$CH_3CO(CH_2)_8CO_2C_2H_5$	n-$C_{16}H_{33}MgBr$	After hydrogen'n: n-$C_{16}H_{33}CH(CH_3)(CH_2)_8CO_2H$	*407*
$C_{13}H_{26}O$			
$CH_3CO(CH_2)_3CH(CH_3)$-i-C_6H_{13} (96 g.)	$C_2H_5O(CH_2)_3Br$ (100 g.) + Mg (15.2 g.)	$C_2H_5O(CH_2)_2CH{=}C(CH_3)(CH_2)_3CH(CH_3)$-$i$-$C_6H_{13}$ (52%)	*411*
$(n\text{-}C_6H_{13})_2CO$	n-C_4H_9MgBr	n-$C_4H_9(n\text{-}C_6H_{13})_2COH$	*298*
$(n\text{-}C_6H_{13})_2CO$	n-$C_8H_{17}MgBr$	n-$C_8H_{17}(n\text{-}C_6H_{13})_2COH$	*298*
$C_{14}H_8O_2Br_2$			
$(4\text{-}BrC_6H_4CO{-}{-})_2$	$(\equiv CMgBr)_2$	$[HO(4\text{-}BrC_6H_4)(4\text{-}BrC_6H_4CO)CC\equiv]_2$; $HO(4\text{-}BrC_6H_4)(4\text{-}BrC_6H_4CO)CC\equiv CH$	*85*
$C_{14}H_{10}O$			
$(C_6H_5)_2C{=}CO$	C_6H_5MgBr (1.5 equiv.)	$(C_6H_5)_2C{=}C(C_6H_5)OH$	*445,425*
$(C_6H_5)_2C{=}CO$ (9.7 g.)	$C_6H_5C\equiv CMgBr$ (5.5 ml. $C_6H_5C\equiv CH$)	$C_6H_5C\equiv CCOCH(C_6H_5)_2$ (12 g., crude)	*446*
$C_{14}H_{10}O_2$			
$(C_6H_5CO{-}{-})_2$	CH_3MgI	$[HO(CH_3)(C_6H_5)C{-}{-}]_2$, m.p. 118° (52%); isomer, m.p. 45°	*413,439*
$(C_6H_5CO{-}{-})_2$	$(\equiv MgBr)_2$ (1 equiv.)	$[HO(C_6H_5)(C_6H_5CO)CC\equiv]_2$	*412*
$(C_6H_5CO{-}{-})_2$	n-C_4H_9MgBr	n-$C_4H_9(C_6H_5)(C_6H_5CO)COH$ (0.5–5.6%); $C_6H_5CH(OH)COC_6H_5$ (0.5–13.0%)	*217*

TABLE VI-XVIII (Continued)

Ketonic Comp'd	RMgX	Product(s)	Ref.
$C_{14}H_{10}O_2$ (*cont.*)			
$(C_6H_5CO—)_2$	$H_2C{=}CHCH_2Br$ + Mg	$[HO(H_2C{=}CHCH_2)(C_6H_5)C—]_2$ (25–30%)	*86*
$(C_6H_5CO—)_2$	$4\text{-}BrC_6H_4MgBr$ (*ca.* 1 equiv.)	$4\text{-}BrC_6H_4(C_6H_5)(C_6H_5CO)COH$	*359*
$(C_6H_5CO—)_2$	$4\text{-}BrC_6H_4MgBr$ (*ca.* 2 equiv.)	$[HO(4\text{-}BrC_6H_4)(C_6H_5)C—]_2$	*359*
$(C_6H_5CO—)_2$ (7 g.)	$4\text{-}ClC_6H_4MgI$ (10 g. C_6H_4ClI)	$4\text{-}ClC_6H_4(C_6H_5)(C_6H_5CO)COH$	*359*
$(C_6H_5CO—)_2$ (5 g.)	$4\text{-}ClC_6H_4MgI$ (15 g. C_6H_4ClI)	$[HO(4\text{-}ClC_6H_4)(C_6H_5)C—]_2$	*359*
$(C_6H_5CO—)_2$ (50.g.)	$(CH_2)_5CHMgCl$ (120 g. $C_6H_{11}Cl$)	$\{HO(C_6H_5)[(CH_2)_5CH]C—\}_2$ (*ca.* quant.)	*440*
$(C_6H_5CO—)_2$	$C_6H_5CH_2MgCl$	$C_6H_5(C_6H_5CH_2)(C_6H_5CO)COH$; $C_6H_5CH(OH)COC_6H_5$; $(C_6H_5CH_2—)_2$	*362*
$(C_6H_5CO—)_2$	$C_6H_5CH_2MgCl$	$[HO(C_6H_5)(C_6H_5CH_2)C—]_2$	*435*
$(C_6H_5CO—)_2$ (21 g.)	$2\text{-}CH_3C_6H_4MgBr$ (20 g. C_7H_7Br)	$2\text{-}CH_3C_6H_4COC(C_6H_5)_2OH$ (?) (8 g.)	*414*
$(C_6H_5CO—)_2$ (21 g.)	$3\text{-}CH_3C_6H_4MgBr$ (25 g. C_7H_7Br)	$C_6H_5(C_6H_5CO)(3\text{-}CH_3C_6H_4)COH$ (4 g.); $C_6H_5CH(OH)COC_6H_5$; recovered benzil	*414*
$(C_6H_5CO—)_2$	$4\text{-}CH_3C_6H_4MgBr$	Product yielding, on HI-P red'n, $C_6H_5(4\text{-}CH_3C_6H_4)CHCOC_6H_5$*	*414*
$(C_6H_5CO—)_2$	$4\text{-}CH_3C_6H_4MgBr$	Two isomeric pinacolins†	*414*
$(C_6H_5CO—)_2$	$4\text{-}C_2H_5OC_6H_4MgBr$	$[HO(C_6H_5)(4\text{-}C_2H_5OC_6H_4)C—]_2$ (41%)	*415*
$(C_6H_5CO—)_2$ (10.5 g.)	$2\text{-}(p\text{-}ClC_6H_4)C_6H_4MgI$ (18.9 g. $C_{12}H_8ClI$)	$C_6H_5(C_6H_5CO)(2\text{-}p\text{-}ClC_6H_4C_6H_4)COH$ (6.6 g., 33%)	*421*
$(C_6H_5CO—)_2$ (10.5 g.)	$2\text{-}C_6H_5C_6H_4MgI$ (16.8 g. $C_{12}H_9I$)	$C_6H_5(C_6H_5CO)(2\text{-}C_6H_5C_6H_4)COH$ (9.04 g., 50%)	*421*
α-Furfurylidene-*p*-methylacetophenone (45 g.)	CH_3MgI (0.5 mole CH_3I)	$CH_3(\alpha\text{-}C_4H_3O)CHCH_2COC_6H_4\text{-}4\text{-}CH_3$ (50%)	*346*
α-Furfurylidene-*p*-methylacetophenone (45 g.)	C_2H_5MgBr (60 g. C_2H_5Br)	$C_2H_5(\alpha\text{-}C_4H_3O)CHCH_2COC_6H_4\text{-}4\text{-}CH_3$ (50 g.)	*346*
α-Furfurylidene-*p*-methylacetophenone (45 g.)	$i\text{-}C_3H_7MgBr$ (0.5 mole C_3H_7Br)	$i\text{-}C_3H_7(\alpha\text{-}C_4H_3O)CHCH_2COC_6H_4\text{-}4\text{-}CH_3$ (80%).	*346*

*Addition of Grignard reagent solution to ether-benzil solution; one hour reflux.

†Addition of ether-benzil solution to Grignard reagent solution; one hour reflux.

TABLE VI-XVIII (Continued)

Ketonic Comp'd	RMgX	Product(s)	Ref.
$C_{14}H_{10}O_2$ (*cont.*)			
α-Furfurylidene-*p*-methylacetophenone (45 g.)	*i*-C_4H_9MgBr (0.5 mole C_4H_9Br)	α-C_4H_3O(*i*-C_4H_9)$CHCH_2COC_6H_4$-4-CH_3 (70%)	*346*
α-Furfurylidene-*p*-methylacetophenone (45 g.)	C_6H_5MgBr (80 g. C_6H_5Br)	α-$C_4H_3O(C_6H_5)CHCH_2COC_6H_4$-4-$CH_3$ (80%)	*346*
$C_{14}H_{10}O_3$			
$C_6H_5COC_6H_4$-2-CO_2H	CH_3MgI	3-Methyl-3-phenylphthalide	*416*
$C_6H_5COC_6H_4$-2-CO_2H	C_6H_5MgBr	3,3-Diphenylphthalide	*417,416*
$C_{14}H_{11}OCl$			
$C_6H_5COCHClC_6H_5$ (20 g.)	C_6H_5MgBr (34 g. C_6H_5Br)	$(C_6H_5)_2CHC(C_6H_5)_2OH$ (3.5 g.); $C_6H_5COCH(C_6H_5)_2$ (2.0 g.)*	*426*
$C_6H_5COCHClC_6H_5$	C_6H_5MgBr	$(C_6H_5)_2CHC(C_6H_5)_2OH$ (< 3.5 g.); $C_6H_5COCH(C_6H_5)_2$ (< 2.0 g.)†	*426*
$C_6H_5COCHClC_6H_5$	2-$CH_3C_6H_4MgBr$	No isolable product‡	*426*
$C_6H_5COCHClC_6H_5$ (25 g.)	2-$CH_3C_6H_4MgBr$ (40 g. C_7H_7Br)	$(C_6H_5CO—)_2$; C_6H_5(2-$CH_3C_6H_4$)$CHCOC_6H_5$; $C_{28}H_{22}O_3$, m. 185° §	*426*
$C_6H_5COCHClC_6H_5$ (20 g.)	3-$CH_3C_6H_4MgBr$ (30 g. C_7H_7Br)	C_6H_5(3-$CH_3C_6H_4$)$CHCOC_6H_5$ (2 g.); $C_{28}H_{22}O_3$, m. 185°	*426*
4-$ClC_6H_4COC_6H_4$-4-CH_3	4-$CH_3C_6H_4MgBr$	4-ClC_6H_4(4-$CH_3C_6H_4$)$_2COH$ (62%)	*431*
$C_{14}H_{11}O_2N$			
$C_6H_5COC({=}NOH)C_6H_5$ (22.5 g.)	CH_3MgI (57 g. CH_3I)	$HO(CH_3)(C_6H_5)CC({=}NOH)C_6H_5$	*207*
$C_6H_5COC({=}NOH)C_6H_5$ (22.5 g.)	C_6H_5MgBr (48 g. C_6H_5Br)	$HO(C_6H_5)_2CC({=}NOH)C_6H_5$ (65%)	*207*

*Addition of ether-ketone solution to Grignard reagent solution; two hours reflux.
†Addition of Grignard reagent solution to ether-ketone solution.
‡Usual order of addition.
§Addition of Grignard reagent solution to ether-ketone solution; seven hours reflux.

TABLE VI-XVIII (Continued)

Ketonic Comp'd	RMgX	Product(s)	Ref.
$C_{14}H_{11}O_2N$ (*cont.*)			
$C_6H_5COC({=}NOH)C_6H_5$ (22.6 g.)	1-$C_{10}H_7MgBr$ (83 g. $C_{10}H_7Br$)	$HO(C_6H_5)(1\text{-}C_{10}H_7)CC({=}NOH)C_6H_5$ (10–15 g.)	*207*
$C_6H_5COCONHC_6H_5$ (0.05 mole)	C_6H_5MgBr (*ca.* 0.15 mole)	$HO(C_6H_5)_2CCONHC_6H_5$ (88%)	*427*
$C_{14}H_{21}O$			
$CH_3COC_6H_4$-4-C_6H_5	*i*-C_3H_7MgBr	$CH_3(i\text{-}C_3H_7)(4\text{-}C_6H_5C_6H_4)COH$	*418*
$C_6H_5COCH_2C_6H_5$ (18 g.)	CH_3MgI (30 g. CH_3I)	$CH_3(C_6H_5)C{=}CHC_6H_5$	*350*
$C_6H_5COCH_2C_6H_5$	CH_3MgI	$CH_3(C_6H_5)(C_6H_5CH_2)COH$	*353*
$C_6H_5COCH_2C_6H_5$	C_2H_5MgI	$C_2H_5(C_6H_5)(C_6H_5CH_2)COH$	*353*
$C_6H_5COCH_2C_6H_5$ (0.10 mole)	*n*-C_3H_7MgBr (0.12 g. C_3H_7Br)	$C_6H_5(C_6H_5CH_2)CHOH$ (9%)*	*287*
$C_6H_5COCH_2C_6H_5$	*n*-C_4H_9MgBr	$(C_6H_5CH{=})_2$ (2.5–7.4%); reduction; *no* addition; pinacol (traces in some exp'ts.)	*217*
$C_6H_5COCH_2C_6H_5$	C_6H_5MgBr	$C_6H_5CH_2(C_6H_5)_2COH$ ("good yield")	*353,225, 449,619*
$C_6H_5COCH_2C_6H_5$	$(CH_2)_2CHMgBr$ (2 equiv.)	$C_6H_5[(CH_2)_5CH](C_6H_5CH_2)COH$	*441*
$C_6H_3COCH_2C_6H_5$	3-$CH_3C_6H_4MgBr$	$C_6H_5(C_6H_5CH_2)(3\text{-}CH_3C_6H_4)COH$	*441*
$C_6H_5COCH_2C_6H_5$	$(C_2H_5)_2N(CH_2)_3Cl$ + Mg	$(C_2H_5)_2N(CH_2)_3(C_6H_5)(C_6H_5CH_2)COH$	*226*
$C_6H_5COCH_2C_6H_5$ (14.8 g.)	$C_6H_5CH(CO_2MgCl)MgCl$† (9.65 g. $C_6H_5CH_2CO_2H$)	$C_6H_5(C_6H_5CH_2)[HO_2C(C_6H_5)CH]COH$ (14.2 g.)	*442*
$C_6H_5COC_6H_4$-4-CH_3	$H_2C{=}CHCH_2Br$ + Mg	$H_2C{=}CHCH_2(C_6H_5)(4\text{-}CH_3C_6H_4)COH$ (90%, crude)	*419*
$C_6H_5COC_6H_4$-4-CH_3	$C_6H_5CH_2MgCl$	$C_6H_5(C_6H_5CH_2)(4\text{-}CH_3C_6H_4)COH$	*345*
$C_6H_5COC_6H_4$-4-CH_3	$C_6H_5C{\equiv}CMgBr$	$C_6H_5(4\text{-}CH_3C_6H_4)(C_6H_5C{\equiv}C)COH$ (60%)	*344*

*From a study of the reducing properties of Grignard reagents in which yields of reduction products only are reported.

†In the opinion of Schlenk, Hilleman, and Rodloff, *Ann.*, *487*, 135–54 (1931), this "Grignard reagent" should be formulated as an enolate.

TABLE VI-XVIII (Continued)

Ketonic Comp'd	RMgX	Product(s)	Ref.
$C_{14}H_{12}O$ (*cont.*)			
$C_6H_5COC_6H_4$-4-CH_3 (39 g.)	4-$C_2H_5C_6H_4MgBr$ (40 g. C_8H_9Br)	$C_6H_5(4\text{-}CH_3C_6H_4)(4\text{-}C_2H_5C_6H_4)COH$ (yielding 8 g. chloride)	382
$C_6H_5COC_6H_4$-4-CH_3 (60 g.)	4-*t*-$C_4H_9C_6H_4MgBr$ (71 g. $C_{10}H_9Br$)	$C_6H_5(4\text{-}CH_3C_6H_4)(4\text{-}t\text{-}C_4H_9C_6H_4)COH$ (yielding 17 g. chloride)	382
$C_{14}H_{12}O_2$			
$C_6H_5COCH(OH)C_6H_5$	$CH_3MgCl + MgCl_2$	$HO(CH_3)(C_6H_5)CCH(OH)C_6H_5$ (65%)*	420
$C_6H_5COCH(OH)C_6H_5$	$CH_3MgI + (CH_3)_2Mg$	$HO(CH_3)(C_6H_5)CCH(OH)C_6H_5$ (94%)†	420
$C_6H_5COCH(OH)C_6H_5$	CH_3MgI	$HO(CH_3)(C_6H_5)CCH(OH)C_6H_5$	429
DL-$C_6H_5COCH(OH)C_6H_5$ (12 g.)	CH_3MgI (30.3 g. CH_3I)	DL-$HO(CH_3)(C_6H_5)CCH(OH)C_6H_5$ (11.5 g.)	428
(−)-$C_6H_5COCH(OH)C_6H_5$	CH_3MgI	(+)-$HO(CH_3)(C_6H_5)CCH(OH)C_6H_5$	428
$C_6H_5COCH(OH)C_6H_5$ (10 g.)	($\equiv CMgBr$) (24 g. Mg)	$HO(HC\equiv C)(C_6H_5)CCH(OH)C_6H_5$ (80%)	447
$C_6H_5COCH(OH)C_6H_5$	C_2H_5MgBr	$HO(C_2H_5)(C_6H_5)CCH(OH)C_6H_5$	429
$C_6H_5COCH(OH)C_6H_5$ (12 g.)	C_2H_5MgI	$HO(C_2H_5)(C_6H_5)CCH(OH)C_6H_5$ (13 g.)	433
(−)-$C_6H_5COCH(OH)C_6H_5$ (4.0 g.)	C_2H_5MgI (11.8 g. C_2H_5I)	(+)-$HO(C_2H_5)(C_6H_5)CCH(OH)C_2H_5$ (4.3 g., crude)	428
(−)-$C_6H_5COCH(OH)C_6H_5$	C_6H_5MgBr	(+)-$HO(C_6H_5)_2CCH(OH)C_6H_5$	428
$C_6H_5COCH(OH)C_6H_5$ (106 g.)	$C_6H_5CH_2MgCl$ (189 g. C_7H_7Cl)	$HO(C_6H_5)(C_6H_5CH_2)CCH(OH)C_6H_5$ (142 g., 93%)	443
DL-$C_6H_5COCH(OH)C_6H_5$ (10.0 g.)	2-$CH_3C_6H_4MgBr$ (25.0 g. C_7H_7Br)	α-DL-$HO(C_6H_5)(2\text{-}CH_3C_6H_4)CCH(OH)C_6H_5$ (9.8 g.)	434
D(−)-$C_6H_5COCH(OH)C_6H_5$ (9.0 g.)	2-$CH_3C_6H_4MgBr$ (32.0 g. C_7H_7Br)	α-D(+)-$HO(C_6H_5)(2\text{-}CH_3C_6H_4)CCH(OH)C_6H_5$ (4.2 g.); DL-$C_6H_5COCH(OH)C_6H_5$ (1.4 g.)	434
DL-$C_6H_5COCH(OH)C_6H_5$ (10.0 g.)	3-$CH_3C_6H_4MgBr$ (40.0 g. C_7H_7Br)	α-DL-$HO(C_6H_5)(3\text{-}CH_3C_6H_4)CCH(OH)C_6H_5$ (10.1 g.)	434

*Reaction in dioxane suspension.
†Reaction in isoamyl ether solution.

TABLE VI-XVIII (Continued)

Ketonic Comp'd	RMgX	Product(s)	Ref.
$C_{14}H_{12}O_2$ (*cont.*)			
D(−)-$C_6H_5COCH(OH)C_6H_5$ (4.6 g.)	3-$CH_3C_6H_4MgBr$ (17.0 g. C_7H_7Br)	α-D(+)-$HO(C_6H_5)$(3-$CH_3C_6H_4$)$CCH(OH)C_6H_5$ (4.0 g.)	*434*
D(−)-$C_6H_5COCH(OH)C_6H_5$ (4.2 g.)	4-$CH_3C_6H_4MgBr$ (15.0 g. C_7H_7Br)	α-D(+)-$HO(C_6H_5)$(4-$CH_3C_6H_4$)$CCH(OH)C_6H_5$	*434*
$C_6H_5COCH(OH)C_6H_5$	$C_6H_5CH(CO_2Na)MgCl$*	α,β,γ-Triphenyl-γ-hydroxybutyric acid γ-lactone ("good yield")	*149*
$C_6H_5COCH(OH)C_6H_5$	2-$C_6H_5C_6H_4MgI$ (2^+ equiv.)	$HO(C_6H_5)$(2-$C_6H_5C_6H_4$)$CCH(OH)C_6H_5$ (yielding 29% phenanthrene deriv. on cyclohehydr'n)	*421*
$C_6H_5COC_6H_4$-2-OCH_3	CH_3MgI	$CH_3(C_6H_5)$(2-$CH_3OC_6H_4$)COH	*432*
$C_6H_5COC_6H_4$-2-OCH_3	2-$C_2H_5OCH_2C_6H_4MgBr$	C_6H_5(2-$CH_3OC_6H_4$)(2-$C_2H_5OCH_2C_6H_4$)COH	*363*
$C_6H_5COC_6H_4$-3-OCH_3	CH_3MgI	$CH_3(C_6H_5)$(3-$CH_3OC_6H_4$)COH	*432*
$C_6H_5COC_6H_4$-3-OCH_3	2-$C_2H_5OCH_2C_6H_4MgBr$	C_6H_5(3-$CH_3OC_6H_4$)(2-$C_2H_5OCH_2C_6H_4$)COH	*363*
$C_6H_5COC_6H_4$-4-OCH_3	C_6H_5MgBr	4-$CH_3OC_6H_4(C_6H_5)_2COH$	*395*
$C_6H_5COC_6H_4$-4-OCH_3	$C_6H_5CH_2MgCl$	$C_6H_5(C_6H_5CH_2)$(4-$CH_3OC_6H_4$)COH	*345*
$C_6H_5COC_6H_4$-4-OCH_3	2-$CH_3OC_6H_4MgI$	C_6H_5(2-$CH_3OC_6H_4$)(4-$CH_3OC_6H_4$)COH	*395*
$C_6H_5COC_6H_4$-4-OCH_3	4-$CH_3OC_6H_4MgI$	C_6H_5(4-$CH_3OC_6H_4)_2COH$	*395*
$C_6H_5COC_6H_4$-4-OCH_3	2-$C_2H_5OCH_2C_6H_4MgBr$	C_6H_5(4-$CH_3OC_6H_4$)(2-$C_2H_5OCH_2C_6H_4$)COH	*363*
$C_6H_5COC_6H_4$-4-OCH_3	4-$C_6H_5C_6H_4MgBr$	C_6H_5(4-$CH_3OC_6H_4$)(4-$C_6H_5C_6H_4$)COH	*373*
$C_{14}H_{12}O_2ClN$			
2-H_2N-5-ClC_6H_3CO-C_6H_3-2-OH-5-CH_3 (12 g.)	CH_3MgI (45 g. CH_3I)	2-H_2N-5-ClC_6H_3(2-HO-5-$CH_3C_6H_3$)$C{=}CH_2$ (*ca.* 50%)	*391*
$C_{14}H_{12}O_3$			
α-Furfurylidene-*p*-methoxyacetophenone (25 g.)	C_2H_5MgBr (27 g. C_2H_5Br)	C_2H_5(α-C_4H_3O)$CHCH_2COC_6H_4$-4-OCH_3 (20 g.)	*347*

*In the opinion of Schlenk, Hilleman, and Rodloff, *Ann.*, *487*, 135–54 (1931), this "Grignard reagent" should be formulated as an enolate.

TABLE VI-XVIII (Continued)

Ketonic Comp'd	RMgX	Product(s)	Ref.
$C_{14}H_{12}O_3$ *(cont.)*			
α-Furfurylidene-*p*-methoxyacetophenone (25 g.)	*n*-C_3H_7MgBr (31 g. C_3H_7MgBr)	*n*-$C_3H_7(\alpha\text{-}C_4H_3O)CHCH_2COC_6H_4\text{-}4\text{-}OCH_3$ (67%)	347
$C_{14}H_{12}O_4$			
2,4-$(HO)_2C_6H_3COC_6H_4\text{-}4\text{-}OCH_3$	C_6H_5MgBr	$C_6H_5[2,4\text{-}(HO)_2C_6H_3)(4\text{-}CH_3OC_6H_4)COH$	392
$C_{14}H_{13}ON$			
2-$H_2NC_6H_4COC_6H_4\text{-}4\text{-}CH_3$ (21 g.)	CH_3MgI (60 g. CH_3I)	$CH_3(2\text{-}H_2NC_6H_4)(4\text{-}CH_3C_6H_4)COH$	397
$C_{14}H_{13}O_2N$			
2-$H_2NC_6H_4COC_6H_4\text{-}4\text{-}OCH_3$ (25 g.)	C_2H_5MgI (110 g. C_2H_5I)	$C_2H_5(2\text{-}H_2NC_6H_4)(4\text{-}CH_3OC_6H_4)COH$	398
2-$H_2NC_6H_4COC_6H_4\text{-}4\text{-}CH_3$ (15 g.)	$C_6H_5CH_2MgCl$ (44 ml. C_7H_7Cl)	2-$H_2NC_6H_5(C_6H_5CH_2)(4\text{-}CH_3OC_6H_4)COH$ (18.3 g.)	398
$C_{14}H_{14}O$			
1-$CH_3COC_{10}H_5\text{-}3,4\text{-}(CH_3)_2$ (18 g.)	CH_3MgI	1-$[HO(CH_3)_2C]C_{10}H_5\text{-}3,4\text{-}(CH_3)_2$ (yielding 14 g., 79% olefin)	334
1-$CH_3COC_{10}H_5\text{-}3,4\text{-}(CH_3)_2$	C_2H_5MgBr	1-$[HO(CH_3)(C_2H_5)C]C_{10}H_5\text{-}3,4\text{-}(CH_3)_2$ (yielding 80% olefin)	334
$C_{14}H_{14}OClN$			
(−)-$C_6H_5COCH(NH_2{\cdot}HCl)C_6H_5$ (4.5 g.)	CH_3MgI (15.5 g. CH_3I)	(+)-$HO(CH_3)(C_6H_5)CCH(NH_2)C_6H_5$ (2.5 g.)	422
$C_6H_5COCH(NH_2{\cdot}HCl)C_6H_5$ (30 g.)	4-$CH_3C_6H_4MgBr$ (145 g. C_7H_7Br)	$HO(C_6H_4)(4\text{-}CH_3C_6H_4)CCH(NH_2)C_6H_5$ (27 g.)	238
DL-$C_6H_5COCH(NH_2{\cdot}HCl)C_6H_5$ (20 g.)	4-$CH_3OC_6H_4MgBr$ (76 g. C_7H_7BrO)	DL-$HO(C_6H_5)(4\text{-}CH_3OC_6H_4)CCH(NH_2)C_6H_5$ (17 g.)	422
(+)-$C_6H_5COCH(NH_2{\cdot}HCl)C_6H_5$ (4 g.)	4-$CH_3OC_6H_4MgBr$ (15 g. C_7H_7BrO)	(−)-$HO(C_6H_5)(4\text{-}CH_3OC_6H_4)CCH(NH)_2C_6H_5$ (*ca.* 1.3 g.)	422
$C_6H_5COCH(NH_2{\cdot}HCl)C_6H_5$	1-$C_{10}H_7MgBr$	$HO(C_6H_5)(1\text{-}C_{10}H_7)CCH(NH_2)C_6H_5$	444

TABLE VI-XVIII (Continued)

Ketonic Comp'd	RMgX	Product (s)	Ref.
$C_{14}H_{14}OClN$ (*cont.*)			
(+)-$C_6H_5COCH(NH_2{\cdot}HCl)C_6H_5$ (5 g.)	1-$C_{10}H_7MgBr$ (25 g. $C_{10}H_7Br$)	(−)-$HO(C_6H_5)(1\text{-}C_{10}H_7)CCH(NH_2)C_6H_5$	*422*
$C_{14}H_{14}OS$			
2-(α-Phenylbutyryl)thiophene	C_6H_5MgBr	$C_2H_5(C_6H_5)C{=}C(\alpha\text{-}C_4H_3S)C_6H_5$	*301*
2-(α-Phenylbutyryl)thiophene	$C_6H_5CH_2MgBr$	$C_2H_5(C_6H_5)C{=}C(\alpha\text{-}C_4H_3S)CH_2C_6H_5$	*301*
$C_{14}H_{14}O_2$			
$(4\text{-}CH_3C_6H_4CO{-})_2$ (0.1 mole)	CH_3MgI (0.3 mole)	$[HO(CH_3)(4\text{-}CH_3C_6H_4)C{-}]_2$, m.p. 136–137° and m.p. 134.5–135.0°; $HO(CH_3)(4\text{-}CH_3C_6H_4)CCOC_6H_4\text{-}4\text{-}CH_3$	*88*
$C_{14}H_{16}O_2$			
2-*p*-Xyloylcyclopentanone	C_2H_5MgBr	1-Ethyl-2-*p*-xyloylcyclopentene	*400*
$C_{14}H_{18}O$			
$CH_3COC_6H_4\text{-}4\text{-}CH(CH_2)_5$	C_2H_5MgBr	$CH_3[4\text{-}(CH_2)_5CHC_6H_4]C{=}CHCH_3$	*423*
$CH_3COC_6H_4\text{-}4\text{-}CH(CH_2)_5$	$n\text{-}C_3H_7MgBr$	$CH_3[4\text{-}(CH_2)_5CHC_6H_4]C{=}CHC_2H_5$	*423*
$CH_3COC_6H_4\text{-}4\text{-}CH(CH_2)_5$	$n\text{-}C_4H_9MgBr$	$CH_3[4\text{-}(CH_2)_5CHC_6H_4]C{=}CH\text{-}n\text{-}C_3H_7$	*423*
$CH_3COC_6H_4\text{-}4\text{-}CH(CH_2)_5$	C_6H_5MgBr	$C_6H_5[4\text{-}(CH_2)_5CHC_6H_4]C{=}CH_2$	*423*
$C_{14}H_{18}O_3$			
$C_6H_5COC(CH_3)_2CH_2CO_2C_2H_5$	C_6H_5MgBr	$C_{18}H_{38}O_2$, m. 146–147°; β,β-dimethyl-γ,γ-diphenyl-γ-butyrolactone (?)	*665*
$C_{14}H_{18}O_4$			
$4\text{-}CH_3OC_6H_4COCH_2CH(CH_3)CO_2C_2H_5$ (25 g.)	CH_3MgI (7.5 ml. CH_3I)	$HO(CH_3)(4\text{-}CH_3OC_6H_4)CCH_2CH(CH_3)CO_2C_2H_5$ (15 g.); corresponding lactone (5 g.)	*436*

TABLE VI-XVIII (Continued)

Ketonic Comp'd	RMgX	Product(s)	Ref.
$C_{14}H_{20}O$			
$CH_3CO(CH_2)_2CH(CH_3)C_6H_3$-2,4-$(CH_3)_2$	CH_3MgI	$HO(CH_3)_2C(CH_2)_2CH(CH_3)C_6H_3$-2,4-$(CH_3)_2$ (87%)	*448*
$CH_3CO(CH_2)_2CH(CH_3)C_6H_3$-2,5-$(CH_3)_2$	CH_3MgI	$HO(CH_3)_2C(CH_2)_2CH(CH_3)C_6H_3$-2,5-$(CH_3)_2$ (85%)	*448*
t-$C_4H_9COC_6H_2$-2,4,6-$(CH_3)_3$ (21 g.)	CH_3MgI	No isolable product; recovered ketone (17 g.)	*424*
$C_6H_5COC(C_2H_5)_3$	CH_3MgI	$CH_3(C_6H_5)[(C_2H_5)_3C]COH$ (85%)	*234*
$C_6H_5COC(C_2H_5)_3$	C_6H_5MgBr	$(C_2H_5)_3C(C_6H_5)_2COH$*	*234*
$C_{15}H_{10}O$			
$C_6H_5COC{\equiv}CC_6H_5$ (0.5 g.)	*t*-C_4H_9MgCl (2.0 g. C_4H_9Cl)	*t*-$C_4H_9(C_6H_5)(C_6H_5C{\equiv}C)COH$ ("poor yield")	*310*
$C_6H_5COC{\equiv}CC_6H_5$ (13.8 g.)	C_6H_5MgBr (17.5 g. C_6H_5Br)	$C_6H_5C{\equiv}C(C_6H_5)_2COH$ (15.4 g., 81%)	*663,111*
$C_6H_5COC{\equiv}CC_6H_5$ (2.0 g.)	1-$C_{10}H_7MgBr$ (2.0 g. $C_{10}H_7Br$)	$C_6H_5(C_6H_5C{\equiv}C)(1\text{-}C_{10}H_7)COH$ (2-5 g.)	*65*
$C_6H_5COC{\equiv}CC_6H_5$	$C_6H_5C{\equiv}CMgBr$	$C_6H_5(C_6H_5C{\equiv}C)_2COH$ (43%)	*367*
$C_{15}H_{10}OS$			
3-Benzoylthianaphthene (3.0 g.)	$C_6H_5CH_2MgCl$ (3.5 g. C_7H_7Cl)	1,2-Diphenyl-1-(3-thianaphthenyl)ethene (90%)	*485*
$C_{15}H_{10}O_2$			
2-Benzoylbenzofuran (8.12 g.)	C_6H_5MgBr (0.05 mole)	α-(2-Benzofuryl)benzhydrol (8.9 g.)	*451*
Benzylideneacetophenone oxide (35 g.)	C_2H_5MgBr (5 equiv.)	$C_6H_5(C_2H_5)_2COH$ (17 g., 66%); gum	*430*
Benzylideneacetophenone oxide	C_6H_5MgBr (5 equiv.)	$(C_6H_5)_3COH$ (*ca.* 70%); gum	*430*
Benzylideneacetophenone oxide (34 g.)	C_6H_5MgBr (47 g. C_6H_5Br)	1,1,3-Triphenyl-2,3-epoxy-1-propanol (22 g.) recovered ketone; unidentified products	*430*

*Distillation of product at ordinary pressure yields $(C_6H_5)_2CO + C_7H_{14}$.

TABLE VI-XVIII (Continued)

Ketonic Comp'd	RMgX	Product(s)	Ref.
$C_{15}H_{10}O_2Br_2$			
$(C_6H_5CO)_2CBr_2$ (85 g.)	C_6H_5MgBr (140 g. C_6H_5Br)	$HO(C_6H_5)_2CCHBrCOC_6H_5$	430
$(C_6H_5CO)_2CBr_2$	$C_6H_5C{\equiv}CMgBr$	$HO(C_6H_5)(C_6H_5C{\equiv}C)CCHBrCOC_6H_5$	437
$C_{15}H_{10}O_3$			
$(C_6H_5CO)_2CO$ (14.5 g.)	C_6H_5MgBr (11.0 g. Mg)	$(C_6H_5)_3COH$ (9.8 g., 62%); $C_6H_5COCH(OH)C_6H_5$	450
$(C_6H_5CO)_2CO$ (14.3 g.)	C_6H_5MgBr (1.82 g. Mg)	$C_6H_5COCH(O_2CC_6H_5)C_6H_5$	450
$C_{15}H_{11}OBr$			
$4\text{-}BrC_6H_4COCH{=}CHC_6H_5$	$(CH_2)_4CHMgBr$	$4\text{-}BrC_6H_4COCH_2CH(C_6H_5)CH(CH_2)_4$ (48%)	452
$4\text{-}BrC_6H_4COCH{=}CHC_6H_5$ (34 g.)	$4\text{-}BrC_6H_4MgBr$ (42 g. $C_6H_4Br_2$)	$4\text{-}BrC_6H_4COCH_2CH(C_6H_5)C_6H_4\text{-}4\text{-}Br$ (18 g.)	453
$C_6H_5COCBr{=}CHC_6H_5$ (28 g.)	C_6H_5MgBr (33 g. C_6H_5Br)	$C_6H_5COCHBrCH(C_6H_5)_2$ (35 g.)	275
$C_6H_5COCBr{=}CHC_6H_5$ (40.0 g.)	$4\text{-}CH_3C_6H_4MgBr$ (48.5 g. C_7H_7Br)	$C_6H_5COCHBrCH(C_6H_5)C_6H_4\text{-}4\text{-}CH_3$ (91%)	603
$C_{15}H_{11}OCl$			
$4\text{-}ClC_6H_4COCH{=}CHC_6H_5$ (60 g.)	C_6H_5MgBr (47 g. C_6H_5Br)	$4\text{-}ClC_6H_4COCH_2CH(C_6H_5)_2$ (53 g.)	453
$C_{15}H_{11}O_2Br$			
$(C_6H_5CO)_2CHBr$ (12.5 g.)	C_6H_5MgBr (1.0 g. Mg)	$(C_6H_5CO)_2CH_2$ (9.0 g.)	437
$(C_6H_5CO)_2CHBr$ (12.5 g.)	C_6H_5MgBr (2.5 g. Mg)	$C_6H_5COCH_2C(C_6H_5)_2OH$ (10.5 g.)	437
$C_{15}H_{11}O_2Cl$			
1-Benzoyl-2-o-chlorophenyl-1,2-epoxyethane (15.0 g.)	C_6H_5MgBr (2.82 g. Mg)	1,1-Diphenyl-2,3-epoxy-3-o-chlorophenyl-1-propanol (13.5 g.); recovered ketone (2.0 g.)	647

TABLE VI-XVIII (Continued)

Ketonic Comp'd	RMgX	Product(s)	Ref.
$C_{15}H_{12}O$			
$C_6H_5COCH{=}CHC_6H_5$ (0.19 mole)	CH_3MgBr (0.26 mole)	$C_6H_5COCH_2CH(CH_3)C_6H_5$ (54.9–56.1%); CH_3-$(C_6H_5)CH(C_6H_5CO)CHC(OH)(C_6H_5)CH{=}CHC_6H_5$ (37.1–39.0%)	*611*
$C_6H_5COCH{=}CHC_6H_5$	CH_3MgI	$CH_3(C_6H_5)(C_6H_5CH{=}CH)COH$ (chief product); $C_6H_5COCH_2CH(CH_3)C_6H_5$	*108*
$C_6H_5COCH{=}CHC_6H_5$ (105 g.)	C_2H_5MgBr (58 g. C_2H_5Br)	$C_6H_5COCH_2CH(C_2H_5)C_6H_5$ (70 g.)	*449,111, 147,464*
$C_6H_5COCH{=}CHC_6H_5$	C_2H_5MgBr	$C_6H_5COCH_2CH(C_2H_5)C_6H_5$ (*ca.* 60%); $HO(C_2H_5)(C_6H_5)CCH{=}CHC_6H_5$ (*ca.* 40%)	*611*
$C_6H_5COCH{=}CHC_6H_5$ (30 g., 0.205 mole)	C_2H_5MgBr (0.292 mole)	$C_6H_5COCH_2CH(C_2H_5)C_6H_5$ (17.5 g.); $C_2H_5(C_6H_5)(C_6H_5CH{=}CH)COH$ (13.5 g.)*	*454*
$C_6H_5COCH{=}CHC_6H_5$	$H_2C{=}CHCH_2Br$ + Mg	$H_2C{=}CHCH_2(C_6H_5)(C_6H_5CH{=}CH)COH$ (18.7%)	*599*
$C_6H_5COCH{=}CHC_6H_5$	C_6H_5MgBr (2 equiv.).	$(C_6H_5)_2C{=}CH(C_6H_5)_2COH$; $[(C_6H_5)_2C{=}]_2C$	*455*
$C_6H_5COCH{=}CHC_6H_5$ (50 g.)	C_6H_5MgBr	$C_6H_5COCH_2CH(C_6H_5)_2$ (58.5 g., 85.2%); $C_6H_5CH{=}CH(C_6H_5)_2COH$ (3.6%)	*111,147, 449,464, 569,611*
$C_6H_5COCH{=}CHC_6H_5$	$(CH_2)_5CHMgBr$ (excess)	$C_6H_5COCH_2CH(C_6H_5)CH(CH_2)_5$ (*ca.* 95%)	*278*
$C_6H_5COCH{=}CHC_6H_5$ (80 g.)	4-$CH_3C_6H_4MgBr$ (80 g. C_7H_7Br)	$C_6H_5COCH_2CH(C_6H_5)C_6H_4$-4-$CH_3$	*449*
$C_6H_5COCH{=}CHC_6H_5$ (105 g.)	4-$CH_3OC_6H_4MgBr$ (120 g. C_7H_7BrO)	$C_6H_5COCH_2CH(C_6H_5)C_6H_4$-4-$OCH_3$	*449*
$C_6H_5COCH{=}CHC_6H_5$	4-$(CH_3)_2NC_6H_4MgI$	$C_6H_5COCH_2CH(C_6H_5)C_6H_4$-4-$N(CH_3)_2$ (71%)	*465*
$C_6H_5COCH{=}CHC_6H_5$	1-$C_{10}H_7MgBr$	$C_6H_5COCH_2CH(C_6H_5)$-1-$C_{10}H_7$	*275*
$C_{15}H_{12}OBr_2$			
$C_6H_5COCHBrCHBrC_6H_5$	C_6H_5MgBr	$C_6H_5COCHBrCH(C_6H_5)_2$; $C_6H_5COCH_2CH(C_6H_5)_2$	*275*
$C_6H_5COCHBrCHBrC_6H_5$	1-$C_{10}H_7MgBr$	$C_6H_5COCH_2CH(C_6H_5)$-1-$C_{10}H_7$	*275*

*Reaction at $-70°$; similar results at $30°$.

TABLE VI-XVIII (Continued)

Ketonic Comp'd	RMgX	Product (s)	Ref.
$C_{15}H_{12}O_2$			
$C_6H_5COCH{=}CHC_6H_4$-2-OH (22.4 g.)	C_6H_5MgBr (47 g. C_6H_5Br)	2,4-Diphenyl-2-chromanol (80%)	438
$C_6H_5COCH{=}CHC_6H_4$-2-OH (5 g.)	4-$CH_3C_6H_4MgBr$ (11.5 g. C_7H_7Br)	2-Phenyl-4-*p*-tolyl-2-chromanol (4 g.)	438
$(C_6H_5CO)_2CH_2$ (10 g.)	C_6H_5MgBr (21 g. C_6H_5Br)	Recovered ketone (chiefly); $C_6H_5COCH{=}C(C_6H_5)_2$ (?)*	457
$(C_6H_5CO)_2CH_2$ (5 g.)	C_6H_5MgBr (7.5 g. C_6H_5Br)	$C_6H_5COC(C_6H_5)_2OH$†	456
$(C_6H_5CO)_2CH_2$ (10 g., sl. excess)	C_6H_5MgBr	Recovered ketone (9.65 g.)‡	450
$(C_6H_5CO)_2CH_2$	C_6H_5MgBr (excess)	$C_6H_5COCH_2C(C_6H_5)_2OH$ (82%); $CH_3COC_6H_5$; $(C_6H_5)_2CO$§	450
$(C_6H_5CO)_2CH_2$ (1.45 g.)	C_6H_5MgBr (0.7 g. C_6H_5Br)	$C_6H_5COCH_2C(C_6H_5)_2OH$ (1.25 g.)¶	479
$(C_6H_5CO)_2CH_2$ (0.4 g.)	C_6D_5MgBr (0.2 g. C_6D_5Br)	$C_6H_5COCH_2(C_6H_5)(C_6D_5)OH$ (0.3 g.)¶	479
$(C_6H_5CO)_2CH_2$ (7.2 g.)	4-$CH_3C_6H_4MgBr$ (25 g. C_7H_7Br)	$C_6H_5COCH_2(C_6H_5)(C_6H_4$-4-$CH_3)OH$ (6.5–6.8 g.)¶	479
$C_6H_5COCOCH_2C_6H_5$	C_6H_5MgBr	$C_6H_5CH_2COC(C_6H_5)_2OH$ (89%)	466
$C_{15}H_{12}O_3$			
$C_6H_5COC_6H_4$-2-CO_2CH_3	C_6H_5MgBr ("large excess")	1,3,3-Triphenyl-1-phthalanol‖ (90%)	459,625
$C_{15}H_{12}O_3Br_2$			
(3-Br-4-$CH_3OC_6H_3)_2CO$ (6.0 g.)	2-$C_2H_5OCH_2C_6H_4MgBr$ (4.3 g. $C_9H_{11}BrO$)	2-$C_2H_5OCH_2C_6H_4$(3-Br-4-$CH_3OC_6H_4)_2COH$ (5.6 g.)	467

* Addition of Grignard reagent solution to ether-ketone solution; overnight at room temperature; six hours reflux.

† Dropwise addition of ether-ketone solution to Grignard reagent solution; three-quarters hour on water-bath.

‡ Addition of Grignard reagent solution to ether-ketone solution; one hour reflux.

§ Addition of ketone to Grignard reagent solution; "prolonged" reflux.

¶ Gradual (fifteen minutes) addition of benzene-ketone solution to Grignard reagent solution at 10°; overnight standing.

‖ Pérard *(486)* suggests that this product should be formulated as $C_6H_5COC_6H_4$-2-$C(C_6H_5)_2OH$.

TABLE VI-XVIII (Continued)

Ketonic Comp'd	RMgX	Product(s)	Ref.
$C_{15}H_{12}O_3S$			
trans-$C_6H_5COCH{=}CHSO_2C_6H_5$ (4.08 g.)	C_6H_5MgBr (1.44 g. Mg)	$HO(C_6H_5)_2CCH{=}CHSO_2C_6H_5$; $C_6H_5COCH_2CH(C_6H_5)_2$; $(C_6H_5)_2SO$*	*653*
$C_{15}H_{13}O_2$			
$CH_3COC(C_6H_5)_2OH$ (10 g.)	CH_3MgBr (50 g. CH_3Br)	$HO(CH_3)_2CC(C_6H_5)_2OH$; "much" recovered ketone	*292*
$C_{15}H_{13}O_2N$			
$C_6H_5COCON(CH_3)C_6H_5$ (0.05 mole)	C_6H_5MgBr (0.25 mole)	$HO(C_6H_5)_2CCON(CH_3)C_6H_5$ (81%)	*427*
$C_{15}H_{14}O$			
$C_6H_5COCH_2CH_2C_6H_5$	C_6H_5MgBr	$C_6H_5CH_2CH_2(C_6H_5)_2COH$ (69%)	*619*
$C_6H_5COCH(CH_3)C_6H_5$	*t*-C_4H_9MgCl	$C_6H_5[CH_3(C_6H_5)CH]CHOH$	*648*
$(C_6H_5CH_2)_2CO$ (21 g.)	CH_3MgI	$CH_3(C_6H_5CH_2)_2COH$ (8 g.)	*468,260*
$(C_6H_5CH_2)_2CO$ (31 g.)	2-$CH_3C_6H_4MgBr$	Recovered ketone (20 g.); $[C_6H_5CH_2CH(OH)-]_2$ (?)	*469*
$(C_6H_5CH_2)_2CO$	$C_6H_5CH(CO_2Na)MgX$*	$C_6H_5CH(CO_2H)C(CH_2C_6H_5)_2OH$ ("good yield")	*200*
$C_6H_5CH_2COC_6H_4$-4-CH_3	C_2H_5MgI (3 equiv)	$C_2H_5(C_6H_5CH_2)(4\text{-}CH_3C_6H_4)COH$	*441*
$C_6H_5CH_2COC_6H_4$-4-CH_3	*n*-C_3H_7MgBr	*n*-$C_3H_7(C_6H_5CH_2)(4\text{-}CH_3C_6H_4)COH$	*441*

*Apparently, one of the competing primary reactions is sulfone cleavage:

$$trans\text{-}C_6H_5COCH{=}CHSO_2C_6H_5 \xrightarrow{C_6H_5MgBr} C_6H_5COCH{=}CHC_6H_5 + C_6H_5S(\rightarrow O)OMgBr$$

Presumably, 1,4-addition of the Grignard reagent to the unsaturated ketone formed in the cleavage accounts for the saturated ketone isolated. Bromomagnesium benzenesulfinate has been shown to react with phenylmagnesium bromide to yield phenyl sulfoxide [Kohler and Larsen (*652*)].

†In the opinion of Schlenk, Hilleman, and Rodloff, *Ann.*, *487*, 135–54 (1931), this "Grignard reagent" should be formulated as an enolate.

TABLE VI-XVIII (Continued)

Ketonic Comp'd	RMgX	Product(s)	Ref.
$C_{15}H_{14}O$ (*cont.*)			
$C_6H_5CH_2COC_6H_4$-4-CH_3	*n*-C_4H_9MgBr	*n*-$C_4H_9(C_6H_5CH_2)$(4-$CH_3C_6H_4$)COH	*441*
$C_6H_5CH_2COC_6H_4$-4-CH_3	3-$CH_3C_6H_4MgBr$	$C_6H_5CH_2$(3-$CH_3C_6H_4$)(4-$CH_3C_6H_4$)COH	*441*
$C_6H_5COC_6H_4$-2-C_2H_5 (21 g.)	C_6H_5MgBr (11.5 g. C_7H_7Br)	[HO(C_6H_5)(2-$C_2H_5C_6H_4$)C—] (2.5 g.); 2-$C_2H_5C_6H_4(C_6H_5)_2COH$	*480*
$(4\text{-}CH_3C_6H_4)_2CO$	$C_6H_5CH_2MgCl$	$C_6H_5CH_2(4\text{-}CH_3C_6H_4)_2COH$	*345*
$(4\text{-}CH_3C_6H_4)_2CO$	4-$CH_3C_6H_4MgBr$	$(4\text{-}CH_3C_6H_4)_3COH$ (57%)	*365*
$(4\text{-}CH_3C_6H_4)_2CO$	4-$CH_3OC_6H_4CH_2MgCl$	4-$CH_3OC_6H_4CH_2(4\text{-}CH_3C_6H_4)_2COH$ (75–85%)	*481*
$(4\text{-}CH_3C_6H_4)_2CO$ (6.5 g.)	4-*t*-$C_4H_9C_6H_4MgBr$ (71 g. $C_{10}H_{13}Br$)	4-*t*-$C_4H_9C_6H_4(4\text{-}CH_3C_6H_4)_2COH$ (yielding 30 g. chloride)	*382*
$C_{15}H_{14}O_2$			
$CH_3COC(C_6H_5)_2OH$	CH_3MgBr	$HO(CH_3)_2CC(C_6H_5)_2OH$	*285*
$CH_3OCH_2COC_6H_4$-2-C_6H_5	CH_3MgI	$CH_3(CH_3OCH_2)$(2-$C_6H_5C_6H_4$)COH	*16*
$CH_3OCH_2COC_6H_4$-2-C_6H_5	C_2H_5MgBr	$C_2H_5(CH_3OCH_2)$(2-$C_6H_5C_6H_4$)COH (yielding 53% 9-ethylphenanthrene)	*470*
$CH_3COCH_2COC_6H_4$-2-C_6H_5	*n*-C_3H_7MgBr	CH_3OCH_2(*n*-C_3H_7)(2-$C_6H_5C_6H_4$)COH (yielding 53% 9-*n*-propylphenanthrene)	*470*
$CH_3COCH_2COC_6H_4$-2-C_6H_5	*i*-C_3H_7MgBr	CH_3OCH_2(*i*-C_3H_7)(2-$C_6H_5C_6H_4$)COH (yielding 51% 9-*i*-propylphenanthrene)	*470*
$CH_3OCH_2COC_6H_4$-2-C_6H_5	*n*-C_4H_9MgCl	CH_3OCH_2(*n*-C_4H_9)(2-$C_6H_5C_6H_4$)COH (yielding 40% 9-*n*-butylphenanthrene)	*470*
$CH_3OCH_2COC_6H_4$-2-C_6H_5	$C_6H_5CH_2MgCl$	$CH_3OCH_2(C_6H_5CH_2)$(2-$C_6H_5C_6H_4$)COH (yielding 70% 9-benzylphenanthrene)	*470*
$C_6H_5COCH_2C_6H_4$-4-OCH_3 (26 g.)	C_6H_5MgBr (165 g. C_6H_5Br)	4-$CH_3OC_6H_4CH_2(C_6H_5)_2COH$ (yielding 170 g., 81% olefin)	*180*
$C_6H_5COCH(OC_6H_5)CH_3$	2-$C_6H_5C_6H_4MgI$	$C_6H_5[CH_3(C_6H_5O)CH]$(2-$C_6H_5C_6H_4$)COH	*471*
DL-$C_6H_5COCH(OCH_3)C_6H_5$ (2.7 g.)	C_6H_5MgBr (2.5 g. C_6H_5Br)	DL-$HO(C_6H_5)_2CCH(OCH_3)C_6H_5$ (3.2 g.)	*428*

TABLE VI-XVIII (Continued)

Ketonic Comp'd	RMgX	Product(s)	Ref.
$C_{15}H_{14}O_2$ (*cont.*)			
DL-$C_6H_5COCH(OH)CH_2C_6H_5$ (2.0 g.)	C_6H_5MgBr (6.0 g.)	DL-$HO(C_6H_5)_2CCH(OH)CH_2C_6H_5$ (2.5 g., crude)	*463*
$C_6H_5CH_2COC_6H_4$-4-OCH_3 (20 g.)	1-$C_{10}H_7MgBr$ (25 g. $C_{10}H_7Br$)	$C_6H_5CH{=}C(C_6H_4\text{-}4\text{-}OCH_3)(1\text{-}C_{10}H_7)$ (70%)	*485*
$C_{15}H_{14}O_3$			
$C_6H_5COCH(OH)C_6H_4$-4-OCH_3	C_2H_5MgBr	β-$HO(C_2H_5)(C_6H_5)CCH(OH)C_6H_4$-4-$OCH_3$	*322*
$C_6H_5COC_6H_3$-2,4-$(OCH_3)_2$	2-$CH_3OC_6H_4MgI$	$C_6H_5(2\text{-}CH_3OC_6H_4)[2,4\text{-}(CH_3O)_2C_6H_3]COH$	*395*
$C_6H_5COC_6H_3$-2,4-$(OCH_3)_2$ (9.2 g.)	2,4-$(CH_3O)_2C_6H_3MgI$ (16 g. $C_8H_9IO_2$)	$C_6H_5[2,4\text{-}(CH_3O)_2C_6H_3]_2COH$ (4.5 g.)	*474*
$C_6H_5COC_6H_3$-2,5-$(OCH_3)_2$	$C_6H_5CH_2MgCl$ (2 equiv.)	$C_6H_5(C_6H_5CH_2)[2,5\text{-}(CH_3O)_2C_6H_3]COH$ (88%)	*458,473*
$C_6H_5COC_6H_3$-2,5-$(OCH_3)_2$ (235 g.)	$C_6H_5CH(CO_2MgCl)MgCl$* (120 g. $C_6H_5CH_2CO_2H$)	$C_6H_5[2,5\text{-}(CH_3O)_2C_6H_3][C_6H_5CH(CO_2H)]COH$ (249 g., 75%)	*458*
$C_6H_5COC_6H_3$-2,5-$(OCH_3)_2$	2,5-$(CH_3O)_2C_6H_3MgI$	$C_6H_5[2,5\text{-}(CH_3O)_2C_6H_3]_2COH$	*472*
$C_6H_5COC_6H_3$-3,4-$(OCH_3)_2$	C_6H_5MgBr	3,4-$(CH_3O)_2C_6H_3(C_6H_5)_2COH$	*475,395*
$(2\text{-}CH_3OC_6H_4)_2CO$	2-$C_2H_5OCH_2C_6H_4MgBr$	2-$C_2H_5OCH_2C_6H_4(2\text{-}CH_3OC_6H_4)_2COH$	*363*
2-$CH_3OC_6H_4COC_6H_4$-4-OCH_3	CH_3MgI	$CH_3(2\text{-}CH_3OC_6H_4)(4\text{-}CH_3OC_6H_4)COH$	*432*
2-$CH_3OC_6H_4COC_6H_4$-4-OCH_3	2-$CH_3C_6H_4MgBr$	2-$CH_3C_6H_4(2\text{-}CH_3OC_6H_4)(4\text{-}CH_3OC_6H_4)COH$	*363*
2-$CH_3OC_6H_4COC_6H_4$-4-OCH_3	2-$C_2H_5OCH_2C_6H_4MgBr$	2-$CH_3OC_6H_4(4\text{-}CH_3OC_6H_4)(2\text{-}C_2H_5OCH_2C_6H_4)$-COH	*363*
3-$CH_3OC_6H_4COC_6H_4$-4-OCH_3	CH_3MgI	$CH_3(3\text{-}CH_3OC_6H_4)(4\text{-}CH_3OC_6H_4)COH$	*432*
3-$CH_3OC_6H_4COC_6H_4$-4-OCH_3	2-$C_2H_5OCH_2C_6H_4MgBr$	3-$CH_3OC_6H_4(4\text{-}CH_3OC_6H_4)(2\text{-}C_2H_5OCH_2C_6H_4)$-COH	*363*
$(4\text{-}CH_3OC_6H_4)_2CO$ (10 g.)	4-$ClC_6H_4CH_2MgCl$ (14 g. $C_7H_6Cl_2$)	4-$ClC_6H_4CH_2(4\text{-}CH_3OC_6H_4)_2COH$ (*ca.* quant.)	*387*
$(4\text{-}CH_3OC_6H_4)_2CO$	$C_6H_5CH_2MgCl$	$C_6H_5CH_2(4\text{-}CH_3OC_6H_4)_2COH$	*345*

*In the opinion of Schlenk, Hilleman, and Rodloff, *Ann.*, *487*, 135–54 (1931), this "Grignard reagent" should be formulated as an enolate.

TABLE VI-XVIII (Continued)

Ketonic Comp'd	RMgX	Product(s)	Ref.
$C_{15}H_{14}O_3$ (*cont.*)			
$(4\text{-}CH_3OC_6H_4)_2CO$	$2\text{-}CH_3C_6H_4MgBr$	$2\text{-}CH_3C_6H_4(4\text{-}CH_3OC_6H_4)_2COH$	363
$(4\text{-}CH_3OC_6H_4)_2CO$	$C_6H_5CH{=}CHMgBr$ (+ $HClO_4$)	$C_6H_5CH{=}CH(4\text{-}CH_3OC_6H_4)_2CClO_4$ (40%)	476
$(4\text{-}CH_3OC_6H_4)_2CO$	$2\text{-}C_2H_5OCH_2C_6H_4MgBr$	$2\text{-}C_2H_5OCH_2C_6H_4(4\text{-}CH_3OC_6H_4)_2COH$	363
$(4\text{-}CH_3OC_6H_4)_2CO$	$(C_6H_5)_2C{=}CHMgBr$ (+ $HClO_4$)	$(C_6H_5)_2C{=}CH(4\text{-}CH_3OC_6H_4)_2CClO_4$ (50–60%)	476
$C_{15}H_{15}ON$			
$C_6H_5COC_6H_4\text{-}3\text{-}N(CH_3)_2$	$2\text{-}(CH_3)_2NC_6H_4MgI$	$C_6H_5[2\text{-}(CH_3)_2NC_6H_4][3\text{-}(CH_3)_2NC_6H_4]COH$	394
$C_6H_5COC_6H_4\text{-}4\text{-}N(CH_3)_2$	CH_3MgI	$C_6H_5[4\text{-}(CH_3)_2NC_6H_4]C{=}CH_2$	477
$C_6H_5COC_6H_4\text{-}4\text{-}N(CH_3)_2$ (2.00 g.)	C_2H_5MgBr (6.72 g. C_2H_5Br)	$C_2H_5(C_6H_5)[4\text{-}(CH_3)_2NC_6H_4]COH$	389
$C_6H_5COC_6H_4\text{-}4\text{-}N(CH_3)_2$	C_2H_5MgI	$C_6H_5[4\text{-}(CH_3)_2NC_6H_4]C{=}CHCH_3$	477
$C_6H_5COC_6H_4\text{-}4\text{-}N(CH_3)_2$	$C_6H_5CH_2MgCl$	$C_6H_5(C_6H_5CH_2)[4\text{-}(CH_3)_2NC_6H_4]COH$	477
$C_6H_5COC_6H_4\text{-}4\text{-}N(CH_3)_2$	$2\text{-}(CH_3)_2NC_6H_4MgI$	$C_6H_5[2\text{-}(CH_3)_2NC_6H_4][4\text{-}(CH_3)_2NC_6H_4]COH$	394
$C_{15}H_{16}OClN$			
$C_6H_5COCH(NH_2{\cdot}HCl)CH_2C_6H_5$ (5.0 g.)	$C_6H_5CH_2MgCl$ (14.5 g. C_7H_7Cl)	$HO(C_6H_5)(C_6H_5CH_2)CCH(NH_2{\cdot}HCl)CH_2C_6H_5$ (5.5 g.)	478
$C_6H_5COCH(NH_2{\cdot}HCl)CH_2C_6H_5$ (5.0 g.)	$4\text{-}CH_3C_6H_4MgBr$ (19.7 g. C_7H_7Br)	$HO(C_6H_5)(4\text{-}CH_3C_6H_4)CCH(NH_2{\cdot}HCl)CH_2C_6H_5$ (4.2 g.)	478
$C_6H_5COCH(NH_2{\cdot}HCl)CH_2C_6H_5$ (5.0 g.)	$1\text{-}C_{10}H_7MgBr$ (23.8 g. $C_{10}H_7Br$)	$HO(C_6H_5)(1\text{-}C_{10}H_7)CCH(NH_2{\cdot}HCl)CH_2C_6H_5$ (4.3 g.)	478
$C_{15}H_{16}O_3$			
$CH_3(H_3CO_2C)CHCH_2CO\text{-}1\text{-}C_{10}H_7$	CH_3MgI	$CH_3(1\text{-}C_{10}H_7)C{=}CHCH(CH_3)CO_2CH_3$ (75%)	460
$C_{15}H_{16}O_4$			
$4\text{-}CH_3OC_6H_4COCH(OH)C_6H_4\text{-}4\text{-}OCH_3$	C_2H_5MgI	$HO(C_2H_5)(4\text{-}CH_3OC_6H_4)CCH(OH)C_6H_4\text{-}4\text{-}OCH_3$	483

TABLE VI-XVIII (Continued)

Ketonic Comp'd	RMgX	Product(s)	Ref.
$\mathbf{C_{15}H_{17}O_2N}$			
2-Piperidinoacetylbenzofuran (8.5 g.)	C_2H_5MgBr (11.6 g. C_2H_5Br)	2-(1-Ethyl-1-hydroxy-2-piperidinoethyl)benzofuran (38%)	*462*
$\mathbf{C_{15}H_{18}O}$			
$CH_3(CH{=}CH)_2COC_6H_2$-2,4,6-$(CH_3)_3$ (46.5 g.)	C_6H_5MgBr (39.3 g. C_6H_5Br)	$CH_3CH{=}CHCH(C_6H_5)CH_2COC_6H_2$-2,4,6-$(CH_3)_3$ (51.3 g., 81%)	*640*
$(CH_2)_5CHCOCH{=}CHC_6H_5$	C_2H_5MgBr	$(CH_2)_5CHCOCH_2CH(C_2H_5)C_6H_5$	*278*
$(CH_2)_5CHCOCH{=}CHC_6H_5$	C_6H_5MgBr	$(CH_2)_5CHCOCH_2CH(C_6H_5)_2$; $(CH_2)_5CH(C_6H_5)(C_6H_5CH{=}CH)COH$ (trace)	*278*
$\mathbf{C_{15}H_{20}O_2}$			
t-$C_4H_9COCOC_6H_2$-2,4,6-$(CH_3)_3$ (8 g.)	CH_3MgI (8.5 g. CH_3I)	$HO(CH_3)(t\text{-}C_4H_9)CCOC_6H_2$-2,4,6-$(CH_3)_3$ (4 g.); *t*-$C_4H_9COC(OH)(CH_3)C_6H_2$-2,4,6-$(CH_3)_3$ (1.5 g.)	*424*
$\mathbf{C_{15}H_{20}O_3}$			
$CH_3COCH(O_2CC_6H_5)$-*n*-C_5H_{11} (13.2 g.)	CH_6MgBr (10 g. Mg)	$C_6H_5(CH_3)_2COH$ (3 g.); $HO(CH_3)_2CCH(OH)$-*n*-C_5H_{11} (6 g.)	*295*
$\mathbf{C_{15}H_{22}O}$			
$CH_3COCH_2CH(i\text{-}C_5H_{11})C_6H_5$	*i*-$C_5H_{11}MgBr$	$CH_3(i\text{-}C_5H_{11})[i\text{-}C_5H_{11}(C_6H_5)CHCH_2]COH$ (?) (15–18%)	*277*
$\mathbf{C_{16}H_{10}O_2Br_2}$			
$(4\text{-}BrC_6H_4COCH{=})_2$	C_6H_5MgBr	4-$BrC_6H_4COCH_2CH(C_6H_5)COC_6H_4$-4-Br (53%)	*488*
$\mathbf{C_{12}H_{12}O}$			
2-Acetophenanthrene	CH_3MgI	2-(2-Phenanthryl)-2-propanol (80%, crude)	*489*

TABLE VI-XVIII (Continued)

Ketonic Comp'd	RMgX	Product (s)	Ref.
$C_{16}H_{12}O_2$			
$(C_6H_5COCH{=})_2$	C_6H_5MgBr	$C_6H_5COCH_2CH(C_6H_5)COC_6H_5$ (60–65%)	*488*
$(C_6H_5COCH{=})_2$ (4.0 g.)	C_6H_5MgBr (10 ml. C_6H_5Br) [+ I (9.0 g.)]	*cis*-$C_6H_5COCH{=}C(C_6H_5)COC_6H_5$ (0.65 g., 12.3%)	*641*
$(C_6H_5COCH{=})_2$ (4.75 g.)	C_6H_5MgBr (3.00 g. Mg) [+ I]	Tetraphenylfuran (2.1 g., 38%)	*641*
$C_{16}H_{12}O_3$			
$C_6H_5COCH{=}CHC_6H_3{=}3,4{=}O_2CH_2$ (120 g.)	CH_3MgI (70 g. CH_3I)	$C_6H_5COCH_2CH(CH_3)C_6H_3{=}3,4{=}O_2CH_2$ (50 g.)	*449*
$C_6H_5COCH{=}CHC_6H_3{=}3,4{=}O_2CH_2$ (126 g.)	C_2H_5MgBr (55 g. C_2H_5Br)	$C_6H_5COCH_2CH(C_2H_5)C_6H_3{=}3,4{=}O_2CH_2$	*449*
$C_6H_5COCH{=}CHC_6H_3{=}3,4{=}O_2CH_2$ (126 g.)	C_6H_5MgBr (100 g. C_6H_5Br)	$C_6H_5COCH_2CH(C_6H_5)C_6H_3{=}3,4{=}O_2CH_2$	*449*
$C_{16}H_{14}O$			
$C_6H_5COC(CH_3){=}CHC_5H_5$	CH_3MgI	1-Phenyl-2,3-dimethylindene (68–75%)*	*490*
$C_6H_5COC(CH_3){=}CHC_6H_5$	CH_3MgI	$CH_3(C_6H_5)[C_6H_5CH{=}C(CH_3)]COH$ (91%)†	*490*
$C_6H_5COC(CH_3){=}CHC_6H_5$	C_2H_5MgBr (excess)	$C_6H_5COCH(CH_3)CH(C_2H_5)C_6H_5$	*147*
$C_6H_5COC(CH_3){=}CHC_6H_5$	C_6H_5MgBr	$C_6H_5COCH(CH_3)CH(C_6H_5)_2$	*569*
$C_6H_5COCH{=}C(CH_3)C_6H_5$ (20 g.)	C_2H_5MgBr	$C_6H_5COCH_2C(CH_3)(C_2H_5)C_6H_5$ (10 g.)	*111*
$C_6H_5COCH{=}C(CH_3)C_6H_5$ (20 g.)	C_6H_5MgBr	$C_6H_5COCH_2C(C_6H_5)_2CH_3$ (10.1 g.)	*111*
$C_6H_5COCH{=}C(CH_3)C_6H_5$	$C_6H_5CH(CO_2Na)MgCl$‡	$C_6H_5COCH_2C(CH_3)(C_6H_5)CH(CO_2H)C_6H_5$	*149*

*Decomposition of the addition intermediate with iced dilute hydrochloric acid. The substituent numbering of the product is that of Patterson and Capell, "The Ring Index," Rheinhold Publishing Corp., New York City, *1940*, p. 134, *876*, rather than that of the article cited.

†Decomposition of the addition intermediate with iced aqueous ammonium chloride.

‡In the opinion of Schlenk, Hilleman, and Rodloff, *Ann.*, *487*, 135–54 (1931), this "Grignard reagent" should be formulated as an enolate.

TABLE VI-XVIII (Continued)

Ketonic Comp'd	RMgX	Product(s)	Ref.
$C_{16}H_{14}O_2$			
$(C_6H_5CO)_2CHCH_3$	C_6H_5MgBr	$(C_6H_5)_3COH$; $C_2H_5COC_6H_5$	*450*
$C_6H_5COCH{=}CHC_6H_4$-4-OCH_3 (45.0 g.)	C_2H_5MgBr	$C_6H_5COCH_2CH(C_2H_5)C_6H_4$-4-$OCH_3$ (47.5 g.); $C_2H_5(C_6H_5)(4\text{-}CH_3OC_6H_4CH{=}CH)COH$ (yielding 0.35 g. anisic acid)	*111*
$C_6H_5COCH{=}CHC_6H_4$-4-OCH_3 (50.0 g.)	C_6H_5MgBr	$C_6H_5COCH_2CH(C_6H_5)C_6H_4$-4-$OCH_3$ (63.5 g.); 4-$CH_3OC_6H_4CH{=}CH(C_6H_5)_2COH$ (yielding 1.1 g. anisic acid)	*111*
4-$CH_3OC_6H_4COCH{=}CHC_6H_5$ (30.0 g.)	C_2H_5MgBr	4-$CH_3OC_6H_4COCH_2CH(C_2H_5)C_6H_5$ (32.0 g.); carbinol (trace)	*111*
4-$CH_3OC_6H_4COCH{=}CHC_6H_5$ (25.0 g.)	C_6H_5MgBr	4-$CH_3OC_6H_4COCH_2CH(C_6H_5)_2$ (32.0); carbinol (trace)	*111*
4-$CH_3OC_6H_4COCH{=}CHC_6H_4$-2-OH	C_6H_5MgBr	2-*p*-Tolyl-4-phenyl-2-chromanol	*438*
$C_{16}H_{14}O_3$			
$C_6H_5COC_6H_4$-2-$CO_2C_2H_5$ (52 g.)	CH_3MgI (14.3 ml. CH_3I)	$H_2C{=}C(C_6H_5)C_6H_4$-2-CO_2H (11–15 g.); 3-methyl-3-phenylphthalide (7–15 g.)	*480*
Benzylidene-*p*-methoxyacetophenone oxide (5 g.)	C_6H_5MgBr (10.5 g. C_6H_5Br)	$HO(C_6H_5)(4\text{-}CH_3OC_6H_4)CCH(C_6H_5)CH(OH)\text{-}C_6H_5$ (3 g.)	*492*
Benzylidene-*p*-methoxyacetophenone oxide (15.0 g.)	C_6H_5MgBr (1 equiv.)	$HO(C_6H_5)(4\text{-}CH_3OC_6H_4)CCH(OH)CH(C_6H_5)_2$ (12.0 g.); recovered ketone (7.5 g.)*	*649*
Benzylidene-*p*-methoxyacetophenone oxide (15.0 g.)	C_6H_5MgBr (4 equiv.)	$HO(C_6H_5)(4\text{-}CH_3OC_6H_4)CCH(OH)CH(C_6H_5)_2$ (23.5 g.)†	*649*
$C_6H_5COCH_2COC_6H_4$-4-OCH_3 (25 g.)	C_6H_5MgBr (4 equiv.)	$HO(C_6H_5)_2CCH_2COC_6H_4$-4-$OCH_3$ (*ca.* 7 g.); $C_6H_5COCH_2C(OH)(C_6H_5)C_6H_4$-4-$OCH_3$ (*ca.* 7 g.)	*649*

*Inverse addition at $-15°$; half-hour stirring.
†Normal addition; one-hour reflux.

TABLE VI-XVIII (Continued)

Ketonic Comp'd	RMgX	Product (s)	Ref.
$C_{16}H_{14}O_3Cl_2$			
2-CH_3O-3,5-$Cl_2C_6H_2COCH(OC_6H_5)CH_3$ (3.25 g.)	2-$C_6H_5C_6H_4MgI$ (3.5 g. $C_{12}H_9I$)	2-CH_3O-3,5-$Cl_2C_6H_2[CH_3(C_6H_5O)CH]$(2-$C_6H_5C_6H_4)COH$ (1.55 g., crude)	*257*
$C_{16}H_{14}O_4$			
(4-$CH_3OC_6H_4CO$—)$_2$	4-ClC_6H_4MgBr	[HO(4-ClC_6H_4)(4-$CH_3OC_6H_4$)C—]$_2$ (48%)	*415*
(4-$CH_3OC_6H_4CO$—)$_2$	4-$CH_3C_6H_4MgBr$	[HO(4-$CH_3C_6H_4$)(4-$CH_3OC_6H_4$)C—]$_2$ (46%)	*415*
$C_{16}H_{15}OBr$			
4-$BrC_6H_4COC_6H_2$-2,4,6-$(CH_3)_3$ (10 g.)	C_6H_5MgBr + Mg (0.5 g. C_6H_5Br + 1.0 g. Mg)	[2,4,6-$(CH_3)_3C_6H_2COC_6H_4$-4—]$_2$ (2 g.)	*342*
4-$BrC_6H_4COC_6H_2$-2,4,6-$(CH_3)_3$	C_6H_5MgBr	$C_{22}H_{21}BrO$ (?)*, m.p. 121° (17 g., 43%); $C_{22}H_{21}BrO_2$, m.p. 131°	*491*
4-$BrC_6H_4COC_6H_2$-2,4,6-$(CH_3)_3$	1-$C_{10}H_7MgBr$	$C_{26}H_{23}BrO$ (?), m.p. 195° (chief product); $C_{26}H_{23}BrO$ (?), m.p. 143°	*491*
$C_{16}H_{15}O_3Cl$			
4-$CH_3OC_6H_4COCHClC_6H_4$-4-OCH_3 (170 g.)	C_2H_5MgBr (138 g. C_2H_5Br)	(4-$CH_3OC_6H_4)_2CHC(C_2H_5)_2OH$ (72 g.)	*404*
$C_{16}H_{16}O$			
i-$C_3H_7COC_6H_4$-4-C_6H_5	CH_3MgI	$HO(CH_3)(i\text{-}C_3H_7)(4\text{-}C_6H_5C_6H_4)COH$	*418*
$C_6H_5COCH(C_2H_5)C_6H_5$	$H_2C{=}CHCH_2MgX$	$H_2C{=}CHCH_2(C_6H_5)[C_2H_5(C_6H_5)CH]COH$	*461*
$C_6H_5COCH(C_2H_5)C_6H_5$	*n*-C_3H_7MgX	*n*-$C_3H_7(C_6H_5)[C_2H_5(C_6H_5)CH]COH$	*461*
$C_6H_5COCH(C_2H_5)C_6H_5$	*n*-C_4H_9MgX	*n*-$C_4H_9(C_6H_5)[C_2H_5(C_6H_5)CH]COH$	*461*

*It appears possible that the product actually isolated is 4-bromo-2′-mesitoylbiphenyl ($C_{22}H_{19}BrO$); either the enolate formed by 1,4-addition of the Grignard reagent to the hindered ketone or its hydrolysis product would be susceptible to atmospheric oxidation.

TABLE VI-XVIII (Continued)

Ketonic Comp'd	RMgX	Product(s)	Ref.
$C_{16}H_{16}O$ (*cont.*)			
$C_6H_5COCH(C_2H_5)C_6H_5$	t-C_4H_9MgCl	$C_6H_5[C_2H_5(C_6H_5)CH]CHOH$; t-$C_4H_9(C_6H_5)[C_2H_5(C_6H_5)CH]COH$	*648*
$C_6H_5COCH(C_2H_5)C_6H_5$	n-$C_5H_{11}MgX$	n-$C_5H_{11}(C_6H_5)[C_2H_5(C_6H_5)CH]COH$	*461*
$C_6H_5COCH(C_2H_5)C_6H_5$	i-$C_5H_{11}MgX$	i-$C_5H_{11}(C_6H_5)[C_2H_5(C_6H_5)CH]COH$	*461*
$C_6H_5COCH(C_2H_5)C_6H_5$	1-$C_{10}H_7MgX$	$C_6H_5[C_2H_5(C_6H_5)CH](1$-$C_{10}H_7)COH$	*461*
$C_6H_5COC_6H_2$-$2,4,6$-$(CH_3)_3$	CH_3MgI	$C_6H_5[2,4,6$-$(CH_3)_3C_6H_2]C{=}CH_2$ (64%)	*221*
$C_6H_5COC_6H_2$-$2,4,6$-$(CH_3)_3$	C_6H_5MgBr	2-$C_6H_5C_6H_4COC_6H_2$-$2,4,6$-$(CH_3)_3$ (18%)	*491*
$C_6H_5CH_2COC_6H_4$-4-C_2H_5	C_2H_5MgX (2 equiv.)	$C_2H_5(C_6H_5CH_2)(4$-$C_2H_5C_6H_4)COH$	*441*
$C_6H_5CH_2COC_6H_3$-$2,4$-$(CH_3)_2$	C_6H_5MgBr	$C_6H_5(C_6H_5CH_2)[2,4$-$(CH_3)_2C_6H_3]COH$	*441*
$C_6H_5CH_2COC_6H_3$-$2,4$-$(CH_3)_2$	3-$CH_3C_6H_4MgBr$	$C_6H_5(3$-$CH_3C_6H_4)[2,4$-$(CH_3)_2C_6H_3]COH$	*441*
4-$CH_3C_6H_4COCH_2C_6H_4$-4-CH_3 (3 g.)	4-$CH_3C_6H_4MgBr$ (7.5 g. C_7H_7Br)	$(4$-$CH_3C_6H_4)_2C{=}CHC_6H_4$-$4$-$CH_3$	*503*
4-$CH_3C_6H_4COC_6H_4$-4-C_2H_5 (63 g.)	4-i-$C_3H_7C_6H_4MgBr$ (100 g. $C_9H_{11}Br$)	4-$CH_3C_6H_4(4$-$C_2H_5C_6H_4)(4$-i-$C_3H_7C_6H_4)COH$ (yielding 15 g. chloride)	*382*
$C_6H_5[2,4,6$-$(CH_3)_3C_6H_2]C{=}CO$	$(CH_2)_5CHMgCl$	$C_6H_5[2,4,6$-$(CH_3)_3C_6H_2]C{=}CHOH$ (80%)	*501*
$C_{16}H_{16}O_2$			
$C_6H_5COCH_2C_6H_4$-4-OC_2H_5	4-$CH_3OC_6H_4MgBr$	$C_6H_5(4$-$CH_3OC_6H_4)(4$-$C_2H_5OC_6H_4CH_2)COH$	*497*
$C_6H_5COCH(OC_6H_5)C_2H_5$	2-$C_6H_5C_6H_4MgI$	$C_6H_5(2$-$C_6H_5C_6H_4)[C_2H_5(C_6H_5O)CH]COH$ (47%)	*471*
$C_{16}H_{16}O_3$			
$H_3CO_2C(CH_2)_2CO$-2-$C_{10}H_6$-6-CH_3 (26 g.)	CH_3MgI (21.5 g. CH_3I)	$CH_3(6$-$CH_3C_{10}H_6$-2-$)C{=}CHCH_2CO_2H$ (22 g.)	*330*
$H_3CO_2C(CH_2)_2CO$-2-$C_{10}H_6$-6-CH_3	C_2H_5MgI	$C_2H_5(6$-$CH_3C_{10}H_6$-2-$)C{=}CHCH_2CO_2H$	*493*
$C_6H_5COCH(OH)CH(OCH_3)C_6H_5$	C_6H_5MgBr (excess)	$HO(C_6H_5)_2CCH(OH)CH(OCH_3)C_6H_5$ (*ca.* quant.)	*430*

TABLE VI-XVIII (Continued)

Ketonic Comp'd	RMgX	Product (s)	Ref.
$C_{16}H_{16}O_3$ (*cont.*)			
$H_5C_2O_2C(CH_2)_2CO$-2-$C_{10}H_7$ (31 g.)	CH_3MgI (18 g. CH_3I)	CH_3(2-$C_{10}H_7$)$C{=}CHCO_2H$ (24 g.); γ-hydroxy-γ-2-naphthylvaleric acid γ-lactone	*482*
$C_{16}H_{16}O_4$			
$C_6H_5COC_6H_2$-2,3,4-$(OCH_3)_3$ (4.0 g.)	C_6H_5MgBr (3.5 g. C_6H_5Br)	2,3,4-$(CH_3O)_3C_6H_2(C_6H_5)_2COH$	*474*
$C_6H_5COC_6H_2$-2,4,6-$(OCH_3)_3$ (3.0 g.)	C_6H_5MgBr (3.6 g. C_6H_5Br)	2,4,6-$(CH_3O)_3C_6H_2(C_6H_5)_2COH$	*474*
4-$CH_3OC_6H_4COCH(OH)C_6H_4$-4-$OCH_3$	CH_3MgI (5 equiv.)	β-$HO(CH_3)$(4-$CH_3OC_6H_4$)$CCH(OH)C_6H_4$-4-OCH_3	*322*
4-$CH_3OC_6H_4COCH(OH)C_6H_4$-4-$OCH_3$	C_2H_5MgBr	β-$HO(C_2H_5)$(4-$CH_3OC_6H_4$)$CCH(OH)C_6H_4$-4-OCH_3	*322*
4-$CH_3OC_6H_4COCH(OH)C_6H_4$-4-$OCH_3$ (27 g.)	C_6H_5MgBr (47 g. C_6H_5Br)	$HO(C_6H_5)$(4-$CH_3OC_6H_4$)$CCH(OH)C_6H_4$-4-OCH_3 (25–30 g., 70–80%)	*498*
4-$CH_3OC_6H_4COCH(OH)C_6H_4$-4-$OCH_3$	2-$C_6H_5C_6H_4MgI$	HO(4-$CH_3OC_6H_4$)(2-$C_6H_5C_6H_4$)$CCH(OH)C_6H_4$-4-OCH_3 (yielding 28%)phenanthrene deriv. on cyclodehydr'n)	*494*
4-$CH_3OC_6H_4COC_6H_3$-2,3-$(OCH_3)_2$	$(C_6H_5)_2C{=}CHMgBr$	4-$CH_3OC_6H_4$[2,3-$(CH_3O)_2C_6H_3$][$(C_6H_5)_2C{=}CH$]COH (60–70%)	*378*
$CH_3(CH{=}CH)_2COC_6H$-2,3,5,6-$(CH_3)_4$	C_6H_5MgBr	$CH_3CH{=}CHCH(C_6H_5)CH_2COC_6H$-2,3,5,6-$(CH_3)_4$ (73%)	*640*
$CH_3(CH{=}CH)_2COC_6H$-2,3,5,6-$(CH_3)_4$	$C_6H_5CH_2MgCl$	$CH_3CH{=}CHCH(CH_2C_6H_5)CH_2COC_6H$-2,3,5,6-$(CH_3)_4$ (88%)	*640*
$C_{16}H_{22}O_{11}$			
Pentaäcetylfructose	C_2H_5MgI	$C_{16}H_{22}O_{11}\cdot 2C_2H_5MgI$ (regenerating pentaacetylfructose on hydrolysis)	*499*

TABLE VI-XVIII (Continued)

Ketonic Comp'd	RMgX	Product(s)	Ref.
$C_{16}H_{24}O$			
$C_6H_5COCH(t\text{-}C_4H_9)_2$	CH_3MgBr	Addition (quant.)*	324
$C_6H_5COCH(t\text{-}C_4H_9)_2$	CH_3MgI	$CH_3(C_6H_5)[(t\text{-}C_4H_9)_2CH]COH$ (61%)	324
$C_{16}H_{24}O_3$			
$CH_3(C_2H_5)CHCH_2COCH(CH_3)C_6H_3\text{-}3,5\text{-}(OCH_3)_2$ (32 g.)	CH_3MgI (2 equiv.)	$CH_3[CH_3(C_2H_5)CHCH_2][3,5\text{-}(CH_3O)_2C_6H_4CH(CH_3)]COH$ (yielding 24.5 g., 81% of the 2-heptene deriv.)	504
$C_{16}H_{25}ON$			
$(C_2H_5)_2NCH_2COC_6H_3\text{-}2\text{-}CH_3\text{-}5\text{-}i\text{-}C_3H_7$	$n\text{-}C_3H_7MgBr$	$(C_2H_5)_2NCH_2(2\text{-}CH_3\text{-}5\text{-}i\text{-}C_3H_7C_6H_3)CHOH$	502
$C_{16}H_{30}O_2$			
$n\text{-}C_4H_9COCH_2CH(n\text{-}C_4H_9)CO\text{-}n\text{-}C_4H_9$ (6 g.)	C_6H_5MgBr (30 g. C_6H_5Br)	$HO(n\text{-}C_4H_9)(C_6H_5)CCH_2CH(n\text{-}C_4H_9)C(C_6H_5)\text{-}(n\text{-}C_4H_9)OH$ (0.3 g.); dehydration product (?)	495
$C_{16}H_{32}O$			
$n\text{-}C_4H_9CO\text{-}n\text{-}C_{11}H_{23}$ (97 g.)	$n\text{-}C_{10}H_{21}MgBr$ (212 g. $C_{10}H_{21}Br$)	$n\text{-}C_4H_9(n\text{-}C_{10}H_{21})(n\text{-}C_{11}H_{23})COH$	496
$C_{17}H_{12}O$			
$C_6H_5CO\text{-}1\text{-}C_{10}H_7$ (0.10 mole)	$n\text{-}C_3H_7MgBr$ (0.12 mole C_3H_7Br)	$C_6H_5(1\text{-}C_{10}H_7)CHOH$ (65%)†	287
$C_6H_5CO\text{-}1\text{-}C_{10}H_7$	2-Thienyl-MgBr	$\alpha\text{-}C_4H_3S(C_6H_5)(1\text{-}C_{10}H_7)COH$	272
$C_6H_5CO\text{-}1\text{-}C_{10}H_7$ (5 g.)	C_6H_5MgBr (5 g. C_6H_5Br)	$1\text{-}C_{10}H_7(C_6H_5)_2COH$ (3.5 g.)	360
$C_6H_5CO\text{-}1\text{-}C_{10}H_7$	$C_6H_5C{\equiv}CMgBr$	$C_6H_5(C_6H_5C{\equiv}C)(1\text{-}C_{10}H_7)COH$	65
$C_6H_5CO\text{-}1\text{-}C_{10}H_7$ (45 g.)	9-Phenanthryl-MgBr (50 g. $C_{14}H_9Br$)	$C_6H_5(1\text{-}C_{10}H_7)(9\text{-}C_{14}H_9)COH$ (12 g., 14.5%)	511

*"Grignard machine" study.

†From a study of the reducing properties of Grignard reagents in which yields of reduction products only are reported.

TABLE VI-XVIII (Continued)

Ketonic Comp'd	RMgX	Product(s)	Ref.
$C_{17}H_{12}O$ (*cont.*)			
C_6H_5CO-2-$C_{10}H_7$	C_6H_5MgBr	2-$C_{10}H_7(C_6H_5)_2COH$	*505*
$C_{17}H_{12}OS$			
4-(2-Thenoyl)biphenyl (5.5 g.)	$C_6H_5CH_2MgCl$ (5.0 g.)	α-$C_4H_3S(C_6H_5CH_2)$(4-$C_6H_5C_6H_4$)COH (yielding *ca.* 7.0 g. crude ethene deriv.)	*254*
$C_{17}H_{12}O_2$			
4-(2-Furoyl)biphenyl (12 g.)	$C_6H_5CH_2MgCl$ (12.5 g. C_7H_7Cl)	α-C_4H_3O(4-$C_6H_5C_6H_4$)C=CHC_6H_5 (8 g.)	*485*
2-$C_6H_5COC_{10}H_6$-6-OH	C_6H_5MgBr (excess)	6-HO-2-$C_{10}H_6(C_6H_5)_2COH$ (75%)	*527*
3-$C_6H_5COC_{10}H_6$-2-OH (3.7 g.)	1-$C_{10}H_7MgBr$ (25 g. $C_{10}H_7Br$)	C_6H_5(1-$C_{10}H_7$)(2-HO-3-$C_{10}H_6$)COH (yielding 3.7 g., 67% 14-phenyl-14*H*-dibenzo-[*a,i*]xanthene)	*512*
3-$C_6H_5COC_{10}H_6$-2-OH (3.7 g.)	1-$CH_3C_{10}H_6$-2-MgI (20 g. $C_{11}H_9I$)	C_6H_5(2-HO-3-$C_{10}H_6$)(1-CH_3-2-$C_{10}H_6$)COH	*512*
$C_{17}H_{13}OBr$			
4-$BrC_6H_4CO(CH=CH)_2C_6H_5$	$C_6H_5CH_2MgCl$	4-$BrC_6H_4COCH_2CH(CH_2C_6H_5)CH=CHC_6H_5$	*506*
$C_{17}H_{14}O$			
$C_6H_5CO(CH=CH)_2C_6H_5$	C_2H_5MgBr	$C_6H_5COCH_2CH(C_2H_5)CH=CHC_6H_5$*	*507*
$C_6H_5CO(CH=CH)_2C_6H_5$	C_6H_5MgBr	$C_6H_5COCH_2CH(C_6H_5)CH=CHC_6H_5$ (73%)	*507*
$C_6H_5CO(CH=CH)_2C_6H_5$	$C_6H_5CH_2MgCl$	$C_6H_5COCH_2CH(CH_2C_6H_5)CH=CHC_6H_5$*	*507*
$(C_6H_5CH=CH)_2CO$ (50 g.)	C_2H_5MgBr	$C_6H_5CH=CHCOCH_2CH(C_2H_5)C_6H_5$ (51 g.)	*111*
$(C_6H_5CH=CH)_2CO$	$H_2C=CHCH_2Br$ + Mg	$C_{37}H_{34}O_2$, m.p. 89°	*600*
$(C_6H_5CH=CH)_2CO$ (200 g.)	*t*-C_4H_9MgCl (48 g. Mg)	$C_6H_5CH=CHCOCH_2CH$(*t*-C_4H_9)C_6H_5 (190 g.)	*276*
$(C_6H_5CH=CH)_2CO$ (60 g.)	C_6H_5MgBr	$C_6H_5CH=CHCOCH_2CH(C_6H_5)_2$ (57 g.)	*111*
$(C_6H_5CH=CH)_2CO$	$C_6H_5C\equiv CMgBr$	$C_6H_5C\equiv C(C_6H_5CH=CH)_2COH$ (?)	*367*

*Reported by Bauer, *Ber.*, *38*, 688–90 (1905), as the tertiary alcohol.

TABLE VI-XVIII (Continued)

Ketonic Comp'd	RMgX	Product(s)	Ref.
$C_{17}H_{15}OBr$			
$C_6H_5[2,4,6\text{-}(CH_3)_3\text{-}3\text{-}BrC_6H]C{=}CO$ (2.8 g.)	$t\text{-}C_4H_9MgCl$ (excess)	$C_6H_5[2,4,6\text{-}(CH_3)_3\text{-}3\text{-}BrC_6H]C{=}CHOH$ (2.3 g.)	*501*
$C_{17}H_{16}O$			
$C_6H_5[2,4,6\text{-}(CH_3)_3C_6H_2]C{=}CO$ (1 g.)	CH_3MgI (3.5 g. CH_3I)	$C_6H_5[2,4,6\text{-}(CH_3)_3C_6H_2]CHCOCH_3$	*500,501, 530*
$C_6H_5[2,4,6\text{-}(CH_3)_3C_6H_2]C{=}CO$ (9.5 g.)	C_6H_5MgBr (9.7 g. C_6H_5Br)	$C_6H_5[2,4,6\text{-}(CH_3)_3C_6H_2]CHCOC_6H_5$	*500*
$C_6H_5[2,4,6\text{-}(CH_3)_3C_6H_2]C{=}CO$	$(CH_2)_5CHMgCl$	$C_6H_5[2,4,6\text{-}(CH_3)_3C_6H_2]C{=}CHOH$ (80%)	*501*
$C_6H_5[2,4,6\text{-}(CH_3)_3C_6H_2]C{=}CO$ (8.0 g.)	$2,4,6\text{-}(CH_3)_3C_6H_2MgBr$ (12.6 g. $C_9H_{11}Br$)	$C_6H_5[2,4,6\text{-}(CH_3)_3C_6H_2]C{=}C[C_6H_2\text{-}2,4,6\text{-}(CH_3)_3]OH$ (8.0 g.)	*530*
$C_{17}H_{16}O_2$			
$C_6H_5COCH{=}C(OC_2H_5)C_6H_5$	C_2H_5MgBr	$C_2H_5(C_6H_5)[C_2H_5O(C_6H_5)C{=}CH]COH$; $C_6H_5COCH_2C(C_2H_5)(OC_2H_5)C_6H_5$; $C_6H_5[C_2H_5O(C_6H_5)C{=}CH]C{=}CHCH_3$; $C_{34}H_{32}O_3$	*147*
$C_6H_5COCH{=}C(OC_2H_5)C_6H_5$	C_6H_5MgBr	$C_2H_5O(C_6H_5)C{=}CH(C_6H_5)_2COH$*	*147*
$C_6H_5COCH{=}C(OC_2H_5)C_6H_5$	C_6H_5MgBr	$(C_6H_5)_2C{=}CH(C_6H_5)_2COH$; $[(C_6H_5)_2C{=}]_2C$†	*147*
$(C_6H_5CO)_2C(CH_3)_2$ (5 g.)	CH_3MgI (6 g. CH_3I)	$C_6H_5CO(CH_3)_2CC(CH_3)(C_6H_5)OH$‡	*457*
$(C_6H_5CO)_2C(CH_3)_2$	C_6H_5MgBr	$(C_6H_5)_3COH$ (*ca.* quant.)	*450*
$C_6H_5COCOC_6H_2\text{-}2,4,6\text{-}(CH_3)_3$	CH_3MgI	$HO(CH_3)(C_6H_5)CCOC_6H_2\text{-}2,4,6\text{-}(CH_3)_3$	*508*
$C_6H_5COCOC_6H_2\text{-}2,4,6\text{-}(CH_3)_3$	C_6H_5MgBr	$HO(C_6H_5)_2CCOC_6H_2\text{-}2,4,6\text{-}(CH_3)_3$	*509*

* Portionwise addition of solid ketone to concentrated Grignard reagent solution.

† Portionwise addition of solid ketone to dilute Grignard reagent solution.

‡ According to Kohler and Erickson (*450*) this product is probably a mixture of $i\text{-}C_3H_7COC_6H_5$ and $CH_3(C_6H_5)CHOH$.

TABLE VI-XVIII (Continued)

Ketonic Comp'd	RMgX	Product(s)	Ref.
$C_{17}H_{16}O_3$			
4-$CH_3OC_6H_4COCH{=}CHC_6H_4$-4-$OCH_3$	CH_3MgI (3 equiv.)	4-$CH_3OC_6H_4COCH_2CH(CH_3)C_6H_4$-4-$OCH_3$ (45%)	*513*
4-$CH_3OC_6H_4COCH{=}CHC_6H_4$-4-$OCH_3$	C_2H_5MgBr (3 equiv.)	4-$CH_3OC_6H_4COCH_2CH(C_2H_5)C_6H_4$-4-$OCH_3$ (80%)	*513*
4-$CH_3OC_6H_4COCH{=}CHC_6H_4$-4-$OCH_3$	*n*-C_3H_7MgBr (3 equiv.)	4-$CH_3OC_6H_4COCH_2CH$(*n*-$C_3H_7)C_6H_4$-4-OCH_3 (80%)	*513*
4-$CH_3OC_6H_4COCH{=}CHC_6H_4$-4-$OCH_3$	*i*-C_3H_7MgBr (3 equiv.)	4-$CH_3OC_6H_4COCH_2CH$(*i*-$C_3H_7)C_6H_4$-4-OCH_3 (75%)	*513,514*
4-$CH_3OC_6H_4COCH{=}CHC_6H_4$-4-$OCH_3$	*n*-C_4H_9MgBr (3 equiv.)	4-$CH_3OC_6H_4COCH_2CH$(*n*-$C_4H_9)C_6H_4$-4-OCH_3 (70%)	*513*
4-$CH_3OC_6H_4COCH{=}CHC_6H_4$-4-$OCH_3$	*n*-$C_5H_{11}MgBr$ (3 equiv.)	4-$CH_3OC_6H_4COCH_2CH$(*n*-$C_5H_{11})C_6H_4$-4-OCH_3 (75%)	*513*
4-$CH_3OC_6H_4COCH{=}CHC_6H_4$-4-$OCH_3$	C_6H_5MgBr (3 equiv.)	4-$CH_3OC_6H_4COCH_2CH(C_6H_5)C_6H_4$-4-$OCH_3$ (75%)	*513*
4-$CH_3OC_6H_4CH{=}CHC_6H_4$-4-OCH_3	$(CH_2)_5CHMgCl$	4-$CH_3OC_6H_4COCH_2CH[CH(CH_2)_5]C_6H_4$-4-$OCH_3$ (85%)	*514*
4-$CH_3OC_6H_4CH{=}CHC_6H_4$-4-OCH_3	$C_6H_5CH_2MgCl$ (3 equiv.)	4-$CH_3OC_6H_4COCH_2CH(CH_2C_6H_5)C_6H_4$-4-$OCH_3$ (70%)	*513*
4-$CH_3OC_6H_4CH{=}CHC_6H_4$-4-OCH_3	4-$CH_3OC_6H_4MgBr$ (3 equiv.)	4-$CH_3OC_6H_4COCH_2CH(C_6H_4$-4-$OCH_3)_2$ (70%)	*513*
$H_5C_2O_2CCOCH(C_6H_5)_2$* (10 g.)	C_6H_5MgBr (excess)	$(C_6H_5)_2CHC(OH)(C_6H_5)CO_2C_2H_5$ (8 g.)†	*430*
$H_5C_2O_2CCOCH(C_6H_5)_2$*	C_6H_5MgBr ("large excess")	$(C_6H_5)_2CHC(OH)(C_6H_5)CO_2C_2H_5$; $(C_6H_5)_2CHC(OH)(C_6H_5)C(C_6H_5)_2OH$‡	*430*

* According to Kohler *et al.* (*430*) this is the ester actually investigated by Bardon and Ramart, *Compt. rend.*, *183*, 214–6 (1926), who supposed that they were dealing with the isomeric epoxy compound.

† Addition of ether-ketone solution to ice-cold Grignard reagent solution. Similar inverse addition yielded 10 g. of the same product.

‡ Addition of ketone to Grignard reagent solution; several days at room temperature or 3–4 hours reflux.

TABLE VI-XVIII (Continued)

Ketonic Comp'd	RMgX	Product(s)	Ref.
$C_{17}H_{17}OBr$			
$C_6H_5COC_6$-2,3,5,6-$(CH_3)_4$-4-Br (13.0 g.)	t-C_4H_9MgCl (30.0 ml. C_4H_9Cl)	4-t-$C_4H_9C_6H_4COC_6$-2,3,5,6-$(CH_3)_4$-4-Br (6.1 g., 40%)	*510*
$C_{17}H_{17}ON$			
$C_6H_5COCH{=}CHC_6H_4$-4-$N(CH_3)_2$	C_6H_5MgBr	$C_6H_5COCH_2CH(C_6H_5)C_6H_4$-4-$N(CH_3)_2$ (66%)	*465*
4-(2,5-Dimethyl-1-pyrryl)benzophenone (14 g.)	$C_6H_5CH_2MgCl$ (15 g. C_7H_7Cl)	1,2-Diphenyl-1-[4-(2,5-dimethyl-1-pyrryl)-phenyl]ethylene	*485*
$C_{17}H_{17}O_3N$			
$C_6H_5COCON(CH_3)C_6H_4$-4-OC_2H_5 (20 g.)	C_6H_5MgBr (excess)	$HO(C_6H_5)_2CCON(CH_3)C_6H_4$-4-$OC_2H_5$ (23 g., 93%)	*427*
$C_{17}H_{18}O$			
$C_6H_5COCH(n$-$C_3H_7)C_6H_5$	n-C_3H_7MgX	n-$C_3H_7(C_6H_5)[n$-$C_3H_7(C_6H_5)CH]COH$	*461*
$C_6H_5COCH(n$-$C_3H_7)C_6H_5$	n-C_4H_9MgX	n-$C_4H_9(C_6H_5)[n$-$C_3H_7(C_6H_5)CH]COH$	*461*
$C_6H_5COC_6H$-2,3,4,5-$(CH_3)_4$	CH_3MgI	$C_6H_5[$2,3,4,5-$(CH_3)_4C_6H]C{=}CH_2$ (42%)	*221*
$C_6H_5COC_6H$-2,3,5,6-$(CH_3)_4$ (100 g.)	CH_3MgI (198 g. CH_3I)	$C_6H_5[$2,3,5,6-$(CH_3)_4C_6H]C{=}CH_2$ (15 g.); dihydro-o-toluyldurene, *A* isomer, m.p. 123–124° (34 g.); *p*-toluyldurene (0.5 g.); $\{C_6H_5[$2,3,5,6-$(CH_3)_4C_6H]CH\}_2O$ (3 g.); *o*-toluyldurene*	*228*
$C_6H_5COC_6H$-2,3,5,6-$(CH_3)_4$ (20 g.)	CH_3MgI (39.6 g. CH_3I)	$C_6H_5[$2,3,5,6-$(CH_3)_4C_6H]C{=}CH_2$ (3 g., crude); dihydro-*o*-toluyldurene, *B* isomer, m.p. 103.0–103.5° (6 g.)†	*228*
$C_6H_5COC_6H$-2,3,5,6-$(CH_3)_4$ (9.5 g.)	i-C_3H_7MgBr (0.12 mole)	4-i-$C_3H_7C_6H_4COC_6H$-2,3,5,6-$(CH_3)_4$ (38%)	*528*

* Addition of solid ketone and butyl ether to Grignard reagent solution; slow distillation of ethyl ether with addition of butyl ether; six hours under nitrogen at 130° with stirring; dilute aqueous sulfuric acid hydrolysis at 0°.

† Procedure as described in preceding footnote*; hydrolysis with aqueous ammonium chloride at 0°.

TABLE VI-XVIII (Continued)

Ketonic Comp'd	RMgX	Product(s)	Ref.
$C_{17}H_{18}O$ (*cont.*)			
$C_6H_5COC_6H$-2,3,5,6-$(CH_3)_4$	*s*-C_4H_9MgBr	4-*s*-$C_4H_9C_6H_4COC_6H$-2,3,5,6-$(CH_3)_4$ (63%)	528
$C_6H_5COC_6H$-2,3,5,6-$(CH_3)_4$ (10 g.)	*t*-C_4H_9MgCl (28 ml. C_4H_9Cl)	4-*t*-$C_4H_9C_6H_4COC_6H$-2,3,5,6-$(CH_3)_4$ (33%)	510
$C_6H_5COC_6H$-2,3,5,6-$(CH_3)_4$	$(CH_2)_5CHMgCl$	4-$(CH_2)_5CHC_6H_4COC_6H$-2,3,5,6-$(CH_3)_4$ (38%)	528
$C_6H_5COC_6H$-2,3,5,6-$(CH_3)_4$	$C_6H_5CH_2MgCl$	4-$C_6H_5CH_2C_6H_4COC_6H$-2,3,5,6-$(CH_3)_4$	510
4-$CH_3C_6H_4COCH(C_2H_5)C_6H_5$	C_2H_5MgI	$C_2H_5(4\text{-}CH_3C_6H_4)[C_2H_5(C_6H_5)CH]COH$	441
4-$CH_3C_6H_4COC_6H_2$-2,4,6-$(CH_3)_3$	CH_3MgI	4-$CH_3C_6H_4[2,4,6\text{-}(CH_3)_3C_6H_4]C{=}CH_2$	221
4-$CH_3C_6H_4COC_6H_2$-2,4,6$(CH_3)_3$	4-$CH_3C_6H_4MgBr$	2-Mesitoyl-4′,5-dimethylbiphenyl; recovered ketone; unidentified oil	491
$C_6H_5COC_6H$-2,3,5,6-$(CH_3)_4$ (11.9 g.)	2-Thianaphthenylmethyl-MgCl (0.0361 mole)	1-Phenyl-1-duryl-2-thianaphthenylethanol (4.27 g., 31%)	661
$C_6H_5COC_6H$-2,3,5,6-$(CH_3)_4$ (11.9 g.)	3-Thianaphthenylmethyl-MgCl (0.0825 mole)	α-Duryl-β-3-thianaphthenylstyrene (3.9 g., 30%)	659
$C_6H_5COC_6H$-2,3,5,6-$(CH_3)_4$	3-Methyl-2-thianaphthenyl-MgBr + Mg	$\{2\text{-}[2,3,5,6\text{-}(CH_3)_4C_6H]C_6H_4\text{—}\}_2$	659
$C_{17}H_{18}O_2$			
$C_6H_5COCH_2C_6H_4$-4-O-*n*-C_3H_7 (2 parts)	4-$CH_3OC_6H_4MgBr$ (7.2 parts C_7H_7BrO)	$C_6H_5(4\text{-}CH_3OC_6H_4)(4\text{-}n\text{-}C_3H_7OC_6H_4)COH$	497
2-$CH_3OC_6H_4COC_6H_2$-2,4,6-$(CH_3)_3$	C_6H_5MgBr	2-$C_6H_5C_6H_4COC_6H_2$-2,4,6-$(CH_3)_3$ (35%)*	519
2-$CH_3OC_6H_4COC_6H_2$-2,4,6-$(CH_3)_3$	C_6H_5MgBr	2,6-$(C_6H_5)_2C_6H_3COC_6H_2$-2,4,6-$(CH_3)_3$ (20%)†	519
2-$CH_3OC_6H_4COC_6H_2$-2,4,6-$(CH_3)_3$	2-$CH_3OC_6H_4MgBr$	2-*o*-$CH_3OC_6H_4C_6H_4COC_6H_2$-2,4,6-$(CH_3)_3$ (47%)†	519
2-$CH_3OC_6H_4COC_6H_2$-2,4,6-$(CH_3)_3$ (12.7 g.)	2-$[2,4,6\text{-}(CH_3)_3C_6H_2CH_2]C_6H_4MgBr$ (14.5 g. $C_{16}H_{17}Br$)	2-$[2,4,6\text{-}(CH_3)_3C_6HCO]C_6H_4C_6H_4$-2-$[CH_2C_6H_2$-2,4,6-$(CH_3)_3]$ (7.8 g., 33%)	642
3-$CH_3OC_6H_4COC_6H_4$-2,4,6-$(CH_3)_3$ (6.4 g.)	C_6H_5MgBr (8 g. C_6H_5Br)	2-C_6H_5-5-$CH_3OC_6H_3COC_6H_2$-2,4,6-$(CH_3)_3$ (?) (0.5 g., crude)†	519

* Reaction at 30°.

† Addition of benzene-ketone solution to Grignard reagent solution; eight hours reflux at 60°.

TABLE VI-XVIII (Continued)

Ketonic Comp'd	RMgX	Product(s)	Ref.
$C_{17}H_{18}O_2$ (*cont.*)			
3-$CH_3OC_6H_4COC_6H_2$-2,4,6-$(CH_3)_3$ (5 g.)	$C_6H_5CH_2MgCl$	3-CH_3O-4-$C_6H_5CH_2C_6H_3COC_6H_2$-2,4,6-$(CH_3)_3$ (0.6 g., 9%)	*515*
4-$CH_3OC_6H_4COC_6H_2$-2,4,6-$(CH_3)_3$ (10 g.)	$C_6H_5CH_2MgCl$	2-Benzyl-4-methoxy-1,2-dihydrophenyl mesityl ketone (2.7 g., 20%)	*515*
$C_{17}H_{18}O_3$			
4-$CH_3OC_6H_4CO(CH_2)_2C_6H_4$-3-$OCH_3$ (21.6 g.)	*n*-C_3H_7MgI	Oily carbinol (yielding 18 g. crude olefin)	*531*
4-$CH_3OC_6H_4CO(CH_2)_2C_6H_4$-4-$OCH_3$	$(CH_2)_5CHMgCl$	$(CH_2)_5CH$(4-$CH_3OC_6H_4$)(4-$CH_3OC_6H_4$-CH_2CH_2)COH	*514*
4-$CH_3OC_6H_4COCH(C_2H_5)C_6H_4$-4-$OCH_3$	C_2H_5MgBr	C_2H_5(4-$CH_3OC_6H_4$)[C_2H_5(4-$CH_3OC_6H_4$)CH]-COH, two isomers (75%)	*520*
(4-$C_2H_5OC_6H_4)_2CO$ (10 g.)	$C_6H_5CH_2MgCl$ (14 g. C_7H_7Cl)	$C_6H_5CH_2$(4-$C_2H_5OC_6H_4)_2COH$ (*ca.* quant.)	*387*
$C_{17}H_{18}O_4$			
4-$CH_3OC_6H_4COCH(OCH_3)C_6H_4$-4-$OCH_3$	2-(*p*-$ClC_6H_4)C_6H_4MgI$ (6.94 g. $C_{12}H_8ClI$)	4-$CH_3OC_6H_4$[2-(*p*-$ClC_6H_4)C_6H_4$][CH_3O(4-$CH_3OC_6H_4$)CH]COH [yielding 1 g., 13%) of 2-chloro-9,10-bis-(*p*-hydroxyphenyl)-phenanthrene]	*421*
$C_{17}H_{18}O_5$			
[2,5-$(CH_3O)_2C_6H_3]_2CO$	C_2H_5MgBr	C_2H_5[2,5-$(CH_3O)_2C_6H_3]_2COH$ (88%)	*522,473*
[2,5-$(CH_3O)_2C_6H_3]_2CO$	2,5-$(CH_3O)_2C_6H_3MgI$	[2,5-$(CH_3O)_2C_6H_3]_3COH$ (76%)	*472*
[3,4-$(CH_3O)_2C_6H_3]_2CO$	CH_3MgI	[3,4-$(CH_3O)_2C_6H_3]_2C{=}CH_2$ ("low yield")	*516*
$C_{17}H_{20}O$			
8-Benzoylcamphene	CH_3MgI	8-(α-Phenylvinyl)camphene	*339*

TABLE VI-XVIII (Continued)

Ketonic Comp'd	RMgX	Product (s)	Ref.
$C_{17}H_{20}ON_2$			
$[2\text{-}(CH_3)_2NC_6H_4]_2CO$	$2\text{-}(CH_3)_2NC_6H_4MgI$ (excess)	$[2\text{-}(CH_3)_2NC_6H_4]_3COH$ ("good yield")	394
$[3\text{-}(CH_3)_2NC_6H_4]_2CO$	C_6H_5MgBr	$C_6H_5[3\text{-}(CH_3)_2NC_6H_4]_2COH$	394
$[3\text{-}(CH_3)_2NC_6H_4]_2CO$	$2\text{-}(CH_3)_2NC_6H_4MgI$	$2\text{-}(CH_3)_2NC_6H_4[3\text{-}(CH_3)_2NC_6H_4]_2COH$	394
$3\text{-}(CH_3)_2NC_6H_4COC_6H_4\text{-}4\text{-}N(CH_3)_2$	C_6H_5MgBr	$C_6H_5[3\text{-}(CH_3)_2NC_6H_4][4\text{-}(CH_3)_2NC_6H_4]COH$	394
$[4\text{-}(CH_3)_2NC_6H_4]_2CO$	C_2H_5MgBr (4 equiv.)	$[4\text{-}(CH_3)_2NC_6H_4]_2C{=}CH_2$	477
$[4\text{-}(CH_3)_2NC_6H_4]_2CO$	C_2H_5MgBr (4 equiv.)	$C_2H_5[4\text{-}(CH_3)_2NC_6H_4]_2COH$	389
$[4\text{-}(CH_3)_2NC_6H_4]_2CO$	C_2H_5MgI	$[4\text{-}(CH_3)_2NC_6H_4]_2C{=}CHCH_3$	477
$[4\text{-}(CH_3)_2NC_6H_4]_2CO$ (13.5 g.)	$i\text{-}C_3H_7MgI$ (45 g. C_3H_7I)	$[4\text{-}(CH_3)_2NC_6H_4]_2C{=}C(CH_3)_2$ (*ca.* 9 g.)	517
$[4\text{-}(CH_3)_2NC_6H_4]_2CO$	2-Thienyl-MgBr	$\alpha\text{-}C_4H_3S[4\text{-}(CH_3)_2NC_6H_4]_2COH$	523
$[4\text{-}(CH_3)_2NC_6H_4]_2CO$	$i\text{-}C_5H_{11}MgI$	$[4\text{-}(CH_3)_2NC_6H_4]_2C{=}CH\text{-}i\text{-}C_3H_7$	477
$[4\text{-}(CH_3)_2NC_6H_4]_2CO$ (0.005 mole)	C_6H_5MgBr (0.005 mole)	$C_6H_5[4\text{-}(CH_3)_2NC_6H_4]_2COH$ (42%); recovered ketone (45%)	529
$[4\text{-}(CH_3)_2NC_6H_4]_2CO$	$(CH_2)_5CHMgBr$	$[4\text{-}(CH_3)_2NC_6H_4]_2C{=}C(CH_2)_5$ ("very poor yield"; much recovered ketone)	524
$[4\text{-}(CH_3)_2NC_6H_4]_2CO$ (50 g.)	$C_6H_5CH_2MgCl$ (24 ml. C_7H_7Cl)	$[4\text{-}(CH_3)_2NC_6H_4]_2C{=}CHC_6H_5$ (47 g. hydrochloride)	525
$[4\text{-}(CH_3)_2NC_6H_4]_2CO$	$2\text{-}CH_3OC_6H_4MgI$	$2\text{-}CH_3OC_6H_4[4\text{-}(CH_3)_2NC_6H_4]_2COH$	526
$[4\text{-}(CH_3)_2NC_6H_4]_2CO$	$3\text{-}CH_3OC_6H_4MgI$	$3\text{-}CH_3OC_6H_4[4\text{-}(CH_3)_2NC_6H_4]_2COH$	526
$[4\text{-}(CH_3)_2NC_6H_4]_2CO$	$4\text{-}CH_3OC_6H_4MgBr$	$4\text{-}CH_3OC_6H_4[4\text{-}(CH_3)_2NC_6H_4]_2COH$	526
$[4\text{-}(CH_3)_2NC_6H_4]_2CO$	$4\text{-}C_2H_5OC_6H_4MgBr$	$4\text{-}C_2H_5OC_6H_4[4\text{-}(CH_3)_2NC_6H_4]_2COH$	526
$[4\text{-}(CH_3)_2NC_6H_4]_2CO$	$4\text{-}(CH_3)_2NC_6H_4MgBr$	$[4\text{-}(CH_3)_2NC_6H_4]_3COH$	371,417
$[4\text{-}(CH_3)_2NC_6H_4]_2CO$	$2\text{-}CH_3C_{10}H_6\text{-}1\text{-}MgBr$	$2\text{-}CH_3\text{-}1\text{-}C_{10}H_6[4\text{-}(CH_3)_2C_6H_4]_2COH$	532
$[4\text{-}(CH_3)_2NC_6H_4]_2CO$	$4\text{-}CH_3C_{10}H_6\text{-}1\text{-}MgBr$	$4\text{-}CH_3\text{-}1\text{-}C_{10}H_6[4\text{-}(CH_3)_2NC_6H_4]_2COH$	532
$C_{17}H_{20}O_3$			
$CH_3CO(CH_2)_2\text{-}2\text{-}C_{10}H_4\text{-}1,4\text{-}(OCH_3)_2\text{-}3\text{-}CH_3$ (6.8 g.)	CH_3MgI (0.075 mole)	$HO(CH_3)_2C(CH_2)_2\text{-}2\text{-}C_{10}H_4\text{-}1,4\text{-}(OCH_3)_2\text{-}3\text{-}CH_3$ (6.6 g.)	521

TABLE VI-XVIII (Continued)

Ketonic Comp'd	RMgX	Product(s)	Ref.
$C_{17}H_{26}O$			
$2\text{-}CH_3C_6H_4COCH(t\text{-}C_4H_9)_2$	CH_3MgBr	Addition (quant.)*	324
$CH_3COCH{=}CHC(CH_3){=}CHCH_2R^{\dagger}$ (450 mg.)	C_2H_5MgBr (100 mg. Mg)	$HO(CH_3)(C_2H_5)CCH{=}CHC(CH_3){=}CHCH_2R^{\dagger}$ (143 mg.)	643
$C_{18}H_{11}O_3Cl$			
$2\text{-}(o\text{-}ClC_6H_4CO)C_{10}H_6\text{-}1\text{-}CO_2H$ (6.21 g.)	CH_3MgBr (20 ml., 0.214 *M*)	3-Methyl-3-*o*-chlorophenyl-6,7-benzophthalide (4.86 g., 79%)	533
$2\text{-}(p\text{-}ClC_6H_4CO)C_{10}H_6\text{-}1\text{-}CO_2H$ (0.029 mole)	CH_3MgBr (0.073 mole)	3-Methyl-3-*p*-chlorophenyl-6,7-benzophthalide (7.1 g., 80%)	534
$C_{18}H_{12}O_3$			
$2\text{-}C_6H_5COC_{10}H_6\text{-}1\text{-}CO_2H$	CH_3MgBr (3 equiv.)	3-Methyl-3-phenyl-6,7-benzophthalide (89%)	331
$2\text{-}(\alpha\text{-}C_{10}H_7CO)C_6H_4\text{-}1\text{-}CO_2H$ (13.8 g.)	CH_3MgBr (7.29 g. Mg)	3-Methyl-3-α-naphthylphthalide (8.0 g., 58%)	535
$C_{18}H_{14}OS$			
4-(5-Methyl-2-thenoyl)biphenyl (4 g.)	$C_6H_5CH_2MgCl$ (3.7 g. C_7H_7Cl)	$\alpha'\text{-}CH_3\text{-}\alpha\text{-}C_4H_3S(C_6H_5CH_2)(4\text{-}C_6H_4C_6H_5)COH$ (yielding ethene *ca.* quant.)	254
$C_{18}H_{14}O_2$			
$1\text{-}C_6H_5COC_{10}H_6\text{-}4\text{-}OCH_3$	C_6H_5MgBr	$1\text{-}(4\text{-}CH_3OC_{10}H_6)(C_6H_5)_2COH$	537
$C_{18}H_{16}O$			
$C_6H_5C{\equiv}CCOC_6H_2\text{-}2,4,6\text{-}(CH_3)_3$ (1 g.)	CH_3MgI (3 ml. CH_3I)	$CH_3(C_6H_5)C{=}CHCOC_6H_2\text{-}2,4,6\text{-}(CH_3)_3$ (0.78 g., 73%)	393
$C_6H_5C{\equiv}CCOC_6H_2\text{-}2,4,6\text{-}(CH_3)_3$	C_6H_5MgBr	$(C_6H_5)_2C{=}CHCOC_6H_2\text{-}2,4,6\text{-}(CH_3)_3$	393

* "Grignard machine" study.

† R = 1,3,3-trimethyl-2-cyclohexen-1-yl.

TABLE VI-XVIII (Continued)

Ketonic Comp'd	RMgX	Product(s)	Ref.
$C_{18}H_{16}O$ (*cont.*)			
$C_6H_5C{\equiv}CCOC_6H_2$-2,4,6-$(CH_3)_3$ (1 g.)	2,4,6-$(CH_3)_3C_6H_2MgBr$ (4.5 g. $C_9H_{11}Br$)	$C_6H_5[2,4,6\text{-}(CH_3)_3C_6H_2]C{=}CHCOC_6H_2$-2,4,6-$(CH_3)_3$, m.p. 118.5–119.5° (67%)	393
$C_{18}H_{16}O_2$			
4-$CH_3OC_6H_4CO(CH{=}CH)_2C_6H_5$	$C_6H_5CH_2MgCl$	4-$CH_3OC_6H_4COCH_2CH(CH_2C_6H_5)CH{=}CHC_6H_5$	*506*
$C_6H_5COCH_2COC_6H_2$-2,4,6-$(CH_3)_3$	C_6H_5MgBr	$HO(C_6H_5)_2CCH_2COC_6H_2$-2,4,6-$(CH_3)_3$	*538*
2-Mesitoylbenzofuran	C_6H_5MgBr	2-Mesitoyl-3-phenyl-2,3-dihydrobenzofuran	*451*
$C_{18}H_{17}ON$			
2-$NCC_6H_4COC_6H$-2,3,5,6-$(CH_3)_4$ (2.6 g.)	CH_3MgI (7.1 g. CH_3I)	1,1-Dimethyl-3-durylpseudoïsoindole (2.6 g., 83%)	*235*
2-$NCC_6H_4COC_6H$-2,3,5,6-$(CH_3)_4$ (7.9 g.)	$H_2C{=}CHCH_2MgBr$ (0.15 mole)	1,1-Diallyl-3-durylpseudoïsoindole (7.5 g., 76%)	*235*
2-$NCC_6H_4COC_6H$-2,3,5,6-$(CH_3)_4$ (2.6 g.)	C_6H_5MgBr (15.7 g. C_6H_5Br)	1,1-Diphenyl-3-durylpseudoïsoindole (2.1 g., 51%)	*235*
2-$NCC_6H_4COC_6H$-2,3,5,6-$(CH_3)_4$ (5.2 g.)	4-$CH_3C_6H_4MgBr$ (17.0 g. C_7H_7Br)	1,1-Di-*p*-tolyl-3-durylpseudoïsoindole (2.6 g., 31%)	*235*
2-$NCC_6H_4CCC_6H$-2,3,5,6-$(CH_3)_4$ (7.9 g.)	4-$CH_3OC_6H_4MgBr$ (28.0 g. C_7H_7BrO)	1,1-Di-*p*-anisyl-3-durylpseudoïsoindole (5.0 g., 36%)	*235*
2-$NCC_6H_4COC_6H$-2,3,5,6-$(CH_3)_4$ (7.9 g.)	1-$C_{10}H_7MgBr$ (20.7 g. $C_{10}H_7Br$)	1,1-Di-α-naphthyl-3-durylpseudoïsoindole (9.3 g., 65%)	*235*
3-$NCC_6H_4COC_6H$-2,3,5,6-$(CH_3)_4$ (1.3 g.)	*s*-C_4H_9MgBr (3.4 g. C_4H_9Br)	3-*s*-$C_4H_9COC_6H_4COC_6H$-2,3,5,6-$(CH_3)_4$ (0.5 g., 31%)	*235*
3-$NCC_6H_4COC_6H$-2,3,5,6-$(CH_3)_4$ (1.3 g.)	$C_6H_5CH_2MgCl$ (3.2 g. C_7H_7Cl)	3-$C_6H_5CH_2COC_6H_4COC_6H$-2,3,5,6-$(CH_3)_4$ (0.95 g., 53%)	*235*
4-$NCC_6H_4COC_6H$-2,3,5,6-$(CH_3)_4$ (2.6 g.)	CH_3MgI (7.1 g. CH_3I)	Recovered ketone (*ca.* 50%); 4-$CH_3C_6H_4COC_6H$-2,3,5,6-$(CH_3)_4$ (14%)	*235*

TABLE VI-XVIII (Continued)

Ketonic Comp'd	RMgX	Product (s)	Ref.
$C_{18}H_{17}ON$ (*cont.*)			
4-NCC_6H_4COCH-2,3,5,6-$(CH_3)_4$ (1.3 g.)	$C_6H_5CH_2MgCl$ (3.2 g. C_7H_7Cl)	4-$C_6H_5CH_2C_6H_4COC_6H$-2,3,5,6-$(CH_3)_4$ (44%)	*235*
$C_{18}H_{17}O_2N$			
4-$CH_3OC_6H_4COCH(C_2H_5)C_6H_4$-4-CN (5 g.)	CH_3MgBr (5 g. Mg)	CH_3(4-$CH_3OC_6H_4$)C=C(C_2H_5)C_6H_4-4-$COCH_3$ (4 g.)*	*536*
4-$CH_3OC_6H_4COCH(C_2H_5)C_6H_4$-4-CN (6 g.)	C_2H_5MgBr (3.6 g. C_2H_5Br)	C_2H_5(4-$CH_3OC_6H_4$)[C_2H_5(4-NCC_6H_4)CH]COH (5 g.)†	*536*
$C_{18}H_{18}O$			
C_6H_5COCH=CHC_6H_2-2,4,6-$(CH_3)_3$	RMgX	1,4-Addition products, only	*401*
C_6H_5CH=$CHCOC_6H_2$-2,4,6-$(CH_3)_3$ (50 g.)	C_6H_5MgBr	$(C_6H_5)_2CHCH_2COC_6H_2$-2,4,6-$(CH_3)_3$ (62 g.)	*111*
C_6H_5CH=$CHCOC_6H_2$-2,4,6-$(CH_3)_3$	C_6H_5MgBr (+ Br_2)	$(C_6H_5)_2CHCHBrCOC_6H_2$-2,4,6-$(CH_3)_3$ (80–90%)	*539*
C_6H_5CH=$CHCOC_6H_2$-2,4,6-$(CH_3)_3$ (5 g.)	2,4,6-$(CH_3)_3C_6H_2MgBr$ (8 g. $C_9H_{11}Br$)	2,4,6-$(CH_3)_3C_6H_2(C_6H_5)CHCH_2COC_6H_2$-2,4,6-$(CH_3)_3$	*393*
$C_6H_5COC(=CH_2)C_6H_2$-2,4,6-$(CH_3)_3$	C_6H_5MgBr	No addition product obtained	*500*
C_6H_5[2,3,5,6-$(CH_3)_4C_6H$]C=CO (6 g.)	*t*-C_4H_9MgCl (9.3 g. C_4H_9Cl)	C_6H_5[2,3,5,6-$(CH_3)_4C_6H$]C=CHOH (6.5 g., 80%)	*501*
$C_{18}H_{18}O_2$			
$C_6H_5COCH_2COC_6H_2$-2,4,6-$(CH_3)_3$	CH_3MgI	$HO(CH_3)(C_6H_5)CCH_2COC_6H_2$-2,4,6-$(CH_3)_3$ (92.4%)	*538*

* Slow addition of ether-ketone solution to cooled, stirred Grignard reagent solution; twelve hours reflux.

† Dropwise addition of ether-ketone solution to stirred, ice-cooled Grignard reagent solution; one hour stirring with cooling; twelve hours at room temperature.

TABLE VI-XVIII (Continued)

Ketonic Comp'd	RMgX	Product(s)	Ref.
$C_{18}H_{18}O_2$ (*cont.*)			
$C_6H_5COCH_2COC_6H_2$-2,4,6-$(CH_3)_3$	C_6H_5MgBr	$HO(C_6H_5)_2CCH_2COC_6H_2$-2,4,6-$(CH_3)_3$	538
$C_6H_5COCOC_6H$-2,3,5,6-$(CH_3)_4$	CH_3MgI	$HO(CH_3)(C_6H_5)CCOC_6H_4$-2,3,5,6-$(CH_3)_4$	508
$C_{18}H_{18}O_3$-$C_{20}H_{22}O_3$			
4-$CH_3OC_6H_4COCR{=}CHC_6H_4$-4-$OCH_3$*	CH_3MgI (3 equiv.)	Principal products apparently indenes (1,2 add'n); traces of 1,4 add'n products	518
4-$CH_3OC_6H_4COCR{=}CHC_6H_4$-4-$OCH_3$*	$R'MgBr$†	4-$CH_3C_6H_4COCHRCHR'C_6H_4$-4-$OCH_3$*† (*ca.* 80%)	518
$C_{18}H_{18}O_4$			
4-$CH_3OC_6H_4COCH(C_2H_5)C_6H_4$-3-$CO_2H$	C_2H_5MgI	C_2H_5(4-$CH_3OC_6H_4$)[C_2H_5(3-$HO_2CC_6H_4$)CH]COH	540
$C_{18}H_{20}O$			
$C_6H_5COCH(n\text{-}C_4H_9)C_6H_5$	n-C_4H_9MgX	n-$C_4H_9(C_6H_5)[n\text{-}C_4H_9(C_6H_5)CH]COH$	461
$C_6H_5COCH(n\text{-}C_4H_9)C_6H_5$	n-$C_5H_{11}MgX$	n-$C_5H_{11}(C_6H_5)[n\text{-}C_4H_9(C_6H_5)CH]COH$	461
$C_6H_5CH_2COC_6H_4$-4-t-C_4H_9	C_2H_5MgX	$C_6H_5CH{=}C(C_2H_5)C_6H_4$-4-$t$-$C_4H_9$	441
2-$CH_3C_6H_4COC_6H$-2,3,5,6-$(CH_3)_4$	t-C_4H_9MgCl	2-CH_3-4-t-$C_4H_9C_6H_3COC_6H_4$-2,3,5,6-$(CH_3)_4$	528
4-$CH_3C_6H_4COCH(n\text{-}C_3H_7)C_6H_5$	C_2H_5MgI	$HO(C_2H_5)(4\text{-}CH_3C_6H_4)CCH(n\text{-}C_3H_7)C_6H_5$	441
$C_{18}H_{20}O_2$			
2-CH_3O-5-$CH_3C_6H_3COC_6H_4$-2,4,6-$(CH_3)_3$	C_2H_5MgBr	2-C_2H_5-5-$CH_3C_6H_3COC_6H_2$-2,4,6-$(CH_3)_3$ (28%)‡	519

*R = CH_3, C_2H_5, n-C_3H_7.

†R′ = C_2H_5, n-C_3H_7.

‡Reaction at 30°.

TABLE VI-XVIII (Continued)

Ketonic Comp'd	RMgX	Product(s)	Ref.
$C_{18}H_{20}O_2$ (*cont.*)			
2-CH_3O-5-$CH_3C_6H_3COC_6H_2$-2,4,6-$(CH_3)_3$	C_6H_5MgBr	2-C_6H_5-5-$CH_3C_6H_3COC_6H_2$-2,4,6-$(CH_3)_3$ (18%)*	*519* *519*
2-CH_3O-5-$CH_3C_6H_3COC_6H_2$-2,4,6-$(CH_3)_3$ (13.4 g.)	C_6H_5MgBr (16 g. C_6H_5Br)	2,6-$(C_6H_5)_2$-3-$CH_3C_6H_2COC_6H_2$-2,4,6-$(CH_3)_3$ (3.5 g., 20%)†	*519*
2-$CH_3OC_6H_4COC_6H$-2,3,5,6-$(CH_3)_4$ (10.0 g.)	2-[2,4,6-$(CH_3)_3C_6H_2CH_2$]C_6H_4MgBr (14.5 g. $C_{16}H_{17}Br$)	2-[2,3,5,6-$(CH_3)_3C_6HCO$]$C_6H_4C_6H_4$-2-[$CH_2C_6H_2$-2,4,6-$(CH_3)_3$] (8.2 g., 49%)	*644*
3-$CH_3OC_6H_4COC_6H$-2,3,5,6-$(CH_3)_4$ (10 g.)	$C_6H_5CH_2MgCl$	3-CH_3O-4-$C_6H_5CH_2C_6H_3COC_6H$-2,3,5,6-$(CH_3)_4$ (4.6 g., 34%)	*515*
4-$CH_3OC_6H_4COC_6H$-2,3,5,6-$(CH_3)_4$ (10 g.)	$C_6H_5CH_2MgCl$	2-Benzyl-4-methoxy-1,2-dihydrophenyl duryl ketone (0.28 g.)	*515*
$C_{18}H_{20}O_3$			
2-$(H_3CO_2CCH_2CH_2CO)C_{10}H_6$-6-*i*-$C_3H_7$	CH_3MgI	6-*i*-C_3H_7-2-$C_{10}H_6C(CH_3)$=$CHCH_2CO_2H$	*330*
2-$(H_3CO_2CCH_2CH_2CO)C_{10}H_6$-6-*i*-$C_3H_7$	C_2H_5MgI	6-*i*-C_3H_7-2-$C_{10}H_6C(C_2H_5)$=$CHCH_2CO_2H$	*439*
4-$CH_3OC_6H_4COCH(C_2H_5)C_6H_4$-4-$OCH_3$ (10 g.)	C_2H_5MgBr (2.5 g. Mg)	$HO(C_2H_5)$(4-$CH_3OC_6H_4$)$CCH(C_2H_5)C_6H_4$-4-OCH_3, 2 isomers (10.12 g., 91%)	*520*
2,3-$(CH_3O)_2C_6H_3COC_6H_2$-2,4,6-$(CH_3)_3$ (4.5 g.)	$C_6H_5CH_2MgCl$	2-$C_6H_5CH_2$-3-$CH_3OC_6H_3COC_6H_2$-2,4,6-$(CH_3)_3$ (0.38 g., 7%)	*515*
3,4-$(CH_3O)_2C_6H_3COC_6H_2$-2,4,6-$(CH_3)_3$ (12 g.)	C_6H_5MgBr	3-CH_3O-4-$C_6H_5C_6H_3COC_6H_2$-2,4,6-$(CH_3)_3$ (15%)	*515*
3,4-$(CH_3O)_2C_6H_3COC_6H_2$-2,4,6-$(CH_3)_3$ (8 g.)	$C_6H_5CH_2MgCl$ (8.9 g. C_7H_7Cl)	3-CH_3O-4-$C_6H_5CH_2C_6H_3COC_6H_2$-2,4,6-$(CH_3)_3$ (2.1 g., 22%)	*515*
$C_{18}H_{26}O$			
CH_3COCH=$CHCH$=$C(CH_3)R$‡	$C_2H_5OC{\equiv}CMgBr$	$HO(CH_3)(C_2H_5OC{\equiv}C)CCH$=$CHCH$=$C(CH_3)R$	*487*

* Reaction at 30°.

† Addition of benzene-ketone solution to Grignard reagent solution; eight hours reflux at 60°.

‡ R = β-(1,3,3-trimethyl-2-cyclohexenyl)vinyl.

TABLE VI-XVIII (Continued)

Ketonic Comp'd	RMgX	Product(s)	Ref.
$C_{18}H_{26}O_3N_2$			
3,4-Di-4-morpholinyl-4-phenyl-2-butanone (10 g., 1 equiv.)	CH_3MgI (3.02 g., 4 equiv. Mg)	$HO(CH_3)_2CCH(C_4H_8NO)CH(C_4H_8NO)C_6H_5$ (5.5 g., 53%); recovered ketone (2 g.)	*542*
3,4-Di-4-morpholinyl-4-phenyl-2-butanone (16 g., 1 equiv.)	C_2H_5MgBr (4.8 g., 4 equiv. Mg)	$HO(CH_3)(C_2H_5)CCH(C_4H_8NO)CH(C_4H_8NO)$-$C_6H_5$ (10 g., 57%); recovered ketone (4 g.)	*542*
3,4-Di-4-morpholinyl-4-phenyl-2-butanone (5.9 g.)	C_6H_5MgBr (1.79 g. Mg)	$HO(CH_3)(C_6H_5)CCH(C_4H_8NO)CH(C_4H_8NO)$-$C_6H_5$ (3.6 g.); recovered ketone (1.4 g.)	*544*
$C_{18}H_{28}O$			
C_6H_5CO-*n*-$C_{11}H_{23}$ (1.86 mole)	*n*-$C_8H_{17}MgBr$ (1.8 mole)	C_6H_5(*n*-C_8H_{17})(*n*-$C_{11}H_{23}$)COH (yielding 90% crude olefin)	*231*
$C_{18}H_{36}O$			
n-C_4H_9CO-*n*-$C_{13}H_{27}$	*n*-$C_8H_{17}MgBr$	*n*-C_4H_9(*n*-C_8H_{17})(*n*-$C_{13}H_{27}$)COH	*496*
n-C_4H_9CO-*n*-$C_{13}H_{27}$	*n*-$C_{10}H_{21}MgBr$	*n*-C_4H_9(*n*-$C_{10}H_{21}$)(*n*-$C_{13}H_{27}$)COH	*496*
$C_{19}H_{13}OBr$			
4-$BrC_6H_4COC_6H_4$-4-C_6H_5	C_6H_5MgBr	4-$BrC_6H_4(C_6H_5)$(4-$C_6H_5C_6H_4$)COH (yielding 53% triarylmethane)	*547*
$C_{19}H_{13}OCl$			
4-$ClC_6H_4COC_6H_4$-4-C_6H_5 (15 g.)	C_6H_5MgBr (sl. excess)	4-$ClC_6H_4(C_6H_5)$(4-$C_6H_5C_6H_4$)COH (62%)	*547*
$C_{19}H_{14}O$			
$C_6H_5COC_6H_4$-2-C_6H_5 (6.5 g.)	C_6H_5MgBr (8 g. C_6H_5Br)	2-$C_6H_5C_6H_4(C_6H_5)_2COH$ (5.2 g., 63%)	*541*
$C_6H_5COC_6H_4$-4-C_6H_5	CH_3MgI (3 equiv.)	$CH_3(C_6H_5)$(4-$C_6H_5C_6H_4$)COH (94%, crude)	*418*
$C_6H_5COC_6H_4$-4-C_6H_5 (0.10 mole)	*n*-C_3H_7MgBr (0.12 mole C_3H_7Br)	C_6H_5(4-$C_6H_5C_6H_4$)CHOH (48%)*	*287*
5-Benzoylacenaphthene	C_6H_5MgBr	Diphenyl-5-acenaphthenylmethanol (55%)	*374,545*

*From a study of the reducing properties of Grignard reagents in which the yields of reduction products only are reported.

TABLE VI-XVIII (Continued)

Ketonic Comp'd	RMgX	Product(s)	Ref.
$C_{19}H_{14}O_3$			
2-$C_6H_5COC_{10}H_6$-1-CO_2CH_3	CH_3MgI (*ca.* 1 equiv.)	3-Methyl-3-phenyl-6,7-benzophthalide (56%)	*331*
2-*o*-$CH_3C_6H_4COC_{10}H_6$-1-CO_2H	CH_3MgBr (excess)	3-Methyl-3-*o*-tolyl-6,7-benzophthalide (85%)	*331*
2-*o*-$CH_3C_6H_4COC_{10}H_6$-1-CO_2H	C_2H_5MgBr (3 equiv.)	3-*o*-Tolyl-6,7-benzophthalide (34%); 3-ethyl-3-*o*-tolyl-6,7-benzophthalide (23%)	*331*
2-*o*-$CH_3C_6H_4COC_{10}H_6$-1-CO_2H	*n*-$C_{18}H_{37}MgBr$ (3 equiv.)	3-*o*-Tolyl-6,7-benzophthalide (28%); *n*-$C_{36}H_{74}$	*331*
1-*o*-$HO_2CC_6H_4C_{10}H_6$-8-CH_3 (18.5 g.)	CH_3MgCl (5 g. Mg)	Recovered keto acid (1.5 g.); unsaponifiable oil (16.5 g.)	*205*
1-(*o*-CH_3-*o*′-$HO_2CC_6H_4CO)C_{10}H_7$ (8.7 g.)	CH_3MgBr (18 g. Mg)	3,7-Dimethyl-3-α-naphthylphthalide (6.4 g., 74%)	*535*
$C_{19}H_{14}O_4$			
2-*o*-$CH_3OC_6H_4COC_{10}H_6$-1-CO_2H (5 g.)	CH_3MgBr (17.5 ml., 1.96 *M*)	3-Methyl-3-*o*-methoxyphenyl-6,7-benzophthalide (3.9 g., 78%); recovered ketone	*548*
2-*o*-$CH_3OC_6H_4COC_{10}H_6$-1-CO_2H (1.186 g.)	2-$CH_3OC_6H_4MgBr$ (7.5 ml., 1.0 *M*)	3,3-Di-*o*-methoxyphenyl-6,7-benzophthalide (1.168 g., 76%)	*548*
$C_{19}H_{16}O$			
$CH_3(C_6H_5)CHCO$-1-$C_{10}H_7$ (16 g.)	CH_3MgI (26 g. CH_3I)	$CH_3[CH_3(C_6H_5)CH](1\text{-}C_{10}H_7)COH$ (5 g., crude); $CH_3(C_6H_5)C=C(CH_3)$-1-$C_{10}H_7$	*543*
$CH_3(G_6H_5)CHCO$-1-$C_{10}H_7$ (16.2 g.)	C_2H_5MgBr (22.0 g. C_2H_5Br)	$C_2H_5[CH_3(C_6H_5)CH](1\text{-}C_{10}H_7)COH$ + $CH_3(C_6H_5)C=C(C_2H_5)$-1-$C_{10}H_7$ (totaling 14.5 g.)	*543*
$C_{19}H_{16}O_2$			
6-*p*-$CH_3OC_6H_4COC_{10}H_6$-2-OCH_3 (5.9 g.)	CH_3MgI (4.7 g. CH_3I)	4-$CH_3OC_6H_4(2\text{-}CH_3O\text{-}6\text{-}C_{10}H_6)C=CH_2$ (4.4 g., 75%)	*550*

TABLE VI-XVIII (Continued)

Ketonic Comp'd	RMgX	Product (s)	Ref.
$C_{19}H_{17}ON$			
4-(2,5-Dimethyl-1-pyrryl)benzophenone (15 g.)	$C_6H_5CH_2MgCl$ (15 g. C_7H_7Cl)	1,2-Diphenyl-2-[4-(2,5-dimethyl-1-pyrryl)phenyl]ethene	*485*
$C_{19}H_{20}O$			
$CH_3(C_6H_5)C{=}CHCOC_6H_2$-2,4,6-$(CH_3)_3$	CH_3MgI	$C_6H_5(CH_3)_2CCH_2COC_6H_2$-2,4,6-$(CH_3)_3$	*538*
$CH_3(C_6H_5)C{=}CHCOC_6H_2$-2,4,6-$(CH_3)_3$	C_6H_5MgBr	$CH_3(C_6H_5)_2CCH_2COC_6H_2$-2,4,6-$(CH_3)_3$ (62%); recovered ketone (25%)	*538*
$C_{19}H_{21}ON$			
$(CH_2)_5NCH_2COC_6H_4$-4-C_6H_5	CH_3MgI (*ca.* 10 equiv.)	$CH_3[(CH_2)_5NCH_2](4\text{-}C_6H_5C_6H_4)COH$	*418*
3-[3,4-Dihydro-2(1*H*)-isoquinolyl]-4-phenyl-2-butanone	CH_3MgI	2-Methyl-3-[3,4-dihydro-2(1*H*)-isoquinolyl]-4-phenyl-2-butanol (46%)	*551*
3-[3,4-Dihydro-2(1*H*)-isoquinolyl]-4-phenyl-2-butanone (10 g., 0.036 mole)	C_6H_5MgBr (3.5 g., 0.144 mole Mg)	2,4-Diphenyl-3-[3,4-dihydro-2(1*H*)-isoquinolyl]-2-butanol (5.5 g., 43%)	*551*
$C_{19}H_{22}O$			
$C_2H_5(C_6H_5)CHCH_2COCH{=}CHC_6H_5$	C_2H_5MgBr	$[C_2H_5(C_6H_5)CHCH_2]_2CO$ (*ca.* quant.)	*111*
$C_2H_5(C_6H_5)CHCH_2COCH{=}CHC_6H_5$ (20 g.)	C_6H_5MgBr	$C_2H_5(C_6H_5)CHCH_2COCH_2CH(C_6H_5)_2$ (23 g.); $C_6H_5(C_6H_5CH{=}CH)[C_2H_5(C_6H_5)CHCH_2]$-COH (*ca.* 7%)	*111*
$C_6H_5COCH(n\text{-}C_5H_{11})C_6H_5$	1-$C_{10}H_7MgX$	$C_6H_5(1\text{-}C_{10}H_7)[n\text{-}C_5H_{11}(C_6H_5)CH]COH$	*461*
2,6-$(CH_3)_2C_6H_3COC_6H$-2,3,5,6-$(CH_3)_4$	*t*-C_4H_9MgCl	2,6-$(CH_3)_2$-4-*t*-$C_4H_9C_6H_2COC_6H$-2,3,5,6-$(CH_3)_4$ (low yield)	*528*
4-$CH_3C_6H_4COCH(n\text{-}C_4H_9)C_6H_5$	C_2H_5MgBr (2 equiv.)	$C_2H_5(4\text{-}CH_3C_6H_4)[n\text{-}C_4H_9(C_6H_5)CH]COH$	*441*

TABLE VI-XVIII (Continued)

Ketonic Comp'd	RMgX	Product(s)	Ref.
$C_{19}H_{22}O_3$			
$4\text{-}CH_3OC_6H_4COCH(C_2H_5)C_6H_4\text{-}3\text{-}OC_2H_5$ (2.6 g.)	C_2H_5MgI (1.5 g. C_2H_5I)	$C_2H_5(4\text{-}CH_3OC_6H_4)[C_2H_5(3\text{-}C_2H_5OC_6H_4CH]COH$ (2.4 g.)	*546*
$2,6\text{-}(CH_3O)_2C_6H_3COC_6H\text{-}2,3,5,6\text{-}(CH_3)_4$	CH_3MgI	$2,6\text{-}(CH_3)_2C_6H_3COC_6H\text{-}2,3,5,6\text{-}(CH_3)_4$ (47%)	*528*
$3,4\text{-}(CH_3O)_2C_6H_3COC_6H\text{-}2,3,5,6\text{-}(CH_3)_4$ (3.9 g.)	$C_6H_5CH_2MgCl$	$3\text{-}CH_3O\text{-}4\text{-}C_6H_5CH_2C_6H_3COC_6H\text{-}2,3,5,6\text{-}(CH_3)_4$ (2 g., 42%)	*515*
$3,5\text{-}(CH_3O)_2C_6H_3COC_6H\text{-}2,3,5,6\text{-}(CH_3)_4$ (2.4 g.)	$C_6H_5CH_2MgCl$	$3,5\text{-}(CH_3O)_2\text{-}4\text{-}C_6H_5CH_2C_6H_2COC_6H\text{-}2,3,5,6\text{-}(CH_3)_4$ (0.74 g., 21%)	*515*
$(4\text{-}i\text{-}C_3H_7OC_6H_4)_2CO$	$C_6H_5CH_2MgCl$	$(4\text{-}i\text{-}C_3H_7OC_6H_4)_2C{=}CHC_6H_5$	*549*
$C_{19}H_{22}O_3\text{-}C_{20}H_{24}O_3$			
$4\text{-}CH_3OC_6H_4COCH_2CHRC_6H_4\text{-}4\text{-}OCH_3$*	$R'MgX$† (2 equiv.)	$R'(4\text{-}CH_3OC_6H_4)[R(4\text{-}CH_3OC_6H_4)CHCH_2]COH$ (yielding 80–90% olefin)	*518*
$C_{20}H_{14}O$			
2-Benzoylfluorene (10 g.)	C_6H_5MgBr (10 g. C_6H_5Br)	Diphenyl-2-fluorenylmethanol (10 g., 78%)	*554*
$C_{20}H_{14}O_2$			
$1,2\text{-}(C_6H_5CO)_2C_6H_4$	C_6H_5MgBr	$2\text{-}C_6H_5COC_6H_4(C_6H_5)_2COH$ or the corresponding hydroxyphthalan (isolated, after heating at 300°, as 10,10-diphenyl-9-anthrone); recovered ketone	*555*
$C_{20}H_{16}O$			
$C_6H_5COCH(C_6H_5)_2$	C_2H_5MgBr	$HO(C_2H_5)(C_6H_5)CCH(C_6H_5)$	*645*
$C_6H_5COCH(C_6H_5)_2$ (24 g.)	C_6H_5MgBr (42 g. C_6H_5Br)	$(C_6H_5)_2C{=}C(C_6H_5)OH$ (*ca.* 21 g., crude); $(C_6H_5)_2CH(C_6H_5)_2COH$ (5 g.)‡	*552*

* R = C_2H_5, $n\text{-}C_3H_7$.

† $R'MgX$ = CH_3MgI, C_2H_5MgBr, $n\text{-}C_3H_7MgBr$.

‡ Gradual (twenty minutes) addition of powdered ketone to Grignard reagent solution; 4 hours reflux.

TABLE VI-XVIII (Continued)

Ketonic Comp'd	RMgX	Product(s)	Ref.
$C_{20}H_{16}O$ (*cont.*)			
$C_6H_5COCH(C_6H_5)_2$ (20 g.)	C_6H_5MgBr (70 g. C_6H_5Br)	$(C_6H_5)_2C{=}C(C_6H_5)OH$ (8.7 g.); $(C_6H_5)_2CH(C_6H_5)_2COH$ (5 g.)*	*552*
$C_6H_5COCH(C_6H_5)_2$ (54.5 g.)	$C_6H_5CH_2MgCl$ (90 ml. C_7H_7Cl)	$C_6H_5(C_6H_5CH_2)[(C_6H_5)_2CH]COH$ (60 g.)	*556*
$C_6H_5CH_2COC_6H_4$-4-C_6H_5	C_6H_5MgBr	$C_6H_5(C_6H_5CH_2)(4\text{-}C_6H_5C_6H_4)COH$	*441*
4-$CH_3C_6H_4COC_6H_4$-4-C_6H_5	4-$CH_3C_6H_4MgBr$	4-$C_6H_5C_6H_4(4\text{-}CH_3C_6H_4)_2COH$	*431*
$C_{20}H_{16}O_2$			
$C_6H_5COCH(OC_6H_5)C_6H_5$	2-$C_6H_5C_6H_4MgI$	$C_6H_5(4\text{-}C_6H_5C_6H_4)[C_6H_5(C_6H_5O)CH]COH$	*471*
4-$CH_3OC_6H_4COC_6H_4$-4-C_6H_5 (20 g.)	$C_6H_5CH_2MgCl$ (15 g. C_7H_7Cl)	4-$CH_3OC_6H_4(4\text{-}C_6H_5C_6H_4)C{=}CHC_6H_5$ (10 g.)	*485*
4-$CH_3OC_6H_4COC_6H_4$-4-C_6H_5	4-$CH_3OC_6H_4MgBr$	4-$C_6H_5C_6H_4(4\text{-}CH_3OC_6H_4)_2COH$	*431*
5-Anisoylacenaphthene (25 g.)	$C_6H_5CH_2MgCl$ (15 g. C_7H_7Cl)	1-Anisyl-1-(5-acenaphthenyl)-2-phenylethene (70%)	*485*
$C_{20}H_{16}O_3$			
2-*o*-$CH_3C_6H_4COC_{10}H_6$-1-CO_2CH_3	CH_3MgI (*ca.* 1 equiv.)	3-Methyl-3-*o*-tolyl-6,7-benzophthalide (51% on basis of ketone consumed); recovered ketone	*331*
$C_{20}H_{18}O$			
$C_2H_5(C_6H_5)CHCO$-2-$C_{10}H_7$ (10 g.)	CH_3MgI (excess)	$C_2H_5(C_6H_5)C{=}C(CH_3)$-2-$C_{10}H_7$ (8 g.); a little carbinol	*543*
$C_2H_5(C_6H_5)CHCO$-2-$C_{10}H_7$ (10 g.)	C_2H_5MgBr (excess)	$C_2H_5(C_6H_5)C{=}C(C_2H_5)$-2-$C_{10}H_7$ (8.75 g.); a little carbinol	*543*
2,4,6-$(CH_3)_3C_6H_2CO$-1-$C_{10}H_7$ (54.8 g.)	CH_3MgI (42.6 g. CH_3I)	3-Mesitoyl-2-methyl-1,2-dihydronaphthalene (58%)	*327*

* Addition of ketone to Grignard reagent solution; seven hours reflux.

TABLE VI-XVIII (Continued)

Ketonic Comp'd	RMgX	Product(s)	Ref.
$C_{20}H_{18}O$ (*cont.*)			
2,4,6-$(CH_3)_3C_6H_2CO$-1-$C_{10}H_7$ (5 g.)	C_6H_5MgBr (10.5 g. C_6H_5Br)	1-HO-2-$C_6H_5C_{10}H_6$ (1.0 g.); 2,4,6-$(CH_3)_3C_6H_2CO_2H$ (0.4 g.); tar	*491*
2,4,6-$(CH_3)_3C_6H_2CO$-2-$C_{10}H_7$ (27.4 g.)	CH_3I (excess)	1-$CH_3C_{10}H_6$-2-[COC_6H_2-2,4,6-$(CH_3)_3$] (2.0 g.); 1-methyl-2-mesitoyl-1,2-dihydronaphthalene; 2 unidentified products	327
2,4,6-$(CH_3)_3C_6H_2CO$-2-$C_{10}H_7$	RMgX*	Intractable oils	*646*
2,4,6-$(CH_3)_3C_6H_2CO$-2-$C_{10}H_7$	4-$CH_3C_6H_4MgBr$	1-*p*-$CH_3C_6H_4C_{10}H_6$-2-[COC_6H_2-2,4,6-$(CH_3)_3$] (48%)	*646*
2,4,6-$(CH_3)_3C_6H_2CO$-2-$C_{10}H_7$	4-*i*-$C_3H_7C_6H_4MgBr$	1-*p*-*i*-$C_3H_7C_6H_4C_{10}H_6$-2-[COC_6H_2-2,4,6-$(CH_3)_3$] (44%)	*646*
$C_{20}H_{21}ON$			
$C_6H_5COC[N(CH_2)_5]{=}CHC_6H_5$ (11 g.)	C_6H_5MgBr (2.5 g. Mg)	$C_6H_5COCH[N(CH_2)_5]CH(C_6H_5)_2$ (61%)	*559*
$C_{20}H_{22}O$			
[2,4,6-$(CH_3)_3C_6H_2]_2CO$ (8.4 g.)	CH_3MgI (3 ml. CH_3I)	[2,4,6-$(CH_3)_3C_6H_2]_2C{=}C(CH_3)OH$ (7 g., crude)	*500*
[2,4,6-$(CH_3)_3C_6H_2]_2CO$	*t*-C_4H_9MgCl	[2,4,6-$(CH_3)_3C_6H_2]_2C{=}CHOH$ (86%)	*501*
[2,4,6-$(CH_3)_3C_6H_2]_2CO$ (5.6 g.)	C_6H_5MgBr (4.8 g. C_6H_5Br)	[2,4,6-$(CH_3)_3C_6H_2]_2C{=}C(C_6H_5)OH$ (3 g.)	*500*
$C_{20}H_{23}ON$			
$C_6H_5COCH[N(CH_2)_5]CH_2C_6H_5$ (2.9 g.)	C_6H_5MgBr (0.96 g. Mg)	$HO(C_6H_5)_2CCH[N(CH_2)_5]CH_2C_6H_5$	*559*
$C_{20}H_{24}O$			
2,4,6-$(CH_3)_3C_6H_2COCH_2C_6H_2$-2,4,6-$(CH_3)_3$	CH_3MgX	Enolization (96%)†	*312*

* RMgX = $(CH_2)_5CHMgX$, 4-ClC_6H_4MgBr, $C_6H_5CH_2MgCl$.
† "Grignard machine" study.

TABLE VI-XVIII (Continued)

Ketonic Comp'd	RMgX	Product(s)	Ref.
$C_{20}H_{24}O$ (*cont.*)			
2,4,6-$(CH_3)_3C_6H_2COCH_2C_6H_2$-2,4,6-$(CH_3)_3$	C_2H_5MgBr	Enolization*	*312*
2,4,6-$(CH_3)_3C_6H_2COC_6H$-2,3,5,6-$(CH_3)_4$	*s*-C_4H_9MgBr	"No product"	*528*
$C_{20}H_{24}ON_2$			
N-Methylcinchotoxine	CH_3MgI (or C_6H_5MgBr)	Recovered ketone	*418*
$C_{20}H_{24}O_3$			
4-$CH_3OC_6H_4COCH_2CH$(*i*-C_3H_7)C_6H_4-4-OCH_3	$(CH_2)_5CHMgCl$	$(CH_2)_5CH(4\text{-}CH_3OC_6H_4)$[*i*-$C_3H_7$(4-$CH_3OC_6H_4$)-$CHCH_2$]COH	*514*
4-$CH_3OC_6H_4COCH(CH_3)CH(C_2H_5)C_6H_4$-4-$OCH_3$ ("B" isomer, m.p., 72°)	CH_3MgI (2 equiv.)	After dehydr'n: 4-$CH_3OC_6H_4C$(=CH_2)-$CH(CH_3)CH(C_2H_5)C_6H_4$-4-OCH_3, b.p. (1 mm.), 175–177° (*ca.* 80%)	*553*
4-$CH_3OC_6H_4COCH(CH_3)CH(C_2H_5)C_6H_4$-4-$OCH_3$ ("A" isomer, m.p., 52°)	C_2H_5MgBr (2 equiv.)	After dehydr'n: 4-$CH_3OC_6H_4C$(=$CHCH_3$)-$CH(CH_3)CH(C_2H_5)C_6H_4$-4-OCH_3, b.p. (1 mm.), 175° (*ca.* 80%)	*553*
$C_{20}H_{24}O_4$			
$CH_3COC(CH_3)(CO_2C_2H_5)CH_2CH_2$-1-$C_{10}H_6$-6-$OCH_3$ (7.7 parts)	C_2H_5MgBr (3.3 parts C_2H_5Br)	$HO(CH_3)(C_2H_5)CC(CH_3)(CO_2C_2H_5)CH_2CH_2$-1-$C_{10}H_6$-6-$OCH_3$ (8.1 parts)	*560*
$C_{20}H_{30}ON_2$			
$CH_3COCH[N(CH_2)_5]CH[N(CH_2)_5]C_6H_5$	C_6H_5MgBr	$HO(CH_3)(C_6H_5)CCH[N(CH_2)_5]CH[N(CH_2)_5]$-$C_6H_5$ (13%)	*561*

*"Grignard machine" study.

TABLE VI-XVIII (Continued)

Ketonic Comp'd	RMgX	Product(s)	Ref.
$C_{20}H_{32}O_3$			
2,5-$(CH_3O)_2C_6H_3CO$-*n*-$C_{11}H_{23}$	CH_3MgI	$CH_3[2,5\text{-}(CH_3O)_2C_6H_3]C{=}CH$-*n*-$C_{10}H_{21}$ (60–70%)	*557*
$C_{20}H_{38}O_2$			
$[C_2H_5CO(CH_2)_7—]_2$	*n*-$C_{16}H_{33}C{\equiv}CMgBr$	$[HO(C_2H_5)$(*n*-$C_{16}H_{32}C{\equiv}C)C(CH_2)_7—]_2$ (88%)	*558*
$C_{20}H_{40}O$			
n-C_4H_9CO-*n*-$C_{15}H_{31}$	*n*-$C_6H_{13}MgBr$	*n*-C_4H_9(*n*-C_6H_{13})(*n*-$C_{15}H_{31}$)COH	*496*
n-C_4H_9CO-*n*-$C_{15}H_{31}$	*n*-$C_{10}H_{21}MgBr$	*n*-C_4H_9(*n*-$C_{10}H_{21}$)(*n*-$C_{15}H_{21}$)COH	*496*
$C_{21}H_{14}O$			
2-Benzoylphenanthrene	C_6H_5MgBr	Diphenyl-2-phenanthrylmethanol (53%)	*562*
3-Benzoylphenanthrene	C_6H_5MgBr	Diphenyl-3-phenanthrylmethanol (89%)	*562*
Anthraphenone (5 g.)	C_6H_5MgBr (4 equiv.)	Recovered ketone (3.5 g.); 9,9′-bis-(10-benzoyl-9,10-dihydroanthracyl)	*565*
$(1\text{-}C_{10}H_7)_2CO$	$C_6H_5C{\equiv}CMgBr$	$C_6H_5C{\equiv}C(1\text{-}C_{10}H_7)_2COH$ (90%)	*65*
$(1\text{-}C_{10}H_7)_2CO$	$1\text{-}C_{10}H_7MgBr$	$(1\text{-}C_{10}H_7)_3COH$	*563,564*
$C_{21}H_{16}O$			
$C_6H_5COCH{=}C(C_6H_5)_2$ (40 g.)	C_6H_5MgBr	$(C_6H_5)_2C{=}CH(C_6H_5)_2COH$; diene; $C_6H_5COCH_2C(C_6H_5)_3$ (8 g.)	*111*
$C_6H_5COCH{=}C(C_6H_5)_2$	C_6H_5MgBr (2 equiv.)	$(C_6H_5)_2C{=}CH(C_6H_5)_2COH$; diene	*111,455*
$C_6H_5COC(C_6H_5){=}CHC_6H_5$	CH_3MgI (4 equiv.)	$HO(CH_3)(C_6H_5)C(C_6H_5){=}CHC_6H_5$ (53.6–63.4%)	*591*
$C_6H_5COC(C_6H_5){=}CHC_6H_5$, m. 102° (5.0 g.)	C_2H_5MgBr	$C_6H_5COCH(C_6H_5)CH(C_2H_5)C_6H_5$ (6.2 g., yielding 0.8 g. of isomer m. 170° and 5.1 g. of isomer m. 92°)	*645*

TABLE VI-XVIII (Continued)

Ketonic Comp'd	RMgX	Product (s)	Ref.
$C_{21}H_{16}O$ (*cont.*)			
$C_6H_5COC(C_6H_5){=}CHC_6H_5$, m. 88–89° (5.0 g.)	C_2H_5MgBr	$C_6H_5COCH(C_6H_5)CH(C_2H_5)C_6H_5$ (6.3 g., yielding 0.7 g. of isomer m. 170° and 5.3 g. of isomer m. 92°)	645
$C_6H_5COC(C_6H_5){=}CHC_6H_5$ (50 g.)	C_6H_5MgBr (10 g. Mg)	$C_6H_5COCH(C_6H_5)CH(C_6H_5)_2$ (61 g., 95.8%)	591
$C_6H_5COC(C_6H_5){=}CHC_6H_5$ (25 g.)	$C_6H_5CH_2MgCl$ (12.6 g. C_7H_7Cl)	$C_6H_5COCH(C_6H_5)CH(C_6H_5)CH_2C_6H_5$ (8.5 g.)	435
2-Benzoyl-9-methylfluorene	C_6H_5MgBr	Diphenyl-2-(9-methylfluorenyl)methanol	554
Dihydroanthraphenone (5.0 g.)	C_6H_5MgBr (9.5 g. C_6H_5Br)	9-(9,10-Dihydroanthracyl)diphenylmethanol (4.0 g.)	565
$C_{21}H_{16}O_2$			
$C_6H_5COCOCH(C_6H_5)_2$	CH_3MgI	$C_6H_5COC(OH)(CH_3)CH(C_6H_5)_2$*	566
$C_6H_5COCOCH(C_6H_5)_2$	CH_3MgI	$(C_6H_5)_2CHCOC(OH)(CH_3)C_6H_5$†	566
$C_6H_5COCOCH(C_6H_5)_2$ (10 g.)	C_6H_5MgBr (excess)	$C_6H_5COC(OH)(C_6H_5)CH(C_6H_5)_2$ (9.5 g.)	566
Benzylidene-4-phenylacetophenone oxide	C_6H_5MgBr	$[C_6H_5(p\text{-}C_6H_5C_6H_4)COH{-}]_2$; $HO(C_6H_5)$-$CHCH(C_6H_5)C(C_6H_5)(C_6H_4\text{-}4\text{-}C_6H_5)OH$	492
1,1-Diphenyl-2-benzoylepoxyethane	C_2H_5MgI (excess)	$(C_6H_5)_2CHCHO$	430
1,1-Diphenyl-2-benzoylepoxyethane	C_6H_5MgBr (excess)	$(C_6H_5)_2CHCHO$; $(C_6H_5)_2CHCH_2OH$; $(C_6H_5{-})_2$	430
$C_{21}H_{16}O_3S$			
$C_6H_5COCH{=}C(C_6H_5)SO_2C_6H_5$ (7.0 g.)	C_6H_5MgBr (4 equiv.)	$HO(C_6H_5)_2CCH{=}C(C_6H_5)SO_2C_6H_5$‡	654
$C_6H_5COCH{=}C(C_6H_5)SO_2C_6H_5$ (10.0 g.)	C_6H_5MgBr (2.25 g. Mg)	$HO(C_6H_5)_2CCH{=}C(C_6H_5)SO_2C_6H_5$ (57%); $HO(C_6H_5)_2CCH(C_6H_5)CH(C_6H_5)SO_2C_6H_5$, m. 178° (15%); $HO(C_6H_5)_2CCH(C_6H_5)CH$-$(C_6H_5)SO_2C_6H_5$, m. 223° (12%)§	654

* Addition of Grignard reagent solution to Et_2O-ketone solution.
† Addition of Et_2O-ketone solution to Grignard reagent solution.
‡ Several hours stirring at room temperature.
§ Two hours reflux.

TABLE VI-XVIII (Continued)

Ketonic Comp'd	RMgX	Product(s)	Ref.
$C_{21}H_{16}O_3S$ (*cont.*)			
$C_6H_5COCH{=}C(C_6H_5)SO_2C_6H_5$ (10.0 g.)	C_6H_5MgBr (2.25 g. Mg)	$HO(C_6H_5)_2CCH{=}C(C_6H_5)SO_2C_6H_5$ (22%); $HO(C_6H_5)_2CCH(C_6H_5)CH(C_6H_5)SO_2C_6H_5$, m. 178° (26%); $(C_6H_5)_2C{=}C(C_6H_5)CH(C_6H_5)SO_2C_6H_5$ (?), m. 196° (32%)*	654
$C_{21}H_{17}OBr$			
$C_6H_5COCHBrCH(C_6H_5)_2$	C_6H_5MgBr	$C_6H_5COCH_2CH(C_6H_5)_2$; $(C_6H_5{-}{-})_2$	275
$C_6H_5COCHBrCH(C_6H_5)_2$ (25 g.)	$C_6H_5C{\equiv}CMgBr$ (11.5 g. $C_6H_5C{\equiv}CH$)	$HO(C_6H_5)(C_6H_5C{\equiv}C)CCHBrCH(C_6H_5)_2$ (19 g.)	567
$C_{21}H_{17}OCl$			
$4\text{-}ClC_6H_4COCH_2CH(C_6H_5)_2$ (45 g.)	C_6H_5MgBr (25 g. C_6H_5Br)	$4\text{-}ClC_6H_4(C_6H_5)[(C_6H_5)_2CHCH_2]COH$ (40 g.)	453
$C_{21}H_{17}OI$			
$C_6H_5COCHICH(C_6H_5)_2$	C_6H_5MgBr	$C_6H_5COCH_2CH(C_6H_5)_2$ (94%); C_6H_5I (96.5%)	437
$C_{21}H_{18}O$			
$C_6H_5COCH_2CH(C_6H_5)_2$	CH_3MgBr	$CH_3(C_6H_5)C{=}CHCH(C_6H_5)_2$	223
$C_6H_5COCH_2CH(C_6H_5)_2$	C_6H_5MgBr	$(C_6H_5)_2CHCH_2(C_6H_5)_2COH$	569
$C_6H_5COCH(C_6H_5)CH_2C_6H_5$	$t\text{-}C_4H_9MgCl$	$t\text{-}C_4H_9(C_6H_5)[C_6H_5(C_6H_5CH_2)CH]COH$	648
DL-$C_6H_5COCH(C_6H_5)CH_2C_6H_5$ (5 g.)	C_6H_5MgBr (11.5 g. C_6H_5Br)	$C_6H_5CH_2(C_6H_5)CH(C_6H_5)_2COH$ (4 g.)	568
$C_6H_5COCH(C_6H_5)CH_2C_6H_5$ (23 g.)	$C_6H_5CH_2MgCl$ (14 ml. C_7H_7Cl)	$C_6H_5(C_6H_5CH_2)[C_6H_5CH_2(C_6H_5)CH]COH$ (22 g., purified)	435
$C_6H_5COCH(C_6H_5)C_6H_4\text{-}4\text{-}CH_3$ (2 g.)	$4\text{-}CH_3C_6H_4MgBr$	$C_6H_5(4\text{-}CH_3C_6H_4)[C_6H_5(4\text{-}CH_3C_6H_4)CH]COH$ (0.5 g.)	426

*Six hours reflux.

TABLE VI-XVIII (Continued)

Ketonic Comp'd	RMgX	Product(s)	Ref.
$C_{21}H_{18}OS$			
$C_6H_5COCH(C_6H_5)SC_6H_4$-4-$CH_3$	C_6H_5MgBr (excess)	$HO(C_6H_5)_2CCH(C_6H_5)SC_6H_4$-4-$CH_3$ (*ca.* quant.)	*652*
$C_{21}H_{18}O_2$			
$C_6H_5COC(OCH_3)(C_6H_5)_2$	C_6H_5MgBr	$HO(C_6H_5)_2CC(OCH_3)(C_6H_5)_2$ (66%)	*570*
$C_6H_5COCH_2CH(C_6H_5)C_6H_4$-2-OH (5 g.)	C_6H_5MgBr	2-$HOC_6H_4(C_6H_5)CHCH_2(C_6H_5)_2COH$ (4.3 g.)	*571,572*
$C_6H_5COCH_2CH(C_6H_5)C_6H_4$-2-OH	C_6H_5MgBr	2,4-Diphenylflavan	*572*
4-$CH_3OC_6H_4COC_6H_4$-2-$CH_2C_6H_5$	4-$CH_3OC_6H_4MgI$	2-$C_6H_5CH_2C_6H_4(4$-$CH_3OC_6H_4)_2COH$	*573*
$C_{21}H_{19}O_5Br$			
1,1-Dicarbomethoxy-2-benzoyl-3-(3-bromo-4-methoxyphenyl)cyclopropane	C_2H_5MgBr	1,1-Dicarbomethoxy-2-(α-hydroxy-α-phenylpropyl)-3-(3-bromo-4-methoxyphenyl)cyclopropane (2 isomers, m. 135° and 161°)	*574*
$C_{21}H_{20}O_2$			
2,4,6-$(CH_3)_3C_6H_2CO$-1-$C_{10}H_6$-2-OCH_3	CH_3MgI	2,4,6-$(CH_3)_3C_6H_2CO$-1-$C_{10}H_6$-2-CH_3 (56%)	*519*
2,4,6-$(CH_3)_3C_6H_2CO$-1-$C_{10}H_6$-2-OCH_3 (7.6 g.)	C_2H_5MgBr (4.2 g. C_2H_5Br)	2,4,6-$(CH_3)_3C_6H_2CO$-1-$C_{10}H_6$-2-C_2H_5 (6 g., 80%)	*519*
2,4,6-$(CH_3)_3C_6H_2CO$-1-$C_{10}H_6$-2-OCH_3	*n*-C_4H_9MgBr	2,4,6-$(CH_3)_3C_6H_2CO$-1-$C_{10}H_6$-2-*n*-C_4H_9 (55%)	*519*
2,4,6-$(CH_3)_3C_6H_5$ CO-1-$C_{10}H_6$-2-OCH_3	C_6H_5MgBr	2,4,6-$(CH_3)_3C_6H_2CO$-1-$C_{10}H_6$-2-C_6H_5 (59%)	*519*
2,4,6-$(CH_3)_3C_6H_2CO$-1-$C_{10}H_6$-2-OCH_3	1-$C_{10}H_7MgBr$	2,4,6-$(CH_3)_3C_6H_2CO$-1-$C_{10}H_6$-2-α-$C_{10}H_7$ (76%)	*519*
2,4,6-$(CH_3)_3C_6H_2CO$-2-$C_{10}H_6$-1-OCH_3 (0.5 g.)	CH_3MgI (1.2 g. CH_3I)	2,4,6-$(CH_3)_3C_6H_2CO$-2-$C_{10}H_6$-1-CH_3 (74%)	*646*
2,4,6-$(CH_3)_3C_6H_2CO$-2-$C_{10}H_6$-1-OCH_3	C_2H_5MgBr	2,4,6-$(CH_3)_3C_6H_2CO$-2-$C_{10}H_6$-1-C_2H_5 (73%)	*646*
2,4,6-$(CH_3)_3C_6H_2CO$-2-$C_{10}H_6$-1-OCH_3	C_6H_5MgBr	2,4,6-$(CH_3)_3C_6H_2CO$-2-$C_{10}H_6$-1-C_6H_5 (69%)	*646*
2,4,6-$(CH_3)_3C_6H_2CO$-2-$C_{10}H_6$-1-OCH_3 (1.1 g.)	$C_6H_5CH_2MgCl$ (0.9 g. C_7H_7Cl)	2,4,6-$(CH_3)_3C_6H_2CO$-2-$C_{10}H_6$-1-$CH_2C_6H_5$ (91%)	*646*

TABLE VI-XVIII (Continued)

Ketonic Comp'd	RMgX	Product(s)	Ref.
$C_{21}H_{20}O_2$ (*cont.*)			
2,4,6-$(CH_3)_3C_6H_2CO$-2-$C_{10}H_6$-1-OCH_3	4-$CH_3C_6H_4MgBr$	2,4,6-$(CH_3)_3C_6H_2CO$-2-$C_{10}H_6$-1-C_6H_4-4-CH_3 (75%)	*646*
2,4,6-$(CH_3)_3C_6H_2CO$-2-$C_{10}H_6$-1-OCH_3	4-*i*-$C_3H_7C_6H_4MgBr$	2,4,6-$(CH_3)_3C_6H_2CO$-2-$C_{10}H_6$-1-C_6H_4-4-*i*-C_3H_7 (56%)	*646*
$C_{21}H_{22}O$			
1-Mesitoyl-2-methyl-1,2-dihydronaphthalene	CH_3MgI	CH_4 (0.98 equiv.); enolate, isolated as acetate	*327*
1-Mesitoyl-2-methyl-1,2-dihydronaphthalene	C_2H_5MgI (3-fold excess)	Enolate, isolated as peroxide, which on decomp'n yielded mesitoic acid and 3,3'-dimethyl-4,4'-dihydroxy-1,1'-binaphthyl	*327*
2,4,6-$(CH_3)_3C_6H_2COC \equiv CC_6H_2$-2,4,6-$(CH_3)_3$ (4.39 g.)	CH_3MgI (6.5 g. CH_3I)	2,4,6-$(CH_3)_3C_6H_2COCH = C(CH_3)C_6H_2$-2,4,6-$(CH_3)_3$ (4.2 g., 91%), separated into isomer "A," m. 101–103° (3.28 g., 72%) and isomer "B," m. 75–76° (0.13 g., 2.9%)	*393*
2,4,6-$(CH_3)_3C_6H_2COC \equiv CC_6H_2$-2,4,6-$(CH_3)_3$	C_6H_5MgBr	$C_6H_5[2,4,6\text{-}(CH_3)_3C_6H_2]C = CHCOC_6H_2$-2,4,6-$(CH_3)_3$, m. 119–120°	*393*
2,4,6-$(CH_3)_3C_6H_2COC \equiv CC_6H_2$-2,4,6-$(CH_3)_3$	2,4,6-$(CH_3)_3C_6H_2MgBr$	$[2,4,6\text{-}(CH_3)_3C_6H_2]_2C = CHCOC_6H_2$-2,4,6-$(CH_3)_3$ (35%); $C_{30}H_{36}O$, m. 182–183°	*393*
$C_{21}H_{24}O$			
2,4,6-$(CH_3)_3C_6H_2COCH = CHC_6H_2$-2,4,6-$(CH_3)_3$	RMgX	1,4-Addition products, only	*401*
2,4,6-$(CH_3)_3C_6H_2COCH = CHC_6H_2$-2,4,6-$(CH_3)_3$ (11.5 g.)	CH_3MgI (13.0 g. CH_3I)	2,4,6-$(CH_3)_3C_6H_2COCH_2CH(CH_3)C_6H_2$-2,4,6-$(CH_3)_3$ ("high yield")	*393*
2,4,6-$(CH_3)_3C_6H_2COCH = CHC_6H_2$-2,4,6-$(CH_3)_3$	C_6H_5MgBr	2,4,6-$(CH_3)_3C_6H_2COCH_2CH(C_6H_5)C_6H_2$-2,4,6-$(CH_3)_3$	*393*

TABLE VI-XVIII (Continued)

Ketonic Comp'd	RMgX	Product(s)	Ref.
$C_{21}H_{24}O$ (*cont.*)			
2,4,6-$(CH_3)_3C_6H_2COCH{=}CHC_6H_2$-2,4,6-$(CH_3)_3$ (8.42 g.)	2,4,6-$(CH_3)_3C_6H_2MgBr$ (*ca.* 0.1 mole)	2,4,6-$(CH_3)_3C_6H_2COCH_2CH[C_6H_2$-2,4,6-$(CH_3)_3]_2$ (46%)	393
2,4,6-$(CH_3)_3C_6H_2COC[C_6H_2$-2,4,6-$(CH_3)_3]{=}CH_2$	CH_3MgI	$C_2H_5[2,4,6\text{-}(CH_3)_3C_6H_2]C{=}C[C_6H_2$-2,4,6-$(CH_3)_3]OH$	575
2,4,6-$(CH_3)_3C_6H_2COC[C_6H_2$-2,4,6-$(CH_3)_3]{=}CH_2$	C_6H_5MgBr	$C_6H_5CH_2[2,4,6\text{-}(CH_3)_3C_6H_2]C{=}C[C_6H_2$-2,4,6-$(CH_3)_3]OH$	575
$C_{21}H_{26}O$			
2,3,5,6-$(CH_3)_4C_6HCOC_6H_4$-4-*t*-C_4H_9 (4.4 g.)	CH_3MgI (2.8 ml. CH_3I)	2,3,5,6-$(CH_3)_4C_6HCOC_6H_3$-2-CH_3-4-*t*-C_4H_9	528
$C_{21}H_{26}O_3$			
4-$CH_3OC_6H_4COCH(C_2H_5)CH(C_2H_5)$-$C_6H_4$-4-$OCH_3$ ["A" isomer, b. (2 mm.) 181–183°]	CH_3MgI (2 equiv.)	After dehydration: 4-$CH_3OC_6H_4C({=}CH_2)$-$[CH(C_2H_5)]_2C_6H_4$-4-OCH_3, b. (1 mm.) 174–176°. (*ca.* 80%)	353
4-$CH_3OC_6H_4COCH(C_2H_5)CH(C_2H_5)$-$C_6H_4$-4-$OCH_3$ ["A" isomer, b. (2 mm.) 181–183°]	C_2H_5MgBr (2 equiv.)	After dehydration: 4-$CH_3OC_6H_4C({=}CHCH_3)$-$[CH(C_2H_5)]_2C_6H_4$-4-OCH_3, b. (1 mm.) 178° (*ca.* 80%)	353
4-$CH_3OC_6H_4COCH(C_2H_5)CH(C_2H_5)$-$C_6H_4$-4-$OCH_3$ ["A" isomer, b. (2 mm.) 181–183°]	*n*-C_3H_7MgBr (2 equiv.)	After dehydration: 4-$CH_3OC_6H_4C$-$({=}CHC_2H_5)[CH(C_2H_5)]_2C_6H_4$-4-$OCH_3$, b. (1 mm.) 190°, (*ca.* 80%)	353
4-$CH_3OC_6H_4COCH(C_2H_5)CH(C_2H_5)$-$C_6H_4$-4-$OCH_3$)"B" isomer, m. 82°)	CH_3MgI (2 equiv.)	After dehydration: 4-$CH_3OC_6H_4C({=}CH_2)$-$[CH(C_2H_5)]_2C_6H_4$-4-OCH_3, m. 44° (*ca.* 80%)	353
4-$CH_3OC_6H_4COCH(C_2H_5)CH(C_2H_5)$-$C_6H_4$-4-$OCH_3$ ("B" isomer, m. 82°)	C_2H_5MgBr (2 equiv.)	After dehydration: 4-$CH_3OC_6H_4C({=}CHCH_3)$-$[CH(C_2H_5)]_2C_6H_4$-4-OCH_3 b. (1 mm.) 190° (*ca.* 80%)	353
4-$CH_3OC_6H_4COCH(C_2H_5)CH(C_2H_5)$-$C_6H_4$-4-$OCH_3$ ("B" isomer, m. 82°)	*n*-C_3H_7MgBr (2 equiv.)	After dehydration: 4-$CH_3OC_6H_4C$-$({=}CHC_2H_5)[CH(C_2H_5)]_2C_6H_4$-4-$OCH_3$, b. (1 mm.) 190° (*ca.* 80%)	353

TABLE VI-XVIII (Continued)

Ketonic Comp'd	RMgX	Product(s)	Ref.
$C_{21}H_{28}ON_2$			
$[4\text{-}(C_2H_5)_2NC_6H_4]_2CO$	CH_3MgI	$[4\text{-}(C_2H_5)_2NC_6H_4]_2C{=}CH_2$	477
$[4\text{-}(C_2H_5)_2NC_6H_4]_2CO$	C_2H_5MgI	$[4\text{-}(C_2H_5)_2NC_6H_4]_2C{=}CHCH_3$	477
$C_{22}H_{16}O_2$			
$C_6H_5COCH{=}C(C_6H_5)COC_6H_5$ (15 parts)	C_6H_5MgBr (35 parts C_6H_5Br)	2,3,4,5-Tetraphenylfuran (40-60%); $[C_6H_5(C_6H_5CO)CH\text{—}]_2$; $[C_6H_5(C_6H_5CO)\text{-}C{=}]_2$; "dihydroxylepidine"	602
$C_{22}H_{19}ON$			
1-Benzyl-2-phenyl-3-benzoylethyleneimine	CH_3MgI (4 equiv.)	1-Benzyl-2,4-diphenyl-4-hydroxy-α-butyleneimine (85%)	484
1-Benzyl-2-phenyl-3-benzoylethyleneimine	C_6H_5MgBr (4 equiv.)	1-Benzyl-2,4,4-triphenyl-4-hydroxypropyleneimine (90%)	484
1-Benzyl-2-phenyl-3-benzoylethyleneimine	$4\text{-}CH_3C_6H_4MgBr$ (4 equiv.)	1-Benzyl-2,4-diphenyl-4-*p*-tolyl-4-hydroxypropyleneimine, m.p. 138° (85%)	484
$C_{22}H_{20}O$			
$C_6H_5CH_2COCH(C_6H_5)CH_2C_6H_5$ (3.0 g.)	$C_6H_5CH_2MgCl$ (3.8 g. C_7H_7Cl)	$C_6H_5(C_6H_5CH_2)CH(C_6H_5CH_2)_2COH$ (3.6 g., 92%)	498
$C_{22}H_{20}O_2$			
$C_6H_5COC(OC_2H_5)(C_6H_5)_2$	C_6H_5MgBr	$HO(C_6H_5)_2CC(OC_2H_5)(C_6H_5)_2$ (75%)	570
$HO(CH_3)(C_6H_5)CCOCH(C_6H_5)_2$ (2 g.)	C_6H_5MgBr (2 g. Mg)	$HO(CH_3)(C_6H_5)CC(OH)(C_6H_5)CH(C_6H_5)_2$ (0.5 g.)	566
$C_{22}H_{24}O_2$			
$[2,4,6\text{-}(CH_3)_3C_6H_2COCH{=}]_2$ (50 g.)	$t\text{-}C_4H_9MgCl$ (5 equiv.)	$2,4,6\text{-}(CH_3)_3C_6H_2C(OH){=}CHCH(t\text{-}C_4H_9)COC_6H_2\text{-}2,4,6\text{-}(CH_3)_3$ (29.6 g.)	576

TABLE VI-XVIII (Continued)

Ketonic Comp'd	RMgX	Product(s)	Ref.
$C_{22}H_{24}O_2$ (*cont.*)			
$[2,4,6\text{-}(CH_3)_3C_6H_2COCH{=}]_2$	C_6H_5MgBr	$2,4,6\text{-}(CH_3)_3C_6H_2COCH_2CH(C_6H_5)COC_6H_2\text{-}2,4,6\text{-}(CH_3)_3$ (59–60%)	488
$C_{22}H_{26}O$			
$2,4,6\text{-}(CH_3)_3C_6H_2COC(CH_3){=}CHC_6H_2\text{-}2,4,6\text{-}(CH_3)_3$ (8.9 g.)	$2,4,6\text{-}(CH_3)_3C_6H_2MgBr$ (0.08 mole)	$2,4,6\text{-}(CH_3)_3C_6H_2COCH(CH_3)CH[C_6H_2\text{-}2,4,6\text{-}(CH_3)_3]_2$ (46%)	393
$2,3,4,6\text{-}(CH_3)_4C_6HCOC[C_6H_2\text{-}2,4,6\text{-}(CH_3)_3]{=}CH_2$	C_6H_5MgBr	$2,3,4,6\text{-}(CH_3)_4C_6HC(OH){=}C(C_6H_5)C_6H_2\text{-}2,4,6\text{-}(CH_3)_3$	575
$2,3,5,6\text{-}(CH_3)_4C_6HCOC[C_6H_2\text{-}2,4,6\text{-}(CH_3)_3]{=}CH_2$	CH_3MgI	$2,3,5,6\text{-}(CH_3)_4C_6HC(OH){=}C(C_2H_5)C_6H_2\text{-}2,4,6\text{-}(CH_3)_3$	575
$C_{22}H_{28}O_3$			
$4\text{-}CH_3OC_6H_4COCH(n\text{-}C_3H_7)CH(C_2H_5)\text{-}C_6H_4\text{-}4\text{-}OCH_3$ ["A" isomer; b. (2 mm.), 183–185°]	CH_3MgI (2 equiv.)	After dehydration: $4\text{-}CH_3OC_6H_4C({=}CH_2)\text{-}CH(n\text{-}C_3H_7)CH(C_2H_5)C_6H_4\text{-}4\text{-}OCH_3$, b. (1 mm.), 186–188° (*ca.* 80%)	553
$4\text{-}CH_3OC_6H_4COCH(n\text{-}C_3H_7)CH(C_2H_5)\text{-}C_6H_4\text{-}4\text{-}OCH_3$ ["A" isomer; b. (2 mm.), 182–185°]	C_2H_5MgBr (2 equiv.)	After dehydr'n: $4\text{-}CH_3OC_6H_4C({=}CHCH_3)\text{-}CH(n\text{-}C_3H_7)CH(C_2H_5)C_6H_4\text{-}4\text{-}OCH_3$, b. (1 mm.), 185° (*ca.* 80%)	553
$4\text{-}CH_3OC_6H_4COCH(n\text{-}C_3H_7)CH(C_2H_5)\text{-}C_6H_4\text{-}4\text{-}OCH_3$ ("B" isomer, m. 69°)	CH_3MgI (2 equiv.)	After dehydr'n: $4\text{-}CH_3OC_6H_4C({=}CH_2)CH\text{-}(n\text{-}C_3H_7)CH(C_2H_5)C_6H_4\text{-}4\text{-}OCH_3$, b. (1 mm.), 185° (*ca.* 80%)	553
$4\text{-}CH_3OC_6H_4COCH(n\text{-}C_3H_7)CH(C_2H_5)\text{-}C_6H_4\text{-}4\text{-}OCH_3$ ("B" isomer, m. 69°)	C_2H_5MgBr (2 equiv.)	After dehydr'n: $4\text{-}CH_3OC_6H_4C({=}CHCH_3)\text{-}CH(n\text{-}C_3H_7)CH(C_2H_5)C_6H_4\text{-}4\text{-}OCH_3$, b. (1 mm.), 174–177° (*ca.* 80%)	553
$4\text{-}CH_3OC_6H_4COCH(C_2H_5)CH(n\text{-}C_3H_7)\text{-}C_6H_4\text{-}4\text{-}OCH_3$ ("A" isomer, m. 62°)	CH_3MgI (2 equiv.)	After dehydr'n: $4\text{-}CH_3OC_6H_4C({=}CH_2)CH\text{-}(C_2H_5)CH(n\text{-}C_3H_7)C_6H_4\text{-}4\text{-}OCH_3$, b. (1 mm.), 185° (*ca.* 80%)	553

TABLE VI-XVIII (Continued)

Ketonic Comp'd	RMgX	Product (s)	Ref.
$C_{22}H_{28}O_3$ *(cont.)*			
4-$CH_3OC_6H_4COCH(C_2H_5)CH(n\text{-}C_3H_7)$-$C_6H_4$-4-$OCH_3$ ("B" isomer, m. 93°)	CH_3MgI (2 equiv.)	After dehydr'n: 4-$CH_3OC_6H_4C(=CH_2)$-$CH(C_2H_5)CH(n\text{-}C_3H_7)C_6H_4$-4-$OCH_3$, b. (1 mm.), 187° (*ca.* 80%)	*553*
$C_{22}H_{36}O$			
C_6H_5CO-*n*-$C_{15}H_{31}$	*n*-C_4H_9MgBr	*n*-$C_4H_9(C_6H_5)(n\text{-}C_{15}H_{31})COH$; "olefin" (*i.e.*, dehydr'n product)	*222*
$C_{22}H_{36}O_3$			
2,5-$(CH_3O)_2C_6H_3CO$-*n*-$C_{13}H_{27}$	CH_3MgI	2,5-$(CH_3O_2)C_6H_3C(CH_3)=CH$-*n*-$C_{12}H_{25}$ (60-70%)	*557*
$C_{23}H_{12}OBr_2$			
1-Benzoyl-6,8-dibromopyrene* (25 g.)	C_6H_5MgBr (24 g. C_6H_5Br)	Diphenyl-6,8-dibromo-1-pyrenylmethanol* (22 g.)	*579*
$C_{23}H_{14}O$			
1-Benzoylpyrene* (16 g.)	C_6H_5MgBr (14 g. C_6H_5Br)	Diphenyl-1-pyrenylmethanol* (19.5 g., with 1 mole EtOH of cryst'n)	*579*
$C_{23}H_{18}O_2$			
4-Phenacylflavene†	C_6H_5MgBr	4-(β-Hydroxy-β, β-diphenylethyl)flavene	*572,571*
$C_{23}H_{20}O$			
$C_6H_5COCH_2CH(C_6H_5)CH=CHC_6H_5$	C_6H_5MgBr (2 equiv.)	$HO(C_6H_5)_2CCH_2CH(C_6H_5)CH\equiv CHC_6H_5$ (quant.)	*581*

*The numbering of "The Ring Index" rather than that of the authors cited is here employed.

†2-Phenyl-4-phenacyl-1,4-benzopyran, or 2-phenyl-4-phenacyl-1,4-chromene.

TABLE VI-XVIII (Continued)

Ketonic Comp'd	RMgX	Product(s)	Ref.
$C_{23}H_{20}O$ (*cont.*)			
$(C_6H_5)_2CHCH_2COCH{=}CHC_6H_5$ (20.0 g.)	C_2H_5MgBr	$(C_6H_5)_2CHCH_2COCH_2CH(C_2H_5)C_6H_5$ (24.6 g.);* *no* carbinol	*111*
$(C_6H_5)_2CHCH_2COCH{=}CHC_6H_5$ (40.0 g.)	C_6H_5MgBr	$[(C_6H_5)_2CHCH_2]_2CO$ (23.2 g.); $C_6H_5(C_6H_5CH{=}CH)[(C_6H_5)_2CHCH_2]COH$ (trace)	*111*
$C_{23}H_{20}O_3$			
$(C_6H_5COCH_2)_2CHC_6H_4$-2-OH	C_6H_5MgBr	1,1,3-Triphenyl-3-(*o*-hydroxyphenyl)-1-propanol (?)†‡	*572*
$(C_6H_5COCH_2)_2CHC_6H_4$-2-OH	C_6H_5MgBr	2,2,4-Triphenylchroman§¶	*572*
$(C_6H_5COCH_2)_2CHC_6H_4$-2-OH	C_6H_5MgBr	2,2-Diphenyl-4-(β, β-diphenyl-vinyl)-1,4-benzopyran‖**	*571*
$(C_6H_5COCH_2)_2CHC_6H_4$-2-OH	C_6H_5MgBr	1,7,7-Triphenyl-3,4-benzo-2,8-dioxabicyclo-[3.3.1] non-3-ene††	*571*
$C_{23}H_{21}ON$			
1-Benzyl-2-phenyl-3-*p*-toluylethyleneimine	C_6H_5MgBr (4 equiv.)	1-Benzyl-2,4-diphenyl-4-*p*-tolyl-4-hydroxy-propyleneimine, m.p. 117° (80%)	*484*
1-Benzyl-2-*p*-tolyl-3-benzoylethyleneimine	C_6H_5MgBr (4 equiv.)	1-Benzyl-2-*p*-tolyl-4,4-diphenyl-4-hydroxy-propyleneimine (95%)	*484*

* This is probably a misprint; the reported yield is obviously more than 100% of the theoretical.

† According to Geissman *(571)* the product tentatively so designated by Gomm and Hill *(572)* is in fact 1,7,7-triphenyl-3,4-benzo-2,8-dioxabicyclo[3.3.1]non-3-ene.

‡ Slow addition of Grignard reagent solution to Et_2O-ketone suspension; overnight standing.

§ 2,2,4-Triphenyl-2,3-dihydro-1,4-benzopyran, or 2,4-diphenylflavan.

¶ Slow addition of Grignard reagent solution to boiling C_6H_6-ketone solution; one-hour reflux; overnight standing.

‖ 2-Phenyl-4-(β,β-diphenylvinyl)flavene, or 2,2-diphenyl-4-(β,β-diphenylvinyl)-chromene.

** Addition of C_6H_6-ketone solution to ethereal Grignard reagent solution; two and one-half hours reflux.

†† Addition of Grignard reagent solution to cooled (5–10°) Et_2O-ketone suspension.

TABLE VI-XVIII (Continued)

Ketonic Comp'd	RMgX	Product(s)	Ref.
$C_{23}H_{22}O$			
$C_6H_5COCH(C_6H_5)C_6H_2$-2,4,6-$(CH_3)_3$	*i*-C_3H_7MgBr	$C_6H_5CH(OH)CH(C_6H_5)C_6H_2$-2,4,6-$(CH_3)_3$	*500*
$C_{23}H_{22}O_2$			
$CH_3CO(CH_2)_2OC(C_6H_5)_3$	1-Cyclohexenylethynyl-MgBr	"Condensation products"	*97*
$C_6H_5CH_2COCH(CH_2C_6H_5)C_6H_4$-4-$OCH_3$	$C_6H_5CH_2MgCl$	$HO(C_6H_5CH_2)_2CCH(CH_2C_6H_5)C_6H_4$-4-$OCH_3$	*582*
$C_{23}H_{28}O_2$			
$C_6H_5COCOC_6H_2$-2,4,6-(*i*-$C_3H_7)_3$	CH_3MgI	$HO(CH_3)(C_6H_5)CCOC_6H_2$-2,4,6-(*i*-$C_3H_7)_3$	*508*
$C_{23}H_{28}O_2N_2$			
3-(4-Morpholino)-4-phenyl-4-(1,2,3,4-tetrahydro-1-quinolyl)butanone	CH_3MgI	"No reaction"	*561*
$C_{23}H_{28}O_3$			
4-$CH_3OC_6H_4COCH_2CH[CH(CH_2)_5]C_6H_4$-4-$OCH_3$	CH_3MgI	$HO(CH_3)(4$-$CH_3OC_6H_4)CCH_2CH[CH(CH_2)_5]$-$C_6H_4$-4-$OCH_3$	*514*
4-$CH_3OC_6H_4COCH_2CH[CH(CH_2)_5]C_6H_4$-4-$OCH_3$	C_2H_5MgI	$HO(C_2H_5)(4$-$CH_3OC_6H_4)CCH_2CH[CH(CH_2)_5]$-$C_6H_4$-4-$OCH_3$	*514*
$C_{23}H_{28}O_3N_2$			
α,β-Di-4-morpholinylbenzylacetophenone	CH_3MgI (0.50 g. Mg)	2,4-Diphenyl-3,4-di-4-morpholinyl-2-butanol (0.05 g.); intractable oil	*544*
$C_{23}H_{30}O_5$			
3-CH_3O-4-$C_2H_5OC_6H_3CH(CH_3)CO$-$(CH_2)_2C_6H_3$-3-OCH_3-4-OC_2H_5	CH_3MgI	3-CH_3O-4-$C_2H_5OC_6H_3CH(CH_3)C(OH)(CH_3)$-$(CH_2)_2C_6H_3$-3-$OCH_3$-4-$OC_2H_5$	*583*

TABLE VI-XVIII (Continued)

Ketonic Comp'd	RMgX	Product(s)	Ref.
$C_{24}H_{22}O$			
2,4,6-$(CH_3)_3C_6H_2COCH{=}C(C_6H_5)_2$ (5 g.)	CH_3MgI (1.6 g. Mg.)	2,4,6-$(CH_3)_3C_6H_2COCH_2C(C_6H_5)_2CH_3$ (82%)	*538*
2,4,6-$(CH_3)_3C_6H_2COCH{=}C(C_6H_5)_2$	C_2H_5MgBr	2,4,6-$(CH_3)_3C_6H_2COCH_2C(C_6H_5)_2C_2H_5$	*538*
2,4,6-$(CH_3)_3C_6H_2COCH{=}C(C_6H_5)_2$ (5 g.)	C_6H_5MgBr (1.6 g. Mg.)	2,4,6-$(CH_3)_3C_6H_2COCH_2C(C_6H_5)_3$ (60%)	*538*
$C_{24}H_{24}O_2$			
2-*o*-$CH_3OC_6H_4C_6H_4COC_6H$-2,3,5,6-$(CH_3)_4$ (4.2 g.)	$C_6H_5CH_2MgCl$ (13 g. C_7H_7Cl)	2-*o*-$CH_3OC_6H_4$-4-$C_6H_5CH_2C_6H_3COC_6H$-2,3,5,6-$(CH_3)_4$ (0.2 g.)	*515*
$C_{24}H_{26}ON_2$			
$C_6H_5COCH[C_6H_4\text{-}4\text{-}N(CH_3)_2]_2$	C_6H_5MgBr	$HO(C_6H_5)_2CCH[C_6H_4\text{-}4\text{-}N(CH_3)_2]_2$	*203*
$C_{24}H_{26}O_2$			
2-Methyl-3-mesitoyl-5-mesitylfuran	CH_3MgI (6 equiv.)	2,4,6-$(CH_3)_3C_6H_2C(OH){=}CHCH$(*t*-$C_4H_9)CH_2C_6H_2$-2,4,6-$(CH_3)_3$	*576*
$C_{24}H_{28}O_2$			
2-(2,4,6-Triisopropylbenzoyl)benzofuran (25 g.)	C_6H_5MgBr (0.1 mole)	2-(2,4,6-Triisopropylbenzoyl)-3-phenyl-2,3-dihydrobenzofuran (21 g., crude)	*451*
$C_{24}H_{30}ON_2$			
3-(1-Piperidyl)-4-phenyl-4-(1,2,3,4-tetrahydro-1-quinolyl)butanone	CH_3MgI	"No reaction"	*561*
3-(1-Piperidyl)-4-phenyl-4-(1,2,3,4-tetrahydro-2-isoquinolyl)butanone	CH_3MgI	2-Methyl-3-(1-piperidyl)-4-phenyl-4-(1,2,3,4-tetrahydro-2-isoquinolyl)-2-butanol (14%)	*561*
3-(1-Piperidyl)-4-phenyl-4-(1,2,3,4-tetrahydro-2-isoquinolyl)butanone	C_6H_5MgBr	2,4-Diphenyl-3-(1-piperidyl)-4-(1,2,3,4-tetrahydro-2-isoquinolyl)-2-butanol (47%)	*561*

TABLE VI-XVIII (Continued)

Ketonic Comp'd	RMgX	Product(s)	Ref.
$C_{24}H_{40}O_3$			
2,5-$(CH_3O)_2C_6H_3CO$-*n*-$C_{15}H_{31}$	CH_3MgI	2,4-$(CH_3O)_2C_6H_3C(CH_3){=}CH$-*n*-$C_{14}H_{29}$ (60–70%)*	557
$C_{25}H_{18}O$			
$(4-C_6H_5C_6H_4)_2CO$	*t*-C_4H_9MgCl	*t*-$C_4H_9(4-C_6H_5C_6H_4)_2COH$ (5%);† recovered ketone	403
$(4-C_6H_5C_6H_4)_2CO$	3-ClC_6H_4MgI	3-$ClC_6H_4(4-C_6H_5C_6H_4)_2COH$ (quant.)	415
$(4-C_6H_5C_6H_4)_2CO$ (40 g.)	C_6H_5MgBr (40 g. C_6H_5Br)	$C_6H_5(4-C_6H_5C_6H_4)_2COH$ (35 g.)	375
$(4-C_6H_5C_6H_4)_2CO$ (6.7 g.)	3-$CH_3C_6H_4MgBr$ (7.25 g. C_6H_5Br)	3-$CH_3C_6H_4(4-C_6H_5C_6H_4)_2COH$ (5.32 g.)	431
$(4-C_6H_5C_6H_4)_2CO$	4-$CH_3C_6H_4MgBr$	4-$CH_3C_6H_4(4-C_6H_5C_6H_4)_2COH$ (58%)	431
$(4-C_6H_5C_6H_4)_2CO$ (30 g.)	1-$C_{10}H_7MgBr$ (32 g. $C_{10}H_7Br$)	1-$C_{10}H_7(4-C_6H_5C_6H_4)_2COH$ (35 g., crude)	583
$(4-C_6H_5C_6H_4)_2CO$	4-$C_6H_5C_6H_4MgI$	$(4-C_6H_5C_6H_4)_3COH$	375
$C_{25}H_{24}O_2$			
$C_6H_5CH_2COCH_2CH(CH_2C_6H_5)$-$COCH_2C_6H_5$ (0.6 g.)	C_6H_5MgBr (1.0 g. C_6H_5Br)	$HO(C_6H_5)(C_6H_5CH_2)CCH_2CH(CH_2C_6H_5)$-$COCH_2C_6H_5$ (250 mg.)	495
$C_{25}H_{38}O_3$			
3-Acetoxy-20-iso-5-ternorcholenyl methyl ketone (23.2 g.)	CH_3MgBr (85 g. CH_3Br)	3-Hydroxy-20-iso-5-ternorcholenyldimethylmethanol (17.1 g.)	577
$C_{25}H_{40}O_3$			
3-Acetoxy-20-ternor*allo*cholanyl methyl ketone (23.2 g.)	CH_3MgBr (85 g. CH_3Br)	3-Hydroxy-20-ternor*allo*cholanyldimethylmethanol (15.2 g.)	577
3-Acetoxy-20-isoternor*allo*cholanyl methyl ketone (23.2 g.)	CH_3MgBr (85 g. CH_3Br)	3-Hydroxy-20-isoternor*allo*cholanyldimethylmethanol (21.3 g.)	577

*The figures recorded represent the range of yields reported for a series of reactions studied.

†"Boiling the solution for many hours with and without the addition of benzene, toluene, or xylene, or even heating to 150° in ether in a sealed tube for eight hours failed to increase the yield of carbinol to more than 10 percent...."

TABLE VI-XVIII (Continued)

Ketonic Comp'd	RMgX	Product(s)	Ref.
$C_{26}H_{16}O_2Cl_2$			
$[2\text{-}(2\text{-}ClC_6H_4CO)C_6H_4—]_2$	C_2H_5MgBr	$\{2\text{-}[2\text{-}ClC_6H_4C(OH)(C_2H_5)]C_6H_4—\}_2$ (23%)	584
$C_{26}H_{18}O$			
9-(2-Benzoylphenyl)fluorene	C_6H_5MgBr	2-(9-Fluorenyl)triphenylmethanol	585
$C_{26}H_{18}O_2$			
$(2\text{-}C_6H_5COC_6H_4—)_2$	C_2H_5MgBr	$[2\text{-}HO(C_2H_5)(C_6H_5)CC_6H_4—]_2$ (46%)	584
$(4\text{-}C_6H_5COC_6H_4—)_2$ (9 g.)	C_6H_5MgBr (12 g. C_6H_5Br)	$[4\text{-}HO(C_6H_5)_2CC_6H_4—]_2$ (10 g.)	578
$C_{26}H_{20}O$			
$C_6H_5COC(C_6H_5)_3$	$n\text{-}C_3H_7MgBr$	$C_6H_5[(C_6H_5)_3C]CHOH$	587
$C_6H_5COC(C_6H_5)_3$ (20 g.)	C_6H_5MgI (100 g. C_6H_5I)	$(C_6H_5)_3C(C_6H_5)_2COH$ (10 g., crude)	589
$C_6H_5COC_6H_4\text{-}4\text{-}CH(C_6H_5)_2$ (7 g.)	$4\text{-}BrC_6H_4MgBr$ (13 g. $C_6H_4Br_2$)	$4\text{-}BrC_6H_4(C_6H_5)[4\text{-}(C_6H_5)_2CHC_6H_4]COH$ (converted to bromide, 5 g.)	588
$C_6H_5COC_6H_4\text{-}4\text{-}CH(C_6H_5)_2$	C_6H_5MgBr (18 g. C_6H_5Br)	$4\text{-}(C_6H_5)_2CHC_6H_4(C_6H_5)_2COH$ (22 g., crude)	588
$C_6H_5COC_6H_4\text{-}4\text{-}CH(C_6H_5)_2$ (10 g.)	$4\text{-}CH_3C_6H_4MgBr$ (10 g. C_6H_5Br)	$C_6H_5(4\text{-}CH_3C_6H_4)[4\text{-}(C_6H_5)_2CHC_6H_4]COH$ (converted to bromide, 10.5 g.)	588
$C_6H_5COC_6H_4\text{-}4\text{-}CH(C_6H_5)_2$ (10 g.)	$1\text{-}C_{10}H_7MgBr$ (13.5 g. C_6H_5Br)	$C_6H_5(1\text{-}C_{10}H_7)[4\text{-}(C_6H_5)_2CHC_6H_4]COH$ (converted to chloride, 12 g.)	588
$4\text{-}C_6H_5C_6H_4COCH_2C_6H_4\text{-}4\text{-}C_6H_5$	C_6H_5MgBr	$C_6H_5(4\text{-}C_6H_5C_6H_4)(4\text{-}C_6H_5C_6H_4CH_2)COH$	586
$4\text{-}C_6H_5C_6H_4COCH_2C_6H_4\text{-}4\text{-}C_6H_5$	$1\text{-}C_{10}H_7MgBr$	$1\text{-}C_{10}H_7(4\text{-}C_6H_5C_6H_4)(4\text{-}C_6H_5C_6H_4CH_2)COH$	586
$C_{26}H_{20}O_2$			
$C_6H_5COC(C_6H_5)_2OC_6H_5$	C_6H_5MgBr	$C_6H_5O(C_6H_5)_2CC(C_6H_5)_2OH$ (88%)	570
$C_{26}H_{27}ON$			
$C_6H_5COCH[N(CH_2)_5]CH(C_6H_5)_2$ (1.0 g.)	C_6H_5MgBr (0.2 g. Mg)	$HO(C_6H_5)_2CCH[N(CH_2)_5]CH(C_6H_5)_2$	559

TABLE VI-XVIII (Continued)

Ketonic Comp'd	RMgX	Product(s)	Ref.
$C_{26}H_{32}O_2$			
2,4,6-$(CH_3)_3C_6H_2COCH=C(t\text{-}C_4H_9)COC_6H_2$-2,4,6-$(CH_3)_3$ (0.32 g.)	C_6H_5MgBr (4 equiv.)	2,4,6-$(CH_3)_3C_6H_2COCH(C_6H_5)$-$CH(t\text{-}C_4H_9)COC_6H_2$-2,4,6-$(CH_3)_3$ (0.12 g.)*	*590*
2,4,6-$(CH_3)_3C_6H_2COCH=C(t\text{-}C_4H_9)COC_6H_2$-2,4,6-$(CH_3)_3$ (1.15 g.)	C_6H_5MgBr (4 equiv.)	2,4,6-$(CH_3)_3C_6H_2COC(C_6H_5)=C(t\text{-}C_4H_9)COC_6H_2$-2,4,6-$(CH_3)_3$ (0.96 g.)†	*590*
$C_{26}H_{33}O_2Br$			
2,4,6-$(CH_3)_3C_6H_2COCHBrCH$-$(t\text{-}C_4H_9)COC_6H_2$-2,4,6-$(CH_3)_3$	CH_3MgX‡ (2 equiv.)	2,4,6-$(CH_3)_3C_6H_2C(OH)=CHCH$-$(t\text{-}C_4H_9)COC_6H_2$-2,4,6-$(CH_3)_3$ (*ca.* quant.)	*576*
2,4,6-$(CH_3)_3C_6H_2COCHBrCH$-$(t\text{-}C_4H_9)COC_6H_2$-2,4,6-$(CH_3)_3$ (0.5 g.)	$t\text{-}C_4H_9MgCl$	2,4,6-$(CH_3)_3C_6H_2C(OH)=CHCH(t\text{-}C_4H_9)COC_6H_2$-2,4,6-$(CH_3)_3$ (0.24 g.)	*576*
$C_{26}H_{44}O_3$			
2,5-$(CH_3O)_2C_6H_3CO$-n-$C_{17}H_{35}$	CH_3MgI	2,5-$(CH_3O)_2C_6H_3C(CH_3)=CH$-$n$-$C_{16}H_{33}$ (60–70%)§	*557*
$C_{27}H_{20}O$			
$C_6H_5COC(C_6H_5)=C(C_6H_5)_2$	CH_3MgI (4 equiv.)	$HO(CH_3)(C_6H_5)CC(C_6H_5)=C(C_6H_5)_2$ (53.6–63.4%)	*591*

* Addition of ketone to Grignard reagent solution at room temperature; ten minutes standing.

† Addition of ketone to Grignard reagent solution at 0°; fifteen minutes standing; treatment with $EtOH$-Br_2 at −10°.

‡ X = Br, I.

§ The figure here recorded represents the range of yields reported for a series of reactions studied.

TABLE VI-XVIII (Continued)

Ketonic Comp'd	RMgX	Product(s)	Ref.
$C_{27}H_{20}O$ (*cont.*)			
$C_6H_5COC(C_6H_5){=}C(C_6H_5)_2$	C_6H_5MgBr (4 equiv.)	"Enol peroxide" (37.3%);* $HO(C_6H_5)_2CC(C_6H_5){=}C(C_6H_5)_2$ (31.9%)	*591*
9-Phenyl-10-benzoyl-9,10-dihydroanthracene (3.5 g.)	C_6H_5MgBr	Recovered ketone (1.2 g.); phenylanthrapheneone (0.7 g.)	*565*
$C_{27}H_{21}OBr$			
$C_6H_5COCBr(C_6H_5)CH(C_6H_5)_2$	C_6H_5MgBr	$C_6H_5COCH(C_6H_5)CH(C_6H_5)_2$; "1-hydroxy-1,2,3,3-tetraphenylpropene peroxide"†	*437*

*Kohler (*591*, etc.) formulated his "enol peroxides" as compounds containing a 2-oxygen 2-carbon four-membered ring—in this instance,

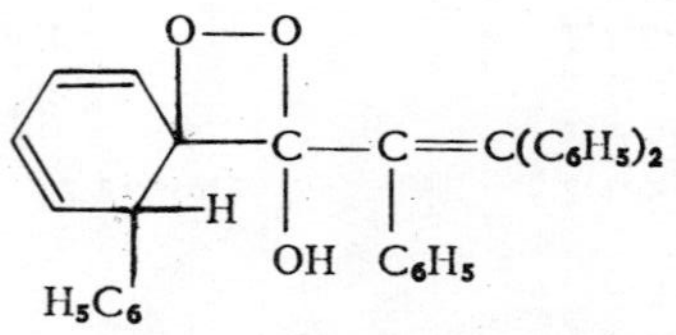

Rigaudy, *Compt. rend.*, *226*, 1993–5 (1948), has pointed out the probable instability of such structures, has cited the similarity in chemical properties between Kohler's "enol peroxides" and known hydroperoxides, and has shown that the ultraviolet absorption spectrum of one of Kohler's "enol peroxides" bears evidence of the presence of a carbonyl group and is closely similar to those of analogous ketones but quite different from that of an analogous carbinol. The more probable formulation would seem to be:

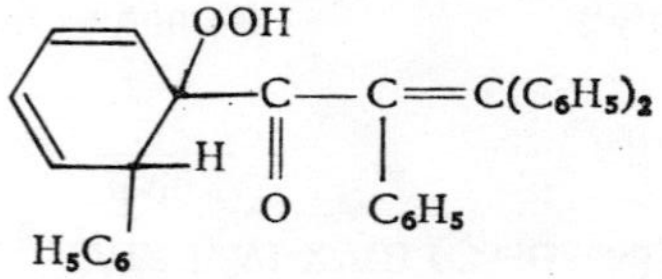

†Probably the hydroperoxide, $C_6H_5(C_6H_5CO)[(C_6H_5)_2CH]COOH$.

TABLE VI-XVIII (Continued)

Ketonic Comp'd	RMgX	Product(s)	Ref.
$C_{27}H_{22}O$			
$C_6H_5COCH(C_6H_5)CH(C_6H_5)_2$ (15 g.)	CH_3MgI (4 g. Mg)	$CH_3(C_6H_5)[(C_6H_5)_2CHCH(C_6H_5)]COH$ (>12.5 g.)	*591*
$C_6H_5COCH(C_6H_5)CH(C_6H_5)_2$ (5 g.)	C_6H_5MgBr (1.4 g. Mg)	$HO(C_6H_5)_2CCH(C_6H_5)CH(C_6H_5)_2$ (33%)	*591*
$C_{28}H_{18}O_2$			
2-*p*-Benzoylphenyl-3-phenylindone	C_6H_5MgBr (excess)	1,3-Diphenyl-2-(*p*-α-hydroxybenzhydrylphenyl)indenol	*592*
$C_{28}H_{20}O_2$			
$C_6H_5COC(C_6H_5)=C(C_6H_5)COC_6H_5$ (15 g.)	C_6H_5MgBr (35 g. C_6H_5Br)	$HO(C_6H_5)_2CC(C_6H_5)=C(C_6H_5)COC_6H_5$ (70-90%)	*602*
2-Benzoyl-3,4,5-triphenylfuran	C_6H_5MgBr	Diphenyl-2-(3,4,5-triphenylfuryl)methanol (70%)	*593*
$C_{28}H_{22}O_2$			
$[2\text{-}(3\text{-}CH_3C_6H_4CO)C_6H_4—]_2$	C_2H_5MgBr	$\{2\text{-}[HO(C_2H_5)(3\text{-}CH_3C_6H_4)C]C_6H_4—\}_2$ (35%)	*584*
$C_{28}H_{28}O_2$			
$2,4,6\text{-}(CH_3)_3C_6H_2COC(C_6H_5)=CHCOC_6H_2\text{-}2,4,6\text{-}(CH_3)_3$	*t*-C_4H_9MgCl	$2,4,6\text{-}(CH_3)_3C_6H_2COC(t\text{-}C_4H_9)(C_6H_5)CH_2CO\text{-}C_6H_2\text{-}2,4,6\text{-}(CH_3)_3$	*590*
$C_{28}H_{40}O$			
$C_6H_5CO\text{-}n\text{-}C_{21}H_{43}$ (55 g.)	*n*-C_4H_9MgCl	$n\text{-}C_4H_9(C_6H_5)(n\text{-}C_{21}H_{43})COH$ (62 g., crude)	*594*
$C_{29}H_{24}O$			
$C_6H_5COCH(C_6H_5)CH(C_6H_5)CH=CHC_6H_5$	C_6H_5MgBr (3 equiv.)	$HO(C_6H_5)_2CCH(C_6H_5)CH(C_6H_5)CH=CHC_6H_5$	595

TABLE VI-XVIII (Continued)

Ketonic Comp'd	RMgX	Product(s)	Ref.
$C_{29}H_{24}O_2$			
2,2-Diphenyl-4-phenacylchroman*	C_6H_5MgBr	2,2-Diphenyl-4-(β-hydroxy-β,β-diphenylethyl)chroman	571
$C_{29}H_{32}ON_2$			
α-Piperidyl-β-phenyl-β-(1,2,3,4-tetrahydroquinolyl)propiophenone	CH_3MgI	2,4-Diphenyl-3-piperidyl-4-(1,2,3,4-tetrahydroquinolyl)-2-butanol (20%)	561
$C_{30}H_{16}O_2Br_2$			
1,6-Dibenzoyl-3,6-dibromopyrene† (15 g.)	C_6H_5MgBr (36 g. C_6H_5Br)	1,6-Bis(diphenylhydroxymethyl)-3,8-dibromopyrene† (14.5 g.)	579
1,8-Dibenzoyl-3,6-dibromopyrene† (17 g.)	C_6H_5MgBr (36 g. C_6H_5Br)	1,8-Bis(diphenylhydroxymethyl)-3,6-dibromopyrene† (12 g.)	579
$C_{30}H_{18}O_2$			
1,6-Dibenzoylpyrene† (16 g.)	C_6H_5MgBr (36 g. C_6H_5Br)	1,6-Bis(diphenylhydroxymethyl)pyrene† (17 g.)	579
1,8-Dibenzoylpyrene† (16 g.)	C_6H_5MgBr (36 g. C_6H_5Br)	1,8-Bis(diphenylhydroxymethyl)pyrene† (18 g.)	579
$C_{30}H_{20}O_3$			
$C_6H_5COC{\equiv}CC(COC_6H_5)_2C_6H_5$	CH_3MgBr	$HO(CH_3)(C_6H_5)CC{\equiv}CC(COC_6H_5)_2C_6H_5$	85
$C_{30}H_{25}ON$			
2,4,6-Triphenyl-3-benzoyl-2,3,4,5-tetrahydropyridine (0.16 g., 0.00145 mole)	CH_3MgCl (excess)	2,4,6-Triphenyl-3-(1-hydroxy-1-phenylethyl)-2,3,4,5-tetrahydropyridine (97%)	596

*2,2-Diphenyl-4-phenacyl-2,3-dihydro-1,4-benzopyran.

†The numbering here employed is that of the "Ring Index" rather than that of the authors cited.

TABLE VI-XVIII (Continued)

Ketonic Comp'd	RMgX	Product(s)	Ref.
$C_{30}H_{25}ON$ (*cont.*)			
2,4,6-Triphenyl-3-benzoyl-2,3,4,5-tetrahydropyridine (2.0 g., 0.0048 mole)	C_6H_5MgBr (0.012 mole)	2,4,6-Triphenyl-3-(α-hydroxy-benzhydryl)-2,3,4,5-tetrahydropyridine (1.69 g., 0.0034 mole, 71%)	596
$C_{30}H_{26}O_4$			
$[2\text{-}(4\text{-}C_2H_5OC_6H_4CO)C_6H_4\text{—}]_2$	C_2H_5MgBr	$\{2\text{-}[HO(C_2H_5)(4\text{-}C_2H_5OC_6H_4C]C_6H_4\text{—}\}_2$ (33%)	584
$C_{30}H_{30}O_2$			
2-Methyl-3-mesitoyl-4-phenyl-5-mesitylfuran (9.7 g.)	CH_3MgI (5 equiv.)	$2,4,6\text{-}(CH_3)_3C_6H_2COCH(C_6H_5)CH(t\text{-}C_4H_9)\text{-}COC_6H_2\text{-}2,4,6\text{-}(CH_3)_3$ (5.85 g.)	590
$C_{31}H_{62}O$			
$(n\text{-}C_{15}H_{31})_2CO$	CH_3MgBr (3 equiv.)	$CH_3(C_{15}H_{31})_2COH$	598
$(n\text{-}C_{15}H_{31})_2CO$	C_2H_5MgBr (3 equiv.)	$C_2H_5(C_{15}H_{31})_2COH$	598
$(n\text{-}C_{15}H_{31})_2CO$	$n\text{-}C_4H_9MgBr$ (3 equiv.)	$n\text{-}C_4H_9(C_{15}H_{31})_2COH$ (*ca.* 80%); recovered ketone; $(C_{15}H_{31})_2CHOH$; $C_{31}H_{64}$	598
$(n\text{-}C_{15}H_{31})_2CO$ (63 g.)	$n\text{-}C_{16}H_{33}Br$ (26 g.) + Mg (3.6 g.)	$n\text{-}C_{16}H_{33}(n\text{-}C_{15}H_{31})_2COH$ (3.2 g.)	598
$C_{32}H_{22}O$			
5-Benzoyl-9,9-diphenylfluorene	C_6H_5MgBr	Diphenyl-9,9-diphenyl-5-fluorenylmethanol	597
$C_{32}H_{38}O_2$			
$2,4,6\text{-}(CH_3)_3C_6H_2COCH(C_6H_5)CH(t\text{-}C_4H_9)COC_6H_2\text{-}2,4,6\text{-}(CH_3)_3$	CH_3MgI	$2,4,6\text{-}(CH_3)_3C_6H_2COC(C_6H_5)=C(t\text{-}C_4H_9)\text{-}COC_6H_2\text{-}2,4,6\text{-}(CH_3)_3$ (40%)	590
$C_{32}H_{50}O$			
$2\text{-}C_{10}H_7CO\text{-}n\text{-}C_{21}H_{43}$	$n\text{-}C_4H_9MgCl$	$n\text{-}C_4H_9(2\text{-}C_{10}H_7)(n\text{-}C_{21}H_{43})COH$	594

TABLE VI-XVIII (Continued)

Ketonic Comp'd	RMgX	Product (s)	Ref.
$C_{32}H_{54}O$			
n-Heneicosyl 6-(1,2,3,4-tetrahydronaphthyl) ketone	*n*-C_4H_9MgCl	*n*-$C_4H_9(C_{10}H_{11})$(*n*-$C_{21}H_{43}$)COH	594
$C_{32}H_{54}O$			
4-$C_6H_5C_6H_4CO$-*n*-$C_{21}H_{43}$	*n*-C_4H_9MgCl	*n*-$C_4H_9(4\text{-}C_6H_5C_6H_4)$(*n*-$C_{21}H_{43}$)COH	594
$C_{38}H_{26}O_2$			
[2-(4-$C_6H_5C_6H_4CO)C_6H_4$—]$_2$	C_2H_5MgBr	{2-[HO(C_2H_5)(4-$C_6H_5C_6H_4$)C]C_6H_4—}$_2$	584

REFERENCES FOR TABLE VI-XVIII

(1) Dashkevich, *J. Gen. Chem.* (U.S.S.R.), *18*, 205-8 (1948); *Chem. Abstr.*, *42*, 7244 (1948).
(2) Dashkevich, *J. Gen. Chem.* (U.S.S.R.), 8, 779-81 (1938); *Chem. Abstr.*, 33, 1293 (1939).
(3) Henry, *Bull. soc. chim. Belg.*, *20*, 152-6 (1906).
(4) Shtukin, *J. Gen. Chem.* (U.S.S.R.), *10*, 77-81 (1940); *Chem. Abstr.*, *34*, 4725 (1940).
(5) Christie, McKenzie, and Ritchie, *J. Chem. Soc.*, *1935*, 153-5.
(6) Huston, Jackson, and Spero, *J. Am. Chem. Soc.*, *63*, 1459-60 (1941).
(7) Henry, *Compt. rend.*, *145*, 21-5 (1907); *Chem. Zentr.*, *1907,II*, 889.
(8) Tiffeneau, *Compt. rend.*, *134*, 774-5 (1902); *Chem. Zentr.*, *1902,I*, 1092.
(9) Fourneau and Tiffeneau, *Compt. rend.*, *145*, 437-9 (1907); *Chem. Zentr.*, 1907,*II*, 1320.
(10) Kyriakides, *J. Am. Chem. Soc.*, *36*, 657-63 (1914).
(11) Kinney and Spliethoff, *J. Org. Chem.*, *14*, 71-8 (1949).
(12) Tiffeneau, *Compt. rend.*, *137*, 989-91 (1903); *J. Chem. Soc.*, 86,*I*, 63 (1904).
(13) Tiffeneau, *Bull. soc. chim.*, [3], *29*, 1156-8 (1903).
(14) Temnikova and Veksler, *J. Gen. Chem.* (U.S.S.R.), *19*, 1318-23 (1949); *Chem. Abstr.*, *44*, 1056 (1950).
(15) Tiffeneau and Deux, *Compt. rend.*, *213*, 753-8 (1941); *Chem. Abstr.*, 37, 4049 (1943).
(16) Bradsher and Tess, *J. Am. Chem. Soc.*, *61*, 2184-5 (1939).
(17) Fréon, *Ann. chim.*, [11], *11*, 435-518 (1939).
(18) Grignard, *Ann. chim.*, [7], *24*, 433-90 (1901).
(19) Iotsitch, *J. Russ. Phys.-Chem. Soc.*, *34*, 242-4 (1902); *Bull. soc. chim.*, [3], *30*, 210 (1903).
(20) Iotsitch, *J. Russ. Phys.-Chem. Soc.*, *36*, 1545-51 (1904); *Bull. soc. chim.*, [3], *36*, 177 (1906).
(21) Dupont, *Ann. chim.*, [8], *30*, 485-587 (1913).
(22) Zal'kind and Labuzov, *J. Gen. Chem.* (U.S.S.R.), 9, 1525-32 (1939); *Chem. Abstr.*, *34*, 2788 (1940).
(23) Salkind and Teterin, *Ber.*, *66B*, 321-5 (1933).
(24) Meisenheimer, *Ann.*, *442*, 180-210 (1925).
(25) Henze, Allen, and Leslie, *J. Org. Chem.*, 7, 326-35 (1942).
(26) Jaworski, *J. Russ. Phys.-Chem. Soc.*, *40*, 782-7 (1908); *Chem. Zentr.*, *1908,II*, 1412.
(27) Jaworski, *J. Russ. Phys.-Chem. Soc.*, *40*, 1746-8 (1909); *Chem. Zentr.*, *1909,I*, 856.
(28) Jaworsky, *Ber.*, *42*, 435-8 (1909).
(29) Bacon and Farmer, *J. Chem. Soc.*, *1937*, 1065-77.
(30) Ou Kuin-Houo, *Ann. chim.*, [11], *13*, 175-241 (1940).
(31) Wibaut, Hoog, Langedijk, Overhoff, and Smittenberg, *Rec. trav. chim.*, *58*, 329-77 (1939).
(32) Deschamps, *J. Am. Chem. Soc.*, *42*, 2670-3 (1920).
(33) Whitmore and Badertsher, *J. Am. Chem. Soc.*, *55*, 1559-67 (1933).
(34) Schreiner, *J. prakt. Chem.*, [2], *82*, 292-6 (1910).
(35) Norton and Hass, *J. Am. Chem. Soc.*, *58*, 2147-50 (1936).
(36) Iotsitch, Breitfous, Roudolf, Stassévitch, Elmanovitch, Kondyref, and Fomine, *J. Russ. Phys.-Chem. Soc.*, *39*, 652-7 (1907); *Bull. soc. chim.*, [4], 6, 98-100 (1909).
(37) Stas, *Bull. soc. chim. Belg.*, *35*, 379-86 (1926).

(38) Carothers and Berchet, *J. Am. Chem. Soc.*, *55*, 1094–6 (1933).
(39) Zal'kind and Pletz, *Trans. Leningrad Chem.-Tech. Inst.*, *1*, 57–60 (1934); *Chem. Abstr.*, *29*, 2908 (1935).
(40) Nazarov and Elizarova, *Bull. acad. sci. U.R.S.S.*, *Classe sci. chim.*, *1940*, 189–94; *Chem. Abstr.*, *36*, 741 (1942).
(41) Thomas, *Bull. soc. chim.*, [4], *5*, 730–6 (1909).
(42) Dupont, *Compt. rend.*, *148*, 1522–4 (1909); *Chem. Abstr.*, *3*, 2674 (1909).
(43) Shchukina and Rubstov, *J. Gen. Chem.* (U.S.S.R.), *18*, 1645–52 (1948); *Chem. Abstr.*, *43*, 2570 (1949).
(44) Tamele, Ott, Marple, and Hearne, *Ind. Eng. Chem.*, *33*, 115–20 (1941).
(45) Roberts and Young, *J. Am. Chem. Soc.*, *67*, 148–50 (1945).
(46) Edgar, Calingaert, and Marker, *J. Am. Chem. Soc.*, *51*, 1483–91 (1929).
(47) Church, Whitmore, and McGrew, *J. Am. Chem. Soc.*, *56*, 176–84 (1934).
(48) Petrov and Kurbskiĭ, *J. Gen. Chem.* (U.S.S.R.), *14*, 492–4 (1944); *Chem. Abstr.*, *39*, 4600 (1945).
(49) Pierotti and Stewart, *J. Am. Chem. Soc.*, *59*, 1773–5 (1937).
(50) Konowalow, *J. Russ. Phys.-Chem. Soc.*, *37*, 910–1 (1906); *Chem. Zentr.*, *1906,I*, 330.
(51) Willcox and Brunel, *J. Am. Chem. Soc.*, *38*, 1821–41 (1916).
(52) Henry, *Bull. acad. roy. Belg.*, *1906*, 352–63; *Chem. Zentr.*, *1906,II*, 748.
(53) Elliott and Linstead, *J. Chem. Soc.*, *1938*, 660–5.
(54) Meyer and Tuot, *Compt. rend.*, *196*, 1231–3 (1933).
(55) Halse, *J. prakt. Chem.*, [2], *89*, 451–65 (1914).
(56) Tissier and Grignard, *Compt. rend.*, *132*, 1182–4 (1901); *Chem. Zentr.*, *1901,I*, 1357.
(57) Bergmann, Taubadel, and Weiss, *Ber.*, *64B*, 1493–501 (1931).
(58) Sabatier and Mailhe, *Compt. rend.*, *139*, 343–6 (1904); *J. Chem. Soc.*, *86,I*, 809 (1904).
(59) Sabatier and Mailhe, *Ann. chim.*, [8], *10*, 527–74 (1907).
(60) Sontag, *Ann. chim.*, [11], *1*, 359–438 (1934).
(61) Grignard, *Compt. rend.*, *130*, 1322–4 (1900); *J. Chem. Soc.*, *78,I*, 382 (1900).
(62) Sabatier and Murat, *Compt. rend.*, *156*, 184–7 (1913); *Chem. Abstr.*, *7*, 1485 (1913).
(63) Iotsitch, *J. Russ. Phys.-Chem. Soc.*, *36*, 8–9 (1904); *Bull. soc. chim.*, [3], *34*, 204 (1905).
(64) Iotsitch, *J. Russ. Phys.-Chem. Soc.*, *34*, 100–2 (1902); *Bull. soc. chim.*, [3], *28*, 922 (1902).
(65) Willemart, *Ann. chim.*, [10], *12*, 345–422 (1929).
(66) Jacobs, Cramer, and Weiss, *J. Am. Chem. Soc.*, *62*, 1849–54 (1940).
(67) Lepin, *J. Russ. Phys.-Chem. Soc.*, *44*, 1190–6 (1912); *Chem. Zentr.*, *1912,II*, 2080.
(68) Bogert and Davidson, *J. Am. Chem. Soc.*, *56*, 185–90 (1934).
(69) Courtot, *Ann. chim.*, [9], *4*, 58–136 (1915).
(70) Oddo and Perotti, *Gazz. chim. ital.*, *60*, 13–21 (1930); *Chem. Zentr.*, *1930,I*, 3051.
(71) Bogert, Davidson, Appelbaum, *J. Am. Chem. Soc.*, *56*, 959–63 (1934).
(72) Shurakowski, *J. Russ. Phys.-Chem. Soc.*, *41*, 1687–94 (1910); *Chem. Zentr.*, *1910,I*, 1144.
(73) von Braun and Kirschbaum, *Ber.*, *52B*, 1725–30 (1919).
(74) Malmgren, *Ber.*, *35*, 3910–2 (1902).
(75) Malmgren, *Ber.*, *36*, 2608–42 (1903).
(76) Clément and Savard, *Compt. rend.*, *204*, 1742–3 (1937); *Chem. Abstr.*, *31*, 7044 (1937).

(77) Clément, *Ann. chim.*, [11], *13*, 243–316 (1940).
(78) Savard and Hösögüt, *Rev. faculté sci. univ. Istanbul*, [N.S.], *3*, 164–73 (1938); *Chem. Abstr.*, *32*, 5795 (1938).
(79) Smith and Miller, *J. Am. Chem. Soc.*, *64*, 440–5 (1942).
(80) Smith and Miller, U. S. Patent 2,372,132, March 20, 1945; *Chem. Abstr.*, *39*, P4894 (1945).
(81) Schmidlin and Hodgson, *Ber.*, *41*, 430–7 (1907).
(82) Kling, *Bull. soc. chim.*, [3], *31*, 16–9 (1904).
(83) Cymerman, Heilbron, and Jones, *J. Chem. Soc.*, *1944*, 144–7.
(84) Milas, Grossi, Penner, and Kahn, *J. Am. Chem. Soc.*, *70*, 1292 (1948).
(85) Kleinfeller, *Ber.*, *72B*, 249–56 (1939).
(86) Yushchenko, *Mem. Inst. Chem. Acad. Sci. Ukrain. S.S.S.R.*, *5*, No. 1, 101–11 (1938); *Chem. Abstr.*, *32*, 7894 (1938).
(87) Grignard and Vignon, *Compt. rend.*, *144*, 1358–60 (1907); *Chem. Zentr.*, *1907,II*, 681.
(88) Backer, Stevens, and van der Bij, *Rec. trav. chim.*, *59*, 1141–55 (1940).
(89) Deakin and Wilsmore, *J. Chem. Soc.*, *97*, 1968–78 (1910).
(90) Diels and ter Meer, *Ber.*, *42*, 1940–5 (1909).
(91) Campbell, Campbell, and Eby, *J. Am. Chem. Soc.*, *60*, 2882–4 (1938).
(92) Cottle and Powell, *J. Am. Chem. Soc.*, *58*, 2267–72 (1936).
(93) Pariselle and Simon, *Compt. rend.*, *173*, 86–9 (1921).
(94) Thompson and Margnetti, *J. Am. Chem. Soc.*, *64*, 573–6 (1942).
(95) Milas and McAlevy, *J. Am. Chem. Soc.*, *57*, 580–3 (1935).
(96) Dubois, *Compt. rend.*, *224*, 1018–20 (1947); *Chem. Abstr.*, *43*, 5004 (1949).
(97) Sobotka and Chanley, *J. Am. Chem. Soc.*, *70*, 3914–8 (1948).
(98) van Risseghem, *Bull. soc. chim. Belg.*, *39*, 369–73 (1930).
(99) Whitmore and Woodburn, *J. Am. Chem. Soc.*, *55*, 361–5 (1933).
(100) Davies, Dixon, and Jones, *J. Chem. Soc.*, *1930*, 468–73.
(101) Konowaloff, *J. Russ. Phys.-Chem. Soc.*, *36*, 228–32 (1904); *Chem. Zentr.*, *1904,I*, 1496.
(102) Konowalow, Miller, and Timtschenko, *J. Russ. Phys.-Chem. Soc.*, *38*, 447–8 (1906); *Chem. Zentr.*, *1906,II*, 311.
(103) Thompson, Burr, and Shaw, *J. Am. Chem. Soc.*, *63*, 186–8 (1941).
(104) Davies and Kipping, *J. Chem. Soc.*, *99*, 296–301 (1911).
(105) Rupe and Bürgin, *Ber.*, *44*, 1218–25 (1911).
(106) Nightingale and Shanholtzer, *J. Org. Chem.*, *7*, 6–14 (1942).
(107) Lemaire, *Bull. acad. roy. Belg.*, *1909*, 83–159; *Chem. Zentr.*, *1909,I*, 1982.
(108) Whitby and Gallay, *Can. J. Research*, *6*, 280–91 (1932); *Chem. Abstr.*, *26*, 3479 (1932).
(109) Gry, *Bull. soc. chim.*, [4], *1*, 1042 (1907).
(110) Gry, *Bull. soc. chim.*, [4], *3*, 377–8 (1908).
(111) Kohler, *Am. Chem. J.*, *38*, 511–61 (1907).
(112) Stevens, *J. Am. Chem. Soc.*, *57*, 1112–7 (1934).
(113) Zelinsky, *Ber.*, *34*, 2877–84 (1901).
(114) Bruylants, *Bull. acad. roy. Belg.*, *1908*, 1011–84; *Chem. Zentr.*, *1909,I*, 1859.
(115) Bruylants, *Bull. soc. chim. Belg.*, *36*, 153–64 (1927).
(116) Khaletskiĭ, *J. Gen. Chem.* (U.S.S.R.), *11*, 319–23 (1941); *Chem. Abstr.*, *35*, 5853 (1941).
(117) Maire, *Bull. soc. chim.*, [4], *3*, 280–6 (1908).
(118) Iotsitch, *J. Russ. Phys.-Chem. Soc.*, *35*, 1269–75 (1903); *Bull. soc. chim.*, [3], *34*, 181 (1905).

(*119*) Lapkin and Golovkova, *J. Gen. Chem.* (U.S.S.R.), *18*, 485–94 (1948); *Chem. Abstr.*, *42*, 7273 (1948).
(*120*) Greenburg and Aston, *J. Am. Chem. Soc.*, *62*, 3135 (1940).
(*121*) Whitmore and Evers, *J. Am. Chem. Soc.*, *55*, 812–6 (1933).
(*122*) Pétroff, Karasseff, and Tschelzowa, *Bull. soc. chim.*, [5], *3*, 169–76 (1936).
(*123*) Malenok, *J. Gen. Chem.* (U.S.S.R.), 9, 1947–52 (1939); *Chem. Abstr.*, *34*, 4385 (1940).
(*124*) Whitmore and Block, *J. Am. Chem. Soc.*, *64*, 1619–21 (1942).
(*125*) Iotsitch, *J. Russ. Phys.-Chem. Soc.*, *38*, 656–9 (1906); *Bull. soc. chim.*, [4], *4*, 1203 (1906).
(*126*) Clarke, *J. Am. Chem. Soc.*, *33*, 520–31 (1911).
(*127*) Ivanoff and Spassoff, *Bull. soc. chim.*, [5], *2*, 1435–8 (1935).
(*128*) Whitmore and Southgate, *J. Am. Chem. Soc.*, *60*, 2571–3 (1939).
(*129*) Clarke and Riegel, *J. Am. Chem. Soc.*, *34*, 674–9 (1912).
(*130*) Nazarov, *Bull. acad. sci. U.R.S.S., Classe sci. chim.*, *1940*, 195–202; *Chem. Abstr.*, *36*, 742 (1942).
(*131*) Gauthier, *Compt. rend.*, *152*, 1100–2 (1911); *Chem. Zentr.*, *1911,I*, 1809.
(*132*) Blicke and Tsao, *J. Am. Chem. Soc.*, *66*, 1645–8 (1944).
(*133*) Levina, Faĭnzil'berg, and Shusherina, *J. Gen. Chem.* (U.S.S.R.), *18*, 1775–80 (1948); *Chem. Abstr.*, *43*, 3344 (1949).
(*134*) Colonge and Lagier, *Bull. soc. chim. France*, *1949*, 15–7.
(*135*) Harries, *Ann.*, *343*, 311–74 (1905).
(*136*) Polgar and Robinson, *J. Chem. Soc.*, *1945*, 389–95.
(*137*) Dupont and Menut, *Bull. soc. chim.*, [5], *6*, 1215–20 (1939).
(*138*) von Fellenberg, *Ber.*, *37*, 3578–81 (1904).
(*139*) Pastereau and Bernard, *Compt. rend.*, *177*, 327–9 (1923).
(*140*) Esafov, *J. Gen. Chem.* (U.S.S.R.), *9*, 467–70 (1939); *Chem. Abstr.*, *33*, 9282 (1939).
(*141*) Esafov, *J. Gen. Chem.* (U.S.S.R.), *14*, 84–7 (1944); *Chem. Abstr.*, *39*, 905 (1945).
(*142*) Bodroux and Taboury, *Bull. soc. chim.*, [4], *5*, 812–4 (1909).
(*143*) Knorr, German Patent 544,388, Jan. 28, 1932; *Friedländer*, *18*, 180–4 (1933).
(*144*) Petrov, Lapteva, and Pchelkina, *J. Gen. Chem.* (U.S.S.R.), *14*, 495–7 (1944); *Chem. Abstr.*, *39*, 4598 (1945).
(*145*) Esafov and Smirnov, *J. Gen. Chem.* (U.S.S.R.), *10*, 1535–8 (1940); *Chem. Abstr.*, *35*, 2855 (1941).
(*146*) Klages, *Ber.*, *37*, 2301–17 (1904).
(*147*) Reynolds, *Am. Chem. J.*, *44*, 305–31 (1910).
(*148*) von Fellenberg, *Ber.*, *39*, 2064–6 (1906).
(*149*) Ivanoff, Mihova, and Christova, *Bull. soc. chim.*, [4], *51*, 1321–5 (1932).
(*150*) Colonge, *Bull. soc. chim.*, [5], *2*, 754–61 (1935).
(*151*) Grignard, *Ann. chim.*, [7], *27*, 548–74 (1902).
(*152*) Grignard, *Compt. rend.*, *134*, 849–51 (1902); *Chem. Zentr.*, *1902,I*, 1197.
(*153*) Benary, *Ber.*, *64B*, 2543–5 (1931).
(*154*) Pastereau and Bernard, *Compt. rend.*, *174*, 1555–7 (1922).
(*155*) Pastereau and Bernard, *Compt. rend.*, *176*, 1400–2 (1923).
(*156*) Clarke, *J. Am. Chem. Soc.*, *31*, 585–90 (1909).
(*157*) Konowaloff, *J. Russ. Phys.-Chem. Soc.*, *34*, 26–31 (1902); *Chem. Zentr.*, *1902,I*, 1271.
(*158*) Clarke, *J. Am. Chem. Soc.*, *34*, 680–3 (1912).

(159) Whitmore, Popkin, Whitaker, Mattil, and Zech, *J. Am. Chem. Soc.*, *60*, 2458–62 (1938).
(160) Marvel, Mozingo, and Kirkpatrick, *J. Am. Chem. Soc.*, *61*, 2003–8 (1939).
(161) Richard and Mirjollet, *Compt. rend.*, *224*, 284–6 (1947); *Chem. Abstr.*, *41*, 3754 (1947).
(162) Clarke, *J. Am. Chem. Soc.*, *30*, 1144–52 (1908).
(163) Clarke and Beggs, *J. Am. Chem. Soc.*, *34*, 54–60 (1912).
(164) Clarke and Beggs, *J. Am. Chem. Soc.*, *34*, 60–2 (1912).
(165) Hickinbottom and Schlüchterer, *Nature*, *155*, 19 (1945).
(166) Henry, *Rec. trav. chim.*, *26*, 106–15 (1907).
(167) Tolstopjatow, *J. Russ. Phys.-Chem. Soc.*, *62*, 1813–28 (1930); *Chem. Zentr.*, *1931,I*, 2738.
(168) Whitmore and Lewis, *J. Am. Chem. Soc.*, *64*, 2964–6 (1942).
(169) Clarke and Jones, *J. Am. Chem. Soc.*, *34*, 170–4 (1912).
(170) Whitmore and Laughlin, *J. Am. Chem. Soc.*, *54*, 4011–4 (1932).
(171) Leroide, *Ann. chim.*, [9], *16*, 354–410 (1921).
(172) Ramart-Lucas, *Compt. rend.*, *154*, 708–10 (1912); *Chem. Abstr.*, 6, 1603 (1912).
(173) Ruggli and Businger, *Helv. Chim. Acta*, *24*, 1112–26 (1941).
(174) Lemaire, *Rec. trav. chim.*, *29*, 22–84 (1910).
(175) Lespieau and Wakeman, *Bull. soc. chim.*, [4], *51*, 384–400 (1932).
(176) Jacquemaine, *Compt. rend.*, *199*, 1315–7 (1934).
(177) Franke and Kohn, *Ber.*, *37*, 4730–1 (1904).
(178) Franke and Kohn, *Monatsh.*, *28*, 997–1015 (1907).
(179) Tiffeneau and Lévy, *Bull. soc. chim.*, [4], *33*, 735–59 (1923).
(180) Hurd and Webb, *J. Am. Chem. Soc.*, *49*, 546–59 (1927).
(181) Domratschewa, *J. Russ. Phys.-Chem. Soc.*, *46*, 864–7 (1914); *Chem. Zentr.*, *1915,I*, 878.
(182) Heilbron, Jones, and Richardson, *J. Chem. Soc.*, *1949*, 287–93.
(183) Grignard and Dubien, *Ann. chim.*, [10], *2*, 298–318 (1924).
(184) Esafov and Molchanova, *J. Gen. Chem.* (U.S.S.R.), *16*, 1885–90 (1946); *Chem. Abstr.*, *41*, 6185 (1947).
(185) Colonge, *Bull. soc. chim.*, [5], *3*, 413–8 (1936).
(186) Smith, Chase, and Rhodes, *J. Am. Chem. Soc.*, *66*, 1547–9 (1944).
(187) Grignard, *Compt. rend.*, *135*, 627–30 (1902); *Chem. Zentr.*, *1902,II*, 1359.
(188) Frank, Arvan, Richter, and Vanneman, *J. Am. Chem. Soc.*, *66*, 4–6 (1944).
(189) LaForge and Barthel, *J. Org. Chem.*, *10*, 222–7 (1945).
(190) Huston and Guile, *J. Am. Chem. Soc.*, *61*, 69–71 (1939).
(191) Whitmore and Williams, *J. Am. Chem. Soc.*, *55*, 406–11 (1933).
(192) Whitmore and Lewis, *J. Am. Chem. Soc.*, *64*, 1619–21 (1942).
(193) Stas, *Bull. soc. chim. Belg.*, *34*, 188–90 (1925).
(194) Blatt and Stone, *J. Am. Chem. Soc.*, *54*, 1495–9 (1932).
(195) Murat and Amouroux, *J. Pharm. Chim.*, [7], *5*, 473–8 (1912); *Chem. Zentr.*, *1912,II*, 103.
(196) Whitmore and George, *J. Am. Chem. Soc.*, *64*, 1239–42 (1942).
(197) Young and Roberts, *J. Am. Chem. Soc.*, *67*, 319–21 (1945).
(198) Béhal and Sommelet, *Compt. rend.*, *138*, 89–92 (1904); *Chem. Zentr.*, *1904,I*, 504.
(199) Tuot and Guyard, *Bull. soc. chim.*, [5], *14*, 1087–96 (1947).
(200) Ivanoff and Spassoff, *Bull. soc. chim.*, [4], *49*, 377–9 (1931).
(201) Young and Roberts, *J. Am. Chem. Soc.*, *66*, 1444–5 (1944).
(202) de Coster, *Bull. acad. roy. Belg.*, [5], *11*, 661–5 (1925); *Chem. Zentr.*, *1926,I*, 3146.

(*203*) Madelung and Oberwegner, *Ber.*, *65B*, 931–41 (1932).
(*204*) Gilman and Kirby, *J. Am. Chem. Soc.*, *54*, 345–55 (1932).
(*205*) Fieser and Seligman, *J. Am. Chem. Soc.*, *61*, 136–42 (1939).
(*206*) Klages, *Ber.*, *35*, 2633–41 (1902).
(*207*) Orékhoff and Tiffeneau, *Bull. soc. chim.*, [4], *41*, 839–43 (1927).
(*208*) Chang and Tseng, *Trans. Science Soc. China*, 7, 225–32 (1932); *Chem. Abstr.*, *26*, 5555 (1932).
(*209*) Simons and Ramler, *J. Am. Chem. Soc.*, *65*, 389–92 (1943).
(*210*) Marvel, Allen, and Overberger, *J. Am. Chem. Soc.*, *68*, 1088–91 (1946).
(*211*) Pochinok, *J. Gen. Chem.* (U.S.S.R.), *16*, 1306–10 (1946); *Chem. Abstr.*, *41*, 3066 (1947).
(*212*) Sudzuki, *J. Chem. Soc., Japan*, *63*, 124–7 (1942); *Chem. Abstr.*, *41*, 3046 (1947).
(*213*) Tiffeneau, *Ann. chim.*, [8], *10*, 322–78 (1907).
(*214*) Salkind and Rosenfeld, *Ber.*, *57B*, 1690–2 (1924).
(*215*) Nesmeyanov and Sazanova, *Bull. acad. sci. U.S.S.R., Classe sci. chim.*, *1941*, 499–519; *Chem. Abstr.*, *37*, 2723 (1943).
(*216*) Gilman and McGlumphy, *Bull. soc. chim.*, [4], *43*, 1322–8 (1928).
(*217*) Crawford, Saeger, and Warneke, *J. Am. Chem. Soc.*, *64*, 2862–4 (1942).
(*218*) Proost and Wibaut, *Rec. trav. chim.*, *59*, 971–7 (1940).
(*219*) Sabatier and Murat, *Compt. rend.*, *154*, 1771–3 (1912); *Chem. Abstr.*, *6*, 2738 (1912).
(*220*) Hell, *Ber.*, *37*, 453–8 (1904).
(*221*) Fuson, Armstrong, Wallace, and Kneisley, *J. Am. Chem. Soc.*, *66*, 681–4 (1944).
(*222*) Petrov and Chel'tsova, *J. Gen. Chem.* (U.S.S.R.), *12*, 87–94 (1942); *Chem. Abstr.*, *37*, 1993 (1943).
(*223*) Ziegler and Sauermilch, *Ber.*, *63B*, 1851–64 (1930).
(*224*) Chelintsev and Till, *Uchenye Zapiski Saratov Gosudarst. Univ. N.G. Chernyshevskogo, Khim.*, *15*, No. 4, 24–31 (1940); *Chem. Abstr.*, *35*, 6953 (1941).
(*225*) Stoermer, *Ber.*, *39*, 2288–306 (1906).
(*226*) Miescher and Marxer, U. S. Patent 2,411,664, Nov. 26, 1946; *Chem. Abstr.*, *41*, P6276 (1947).
(*227*) Stoermer and Simon, *Ber.*, *37*, 4163–8 (1904).
(*228*) Fuson, McKusick, and Mills, *J. Org. Chem.*, *11*, 60–6 (1946).
(*229*) Vavon, Rivière, and Angelo, *Compt. rend.*, *222*, 959–61 (1946); *Chem. Abstr.*, *40*, 4365 (1946).
(*230*) Vavon and Angelo, *Compt. rend.*, *224*, 1435–7 (1947); *Chem. Abstr.*, *41*, 6221 (1947).
(*231*) Whitmore, Schiessler, Rowland, and Cosby, *J. Am. Chem. Soc.*, *69*, 235–7 (1947).
(*232*) Jacquemain, *Compt. rend.*, *198*, 482–4 (1934); *Chem. Abstr.*, *28*, 2328 (1934).
(*233*) Arens, van Dorp, van Dijk, Brandt, Hubers, and Pieters, *Rec. trav. chim.*, *67*, 973–9 (1948).
(*234*) Ramart-Lucas, *Ann. chim.*, [8], *30*, 349–432 (1913).
(*235*) Oparin, *J. Russ. Phys.-Chem. Soc.*, *61*, 2011–5 (1929); *Chem. Zentr.*, *1930,I*, 3556; *Chem. Abstr.*, *24*, 4785 (1930).
(*236*) Kanao and Shinozuka, *J. Pharm. Soc. Japan*, *50*, 148–52 (1930); *Chem. Zentr.*, *1931,I*, 1743.
(*237*) Sackur, *Compt. rend.*, *208*, 1092–4 (1939); *Chem. Abstr.*, *33*, 9296 (1939).
(*238*) McKenzie, Mills, and Myles, *Ber.*, *63B*, 904–11 (1930).

(239) Esafov, Gulyakov, Kargapol'tseva, Kulekova, Razmyslov, and Toporov, *J. Gen. Chem.* (U.S.S.R.), *10*, 1973–7 (1940); *Chem. Abstr.*, *35*, 3958 (1941).
(240) Bruylants, *Bull. soc. chim. Belg.*, *36*, 519–32 (1927).
(241) Harries and Weil, *Ber.*, *37*, 845–50 (1904).
(242) Escourru, *Bull. soc. chim.*, [4], *39*, 1121–38 (1926).
(243) Barbier, *Compt. rend.*, *128*, 110–1 (1899); *J. Chem. Soc.*, *76*,*I*, 323 (1899).
(244) Sand and Singer, *Ber.*, *35*, 3170–87 (1902).
(245) Nazarov and Terekhova, *Bull. acad. sci. U.R.S.S.*, *Classe sci. chim.*, *1943*, 286–95; *Chem. Abstr.*, *38*, 5489 (1944).
(246) Speck and Bost, *J. Org. Chem.*, *11*, 788–94 (1946).
(247) Slavianov, *J. Russ. Phys.-Chem. Soc.*, *39*, 140–60 (1907); *Chem. Abstr.*, *1*, 2077 (1907).
(248) Gredy, *Bull. soc. chim.*, [5], *2*, 1038–44 (1935).
(249) Calingaert and Soroos, *J. Am. Chem. Soc.*, *58*, 635–6 (1936).
(250) Brokaw and Brode, *J. Org. Chem.*, *13*, 194–9 (1948).
(251) Wilson, Roberts, and Young, *J. Am. Chem. Soc.*, *72*, 218–9 (1950).
(252) Tiffeneau and Lévy, *Bull. soc. chim.*, [4], *33*, 759–79 (1923).
(253) Spaeth, Geissman, and Jacobs, *J. Org. Chem.*, *11*, 399–404 (1946).
(254) Buu-Hoï and Nguyen-Hoán, *Rec. trav. chim.*, *68*, 5–33 (1949).
(255) Young and Roberts, *J. Am. Chem. Soc.*, *68*, 649–52 (1946).
(256) Kohler, *Am. Chem. J.*, *42*, 375–401 (1909).
(257) Tarbell and Sato, *J. Am. Chem. Soc.*, *68*, 1094–6 (1946).
(258) Temnikova, *Vestnik Leningrad Univ.*, *1947*, 138–45; *Chem. Abstr.*, *42*, 4155 (1948).
(259) Levy and Cope, *J. Am. Chem. Soc.*, *66*, 1684–8 (1944).
(260) Sabatier and Murat, *Compt. rend.*, *156*, 1430–4 (1913); *Chem. Abstr.*, *7*, 3109 (1913).
(261) Gilman and Harris, *J. Am. Chem. Soc.*, *54*, 2072–5 (1932).
(262) Mills and Grigor, *J. Chem. Soc.*, *1934*, 1568–70.
(263) Tiffeneau, Lévy, and Dietz, *Bull. soc. chim.*, [5], *2*, 1848–55 (1935).
(264) Tiffeneau, Orékhoff, and Roger, *Bull. soc. chim.*, [4], *49*, 1757–65 (1931).
(265) Meyer, *Helv. Chim. Acta*, *18*, 101–3 (1935).
(266) Barbier and Locquin, *Bull. soc. chim.*, [4], *9*, 717–22 (1911).
(267) Werner and Bogert, *J. Org. Chem.*, *3*, 578–87 (1939).
(268) Houben, *Ber.*, *35*, 3587–92 (1902).
(269) Cason and Prout, *J. Am. Chem. Soc.*, *66*, 46–50 (1944).
(270) Mannich and Hof, *Arch. Pharm.*, *265*, 589–98 (1927); *Chem. Zentr.*, *1928*,*I*, 201.
(271) Mironescu, Ioanid, and Nicolescu, *Bul. soc. chim. România*, *14*, 187 (1932); *Chem. Abstr.*, *27*, 4231 (1933).
(272) Minnis, *J. Am. Chem. Soc.*, *51*, 2143–7 (1929).
(273) Shriner and Sharp, *J. Org. Chem.*, *4*, 575–82 (1939).
(274) Buchta and Haagner, *Ber.*, *81B*, 251–3 (1948); *Chem. Abstr.*, *43*, 1039 (1949).
(275) Kohler and Johnstin, *Am. Chem. J.*, *33*, 35–45 (1905).
(276) Koelsch, *J. Am. Chem. Soc.*, *65*, 1640–3 (1943).
(277) Ponomarev, *Uchenye Zapiski Saratov Gosudarst. Univ.*, *Sbornik Nauch.*, *Rabot Studentov*, *1938*, 20–4; *Khim. Referat. Zhur.*, *1939*, No. 9, 31; *Chem. Abstr.*, *34*, 5830 (1940).
(278) Kohler and Burnley, *Am. Chem. J.*, *43*, 412–8 (1910).
(279) Lipp, Buchkremer, and Seeles, *Ann.*, *499*, 1–25 (1932).
(280) Burmistrov and Shilov, *J. Gen. Chem.* (U.S.S.R.), *16*, 295–9 (1946); *Chem. Abstr.*, *41*, 474 (1947).

(281) Lauer and Renfrew, *J. Am. Chem. Soc.*, *67*, 808–10 (1945).
(282) Orechoff and Meerson, *Ber.*, *45*, 1926–30 (1912).
(283) Mazurewitsch, *J. Russ. Phys.-Chem. Soc.*, *43*, 973–90 (1911); *Chem. Zentr.*, *1911,II*, 1921.
(284) Grischkewitsch-Trochimowski, *J. Russ. Phys.-Chem. Soc.*, *41*, 1326–32 (1909); *Chem. Zentr.*, *1910,I*, 739.
(285) Yéramian, *Compt. rend.*, *173*, 362–4 (1921).
(286) Klages, *Ber.*, *37*, 1721–6 (1904).
(287) Blicke and Powers, *J. Am. Chem. Soc.*, *51*, 3378–83 (1929).
(288) Schwartzkopf and Bush, British Patent 584,705, Jan. 21, 1947; *Chem. Abstr.*, *41*, P4515 (1947).
(289) Temnikova, *J. Gen. Chem.* (U.S.S.R.), *11*, 77–91 (1941); *Chem. Abstr.*, *35*, 6580 (1941).
(290) Venus-Danilova and Brichko, *J. Gen. Chem.* (U.S.S.R.), *17*, 1549–58 (1947); *Chem. Abstr.*, *42*, 2243 (1948).
(291) Weill, *Bull. soc. chim.*, [4], *49*, 1795–1806 (1931).
(292) Temnikova, *J. Gen. Chem.* (U.S.S.R.), *15*, 514–23 (1945); *Chem. Abstr.*, *40*, 4695 (1946).
(293) Skita, Keil, and Baesler, *Ber.*, *66B*, 858–66 (1933).
(294) Esafov, Vladimirtsev, Kassiklina, and Raikher, *J. Gen. Chem.* (U.S.S.R.), *13*, 818–22 (1943); *Chem. Abstr.*, *39*, 904 (1945).
(295) Temnikova and Veksler, *J. Gen. Chem.* (U.S.S.R.), *11*, 3–8 (1941); *Chem. Abstr.*, *35*, 5459 (1941).
(296) Montagne and Rousseau, *Compt. rend.*, *196*, 1165–7 (1933).
(297) Karrer, Shibata, Wettstein, and Jacubowiecz, *Helv. Chem. Acta*, *13*, 1292–308 (1930).
(298) Petrov and Vittikh, *Bull. acad. sci. U.R.S.S.*, *Classe sci. chim.*, *1944*, 152–5; *Chem. Abstr.*, *39*, 1618 (1945).
(299) Whitmore and Laughlin, *J. Am. Chem. Soc.*, *56*, 1128–30 (1934).
(300) Brachin, *Bull. soc. chim.*, [3], *35*, 1163–79 (1906).
(301) Buu-Hoï and Hiong-Ki-Wei, *Compt. rend.*, *220*, 175–7 (1945); *Chem. Abstr.*, *40*, 2828 (1946).
(302) Padbury and Lindwall, *J. Am. Chem. Soc.*, *67*, 1268–70 (1945).
(303) Strating and Backer, *Rec. trav. chim.*, *62*, 57–67 (1943); *Chem. Abstr.*, *39*, 2497 (1945).
(304) Kondo and Osawa, *J. Pharm. Soc. Japan*, *56*, 73–4 (1936); *Chem. Abstr.*, *32*, 5837 (1938).
(305) Whitmore, Whitaker, Mosher, Breivik, Wheeler, Miner, Sutherland, Wagner, Clapper, Lewis, Lux, and Popkin, *J. Am. Chem. Soc.*, *63*, 643–54 (1941).
(306) Kondo and Kokeguchi, *J. Pharm. Soc. Japan*, *57*, 573–9 (1937); *Chem. Abstr.*, *31*, 6230 (1937).
(307) Lüttringhaus, Wagner-von Sääf, Sucker, and Borth, *Ann.*, *557*, 26–45 (1945); *Chem. Abstr.*, *40*, 5418 (1946).
(308) Maxim and Georgescu, *Bull. soc. chim.*, [5], *3*, 1114–24 (1936).
(309) Young and Roberts, *J. Am. Chem. Soc.*, *68*, 1472–5 (1946).
(310) Willemart, *Bull. soc. chim.*, [5], *2*, 867–82 (1935).
(311) Venus-Danilova and Brichko, *J. Gen. Chem.* (U.S.S.R.), *17*, 1849–57 (1947); *Chem. Abstr.*, *42*, 4160 (1948).
(312) Fuson, Armstrong, and Shenk, *J. Am. Chem. Soc.*, *66*, 964–7 (1944).
(313) Temnikova, *J. Gen. Chem.* (U.S.S.R.), *8*, 1022–8 (1939); *Chem. Abstr.*, *33*, 3777 (1939).
(314) Kloetzel, *J. Am. Chem. Soc.*, *62*, 3405–10 (1940).
(315) Adams and Gross, *J. Am. Chem. Soc.*, *64*, 1786–90 (1942).

(*316*) Young and Roberts, *J. Am. Chem. Soc.*, *66*, 2131 (1944).
(*317*) Dev, *Current Sci.*, *16*, 377–8 (1947); *Chem. Abstr.*, *42*, 5890 (1948).
(*318*) Chichibabin and Stepanov, *Ber.*, *62B*, 1068–75 (1929).
(*319*) Mironescu and Ioanid, *Bul. soc. chim. România*, *17*, 107–29 (1935); *Chem. Abstr.*, *30*, 1053 (1936).
(*320*) Lucas, *Compt. rend.*, *150*, 1058–61 (1910); *Chem. Zentr.*, *1910,II*, 77.
(*321*) Lucas, *Compt. rend.*, *152*, 1771–4 (1911); *Chem. Zentr.*, *1911,II*, 360.
(*322*) Weill, *Bull. soc. chim.*, [4], *49*, 1811–23 (1931).
(*323*) Petrov and Karlik, *J. Gen. Chem.* (U.S.S.R.), *11*, 1100–3 (1941); *Chem. Abstr.*, *37*, 4049 (1942).
(*324*) Whitmore and Lester, *J. Am. Chem. Soc.*, *64*, 1247–51 (1942).
(*325*) Tschitschibabin, *J. prakt. Chem.*, [2], *75*, 526–8 (1905); *Chem. Abstr.*, *1*, 2478 (1907).
(*326*) Tschitschibabin, *J. Russ. Phys.-Chem. Soc.*, 7, 1056–7 (1906); *Chem. Abstr.*, *1*, 1414 (1907).
(*327*) Fuson, McKusick, and Spangler, *J. Am. Chem. Soc.*, *67*, 597–601 (1945).
(*328*) Bergmann and Weizmann, *J. Org. Chem.*, *9*, 352–8 (1944).
(*329*) Bauer, *Ber.*, *38*, 688–90 (1905).
(*330*) Haworth, Letsky, and Mavin, *J. Chem. Soc.*, *1932*, 1784–92.
(*331*) Fieser and Newman, *J. Am. Chem. Soc.*, *58*, 2376–82 (1936).
(*332*) Tarbell and Weaver, *J. Am. Chem. Soc.*, *62*, 2747–50 (1940).
(*333*) Adams, Chen, and Loewe, *J. Am. Chem. Soc.*, *67*, 1534–7 (1945).
(*334*) Bergmann and Weizmann, *J. Org. Chem.*, *11*, 592–9 (1946).
(*335*) Tsatsas, *Ann. chim.*, [12], *1*, 342–94 (1946).
(*336*) Tsatsas, *Compt. rend.*, *220*, 889–91 (1945); *Chem. Abstr.*, *40*, 3739 (1946).
(*337*) Rajagopalan, *J. Indian Chem. Soc.*, *17*, 576–82 (1940).
(*338*) Walther, *J. pharm. chim.*, *27*, 467–9 (1938); *Chem. Abstr.*, *32*, 6237 (1938).
(*339*) Lipp and Quaedvlieg, *Ber.*, *62B*, 2311–22 (1929).
(*340*) Morton and Peakes, *J. Am. Chem. Soc.*, *55*, 2110–2 (1933).
(*341*) Forrest, *J. Chem. Soc.*, *1946*, 333–9.
(*342*) Fuson and Armstrong, *J. Am. Chem. Soc.*, *63*, 2650–2 (1941).
(*343*) Marvel, Dietz, and Himel, *J. Org. Chem.*, 7, 392–6 (1942).
(*344*) Loury, *Compt. rend.*, *194*, 1747–9 (1932).
(*345*) Koelsch, *J. Am. Chem. Soc.*, *54*, 2487–93 (1932).
(*346*) Maxim and Angelesco, *Bull. soc. chim.*, [4], *51*, 1365–70 (1932).
(*347*) Maxim and Angelesco, *Bull. soc. chim.*, [5], *1*, 1128–33 (1934).
(*348*) Grummit, Buck, and Becker, *J. Am. Chem. Soc.*, *67*, 2265–6 (1945).
(*349*) Bergmann and Bondi, *Ber.*, *64B*, 1455–80 (1931).
(*350*) Klages, *Ber.*, *35*, 2646–9 (1902).
(*351*) Kharasch and Weinhouse, *J. Org. Chem.*, *1*, 209–30 (1936).
(*352*) Tarassow, *J. Russ. Phys.-Chem. Soc.*, *41*, 1309–13 (1910); *Chem. Zentr.*, *1910,I*, 739.
(*353*) Klages and Heilmann, *Ber.*, *37*, 1447–57 (1904).
(*354*) LaGrave, *Ann. chim.*, [10], *8*, 363–446 (1927).
(*355*) Kharasch, Kleiger, Martin, and Mayo, *J. Am. Chem. Soc.*, *63*, 2305–7 (1941).
(*356*) Noller, Grebe, and Knox, *J. Am. Chem. Soc.*, *54*, 4690–6 (1932).
(*357*) Davies, Dixon, and Jones, *J. Chem. Soc.*, *1930*, 1916–21.
(*358*) Grignard and Courtot, *Compt. rend.*, *158*, 1763–6 (1914); *Chem. Abstr.*, *8*, 3436 (1914).
(*359*) Mihaïlescu and Caragea, *Bull. sect. sci. acad. romaine*, *12*, No. 4/5, 7–18 (1929); *Chem. Abstr.*, *24*, 2116 (1930).
(*360*) Acree, *Ber.*, *37*, 2753–64 (1904).
(*361*) Tadros, *Nature*, *148*, 53 (1941).

(362) Banus and Vila, *Anales soc. españ. fís. quím.*, *19*, 326–46 (1921); *Chem. Zentr.*, *1924,I*, 1525.
(363) Blicke and Weinkauff, *J. Am. Chem. Soc.*, *54*, 1446–53 (1932).
(364) Acree, *Ber.*, *37*, 990–4 (1904).
(365) Kovache, *Ann. chim.*, [9], *10*, 184–248 (1918).
(366) Marxer, *Helv. Chim. Acta*, *24*, 209–15E (1941).
(367) Hess and Weltzien, *Ber.*, *54B*, 2511–21 (1921).
(368) Acree, *Ber.*, *37*, 625–8 (1904).
(369) Meyer and Schuster, *Ber.*, *55B*, 815–9 (1922).
(370) Straus and Ehrenstein, *Ann.*, *442*, 93–118 (1925).
(371) Ehrlich and Sachs, *Ber.*, *36*, 4296–9 (1903).
(372) Sweet and Marvel, *J. Am. Chem. Soc.*, *54*, 1184–90 (1932).
(373) Bowden, Harris, and Roberts, *J. Chem. Soc.*, *1939*, 302–7.
(374) Bowden and Harris, *J. Chem. Soc.*, *1939*, 307–10.
(375) Schlenk and Weickel, *Ann.*, *368*, 295–304 (1909).
(376) Grignard and Courtot, *Compt. rend.*, *152*, 1493–5 (1911); *Chem. Abstr.*, *5*, 3409 (1911).
(377) Bachmann, *J. Am. Chem. Soc.*, *56*, 1363–7 (1934).
(378) Ziegler, *Ann.*, *434*, 34–78 (1923).
(379) Koelsch, *J. Am. Chem. Soc.*, *54*, 3384–9 (1932).
(380) Tschelinzew, Tronow, and Terentjew, *J. Russ. Phys.-Chem. Soc.*, *47*, 1211–23 (1915); *Chem. Zentr.*, *1916,I*, 1247.
(381) Bachmann and Hetzner, *Organic Syntheses*, *23*, 98–100 (1943).
(382) Marvel, Kaplan, and Himel, *J. Am. Chem. Soc.*, *63*, 1892–6 (1941).
(383) Nesmeyanov and Pecherskaya, *Bull. acad. sci. U.R.S.S., Classe sci. chim.*, *1943*, 317–8; *Chem. Abstr.*, *38*, 5492 (1944).
(384) Ivanoff and Pchenitchny, *Bull. soc. chim.*, [5], *1*, 223–33 (1934).
(385) Courtot and Tchelitcheff, *Compt. rend.*, *217*, 201–3 (1943); *Chem. Abstr.*, *38*, 5502 (1944).
(386) Bachmann and Kloetzel, *J. Org. Chem.*, *3*, 55–61 (1938).
(387) Tadros, Farahat, and Robson, *J. Chem. Soc.*, *1949*, 439–41.
(388) Petrov and Kaplan, *Isvest. Akad. Nauk. S.S.S.R., Otdel Khim. Nauk.*, *1947*, 295–308; *Chem. Abstr.*, *43*, 1718 (1949).
(389) Pfeiffer and Blank, *J. prakt. Chem.*, [2], *153*, 242–56 (1939).
(390) Soc. pour l'ind. chim. à Bâle, Swiss Patents 235,496, Apr. 3, 1945, 235,497, Apr. 16, 1945; *Chem. Abstr.*, *43*, P7056 (1949).
(391) Simpson and Stephenson, *J. Chem. Soc.*, *1942*, 353–8.
(392) Baeyer, *Ann.*, *372*, 80–151 (1910).
(393) Fuson and Meek, *J. Org. Chem.*, *10*, 551–61 (1945).
(394) Baeyer, *Ann.*, *354*, 152–204 (1907).
(395) Kauffmann and Pannwitz, *Ber.*, *45*, 766–76 (1912).
(396) Porter and Hirst, *J. Am. Chem. Soc.*, *41*, 1264–7 (1919).
(397) Stoermer and Fincke, *Ber.*, *42*, 3115–34 (1909).
(398) Simpson, *J. Chem. Soc.*, *1946*, 673–5.
(399) Dziewoński and Marusińska, *Bull. intern. polon. sci., Classe sci. math. nat.*, *1938A*, 316–23; *Chem. Abstr.*, *33*, 1712 (1939).
(400) Grateau, *Compt. rend.*, *196*, 1619–21 (1933).
(401) Kohler and Blanchard, *J. Am. Chem. Soc.*, *57*, 367–71 (1935).
(402) Campbell and Soffer, *J. Am. Chem. Soc.*, *64*, 417–25 (1943).
(403) Conant and Schultz, *J. Am. Chem. Soc.*, *55*, 2098–104 (1933).
(404) Földi and Demjén, *Ber.*, *74B*, 930–4 (1941).
(405) Giacolone, *Gazz. chim. ital.*, *67*, 464–8 (1937); *Chem. Abstr.*, *32*, 1689 (1938).

(406) Neunhoeffer, *Ann.*, *509*, 115–30 (1934).
(407) Schneider and Spielmann, *J. Biol. Chem.*, *142*, 345–54 (1942).
(408) Clark and Linnell, *J. Pharm. Pharmacol.*, *1*, 211–8 (1949); *Chem. Abstr.*, *43*, 8367 (1949).
(409) Smith and Sprung, *J. Am. Chem. Soc.*, *65*, 1276–83 (1943).
(410) Preobrazhenskiĭ and Shokina, *J. Gen. Chem.* (U.S.S.R.), *15*, 65–9 (1945); *Chem. Abstr.*, *40*, 1793 (1946).
(411) Smith and Sprung, U. S. Patent 2,241,090, May 27, 1947; *Chem. Abstr.*, *41*, P5543 (1947).
(412) Kleinfeller and Eckert, *Ber.*, *62B*, 1598–600 (1929).
(413) Chu and Chu, *J. Chinese Chem. Soc.*, *9*, 190–5 (1942).
(414) Roger and McGregor, *J. Chem. Soc.*, *1934*, 442–4.
(415) Bachmann and Ferguson, *J. Am. Chem. Soc.*, *56*, 2081–4 (1934).
(416) Ostersetzer, *Monatsh.*, *34*, 795–6 (1913).
(417) Chamberlain and Dull, *J. Am. Chem. Soc.*, *50*, 3088–92 (1928).
(418) Carpenter and Turner, *J. Chem. Soc.*, *1934*, 869–72.
(419) Kusjimin, *J. Russ. Phys.-Chem. Soc.*, *41*, 1314–9 (1909); *Chem. Zentr.*, *1910,I*, 739.
(420) Wright, *J. Am. Chem. Soc.*, *61*, 1152–6 (1939).
(421) Bradsher and Wissow, *J. Am. Chem. Soc.*, *68*, 1094–6 (1946).
(422) McKenzie and Mills, *Ber.*, *62B*, 1784–94 (1929).
(423) Zugrăvescu and Zugrăvescu, *Bul. soc. chim. România*, *20A*, 225–30 (1938); *Chem. Abstr.*, *34*, 1974 (1940).
(424) Fuson and Robertson, *J. Org. Chem.*, *7*, 466–71 (1942).
(425) Staudinger, *Ann.*, *356*, 51–123 (1907).
(426) Roger and McGregor, *J. Chem. Soc.*, *1934*, 1850–3.
(427) Reeves and Lindwall, *J. Am. Chem. Soc.*, *64*, 1086–9 (1942).
(428) McKenzie and Wren, *J. Chem. Soc.*, *97*, 473–86 (1910).
(429) Tiffeneau and Dorlencourt, *Compt. rend.*, *143*, 126–8 (1906); *Chem. Zentr.*, *1906,II*, 670.
(430) Kohler, Richtmyer, and Hester, *J. Am. Chem. Soc.*, *53*, 205–21 (1931).
(431) Bachmann and Moser, *J. Am. Chem. Soc.*, *54*, 1124–33 (1932).
(432) Lévy and Pernot, *Bull. soc. chim.*, [4], *49*, 1730–8 (1931).
(433) Acree, *Am. Chem. J.*, *33*, 180–95 (1905).
(434) Roger and McKay, *J. Chem. Soc.*, *1931*, 2229–38.
(435) Bergmann, Winter, and Schreiber, *Ann.*, *500*, 122–36 (1933).
(436) Mitter and De, *J. Indian Chem. Soc.*, *16*, 199–208 (1939).
(437) Kohler and Tishler, *J. Am. Chem. Soc.*, *54*, 1594–600 (1932).
(438) Löwenbein, Pongrácz, and Spiess, *Ber.*, *57B*, 1517–26 (1924).
(439) Johlin, *J. Am. Chem. Soc.*, *39*, 291–3 (1917).
(440) Neunhoeffer and Nerdel, *Ann.*, *526*, 47–58 (1936).
(441) Buu-Hoï, *Bull. soc. chim.*, [5], *13*, 117–23 (1946).
(442) Ivanoff and Spassoff, *Bull. soc. chim.*, [4], *49*, 371–5 (1931).
(443) Orékhoff, *Bull. soc. chim.*, [4], *25*, 108–11 (1919).
(444) McKenzie and Richardson, *J. Chem. Soc.*, *123*, 79–91 (1923).
(445) Gilman and Heckert, *J. Am. Chem. Soc.*, *42*, 1010–4 (1920).
(446) Smith and Hoehn, *J. Am. Chem. Soc.*, *63*, 1176–8 (1941).
(447) Gverdsiteli, *J. Gen. Chem.* (U.S.S.R.), *18*, 1187–8 (1948); *Chem. Abstr.*, *43*, 1754 (1949).
(448) Colonge and Pichat, *Compt. rend.*, *226*, 673–5 (1948); *Chem. Abstr.*, *42*, 4993 (1948).
(449) Albesco, *Ann. chim.*, [9], *18*, 216–62 (1922).
(450) Kohler and Erickson, *J. Am. Chem. Soc.*, *53*, 2301–9 (1931).

(451) Fuson, Kaiser, and Speck, *J. Org. Chem.*, 6, 845-51 (1941).
(452) Taylor and Connor, *J. Org. Chem.*, 6, 696-704 (1941).
(453) Bergmann and Hampson, *J. Chem. Soc.*, *1935*, 989-93.
(454) Newman and Smith, *J. Org. Chem.*, *13*, 592-8 (1948).
(455) Vorländer and Siebert, *Ber.*, *39*, 1024-35 (1906).
(456) Vorländer, Osterburg, and Meye, *Ber.*, *56B*, 1136-44 (1923).
(457) Smedley, *J. Chem. Soc.*, 97, 1484-94 (1910).
(458) Koelsch and Prill, *J. Am. Chem. Soc.*, *67*, 1296-9 (1945).
(459) Guyot and Catel, *Compt. rend.*, *140*, 254-6 (1905); *Chem. Zentr.*, *1905,I*, 679.
(460) Haworth, Mavin, and Sheldrick, *J. Chem. Soc.*, *1934*, 454-61.
(461) Buu-Hoï, Hiong-Ki-Wei, Lacassagne, and Lecocq, *Compt. rend.*, *219*, 589-91 (1944); *Chem. Abstr.*, *40*, 1489 (1946).
(462) Burger and Deiner, *J. Am. Chem. Soc.*, *67*, 566-9 (1945).
(463) McKenzie, Martin, and Rule, *J. Chem. Soc.*, *105*, 1583-91 (1914).
(464) Ramart and Albesco, *Compt. rend.*, *174*, 1289-91 (1922); *Chem. Zentr.*, *1922,III*, 1290.
(465) Gilman and Kirby, *J. Am. Chem. Soc.*, *63*, 2046-8 (1941).
(466) Kohler and Barnes, *J. Am. Chem. Soc.*, *56*, 211-4 (1934).
(467) Blicke, Smith, and Powers, *J. Am. Chem. Soc.*, *54*, 1465-71 (1932).
(468) Campbell, Anderson, and Gilmore, *J. Chem. Soc.*, *1940*, 819-21.
(469) Austin and Johnson, *J. Am. Chem. Soc.*, *54*, 647-60 (1932).
(470) Bradsher and Amore, *J. Am. Chem. Soc.*, *63*, 493-5 (1941).
(471) Bradsher and Rosher, *J. Am. Chem. Soc.*, *61*, 1524-5 (1939).
(472) Kauffmann and Fritz, *Ber.*, *41*, 4423-7 (1908).
(473) Kauffmann and Grombach, *Ber.*, *38*, 794-801 (1905).
(474) Kauffmann and Kieser, *Ber.*, *46*, 3788-801 (1913).
(475) Sachs and Thonet, *Ber.*, *37*, 3327-34 (1904).
(476) Ziegler and Ochs, *Ber.*, *55B*, 2257-77 (1922).
(477) Busignies, *Compt. rend.*, *149*, 348-50 (1909); *Chem. Zentr.*, *1909,II*, 1450.
(478) Mills, *J. Chem. Soc.*, *1934*, 1565-8.
(479) Clemo, Kefford, and Osborne, *J. Chem. Soc.*, *1939*, 360-1.
(480) Bergmann, *J. Org. Chem.*, *4*, 1-13 (1939).
(481) Shelton and Van Campen, U. S. Patent 2,430,891, Nov. 18, 1947; *Chem. Abstr.*, *42*, P1968 (1948).
(482) Robinson and Slater, *J. Chem. Soc.*, *1941*, 376-85.
(483) Sah, *J. Chinese Chem. Soc.*, *13*, 89-95 (1946); *Chem. Abstr.*, *41*, 5869 (1947).
(484) Cromwell, *J. Am. Chem. Soc.*, *69*, 258-60 (1947).
(485) Buu-Hoï, Nguyen-Hoàn, Lecocq, and de Clercq, *Rec. trav. chim.*, *67*, 795-812 (1948).
(486) Pérard, *Ann. chim.*, [9], 7, 344, ftnote (1917).
(487) van Dorp and Arens, *Nature*, *160*, 189 (1947).
(488) Lutz and Tyson, *J. Am. Chem. Soc.*, *56*, 1341-2 (1934).
(489) Fieser and Price, *J. Am. Chem. Soc.*, *58*, 1838-43 (1936).
(490) Smith and Hanson, *J. Am. Chem. Soc.*, *57*, 1326-8 (1935).
(491) Fuson, Armstrong, and Speck, *J. Org. Chem.*, 7, 297-302 (1942).
(492) Bergmann and Wolff, *J. Am. Chem. Soc.*, *54*, 1644-7 (1932).
(493) Haworth, *J. Chem. Soc.*, *1932*, 2717-20.
(494) Bradsher and Wissow, *J. Am. Chem. Soc.*, *65*, 2034-5 (1943).
(495) Weizmann and Bergmann, *J. Am. Chem. Soc.*, *60*, 2647-50 (1938).
(496) Whitmore, Sutherland, and Cosby, *J. Am. Chem. Soc.*, *64*, 1360-4 (1942).
(497) Hey and Carter, British Patent 586,493, March 20, 1947; *Chem. Abstr.*, *42*, P1967 (1948).

(498) Orékhoff, *Bull. soc. chim.*, [4], *25*, 111–5 (1919).
(499) Frösch, Zellner, and Zak, *Monatsh.*, *55*, 25–46 (1930).
(500) Fuson, Armstrong, Chadwick, Kneisley, Rowland, Shenk, and Soper, *J. Am. Chem. Soc.*, *67*, 386–93 (1945).
(501) Fuson, Foster, Shenk, and Maynert, *J. Am. Chem. Soc.*, *67*, 1937–9 (1945).
(502) Lutz, Allison, Ashburn, Bailey, Clarke, Codington, Deintert, Freek, Jordon, Leake, Martin, Nicodemus, Rowlett, Shearer, Smith, and Wilson, *J. Org. Chem.*, *12*, 617–703 (1947).
(503) Buu-Hoï, Nguyen-Hoàn, and Royer, *Bull. soc. chim.*, [5], *14*, 84–6 (1947).
(504) Adams, Harfenist, and Loewe, *J. Am. Chem. Soc.*, *71*, 1624–8 (1949).
(505) Ullmann and Mourawiew-Winigradoff, *Ber.*, *38*, 2213–9 (1905).
(506) Bauer and Breit, *Ber.*, *39*, 1916–21 (1906).
(507) Kohler, *Ber.*, *38*, 1203–8 (1905).
(508) Fuson, Byers, Sperati, Foster, and Warfield, *J. Org. Chem.*, *10*, 69–75 (1945).
(509) Weinstock and Fuson, *J. Am. Chem. Soc.*, *58*, 1233–6 (1936).
(510) Fuson and McKusick, *J. Am. Chem. Soc.*, *65*, 60–4 (1943).
(511) Bergmann and Israelashvili, *J. Am. Chem. Soc.*, *68*, 1–5 (1946).
(512) Dilthey and Stephen, *J. prakt. Chem.*, [2], *152*, 114–25 (1939).
(513) Stuart and Tallman, *J. Am. Chem. Soc.*, *65*, 1579–81 (1943).
(514) Winternitz and Mousseron, *Bull. soc. chim.*, [5], *15*, 567–70 (1948); *Chem. Abstr.*, *42*, 7279 (1948).
(515) Fuson and Gaertner, *J. Org. Chem.*, *13*, 496–501 (1948).
(516) Tarbell and Lindstrom, *J. Am. Chem. Soc.*, *68*, 1930–2 (1946).
(517) Wizinger and Cyriax, *Helv. Chim. Acta*, *28*, 1018–27 (1945).
(518) Stuart, Shukis, and Tallman, *J. Am. Chem. Soc.*, *67*, 1475–8 (1945).
(519) Fuson and Speck, *J. Am. Chem. Soc.*, *64*, 2446–8 (1942).
(520) Wilds and Biggerstaff, *J. Am. Chem. Soc.*, *67*, 789–93 (1945).
(521) Smith, Wawzonek, and Miller, *J. Org. Chem.*, *6*, 229–35 (1941).
(522) Kauffmann, *Ann.*, *344*, 30–76 (1906).
(523) Thomas, *Compt. rend.*, *146*, 642–5 (1908); *Chem. Zentr.*, *1908,I*, 1784.
(524) Wahl and Meyer, *Bull. soc. chim.*, [4], *7*, 28–31 (1910).
(525) Kohlstadt, *Helv. Chim. Acta*, *27*, 685–701 (1944).
(526) Votoček and Matějka, *Ber.*, *46*, 1755–9 (1913).
(527) Anderson and Thomas, *J. Am. Chem. Soc.*, *65*, 234–8 (1943).
(528) Fuson and Tull, *J. Am. Chem. Soc.*, *71*, 2543–6 (1949).
(529) Gilman and Jones, *J. Am. Chem. Soc.*, *62*, 1243–7 (1940).
(530) Fuson, Armstrong, Kneisley, and Shenk, *J. Am. Chem. Soc.*, *66*, 1464–6 (1944).
(531) Hudson, *J. Chem. Soc.*, *1946*, 754–5.
(532) Willstaedt, Swedish Patent 115,343, Nov. 13, 1945; *Chem. Abstr.*, *41*, P158 (1947).
(533) Newman, *J. Am. Chem. Soc.*, *60*, 1368–70 (1938).
(534) Newman and Orchin, *J. Am. Chem. Soc.*, *60*, 586–9 (1938).
(535) Newman, *J. Am. Chem. Soc.*, *59*, 1003–6 (1937).
(536) Jaeger and Robinson, *J. Chem. Soc.*, *1941*, 744–7.
(537) Julian and Gist, *J. Am. Chem. Soc.*, *57*, 2030–2 (1935).
(538) Kohler and Barnes, *J. Am. Chem. Soc.*, *55*, 690–5 (1933).
(539) Kohler and Sonnichsen, *J. Am. Chem. Soc.*, *60*, 2650–2 (1938).
(540) Linnell and Roushdi, *Quart. J. Pharm. Pharmacol.*, *14*, 270–80 (1941); *Chem. Abstr.*, *36*, 2544 (1942).
(541) Clarkson and Gomberg, *J. Am. Chem. Soc.*, *52*, 2881–91 (1930).
(542) Cromwell, *J. Am. Chem. Soc.*, *69*, 1857–60 (1947).
(543) Badger, *J. Chem. Soc.*, *1941*, 535–8.

(544) Cromwell, *J. Am. Chem. Soc.*, *62*, 3470–3 (1940).
(545) Chu, *J. Chinese Chem. Soc.*, 7, 14–9 (1939).
(546) Linnell and Sharma, *Quart. J. Pharm. Pharmacol.*, *14*, 259–69 (1941); *Chem. Abstr.*, 36, 2546 (1942).
(547) Schoepfle and Trepp, *J. Am. Chem. Soc.*, *54*, 4059–65 (1932).
(548) Newman and Wise, *J. Am. Chem. Soc.*, *63*, 2109–11 (1941).
(549) Tadros, British Patent, 602,269, May 24, 1948; *Chem. Abstr.*, *42*, P8214 (1948).
(550) Hudson, *J. Chem. Soc.*, *1946*, 76–8.
(551) Cromwell and Burch, *J. Am. Chem. Soc.*, *66*, 872–3 (1944).
(552) McKenzie and Boyle, *J. Chem. Soc.*, *119*, 1131–40 (1921).
(553) Stuart, Shukis, Tallman, McCann, and Treves, *J. Am. Chem. Soc.*, *68*, 728–33 (1946).
(554) Bachmann, Hoffman, and Whitehead, *J. Org. Chem.*, *8*, 320–30 (1943).
(555) Barnett, Cook, and Nixon, *J. Chem. Soc.*, *1927*, 504–12.
(556) Bergmann and Weiss, *Ber.*, *64B*, 1485–93 (1931).
(557) Cook, Heilbron, and Lewis, *J. Chem. Soc.*, *1942*, 659–61.
(558) Meyer and Streuli, *Helv. Chim. Acta*, *20*, 1179–83 (1937).
(559) Kohler and Bruce, *J. Am. Chem. Soc.*, *53*, 1994–8 (1931).
(560) Miescher and Anner, U. S. Patent 2,459,949, Jan. 5, 1949; *Chem. Abstr.*, *43*, P3849 (1949).
(561) Cromwell and Cram, *J. Am. Chem. Soc.*, *71*, 2579–80 (1949).
(562) Bachmann, *J. Am. Chem. Soc.*, *57*, 555–9 (1935).
(563) Tschitschibabin, *J. prakt. Chem.*, [2], *84*, 760–77 (1911).
(564) Tschitschibabin, *Ber.*, *46*, 2554–6 (1913).
(565) Julian, Cole, and Wood, *J. Am. Chem. Soc.*, *57*, 2508–13 (1935).
(566) Kohler and Weiner, *J. Am. Chem. Soc.*, *56*, 434–8 (1934).
(567) Kohler and Tishler, *J. Am. Chem. Soc.*, *57*, 217–24 (1935).
(568) McKenzie and Winton, *J. Chem. Soc.*, *1940*, 840–4.
(569) Kohler, *Am. Chem. J.*, *31*, 642–61 (1904).
(570) Schuster, *Ber.*, *63B*, 2397–9 (1930).
(571) Geissman, *J. Am. Chem. Soc.*, *62*, 1363–7 (1940).
(572) Gomm and Hill, *J. Chem. Soc.*, *1935*, 1118–20.
(573) Blicke and Patelski, *J. Am. Chem. Soc.*, *60*, 2638–41 (1938).
(574) Kohler and Conant, *J. Am. Chem. Soc.*, *39*, 1699–715 (1917).
(575) Fuson, Byers, Rowland, Southwick, and Sperati, *J. Am. Chem. Soc.*, *66*, 1873–5 (1944).
(576) Lutz and Reveley, *J. Am. Chem. Soc.*, *63*, 3180–9 (1941).
(577) Julian, Cole, Meyer, and Herness, *J. Am. Chem. Soc.*, *67*, 1375–81 (1945).
(578) Schlenk and Brauns, *Ber.*, *48*, 716–28 (1915).
(579) Lund and Berg, *Kgl. Danske Videnskab. Selskab. Math.-fys. Medd.*, *18*, No. 9, 22 pp. (1941); *Chem. Abstr.*, *36*, 87 (1942).
(580) Arnold, *J. Am. Chem. Soc.*, *69*, 2322–5 (1947).
(581) Reynolds, *Am. Chem. J.*, *46*, 198–211 (1911).
(582) Tiffeneau, Lévy, and Weill, *Bull. soc. chim.*, [4], *49*, 1709–21 (1931).
(583) Schlenk and Bornhardt, *Ber.*, *46*, 1482–3 (1913).
(584) Chu, *J. Chinese Chem. Soc.*, 7, 24–6 (1939).
(585) Koelsch, *J. Am. Chem. Soc.*, *55*, 3394–9 (1933).
(586) Shilov and Yudin, *J. Gen. Chem.* (U.S.S.R.), *9*, 167–72 (1939); *Chem. Abstr.*, *33*, 6283 (1939).
(587) Gorski, *J. Russ. Phys.-Chem. Soc.*, *45*, 163–9 (1913); *Chem. Zentr.*, *1913,I*, 2021.
(588) Tschitschibabin, *Ber.*, *41*, 2770–8 (1908).
(589) Schmidlin and Wohl, *Ber.*, *43*, 1145–61 (1910).

(590) Lutz and Reveley, *J. Am. Chem. Soc.*, *63*, 3178–80 (1941).
(591) Kohler and Nygaard, *J. Am. Chem. Soc.*, *52*, 4128–39 (1930).
(592) Koelsch, *J. Am. Chem. Soc.*, *58*, 1331–3 (1935).
(593) French and Smith, *J. Am. Chem. Soc.*, *67*, 1949–50 (1945).
(594) Mikeska and Cohen, *J. Org. Chem.*, *6*, 787–94 (1941).
(595) Reimer and Reynolds, *Am. Chem. J.*, *40*, 428–44 (1908).
(596) Piper and Wright, *J. Am. Chem. Soc.*, *72*, 1669–74 (1950).
(597) Ssergejew, *J. Russ. Phys.-Chem. Soc.*, *61*, 1421–49 (1929); *Chem. Zentr.*, *1930,II*, 391.
(598) Suida and Planckh, *Ber.*, *66B*, 1445–54 (1933).
(599) Maxim, *Bull. soc. chim.*, [4], *49*, 887–91 (1931).
(600) Pel'kis, *Mem. Inst. Chem. Ukrain. Acad. Sci.*, *3*, 45–58 (1936); *Chem. Abstr.*, *31*, 4642 (1937).
(601) Pel'kis and Pazenko, *Zapiski Inst. Khim., Akad. Nauk U.R.S.R., Inst. Khim.*, *6*, Nos. 3–4, 311–39 (1940); *Chem. Abstr.*, *35*, 2469 (1941).
(602) Hahn and Murray, *J. Am. Chem. Soc.*, *36*, 1484–97 (1914).
(603) Badoche, *Bull. soc. chim.*, [4], *43*, 337–43 (1928).
(604) Jacquemain, *Ann. chim.*, [11], *19*, 522–48 (1944).
(605) Kharasch and Lambert, *J. Am. Chem. Soc.*, *63*, 2315–6 (1941).
(606) Hurd, Jones, and Blunck, *J. Am. Chem. Soc.*, *57*, 2033–6 (1935).
(607) Cason, Adams, Bennett, and Register, *J. Am. Chem. Soc.*, *66*, 1764–7 (1944).
(608) Iotsitch, *J. Russ. Phys.-Chem. Soc.*, *42*, 1490–1 (1910); *Bull. soc. chim.*, [4], *10*, 1294 (1911).
(609) Oddo, *Gazz. chim. ital.*, *41,I*, 273–94 (1911); *Chem. Abstr.*, *5*, 2639 (1911).
(610) Truce and Wise, *J. Am. Chem. Soc.*, *72*, 2300 (1950).
(611) Kharasch and Sayles, *J. Am. Chem. Soc.*, *64*, 2972–5 (1942).
(612) Mosher and La Combe, *J. Am. Chem. Soc.*, *72*, 3994–9 (1950).
(613) Hurd and Cohen, *J. Am. Chem. Soc.*, *53*, 1917–22 (1931).
(614) Barré and Repentigny, *Can. J. Research*, *27B*, 716–20 (1949).
(615) Dev, *J. Indian Chem. Soc.*, *25*, 69–80 (1948).
(616) Dev, *J. Indian Chem. Soc.*, *25*, 315–22 (1948).
(617) Bergmann and Bergmann, *J. Am. Chem. Soc.*, *59*, 1443–50 (1937).
(618) Swain and Boyles, *J. Am. Chem. Soc.*, *73*, 870–2 (1951).
(619) Kharasch and Burt, *J. Org. Chem.*, *16*, 150–60 (1951).
(620) Faworsky, *J. prakt. Chem.*, [2], *88*, 641–98 (1913).
(621) Herstein, *J. Gen. Chem.* (U.S.S.R.), *9*, 361–8 (1939); *Chem. Zentr.*, *1939,II*, 2910.
(622) Alexander and Coraor, *J. Am. Chem. Soc.*, *73*, 2721–3 (1951).
(623) Fuson, Emmons, and Tull, *J. Org. Chem.*, *16*, 648–51 (1951).
(624) Maxim, *Bul. soc. chim. România*, *12*, 24–7 (1930); *Chem. Zentr.*, *1930,II*, 3023.
(625) Guyot and Catel, *Bull. soc. chim.*, [3], *35*, 551–62 (1906).
(626) Tucker and Whalley, *J. Chem. Soc.*, *1949*, 50–5.
(627) Schokina, Kildischeva, and Preobrashenski, *J. Gen. Chem.* (U.S.S.R.), *11*, 425–8 (1941); *Brit. Chem. Abstr.*, *A,II*, 224 (1942).
(628) Salkind, *J. Russ. Phys.-Chem. Soc.*, *45*, 1875–95 (1914); *Bull. soc. chim.*, [4], *16*, 536 (1914).
(629) Jones and Weedon, *J. Chem. Soc.*, *1946*, 937–9.
(630) Heilbron, *J. Chem. Soc.*, *1948*, 386–93.
(631) Blomquist and Marvel, *J. Am. Chem. Soc.*, *55*, 1655–62 (1933).
(632) Teterin and Ivanov, *J. Gen. Chem.* (U.S.S.R.), *7*, 1629–31 (1937); *Chem. Abstr.*, *31*, 8503 (1937).
(633) Cymerman, Heilbron, Johnson, and Jones, *J. Chem. Soc.*, *1944*, 141–4.

(634) Schmitt, *Ann.*, 547, 115–22 (1941).
(635) Karrer, Salomon, Morf, and Walker, *Helv. Chim. Acta*, 15, 878–89 (1932).
(636) Thompson, Milas, and Rovno, *J. Am. Chem. Soc.*, 63, 752–5 (1941).
(637) Zal'kind, Zonis, and Blokhin, *Compt. rend. acad. sci. U.R.S.S.*, 2, 57–60 (1935); *Chem. Abstr.*, 29, 5819 (1935).
(638) Teterin and Ivanov, *Compt. rend. acad. sci. U.R.S.S.*, 2, 259–60 (1935); *Chem. Abstr.*, 29, 6214 (1935).
(639) Krauze and Slobodin, *J. Gen. Chem.* (U.S.S.R.), 10, 907–12 (1940); *Chem. Abstr.*, 35, 3237 (1941).
(640) Fuson and Libby, *J. Org. Chem.*, 16, 626–30 (1951).
(641) Lutz and Revely, *J. Am. Chem. Soc.*, 61, 1854–9 (1940).
(642) Fuson and Hornberger, *J. Org. Chem.*, 16, 631–6 (1951).
(643) Heilbron, Johnson, Jones, and Spinks, *J. Chem. Soc.*, *1942*, 727–33.
(644) Fuson and Hornberger, *J. Org. Chem.*, 16, 637–42 (1951).
(645) Kohler, *Am. Chem. J.*, 36, 177–95 (1906).
(646) Fuson and Shealy, *J. Org. Chem.*, 16, 643–7 (1951).
(647) Kohler and Bickel, *J. Am. Chem. Soc.*, 57, 1099–101 (1935).
(648) Kayser, *Ann. chim.*, [11], 6, 145–248 (1936).
(649) Bickel, *J. Am. Chem. Soc.*, 59, 325–8 (1937).
(650) Glattfeld and Cameron, *J. Am. Chem. Soc.*, 49, 1043–8 (1927).
(651) Kohler and Potter, *J. Am. Chem. Soc.*, 57, 1316–21 (1935).
(652) Kohler and Larsen, *J. Am. Chem. Soc.*, 57, 1448–52 (1935).
(653) Kohler and Larsen, *J. Am. Chem. Soc.*, 58, 1518–22 (1936).
(654) McBee, Pierce and Higgins, *J. Am. Chem. Soc.*, 74, 1736–7 (1952).
(655) Carré, *Bull. soc. chim.*, [4], 5, 486–9 (1909).
(656) Ford, Thompson, and Marvel, *J. Am. Chem. Soc.*, 57, 2619–23 (1935).
(657) Diels and Johlin, *Ber.*, *44*, 403–10 (1911).
(658) Marshall, *J. Chem. Soc.*, 107, 509–23 (1915).
(659) Gaertner, *J. Am. Chem. Soc.*, 74, 2185–8 (1952).
(660) Landrieu and Blatt, *Bull. soc. chim.*, [4], 1424–36 (1924).
(661) Gaertner, *J. Am. Chem. Soc.*, 74, 766–7 (1952).
(662) Harmon and Marvel, *J. Am. Chem. Soc.*, 55, 1716–22 (1933).
(663) Moureu, Dufraisse, and Mackall, *Bull. soc. chim.*, [4], 33, 934–42 (1923).
(664) Moureu, Dufraisse, and Blatt, *Bull. soc. chim.*, [4], 35, 1412–24 (1924).
(665) Haller and Ramart-Lucas, *Compt. rend.*, 159, 143–9 (1914); *Chem. Abstr.*, 8, 3437 (1941).

TABLE VI-XIX

REACTIONS OF GRIGNARD REAGENTS WITH CYCLIC KETONES

Ketone	RMgX	Product(s)	Ref.
C_5H_7OCl			
2-Chlorocyclopentanone	CH_3MgX	2-Methylcyclopentanone (poor yield)	*201*
2-Chlorocyclopentanone	C_2H_5MgX	2-Ethylcyclopentanone (poor yield)	*201*
2-Chlorocyclopentanone	i-C_3H_7MgX	2-Isopropylcyclopentanone (poor yield)	*201*
2-Chlorocyclopentanone	C_6H_5MgX	2-Phenylcyclopentanone (poor yield)	*201*
C_5H_8O			
$(CH_2)_4CO$	CH_3MgI	$(CH_2)_4C(CH_3)OH$ (65–75%)	*359*
$(CH_2)_4CO$ (8.4 g.)	CH_3MgI (14.2 g. CH_3I)	$(CH_2)_4C(CH_3)OH$ (7.0 g., crude)	*319,351*
$(CH_2)_4CO$	CH_3MgI	$(CH_2)_4C(CH_3)OH$; unidentified product, b.p., 246–248°	*269*
$(CH_2)_4CO$ (42 g.)	$(\equiv CMgBr)_2$ (12 g. Mg, 55 g. C_2H_5Br)	$[\equiv CC(OH)(CH_2)_4]_2$ (45.2%); $HC\equiv CC(OH)(CH_2)_4$	*344*
$(CH_2)_4CO$	C_2H_5MgBr	$(CH_2)_4C(OH)C_2H_5$ (*ca.* 75%)	*350,352*
$(CH_2)_4CO$	C_2H_5MgI	$(CH_2)_4C(OH)C_2H_5$	*353,354*
$(CH_2)_4CO$ (504 g., 6 moles)	$H_2C{=}CHCH_2Cl$ (536 g., 7 moles) + Mg (146 g., 6 g.-atoms)	$(CH_2)_4C(OH)CH_2CH{=}CH_2$ (54%)*	*343*
$(CH_2)_4CO$ (122.5 g.)	n-C_3H_7MgBr (1 equiv.)	$(CH_2)_4C(OH)$-n-C_3H_7 (107.5 g., crude); $(CH_2)_4CHOH$; cond'n product	*350,352,343*
$(CH_2)_4CO$	i-C_3H_7MgCl	Ketol (36%)	*146*
$(CH_2)_4CO$	i-C_3H_7MgCl	"Cyclopentenylcyclopentanone" (chief product)	*352*
$(CH_2)_4CO$	i-C_3H_7MgBr	"Cyclopentenylcyclopentanone" (chief product)	*352*
$(CH_2)_4CO$ (70 g.)	i-C_3H_7MgI (150 g. C_3H_7I)	$(CH_2)_4C(OH)$-i-C_3H_7 (16 g., crude); cond'n product	*351,343*

* Copper reaction vessel.

TABLE VI-XIX (Continued)

Ketone	RMgX	Product(s)	Ref.
C_5H_8O (*cont.*)			
$(CH_2)_4CO$	$H_2C{=}C(CH_3)CH_2Cl$ + Mg	$(CH_2)_4C(OH)CH_2C(CH_3){=}CH_2$ (25%)*	343
$(CH_2)_4CO$	n-C_4H_9MgBr	$(CH_2)_4C(OH)$-n-C_4H_9 (*ca.* 60%); $(CH_2)_4CHOH$	350,352
$(CH_2)_4CO$	s-C_4H_9MgBr	Ketol (42%)†	146
$(CH_2)_4CO$ (42 g.)	$BrMgO(CH_3)_2CC{\equiv}CMgBr$ (42 g. C_5H_8O)	$HO(CH_3)_2CC{\equiv}CC(OH)(CH_2)_4$	344
$(CH_2)_4CO$	i-$C_5H_{11}MgBr$	$(CH_2)_4C(i$-$C_5H_{11})OH$	124
$(CH_2)_4CO$	C_6H_5MgBr	$(CH_2)_4C(C_6H_5)OH$ ("good yield")	313,105
$(CH_2)_4CO$	$BrMgO(CH_3)(C_2H_5)CC{\equiv}CMgBr$	$(CH_2)_4C(OH)C{\equiv}CC(CH_3)(C_2H_5)OH$ (43–45%)	106
$(CH_2)_4CO$ (31 g.)	$(CH_2)_5CHMgBr$ (60 g. $C_6H_{11}Br$)	$(CH_2)_4C(OH)CH(CH_2)_5$ (21 g.)	314
$(CH_2)_4CO$	n-$C_6H_{13}MgBr$	$(CH_2)_4C(n$-$C_6H_{13})OH$ (27%); n-hexylcyclopentene	317
$(CH_2)_4CO$	n-$C_8H_{17}MgBr$	$(CH_2)_4C(n$-$C_8H_{17})OH$	317
$(CH_2)_4CO$	1-Ethynyl-4-methoxycyclohexanol + C_2H_5MgBr	1-(1-Hydroxycyclopentyl)-2-(1-hydroxy-4-methoxycyclohexyl)ethyne	188
$(CH_2)_4CO$ (48.6 g.)	1-$C_{10}H_7MgBr$ (27.6 ml. $C_{10}H_7Br$)	$(CH_2)_4C(1$-$C_{10}H_7)OH$, yielding 13.1 g. olefin	26
$(CH_2)_4CO$	$C_6H_5(CH_2)_4MgCl$	$(CH_2)_4C[(CH_2)_4C_6H_5]OH$ (65%)	84
$(CH_2)_4CO$ (8.4 g.)	6-$CH_3OC_{10}H_6$-2-MgBr (23.7 ml. $C_{11}H_9BrO$)	$(CH_2)_4C(2$-$C_{10}H_6$-6-$OCH_3)OH$, yielding 15.0 g. olefin	26
$(CH_2)_4CO$	$C_6H_5(CH_2)_5MgCl$	$(CH_2)_4C[(CH_2)_5C_6H_5]OH$ (65%)	84
$(CH_2)_4CO$ (50.4 g.)	1-$C_{10}H_7CH_2CH_2MgCl$ (114.0 g., $C_{12}H_{11}Cl$)	$(CH_2)_4C(CH_2CH_2$-1-$C_{10}H_7)OH$ (85.0 g.)	362
$(CH_2)_4CO$ (8.4 g.)	9-Phenanthryl-MgBr (25.7 ml. $C_{14}H_9Br$)	$(CH_2)_4C(9$-$C_{14}H_9)OH$ (yielding 5.0 g. olefin)	26

* Glass reaction vessel.

† Identified as semicarbazone of 2-cyclopentylidenecyclopentanone.

TABLE VI-XIX (Continued)

Ketone	RMgX	Product(s)	Ref.
C_5H_8O (*cont.*)			
$(CH_2)_4CO$ (10.8 ml.)	9-Phenanthryl-CH_2CH_2MgCl (29.6 g. $C_{16}H_{13}Cl$)	$(C_{14}H_9CH_2CH_2—)_2$ (1.75 g.); $(CH_2)_4C(CH_2CH_2C_{14}H_9)OH$ (17.1 g.)	360
C_6H_8O			
2-Cyclohexen-1-one (48.0 g., 0.5 mole)	CH_3MgBr (24.3 g., 1.0 g.-atom Mg)	3-Methylcyclohexanone (8.0 g., 15%); 1-methyl-2-cyclohexen-1-ol (38%); condens'n products (18%)	337
2-Cyclohexen-1-one (48.0 g., 0.5 mole)	C_2H_5MgBr (1.0 mole)	3-Ethylcyclohexanone (15.2 g., 24%); 1-ethyl-2-cyclohexen-1-ol (52%); condens'n products (13%)	337
2-Cyclohexen-1-one (0.5 mole)	C_2H_5MgBr (1.0 mole C_2H_5Br)	3-Ethylcyclohexanone (22.8*x*%)*	338
2-Cyclohexen-1-one (48.0 g., 0.5 mole)	*i*-C_3H_7MgCl (1.0 mole)	3-Isopropylcyclohexanone (31.0 g., 44%); 1-isopropyl-2-cyclohexen-1-ol (10%); 2-cyclohexen-1-ol (12%); condens'n products (16%)	337
2-Cyclohexen-1-one (0.5 mole)	*i*-C_3H_7MgBr (1.0 mole C_3H_7Br)	3-Isopropylcyclohexanone (64.5*x*%)*	338
2-Cyclohexen-1-one (48.0 g., 0.5 mole)	*t*-C_4H_9MgCl (1.0 mole)	Recovered ketone (10%); 3-*t*-butylcyclohexanone (70%); condens'n products (14%)	337
2-Cyclohexen-1-one (0.5 mole)	*t*-C_4H_9MgCl (1.0 mole C_4H_9Cl)	3-*t*-Butylcyclohexanone (61.6*x*%)*	338
$C_6H_8O_2$			
Cyclohexane-1,2-dione (112 g.)	CH_3MgI (298 g. CH_3I)	2-Hydroxy-2-methylcyclohexanone (*ca.* 95 g., crude)	56

* In this study only the relative yields of 1,4-addition products were evaluated. Total yield of addition products for the reactions studied is said to range from 86 to 100% (*i.e.*, $x = 0.86–1.00$).

TABLE VI-XIX (Continued)

Ketone	RMgX	Product(s)	Ref.
$C_6H_8O_2$ (*cont.*)			
Dihydroresorcinol* (25 g.)	C_6H_5MgBr (1 equiv. C_6H_5Br)	3-Hydroxy-3-phenylcyclohexanone (8 g.); 1-phenylcyclohexen-3-one (15–20 g.); 1,3-diphenyl-1,3-cyclohexadiene (5 g.)	309
C_6H_9OCl			
2-Chlorocyclohexanone	CH_3MgI	1-Methyl-2-chlorocyclohexanol	266,46
2-Chlorocyclohexanone	CH_3MgI	2-Methylcyclohexanone (2 parts); acetylcyclopentane (1 part)	277,266
2-Chlorocyclohexanone	CH_3MgI	1-Methyl-2-chlorocyclohexanol (*cis* and *trans* chlorohydrins)	267
2-Chlorocyclohexanone	C_2H_5MgBr	1-Ethyl-2-chlorocyclohexanol	266
2-Chlorocyclohexanone	C_2H_5MgBr	2-Ethylcyclohexanone; propionylcyclopentane (total yield, 50–60%)	276,266
2-Chlorocyclohexanone	C_2H_5MgBr	1-Ethyl-2-chlorocyclohexanol (*cis* and *trans* chlorohydrins)	267
2-Chlorocyclohexanone	*i*-C_3H_7MgX	2-Chlorocyclohexanol (27–28% *A*-isomer; 72–73% *B*-isomer); $(CH_3)_2C{=}CH_2$ (total yield crude reduction products, 64%)	22
2-Chlorocyclohexanone	*n*-C_4H_9MgX† (1.5 equiv.)	2-*n*-Butylcyclohexanone; pentanoylcyclopentane (total yield, 27–30%)	275
2-Chlorocyclohexanone	*n*-C_4H_9MgBr	1-*n*-Butyl-2-chlorocyclohexanol (*cis* and *trans* chlorohydrins)	267
2-Chlorocyclohexanone	*t*-C_4H_9MgCl	2-Chlorocyclohexanol (27–28% *A*-isomer; 72–73% *B*-isomer); C_4H_8 (total yield crude reduction products, 72%)	22,342

*A strongly enolic diketone formulated as 3-hydroxycyclohex-2-en-1-one.

†X = Br, Cl.

TABLE VI-XIX (Continued)

Ketone	RMgX	Product(s)	Ref.
C_6H_9OCl (*cont.*)			
2-Chlorocyclohexanone (280 g.)	C_6H_5MgBr (750 ml., 3.22 *M*)	2-Phenylcyclohexanone (58%)	*212*
2-Chlorocyclohexanone	$(CH_2)_5CHMgX$	2-Chlorocyclohexanol (27–28% *A*-isomer; 72–73% *B*-isomer); C_6H_{10} (total yield crude reduction products, 27%)	*22*
C_6H_9ON			
1,5-Dimethyl-2-pyrrolone	CH_3MgBr	1,2,5-Trimethylpyrrole*	*182*
$C_6H_{10}O$			
2-Methylcyclopentanone	CH_3MgI (15% excess)	1,2-Dimethylcyclopentanol	*63,361*
2-Methylcyclopentanone (17 g.)	$CH_3O_2CCH_2Br$ (25 g.) + Mg (5 g.)	1-Carbomethoxymethyl-2-methylcyclohexanol (14 g.)	*170*
2-Methylcyclopentanone	*n*-C_4H_9MgBr	1-*n*-Butyl-2-methylcyclopentanol	*63*
2-Methylcyclopentanone (6 g.)	6-$CH_3OC_{10}H_6$-1-CH_2CH_2MgCl (12 g. $C_{13}H_{13}ClO$)	1-β-6-Methoxy-1-naphthylethyl)-2-methylcyclopentanol (6 g.)	*363*
2-Methylcyclopentanone (7.6 g.)	9-Phenanthryl-CH_2CH_2MgCl (19.2 g. $C_{16}H_{13}Cl$)	1,4-Bis-(9-phenanthryl)butane (1.2 g.); 9-ethylphenanthrene; 1-methyl-2-(β-9-phenanthrylethyl)cyclopentene ("very poor yield")	*360*
3-Methylcyclopentanone (10 g.)	CH_3MgI	1,3-Dimethylcyclopentanol	*312,63,313*
3-Methylcyclopentanone	C_2H_5MgI	1-Ethyl-3-methylcyclopentanol	*313*
3-Methylcyclopentanone	$(CH_2)_5CHMgBr$	1-Cyclohexyl-3-methylcyclopentanol	*314*
$(CH_2)_5CO$	RMgX†	$(CH_2)_5CROH$	*239*
$(CH_2)_5CO$ (2.9 g.)	CH_3MgI (4.5 g. CH_3I)	$(CH_2)_5C(CH_3)OH$ (2.2 g.)	*311*
$(CH_2)_5CO$	CH_3MgX	$(CH_2)_5C(CH_3)OH$ (64%)	*255*

* The *Chemical Abstracts* report contains a misprint: "1,3,5-" for 1,2,5-.

† R = CH_3, C_2H_5, *n*-C_3H_7, *i*-C_4H_9, *i*-C_5H_{11}, C_6H_5, $(CH_2)_5CH$, $C_6H_5CH_2$, 4-$CH_3C_6H_4$.

TABLE VI-XIX (Continued)

Ketone	RMgX	Product(s)	Ref.
$C_6H_{10}O$ (*cont.*)			
$(CH_2)_5CO$	$(\equiv CMgBr)_2$	$[(CH_2)_5C(OH)C\equiv]_2$	*95*
$(CH_2)_5CO$	$(\equiv CMgI)_2$	$[(CH_2)_5C(OH)C\equiv]_2$	*144*
$(CH_2)_5CO$	RMgX*	$(CH_2)_5CROH$ (41–72%)	*303*
$(CH_2)_5CO$	C_2H_5MgX	$(CH_2)_5C(C_2H_5)OH$ (62%)	*255*
$(CH_2)_5CO$ (34 g.)	$BrMgOCH_2C\equiv CMgBr$ (0.5 mole $HOCH_2C\equiv CH$)	3-(1-Hydroxycyclohexyl)-2-propyn-1-ol (50% crude)	*310*
$(CH_2)_5CO$	2-Thienyl-MgX	1-α-Thienylcyclohexene (91.5%)	*105*
$(CH_2)_5CO$	$H_2C=CHCH_2Br$ + Mg	1-Allylcyclohexanol (81%)	*190*
$(CH_2)_5CO$	n-C_3H_7MgX	$(CH_2)_5C(n\text{-}C_3H_7)OH$ (57%)	*255*
$(CH_2)_5CO$	i-C_3H_7MgX	$(CH_2)_5C(i\text{-}C_3H_7)OH$	*105*
$(CH_2)_5CO$ (19.6 g.)	i-C_3H_7MgCl	Ketol (3 g.), identified as semicarbazone of corresponding unsat'd ketone (2-cyclohexylidenecyclohexanone)	*146*
$(CH_2)_5CO$	i-C_3H_7MgBr	$(CH_2)_5C(i\text{-}C_3H_7)OH$ (41%); $(CH_2)_5CHOH$	*255,281*
$(CH_2)_5CO$	n-C_4H_9MgX	$(CH_2)_5C(n\text{-}C_4H_9)OH$ (48%)	*255*
$(CH_2)_5CO$	i-C_4H_9MgBr	$(CH_2)_5CHOH$; $(CH_2)_5C(i\text{-}C_4H_9)OH$ (10%)	*241*
$(CH_2)_5CO$	t-C_4H_9MgCl	$(CH_2)_5C(t\text{-}C_4H_9)OH$ (poor yield); $(CH_2)_5CHOH$	*23*
$(CH_2)_5CO$	n-$C_5H_{11}MgX$	$(CH_2)_5C(n\text{-}C_5H_{11})OH$ (54%)	*255,105*
$(CH_2)_5CO$	i-$C_5H_{11}MgX$	$(CH_2)_5C(i\text{-}C_5H_{11})OH$ (58%)	*255*
$(CH_2)_5CO$	C_6H_5MgX	$(CH_2)_5C(C_6H_5)OH$ (60%)	*255*
$(CH_2)_5CO$	C_6H_5MgBr	$(CH_2)_5C(C_6H_5)OH$ (85%)	*151,287,105, 314*
$(CH_2)_5CO$	$(CH_2)_5CHMgX$	$(CH_2)_5C[CH(CH_2)_5]OH$ (53%)	*255*
$(CH_2)_5CO$	$(CH_2)_5CHMgCl$	$(CH_2)_5CHOH$, only	*241*
$(CH_2)_5CO$	$(CH_2)_5CHMgCl$	$(CH_2)_5C[CH(CH_2)_5]OH$ (61%)	*151,105*
$(CH_2)_5CO$ (8 g.)	$C_6H_5CH_2MgCl$ (12.7 g. C_7H_7Cl)	$(CH_2)_5C(CH_2C_6H_5)OH$	*287*
$(CH_2)_5CO$	$2\text{-}CH_3C_6H_4MgBr$	$(CH_2)_5C(C_6H_4\text{-}2\text{-}CH_3)OH$ (50%)	*246*

*R = C_2H_5, n-C_4H_9, n-C_6H_{13}, n-C_7H_{15}, n-C_8H_{17}, n-$C_{12}H_{25}$.

TABLE VI-XIX (Continued)

Ketone	RMgX	Product(s)	Ref.
$C_6H_{10}O$ (*cont.*)			
$(CH_2)_5CO$	$3\text{-}CH_3C_6H_4MgBr$	$(CH_2)_5C(C_6H_4\text{-}3\text{-}CH_3)OH$ (48%)	*246*
$(CH_2)_5CO$	$4\text{-}CH_3OC_6H_4MgBr$	$(CH_2)_5C(C_6H_4\text{-}4\text{-}OCH_3)OH$ (44%)	*246,193*
$(CH_2)_5CO$	$4\text{-}CH_3OC_6H_4MgBr$	$(CH_2)_5C(C_6H_4\text{-}4\text{-}OCH_3)OH$ + 1-anisylcyclohexene (aggregating 73%)	*105,151*
$(CH_2)_5CO$	$C_6H_5C{\equiv}CMgX$	$(CH_2)_5C(C{\equiv}CC_6H_5)OH$ (97%)	*140*
$(CH_2)_5CO$	$C_6H_5CH(CO_2Na)MgX$*	$C_6H_5CH(CO_2H)C(CH_2)_5OH$ (80%)	*145*
$(CH_2)_5CO$ (49 g.)	$C_6H_5CH_2CH_2MgCl$ (77 g. C_8H_9Cl)	$(CH_2)_5C(CH_2CH_2C_6H_5)OH$ (49 g.)	*362*
$(CH_2)_5CO$ (30 g.)	$C_6H_5CH_2CH_2MgCl$ (42 g. C_8H_9Cl)	$(CH_2)_5C(CH_2CH_2C_6H_5)OH$ (40 g.)	*358*
$(CH_2)_5CO$	$C_6H_5CH_2CH_2MgBr$	$(CH_2)_5C(CH_2CH_2C_6H_5)OH$ (54%)	*218*
$(CH_2)_5CO$ (12 g.)	$2,3\text{-}(CH_3)_2C_6H_3MgBr$ (22 g. C_8H_9Br)	$(CH_2)_5C[C_6H_3\text{-}2,3\text{-}(CH_3)_2]OH$	*64*
$(CH_2)_5CO$ (17 g.)	$3,4\text{-}(CH_3)_2C_6H_3MgBr$ (32 g. C_8H_9Br)	$(CH_2)_5C[C_6H_3\text{-}3,4\text{-}(CH_3)_2]OH$, (20 g., crude)	*64*
$(CH_2)_5CO$ (25 g.)	$4\text{-}C_2H_5OC_6H_4MgBr$	$(CH_2)_5C(C_6H_4\text{-}4\text{-}OC_2H_5)OH$ (19 g.)	*193*
$(CH_2)_5CO$	$2\text{-}CH_3O\text{-}5\text{-}CH_3C_6H_3MgBr$	$2\text{-}CH_3O\text{-}5\text{-}CH_3C_6H_3(HO)CH(CH_2)_5$ (36%)	*246*
$(CH_2)_5CO$ (25 g.)	$1\text{-}C_{10}H_7MgBr$ (50 g. $C_{10}H_7Br$)	$(CH_2)_5C(1\text{-}C_{10}H_7)OH$ (40%)	*157,105*
$(CH_2)_5CO$ (4.2 g.)	$1\text{-}C_{10}H_7MgBr$ (10.0 g. $C_{10}H_7Br$)	1-(1-Cyclohexenyl)naphthalene (6.0 g.)	*301,32*
$(CH_2)_5CO$	$i\text{-}C_3H_7(CH_2)_3CH(CH_3)(CH_2)_2MgX$	$(CH_2)_5C(C_{10}H_{21})OH$ (82.5%)	*105*
$(CH_2)_5CO$ (40 g., 0.4 mole)	$4\text{-}CH_3C_{10}H_6\text{-}1\text{-}MgBr$ (44 g., 0.2 mole $C_{11}H_9Br$)	$(CH_2)_5C(C_{11}H_9)OH$ (yielding 50% olefin)	*32*
$(CH_2)_5CO$	$(n\text{-}C_4H_9)_2N(CH_2)_3MgCl$	$(CH_2)_5C[(CH_2)_3N(n\text{-}C_4H_9)_2]OH$	*189*
$(CH_2)_5CO$	$(n\text{-}C_4H_9)_2N(CH_2)_3Cl$ + Mg	$(CH_2)_5C[(CH_2)_3N(n\text{-}C_4H_9)_2]OH$	*197*
$(CH_2)_5CO$	$CH_3(C_6H_5)N(CH_2)_3MgBr$	$(CH_2)_5C[(CH_2)_3N(CH_3)C_6H_5]OH$; $CH_3(n\text{-}C_3H_7)(C_6H_5)N$	*290*
$(CH_2)_5CO$	$3,4\text{-}(CH_3)_2C_{10}H_5\text{-}1\text{-}MgBr$	$(CH_2)_5C[1\text{-}C_{10}H_5\text{-}3,4\text{-}(CH_3)_2]OH$ (yielding 64% olefin)	*32*
$(CH_2)_5CO$	$n\text{-}C_{12}H_{25}MgBr$	$(CH_2)_5C(n\text{-}C_{12}H_{25})OH$ (74.6%)	*105*

* In the opinion of Schlenk, Hilleman, and Rodloff, *Ann.*, *487*, 135–54 (1931), this "Grignard reagent" should be formulated as an enolate.

TABLE VI-XIX (Continued)

Ketone	RMgX	Product(s)	Ref.
$C_6H_{10}O$ (*cont.*)			
$(CH_2)_5CO$ (23.5 g.)	n-$C_{12}H_{25}MgBr$ (59 g. $C_{12}H_{25}Br$)	$(CH_2)_5C(n\text{-}C_{12}H_{25})OH$ (yielding 25.6 g. olefin)	*251*
$(CH_2)_5CO$ (10 g.)	9-Phenanthryl-MgBr (25.7 ml. $C_{14}H_9Br$)	$(CH_2)_5C(C_{14}H_9)OH$ (yielding 5 g. olefin)	*26,105,32*
$(CH_2)_5CO$	n-$C_{14}H_{29}MgX$	$(CH_2)_5C(n\text{-}C_{14}H_{29})OH$ (81%)	*105*
$(CH_2)_5CO$	n-$C_{16}H_{33}MgX$	$(CH_2)_5C(n\text{-}C_{16}H_{33})OH$ (80%)	*105*
$(CH_2)_5CO$	n-$C_{18}H_{37}MgX$	$(CH_2)_5C(n\text{-}C_{18}H_{37})OH$ (70%)	*105*
$(CH_2)_5CO$	i-$C_3H_7(CH_2)_3[CH(CH_3)(CH_2)_3]_2$-$CH(CH_3)(CH_2)_2MgX$	$(CH_2)_5C(C_{20}H_{41})OH$ (80%)	*105*
$(CH_2)_5CO$	n-$C_{26}H_{53}MgX$	$(CH_2)_5C(n\text{-}C_{26}H_{53})OH$ (75%)	*105*
$C_6H_{10}O_2$			
2,2-Dimethyl-3-tetrahydrofuranone	CH_3MgBr	2,2,3-Trimethyl-3-tetrahydrofuranol (60%)	356
2,2-Dimethyl-3-tetrahydrofuranone	C_2H_5MgBr	2,2-Dimethyl-3-ethyl-3-tetrahydrofuranol	356
2,2-Dimethyl-3-tetrahydrofuranone	C_6H_5MgBr	2,2-Dimethyl-3-phenyl-3-tetrahydrofuranol (50%)	356
2,2-Dimethyl-3-tetrahydrofuranone	$C_6H_5CH_2MgCl$	2,2-Dimethyl-3-benzyl-3-tetrahydrofuranol	356
2,2-Dimethyl-3-tetrahydrofuranone	$4\text{-}CH_3C_6H_4MgBr$	2,2-Dimethyl-3-p-tolyl-3-tetrahydrofuranol	356
$C_6H_{11}ON$			
1-Methyl-2-piperidone	n-C_3H_7MgBr	N-Methyl-γ-coniceine;* 1-methyl-2,2-dipropylpiperidine	*183*
1-Methyl-2-piperidone (11.3 g.)	C_6H_5MgBr (23.5 g. C_6H_5Br)	1-Methyl-2-hydroxy-2-phenylpiperidine	*175,176*
1-Methyl-2-piperidone	$(CH_2)_5CHMgCl$	1-Methyl-2-hydroxy-2-(1-methyl-2-oxo-3-piperidyl)piperidine	*175*
1-Methyl-2-piperidone (22.6 g.)	$C_6H_5CH_2MgBr$ (34.2 g. C_7H_7Br)	1-Methyl-2-benzyl-1,4,5,6-tetrahydropyridine	*175,176*

* 1-Methyl-6-propyl-1,2,3,4-tetrahydropyridine.

TABLE VI-XIX (Continued)

Ketone	RMgX	Product(s)	Ref.
$C_6H_{11}ON$ (*cont.*)			
1-Methyl-2-piperidone (0.2 mole)	$4\text{-}CH_3OC_6H_4MgBr$ (0.2 mole C_7H_7BrO)	1-Methyl-2-*p*-anisyl-1,4,5,6-tetrahydropyridine	*175,176*
1-Methyl-2-piperidone (37.3 g.)	$6\text{-}CH_3OC_{10}H_6\text{-}2\text{-}MgBr$ (50.0 g. $C_{11}H_9BrO$)	1-Methyl-2-(6-methoxy-2-naphthyl)-1,4,5,6-tetrahydropyridine	*175,176*
1-Methyl-4-piperidone (11.3 g.)	C_6H_5MgBr (24.0 g. C_6H_5Br)	1-Methyl-4-phenyl-4-piperidinol	*15,2*
1-Methyl-4-piperidone (23 g.)	$4\text{-}CH_3OC_6H_4MgBr$ (38 g. C_7H_7BrO)	1-Methyl-4-anisyl-4-piperidinol (10 g.)	*322*
$C_7H_{10}O$			
2-Methyl-2-cyclohexen-1-one	CH_3MgI	1,2-Dimethyl-2-cyclohen-1-ol	*127*
3-Methyl-2-cyclohexen-1-one (22.0 g., 0.2 mole) + CuCl (400 mg.)	CH_3MgI (6.5 g., 0.27 g.-atom Mg)	3,3-Dimethylcyclohexanone (15.0 g.)	*331*
3-Methyl-2-cyclohexen-1-one	$H_2C{=}CHCH_2Br$ + Mg	1-Allyl-3-methyl-2-cyclohexen-1-ol (92.7%)	*190*
3-Methyl-2-cyclohexen-1-one	$2\text{-}CH_3C_6H_4MgBr$	1-Methyl-3-*o*-tolyl-1,3-cyclohexadiene*	*159*
3-Methyl-2-cyclohexen-1-one	$3\text{-}CH_3OC_6H_4(CH_2)_2MgCl$ (45 g. $C_9H_{11}ClO$)	3-Methyl-3′-methoxy-4,5-dihydrobibenzyl (32 g.)	*209*
$C_7H_{11}OCl$			
2-Chloro-4-methylcyclohexanone	CH_3MgI	2,4-Dimethylcyclohexanone	*110*
2-Chloro-4-methylcyclohexanone	CH_3MgI	1,4-Dimethyl-2-chlorocyclohexanol (*cis* and *trans* chlorohydrins)	*267*
2-Chloro-4-methylcyclohexanone (low-boiling) (117 g., 1.22 mole)	C_6H_5MgBr (600 ml., 2 *M*)	Phenylmethylcyclohexanones (150 g., 67%): *ca.* 3 parts 2-phenyl-4-methyl-, *ca.* 1 part 2-phenyl-5-methyl	*211*
2-Chloro-5-methylcyclohexanone	CH_3MgI	1,5-Dimethyl-2-chlorocyclohexanol	*266*

* After sulfuric acid hydrolysis of the Grignard intermediate and distillation of the product.

TABLE VI-XIX (Continued)

Ketone	RMgX	Product(s)	Ref.
$C_7H_{11}OCl$ (*cont.*)			
2-Chloro-5-methylcyclohexanone (liquid)	CH_3MgI	2,5-Dimethylcyclohexanone (semicarbazone, m. 155°)	*111*
2-Chloro-5-methylcyclohexanone (solid)	CH_3MgI	2,5-Dimethylcyclohexanone (semicarbazone, m. 122°)	*111*
2-Chloro-5-methylcyclohexanone	CH_3MgI	1,5-Dimethyl-2-chlorocyclohexanol (*cis* and *trans* chlorohydrins)	*267*
$C_7H_{11}ON$			
1-Methyl-5-ethyl-2-pyrrolone	CH_3MgBr	1,2-Dimethyl-5-ethylpyrrole	*182*
1-Methyl-5-ethyl-2-pyrrolone	C_2H_5MgBr	1-Methyl-2,5-diethylpyrrole; 1-methyl-2,5,5-triethyl-Δ^2-pyrroline; $(C_2H_5COCH-)_2$; C_2H_6	*182*
1-Methyl-5-ethyl-2-pyrrolone	$C_6H_5CH_2MgCl$	1-Methyl-2-ethyl-5-benzylpyrrole (29*x*%); $C_2H_5CO(CH_2)_2COCH_2C_6H_5$ (71*x*%) (Total yield not stated.)	*182*
$C_7H_{12}O$			
2,5-Dimethylcyclopentanone	C_2H_5MgI	1-Ethyl-2,5-dimethylcyclopentanol	*314*
"Methylcyclohexanone"	$(\equiv CMgX)_2$*	"Glycol" (75%)	*142,334*
2-Methylcyclohexanone	CH_3MgX	1,2-Dimethylcyclohexanol (67%)	*255*
2-Methylcyclohexanone	CH_3MgI	1,2-Dimethylcyclohexanol	*23,240,351*
2-Methylcyclohexanone	$(\equiv CMgBr)_2$	Bis-(1-hydroxy-2-methylcyclohexyl)ethyne	*345*
2-Methylcyclohexanone	C_2H_5MgX	1-Ethyl-2-methylcyclohexanol (92%)	*255*
2-Methylcyclohexanone	C_2H_5MgI	1-Ethyl-2-methylcyclohexanol (20%)	*204*
2-Methylcyclohexanone	n-C_3H_7MgX	1-*n*-Propyl-2-methylcyclohexanol (57%)	*255*
2-Methylcyclohexanone	n-C_3H_7MgI	1-*n*-Propyl-2-methylcyclohexanol (15%)	*204*
2-Methylcyclohexanone	$H_2C=CH(CH_2)_2MgBr$	1-(3-Butenyl)-2-methylcyclohexanol (35%)	*99*

* X = Br, I.

TABLE VI-XIX (Continued)

Ketone	RMgX	Product(s)	Ref.
$C_7H_{12}O$ (*cont.*)			
2-Methylcyclohexanone	n-C_4H_9MgX	1-n-Butyl-2-methylcyclohexanol (65%)	*255*
2-Methylcyclohexanone	i-C_4H_9MgCl	1-Isobutyl-2-methylcyclohexanol	*204*
2-Methylcyclohexanone	$H_2C{=}CH(CH_2)_3MgBr$	1-(4-Pentenyl)-2-methylcyclohexanol (57–68%)	*97*
2-Methylcyclohexanone	n-$C_5H_{11}MgX$	1-n-Amyl-2-methylcyclohexanol (63%)	*255*
2-Methylcyclohexanone	i-$C_5H_{11}MgX$	1-Isoamyl-2-methylcyclohexanol	*204*
2-Methylcyclohexanone	$(CH_2)_5CHMgCl$	1-Cyclohexyl-2-methylcyclohexanol (which dehydrates on distillation)	*204*
2-Methylcyclohexanone	$C_6H_5CH_2MgCl$	1-Benzyl-6-methylcyclohexene	*204*
2-Methylcyclohexanone (24.6 g.)	$C_6H_5CH_2MgCl$ (25.2 g. C_7H_7Cl)	1-Benzyl-2-methylcyclohexanol (25 g.)	*75*
2-Methylcyclohexanone	2-$CH_3C_6H_4MgCl$	1-*o*-Tolyl-6-methylcyclohexene	*204*
2-Methylcyclohexanone (11.5 g.)	$C_6H_5CH_2CH_2MgCl$ (14.0 g. C_8H_9Cl)	1-Phenethyl-2-methylcyclohexanol (7.0 g.)	*358*
2-Methylcyclohexanone	$C_6H_5CH_2CH_2MgBr$	1-Phenethyl-2-methylcyclohexanol (46%)	*218*
2-Methylcyclohexanone	1-$C_{10}H_7MgBr$	1-α-Naphthyl-2-methylcyclohexanol	*74*
2-Methylcyclohexanone	n-$C_{12}H_{25}MgBr$	1-Dodecyl-2-methylcyclohexanol; "olefin" (*i.e.*, dehydr'n product)	*218*
3-Methylcyclohexanone	CH_3MgX	1,3-Dimethylcyclohexanol (80%)	*255*
3-Methylcyclohexanone	CH_3MgI	1,3-Dimethylcyclohexanol (90%)	*311,240*
3-Methylcyclohexanone	$({\equiv}CMgBr)_2$	1,2-Bis-(1-hydroxy-3-methylcyclohexyl)ethyne (93%)	*141,345*
3-Methylcyclohexanone	$HC{\equiv}CMgBr$	1-Ethynyl-3-methylcyclohexanol	*143*
3-Methylcyclohexanone	C_2H_5MgX	1-Ethyl-3-methylcyclohexanol (93%)	*255*
3-Methylcyclohexanone	C_2H_5MgBr	1-Ethyl-3-methylcyclohexanol (70%)	*186*
3-Methylcyclohexanone	C_2H_5MgI	1-Ethyl-3-methylcyclohexanol ("good" yield)	*311,312*
3-Methylcyclohexanone	n-C_3H_7MgX	1-n-Propyl-3-methylcyclohexanol (72%)	*255*
3-Methylcyclohexanone	n-C_3H_7MgBr	1-n-Propyl-3-methylcyclohexanol ("poor" yield)	*186*
3-Methylcyclohexanone (16.8 g.)	n-C_3H_7MgI	1-n-Propyl-3-methylcyclohexanol (9 g.)	*311*

TABLE VI-XIX (Continued)

Ketone	RMgX	Product(s)	Ref.
$C_7H_{12}O$ *(cont.)*			
3-Methylcyclohexanone	i-C_3H_7MgX*	1-Isopropyl-3-methylcyclohexanol; high-boiling hydrocarbons	*311*
3-Methylcyclohexanone (11.2 g.)	$H_5C_2O_2CCH_2Br$ (16.7 g.) + Mg (2.4 g.)	Ethyl α-(1-hydroxy-3-methyl-1-cyclohexyl)acetate (14.0 g.)	*315*
3-Methylcyclohexanone	n-C_4H_9MgX	1-n-Butyl-3-methylcyclohexanol (70%)	*255*
3-Methylcyclohexanone	i-C_4H_9MgX	1-Isobutyl-3-methylcyclohexanol (6%); 3-methylcyclohexanol	*255*
3-Methylcyclohexanone	i-C_4H_9MgCl	1-Isobutyl-3-methylcyclohexanol ("poor" yield)	*186*
3-Methylcyclohexanone (17.5 g.)	$H_5C_2O_2CCH(CH_3)CH_2Br$ (28.3 g.) + Mg (3.8 g.)	Ethyl α-methyl-β-(1-hydroxy-3-methyl-1-cyclohexyl)propionate (9.0 g., 30%)	*315*
3-Methylcyclohexanone (28 g.)	$H_5C_2O_2CCH(CH_3)CH_2I$ (55 g.) + Mg (6 g.)	Ethyl α-methyl-β-(1-hydroxy-3-methyl-1-cyclohexyl)propionate (24 g., 45%)	*315*
3-Methylcyclohexanone	i-$C_5H_{11}MgBr$	1-Isoamyl-3-methylcyclohexanol (70%)	*186*
3-Methylcyclohexanone	C_6H_5MgBr	1-Phenyl-3-methylcyclohexanol (yield "considerable")	*186*
3-Methylcyclohexanone	$(CH_2)_5CHMgCl$	1-Cyclohexyl-3-methylcyclohexanol ("satisfactory" yield)	*186*
3-Methylcyclohexanone (28 g.)	$H_5C_2O_2CCH(C_2H_5)CH_2Br$ (29 g.) + Mg (6 g.)	Ethyl α-ethyl-β-(1-hydroxy-3-methyl-1-cyclohexyl)propionate (31 g., 50%)	*315*
3-Methylcyclohexanone	$C_6H_5CH_2MgCl$	1-Benzyl-3-methylcyclohexanol ("poor" yield)	*186*
3-Methylcyclohexanone (11.5 g.)	$C_6H_5CH_2CH_2MgCl$ (14.0 g. C_8H_9Cl)	1-Phenethyl-3-methylcyclohexanol (10.0 g.)	*358*
3-Methylcyclohexanone	1-$C_{10}H_7MgBr$	1-α-Naphthyl-3-methylcyclohexanol	*36*
3-Methylcyclohexanone	n-$C_{12}H_{25}MgBr$	1-Dodecyl-3-methylcyclohexanol; "olefin" (*i.e.*, dehydr'n product)	*219*

* X = Br, I.

TABLE VI-XIX (Continued)

Ketone	RMgX	Product(s)	Ref.
$C_7H_{12}O$ (*cont.*)			
4-Methylcyclohexanone	CH_3MgI	1,3-Dimethylcyclohexanol ("very good" yield)	*240,242,294*
4-Methylcyclohexanone	C_2H_5MgX	1-Ethyl-4-methylcyclohexanol (69%)	*255*
4-Methylcyclohexanone	C_2H_5MgI	1-Ethyl-4-methylcyclohexanol ("good" yield)	*242*
4-Methylcyclohexanone	*n*-C_3H_7MgX	1-*n*-Propyl-4-methylcyclohexanol (52%)	*255*
4-Methylcyclohexanone	*n*-C_3H_7MgX	1-*n*-Propyl-4-methylcyclohexanol; 4-methylcyclohexanol	*242*
4-Methylcyclohexanone	*i*-C_3H_7MgI	1-Isopropyl-4-methylcyclohexanol ("very little"); 4-methylcyclohexanol	*242,217*
4-Methylcyclohexanone	*n*-C_4H_9MgX	1-*n*-Butyl-4-methylcyclohexanol	*255*
4-Methylcyclohexanone	*i*-C_4H_9MgBr	4-Methylcyclohexanol; C_4H_8	*242*
4-Methylcyclohexanone	*i*-$C_5H_{11}MgBr$	1-Isoamyl-4-methylcyclohexanol ("a little"); 4-methylcyclohexanol	*242*
4-Methylcyclohexanone	C_6H_5MgBr	1-Phenyl-4-methylcyclohexanol	*242*
4-Methylcyclohexanone	$C_6H_5CH_2MgCl$	1-Benzyl-4-methylcyclohexanol ("good" yield)	*242*
4-Methylcyclohexanone (11.5 g.)	$C_6H_5CH_2CH_2MgCl$ (14.0 g., C_8H_9Cl)	1-Phenethyl-4-methylcyclohexanol (9.0 g.)	*358*
4-Methylcyclohexanone	"Secondary" $C_8H_{17}MgI$	"1-*s*-Octyl-4-methylcyclohexanol" (25%)	*242*
4-Methylcyclohexanone	1-$C_{10}H_7MgBr$	1-α-Naphthyl-4-methylcyclohexanol	*36*
$(CH_2)_6CO$*	CH_3MgI	$(CH_2)_6C(CH_3)OH$	*291*
$(CH_2)_6CO$* (11 g.)	CH_3MgI (28 g. CH_3I)	1-Methylcycloheptene (b. 74-75°/100 mm.) (88 g.)	*236*
$(CH_2)_6CO$*	$(\equiv CMgI)_2$	$[(CH_2)_6C(OH)C\equiv]_2$	*144*
$(CH_2)_6CO$*	$H_5C_2O_2CCH_2Br$ (17.0 g.) + Mg (2.5 g.)	Ethyl α-(1-hydroxycycloheptyl)acetate (11.0 g.)	*315*
$(CH_2)_6CO$*	$C_6H_5CH_2MgCl$	1-Benzylcycloheptanol	*96*

* Suberone.

TABLE VI-XIX (Continued)

Ketone	RMgX	Product(s)	Ref.
$C_7H_{12}O_2$			
4-Methoxycyclohexanone	C_2H_5MgBr	1-Ethyl-4-methoxycyclohexanol (60%)	*188*
4-Methoxycyclohexanone	1-Ethynylcyclohexanol + C_2H_5MgBr	1,1′-Dihydroxy-4-methoxydicyclohexylethyne (78%, crude; 2 isomers)	*188*
4-Methoxycyclohexanone	1-Ethynyl-4-methoxycyclohexanol + C_2H_5MgBr	Bis-(1-hydroxy-4-methoxycyclohexyl)ethyne	*188*
3-Methylcyclohexan-1-ol-2-one	CH_3MgI	2,3-Dimethylcyclohexanone	*172*
$C_8H_4O_2BrN$			
5-Bromoïsatin*	CH_3MgI	3-Hydroxy-3-methyl-5-bromoöxindole†	*167*
5-Bromoïsatin	C_6H_5MgBr	3-Hydroxy-3-phenyl-5-bromoöxindole	*167*
$C_8H_5O_2N$			
Isatin‡	CH_3MgI	3-Hydroxy-3-methyloxindole§	*167*
Isatin	RMgBr¶ (2.5 equiv.)	3-Hydroxy-3-R-oxindole	*166*
Isatin	C_6H_5MgBr	3-Hydroxy-3-phenyloxindole	*139*
Isatin	$2-CH_3C_6H_4MgI$	3-Hydroxy-3-*o*-tolyloxindole	*139*
Isatin	$3-CH_3C_6H_4MgI$	3-Hydroxy-3-*m*-tolyloxindole	*139*
Isatin	$4-CH_3C_6H_4MgI$	3-Hydroxy-3-*p*-tolyloxindole	*139*
Isatin	$2-CH_3OC_6H_4MgI$	3-Hydroxy-3-*o*-methoxyphenyloxindole	*139*
Isatin	$3-CH_3OC_6H_4MgI$	3-Hydroxy-3-*m*-methoxyphenyloxindole	*139*
Isatin	$4-CH_3OC_6H_4MgI$	3-Hydroxy-3-*p*-anisyloxindole	*139*

* 5-Bromo-2,3-indolinedione; 5-bromoïsatic acid lactam.

† 3-Hydroxy-3-methyl-5-bromo-2(3*H*)-indolone.

‡ 2,3-Indolinedione; isatic acid lactam.

§ 3-Hydroxy-3-methyl-2(3*H*)-indolone.

¶ R = $4-BrC_6H_4$, C_6H_5, $C_6H_5CH_2$, $1-C_{10}H_7$.

TABLE VI-XIX (Continued)

Ketone	RMgX	Product(s)	Ref.
$C_8H_7OCl_3$			
4-Methyl-4-trichloromethyl-2,5-cyclohexadien-1-one	CH_3MgI	1,4-Dimethyl-4-trichloromethyl-2,5-cyclohexadien-1-ol (80–90%)	*323*
$C_8H_8OCl_2$			
4-Methyl-4-dichloromethyl-2,5-cyclohexadien-1-one (19.1 g.)	CH_3MgI (14.2 g. CH_3I)	1,4-Dimethyl-4-dichloromethyl-2,5-cyclohexadien-1-ol (8 g. or less)	*283,282*
4-Methyl-4-dichloromethyl-2,5-cyclohexadien-1-one	C_2H_5MgI (2 equiv.)	1-Ethyl-4-methyl-4-dichloromethyl-2,5-cyclohexadien-1-ol	*278*
4-Methyl-4-dichloromethyl-2,5-cyclohexadien-1-one	*n*-C_3H_7MgX* (2 equiv.)	1-*n*-Propyl-4-methyl-4-dichloromethyl-2,5-cyclohexadien-1-ol (*ca.* quant.)	*279*
4-Methyl-4-dichloromethyl-2,5-cyclohexadien-1-one	*i*-C_3H_7MgBr	1-Isopropyl-4-methyl-4-dichloromethyl-2,5-cyclohexadien-1-ol (*ca.* quant.)	*279*
4-Methyl-4-dichloromethyl-2,5-cyclohexadien-1-one	$C_6H_5CH_2MgCl$ (2 equiv.)	1-Benzyl-4-methyl-4-dichloromethyl-2,5-cyclohexadien-1-ol	*279*
$C_8H_{12}O$			
2,3-Dimethyl-2-cyclohexen-1-one (12.5 g.)	$C_6H_5(CH_2)_2MgCl$ (14.2 g. C_8H_9Cl)	1,2-Dimethyl-3-phenethyl-1,3-cyclohexadiene (6 g.)	*35*
2,3-Dimethyl-2-cyclohexen-1-one (9.2 g.)	3-$CH_3OC_6H_4(CH_2)_2MgCl$ (11.0 g. $C_9H_{11}ClO$)	1,2-Dimethyl-3-*m*-methoxyphenethyl-1,3-cyclohexadiene (7.5 g.)	*35*
3,5-Dimethyl-2-cyclohexen-1-one (1.00 mole)	CH_3MgI (1.05 mole)	1,3,5-Trimethyl-2-cyclohexen-1-ol	*346*
3,5-Dimethyl-2-cyclohexen-1-one	C_2H_5MgBr (2 equiv.)	1-Ethyl-3,5-dimethyl-2-cyclohexen-1-ol	*346*
3,5-Dimethyl-2-cyclohexen-1-one	$H_2C{=}CHCH_2Br$ + Mg	1-Allyl-3,5-dimethyl-2-cyclohexen-1-ol (95%)	*190*
3,5-Dimethyl-2-cyclohexen-1-ol	*i*-C_3H_7MgBr (2 equiv.)	1-Isopropyl-3,5-dimethyl-2-cyclohexen-1-ol	*346*
3,5-Dimethyl-2-cyclohexen-1-one (25 g.)	C_6H_5MgBr	3,5-Dimethyl-1-phenyl-2-cyclohexen-1-ol (36 g., pure)	*164,287*

*X = Br, I.

TABLE VI-XIX (Continued)

Ketone	RMgX	Product(s)	Ref.
$C_8H_{12}O$ (*cont.*)			
cis-Bicyclo[3.3.0]octan-2-one (15.0 g.)	$C_6H_5CH_2MgCl$ (15.5 g. C_7H_7Cl)	2-Benzyl-*cis*-bicyclo[3.3.0]octan-2-ol (12.4 g.); liquid isomer (6.1 g.)	21
4-Methyl-4-dichloromethylcyclohexanone	CH_3MgI	1,4-Dimethyl-4-dichloromethylcyclohexanol (*ca.* quant.)	286
$C_8H_{12}O_2$			
Tetramethyl-1,3-cyclobutanedione (15.0 g., 0.106 mole)	CH_3MgBr (60.0 g. CH_3Br)	$(CH_3)_2CO$ (0.8 g.); $(i\text{-}C_3H_7)_2CO$ (1.8 g.); $HO(CH_3)_2CC(CH_3)_2CO\text{-}i\text{-}C_3H_7$ (12 g., 65%)	98
Tetramethyl-1,3-cyclobutanedione (4.2 g.)	C_2H_5MgBr (7.0 g. C_2H_5Br)	1,3-Diethyl-2,2,4,4-tetramethyl-1,3-cyclobutanediol* (*ca.* quant.)	296
Tetramethyl-1,3-cyclobutanedione (20.0 g.)	C_2H_5MgBr (85.0 g. C_2H_5Br)	$C_2H_5CH(OH)C(CH_3)_2CO\text{-}i\text{-}C_3H_7$ (21.8 g., 84%)†	98
Tetramethyl-1,3-cyclobutanedione (12.0 g.)	C_2H_5MgBr (11.0 g. C_2H_5Br)	Recovered ketone (7.3 g., 60%); $C_2H_5CH(OH)C(CH_3)_2CO\text{-}i\text{-}C_3H_7$ (3.8 g., 83% on basis of ketone consumed)‡	98
Tetramethyl-1,3-cyclobutanedione (21.0 g.)	C_6H_5MgBr (119.6 g. C_6H_5Br)	$(i\text{-}C_3H_7)_2CO$ (14.5 g., 85%); $(C_6H_5)_2CO$ (26.1 g., 95%)§	98
Tetramethyl-1,3-cyclobutanedione (12.0 g.)	C_6H_5MgBr (16.8 g. C_6H_5Br)	Recovered ketone (7.1 g., 59%); $(i\text{-}C_3H_7)_2CO$ (2.1 g., 53% on basis of ketone consumed); $(C_6H_5)_2CO$ (5.8 g., 91%)¶	98
Tetramethyl-1,3-cyclobutanedione (5.0 g.)	2,4,6-$(CH_3)_3C_6H_2MgBr$ (23.0 g., $C_9H_{11}Br$)	Recovered ketone (4.2 g., 84%)	98

* According to Erickson and Kitchens (98), this product, erroneously characterized, is actually $C_2H_5CH(OH)C(CH_3)_2CO\text{-}i\text{-}C_3H_7$.

† Portionwise addition of ketone to Grignard reagent solution; fifteen minutes reflux.

‡ Slow (forty-five minutes) addition of Grignard reagent solution to Et_2O-ketone solution.

§ Portionwise addition of ketone to Grignard reagent solution.

¶ Slow (one hour) addition of Grignard reagent solution to Et_2O-ketone solution.

TABLE VI-XIX (Continued)

Ketone	RMgX	Product(s)	Ref.
$C_8H_{12}O_2$ (*cont.*)			
Dihydroresorcinol enol ethyl ether*	RMgX† (1.58 equiv.)	3-R-2-Cyclohexen-1-one (12–85%)	307
Dihydroresorcinol enol ethyl ether* (70 g.)	C_6H_5MgBr (0.75 mole)	3-Phenyl-2-cyclohexen-1-one (71 g., 87%)	309
Dihydroresorcinol enol ethyl ether* (92.0 g.)	3-$C_6H_5C_6H_4MgBr$ (114.6 g. $C_{12}H_9Br$)	3-(3-Biphenylyl)-2-cyclohexen-1-one (70.0 g., crude)	308
Dimedone‡ (50 g., 0.35 mole)	C_6H_5MgBr (1.5 mole C_6H_5Br)	1-Phenyl-5,5-dimethylcyclohexen-3-one (21.5 g., 31%); 1,3-diphenyl-5,5-dimethyl-1,3-cyclohexadiene (15.9 g., 18%); tar (10–20 g.)	307
$C_8H_{12}O_2Br_2$			
2,2,5,5-Tetramethyl-4,4-dibromotetrahydrofuran-3-one	C_2H_5MgBr	2,2,5,5-Tetramethyl-4-bromotetrahydrofuran-3-one; 2,2,5,5-tetramethyl-4-bromo-4-ethyltetrahydrofuran-3-one (20%)	222
$C_8H_{12}O_3$			
3-Carbethoxycyclopentanone (15.6 g.)	6-$CH_3OC_{10}H_6$-2-MgBr (18.0 g. $C_{11}H_9BrO$)	3-Hydroxy-3-(6-methoxy-2-naphthyl)cyclopentanecarboxylic acid lactone (9.0 g., crude)	223
$C_8H_{13}ON$			
1-Oxoöctahydropyrrocoline§ (1.85 g.)	CH_3MgI (13.5 g. CH_3I)	1-Hydroxy-1-methyloctahydropyrrocoline (1.28 g.)	72

* Formulated as 3-ethoxy-2-cyclohexen-1-one.

† The Grignard reagents studied and the corresponding yields of the indicated products are as follows: CH_3, 34%; C_2H_5, 75%; i-C_3H_7, 12%; n-C_4H_9, 85%; i-C_4H_9, 43%; s-C_4H_9, 15%; t-C_4H_9, 13%.

‡ 5,5-Dimethyl-1,3-cyclohexanedione.

§ 1-Oxoïndolizidine, 1-oxopiperolidine.

TABLE VI-XIX (Continued)

Ketone	RMgX	Product(s)	Ref.
$C_8H_{13}ON$ (*cont.*)			
2-Oxoöctahydropyrrocoline	C_2H_5MgI	2-Hydroxy-2-ethyloctahydropyrrocoline ("very good" yield)	*72*
$C_8H_{13}O_2Br$			
2,2,5,5-Tetramethyl-4-bromo-tetrahydrofuran-3-one	C_2H_5MgBr	2,2,5,5-Tetramethyltetrahydrofuran-3-one (chiefly); 2,2,5,5-Tetramethyl-4-ethyl-tetrahydrofuran-3-one (20%)	*222*
$C_8H_{14}O$			
2-Methyl-4-ethylcyclopentanone (30.0 g.)	C_6H_5MgBr (56.3 g. C_6H_5Br)	1-Phenyl-2-methyl-5-ethylcyclopentanol (18.0 g., 37%); recovered ketone (16.0 g., 53%)	*263*
2-Ethylcyclohexanone (20 g.)	*n*-C_4H_9MgBr (23 g. C_4H_9Br)	1-*n*-Butyl-2-ethylcyclohexanol (20 g.)	*152*
2,2-Dimethylcyclohexanone	CH_3MgI	1,2,2-Trimethylcyclohexanol (*ca.* quant.)	*286*
2,3-Dimethylcyclohexanone (6.0 g.)	CH_3MgI (11.3 g. CH_3I)	1,2,3-Trimethylcyclohexanol	*285*
2,5-Dimethylcyclohexanone	*i*-C_3H_7MgI	2,5-Dimethylcyclohexanol	*242*
2,6-Dimethylcyclohexanone	3-*i*-$C_3H_7C_6H_4(CH_2)_2MgBr$	1-(*m*-Isopropylphenethyl)-2,6-dimethylcyclohexanol	*44*
3,3-Dimethylcyclohexanone	CH_3MgBr	1,3,3-Trimethylcyclohexanol (70%)	*81*
3,3-Dimethylcyclohexanone	C_2H_5MgBr	1-Ethyl-3,3-dimethylcyclohexanol	*81*
3,5-Dimethylcyclohexanone	CH_3MgI	1,3,5-Trimethylcyclohexanol	*294*
$(CH_2)_7CO$	C_6H_5MgBr	$(CH_2)_7C(C_6H_5)OH$ + 1-phenylcyclooöctene (aggregating 73.5%)	
$(CH_2)_7CO$	*n*-$C_{18}H_{37}MgBr$	$(CH_2)_7C(n\text{-}C_{18}H_{37})OH$ (70%)	*105*
$C_8H_{14}O_2$			
2,2,5,5-Tetramethyl-3-tetrahydro-furanone	CH_3MgBr	2,2,3,5,5-Pentamethyl-3-tetrahydrofuranol	*356*

TABLE VI-XIX (Continued)

Ketone	RMgX	Product(s)	Ref.
$C_8H_{14}O_2$ (*cont.*)			
2,2,5,5-Tetramethyl-3-tetrahydrofuranone	CH_3MgI	2,2,3,5,5-Pentamethyl-3-tetrahydrofuranol	355
2,2,5,5-Tetramethyl-3-tetrahydrofuranone	$(\equiv CMgBr)_2$	$[\equiv CC(OH)(C_7H_{14}O)]_2$	355
2,2,5,5-Tetramethyl-3-tetrahydrofuranone	C_2H_5MgBr	2,2,5,5-Tetramethyl-3-ethyl-3-tetrahydrofuranol (40-50%)	222
2,2,5,5-Tetramethyl-3-tetrahydrofuranone	$H_2C{=}CHCH_2MgBr$	2,2,5,5-Tetramethyl-3-allyl-3-tetrahydrofuranol	356
2,2,5,5-Tetramethyl-3-tetrahydrofuranone	$C_6H_5CH_2MgBr$	2,2,5,5-Tetramethyl-3-benzyl-3-tetrahydrofuranol	356
2,2,5,5-Tetramethyl-3-tetrahydrofuranone	RMgX*	Enolate	356
$C_9H_4OBr_3$			
2,3-Dibromo-1-indone (10.0 g.)	CH_3MgI (5.8 g. CH_3I)	1-Methyl-2,3-dibromo-1-indenol (3.7 g.)	256
2,3-Dibromo-1-indone	C_2H_5MgBr (2 equiv.)	1-Ethyl-2,3-dibromo-1-indenol (85%)	256
C_9H_4OBrI			
2-Iodo-3-bromo-1-indone	CH_3MgI	1-Methyl-2-iodo-3-bromoinden-1-ol (81%)	256
$C_9H_7O_2N$			
1-Methylisatin (0.05 mole)	C_6H_5MgBr (0.25 mole)	1-Methyl-2,3-epoxy-2,3-diphenylindoline (*ca.* 52%); 1-methyl-3,3-diphenyloxindole	206
C_9H_8O			
Indone	CH_3MgI	1-Methyl-1-indanol	289,262,162

* RMgX = "most Grignard reagents."

TABLE VI-XIX (Continued)

Ketone	RMgX	Product(s)	Ref.
C_9H_8O (*cont.*)			
Indone (66 g.)	$H_2C{=}CH(CH_2)_3MgBr$	1-(Δ^4-Pentenyl)-1-indanol (53 g.)	*187*
Indone (13.5 g.)	9-Phenanthryl-MgBr (25.7 ml. $C_{14}H_9Br$)	1-(9-Phenanthryl)-1-indanol + corresponding olefin (aggregating (10.0 g.)	*26*
2-Indanone	CH_3MgI	2-Methyl-2-indanol (73%)	*162*
$C_9H_{10}OCl_2$			
2,4-Dimethyl-4-dichloromethyl-2,5-cyclohexadien-1-one	CH_3MgI	1,2,4-Trimethyl-4-dichloromethyl-2,5-cyclohexadien-1-ol	284
2,4-Dimethyl-4-dichloromethyl-2,5-cyclohexadien-1-one	C_2H_5MgI	1-Ethyl-2,4-dimethyl-4-dichloromethyl-2,5-cyclohexadien-1-ol	284
3,4-Dimethyl-4-dichloromethyl-2,5-cyclohexadien-1-one	CH_3MgI	1,3,4-Trimethyl-4-dichloromethyl-2,5-cyclohexadien-1-ol	284
3,4-Dimethyl-4-dichloromethyl-2,5-cyclohexadien-1-one	C_2H_5MgI	1-Ethyl-3,4-dimethyl-4-dichloromethyl-2,5-cyclohexadien-1-ol	284
$C_9H_{14}O$			
4-Isopropyl-2-cyclohexen-1-one	CH_3MgI	1-Methyl-4-isopropyl-2-cyclohexen-1-ol; α-Phellandrene (1-methyl-4-isopropyl-1,5-cyclohexadiene)	293
3-Methyl-5-ethyl-2-cyclohexen-1-one	$H_2C{=}CHCH_2Br$ + Mg	1-Allyl-3-methyl-5-ethyl-2-cyclohexen-1-ol (99.2%)	*190*
Isophorone*	CH_3MgBr	1,3,5,5-Tetramethyl-2-cyclohexen-1-ol (42.6%); 1,3,5,5-tetramethyl-1,3-cyclohexadiene (48.2%)†	*153*

* 3,5,5-Trimethyl-2-cyclohexen-1-one.

† Slow addition of Et_2O-ketone solution to stirred Grignard reagent solution at 10–20°; one hour heating; overnight standing.

TABLE VI-XIX (Continued)

Ketone	RMgX	Product(s)	Ref.
$C_9H_{14}O$ (*cont.*)			
Isophorone*	CH_3MgBr	1,3,5,5-Tetramethyl-2-cyclohexen-1-ol (67.2%); 1,3,5,5-tetramethylcyclohexadiene (23.6)†	*153*
Isophorone* (50 g.)	CH_3MgBr (2 equiv.)	1,3,5,5-Tetramethyl-1,3-cyclohexadiene (43 g.)	*250*
Isophorone* + CuCl (1 mole-%)	CH_3MgBr	1,3,5,5-Tetramethylcyclohexadiene (6.9%); 3,3,5,5-tetramethylcyclohexanone (82.5%)	*153*
Isophorone* (1.5 mole)	CH_3MgBr (2.0 moles)	Recovered ketone (10%); 1,3,5,5-tetramethyl-2-cyclohexen-1-ol (83%)	*337*
Isophorone*	C_2H_5MgBr	Recovered ketone (10%); 1-ethyl-3,5,5-trimethyl-2-cyclohexen-1-ol (80%)	*337*
Isophorone*	i-C_3H_7MgBr	3,5,5-Trimethyl-3-isopropylcyclohexanone (8%)	*337*
Isophorone* (17.2 g.)	n-$C_4H_9C{\equiv}CMgBr$ (12.5 g. C_6H_{10})	1-(1-Hexynyl)-3,5,5-trimethyl-2-cyclohexen-1-ol (10.1 g.)	*347*
Sabinaketone‡	CH_3MgI	Sabinene hydrate§	*249*
Camphenilone¶	$({\equiv}CMgBr)_2$	$[C_8H_{14}{=}C(OH)C{\equiv}]_2$ (35.4%)	*94*
Camphenilone¶	n-C_3H_7MgBr	Camphenilol‖	*179*
Nopinone**	CH_3MgI	Pinene hydrate†† (80%)	*292*

* 3,5,5-Trimethyl-2-cyclohexen-1-one.

† Addition of Grignard reagent solution to Et_2O-ketone solution.

‡ 5-Isopropylbicyclo[3.1.0]hexan-2-one.

§ 2-Methyl-5-isopropylbicyclo[3.1.0]hexan-2-ol.

¶ 2,2-Dimethylbicyclo[2.2.1]heptan-3-one.

‖ 2,2-Dimethylbicyclo[2.2.1]heptan-3-ol.

** 6,6-Dimethylbicyclo[3.1.1]heptan-2-one.

†† Homopinol; 2,6,6-trimethylbicyclo[3.1.1]heptan-2-ol.

TABLE VI-XIX (Continued)

Ketone	RMgX	Product(s)	Ref.
$C_9H_{14}O$ (*cont.*)			
Nopinone*	C_2H_5MgI	Ethylnopinol†	*292*
α-Fenchocamphorone‡	CH_3MgI	2,7,7-Trimethylbicyclo[2.2.1]heptan-2-ol	*169*
$C_9H_{14}O_3$			
2-Carbethoxymethylcyclopentanone	CH_3MgX	2-Hydroxy-2-methylcyclopentaneacetic acid γ-lactone	*336*
2-Methyl-2-carbethoxycyclopentanone	$C_2H_5O_2CCH_2Br$ + Mg	Ethyl α-(1-hydroxy-2-methyl-2-carbethoxycyclopentyl)acetate	*99*
$C_9H_{15}ON$			
2-Oxoöctahydropyridocoline§	CH_3MgI	2-Hydroxy-2-methyloctahydropyridocoline ("extremely small yield")	*72*
$C_9H_{17}ON$			
2-Dimethylaminomethylcyclohexanone	$4-CH_3OC_6H_4MgBr$	1-Anisyl-2-dimethylaminomethylcyclohexanol	*175*
2-Dimethylaminomethylcyclohexanone (14.1 g.)	2-(1-Tetralylidene)ethyl-MgBr (22.9 g. $C_{12}H_{13}Br$)	1-[2-(1-Tetralylidene)ethyl]-2-dimethylaminomethylcyclohexanol; $(C_{12}H_{19})_2$	*89*
1-Butyl-4-piperidone (15.5 g.)	C_6H_5MgBr (23.5 g. C_6H_5Br)	1-Butyl-4-phenyl-4-piperidinol (8 g.)	*322*
Triacetonamine¶	C_2H_5MgI	2,2,6,6-Tetramethyl-4-ethyl-4-piperidinol	*70*
$C_9H_{17}O_2N$			
2-Dimethylaminomethyl-3-hydroxycyclohexanone	CH_3MgI	1-Methyl-2-dimethylaminomethylcyclohexane-1,3-diol	*90*

* 6,6-Dimethylbicyclo[3.1.1]heptan-2-one.
† 2-Ethyl-6,6-dimethylbicyclo[3.1.1]heptan-2-ol.
‡ 7,7-Dimethylbicyclo[2.2.1]heptan-2-one.
§ 2-Oxoöctahydro-4-quinazoline, 2-oxoöctahydro-4-pyrido[1.2-a]pyridine, 2-oxonorlupinane.
¶ 2,2,6,6-Tetramethyl-4-piperidone.

TABLE VI-XIX (Continued)

Ketone	RMgX	Product(s)	Ref.
$C_9H_{17}O_2N$ (*cont.*)			
2-Dimethylaminomethyl-5-hydroxy-cyclohexanone	CH_3MgI	1-Methyl-2-dimethylaminomethylcyclo-hexane-1,5-diol	*90*
$C_{10}H_8O$			
2-Methyl-1-indenone	CH_3MgI (excess)	1,2-Dimethyl-1-indenol	*262*
$C_{10}H_9O_2N$			
1-Ethylisatin	*n*-C_4H_9MgBr (1 equiv.)	1-Ethyl-3-hydroxy-3-*n*-butyloxindole ("good yield")	*264*
1-Ethylisatin	*n*-C_4H_9MgBr (4 equiv.)	1-Ethyl-2,3-dibutyl-2,3-epoxyindoline	*264*
1-Ethylisatin	C_6H_5MgBr (5 equiv.)	1-Ethyl-2,3-diphenyl-2,3-epoxyindoline (56%); 1-ethyl-3,3-diphenyloxindole (16%)	*206*
$C_{10}H_{10}O$			
2-Methyl-1-indanone (5.0 g.)	CH_3MgI (7.3 g. CH_3I)	1,2-Dimethyl-1-indanol (4.0 g.)	*262,289*
3-Methyl-1-indanone	CH_3MgI	1,3-Dimethylindone	*289*
α-Tetralone*	4-BrC_6H_4MgBr	1-*p*-Bromophenyl-1-tetralol	*288*
α-Tetralone	C_6H_5MgBr	1-Phenyl-1-tetralol	*288*
α-Tetralone (50 g.)	C_6H_5MgBr (61.5 g. C_6H_5Br)	1-Phenyl-3,4-dihydronaphthalene (28 g.)	*301*
α-Tetralone (36.5 g.)	$(CH_2)_5CHMgCl$ (30 g. $C_6H_{11}Cl$)	Recovered ketone (21.5 g.); 1-cyclohexyl-1-tetralol and 1-cyclohexyl-3,4-dihydro-naphthalene (yielding 3.8 g. hydrocarbon on complete dehydr'n); 1-oxo-2-(1-tetralylidene)-1,2,3,4-tetrahydro-naphthalene (?) (3.7 g.)	*77,36*
α-Tetralone	4-$CH_3C_6H_4MgBr$	1-*p*-Tolyl-1-tetralol	*288*
α-Tetralone	4-$CH_3OC_6H_4MgBr$	1-Anisyl-1-tetralol	*193*

* 3,4-Dihydro-1(2*H*)-naphthalenone.

TABLE VI-XIX (Continued)

Ketone	RMgX	Product(s)	Ref.
$C_{10}H_{10}O$ (*cont.*)			
α-Tetralone (15.0 g.)	$C_6H_5CH_2CH_2MgCl$ (14.0 g. C_8H_9Cl)	1-Phenethyl-1-tetralol (9.5 g.)	*358*
α-Tetralone (8.8 g.)	2-$C_{10}H_7MgBr$ (15 g. $C_{10}H_7Br$)	1-β-Naphthyl-1-tetralol (yielding 11.3 g. hydrocarbon)	*134,216*
α-Tetralone (9.0 g.)	9-Phenanthryl-MgBr (15 ml. $C_{14}H_9Br$)	1-(9-Phenanthryl)-1-tetralol (yielding 1.0 g. hydrocarbon)	*26*
$C_{10}H_{12}OCl_2$			
2,4,5-Trimethyl-4-dichloromethyl-2,5-cyclohexadien-1-one	CH_3MgI	1,2,4,5-Tetramethyl-4-dichloromethyl-2,5-cyclohexadien-1-ol	*284*
$C_{10}H_{14}O$			
Carvone*	CH_3MgX†	1,2-Dimethyl-5-isopropenyl-2-cyclohexen-1-ol (*ca.* quant.)	*156,227,280*
Carvone*	CH_3MgI	2,3-Dimethyl-5-isopropenyl-1,3-cyclohexadiene; 2,3-dimethyl-5-isopropenylcyclohexanone	*229*
Carvone* (15.2 g.) + CuBr (0.1 g.)	CH_3MgI (16.0 g. CH_3I)	2,3-Dimethyl-5-isopropenylcyclohexanone (11.0 g.); diene (?) (2.5 g.)	*330*
Carvone*	$(\equiv CMgBr)_2$	Glycol, m.p. 145–147°	*334*
Carvone* (30 g.)	C_2H_5MgBr (50 g. C_2H_5Br)	1-Ethyl-2-methyl-5-isopropenyl-2-cyclohexen-1-ol (27 g.)	*156*
Carvone* (12.0 g.)	*n*-C_3H_7MgBr (12.5 g.)	1-*n*-Propyl-2-methyl-5-isopropenyl-2-cyclohexen-1-ol (11.0 g.)	*155*
Carvone*	*i*-$C_5H_{11}MgBr$	2-Methyl-3-isoamyl-5-isopropenylcyclohexanone; 1-isoamyl-2-methyl-5-isopropenyl-2-cyclohexen-1-ol	*245*

* 2-Methyl-5-isopropenyl-2-cyclohexen-1-one; 6,8(9)-*p*-menthadien-2-one.
† X = Br, I.

TABLE VI-XIX (Continued)

Ketone	RMgX	Product(s)	Ref.
$C_{10}H_{14}O$ (*cont.*)			
Carvone* (30 g.)	C_6H_5MgBr (50 g. C_6H_5Br)	1-Phenyl-2-methyl-5-isopropenyl-2-cyclohexen-1-ol	*155*
Carvone*	$C_6H_5CH_2MgCl$	2-Methyl-3-benzyl-5-isopropenylcyclohexanone; 2 isomeric hydrocarbons ($C_{17}H_{20}$)	*230*
Carvone*	$CH_3(C_6H_5)CHMgBr$	$C_{18}H_{20}$	*230*
Pinocarvone† (150 g., 1.0 mole)	CH_3MgX‡ (1.2 mole CH_3X‡)	Ethylapopinocamphone§ (95.9%, crude)	*335*
Pinocarvone† (150 g., 1.0 mole)	C_2H_5MgBr (1.2 mole)	*n*-Propylapopinocamphone (88%, crude)	*335*
Pinocarvone† (150 g., 1.0 mole)	*n*-C_3H_7MgBr (1.2 mole)	*n*-Butylapopinocamphone (82%, crude)	*335*
Pinocarvone† (150 g., 1.0 mole)	*i*-C_3H_7MgBr (1.2 mole)	*i*-Butylapopinocamphone (45%, crude)	*335*
Pinocarvone† (150 g., 1.0 mole)	*n*-C_4H_9MgBr (1.2 mole)	*n*-Amylapopinocamphone (68%, crude)	*335*
Pinocarvone† (150 g., 1.0 mole)	C_6H_5MgBr (1.2 mole)	Benzylapopinocamphone (55%, crude)	*335*
Pinocarvone† (150 g., 1.0 mole)	$C_6H_5CH_2MgCl$ (1.2 mole)	Resinous products, only	*335*
3,4,5,6,7,8-Hexahydro-1(2*H*)-naphthalenone	CH_3MgCl	1-Methyl-1,2,3,4,5,6,7,8-octahydro-1-naphthol	*125*
4,4a,5,6,7,8-Hexahydro-2(3*H*)-naphthalenone (12.0 g.) + CuBr (0.2 g.)	CH_3MgI (19.5 g. CH_3I)	*cis*-8a-Methyl-2-decalone (5.0 g.)	*330*
Cyclopentenocycloheptan-4-one (20 g.)	CH_3MgI (35 g. CH_3I)	4-Methyl-1,2,3,6,7,8-hexahydrocyclopentacycloheptane (12 g.)	*244*
Cyclopentenocycloheptan-4-one (40.0 g.)	C_2H_5MgBr (60.0 g. C_2H_5Br)	4-Ethyl-1,2,3,6,7,8-hexahydrocyclopentacycloheptane (25.6 g.)	*244*

* 2-Methyl-5-isopropenyl-2-cyclohexen-1-one; 6,8(9)-*p*-menthadien-2-one.
† 2-Methylene-6,6-dimethylbicyclo[3.1.1]heptan-3-one.
‡ X = Br, I.
§ 2-Ethyl-6,6-dimethylbicyclo[3.1.1]heptan-3-one.

TABLE VI-XIX (Continued)

Ketone	RMgX	Product(s)	Ref.
$C_{10}H_{14}O$ (*cont.*)			
Cyclopentenocycloheptan-4-one (20 g.)	C_6H_5MgBr (45 g. C_6H_5MgBr)	4-Phenyl-1,2,3,6,7,8-hexahydrocyclopentacycloheptane + 4-phenyl-4-cyclopentenocycloheptanol (totaling 20 g.)	*244*
$C_{10}H_{14}O_2$			
DL-Camphorquinone[*] (15 g.)	C_6H_5MgBr (25 g. C_6H_5Br)	Product, m. 193° (8.4 g., 38%); product, m. 114-115° (9.5 g.); $(C_6H_5-)_2$	*119*
DL-Camphorquinone[*]	C_6H_5MgBr	2-Hydroxy-2-phenylepicamphor; 3-hydroxy-3-phenylcamphor	*120*
DL-Camphorquinone[*] (40 g.)	$1-C_{10}H_7MgBr$	3-Hydroxy-3-α-naphthylcamphor (12 g., 17%)	*119*
2-Hydroxycarvone[†] (20 g.)	C_2H_5MgBr (35 g. C_2H_5Br)	2-Ethylcarvone[‡]	*268*
$C_{10}H_{15}O_3$			
2-Carboxymethylcyclohexanone (10 g.)	$C_6H_5(CH_2)_2MgBr$ (10 g. C_8H_9Br)	2-Hydroxy-2-phenethylcyclohexylacetic acid lactone (7 g.)	*115*
$C_{10}H_{16}O$			
Dihydrocarvone[§]	CH_3MgI	*t*-Methyldihydrocarveol[¶] (87%)	*227*
Carvenone[‖] (45.5 g.)	CH_3MgI (58.5 g. CH_3I)	2-Methylcarvenol;[**] 2-methyl-α-terpinene[††]	*228*

[*] Camphane-2,3-dione; 3-oxocamphor.
[†] 2-Methyl-3-hydroxy-5-isopropenyl-2-cyclohexen-1-one.
[‡] 2-Methyl-3-ethyl-5-isopropenyl-2-cyclohexen-1-one.
[§] 2-Methyl-5-isopropenylcyclohexanone.
[¶] 2,3-Dimethyl-5-isopropenylcyclohexanol.
[‖] 2-Methyl-5-isopropyl-5-cyclohexen-1-one; 3-*p*-menthen-2-one.
[**] 1,2-Dimethyl-5-isopropyl-5-cyclohexen-1-one; 2-methyl-3-*p*-menthadien-2-ol.
[††] 1,2-Dimethyl-4-isopropyl-1,3-cyclohexadiene.

TABLE VI-XIX (Continued)

Ketone	RMgX	Product(s)	Ref.
$C_{10}H_{16}O$ (*cont.*)			
Pulegone*	CH_3MgI	$C_{11}H_{18}$	*116,228,280*
Pulegone*	CH_3MgI	*t*-Methylpulegol†	*117*
Pulegone*	$H_2C{=}CHCH_2Br$ + Mg	*t*-Allylpulegol (*ca.* 90%)	*147*
Pulegone* (100 g.)	*i*-$C_5H_{11}MgBr$ (150 g. $C_5H_{11}Br$)	Recovered ketone (75 g.); *t*-isomylpulegol (*ca.* 8 g.); 8-isoamylmenthone‡ (*ca.* 12 g.)	*92*
Isopulegone§	CH_3MgI	*t*-Methylisopulegol¶	*190*
3-Methyl-5-*n*-propyl-2-cyclohexen-1-one	$H_2C{=}CHCH_2Br$ + Mg	1-Allyl-3-methyl-5-*n*-propyl-2-cyclohexen-1-ol (97.1%)	*190*
3-Methyl-5-isopropyl-2-cyclohexen-1-one	$H_2C{=}CHCH_2Br$ + Mg	1-Allyl-3-methyl-5-isopropyl-2-cyclohexen-1-ol (91.2%)	*190*
trans-2-Decalone (120 g.)	$H_2C{=}CH(CH_2)_2MgBr$ (105 g. C_4H_7Br)	*trans*-2-(Δ^3-Butenyl)-2-decalol (25 g., purified)	*99*
trans-2-Decalone (15.0 g.)	$C_6H_5CH_2MgCl$ (12.5 g. C_7H_7Cl)	*trans*-2-Benzyl-2-decalol (16.0 g.)	*76*
trans-2-Decalone	3-CH_3-4-$CH_3OC_6H_3(CH_2)_2MgCl$	*trans*-2-(3-Methyl-4-methoxyphenethyl)-2-decalol	*78*
Fenchone‖	CH_3MgI	*t*-Methylfenchol**	*311,50*
Fenchone‖	$({\equiv}CMgBr)_2$	$[C_9H_{16}{=}C(OH)C{\equiv}]_2$ (20%)	*94*
Fenchone‖	C_2H_5MgI	*t*-Ethylfenchol; fenchyl alcohol	*171*
Fenchone‖	C_6H_5MgBr	*t*-Phenylfenchol (7%)	*306*
Fenchone‖	C_6H_5MgBr†† (4 equiv.)	*t*-Phenylfenchol (36%)	*328*

* 2-Isopropylidene-5-methylcyclohexanone; 4(8*H*)-*p*-menthen-3-one.
† 1,5-Dimethyl-2-isopropylidenecyclohexanol.
‡ 2-(2,5-Dimethyl-2-hexyl)-5-methylcyclohexanone.
§ 3-Methyl-6-isopropenylcyclohexanone.
¶ 1,3-Dimethyl-6-isopropenylcyclohexanol.
‖ 1,3,3-Trimethylbicyclo[2.2.1]heptan-2-one.
** 1,2,3,3-Tetramethylbicyclo[2.2.1]heptan-2-ol.
†† Reaction at 110–120° in Bu_2O.

TABLE VI-XIX (Continued)

Ketone	RMgX	Product(s)	Ref.
$C_{10}H_{16}O$ (*cont.*)			
Fenchone*	$C_6H_5CH_2MgCl$	*t*-Benzylfenchol (45%)	*306*
Fenchone*	$2\text{-}CH_3C_6H_4MgBr$	*t*-*o*-Tolylfenchol	*306*
Fenchone*	$4\text{-}CH_3C_6H_4MgBr$	*t*-*p*-Tolylfenchol	*306*
Isofenchone† (10.0 g.)	CH_3MgI (12.3 g. CH_3I)	*t*-Methylisofenchol‡ (5.0 g.)	*168*
Camphor§	CH_3MgI	*t*-Methylborneol¶	*311,49*
Camphor§	$(\equiv MgBr)_2$	$[C_9H_{16}{=}C(OH)C{\equiv}]_2$ (35.8%)	*94,144*
Camphor§	$H_2C{=}CHCH_2MgBr$	*t*-Allylborneol	*208*
Camphor§	$H_2C{=}CHCH_2Br$ + Mg	*t*-Allylborneol	*66,147*
Camphor§	*n*-C_3H_7MgBr	Borneol and isoborneol‖	*179*
Camphor§	C_6H_5MgBr	*t*-Phenylborneol	*49*
Camphor§	1-$C_{10}H_7MgBr$	*t*-α-Naphthylborneol	*49*
Camphor§	α-Camphoryl-MgBr	2-Hydroxy-2-(2-oxo-3-camphanyl)camphane	*185*
Camphor§	$(n\text{-}C_4H_9)_2N(CH_2)_3Cl$ + Mg	*t*-3-(Di-*n*-butylaminopropyl)borneol	*197*
Epicamphor** (20 g.)	CH_3MgI (25 g. CH_3I)	*t*-Methylepiborneol†† (30–40%)	*214*
cis-Bicyclo[5.3.0]decan-4-one (4.9 g.)	CH_3MgI	4-Methyl-*cis*-bicyclo[5.3.0]decan-4-ol (5.1 g., 94%)	*260*
cis-Bicyclo[5.3.0]decan-5-one (19.1 g.)	CH_3MgI (48.0 g. CH_3I)	5-Methyl-*cis*-bicyclo[5.3.0]decan-5-ol (87%)	*259*

* 1,3,3-Trimethylbicyclo[2.2.1]heptan-2-one.
† 1,3,3-Trimethylbicyclo[2.2.1]heptan-6-one.
‡ 1,3,3,6-Tetramethylbicyclo[2.2.1]heptan-6-ol.
§ 1,7,7-Trimethylbicyclo[2.2.1]heptan-2-one.
¶ 1,2,7,7-Tetramethylbicyclo[2.2.1]-heptan-2-ol.
‖ (−)- and (+)-1,7,7-Trimethylbicyclo[2.2.1]heptan-2-ol.
** 1,7,7-Trimethylbicyclo[2.2.1]heptan-3-one.
†† 1,3,7,7-Tetramethylbicyclo[2.2.1]heptan-3-ol.

TABLE VI-XIX (Continued)

Ketone	RMgX	Product(s)	Ref.
$C_{10}H_{16}O_2$			
2-Ketocineole[*]	CH_3MgI	2-Hydroxy-2-methylcineole[†] (2 isomers)	*327*
2-Ketocineole[*]	C_2H_5MgI	2-Hydroxy-2-ethylcineole (2 isomers)	*327*
2-Ketocineole[*]	C_6H_5MgBr	2-Hydroxy-2-phenylcineole (2 isomers)	*327*
Dimedone enol ethyl ether[‡] (84 g., 0.5 mole)	C_6H_5MgBr (1 mole C_6H_5Br)	3-Phenyl-5,5-dimethyl-2-cyclohexen-1-one (74 g., 74%)	*307*
$C_{10}H_{16}O_3$			
2-Carboxymethylcyclohexanone	C_6H_5MgBr	1-Phenyl-2-carboxymethylcyclohexanol	*62*
2-Methyl-2-carboxycyclohexanone	$C_6H_5(CH_2)_2MgBr$	1-Phenethyl-6-methyl-6-carboxycyclohexene (after dehydr'n)	*129*
$C_{10}H_{18}O$			
Tetrahydrocarvone[§] (38.5 g.)	$C_6H_5CH_2MgCl$ (40 g. C_7H_7Cl)	1-Benzyl-2-methyl-5-isopropylcyclohexanol (43 g.)	*76*
Tetrahydrocarvone[§] (31 g.)	1-$C_{10}H_7(CH_2)_2MgCl$ (47 g. $C_{12}H_{11}Cl$)	1-[β-(α-Naphthyl)ethyl]-2-methyl-5-isopropylcyclohexan-1-ol (10 g. crude)	*78*
Menthone[¶]	CH_3MgI	$C_{12}H_{20}$	*116*
Menthone[¶]	CH_3MgI	*t*-Methylmenthol[‖] (75.5%)	*295,312*
Menthone[¶]	$HC{\equiv}CMgBr$	*t*-Ethynylmenthol	*143*
Menthone	$H_2C{=}CHCH_2Br$ + Mg	*t*-Allylmenthol (*ca.* 90%)	*147*
(–)- or DL-Menthone	C_6H_5MgBr	*t*-Phenylmenthol	*205*

[*] 1,3,3-Trimethyl-2-oxabicyclo[2.2.2]octan-6-one.
[†] 1,3,3,6-Tetramethyl-2-oxabicyclo[2.2.2]octan-6-ol.
[‡] 3-Ethoxy-5,5-dimethyl-2-cyclohexen-1-one.
[§] 2-Methyl-5-isopropylcyclohexanone.
[¶] 2-Isopropyl-5-methylcyclohexanone.
[‖] 1,3-Dimethyl-6-isopropylcyclohexanol.

TABLE VI-XIX (Continued)

Ketone	RMgX	Product(s)	Ref.
$C_{10}H_{18}O$ (*cont.*)			
(−)- or DL-Menthone	$(CH_2)_5CHMgCl$	*t*-Cyclohexylmenthol	*205*
2,2,6,6-Tetramethylcyclohexanone (15 g.)	CH_3MgI (1 equiv.)	1,2,2,6,6-Pentamethylcyclohexanol (12 g.)	*79*
$C_{10}H_{18}O_2$			
"Dimethyldiethyltetrahydrofuran-2-one"	RMgX	Enolate (quant.)	*356*
$C_{10}H_{19}ON$			
1,2,2,6,6-Pentamethyl-4-piperidone (16.9 g.)	C_6H_5MgBr (24.0 g. C_6H_5Br)	1,2,2,6,6-Pentamethyl-4-hydroxy-4-phenylpiperidine	*15*
$C_{11}H_{10}O$			
1-Phenyl-1-cyclopenten-3-one (5 g.)	CH_3MgI (8.6 g. CH_3I)	1-Phenyl-3-methyl-1,3-cyclopentadiene (3.5 g.)	*45*
1-Phenyl-1-cyclopenten-3-one	C_2H_5MgBr	1-Phenyl-3-ethyl-1,3-cyclopentadiene	*45*
1-Phenyl-1-cyclopenten-3-one	C_6H_5MgBr	1,3-Diphenyl-1,3-cyclopentadiene	*45*
2-Methyl-1-indenone (2.2 g.)	CH_3MgI (4.2 g. CH_3I)	1,2-Dimethyl-1-indenol	*289*
$C_{11}H_{10}O_2$			
2,2-Dimethyl-1,3-indandione (2.0 g.)	C_6H_5MgBr (1.8 g. C_6H_5Br)	2,2-Dimethyl-3-hydroxy-3-phenyl-1-indanone (20%)	*300*
2,2-Dimethyl-1,3-indandione (4 g.)	C_6H_5MgBr (1 equiv.)	2,2-Dimethyl-3-hydroxy-3-phenyl-1-indanone; 1,3-diphenyl-2,2-dimethyl-1,3-indandiol*	*108*
2,2-Dimethyl-1,3-indandione (4 g.)	C_6H_5MgBr (3 equiv.)	1,3-Diphenyl-2,2-dimethyl-1,3-indandiol (6.5 g., 86%)†	*108*

* Addition of Grignard reagent solution to Et_2O-ketone solution; two hours standing.
† Gradual (fifteen minutes) addition of Grignard reagent solution to C_6H_6-ketone solution; three hours standing.

TABLE VI-XIX (Continued)

Ketone	RMgX	Product(s)	Ref.
$C_{11}H_{10}O_2$ *(cont.)*			
2,2-Dimethyl-1,3-indandione (20 g., 0.11 mole)	C_6H_5MgBr (0.03 mole)	2,2-Dimethyl-3-hydroxy-3-phenyl-1-indanone (5.7 g., 75%); recovered ketone (13 g.)*	*108*
2,2-Dimethyl-1,3-indandione (8 g.)	C_6H_5MgBr (0.025 mole)	1,3-Diphenyl-2,2-dimethyl-1,3-indandiol (79%)†	*108*
$C_{11}H_{12}O$			
3,3-Dimethyl-1-indanone (10.0 g.)	C_6H_5MgBr (14.4 ml. C_6H_5Br)	1-Phenyl-3,3-dimethyl-1-indanol (9.5 g.)	*33*
2-Methyl-α-tetralone‡ (2.9 g.)	C_2H_5MgBr (1.9 g. C_2H_5Br)	1-Ethyl-2-methyl-3,4-dihydronaphthalene (1.5 g.)	*51*
5-Methyl-α-tetralone§ (1.0 g.)	*n*-C_3H_7MgI (3.3 g. C_3H_7I)	1-*n*-Propyl-5-methyl-1,2,3,4-tetrahydro-1-naphthol (1.3 g.)	*126*
5-Methyl-α-tetralone§	β-(5-Methyl-1,2,3,4-tetrahydro-1-naphthyl)ethyl-MgBr	α-(5-Methyl-1,2,3,4-tetrahydro-1-naphthyl)-β-(5-methyl-3,4-dihydronaphthyl)ethane	*234*
7-Methyl-α-tetralone¶	CH_3MgX	1,7-Dimethyl-1,2,3,4-tetrahydro-1-naphthol (*ca.* 70%)	*20*
7-Methyl-α-tetralone¶ (7 g.)	C_2H_5MgBr (6 g. C_2H_5Br)	1-Ethyl-7-methyl-3,4-dihydronaphthalene (6 g.)	*51*
7-Methyl-α-tetralone¶	*i*-C_3H_7MgX	1-Isopropyl-7-methyl-1,2,3,4-tetrahydro-1-naphthol (*ca.* 70%)	*20*
6-Methyl-β-tetralone‖ (2.0 g.)	CH_3MgI (5.4 g. CH_3I)	2,6-Dimethyl-1,2,3,4-tetrahydro-2-naphthol (1.5 g.)	*224,225*

* Slow (two to three hours) dropwise addition of Grignard reagent solution to cooled C_6H_6-ketone solution; overnight standing.

† Addition of Grignard reagent solution to C_6H_6-ketone solution; partial distillation of Et_2O; sixteen hours at 80°; addition of excess Grignard reagent.

‡ 2-Methyl-3,4-dihydro-1(2*H*)-naphthalenone.

§ 5-Methyl-3,4-dihydro-1(2*H*)-naphthalenone.

¶ 7-Methyl-3,4-dihydro-1(2*H*)-naphthalenone.

‖ 6-Methyl-3,4-dihydro-2(1*H*)-naphthalenone.

TABLE VI-XIX (Continued)

Ketone	RMgX	Product(s)	Ref.
$C_{11}H_{12}O_2$			
6-Methoxy-α-tetralone*	$H_5C_2O_2CCH_2CH_2X$† (1 equiv.) + Mg (1 equiv.)	β-(6-Methoxy-3,4-dihydro-1-naphthyl)propionic acid	*121*
7-Methoxy-α-tetralone‡	CH_3MgI	1-Methyl-7-methoxy-1,2,3,4-tetrahydro-1-naphthol§	*131*
7-Methoxy-α-tetralone‡ (27.0 g.)	CH_3MgI (22.0 ml. CH_3I)	1-Methyl-7-methoxy-3,4-dihydronaphthalene (21.5 g.)	*202*
$C_{11}H_{16}O$			
4a-Methyl-4,4a,5,6,7,8-hexahydro-2(3*H*)-naphthalenone (2.4 g.) + CuBr (0.05 g.)	CH_3MgI (3.0 g. CH_3I)	4a,8a-Dimethyl-2-decalone (120 mg.)	*330*
cis-8a-Methyl-1-decalone	$C_2H_5O(CH_2)_3MgBr$	1-γ-Ethoxypropyl-8a-methyl-1-decalol	*17*
$C_{11}H_{18}O$			
3-Methyl-5-isobutyl-2-cyclohexen-1-one	$H_2C{=}CHCH_2Br$ + Mg	1-Allyl-3-methyl-5-isobutyl-2-cyclohexen-1-ol (98%)	*190*
$C_{11}H_{18}O_3$			
2,6-Dimethyl-2-carbethoxycyclohexanone	$C_6H_5(CH_2)_2MgBr$	After dehydr'n, 1-Phenethyl-2,6-dimethyl-6-carbethoxycyclohexene	*129*
2,6-Dimethyl-2-carbethoxycyclohexanone	$4\text{-}CH_3OC_6H_4(CH_2)_2MgCl$	1-*p*-Methoxyphenethyl-2,6-dimethyl-2-carbethoxycyclohexanol; 1-*p*-methoxyphenethyl-2,6-dimethyl-6-carbethoxycyclohexene	*37*

* 6-Methoxy-3,4-dihydro-1(2*H*)-naphthalenone.
† X = Cl, Br.
‡ 7-Methoxy-3,4-dihydro-1(2*H*)-naphthalenone.
§ Isolated, after dehydration and dehydrogenation, as 1-methyl-7-methoxynaphthalene (22.5 g. from 26.0 g. ketone).

TABLE VI-XIX (Continued)

Ketone	RMgX	Product(s)	Ref.
$C_{11}H_{18}O_3$ (*cont.*)			
2,6-Dimethyl-2-carbethoxycyclohexanone	3-*i*-$C_3H_7C_6H_4(CH_2)_2MgBr$	After dehydr'n, 1-*m*-Isopropylphenethyl-2,6-dimethyl-6-carbethoxycyclohexene	*129*
$C_{11}H_{19}O_3N$			
2-Dimethylaminomethyl-3-acetoxycyclohexanone	2-(1-Decalylidene)ethyl-MgBr	1-(2-α-Decalylidenethyl)-2-dimethylaminomethyl-3-acetoxycyclohexanol	*91*
2-Dimethylaminomethyl-5-acetoxycyclohexanone	2-(1-Decalylidene)ethyl-MgBr	1-(2-α-Decalylidenethyl)-2-dimethylaminomethyl-5-acetoxycyclohexanol	*91*
$C_{12}H_{12}O$			
3-Phenyl-2-cyclohexen-1-one (10.0 g.)	C_6H_5MgBr (18.3 g. C_6H_5Br)	1,3-Diphenyl-1,3-cyclohexadiene (14.0 g., crude)	*310*
$C_{12}H_{14}O$			
2-Phenylcyclohexanone (118 g.)	C_2H_5MgBr (78 g. C_2H_5Br)	1-Ethyl-2-phenylcyclohexanol (117.4 g., 85%); gas (1.3 1.)	*215*
2-Ethyl-α-tetralone* (3.0 g.)	CH_3MgI (2.9 g. CH_3I)	1-Methyl-2-ethyl-3,4-dihydronaphthalene (2.4 g.)	*51*
2-Ethyl-α-tetralone* (78.8 g.)	C_2H_5MgBr (98.0 g. C_2H_5Br)	1,2-Diethyl-1,2,3,4-tetrahydronaphthol (90.5 g., 98%)	*158*
2,5-Dimethyl-α-tetralone†	C_2H_5MgI (10 equiv.)	1-Ethyl-2,5-dimethyl-1,2,3,4-tetrahydro-1-naphthol; dehydr'n product	*232*

* 2-Ethyl-3,4-dihydro-1(2*H*)-naphthalenone.
† 2,5-Dimethyl-3,4-dihydro-1(2*H*)-naphthalenone.

TABLE VI-XIX (Continued)

Ketone	RMgX	Product(s)	Ref.
$C_{12}H_{14}O$ (*cont.*)			
2,7-Dimethyl-α-tetralone*	C_2H_5MgI (10 equiv.)	1-Ethyl-2,7-dimethyl-1,2,3,4-tetrahydro-1-naphthol; dehydr'n product	232
5,6-Dimethyl-α-tetralone†	2-(5-Methyl-1,2,3,4-tetrahydro-1-naphthyl)ethyl-MgBr	1-(5-Methyl-1,2,3,4-tetrahydro-1-naphthyl)-2-(5,6-dimethyl-3,4-dihydro-1-naphthyl)ethane	234
5,6-Dimethyl-α-tetralone†	2-(7-Methyl-1,2,3,4-tetrahydro-1-naphthyl)ethyl-MgBr	1-(7-Methyl-1,2,3,4-tetrahydro-1-naphthyl)-2-(5,6-dimethyl-3,4-dihydro-1-naphthyl)ethane	234
5,6-Dimethyl-α-tetralone†	2-(5,6-Dimethyl-1,2,3,4-tetrahydro-1-naphthyl)ethyl-MgBr	1-(5,6-Dimethyl-1,2,3,4-tetrahydro-1-naphthyl)-2-(5,6-dimethyl-3,4-dihydro-1-naphthyl)ethane	234
6,7-Dimethyl-α-tetralone‡	CH_3MgX	1,6,7-Trimethyl-1,2,3,4-tetrahydro-1-naphthol (*ca.* 70%)	20
$C_{12}H_{14}O_2$			
2-Methyl-6-furfurylidenecyclohexanone	C_6H_5MgBr	1-Methyl-6-(phenyl-α-furylmethyl)-cyclohexanone	305
2-Methyl-6-furfurylidenecyclohexanone	$C_6H_5CH_2MgCl$	1-Methyl-6-[1-(α-furyl)-2-phenylethyl]cyclohexanone	305
2-Methyl-6-furfurylidenecyclohexanone	$4-CH_3C_6H_4MgBr$	1-Methyl-6-(phenyl-*p*-tolylmethyl)cyclohexanone	305
2-Methyl-7-methoxy-α-tetralone§ (10.0 g.)	CH_3MgI (4.5 ml. CH_3I)	1,2-Dimethyl-7-methoxy-1,2,3,4-tetrahydro-1-naphthol + 1,2-dimethyl-7-methoxy-3,4-dihydronaphthalene (totaling 8.0 g.)	203

* 2,7-Dimethyl-3,4-dihydro-1(2*H*)-naphthalenone.
† 5,6-Dimethyl-3,4-dihydro-1(2*H*)-naphthalenone.
‡ 6,7-Dimethyl-3,4-dihydro-1(2*H*)-naphthalenone.
§ 2-Methyl-7-methoxy-3,4-dihydro-1(2*H*)-naphthalenone.

TABLE VI-XIX (Continued)

Ketone	RMgX	Product(s)	Ref.
$C_{12}H_{15}ON$			
2-(α-Piperidylmethyl)cyclohexanone	$3\text{-}CH_3OC_6H_4MgBr$	1-(*m*-Methoxyphenyl)-2-(α-piperidylmethyl)cyclohexanol (30%)	*175*
$C_{12}H_{18}O$			
2-Ethylcarvone*	C_2H_5MgBr	2,6-Diethylmenthatriene†	*268*
$\Delta^{1(7)}$-Bicyclo[5.5.0]dodecen-2-one (5.0 g.)	CH_3MgI (11.8 g. CH_3I)	2-Methylbicyclo[5.5.0]dedecadiene (probably $\Delta^{2,12(1)}$) (3.0 g. 60%)	*52*
$C_{12}H_{20}O$			
2,8-Dimethylbicyclo[5.3.0]decan-5-one (2.7 g.)	CH_3MgI (4.0 CH_3I)	2,5,8-Trimethylbicyclo[5.3.0]decan-5-ol	*220*
2,8-Dimethylbicyclo[5.3.0]decan-5-one (1.0 g.)	*i*-C_3H_7MgBr (1.4 g. C_3H_7Br)	"Dihydroguaiaene"	*220*
$C_{13}H_7OBr$			
2-Bromo-9-fluorenone (12.9 g.)	2-*p*-$CH_3C_6H_4OC_6H_4MgI$ (15.5 g. $C_{13}H_{11}IO$)	2-Bromo-9-*o*-toloxyphenyl-9-fluorenol (14.0 g.)	*71*
$C_{13}H_7O_2Br$			
3-Bromoxanthone	C_6H_5MgBr (3 equiv.)	3-Bromo-9-phenylxanthhydrol	*112*
$C_{13}H_7O_2Cl$			
3-Chloroxanthone	C_6H_5MgBr (3 equiv.)	3-Chloro-9-phenylxanthhydrol (80%)	*112*

* 2-Methyl-3-ethyl-5-isopropenyl-2-cyclohexen-1-one.

† 1,3-Diethyl-2-methyl-5-isopropenyl-1,3-cyclohexadiene.

TABLE VI-XIX (Continued)

Ketone	RMgX	Product(s)	Ref.
$C_{13}H_8O$			
9-Fluorenone (5.2 g.)	CH_3MgI (8.5 g. CH_3I)	9-Methyl-9-fluorenol (5.5 g., crude)	*273,14,215*
9-Fluorenone (20 g.)	$(\equiv CMgBr)_2$	1,4-Dibiphenylene-2-butyne-1,4-diol (6 g.)	*29*
9-Fluorenone	C_2H_5MgI	9-Ethyl-9-fluorenol (72.7%)	*273*
9-Fluorenone	2-Thienyl-MgI	9-α-Thienyl-9-fluorenol	*200*
9-Fluorenone (100 g.)	C_6H_5MgBr	9-Phenyl-9-fluorenol (140 g.)	*10,173,272*
9-Fluorenone	$C_6H_5CH_2MgCl$	9-Benzyl-9-fluorenol (76%)	*273,173*
9-Fluorenone (5.4 g.)	2-$C_6H_5OC_6H_4MgI$ (8.9 g. $C_{12}H_9IO$)	9-*o*-Phenoxyphenyl-9-fluorenol (5.7 g.)	*71*
9-Fluorenone (9 g.)	2-$C_6H_5CH_2C_6H_4MgBr$ (1.2 g. Mg)	9-*o*-Benzylphenyl-9-fluorenol (10.4 g.)	*71*
9-Fluorenone (1.35 g.)	9-Anthryl-MgBr (0.257 g. $C_{14}H_9Br$)	9-(9-Anthryl)-9-fluorenol (1.09 g., 30%)	*12*
9-Fluorenone	9-Phenanthryl-MgBr	9-(9-Phenanthryl)-9-fluorenol (60%)	*11*
9-Fluorenone	$(C_6H_5)_2C{=}CHMgBr$	9-(β,β-Diphenylvinyl)-9-fluorenol	*160*
9-Fluorenone	2-$[(C_6H_5)_2CH]C_6H_4MgBr$	9-*o*-Benzhydrylphenyl-9-fluorenol (51%)	*171*
9-Fluorenone (35 g.)	1-Phenyl-2-biphenylenevinyl-MgBr (70 g. $C_{20}H_{13}Br$)	9-(α-Phenyl-β-biphenylenevinyl)-9-fluorenol (38.5 g.)	*159*
9-Fluorenone (2 g.)	$(C_6H_5)_2C{=}(C_6H_5)CMgBr$ (5 g. $C_{20}H_{15}Br$)	9-(α,β,β-Triphenylvinyl)-9-fluorenol	*325*
$C_{13}H_8OS$			
Thioxanthone	CH_3MgI	Product isolated as double salt; 9-Methylthioxanthylium chloride-mercuric chloride	*82*
Thioxanthone	C_6H_5MgBr	9-Phenyl-9-thioxanthenol	*53*
Thioxanthone	$C_6H_5CH_2MgCl$ (2 equiv.)	9-Benzyl-9-thioxanthenol; 9-Benzylidenethioxanthene	*82*
$C_{13}H_8O_2$			
Xanthone	CH_3MgI	9-Methyl-9-xanthenol	*82*
Xanthone	2-Thienyl-MgI	9-α-Thienyl-9-xanthenol	*200*
Xanthone	4-BrC_6H_4MgBr	9-*p*-Bromophenyl-9-xanthenol (50–60%)	*112,177*

TABLE VI-XIX (Continued)

Ketone	RMgX	Product(s)	Ref.
$C_{13}H_8O_2$ (*cont.*)			
Xanthone	$4\text{-}ClC_6H_4MgI$	9-*p*-Chlorophenyl-9-xanthenol	*112,177*
Xanthone	C_6H_5MgBr	9-Phenyl-9-xanthenol (93%)	*53,112,173, 270*
Xanthone (5.0 g.)	C_6H_5MgBr (15.0 g. C_6H_5Br)	9,9-Diphenylxanthene (0.5 g.)	*252*
Xanthone	$C_6H_5CH_2MgCl$	9-Benzyl-9-xanthenol; 9-benzylidene-xanthene	*82*
Xanthone	$2\text{-}CH_3C_6H_4MgBr$	9-*o*-Tolyl-9-xanthenol; unidentified byproduct	*83,41*
Xanthone	$2\text{-}CH_3C_6H_4MgBr$	9,9-Di-*o*-tolylxanthene	*252*
Xanthone	$4\text{-}CH_3C_6H_4MgBr$	9-*p*-Tolyl-9-xanthenol (70%)	*173,112*
Xanthone	$4\text{-}CH_3OC_6H_4MgBr$	9-Anisyl-9-xanthenol (72%)	*173*
Xanthone	$C_6H_5CH{=}CHMgBr$ (+ $HClO_4$)	9-Styryl-9-xanthenyl perchlorate (56%)	*321*
Xanthone	$C_6H_5CH{=}CHMgBr$	9-Styryl-9-xanthenol (isolated as corresponding chloride, 60%)	*321*
Xanthone	$2\text{-}C_2H_5OCH_2C_6H_4MgBr$	9-(α-Ethoxy-*o*-tolyl)-9-xanthenol	*41*
Xanthone	$1\text{-}C_{10}H_7MgBr$	9-α-Naphthyl-9-xanthenol (76%)	*173*
Xanthone (4.9 g.)	$2\text{-}C_6H_5C_6H_4MgI$ (7.0 g. $C_{12}H_9I$)	9-*o*-Biphenylyl-9-xanthenol (4.3 g.)	*71*
Xanthone (4.9 g.)	$2\text{-}C_6H_5OC_6H_4MgI$ (7.4 g. $C_{12}H_9IO$)	9-*o*-Phenoxyphenyl-9-xanthenol (6.3 g.)	*71*
Xanthone (4.9 g.)	$2\text{-}C_6H_5CH_2C_6H_4MgBr$ (6.2 g. $C_{13}H_{11}Br$)	9-*o*-Benzylphenyl-9-xanthenol (6.9 g.)	*71*
Xanthone	$(C_6H_5)_2C{=}CHMgBr$	9-(β,β-Diphenylvinyl)-9-xanthenol	*320*
Xanthone	$2\text{-}[(C_6H_5)_2CH]C_6H_4MgBr$	9-*o*-Benzhydrylphenyl-9-xanthenol	*71*
$C_{13}H_8O_4$			
Euxanthone* (3 g.)	CH_3MgI (14 g. CH_3I)	1,7,9-Trihydroxy-9-methylxanthene	*317*
Euxanthone* (4 g.)	C_6H_5MgBr (20 g. C_6H_5Br)	1,7,9-Trihydroxy-9-phenylxanthene (4 g.)	*317*
1,8-Dihydroxyxanthone (3 g.)	C_6H_5MgBr (10 g. C_6H_5Br)	1,8,9-Trihydroxy-9-phenylxanthene	*16*

* 1,7-Dihydroxyxanthone.

TABLE VI-XIX (Continued)

Ketone	RMgX	Product(s)	Ref.
$C_{13}H_9ON$			
9(10*H*)-Acridone (18.0 g., 0.092 mole)	CH_3MgI* (0.3 mole)	9-Methylacridine (6.0 g., 44%); 9,9-dimethylacridan (2.5 g., 17%); recovered ketone (4.0 g.)	*348*
9(10*H*)-Acridone (13 g. 0.067 mole)	*n*-C_4H_9MgBr (0.4 mole)	9,9-Di-*n*-butylacridan (4 g., 24%)	*348*
9(10*H*)-Acridone (9.8 g.)	C_6H_5MgBr (2.5 equiv.)	Recovered ketone (7.2 g.); 9-phenylacridine (2.6 g., 19%)	*178*
$C_{13}H_{14}O$			
2,4,6-Trimethyl-1(2*H*)-naphthalenone	*i*-C_3H_7MgBr	1-Isopropyl-2,4,6-trimethyl-1,2-dihydronaphthol	*85*
$C_{13}H_{14}O_2$			
2-*p*-Toluylcyclopentanone	C_2H_5MgBr	2-(α-*p*-Tolylpropylidene)cyclopentanone; 1-ethyl-2-*p*-toluylcyclopentene	*113*
$C_{13}H_{16}O$			
7-Isopropyl-α-tetralone †	CH_3MgX	1-Methyl-7-isopropyl-1,2,3,4-tetrahydro-1-naphthol (*ca.* 70%)	*20*
4-Ethyl-7-methyl-α-tetralone ‡ (9 g.)	*i*-C_3H_7MgBr (8 ml. C_3H_7Br)	1-Isopropyl-4-ethyl-7-methyl-1,2,3,4-tetrahydro-1-naphthol (10 g., crude)	*87*
2,4,7-Trimethyl-α-tetralone § (15.0 g.)	*i*-C_3H_7MgBr (15.6 g. C_3H_7Br)	1-Isopropyl-2,4,7-trimethyl-1,2,3,4-tetrahydro-1-naphthol (yielding 13.0 g., 76% hydrocarbon)	*86*

* In Bu_2O solution.
† 7-Isopropyl-3,4-dihydro-1(2*H*)-naphthalenone.
‡ 4-Ethyl-7-methyl-3,4-dihydro-1(2*H*)-naphthalenone.
§ 2,4,7-Trimethyl-3,4-dihydro-1(2*H*)-naphthalenone.

TABLE VI-XIX (Continued)

Ketone	RMgX	Product(s)	Ref.
$C_{13}H_{16}O$ (*cont.*)			
2,5,6-Trimethyl-α-tetralone*	CH_3MgI	1,2,5,6-Tetramethyl-1,2,3,4-tetrahydro-1-naphthol	*232*
2,5,7-Trimethyl-α-tetralone†	CH_3MgI (10 equiv.)	1,2,5,7-Tetramethyl-1,2,3,4-tetrahydro-1-naphthol; dehydr'n product	*232*
3,4,5-Trimethyl-α-tetralone‡	CH_3MgI (2 equiv.)	1,3,4,5-Tetramethyl-1,2,3,4-tetrahydro-1-naphthol; dehydr'n product	*232*
4,5,7-Trimethyl-α-tetralone§ (10 g.)	*i*-C_3H_7MgBr	1-Isopropyl-4,5,7-trimethyl-1,2,3,4-tetrahydro-1-naphthol (11 g., crude)	*86,85*
$C_{13}H_{20}O$			
Decahydro-1-benz[*e*]-inden-4(2*H*)-one (4.5 g.)	CH_3MgI (8.0 g. CH_3I)	4-Methyldodecahydro-1-benz[*e*]inden-4-ol (4.0 g.)	*223*
$C_{14}H_{10}O$			
Anthrone¶	CH_3MgX (3 equiv.)	9-Methylanthracene	*254,69,174*
Anthrone¶	C_2H_5MgBr	9-Ethyl-9,10-dihydro-9-anthrol	*254,174*
Anthrone¶	*n*-C_4H_9MgBr	9-*n*-Butylanthracene (43%)	*247*
Anthrone¶	*i*-$C_5H_{11}MgBr$	9-Isoamyl-9,10-dihydro-9-anthrol	*254,174*
Anthrone¶	C_6H_5MgBr	9-Phenyl-9,10-dihydro-9-anthrol	*254*
Anthrone¶	C_6H_5MgBr (3 equiv.)	9-Phenylanthracene (50%)	*93*
Anthrone¶	$(CH_2)_5CHMgCl$	9-Cyclohexylanthracene	*302*
Anthrone¶ (368 g., 2 moles)	*n*-$C_{12}H_{25}MgBr$ (1668 g., 6.7 moles $C_{12}H_{25}Br$)	9-*n*-Dodecylanthracene (375 g., 49.5%)	*247*

* 2,5,6-Trimethyl-3,4-dihydro-1(2*H*)-naphthalenone.
† 2,5,7-Trimethyl-3,4-dihydro-1(2*H*)-naphthalenone.
‡ 3,4,5-Trimethyl-3,4-dihydro-1(2*H*)-naphthalenone.
§ 4,5,7-Trimethyl-3,4-dihydro-1(2*H*)-naphthalenone.
¶ 9(10*H*)-Anthracenone.

TABLE VI-XIX (Continued)

Ketone	RMgX	Product(s)	Ref.
$C_{14}H_{10}O_3$			
2-Methoxyxanthone	C_6H_5MgBr	2-Methoxy-9-phenyl-9-xanthenol	*16*
2-Methoxyxanthone	C_6H_5MgBr	Product isolated as double salt; 2-methoxy-9-phenylxanthylium chloride-ferric chloride	*83*
3-Methoxyxanthone	C_6H_5MgBr	Product isolated as isomer of double salt described above	*83*
3-Methoxyxanthone	C_6H_5MgBr	3-Methoxy-9-phenyl-9-xanthenol	*16*
4-Methoxyxanthone	C_6H_5MgBr	4-Methoxy-9-phenyl-9-xanthenol	*16*
$C_{14}H_{10}O_4$			
1-Hydroxy-7-methoxyxanthone	C_6H_5MgBr	9-(1-Hydroxy-7-methoxy-9-phenyl-xanthenyl)ether	*317*
1-Methoxy-7-hydroxyxanthone	C_6H_5MgBr	1-Methoxy-7,9-dihydroxy-9-phenylxanthene	*318*
$C_{14}H_{12}O$			
3,4-Dihydro-1(2*H*)-phenanthrone (4 g.)	CH_3MgI (3 g. CH_3I)	$C_{15}H_{14}$ (dehydration products of 1-methyl-1,2,3,4-tetrahydro-1-phenanthrol) (4 g.)	*128*
2,3-Dihydro-4(1*H*)-phenanthrone	CH_3MgI	4-Methyl-1,2,3,4-tetrahydro-4-phenanthrol	*128*
2,3-Dihydro-4(1*H*)-phenanthrone	C_6H_5MgBr	1,2,3,4-Tetrahydro-4-phenanthrol	*75*
2,3-Dihydro-4(1*H*)-phenanthrone (6.5 g.)	$(CH_2)_5CHMgCl$ (5.9 g. C_7H_7Cl)	1,2,3,4-Tetrahydro-4-phenanthrol (2.2 g.)	*75*
2,3-Dihydro-4(1*H*)-phenanthrone	$C_6H_5(CH_2)_2MgBr$	After dehydr'n, 4-phenethyl-1,2-dihydrophenanthrene	*25*
$C_{14}H_{16}O$			
2-Methyl-2-carbomethoxy-6-methoxy-α-tetralone* (10.3 g.)	C_2H_5MgBr (0.00125 mole)	1-Ethyl-2-methyl-2-carbomethoxy-6-methoxy-1,2,3,4-tetrahydro-1-naphthol (9.8 g., 87%)	*137*

* 2-Methyl-2-carbomethoxy-6-methoxy-3,4-dihydro-1(2*H*)-naphthalenone.

TABLE VI-XIX (Continued)

Ketone	RMgX	Product(s)	Ref.
$C_{14}H_{16}O$ (*cont.*)			
2-Methyl-2-carbomethoxy-7-methoxy-α-tetralone* (10.3 g.)	C_2H_5MgBr (0.00125 mole)	1-Ethyl-2-methyl-2-carbomethoxy-7-methoxy-1,2,3,4-tetrahydro-1-naphthol (9.5 g., 82%)	*137*
3-Phenyl-5,5-dimethyl-2-cyclohexen-1-one (20 g., 0.1 mole)	C_6H_5MgBr (0.5 mole C_6H_5Br)	1,3-Diphenyl-5,5-dimethyl-1,3-cyclohexadiene (14 g., 54%)	*307*
$C_{14}H_{16}O_2$			
2-*p*-Xyloylcyclopentanone	C_2H_5MgBr	1-Ethyl-2-*p*-xyloylcyclopentene	*113*
$C_{14}H_{18}O$			
2,4,6,7-Tetramethyl-α-tetralone †	*i*-C_3H_7MgCl	1-Isopropyl-2,4,6,7-tetramethyl-1-tetralol	*58*
3,4,5,7-Tetramethyl-α-tetralone ‡	CH_3MgI (excess)	1,3,4,5,7-Pentamethyl-3,4-dihydronaphthalene	*232*
3,4,5,8-Tetramethyl-α-tetralone §	CH_3MgI (excess)	1,3,4,5,8-Pentamethyl-3,4-dihydronaphthalene	*232*
3,4,6,7-Tetramethyl-α-tetralone ¶	*i*-C_3H_7MgCl	1-Isopropyl-3,4,6,7-tetramethyl-1-tetralol	*58*
$C_{14}H_{20}O_6$			
2,4-Diethyl-2,4-dicarbethoxy-1,3-cyclobutanedione (25 g.)	C_6H_5MgBr (1 equiv.)	Recovered ketone; $C_2H_5(H_5C_2O_2C)C{=}CO$; ‖ 1,3-diphenyl-2,4-diethyl-2,4-dicarbethoxy-1,3-cyclobutanediol (15 g., crude); $C_2H_5(C_6H_5CO)CHCO_2C_2H_5$ (15 g., crude)	*138*

* 2-Methyl-2-carbomethoxy-7-methoxy-3,4-dihydro-1(2*H*)-naphthalenone.
† 2,4,6,7-Tetramethyl-3,4-dihydro-1(2*H*)-naphthalenone.
‡ 3,4,5,7-Tetramethyl-3,4-dihydro-1(2*H*)-naphthalenone.
§ 3,4,5,8-Tetramethyl-3,4-dihydro-1(2*H*)-naphthalenone.
¶ 3,4,6,7-Tetramethyl-3,4-dihydro-1(2*H*)-naphthalenone.
‖ The cyclic diketone is a ketene dimer which, on distillation, is converted in part into the monomer.

TABLE VI-XIX (Continued)

Ketone	RMgX	Product(s)	Ref.
$C_{15}H_9OBr$			
2-Bromo-3-phenylindenone (2.0 g.)	C_6H_5MgBr (2.4 g. C_6H_5Br)	1,3-Diphenyl-2-bromo-1-indenol (isolated as the acetate)	*300*
$C_{15}H_{10}O_3$			
1-Methoxyxanthone	$C_6H_5CH{=}CHMgBr$ (+ $HClO_4$)	1-Methoxy-9-styryl-9-xanthenyl perchlorate	*321*
$C_{15}H_{12}O$			
3-Phenyl-1-indanone	$H_2C{=}CH(CH_2)_3MgBr$	1-(4-Pentenyl)-3-phenyl-1-indanol	*187*
1-Oxo-4,5-methylene-1,2,3,4-tetrahydrophenanthrene* (0.5 g.)	CH_3MgI	1-Methyl-4,5-methylene-1,2,3,4-tetrahydrophenanthren-1-ol† (>0.45 g.)‡	*13*
1-Oxo-4,5-methylene-1,2,3,4-tetrahydrophenanthrene*	C_2H_5MgBr	1-Ethyl-4,5-methylene-1,2,3,4-tetrahydrophenanthren-1-ol§ (>77%)‡	*13*
$C_{15}H_{12}O_2$			
2-Methoxyanthrone¶ (9.4 g.)	$4\text{-}CH_3OC_6H_4MgI$ (23.4 g. C_7H_7IO)	2-Methoxy-9-anisylanthracene (5.2 g.)	*42*
10-Methoxyanthrone‖	$C_6H_5CH_2MgCl$ (3 equiv.)	Anthraquinone; 9,9′-dioxo-10,10′-dimethoxy-10,10′-bis-(9,10-dihydroanthracyl); 9-benzyl-10-methoxy-9,10-dihydro-9-anthrol	*18*
7-Ethoxy-*peri*-naphthindenone-9**	C_6H_5MgBr (2 equiv.)	3-Ethoxy-9-phenyl-9,9a-dihydrobenzonaphthenone	*163*

* 3,3a-Dihydro-4-cyclopenta[*def*]phenanthren-1(2*H*)-one.
† 1-Methyl-1,2,3,3a-tetrahydro-4-cyclopenta[*def*]phenanthren-1-ol.
‡ The figure reported represents the yield of hydrocarbon after dehydration and dehydrogenation of the alcohol.
§ 1-Ethyl-1,2,3,3a-tetrahydro-4-cyclopenta[*def*]phenanthren-1-ol.
¶ 2-Methoxy-9(10*H*)-anthracenone.
‖ 10-Methoxy-9(10*H*)-anthracenone.
** 3-Ethoxybenzonaphthenone.

TABLE VI-XIX (Continued)

Ketone	RMgX	Product(s)	Ref.
$C_{15}H_{12}O_2$ (*cont.*)			
8,8-Dimethyl-*peri*-naphthindandione-7,9 (3.3 g.)*	C_6H_5MgBr (1 equiv.)	Recovered ketone (1.5 g.); 2,2-dimethyl-3-hydroxy-3-phenyl-2,3-dihydro-1-benzonaphthenone (1.3 g.)	*107*
8,8-Dimethyl-*peri*-naphthindandione-7,9*	C_6H_5MgBr (3 equiv.)	1,3-Diphenyl-2,2-dimethyl-2,3-dihydrobenzonaphthene-1,3-diol[†]	*107*
8,8-Dimethyl-*peri*-naphthindandione-7,9*	C_6H_5MgBr (3 equiv.)	1,3-Diphenyl-2,2-dimethyl-2,3-dihydrobenzonaphthene-1,3-diol (small am't); 2,2-dimethyl-3-hydroxy-3,9-diphenyl-2,3-dihydro-1-benzonaphthenone[‡]	*107*
Flavanone[§] (10 g.)	C_6H_5MgBr (22 g. C_6H_5Br)	2,4-Diphenyl-4-chromanol (10 g.)	*181*
2,7-Dimethylxanthone (6.0 g.)	C_6H_5MgBr (10.0 g. C_6H_5Br)	2,7-Dimethyl-9-phenyl-9-xanthenol (6.2 g.)	*221*
$C_{15}H_{12}O_4$			
2,2-Dimethoxyxanthone	C_6H_5MgBr	2,2-Dimethoxy-9-phenyl-9-xanthenol	*16*
$C_{15}H_{14}O$			
5-Methyl-3,4-dihydro-1(2*H*)-anthracenone	CH_3MgI	1,5-Dimethyl-1,2,3,4-tetrahydro-1-anthracenol[¶]	*131*
9-Methyl-3,4-dihydro-1(2*H*)-phenanthrene	CH_3MgI	1,9-Dimethyl-1,2,3,4-tetrahydro-1-phenanthrol (>50%)[‖]	*130*

* 2,2-Dimethyl-1,3(2*H*)-benzonaphthenedione.

[†] Addition of Grignard reagent solution to ice-cooled C_6H_6-ketone solution; three hours standing; four hours at room temperature.

[‡] Slow (two hours) addition of Grignard reagent solution to boiling C_6H_6-ketone solution.

[§] 2-Phenylchromanone.

[¶] Isolated, after dehydration and dehydrogenation, as 1,5-dimethylanthracene.

[‖] The figure reported represents the yield of hydrocarbon after dehydration and dehydrogenation of the alcohol.

TABLE VI-XIX (Continued)

Ketone	RMgX	Product(s)	Ref.
$C_{15}H_{16}O$			
2-Cyclopentadecen-1-one (11.1 g.) + $CuCl_2$ (50 mg.)	CH_3MgBr (1.5 g. Mg)	Muscone* (3.0 g.); 1-methyl-2-cyclopentadecen-1-ol (5.2 g.)	*332*
3,5-Dimethyl-6-benzylidene-2-cyclohexen-1-one	C_6H_5MgBr ("large excess")	1-Phenyl-3,5-dimethyl-6-(α-hydroxybenzyl)-2-cyclohexen-1-ol	*164*
$C_{15}H_{16}O_2$			
Furfurylidenecarvone† (10.0 g.)	C_2H_5MgBr (15.5 g. C_2H_5Br)	2-Methyl-3-ethyl-5-isopropenyl-6-furfurylidenecyclohexanone (26.5%)	*192*
Furfurylidenecarvone† (10 g.)	n-C_3H_7MgBr (17 g. C_3H_7Br)	2-Methyl-3-*n*-propyl-5-isopropenyl-6-furfurylidenecyclohexanone (16.8%)	*192*
Furfurylidenecarvone† (10 g.)	i-C_4H_9MgCl (13 g. C_4H_9Cl)	2-Methyl-3-isobutyl-5-isopropenyl-6-furfurylidenecyclohexanone (24%)	*192*
Furfurylidenecarvone† (10 g.)	C_6H_5MgBr (21 g. C_6H_5Br)	2-Methyl-3-phenyl-5-isopropenyl-6-furfurylidenecyclohexanone (22%)	*192*
Furfurylidenecarvone† (8 g.)	$C_6H_5CH_2MgCl$ (14 g. C_7H_7Cl)	2-Methyl-3-benzyl-5-isopropenyl-6-furfurylidenecyclohexanone (18%)	*192*
$C_{15}H_{18}O_2$			
2-Furfurylidenepulegone‡ (15 g.)	C_2H_5MgBr (23 g. C_2H_5Br)	2-Furfurylidene-8-ethyl-*p*-menthone§ (6 g.)	*191*
2-Furfurylidenepulegone‡ (20 g.)	n-C_3H_7MgBr (34 g. C_3H_7Br)	2-Furfurylidene-8-*n*-propylmenthone (5 g.)	*191*
2-Furfurylidenepulegone‡ (15 g.)	i-C_4H_9MgCl (20 g. C_4H_9Cl)	2-Furfurylidene-8-*i*-butylmenthone (6 g.)	*191*
2-Furfurylidenepulegone‡ (20 g.)	C_6H_5MgBr (44 g. C_6H_5Br)	2-Furfurylidene-8-phenylmenthone (11 g.)	*191*
2-Furfurylidenepulegone‡ (20.0 g.)	$C_6H_5CH_2MgCl$ (36.0 g. C_7H_7Cl)	2-Furfurylidene-8-benzylmenthone (12.5 g.)	*191*

* 3-Methylcyclopentadecanone.

† 2-Methyl-5-isopropenyl-6-furfurylidene-2-cyclohexen-1-one.

‡ 2-Furfurylidene-3-methyl-6-isopropylidenecyclohexanone; 2-furfurylidene-$\Delta^{4(8)}$-*p*-menthen-3-one.

§ 2-Furfurylidene-3-methyl-6-*t*-amylcyclohexanone.

TABLE VI-XIX (Continued)

Ketone	RMgX	Product(s)	Ref.
$C_{15}H_{18}O_2$ (*cont.*)			
α-Furfurylidenecamphor*	C_6H_5MgBr (sl. excess)	Phenyl-α-camphoryl-α-furylmethane	*304,305*
α-Furfurylidenecamphor*	$C_6H_5CH_2MgCl$	Benzyl-α-camphoryl-α-furylmethane	*304,305*
α-Furfurylidene camphor*	$4-CH_3C_6H_4MgBr$	*p*-Tolyl-α-camphoryl-α-furylmethane	*304,305*
α-Furfurylidenecamphor*	$4-CH_3OC_6H_4MgBr$	Anisyl-α-camphoryl-α-furylmethane	*304,305*
$C_{15}H_{18}O_3$			
2-(α-Carboxyphenethyl)cyclohexanone (18 g.)	CH_3MgI (26 g. CH_3I)	1-Methyl-2-(α-carboxyphenethyl)cyclohexanol (15 g.)	*114*
$C_{15}H_{20}O$			
2,5-Dimethyl-8-isopropyl-α-tetralone (10 g.)	CH_3MgI (10 g. CH_3I)	After dehydr'n, 1,2,5-Trimethyl-8-isopropyl-3,4-dihydronaphthalene (9 g., 90%)	*85,86*
$C_{15}H_{20}O_2$			
2-Furfurylidenementhone†	CH_3MgX	2-[α-(α-Furyl)ethyl]menthone‡	*43*
2-Furfurylidenementhone†	C_2H_5MgX	2-[α-(α-Furyl)propyl]menthone	*43*
2-Furfurylidenementhone†	$n-C_3H_7MgX$	2-[α-(α-Furyl)butyl]menthone	*43*
2-Furfurylidenementhone†	$i-C_3H_7MgX$	2-[α-(α-Furyl)isobutyl]menthone	*43*
2-Furfurylidenementhone†	$n-C_4H_9MgX$	2-[α-(α-Furyl)amyl]menthone	*43*
2-Furfurylidenementhone†	$i-C_4H_9MgX$	2-[α-(α-Furyl)isoamyl]menthone	*43*
2-Furfurylidenementhone†	$i-C_5H_{11}MgX$	2-[α-(α-Furyl)isohexyl]menthone	*43*
2-Furfurylidenementhone†	C_6H_5MgX	2-(Phenyl-α-furylmethyl)menthone	*43*

* 1,7,7-Trimethyl-3-furfurylidenebicyclo[2.2.1]heptan-2-one.
† 2-Furfurylidene-3-methyl-6-isopropylcyclohexanone.
‡ 2-[α-(α-Furyl)ethyl]-3-methyl-6-isopropylcyclohexanone.

TABLE VI-XIX (Continued)

Ketone	RMgX	Product(s)	Ref.
$C_{15}H_{20}O_5$			
2-Carbethoxy-2-carbethoxymethylcyclohexanone	C_6H_5MgBr	1-Phenyl-2-carbethoxy-2-carboxymethylcyclohexanol lactone	*62*
$C_{15}H_{26}O$			
1,4a-Dimethyl-7-*n*-propyl-2-decalone	CH_3MgI	1,3,4a-Trimethyl-7-*n*-propyl-2-decalol	*48*
Tetrahydro-α-cyperone*	CH_3MgI	1,3,4a-Trimethyl-7-isopropyl-2-decalol + dehydr'n product	*47*
$C_{16}H_8O_2S_2$			
Thioïndigo	RMgBr †	Thioïndigo white (?)	*24*
$C_{16}H_{10}O_2$			
2-Benzylidene-1,3-indandione	C_6H_5MgBr	10-Phenyl-9-bindenone ‡	*164*
$C_{16}H_{10}O_2N_2$			
Indigotin §	RMgBr ¶	Reaction in 1 : 1 molecular ratio	*243*
$C_{16}H_{12}O$			
2-Methyl-3-phenyl-1-indone	CH_3MgI (2 equiv.)	1,2-Dimethyl-3-phenyl-1-indenol (87%)	*257*
2-Methyl-3-phenyl-1-indone (11.0 g.)	$C_6H_5CH_2MgCl$ (17.3 g. C_7H_7Cl)	1-Benzyl-2-methyl-3-phenyl-1-indenol (16.0 g., crude)	*34*

* 1,4a-Dimethyl-7-isopropyl-2-decalone.

† R = CH_3, C_2H_5, C_6H_5.

‡ 10-Phenylindeno[1.2-*a*]inden-9(10*H*)-one.

§ $\Delta^{2(2')}$-Bipseudoïndoxyl.

¶ R = CH_3, C_2H_5, *i*-C_4H_9, *i*-C_5H_{11}, C_6H_5, $C_6H_5CH_2$, 4-$CH_3C_6H_4$.

TABLE VI-XIX (Continued)

Ketone	RMgX	Product(s)	Ref.
$C_{16}H_{12}O_3$			
10-Acetoxyanthrone*	CH_3MgBr	9,10-Dimethylanthracene (58.0%); anthraquinone† (40.5%)‡	*103*
10-Acetoxyanthrone*	CH_3MgBr	9,10-Dimethyl-9,10-dihydro-9-anthrol (18.5%); anthraquinone† (38.0%)§	*103*
$C_{16}H_{14}O$			
2-Methyl-3-phenyl-1-indanone	CH_3MgI (2 equiv.)	1,2-Dimethyl-3-phenyl-1-indanol (62%)	*257*
2-Phenyl-α-tetralone¶	C_2H_5MgI	1-Ethyl-2-phenyl-1-tetralol‖	*57*
2-Phenyl-α-tetralone¶	n-C_3H_7MgX	1-n-Propyl-2-phenyl-1-tetralol	*57*
2-Phenyl-α-tetralone¶	i-C_3H_7MgX	1-Isopropyl-2-phenyl-1-tetralol	*57*
2-Phenyl-α-tetralone¶	C_6H_5MgBr	1,2-Diphenyl-1-tetralol	*27*
1,3-Dimethylanthrone**	CH_3MgBr	1,3-Dimethylanthraquinone (32%); 1,3-dimethylanthracene;†† 1,3,9,10-tetramethylanthracene††	*103*
$C_{16}H_{16}O$			
2,8-Dimethyl-3,4-dihydro-1(2*H*)-phenanthrone	CH_3MgI	1,2,8-Trimethyl,1,2,3,4-tetrahydro-1-phenanthrol (>60%)‡‡	*130*

* 10-Acetoxy-9(10*H*)-anthracenone.

† By atmospheric oxidation of anthrahydroquinone.

‡ Addition of Et_2O-ketone solution to stirred CH_3Br-free Grignard reagent solution; fifteen hours stirring at room temperature.

§ Addition of Et_2O-ketone solution to Mg-free Grignard reagent solution containing excess CH_3Br; fifteen hours stirring.

¶ 2-Phenyl-3,4-dihydro-1(2*H*)-naphthalenone.

‖ 1-Ethyl-2-phenyl-1,2,3,4-tetrahydro-1-naphthol.

** 1,3-Dimethyl-9(10*H*)-anthracenone.

†† By reduction of residual reddish oil.

‡‡ The figure recorded represents the overall yield of hydrocarbon after dehydration and dehydrogenation of the Grignard product.

TABLE VI-XIX (Continued)

Ketone	RMgX	Product(s)	Ref.
$C_{16}H_{16}O_2$			
2-Methyl-7-methoxy-3,4-dihydro-1(2*H*)-phenanthrone	$H_5C_2O_2CCH_2CH_2Br$ + Mg	α-(1-Hydroxy-2-methyl-7-methoxy-1,2,3,4-tetrahydro-1-phenthryl)propionic acid lactone	*121*
7-Methyl-9-methoxy-3,4-dihydro-1(2*H*)-phenanthrone	CH_3MgI	1,7-Dimethyl-9-methoxy-1,2,3,4-tetrahydro-1-phenanthrol (50%)	*237*
$C_{16}H_{16}O_3$			
5,9-Dimethoxy-3,4-dihydro-1(2*H*)-phenanthrone (4.6 g.)	CH_3MgI (1.8 ml. CH_3I)	1-Methyl-5,9-dimethoxy-3,4-dihydrophenanthrene (3.4 g.); recovered ketone (*ca.* 0.7 g.)	*132*
$C_{16}H_{18}O_3$			
4a-Carbomethoxy-3,4,4a,9,10,10a-hexahydro-2(1*H*)-phenanthrone (2.1 g.)	CH_3MgI (1.28 g. CH_3I)	After dehydration and dehydrogenation, 2-methylphenanthrene (0.7 g., crude)	*133*
$C_{17}H_8OS_3$			
2,3,6,5-Dithianaphtheno-1,4-thiapyrone (1 g.)	C_6H_5MgBr (9 g. C_6H_5Br)	4,4-Diphenyl-2,3,6,5-dithianaphtheno-1,4-thiapyran	*252*
2,3,6,5-Dithianaphtheno-1,4-thiapyrone (1.0 g.)	$C_6H_5CH_2MgCl$ (5.5 g. C_7H_7Cl)	4,4-Dibenzyl-2,3,6,5-dithianaphtheno-1,4-thiapyran (0.3 g.); 4-hydroxy-4-benzyl-2,3,6,5-dithianaphtheno-1,4-thiapyran	*252*
2,3,6,5-Dithianaphtheno-1,4-thiapyrone (1 g.)	3-$CH_3C_6H_5MgBr$ (9 g. C_7H_7Br)	4,4-Di-*m*-tolyl-2,3,6,5-dithianaphtheno-1,4-thiapyran	*252*
$C_{17}H_{10}O$			
Chrysofluorenone* (2.60 g.)	CH_3MgI (4.26 g. CH_3I)	11-Methyl-11-chrysofluorenol (2.30 g.)	*14*

* 11-Benzo[*a*]fluoren-11-one.

TABLE VI-XIX (Continued)

Ketone	RMgX	Product(s)	Ref.
$C_{17}H_{10}O$ (*cont.*)			
Chrysofluorenone*	C_6H_5MgBr	11-Phenyl-11-chrysofluorenol (88%)	*271*
Benzanthrone† (20.0 g.)	CH_3MgI (35.5 g. CH_3I)	7-Methylene-5,6-dihydro-7-benz[*de*]anthracene (10.0 g.); 6-methyl-7-benz[*de*]anthracen-7-one	*60*
Benzanthrone†	C_2H_5MgI (3 equiv.)	6-Ethyl-7-benz[*de*]anthracen-7-one	*60*
Benzanthrone†	n-C_3H_7MgI	6-*n*-Propyl-7-benz[*de*]anthracen-7-one	*61*
Benzanthrone†	n-C_4H_9Br	3-*n*-Butyl-7-benz[*de*]anthracen-7-one‡	*207*
Benzanthrone†	n-C_4H_9MgI	6-*n*-Butyl-7-benz[*de*]anthracen-7-one (60%)	*61*
Benzanthrone†	t-C_4H_9MgCl (3 equiv.)	7-*t*-Butyl-7-benz[*de*]anthracen-7-ol (20%)	*4*
Benzanthrone†	C_6H_5MgBr	1-Phenyl-7-benz[*de*]anthracen-7-one§	*68*
Benzanthrone†	C_6H_5MgBr	3-Phenyl-7-benz[*de*]anthracen-7-one‡	*207*
Benzanthrone†	C_6H_5MgBr	6-Phenyl-7-benz[*de*]anthracen-7-one (75%)	*61*
Benzanthrone†	C_6H_5MgBr (3 equiv.)	6-Phenyl-7-benz[*de*]anthracen-7-one (42%)	*4*
Benzanthrone†	$(CH_2)_5CHMgCl$	6-Cyclohexyl-7-benz[*de*]anthracen-7-one (15%)	*4*
Benzanthrone†	$C_6H_5CH_2MgCl$	6-Benzyl-7-benz[*de*]anthracen-7-one (22%)	*4*
Benzanthrone†	$C_6H_5CH_2MgCl$	6-Benzyl-7-benz[*de*]anthracen-7-one (?)	*68*
Benzanthrone†	n-$C_7H_{15}MgBr$	6-*n*-Heptyl-7-benz[*de*]anthracen-7-one (61%)	*4*
Benzanthrone†	1-$C_{10}H_7MgBr$	1-α-Naphthyl-7-benz[*de*]anthracen-7-one§	*68*

* 11-Benzo[*a*]fluoren-11-one.

† 7-Benz[*de*]anthracen-7-one.

‡ It is not specified in the available abstract whether the 3 position of the *Chemical Abstracts* and "Ring Index" system or the 3-*Bz* position of the system of numbering employed by Clar (*68*) (*i.e.*, the 1 position) is intended. In either case, however, the work of Charrier and Ghigi (*61*) and of Allen and Overbaugh (*4*) shows the constitution assigned to be erroneous. Undoubtedly, the 6 derivative was isolated.

§ In view of the work of Charrier and Ghigi (*61*) and of Allen and Overbaugh (*4*) there can be no doubt that the constitution here assigned is erroneous, and that the product isolated was the 6-phenyl derivative.

TABLE VI-XIX (Continued)

Ketone	RMgX	Product(s)	Ref.
$C_{17}H_{12}O_2$			
Bis-1-indanone-3,3-spiran (2.48 g.)	C_6H_5MgBr (3.14 g. C_6H_5Br)	1,1′-Diphenylbis-1-indanol-3,3-spiran (75%); corresponding anhydride (0.3 g.)	*180*
Bis-1-indanone-3,3-spiran (2.48 g.)	$C_6H_5CH_2MgCl$ (2.53 g. C_7H_7Cl)	1,1′-Dibenzylbis-1-indanol-3,3-spiran (I) (2.1 g.); 1-benzyl-1-indanol-1′-indanone-3,3-spiran (II) (0.9 g.); dehydration product of I (0.4 g.)	*180*
1,2-Cyclopenteno-9,10-phenanthraquinone (505 mg.)	CH_3MgI (6 ml. CH_3I)	After dehydr'n, 9,10-dimethyl-1,2-cyclopentenophenanthrene (31.7 mg.)	*55*
$C_{17}H_{14}O_2$			
2-Methyl-2-benzoyl-1-indanone (4.0 g.)	C_6H_5MgBr (3 equiv.)	(1-Hydroxy-1-phenyl-2-methyl-2-indanyl)diphenylmethanol (>3.9 g.); $(C_6H_5)_3COH$ (1.3 g.); 2-methyl-1-indanone	*109*
$C_{17}H_{14}O_3$			
2-Methyl-10-acetoxyanthrone*	CH_3MgBr	2,9,10-Trimethylanthracene (28%); 2-methylanthraquinone† (27%)	*103*
$C_{17}H_{15}O_3$			
2-Methyl-2-carbomethoxy-7-methoxybenz[*e*]indan-3-one (2.0 g.)	C_2H_5MgBr (0.8 g. C_2H_5Br)	2-Methyl-2-carbomethoxy-7-methoxybenz[*e*]indan-3-ol (250 mg.); recovered ketone (0.8 g.)	*38*
$C_{17}H_{16}O$			
1,2-Dihydro-1,2-cyclopentenophenanthren-4(3*H*)-one (1.45 g.)	CH_3MgI	4-Methyl-1,2,3,4-tetrahydro-1,2-cyclopentenophenanthren-4-ol (yielding 124.5 mg. 4-methyl-1,2-cyclopentenophenanthrene)	*55*

* 2-Methyl-10-acetoxy-9(10*H*)-anthracenone.

† [illegible]

TABLE VI-XIX (Continued)

Ketone	RMgX	Product(s)	Ref.
$C_{17}H_{16}O_2$			
2,2-Dimethyl-3-hydroxy-3-phenyl-1-indanone (2.6 g.)	C_6H_5MgBr (1 equiv.)	Recovered ketone (70%); no isolable product	*108*
1,4-Dimethyl-10-methoxyanthrone*	CH_3MgI (3 equiv.)	1,4,9-Trimethyl-10-methoxy-9-anthrol	*18*
1,4-Dimethyl-10-methoxyanthrone*	C_6H_5MgBr	1,4-Dimethyl-9-phenyl-10-methoxy-9-anthrol	*18*
$C_{17}H_{18}O$			
Benzylidenecarvone† (15 g.)	C_2H_5MgBr (22 g. C_2H_5Br)	2-Methyl-3-ethyl-5-isopropenyl-6-benzylidenecyclohexanone (35.5%)	*192*
Benzylidenecarvone† (10 g.)	*n*-C_3H_7MgBr (16 g. C_3H_7Br)	2-Methyl-3-*n*-propyl-5-isopropenyl-6-benzylidenecyclohexanone (3 g.)	*192*
Benzylidenecarvone† (15 g.)	*i*-C_4H_9MgCl (19 g. C_4H_9Cl)	2-Methyl-3-isobutyl-5-isopropenyl-6-benzylidenecyclohexanone (48.5%)	*192*
Benzylidenecarvone† (18 g.)	C_6H_5MgBr (39 g. C_6H_5Br)	2-Methyl-3-phenyl-5-isopropenyl-6-benzylidenecyclohexanone (33.5%)	*192*
Benzylidenecarvone† (10 g.)	$C_6H_5CH_2MgCl$ (17 g. C_7H_7Cl)	2-Methyl-3-benzyl-5-isopropenyl-6-benzylidenecyclohexanone (36.0%)	*192*
$C_{17}H_{20}O$			
Benzylidenepulegone‡ (15 g.)	C_2H_5MgBr (22 g. C_2H_5Br)	2-Benzylidene-8-ethylmenthone (8 g.)§	*191*
Benzylidenepulegone‡ (30 g.)	*n*-C_3H_7MgBr (49 g.) C_3H_7Br)	2-Benzylidene-8-*n*-propylmenthone (12 g.)	*191*
Benzylidenepulegone‡ (20 g.)	*i*-C_4H_9MgCl (22 g. C_4H_9Cl)	2-Benzylidene-8-isobutylmenthone (7 g.)	*191*
Benzylidenepulegone‡ (20 g.)	C_6H_5MgBr (41 g. C_6H_5Br)	2-Benzylidene-8-phenylmenthone (12 g.)	*191*
Benzylidenepulegone‡ (20 g.)	$C_6H_5CH_2MgCl$ (24 g. C_7H_7Cl)	2-Benzylidene-8-benzylmenthone (14.5 g.)	*191*

* 1,4-Dimethyl-10-methoxy-9(10*H*)-anthracenone.
† 2-Methyl-5-isopropenyl-6-benzylidene-2-cyclohexen-1-one.
‡ 2-Benzylidene-3-methyl-6-isopropylidenecyclohexanone.
§ 2-Benzylidene-3-methyl-6-*t*-amylcyclohexanone.

TABLE VI-XIX (Continued)

Ketone	RMgX	Product(s)	Ref.
$C_{17}H_{20}O$ (*cont.*)			
α-Benzylidenecamphor*	CH_3MgX	1-Phenyl-1-α-camphorylethane	*122*
α-Benzylidenecamphor*	C_2H_5MgX	1-Phenyl-1-α-camphorylpropane	*122*
α-Benzylidenecamphor*	C_6H_5MgX	Diphenyl-α-camphorylmethane	*122*
$C_{17}H_{22}O$			
2-Methyl-3-benzyl-5-isopropenyl-cyclohexanone	CH_3MgI	1,2-Dimethyl-3-benzyl-5-isopropenyl-cyclohexanol	*230*
$C_{17}H_{28}O$			
1-(1,5-Dimethylhexyl)-6,7-dihydro-4(5*H*)-indanone	CH_3MgI	1-(1,5-Dimethylhexyl)-7a-methyl-3a,6,7,7a-tetrahydro-4(5*H*)-indanone	*199*
$C_{17}H_{28}O_2$			
4b,8,8-Trimethyl-10a-hydroxy-perhydrophenanthren-2-one (5 g.)	CH_3MgI (17 g. CH_3I)	2,4b,8,8-Tetramethyl-3,4,4a,4b,5,6,7,8,8a,9-decahydrophenanthrene	*135,238*
$C_{17}H_{32}O$			
2,6,Di-*n*-propyl-2,6-diisopropyl-cyclopentanone	CH_3MgI (5–6 equiv.)	No reaction	*79*
$C_{18}H_{12}O$			
5(12*H*)-Naphthacenone	CH_3MgI	5-Methyl-5,12-dihydro-5-naphthacenol	*69*
1,2-Benz-9-anthrone †	CH_3MgCl	7-Methylbenz[*a*]anthracene (56%)	*102*
1,2-Benz-10-anthrone ‡	*i*-C_3H_7MgCl	12-Isopropyl-7,12-dihydrobenz[*a*]anthracen-12-ol	*73*

* 1,7,7-Trimethyl-3-benzylidenebicyclo[2.2.1]heptan-2-one.
† Benz[*a*]anthracen-7(12*H*)-one.
‡ Benz[*a*]anthracen-12(7*H*)-one.

TABLE VI-XIX (Continued)

Ketone	RMgX	Product(s)	Ref.
$C_{18}H_{12}O_2$			
Benz[*a*]anthracene-5(6*H*), 7(12*H*)-dione (1.5 g.)	CH_3MgBr ("large excess")	5,7-Dimethylbenz[*a*]anthracene (810 mg., 54%)	*213*
$C_{18}H_{14}O$			
3,4-Dihydrobenz[*a*]anthracen-1(2*H*)-one	CH_3MgI	1-Methyl-1,2,3,4,-Tetrahydrobenz[*a*]anthracen-1-ol	*78*
7,12-Dihydrobenz[*a*]anthracen-5(6*H*)-one (700 mg.)	CH_3MgBr	5-Methyl-5,6,7,12-tetrahydrobenz[*a*]anthracen-5-ol (422 mg., 61.6%)	*213*
10,11-Dihydrobenz[*a*]anthracen-8(9*H*)-one (13.8 g.)	C_2H_5MgBr (22 g. C_2H_5Br)	After Pd-charcoal treatment, 8-ethyl-10,11-dihydrobenz[*a*]anthracene (79%)	*8*
10,11-Dihydrobenz[*a*]anthracen-8(9*H*)-one	$H_2C{=}CHCH_2Br$ + Mg	8-Allyl-8,9,10,11-tetrahydrobenz[*a*]anthracen-8-ol (84%)	*8*
10,11-Dihydrobenz[*a*]anthracene-8(9*H*)-one (5.0 g.)	*n*-C_3H_7MgBr (4.0 ml. C_3H_7Br)	8-*n*-Propyl-8,9,10,11-tetrahydrobenz[*a*]anthracen-8-ol (2.2 g.)	*8*
$C_{18}H_{14}O_2$			
11-Methoxy-15,16-dihydro-17-cyclopenta[*a*]phenanthren-17-one (1.0 g.)	C_2H_5MgBr (3.0 g. C_2H_5Br)	11-Methoxy-17-ethyl-15-cyclopenta[*a*]phenanthrene (0.6 g.)	*223*
$C_{18}H_{16}O$			
3-*m*-Biphenylyl-2-cyclohexen-1-one (25.0 g.)	C_6H_5MgBr (25.0 g. C_6H_5Br)	2-Phenyl-4-*m*-biphenylyl-1,3-cyclohexadiene (22.7 g., crude)	*309*
3-*m*-Biphenylyl-2-cyclohexen-1-one	3-$C_6H_5C_6H_4MgBr$ (30.3 g. $C_{12}H_9Br$)	2,4-Bis-*m*-biphenylyl-1,3-cyclohexadiene (11.4 g., crude)	*309*
3-*p*-Biphenylyl-2-cyclohexen-1-one (10.0 g., 0.04 mole)	C_6H_5MgBr (18.7 g. C_6H_5Br)	1-*p*-Biphenylyl-3-phenyl-1,3-cyclohexadiene	

TABLE VI-XIX (Continued)

Ketone	RMgX	Product(s)	Ref.
$C_{18}H_{16}O$ (*cont.*)			
3-*p*-Biphenylyl-2-cyclohexen-1-one (15.0 g.)	3-$C_6H_5C_6H_4MgBr$ (25.0 g. C_6H_5Br)	2-*m*-Biphenylyl-4-*p*-biphenylyl-1,3-cyclohexadiene (9.6 g.)	*309*
3,5-Diphenyl-2-cyclohexen-1-one	C_2H_5MgBr (excess)	1,5-Diphenyl-3-ethylidenecyclohexene; 3-ethyl-3,5-diphenylcyclohexanone	*164*
3,5-Diphenyl-2-cyclohexen-1-one	C_6H_5MgBr (excess)	1,3,5-Triphenyl-1,3-cyclohexadiene	*164*
5,6,8,9-Tetrahydrobenz[*a*]anthracen-11(10*H*)-one	CH_3MgCl	11-Methyl-5,6,8,9-tetrahydrobenz[*a*]anthracene (86%)	*104*
$C_{18}H_{16}O_2$			
2,3-Dimethyl-4-hydroxy-4-phenyl-1(4*H*)-naphthalenone	C_6H_5MgBr (excess)	1,2-Diphenyl-2,3-dimethyl-1,2-dihydronaphthalene-1,4-diol	*326*
$C_{18}H_{18}O_2$			
2,2-Dimethyl-3-methoxy-3-phenyl-1-indanone	C_6H_5MgBr	1,3-Diphenyl-2,2-dimethyl-3-methoxy-1-indanol	*108,300*
$C_{18}H_{18}O_3$			
2-Anisyl-6-methoxy-3,4-dihydro-1(2*H*)-naphthalenone	CH_3MgI	1-Methyl-2-anisyl-6-methoxy-3,4-dihydronaphthalene	*194*
$C_{18}H_{18}O_4$			
2-Methyl-2-carbomethoxy-7-methoxy-3,4-dihydrophenanthren-1(2*H*)-one (8 parts)	C_2H_5MgBr (12 parts C_2H_5Br)	1-Ethyl-2-methyl-2-carbomethoxy-7-methoxy-1,2,3,4-tetrahydrophenanthren-1-ol	*258,196*
$C_{18}H_{20}O_4$			
2-Methyl-2-carbomethoxy-7-methoxy-3,4,9,10-tetrahydrophenanthren-1(2*H*)-one	C_2H_5MgI (1 equiv.)	1-Ethylidene-2-methyl-2-carbomethoxy-1,2,3,4,9,10-hexahydrophenanthrene	*136*

TABLE VI-XIX (Continued)

Ketone	RMgX	Product(s)	Ref.
$C_{18}H_{26}O$			
2,2,6,6-Tetraällylcyclohexanone (15 g.)	CH_3MgI (5 equiv.)	Recovered ketone (7 g.); "polymerization" products	*79*
$C_{18}H_{26}O_3$			
4b,8-Dimethyl-8-carbomethoxy-4,-4a,4b,5,6,7,8,8a,9,10-decahydrophenanthren-2(3*H*)-one (5.8 g.)	CH_3MgI (5.7 g. CH_3I)	2,4b,8-Trimethyl-8-carbomethoxy-2,3,4,4a,4b,5,6,7,8,8a,9,10-dodecahydrophenanthren-2-ol (3.0 g.)	*126*
$C_{18}H_{34}O$			
2,2,6,6-Tetra-*n*-propylcyclohexanone (13 g.)	CH_3MgI (5 equiv.)	1-Methylene-2,2,6,6-tetra-*n*-propylcyclohexane (11 g.)	*79*
10-Phenyl-9(10*H*)-acridone (3.7 g.)	C_6H_5MgBr (6.0 ml. C_6H_5Br)	9,10-Diphenyl-9-acridanol (4.0 g.)	*349*
$C_{19}H_{14}O$			
Fuchsone*	CH_3MgI (3 equiv.)	*p*-$HOC_6H_4(C_6H_5)_2CCH_3$	*150*
$C_{19}H_{16}O_2$			
3-Methyl-11-methoxy-15,16-dihydro-17-cyclopenta[*a*]phenanthren-17-one (7 g.)	CH_3MgI	3,17-Dimethyl-11-methoxy-15-cyclopenta[*a*]phenanthrene (6 g.)	*170*
$C_{19}H_{20}O_4$			
2-Methyl-2-carbethoxy-7-methoxy-3,4-dihydrophenanthren-1(2*H*)-one	C_2H_5MgBr	1-Ethyl-2-methyl-2-carbethoxy-7-methoxy-1,2,3,4-tetrahydrophenanthren-1-ol	*258*

* 4-Benzhydrylidene-2,5-cyclohexadiene-1-one.

TABLE VI-XIX (Continued)

Ketone	RMgX	Product(s)	Ref.
$C_{19}H_{21}O_2N$			
2-Piperidinomethyl-1-benzo-[*f*]chromanone (17.8 g., 0.06 mole)	CH_3MgI (17.0 g., 0.12 mole CH_3I)	1-Methyl-2-piperidinomethyl-1-benzo-[*f*]chromanol (yielding 4.7 g., 22.6% of the chromene hydrochloride)	*9*
2-Piperidinomethyl-1-benzo-[*f*]chromanone (29.5 g., 0.1 mole)	C_2H_5MgBr (54.5 g., 0.5 mole C_2H_5Br)	1-Ethyl-2-piperidinomethyl-1-benzo-[*f*]chromanol (44.5%)	*9*
$C_{20}H_{22}O_4$			
2-Ethyl-2-carbethoxy-7-methoxy-3,4-dihydrophenanthren-1(2*H*)-one	C_2H_5MgBr	1,2-Diethyl-2-carbethoxy-7-methoxy-1,2,3,4-tetrahydrophenanthren-1-ol	*258,196*
$C_{19}H_{36}O$			
2,2,6,6-Tetra-*n*-propyl-3-methylcyclohexanone (15 g.)	CH_3MgI (5 equiv.)	Recovered ketone; dehydr'n product (total recovery, 8 g.)	*79*
2,2,6,6-Tetra-*n*-propyl-4-methylcyclohexanone (15 g.)	CH_3MgI (5 equiv.)	Dehydr'n product (12 g.)	*79*
$C_{20}H_{13}ON$			
10-Phenyliminoanthrone (8.0 g., 0.028 mole)	C_6H_5MgBr (9.0 g. C_6H_5Br)	9-Phenyl-10-phenylimino-9,10-dihydro-9-anthrol (8.7 g., 85%)	*149*
$C_{20}H_{14}O$			
Acebenzanthrone*	CH_3MgI	7-Methyl-4,5-dihydrobenz[*k*]acephenanthrylene (30%)	*198*
Acebenzanthrone*	C_2H_5MgBr	7-Ethyl-4,5-dihydrobenz[*k*]acephenanthrylene (28.6%)	*198*

* 4,5-Dihydrobenz[*k*]acephenanthrylen-7(12*H*)-one.

TABLE VI-XIX (Continued)

Ketone	RMgX	Product(s)	Ref.
$C_{20}H_{14}O$ (*cont.*)			
Acebenzanthrone*	*n*-C_3H_7MgBr	7-*n*-Propyl-4,5-dihydrobenz[*k*]acephenanthrylene (25%)	*198*
Acebenzanthrone*	*n*-C_4H_9MgBr	7-*n*-Butyl-4,5-dihydrobenz[*k*]acephenanthrylene (20.7%)	*198*
10-Phenylanthrone†	$(CH_2)_5CHMgCl$	9-Phenyl-10-cyclohexylanthracene	*302*
9,10-Dihydrobenzo[*a*]pyren-7(8*H*)-one	CH_3MgI	7-Methyl-9,10-dihydrobenzo[*a*]pyrene	*101*
$C_{20}H_{14}O_3$			
10-Benzoxyanthrone‡	CH_3MgCl	Benzoic acid (11%); anthraquinone§ (25%); 9,10-dimethylanthracene (50%)	*103*
10-Benzoxyanthrone‡	CH_3MgBr (2.75 equiv.)	Benzoic acid (13%); anthrahydroquinone monobenzoate (7.5%); 9,10-dimethylanthracene (9%); anthraquinone§ (60%)	*103*
$C_{20}H_{24}O$			
17-Isopropyl-6,7,8,14,16,17-hexahydro-15-cyclopenta[*a*]phenanthren-11(9*H*)-one (2.0 g.) + CuBr¶ (0.1 g.)	CH_3MgI¶ (1.0 g. CH_3I)	11-Methyl-17-isopropyl-6,7,8,14,16,17-hexahydro-15-cyclopenta[*a*]phenanthrene (1.4 g.)	*333*

* 4,5-Dihydrobenz[*k*]acephenanthrylen-7(12*H*)-one.

† 10-Phenylanthracen-9(10*H*)-one.

‡ 10-Benzoxyanthracen-9(10*H*)-one.

§ By atmospheric oxidation of anthrahydroquinone.

¶ "Repetition of the Grignard addition under varying conditions, using methylmagnesium bromide and cuprous chloride, gave essentially the same results."

TABLE VI-XIX (Continued)

Ketone	RMgX	Product(s)	Ref.
$C_{21}H_{12}O_2$			
7-Dibenzo[*c,h*]xanthone	C_6H_5MgBr	7-Phenyl-7-dibenzo[*c,h*]xanthen-7-ol	*67*
$C_{21}H_{14}O$			
2,3-Diphenyl-1-indone	$C_6H_5CH_2MgCl$	1-Benzyl-2,3-diphenyl-1-indenol	*34*
2,3-Diphenyl-1-indone	$4-CH_3C_6H_4MgBr$	1-*p*-Tolyl-2,3-diphenyl-1-indenol	*161*
10-Benzalanthrone* (14 g.)	CH_3MgI (22 g. CH_3I)	9-Methyl-10-benzylidene-9,10-dihydro-9-anthrol (13 g., crude)	*148*
10-Benzalanthrone*	C_6H_5MgBr	Anthrafuchsone†	*207*
14-Dibenzo[*a,f*]xanthen-14-one (3 g.)	C_6H_5MgBr (14 g. C_6H_5Br)	14-Phenyl-14-dibenzo[*a,f*]xanthen-14-ol	*88*
14-Dibenzo[*a,i*]xanthen-14-one (3 g.)	C_6H_5MgBr (14 g. C_6H_5Br)	14-Phenyl-14-dibenzo[*a,i*]xanthen-14-ol	*88*
$C_{21}H_{16}O$			
2,3-Diphenyl-1-indanone (2.3 g.)	CH_3MgI (0.255 g. Mg)	1,2-Diphenyl-3-methylindene (1.6 g., 70%)	*162*
2,3-Diphenyl-1-indanone (1.4 g.)	$C_6H_5CH_2MgCl$ (1.8 g. C_7H_7Cl)	1-Benzyl-2,3-diphenyl-1-indanol (0.8 g.)	*31*
2,3-Diphenyl-1-indanone (18 g.)	$4-CH_3C_6H_4MgBr$ (2.4 g. C_7H_7Br)	1-*p*-Tolyl-2,3-diphenyl-1-indanol (9.4 g.)	*161*
$C_{21}H_{16}O_2$			
10-Methoxy-10-phenylanthrone	Furyl-MgBr	9-Furyl-10-methoxy-10-phenyl-9,10-dihydroanthrol	*100*
$C_{21}H_{20}O$			
2,6-Dibenzylidene-3-methylcyclohexanone	C_6H_5MgBr (excess)	2-Benzylidene-3-methyl-6-benzhydrylcyclohexanone; 2-benzhydryl-3-methyl-6-benzylidenecyclohexanone	*164*

* 10-Benzylidene-9(10*H*)-anthracenone.

† 10-Benzhydrylideneanthracen-9(10*H*)-one.

TABLE VI-XIX (Continued)

Ketone	RMgX	Product(s)	Ref.
$C_{21}H_{25}OS$			
3-Ethyl thio enol ether of Δ^4-androstene-3,17-dione (2.9 g.)	HC≡CMgBr (15 g. C_2H_5MgBr)	3-Ethyl thio enol ether of 17-ethynyltestosterone	*195*
$C_{21}H_{26}OS_2$			
3-Ethylene mercaptole of Δ^4-androstene-3,17-dione (2.9 g.)	CH_3MgBr (3.6 g.)	3-Ethylene mercaptole of 17-methyltestosterone	*195*
$C_{21}H_{30}O_2$			
Δ^4-Androstene-3,17-dione 3-enol ethyl ether	CH_3MgX	17-Methyltestosterone	*341*
Δ^4-Androstene-3,17-dione 3-enol ethyl ether	HC≡CMgBr	17-Ethynyltestosterone	*341*
Δ^4-Androstene-3,17-dione 3-enol ethyl ether	C_2H_5MgX	17-Ethyltestosterone	*341*
$C_{21}H_{30}O_3$			
Δ^4-Androstene-3,17-dione 3-glycol acetal	CH_3MgX	17-Methyltestosterone 3-glycol acetal	*340*
Δ^4-Androstene-3,17-dione 3-glycol acetal	HC≡CMgBr	17-Ethynyltestosterone 3-glycol acetal	*340*
Δ^4-Androstene-3,17-dione 3-glycol acetal	C_2H_5MgX	17-Ethyltestosterone 3-glycol acetal	*340*
trans-Dehydroandrosterone acetate (3.3 g.)	CH_3MgI (1.2 g. Mg)	Normal addition product, which was further treated without isolation	*77*
$C_{21}H_{32}O_2$			
Androstane-3,17-dione	CH_3MgX	17-Methylandrastan-3-on-17-ol	*339*
Androstane-3,17-dione	C_2H_5MgX	17-Ethylandrastan-3-on-17-ol	*339*

TABLE VI-XIX (Continued)

Ketone	RMgX	Product(s)	Ref.
$C_{22}H_{14}O$			
6(13*H*)-Pentacenone	CH_3MgI	6-Methyl-6,13-dihydropentacen-6-ol; $C_{46}H_{32}$, m.p. 420°	*69*
$C_{22}H_{16}O$			
2-Benzyl-3-phenyl-1-indone (3.2 g.)	C_6H_5MgBr (7.5 g. C_6H_5Br)	1,3-Diphenyl-2-benzyl-1-indenol (2.0 g.)	*34*
2-Phenyl-3-benzyl-1-indone	$C_6H_5CH_2MgCl$	1,3-Dibenzyl-2-phenyl-1-indenol	*298*
2-Phenyl-3-*p*-tolyl-1-indone (15.0 g.)	C_6H_5MgBr (2.2 g. Mg)	1,2-Diphenyl-3-*p*-tolyl-1-indenol (15.0 g.)	*161*
$C_{22}H_{16}O_2$			
2-Benzoyl-3-phenyl-1-indanone (2.5 g.)	C_6H_5MgBr (6.4 g. C_6H_5Br)	$C_{28}H_{20}O$, m.p. 145–146°	*184*
$C_{22}H_{18}O$			
2,2,3-Triphenylcyclobutanone	CH_3MgI	1-Methyl-2,2,3-triphenylcyclobutanol (87%)	*261*
2-Phenyl-3-*p*-tolyl-1-indanone	C_6H_5MgBr	1,2-Diphenyl-3-*p*-tolyl-1-indanol (55%)	*161*
6a,13,14,14a-Tetrahydropicen-5(6*H*)-one	CH_3MgBr (excess)	5-Methyl-5,6,6a,13,14,14a-hexahydropicen-5-ol	*210*
6b,7,8,12b-Tetrahydropicen-14(13*H*)-one	CH_3MgBr (excess)	14-Methyl-6b,7,8,12b,13,14-hexahydropicen-14-ol	*210*
$C_{22}H_{24}O$			
2,3-Diphenyl-α-tetralone*	C_6H_5MgBr	1,2,3-Triphenyl-1,2,3,4-tetrahydro-1-naphthol (70%, crude)	*30*
$C_{23}H_{14}O$			
3-Phenyl-7-benz[*de*]anthracen-7-one	C_2H_5MgX	3-Phenyl-6-ethyl-7-benz[*de*]anthracen-7-one (35%)	*5*

* 2,3-Diphenyl-3,4-dihydro-1(2*H*)-naphthalenone.

TABLE VI-XIX (Continued)

Ketone	RMgX	Product(s)	Ref.
$C_{23}H_{14}O$ (*cont.*)			
3-Phenyl-7-benz[*de*]anthracen-7-one	*n*-C_4H_9MgX	3-Phenyl-6-*n*-butyl-7-benz[*de*]anthracen-7-one (53%)	*5*
3-Phenyl-7-benz[*de*]anthracen-7-one	*t*-C_4H_9MgCl	3-Phenyl-7-*t*-butyl-7-benz[*de*]anthracen-7-ol (10%)	*5*
3-Phenyl-7-benz[*de*]anthracen-7-one	C_6H_5MgBr	3,6-Diphenyl-7-benz[*de*]anthracen-7-one (45%)	*5*
3-Phenyl-7-benz[*de*]anthracen-7-one	$(CH_2)_5CHMgX$	3-Phenyl-6-cyclohexyl-7-benz[*de*]anthracen-7-one (22%)	*5*
3-Phenyl-7-benz[*de*]anthracen-7-one	*n*-$C_6H_{13}MgX$	3-Phenyl-6-*n*-hexyl-7-benz[*de*]anthracen-7-one (47%)	*5*
3-Phenyl-7-benz[*de*]anthracen-7-one	$C_6H_5CH_2MgCl$	3-Phenyl-6-benzyl-7-benz[*de*]anthracen-7-one (19%)	*5*
3-Phenyl-7-benz[*de*]anthracen-7-one	$C_6H_5CH{=}CHMgX$	3-Phenyl-6-styryl-7-benz[*de*]anthracen-7-one (6%)	*5*
$C_{23}H_{16}O$			
Naphthofuchsone*	CH_3MgI	1-$(4\text{-}HOC_{10}H_6)(C_6H_5)_2CCH_3$	*150*
$C_{23}H_{16}O_2$			
1,2,4-Triphenylcyclopentene-3,5-dione (16.2 g.)	C_6H_5MgBr (40.0 g. C_6H_5Br)	2,4,5-Triphenylcyclopentane-1,3-dione (8.7 g.); 1,2,3,4-tetraphenylcyclopenten-3-ol-5-one (0.8 g.)	*357*
$C_{23}H_{20}O$			
2,7-Diphenyl-4,5-benzocycloheptanone (1.4 g.)	CH_3MgI (1.8 g. CH_3I)	1-Methyl-2,7-diphenyl-4,5-benzocycloheptanol (1.2 g.)	*265*

* 4-Benzhydrylidene-1(4*H*)-naphthalenone.

TABLE VI-XIX (Continued)

Ketone	RMgX	Product(s)	Ref.
$C_{24}H_{20}O$			
2,3-Dimethyl-2,4-diphenyl-1(2*H*)-naphthalenone	C_6H_5MgBr (excess)	1,2,4-Triphenyl-2,3-dimethyl-1,2-dihydro-1-naphthol	*326*
2,3-Dimethyl-4,4-diphenyl-1(4*H*)-naphthalenone	C_6H_5MgBr	1,4,4-Triphenyl-2,3-dimethyl-1,4-dihydro-1-naphthol (90%)	*326*
$C_{25}H_{24}O$			
1,3-Diphenyl-9-fluorenone	C_6H_5MgBr	1,3,9-Triphenyl-9-fluorenol	*165*
$C_{26}H_{13}O_2$			
1-(9-Hydroxy-9-fluorenyl)-9-fluorenone	C_6H_5MgBr	1-(9-Hydroxy-9-fluorenyl)-9-phenyl-9-fluorenol	*159*
$C_{26}H_{18}O$			
10,10-Diphenylanthrone*	C_6H_5MgBr	9,10-10-Triphenyl-9-anthrol (*ca.* quant.)	*123,173,19*
10,10-Diphenylanthrone* (30.0 g.)	4-$CH_3OC_6H_4MgI$ (35.4 g. C_7H_7IO)	9-*p*-Anisyl-10,10-diphenyl-9-anthrol (22.5 g.)	*39*
$C_{27}H_{18}O$			
Anthrafuchsone†	CH_3MgI	9-Methyl-10-benzhydrylidene-9,10-dihydro-9-anthrol	*150*
$C_{27}H_{26}O$			
2-Benzylidene-3-methyl-6-benzhydrylcyclohexanone	C_6H_5MgBr	2,6-Dibenzhydryl-3-methylcyclohexanone	*164*
2-Benzhydryl-3-methyl-6-benzylidenecyclohexanone	C_6H_5MgBr	2,6-Dibenzhydryl-3-methylcyclohexanone	*164*

* 10,10-Diphenylanthracen-9(10*H*)-one.

† 10-Benzhydrylideneanthrone; 10-benzhydrilideneanthracen-9(10*H*)-one.

TABLE VI-XIX (Continued)

Ketone	RMgX	Product(s)	Ref.
$C_{27}H_{44}O$			
Cholestenone (5.0 g.)	C_6H_5MgBr (6.2 g. C_6H_5Br)	3-Phenyl-4-cholesten-3-ol (80%)	*28,274*
Cholestenone	1-$C_{10}H_7MgBr$ (3 equiv.)	After dehydr'n, a 3-α-naphthyl-cholestadiene	*274*
$C_{27}H_{46}O$			
3-Cholestanone	CH_3MgI	3-Methyl-3-cholestanol	*170*
3-Cholestanone	CH_3MgI (excess)	3-Methylcholestene	*170*
$C_{27}H_{46}O_2$			
6-Ketocholestanol	CH_3MgI	6(α)-Methylcholestane-3(β),6(β)-diol	*364*
6-Ketocholestanol	C_6H_5MgBr	6-Phenyl-3,6-cholestanediol	*65*
$C_{28}H_{16}O_2$			
Dianthraquinone*	2-ClC_6H_4MgX	9,9′-Di-o-chlorophenyl-$\Delta^{10(9H),10'(9'H)}$-bi-9-anthrol †	*329*
Dianthraquinone* (4.0 g.)	C_6H_5MgBr (7.2 g. C_6H_5Br)	9,9′-Diphenyl-$\Delta^{10(9H),10'(9'H)}$-bi-9-anthrol	*329*
Dianthraquinone*	$C_6H_5CH_2MgX$	9,9′-Dibenzyl-$\Delta^{10(9H),10'(9'H)}$-bi-9-anthrol	*329*
Dianthraquinone*	1-$C_{10}H_7MgX$	9,9′-Di-α-naphthyl-$\Delta^{10(9H),10'(9'H)}$-bi-9-anthrol	*329*
$C_{28}H_{22}O_3$			
10,10-Dianysylanthrone ‡ (16.0 g.)	4-$CH_3OC_6H_4MgI$ (18.9 g. C_7H_7IO)	9,10,10-Trianisyl-9,10-dihydro-9-anthrol (15.0 g.)	*39*

* $\Delta^{10,10'}$-Bianthrone; 10,10′-Dioxo-$\Delta^{9,9'}$-9,9′,10,10′-Tetrahydro-9,9′-bianthracyl.

† 10,10′-Dihydroxy-10,10′-di-o-chlorophenyl-$\Delta^{10,10'}$-9,9′,10,10′-tetrahydro-9,9′-bianthracyl.

‡ 10,10-Dianysylanthracen-9(10*H*)-one.

TABLE VI-XIX (Continued)

Ketone	RMgX	Product(s)	Ref.
$C_{29}H_{18}O$			
1,3-Diphenyl-2-cyclopenta-[*l*]phenanthren-2-one	C_2H_5MgBr	1,3-Diphenyl-2-ethyl-2-cyclopenta[*l*]phenanthren-2-ol (53-75%)*	*1*
1,3-Diphenyl-2-cyclopenta-[*l*]phenanthren-2-one	*n*-C_4H_9MgBr	1,3-Diphenyl-2-*n*-butyl-2-cyclopenta[*l*]phenanthren-2-ol (53-75%)*	*1*
1,3-Diphenyl-2-cyclopenta-[*l*]phenanthren-2-one	C_6H_5MgBr	1,2,3-Triphenyl-2-cyclopenta[*l*]phenanthren-2-ol (53-75%)*	*1*
1,3-Diphenyl-2-cyclopenta-[*l*]phenanthren-2-one	$C_6H_5CH_2MgCl$	1,3-Diphenyl-2-benzyl-2-cyclopenta[*l*]phenanthren-2-ol (53-75%)*	*1*
$C_{29}H_{18}OBr_2$			
2,5-Diphenyl-3,4-di-*p*-bromophenyl-2,4-cyclopentadien-1-one (5.4 g.)	C_6H_5MgBr	1,2,5-Triphenyl-3,4-di-*p*-bromophenyl-2,4-cyclopentadien-1-ol (4.1 g.)	*6*
$C_{29}H_{22}O$			
1,1,4-Triphenyl-3-methylnaphthalen-2(1*H*)-one	CH_3MgI	1,1,4-Triphenyl-2-methylene-3-methyl-1,2-dihydronaphthalene	*326*
$C_{29}H_{24}O_4$			
2-Methoxy-10,10-dianysylanthrone†	4-$CH_3OC_6H_4MgI$	2-Methoxy-9,10,10-trianysyl-9,10-dihydro-9-anthrol	*42*
3-Methoxy-10,10-dianysylanthrone†	4-$CH_3OC_6H_4MgI$	3-Methoxy-9,10-,10-trianysyl-9,10-dihydro-9-anthrol	*42*
$C_{29}H_{46}O_3$			
7-Ketocholesteryl acetate (6.6 g., 0.015 mole)	CH_3MgX (0.1 mole)	7-Hydroxy-7-methylcholesterol (2.25 g.)	*297*

* The available abstract reports the yields of a series of reactions as ranging from 53% to 75%.

† 2-Methoxy-10,10-dianysylanthracen-9(10*H*)-one.

TABLE VI-XIX (Continued)

Ketone	RMgX	Product(s)	Ref.
$C_{29}H_{46}O_3$ (*cont.*)			
7-Ketocholesteryl acetate	C_2H_5MgX	7-Ethylidenecholesterol	*297*
7-Ketocholesteryl acetate	i-C_4H_9MgX	7-Hydroxy-7-isobutylcholesterol	*297*
7-Ketocholesteryl acetate	C_6H_5MgBr	7-Hydroxy-7-phenylcholesterol	*297,274*
$C_{30}H_{46}O$			
trans-Dehydroandrosterone	CH_3MgI	17-Methyl-3,17-androstenediol (74%)	*154*
trans-Dehydroandrosterone (2.0 g.)	CH_3MgI (8.0 g. CH_3I)	17-Methyl-*trans*-$\Delta^{5,6}$-androstene-3,17-diol (1.2 g.)	*233*
trans-Dehydroandrosterone	C_2H_5MgI	17-Ethyl-$\Delta^{5,6}$-androstene-3-*trans*-17-(?)-diol; $\Delta^{5,6}$-androstene-3-*trans*-17-*cis*-diol	*235*
$C_{30}H_{46}O_2$			
Androstane-3,17-dione (100 g.)	CH_3MgI (400 mg. CH_3I)	3,17-Dimethylandrostane-3,17-diol	*233*
$C_{30}H_{48}O$			
Androsterone (0.5 g.)	CH_3MgI (2.0 g. CH_3I)	3-*epi*-Hydroxy-17-methylandrostan-17-ol (340 mg.)	*233*
Androsterone	C_2H_5MgI	17-Ethyl-*cis*-androstane-3,17-diol	*233*
trans-Androsterone	CH_3MgI	17-Methyl-*trans*-androstane-3,17-diol	*233*
trans-Androsterone	C_2H_5MgI	17-Ethylandrostane-3-*trans*-17-(?)-diol; androstane-3-*trans*-17-*cis*-diol	*233*
trans-Androsterone	n-C_3H_7MgBr	17-*n*-Propylandrostane-3-*trans*-17-(?)-diol (very little); antrostane-3-*trans*-17-*cis*-diol	*235*
$C_{30}H_{56}O_2$			
Cyclotriacontane-1,16-dione	CH_3MgI	1,16-Dimethylcyclotriacontane-1,16-diol (or partial dehydr'n product)	*231*

TABLE VI-XIX (Continued)

Ketone	RMgX	Product(s)	Ref.
$C_{33}H_{22}O$			
2,3,5,6-Tetraphenylindone	C_6H_5MgBr	1,2,3,5,6-Pentaphenyl-1-indenol (87%)	3
$C_{33}H_{23}OBr$			
2-Bromo-2,3,5,6-tetraphenyl-1-indanone (6 g.)	C_6H_5MgBr (0.1 mole)	2,3,5,6-Tetraphenyl 2,7a-di-hydroinden-1-one (3 g.)	3
2,3,5,6-Tetraphenyl-4-bromo-3a,4-dihydroinden-1-one	CH_3MgI	2,3,5,6-Tetraphenyl-7-methyl-3a,7a-dihydroinden-1-one; unidentified products	3
2,3,5,6-Tetraphenyl-4-bromo-3a,4-dihydroinden-1-one	C_6H_5MgBr	2,3,5,6,7-Pentaphenyl-3a,7a-dihydroinden-1-one; a bimolecular (brominated) comp'd	3
$C_{33}H_{24}O$			
2,3,5,6-Tetraphenyl-3a,4-dihydroinden-1-one	C_6H_5MgBr	1,2,3,5,6-Pentaphenyl-3a,4-dihydroinden-1-ol (25%); 2,3,5,6,7-Pentaphenyl-3a,4-7,7a-tetrahydroinden-1-one	3
$C_{34}H_{21}O_2Br_3$			
2,3,5,6-Tetraphenyl-4,7,7a-tribromo-4,7-methano-3a,4,7,7a-tetrahydroindene-1,8-dione	CH_3MgI	1,8-Dihydroxy-1,8-dimethyl-2,3,5,6-tetraphenyl-4,7,7a-tribromo-4,7-methano-3a,4,7,7a-tetrahydriondene	3
$C_{34}H_{34}O$			
2,2,6,6-Tetrabenzylcyclohexanone (13.5 g.)	CH_3MgI (5 equiv.)	Recovered ketone (1 part); 1-methyl-2,2,6,6-tetrabenzylcyclohexanol (2 parts) (Total recovery, 10 g.)	79
$C_{36}H_{28}O_2$			
2,7-Dimethyl-3,3a,5,6-tetraphenyl-3a,4,7,7a-tetrahydro-4,7-methanoindene-1,8-dione	CH_3MgI	2,7,8-Trimethyl-3,3a,5,6-tetraphenyl-8-hydroxy-3a,4,7,7a-tetrahydro-4,7-methanoinden-1-one (90–98%)	7

Ketone	RMgX	Product(s)	Ref.
$C_{36}H_{28}O_2$ *(cont.)*			
2,7-Dimethyl-3,3a,5,6-tetraphenyl-3a,4,7,7a-tetrahydro-4,7-methanoindene-1,8-dione	C_6H_5MgBr	2,7-Dimethyl-3,3a,5,6,8-pentaphenyl-8-hydroxy-3a,4,7,7a-tetrahydro-4,7-methanoinden-1-one (90-98%)	7
2,7-Dimethyl-3,3a,5,6-tetraphenyl-3a,4,7,7a-tetrahydro-4,7-methanoindene-1,8-dione	$4\text{-}CH_3OC_6H_4MgBr$	2,7-Dimethyl-3,3a,5,6-tetraphenyl-8-hydroxy-8-*p*-anisyl-3a,4,7,7a-tetrahydro-4,7-methanoinden-1-one (90-98%)	7
$C_{38}H_{32}O_2$			
2,4,7,7a-Tetramethyl-3,3a,5,6-tetraphenyl-3a,4,7,7a-tetrahydro-4,7-methanoindene-1,8-dione	CH_3MgI	1-(or 8-)Hydroxy-1,2,4,7,7a-(or 2,4,7,7a,8-)pentamethyl-3,3a,5,6-tetraphenyl-3a,4,7,7a-tetrahydro-4,7-methanoinden-8-(or 1-)one	7
2,4,7,7a-Tetramethyl-3,3a,5,6-tetraphenyl-3a,4,7,7a-tetrahydro-4,7-methanoindene-1,8-dione	C_6H_5MgBr	1-(or 8-)Hydroxy-1,3,3a,5,6-(or 3,3a,5,6,8-)pentaphenyl-2,4,7,7a-tetramethyl-3a,4,7,7a-tetrahydro-4,7-methanoinden-8-(or 1-)one	7
2,4,7,7a-Tetramethyl-3,3a,5,6-tetraphenyl-3a,4,7,7a-tetrahydro-4,7-methanoindene-1,8-dione	$4\text{-}CH_3OC_6H_4MgBr$	1-Anisyl-2,5-dimethyl-3,4-diphenylcyclopentadien-1-ol*	7
$C_{39}H_{28}O$			
2,3,5,6,7-Pentaphenyl-3a,7a-dihydroinden-1-one	C_6H_5MgBr	1,2,3,5,6,7-Hexaphenyl-3a,7a-dihydroinden-1-ol	3
$C_{44}H_{44}O_2$			
2,7-Di-*n*-amyl-3,3a,5,6-tetraphenyl-3a,4,7,7a-tetrahydro-4,7-methanoindene-1,8-dione	C_6H_5MgBr	2,7-Di-*n*-amyl-3,3a,5,6,8-pentaphenyl-8-hydroxy-3a,4,7,7a-tetrahydro-4,7-methanoinden-1-one (90-98%)	7

* The diketone is a cyclopentadienone dimer. Evidently depolymerization takes place under the experimental conditions imposed.

REFERENCES FOR TABLE VI-XIX

(1) Abramov and Malskiĭ, *J. Gen. Chem.*, (U.S.S.R.), *9*, 1533–6 (1939); *Chem. Abstr.*, *34*, 2839 (1940).
(2) Aktieselskabet "Ferrosan," Danish Patent 60,592, Feb. 15, 1943; *Chem. Abstr.*, *40*, P4086 (1946).
(3) Allen and Gates, *J. Am. Chem. Soc.*, *64*, 2123–7 (1942).
(4) Allen and Overbaugh, *J. Am. Chem. Soc.*, *57*, 740–4 (1935).
(5) Allen and Overbaugh, *J. Am. Chem. Soc.*, *57*, 1322–5 (1935).
(6) Allen and Van Allan, *J. Am. Chem. Soc.*, *66*, 7–8 (1944).
(7) Allen and Van Allan, *J. Am. Chem. Soc.*, *68*, 2387–90 (1946).
(8) Bachmann and Chemerda, *J. Am. Chem. Soc.*, *61*, 2358–61 (1939).
(9) Bachmann and Levine, *J. Am. Chem. Soc.*, *69*, 2341–6 (1947).
(10) Bachmann, *J. Am. Chem. Soc.*, *52*, 3287–90 (1930).
(11) Bachmann, *J. Am. Chem. Soc.*, *56*, 1363–7 (1934).
(12) Bachmann and Kloetzel, *J. Org. Chem.*, *3*, 55–61 (1938).
(13) Bachmann and Sheehan, *J. Am. Chem. Soc.*, *63*, 2598–600 (1941).
(14) Badger, *J. Chem. Soc.*, *1941*, 535–8.
(15) Badger, Carrington, and Hendry, British Patent 576,962, Apr. 29, 1946; *Chem. Abstr.*, *42*, P3782 (1948).
(16) Baeyer, *Ann.*, *372*, 80–151 (1910).
(17) Banerjee, *Science and Culture*, *12*, 508–9 (1947); *Chem. Abstr.*, *41*, 6557 (1947).
(18) Barnett, *J. Chem. Soc.*, *1931*, 3340–1.
(19) Barnett, Cook, and Nixon, *J. Chem. Soc.*, *1927*, 504–12.
(20) Barnett and Sanders, *J. Chem. Soc.*, *1933*, 434–7.
(21) Barrett and Linstead, *J. Chem. Soc.*, *1936*, 611–6.
(22) Bartlett, *J. Am. Chem. Soc.*, *57*, 224–7 (1935).
(23) Bateman and Koch, *J. Chem. Soc.*, *1944*, 600–6.
(24) Béchamp, *Compt. rend.*, *148*, 1677–9 (1909); *Chem. Zentr.*, *1909,II*, 714.
(25) Bergmann, *J. Chem. Soc.*, *1938*, 1291–2.
(26) Bergmann and Bergmann, *J. Am. Chem. Soc.*, *59*, 1443–50 (1937).
(27) Bergmann, Eschinazi, and Shapiro, *J. Am. Chem. Soc.*, *64*, 557–8 (1942).
(28) Bergmann and Hirschmann, *J. Org. Chem.*, *4*, 40–7 (1939).
(29) Bergmann, Hoffmann, and Winter, *Ber.*, *66B*, 46–54 (1933).
(30) Bergmann, Shapiro, and Eschinazi, *J. Am. Chem. Soc.*, *64*, 559–61 (1942).
(31) Bergmann and Schreiber, *Ann.*, *500*, 118–22 (1933).
(32) Bergmann and Szmuszhowicz, *J. Am. Chem. Soc.*, *69*, 1367–70 (1947).
(33) Bergmann, Taubadel, and Weiss, *Ber.*, *64B*, 1493–1501 (1931).
(34) Bergmann and Weiss, *Ann.*, *480*, 64–75 (1930).
(35) Bergmann and Weizmann, *J. Org. Chem.*, *4*, 266–9 (1939).
(36) Bergmann and Weizmann, *J. Org. Chem.*, *9*, 352–8 (1944).
(37) Bhattacharyya, *J. Indian Chem. Soc.*, *22*, 165–8 (1945); *Chem. Abstr.*, *40*, 5044 (1946).
(38) Billeter and Miescher, *Helv. Chim. Acta*, *29*, 859–71 (1946).
(39) Blicke and Patelski, *J. Am. Chem. Soc.*, *60*, 2636–8 (1938).
(40) Blicke and Patelski, *J. Am. Chem. Soc.*, *60*, 2638–41 (1938).
(41) Blicke and Weinkauff, *J. Am. Chem. Soc.*, *54*, 1446–53 (1932).
(42) Blicke and Weinkauff, *J. Am. Chem. Soc.*, *54*, 1460–4 (1932).
(43) Boedtker, *J. pharm. chim.*, [8], *6*, 193–203 (1927); *Chem. Zentr.*, *1927,II*, 2189.
(44) Bogert and Sterling, *Science*, 87, 196, 234 (1938); *Chem. Abstr.*, 32, 4147 (1938).
(45) Borsche and Menz, *Ber.*, *41*, 190–210 (1908).

(46) Bouveault and Chereau, *Compt. rend.*, *142*, 1086–7 (1906); *Chem. Zentr.*, *1906,II*, 125.
(47) Bradfield, Hegde, Rao, Simonsen, and Gillam, *J. Chem. Soc.*, *1936*, 667–77.
(48) Bradfield, Jones, and Simonsen, *J. Chem. Soc.*, *1936*, 1137–43.
(49) Bredt, *J. prakt. Chem.*, [2], *98*, 96–105 (1918).
(50) Bredt-Savelsburg and Buchkremer, *Ber.*, *64B*, 600–10 (1931).
(51) Brunner and Grof, *Monatsh*, *64*, 76–9 (1934).
(52) Büchi and Jeger, *Helv. Chim. Acta*, *32*, 538–44 (1949).
(53) Bünzly and Decker, *Ber.*, *37*, 2931–8 (1904).
(54) Butenandt, Dannenberg, and von Dresler, *Z. Naturforsch.*, *1*, 151–6 (1946); *Chem. Abstr.*, *41*, 5887 (1947).
(55) Butenandt, Dannenberg, and von Dresler, *Z. Naturforsch.*, *1*, 222–6 (1946); *Chem. Abstr.*, *41*, 5888 (1947).
(56) Butz, Davis, and Gaddis, *J. Org. Chem.*, *12*, 122–32 (1947).
(57) Buu-Hoï, *Bull. soc. chim.*, [5], *13*, 117–23 (1946).
(58) Campbell and Soffer, *J. Am. Chem. Soc.*, *64*, 417–25 (1943).
(59) Candini, *Gazz. chim. ital.*, *64*, 594–604 (1934); *Chem. Abstr.*, *29*, 1408 (1935).
(60) Charrier and Ghigi, *Gazz. chim. ital.*, *62*, 928–36 (1932); *Chem. Abstr.*, *27*, 1344 (1933).
(61) Charrier and Ghigi, *Ber.*, *69B*, 2211–32 (1936).
(62) Chatterjee, *J. Indian Chem. Soc.*, *12*, 591–4 (1935).
(63) Chavanne and Miller, *Bull. soc. chim. Belg.*, *39*, 287–97 (1930).
(64) Chigi, *Ber.*, *71B*, 684–9 (1938).
(65) Chinaeva and Ushakov, *J. Gen. Chem.* (U.S.S.R.), *11*, 335–8 (1941); *Chem. Abstr.*, *35*, 5903 (1941).
(66) Choin, *J. Russ. Phys.-Chem. Soc.*, *44*, 1844–53 (1912); *Chem. Zentr.*, *1913,I* 1421.
(67) Clar, *Ber.*, *62B*, 350–9 (1929).
(68) Clar, *Ber.*, *65B*, 846–58 (1932).
(69) Clar and Wright, *Nature*, *163*, 921–2 (1949).
(70) Clarke and Francis, *Ber.*, *45*, 2060–5 (1912).
(71) Clarkson and Gomberg, *J. Am. Chem. Soc.*, *52*, 2881–91 (1930).
(72) Clemo and Metcalfe, *J. Chem. Soc.*, *1937*, 1518–23.
(73) Cook, *J. Chem. Soc.*, *1932*, 456–72.
(74) Cook and Lawrence, *J. Chem. Soc.*, *1936*, 1431–4.
(75) Cook and Hewett, *J. Chem. Soc.*, *1933*, 398–405.
(76) Cook and Hewett, *J. Chem. Soc.*, *1936*, 62–71.
(77) Mikeska and Cohen, *J. Org. Chem.*, *6*, 787–94 (1941).
(78) Cook and Robinson, *J. Chem. Soc.*, *1938*, 505–13.
(79) Cornubert, Borrel, De Demo, Garner, Humeau, Le Bihan, and Sarkis, *Bull. soc. chim.*, [5], *2*, 195–220 (1935).
(80) Courtot, *Ann. chim.*, [9], *4*, 58–136 (1915).
(81) Crossley and Gilling, *J. Chem. Soc.*, *97*, 2218–23 (1910).
(82) Decker, *Ber.*, *38*, 2493–511 (1905).
(83) Decker and von Fellenberg, *Ann.*, *356*, 281–342 (1907).
(84) Denisenko and Naber, *Bull. acad. sci. U. R. S. S., Classe sci. math. nat., Ser. chim.*, *1938*, 1015–8; *Chem. Abstr.*, *33*, 7280 (1939).
(85) Dev, *Current Sci.*, *16*, 377–8 (1947); *Chem. Abstr.*, *42*, 5890 (1948).
(86) Dev, *J. Indian Chem. Soc.*, *25*, 69–80 (1948).
(87) Dev, *J. Indian Chem. Soc.*, *25*, 315–22 (1948).
(88) Dilthey and Stephen, *J. prakt. Chem.*, [2], *152*, 114–25 (1939).
(89) Dimroth and Stockstrom, *Ber.*, *75B*, 180–97 (1942).

(90) Dimroth and Stockstrom, *Ber.*, *75B*, 326–31 (1942).
(91) Dimroth and Stockstrom, *Ber.*, *75B*, 510–21 (1942).
(92) Doeuvre, *Bull. soc. chim.*, [5], *6*, 1067–9 (1939).
(93) Dufraisse, Velluz, and Velluz, *Bull. soc. chim.*, [5], *4*, 1260–4 (1937).
(94) Dulou, *Bull. inst. pin*, *1934*, 164–5, 178–82, 197–204; *Chem. Abstr.*, *29*, 2945 (1935).
(95) Dupont, *Ann. chim.*, [8], *30*, 485–587 (1913).
(96) Elagina and Zelinskiĭ, *Compt. rend. acad. sci. U. R. S. S.*, *30*, 728–31 (1941); *Chem. Abstr.*, *37*, 616 (1943).
(97) Elliott and Linstead, *J. Chem. Soc.*, *1938*, 660–5.
(98) Erickson and Kitchens, *J. Am. Chem. Soc.*, *68*, 492–6 (1946).
(99) Errington and Linstead, *J. Chem. Soc.*, *1938*, 666–72.
(100) Étienne and Brisson, *Compt. rend.*, *224*, 1775–7 (1947); *Chem. Abstr.*, *42*, 1259, (1948).
(101) Fieser and Fieser, *J. Am. Chem. Soc.*, *57*, 782–3 (1935).
(102) Fieser and Hershberg, *J. Am. Chem. Soc.*, *61*, 1272–81 (1939).
(103) Fieser and Heymann, *J. Am. Chem. Soc.*, *64*, 376–82 (1942).
(104) Fieser and Johnson, *J. Am. Chem. Soc.*, *61*, 168–71 (1939).
(105) Fieser and Szmuszkovicz, *J. Am. Chem. Soc.*, *70*, 3352–5 (1948).
(106) Gversiteli and Pataraya, *J. Gen. Chem.* (U.S.S.R.), *19*, 1479–82 (1949); *Chem. Abstr.*, *44*, 1038 (1950).
(107) Geissman and Morris, *J. Am. Chem. Soc.*, *66*, 716–9 (1944).
(108) Geissman and Tulagin, *J. Am. Chem. Soc.*, *63*, 3352–6 (1941).
(109) Geissman and Tulagin, *J. Am. Chem. Soc.*, *66*, 719–22 (1944).
(110) Godchot and Bedos, *Compt. rend.*, *180*, 751–4 (1925).
(111) Godchot and Bedos, *Bull. soc. chim.*, [4], *39*, 83–99 (1926).
(112) Gomberg and Cone, *Ann.*, *370*, 142–208 (1909).
(113) Grateau, *Compt. rend.*, *196*, 1619–21 (1933).
(114) Grewe, *Ber.*, *72B*, 785–90 (1939).
(115) Grewe, *Ber.*, *72B*, 1314–7 (1939).
(116) Grignard, *Ann. Univ. Lyon*, N.S., *6*, 1–116 (1901); *Chem. Zentr.*, *1901,II*, 622.
(117) Grignard and Savard, *Compt. rend.*, *181*, 589–92 (1925).
(118) Grignard and Savard, *Bull. soc. chim. Belg.*, *36*, 97–107 (1927).
(119) Gripenberg, *Suomen Kemistilehti*, *18B*, 53–6 (1945); *Chem. Abstr.*, *41*, 739 (1947).
(120) Gripenberg, *Suomen Kemistilehti*, *19B*, 46–9 (1946); *Chem. Abstr.*, *41*, 5488 (1947).
(121) Haberland and Heinrich, *Ber.*, *72B*, 1222–6 (1939).
(122) Haller and Bauer, *Compt. rend.*, *142*, 971–6 (1906); *Chem. Zentr.*, *1906,I*, 1827.
(123) Haller and Guyot, *Bull. soc. chim.*, [3], *31*, 979–85 (1904).
(124) Harris, *J. Am. Chem. Soc.*, *51*, 2591 (1929).
(125) Harris, *J. Am. Chem. Soc.*, *64*, 720 (1942).
(126) Harris and Sanderson, *J. Am. Chem. Soc.*, *70*, 339–43 (1948).
(127) Haworth, *J. Chem. Soc.*, *103*, 1242–50 (1913).
(128) Haworth, *J. Chem. Soc.*, *1932*, 1125–33.
(129) Haworth and Barker, *J. Chem. Soc.*, *1939*, 1299–303.
(130) Haworth and Mavin, *J. Chem. Soc.*, *1932*, 2720–3.
(131) Haworth and Sheldrick, *J. Chem. Soc.*, *1934*, 1950–2.
(132) Hill, Short, and Stromberg, *J. Chem. Soc.*, *1937*, 937–41.
(133) Holmes and Mann, *J. Am. Chem. Soc.*, *69*, 2000–3 (1947).
(134) Hooker and Fieser, *J. Am. Chem. Soc.*, *58*, 1216–23 (1936).

(135) Hosking, *Ber.*, *69B*, 780–5 (1936).
(136) Hunter and Hogg, *J. Am. Chem. Soc.*, *68*, 1676–7 (1946).
(137) Hunter and Korman, *J. Am. Chem. Soc.*, *69*, 2124–6 (1947).
(138) Hurd, Jones, and Blunck, *J. Am. Chem. Soc.*, *57*, 2033–6 (1935).
(139) Inagaki, *J. Pharm. Soc. Japan*, *59*, 5–17 (1939); *Chem. Abstr.*, *33*, 3790 (1939).
(140) Iotsitch, *J. Russ. Phys.-Chem. Soc.*, *34*, 100–2 (1902); *Bull. soc. chim.*, [3], *28*, 922 (1902).
(141) Iotsitch, *J. Russ. Phys.-Chem. Soc.*, *35*, 1269–75 (1905); *Bull. soc. chim.*, [3], *34*, 181 (1905).
(142) Iotsitch, *J. Russ. Phys.-Chem. Soc.*, *36*, 1545–51 (1904); *Bull. soc. chim.*, [3], *36*, 177 (1906).
(143) Iotsitch, *J. Russ. Phys.-Chem. Soc.*, *38*, 252–3 (1906); *Bull. soc. chim.*, [4], *4*, 981, (1908).
(144) Iotsitch, *J. Russ. Phys.-Chem. Soc.*, *38*, 656–9 (1906); *Bull. soc. chim.*, [4], *4*, 1203 (1908).
(145) Ivanoff and Spassoff, *Bull. soc. chim.*, [4], *49*, 377–9 (1931).
(146) Ivanoff and Spassoff, *Bull. soc. chim.*, [5], *2*, 1435–8 (1935).
(147) Jaworski, *J. Russ. Phys.-Chem. Soc.*, *40*, 1746–8 (1909); *Chem. Zentr.*, *1909,I*, 856.
(148) Julian, Cole, and Wood, *J. Am. Chem. Soc.*, *57*, 2508–13 (1935).
(149) Julian, Cole, and Schroeder, *J. Am. Chem. Soc.*, *71*, 2368–70 (1949).
(150) Julian and Gist, *J. Am. Chem. Soc.*, *57*, 2030–2 (1935).
(151) Kharasch and Burt, *J. Org. Chem.*, *16*, 150–60 (1951).
(152) Kharasch and Sternfeld, *J. Am. Chem. Soc.*, *61*, 2318–22 (1939).
(153) Kharasch and Tawney, *J. Am. Chem. Soc.*, *63*, 2308–15 (1941).
(154) Kiprianov and Frenkel, *J. Gen. Chem.* (U.S.S.R.), *9*, 1682–6 (1939); *Chem. Abstr.*, *34*, 3756 (1940).
(155) Klages, *Ber.*, *40*, 2360–76 (1907).
(156) Klages and Sommer, *Ber.*, *39*, 2306–15 (1906).
(157) Kleene, *J. Am. Chem. Soc.*, *63*, 1768 (1941).
(158) Kloetzel and Close, *J. Org. Chem.*, *11*, 395–8 (1946).
(159) Koelsch, *J. Am. Chem. Soc.*, *54*, 4744–9 (1932).
(160) Koelsch, *J. Am. Chem. Soc.*, *55*, 3394–9 (1933).
(161) Koelsch, *J. Am. Chem. Soc.*, *56*, 1337–9 (1934).
(162) Koelsch and Johnson, *J. Am. Chem. Soc.*, *65*, 567–73 (1943).
(163) Koelsch and Richter, *J. Org. Chem.*, *3*, 462–4 (1938).
(164) Kohler, *Am. Chem. J.*, *37*, 369–92 (1907).
(165) Kohler and Blanchard, *J. Am. Chem. Soc.*, *57*, 367–71 (1935).
(166) Kohn, *Monatsh.*, *31*, 747–51 (1910).
(167) Kohn and Ostersetzer, *Monatsh.*, *32*, 905–16 (1911).
(168) Komppa, *Ann.*, *472*, 179–84 (1929).
(169) Komppa and Roschier, *Ann. Acad. Sci. Fennica* (A) *10*, III, 3–15 (1916); *Chem. Zentr.*, *1917,I*, 751; *Chem. Abstr.*, *11*, 3276 (1917).
(170) Kon and Woolman, *J. Chem. Soc.*, *1939*, 794–800.
(171) Konowalow, Miller, and Timtschenko, *J. Russ. Phys.-Chem. Soc.*, *38*, 447–8 (1906); *Chem. Zentr.*, *1906,II*, 311.
(172) Kotz, Blendermann, Rosenbusch, and Sirringhaus, *Ann.*, *400*, 55–72 (1913).
(173) Kovache, *Ann. chim.*, [9], *10*, 184–248 (1918).
(174) Krollpfeiffer and Branscheid, *Ber.*, *56B*, 1617–9 (1923).
(175) Lee, Ziering, Berger, and Heineman, *Jubilee Vol. Emil Barell*, *1946*, 264–305; *Chem. Abstr.*, *41*, 6246 (1947).
(176) Lee, Ziering, Heineman, and Berger, *J. Org. Chem.*, *12*, 885–93 (1947).

(*177*) Le Fevre and Pearson, *J. Chem. Soc.*, *1933*, 482-4.
(*178*) Lehmstedt and Dostal, *Ber.*, *72B*, 804-6 (1939).
(*179*) Leroide, *Ann. chim.*, [9], *16*, 354-410 (1921).
(*180*) Leuchs and Lock, *Ber.*, *48*, 1432-43 (1915).
(*181*) Löwenbein, Pongrácz, and Spiess, *Ber.*, *57B*, 1517-26 (1924).
(*182*) Lukeš, *Collection Czechoslov. Chem. Commun.*, *4*, 181-92 (1932); *Chem. Zentr.*, *1932,II*, 873; *Chem. Abstr.*, *26*, 4328 (1932).
(*183*) Lukeš and Smetáčková, *Collection Czechoslov. Chem. Commun.*, 6, 433 (1934); *Chem. Abstr.*, *29*, 794 (1935).
(*184*) Lüttringhaus and Sholtis, *Ann.*, *557*, 70-82 (1945).
(*185*) Malmgren, *Ber.*, *35*, 3910-2 (1902).
(*186*) Mailhe and Murat, *Bull. soc. chim.*, [4], 7, 1083-9 (1910).
(*187*) Marvel and Brooks, *J. Am. Chem. Soc.*, *63*, 2853 (1941).
(*188*) Marvel and Walton, *J. Org. Chem.*, 7, 88-97 (1942).
(*189*) Marxer, *Helv. Chim. Acta*, *24*, 209-15E (1941).
(*190*) Matzurewitsch, *J. Russ. Phys.-Chem. Soc.*, *43*, 973-90 (1911); *Chem. Abstr.*, 6, 480 (1912).
(*191*) Maxim, Zugrăvescu, and Teodorescu, *Bull. soc. chim.*, [5], 7, 382-93 (1940).
(*192*) Maxim, Zugrăvescu, and Teodorescu, *Bul. Chim. pură apl.*, *Soc. Chim. România*, [2], 3, A24-31 (1941-1942); *Chem. Zentr.*, *1943,II*, 1278.
(*193*) Mentzer, Molho, and Xuong, *Bull. soc. chim.*, [5], *15*, 263-8 (1948).
(*194*) Mentzer and Urbain, *Compt. rend.*, *215*, 554-6 (1942); *Chem. Abstr.*, 38, 2645 (1944).
(*195*) Miescher, U. S. Patent 2,435,013, Jan. 27, 1948; *Chem. Abstr.*, *42*, P2996 (1948).
(*196*) Miescher, Heer, and Billeter, U.S. Patent 2,459,834, Jan. 25, 1949; *Chem. Abstr.*, *43*, P3848 (1949).
(*197*) Miescher and Marxer, U. S. Patent 2,411,664, Nov. 26, 1946; *Chem. Abstr.*, *41*, P6276 (1947).
(*198*) Mikhaĭlov and Blokhina, *J. Gen. Chem.* (U.S.S.R.), *13*, 609-15 (1943); *Chem. Abstr.*, *39*, 702 (1945).
(*199*) Milas, U. S. Patent 2,407,672, Sept. 17, 1946; *Chem. Abstr.*, *41*, P996 (1947).
(*200*) Minnis, *J. Am. Chem. Soc.*, *51*, 2143-7 (1929).
(*201*) Mitchovitch, *Compt. rend.*, *200*, 1601-3 (1935).
(*202*) Mitter and De, *J. Indian Chem. Soc.*, *16*, 35-42 (1939).
(*203*) Mitter and De, *J. Indian Chem. Soc.*, *16*, 199-208 (1939).
(*204*) Murat, *Ann. chim.*, [8], *16*, 108-26 (1909).
(*205*) Murat, *J. pharm. chim.*, *4*, 294-9 (1911); *J. Soc. Chem. Ind.*, *30*, 1332 (1911); *Chem. Abstr.*, 6, 1156 (1912).
(*206*) Myers and Lindwall, *J. Am. Chem. Soc.*, *60*, 2153-5 (1938).
(*207*) Nakanishi, *Proc. Imp. Acad.* (Tokyo), *9*, 394-7 (1933); *Chem. Abstr.*, *28*, 762 (1934).
(*208*) Nametkin and Shawrigin, *Ber.*, *66B*, 511-4 (1933).
(*209*) Natelson and Gottfried, *J. Am. Chem. Soc.*, *61*, 1001-2 (1939).
(*210*) Newman, *J. Org. Chem.*, *9*, 518-28 (1944).
(*211*) Newman and Booth, *J. Org. Chem.*, *12*, 737-9 (1947).
(*212*) Newman and Farbman, *J. Am. Chem. Soc.*, *66*, 1550-2 (1944).
(*213*) Newman and Hart, *J. Am. Chem. Soc.*, *69*, 298-30 (1947).
(*214*) Nyman and Kuvaja, *Ann.*, *538*, 68-84 (1939).
(*215*) Orchin, *J. Am. Chem. Soc.*, *68*, 571-2 (1946).
(*216*) Orchin and Reggel, *J. Am. Chem. Soc.*, *69*, 505-9 (1947).

(217) Perkin, *Proc. Chem. Soc.*, *21*, 255–6 (1905).
(218) Perlman, Davidson, and Bogert, *J. Org. Chem.*, *1*, 288–99 (1936).
(219) Petrov and Chel'tsova, *J. Gen. Chem.* (U.S.S.R.), *12*, 87–94 (1942); *Chem. Abstr.*, *37*, 1993 (1943).
(220) Plattner and Magyar, *Helv. Chim. Acta*, *25*, 581–90 (1942).
(221) Reilly and Drumm, *J. Chem. Soc.*, *1930*, 455–8.
(222) Richet, *Ann. chim.*, [12], *3*, 317–54 (1948).
(223) Robinson and Slater, *J. Chem. Soc.*, *1941*, 376–85.
(224) Royer, *Ann. chim.*, [12], *1*, 395–445 (1946).
(225) Royer and Buu-Hoï, *Compt. rend.*, *222*, 746–7 (1946); *Chem. Abstr.*, *40*, 4051 (1946).
(226) Rupe and Ebert, *Ber.*, *41*, 2067–71 (1908).
(227) Rupe and Emmerich, *Ber.*, *41*, 1393–403 (1908).
(228) Rupe and Emmerich, *Ber.*, *41*, 1750–4 (1908).
(229) Rupe and Liechtenhahn, *Ber.*, *39*, 1119–26 (1906).
(230) Rupe and Tomi, *Ber.*, *47*, 3064–93 (1914).
(231) Ruzicka and Boekenoogen, *Helv. Chim. Acta*, *14*, 1319–35 (1931).
(232) Ruzicka, Ehmann, and Morgeli, *Helv. Chim. Acta*, *16*, 314–26 (1933).
(233) Ruzicka, Goldberg, and Rosenberg, *Helv. Chim. Acta*, *18*, 1487–98 (1935).
(234) Ruzicka and Hofmann, *Helv. Chim. Acta*, *22*, 126–34 (1939).
(235) Ruzicka and Rosenberg, *Helv. Chim. Acta*, *19*, 357–66 (1936).
(236) Ruzicka and Seidel, *Helv. Chim. Acta*, *19*, 424–33 (1936).
(237) Ruzicka and Waldmann, *Helv. Chim. Acta*, *15*, 907–14 (1932).
(238) Ruzicka, Zwicky, and Jeger, *Helv. Chim. Acta*, *31*, 2143–7 (1948).
(239) Sabatier and Mailhe, *Compt. rend.*, *138*, 1321–4 (1904); *J. Chem. Soc.*, *86,I*, 666, (1904).
(240) Sabatier and Mailhe, *Compt. rend.*, *141*, 20–22 (1905); *Chem. Zentr.*, *1905,II*, 482.
(241) Sabatier and Mailhe, *Compt. rend.*, *141*, 298–301 (1905); *J. Chem. Soc.*, *88,I*, 254, (1905).
(242) Sabatier and Mailhe, *Compt. rend.*, *142*, 438–40 (1906); *Chem. Zentr.*, *1906,I*, 1096.
(243) Sachs and Kantorowicz, *Ber.*, *42*, 1565–76 (1909).
(244) St. Pfau and Plattner, *Helv. Chim. Acta*, *19*, 858–79 (1936).
(245) Semmler, Jonas, and Oelsner, *Ber.*, *50*, 1838–42 (1917).
(246) Sherwood, Short, and Stansfield, *J. Chem. Soc.*, *1932*, 1832–5.
(247) Schiessler, Rytina, and Whitmore, *J. Am. Chem. Soc.*, *70*, 529–30 (1948).
(248) Schlenk and Herzenstein, *Ann.*, *372*, 21–31 (1910).
(249) Schmidt, *Jahrbuch der organishen Chemie*, *I*, 218 (1907).
(250) Schmitt, *Ann.*, *547*, 256–70 (1941).
(251) Schneider and Spielman, *J. Biol. Chem.*, *142*, 345–54 (1942).
(252) Schönberg and Asker, *J. Chem. Soc.*, *1946*, 609–10.
(253) Sen and Sidhu, *J. Indian Chem. Soc.*, *25*, 437–8 (1948).
(254) Sieglitz and Marx, *Ber.*, *56B*, 1619–21 (1923).
(255) Signaigo and Cramer, *J. Am. Chem. Soc.*, *55*, 3326–32 (1933).
(256) Simonis and Kirschsten, *Ber.*, *45*, 567–79 (1912).
(257) Smith and Hanson, *J. Am. Chem. Soc.*, *57*, 1326–8 (1935).
(258) Soc. pour l'ind. chim. à Bâle, British Patent 591,994, Sept. 4, 1947; *Chem. Abstr.*, *42*, P1609 (1948).
(259) Šorm, *Collection Czech. Chem. Commun.*, *12*, 251–61 (1947); *Chem. Abstr.*, *42*, 555 (1948).
(260) Šorm and Fajkoš, *Collection Czech. Chem. Commun.*, *12*, 81–100 (1947); *Chem. Abstr.*, *41*, 4140 (1947).

(261) Staudinger and Rheiner, *Helv. Chim. Acta*, 7, 8–18 (1924).
(262) Stoermer and Laage, *Ber.*, *50*, 981–9 (1917).
(263) Sulzbacher and Bachmann, *J. Org. Chem.*, *13*, 303–8 (1948).
(264) Sumpter, *Trans. Kentucky Acad. Sci.*, *9*, 61–4 (1941); *Chem. Abstr.*, *36*, 4508 (1942).
(265) Thiele and Weitz, *Ann.*, *377*, 1–22 (1910).
(266) Tiffeneau and Tchoubar, *Compt. rend.*, *198*, 941–3 (1934).
(267) Tiffeneau, Tchoubar, and Le Tellier, *Compt. rend.*, *216*, 856–60 (1943); *Chem. Abstr.*, *38*, 4584 (1944).
(268) Treibs, *Ber.*, *65B*, 1324–9 (1932).
(269) Tschitschibabin, *J. Russ. Phys.-Chem. Soc.*, *45*, 184–8 (1913); *Chem. Zentr.*, *1913,I*, 2028.
(270) Ullmann and Engi, *Ber.*, *37*, 2367–74 (1904).
(271) Ullmann and Mourawiew-Winigradoff, *Ber.*, *38*, 2213–9 (1905).
(272) Ullmann and von Wurstemburger, *Ber.*, *37*, 73–8 (1904).
(273) Ullmann and von Wurstemburger, *Ber.*, *38*, 4105–10 (1905).
(274) Urushibara, Ando, Araki, and Ozawa, *Bull. Chem. Soc., Japan*, *12*, 353–5 (1937); *Chem. Abstr.*, *31*, 7881 (1937).
(275) Vavon and Guédon, *Bull. soc. chim.*, [4], *47*, 901–10 (1930).
(276) Vavon and Mitchovitch, *Bull. soc. chim.*, [4], *45*, 961–72 (1929).
(277) Vavon and Perlin-Borrel, *Bull. soc. chim.*, [4], *51*, 993–4 (1932).
(278) von Auwers, *Ber.*, *38*, 1697–711 (1905).
(279) von Auwers, *Ber.*, *49*, 2389–410 (1916).
(280) von Auwers and Eisenlohr, *Ber.*, *43*, 827–34 (1910).
(281) von Auwers and Ellinger, *Ann.*, *387*, 200–39 (1912).
(282) von Auwers and Hessenland, *Ann.*, *352*, 273–87 (1907).
(283) von Auwers and Keil, *Ber.*, *36*, 1861–77 (1903).
(284) von Auwers and Kockritz, *Ann.*, *352*, 288–321 (1907).
(285) von Auwers and Krollpfeiffer, *Ber.*, *48*, 1226–33 (1915).
(286) von Auwers and Lange, *Ann.*, *401*, 303–26 (1911).
(287) von Auwers and Treppmann, *Ber.*, *48*, 1207–25 (1915).
(288) von Braun and Anton, *Ber.*, *67B*, 1051–6 (1934).
(289) von Braun and Kirschbaum, *Ber.*, *46*, 3041–50 (1913).
(290) von Braun and Kirschbaum, *Ber.*, *52B*, 1725–30 (1919).
(291) Wallach, *Ann.*, *345*, 139–54 (1906).
(292) Wallach, *Ann.*, *356*, 227–49 (1907).
(293) Wallach, *Ann.*, *359*, 265–86 (1908).
(294) Wallach, *Ann.*, *396*, 264–84 (1913).
(295) Wanin, *J. Russ. Phys.-Chem. Soc.*, *44*, 1068–75 (1912); *Chem. Zentr.*, *1913,I*, 24.
(296) Wedekind and Miller, *Ber.*, *44*, 3285–7 (1911).
(297) Weinhouse and Kharasch, *J. Org. Chem.*, *1*, 490–5 (1936).
(298) Weiss and Alberti, *Monatsh.*, *59*, 220–7 (1932).
(299) Weiss and Knapp, *Monatsh.*, *61*, 61–8 (1932).
(300) Weiss and Luft, *Monatsh.*, *48*, 337–45 (1927).
(301) Weiss and Woidich, *Monatsh.*, *46*, 453–8 (1925).
(302) Willemart, *Compt. rend.*, *207*, 536–8 (1938); *Chem. Abstr.*, *33*, 571 (1939).
(303) Williams and Edwards, *J. Am. Chem. Soc.*, *69*, 336–8 (1947).
(304) Wolff, *Compt. rend.*, *172*, 1357–60 (1921).
(305) Wolff, *Ann. chim.*, [9], *20*, 82–130 (1923).
(306) Leroide, *Compt. rend.*, *148*, 1611–3 (1909); *Chem. Abstr.*, *3*, 2675 (1909).
(307) Woods, *J. Am. Chem. Soc.*, *69*, 2549–52 (1947).
(308) Woods, Griswold, Armbrecht, Blumethal, and Plapinger, *J. Am. Chem. Soc.*, *71*, 2028–31 (1949).

(309) Woods and Reed, *J. Am. Chem. Soc.*, *71*, 1348–50 (1949).
(310) Woods and Tucker, *J. Am. Chem. Soc.*, *70*, 2174–7 (1948).
(311) Zeile and Meyer, *Ber.*, *75B*, 356–62 (1942).
(312) Zelinsky, *Ber.*, *34*, 3877–84 (1901).
(313) Zelinsky, *Ber.*, *34*, 3950–2 (1901).
(314) Zelinsky, *Ber.*, *58B*, 2755–63 (1925).
(315) Zelinsky and Glinka, *J. Russ. Phys.-Chem. Soc.*, *39*, 1170 (1908); *Chem. Abstr.*, *2*, 1265 (1908).
(316) Zelinsky and Gutt, *Ber.*, *35*, 2140–4 (1902).
(317) Zerner and Loti, *Monatsh.*, *34*, 981–94 (1913).
(318) Zelinsky, Michlina, and Eventowa, *Ber.*, *66B*, 1422–6 (1933).
(319) Zelinsky and Namjetkin, *Ber.*, *35*, 2683 (1902).
(320) Ziegler, *Ann.*, *434*, 34–78 (1923).
(321) Ziegler and Ochs, *Ber.*, *54B*, 3003–9 (1921).
(322) Ziegler and Ochs, *Ber.*, *55B*, 2257–77 (1922).
(323) Ziering, Berger, Heineman, and Lee, *J. Org. Chem.*, *12*, 894–903 (1947).
(324) Zincke and Schwabe, *Ber.*, *41*, 897–902 (1908).
(325) Koelsch, *J. Am. Chem. Soc.*, *54*, 3384–9 (1932).
(326) Crawford, *J. Am. Chem. Soc.*, *61*, 3310–4 (1939).
(327) Gandini, *Gazz. chim. ital.*, *64*, 594–604 (1934); *Chem. Abstr.*, *29*, 1408 (1935).
(328) Obtemperanskaya, *Vestnik Moskov. Univ.*, *1946*, No. 3/4, 132–42; *Chem. Abstr.*, *42*, 4554 (1948).
(329) Schönberg and Ismail, *J. Chem. Soc.*, *1945*, 201–2.
(330) Birch and Robinson, *J. Chem. Soc.*, *1943*, 501–2.
(331) Büchi, Jeger, and Ruzicka, *Helv. Chim. Acta*, *31*, 241–8 (1948).
(332) Stoll and Commarmont, *Helv. Chim. Acta*, *31*, 554–5 (1948).
(333) Birch and Robinson, *J. Chem. Soc.*, *1944*, 503–6.
(334) Iotsitch, *J. Russ. Phys.-Chem. Soc.*, *34*, 242–4 (1902); *Bull. soc. chim*,. [3], *30*, 210 (1903).
(335) Treibs, *Ber.*, *77B*, 572–9 (1944).
(336) Ghosh, *Science and Culture*, 3, 120–1 (1937); *Chem. Abstr.*, *32*, 145 (1938).
(337) Whitmore and Pedlow, *J. Am. Chem. Soc.*, *63*, 758–60 (1941).
(338) Alexander and Coraor, *J. Am. Chem. Soc.*, *73*, 2721–3 (1951).
(339) Reimer and Reynolds, *Am. Chem. J.*, *40*, 428–44 (1908).
(340) French and Smith, *J. Am. Chem. Soc.*, *67*, 1949–50 (1945).
(341) Koelsch, *J. Am. Chem. Soc.*, *58*, 1331–3 (1935).
(342) Mousseron and Winternitz, *Bull. soc. chim.*, [5], *13*, 604–10 (1946).
(343) Crane, Boord, and Henne, *J. Am. Chem. Soc.*, *67*, 1237–9 (1945).
(344) Zal'kind and Gverdtsiteli, *J. Gen. Chem.* (U.S.S.R.), *9*, 855–62; *Chem. Abstr.*, *34*, 387 (1940).
(345) Schokina, Kildischeva, and Preobrashenski, *J. Gen. Chem.* (U.S.S.R.), *11*, 425–8 (1941); *Brit. Chem. Abstr.*, *A,II*, 224 (1942).
(346) von Auwers and Peters, *Ber.*, *43*, 3076–94 (1910).
(347) Cymerman, Heilbron, and Jones, *J. Chem. Soc.*, *1945*, 90–4.
(348) Semon and Craig, *J. Am. Chem. Soc.*, *58*, 1278–82 (1936).
(349) Ullmann and Maag, *Ber.*, *40*, 2515–24 (1907).
(350) Chavanne and Becker, *Bull. soc. chim. Belg.*, *36*, 591–604 (1927).
(351) Meerwein, *Ann.*, *405*, 129–75 (1914).
(352) Pines and Ipatieff, *J. Am. Chem. Soc.*, *61*, 1076–7 (1939).
(353) Wallach, *Ann.*, *365*, 255–77 (1909).
(354) Zelinsky and Pappe, *J. Russ. Phys.-Chem. Soc.*, 37, 625–6 (1905); *Bull. soc. chim.*, [4], *2*, 1119 (1907).
(355) Dupont, *Compt. rend.*, *152*, 1486–8 (1911); *Chem. Abstr.*, *5*, 3408 (1911).

(356) Dupont, *Compt. rend.*, *154*, 599–601 (1912); *Chem. Abstr.*, 6, 1287 (1912).
(357) Koelsch and Wawzonek, *J. Org. Chem.*, 6, 684–9 (1941).
(358) Bergs, Wittfeld, and Wildt, *Ber.*, *67B*, 238–44 (1934).
(359) Chavanne and de Vogel, *Bull. soc. chim. Belg.*, 37, 141–52 (1928).
(360) Bergmann and Blum-Bergmann, *J. Am. Chem. Soc.*, *58*, 1678–81 (1936).
(361) van Rysselberge, *Bull. acad. roy. Belg.*, *Classe sci.*, [5], *12*, 171–92 (1926); *Chem. Zentr.*, *1926,II*, 1846.
(362) Cook and Hewett, *J. Chem. Soc.*, *1933*, 1098–111.
(363) Cohen, Cook, Hewett, and Girard, *J. Chem. Soc.*, *1934*, 653–8.
(364) Fieser and Rigaudy, *J. Am. Chem. Soc.*, 73, 4660–2 (1951).

CHAPTER VII

Reactions of Grignard Reagents with Quinones

Whereas the true quinones are in fact bifunctional α,β-unsaturated cyclic ketones, they undergo many of the reactions already discussed in Chapter VI. Single and double 1,2-addition, 1,4-addition, and combined 1,2- and 1,4-addition have all been reported.

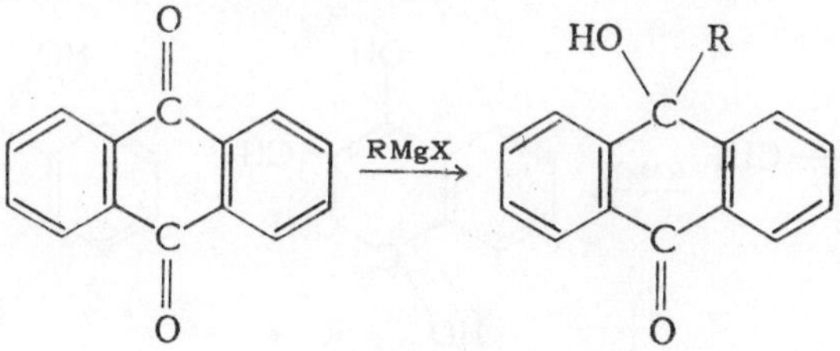

RMgX → (Ref. *1,2,3*)

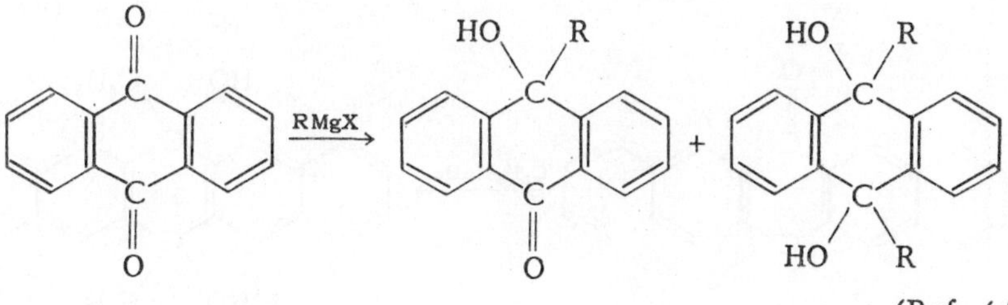

RMgX → + (Ref. *4,5*)

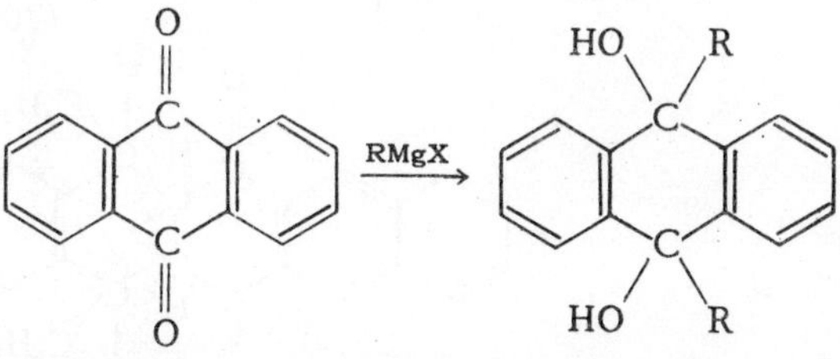

RMgX → (Ref. *6*)

[1]Julian, Cole, and Wood, *J. Am. Chem. Soc.*, *57*, 2508–13 (1935).

[2]Haller and Guyot, *Compt. rend.*, *138*, 1251–4 (1904); *Chem. Zentr.*, *1904,II*, 117.

[3]Blicke and Weinkauff, *J. Am. Chem. Soc.*, *54*, 1460–4 (1932).

[4]Padova, *Ann. chim.*, [8], *19*, 353–440 (1910).

[5]Guyot and Staehling, *Bull. soc. chim.*, [3], *33*, 1104–21 (1905).

[6]Clarkson and Gomberg, *J. Am. Chem. Soc.*, *52*, 2881–91 (1930).

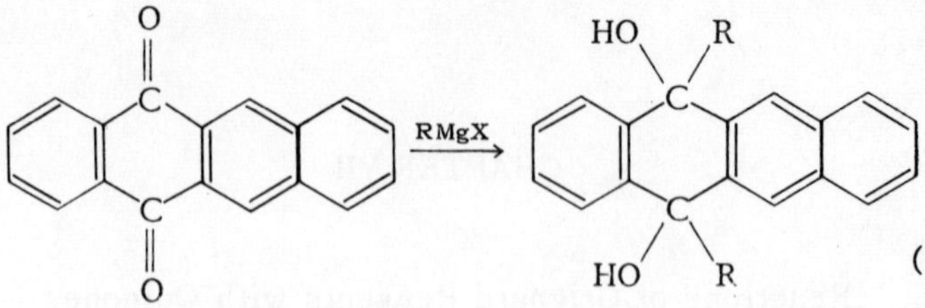

(Ref. 7)

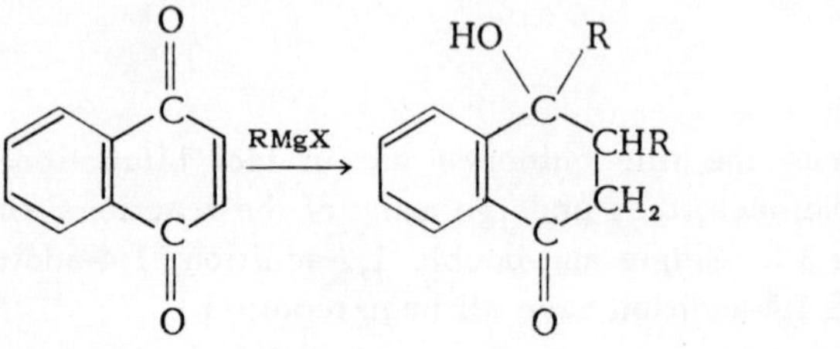

(Ref. 8)

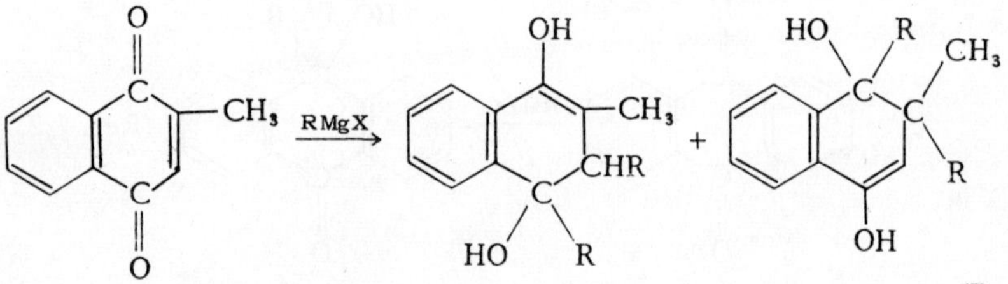

(Ref. 9)

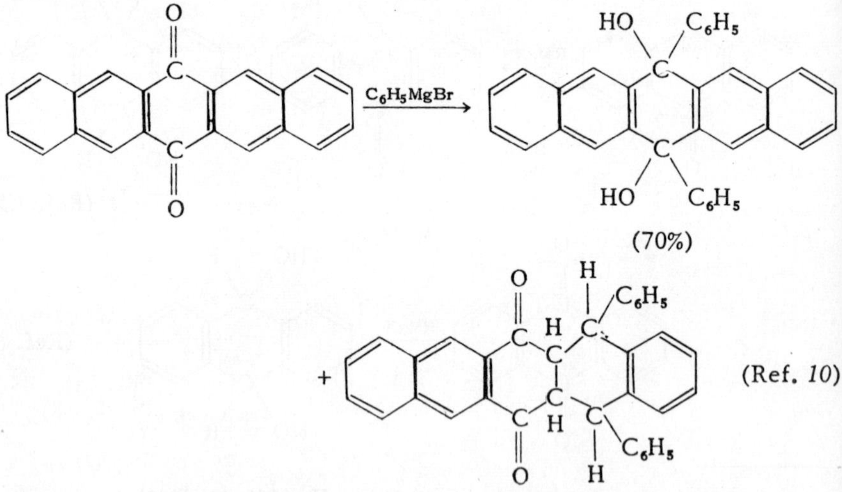

(70%)

(Ref. 10)

(15%)

[7]Dufraisse and Horclois, *Bull. soc. chim.*, [5], 3, 1894–905 (1936).
[8]Smith and Hoehn, *J. Am. Chem. Soc.*, *61*, 2619–24 (1939).
[9]Crawford, *J. Am. Chem. Soc.*, 63, 1070–3 (1941).
[10]Allen and Bell, *J. Am. Chem. Soc.*, *64*, 1253–60 (1942).

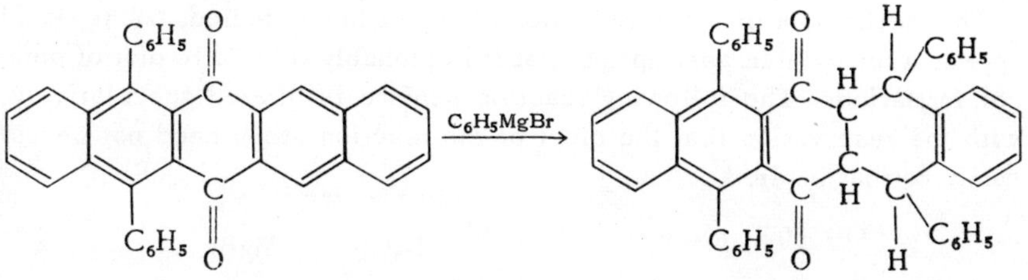

$\xrightarrow{C_6H_5MgBr}$

(60%) (Ref. *10*)

With a few exceptions the quinones react with Grignard reagents to give only small percentage yields of readily isolable and identifiable products. In most cases the major portion of the reaction product consists of a refractory oil, or tar, or both. Consequently the side-reactions in general have been but little studied.

Reductions of addition products of reactions of quinones with non-reducing Grignard reagents have been reported by Bamberger and Blangey,[11] by Barnett *et al.*,[12] and by Allen and Bell.[13] Allen and Bell maintain, despite the statement of Barnett *et al.* to the contrary, that such reductions take place only in the presence of metallic magnesium. In view of the supplementary evidence on the Grignard reductions of aldehydes and ketones (see Magnesious Halide Reduction, Chapter VI), of the fact that Allen and Bell, as well as others, have found suspended magnesium which has passed through a glass-wool plug capable of effecting such reductions, and of the fact that Barnett *et al.* describe no special precautions taken to free their Grignard reagents of residual magnesium, it appears fairly certain that these reductions are of the Gomberg (*i.e.*, magnesious halide) type.

The results of some experiments by Allen and Bell on 5,12-diphenyl-5,12-dihydro-5,12-naphthacenediol, one of the primary products of the reaction of phenylmagnesium bromide with 5,12-naphthacenequinone (Dufraisse and Horclois;[14] Allen and Bell, *loc. cit.*[13]) are recorded in Table VII-I.

TABLE VII-I

PRODUCTS OF THE TREATMENT OF 5,12-DIPHENYL-5,12-DIHYDRO-5,12-NAPHTHACENEDIOL WITH VARIOUS REAGENTS

Reagent	Recovered diol (%)	5,12-Diphenylnaphthacene (%)
C_6H_5MgBr	80	0
Mg	80	0
C_6H_5MgBr + Mg	0	65
Mg + $MgBr_2$	0	73

[11]Bamberger and Blangey, *Ann.*, *384*, 272–322 (1911).
[12]Barnett, Cook, and Wiltshire, *J. Chem. Soc.*, *1927*, 1724–32.
[13]Allen and Bell, *J. Am. Chem. Soc.*, *62*, 2408–12 (1940).
[14]Dufraisse and Horclois, *Bull. soc. chim.*, [5], *3*, 1894–905 (1936).

The mechanism of these reductions has not been studied, but it would appear a reasonable assumption that it is probably related to that of pinacol formation. The following reaction scheme is offered speculatively, with the reservation that the order of the reaction steps need not necessarily be that implied.

$$\text{naphthacenequinone} \xrightarrow{2\ C_6H_5MgBr} \text{(5,12-}H_5C_6\text{, 5,12-OMgBr adduct)} \xrightarrow{\cdot MgBr} \text{(}H_5C_6\text{, OMgBr; }\dot{C}\text{-}H_5C_6\text{ radical)} + MgO + MgBr_2$$

$$2\ \text{(}H_5C_6\text{, OMgBr; }\dot{C}\text{-}H_5C_6\text{ radical)} \longrightarrow 2\ \text{(5,12-di-}C_6H_5\text{-naphthacene)} + MgO + MgBr_2$$

A similar reaction mechanism would account for the reduction of the quinones themselves, as reported by Schmidlin *et al.*[15] (benzoquinone ⟶ quinhydrone), Worrall and Cohen[16] (benzoquinone ⟶ hydroquinone), Smith and Crawford[17] (duroquinone ⟶ durohydroquinone), and Bamberger and Blangey (*loc. cit.*[11]) (toluquinone ⟶ toluhydroquinone).

$$\text{benzoquinone} \xrightarrow{\cdot MgX} \text{(}\dot{C}\text{-OMgX radical)} \longrightarrow \tfrac{1}{2}\ XMgO\text{-}C_6H_4\text{-}OMgX + \tfrac{1}{2}\ \text{benzoquinone}$$

---

[15]Schmidlin, Wohl, and Thommen, *Ber.*, 43, 1298–1303 (1910).
[16]Worrall and Cohen, *J. Am. Chem. Soc.*, 58, 533 (1936).
[17]Smith and Crawford, *J. Am. Chem. Soc.*, 50, 869–83 (1928).

If any of the intermediate free radicals so formed proved capable of coupling rather than disproportionating, bimolecular reduction products such as those reported by Schmidlin *et al.* (*loc. cit.*[15]) and Bamberger and Blangey (*loc. cit.*[11]) could be expected.

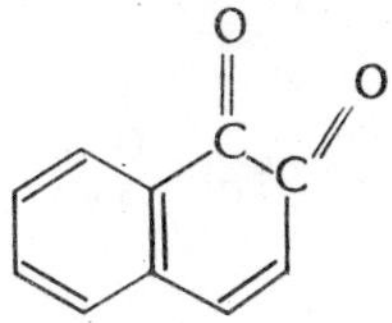

→ "dinaphthyldiquinhydrone" (Ref. *15*)

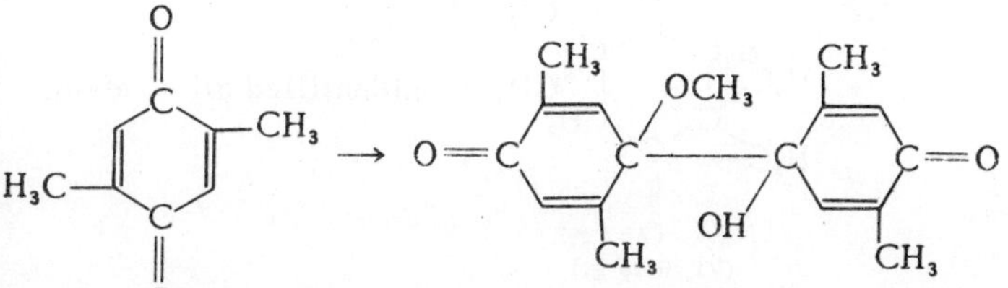

→ (Ref. *11*)

The methoxyl group in the Bamberger and Blangey product is, of course, not the result of a species of reverse Grignard reagent addition (as they suggest) but of a variety of Williamson etherification fairly well known as a side-reaction in ketone-Grignard reagent reactions.

The possibility of oxidation-reduction reactions among the various products of quinone-Grignard reagent interaction or between products and the quinone themselves is, of course, not excluded.

The reaction of phlorone with methylmagnesium iodide may be cited as an example of the few that have been studied in some detail (Bamberger and Blangey, *loc. cit.*[11]).

(120 g.) $\xrightarrow{CH_3MgI}$ (125.6 g. CH_3I) Recovered quinone (I, 26.4 g.)

+ (II, 2.4 g.) + (III, 5.3 g.)

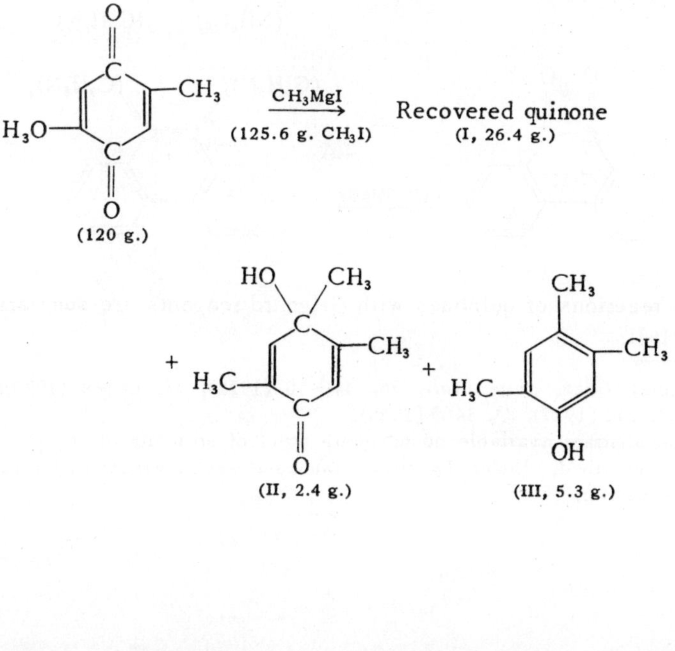

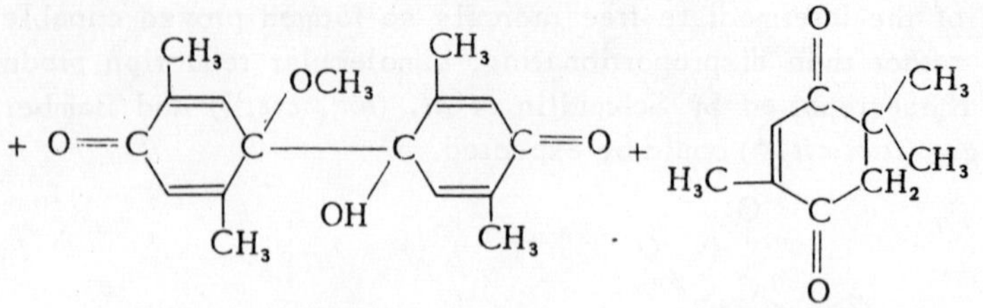

(IV, 1.7 g.) (V, 5.3 g.)

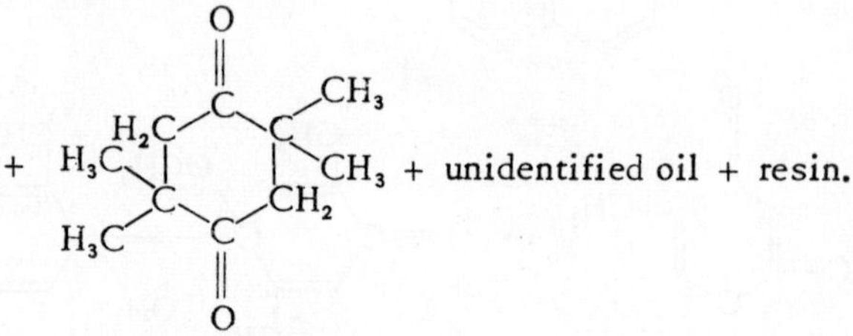

+ unidentified oil + resin.

(VI, 0.26 g.)

When two equivalents of methylmagnesium iodide were used no pseudocumoquinol (**II**) was isolated, but a small amount of prehnitol (2,3,4,5-tetramethylphenol) was found.

Two reactions described by Mingoia,[18] namely, those of 3-methylindolylmagnesium bromide with anthraquinone and 9,10-phenanthrenequinone, await satisfactory elucidation.*

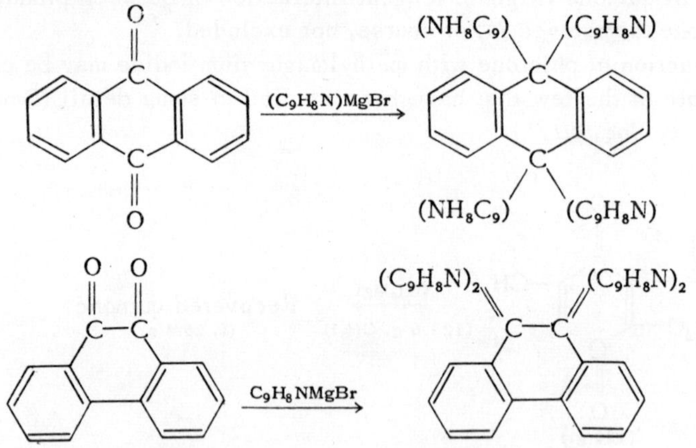

$(C_9H_8N)MgBr$

C_9H_8NMgBr

Other reactions of quinones with Grignard reagents are summarized in Table VII-II.

[18]Mingoia, *Gazz. chim. ital.*, *56*, 446–50 (1926); *58*, 673–9 (1929); *Chem. Abstr.*, *21*, 242 (1927); *23*, 3465 (1929).

*In the abstract available no adequate proof of structure of the products reported is described. Under the circumstances it seems wisest to forego speculative discussion.

TABLE VII-II

REACTIONS OF GRIGNARD REAGENTS WITH QUINONES

Quinone	RMgX	Product(s)	Ref.
$C_6H_4O_2$			
o-Quinone	$(C_6H_5)_3CMgCl$	$[(C_6H_5)_3C]_2O_2$ (0.11 g.); black C_6H_6-insoluble powder	*42*
Quinone (0.4 mole)	$4\text{-}C_6H_5C_6H_4MgBr$ (0.1 mole $C_{12}H_9Br$)	$(4\text{-}C_6H_5C_6H_4—)_2$; $(C_6H_5—)_2$; hydroquinone; unidentified oily products; tar.	*51*
Quinone (10 g.)	$(C_6H_5)_3CMgCl$ (20 g. $C_{19}H_{15}Cl$)	1,4-$[(C_6H_5)_3CO]_2C_6H_4$ (6 g.); quinhydrone	*42*
$C_7H_6O_2$			
p-Toluquinone	CH_3MgI	3,4-Xyloquinol; *p*-toluhydroquinone; *p*-xyloquinone; *p*-xylohydroquinone; oil; resin	*12,11*
"Toluquinone" (9.2 g.)	$(C_6H_5)_3CMgCl$ (14.0 g. $C_{19}H_{15}Cl$)	$[(C_6H_5)_3C]_2O_2$ (0.01 g.); $(C_6H_5)_3COH$; "toluquinhydrone"	*42*
$C_8H_8O_2$			
Phlorone (120.0 g.)	CH_3MgI (125.6 g. CH_3I)	Recovered quinone (26.4 g.); pseudocumoquinol (2,4,5-trimethyl-4-hydroxy-2,5-cyclohexadien-1-one) (2.4 g.); pseudocumenol (2,4,5-trimethylphenol) (5.3 g.); 1-hydroxy-1′-methoxy-1,1′-bis(2,5-dimethyl-4-oxo-2,5-cyclohexadienyl) (1.7 g.); dihydrotrimethylquinone (5.3 g.); 2,2,5,5-tetramethylcyclohexane-1,4-dione (0.26 g.); unidentified oil; resin	*12,11*
Phlorone (285 g.)	CH_3MgI (298 g. CH_3I)	Recovered quinone (66.7 g.); pseudocumenol (16.6 g.); dihydrotrimethylquinone (17.9 g.); bi-*p*-xyloquinol monomethyl ether (3.2 g.); prehnitol (2.1 g.); 2,2,5,5-tetramethylcyclohexane-1,4-dione (0.5 g.); oil (7.3 g.); resin	*12,11*

TABLE VII-II (Continued)

Quinone	RMgX	Product(s)	Ref.
$C_{10}H_6O_2$			
1,2-Naphthoquinone	C_6H_5MgBr	$C_{16}H_{10}O_2$	*26*
1,2-Naphthoquinone	$(C_6H_5)_3CMgCl$	$[(C_6H_5)_3C]_2O_2$ (0.8 g.); $(C_6H_5)_2CH$ (5.2 g.); "dinaphthyldiquinhydrone" (7.7 g.)	*42*
1,4-Naphthoquinone (20 g.)	C_6H_5MgBr (99 g. C_6H_5Br)	3,4-Diphenyl-4-hydroxy-3,4-dihydro-1(2*H*)-naphthalenone (8.1 g.)	*47,26,27*
1,4-Naphthoquinone	$(C_6H_5)_3CMgCl$	$[(C_6H_5)_3C]_2O_2$ (1.0 g.); "α-hydronaphthoquinone" (0.3 g.)	*42*
$C_{10}H_{12}O_2$			
Duroquinone	C_6H_5MgBr (1 equiv.)	2,3,5,6-Tetramethyl-4-hydroxy-4-phenyl-2,5-cyclohexadien-1-one; 2,3,5,6-tetramethyl-4-hydroxy-6-phenyl-2,4-cyclohexadien-1-one; 2,3,5,6-tetramethyl-6-phenyl-2-cyclohexene-1,4-dione; hydroduroquinone; biphenyl; oil.	*46*
Duroquinone	C_6H_5MgBr (4 equiv.)	2,3,5,6-Tetramethyl-4-hydroxy-6-phenyl-2,4-cyclohexadien-1-one; 2,3,5,6-tetramethyl-3,6-diphenyl-1,4-cyclohexadiene-1,4-diol; hydroduroquinone; biphenyl; oil.	*46*
$C_{11}H_8O_2$			
2-Methyl-1,4-naphthoquinone	C_6H_5MgBr	2-Methyl-3,4-diphenyl-3,4-dihydro-1,4-naphthalenediol (5–12.2%); 2-methyl-1,2-diphenyl-1,2-dihydro-1,4-naphthalenediol	*20*
$C_{11}H_8O_3$			
2-Methoxy-1,4-naphthoquinone (30 g.)	C_6H_5MgBr (157 g. C_6H_5Br)	1-Hydroxy-1,4-diphenyl-2(1*H*)-naphthalenone (*ca.* 15 g.)	*48*
$C_{12}H_6O_2$			
Acenaphthenequinone	C_6H_5MgBr	1,2-Diphenyl-1,2-acenaphthenediol	*1*

TABLE VII-II (Continued)

Quinone	RMgX	Product(s)	Ref.
$C_{12}H_{10}O_2$			
2,3-Dimethyl-1,4-naphthoquinone	C_6H_5MgBr	1,2-Diphenyl-2,3-dimethyl-1,2-dihydro-1,4-naphthalenediol (chief solid product); 1,4-diphenyl-2,3-dimethyl-1,4-naphthalenediol; 2,3-dimethyl-4-hydroxy-4-phenyl-1(*4H*)-naphthalenone; reduction products; dehydration products	*18,19*
$C_{14}H_6O_2Cl_2$			
1,4-Dichloroanthraquinone (5.54 g.)	C_6H_5MgBr (2.92 g. Mg)	1,4-Dichloro-9,10-diphenyl-9,10-dihydro-9,10-anthradiol (3.4 g.)	*25*
1,5-Dichloroanthraquinone (12 g.)	C_6H_5MgBr (4 equiv.)	1,5-Dichloro-9,10-diphenyl-9,10-dihydro-9,10-anthradiol (5 g.); 1,5-dichloroanthraquinone*	*13*
1,5-Dichloroanthraquinone (5.54 g.)	C_6H_5MgBr (8.4 g. C_6H_5Br)	1,5-Dichloro-9,10-diphenyl-9,10-dihydro-9,10-anthradiol (3.1 g.)	*25*
$C_{14}H_7O_2Br$			
2-Bromoanthraquinone (78 g.)	C_6H_5MgBr (120 g. C_6H_5Br)	2-Bromo-9,10-diphenyl-9,10-dihydro-9,10-anthradiol	*34*
$C_{14}H_7O_2Cl$			
1-Chloroanthraquinone	C_6H_5MgBr (4 equiv.)	1-Chloro-9,10-diphenyl-9,10-dihydro-9,10-anthradiol; 1-chloro-9,10-diphenylanthracene	*13*
1-Chloroanthraquinone	C_6H_5MgBr	1-Chloro-9,10-diphenyl-9,10-dihydro-9,10-anthradiol (83%)	*2*
2-Chloroanthraquinone	C_6H_5MgBr	2-Chloro-9,10-diphenyl-9,10-dihydro-9,10-anthradiol (90%)	*2*
2-Chloroanthraquinone	C_6H_5MgBr	2-Chloro-9,10-diphenyl-9,10-dihydro-9,10-anthradiol	*13,34*
$C_{14}H_8O_2$			
Anthraquinone (208 g.)	CH_3MgBr (0.5 mole)	10-Hydroxy-10-methyl-9-anthrone (52 g.)	*36*

*Attributed to atmospheric oxidation of the anthraquinol.

TABLE VII-II (Continued)

Quinone	RMgX	Product(s)	Ref.
$C_{14}H_8O_2$ *(cont.)*			
Anthraquinone	CH_3MgI (1 equiv.)	9,10-Dimethyl-9,10-dihydro-9,10-anthradiol	*29*
Anthraquinone (140 g.)	C_2H_5MgBr (65 g. C_2H_5Br)	10-Hydroxy-10-ethyl-9-anthrone (65 g., crude)	*38*
Anthraquinone	C_2H_5MgBr	9,10-Diethyl-9,10-dihydro-9,10-anthradiol; yellow rhombic plates, m. 161° [9-(9-ethyl-10-ethylidene-9,10-dihydro) anthryl ether (?)]; yellow prisms, m. 226° [$C_{36}H_{34}O$ (?)]	*16*
Anthraquinone	2-Furyl-MgBr	9,10-Difuryl-9,10-dihydro-9,10-anthradiol	*24*
Anthraquinone (10.4 g.)	Pyrryl-MgBr (6.7 g. pyrrole)	9,10-Dipyrrolenyl-9,10-dihydroanthracene	*39*
Anthraquinone (150 g.)	n-C_4H_9MgBr (0.5 mole)	10-Hydroxy-10-*n*-butyl-9-anthrone (66 g.)	*37*
Anthraquinone	i-$C_5H_{11}MgBr$ (25 g. $C_5H_{11}Br$)	10-Hydroxy-10-isoamyl-9-anthrone	*37*
Anthraquinone (25 g.)	4-BrC_6H_4MgI (90 g. C_6H_4IBr)	9,10-Di-*p*-bromophenyl-9,10-dihydro-9,10-anthradiol	*34*
Anthraquinone (30 g.)	4-ClC_6H_4MgI (95 g. C_6H_4ICl)	9,10-Di-*p*-chlorophenyl-9,10-dihydro-9,10-anthradiol	*34*
Anthraquinone	C_6H_5MgBr (1 equiv.)	10-Hydroxy-10-phenyl-9-anthrone; 9,10-diphenyl-9,10-dihydro-9,10-anthradiol (10%)	*32*
Anthraquinone	C_6H_5MgBr	9,10-Diphenyl-9,10-dihydro-9,10-anthradiol (34%); unchanged anthraquinone	*34*
Anthraquinone	C_6H_5MgBr	9,10-Diphenyl-9,10-dihydro-9,10-anthradiol (50%); 9,10-diphenylanthracene	*13*
Anthraquinone (60 g.)	C_6H_5MgBr (30 g. Mg)	9,10-Diphenyl-9,10-dihydro-9,10-anthradiol (55%)	*22*
Anthraquinone (large excess)	$C_6H_5CH_2MgCl$	9,10-Dibenzyl-9,10-dihydro-9,10-anthradiol (poor yield); 10-hydroxy-10-benzyl-9-anthrone	*41*

TABLE VII-II (Continued)

Quinone	RMgX	Product(s)	Ref.
$C_{14}H_8O_2$ (*cont.*)			
Anthraquinone (72 g.)	$C_6H_5CH_2Cl$ (64 g.) + Mg (12.5 g.)	10-Hydroxy-10-benzyl-9-anthrone (18–25 g.); recovered anthrone (15–20 g.)	*41*
Anthraquinone (45.5 g.)	$4\text{-}CH_3C_6H_4MgI$ (100 g. C_7H_7I)	9,10-Di-*p*-tolyl-9,10-dihydro-9,10-anthradiol (18%)	*34*
Anthraquinone	$2\text{-}CH_3OC_6H_4MgBr$	9,10-Di-*o*-anisyl-9,10-dihydro-9,10-anthradiol.	*31*
Anthraquinone (40 g.)	$4\text{-}CH_3OC_6H_4MgBr$ (93.5 g. C_7H_7BrO	9,10-Di-*p*-anisyl-9,10-dihydro-9,10-anthradiol (31 g.)	*34,13,31*
Anthraquinone (40 g.)	$4\text{-}CH_3OC_6H_4MgI$ (23.4 g. C_7H_7IO)	10-Hydroxy-10-*p*-anisyl-9-anthrone	*14*
Anthraquinone	$C_6H_5C{\equiv}CMgBr$	9,10-Di(phenylethynyl)-9,10-dihydro-9,10-anthradiol	*23*
Anthraquinone (5.2 g.)	2-Methylindolyl-MgBr (13.0 g. 2-methylindole)	9,9,10,10-Tetra-(2-methyl-3-indolyl)-9,10-dihydroanthracene	*39*
Anthraquinone	$1\text{-}C_{10}H_7MgBr$	9,10-Di-α-naphthyl-9,10-dihydro-9,10-anthradiol; 10-hydroxy-10-α-naphthyl-9-anthrone.	*28*
Anthraquinone (5.8 g.)	$2\text{-}C_6H_5C_6H_4MgI$ (15.6 g. $C_{12}H_9I$)	$(C_6H_5\text{—})_2$ (3.7 g.); recovered quinone; 9,10-di-*o*-biphenylyl-9,10-dihydro-9,10-anthradiol (3.6 g., 25%)	*17*
Anthraquinone	$2\text{-}C_6H_5OC_6H_4MgI$	9,10-Di-*o*-phenoxyphenyl-9,10-dihydro-9,10-anthradiol (47%)	*17*
9,10-Phenanthrenequinone (15 g.)	CH_3MgI (30 g. CH_3I)	9,10-Dimethyl-9,10-dihydro-9,10-phenanthrenediol (60%)	*52*
9,10-Phenanthrenequinone (15 g.)	C_2H_5MgBr (25 g. C_2H_5Br)	9,10-Diethyl-9,10-dihydro-9,10-phenanthrenediol (*ca.* 40%)	*52*
9,10-Phenanthrenequinone (15 g.)	C_2H_5MgI (33 g. C_2H_5I)	9,10-Diethyl-9,10-dihydro-9,10-phenanthrenediol (*ca.* 40%)	*52*
9,10-Phenanthrenequinone (10 g.)	$n\text{-}C_3H_7MgBr$ (21 g. C_3H_7Br)	9,10-Di-*n*-propyl-9,10-dihydro-9,10-phenanthrenediol (60–70%)	*52*
9,10-Phenanthrenequinone (5.2 g.)	Pyrryl-MgBr (3.4 g. pyrrole)	9,10-Dipyrrolenyl-9,10-dihydrophenanthrene	*40*

TABLE VII-II (Continued)

Quinone	RMgX	Product(s)	Ref.
$C_{14}H_8O_2$ (*cont.*)			
9,10-Phenanthrenequinone (10.4 g.)	4-ClC_6H_4MgBr (0.2 mole C_6H_4BrCl)	9,10-Di-*p*-chlorophenyl-9,10-dihydro-9,10-phenanthrenediol (44%)	9
9,10-Phenanthrenequinone (10.4 g.)	4-FC_6H_4MgBr (0.2 mole C_6H_4BrF)	9,10-Di-*p*-fluorophenyl-9,10-dihydro-9,10-phenanthrenediol (30%).	9
9,10-Phenanthrenequinone (20 g.)	C_6H_5MgBr	9,10-Diphenyl-9,10-dihydro-9,10-phenanthrenediol (25 g.)	1
9,10-Phenanthrenequinone	C_6H_5MgI	9,10-Diphenyl-9,10-dihydro-9,10-phenanthrenediol	50
9,10-Phenanthrenequinone	$C_6H_5CH_2MgCl$ (4 equiv.)	9,10-Dibenzyl-9,10-dihydro-9,10-phenanthrenediol (80–90%)	52
9,10-Phenanthrenequinone	2-$CH_3C_6H_4MgBr$	9,10-Di-*o*-tolyl-9,10-dihydro-9,10-phenanthrenediol (51%)	35
9,10-Phenanthrenequinone (10.4 g.)	3-$CH_3C_6H_4MgBr$ (0.2 mole C_7H_7Br)	9,10-Di-*m*-tolyl-9,10-dihydro-9,10-phenanthrenediol (40%)	9,35
9,10-Phenanthrenequinone (17 g.)	4-$CH_3C_6H_4MgBr$ (42 g. C_7H_7Br)	9,10-Di-*p*-tolyl-9,10-dihydro-9,10-phenanthrenediol (57%)	5,35
9,10-Phenanthrenequinone	2-$CH_3OC_6H_4MgBr$	9,10-Di-*o*-anisyl-9,10-dihydro-9,10-phenanthrenediol (43%)	35
9,10-Phenanthrenequinone	3-$CH_3OC_6H_4MgBr$	9,10-Di-*m*-anisyl-9,10-dihydro-9,10-phenanthrenediol (48%)	35
9,10-Phenanthrenequinone (17 g.)	4-$CH_3OC_6H_4MgBr$ (46 g. C_7H_7BrO)	9,10-Di-*p*-anisyl-9,10-dihydro-9,10-phenanthrenediol (47%)	35,5
9,10-Phenanthrenequinone	3,4-$(CH_3)_2C_6H_3MgBr$	9,10-Di-(3,4-dimethylphenyl)-9,10-dihydro-9,10-phenanthrenediol (23%)	35
9,10-Phenanthrenequinone	2-$C_2H_5OC_6H_4MgBr$	9, 10-Di-*o*-phenetyl-9,10-dihydro-9,10-phenanthrenediol (52%)	35
9,10-Phenanthrenequinone	3-$C_2H_5OC_6H_4MgBr$	9,10-Di-*m*-phenetyl-9,10-dihydro-9,10-phenanthrenediol (39%)	35

TABLE VII-II (Continued)

Quinone	RMgX	Product(s)	Ref.
$C_{14}H_8O_2$ (*cont.*)			
9,10-Phenanthrenequinone (10.4 g.)	4-$C_2H_5OC_6H_4MgBr$ (0.2 mole C_8H_9BrO)	9,10-Di-*p*-phenetyl-9,10-dihydro-9,10-phenanthrenediol (33%)	*9,35*
9,10-Phenanthrenequinone (2.6 g.)	2-Methylindolyl-MgBr (6.5 g. 2-methylindole)	9,9,10,10-Tetra-(2-methyl-3-indolyl)-9,10-dihydrophenanthrene	*40*
9,10-Phenanthrenequinone (10.4 g.)	1-$C_{10}H_7MgBr$ (0.2 mole $C_{10}H_7Br$)	9,10-Di-α-naphthyl-9,10-dihydro-9,10-phenanthrenediol (31%)	*9*
9,10-Phenanthrenequinone (10.4 g.)	4-$C_6H_5C_6H_4MgBr$ (0.2 mole $C_{12}H_9Br$)	9,10-Di-*p*-biphenylyl-9,10-dihydro-9,10-phenanthrenediol (65%)	*9*
$C_{15}H_{10}O_2$			
2-Methylanthraquinone	C_6H_5MgBr (excess)	2-Methyl-9,10-diphenyl-9,10-dihydro-9,10-anthradiol (95%); 2-methyl-10-hydroxy-10-phenyl-9-anthrone	*28*
2-Methylanthraquinone	C_6H_5MgBr	2-Methyl-9,10-diphenyl-9,10-dihydro-9,10-anthradiol (86%)	*2*
2-Methylanthraquinone	4-$CH_3C_6H_4MgBr$ (excess)	2-Methyl-9,10-di-*p*-tolyl-9,10-dihydro-9,10-anthradiol ("excellent yield")	*30*
2-Methylanthraquinone	4-$CH_3OC_6H_4MgBr$	2-Methyl-9,10-di-*p*-anisyl-9,10-dihydro-9,10-anthradiol	*31*
$C_{15}H_{10}O_3$			
2-Methoxyanthraquinone (4.7 g.)	4-$CH_3OC_6H_4MgI$ (5.8 g. C_7H_7IO)	2-Methoxy-10-hydroxy-10-*p*-anisyl-9-anthrone (2.3 g.)	*14*
$C_{16}H_8O_2S$			
5,6-Benzo-4,9-thiophenanthrenequinone (0.95 g.)	CH_3MgI (1 g. Mg)	4,9-Dimethyl-5,6-benzothiophenanthrene (0.7 g.)*	*53*

* After treatment with HI and reduction with $SnCl_2$.

TABLE VII-II (Continued)

Quinone	RMgX	Product(s)	Ref.
$C_{16}H_8O_2S$ (*cont.*)			
7,8-Benzo-4,9-thiophenanthrenequinone	CH_3MgI	4,9-Dimethyl-7,8-benzothiophenanthrene*	53
$C_{16}H_{12}O_2$			
1,2-Dimethylanthraquinone (7.1 g.)	CH_3MgI (8.4 ml. CH_3I)	1,2,9,10-Tetramethyl-9,10-anthradiol (3.2 g.)	10
1,4-Dimethylanthraquinone (5.9 g.)	C_6H_5MgBr (3.95 g. C_6H_5Br)	Recovered quinone (5.5 g.); 1,4-dimethyl-10-hydroxy-10-phenyl-9-anthrone (0.6 g.)	43
1,4-Dimethylanthraquinone 5.9 g.)	C_6H_5MgBr (40 g., *ca.* 10 equiv., C_6H_5Br)	1,4-Dimethyl-9,10-diphenyl-9,10-dihydro-9,10-anthradiol (55%)	43
2,3-Dimethylanthraquinone	C_6H_5MgBr	2,3-Dimethyl-9,10-diphenyl-9,10-dihydro-9,10-anthradiol (77%)	2
$C_{16}H_{12}O_4$			
1,2-Dimethoxyanthraquinone	C_2H_5MgI (1.5 equiv.)	1,2-Dimethoxy-10-hydroxy-10-ethyl-9-anthrone (*ca.* 22%)	45
1,2-Dimethoxyanthraquinone	C_2H_5MgI (2.5 equiv.)	1,2-Dimethoxy-9,10-diethyl-9,10-dihydro-9,10-anthradiol (*ca.* 18%); 1,2-dimethoxy-10-hydroxy-10-ethyl-9-anthrone; recovered quinone	45
$C_{18}H_{12}O_2$			
Benz[*a*]anthracene-7,12-dione (5.16 g.)	*n*-C_3H_7MgBr	7,12-Di-*n*-propyl-7,12-dihydrobenz[*a*]anthracene-7,12-diol (isolated as the dimethyl ether, 3.9 g.)	8,6
Benz[*a*]anthracene-7,12-dione	C_6H_5MgBr	7,12-Diphenyl-7,12-dihydrobenz[*a*]anthracene-7,12-diol (78%)†	2

* After treatment with HBr-HI and reduction with $SnCl_2$.

† Add'n of *n*-Bu_2O-quinone sol'n to Mg-free Et_2O-G.r. sol'n; 3 hrs. stirring at 100° with dist'n of Et_2O.

TABLE VII-II (Continued)

Quinone	RMgX	Product(s)	Ref.
$C_{18}H_{12}O_2$ (*cont.*)			
Benz[*a*]anthracene-7,12-dione	C_6H_5MgBr	7,12-Diphenyl-7,12-dihydrobenz[*a*]anthracene-7,12-diol (70%)*	*2*
5,12-Naphthacenequinone	C_6H_5MgBr (6 equiv.)	6,11-Diphenyl-5a,6,11,11a-tetrahydro-5,12-naphthacenequinone (20.4%); 5,12-diphenylnaphthacene (25.0%); *no diol*†	*4,2*
5,12-Naphthacenequinone	C_6H_5MgBr	5,12-Diphenyl-5,12-dihydro-5,12-naphthacenediol (58%); 6,11-diphenyl-5a,6,11,11a-tetrahydro-5,12-naphthacenequinone (6%)‡	*2*
5,12-Naphthacenequinone	C_6H_5MgBr + Mg	5,12-Diphenyl-5,12-dihydro-5,12-naphthacenediol (27%); 6,11-diphenyl-5a,6,11,11a-tetrahydronaphthacenequinone (15%); 5,12-diphenylnaphthacene (12%)§	*2*
5,12-Naphthacenequinone	C_6H_5MgBr	5,12-Diphenyl-5,12-dihydro-5,12-naphacenediol (40%); 6,11-diphenyl-5a,6,11,11a-tetrahydronaphthacenequinone (15%)	*2*
5,12-Naphthacenequinone (0.4 g.)	C_6H_5MgBr (2 g. C_6H_5Br)	5,12-Diphenyl-5,12-dihydro-5,12-naphthacenediol (0.32 g., 50%)	*21*
$C_{18}H_{14}O_2$			
1,2,3,4-Tetrahydrobenz[*a*]anthracene-7,12-dione	C_6H_5MgBr	7,12-Diphenyl-1,2,3,4,7,12-hexahydrobenz[*a*]anthracene-7,12-diol (70%)	*2*
$C_{18}H_{16}O_2$			
7,8,9,10-Tetrahydronaphthacenequinone	C_6H_5MgBr	5,12-Diphenyl-5,7,8,9,10,12-hexahydro-5,12-naphthacenediol (60%)	*21*
Retenequinone¶	C_6H_5MgBr	9,10-Diphenyl-9,10-dihydro-9,10-retenediol	*33*

*Add'n of C_6H_6-quinone sol'n to Mg-free Et_2O-G.r. sol'n; 3 hrs. stirring on steam bath with dist'n of Et_2O.

†Portionwise add'n of quinone to filtered Et_2O-*n*-Bu_2O-G.r. sol'n; 2 hrs. stirring at 85–90°.

‡Add'n of C_7H_8-quinone sol'n to Mg-free Et_2O-G.r. sol'n; 3 hrs. stirring at 100° with dist'n of Et_2O.

§As above, save for presence of traces of Mg.

¶1-Methyl-7-isopropyl-9,10-phenanthrenedione.

TABLE VII-II (Continued)

Quinone	RMgX	Product(s)	Ref.
$C_{19}H_{12}O_2$			
8-Methylbenz[*a*]anthracene-7,12-dione (3.56 g.)	CH_3MgI (3.3 ml. CH_3I)	7,8,12-Trimethyl-7,12-dihydrobenz[*a*]anthracene-7,12-diol (3.6 g., 91%)	*7*
9-Methylbenz[*a*]anthracene-7,12-dione (7.1 g.)	CH_3MgI (6.6 ml. CH_3I)	7,9,12-Trimethyl-7,12-dihydrobenz[*a*]anthracene-7,12-diol (yielding 2.35 g. of the dimethyl ether)	*10*
$C_{20}H_{12}O_2$			
1-Phenylanthraquinone	C_6H_5MgBr (10 equiv.)	1,9,10-Triphenyl-9,10-dihydro-9,10-anthradiol	*49*
2-Phenylanthraquinone	C_6H_5MgBr	2,9,10-Triphenyl-9,10-dihydro-9,10-anthradiol (80%)	*2*
$C_{20}H_{14}O_2$			
8-Ethylbenz[*a*]anthracene-7,12-dione (3.75 g.)	CH_3MgI (5.0 ml. CH_3I)	7,12-Dimethyl-8-ethyl-7,12-dihydrobenz[*a*]anthracene-7,12-diol (3.54 g.)	*8*
8,9-Dimethylbenz[*a*]anthracene-7,12-dione (5.0 g.)	CH_3MgI (5.0 ml. CH_3I)	7,8,9,12-Tetramethyl-7,12-dihydrobenz[*a*]anthracene-7,12-diol (2.2 g.)	*10*
$C_{21}H_{16}O_2$			
8-*n*-Propylbenz[*a*]anthracene-7,12-dione (4.42 g.)	CH_3MgI	7,12-Dimethyl-8-*n*-propyl-7,12-dihydrobenz[*a*]anthracene-7,12-diol (3.9 g.)	*8*
$C_{22}H_{10}O_4$			
5,7,12,14-Pentacenetetrone	C_6H_5MgBr	5,7,12,14-Tetraphenyl-5,7,12,14-tetrahydro-5,7,12,14-pentacenetetrol (76%)	*3*

TABLE VII-II (Continued)

Quinone	RMgX	Product(s)	Ref.
$C_{22}H_{12}O_2$			
6,13-Pentacenedione	C_6H_5MgBr	*trans*-6,13-Diphenyl-6,13-dihydropentacene-6,13-diol (70%); 5,14-diphenyl-5,5a,13a,14-tetrahydro-6,13-pentacenedione (15%)	3
$C_{22}H_{16}O_2$			
1,2,3,4-Tetrahydro-6,13-pentacenedione	C_6H_5MgBr	6,13-Diphenyl-1,2,3,4,6,13-hexahydropentacene (66%)	2
$C_{24}H_{18}O_4$			
6,13-Diphenyl-5,7,12,-14-pentacentetrone	C_6H_5MgBr	5,6,7,12,13,14-Hexaphenyl-5,7,12,14-tetrahydro-5,7,12,14-pentacene-tetrol	3
$C_{26}H_{16}O_2$			
1,4-Diphenylanthraquinone (3 g.)	C_6H_5MgBr (15.6 g. C_6H_5Br)	1,4,9,10-Tetraphenyl-9,10-dihydro-9,10-anthradiol.	49
2,3-Diphenylanthraquinone	C_6H_5MgBr	2,3,9,10-Tetraphenyl-9,10-dihydro-9,10-anthradiol (80%)	2
$C_{28}H_{16}O_2$			
Bianthraquinone	$2-ClC_6H_4MgX$	"10,10′-Dihydroxy-10,10′-di(*o*-chlorophenyl)dianthranene"	44
Bianthraquinone (4 g.)	C_6H_5MgBr (7.2 g. C_6H_5Br)	"10,10′-Dihydroxy-10,10′-diphenyldianthranene" (3.6 g., crude)	44
Bianthraquinone	$C_6H_5CH_2MgBr$	"10,10′-Dihydroxy-10,10′-dibenzyldianthranene"	44
Bianthraquinone	$1-C_{10}H_7MgX$	"10,10′-Dihydroxy-10,10′-di-α-naphthyldianthranene"	44

TABLE VII-II (Continued)

Quinone	RMgX	Product(s)	Ref.
$C_{30}H_{20}O_2$			
6,11-Diphenylnaphthacenequinone	C_6H_5MgBr	No isolable product; 70% quinone recovery	4,2
6,11-Diphenylnaphthacenequinone	C_6H_5MgBr	5,6,11,12-Tetraphenyl-5,12-dihydro-5,12-naphthacenediol (50%)	2
$C_{34}H_{20}O_2$			
5,14-Diphenyl-6,13-pentacenedione	C_6H_5MgBr	Mixture of stereoisomers: 5,7,12,14-tetraphenyl-6a,7,12,12a-tetrahydro-6,13-pentacenedione (60%)	3

REFERENCES FOR TABLE VII-II

(*1*) Acree, *Am. Chem. J.*, *33*, 180–95 (1905).
(*2*) Allen and Bell, *J. Am. Chem. Soc.*, *62*, 2408–12 (1940).
(*3*) Allen and Bell, *J. Am. Chem. Soc.*, *64*, 1253–60 (1942).
(*4*) Allen and Gilman, *J. Am. Chem. Soc.*, *58*, 937–40 (1936).
(*5*) Bachmann, *J. Am. Chem. Soc.*, *54*, 1969–74 (1932).
(*6*) Bachmann and Bradbury, *J. Org. Chem.*, *2*, 175–82 (1937).
(*7*) Bachmann and Chemerda, *J. Am. Chem. Soc.*, *60*, 1023–6 (1938).
(*8*) Bachmann and Chemerda, *J. Am. Chem. Soc.*, *61*, 2358–61 (1939).
(*9*) Bachmann and Chu, *J. Am. Chem. Soc.*, *57*, 1095–8 (1935).
(*10*) Badger, Cook, and Goulden, *J. Chem. Soc.*, *1940*, 16–8.
(*11*) Bamberger and Blangey, *Ber.*, *36*, 1625–8 (1903).
(*12*) Bamberger and Blangey, *Ann.*, *384*, 272–322 (1911).
(*13*) Barnett, Cook, and Wiltshire, *J. Chem. Soc.*, *1927*, 1724–32.
(*14*) Blicke and Weinkauff, *J. Am. Chem. Soc.*, *54*, 1460–4 (1932).
(*15*) Clarke, *Ber.*, *41*, 935–6 (1908).
(*16*) Clarke and Carleton, *J. Am. Chem. Soc.*, *33*, 1966–73 (1911).
(*17*) Clarkson and Gomberg, *J. Am. Chem. Soc.*, *52*, 2881–91 (1930).
(*18*) Crawford, *J. Am. Chem. Soc.*, *57*, 2000–4 (1935).
(*19*) Crawford, *J. Am. Chem. Soc.*, *61*, 3310–4 (1939).
(*20*) Crawford, *J. Am. Chem. Soc.*, *63*, 1070–3 (1941).
(*21*) Dufraisse and Horclois, *Bull. soc. chim.*, [5], *3*, 1894–905 (1936).
(*22*) Dufraisse and Le Bras, *Bull. soc. chim.*, [5], *4*, 1037–45 (1937).
(*23*) Dufraisse, Mathieu, and Rio, *Compt. rend.*, *227*, 937–9 (1948); *Chem. Abstr.*, *43*, 3401 (1949).
(*24*) Etienne and Brisson, *Compt. rend.*, *224*, 1775–7 (1947); *Chem. Abstr.*, *42*, 1259 (1948).
(*25*) Fedorov, *Bull. acad. sci. U.R.S.S., Classe sci. chim.*, *1947*, 397–404; *Chem. Abstr.*, *42*, 1585 (1948).
(*26*) Franssen, *Bull. soc. chim.*, [4], *37*, 902–13 (1925).
(*27*) Franssen, *Bull. soc. chim.*, [4], *45*, 1030–44 (1929).
(*28*) Guyot and Staehling, *Bull. soc. chim.*, [3], 33, 1104–21 (1905).
(*29*) Guyot and Staehling, *Bull. soc. chim.*, [3], 33, 1144–52 (1905).
(*30*) Guyot and Vallette, *Ann. chim.*, [8], 23, 363–97 (1911).
(*31*) Haller and Comtesse, *Compt. rend.*, *150*, 1290–5 (1910); *Chem. Zentr.*, *1910,II*, 218.
(*32*) Haller and Guyot, *Compt. rend.*, *138*, 1251–4 (1904); *Chem. Zentr.*, *1904,II*, 117.
(*33*) Heiduschka and Grimm, *Arch. Pharm.*, *248*, 89–101 (1909); *Chem. Zentr.*, *1910,I*, 1975.
(*34*) Jezierski, *Roczniki Chem.*, *19*, 307–16 (1939); *Chem. Abstr.*, *34*, 3729 (1940).
(*35*) Julian, Cole, and Diemer, *J. Am. Chem. Soc.*, *67*, 1721–3 (1945).
(*36*) Julian, Cole, and Meyer, *J. Am. Chem. Soc.*, *67*, 1724–7 (1945).
(*37*) Julian, Cole, and Wood, *J. Am. Chem. Soc.*, *57*, 2508–13 (1935).
(*38*) Mingoia, *Gazz. chim. ital.*, *56*, 446–50 (1926); *Chem. Abstr.*, *21*, 242 (1927).
(*39*) Mingoia, *Gazz. chim. ital.*, *58*, 673–9 (1928); *Chem. Abstr.*, *23*, 3465 (1929).
(*40*) Schmidlin, Wohl, and Thommen, *Ber.*, *43*, 1298–303 (1910).
(*41*) Scholl and Meyer, *Ann.*, *512*, 112–24 (1934).
(*42*) Schönberg and Ismail, *J. Chem. Soc.*, *1945*, 201–2.
(*43*) Sirker, *J. Chem. Soc.*, *107*, 1241–7 (1915).
(*44*) Smith and Crawford, *J. Am. Chem. Soc.*, *50*, 869–83 (1928)
(*45*) Smith and Hoehn, *J. Am. Chem. Soc.*, *61*, 2619–24 (1939).
(*46*) Smith and Hoehn, *J. Am. Chem. Soc.*, *63*, 1178–9 (1941).

(47) Weizmann, Bergmann, and Haskelberg, *J. Chem. Soc.*, *1939*, 391–7.
(48) Werner and Grob, *Ber.*, *37*, 2887–903 (1904).
(49) Worrall and Cohen, *J. Am. Chem. Soc.*, *58*, 533 (1936).
(50) Zincke and Tropp, *Ann.*, *362*, 242–59 (1908).
(51) Sandin and Kitchen, *J. Am. Chem. Soc.*, *67*, 1305–7 (1945).

CHAPTER VIII

Reactions of Grignard Reagents with Esters and Lactones

"NORMAL" ADDITION TO CARBOXYLIC ESTERS

The reaction between a carboxylic ester of the type RCO_2R' and a Grignard reagent commonly regarded as the "normal" one is that in which one molecule of the former reacts with two molecules of the latter to form a halomagnesium *t*-alkoxide (a *s*-alkoxide in the special case of a formic ester) and the halomagnesium alkoxide corresponding to the ester alcohol.

$$RCO_2R' + 2\,R''MgX \longrightarrow RR_2''COMgX + R'OMgX$$

Grignard[1] represented the reaction as taking place in two stages:

$$(1)\qquad R{-}C({=}O){-}OR' + R''MgX \longrightarrow R{-}C(OMgX)(OR')(R'')$$

$$(2)\qquad R{-}C(OMgX)(OR')(R'') + R''MgX \longrightarrow R{-}C(OMgX)(R'')(R'') + R'OMgX$$

This representation is, of course, satisfactory from a stoichiometric point of view, but there is a reasonable question that it adequately describes the mechanism of the reaction. Equally satisfactory from a stoichiometric standpoint would be the sequence:

$$(1a)\qquad R{-}C({=}O){-}OR' + R''MgX \longrightarrow R{-}C(OMgX)(OR')(R'') \longrightarrow RCOR'' + R'OMgX$$

$$(2a)\qquad RCOR'' + R''MgX \longrightarrow R{-}C(OMgX)(R'')(R'')$$

---

[1]Grignard, *Compt. rend.*, *132*, 336–8 (1901); *J. Chem. Soc.*, *80,I*, *250* (1901); *Ann. chim.*, [7], *24*, 433–90 (1901).

The available evidence upon which to base a choice between the two reaction schemes is inconclusive, but, on the whole, would appear to favor the former except, possibly, in the case of "sterically hindered" esters.

Although it is true that ketones are among the final products of reaction of some esters with some Grignard reagents, it has not been demonstrated that they are present prior to hydrolysis; they may result from the hydrolysis of relatively stable products of the type postulated by Grignard.

$$R—C(OMgX)(R'')—OR' \xrightarrow{H_2O} RCOR'' + MgXOH + R'OH$$

Boyd and Hatt[2] found that, in the presence of free magnesium, phenylmagnesium bromide reacts with ethyl *o*-toluate to form a pinacol as well as a carbinol.

$$C_6H_5MgBr + Mg + 2\text{-}CH_3C_6H_4CO_2C_2H_5 \longrightarrow 2\text{-}CH_3C_6H_4(C_6H_5)_2COH\ (23\%)$$
$$+ [HO(C_6H_5)(2\text{-}CH_3C_6H_4)C—]_2\ (38\%)$$

They argue that pinacol formation is evidence of the presence of free ketone, from which the pinacol is derived by a Gomberg (*i.e.*, magnesious halide) reaction. This argument can be conclusive, however, only if the possibility of such a reaction sequence as

$$C_6H_5(2\text{-}CH_3C_6H_4)C(OC_2H_5)OMgBr + \cdot MgBr \longrightarrow$$
$$BrMgO(C_6H_5)(2\text{-}CH_3C_6H_4)C\cdot + C_2H_5OMgBr$$
$$2\ BrMgO(C_6H_5)(2\text{-}CH_3C_6H_4)C\cdot \longrightarrow [BrMgO(C_6H_5)(2\text{-}CH_3C_6H_4)C—]_2$$

is excluded.

Whitmore and Lewis[3] found that, when treated with methylmagnesium bromide in the "Grignard machine," the non-enolizable ethyl and butyl esters of α-methyl-α-ethylbutyric acid (**I**) underwent apparent enolization to the extent of 25 percent and 22 percent, respectively. They attributed this phenomenon to intermediate ketone formation and enolization of the ketone.

$$CH_3(C_2H_5)_2CCO_2R\ (\mathbf{I}) \xrightarrow{CH_3MgBr} CH_3(C_2H_5)_2CCOCH_3\ (\mathbf{II})$$
$$+ ROMgBr \xrightarrow{CH_3MgBr} [CH_3(C_2H_5)_2CCO{=}CH_2]^-MgBr^+$$
$$+ CH_4\ (22\text{–}25\%) + ROMgBr$$

It may or may not be significant that under essentially the same conditions 3-methyl-3-ethyl-2-pentanone (**II**) undergoes 84 percent enolization, or that the ethyl ester of α,α-dimethylbutyric acid (**III**) shows no apparent enolization, whereas 3,3-dimethyl-2-pentanone (**IV**) undergoes 14 percent enolization (Whitmore and Lewis, *loc. cit.*[3]).

---

[2]Boyd and Hatt, *J. Chem. Soc.*, *1927*, 898–910.
[3]Whitmore and Lewis, *J. Am. Chem. Soc.*, *64*, 2964–6 (1942).

$CH_3(C_2H_5)_2CCO_2C_2H_5$ **(IA)** $\xrightarrow{2\ CH_3MgBr}$ Add'n. (45%); enolization (25%)

$CH_3(C_2H_5)_2CCO_2\text{-}n\text{-}C_4H_9$ **(IB)** $\xrightarrow{2\ CH_3MgBr}$ Add'n. (60%); enolization (22%)

$CH_3(C_2H_5)_2CCOCH_3$ **(II)** $\xrightarrow{CH_3MgBr}$ Add'n. (0%); enolization (84%)

$C_2H_5(CH_3)_2CCO_2C_2H_5$ **(III)** $\xrightarrow{2\ CH_3MgBr}$ Add'n. (100%); enolization (0%)

$C_2H_5(CH_3)_2CCOCH_3$ **(IV)** $\xrightarrow{CH_3MgBr}$ Add'n. (74%); enolization (14%)

There is, however, at least a strong suggestion (which it would be imprudent to ignore altogether) that the initial reaction product is an intermediate (possibly a hemiketal derivative) which is more susceptible to further Grignard reagent addition, and less susceptible to Grignard reagent enolization, than is the corresponding free ketone.*

The postulate that the initially-formed intermediate is more reactive (with respect to further addition of the Grignard reagent) than is the corresponding ketone would necessarily imply that, in general, the second stage of addition is considerably more rapid than the first, for, although misdirected ingenuity may discover apparent exceptions (notably among the "hindered" ketones), it is generally true that a ketonic function is more reactive (with respect to Grignard reagent addition) than a reasonably comparable ester function. With regard to the more reactive esters, at least, this implication is consistent with experimental observation, for the treatment of one molecular equivalent of ester with one molecular equivalent of Grignard reagent is much more likely to result in the formation of approximately one-half molecular equivalent of tertiary alcohol and the recovery of approximately one-half molecular equivalent of ester than in anything approaching the formation of one molecular equivalent of ketone.

Approaching the point in question from a somewhat different direction, Morton and Peakes[4] argue that if a free ketone is indeed an intermediate in the Grignard preparation of tertiary alcohols from esters, the yield of tertiary alcohol from the appropriate ketone should be as high as, or higher than, that from the ester. They cite the preparations of 2,2′,4,4′-tetramethoxytriphenylmethanol from 2,4-dimethoxyphenylmagnesium iodide and 2,4-dimethoxybenzophenone by Kauffman and Kieser[5] (37 percent) and from 2,4-dimethoxyphenylmagnesium iodide and methyl benzoate by Lund[6] (60 percent). They also found that the reaction between phenylmagnesium bromide and methyl 2,4,6-tribromobenzoate yielded 28 percent of the expected carbinol, whereas under the same conditions the same Grignard

*This need not, of course, be construed as a generalization; the relative reactivities of hemiketal derivatives and corresponding ketones with respect to addition and enolization might well vary from case to case.

[4]Morton and Peakes, *J. Am. Chem. Soc.*, *55*, 2110–2 (1933).

[5]Kauffman and Kieser, *Ber.*, *45*, 2333–7 (1912).

[6]Lund, *J. Am. Chem. Soc.*, *49*, 1346–60 (1927).

reagent and the appropriate ketone yielded only traces of carbinol (and quantities of tar).

Ivanoff and Spassoff,[6.1] on the other hand, although they accept in part the reaction scheme of Grignard, believe that the hemiketal-type intermediate first formed is unstable and decomposes spontaneously to liberate free ketone. In support of this opinion they claim that substantially the same amount of gas is liberated whether an alkyl Grignard reagent is caused to react with an aliphatic ester or with the ketone corresponding to the first stage of ester-Grignard reagent addition. Although the Grignard reagents actually employed are potentially reducing agents, it is assumed, in view of the relatively high yields of ketols isolated from some of the ester reactions, that the gas liberated is essentially an enolization product. A summary of the corroborative data offered is reproduced in Table VIII-I. No explicit statement concerning the basis of calculation employed is made, but percentage of gas liberated would presumably be related, in the case of ketones, to the amount of Grignard reagent consumed, and, in the case of esters, to the second equivalent of Grignard reagent consumed.

TABLE VIII-I

RELATIVE AMOUNTS OF GASES LIBERATED IN THE REACTIONS OF CERTAIN ALKYLMAGNESIUM HALIDES WITH CERTAIN ALIPHATIC ESTERS AND WITH THE RESPECTIVE KETONES CORRESPONDING TO THE FIRST STAGE OF ESTER ADDITION

RMgX	Gas Evolution (%)			
	Ester		Ketone	
C_2H_5MgBr	$CH_3CO_2C_2H_5$,	1.5	$CH_3COC_2H_5$,	5.9
n-C_3H_7MgBr	$CH_3CO_2C_2H_5$,	5.0	CH_3CO-n-C_3H_7,	10.0
i-C_3H_7MgCl	$CH_3CO_2C_2H_5$,	92.6	CH_3CO-i-C_3H_7,	86.6
C_2H_5MgBr	$C_2H_5CO_2C_2H_5$,	0.7	$(C_2H_5)_2CO$,	0.9
i-C_3H_7MgCl	$C_2H_5CO_2C_2H_5$,	72.0	C_2H_5CO-i-C_3H_7,	70.6

In the opinion of the present authors the evidence offered by Ivanoff and Spassoff is susceptible of at least three interpretations. (1) Ivanoff and Spassoff are correct in their primary premise, and the intermediate resulting from the first stage of carboxylic ester-Grignard reagent addition is, in fact, a free ketone. (2) The stability of the postulated hemiketal-type intermediate varies with the individual case, and further reaction may take place either through the hemiketal derivative itself or through its decomposition product, the free ketone. (3) The true intermediate is indeed the postulated hemiketal derivative, but the choice of reactants by Ivanoff and Spassoff is fortuitously such that in the cases studied the respective relative susceptibilities of the hemiketal derivatives and the corresponding ketones to addition and enolization do not differ markedly.

[6.1] Ivanoff and Spassoff, *Bull. soc. chim.*, [5], *2*, 816–24 (1935).

In the light of all the evidence here outlined, and of a survey of the (rather fragmentary) relevant quantitative data to be gleaned from Tables VI-XVIII and VIII-III, the present authors are inclined to reject interpretation 1 (at least as a general proposition) and to favor interpretation 3 (at least tentatively), without, however, excluding interpretation 2 as a reasonable possibility.

Probable mechanisms of carboxylic ester reactions. Doubtless reaction of any kind is preceded, as in the case of ketones (and, presumably, aldehydes), by Werner complex formation.

$$\begin{array}{c} R \\ \quad\diagdown \\ \quad\quad C{=}O : \underset{\displaystyle R''}{\overset{\displaystyle X}{\overset{|}{\underset{|}{Mg}}}} : O(C_2H_5)_2 \\ \quad\diagup \\ R'O \end{array}$$

In favorable cases such complexes are isolable. Stadnikoff[7] found, for example, that when 0.1 mole (23 g.) of benzhydryl acetate is added dropwise to one equivalent of a cooled, agitated ethereal solution of ethylmagnesium iodide a white precipitate is formed. In the experiment described, after twenty minutes of additional cooling and shaking, the precipitate was separated and treated with water, whereupon 21 g. of the original ester was recovered.

For reasons discussed in connection with the ketone-Grignard reagent complexes (Chapter VI), a complex of the oxonium salt type, as postulated by Stadnikoff (*loc. cit.*[7]), appears highly improbable. Indeed, some of the ("abnormal") reaction products upon which, in part, Stadnikoff bases his argument have since been shown by Boyd and Hatt (*loc. cit.*[2]) to have been erroneously characterized.

The direct experimental evidence available at this writing appears insufficient to support a conclusion as to whether the first stage of the "normal" addition reaction is effected through complex rearrangement (or rearrangement and dissociation) or through complex reaction with an additional molecule of Grignard reagent. In the absence of any extremely cogent indications to the contrary, however, it seems reasonable to accept tentatively the hypothesis that the addition reactions of ketones, aldehydes, and carboxylic esters are analogous. For reasons already discussed (Chapter VI), a trimolecular process appears, in the light of present knowledge, the most probable for ketones. The rather generally applicable and, on the whole, attractive concept of a quasi six-membered ring transition state may be invoked to propose a mechanism leading to the formation of a reasonably probable (though as yet hypothetical) intermediate of the hemiketal type.

---

[7]Stadnikoff, *Ber.*, 47, 2133–42 (1914).

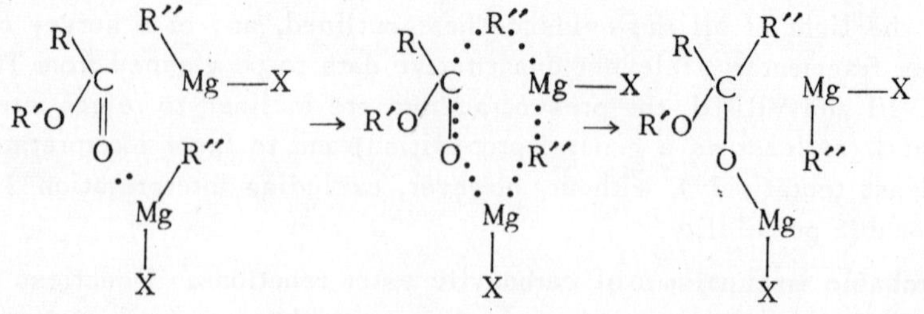

If this choice of intermediate is correct it seems probable that the succeeding reaction stage resembles that of an acetal or ketal (*q.v.*, Chapter XV), or of an ortho ester. A slightly modified version of the quasi six-membered ring transition state concept may be employed without obvious violence to the *a priori* probabilities.

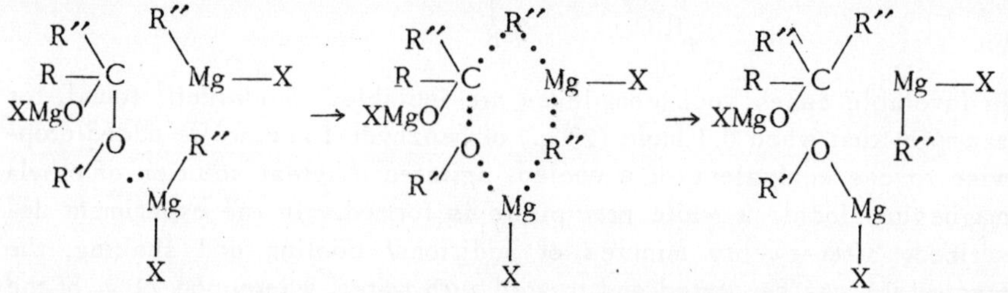

The fundamental principles applicable to the elucidation of ketone enolization (see Enolate Formation by Grignard Reagents, Chapter VI) are readily extensible to a hemiketal-type intermediate of the sort postulated. Enolate formation may be conveniently represented as a concerted displacement reaction involving a quasi six-membered ring transition state.

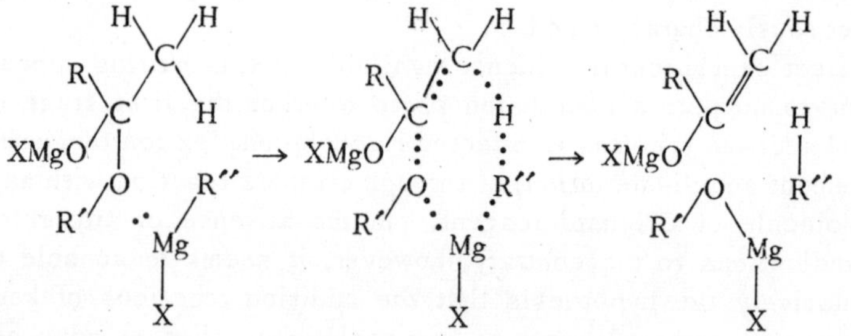

RELATIVE REACTIVITIES OF CARBOXYLIC ESTERS

Although there are a few exceptions, which will be noted in appropriate connections, the generally-prevailing impression that the course of reaction of an ester with a given Grignard reagent (say methylmagnesium bromide) is determined by the acidic constituent of the ester is not far off the mark. When no competing reaction seriously interferes, actual rates of addition are, however, affected by both the acidic and alcoholic constituents of the ester. According to a kinetic study by Treibs,[8] the influences of both acidic and alcoholic constituents upon addition rates are primarily steric rather than energetic.

The relatively simple technique of Treibs involves evaluation of a measured sample of a standard solution of methylmagnesium iodide in a 1:1 mixture of *n*-amyl ether and tetralin by measurement of the amount of methane evolved upon addition of an excess of relatively non-volatile alcohol (*e.g.*, butyl, amyl, or benzyl). To a similar measured sample of standard Grignard solution (usually 2.0–2.5 ml.) is added 1 mole of ester, and, after a uniform time period (usually two or three minutes), residual Grignard reagent is evaluated by addition of an excess of the same non-volatile alcohol used in the control measurement. This technique, of course, makes no distinction between the first and second stages of addition, but, in so far as it is generally true that the second stage is very rapid as compared with the first, it is actually the rate of the first stage of addition that is measured.

In the cases of citronellyl

$$[(CH_3)_2C{=}CH(CH_2)_2CH(CH_3)(CH_2)_2{-}]$$

geranyl

$$[(CH_3)_2C{=}CH(CH_2)_2C(CH_3){=}CHCH_2{-}],$$

or phenethyl $[C_6H_5(CH_2)_2{-}]$ esters of the fatty acids, the formic esters react considerably more rapidly than the corresponding acetic esters. As the acid chain is lengthened there is a further gradual drop in reactivity until the butyl esters are reached, after which further differences become negligible. That these effects are predominantly steric rather than energetic is indicated by the fact that differences in reactivity between the esters of saturated and corresponding unsaturated acids are very slight even when the unsaturation is adjacent to the functional group. Branching of the acid chain, at least in the vicinity of the functional group, retards addition. Thus, butyl butyrate, butyl isobutyrate, and butyl isovalerate are mentioned in the order of decreasing reactivity.

Comparison of the reactivities of corresponding esters of straight-chain, branched-chain, and variously phenylated alcohols suggests that for the alcoholic constituent the steric factor is probably relatively less influential, and the energetic factor somewhat more influential, in determining addition rates than in the case of the acid constituents.

Among the corresponding esters of terpenoid alcohols the general trend is toward greater reactivity of the esters of the less "hindered" alcohols, as the following examples show. (Reactivities are indicated in terms of molecular equivalents of methylmagnesium iodide per molecular equivalent of ester consumed in unit time.)

---

[8]Treibs, *Ann.*, 556, 10–22 (1944).

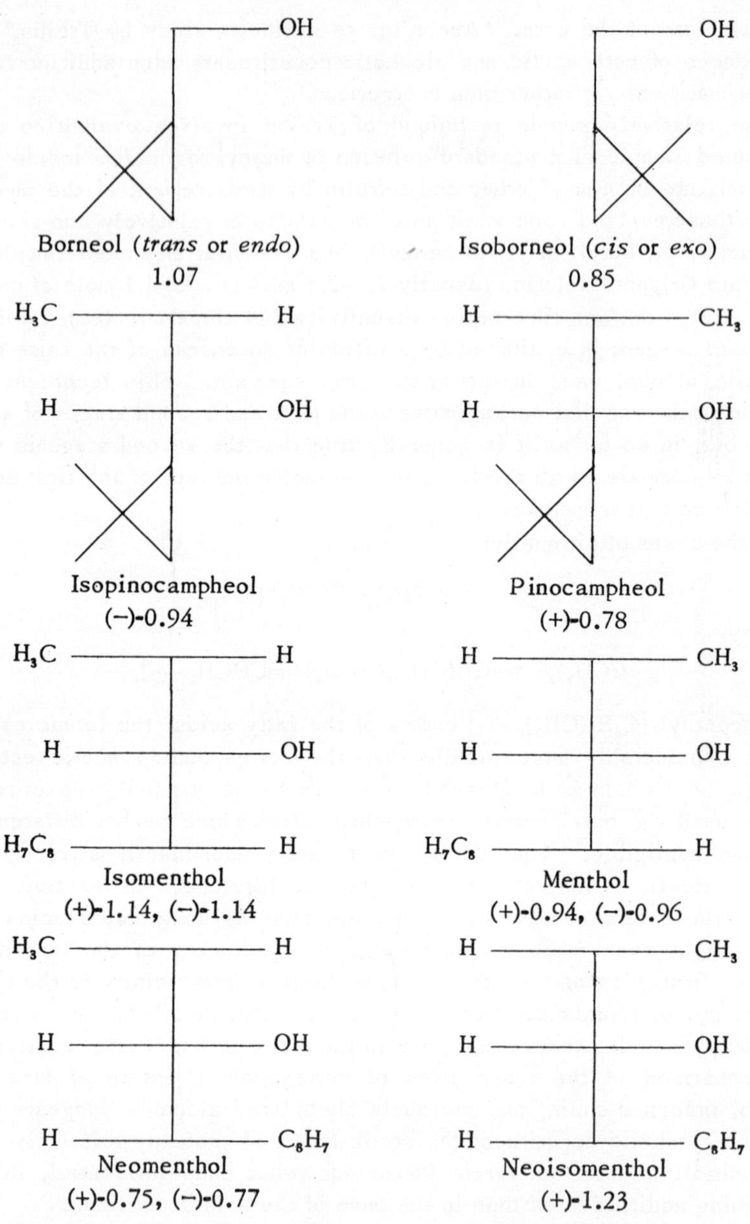

Among the comparable isomeric esters studied, only that of neoisomenthol appears to display a degree of reactivity inconsistent with the configuration assigned to the alcohol. That discrepancy might, conceivably, arise from experimental error. On the basis of the relative reactivities of the respective formic esters, Treibs (*loc. cit.*[8]) deduces that α-fenchol has the *endo* configuration, and β-fenchol the more highly hindered *exo* configuration.

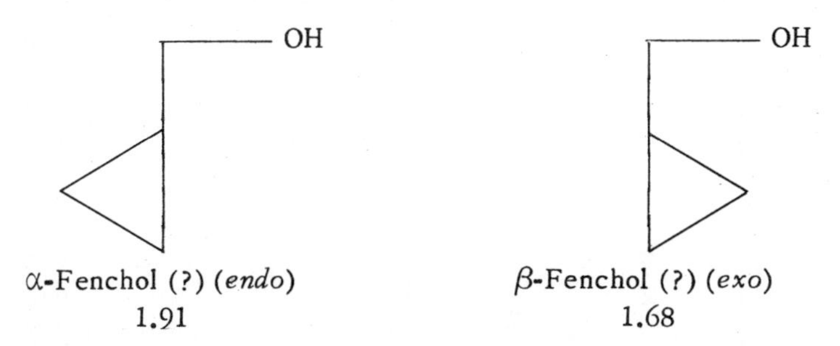

α-Fenchol (?) (*endo*)
1.91

β-Fenchol (?) (*exo*)
1.68

These steric influences on reactivity are compatible with, though they may by no means be regarded as critically confirmative of, the reaction mechanism tentatively proposed.

PREPARATIVE PROCEDURES

Carboxylic esters of the type RCO_2R'. For the preparation of tertiary alcohols by the interaction of organomagnesium halides and esters of the type RCO_2R'; Grignard (*loc. cit.*[1]) employed essentially the same procedure as for the analogous aldehydes and ketones (see Preparative Procedures, Chapter VI). Except in special individual cases this procedure is but little modified by present-day workers. It usually consists in the gradual addition of an ethereal solution of the ester to a stirred ethereal Grignard reagent solution. When the chosen reactant pair is unusually reactive, the rate of reaction may be controlled by slower addition, or by cooling of the reaction mixture, or both. To the less active reaction mixtures heat may be applied as required. Some representative illustrative preparations are briefly outlined in Table VIII-II; references to others may be found in Table VIII-III.

The Barbier-Wieland degradation. The reaction of a Grignard reagent with a carboxylic ester constitutes the first step in a degradative process suggested by Barbier and Locquin[9] for the successive shortening by one carbon atom of the chains of carboxylic acids or by two carbon atoms of the chains of dicarboxylic acids.

$$R(CH_2)_nCH_2CO_2R' \xrightarrow{2\,R''MgX} R(CH_2)_nCH_2CR_2''OH \xrightarrow{[O]} R(CH_2)_nCO_2H + R_2''CO$$

The method has been used by Wieland *et al.*[10] in elucidating the structures of some of the bile acids.

A variation of the method occasionally employed in steroid research consists in dehydrating the carbinol resulting from the Grignard reaction and ozonizing the olefin thus obtained.

---

[9] Barbier and Locquin, *Compt. rend.*, *156*, 1443–6 (1913); *Chem. Abstr.*, 7, 3110 (1913).

[10] Wieland, Schlichting, and von Langsdorff, *Z. physiol. Chem.*, *161*, 74–9 (1926); Wieland, Schlichting, and Jacobi, *ibid.*, *161*, 80–115 (1926); *Chem. Abstr.*, *21*, 590 (1927).

TABLE VIII-II

SOME ILLUSTRATIVE PREPARATIVE REACTIONS OF GRIGNARD REAGENTS WITH CARBOXYLIC, CARBONIC, AND ORTHO ESTERS

Reactants	Reaction Conditions	Yield* (%)	Ref.†
$HCO_2C_2H_5$ (0.25 mole) + C_2H_5MgBr (0.60 mole C_2H_5Br)	Grad'l normal add'n; brief standing.	70	*489*
$HCO_2C_2H_5$ (0.75 mole) + n-C_4H_9MgBr (1.50 mole C_4H_9Br)	Grad'l normal add'n with cooling; 10 min. stirring without cooling.	83–85	*86*
$CH_3CO_2C_2H_5$ (8.30 moles) + n-C_4H_9MgBr (17.25 moles C_4H_9Br)	Slow normal add'n; overnight standing.	79	*74*
$BrCH_2CH_2CO_2CH_3$ (320 g.) + CH_3MgCl (144 g. Mg)	Slow (6 hrs.) normal add'n with cooling; several hrs. at room temp.	84 (crude)	*75*
$C_2H_5CO_2C_2H_5$ + C_2H_5MgBr (4 equiv.)	Slow normal add'n; overnight standing.	83	*101,59*
n-$C_3H_7CO_2C_2H_5$ + CH_3MgX (2 equiv.)	Normal add'n; 4–6 hrs. reflux.	80–85	*259*
Ethyl furoate (7.0 g.) + C_6H_5MgBr (15.7 g. C_6H_5Br)	Normal add'n with reflux; 3–4 hrs. reflux.	70	*147*
i-$C_3H_7CO_2C_2H_5$ + C_2H_5MgX (2 equiv.)	Normal add'n; 4–5 hrs. reflux.	80–85	*259*
Ethyl picolinate (1.00 mole) + CH_3MgI (3.25 moles)	Dropwise normal add'n with cooling; reflux to complete sol'n.	86–90	*392*
t-$C_4H_9CH_2CO_2CH_3$ (0.9 mole) + n-C_4H_9MgBr (3.6 moles)	Slow (*ca.* 3.5 hrs.) normal add'n at room temp.	71	*454*
$(C_2H_5O)_2CHCO_2C_2H_5$ (0.10 mole) + C_6H_5MgBr (0.35 mole C_6H_5Br)	Dropwise normal add'n; 1 hr. reflux.	70	*369*

* The yields recorded are those of the so-called "normal" products, namely: for formates, secondary alcohols; for other carboxylates, tertiary alcohols; for carbonates, tertiary alcohols; for orthoformates, acetals or the corresponding aldehydes; and for orthocarbonates, the ortho esters.

† In the interest of space economy a separate listing of references for this table is omitted; the reference numbers are those of Table VIII-III.

TABLE VIII-II (Continued)

Reactants	Reaction Conditions	Yield (%)	Ref.
2-$BrC_6H_4CO_2CH_3$ (0.9 mole) + 4-ClC_6H_4MgI (1.0 mole C_6H_4ICl)	Normal add'n; 5 hrs. reflux.	74	*131*
$C_6H_5CO_2C_2H_5$ (75 g.) + C_6H_5MgBr (181 g. C_6H_5Br)	Grad'l normal add'n with cooling; 1 hr. reflux.	89–93	*17*
$C_6H_5CO_2C_2H_5$ + $C_6H_5CH_2Cl$ (2 equiv.) + Mg	Barbier synthesis with cooling.	60	*94*
$(CH_2)_5CHCO_2C_2H_5$ (22.5 g.) + *t*-$C_4H_9C{\equiv}CMgBr$ (24.0 g. *t*-$C_4H_9C{\equiv}CH$)	Slow (3–4 hrs.) add'n of half of ester; overnight stirring; slow (4 hrs.) add'n remainder of ester; 3 hrs. stirring.	70	*126*
3-$CH_3C_6H_4CO_2CH_3$ (13.8 g.) + C_6H_5MgBr (31.0 g. C_6H_5Br)	Dropwise normal add'n with warming; 2 hrs. warming.	81	*48*
$CO(OC_2H_5)_2$ (1.32 mole) + C_2H_5MgBr (5.00 moles C_2H_5Br)	Slow (3 hrs.) normal add'n; 1 hr. reflux with stirring.	82–88	*258*
$HC(OC_2H_5)_3$ (42.1 g.) + *n*-C_3H_7MgBr (70.0 g. C_3H_7Br)	Normal add'n; 1 hr. reflux; dist'n of Et_2O.	76	*471*
$HC(OC_2H_5)_3$ + C_6H_5MgBr (2 equiv.)	Slow normal add'n; 15 hrs. at room temp.; 15 min. on water-bath.	95	*389*
$HC(OC_2H_5)_3$ (0.142 mole) + 4-$CH_3C_6H_4MgBr$ (0.122 mole C_7H_7Br)	Rapid normal add'n; 5 hrs. reflux; dist'n Et_2O; overnight standing.	74	*391*
$C(OC_2H_5)_4$ + C_6H_5MgBr (1 equiv.)	Normal add'n; 15 min. on water-bath.	70	*431*

Among others, Dalmer *et al.*[11] have used the Barbier-Wieland degradation for the conversion of 3-hydroxyallocholanic acid to androsterone; Reindel and Niederlander,[12] for the preparation of lower homologs from lithocholic acid; Marker *et al.*,[13] for a part in the preparation of *epi-allo*-pregnanolone; Morsman *et al.*,[14] for the preparation of lower homologs of cholic acid; Steiger and Reichstein,[15] for the degradation of 3-hydroxy-Δ^5-cholenic acid; Hoehn and Mason,[16] for the degradation of desoxycholic acid; Isihara,[17] for the degradation of chenodesoxycholic acid; and Ruzicka *et al.*,[18] for studies of steroids of partially known structure.

Other esters. As has already been indicated, the "normal" reaction of a formate with a Grignard reagent leads to the production of a secondary alcohol.

$$HCO_2R + 2\ R'MgX \longrightarrow R_2'CHOMgX + ROMgX$$

In chloroformic esters, which are at once esters and acid chlorides, the acid chloride function is the more reactive of the two, and among the products of reaction with one equivalent of Grignard reagent an ester usually predominates.

$$ROCOCl + R'MgX \longrightarrow R'CO_2R + MgXCl$$

However, a tertiary alcohol, resulting from interaction of some of the Grignard reagent with the ester first formed is often one of the byproducts of the reaction, and the use of three or more equivalents of Grignard reagent with one equivalent of chloroformate usually leads to production of the carbinol.

$$ROCOCl + 3\ R'MgX \longrightarrow R_3'COH + MgXCl + MgXOR$$

For these reasons most of the chloroformic ester reactions have been listed in the carbonyl halide tabulation (Table IX-II), but some examples are included in Table VIII-III of this chapter.

Although the reaction of ethyl carbonate with *t*-alkylmagnesium halides tends to terminate at the first step,[19]

$$(C_2H_5O)_2CO + t\text{-}C_4H_9MgCl \longrightarrow (C_2H_5O)_2C(OMgCl)\text{-}t\text{-}C_4H_9$$

$$\xrightarrow{H_2O} t\text{-}C_4H_9CO_2C_2H_5 + C_2H_5OH + MgClOH$$

---

[11]Dalmer, von Werder, Honigmann, and Heyns, *Ber.*, *68B*, 1814–25 (1935).

[12]Reindel and Niederlander, *Ber.*, *68B*, 1969–73 (1935).

[13]Marker, Kamm, Jones, Wittle, Oakwood, and Crooks, *J. Am. Chem. Soc.*, *59*, 768 (1937); Marker, Kamm, McGinty, Jones, Wittle, Oakwood, and Crooks, *ibid.*, *59*, 1367–8 (1937).

[14]Morsman, Steiger, and Reichstein, *Helv. Chim. Acta*, *20*, 3–16 (1937).

[15]Steiger and Reichstein, *Helv. Chim. Acta*, *20*, 1040–54 (1937).

[16]Hoehn and Mason, *J. Am. Chem. Soc.*, *60*, 1493–7 (1938).

[17]Isihara, *J. Biochem.* (Japan), *27*, 265–77 (1938); *Chem. Abstr.*, *33*, 4265 (1939).

[18]Ruzicka, Oberlin, Wirz, and Meyer, *Helv. Chim. Acta*, *20*, 1283–90 (1937).

[19]Whitmore and Badertscher, *J. Am. Chem. Soc.*, *55*, 1559–67 (1933).

most Grignard reagents react with it to give tertiary alcohols in which all three carbinol substituents are supplied by the Grignard reagent.

$$(C_2H_5O)_2CO + 3\ RMgX \longrightarrow R_3COMgX + 2\ C_2H_5OMgX$$

$$\xrightarrow{H_2O} R_3COH + 2\ C_2H_5OH + 3\ MgXOH$$

The orthoformates* react readily with one equivalent of Grignard reagent to form acetals, or the corresponding aldehydes, depending on the conditions of reaction and product recovery.

$$HC(OC_2H_5)_3 + RMgX \longrightarrow RCH(OC_2H_5)_2 + MgXOC_2H_5$$

Similarly, orthocarbonic ester reacts with Grignard reagents to form ortho esters.

$$C(OC_2H_5)_4 + RMgX \longrightarrow RC(OC_2H_5)_3 + MgXOC_2H_5$$

KETONE (OR ALDEHYDE) FORMATION

For most saturated esters of the type RCO_2R' it would appear that the second step of the Grignard reaction takes place even more readily than the first, for treatment of an ester with one equivalent of Grignard reagent usually leads, not to the formation of a ketone, but of a tertiary alcohol, and to the recovery of approximately half the ester used.

In this respect formic esters are exceptions to the general rule (probably because of their relatively greater reactivity with respect to the first reaction step), for, although they usually yield secondary alcohols under ordinary Grignard reaction conditions, they can be made to yield aldehydes, as was discovered by Gattermann and Maffezzoli.[20] As might be expected, optimum yields of aldehydes are obtained by employing an excess of ester, by reversing the usual order of reagent addition, and by operating at low temperature. (Gattermann and Maffezzoli used three moles of ester to one of Grignard reagent at $-50°$). Even so, yields are never high (see Table VIII-III), and this method of preparation has been almost entirely abandoned in favor of the orthoformic ester method which gives excellent yields of the acetals (see Tables VIII-II and VIII-III).

As regards "unhindered" saturated esters other than the formates it would appear from the available data that, when the Grignard intermediate originally formed is reasonably ether-soluble, the ability to form ketones is a function primarily of the Grignard reagent employed rather than of the ester. The branched-chain alkylmagnesium halides, the pyrrylmagnesium halides, and the diortho-substituted arylmagnesium halides appear to display a special tendency toward ketone formation. This suggests that the effect is primarily steric, although in the case of the Grignard

*Actually these reactions are more closely related to those of the acetals, ketals, and ethers, (*q.v.*, Chapter XV) than to those of the ordinary carboxylic esters.

[20]Gattermann and Maffezzoli, *Ber.*, *36*, 4152–3 (1903). See also: Houben, *Chem.-Ztg.*, *29*, 667–8 (1905); *Chem. Zentr.*, *1905,II*, 765.

reagents derived from nitrogen heterocycles by hydrogen displacement this effect may be related to one of their atypical properties. In extreme cases steric hindrance may, in itself, be sufficient to account for the inhibition of further addition. Probably, however, it is oftener the case that such inhibition results, in part at least, from the intervention of potentially competing reactions, such as enolization or reduction of the intermediate formed in the first stage of the addition.

When the intermediate formed in the first stage of the Grignard reagent addition is virtually insoluble in the reaction medium, further reaction is necessarily slow. This, as suggested by Long *et al.*,[21] is probably the reason for the isolation of 3(α),11(α)-dihydroxynorcholanyl phenyl ketone as a byproduct of the reaction of methyl 3(α),11(α)-dihydroxycholanate with phenylmagnesium bromide. The detection of ketones as byproducts of the reactions of steroid esters with Grignard reagents is a rather common occurrence.[22]

The α,β-unsaturated esters are exceptions to the general rule in that they display a tendency toward ketone formation regardless of the nature of the Grignard reagents with which they are treated. Usually, though not invariably, ketone formation is accompanied by 1,4-addition (see Table VIII-III). Kohler[23] reported that when methyl α-methylcinnammate, in slight excess, reacts with phenylmagnesium bromide both α-benzylidenepropiophenone and α-benzhydrylpropiophenone are formed.

$$C_6H_5CH{=}C(CH_3)CO_2CH_3 \xrightarrow{C_6H_5MgBr} C_6H_5CH{=}C(CH_3)COC_6H_5 + (C_6H_5)_2CHCH(CH_3)COC_6H_5$$

The reactions of Grignard reagents with the aryl esters of "hindered" acids are probably special cases of ether cleavage (*q.v.*, Chapter XV), and are discussed in the section on Ester Cleavages, p. 567.

REDUCTION

So far as may be judged from published reports, the carboxylic esters as such are not reduced by Grignard reagents. Various investigators, however, have reported the isolation of secondary alcohols corresponding to the ketones which might be expected to result from the first step of the Grignard reaction (see Table VIII-III).

The mechanism of such reductions has not been studied, but it appears that they occur only in reactions involving Grignard reagents of the type RR′CHCR″R‴MgX (*i.e.*, those which also effect aldehyde and ketone reductions), and the predictable alkene byproducts (RR′C=CR″R‴) have been detected by Meerwein,[24] Leroide,[25] Stas,[26] and Ivanoff and

[21] Long, Marshall, and Gallagher, *J. Biol. Chem.*, *165*, 197–209 (1946).

[22] Private communication from Dr. T. F. Gallagher of the Sloan-Kettering Institute for Cancer Research.

[23] Kohler, *Am. Chem. J.*, *36*, 529–38 (1906).

[24] Meerwein, *Ann.*, *396*, 200–63 (1913).

[25] Leroide, *Ann. chim.*, [9], *16*, 354–410 (1921).

[26] Stas, *Bull. soc. chim. Belg.*, *34*, 188–90 (1925).

Spassoff.[27] If, as on the whole appears questionable, a free ketone is an intermediate in the Grignard reaction, the discussion of ketonic reduction (Chapter VI) would apply. Possibly, however, such reductions take a course illustrated by the equation:

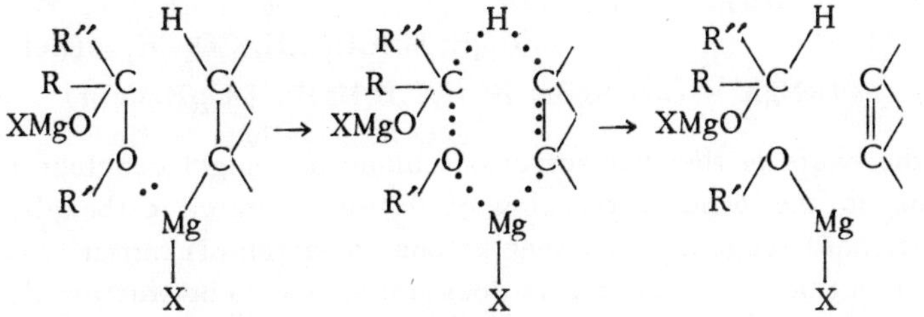

```
 R''    H              R''   .H.            R''    H
   \     \   /           \  .   .  /          \   /
 R--C     C               R--C      C          R--C      C
XMgO/ |   | /  →  XMgO/  :    : /  →  XMgO/     ||
     /O   C          /O   C             /O      C
 R'   ..  /\       R'  ..  ../\       R'  \
        Mg                 Mg               Mg
        |                  |                |
        X                  X                X
```

Some reactions, therefore, may terminate at the first stage merely by reason of competition of the reduction reaction with the second stage of the Grignard reaction, rather than through any intrinsic tendency toward ketone formation.

GRIGNARD REAGENT ADDITION TO α,β-UNSATURATED CARBOXYLIC ESTERS

When treated with Grignard reagents in excess, α,β-unsaturated carboxylic esters usually undergo 1,4-addition, either with or without ketone formation. Several examples of 1,4-addition with ketone formation are recorded in Table VIII-III. Various examples of 1,4-addition without further reaction of the ester group have been reported by Kohler and his students, and by others.

$$(CH_3)_2C{=}C(CO_2C_2H_5)_2 \xrightarrow{RMgX} R(CH_3)_2CCH(CO_2C_2H_5)_2 \quad \text{(Ref. 28)}$$
$$(RMgX = CH_3MgI,\ n\text{-}C_4H_9MgBr)$$

$$C_6H_5CH{=}C(CN)CO_2C_2H_5 \xrightarrow{RMgX} R(C_6H_5)CHCH(CN)CO_2C_2H_5 \quad \text{(Ref. 29)}$$
$$(RMgX = CH_3MgI,\ i\text{-}C_3H_7MgI,\ C_6H_5MgBr,\ 1\text{-}C_{10}H_7MgBr)$$

$$C_6H_5CH{=}C(CO_2C_2H_5)_2 \xrightarrow{RMgX} R(C_6H_5)CHCH(CO_2C_2H_5)_2 \quad \text{(Ref. 30, 31)}$$
$$(RMgX = CH_3MgI,\ C_2H_5MgBr,\ C_6H_5MgBr)$$

$$C_6H_5CH{=}CHCH{=}C(CN)CO_2C_2H_5 \xrightarrow{RMgX}$$
$$C_6H_5CH{=}CHCHRCH(CN)CO_2C_2H_5 \quad \text{(Ref. 32)}$$
$$(R = C_2H_5MgBr,\ C_6H_5MgBr)$$

---

[27]Ivanoff and Spassoff, *Bull. soc. chim.*, [5], 2, 816–24 (1935).

[28]Wideqvist, *Arkiv. Kemi, Mineral. Geol.*, *B23*, No. 4, 6pp. (1946); *Chem. Abstr.*, *41*, 1615 (1947).

[29]Kohler and Reimer, *Am. Chem. J.*, *33*, 333–56 (1905).

[30]Kohler, *Am. Chem. J.*, *34*, 132–47 (1906).

[31]Reynolds, *Am. Chem. J.*, *44*, 305–31 (1910).

[32]MacLeod, *Am. Chem. J.*, *44*, 331–52 (1910).

$$C_6H_5CH{=}CHCH{=}C(CO_2CH_3)_2 \xrightarrow{RMgX} C_6H_5CH{=}CHCHRCH(CO_2CH_3)_2 \quad \text{(Ref. 33)}$$

$$(RMgX = CH_3MgI,\ C_6H_5MgBr,\ C_6H_5CH_2MgCl)$$

$$C_6H_5CH{=}C(C_6H_5)CO_2CH_3 \xrightarrow{RMgX} R(C_6H_5)CHCH(C_6H_5)CO_2CH_3 \quad \text{(Ref. 34, 35)}$$

$$(RMgX = C_6H_5MgBr,\ 2\text{-}CH_3C_6H_4MgBr,\ 1\text{-}C_{10}H_7MgBr)$$

On the basis of these observations alone one might conclude that 1,4-addition is the primary reaction of α,β-unsaturated carboxylic esters with Grignard reagents, and that ketone (or carbinol) formation are secondary reactions. However, this does not appear to be true for all esters, and for a given ester the course of the reaction may vary with the Grignard reagent and the reaction conditions employed. Blaise and Courtot[36] have reported, for example, that, when treated with two equivalents of methylmagnesium iodide at temperatures not exceeding 0°, methacrylic ester yields both saturated ketone and unsaturated carbinol; at 20° the products are unsaturated carbinol and biïsopropenyl (neither involving 1,4-addition).

$$H_2C{=}C(CH_3)CO_2C_2H_5 + CH_3MgI \xrightarrow{0^\circ} CH_3(C_2H_5)CHCOCH_3 + H_2C{=}C(CH_3)C(CH_3)_2OH$$

$$H_2C{=}C(CH_3)CO_2C_2H_5 + CH_3MgI \xrightarrow{20^\circ} H_2C{=}C(CH_3)C(CH_3)_2OH + [H_2C{=}C(CH_3){-}]_2$$

Even at 0° ethylmagnesium iodide yields only the unsaturated carbinol.

Kohler[37] also reports that methyl α-methylcinnamate in slight excess reacts with phenylmagnesium bromide to yield both α-benzylidenepropiophenone and α-benzhydrylpropiophenone.

CLAISEN (ACETOACETIC ESTER-TYPE) CONDENSATIONS*

Like ketones (see Enolate Formation by Grignard Reagents, Chapter VI), many esters with one or more *alpha* hydrogen atoms are capable of undergoing Grignard reagent-enolization. When such esters are also susceptible to enolate addition at the carbonyl double bond self-condensation may occur.

[33] Reimer, *Am. Chem. J.*, *38*, 227–37 (1907).
[34] Kohler, *Am. Chem. J.*, *31*, 642–6 (1904).
[35] Kohler and Heritage, *Am. Chem. J.*, *33*, 153–64 (1905).
[36] Blaise and Courtot, *Compt. rend.*, *140*, 370–2 (1905); *Chem. Zentr.*, *1905*,*I*, 726.
[37] Kohler, *Am. Chem. J.*, *36*, 529–38 (1906).

*For a discussion of this type of reaction in general see: Hauser and Hudson, "The Acetoacetic Ester Condensations and Certain Related Reactions," Chapter 9, Vol. I of "Organic Reactions," edited by Roger Adams, John Wiley & Sons, Inc., New York, pp. 266–302, *1942*.

$$RR'CHCO_2R'' \xrightarrow{R'''MgX} [RR'C{=}C(O^-){-}OR'' \leftrightarrow RR'C^-{-}C(=O){-}OR'']^- MgX^+ + R'''H$$

$$[RR'C{=}C(O^-){-}OR'' \longleftrightarrow RR'C^-{-}C(=O){-}OR'']^- MgX^+ \xrightarrow{RR'CHCO_2R''} RR'C(C(=O)CHRR'){-}C(=O){-}OR'' + R''OMgX$$

Such condensations have been reported by Shivers *et al.*,[38] by Conant and Blatt,[39] by Ivanoff and Spassoff,[40] by Zook *et al.*,[41] and by Spielman and Schmidt,[42] and resultant analogous condensation products have undoubtedly been overlooked or ignored in many instances.

$$CH_3CO_2\text{-}t\text{-}C_4H_9 \xrightarrow{i\text{-}C_3H_7MgBr} CH_3COCH_2CO_2\text{-}t\text{-}C_4H_9\ (41\%) + \text{"gas"}$$
(Ref. 38)

$$i\text{-}C_4H_9CO_2\text{-}t\text{-}C_4H_9 \xrightarrow{i\text{-}C_3H_7MgBr} \text{Recovered ester } (15\%) + i\text{-}C_4H_9CO(i\text{-}C_3H_7)CHCO_2\text{-}t\text{-}C_4H_9\ (29\%) + \text{"gas"}$$
(Ref. 38)

$$C_6H_5CH_2CO_2C_2H_5 \xrightarrow{i\text{-}C_3H_7MgBr} C_6H_5CH_2COCH(C_6H_5)CO_2C_2H_5\ (94\%) + \text{"sat'd. gas"}$$
(Ref. 39)

$$C_6H_5CH_2CO_2C_2H_5 \xrightarrow{i\text{-}C_3H_7MgCl} C_6H_5CH_2COCH(C_6H_5)CO_2C_2H_5 + C_3H_8$$
(Ref. 40)

$$4\text{-}ClC_6H_4CH_2CO_2C_2H_5 \xrightarrow{i\text{-}C_3H_7MgCl} 4\text{-}ClC_6H_4CH_2COCH(C_6H_5)CO_2C_2H_5\ (93\%)$$
(Ref. 40)

$$C_2H_5CO_2C_2H_5 \xrightarrow{t\text{-}C_4H_9MgCl} C_2H_5COCH(CH_3)CO_2C_2H_5\ (50\%) + C_2H_5(t\text{-}C_4H_9)CHOH\ (20\%)$$
(Ref. 41)

$$i\text{-}C_4H_9CO_2C_2H_5 \xrightarrow{2,4,6\text{-}(CH_3)_3C_6H_2MgBr} i\text{-}C_4H_9COCH(i\text{-}C_3H_7)CO_2C_2H_5\ (51\%) + 2,4,6\text{-}(CH_3)_3C_6H_3$$
(Ref. 42)

When, for steric or other reasons, an enolizable ester does not readily undergo enolate addition a cross-condensation may still be possible. Hauser *et al.*[43] have succeeded in benzoylating the enolate of ethyl diphenylacetate with benzoyl chloride.

---

[38] Shivers, Hudson, and Hauser, *J. Am. Chem. Soc.*, *65*, 2051–3 (1943).
[39] Conant and Blatt, *J. Am. Chem. Soc.*, *51*, 1227–36 (1929).
[40] Ivanoff and Spassoff, *Bull. soc. chim.*, [4], *49*, 375–7 (1931).
[41] Zook, McAleer, and Horwin, *J. Am. Chem. Soc.*, *68*, 2404 (1946).
[42] Spielman and Schmidt, *J. Am. Chem. Soc.*, *59*, 2009–10 (1937).
[43] Hauser, Saperstein, and Shivers, *J. Am. Chem. Soc.*, *70*, 606–8 (1948).

$$(C_6H_5)_2CHCO_2C_2H_5 \xrightarrow{i\text{-}C_3H_7MgBr} [(C_6H_5)_2CCO_2C_2H_5]^- MgBr^+$$
$$\xrightarrow{C_6H_5COCl} C_6H_5COC(C_6H_5)_2CO_2C_2H_5$$

Symmetrical ketone formation (R_2CO from 2 RCO_2R'). Numerous examples of symmetrical ketone formation in reactions of esters with Grignard reagents in high-boiling solvents have been reported by Petrov (Pétroff) and co-workers.[44]

$$CH_3CO_2C_2H_5 \xrightarrow{RMgX} (CH_3)_2CO + CH_3COR$$
$$(RMgX = s\text{-}C_4H_9MgBr,\ t\text{-}C_4H_9MgCl)$$

$$n\text{-}C_6H_{13}CO_2C_2H_5 \xrightarrow{t\text{-}C_4H_9MgCl} (n\text{-}C_6H_{13})_2CO$$

$$n\text{-}C_{11}H_{23}CO_2C_2H_5 \xrightarrow{RMgX} (n\text{-}C_{11}H_{23})_2CO$$
$$(RMgX = s\text{-}C_4H_9MgBr,\ t\text{-}C_4H_9MgCl)$$

$$n\text{-}C_{11}H_{23}CO_2\text{-}n\text{-}C_8H_{17} \xrightarrow{t\text{-}C_4H_9MgCl} (n\text{-}C_{11}H_{23})_2CO + n\text{-}C_{11}H_{23}CO_2H$$

$$n\text{-}C_{15}H_{31}CO_2C_2H_5 \xrightarrow{RMgX} (n\text{-}C_{15}H_{31})_2CO$$
$$(RMgX = s\text{-}C_4H_9MgBr,\ t\text{-}C_4H_9MgCl)$$

As a reaction scheme the formulation proposed by Petrov is, of course, a palpable absurdity.

$$2\ RCO_2Et \longrightarrow R_2CO + (EtO)_2CO \longrightarrow R_2CO + Et_2O + CO_2$$

Despite the protests of Petrov,[45] there appears to be no sound reason for rejecting the suggestion of Zook *et al.* (*loc. cit.*[41]) that these reactions take place through the Claisen condensation, for, as they point out, the lower β-keto esters can be isolated by fractional distillation of (acid-hydrolyzed) ethereal reaction mixtures, and they have so isolated a 50 percent yield of ethyl propionylpropionate from the interaction of ethyl propionate and *t*-butylmagnesium chloride in ethereal solution.

$$2\ RCH_2CO_2C_2H_5 \xrightarrow{t\text{-}C_4H_9MgCl} RCH_2COCHRCO_2C_2H_5 \xrightarrow[[OH^-]]{H_2O} (RCH_2)_2CO$$

Zook *et al.* also added an ethereal *t*-butylmagnesium chloride solution (1.08 mole) to a cooled, stirred ethereal methyl myristate (47 g., 0.32 mole) solution. Isobutane (0.17 mole) and isobutylene (0.90 mole) were evolved. After overnight standing, acid aqueous hydrolysis yielded an ether-soluble oil which was subjected to mild alkaline alcoholysis. The

---

[44]Pétroff, Karasseff, and Tschelowa, *Bull. soc. chim.*, [5], 3, 169–76 (1936); Petrov and Sokolova, *J. Gen. Chem.* (U.S.S.R.), 8, 199–206 (1938); *Chem. Abstr.*, 32, 5376 (1938); Petrov, *Sci. Records Gorky State Univ.*, No. 7, 3–9 (1939); *Chem. Abstr.*, 35, 435 (1941); Petrov, Belyaeva, and Kukanova, *Sci. Records Gorky State Univ.*, No. 7, 14–16 (1939); *Khim. Referat. Zhur.*, *1940*, No. 10–11, 20; *Chem. Abstr.*, 37, 1379 (1943).

[45]Petrov, *Isvest. Akad. Nauk S.S.S.R., Otdel Khim. Nauk*, *1950*, 209–15; *Chem. Abstr.*, *44*, 9343 (1950).

products were the relatively ether-insoluble symmetrical ketone [$(n\text{-}C_{13}H_{27})_2CO$; 27.5 g., 44%], *t*-butyltridecanylcarbinol (37 g., 40%), and myristic acid (6 g., 8%) from unchanged ester.

Under the experimental conditions imposed by Petrov *et al.* (*loc. cit.*[44]) the decarbethoxylation would probably take place prior to aqueous hydrolysis.

ESTER CLEAVAGES

"Hindered" alkyl esters. Fuson *et al.*[46] report that methyl, *n*-butyl, and benzyl mesitoates react with Grignard reagents to yield mesitoic acid and the halides corresponding to the respective ester alcohols.

$$MesCO_2CH_3 \xrightarrow{n\text{-}C_4H_9MgBr} \xrightarrow{H_2O} MesCO_2H\ (25\%) + CH_3Br\ (20\%)$$

$$MesCO_2\text{-}n\text{-}C_4H_9 \xrightarrow{C_6H_5MgI} \xrightarrow{H_2O} MesCO_2H\ (61\%) + n\text{-}C_4H_9I\ (54\%)$$

$$MesCO_2CH_2C_6H_5 \xrightarrow{C_6H_5MgI} \xrightarrow{H_2O} MesCO_2H\ (65\%) + C_6H_5CH_2I\ (70\%)$$

This type of reaction would appear to be most readily explicable as a special case of complex rearrangement and decomposition with carbon-oxygen bond cleavage, somewhat related to the epoxide ring openings and ether cleavages, but not closely analogous to either. Because of steric inhibition the "hindered" ester complexes presumably cannot readily react with a second molecule of Grignard reagent to effect the first step of the "normal" addition reaction, and potentially competing, but probably energetically less favored reactions, have an opportunity to come into play.

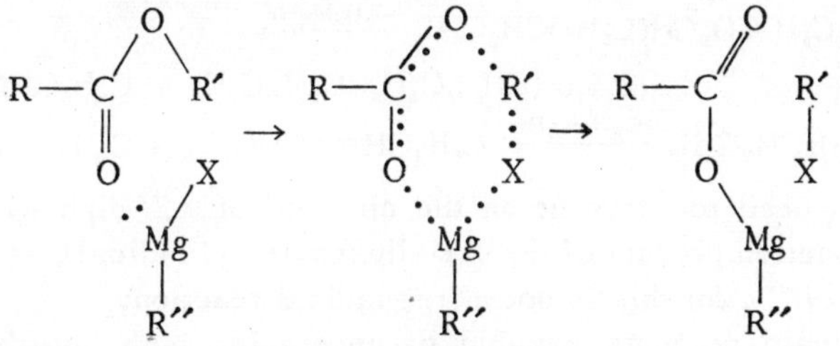

```
        O                     O                    O
       / \                  .'  .                 //
R—C     R'          R—C      R'          R—C     R'
   ||          →         |:      :    →       |       |
   O     X               O.      X             O       X
    ·.  /                  ·.  .·               \
      Mg                    Mg                   Mg
      |                     |                    |
      R''                   R''                  R''
```

Unfortunately no one has as yet (to the knowledge of the present authors) taken the trouble to determine certainly the fate of the group R'' (corresponding to the Grignard reagent, R''MgX). Presumably hydrolysis of the acid salt would yield the corresponding hydrocarbon (R''H), although the possibility of ionic exchange in the sense

$$RCO_2MgR'' + MgX_2 \rightleftharpoons RCO_2MgX + R''MgX$$

or

$$RCO_2MgR'' + R''MgX \rightleftharpoons RCO_2MgX + R''_2Mg$$

would vitiate any conclusions as to the immediate source of the hydro-

[46] Fuson, Bottorff, and Speck, *J. Am. Chem. Soc.*, *64*, 1450–3 (1942).

carbon unless it were possible to isolate the salt itself in a reasonably pure condition.*

Obviously the ultimate fate of the group R′ would depend primarily upon the nature of the group itself, and to a lesser extent upon the nature of the Grignard reagent involved (which would necessarily determine also the identity of the halogen, X), as well as upon the experimental conditions imposed. Under ordinary reaction conditions the primary aliphatic radicals would be largely recoverable as the corresponding halides (R′X). Although benzyl iodide evidently does not react appreciably with the relatively unreactive phenylmagnesium iodide under the conditions employed by Fuson *et al.*, treatment of the benzyl ester with the relatively reactive benzylmagnesium chloride might lead to at least partial reaction of the halide with the Grignard reagent to form bibenzyl.[47]

The triarylmethyl halides react readily with most Grignard reagents to give good yields of hydrocarbons (see Chapter XVI, Table XVI-I). Thus the cleavages of triphenylmethyl acetate by methylmagnesium bromide, reported by Fieser and Heymann,[48] and of triphenylmethyl benzoate by methylmagnesium iodide, reported by Hauser *et al.*,[49] to yield α,α,α-triphenylethane are readily explicable.

α,β-Diphenylethyl mesitoate might be expected to undergo Grignard reagent cleavage to yield highly reactive halides which would undergo dehydrohalogenation or coupling or both, depending on the nature of the Grignard reagent employed (see Chapter XVI). According to Hauser *et al.*, (*loc. cit.*[49]) the products obtained upon treatment of the ester with phenylmagnesium bromide and with methyl- and ethylmagnesium iodides are precisely the ones predictable on this basis.

$$2,4,6\text{-}(CH_3)_3C_6H_4CO_2CH(C_6H_5)CH_2C_6H_5 \xrightarrow{C_6H_5MgBr}$$
$$2,4,6\text{-}(CH_3)_3C_6H_4CO_2MgC_6H_5 + C_6H_5CHBrCH_2C_6H_5$$
$$C_6H_5CHBrCH_2C_6H_5 \xrightarrow{C_6H_5MgBr} C_6H_5CH{=}CHC_6H_5 + C_6H_6 + MgBr_2$$

There is no need to comment on the absence of α,β-diphenylethane (a disproportionation product of the α,β-diphenylethyl radical), as do Hauser *et al.*, (*loc. cit*[49]), for this is not a free-radical reaction.

With Grignard reagents capable of undergoing both homolytic (free-radical) and heterolytic (ionic) dissociation, as is methylmagnesium iodide, both coupling and dehydrohalogenation reactions might be expected to take place simultaneously.

$$C_6H_5CHICH_2C_6H_5 \xrightarrow{CH_3MgI} C_6H_5CH{=}CHC_6H_5 + CH_4 + MgI_2$$
$$C_6H_5CHICH_2C_6H_5 \xrightarrow{CH_3MgI} C_6H_5(C_6H_5CH_2)CH\cdot + CH_3\cdot + MgI_2$$

*There is, of course, the possibility that such cleavages are effected exclusively by the MgX_2 component of the Grignard reagent. Appropriate studies with R_2Mg reagents might throw some light on this point.

[47]See: Spaِth, *Monatsh.*, *34*, 1965–2014 (1913).

[48]Fieser and Heymann, *J. Am. Chem. Soc.*, *64*, 376–82 (1942).

[49]Hauser, Saperstein, and Shivers, *J. Am. Chem. Soc.*, *70*, 606–8 (1948).

Most of the relatively reactive methyl free radicals so liberated would immediately attack the ethereal solvent, abstracting hydrogen and forming methane. A few might encounter diphenylethyl free radicals (also ready hydrogen donors), and extract hydrogen from them.

$$CH_3\cdot + C_6H_5(C_6H_5CH_2)CH\cdot \longrightarrow CH_4 + C_6H_5CH{=}CHC_6H_5$$

For the most part, the relatively unreactive diphenylethyl radicals would accumulate in the solution. Although the possibility of their disproportionation cannot be completely discounted, it appears probable that the predominant reaction of a free radical of this type would be dimerization.

$$2\ C_6H_5(C_6H_5CH_2)CH\cdot \longrightarrow [C_6H_5(C_6H_5CH_2)CH{-}]_2$$

The reaction products of benzhydryl acetate with Grignard reagents (*e.g.*, *n*-propylmagnesium iodide), as reported by Stadnikoff[50] are readily explicable on the basis indicated.

$$CH_3CO_2CH(C_6H_5)_2 \xrightarrow{2\ n\text{-}C_3H_7MgI} CH_3(n\text{-}C_3H_7)_2COMgI + (C_6H_5)_2CHOMgI$$

$$CH_3CO_2CH(C_6H_5)_2 \xrightarrow{n\text{-}C_3H_7MgI} CH_3CO_2Mg\text{-}n\text{-}C_3H_7 + (C_6H_5)_2CHI$$

$$(C_6H_5)_2CHI \xrightarrow{n\text{-}C_3H_7MgI} (C_6H_5)_2CH\cdot + n\text{-}C_3H_7\cdot + MgI_2$$

$$2\ (C_6H_5)_2CH\cdot \longrightarrow [(C_6H_5)_2CH{-}]_2$$

$$2\ (C_6H_5)_2CH\cdot \xrightarrow{O_2} [(C_6H_5)_2CHO{-}]_2$$

$$2\ n\text{-}C_3H_7\cdot \longrightarrow C_3H_8 + C_3H_6$$

In this case the relatively unreactive *n*-propyl free radicals are unable to attack the solvent appreciably and are incapable of dimerization; consequently, they disproportionate.

Allyl halides react readily with most Grignard reagents (except the acetylenic) to give good yields of unsaturated hydrocarbons (see Chapter XVI, Table XVI-I), and one would at first thought be inclined to attribute the cleavage of a "hindered" allyl ester by phenylmagnesium bromide to yield allylbenzene (as reported by Arnold *et al.*[51]) to a two-stage reaction in which allyl halide is formed by ester cleavage and then reacts with Grignard reagent.

$$2,3,4,6\text{-}(CH_3)_4C_6HCO_2CH_2CH{=}CH_2\ (33.7\ g.)$$
$$+\ C_6H_5MgBr\ (\text{from } 32.0\ g.\ C_6H_5Br) \xrightarrow{[H_3O^+]} 2,3,4,6\text{-}(CH_3)_4C_6HCO_2H\ (95\%)$$
$$+\ C_6H_5CH_2CH{=}CH_2\ (13.5\ g.)$$

$$2,3\text{-}(CH_3)_2C_{10}H_5\text{-}1\text{-}CO_2CH_2CH{=}CH_2\ (15.1\ g.)$$
$$+\ C_6H_5MgBr\ (\text{from } 13.0\ g.\ C_6H_5Br) \xrightarrow{[H_3O^+]} 2,3\text{-}(CH_3)_2C_{10}H_5\text{-}1\text{-}CO_2H\ (97\%)$$
$$+\ C_6H_5CH_2CH{=}CH_2\ (6.0\ g.)$$

---

[50] Stadnikoff, *Ber.*, *47*, 2133–42 (1914).

[51] *(a)* Arnold, Bank, and Liggett, *J. Am. Chem. Soc.*, *63*, 3444–6 (1941); *(b)* Arnold and Liggett, *64*, 2875–7 (1942).

Unfortunately there are at least two objections to this happy solution, the first of which might appear (like the reluctant poker player's plea of no funds) to be sufficient in itself. Analysis of the quantitative data included in the two foregoing illustrative equations reveals that in neither case could there be enough Grignard reagent present to account for a two-stage reaction in the sense:

$$RCO_2R' + R''MgX \longrightarrow RCO_2MgR'' + R'X$$

$$RX + R''MgX \longrightarrow R'R'' + MgX_2$$

In the first instance, 0.1553 mole of ester reacts with the Grignard reagent from 0.2038 mole of bromobenzene (presumably about 0.18 mole) to form 0.1475 mole of acid and 0.1144 mole of allylbenzene. In the second, 0.0629 mole of ester reacts with the Grignard reagent from 0.0828 mole of bromobenzene (presumably about 0.08 mole) to form 0.0610 mole of acid and 0.0508 mole of allylbenzene.

Despite its apparent insuperability, however, this contra-indication might be refuted if it could be demonstrated either (*a*) that ionic exchange of RCO_2MgR'' in the sense already indicated is fairly rapid, or (*b*) that salts of the type RCO_2MgR'' (about which little or nothing is known) are to all intents and purposes Grignard reagents capable of reacting readily in the sense:

$$RCO_2MgR'' + BrCH_2CH{=}CH_2 \longrightarrow RCO_2MgBr + R''CH_2CH{=}CH_2$$

If, humanly seeking the easier course, one were inclined, tentatively, to accept the possible refutation as actual, a second objection arises out of the identities of the hydrocarbon products resulting from the phenylmagnesium bromide cleavages of the butenyl mesitoates.[52] Although α-methallyl mesitoate yields crotylbenzene and α-methallylbenzene in approximately the same proportions that result from the treatment of either α-methally or crotyl chloride* with phenylmagnesium bromide, the analogous cleavage of crotyl mesitoate is said to yield crotylbenzene only.

$$H_2C{=}CCH(CH_3)Cl \xrightarrow{C_6H_5MgBr} CH_3CH{=}CHCH_2C_6H_5\ (59 \pm 4\%) + H_2C{=}CHCH(CH_3)C_6H_5 (14 \pm 2\%)$$

$$CH_3CH{=}CHCH_2Cl \xrightarrow{C_6H_5MgBr} CH_3CH{=}CHCH_2C_6H_5\ (46 \pm 3\%) + H_2C{=}CHCH(CH_3)C_6H_5\ (14 \pm 2\%)$$

$$C_4H_7Cl^{\dagger} \xrightarrow{C_6H_5MgBr} CH_3CH{=}CHCH_2C_6H_5\ [(81 \pm 3)x\%] + H_2C{=}CHCH(CH_3)C_6H_5\ [(19 \pm 2)x\%]$$

[52](*a*) Arnold and Liggett, *J. Am. Chem. Soc.*, *67*, 337–8 (1945); (*b*) Arnold and Searles, *ibid.*, *71*, 2021–3 (1949); (*c*) Wilson, Roberts, and Young, *ibid.*, *71*, 2019–20 (1949).

*The chlorides were used in these experiments because, unlike the bromides, which isomerize rapidly at the reaction temperatures employed, they are stable. However, the stability of the *pure* chlorides at these temperatures would seem a very poor guarantee of their stability in the presence of magnesium or organomagnesium halides.

†The butenyl chloride used was a mixture of about 41% crotyl chloride and 59%

$$2,4,6\text{-}(CH_3)_3C_6H_2CO_2CH(CH_3)CH{=}CH_2 \xrightarrow{C_6H_5MgBr}$$
$$CH_3CH{=}CHCH_2C_6H_5\ (63 \pm 5\%) + H_2C{=}CHCH(CH_3)C_6H_5\ (13 \pm 2\%)$$
$$2,4,6\text{-}(CH_3)_3C_6H_2CO_2CH_2CH{=}CHCH_3 \xrightarrow{C_6H_5MgBr}$$
$$CH_3CH{=}CHCH_2C_6H_5\ (76\text{–}86\%)$$

The relatively high yields of crotylbenzene obtained in the cleavage of crotyl mesitoate may or may not be, in themselves, significant, but the inability of two independent research teams to detect α-methallylbenzene among the reaction products (although classifiable as negative evidence) cannot be altogether ignored. Both Arnold and Young (*loc. cit.*[52]) have proposed a mechanism involving a cyclic intermediate complex, which (slightly modified in form, but not materially altered in sense) may be represented as follows.

O O O
R—C R′ → R—C R′ → R—C R′
O R″ O R″ O R″
Mg Mg Mg
X X X

If this formulation be accepted as satisfactory and even necessary for elucidation of the Grignard cleavage of crotyl mesitoate, the question then arises why it should be inadequate to account for the mesityl ester cleavages observed by Fuson *et al.* (*loc. cit.*[46]), or even (completely) for the more closely analogous α-methallyl mesitoate cleavage. At this point there arises the disquieting suspicion that this may be one of the relatively rare, but by no means unknown, situations in which the convenient, and usually harmless, fiction involved in the oversimplified R″MgX formulation of the Grignard reagent (see Chapter IV) constitutes a trap for the unwary. It may well be that our speculations should take into account for any individual cleavage reaction the probable relative abundances, stabilities, and reactivities of at least four theoretically conceivable transition states.

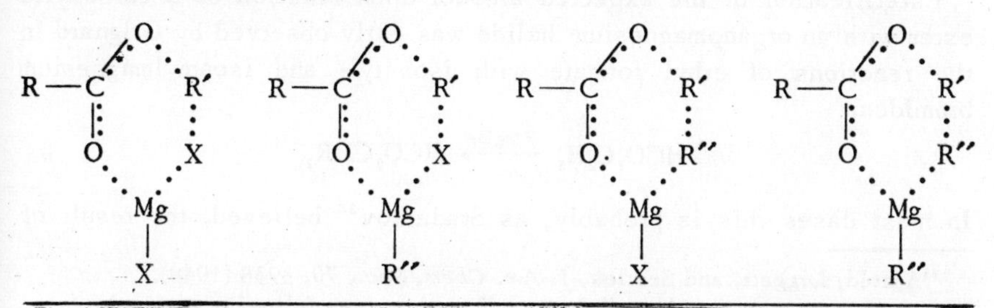

α-methallyl chloride; the products (total yield, 100x%, not stated) were isolated in the ratio indicated.

Obviously, direct experimental investigation of the proposed hypothetical RCO_2R'-$R''MgX$ complexes would be impossible, for no such thing as pure $R''MgX$ exists. Something instructive might, however, develop out of a careful quantitative study of the behavior of various RCO_2R'-MgX_2 and RCO_2R'-$R_2''Mg$ complexes and of the complexes formed by RCO_2R' and variously-proportioned $R_2''Mg$-MgX_2 mixtures.

That "hindrance" may be a function primarily of the Grignard reagent rather than of the ester itself is indicated by the reaction of mesitylmagnesium bromide with allyl benzoate, reported by Arnold *et al.*[53] Under the relatively mild conditions imposed (eighteen hours at 25-35°), 57 percent of the ester reacting yielded cleavage products, whereas 15 percent gave the "normal" addition product (ketone).*

$$C_6H_5CO_2CH_2CH{=}CH_2 + 2,4,6\text{-}(CH_3)_3C_6H_2MgBr \longrightarrow C_6H_5CO_2H\ (57\%)$$
$$+ 2,4,6\text{-}(CH_3)_3C_6H_2CH_2CH{=}CH_2\ (49\%) + 2,4,6\text{-}(CH_3)_3C_6H_2COC_6H_5\ (15\%)$$

"Hindered" aryl esters. The "hindered" aryl esters undergo a different type of cleavage, yielding ketones and phenols. Several instances have been reported by Fuson *et al.*,[54] for example:

$$2,4,6\text{-}(CH_3)_3C_6H_2CO_2C_6H_4\text{-}4\text{-}CH_3 \xrightarrow{C_2H_5MgX} 2,4,6\text{-}(CH_3)_3C_6H_2COC_2H_5 + 4\text{-}CH_3C_6H_4OMgX$$

This has the formal appearance of the first stage of a "normal" ester addition, but steric considerations indicate that it must have a different mechanism. Such reactions are probably best interpreted as special cases of ether cleavage (*q.v.*, Chapter XV).

Granted that "normal" addition is sterically inhibited for both the alkyl and the aryl "hindered" esters, it would seem that the different reaction courses followed by the two types of compounds must be determined primarily by energetic factors arising out of the differences in carbon-oxygen bond polarities.

Readily enolizable ketones obtained in this manner would undoubtedly be prevented from addition by enolization.

MISCELLANEOUS BYPRODUCTS OF ESTER REACTIONS

Esterification of the expected alcohol upon reaction of a carboxylic ester with an organomagnesium halide was early observed by Grignard in the reactions of ethyl formate with isobutyl- and isoamylmagnesium bromides.

$$HCO_2C_2H_5 \xrightarrow{RMgBr} HCO_2CHR_2$$

In most cases this is probably, as Stadnikov[55] believed, the result of

[53] Arnold, Liggett, and Searles, *J. Am. Chem. Soc.*, 70, 3938 (1948).

*The ketone may also be a "cleavage" product (see following section).

[54] Fuson, Bottorf, and Speck, *J. Am. Chem. Soc.*, 64, 1450-3 (1942).

[55] Stadnikov, *J. Russ. Phys.-Chem. Soc.*, 46, 887-9 (1914); 47, 1113-21 (1915); *Chem. Abstr.*, 9, 1755,3051 (1915).

exchange between the halomagnesium alkoxide resulting from the "normal" addition reaction and the original ester. Stadnikov showed that such exchange takes place readily between ethyl acetate and the iodomagnesium derivatives of benzyl alcohol and 2-methylcyclohexanol.

$$CH_3CO_2C_2H_5 \xrightarrow{ROMgI} CH_3CO_2R + C_2H_5OMgI$$

However, he observed no exchange between ethyl acetate and iodomagnesium phenoxide, or between menthyl benzoate and the iodomagnesium derivative of benzhydrol.

Concerning the probability of such exchanges he remarked: "With respect to the nature of the radicals capable of replacing each other..., it was found that with the approach of an alcohol to the phenolic state its radical becomes less capable of replacing more positive alcoholic radicals in esters. While usually the heavier radical replaces the lighter one, the reverse takes place when the difference in mass is not great and the lighter radical is the more positive. With increasing molecular weight of the acidic constituent of the ester the ability of the latter to exchange its alcoholic radical for another seems to diminish. Thus the replacement of ethyl by menthyl is slower with ethyl benzoate than with ethyl acetate or ethyl propionate."

In high-temperature or "forced" reactions it is conceivable that ester formation might result from reaction of the halomagnesium salt of the acid with the halide corresponding to the expected alcohol.

$$RR''_2COMgX + MgX_2 \longrightarrow RR''_2CX + MgO + MgX_2$$

$$RCO_2MgX + RR''_2CX \longrightarrow RCO_2CRR''_2 + MgX_2$$

As is also the case in ketone reactions, one of the products (especially in high-temperature reactions) is sometimes the ether of the expected alcohol. This undoubtedly represents a well-known special case of the Williamson ether synthesis.

$$RR''_2COMgX + MgX_2 \longrightarrow RR''_2CX + MgO + MgX_2$$

$$RR''_2CX + RR''_2COMgX \longrightarrow (RR''_2C)_2O + MgX_2$$

In view of the facility with which many tertiary alcohols are dehydrated it is not surprising that the reaction product isolated is sometimes an olefin or mixture of olefins corresponding to the expected tertiary alcohol. In so far as dehydration occurs during the recovery of the product it may be minimized by taking the obvious precautions of avoiding excessive acidity during hydrolysis (as by the use of ammonium chloride solution), by freeing the product of all traces of acid before distillation, and by distilling at very low pressure. It is probable, however, that in some cases "dehydration" takes place prior to hydrolysis.

$$RR'R''CH_2COMgX \longrightarrow R''CH{=}CRR' + MgXOH$$

In such cases the only hope of avoiding or minimizing "dehydration" resides in conducting the reaction at as low a temperature as possible.

REACTIONS OF GRIGNARD REAGENTS WITH LACTONES

The reactions of Grignard reagents with lactones were first investigated by Houben[56] who studied several of the reactions of coumarin (1,2-benzopyrone).

In view of their relationship to the esters the relatively simple aliphatic γ-lactones might be expected to yield $n,n+3$ glycols.

$$\underset{\text{(RHC}-\text{CH}_2-\text{CH}_2-\text{C(=O)}-\text{O ring)}}{\text{H}_2\text{C}-\text{CH}_2;\ \text{RHC}-\text{O}-\text{C=O}} + 2\,R'MgX \longrightarrow RCH(OMgX)CH_2CH_2CR'_2OMgX$$

$$\xrightarrow{H_2O} RCH(OH)CH_2CH_2CR'_2OH + 2\,MgXOH$$

Such reactions are reported for γ-butyrolactone, γ-valerolactone, α,γ-dihydroxy-α,γ-dimethylvaleric acid γ-lactone, α-amino-α,γ-dimethyl-γ-hydroxyvaleric acid γ-lactone, and others (see Table VIII-IV).

$$\text{H}_2\text{C}-\text{CH}_2,\ \text{H}_2\text{C}-\text{O}-\text{C=O (ring)} \xrightarrow{CH_3MgI} HOCH_2CH_2CH_2(CH_3)_2COH \quad \text{(Henry[57])}$$

$$\text{H}_2\text{C}-\text{CH}_2,\ \text{H}_2\text{C}-\text{O}-\text{C=O (ring)} \xrightarrow{C_6H_5MgBr} HOCH_2CH_2CH_2(C_6H_5)_2COH \quad \text{(Weizmann[58])}$$

$$\text{H}_2\text{C}-\text{CH}_2,\ \text{H}_3\text{CHC}-\text{O}-\text{C=O (ring)} \xrightarrow{CH_3MgI} HOCH(CH_3)CH_2CH_2(CH_3)_2COH$$

(Losanitsch[59])

$$\text{H}_2\text{C}-\text{C(OH)CH}_3,\ (\text{H}_3\text{C})_2\text{C}-\text{O}-\text{C=O (ring)} \xrightarrow{CH_3MgI} HO(CH_3)_2CCH_2C(OH)(CH_3)C(CH_3)_2OH$$

(Kohn[60])

$$\text{H}_2\text{C}-\text{C(NH}_2)\text{CH}_3,\ (\text{H}_3\text{C})_2\text{C}-\text{O}-\text{C=O (ring)} \xrightarrow{CH_3MgI} HO(CH_3)_2CCH_2C(NH_2)(CH_3)C(CH_3)_2OH$$

(Kohn[60])

Cyclic etherification of the primary reaction product of lactones of this type is apparently relatively rare. Kohn (*loc. cit.*[60]) reports that when an

---

[56]Houben, *Ber.*, *37*, 489–502 (1904).
[57]Henry, *Compt. rend.*, *143*, 1221–5 (1906); *Chem. Zentr.*, *1907,I*, 708.
[58]Weizmann and Bergmann, *J. Am. Chem. Soc.*, *60*, 2647–50 (1938).
[59]Losanitsch, *Compt. rend.*, *153*, 390–2 (1911); *Chem. Zentr.*, *1911,II*, 1118.
[60]Kohn, *Monatsh.*, *34*, 1729–40 (1913).

ethereal solution of α,γ-dihydroxy-α,γ-dimethylvaleric acid γ-lactone is permitted to react vigorously with three equivalents of phenylmagnesium bromide the product is a tetrahydrofuran derivative,

$$\begin{array}{l} H_2C \text{—} C(OH)CH_3 \\ (H_3C)_2C \quad C{=}O \\ \quad\; \backslash\; O \;/ \end{array} \xrightarrow{C_6H_5MgBr} \begin{array}{l} H_2C \text{—} C(OH)CH_3 \\ (H_3C)_2C \quad C(C_6H_5)_2 \\ \quad\; \backslash\; O \;/ \end{array}$$

whereas, when the reaction is carried out in very high dilution, the trihydroxy open-chain product is obtained (Kohn and Ostersetzer[61]). With lactones of the coumarin type, however, 1,2-benzopyran (Δ^3-chromene) formation appears to be the commoner reaction.

$$C_6H_4\left<\begin{array}{l}CH{=}CH \\ O\text{—}C{=}O\end{array}\right. \xrightarrow{RMgX} C_6H_4\left<\begin{array}{l}CH{=}CH \\ O\text{—}CR_2\end{array}\right.$$

(Houben, *loc. cit.*,[56] Shriner[62])

(R = CH_3, C_2H_5, n-C_3H_7, n-C_4H_9, n-C_5H_{11}, n-C_6H_{13}, n-C_7H_{15})

Nevertheless, Houben (*loc. cit.*[56]) claimed to have obtained with benzylmagnesium chloride, the o-hydroxystyrylcarbinol.

$$C_6H_4\left<\begin{array}{l}CH{=}CH \\ O\text{—}C{=}O\end{array}\right. \xrightarrow{C_6H_5CH_2MgCl} 2\text{-}HOC_6H_4CH{=}CH(C_6H_5CH_2)_2COH$$

and Smith and Ruoff[63] report that, under carefully controlled conditions, methylmagnesium iodide, ethylmagnesium bromide, and n-butylmagnesium bromide may be made to yield the carbinols (or mixtures of the carbinols with the benzopyrans).

In view of the work of Löwenbein *et al.*,[64] it would appear that Houben (*loc. cit.*[56]) was in error in ascribing the o-hydroxystyrylcarbinol structure to the product of reaction with phenylmagnesium bromide, and that the actual product is a chromanol.

$$C_6H_4\left<\begin{array}{l}CH{=}CH \\ O\text{—}C{=}O\end{array}\right. \xrightarrow{RMgBr} C_6H_4\left<\begin{array}{l}CH(R)\text{—}CH_2 \\ O\text{—}C(OH)R\end{array}\right.$$

(R = C_6H_5, 1-$C_{10}H_7$)

This reaction is the equivalent of the 1,4-addition with ketone formation

[61] Kohn and Ostersetzer, *Monatsh.*, 37, 37–51 (1916).
[62] Shriner and Sharp, *J. Org. Chem.*, 4, 575–82 (1939).
[63] Smith and Ruoff, *J. Am. Chem. Soc.*, 62, 145–8 (1940).
[64] Löwenbein, Pongracz, and Spiess, *Ber.*, 57B, 1517–26 (1924).

observed with the open-chain α,β-unsaturated esters. The lactone ring either is not opened or is reclosed with hemiacetal formation.

When the reaction is carried only to the first stage of 1,2-addition, without 1,4-addition, as may be accomplished by dropwise addition of the Grignard reagent to an ethereal solution of the coumarin, the product is an oxonium (benzopyrylium) salt.

$$\text{coumarin} \xrightarrow{RMgX} \left[C_6H_4(CH{=}CH)(O)C(OMgX)R \right] \rightarrow$$

$$\left[C_6H_4(CH{=}CH)(O)CR \right]^{+}OMgX^{-} \xrightarrow{HX'} \left[C_6H_4(CH{=}CH)(O)CR \right]^{+}X'^{-} + MgXOH$$

This reaction, discovered by Decker and von Fellenberg,[65] has been improved (as to yields) and extended in application by Wilstätter *et al.*[66,67].

Phthalide is reported as reacting "normally" to yield the *o*-hydroxymethylphenylcarbinols,[68,69]

$$\text{phthalide} \xrightarrow{RMgX} 2\text{-}HOCH_2C_6H_4CR_2OH$$

but 3,3-dimethylphthalide is said to yield (with phenylmagnesium bromide) either the hydroxy ketone or the corresponding phthalanol (hemiacetal).[70]

$$\text{3,3-dimethylphthalide} \xrightarrow{C_6H_5MgBr} 2\text{-}C_6H_5COC_6H_4C(CH_3)_2OH$$

or

$$C_6H_4[C(CH_3)_2\text{-}O\text{-}C(OH)(C_6H_5)]$$

[65]Decker and von Fellenberg, *Ann.*, *356*, 281–342 (1907).
[66]Wilstätter, Zechmeister, and Kindler, *Ber.*, *57B*, 1938–44 (1924).
[67]Wilstätter and Schmidt, *Ber.*, *57B*, 1945–50 (1924).
[68]Ludwig, *Ber.*, *40*, 3060–5 (1907).
[69]Seidel, *Ber.*, *61B*, 2267–76 (1928).
[70]Barnett, Cook, and Nixon, *J. Chem. Soc.*, *1927*, 504–12.

The 3-phenylphthalides are also reported as yielding phthalanols with aryl Grignard reagents,[71,72,73] as is phthalophenone (3,3-diphenylphthalide),[74] although it is suggested by Beilstein,[75] as well as by Barnett (*loc. cit.*[70]), that perhaps the latter should be formulated as the hydroxy ketone. Prolonged treatment of phthalophenone with an excess of phenylmagnesium bromide yields the glycol.[76]

$$C_6H_4{<}\binom{C(C_6H_5)_2}{CO}{>}O \xrightarrow{C_6H_5MgBr} C_6H_4\text{-}1,2\text{-}[C(C_6H_5)_2OH]_2$$

The interaction of a 3-arylphthalide with benzylmagnesium chloride leads to the dehydration product of the phthalanol.[77]

$$C_6H_4{<}\binom{CHC_6H_5}{C{=}O}{>}O \xrightarrow{C_6H_5CH_2MgCl} C_6H_4{<}\binom{CHC_6H_5}{C{=}CHC_6H_5}{>}O$$

The products of reaction of 3-*p*-tolylphthalide[72] and 3-α-naphthylphthalide[78] with aryl Grignard reagents undergo a different type of "dehydration" to yield 3,4-benzofurans (isobenzofurans).

$$C_6H_4{<}\binom{CH\text{-}1\text{-}C_{10}H_7}{C{=}O}{>}O \xrightarrow{1\text{-}C_{10}H_7MgBr} C_6H_4{<}\binom{C\text{-}1\text{-}C_{10}H_7}{C\text{-}1\text{-}C_{10}H_7}{>}O$$

With aryl Grignard reagents 3-benzylidenephthalide yields 2-phenyl-3-arylindenones.[79] At first glance it might appear that these reactions must involve a rather unusual type of rearrangement. However, if it be assumed that the Grignard reaction terminates at the first stage with the formation of a product that is at once both an enolate and a ketone, the final product is readily explicable as the result of intramolecular ketolization and "dehydration."

[71] Guyot and Catel, *Compt. rend.*, *140*, 1348-50 (1905); *Chem. Zentr.*, *1905,II*, 137.

[72] Guyot and Valette, *Ann. chim.*, [8], *23*, 363-97 (1911).

[73] Seidel, *Ber.*, *61B*, 2267-76 (1928).

[74] Guyot and Catel, *Bull. soc. chim.*, [3], *35*, 551-62 (1906).

[75] Beilsteins Handuch der organische Chemie, 4th ed., 8, 223 (1925).

[76] Schlenk and Brauns, *Ber.*, *48*, 716-28 (1915).

[77] Weiss and Fastmann, *Monatsh.*, *47*, 727-32 (1926).

[78] Seer and Dischendorfer, *Monatsh.*, *34*, 1493-502 (1914).

[79] Weiss and Sauermann, *Ber.*, *58B*, 2736-40 (1925).

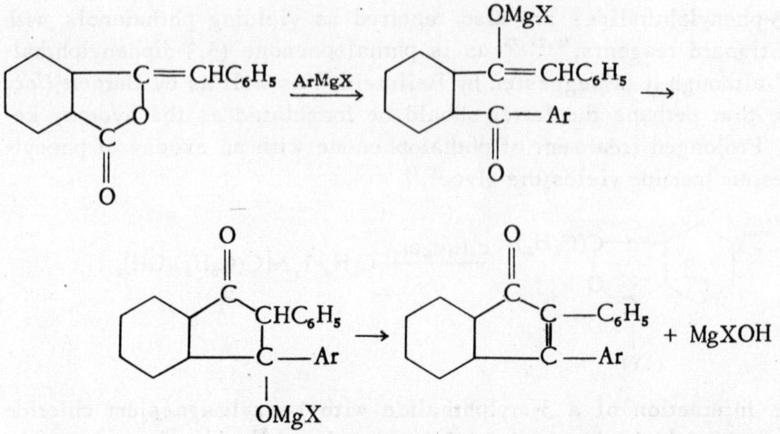

$$C_6H_4(C{=}CHC_6H_5)(O)(C{=}O) \xrightarrow{ArMgX} C_6H_4[C(OMgX){=}CHC_6H_5][C(=O)\text{—}Ar] \longrightarrow$$

$$C_6H_4[C(=O)\text{—}CHC_6H_5][C(OMgX)\text{—}Ar] \longrightarrow C_6H_4[C(=O)\text{—}C(C_6H_5){=}C(Ar)] + MgXOH$$

With benzylmagnesium chloride this lactone undergoes both the type of reaction illustrated above and the ordinary addition-"dehydration" reactions.[80]

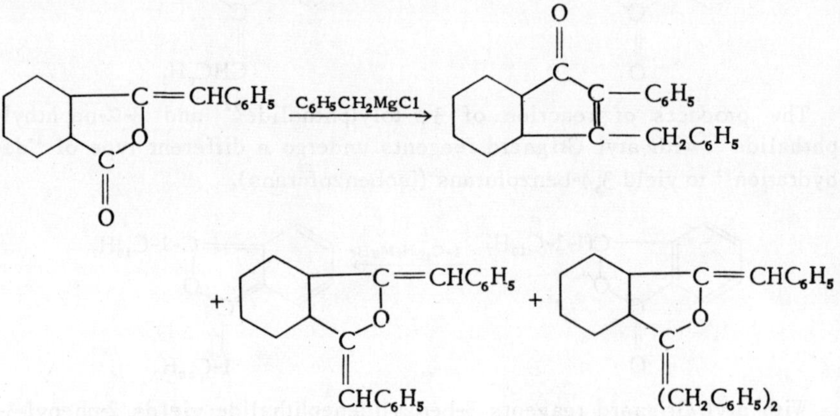

$$C_6H_4(C{=}CHC_6H_5)(O)(C{=}O) \xrightarrow{C_6H_5CH_2MgCl} C_6H_4[C(=O)\text{—}C(C_6H_5){=}C(CH_2C_6H_5)]$$

$$+ \; C_6H_4(C{=}CHC_6H_5)(O)(C{=}CHC_6H_5) \; + \; C_6H_4(C{=}CHC_6H_5)(O)(C(CH_2C_6H_5)_2)$$

[80]Weiss, Grobstein, and Sauermann, *Ber.*, *59B*, 301–6 (1926); Weiss and Alberti, *Ber.*, *59B*, 220–7 (1932).

TABLE VIII-III

REACTIONS OF GRIGNARD REAGENTS WITH CARBOXYLIC, ORTHOFORMIC, CARBONIC, AND ORTHOCARBONIC ESTERS

Ester	RMgX	Product(s)	Ref.
CO_2Cl-R*			
$ClCO_2C_2H_5$	C_2H_5MgX†	$(C_2H_5)_3COH$ (55%)	267
$ClCO_2C_2H_5$	$CH_3C{\equiv}CMgBr$	$(CH_3C{\equiv}C)_3COH$; $CH_3C{\equiv}CCO_2C_2H_5$	178
$ClCO_2C_2H_5$	n-C_3H_7MgBr	$(n$-$C_3H_7)_3COH$	267
$ClCO_2C_2H_5$ (40 g.)	C_6H_5MgBr (53 g. C_6H_5Br)	$C_6H_5CO_2C_2H_5$ (36 g., 75%); $(C_6H_5)_3COH$ (3 g., 8.6%)	*166*
$ClCO_2C_2H_5$ (40 g.)	C_6H_5MgBr (50 g. C_6H_5Br)	$C_6H_5CO_2C_2H_5$ (8 g., 16.6%); $(C_6H_5)_3COH$ (12 g., 34.3%)	*166*
$ClCO_2C_2H_5$ (50 g.)	$C_6H_5CH_2MgCl$ (50 g. C_7H_7Cl)	$C_6H_5CH_2CO_2C_2H_5$ (28 g., 43%); $(C_6H_5CH_2)_3COH$ (6 g.)	*166*
$ClCO_2C_2H_5$	$C_6H_5CH_2MgCl$ (1 equiv.)	2-$CH_3C_6H_4CO_2C_2H_5$; $C_6H_5CH_2CO_2H$; $(C_6H_5CH_2)_3COH$	*10,478*
$ClCO_2C_2H_5$	$C_6H_5CH_2MgCl$ (3 equiv.)	$(C_6H_5CH_2)_3COH$ (principal product)	*10*
$ClCO_2C_2H_5$ (10 g.)	$C_{10}H_{17}MgCl$‡ (0.1 mole)	Unchanged ester (55%); $(C_{10}H_{17})CO_2C_2H_5$ (33%); $(C_{10}H_{17})CH_2OH$ (12%)	*361*
$ClCO_2C_2H_5$ (69 g.)	"Isomerized" $C_{10}H_7MgCl$§ (0.5 mole)	$(C_{10}H_{17})CO_2C_2H_5$ (95%)	*361*
$ClCO_2C_2H_5$ (20 g.)	Isobornyl-MgCl¶ (0.136 mole)	$(C_{10}H_{17})CH_2OH$ (0.039 mole); bornylene	*361*

* For most chloroformic esters see Table IX-II. Reactions of Grignard Reagents with Carbonyl Halides.

† X = Br, I.

‡ From (+)-α-pinene hydrochloride; Rivière (*361*) concludes that this Grignard reagent is an equimolecular mixture of bornylmagnesium and isobornylmagnesium chlorides.

§ Prepared by refluxing in xylene (three hours at 130°) the Grignard reagent from (+)-α-pinene hydrochloride; Rivière (*361*) concludes that the reagent so obtained is substantially pure bornylmagnesium chloride.

¶ Prepared by partial (66%) carbonation of the Grignard reagent from (+)-α-pinene hydrochloride; Rivière (*361*) concludes that the residual reagent is substantially pure isobornylmagnesium chloride.

TABLE VIII-III (Continued)

Ester	RMgX	Product(s)	Ref.
CO_3-R_2			
$CO(OC_2H_5)_2$ (1.32 mole)	C_2H_5MgBr	$(C_2H_5)_3COH$ (82–88%)	*258,452,80*
$CO(OC_2H_5)_2$	$CH_3C{\equiv}CMgBr$	$(CH_3C{\equiv}C)_3COH$; $CH_3C{\equiv}CCO_2C_2H_5$	*178*
$CO(OC_2H_5)_2$	n-C_3H_7MgBr	$(n$-$C_3H_7)_3COH$ (75%)	*258,80*
$CO(OC_2H_5)_2$	$H_2C{\equiv}CHC{\equiv}CMgBr$	Product(s) explosive	*302*
$CO(OC_2H_5)_2$	Pyrryl-MgBr	*N*-Carbethoxypyrrole (chiefly); ethyl 2-pyrrolecarboxylate ("a little")	*517*
$CO(OC_2H_5)_2$	n-C_4H_9MgBr	$(n$-$C_4H_9)_3COH$ (84%)	*258*
$CO(OC_2H_5)_2$	n-C_4H_9MgBr	$(n$-$C_4H_9)_3COH$ (80%)	*462,80*
$CO(OC_2H_5)_2$	t-C_4H_9MgCl (1 equiv.)	t-$C_4H_9CO_2C_2H_5$ (56%)	*452*
$CO(OC_2H_5)_2$	i-$C_3H_7C{\equiv}CMgBr$	$(i$-$C_3H_7C{\equiv}C)_3COH$ (45%)	*411*
$CO(OC_2H_5)_2$ (590 g.)	$(CH_2)_4CHMgBr$ (363 g. C_5H_9Br)	$(CH_2)_4CHCO_2C_2H_5$ (275 g., 48.5%)	*453*
$CO(OC_2H_5)_2$	n-$C_5H_{11}MgBr$	$(n$-$C_5H_{11})_3COH$ (55%)	*461,80*
$CO(OC_2H_5)_2$	n-$C_5H_{11}MgBr$	$(n$-$C_5H_{11})_3COH$ (75%)	*258*
$CO(OC_2H_5)_2$	t-$C_5H_{11}MgCl$ (1 equiv.)	t-$C_5H_{11}CO_2C_2H_5$ (trace); recovered ester	*452*
$CO(OC_2H_5)_2$ (0.33 equiv.)	t-$C_4H_9C{\equiv}CMgBr$ (40 g. C_6H_{10})	$(t$-$C_4H_9C{\equiv}C)_3COH$ (18–23 g., 40–50%)	*518*
$CO(OC_2H_5)_2$	$C_6H_5CH_2MgCl$	$(C_6H_5CH_2)_3COH$ (principal product); low-boiling liquid (trace)	*10*
$CO(OC_2H_5)_2$	$C_6H_5CH_2MgCl$ + i-C_3H_5MgBr	$(C_6H_5CH_2)_3COH$; $C_6H_5CH_2COCH(C_6H_5)CO_2C_2H_5$	*181*
$CO(OC_2H_5)_2$	n-$C_7H_{15}MgBr$	$(n$-$C_7H_{15})_3COH$ (72%)	*258*
$CO(OC_2H_5)_2$	$C_6H_5C{\equiv}CMgBr$	$(C_6H_5C{\equiv}C)_3COH$	*177*
$CO(OC_2H_5)_2$ (12 ml.)	$CH_3(C_2H_5)_2CC{\equiv}CMgBr$ (33 g. C_8H_{14})	$[CH_3(C_2H_5)_2CC{\equiv}C]_3COH$ (30 g., 84%)	*519*

TABLE VIII-III (Continued)

Ester	RMgX	Product(s)	Ref.
CO_3-R_2 *(cont.)*			
$CO(OC_2H_5)_2$ (7.5 moles)	1-$C_{10}H_7MgBr$ (5 moles)	1-$C_{10}H_7CO_2C_2H_5$ (70%)	*246*
$CO(OC_2H_5)_2$ (10.5 g.)	4-*t*-$C_4H_9C_6H_4MgBr$ (75 g. $C_{10}H_{13}Br$)	(4-*t*-$C_4H_9C_6H_4)_3COH$ (34 g.)	*257*
$CO(OC_2H_5)_2$ (0.5 mole)	$C_{10}H_{17}MgCl$* (0.5 mole)	$(C_{10}H_{17})CO_2C_2H_5$ (0.17 mole); $(C_{10}H_{17})CH_2OH$ (0.06 mole); bornylene (0.25 mole)	*361*
$CO(OC_2H_5)_2$ (0.35 mole)	"Isomerized" $C_{10}H_{17}MgCl$† (0.35 mole)	$(C_{10}H_{17})CO_2C_2H_5$ (68%)	*361*
$CO(OC_2H_5)_2$ (13 g.)	4-*t*-$C_5H_{11}C_6H_4MgBr$ (90 g. $C_{11}H_{15}Br$)	(4-*t*-$C_5H_{11}C_6H_4)_3COH$ (yielding 7 g. corresponding chloride)	*257*
$CO(OC_2H_5)_2$ (3 ml.)	3-$C_6H_5C_6H_4MgBr$ (20 g. $C_{12}H_9Br$)	(3-$C_6H_5C_6H_4)_3COH$ (12 g., crude)	*256*
CO_4-R_4			
$C(OC_2H_5)_4$	C_2H_5MgI	$C_2H_5C(OC_2H_5)_3$; $CO(OC_2H_5)_2$ (?); $C_2H_5C(OC_2H_5)_2CH(CH_3)CO_2C_2H_5$	*431*
$C(OC_2H_5)_4$	*i*-$C_5H_{11}MgBr$	*i*-$C_5H_{11}C(OC_2H_5)_3$ (50–60%)	*431*
$C(OC_2H_5)_4$	C_6H_5MgBr	$C_6H_5C(OC_2H_5)_3$ (80%)	*431*
$C(OC_2H_5)_4$	$(CH_2)_5CHMgCl$	$(CH_2)_5CHC(OC_2H_5)_3$ (*ca.* 40%)	*431*
$C(OC_2H_5)_4$	$C_6H_5C{\equiv}CMgI$ (1 equiv.)	$C_6H_5C{\equiv}CC(OC_2H_5)_3$	*491*
$C(OC_2H_5)_4$	$C_6H_5C{\equiv}CMgI$	$(C_6H_5C{\equiv}C)_2C(OC_2H_5)_2$	*492*
$C(OC_2H_5)_4$ (15 ml.)	$({=}CHC_6H_4$-4-$MgI)_2$ (6 g. $C_{14}H_{10}I_2$)	$[{=}CHC_6H_4$-4-$C(OC_2H_5)_3]_2$ (2.5 g., crude)	*365*
CHO_2-R			
HCO_2CH_3	$(CH_2)_5CHMgCl$	$(CH_2)_5CH_2CHOH$ (82.5%, crude)	*303*
HCO_2CH_3	$[{-}(CH_2)_5MgBr]_2$	$[{-}(CH_2)_{10}CH(OH){-}]_x$‡ (88%)	*76*

* From (+)-α-pinene hydrochloride; Rivière (*361*) concludes that this Grignard reagent is an equimolecular mixture of bornylmagnesium and isobornylmagnesium chlorides.

† Prepared by refluxing in xylene (three hours at 130°) the Grignard reagent from (+)-α-pinene hydrochloride; Rivière (*361*) concludes that the reagent so obtained is substantially pure bornylmagnesium chloride.

‡ *x* averages *ca.* 5.

TABLE VIII-III (Continued)

Ester	RMgX	Product(s)	Ref.
CHO_2-R (*cont.*)			
$HCO_2C_2H_5$	$(\equiv CMgBr)_2$	$(HC\equiv C)_2CHOH$	*239*
$HCO_2C_2H_5$	C_2H_5MgBr	$(C_2H_5)_2CHOH$ (73%)	*135,196, 307,467, 493*
$HCO_2C_2H_5$ (500 parts)	C_2H_5MgI (156 parts C_2H_5I)	C_2H_5CHO	*115*
$HCO_2C_2H_5$ (excess)	$CH_3C\equiv CMgBr$	$(CH_3C\equiv C)_2CHOH$	*443,176,178*
$HCO_2C_2H_5$	n-C_3H_7MgBr	$(n$-$C_3H_7)_2CHOH$ (88%)	*433,196,307*
$HCO_2C_2H_5$ (18 g.)	i-C_3H_7MgBr (62 g. C_3H_7Br)	$(i$-$C_3H_7)_2CHOH$	*306*
$HCO_2C_2H_5$	5-Bromo-2-thienyl-MgBr	5-Bromo-2-thiophenecarboxaldehyde (10%)	*124*
$HCO_2C_2H_5$	2-Thienyl-MgBr	2-Thiophenecarboxaldehyde (15%)	*124*
$HCO_2C_2H_5$	Pyrryl-MgBr	2-Pyrrolecarboxaldehyde	*427*
$HCO_2C_2H_5$	Pyrryl-MgI	2-Pyrrolecarboxaldehyde (3.0–3.5 g., 33–35%); recovered pyrrole	*348*
$HCO_2C_2H_5$ (13 g., 0.17 mole)	Butenyl-MgBr (0.35 mole)	[$H_2C\equiv CHCH(CH_3)_2CHOH$ (two forms, totaling 18.6 g., 78%)	*472*
$HCO_2C_2H_5$ (0.75 mole)	n-C_4H_9MgBr (1.5 mole C_4H_9Br)	$(n$-$C_4H_9)_2CHOH$ (83–85%)	*82,95,251, 433*
$HCO_2C_2H_5$	i-C_4H_9MgBr	$(i$-$C_4H_9)_2CHOH$; $HCO_2CH(i$-$C_4H_9)_2$	*135,125*
$HCO_2C_2H_5$	i-C_4H_9MgBr	$(i$-$C_4H_9)_2CHOH$ (74%)	*450,493*
$HCO_2C_2H_5$ (36 g., 0.5 mole)	s-C_4H_9MgBr (1 mole)	$(s$-$C_4H_9)_2CHOH$ (18.2 g., 13%); olefin-containing gas	*472*
$HCO_2C_2H_5$	n-$C_3H_7C\equiv CMgBr$ (2 equiv.)	$(n$-$C_3H_7C\equiv C)_2CHOH$	*245,494*
$HCO_2C_2H_5$	i-$C_5H_{11}MgBr$	$HCO_2CH(i$-$C_5H_{11})_2$	*135*
$HCO_2C_2H_5$	i-$C_5H_{11}MgBr$	$(i$-$C_5H_{11})_2CHOH$	*493*
$HCO_2C_2H_5$ (222 parts)	i-$C_5H_{11}MgBr$ (151 parts $C_5H_{11}Br$)	i-$C_5H_{11}CHO$	*115*
$HCO_2C_2H_5$	4-BrC_6H_4MgBr	4-BrC_6H_4CHO (40%)	*124*

TABLE VIII-III (Continued)

Ester	RMgX	Product(s)	Ref.
CHO_2-R (*cont.*)			
$HCO_2C_2H_5$	C_6H_5MgBr	$(C_6H_5)_2CHOH$	*260*
$HCO_2C_2H_5$	C_6H_5MgBr	C_6H_5CHO	*125,115*
$HCO_2C_2H_5$ (11 g.)	C_6H_5MgBr (34 g. C_6H_5Br)	$C_2H_5OCH(C_6H_5)_2$ (15 g.); $[(C_6H_5)_2CH]_2O$ (6 g.)	*402*
$HCO_2C_2H_5$	2,3-Dimethylpyrryl-MgX	4,5-Dimethyl-2-pyrrolecarboxaldehyde ("moderate yield")	*3*
$HCO_2C_2H_5$	2,5-Dimethylpyrryl-MgX	2,5-Dimethyl-3-pyrrolecarboxaldehyde ("poor yield"); 1-formyl-2,5-dimethylpyrrole (principal product)	*3*
$HCO_2C_2H_5$	n-$C_4H_9C{\equiv}CMgBr$	$(n$-$C_4H_9C{\equiv}C)_2CHOH$	*245,494*
$HCO_2C_2H_5$	t-$C_4H_9C{\equiv}CMgBr$	$(t$-$C_4H_9C{\equiv}C)_2CHOH$	*495*
$HCO_2C_2H_5$ (180 parts)	$C_6H_5CH_2MgCl$ (126.5 parts C_7H_7Cl)	$C_6H_5CH_2CHO$	*115,125*
$HCO_2C_2H_5$ (36 g.)	$C_6H_5CH_2MgCl$ (120 g. C_7H_7Cl)	$(C_6H_5CH_2)_2CHOH$ (42.6%)	*130*
$HCO_2C_2H_5$ (22g.)	2-$CH_3C_6H_4MgBr$ (17.1 g. C_7H_7Br)	2-$CH_3C_6H_4CHO$ (5.4 g., 45%); (2-$CH_3C_6H_4)_2CHOH$	*125,124*
$HCO_2C_2H_5$ (33.4 g.)	2-$CH_3C_6H_4MgBr$ (171 g. C_7H_7Br)	(2-$CH_3C_6H_4)_2CHOH$ (70 g., 73%)	*121*
$HCO_2C_2H_5$	3-$CH_3C_6H_4MgBr$	3-$CH_3C_6H_4CHO$	*125*
$HCO_2C_2H_5$	4-$CH_3OC_6H_4MgBr$	4-$CH_3OC_6H_4CHO$	*125*
$HCO_2C_2H_5$	n-$C_5H_{11}C{\equiv}CMgBr$	$(n$-$C_5H_{11}C{\equiv}C)_2CHOH$	*245,494*
$HCO_2C_2H_5$	n-$C_7H_{15}MgBr$	$(n$-$C_7H_{15})_2CHOH$ (61%)	*433*
$HCO_2C_2H_5$	$CH_3(i$-$C_4H_9)CHCH_2MgBr$	"Secondary products only"	*433*
$HCO_2C_2H_5$	$(i$-$C_3H_7)_2CHMgBr$	$(i$-$C_3H_7)_2CH_2$; i-$C_3H_7CH{=}C(CH_3)_2$; $(i$-$C_3H_7)_2CHCH_2OH$	*433*
$HCO_2C_2H_5$	$C_6H_5C{\equiv}CMgBr$ (1 equiv.)	$C_6H_5C{\equiv}CCHO$	*173*

TABLE VIII-III (Continued)

Ester	RMgX	Product(s)	Ref.
CHO_2-R (*cont.*)			
$HCO_2C_2H_5$	$C_6H_5C\equiv CMgBr$ (2 equiv.)	$(C_6H_5C\equiv C)_2CHOH$	*173,245,494*
$HCO_2C_2H_5$	Indolyl-MgX	3-Indolecarboxaldehyde ("very little"); 1-formylindole (principal product)	*3*
$HCO_2C_2H_5$ (41 parts)	Indolyl-MgBr (50 parts indole)	3-Indolecarboxaldehyde (41%); 1-formylindole (40%)*	*99*
$HCO_2C_2H_5$ (10 ml.)	Indolyl-MgI (3 g. indole)	1-Formylindole (3.0–3.5 g., *ca.* 90%)†	*348*
$HCO_2C_2H_5$ (10 ml.)	Indolyl-MgI (3 g. indole)	3-Indolecarboxaldehyde (1.0–1.2 g.); 1-formylindole (1.0 g.)‡	*348*
$HCO_2C_2H_5$	$2,3-(CH_3)_2-4-BrC_6H_2MgBr$	$2,3-(CH_3)_2-4-BrC_6H_2CHO$ (10%)	*124*
$HCO_2C_2H_5$ (21.4 g.)	$2,4-(CH_3)_2C_6H_3MgBr$ ("twofold excess")	$\{[2,4-(CH_3)_2C_6H_3]_2CH\}_2O$ (17 g.); $[2,4-(CH_3)_2C_6H_3]_2CHOH$	*122*
$HCO_2C_2H_5$ (30 ml.)	$2,5-(CH_3)_2C_6H_3MgBr$ (18.5 g. C_8H_9Br)	$2,5-(CH_3)_2C_6H_3CHO$ (45%)	*124*
$HCO_2C_2H_5$ (22.0 g.)	$2-C_2H_5OC_6H_4MgBr$ (20.1 g. C_8H_9BrO)	$2-C_2H_5OC_6H_4CHO$ (30%)	*124*
$HCO_2C_2H_5$ (5.5 g.)	$2,6-(CH_3O)_2C_6H_3MgI$ (25.0 g. $C_8H_9IO_2$)	$[2,6-(CH_3O)_2C_6H_3]_2CHOH$ (8–10 g.)	*21*
$HCO_2C_2H_5$	$n-C_6H_{13}C\equiv CMgBr$	$(n-C_6H_{13}C\equiv C)_2CHOH$	*245*
$HCO_2C_2H_5$ (47 g.)	$n-C_8H_{17}MgBr$ (245 g. $C_8H_{17}Br$)	$(n-C_8H_{17})_2CHOH$ (41.5 g., crude); $C_{17}H_{34}$	*498*
$HCO_2C_2H_5$	$4-CH_3C_6H_4C\equiv CMgBr$	$(4-CH_3C_6H_4C\equiv C)_2CHOH$	*245*
$HCO_2C_2H_5$	2-Methylindolyl-MgX	2-Methylindole-3-carboxaldehyde ("very little"); 1-formyl-2-methylindole (principal product)	*3*

* The Grignard reagent was prepared with the aid of ethylmagnesium bromide; it is said that when ethylmagnesium chloride is used the yield of 3-indolecarboxaldehyde is negligible.

† Dropwise addition of ester to ice-salt-cooled benzene-Grignard reagent solution.

‡ Dropwise addition of ester to benzene-Grignard reagent solution; twenty minutes at 70–75°.

TABLE VIII-III (Continued)

Ester	RMgX	Product(s)	Ref.
CHO_2-R (*cont.*)			
$HCO_2C_2H_5$	2-Methylindolyl-MgI	1-Formyl-2-methylindole*	*348*
$HCO_2C_2H_5$	2-Methylindolyl-MgI	2-Methylindole-3-carboxaldehyde (yield "not great")†	*348*
$HCO_2C_2H_5$	2,4,6-$(CH_3)_3C_6H_2MgBr$	[2,4,6-$(CH_3)_3C_6H_2]_2CH_2$; 2,4,6-$(CH_3)_3C_6H_2OH$	*235*
$HCO_2C_2H_5$	2,4,6-$(CH_3)_3C_6H_2MgBr$	[2,4,6-$(CH_3)_3C_6H_2]_2CH_2$ ("small am't"); [2,4,6-$(CH_3)_3C_6H_2]_2CO$	*232*
$HCO_2C_2H_5$ (7.5 g.)	1-$C_{10}H_7MgBr$ (50 g. $C_{10}H_7Br$)	(1-$C_{10}H_7)_2CHOH$ (23 g.)	*375*
$HCO_2C_2H_5$ (15 g.)	1-$C_{10}H_7MgBr$ (42 g. $C_{10}H_7Br$)	C_2H_5OCH(1-$C_{10}H_7)_2$	*399*
$HCO_2C_2H_5$ (11 g.)	2-$C_{10}H_7MgI$ (75 g. $C_{10}H_7I$)	(2-$C_{10}H_7)_2CHOH$ (9.5 g.); "β,β-dinaphthofluorene",‡ m. 190.5° (corr.)	*374*
$HCO_2C_2H_5$	2,4-$(CH_3)_2C_6H_3C{\equiv}CMgBr$	[2,4-$(CH_3)_2C_6H_3C{\equiv}C]_2CHOH$	*245,494*
$HCO_2C_2H_5$ (15 g.)	2,3,5,6-$(CH_3)_4C_6HMgBr$ (43 g. $C_{10}H_{13}Br$)	[2,3,5,6-$(CH_3)_4C_6H]_2CH_2$ (2 g.); [2,3,5,6-$(CH_3)_4C_6H]_2CO$	*232*
$HCO_2C_2H_5$	$C_{10}H_{17}MgCl$§	$C_{10}H_{17}CH_2OH$; bornylene; camphane; bibornyl	*60*
$HCO_2C_2H_5$ (0.3 mole)	$C_{10}H_{17}MgCl$¶ (0.3 mole)	$C_{10}H_{17}CH_2OH$ (0.15 mole); bornylene (0.16 mole); recovered ester (0.16 mole)	*361*

* Dropwise addition of ester to ice-salt-cooled Grignard reagent solution.

† Dropwise addition of ester to Grignard reagent solution; warming at 70–75°.

‡ Schmidlin and Huber (*374*) do not attempt to choose between the three formulations which they regard as possible for this product, namely: 12-dibenzo[*b,h*]fluorene, 12-dibenzo[*b,g*]fluorene, and 13-dibenzo[*c,g*]fluorene. The fluorenone obtained upon oxidation of the product melted at 163–165° (corr.).

§ From pinene hydrochloride.

¶ From (+)-α-pinene hydrochloride; Rivière (*361*) concludes that this Grignard reagent is an equimolecular mixture of bornylmagnesium and isobornylmagnesium halides.

TABLE VIII-III (Continued)

Ester	RMgX	Product(s)	Ref.
CHO_2-R (*cont.*)			
$HCO_2C_2H_5$(0.5 mole)	"Isomerized" $C_{10}H_{17}MgCl$* (0.4 mole)	Recovered ester (0.19 mole); bornylene (0.07 mole); $C_{10}H_{17}CHO$ (0.09 mole); $(C_{10}H_{17})_2CHOH$ (0.15 mole); $C_{10}H_{17}CH_2OH$ (0.05 mole).	*361*
$HCO_2C_2H_5$(44 g.)	2-CH_3O-6-$C_{10}H_6MgBr$ (45 g. $C_{11}H_9BrO$)	2-CH_3O-6-$C_{10}H_6CHO$ (6 g., 20%)	*168*
$HCO_2C_2H_5$	$(CH_3)_5C_6MgBr$	$(CH_3)_5C_6CHO$ (34%)	*83*
$HCO_2C_2H_5$	$(CH_3)_5C_6MgBr$	$(CH_3)_5C_6CHROH$†; $(CH_3)_5C_6CHO$	*85*
$HCO_2C_2H_5$ (15 g.)	$(CH_3)_5C_6MgBr$ (46 g. $C_{11}H_{15}Br$)	$[(CH_3)_5C_6]_2CH_2$ (4 g.); $[(CH_3)_5C_6]_2CO$ (3 g.)	*232*
$HCO_2C_2H_5$	*n*-$C_9H_{19}C\equiv CMgBr$	$(n\text{-}C_9H_{19}C\equiv C)_2CHOH$	*245,494*
$HCO_2C_2H_5$ (13.2 g.)	$(C_6H_5)_3CMgCl$ (30 g. $C_{19}H_{15}Cl$)	$(C_6H_5)_3CCHO$ (14.5 g.)	*373*
HCO_2-*n*-C_3H_7	Pyrryl-MgI (1 equiv.)	2-Pyrrolecarboxaldehyde (*ca.* 2.6 g., 28%)	*427*
CHO_3-R_3			
$HC(OCH_3)_3$ (320 g.)	$(\equiv CMgBr)_2$ (109 g. C_2H_5Br)	$[\equiv CCH(OCH_3)_2]_2$ (45–66%); recovered ester	*469*
$HC(OCH_3)_3$	4-$C_2H_5OC_6H_4MgBr$	4-$C_2H_5OC_6H_4CH(OCH_3)_2$	*366*
$HC(OC_2H_5)_3$	CH_3MgI	$CH_3CH(OC_2H_5)_2$ (*ca.* 25%)	*429*
$HC(OC_2H_5)_3$	$(\equiv CMgBr)_2$	$[\equiv CCH(OC_2H_5)_2]_2$ (38%, crude)	*470,177*
$HC(OC_2H_5)_3$	C_2H_5MgBr (2 equiv.)	$C_2H_5CH(OC_2H_5)_2$ (yielding 82% aldehyde)	*471*
$HC(OC_2H_5)_3$	$CH_3C\equiv CMgBr$	$CH_3C\equiv CCH(OC_2H_5)_2$	*442*
$HC(OC_2H_5)_3$ (42.1 g.)	*n*-C_3H_7MgBr (70 g. C_3H_7Br)	*n*-$C_3H_7CH(OC_2H_5)_2$ (yielding 15.5 g., 75.6% aldehyde)	*471*

* Prepared by refluxing in xylene (three hours at 130°) the Grignard reagent from (+)-α-pinene hydrochloride; Rivière (*361*) concludes that the reagent so obtained is substantially pure bornylmagnesium chloride.

† R = CH_3 or C_2H_5, depending upon whether CH_3X or C_2H_5X is used as "entrainer" in the preparation of the Grignard reagent.

TABLE VIII-III (Continued)

Ester	RMgX	Product(s)	Ref.
CHO_3-R_3 *(cont.)*			
$HC(OC_2H_5)_3$	n-C_3H_7MgI	n-$C_3H_7CH(OC_2H_5)_2$ (yielding 22% aldehyde-bisulfite comp'd)	*429*
$HC(OC_2H_5)_3$	n-C_3H_7MgX	n-C_3H_7CHO + n-$C_3H_7CH(OC_2H_5)_2$ (aggregating 75% aldehyde)	*57,56*
$HC(OC_2H_5)_3$ (30 g.)	2-Furyl-MgI (2 moles C_4H_3IO)	$C_4H_3OCH(OC_2H_5)_2$ (yielding 34,4% aldehyde)	*127*
$HC(OC_2H_5)_3$	2-Thienyl-MgI	2-Thiophenecarboxaldehyde	*142*
$HC(OC_2H_5)_3$ (22 g.)	3-Thienyl-MgBr (10 g. C_4H_3BrS)	3-Thiophenecarboxaldehyde ("very poor yield")	*520*
$HC(OC_2H_5)_3$ (25.0 g.)	$H_2C{=}C(CH_3)CH_2MgCl$ (18.1 g. C_4H_7Cl)	$H_2C{=}C(CH_3)CH_2CH(OC_2H_5)_2$ (5.9 g., 24%)	*223*
$HC(OC_2H_5)_3$ (49 g., 0.3 mole)	Butenyl-MgBr (0.27 mole)	$H_2C{=}CHCH(CH_3)CH(OC_2H_5)_2$ (84%); $CH_3CH{=}CHCH_2CH(OC_2H_5)_2$ ($<$4%); recovered ester	*472*
$HC(OC_2H_5)_3$ (48 g.)	Butenyl-MgBr (63 g. crotyl-Br)	$H_2C{=}CHCH(CH_3)CH(OC_2H_5)_2$ (35 g., 73%)	*521*
$HC(OC_2H_5)_3$ (48 g.)	Butenyl-MgBr (63 g. C_4H_7Br)	$H_2C{=}CHCH(CH_3)CH(OC_2H_5)_2$ (35 g., 73%)	*439*
$HC(OC_2H_5)_3$	n-C_4H_9MgBr	n-$C_4H_9CH(OC_2H_5)_2$	*201*
$HC(OC_2H_5)_3$	i-C_4H_9MgX	i-C_4H_9CHO + i-$C_4H_9CH(OC_2H_5)_2$ (aggregating 66% aldehyde)	*57,56*
$HC(OC_2H_5)_3$	$CH_3O(CH_2)_3MgCl$	$CH_3O(CH_2)_3CH(OC_2H_5)_2$ (18%)	*323*
$HC(OC_2H_5)_3$	5-Methyl-2-thienyl-MgBr	5-Methylthiophene-2-carboxaldehyde	*143*
$HC(OC_2H_5)_3$	i-$C_3H_7C{\equiv}CMgBr$	i-$C_3H_7C{\equiv}CCH(OC_2H_5)_2$	*177*
$HC(OC_2H_5)_3$ (148 g.)	n-$C_5H_{11}MgBr$ (189 g. $C_5H_{11}Br$)	n-$C_5H_{11}CH(OC_2H_5)_2$ (yielding 45–50 g., 45–50% aldehyde)	*12,11*
$HC(OC_2H_5)_3$	i-$C_5H_{11}MgBr$	i-$C_5H_{11}CH(OC_2H_5)_2$ (80%)	*429*

TABLE VIII-III (Continued)

Ester	RMgX	Product(s)	Ref.
CHO_3-R_3 (*cont.*)			
$HC(OC_2H_5)_3$	4-BrC_6H_4MgBr	4-BrC_6H_4CHO + 4-$BrC_6H_4CH(OC_2H_5)_2$ (aggregating 60% aldehyde)	*57,56*
$HC(OC_2H_5)_3$	4-BrC_6H_4MgBr	4-$BrC_6H_4CH(OC_2H_5)_2$ (yielding *ca.* 40% aldehyde)	*429*
$HC(OC_2H_5)_3$	4-ClC_6H_4MgBr	4-ClC_6H_4CHO + 4-$ClC_6H_4CH(OC_2H_5)_2$ (aggregating 64% aldehyde)	*57,56*
$HC(OC_2H_5)_3$	C_6H_5MgBr (1 equiv.)	C_6H_5CHO (as bisulfite comp'd, 21.5–89.2%, depending upon reaction conditions)	*389*
$HC(OC_2H_5)_3$	C_6H_5MgBr (2 equiv.)	C_6H_5CHO (as bisulfite comp'd, 95.0%)	*389*
$HC(OC_2H_5)_3$ (74 g.)	C_6H_5MgBr (157 g. C_6H_5Br)	$C_6H_5CH(OC_2H_5)_2$ (yielding 98 g., 93.3% aldehyde-bisulfite comp'd)	*471,55, 57,429*
$HC(OC_2H_5)_3$	$(CH_2)_5CHMgBr$ (1 equiv.)	$(CH_2)_5CHCH(OC_2H_5)_2$ (yielding 61.2% aldehyde-bisulfite comp'd)*	*471*
$HC(OC_2H_5)_3$	$(CH_2)_5CHMgBr$ (2 equiv.)	$(CH_2)_5CHCH(OC_2H_5)_3$ (yielding 56% aldehyde-bisulfite comp'd)*	*471*
$HC(OC_2H_5)_3$	$(CH_2)_5CHMgBr$ (1 equiv.)	$(CH_2)_5CHCH(OC_2H_5)_3$ (yielding 47% aldehyde-bisulfite comp'd)†	*471*
$HC(OC_2H_5)_3$	$(CH_2)_5CHMgBr$	$(CH_2)_5CHCH(OC_2H_5)_3$ (yielding 75% aldehyde-bisulfite comp'd)†	*471*
$HC(OC_2H_5)_3$ (148 g.)	$C_6H_5CH_2MgCl$ (126 g. C_7H_7Cl)	$C_6H_5CH_2CH(OC_2H_5)_2$ (yielding 123 g., 55% aldehyde-bisulfite comp'd)	*471,56*
$HC(OC_2H_5)_3$	2-$CH_3C_6H_4MgBr$	2-$CH_3C_6H_4CHO$ (73.2%)	*391*
$HC(OC_2H_5)_3$	4-$CH_3C_6H_4MgBr$	4-$CH_3C_6H_4CHO$ (74.4%)	*391,57*
$HC(OC_2H_5)_3$	4-$CH_3OC_6H_4MgBr$	4-$CH_3OC_6H_4CH(OC_2H_5)_2$ (yielding 15% aldehyde)	*429*
$HC(OC_2H_5)_3$	$(C_2H_5O)_2CHC{\equiv}CMgBr$	$[{\equiv}CCH(OC_2H_5)_2]_2$	*133,502*

* Gradual addition of ester to stirred Grignard reagent solution; five hours reflux with stirring; distillation of ether.

† Addition of Grignard reagent solution to Et_2O-ester solution.

TABLE VIII-III (Continued)

Ester	RMgX	Product(s)	Ref.
CHO_3-R_3 (*cont.*)			
$HC(OC_2H_5)_3$	3-Methylcyclohexyl-MgBr	1-Methyl-3-diethoxymethylcyclohexane (yielding 4.6 g., 25% aldehyde); "methylcyclohexene"; 3,3′-dimethylbicyclohexyl	430
$HC(OC_2H_5)_3$	4-$CH_3C_6H_4CH_2MgX$	4-$CH_3C_6H_4CH_2CH(OC_2H_5)_2$	42
$HC(OC_2H_5)_3$	4-$C_2H_5OC_6H_4MgBr$	4-$C_2H_5OC_6H_4CH(OC_2H_5)_2$	366
$HC(OC_2H_5)_3$ (25 g.)	4-$H_2C{=}CHCH_2C_6H_4MgBr$ (0.25 mole C_9H_9Br)	4-$H_2C{=}CHCH_2C_6H_4CH(OC_2H_5)_2$ (yielding 12% aldehyde)	347
$HC(OC_2H_5)_3$ (25 g.)	4-$CH_3CH{=}CHC_6H_4MgBr$ (50 g. C_9H_9Br)	4-$CH_3CH{=}CHC_6H_4CH(OC_2H_5)_2$ (yielding 15% aldehyde)	347
$HC(OC_2H_5)_3$	2-$CH_3C_6H_4(CH_2)_2MgX$	2-$CH_3C_6H_4(CH_2)_2CH(OC_2H_5)_2$	42
$HC(OC_2H_5)_3$	4-$CH_3C_6H_4(CH_2)_2MgX$	4-$CH_3C_6H_4(CH_2)_2CH(OC_2H_5)_2$	42
$HC(OC_2H_5)_3$	4-$C_2H_5C_6H_4CH_2MgX$	4-$C_2H_5C_6H_4CH_2CH(OC_2H_5)_2$	42
$HC(OC_2H_5)_3$	2,4-$(CH_3)_2C_6H_3CH_2MgX$	2,4-$(CH_3)_2C_6H_3CH_2CH(OC_2H_5)_2$	42
$HC(OC_2H_5)_3$	2,5-$(CH_3)_2C_6H_3CH_2MgX$	2,5-$(CH_3)_2C_6H_3CH_2CH(OC_2H_5)_2$	42
$HC(OC_2H_5)_3$	2,3,6-$(CH_3)_3C_6H_2MgBr$	2,3,6-$(CH_3)_3C_6H_2CHO$ (61.2%)	391
$HC(OC_2H_5)_3$	2,4,5-$(CH_3)_3C_6H_2MgBr$	2,4,5-$(CH_3)_3C_6H_2CHO$ (71.5%)	391
$HC(OC_2H_5)_3$	2,4,6-$(CH_3)_3C_6H_2MgBr$	2,4,6-$(CH_3)_3C_6H_2CHO$ (57.3%)	391
$HC(OC_2H_5)_3$	1-$C_{10}H_7MgBr$	1-$C_{10}H_7CHO$ + 1-$C_{10}H_7CH(OC_2H_5)_2$ (aggregating 70% aldehyde)	57,56
$HC(OC_2H_5)_3$	4-$CH_3C_6H_4(CH_2)_3MgX$	4-$CH_3C_6H_4(CH_2)_3CH(OC_2H_5)_2$	42
$HC(OC_2H_5)_3$	4-*i*-$C_3H_7C_6H_4CH_2MgX$	4-*i*-$C_3H_7C_6H_4CH_2CH(OC_2H_2)_2$	42
$HC(OC_2H_5)_3$	2,4-$(CH_3)_2C_6H_3(CH_2)_2MgX$	2,4-$(CH_3)_2C_6H_3(CH_2)_2CH(OC_2H_5)_2$	42
$HC(OC_2H_5)_3$	2,5-$(CH_3)_2C_6H_3(CH_2)_2MgX$	2,5-$(CH_3)_2C_6H_3(CH_2)_2CH(OC_2H_5)_2$	42
$HC(OC_2H_5)_3$	2,4,5-$(CH_3)_3C_6H_2CH_2MgX$	2,4,5-$(CH_3)_3C_6H_2CH_2CH(OC_2H_5)_2$	42
$HC(OC_2H_5)_3$	2,3,4,6-$(CH_3)_4C_6HMgBr$	2,3,4,6-$(CH_3)_4C_6HCHO$ (60.2%)	391
$HC(OC_2H_5)_3$	2,3,5,6-$(CH_3)_4C_6HMgBr$	2,3,5,6-$(CH_3)_4C_6HCHO$ (61.4%)	391

TABLE VIII-III (Continued)

Ester	RMgX	Product(s)	Ref.
CHO_3-R_3 *(cont.)*			
$HC(OC_2H_5)_3$	$C_{10}H_{17}MgCl$*	2-Decalincarboxaldehyde (mixture of stereoisomers)	*295*
$HC(OC_2H_5)_3$	4-$(CH_2)_4CHC_6H_4MgBr$	4-$(CH_2)_4CHC_6H_4CHO$	*73*
$HC(OC_2H_5)_3$	2-CH_3-5-*i*-$C_3H_7C_6H_3CH_2MgX$	2-CH_3-5-*i*-$C_3H_7C_6H_3CH_2CH(OC_2H_5)_2$	*42*
$HC(OC_2H_5)_3$	4-*i*-$C_3H_7C_6H_4(CH_2)_2MgX$	4-*i*-$C_3H_7C_6H_4(CH_2)_2CH(OC_2H_5)_2$	*42*
$HC(OC_2H_5)_3$	2,4-$(CH_3)_2C_6H_3(CH_2)_3MgX$	2,4-$(CH_3)_2C_6H_3(CH_2)_3CH(OC_2H_5)_2$	*42*
$HC(OC_2H_5)_3$	2,5-$(CH_3)_2C_6H_3(CH_2)_3MgX$	2,5-$(CH_3)_2C_6H_3(CH_2)_3CH(OC_2H_5)_2$	*42*
$HC(OC_2H_5)_3$	$(CH_3)_5C_6MgBr$	$(CH_3)_5C_6CHO$ (20%); $(CH_3)_5C_6H$; *i*-C_3H_7OH†	*368*
$HC(OC_2H_5)_3$ (excess)	$(CH_3)_5C_6MgBr$	$(CH_3)_5C_6CHO$ (20%); $(CH_3)_5CH$; $(CH_3)_6C_6$‡	*85*
$HC(OC_2H_5)_3$	$(CH_3)_5C_6MgBr$	$(CH_3)_5C_6CHO$ (43.1%)	*391*
$HC(OC_2H_5)_3$	4-$(CH_2)_5CHC_6H_4MgBr$	4-$(CH_2)_5CHC_6H_4CH(OC_2H_5)_2$ (yielding 53% aldehyde)	*58*
$HC(OC_2H_5)_3$	2-CH_3-5-*i*-$C_3H_7C_6H_3(CH_2)_2MgX$	2-CH_3-5-*i*-$C_3H_7C_6H_3(CH_2)_2CH(OC_2H_5)_2$	*42*
$HC(OC_2H_5)_3$	4-*i*-$C_3H_7C_6H_4(CH_2)_3MgX$	4-*i*-$C_3H_7C_6H_4(CH_2)_3CH(OC_2H_5)_2$	*42*
$HC(OC_2H_5)_3$	9-Fluorenyl-MgBr	White crystalline solid, m. 255° (40%); amorphous solid (14%)	*287*
$HC(OC_2H_5)_3$ (30.0 g.)	2-$C_6H_5CH_2C_6H_4MgBr$ (27.5 g. $C_{13}H_{11}Br$)	2-$C_6H_5CH_2C_6H_4CH(OC_2H_5)_2$ (15.5 g.); $(C_6H_5)_2CH_2$ (7.7 g.)	*36*
$HC(OC_2H_5)_3$ (37.5 g.)	9-Phenanthryl-MgBr (32.5 g. $C_{14}H_9Br$)	9-Diethoxymethylphenanthrene	*448*
$HC(OC_2H_5)_3$ (296.4 g., 2.0 moles)	9-Phenanthryl-MgBr (514.0 g., 2.0 moles $C_{14}H_9Br$)	9-Phenanthrenecarboxaldehyde (206–216 g., 50–52%, crude; 166–174 g., 40–42%, pure)	*98,287*
$HC(OC_2H_5)_3$ (7.0 g.)	$(C_6H_5)_2C{=}CHMgBr$ (17.5 g. $C_{14}H_{11}Br$)	$(C_6H_5)_2C{=}CHCHO$ (53%)	*516*

* From 2-chlorodecalin—either stereoisomer.

† Attributable to the action of CH_3MgBr from the CH_3Br used as "entrainer" in the preparation of the Grignard reagent.

‡ Attributable to Wurtz-Fittig side-reaction in the preparation of the Grignard reagent, in which CH_3Br is used as "entrainer".

TABLE VIII-III (Continued)

Ester	RMgX	Product(s)	Ref.
CHO_3-R_3 (*cont.*)			
$HC(OC_2H_5)_3$	3,8-$(CH_3)_2$-5-*i*-$C_3H_7C_{10}H_4$-2-MgBr	2-$(C_2H_5O)_2CH$-3,8-$(CH_3)_2$-5-*i*-$C_3H_7C_{10}H_4$	*141*
$HC(OC_6H_5)_3$ (60 g.)	C_6H_5MgBr (100 g. C_6H_5Br)	C_6H_5CHO (90%)	*55*
$HC(OC_6H_5)_3$	$C_6H_5CH_2MgCl$	$C_6H_5CH_2CHO$ (20%)	*55*
$HC(OC_6H_5)_3$	4-$CH_3C_6H_4MgBr$	4-$CH_3C_6H_4CHO$ (65%); 4-$CH_3C_6H_4CH(OC_2H_5)_2$	*55*
$C_2O_2Cl_3$-R			
$Cl_3CCO_2C_2H_5$	CH_3MgBr	$Cl_3C(CH_3)_2COH$	*160*
$Cl_3CCO_2C_2H_5$	CH_3MgI	$Cl_3C(CH_3)_2COH$	*174*
$C_2O_2F_3$-R			
$CF_3CO_2CH_3$ (0.2–0.3 mole)	C_2H_5MgI (0.8–1.2 mole)	$CF_3(C_2H_5)_2COH$ (56.0%); $CF_3(C_2H_5)CHOH$ (35.0%)	*515*
C_2O_2N-R			
$NCCO_3C_2H_5$ (0.33 mole)	C_2H_5MgBr (1.00 mole)	$(C_2H_5)_3COH$ (16 g.); $C_2H_5COC(C_2H_5)_2OH$	*68*
$NCCO_2C_2H_5$ (6 g.)	C_6H_5MgBr (34 g. C_6H_5Br)	$(C_6H_5)_3COH$ (3 g.)	*268*
C_2O_4-R_2			
$(—CO_2CH_3)_2$	C_2H_5MgI	$[—C(CH_3)(C_2H_5)OH]_2$	*118*
$(—CO_2CH_3)_2$	C_6H_5MgBr	$[—C(C_6H_5)_2OH]_2$	*437*
$(—CO_2CH_3)_2$ (30 g.)	2,4,6-$(CH_3)_3C_6H_2MgBr$ (50 g. $C_9H_{11}Br$)	1,3,5-$(CH_3)_3C_6H_3$ + $(—CO_2CH_3)_2$ (16.1 g.); 2,4,6-$(CH_3)_3C_6H_2COCO_2CH_3$ (6.0 g.)	*233*
$(—CO_2CH_3)_2$ (30 g.)	1-$C_{10}H_7MgBr$ (52 g. $C_{10}H_7Br$)	1-$C_{10}H_7COCO_2CH_3$ (3.5 g., crude)	*233*
$(—CO_2C_2H_5)_2$	CH_3MgI	$[—C(CH_3)_2OH]_2$	*436*
$(—CO_2C_2H_5)_2$ (73 g.)	CH_3MgI (180 g. CH_3I)	$HO(CH_3)_2CCO_2C_2H_5$ (39.6 g., 60%)	*163,152*
$(—CO_2C_2H_5)_2$	C_2H_5MgBr	$[—C(C_2H_5)_2OH]_2$ ("poor yield"); $HO(C_2H_5)_2CCO_2C_2H_5$	*281*

TABLE VIII-III (Continued)

Ester	RMgX	Product(s)	Ref.
$C_2O_4R_2$ (*cont.*)			
$(—CO_2C_2H_5)_2$ (73 g.)	C_2H_5Br (131 g.) + Mg (31 g.)	$HO(C_2H_5)_2CCO_2C_2H_5$ (45.5 g., 57%); recovered ester (*ca.* 4.0 g.)	*163*
$(—CO_2C_2H_5)_2$	C_2H_5MgI	$HO(C_2H_5)_2CCO_2C_2H_5$ (54.3%); $[—C(C_2H_5)_2OH]_2$ (7.1%)	*395*
$(—CO_2C_2H_5)_2$ (65 g.)	n-C_4H_9MgBr (250 g. C_4H_9Br)	$HO(n$-$C_4H_9)_2CCO_2C_2H_5$ (yielding 10 g. acid); $HO(n$-$C_4H_9)_2CCO$-n-C_4H_9 (*ca.* 50 g.)	*331*
$(—CO_2C_2H_5)_2$	n-C_4H_9MgBr ("1 equiv."*)	$HO(n$-$C_4H_9)_2CCO_2C_2H_5$	*331*
$(—CO_2C_2H_5)_2$	t-C_4H_9MgCl ("2 equiv."†)	t-$C_4H_9CH(OH)CO_2C_2H_5$; i-C_4H_8; t-$C_4H_9CH(OC_2H_5)CO_2C_2H_5$; $[—CH(OH)$-t-$C_4H_9]_2$ (?); t-$C_4H_9COCH_2$-t-C_4H_9	*102*
$(—CO_2C_2H_5)_2$ (0.385 mole)	t-C_4H_9MgCl (1.54 mole)	t-$C_4H_9CH(OH)CO_2H$ + t-$C_4H_9CH(OH)CO_2C_2H_5$ (aggregating 28 g. crude acid); i-C_4H_8 (0.7 mole); $(i$-$C_4H_8)_2$; $(t$-$C_4H_9—)_2$‡	*156*
$(—CO_2C_2H_5)_2$ (0.676 mole)	t-C_4H_9MgCl (1.35 mole)	t-$C_4H_9CH(OH)CO_2C_2H_5$ (27 g.); $HO(t$-$C_4H_9)_2CCO_2C_2H_5$ (?) (30 g.); high-boiling material (26 g.)§	*156*
$(—CO_2C_2H_5)_2$ (1 mole)	t-C_4H_9Cl (2 moles) + Mg	t-$C_4H_9CH(OH)CO_2C_2H_5$ (38 g., crude); $HO(t$-$C_4H_9)_2CCO_2C_2H_5$ (40 g.); $HO(t$-$C_4H_9)_2CCO$-t-C_4H_9 (?) (39 g.)¶	*156*
$(—CO_2C_2H_5)_2$ (7 g.)	C_6H_5MgBr (39 g. C_6H_5Br)	$C_6H_5COC(C_6H_5)_3$	*96*
$(—CO_2C_2H_5)_2$ (1.37 ml.)	3,5-Dimethyl-2-pyrryl-MgBr‖ (3.62 g. 2,4-dimethylpyrrole)	Bis(3,5-dimethyl-2-pyrryl)gloxal	*107*

* *I.e.*, two moles of Grignard reagent per mole of ester.

† *I.e.*, four moles of Grignard reagent per mole of ester.

‡ Dropwise addition of ester to filtered Grignard reagent solution.

§ Addition of filtered Grignard reagent solution to ester.

¶ Barbier synthesis.

‖ Concerning the structures of pyrryl Grignard reagents see Nitrogen Heterocycles with "Active" Hydrogen, Chapter II.

TABLE VIII-III (Continued)

Ester	RMgX	Product(s)	Ref.
C_2O_4-R_2 *(cont.)*			
$(—CO_2C_2H_5)_2$ (22 g.)	$(CH_2)_5CHMgCl$ (120 g. $C_6H_{11}Cl$)	$(CH_2)_5CHCOCO_2C_2H_5$ (23 g.); $HO[(CH_2)_5CH]_2CCO_2C_2H_5$ (22 g.); $HO[(CH_2)_5CH]_2CCOCH(CH_2)_5$ (1.8 g.)	*305*
$(—CO_2C_2H_5)_2$ (24.3 g.)	$2\text{-}CH_3C_6H_4MgBr$ (28.5 g. C_7H_7Br)	$2\text{-}CH_3C_6H_4CH(OH)CO_2C_2H_5$ (40%); $HO(2\text{-}CH_3C_6H_4)_2CCO_2C_2H_5$ (7 g., crude)	*234*
$(—CO_2C_2H_5)_2$	$C_6H_5CH(CO_2Na)MgCl$*	$C_6H_5CH_2COCO_2C_2H_5$ (45.9%)	*405*
$(—CO_2C_2H_5)_2$ (2.75 ml.)	Hemopyrryl-MgBr (5.0 g. 2,3-dimethyl-4-ethylpyrrole)	Bis-(3-ethyl-4,5-dimethyl-2-pyrryl)glyoxal (0.8 g.)	*107*
$(—CO_2C_2H_5)_2$ (2.7 ml.)	Cryptopyrryl-MgBr (5.0 g. 2,4-dimethyl-3-ethylpyrrole)	Bis-(3,5-dimethyl-4-ethyl-2-pyrryl)glyoxal (0.72 g.); ethyl 3,5-dimethyl-4-ethyl-2-pyrrylglyoxalate	*107*
$(—CO_2C_2H_5)_2$ (36.5 g.)	$n\text{-}C_8H_{17}MgBr$ (48.3 g. $C_8H_{17}Br$)	$n\text{-}C_8H_{17}CH(OH)CO_2C_2H_5$ (25%)	*234*
$(—CO_2C_2H_5)_2$ (43.0 g.)	$C_6H_5(CH_3)_2CMgBr$ (?)† (58.3 g. $C_9H_{11}Br$)	$[—C(CH_3)_2C_6H_5]_2$ (60%)†	*234*
$(—CO_2C_2H_5)_2$ (18 g.)	$2,4,6\text{-}(CH_3)_3C_6H_2MgBr$ (50 g.)	$2,4,6\text{-}(CH_3)_3C_6H_2CH(OH)CO_2C_2H_5$ (12.5 g.); $[2,4,6\text{-}(CH_3)_3C_6H_2CO—]_2$ (1.5 g.); $2,4,6\text{-}(CH_3)_3C_6H_2COCO_2C_2H_5$ (1.2 g.); $[2,4,6\text{-}(CH_3)_3C_6H_2—]_2$ (3.2 g.)‡	*231*

*In the opinion of Schlenk, Hilleman, and Rodloff, *Ann.*, *487*, 135–54 (1931), this "Grignard reagent" should be formulated as an enolate.

†It is possible that the product reported is attributable entirely to Wurtz reaction in the attempted preparation of the Grignard reagent. Brown, Mighton, and Senkus, *J. Org. Chem.*, *3*, 62–75 (1938), report an unsuccessful attempt to prepare $C_6H_5(CH_3)_2CMgCl$ by the action of magnesium on the appropriate chloride.

‡According to Lapkin (*233*), this reaction also yields acetaldehyde, which would account for the formation of mandelate by a Meerwein-Ponndorf-Verley oxidation-reduction (see Alkoxide Reduction, Chapter VI).

TABLE VIII-III (Continued)

Ester	RMgX	Product(s)	Ref.
C_2O_4-R_2 (*cont.*)			
$(\text{—}CO_2C_2H_5)_2$ (0.25 mole)	$(n\text{-}C_4H_9)_2CHMgBr$ (?) (0.25 mole $C_9H_{19}Br$)	$[(n\text{-}C_4H_9)_2CH\text{—}]_2$ (30%); unidentified acid (2 g.)	*234*
$(\text{—}CO_2C_2H_5)_2$ (36 g.)	$1\text{-}C_{10}H_7MgBr$ (52 g. $C_{10}H_7Br$)	$1\text{-}C_{10}H_7CH(OH)CO_2C_2H_5$ (40%); $(1\text{-}C_{10}H_7CO\text{—})_2$; $1\text{-}C_{10}H_7CH(OH)CO\text{-}1\text{-}C_{10}H_7$	*236*
$(\text{—}CO_2C_2H_5)_2$ (21 g.)	$2,3,4,6\text{-}(CH_3)_4C_6HMgBr$ (30 g. $C_{10}H_{13}Br$)	$2,3,4,6\text{-}(CH_3)_4C_6HCH(OH)CO_2C_2H_5$ (35%)	*236*
$(\text{—}CO_2C_2H_5)_2$ (35 g.)	$2,3,5,6\text{-}(CH_3)_4C_6HMgBr$ (43 g. $C_{10}H_{13}Br$)	$2,3,5,6\text{-}(CH_3)_4C_6HCH(OH)CO_2C_2H_5$ (35%)	*236*
$(\text{—}CO_2C_2H_5)_2$ (35 g.)	$(CH_3)_5C_6MgBr$ (46 g. $C_{11}H_{15}Br$)	$(CH_3)_5C_6CH(OH)CO_2C_2H_5$ (30%)	*236*
$(\text{—}CO_2C_2H_5)_2$ (29.0 g.)	$(C_6H_5)_2CHMgCl$ (?) (40.4 g. $C_{13}H_{11}Cl$)	$[(C_6H_5)_2CH\text{—}]_2$ (90%)	*234*
$(\text{—}CO_2\text{-}i\text{-}C_3H_7)_2$	$2,4,6\text{-}(CH_3)_3C_6H_2MgBr$	$2,4,6\text{-}(CH_3)_3C_6H_2CH(OH)CO_2\text{-}i\text{-}C_3H_7$ (30%)	*231*
$(\text{—}CO_2\text{-}n\text{-}C_4H_9)_2$	$2,4,6\text{-}(CH_3)_3C_6H_2MgBr$	$2,4,6\text{-}(CH_3)_3C_6H_2CH(OH)CO_2C_2H_5$ (40%)*	*231*
$(\text{—}CO_2\text{-}n\text{-}C_4H_9)_2$ (40.4 g.)	$1\text{-}C_{10}H_7MgBr$ (41.4 g. $C_{10}H_7Br$)	$1\text{-}C_{10}H_7CH(OH)CO_2\text{-}n\text{-}C_4H_9$ (40%)	*234*
$(\text{—}CO_2\text{-}i\text{-}C_4H_9)_2$	$2,4,6\text{-}(CH_3)_3C_6H_2MgBr$	$2,4,6\text{-}(CH_3)_3C_6H_2CH(OH)CO_2C_2H_5$ (40%)*	*231*
$(\text{—}CO_2\text{-}i\text{-}C_4H_9)_2$	$1\text{-}C_{10}H_7MgBr$	$1\text{-}C_{10}H_7CH(OH)CO_2C_2H_5$ (40%)	*234*
$(\text{—}CO_2C_6H_5)_2$ (30 g.)	$2,4,6\text{-}(CH_3)_3C_6H_2MgBr$ (25 g. $C_9H_{11}Br$)	$2,4,6\text{-}(CH_3)_3C_6H_2COCO_2C_6H_5$ (1.5 g., crude); C_6H_5OH (8.0 g.)	*233*
C_2O_5-R_2			
$O(CO_2C_2H_5)_2$ (9 g.)	C_6H_5MgBr (35 g. C_6H_5Br)	$C_6H_5CO_2C_2H_5$ (54%); $(C_6H_5)_3COH$ (64%)	*381*
$O(CO_2C_4H_9)_2$	C_6H_5MgBr (23 g. C_6H_5Br)	$C_6H_5CO_2C_2H_5$ (4.0 g.); $(C_6H_5)_3COH$ (6.3 g.)	*381*

* According to Lapkin (*233*), this reaction also yields butyraldehyde (Meerwein-Ponndorf-Verley oxidation-reduction, *q.v.*).

TABLE VIII-III (Continued)

Ester	RMgX	Product(s)	Ref.
$C_2HO_2Cl_2$-R			
$Cl_2CHCO_2C_2H_5$	CH_3MgBr	$Cl_2CH(CH_3)_2COH$	*160*
$Cl_2CHCO_2C_2H_5$	CH_3MgI (2 equiv.)	$Cl_2CHCOCH_3$ (*ca.* 4%); $Cl_2CH(CH_3)_2COH$ (65%)	*175*
$C_2H_2O_2Br$-R			
$BrCH_2CO_2C_2H_5$	CH_3MgBr (4 equiv.)	$CH_3(i\text{-}C_3H_7)CHOH$ (32%)	*171*
$C_2H_2O_2Cl$-R			
$ClCH_2CO_2CH_3$ (196 g.)	CH_3MgCl (120 g. Mg)	$ClCH_2(CH_3)_2COH$ (170–180 g., crude)	*75*
$ClCH_2CO_2CH_3$	$ClCH_2CO_2CH_3$ + Mg	$ClCH_2COCH_2CO_2CH_3$	*150*
$ClCH_2CO_2C_2H_5$	CH_3MgX*	$ClCH_2(CH_3)_2COH$	*224,160*
$ClCH_2CO_2C_2H_5$	CH_3MgBr (4 equiv.)	$CH_3(i\text{-}C_3H_7)CHOH$ (40%)	*171*
$ClCH_2CO_2C_2H_5$	CH_3MgI (2 equiv.)	$ClCH_2(CH_3)_2COH$ (*ca.* 58%)	*175*
$ClCH_2CO_2C_2H_5$	C_2H_5MgBr	$ClCH_2(C_2H_5)_2COH$; $C_2H_5CH(OH)CH(C_2H_5)_2$ (?)	*110*
$ClCH_2CO_2C_2H_5$	C_2H_5MgBr	$ClCH_2(C_2H_5)_2COH$	*410,91*
$ClCH_2CO_2C_2H_5$	$ClCH_2CO_2C_2H_5$ + Mg	$ClCH_2COCH_2COC_2H_5$ (56%); recovered ester	*150*
$ClCH_2CO_2C_2H_5$	$C_6H_5CH(CO_2Na)MgCl$†	$ClCH_2[HO_2C(C_6H_5)CH]_2COH$ (20%); $C_6H_5CH_2CO_2H$	*405*
$ClCH_2CO_2C_2H_5$ (31 g.)	1-$C_{10}H_7MgBr$ (52 g. $C_{10}H_7Br$)	$ClCH_2CO$-1-$C_{10}H_7$ (4 g., crude; 1 g., pure)	*233*
$ClCH_2CO_2$-i-C_4H_9	$ClCH_2CO_2$-i-C_4H_9 + Mg	$ClCH_2COCH_2CO_2$-i-C_4H_9 (*ca.* 7 g. per mole ester)	*150*
$C_2H_2O_3N$-R			
$H_2NOCCO_2C_2H_5$ (10 g.)	C_6H_5MgBr (81 g. C_6H_5Br)	$(C_6H_5)_3COH$ (5 g.)	*268*
$C_2H_3O_2$-R			
$CH_3CO_2CH_3$	CH_3MgI	$(CH_3)_3COH$ (82%)	*135,493*
$CH_3CO_2CH_3$	i-$C_5H_{11}MgBr$	$CH_3(i\text{-}C_5H_{11})_2COH$	*135*

*X = Br, I.

†In the opinion of Schlenk, Hilleman, and Rodloff, *Ann.*, *487*, 135–54 (1931), this "Grignard reagent" should be formulated as an enolate.

TABLE VIII-III (Continued)

Ester	RMgX	Product(s)	Ref.
$C_2H_3O_2$-R (*cont.*)			
$CH_3CO_2C_2H_5$	C_2H_5MgBr	$CH_3(C_2H_5)_2COH$ (67%)	*80,307,379, 467*
$CH_3CO_2C_2H_5$	C_2H_5MgI	$CH_3(C_2H_5)_2COH$	*252*
$CH_3CO_2C_2H_5$	$CH_3C{\equiv}CMgBr$	$CH_3(CH_3C{\equiv}C)_2COH$	*176,178*
$CH_3CO_2C_2H_5$	n-C_3H_7MgBr	$CH_3(n$-$C_3H_7)_2COH$	*149,333*
$CH_3CO_2C_2H_5$	i-C_3H_7MgCl (3 equiv.)	$CH_3(i$-$C_3H_7)C(OH)CH_2CO$-i-C_3H_7 (65%); C_3H_8*	*184*
$CH_3CO_2C_2H_5$	i-C_3H_7MgCl (3 equiv.)	CH_3CO-i-C_3H_7 (60%); i-$C_3H_7COCH{=}C(CH_3)$-i-C_3H_7; C_3H_8†	*184*
$CH_3CO_2C_2H_5$	i-C_3H_7MgCl (3 equiv.)	i-$C_3H_7COCH{=}C(CH_3)$-i-C_3H_7 (principal product); CH_3COCH_2CO-i-C_3H_7; CH_3CO-i-C_3H_7; C_3H_8‡	*184*
$CH_3CO_2C_2H_5$ (20 g.)	$H_2C{=}CHC{\equiv}CMgBr$	$CH_3(H_2C{=}CHC{\equiv}C)_2COH$ (5 g.)	*473*
$CH_3CO_2C_2H_5$	Pyrryl-MgBr	2-Acetylpyrrole (50–60%)	*427*
$CH_3CO_2C_2H_5$ (176 g.)	$ClCH_2CO_2C_2H_5$ (123 g.) +Mg(24 g.)	$CH_3COCH_2CO_2C_2H_5$	*393*
$CH_3CO_2C_2H_5$ (5.0 moles)	n-C_4H_9MgBr (10.6 moles C_4H_9Br)	$CH_3(n$-$C_4H_9)_2COH$ (64%); $CH_3(n$-$C_4H_9)CHOH$ (3%)	*458*
$CH_3CO_2C_2H_5$ (8.30 moles)	n-C_4H_9MgBr (17.25 moles C_4H_9Br)	$CH_3(n$-$C_4H_9)_2COH$ (79%)	*74,462,332, 333*
$CH_3CO_2C_2H_5$	i-C_4H_9MgBr	$CH_3(i$-$C_4H_9)_2COH$	*149*
$CH_3CO_2C_2H_5$	i-C_4H_9MgBr	CH_3CO-i-C_4H_9; $CH_3(i$-$C_4H_9)CHOH$	*383*
$CH_3CO_2C_2H_5$	s-C_4H_9MgBr	$(CH_3)_2CO$; CH_3CO-s-C_4H_9	*327*
$CH_3CO_2C_2H_5$	t-C_4H_9MgCl	$(CH_3)_2CO$ (42%); $(CH_3)_2C{=}CHCOCH_3$; $[(CH_3)_2C{=}CH]_2CO$; CH_3CO-t-C_4H_9; $CH_3CO_2CH(CH_3)$-t-C_4H_9; CH_3COCH_2O-t-C_4H_9	*194,327*

* Addition of Et_2O-ester solution to Grignard reagent solution; one hour reflux; hydrolysis with NH_4Cl or H_2SO_4; distillation at 14 mm.

† Addition of Et_2O-ester solution to Grignard reagent solution; one hour reflux; hydrolysis with NH_4Cl; distillation at barometric pressure.

‡ Addition of Et_2O-ester solution to Grignard reagent solution; one hour reflux; hydrolysis with H_2SO_4; distillation at barometric

TABLE VIII-III (Continued)

Ester	RMgX	Product(s)	Ref.
$C_2H_3O_2$-R (*cont.*)			
$CH_3CO_2C_2H_5$	$H_2C(CH_2CH_2MgBr)_2$	1-Methylcyclohexanol (45%)	*140*
$CH_3C^{13}O_2C_2H_5$ (or $CH_3C^{14}CO_2C_2H_5$)	$H_2C(CH_2CH_2MgBr)_2$	1-Methylcyclohexanol (60–70%)	*490*
$CH_3CO_2C_2H_5$	n-$C_5H_{11}MgBr$	$CH_3(n$-$C_5H_{11})_2COH$ (75%)	*461*
$CH_3CO_2C_2H_5$	i-$C_5H_{11}MgBr$	$CH_3(i$-$C_5H_{11})_2COH$ (45%)	*493,149*
$CH_3CO_2C_2H_5$	C_6H_5MgBr	$(C_6H_5)_2C{=}CH_2$ (80%)	*400*
$CH_3CO_2C_2H_5$	$C_6H_5CH_2MgCl$	$CH_3(C_6H_5CH_2)_2COH$	*421,426*
$CH_3CO_2C_2H_5$	$C_6H_5CH_2MgCl$ (1 equiv.)	$CH_3COCH_2C_6H_5$ (2.7%); high-boiling alcohol (*ca.* 90%)	*459*
$CH_3CO_2C_2H_5$	4-$CH_3SC_6H_4MgBr$	$(4$-$CH_3SC_6H_4)_2C{=}CH_2$	*412*
$CH_3CO_2C_2H_5$ (20 g.)	n-$C_7H_{15}MgBr$ (80 g. $C_7H_{15}Br$)	$CH_3(n$-$C_7H_{15})_2COH$ (32 g.)	*47*
$CH_3CO_2C_2H_5$	$CH_3(i$-$C_4H_9)CHCH_2MgBr$	$C_2H_5CH(CH_3)CH_2CH(CH_3)CH_2OH$; $CH_3(i$-$C_4H_9)CH{=}CH_2$; i-$C_4H_9(CH_3)_2CH$	*433*
$CH_3CO_2C_2H_5$	$(i$-$C_3H_7)_2CHMgBr$	"Secondary products only"	*433*
$CH_3CO_2C_2H_5$	$C_6H_5C{\equiv}CMgX$	$CH_3(C_6H_5C{\equiv}C)_2COH$ (80%)	*399*
$CH_3CO_2C_2H_5$	Indolyl-MgBr	1-Acetylindole (2.8 g.); 3-acetylindole (trace)	*348*
$CH_3CO_2C_2H_5$ (10 g.)	n-$C_8H_{17}MgBr$ (48 g. $C_8H_{17}Br$)	$CH_3(n$-$C_8H_{17})_2COH$ (10 g.)	*47,339*
$CH_3CO_2C_2H_5$	2,4,6-$(CH_3)_3C_6H_2MgBr$	2,4,6-$(CH_3)_3C_6H_2OH$; 2,4,6-$(CH_3)_3C_6H_2COCH_3$; $CH_3CO_2CH[C_6H_2$-2,4,6-$(CH_3)_3]_2$ (?)	*235*
$CH_3CO_2C_2H_5$	$(CH_3)_5C_6MgBr$	$(CH_3)_6C_6$*; t-C_4H_9OH*; $CH_3COC_6(CH_3)_5$ (40%)	*85,82,368*
$CH_3CO_2C_2H_5$ (3.5 ml.)	4-$C_6H_5OC_6H_4MgBr$ (20.0 g. $C_{12}H_9BrO$)	$(4$-$C_6H_5OC_6H_4)_2C{=}CH_2$	*412*
$CH_3CO_2CH_2COCH_3$	C_2H_5MgBr (1 equiv.)	Recovered ester (20%); $CH_3(C_2H_5)_2COH$; $HO(CH_3)(C_2H_5)CCH_2O_2CCH_3$	*207*
CH_3CO_2-t-C_4H_9 (21.5 g., 0.185 mole)	i-C_3H_7MgBr (0.185 mole)	CH_3COCH_2-t-C_4H_9 (6.1 g., 41%); "gas"	*384*

* Attributable to the use of methyl bromide as "entrainer" in the preparation of the Grignard reagent.

TABLE VIII-III (Continued)

Ester	RMgX	Product(s)	Ref.
$C_2H_3O_2$-R (*cont.*)			
$CH_3CO_2CH_2C_6H_5$	C_6H_5MgBr	$CH_3(C_6H_5)_2COH$; $(C_6H_5)_2C{=}CH_2$ (22%); $C_6H_5CH_2OH$	*400,260*
$CH_3CO_2CH(CO_2H)C_6H_5$	CH_3MgBr (2 equiv.)	$C_6H_5CH(OH)CO_2H$ (80.5%)	*105*
$CH_3CO_2CH(COCH_3)$-*n*-C_5H_{11} (12.7 g.)	CH_3MgBr (15.0 g. Mg)	*t*-C_4H_9OH ("a little"); $HO(CH_3)_2CCH(OH)$-*n*-C_5H_{11} (6.5 g.)	*496*
$CH_3CO_2CH(COCH_3)C_6H_4$-4-CH_3 (17.0 g.)	CH_3MgBr (6.0 g. Mg)	*t*-C_4H_9OH; $HO(CH_3)_2CCH(OH)C_6H_4$-4-CH_3 (3.6 g.)	*497*
2-Methyl-3-acetoxy-5-isopropenyl-2-cyclohexen-1-one	C_2H_5MgBr (2 equiv.)	$CH_3(C_2H_5)_2COH$; 2-methyl-3-ethyl-5-isopropenyl-2-cyclohexen-1-one	*425*
9-Fluorenyl acetate	CH_3MgBr (6 equiv.)	9-Fluorenol (89.5%)	*105*
9-Acetoxymethylcarbazole (6.0 g.)	CH_3MgI (8.5 g. CH_3I)	9-Ethylcarbazole (73.9%)	*285*
9-Acetoxymethylcarbazole	C_2H_5MgBr	9-*n*-Propylcarbazole (67.0%)	*285*
9-Acetoxymethylcarbazole	C_6H_5MgBr	9-Benzylcarbazole (75.9%)	*285*
$CH_3CO_2CH(C_6H_5)_2$ (11 g.)	C_2H_5MgI (9 g. C_2H_5I)	$CH_3(C_2H_5)_2COH$ (1.5 g.); $[(C_6H_5)_2CH]_2O$ (3.0 g.); recovered ester; C_2H_4; C_2H_6	*398*
$CH_3CO_2CH(C_6H_5)_2$ (11 g.)	*n*-C_3H_7MgI (18 g. C_3H_7I)	$[(C_6H_5)_2CH{-}]_2$ (1.4 g.); $[(C_6H_5)_2CH]_2O$ (1.2 g.); $(C_6H_5)_2CHOH$ (1.3 g.); $CH_3(n\text{-}C_3H_7)_2COH$ (2.5 g., 40%); oil; C_3H_6; C_3H_8	*398*
$CH_3CO_2CH(C_6H_5)_2$ (22 g.)	*n*-C_4H_9MgI (37 g. C_4H_9I)	$[(C_6H_5)_2CH{-}]_2$ (6 g.); $(C_6H_5)_2CHOH$ (8.6 g.); $CH_3(n\text{-}C_4H_9)_2COH$ (7.0 g.); C_4H_8; C_4H_{10}	*398*
$CH_3CO_2CH(C_6H_5)_2$ (11 g.)	*i*-$C_5H_{11}MgI$ (10 g. $C_5H_{11}I$)	$CH_3(i\text{-}C_5H_{11})_2COH$ (50%); recovered ester	*398*
$CH_3CO_2CH(C_6H_5)_2$ (22 g.)	C_6H_5MgBr (32 g. C_6H_5Br)	$[(C_6H_5)_2CH]_2O$ (7.6 g.); $CH_3(C_6H_5)C{=}C(C_6H_5)_2$; recovered ester	*398*
9-Acetoxyanthracene (10 g.)	CH_3MgBr (0.4 mole)	9-Anthrol (attempted peroxidation yielded bianthrone)	*186*
9-Acetoxy-10-vinylanthracene (2 g.)	CH_3MgBr (0.1 mole)	10-Vinyl-9-anthrol (isolated as peroxide)	*187*
9-Acetoxy-10-ethylanthracene (5 g.)	CH_3MgBr (0.2 mole)	10-Ethyl-9-anthrol (isolated as peroxide, 3.4 g.)	*186*

TABLE VIII-III (Continued)

Ester	RMgX	Product(s)	Ref.
$C_2H_3O_2$-R (*cont.*)			
9-Acetoxy-10-propenylanthracene (2.3 g.)	CH_3MgBr (0.05 mole)	10-Propenyl-9-anthrol (isolated as peroxide, 1.9 g.)	*187*
9-Acetoxy-10-(1-butenyl)anthracene (3 g.)	CH_3MgBr (0.1 mole)	10-(1-Butenyl)-9-anthrol (isolated as peroxide)	*187*
7-Acetoxy-1,2,3,4-tetrahydrobenz[*a*]anthracene (8.0 g.)	*n*-C_4H_9MgBr (14.8 g. C_4H_9Br)	1,2,3,4-Tetrahydrobenz[*a*]anthracen-7(12*H*)-one (5.6 g., 82%)	*104*
$CH_3CO_2C(C_6H_5)_3$ (3.0 g.)	CH_3MgBr (1.2 g. Mg)	$CH_3C(C_6H_5)_3$ (69%)	*105,9*
9-Acetoxy-10-(*β*-isopropylvinyl)anthracene (2.5 g.)	CH_3MgBr (0.05 mole)	10-(*β*-Isopropylvinyl)-9-anthrol (isolated as peroxide, 2.4 g.)	*187*
3,4′-Ace-1,2-Benanthryl 10-acetate* (5.5 g.)	*n*-C_4H_9MgBr (9.0 g. C_4H_9Br)	3,4′-Ace-1,2-benzanthracen-10-ol† (90%, crude)	*286*
9-Acetoxy-10-phenylanthracene (5 g.)	CH_3MgBr (0.15 mole)	10-Phenyl-9-anthrol (isolated as peroxide, 3.5 g.)	*186*
3-Acetoxy-17-cyano-$\Delta^{5,16}$-androstadiene (1.8 g.)	CH_3MgBr (5 g. Mg)	$\Delta^{5,16}$-Pregnadien-3-ol-20-one (1.26 g., 75%)	*70*
3-Acetoxy-17-cyano-$\Delta^{5,16}$-androstadiene	CH_3MgBr	17-Cyano-$\Delta^{5,16}$-androstadien-3-ol	*70*
3-Acetoxy-17-cyano-Δ^{16}-androstene (900 mg.)	CH_3MgBr (2.5 g. Mg)	Δ^{16}-*eso-allo*-Pregnen-3-ol-20-one (450 mg.)	*69*
$(C_2H_3O_2)_x$-R			
3,4-$(CH_3CO_2)_2C_6H_3CON(C_2H_5)_2$	C_2H_5MgBr	$CH_3(C_2H_5)_2COH$	*90*

* 7-Acetoxybenz[*k*]acephenanthrylene.

† 7-Benz[*k*]acephenanthrylenol.

TABLE VIII-III (Continued)

Ester	RMgX	Product(s)	Ref.
$(C_2H_3O_2)_x$-R (*cont.*)			
Triacetyl-L-arabonic acid lactone	C_6H_5MgBr (11 equiv.)	1,1-Diphenyl-L-arabitol* (15–16%); $CH_3(C_6H_5)_2COH$	*316*
Triacetyl-L-arabonic acid lactone (4.5 parts)	$C_6H_5CH_2MgCl$ (25.3 parts C_7H_7Cl)	1,1-Dibenzyl-L-arabitol† (*ca.* 15%); $CH_3(C_6H_5CH_2)_2COH$	*316* *316*
Triacetyl-L-arabonic acid lactone	4-$CH_3C_6H_4MgBr$ (11 equiv.)	1,1-Di-*p*-tolyl-L-arabitol‡ (15%); $CH_3(4\text{-}CH_3C_6H_4)_2COH$	*316*
Triacetyl-D-xylosyl chloride	C_6H_5MgX (*ca.* 10 equiv.)	$CH_3(C_6H_5)_2COH$ (100%, crude); after reacetylation, triacetyl-D-xylopyranosylbenzene (86.6%, crude—25.0% α, 75.0% β)	*169*
Triacetyl-D-xylosyl chloride	4-$CH_3C_6H_4MgX$ (*ca.* 10 equiv.)	$CH_3(4\text{-}CH_3C_6H_4)_2COH$ (100%, crude); after re-acetylation, *p*-(triacetyl-D-xylopyranosyl)toluene. (82.3%, crude—14.0% α, 86.0% β)	*169*
3,4,5-$(CH_3CO_2)_3C_6H_2CON(C_2H_5)_2$	C_2H_5MgBr	$CH_3(C_2H_5)_2COH$	*90*
Tetraäcetyl-D-glucuronic acid γ-lactone	C_6H_5MgBr (12 equiv.)	1,1-Diphenyl-D-sorbitol § (10–12%); $CH_3(C_6H_5)_2COH$	*315*
Tetraäcetyl-D-glucuronic acid γ-lactone	C_6H_5MgBr (13 equiv.)	1,1-Diphenyl-D-sorbitol§ (25%); $CH_3(C_6H_5)_2COH$	*479*
Tetraäcetyl-D-glucuronic acid lactone (5.5 g.)	$C_6H_5CH_2MgCl$ (30 g. C_7H_7Cl)	1,1-Dibenzyl-D-sorbitol;¶ $CH_3(C_6H_5CH_2)_2COH$	*314*
Tetraäcetyl-D-glucuronic acid lactone	4-$CH_3C_6H_4MgBr$ (13 equiv.)	1,1-Di-*p*-tolyl-D-sorbitol;‖ $CH_3(4\text{-}CH_3C_6H_4)_2COH$	*314*

* $HO(C_6H_5)_2C[CH(OH)]_3CH_2OH$.
† $HO(C_6H_5CH_2)_2C[CH(OH)]_3CH_2OH$.
‡ $HO(4\text{-}CH_3C_6H_4)_2C[CH(OH)]_3CH_2OH$.
§ $HO(C_6H_5)_2C[CH(OH)]_4CH_2OH$.
¶ $HO(C_6H_5CH_2)_2C[CH(OH)]_4CH_2OH$.
‖ $HO(4\text{-}CH_3C_6H_4)_2C[CH(OH)]_4CH_2OH$.

TABLE VIII-III (Continued)

Ester	RMgX	Product(s)	Ref.
$(C_2H_3O_2)_x$-R (*cont.*)			
Tetraäcetyl-D-galactonic acid lactone	C_6H_5MgBr (14 equiv.)	1,1-Diphenyldulcitol* (30%); $CH_3(C_6H_5)_2COH$	*480,314*
Tetraäcetyl-D-galactonic acid lactone	$4\text{-}CH_3C_6H_4MgBr$ (14 equiv.)	1,1-Di-*p*-tolyldulcitol†; $CH_3(n\text{-}CH_3C_6H_4)_2COH$	*314*
Tetraäcetyl-α-D-glucosyl chloride	$i\text{-}C_3H_7MgX$ (*ca.* 12 equiv.)	$CH_3(i\text{-}C_3H_7)_2COH$ (50.8%, crude); unidentified syrup mixture	*169*
Tetraäcetyl-α-D-glucosyl chloride	$n\text{-}C_4H_9MgX$ (*ca.* 12 equiv.)	$CH_3(n\text{-}C_4H_9)_2COH$ (95.6%, crude); after reacetylation, 1-(tetraäcetyl-D-glucopyranosyl)butane (59.4%, crude)	*169*
Tetraäcetyl-α-D-glucosyl chloride (0.0136 mole)	C_6H_5MgBr (0.165 mole C_6H_5Br)	$CH_3(C_6H_5)_2COH$ (100%, crude); after reacetylation, tetraäcetyl-D-glucopyranosylbenzene (82%, crude—28.4% α, 71.6% β)	*169*
Tetraäcetyl-α-D-glucosyl chloride	$C_6H_5CH_2MgX$ (*ca.* 12 equiv.)	$CH_3(C_6H_5CH_2)_2COH$ (100%, crude); unidentified syrup mixture	*169*
Tetraäcetyl-α-D-glucosyl chloride	$4\text{-}CH_3C_6H_4MgBr$ (*ca.* 12 equiv.)	$CH_3(4\text{-}CH_3C_6H_4)_2COH$ (98.5%, crude); after reacetylation, *p*-(tetraäcetyl-D-glucopyranosyl)toluene (75.0%, crude—26.6% α, 73.4% β)	*169*
Tetraäcetyl-α-D-glucosyl chloride	$1\text{-}C_{10}H_7MgX$ (*ca.* 12 equiv.)	$CH_3(1\text{-}C_{10}H_7)_2COH$ (66%, crude); after reacetylation, 1-(tetraäcetyl-D-glucopyranosyl)naphthalene (65.0%, crude—33.3% α, 66.7% β)	*169*
Tetraäcetylglucose	CH_3MgI (2 equiv.)	$C_{14}H_{20}O_{10}\cdot 2CH_3MgI$ (regenerating tetraäcetylglucose upon hydrolysis)	*108*
Tetraäcetylfructose	C_2H_5MgI	$C_{14}H_{20}O_{10}\cdot 2C_2H_5MgI$ (regenerating tetraäcetylfructose upon hydrolysis)	*116*
Tetraäcetyl-α-methyl-glucoside	CH_3MgI (2 equiv.)	$C_{15}H_{21}O_9\cdot 2CH_3MgI$	*108*
Pentaäcetyl-α-D-glucose	C_6H_5MgX (*ca.* 14 equiv.)	$CH_3(C_6H_5)_2COH$ (97.8%, crude); unidentified syrup mixture	*169*

* $HO(C_6H_5)_2C[CH(OH)]_4CH_2OH$.
† $HO(4\text{-}CH_3C_6H_4)_2C[CH(OH)]_4CH_2OH$.

TABLE VIII-III (Continued)

Ester	RMgX	Product(s)	Ref.
$(C_2H_3O_2)_x$-R (*cont.*)			
Pentaäcetyl-α-D-glucose	C_6H_5MgX (*ca.* 14 equiv.)	$CH_3(C_6H_5)_2COH$ (89.3%, crude); unidentified syrup mixture	*169*
Octaäcetyllactose (2 g.)	CH_3MgI (from 8 g. CH_3I)	$C_{28}H_{38}O_{19}\cdot 2CH_3MgI$ (regenerating octaäcetyllactose upon hydrolysis)	*116*
$C_2H_3O_3$-R			
$HOCH_2CO_2C_2H_5$ (10 g.)	C_6H_5MgBr (53 g. C_6H_5Br)	1,1-Diphenylepoxyethane (9 g., crude)	*319*
$HOCH_2CO_2C_2H_5$	C_6H_5MgBr (3 equiv.)	$(C_6H_5)_2C(OH)CH_2OH$	*200*
$HOCH_2CO_2C_2H_5$ (52 g.)	$C_6H_5CH_2MgCl$ (260 g. C_7H_7Cl)	$(C_6H_5CH_2)_2C(OH)CH_2OH$ (70 g.)	*420*
$C_2H_4O_2N$-R			
$H_2NCH_2CO_2C_2H_5$	C_2H_5MgBr	$H_2NCH_2C(C_2H_5)_2OH$ (isolated as benzoyl deriv., 62%)	*416*
$H_2NCH_2CO_2C_2H_5$ (from 10 g. hydrochloride)	C_6H_5MgBr (41 g. C_6H_5Br)	$H_2NCH_2C(C_6H_5)_2OH$ (6 g.); $(C_6H_5—)_2$	*317*
$H_2NCH_2CO_2C_2H_5$	C_6H_5MgBr	$H_2NCH_2C(C_6H_5)_2OH$ (60%)	*416*
$C_2H_5O_2ClN$-R			
$HCl\cdot H_2NCH_2CO_2C_2H_5$	CH_3MgI	$H_2NCH_2C(CH_3)_2OH$	*190*
$HCl\cdot H_2NCH_2CO_2C_2H_5$	C_2H_5MgBr	$H_2NCH_2C(C_2H_5)_2OH$ (24%)	*416,190*
$HCl\cdot H_2NCH_2CO_2C_2H_5$ (23.3 g., 0.167 mole)	n-C_3H_7MgCl (68.7 g., 0.668 mole)	$HCl\cdot H_2NCH_2C(n\text{-}C_3H_7)_2OH$ (15.8 g., 52.1%); gas (12.6 l.)*	*134*
$HCl\cdot H_2NCH_2CO_2C_2H_5$ (23.3 g., 0.167 mole)	n-C_3H_7MgCl (68.7 g., 0.668 mole)	$HCl\cdot H_2NCH_2C(n\text{-}C_3H_7)_2OH$ (8.3 g., 27.3%); gas (10.0 l.)†	*134*

* Gradual (three hours) addition of ester to Grignard reagent solution; half-hour stirring; 1.0 hour reflux.

† Gradual (1.5 hour) addition of ester to Grignard reagent solution at –10 to –5°; 3.0 hours at –10°; warming to 30°.

TABLE VIII-III (Continued)

Ester	RMgX	Product(s)	Ref.
$C_2H_5O_2ClN$-R (*cont.*)			
$HCl\cdot H_2NCH_2CO_2C_2H_5$ (23.3 g., 0.167 mole)	n-C_3H_7MgCl (137.3 g., 1.33 mole)	$HCl\cdot H_2NCH_2C(n\text{-}C_3H_7)_2OH$ (22.8 g., 75.2%); gas 12.6 l., including 12.73 g. C_3H_8)*	*134*
$HCl\cdot H_2NCH_2CO_2C_2H_5$ 23.3 g., 0.167 mole)	n-C_3H_7MgCl (137.3 g., 1.33 mole)	$HCl\cdot H_2NCH_2C(n\text{-}C_3H_7)_2OH$; $HCl\cdot H_2NCH_2CO\text{-}n\text{-}C_3H_7$; gas (18.9 l., including 19.78 g. C_3H_8)†	*134*
$HCl\cdot H_2NCH_2CO_2C_2H_5$	n-C_3H_7MgI	$H_2NCH_2C(n\text{-}C_3H_7)_2OH$	*190*
$HCl\cdot H_2NCH_2CO_2C_2H_5$	n-C_4H_9MgI	$H_2NCH_2C(n\text{-}C_4H_9)_2OH$	*190*
$HCl\cdot H_2NCH_2CO_2C_2H_5$ (23.3 g., 0.167 mole)	t-C_4H_9MgCl (1.56 g., 1.33 mole)	Recovered ester (17.04 g.); gas (23.1 l., including 31.06 g. i-C_4H_{10})	*134*
$HCl\cdot H_2NCH_2CO_2C_2H_5$	i-$C_5H_{11}MgI$	$H_2NCH_2C(i\text{-}C_5H_{11})_2OH$	*190*
$HCl\cdot H_2NCH_2CO_2C_2H_5$	C_6H_5MgBr	$H_2NCH_2C(C_6H_5)_2OH$ (68%)	*416,190*
$HCl\cdot H_2NCH_2CO_2C_2H_5$	$C_6H_5CH_2MgBr$	$H_2NCH_2C(CH_2C_6H_5)_2OH$ (49.2%)	*416,190*
$C_3O_2F_5$-R			
$C_2F_5CO_2CH_3$ (0.2–0.3 mole)	C_2H_5MgI (0.8–1.2 mole)	$C_2F_5(C_2H_5)_2COH$ (29.0%); $C_2F_5(C_2H_5)CHOH$ (66.0%)	*515*
$C_3O_4Cl_2$-R_2			
$Cl_2C(CO_2C_2H_5)_2$	CH_3MgBr	A chlorine-containing product b. 215–216°	*237*
C_3O_5-R_2			
$OC(CO_2C_2H_5)_2$	CH_3MgBr (5 equiv.)	$OC[C(CH_3)_2OH]_2$‡	*237*
$OC(CO_2C_2H_5)_2$	C_2H_5MgBr	$H_5C_2O_2CCOC(C_2H_5)_2OH$;§ $C_6H_{11}O$, b. 140–150°; $C_7H_{10}O_3$, b. 190–200°	*237*

* Gradual (one and one-quarter hour) addition of Et_2O-ester suspension to stirred Grignard reagent solution; four hours stirring; one hour reflux.

† Gradual (one hour) addition of Et_2O-ester suspension to stirred Grignard reagent suspension; one and one-quarter hour stirring; two and one-half hours reflux.

‡ According to Lapkin and Golovkova (*481*), this product is probably $HO(CH_3)(CH_3CO)CC(CH_3)_2OH$.

§ According to Lapkin and Golovkova (*481*), this product is probably $HO(C_2H_5)(C_2H_5CO)CCO_2C_2H_5$.

TABLE VIII-III (Continued)

Ester	RMgX	Product(s)	Ref.
C_3HO_4Cl-R_2			
$HClC(CO_2C_2H_5)_2$	CH_3MgBr	Gas evolution; ester recovered on hydrolysis	237
C_3HO_4Na-R_2			
$NaHC(CO_2C_2H_5)_2$	4-$(CH_2)_4CHC_6H_4CH_2CH_2$-MgBr	4-$(CH_2)_4CHC_6H_4(CH_2)_3CO_2H$	73
$C_3H_2O_4$-R_2			
$H_2C(CO_2CH_3)_2$ (20 g.)	C_6H_5MgBr (70 g. C_6H_5Br)	$C_6H_5COCH_2C(C_6H_5)_2OH$ (15 g., crude)	*444*
$H_2C(CO_2C_2H_5)_2$ (16 g.)	CH_3MgI (36 g. CH_3I)	Most of ester recovered (by hydrolysis of enolate)	*163*
$H_2C(CO_2C_2H_5)_2$	C_2H_5MgI	$(C_2H_5)_2C{=}CHC(C_2H_5)_2OH$	*436*
$H_2C(CO_2C_2H_5)_2$ (20 g.)	C_6H_5MgBr (79 g. C_6H_5Br)	$C_6H_5COCH_2C(C_6H_5)_2OH$ (14.9 g.)	*444*,*96*
$H_2C(CO_2C_2H_5)_2$ (0.25 mole)	2,4,6-$(CH_3)_3C_6H_2MgBr$ (0.25 mole $C_9H_{11}Br$)	Recovered ester + C_9H_{12} (nearly quant.); product(s) b. (14 mm.) 165–195° (0.4 g.)	233
$C_3H_3O_3$-R			
$CH_3COCO_2C_2H_5$ (29 g.)	2,4,6-$(CH_3)_3C_6H_2MgBr$ (50 g. $C_9H_{11}Br$)	$HO(CH_3)[2,4,6\text{-}(CH_3)_3C_6H_2]CCO_2C_2H_5$ (20%)	*481*
$CH_3COCO_2C_2H_5$ (14.5 g.)	2,4,6-$(CH_3)_3C_6H_2MgBr$ (50.0 g. $C_9H_{11}Br$)	$HO(CH_3)[2,4,6\text{-}(CH_3)_3C_6H_2]CCO_2C_2H_5$ (50%)	*481*
$C_3H_4O_2Br$-R			
$BrCH_2CH_2CO_2CH_3$ (320 g.)	CH_3MgCl (144 g. Mg)	$BrCH_2CH_2(CH_3)_2COH$ (270 g., crude)	75
$CH_3CHBrCO_2C_2H_5$	$C_6H_5CH(CO_2Na)MgCl$*	$CH_3CH(CO_2H)CH(C_6H_5)CO_2C_2H_5$ (5%)	*405*
$C_3H_4O_2Cl$-R			
$ClCH_2CH_2CO_2C_2H_5$	CH_3MgBr	$ClCH_2CH_2(CH_3)_2COH$	*160*,*324*

*In the opinion of Schlenk, Hilleman, and Rodloff, *Ann.*, *487*, 135–54 (1931), this "Grignard reagent" should be formulated as an enolate.

TABLE VIII-III (Continued)

Ester	RMgX	Product(s)	Ref.
$C_3H_4O_2Cl$-R (*cont.*)			
$ClCH_2CH_2CO_2C_2H_5$	C_2H_5MgBr (3 equiv.)	$ClCH_2CH_2(C_2H_5)_2COH$ (40%); four unidentified products	*294*
$ClCH_2CH_2CO_2C_2H_5$ (42 ml.)	C_2H_5MgBr (57.2 ml. C_2H_5Br)	$ClCH_2CH_2(C_2H_5)_2COH$ (19–25 g.)	*446,110*
$ClCH_2CH_2CO_2C_2H_5$ (41 g.)	n-C_4H_9MgBr (90 g. C_4H_9Br)	$ClCH_2CH_2(n$-$C_4H_9)_2COH$ (46 g.)	*446*
$ClCH_2CH_2CO_2C_2H_5$ (68 g.)	C_6H_5MgBr (104.6 ml. C_6H_5Br)	$(C_6H_5)_2C{=}CHCH_2Cl$; $C_6H_5COCH_2CH_2Cl$	*446*
$ClCH_2CH_2CO_2C_2H_5$ (42 ml.)	$C_6H_5CH_2MgCl$ (77 ml. C_7H_7Cl)	$ClCH_2CH_2(C_6H_5CH_2)_2COH$ (35–46 g.)	*446*
$CH_3CHClCO_2C_2H_5$	CH_3MgBr	$CH_3CHCl(CH_3)_2COH$	*160*
$CH_3CHClCO_2C_2H_5$ (40 g.)	C_2H_5MgBr (from 68 g. bromide)	$CH_3CHCl(C_2H_5)_2COH$ (37%, purified); unidentified products	*294*
$C_3H_4O_2I$-R			
$ICH_2CH_2CO_2C_2H_5$	C_2H_5MgBr (3 equiv.)	$ICH_2CH_2(C_2H_5)_2COH$	*91*
$C_3H_5O_2$-R			
$C_2H_5CO_2CH_3$	n-C_4H_9MgBr	$C_2H_5(n$-$C_4H_9)_2COH$ (35%)	*462*
$C_2H_5CO_2C_2H_5$ (200 g., *ca.* 2 moles)	C_2H_5MgBr (763 g., 7 moles C_2H_5Br)	$(C_2H_5)_3COH$ (765 g.)	*59*
$C_2H_5CO_2C_2H_5$	C_2H_5MgBr (4 moles)	$(C_2H_5)_3COH$ (83%)	*101,379*
$C_2H_5CO_2C_2H_5$	$H_2C{=}CHCH_2MgBr$	$C_2H_5(H_2C{=}CHCH_2)_2COH$ (66%)	*162*
$C_2H_5CO_2C_2H_5$	n-C_3H_7MgBr	$C_2H_5(n$-$C_3H_7)_2COH$ (58%)	*80,149*
$C_2H_5CO_2C_2H_5$	i-C_3H_7MgCl (2.75 equiv.)	C_2H_5CO-i-C_3H_7 (48%); C_3H_8; unidentified product(s)	*184*
$C_2H_5CO_2C_2H_5$	Pyrryl-MgBr	2-Propionylpyrrole (50–60%)	*427*
$C_2H_5CO_2C_2H_5$	n-C_4H_9MgCl	$C_2H_5(n$-$C_4H_9)_2COH$ (75%)	*503*
$C_2H_5CO_2C_2H_5$	n-C_4H_9MgBr	$C_2H_5(n$-$C_4H_9)_2COH$ (73%)	*80*

TABLE VIII-III (Continued)

Ester	RMgX	Product(s)	Ref.
$C_3H_5O_2$-R (*cont.*)			
$C_2H_5CO_2C_2H_5$	s-C_4H_9MgBr	$(C_2H_5)_2CO$; C_2H_5CO-s-C_4H_9	*327*
$C_2H_5CO_2C_2H_5$	t-C_4H_9MgCl	$(C_2H_5)_2CO$; C_2H_5CO-t-C_4H_9*	*327*
$C_2H_5CO_2C_2H_5$ (102 g., 1.0 mole)	t-C_4H_9MgCl (1.7 mole)	$C_2H_5(n\text{-}C_4H_9)CHOH$ (23 g., 20%); $C_2H_5COCH(CH_3)CO_2C_2H_5$ (39 g., 50%)†	*476*
$C_2H_5CO_2C_2H_5$	t-C_4H_9MgCl	$C_2H_5CO_2CH(C_2H_5)$-t-C_4H_9 (44.7%); $(C_2H_5)_2CO$ (trace); $(C_2H_5)_2C{=}C(CH_3)COC_2H_5$ (trace)‡	*194*
$C_2H_5CO_2C_2H_5$	n-$C_5H_{11}MgBr$	$C_2H_5(n\text{-}C_5H_{11})_2COH$ (40%)	*461*
$C_2H_5CO_2C_2H_5$	i-$C_5H_{11}MgBr$	$C_2H_5(i\text{-}C_5H_{11})_2COH$ ("good yield")	*149*
$C_2H_5CO_2C_2H_5$	C_6H_5MgBr	$C_2H_5(C_6H_5)_2COH$	*260*
$C_2H_5CO_2C_2H_5$	$(CH_2)_5CHMgCl$	$C_2H_5COCH(CH_2)_5$; $C_2H_5CH(OH)CH(CH_2)_5$; C_6H_{12}; C_6H_{10}	*433*
$C_2H_5CO_2C_2H_5$	$C_6H_5CH_2Cl$ + Mg	$C_2H_5(C_6H_5CH_2)_2COH$ ("good yield")	*94*
$C_2H_5CO_2C_2H_5$ (2 ml.)	4-$CH_3SC_6H_4MgBr$ (10 g. C_7H_7BrS)	$(4\text{-}CH_3SC_6H_4)_2C{=}CHCH_3$ (4 g.)	*412*
$C_2H_5CO_2C_2H_5$ (15 g.)	n-$C_8H_{17}MgBr$ (48 g. $C_8H_{17}Br$)	$C_2H_5(n\text{-}C_8H_{17})_2COH$ (10 g.)	*47*
$C_2H_5CO_2C_2H_5$	4-$C_6H_5OC_6H_4MgBr$	$(4\text{-}C_6H_5OC_6H_4)_2C{=}CHCH_3$	*412*
$C_2H_5CO_2$-n-C_3H_7	C_2H_5MgBr	$(C_2H_5)_3COH$	*456*
$C_3H_5O_3$-R			
$CH_3OCH_2CO_2C_2H_5$	CH_3MgI	$CH_3OCH_2(CH_3)_2COH$	*322*
$CH_3CH(OH)CO_2C_2H_5$	C_2H_5MgBr	$CH_3CH(OH)C(C_2H_5)_2OH$	*419*
$CH_3CH(OH)CO_2C_2H_5$ (30 g.)	C_6H_5MgBr (80 g. C_6H_5Br)	$CH_3CH(OH)C(C_6H_5)_2OH$ (22g.)	*390,408*
$CH_3CH(OH)CO_2C_2H_5$	2-$CH_3C_6H_4MgBr$	$CH_3COCH(C_6H_4\text{-}2\text{-}CH_3)_2$	*408*

* Reaction in ether "under usual conditions" or at high temperature in toluene.

† Addition of Grignard reagent solution to cooled, stirred Et_2O-ester solution; five days at room temperature.

‡ Reaction at 95–98° [presumably in high-boiling solvent—see Petrov, Karasev, and Cheltzova (*326*)].

TABLE VIII-III (Continued)

Ester	RMgX	Product(s)	Ref.
$C_3H_5O_3$-R (*cont.*)			
$CH_3CH(OH)CO_2C_2H_5$	4-$CH_3C_6H_4MgBr$	$CH_3CH(OH)C(C_6H_4$-4-$CH_3)_2OH$	*408*
$C_3H_6O_2N$-R			
$CH_3CH(NH_2)CO_2C_2H_5$	C_2H_5MgBr	$CH_3CH(NH_2)C(C_2H_5)_2OH$ (isolated as benzoyl deriv., 52%)	*416*
$CH_3CH(NH_2)CO_2C_2H_5$	C_6H_5MgBr	$CH_3CH(NH_2)C(C_6H_5)_2OH$ (59%)	*416*
$C_3H_7O_2ClN$-R			
$CH_3CH(NH_2 \cdot HCl)CO_2C_2H_5$	CH_3MgI (6 equiv.)	$CH_3CH(NH_2 \cdot HCl)C(CH_3)_2OH$ (60–66%)	*30*
L(+)-$CH_3CH(NHNA_2 \cdot HCl)CO_2C_2H_5$ (10.3 g.)	CH_3MgI (57 g. CH_3I)	(+)-$CH_3CH(NH_2 \cdot HCl)C(CH_3)_2OH$	*30*
$CH_3CH(NH_2 \cdot HCl)CO_2C_2H_5$	C_2H_5MgBr	$CH_3CH(NH_2)C(C_2H_5)_2OH$ (55%)	*416*
$CH_3CH(NH_2 \cdot HCl)CO_2C_2H_5$	C_6H_5MgBr	$CH_3CH(NH_2)C(C_6H_5)_2OH$ (67%)	*416*
$CH_3CH(NH_2 \cdot HCl)CO_2C_2H_5$ (20 g.)	C_6H_5MgBr (245 g. C_6H_5Br)	$CH_3CH(NH_2)C(C_6H_5)_2OH$ (20 g., crude)	*275*
D-$CH_3CH(NH_2 \cdot HCl)CO_2C_2H_5$ (15 g.)	C_6H_5MgBr (150 g. C_6H_5Br)	D-$CH_3CH(NH_2)C(C_6H_5)_2OH$ (11 g.)	*274*
$CH_3CH(NH_2 \cdot HCl)CO_2C_2H_5$	$C_6H_5CH_2MgCl$ (9 equiv.)	$CH_3CH(NH_2)C(CH_2C_6H_5)_2OH$	*274*
$CH_3CH(NH_2 \cdot HCl)CO_2C_2H_5$ (5 g.)	4-$CH_3C_6H_4MgBr$ (50 g. C_7H_7Br)	$CH_3CH(NH_2)C(C_6H_4$-4-$CH_3)_2$ (3 g.)	*272*
D-$CH_3CH(NH_2 \cdot HCl)CO_2C_2H_5$ (5 g.)	4-$CH_3C_6H_4MgBr$ (50 g. C_7H_7Br)	$CH_3CH(NH_2)C(C_6H_4$-4-$CH_3)_2$ (5.5 g.)	*272*
$C_4O_2F_7$-R			
n-$C_3F_7CO_2CH_3$ (0.2–0.3 mole)	C_2H_5MgI (0.8–1.2 mole)	*n*-$C_3F_7(C_2H_5)_2COH$ (12.5%); C_2H_5(*n*-C_3F_7)CHOH (68.6%)	*515*
$C_4H_2O_4$-R_2			
$(=CHCO_2CH_3)_2$	C_2H_5MgBr (8 equiv.)	$C_2H_5COCH_2CH(C_2H_5)COC_2H_5$	*447*

TABLE VIII-III (Continued)

Ester	RMgX	Product(s)	Ref.
$C_4H_2O_4$-R_2 (*cont.*)			
$(=CHCO_2CH_3)_2$ (14.4 g.)	*n*-C_4H_9MgBr (8 equiv.)	*n*-$C_4H_9COCH_2CH(n\text{-}C_4H_9)CO\text{-}n\text{-}C_4H_9$ (9 g.); $HO(n\text{-}C_4H_9)_2CCH=CHCO\text{-}n\text{-}C_4H_9$	*447*
$(=CHCO_2CH_3)_2$ (10 g.)	C_6H_5MgBr (44 g. C_6H_5Br)	2,2,5,5-Tetraphenyl-2,5-dihydrofuran; unidentified product(s)	*346*
$(=CHCO_2CH_3)_2$ (7.25 g.)	$C_6H_5CH_2MgCl$ (8 equiv.)	$C_6H_5CH_2COCH_2CH(CH_2C_6H_5)COCH_2C_6H_5$ (2.0 g.)	*447*
$C_4H_2O_5$-R_2			
$HOCH=C(CO_2C_2H_5)_2$	C_2H_5MgBr	$C_2H_5CH=C(CO_2C_2H_5)_2$	*356*
$HOCH=C(CO_2C_2H_5)_2$	C_6H_5MgBr (excess)	$C_6H_5CH=C(CO_2C_2H_5)_2$	*356*
$C_4H_4O_3Cl_3$-R			
DL-$Cl_3CCH(OH)CH_2CO_2C_2H_5$ * (10 g.)	C_6H_5MgBr (40 g. C_6H_5Br)	DL-$Cl_3CCH(OH)CH_2C(C_6H_5)_2OH$ (9 g.)	*64*
$C_4H_4O_4$-R_2			
$(—CH_2CO_2C_2H_5)_2$	CH_3MgBr	$[—CH_2C(CH_3)_2OH]_2$	*67*
$(—CH_2CO_2C_2H_5)_2$ (44 g.)	CH_3MgI (142 g. CH_3I)	$[—CH_2C(CH_3)_2OH]_2$ (*ca.* 45%)	*151,152,342, 436*
$(—CH_2CO_2C_2H_5)_2$ (87 g.)	CH_3I (177 g.) + Mg (30 g.)†	γ-Hydroxy-γ-methylvaleric acid γ-lactone (57 g., 50%)	*163*
$(—CH_2CO_2C_2H_5)_2$ (87 g.)	C_2H_5Br (136 g.) + Mg (30 g.)†	Recovered ester; γ-hydroxy-γ-ethylcaproic acid γ-lactone (33 g., 46%)	*163*
$(—CH_2CO_2C_2H_5)_2$ (40 g.)	*n*-C_4H_9MgBr (137 g. C_4H_9Br)	$[—CH_2C(n\text{-}C_4H_9)_2OH]_2$ (45 g.)	*337*

* Similarly treated, the methyl ester of the levo acid yielded no crystalline product.

† Alternate additions of Et_2O-halide-ester solution and Mg to reacting Mg (10 g.) and halide (10 g.); one hour stirring; overnight

TABLE VIII-III (Continued)

Ester	RMgX	Product(s)	Ref.
$C_4H_4O_4$-R_2 *(cont.)*			
$(\text{—}CH_2CO_2C_2H_5)_2$	C_6H_5MgBr	$[\text{—}CH_2C(C_6H_5)_2OH]_2$ (*ca.* quant.)*	*96,2,437*
$(\text{—}CH_2CO_2C_2H_5)_2$	C_6H_5MgBr	2,2,5,5-Tetraphenyltetrahydrofuran†	*2*
$(\text{—}CH_2CO_2C_2H_5)_2$	2,4,6-$(CH_3)_3C_6H_2MgBr$	Recovered ester + $(CH_3)_3C_6H_3$ (nearly quant.)	*233*
$C_4H_4O_5$-R_2			
(−)-$H_3CO_2CCH_2CH(OH)CO_2CH_3$	C_6H_5MgBr	No identifiable product	*64*
$C_4H_4O_6$-R_2			
D-$[\text{—}CH(OH)CO_2CH_3]_2$ (20 g.)	C_6H_5MgBr (160 g. C_6H_5Br)	D-$[\text{—}CH(OH)C(C_6H_5)_2OH]_2$	*113*
$C_4H_5O_2$-R			
$(CH_2)_2CHCO_2C_2H_5$	CH_3MgBr	$(CH_2)_2CH(CH_3)_2COH$	*66*
$(CH_2)_2CHCO_2C_2H_5$	C_2H_5MgBr	$(CH_2)_2CH(C_2H_5)_2COH$	*66*
$CH_3CH{=}CHCO_2C_2H_5$	CH_3MgBr	$CH_3CH{=}CH(CH_3)_2COH$ (*ca.* 50%); *i*-$C_4H_9CO_2C_2H_5$ (?)	*439*
$CH_3CH{=}CHCO_2C_2H_5$	CH_3MgBr	$CH_3CH{=}CH(CH_3)_2COH$ (36%)	*19*
$H_2C{=}C(CH_3)CO_2C_2H_5$	CH_3MgI (2 equiv.)	$H_2C{=}C(CH_3)C(CH_3)_2OH$; $CH_3CH_2CH(CH_3)COCH_3$	*49,89*
$H_2C{=}C(CH_3)CO_2C_2H_5$	CH_3MgI (2 equiv.)	$H_2C{=}C(CH_3)C(CH_3)_2OH$; $[H_2C{=}C(CH_3)\text{—}]_2$	*49,89*
$H_2C{=}C(CH_3)CO_2C_2H_5$	C_2H_5MgI (2 equiv.)	$H_2C{=}C(CH_3)C(C_2H_5)_2OH$	*49,89*
$C_4H_5O_4N$-R_2			
L-$H_2NCH(CO_2C_2H_5)CH_2CO_2C_2H_5$	CH_3MgI	$HO(CH_3)_2CCH(NH_2)CH_2C(CH_3)_2OH$	*188,189*
L-$H_2NCH(CO_2C_2H_5)CH_2CO_2C_2H_5$	C_2H_5MgBr	$HO(C_2H_5)_2CCH(NH_2)CH_2C(C_2H_5)_2OH$	*188*
L-$H_2NCH(CO_2C_2H_5)CH_2CO_2C_2H_5$	*n*-C_3H_7MgI	$HO(n\text{-}C_3H_7)_2CCH(NH_2)CH_2C(n\text{-}C_3H_7)_2OH$	*188*

* Dropwise addition of Et_2O-ester solution to Grignard reagent solution; standing at room temperature.

† Addition of ester to boiling Grignard reagent solution.

TABLE VIII-III (Continued)

Ester	RMgX	Product(s)	Ref.
$C_4H_5O_4N$-R_2 (*cont.*)			
L-$H_2NCH(CO_2C_2H_5)CH_2CO_2C_2H_5$	n-C_4H_9MgI	$HO(n$-$C_4H_9)_2CCH(NH_2)CH_2C(n$-$C_4H_9)_2OH$	*188*
L-$H_2NCH(CO_2C_2H_5)CH_2CO_2C_2H_5$	C_6H_5MgBr	$HO(C_6H_5)_2CCH(NH_2)CH_2C(C_6H_5)_2OH$	*188,189*
$H_2NCH(CO_2C_2H_5)CH_2CO_2C_2H_5$ (10 g.)	C_6H_5MgBr (50 g. C_6H_5Br)	$HO(C_6H_5)_2CCH(NH_2)CH_2C(C_6H_5)_2OH$ (60–70%)	*320*
$C_4H_6O_2Cl$-R			
$Cl(CH_2)_3CO_2CH_3$ (200 g.)	CH_3MgCl (4 moles)	$Cl(CH_2)_3(CH_3)_2COH$ (200 g., crude)	*75*
$Cl(CH_2)_3CO_2C_2H_5$	CH_3MgBr	$Cl(CH_2)_3(CH_3)_2COH$	*158,160,324*
$Cl(CH_3)_2CCO_2C_2H_5$	CH_3MgBr	t-$C_4H_9C(CH_3)_2OH$	*157*
$C_4H_7O_2$-R			
n-$C_3H_7CO_2CH_3$	n-C_4H_9MgBr	n-$C_3H_7(n$-$C_4H_9)_2COH$ (70%)	*462*
n-$C_3H_7CO_2CH_3$	C_6H_5MgBr	n-$C_3H_7(C_6H_5)_2COH$ (yielding 80–90% olefin)	*377*
n-$C_3H_7CO_2C_2H_5$	CH_3MgX (2 equiv.)	n-$C_3H_7(CH_3)_2COH$ (80–85%); corresponding olefin (*ca.* 1%)	*259,252,467*
n-$C_3H_7CO_2C_2H_5$	C_2H_5MgBr	n-$C_3H_7(C_2H_5)_2COH$ (61%)	*80,149*
n-$C_3H_7CO_2C_2H_5$	C_2H_5MgX (2 equiv.)	n-$C_3H_7(C_2H_5)_2COH$ (80–85%); corresponding olefin (*ca.* 1%)	*259*
n-$C_3H_7CO_2C_2H_5$	n-C_3H_7MgCl	$(n$-$C_3H_7)_3COH$ (69%); $(n$-$C_3H_7)_2CO$ (6%)	*194*
n-$C_3H_7CO_2C_2H_5$	n-C_3H_7MgBr	$(n$-$C_3H_7)_3COH$ ("good yield")	*149*
n-$C_3H_7CO_2C_2H_5$	Pyrryl-MgBr	2-Butyrylpyrrole (50–60%)	*427*
n-$C_3H_7CO_2C_2H_5$	n-C_4H_9MgBr	n-$C_3H_7(n$-$C_4H_9)_2COH$ (73%)	*80*
n-$C_3H_7CO_2C_2H_5$	s-C_4H_9MgBr	$(n$-$C_3H_7)_2CO$; n-C_3H_7CO-s-C_4H_9	*327*
n-$C_3H_7CO_2C_2H_5$	t-C_4H_9MgCl	$(n$-$C_3H_7)_2CO$; n-C_3H_7CO-t-C_4H_9; unidentified product(s)	*335,327*
n-$C_3H_7CO_2C_2H_5$	n-$C_5H_{11}MgBr$	n-$C_3H_7(n$-$C_5H_{11})_2COH$ (58%)	*461*
n-$C_3H_7CO_2C_2H_5$	i-$C_5H_{11}MgBr$	n-$C_3H_7(i$-$C_5H_{11})_2COH$ ("good yield")	*149*

TABLE VIII-III (Continued)

Ester	RMgX	Product(s)	Ref.
$C_4H_7O_2$-R (*cont.*)			
n-$C_3H_7CO_2C_2H_5$	C_6H_5MgBr	n-$C_3H_7(C_6H_5)_2COH$ (60%)	*266,260*
n-$C_3H_7CO_2C_2H_5$	$C_6H_5CH_2MgCl$	n-$C_3H_7(C_6H_5CH_2)_2COH$ (yielding 61.1% olefin)	*341*
i-$C_3H_7CO_2C_2H_5$	i-C_3H_7MgBr	$(i$-$C_3H_7)_2CHOH$; C_3H_6	*404*
i-$C_3H_7CO_2C_2H_5$ (22 g., 0.19 mole)	2,4,6-$(CH_3)_3C_6H_4MgBr$ (0.19 mole)	i-$C_3H_7CO(CH_3)_2CCO_2C_2H_5$ (4.7 g., 26.5%)	*396*
i-$C_3H_7CO_2$-t-C_4H_9	i-C_3H_7MgBr	Recovered ester (45%); no gas evolution	*384*
$C_4H_7O_3$-R			
$C_2H_5OCH_2CO_2C_2H_5$	RMgX*	$C_2H_5OCH_2CH_2OH$ (*ca.* 60%)	*31*
$C_2H_5OCH_2CO_2$-n-C_3H_7	$H_2C{=}CHCH_2MgBr$	$C_2H_5OCH_2(H_2C{=}CHCH_2)_2COH$ (90%)	*162*
$HO(CH_3)_2CCO_2CH_3$ (140 g.)	C_2H_5MgBr (500 g. C_2H_5Br)	$HO(CH_3)_2CC(C_2H_5)_2OH$ (72%)	*280*
$HO(CH_3)_2CCO_2CH_3$	n-C_3H_7MgBr (4 equiv.)	$HO(CH_3)_2CC(n$-$C_3H_7)_2OH$; $HO(CH_3)_2CCH(n$-$C_3H_7)OH$; C_3H_6	*280*
$HO(CH_3)_2CCO_2CH_3$ (59 g.)	n-C_4H_9MgBr (274 g. C_4H_9Br)	$HO(CH_3)_2CC(n$-$C_4H_9)_2OH$ (56%); $HO(CH_3)_2CCH(n$-$C_4H_9)OH$ (total yield glycols, *ca.* 80 g.); C_4H_8	*280*
$HO(CH_3)_2CCO_2CH_3$	C_6H_5MgBr (4 equiv.)	$HO(CH_3)_2CC(C_6H_5)_2OH$ (91%)	*280*
$HO(CH_3)_2CCO_2C_2H_5$	n-C_4H_9MgBr (4 equiv.)	$HO(CH_3)_2CC(n$-$C_4H_9)_2OH$ (45%); $HO(CH_3)_2CCH(n$-$C_4H_9)OH$; n-C_4H_9OH; recovered ester	*281*
$HO(CH_3)_2CCO_2C_2H_5$	n-$C_5H_{11}MgBr$	$HO(CH_3)_2CC(n$-$C_5H_{11})_2OH$; "a hydrocarbon" (chief product)	*47*
$HO(CH_3)_2CCO_2C_2H_5$ (14 g.)	n-$C_7H_{15}MgBr$	$C_{18}H_{34}$ (22 g.)	*47*
$HO(CH_3)_2CCO_2C_2H_5$ (13.2 g.)	n-$C_{12}H_{25}MgBr$	n-$C_{12}H_{26}$ (10 g.); $C_{28}H_{54}$ (21 g.)	*47*
$C_4H_7O_5$-R			
$HOCH_2[CH(OH)]_2CO_2C_2H_5$ (5 g.)	C_6H_5MgBr (4 equiv.)	$HOCH_2[CHOH]_2C(C_6H_5)_2OH$ (4.4 g., 42%)	*321*

*R = CH_3, C_2H_5, $H_2C{=}CHCH_2$, n-C_3H_7, i-C_4H_9, i-C_5H_{11}, C_6H_5.

TABLE VIII-III (Continued)

Ester	RMgX	Product(s)	Ref.
$C_4H_8O_3ClN_2$-R			
$HCl \cdot H_2NCH_2CONHCH_2CO_2C_2H_5$	C_6H_5MgBr	$H_2NCH_2CONHCH_2C(C_6H_5)_2OH$ (66%)	*417*
$C_4H_9O_2ClN$-R			
$C_2H_5CH(NH_2 \cdot HCl)CO_2C_2H_5$ (1.68 g.)	$4\text{-}CH_3OC_6H_4MgBr$ (11.22 g. C_7H_7BrO)	$C_2H_5CH(NH_2)C(C_6H_4\text{-}4\text{-}OCH_3)_2OH$ (2.15 g., 64%)	*388*
$C_5H_3O_2S$-R			
Ethyl 2-thiophenecarboxylate	2-Thienyl-MgBr	Tri-α-thienylmethanol (isolated as perchlorate)	*371*
$C_5H_3O_3$-R			
Ethyl furoate	CH_3MgI	Unstable red-colored liquid	*147*
Ethyl furoate	C_2H_5MgI	α-Furyldiethylmethanol	*147*
Ethyl furoate (8.5 g.)	C_6H_5MgBr (37.5 g. C_6H_5Br)	α-Furyldiphenylmethanol (9.2 g.)	*435,147*
Ethyl furoate	$C_6H_5CH_2MgCl$	α-Furyldibenzylmethanol	*147*
Ethyl furoate (7.0 g.)	$4\text{-}C_6H_5C_6H_4MgBr$ (23.3 g. $C_{12}H_9Br$)	α-Furyldi-*p*-biphenylylmethanol (70%)	*114*
$C_5H_4O_3N$-R			
Ethyl 5-methyl-3-isoxazolecarboxylate (60 g.)	CH_3MgI (137 g. CH_3I)	2-(5-methyl-3-isoxazolyl)-2-propanol (34 g.)	*350*
$C_5H_4O_4$-R_2			
$CH_3CH{=}C(CO_2C_2H_5)_2$ (30 g., 0.16 mole)	$1\text{-}C_{10}H_7CH_2MgCl$ (35 g., 0.21 mole $C_{11}H_9Cl$)	$CH_3(1\text{-}C_{10}H_7CH_2)CHCH(CO_2C_2H_5)_2$ (22 g., 42%)	*360*
$CH_3CH{=}C(CO_2C_2H_5)_2$ (30 g., 0.16 mole)	$1\text{-}C_{10}H_7CH_2MgCl$ (35 g., 0.21 mole $C_{11}H_9Cl$) + $CdCl_2$ (36 g., 0.20 mole)	$CH_3(1\text{-}C_{10}H_7CH_2)CHCH(CO_2C_2H_5)_2$ (60%)	*360*

TABLE VIII-III (Continued)

Ester	RMgX	Product(s)	Ref.
$C_5H_5O_2$-R			
$H_2C{=}CHCH{=}CHCO_2C_2H_5$	C_6H_5MgBr (4 equiv.)	$H_2C{=}CHCH(C_6H_5)CH_2COC_6H_5$ (75%); unidentified product(s) (25%)	*214*
$C_5H_5O_3$-R			
$C_2H_5C({=}CO)CO_2C_2H_5$ (11 g., 0.077 mole)	C_6H_5MgBr (0.2 mole)	$C_2H_5(C_6H_5CO)C{=}C(C_6H_5)_2$ (2.5 g.); $C_2H_5(C_6H_5CO)CHCO_2C_2H_5$ (5 ml.)	*170*
$C_2H_5C({=}CO)CO_2C_2H_5$ (8.5 g., 0.06 mole)	C_6H_5MgBr (0.06 mole)	$C_2H_5(C_6H_5CO)CHCO_2C_2H_5$ (6.0 g.) n-$C_3H_7COC_6H_5$ (<2.0 g.)	*170*
$C_5H_5O_3BrCl$-R			
$C_2H_5CBr(COCl)CO_2C_2H_5$ (8 g.)	C_6H_5MgBr (13 g. C_6H_5Br)	$C_2H_5(C_6H_5CO)C{=}C(C_6H_5)_2$ (0.1 g.)	*170*
$C_5H_5O_4Br$-R_2			
$C_2H_5CBr(CO_2C_2H_5)_2$	C_6H_5MgBr	$[C_2H_5(H_5C_2O_2C)_2C—]_2$; C_6H_5Br	*361*
$C_2H_5CBr(CO_2C_2H_5)_2$	$C_{10}H_{17}MgCl$*	$[C_2H_5(H_5C_2O_2C)_2C—]_2$; pinene hydrobromide	*361*
$C_2H_5CBr(CO_2C_2H_5)_2$	"Bornyl-MgCl"	$[C_2H_5(H_5C_2O_2C)_2C—]_2$; bornyl bromide	*361*
$C_5H_6O_2N$-R			
$NC(C_2H_5)CHCO_2C_2H_5$	C_2H_5MgBr	$(C_2H_5CO)_2CHC_2H_5$ (25–30%)	*261*
$NC(C_2H_5)CHCO_2C_2H_5$	C_6H_5MgBr	$(C_6H_5CO)_2CHC_2H_5$ (60%)	*261*
$C_5H_6O_4$-R_2			
$H_2C(CH_2CO_2C_2H_5)_2$ (64 g.)	CH_3MgI (270 g. CH_3I)	$H_2C[CH_2C(CH_3)_2OH]_2$ (30 g. monohydrate, 20 g. anhydr.)	*301,474*
$H_2C(CH_2CO_2C_2H_5)_2$	CH_3MgBr	$H_2C[CH_2C(CH_3)_2OH]_2$	*67*
$C_2H_5CH(CO_2C_2H_5)_2$ (19 g.)	CH_3MgI (36 g. CH_3I)	$HO(CH_3)_2CCH(C_2H_5)CO_2C_2H_5$ (5 g., crude)	*163*

* From (+)-α-pinene hydrochloride.

TABLE VIII-III (Continued)

Ester	RMgX	Product(s)	Ref.
$C_5H_6O_4$-R_2 *(cont.)*			
$(CH_3)_2C(CO_2C_2H_5)_2$	CH_3MgI	$(CH_3)_2C[C(CH_3)_2OH]$; $HO(CH_3)_2CC(CH_3)_2CO_2C_2H_5$	*387*
$(CH_3)_2C(CO_2C_2H_5)_2$ (19 g.)	CH_3MgI (36 g. CH_3I)	$HO(CH_3)_2CC(CH_3)_2CO_2C_2H_5$ (7 g., crude); recovered ester (9 g.)	*163*
$(CH_3)_2C(CO_2C_2H_5)_2$	n-C_3H_7MgCl	$(CH_3)_2C[CH(OH)$-n-$C_3H_7]_2$; $(n$-$C_3H_7)_3COH$; $(CH_3)_2CHCO_2C_2H_5$; $(n$-$C_3H_7)_2CO$; $(n$-$C_3H_7)_2CHOH$; C_3H_6; C_3H_8; other products	*238*
$(CH_3)_2C(CO_2C_2H_5)_2$	n-C_3H_7MgBr	$(n$-$C_3H_7)_2CHOH$; $(n$-$C_3H_7)_3COH$; $(CH_3)_2C[CH(OH)$-n-$C_3H_7]_2$	*238*
$C_5H_6O_5$-R_2			
L-$H_3CO_2CCH(OCH_3)CH_2CO_2CH_3$ (10 g.)	CH_3MgI (10 g. Mg)	$HO(CH_3)_2CCH(OCH_3)CH_2C(CH_3)_2OH$; $C_9H_{18}O_2$ (dehydr'n product)	*345*
L-$H_3CO_2CCH(OCH_3)CH_2CO_2CH_3$ (30 g.)	C_6H_5MgBr (215 g. C_6H_5Br)	2,2,5,5-Tetraphenyl-2,5-dihydrofuran (*ca.* 36 g.); "triphenylbutyrolactone", m. 160–161°	*346*
$C_5H_7O_2$-R			
$(CH_3)_2C{=}CHCO_2C_2H_5$	CH_3MgI (2 equiv.)	$(CH_3)_2C{=}CHC(CH_3)_2OH$; $(CH_3)_2C{=}CHC(CH_3){=}CH_2$; $(CH_3)_3CCH_2COCH_3$ (?)	*49,89*
$(CH_2)_3CHCO_2C_2H_5$ (24 g.)	C_2H_5MgI	$(CH_2)_3CHC(C_2H_5)_2OH$ (22 g.)	*202*
$C_5H_7O_3$-R			
$CH_3CO(CH_2)_2CO_2C_2H_5$ (130.2 g.)	CH_3MgI (142.0 g. CH_3I)	γ,γ-Dimethylbutyrolactone (63.7 g., 62%)	*504*
$CH_3CO(CH_2)_2CO_2C_2H_5$	C_2H_5MgBr (3 equiv.)	$HO(CH_3)(C_2H_5)C(CH_2)_2C(C_2H_5)_2OH$ (63%)	*138,139*
$CH_3CO(CH_2)_2CO_2C_2H_5$	$CH_3C{\equiv}CMgBr$	$HO(CH_3)(CH_3C{\equiv}C)C(CH_2)_2C(C{\equiv}CCH_3)_2OH$	*176*
$CH_3CO(CH_2)_2CO_2C_2H_5$ (212 g.)	n-C_3H_7MgBr (207 g. C_3H_7Br)	γ-Methyl-γ-n-propylbutyrolactone (157.6 g., 73.3%)	77

TABLE VIII-III (Continued)

Ester	RMgX	Product(s)	Ref.
$C_5H_7O_3$-R (*cont.*)			
$CH_3CO(CH_2)_2CO_2C_2H_5$	*i*-$C_5H_{11}MgBr$ (3 equiv.)	$HO(CH_3)(i\text{-}C_5H_{11})C(CH_2)_2C(i\text{-}C_5H_{11})_2OH$	*138*
$CH_3CO(CH_2)_2CO_2C_2H_5$ (2 moles)	*n*-$C_6H_{13}MgCl$ (2 moles $C_6H_{13}Cl$)	γ-Methyl-γ-decanolactone (103.2 g., 28%); recovered ester (25.1 g.)	*112*
$CH_3CO(CH_2)_2CO_2C_2H_5$ (2 moles)	*n*-$C_6H_{13}MgBr$ (2 moles $C_6H_{13}Br$)	γ-Methyl-γ-decanolactone (113 g., 31%)	*112*
$CH_3CO(CH_2)_2CO_2C_2H_5$ (26.0 g.)	*n*-$C_{10}H_{21}MgBr$ (44.2 g. $C_{10}H_{21}Br$)	γ-Methyl-γ-*n*-decylbutyrolactone (36.4 g., 84.4%)	77
$C_5H_7O_4N$-R_2			
D-$H_5C_2O_2C(CH_2)_2CH(NH_2)CO_2C_2H_5$	CH_3MgI	2-[α′-(α-Pyrrolidonyl)]-2-propanol	*188*
D-$H_5C_2O_2C(CH_2)_2CH(NH_2)CO_2C_2H_5$	C_2H_5MgBr	3-[α′-(α-Pyrrolidonyl)]-3-pentanol	*188*
D-$H_5C_2O_2C(CH_2)_2CH(NH_2)CO_2C_2H_5$	*n*-C_4H_9MgI	5-[α′-(α-Pyrrolidonyl)]-5-nonanol	*188*
D-$H_5C_2O_2C(CH_2)_2CH(NH_2)CO_2C_2H_5$	C_6H_5MgBr	α′-(α-Pyrrolidonyl)diphenylmethanol	*188,189*
D-$H_5C_2O_2C(CH_2)_2CH(NH_2)CO_2C_2H_5$	$C_6H_5CH_2MgCl$	1,3-Diphenyl-2-[α′-(α-pyrrolidonyl)]-2-propanol	*188*
$C_5H_8O_2Br$-R			
$Br(CH_2)_4CO_2CH_3$ (120 g.)	CH_3MgBr (50 g. Mg)	$Br(CH_2)_4C(CH_3)_2OH$ (*ca.* 140 g., crude)	*75*
$C_5H_8O_2Cl$-R			
$(CH_3)_2CClCH_2CO_2C_2H_5$	CH_3MgBr	$(CH_3)_2CClCH_2C(CH_3){=}CH_2$; $(CH_3)_2CClCH_2C(CH_3)_2OH$	*237,112*
$C_5H_8O_2N$-R			
L-Proline ethyl ester*	C_2H_5MgBr	3-α-Pyrrolidyl-3-pentanol	*193*
L-Proline ethyl ester*	C_6H_5MgBr	α-Pyrrolidyldiphenylmethanol	*193*

* L-2-Carbethoxypyrrolidine.

TABLE VIII-III (Continued)

Ester	RMgX	Product(s)	Ref.
$C_5H_8O_3N$-R			
L-Hydroxyproline ethyl ester hydrochloride*	C_6H_5MgBr	4-Hydroxy-2-pyrrolidyldiphenylmethanol	*193*
$C_5H_9O_2$-R			
n-$C_4H_9CO_2CH_3$	n-C_3H_7MgBr	n-$C_4H_9(n$-$C_3H_7)_2COH$ (37%)	*462*
n-$C_4H_9CO_2C_2H_5$	CH_3MgBr	n-$C_4H_9(CH_3)_2COH$	*161,298*
n-$C_4H_9CO_2C_2H_5$	C_2H_5MgCl	n-$C_4H_9(C_2H_5)_2COH$ (30%)	*462*
n-$C_4H_9CO_2C_2H_5$	C_2H_5MgBr	n-$C_4H_9(C_2H_5)_2COH$ (69%)	*80,414*
n-$C_4H_9CO_2C_2H_5$	n-$C_5H_{11}MgBr$	n-$C_4H_9(n$-$C_5H_{11})_2COH$ (59%)	*461*
n-$C_4H_9CO_2C_2H_5$	C_6H_5MgBr	$(C_6H_5)_2C{=}CH$-n-C_3H_7	*224*
i-$C_4H_9CO_2C_2H_5$	CH_3MgI	i-$C_4H_9(CH_3)_2COH$ (80%)	*79,23*
i-$C_4H_9CO_2C_2H_5$	C_2H_5MgX (2 equiv.)	i-$C_4H_9(C_2H_5)_2COH$ (80–85%); corresponding olefin (*ca.* 1%)	*259*
i-$C_4H_9CO_2C_2H_5$ (16.1 g.)	$H_2C{=}CHCH_2Br$ (30 g.) + Mg (5.94 g.)	i-$C_4H_9(H_2C{=}CHCH_2)_2COH$ (72%)	*292*
i-$C_4H_9CO_2C_2H_5$	n-C_3H_7MgBr	i-$C_4H_9(n$-$C_3H_7)_2COH$ ("good yield")	*149*
i-$C_4H_9CO_2C_2H_5$	n-C_4H_9MgBr	i-$C_4H_9(n$-$C_4H_9)_2COH$ (60.5%)	*340,327*
i-$C_4H_9CO_2C_2H_5$	s-C_4H_9MgBr	$(i$-$C_4H_9)_2CO$; i-C_4H_9CO-s-C_4H_9	*327*
i-$C_4H_9CO_2C_2H_5$	t-C_4H_9MgCl	$(i$-$C_4H_9)_2CO$; i-C_4H_9CO-t-C_4H_9	*327*
i-$C_4H_9CO_2C_2H_5$	t-C_4H_9MgCl	i-C_4H_9CO-t-C_4H_9	*335*
i-$C_4H_9CO_2C_2H_5$	i-$C_5H_{11}MgBr$	i-$C_4H_9(i$-$C_5H_{11})_2COH$	*149*
i-$C_4H_9CO_2C_2H_5$ (60 g.)	C_6H_5MgBr (157 g. C_6H_5Br)	$(C_6H_5)_2C{=}CH$-i-C_3H_7 (75 g.); $(C_6H_5{-})_2$	*224*
i-$C_4H_9CO_2C_2H_5$ (24 g.)	2,4,6-$(CH_3)_3C_6H_2MgBr$ (0.189 mole)	i-$C_4H_9COCH(i$-$C_3H_7)CO_2C_2H_5$ (10 g., 51%); $(CH_3)_3C_6H_3$	*396*
i-$C_4H_9CO_2$-t-C_4H_9 (29.2 g., 0.185 mole)	i-C_3H_7MgBr (0.0925 mole)	i-$C_4H_9COCH(i$-$C_3H_7)CO_2$-t-C_4H_9 (5.9 g., 29%); recovered ester (4.5 g., 15%); "gas"	*384*

* L-2-Carbethoxy-4-hydroxyproline hydrochloride.

TABLE VIII-III (Continued)

Ester	RMgX	Product(s)	Ref.
$C_5H_9O_2$-R (*cont.*)			
t-$C_4H_9CO_2CH_3$ (1.87 mole)	C_2H_5MgBr (4.5 moles)	$C_2H_5(t$-$C_4H_9)CHOH$ (8.6%); t-$C_4H_9(C_2H_5)_2COH$ (76.5%)	454
t-$C_4H_9CO_2CH_3$	n-C_3H_7MgBr	n-$C_3H_7(t$-$C_4H_9)CHOH$ (48%); t-$C_4H_9(n$-$C_3H_7)_2COH$ (40%)	454
t-$C_4H_9CO_2CH_3$ (1.5 mole)	i-C_3H_7MgBr (4.5 moles)	i-$C_3H_7(t$-$C_4H_9)CHOH$ (44.8%); recovered ester (34.2%)	454
t-$C_4H_9CO_2CH_3$	n-C_4H_9MgBr	n-$C_4H_9(t$-$C_4H_9)CHOH$ (40%)	454
t-$C_4H_9CO_2CH_3$ (0.5 mole)	i-C_4H_9MgBr (1.7 mole)	i-C_4H_9CO-t-C_4H_9 (29.4%); i-$C_4H_9(t$-$C_4H_9)CHOH$ (25.7%); recovered ester (27.2%)	454
t-$C_4H_9CO_2C_2H_5$	C_2H_5MgI	$C_2H_5(t$-$C_4H_9)CHOH$ (13%); C_2H_4 and C_2H_6 in ratio of 1.7 : 1.0	238
t-$C_4H_9CO_2C_2H_5$	n-C_3H_7MgCl (2.5 equiv.)	n-$C_3H_7(t$-$C_4H_9)CHOH$ (48%); t-$C_4H_9(n$-$C_3H_7)_2COH$ (40%); gas comprising C_3H_6 (84%) and C_3H_8 (6%)	238
t-$C_4H_9CO_2C_2H_5$	n-C_3H_7MgBr	n-$C_3H_7(t$-$C_4H_9)CHOH$ and t-$C_4H_9(n$-$C_3H_7)_2COH$ in ratio of 2.1 : 1.0	238
t-$C_4H_9CO_2C_2H_5$	n-C_3H_7MgI	n-$C_3H_7(t$-$C_4H_9)CHOH$ and t-$C_4H_9(n$-$C_3H_7)_2COH$ in ratio of 10 : 1	238
t-$C_4H_9CO_2C_2H_5$ (1 mole)	n-C_4H_9MgBr (4 moles C_4H_9Br)	n-$C_4H_9(t$-$C_4H_9)CHOH$ (40%); t-$C_4H_9(n$-$C_4H_9)_2COH$ (50%); n-C_4H_9OH	458,451
t-$C_4H_9CO_2C_2H_5$	n-C_4H_9MgI	n-$C_4H_9(t$-$C_4H_9)CHOH$	238
t-$C_4H_9CO_2C_2H_5$ (12 g., 0.1 mole)	t-C_4H_9MgCl (0.6 mole)	Recovered ester (9 g.). [No $(t$-$C_4H_9)_2CO$; no t-$C_4H_9CH_2OH$]	87
t-$C_4H_9CO_2C_2H_5$ (26.8 g.)	t-$C_4H_9C{\equiv}CMgBr$ (38.0 g. t-$C_4H_9C{\equiv}CH$)	t-$C_4H_9(t$-$C_4H_9C{\equiv}C)_2COH$ (78–82%)	126
t-$C_4H_9CO_2CH_2CH{=}CH_2$ (34.6 g.)	C_6H_5MgBr (76.7 C_6H_5Br)	t-$C_4H_9(C_6H_5)_2COH$ (35.0 g.); recovered ester (7–10 g.)	4

TABLE VIII-III (Continued)

Ester	RMgX	Product(s)	Ref.
$C_5H_9O_3$-R			
$HO(CH_3)(C_2H_5)CCO_2CH_3$ (132 g.)	CH_3MgI (568 g. CH_3I)	$HO(CH_3)(C_2H_5)CC(CH_3)_2OH$ (56%)	280
$HO(CH_3)(C_2H_5)CCO_2CH_3$ (33 g.)	C_6H_5MgBr (157 g. C_6H_5Br)	$HO(CH_3)(C_2H_5)CC(C_6H_5)_2OH$ (45 g.)	281
(+)-$CH_3(C_2H_5O)CHCO_2C_2H_5$	CH_3MgCl	(−)-$CH_3(C_2H_5O)CHC(CH_3)_2OH$ (85%)	407
$HOCH_2(CH_3)_2CCO_2C_2H_5$	C_2H_5MgBr	$HOCH_2(CH_3)_2CC(C_2H_5)_2OH$; $HOCH_2(CH_3)_2CCH(C_2H_5)OH$	240
$C_5H_{10}O_3ClN_2$-R			
$HCl\cdot H_2NCH_2CONHCH(CH_3)CO_2C_2H_5$	C_6H_5MgBr	$H_2NCH_2CONHCH(CH_3)C(C_6H_5)_2OH$	45
$HCl\cdot H_2NCH_2COHNCH(CH_3)CO_2C_2H_5$	$C_6H_5CH_2MgBr$	$H_2NCH_2CONHCH(CH_3)C(CH_2C_6H_5)_2OH$	45
$C_6H_2O_5$-R_2			
2,5-Dicarbethoxyfuran	C_6H_5MgBr	2,5-Bis-(α-hydroxybenzhydryl)furan	147
2,5-Dicarbethoxyfuran	$C_6H_5CH_2MgCl$	2,5-Bis-(1,3-diphenyl-2-hydroxyisopropyl)furan	147
$C_6H_4O_2N$-R			
Methyl nicotinate (137 g., 1.0 mole)	CH_3MgI (540 g., 3.25 moles CH_3I)	2-(3-Pyridyl)-2-propanol (78 g., 57%)	15,132
Ethyl picolinate	CH_3MgI	2-(2-Pyridyl)-2-propanol (86–90%)	392
Ethyl picolinate (12 g.)	C_2H_5MgBr (45 g. C_2H_5Br)	3-(2-Pyridyl)-3-pentanol (*ca.* 10 g.)	392
$C_6H_6O_4$-R_2			
$C_2H_5CH{=}C(CO_2C_2H_5)_2$ (0.16 mole)	1-$C_{10}H_7CH_2MgCl$ (0.21 mole $C_{11}H_9Cl$)	$C_2H_5(1\text{-}C_{10}H_7CH_2)CHCH(CO_2C_2H_5)_2$ (55%)	360
$C_2H_5CH{=}C(CO_2C_2H_5)_2$ (0.16 mole)	1-$C_{10}H_7CH_2MgCl$ (0.21 mole $C_{11}H_9Cl$) + $CdCl_2$ (0.20 mole)	$C_2H_5(1\text{-}C_{10}H_7CH_2)CHCH(CO_2C_2H_5)_2$ (65%)	360
$(CH_3)_2C{=}C(CO_2C_2H_5)_2$ (50 g.)	CH_3MgI (40 g. CH_3I)	*t*-$C_4H_9CH(CO_2C_2H_5)_2$ (20 g.)	464

TABLE VIII-III (Continued)

Ester	RMgX	Product(s)	Ref.
$C_6H_6O_4$-R_2 *(cont.)*			
$(CH_3)_2C{=}C(CO_2C_2H_5)_2$ (30 g.)	n-C_4H_9MgBr (23 g. C_4H_9Br)	n-$C_4H_9(CH_3)_2CCH(CO_2C_2H_5)_2$ (11.5 g.)	*464*
$C_6H_6O_2N$-R			
Ethyl 1-pyrrylacetate (23 g.)	CH_3MgI (56.4 g. CH_3I)	2-(1-Pyrrylmethyl)-2-propanol (18 g.)	*50*
Ethyl 1-pyrrylacetate (45 g.)	C_2H_5MgBr (1 mole)	3-(1-Pyrrylmethyl)-3-pentanol (38 g.)	*50*
$C_6H_6O_5$-R_2			
$C_2H_5OCH{=}C(CO_2C_2H_5)_2$	C_2H_5MgBr	$(C_2H_5)_2CHCH(CO_2C_2H_5)_2$	*356*
$C_2H_5OCH{=}C(CO_2C_2H_5)_2$	C_6H_5MgBr	$(C_6H_5)_2CHCH(CO_2C_2H_5)_2$	*356*
$C_6H_8O_4$-R_2			
$(—CH_2CH_2CO_2CH_3)_2$	C_6H_5MgBr	$[—CH_2CH_2C(C_6H_5)_2OH]_2$ (yielding 80–90% alkene)	*377*
$(—CH_2CH_2CO_2C_2H_5)_2$	CH_3MgBr	$[—CH_2CH_2C(CH_3)_2OH]_2$	*284*
$(—CH_2CH_2CO_2C_2H_5)_2$ (20.2 g.)	CH_3MgI (56.6 g. CH_3I)	$[—CH_2CH_2C(CH_3)_2OH]_2$ (16.0 g., 92%)	*61,203,337*
$(—CH_2CH_2CO_2C_2H_5)_2$ (20.2 g.)	C_2H_5MgI (62.4 g. C_2H_5I)	$[—CH_2CH_2C(C_2H_5)_2OH]_2$ (70%)	*61*
$(—CH_2CH_2CO_2C_2H_5)_2$ (20.2 g.)	n-C_3H_7MgI (68.0 g. C_3H_7I)	$[—CH_2CH_2C(n\text{-}C_3H_7)_2OH]_2$ (*ca.* 1.0 g.); unidentified viscous liquid	*61*
$(—CH_2CH_2CO_2C_2H_5)_2$ (40 g.)	n-C_4H_9MgBr (115 g. C_4H_9Br)	$[—CH_2CH_2C(n\text{-}C_4H_9)_2OH]_2$ (62%)	*337*
$(—CH_2CH_2CO_2C_2H_5)_2$ (40 g.)	i-C_4H_9MgBr (160 g. C_4H_9Br)	$[—CH_2CH_2C(i\text{-}C_4H_9)_2OH]_2$ (38 g.); i-C_4H_8; i-C_4H_{10}	*337*
$(—CH_2CH_2CO_2C_2H_5)_2$ (20.2 g.)	C_6H_5MgBr (65.0 g. C_6H_5Br)	$[—CH_2CH_2C(C_6H_5)_2OH]_2$	*61*
$(—CH_2CH_2CO_2C_2H_5)_2$ (20.2 g.)	$(CH_2)_5CHMgCl$ (47.4 g. $C_6H_{11}Cl$)	$\{—CH_2CH_2C[CH(CH_2)_5]_2OH\}_2$ (1.5 g.); $(CH_2)_5CHOC_2H_5$; C_6H_{10}	*61*
$(—CH_2CH_2CO_2C_2H_5)_2$ (20.2 g.)	$C_6H_5CH_2MgCl$ (50.6 g. C_7H_7Cl)	$[—CH_2CH_2C(CH_2C_6H_5)_2OH]_2$ (19.0 g., 40%); $(—CH_2C_6H_5)_2$ (7.0 g.)	*61*

TABLE VIII-III (Continued)

Ester	RMgX	Product(s)	Ref.
$C_6H_8O_6$-R_2			
D-[—$CH(OCH_3)CO_2CH_3]_2$ (20 g.)	CH_3MgI (62 g. CH_3I)	[—$CH(OCH_3)C(CH_3)_2OH]_2$ (9 g.)	*347*
D-[—$CH(OCH_3)CO_2CH_3]_2$	C_6H_5MgBr (6 equiv.)	2,2,5,5-Tetraphenyl-3,4-dimethoxytetrahydrofuran	*347*
$C_6H_9O_2$-R			
$(CH_2)_4CHCO_2C_2H_5$ (45.0 g.)	CH_3MgI (15.3 g. Mg)	$(CH_2)_4CHC(CH_3)_2OH$ (66.6%)	*299*
$(CH_2)_4CHCO_2C_2H_5$ (37 g.)	$(CH_2)_4CHMgCl$ (104 g. C_5H_9Cl)	$[(CH_2)_4CH]_3COH$	*306*
$C_6H_9O_3$-R			
$(CH_2)_4C(OH)CO_2CH_3$ (72 g.)	CH_3MgI (213 g. CH_3I)	$(CH_2)_4C(OH)C(CH_3)_2OH$ (70 g., *ca.* 50%)	*282*
$(CH_2)_4C(OH)CO_2CH_3$	C_2H_5MgBr (4 equiv.)	$(CH_2)_4C(OH)C(C_2H_5)_2OH$ (60%)	*280*
$(CH_2)_4C(OH)CO_2CH_3$	C_2H_5MgBr (5 equiv.)	$(CH_2)_4C(OH)C(C_2H_5)_2OH$ (72%)	*280*
$(CH_2)_4C(OH)CO_2CH_3$ (158 g.)	C_2H_5MgBr (436 g. C_2H_5)	$(CH_2)_4C(OH)C(C_2H_5)_2OH$; $(CH_2)_4C(OH)CH(C_2H_5)OH$ (144 g. glycol mixture)	*281*
$(CH_2)_4C(OH)CO_2CH_3$ (144 g.)	n-C_3H_7MgBr (492 g. C_3H_7Br)	$(CH_2)_4C(OH)C(n\text{-}C_3H_7)_2OH$; $(CH_2)_4C(OH)CH(n\text{-}C_3H_7)OH$ (160 g. glycol mixture, of which *ca.* 60% is the normal product)	*281*
$CH_3CO(C_2H_5)CHCO_2C_2H_5$ (53 g.)	CH_3MgI (3 equiv.)	$HO(CH_3)_2CCH(C_2H_5)CO_2C_2H_5$; recovered ester	*137*
$CH_3CO(C_2H_5)CHCO_2C_2H_5$	CH_3MgI (3 equiv.)	$HO(CH_3)_2CCH(C_2H_5)CO_2C_2H_5$; $[HO(CH_3)_2C]_2CHC_2H_5$ ("very poor yield"); recovered ester (*ca.* 30 g.)	*139,137*
$CH_3CO(CH_3)_2CCO_2C_2H_5$	CH_3MgI	$[HO(CH_3)_2C]_2C(CH_3)_2$	*387*
$C_6H_9O_4N$-R_2			
$H_5C_2O_2C(CH_2)_3CH(NH_2)CO_2C_2H_5$	C_6H_5MgBr	α′-(α-Piperidonyl)diphenylmethanol	*188,189*
$C_6H_{10}O_3N$-R			
$(C_2H_5)_2NCOCO_2C_2H_5$ (20 g.)	C_2H_5MgBr (1.5 equiv.)	$(C_2H_5)_2NCOCOC_2H_5$ (70%); $(C_2H_5)_2NCOC(C_2H_5)_2OH$; recovered ester	*29*
$(C_2H_5)_2NCOCO_2C_2H_5$ (20 g.)	C_2H_5MgBr (2 equiv.)	$(C_2H_5)_2NCOCOC_2H_5$; unchanged ester	*29*

TABLE VIII-III (Continued)

Ester	RMgX	Product(s)	Ref.
$C_6H_{10}O_3N$-R (*cont.*)			
$(C_2H_5)_2NCOCO_2C_2H_5$ (20 g.)	C_2H_5MgBr (2.25 equiv.)	$(C_2H_5)_2NCOC(C_2H_5)_2OH$ (70%); $(C_2H_5)_2NCOCOC_2H_5$ (20%); recovered ester	28,29
$(C_2H_5)_2NCOCO_2C_2H_5$ (20 g.)	C_2H_5MgBr (3 equiv.)	$(C_2H_5)_2NCOC(C_2H_5)_2OH$ (80%); $(C_2H_5)_2NCOCOC_2H_5$ (2–3%); $(C_2H_5CO—)_2$	29
$(C_2H_5)_2NCOCO_2C_2H_5$ (20 g.)	C_2H_5MgBr (5 equiv.)	$(C_2H_5)_2NCOC(C_2H_5)_2OH$; $(C_2H_5CO—)_2$	29
$(C_2H_5)_2NCOCO_2C_2H_5$ (10 g.)	C_2H_5MgI (27 g. C_2H_5I)	$(C_2H_5)_2NCOC(C_2H_5)_2OH$ (5.5 g.)	268
$(C_2H_5)_2NCOCO_2C_2H_5$	*n*-C_4H_9MgBr	$(C_2H_5)_2NCOCO$-*n*-C_4H_9 (90%); $(C_2H_5)_2NCOC$(*n*-$C_4H_9)_2OH$ (trace); diketone (trace)	29
$(C_2H_5)_2NCOCO_2C_2H_5$	C_6H_5MgBr (1.6 equiv.)	$(C_2H_5)_2NCOC(C_6H_5)_2OH$ (63%); $(C_2H_5)_2NCOCOC_6H_5$ (15%)	29
$(C_2H_5)_2NCOCO_2C_2H_5$	C_6H_5MgBr (2 equiv.)	$(C_2H_5)_2NCOCOC_6H_5$ (63%)	29
$(C_2H_5)_2NCOCO_2C_2H_5$ (22 g.)	C_6H_5MgBr (80 g. C_6H_5Br)	$(C_2H_5)_2NCOC(C_6H_5)_2OH$ (23 g.); $(C_6H_5—)_2$	268
$(C_2H_5)_2NCOCO_2C_2H_5$	$C_6H_5CH_2MgCl$	$(C_2H_5)_2NCOCOCH_2C_6H_5$ (70%); $(C_2H_5)_2NCOC(CH_2C_6H_5)_2OH$ (15%)	29
$(C_2H_5)_2NCOCO_2C_2H_5$ (15 g.)	$C_6H_5CH_2MgCl$ (44 g. C_7H_7Cl)	$(C_2H_5)_2NCOC(CH_2C_6H_5)_2OH$ (8 g.)	268
$(C_2H_5)_2NCOCO_2C_2H_5$ (12 g.)	2-$CH_3C_6H_4MgBr$ (48 g. C_7H_7Br)	$(C_2H_5)_2NCOC(C_6H_4$-2-$CH_3)_2OH$ (11 g.)	268
$(C_2H_5)_2NCOCO_2C_2H_5$ (8.8 g.)	4-$CH_3C_6H_4MgBr$ (35 g. C_7H_7Br)	$(C_2H_5)_2NCOC(C_6H_4$-4-$CH_3)_2OH$ (6 g.); (4-$CH_3C_6H_4—)_2$	268
$(C_2H_5)_2NCOCO_2C_2H_5$ (20 g.)	1-$C_{10}H_7MgBr$ (96 g. $C_{10}H_7Br$)	$(C_2H_5)_2NCOC(1$-$C_{10}H_7)_2OH$ (30 g.); (1-$C_{10}H_7—)_2$	268
$C_6H_{11}O_2$-R			
n-$C_5H_{11}CO_2C_2H_5$	CH_3MgCl	*n*-$C_5H_{11}(CH_3)_2COH$ (61%)	461,80
n-$C_5H_{11}CO_2C_2H_5$	CH_3MgX*	*n*-$C_5H_{11}(CH_3)_2COH$	298

* X = Br, I.

TABLE VIII-III (Continued)

Ester	RMgX	Product(s)	Ref.
$C_6H_{11}O_2$-R (*cont.*)			
n-$C_5H_{11}CO_2C_2H_5$	CH_3MgX (2 equiv.)	n-$C_5H_{11}(CH_3)_2COH$ (80–85%); corresponding olefin (*ca.* 1%)	259
n-$C_5H_{11}CO_2C_2H_5$	C_2H_5MgBr	n-$C_5H_{11}(C_2H_5)_2COH$ (73%)	461,80
n-$C_5H_{11}CO_2C_2H_5$	C_2H_5MgX (2 equiv.)	n-$C_5H_{11}(C_2H_5)_2COH$ (80–85%); corresponding olefin (*ca.* 1%)	259
n-$C_5H_{11}CO_2C_2H_5$	n-C_3H_7MgBr	n-$C_5H_{11}(n$-$C_3H_7)_2COH$ (44%)	461,80
n-$C_5H_{11}CO_2C_2H_5$	n-C_4H_9MgBr	n-$C_5H_{11}(n$-$C_4H_9)_2COH$ (76%)	461
n-$C_5H_{11}CO_2C_2H_5$	C_6H_5MgBr	n-$C_5H_{11}(C_6H_5)_2COH$	260,224
n-$C_5H_{11}CO_2C_2H_5$ (154 g.)	n-$C_{10}H_{21}MgBr$ (660 g. $C_{10}H_{21}Br$)	n-$C_5H_{11}(n$-$C_{10}H_{21})_2COH$ (345 g.); $C_{10}H_{22}$ (80 g.); n-$C_5H_{11}CO$-n-$C_{10}H_{21}$ (40 g.)	483
i-$C_5H_{11}CO_2C_2H_5$ (57.6 g.)	C_6H_5MgBr (157 g. C_6H_5Br)	$(C_6H_5)_2C{=}CH$-i-C_4H_9 (50 g.)	224
t-$C_4H_9CH_2CO_2CH_3$ (1 mole)	C_2H_5MgBr (4 moles)	t-$C_4H_9CH_2(C_2H_5)_2COH$ (68.5%); $C_2H_5COCH_2$-t-C_4H_9 (5.0%)	454
t-$C_4H_9CH_2CO_2CH_3$ (1 mole)	n-C_3H_7MgBr (4 moles)	t-$C_4H_9CH_2(n$-$C_3H_7)_2COH$ (61.8%); n-$C_3H_7(t$-$C_4H_9CH_2)CHOH$ (20.4%); n-$C_3H_7COCH_2$-t-C_4H_9 (7.0%)	454
t-$C_4H_9CH_2CO_2CH_3$ (1 mole)	i-C_3H_7MgBr (4 moles)	i-$C_3H_7(t$-$C_4H_9CH_2)CHOH$ (16.1%); i-$C_3H_7COCH_2$-t-C_4H_9 (55.3%)	454
t-$C_4H_9CH_2CO_2CH_3$ (0.9 mole)	n-C_4H_9MgBr (3.6 moles)	t-$C_4H_9CH_2(n$-$C_4H_9)_2COH$ (71.4%); n-$C_4H_9COCH_2$-t-C_4H_9 (trace)	454
t-$C_4H_9CH_2CO_2CH_3$ (0.5 mole)	i-C_4H_9MgBr (1.7 atom Mg)	t-$C_4H_9CH_2(i$-$C_4H_9)_2COH$ (34.2%); i-$C_4H_9(t$-$C_4H_9CH_2)CHOH$ (9.2%); i-$C_4H_9COCH_2$-t-C_4H_9 (32.0%)	454
t-$C_4H_9CH_2CO_2C_2H_5$ (27.0 g.)	2,4,6-$(CH_3)_3C_6H_2MgBr$ (0.194 mole)	t-$C_4H_9CH_2CO(t$-$C_4H_9)CHCO_2C_2H_5$ (7.3 g., 32%)	396
(−)-$CH_3(n$-$C_3H_7)CHCO_2CH_3$ (5.0 g.)	C_6H_5MgBr (18.5 g. C_6H_5Br)	DL-$CH_3(n$-$C_3H_7)CHC(C_6H_5)_2OH$ (3.5 g.)	38
DL-$CH_3(n$-$C_3H_7)CHCO_2CH_3$ (7.0 g.)	C_6H_5MgBr (26.0 g. C_6H_5Br)	DL-$CH_3(n$-$C_3H_7)CHC(C_6H_5)_2OH$ (7.0 g.)	38

TABLE VIII-III (Continued)

Ester	RMgX	Product(s)	Ref.
$C_6H_{11}O_2$-R (*cont.*)			
(−)-CH_3(n-C_3H_7)$CHCO_2C_2H_5$	CH_3MgI	After dehydr'n and hydrogen'n, (−)-CH_3(n-C_3H_7)(i-C_3H_7)CH	*242*
(−)-CH_3(n-C_3H_7)$CHCO_2C_2H_5$ (4.0 g.)	C_2H_5MgBr (11.0 g. C_2H_5Br)	(−)-CH_3(n-C_3H_7)$CHC(C_2H_5)_2OH$ (2.9 g.)	*37*
$(C_2H_5)_2CHCO_2CH_3$	CH_3MgI (3 equiv.)	C_8H_{16} (small quantity)	*137*
$(C_2H_5)_2CHCO_2C_2H_5$	C_6H_5MgBr	$(C_2H_5)_2C{=}C(C_6H_5)_2$	*109*
$(C_2H_5)_2CHCO_2C_2H_5$	4-$CH_3OC_6H_4MgBr$ (2 equiv.)	$(C_2H_5)_2C{=}C(C_6H_4$-4-$OCH_3)_2$	*109*
$(C_2H_5)_2CHCO_2C_2H_5$	n-$C_{10}H_{21}MgBr$	$(C_2H_5)_2CHC$(n-$C_{10}H_{21})_2OH$ (yielding 36% paraffin)	*483*
$(C_2H_5)_2CHCO_2CH_2CH{=}CH_2$ (25.3 g.)	C_6H_5MgBr (45.0 ml. C_6H_5Br)	$(C_2H_5)_2CHCO_2H$ (4.5 g.); $C_6H_5CH_2CH{=}CH_2$ (9.0 g.); $(C_2H_5)_2CHC(C_6H_5)_2OH$ (10.3 g.)	*6*
$C_2H_5(CH_3)_2CCO_2C_2H_5$	CH_3MgBr	Addition (100%); enolization (0%)*	*457*
$C_6H_{11}O_3$-R			
L-$C_2H_5(C_2H_5O)CHCO_2C_2H_5$	CH_3MgI	L-$C_2H_5(C_2H_5O)CHC(CH_3)_2OH$	*243*
$C_6H_{11}O_4$-R			
$(C_2H_5O)_2CHCO_2C_2H_5$	C_6H_5MgBr	$(C_2H_5O)_2CHC(C_6H_5)_2OH$ (70%)	*369*
$C_6H_{12}O_2N$-R			
$(C_2H_5)_2NCH_2CO_2C_2H_5$	C_2H_5MgI	$(C_2H_5)_2NCH_2C(C_2H_5)_2OH$	*318*
$(C_2H_5)_2NCH_2CO_2C_2H_5$ (12 g.)	C_6H_5MgBr (25.7 g. C_6H_5Br)	$(C_2H_5)_2NCH_2C(C_6H_5)_2OH$ (10 g., crude)	*318*
i-$C_4H_9CH(NH_2)CO_2C_2H_5$	C_2H_5MgBr	i-$C_4H_9CH(NH_2)C(C_2H_5)_2OH$	*191*
DL-i-$C_4H_9CH(NH_2)CO_2C_2H_5$	C_6H_5MgBr	DL-i-$C_4H_9CH(NH_2)C(C_6H_3)_2OH$	*191*
DL-i-$C_4H_9CH(NH_2)CO_2C_2H_5$	4-$CH_3C_6H_4MgBr$	DL-i-$C_4H_9CH(NH_2)C(C_6H_4$-4-$CH_3)_2OH$	*191*
L(+)-i-$C_4H_9CH(NH_2)CO_2C_2H_5$	CH_3MgBr	(−)-i-$C_4H_9CH(OH)C(CH_3)_2OH$	*192*

* "Grignard machine" study.

TABLE VIII-III (Continued)

Ester	RMgX	Product(s)	Ref.
$C_6H_{12}O_2N$-R (*cont.*)			
L(+)-*i*-$C_4H_9CH(NH_2)CO_2C_2H_5$	C_2H_5MgBr	(−)-*i*-$C_4H_9CH(OH)C(C_2H_5)_2OH$	*192*
L(+)-*i*-$C_4H_9CH(NH_2)CO_2C_2H_5$	C_6H_5MgBr	L(−)-*i*-$C_4H_9CH(NH_2)C(C_6H_5)_2OH$ (56%)	*191*
L(+)-*i*-$C_4H_9CH(NH_2)CO_2C_2H_5$	C_6H_5MgBr	(−)-*i*-$C_4H_9CH(OH)C(C_6H_5)_2OH$ (72%)	*192*
L(+)-*i*-$C_4H_9CH(NH_2)CO_2C_2H_5$	$C_6H_5CH_2MgCl$	L(+)-*i*-$C_4H_9CH(NH_2)C(CH_2C_6H_5)_2OH$	*191*
L(+)-*i*-$C_4H_9CH(NH_2)CO_2C_2H_5$	4-$CH_3C_6H_4MgBr$	L(−)-*i*-$C_4H_9CH(NH_2)C(C_6H_4$-4-$CH_3)_2OH$	*191*
$C_6H_{13}O_2ClN$-R			
i-$C_4H_9CH(NH_2\cdot HCl)CO_2C_2H_5$	C_6H_5MgBr	*i*-$C_4H_9CH(NH_2)C(C_6H_5)_2OH$ (62%)	*43*
i-$C_4H_9CH(NH_2\cdot HCl)CO_2C_2H_5$	$C_6H_5CH_2MgBr$	*i*-$C_4H_9CH(NH_2)C(CH_2C_6H_5)_2OH$ (61%)	*43*
$C_7H_2O_2Br_3$-R			
2,4,6-$Br_3C_6H_2CO_2CH_3$ (4 g., 0.011 mole)	C_6H_5MgBr (13 g., 0.082 mole C_6H_5Br)	Recovered ester (*ca.* quant.)*	*291*
2,4,6-$Br_3C_6H_2CO_2CH_3$ (4 g., 0.011 mole)	C_6H_5MgBr (13 g., 0.082 mole C_6H_5Br)	2,4,6-$Br_3C_6H_2(C_6H_5)_2COH$ (1.5 g., 28%)†	*291*
$C_7H_3O_2Cl_2$-R			
2,4-$Cl_2C_6H_3CO_2C_2H_5$ (110 g., 0.5 mole)	CH_3MgI (9.1 moles)	2,4-$Cl_2C_6H_3(CH_3)_2COH$ (yielding 64 g., 68% olefin)	*13*
3,4-$Cl_2C_6H_3CO_2C_2H_5$ (410 g.)	CH_3MgI (excess)	3,4-$Cl_2C_6H_3(CH_3)_2COH$ (yielding 248 g., 70% olefin)	*13*
$C_7H_3O_3Br_2$-R			
2-HO-3,5-$Br_2C_6H_2CO_2CH_3$ (10 g.)	C_6H_5MgBr (21 g. C_6H_5Br)	2-HO-3,5-$Br_2C_6H_2(C_6H_5)_2COH$ (10 g.)	*197*
$C_7H_4O_2Br$-R			
2-$BrC_6H_4CO_2CH_3$	4-ClC_6H_4MgI	2-$BrC_6H_4(4\text{-}ClC_6H_4)_2COH$ (isolated as chloride, 74%)	*131*

* Gradual addition of Et_2O-ester solution to Grignard reagent solution; five hours reflux.

† Gradual (thirty minutes) addition of C_6H_5Cl-ester solution to Grignard reagent solution; four hours at 80-85°

TABLE VIII-III (Continued)

Ester	RMgX	Product(s)	Ref.
$C_7H_4O_2Br$-R (*cont.*)			
2-$BrC_6H_4CO_2CH_3$	C_6H_5MgBr	2-$BrC_6H_4(C_6H_5)_2COH$ (54%)	*131*
2-$BrC_6H_4CO_2C_2H_5$	C_6H_5MgBr	2-$BrC_6H_4(C_6H_5)_2COH$	*255*
3-$BrC_6H_4CO_2C_2H_5$	C_6H_5MgBr	3-$BrC_6H_4(C_6H_5)_2COH$	*255*
4-$BrC_6H_4CO_2CH_3$	4-ClC_6H_4MgI	4-BrC_6H_4(4-$ClC_6H_4)_2COH$ (65%)	*131*
4-$BrC_6H_4CO_2C_2H_5$	C_6H_5MgBr	4-$BrC_6H_4(C_6H_5)_2COH$	*255*
$C_7H_4O_2Cl$-R			
2-$ClC_6H_4CO_2CH_3$ (170 g.)	CH_3MgI (355 g. CH_3I)	2-$ClC_6H_4(CH_3)_2COH$ (140 g., 82.5%)	*65*
2-$ClC_6H_4CO_2CH_3$ (12.5 g.)	C_6H_5MgBr (30 g. C_6H_5Br)	2-$ClC_6H_4(C_6H_5)_2COH$ (11.8 g.)	*131,222*
2-$ClC_6H_4CO_2C_2H_5$	CH_3MgI (excess)	2-$ClC_6H_4(CH_3)_2COH$ (yielding 60% olefin)	*13*
2-$ClC_6H_4CO_2C_2H_5$	C_6H_5MgBr	2-$ClC_6H_4(C_6H_5)_2COH$	*255*
3-$ClC_6H_4CO_2C_2H_5$	C_6H_5MgBr	3-$ClC_6H_4(C_6H_5)_2COH$	*255*
4-$ClC_6H_4CO_2C_2H_5$	C_6H_5MgBr	4-$ClC_6H_4(C_6H_5)_2COH$	*255*
$C_7H_4O_2F$-R			
2-$FC_6H_4CO_2C_2H_5$	C_6H_5MgBr	2-$FC_6H_4(C_6H_5)_2COH$	*255*
4-$FC_6H_4CO_2C_2H_5$	C_6H_5MgBr	4-$FC_6H_4(C_6H_5)_2COH$	*255*
$C_7H_4O_2I$-R			
4-$IC_6H_4CO_2C_2H_5$	C_6H_5MgBr	4-$IC_6H_4(C_6H_5)_2COH$	*255*
$C_7H_5O_2$-R			
$C_6H_5CO_2CH_3$	CH_3MgI	$C_6H_5(CH_3)_2COH$ (78%)	*493*
$C_6H_5CO_2CH_3$	C_2H_5I + Mg*	$C_6H_5(C_2H_5)_2COH$	*488*
$C_6H_5CO_2CH_3$	*i*-C_4H_9MgBr	*i*-$C_4H_9(C_6H_5)CHOH$ (*ca.* 35%)	*378*
$C_6H_5CO_2CH_3$	C_6H_5MgBr	$(C_6H_5)_3COH$ (87%); $(C_6H_5—)_2$	*434,424*

* Without solvent (other than the reactants).

TABLE VIII-III (Continued)

Ester	RMgX	Product(s)	Ref.
$C_7H_5O_2$-R (*cont.*)			
$C_6H_5CO_2CH_3$	C_6H_5MgBr	$[(C_6H_5)_3C]_2O$; $(C_6H_5)_3COH$	*401*
$C_6H_5CO_2CH_3$ (14 g.)	C_6H_5MgBr (34 g. C_6H_5Br)	$CH_3OC(C_6H_5)_3$* (9 g.); $(C_6H_5)_3COH$ (7 g.)	*402*
$C_6H_5CO_2CH_3$ (14 g.)	C_6H_5MgBr (34 g. C_6H_5Br)	$(C_6H_5)_3COH$ (13.3 g., 49.7%); $[(C_6H_5)_2COH—]_2$ (0.11 g.); $C_2H_5OC(C_6H_5)_3$ (1.62 g., 5.7%)	*63*
$C_6H_5CO_2CH_3$ (20.9 g.)	C_6H_5MgBr (24.1 g. C_6H_5Br) + Mg + Hg	$(C_6H_5)_3COH$ (8.3 g., 41.5%); $[(C_6H_5)_2COH—]_2$ (2.15 g., 7.8%)	*63*
$C_6H_5CO_2CH_3$ (20.9 g.)	C_6H_5MgBr (24.4 g. C_6H_5Br) + Mg	$(C_6H_5)_3COH$ (8.7 g., 43.5%); $[(C_6H_5)_2COH—]_2$ (0.6 g., 2.2%); $(C_6H_5)_2CO$; $(C_6H_5—)_2$; $C_2H_5OC(C_6H_5)_3$; recovered ester	*63*
$C_6H_5CO_2CH_3$	$4-CH_3C_6H_4MgBr$	$C_6H_5(4-CH_3C_6H_4)_2COH$	*206*
$C_6H_5CO_2CH_3$	$2,4-(CH_3O)_2C_6H_3MgI$	$C_6H_5[2,4-(CH_3O)_2C_6H_3]_2COH$ (*ca.* 60%)	*248*
$C_6H_5CO_2CH_3$	$n-C_{10}H_{21}MgBr$	$C_6H_5(n-C_{10}H_{21})_2COH$ (yielding 75% olefin)	*453*
$C_6H_5CO_2C_2H_5$	CH_3MgBr	$CH_3(C_6H_5)C{=}CH_2$	*182*
$C_6H_5CO_2C_2H_5$	$n-C_4H_9MgCl$	$C_6H_5(n-C_4H_9)_2COH$ (72%)	*328*
$C_6H_5CO_2C_2H_5$	$i-C_4H_9MgX$†	$i-C_4H_9(C_6H_5)CHOH$; $C_6H_5CO_2CH(CH_3)-i-C_4H_9$	*328*
$C_6H_5CO_2C_2H_5$	$t-C_4H_9MgCl$	$(C_6H_5)_2CHOH$ (36%)	*329*
$C_6H_5CO_2C_2H_5$	2-Pyridyl-MgBr	Phenylbis-(2-pyridyl)methanol	*344*
$C_6H_5CO_2C_2H_5$ (30 g.)	C_6H_5MgBr (35 g. C_6H_5Br)	$(C_6H_5)_3COH$ (42%); $C_2H_5OC(C_6H_5)_3$ (31%)	*402*
$C_6H_5CO_2C_2H_5$ (75 g.)	C_6H_5MgBr (181 g. C_6H_5Br)	$(C_6H_5)_3COH$ (116–121 g., 89–93%)	*17*
$C_6H_5CO_2C_2H_5$	$C_6H_5CH_2MgCl$	$C_6H_5(C_6H_5CH_2)_2COH$	*205*
$C_6H_5CO_2C_2H_5$	$C_6H_5CH_2Cl$ + Mg	$C_6H_5(C_6H_5CH_2)_2COH$ (60%)	*94*
$C_6H_5CO_2C_2H_5$ (120 g.)	$2-CH_3C_6H_4MgBr$ (342 g. C_7H_7Br)	$C_6H_5(2-CH_3C_6H_4)_2COH$ (87 g.)	*257*

* *Cf.* Boyd and Hatt (*63*), who suggest that this product is actually the ethyl ether, formed during ethyl alcohol crystallization of the normal product.

†X = Cl, Br.

TABLE VIII-III (Continued)

Ester	RMgX	Product(s)	Ref.
$C_7H_5O_2$-R (*cont.*)			
$C_6H_5CO_2C_2H_5$ (68 g.)	3-$CH_3C_6H_4MgBr$ (171 g. C_7H_7Br)	$C_6H_5(3\text{-}CH_3C_6H_4)_2COH$ (105 g.)	257
$C_6H_5CO_2C_2H_5$ (52 g.)	4-$CH_3C_6H_4MgBr$ (129 g. C_7H_7Br)	$C_6H_5(4\text{-}CH_3C_6H_4)_2COH$ (yielding 19 g. chloride)	257,222
$C_6H_5CO_2C_2H_5$	$C_6H_5CH(CO_2Na)MgCl$*	$C_6H_5COCH_2C_6H_5$ (14.4%); $C_6H_5CH_2OH$	405
$C_6H_5CO_2C_2H_5$ (10 g.)	2-$(CH_3)_2NC_6H_4MgI$ (10 g. $C_8H_{10}IN$)	$C_6H_5[2\text{-}(CH_3)_2NC_6H_4]_2COH$ (10 g.)	20
$C_6H_5CO_2C_2H_5$ (35 g.)	4-*i*-$C_3H_7C_6H_4MgBr$ (100 g. $C_9H_{11}Br$)	$C_6H_5(4\text{-}i\text{-}C_3H_7C_6H_4)_2COH$ (yielding 21 g. chloride)	257
$C_6H_5CO_2C_2H_5$ (37 g.)	2,4,6-$(CH_3)_3C_6H_2MgBr$ (50 g. $C_9H_{11}Br$)	2,4,6-$(CH_3)_3C_6H_2COC_6H_5$ (17.4 g.)	233
$C_6H_5CO_2C_2H_5$ (35 g.)	4-*s*-$C_4H_9C_6H_4MgBr$ (107 g. $C_{10}H_{13}Br$)	$C_6H_5(4\text{-}s\text{-}C_4H_9C_6H_4)_2COH$ (yielding 21 g. chloride)	257
$C_6H_5CO_2C_2H_5$ (21.5 g.)	4-*t*-$C_4H_9C_6H_4MgBr$ (70 g. $C_{10}H_{13}Br$)	$C_6H_5(4\text{-}t\text{-}C_4H_9C_6H_4)_2COH$ (yielding 14 g. chloride)	257
$C_6H_5CO_2C_2H_5$ (22.5 g.)	4-*t*-$C_5H_{11}C_6H_4MgBr$ (76 g. $C_{11}H_{15}Br$)	$C_6H_5(4\text{-}t\text{-}C_5H_{11}C_6H_4)_2COH$ (yielding 9 g. chloride)	257
$C_6H_5CO_2C_2H_5$	$(CH_3)_5C_6MgBr$	$(CH_3)_5C_6C_2H_5$†; $C_2H_5(C_6H_5)CHOH$†; $(CH_3)_5C_6H$; $C_6H_5COC_6(CH_3)_5$	85,84
$C_6H_5CO_2C_2H_5$ (15 g.)	9-Phenanthryl-MgBr (25 g. $C_{14}H_9Br$)	Phenyldi-9-phenanthrylmethanol (20%); di-9-phenanthrylmethane (?)	39
$C_6H_5CO_2CH_2CH{=}CH_2$ (16.2 g.)	2,4,6-$(CH_3)_3C_6H_2MgBr$ (25.0 g. $C_9H_{11}Br$)	2,4,6-$(CH_3)_3C_6H_2COC_6H_5$ (2.4 g., 11%); 2,4,6-$(CH_3)_3C_6H_2CH_2CH{=}CH_2$ (5.7 g., 36%); $C_6H_5CO_2H$ (5.1 g., 42%); recovered ester (26%)	8

* In the opinion of Schlenk, Hilleman, and Rodloff, *Ann.*, *487*, 135–54 (1931), this "Grignard reagent" should be formulated as an enolate.

† Attributable to the use of ethyl bromide as "entrainer" in the preparation of the Grignard reagent.

TABLE VIII-III (Continued)

Ester	RMgX	Product(s)	Ref.
$C_7H_5O_2$-R (*cont.*)			
$C_6H_5CO_2CH_2COCH_3$	C_2H_5MgBr (4 equiv.)	$C_6H_5(C_2H_5)_2COH$; $HOCH_2(CH_3)(C_2H_5)COH$; $C_6H_5CO_2H$	*207*
$C_6H_5CO_2$-*t*-C_4H_9 (0.3 mole)	C_6H_5MgBr (0.5 mole C_6H_5Br)	$(C_6H_5)_3COH$ (41%); $C_6H_5CO_2H$ (10%)	*117*
$C_6H_5CO_2C_6H_5$	$(C_6H_5)_3CMgBr$	$C_6H_5COC(C_6H_5)_3$ (46%)	*16*
$C_6H_5CO_2CH_2C_6H_5$	C_6H_5MgBr	$(C_6H_5)_3COH$ (60%); $C_6H_5CH_2OC(C_6H_5)_3$ (2.3%)*	*401*
$C_6H_5CO_2CH_2C_6H_5$	C_6H_5MgBr	$(C_6H_5)_3COH$ (15%); $C_6H_5CH_2OC(C_6H_5)_3$ (30%); $C_6H_5CH_2Br$†	*401*
$C_6H_5CO_2CH_2C_6H_5$ (40 g.)	C_6H_5MgBr (60 g. C_6H_5Br)	C_6H_5OH; $C_6H_5CO_2H$; $C_6H_5CH_2OH$; $C_6H_5CH{=}C(C_6H_5)_2$‡ (0.55 g.); $(C_6H_5)_3COH$ (35.6 g., 75%); unidentified oil (6.0 g.)§	*398*
$C_6H_5CO_2CH_2C_6H_5$ (20 g.)	C_6H_5MgBr (16 g. C_6H_5Br)	$(C_6H_5)_3COH$ (15%); $C_6H_5CH_2OC(C_6H_5)_3$ (30%)¶	*398*
$C_6H_5CO_2CH_2C_6H_5$ (45 g.)	C_6H_5MgBr (65 g. C_6H_5Br)	$(C_6H_5)_3COH$ (60%); $C_6H_5CH_2OC(C_6H_5)_3$ (2.3%); $C_6H_5CH_2OH$; recovered ester‖	*402*
$C_6H_5CO_2CH_2C_6H_5$ (40 g.)	C_6H_5MgBr (60 g. C_6H_5Br)	$C_6H_5CO_2H$ (0.25 g.); $(C_6H_5)_3COH$ (29.1 g.); C_6H_5Br (5.9 g.); $C_6H_5CH_2OH$ (12.8 g.); $(C_6H_5-)_2$ (0.57 g.)**	*63*
$C_6H_5CO_2CH(COCH_3)$-*n*-C_5H_{11} (13.2 g.)	CH_3MgBr (10.0 g.)	$C_6H_5(CH_3)_2COH$ (3.0 g.); $HO(CH_3)_2CCH(OH)$-*n*-C_5H_{11} (6.0 g.)	*496*
9-Benzoxymethylcarbazole (7.62 g.)	C_6H_5MgBr (4.75 g. C_6H_5Br)	9-Benzylcarbazole; $C_6H_5CO_2H$ (1.4 g.)	*285*

* Reaction at the boiling point of ethyl ether solution.

† Reaction at 100°.

‡ *Cf.* Boyd and Hatt (*63*), who suggest that this product is biphenyl.

§ Moderately rapid addition of ester to intermittently cooled Grignard reagent solution; ten hours reflux.

¶ Addition of ester to ice-cooled Grignard reagent solution; five hours in pressure bottle at 100°.

‖ Gradual addition of ester to Grignard reagent solution; six hours reflux.

** "Method of Stadnikoff" (*398*)§.

Ester	RMgX	Product(s)	Ref.
$C_7H_5O_2$-R (*cont.*)			
$C_6H_5CO_2C(C_6H_5)_3$ (6.0 g., 0.015 mole)	CH_3MgI (13.5 g., 0.098 mole CH_3I)	$CH_3C(C_6H_5)_3$ (2.3 g., 43%); $C_6H_5CO_2H$ (1.0 g., 85%)	*153*
$C_7H_5O_3$-R			
2-$HOC_6H_4CO_2CH_3$	C_6H_5MgBr (4 equiv.)	2-$HOC_6H_4(C_6H_5)_2COH$ (80%)	*20*
2-$HOC_6H_4CO_2CH_3$ (30 g.)	1-$C_{10}H_7MgBr$ (160 g. $C_{10}H_7Br$)	2-HOC_6H_4(1-$C_{10}H_7)_2COH$	*197*
2-$HOC_6H_4CO_2$-*i*-C_4H_9 (48.5 g.)	*i*-C_3H_7MgBr (123.0 g. C_3H_7Br)	2-HOC_6H_4(*i*-$C_3H_7)_2COH$ (15.0 g.)	*328*
3-$HOC_6H_4CO_2C_2H_5$	C_6H_5MgBr	3-$HOC_6H_4(C_6H_5)_2COH$	*20*
$C_7H_5O_4$-R			
2,5-$(HO)_2C_6H_3CO_2C_2H_5$	C_6H_5MgBr	2,5-$(HO)_2C_6H_3(C_6H_5)_2COH$ (60%)	*21*
$C_7H_6O_2ClN_2$-R			
Ethyl 2-methyl-4-chloro-5-pyrimidineacetate	CH_3MgX	2-Methyl-4-chloro-5-(β-hydroxyisobutyl)pyrimidine; 2-methyl-4-chloro-5-acetonylpyrimidine	*308*
$C_7H_6O_2N$-R			
Ethyl 6-methyl-3-pyridinecarboxylate*	CH_3MgI	2-(6-Methyl-3-pyridyl)-2-propanol	*309*
$C_7H_8O_2Cl$-R			
Ethyl 2-chloro-2-cyclohexene-1-carboxylate	C_6H_5MgBr	α,α-Diphenyl-2-chloro-2-cyclohexene-1-methanol	*297*
$C_7H_8O_2N$-R			
Ethyl 3,5-dimethyl-2-pyrrolecarboxylate	C_2H_5MgBr	Recovered ester ("probably through enolate")	*172*

* 2-Methyl-5-carbethoxypyridine.

TABLE VIII-III (Continued)

Ester	RMgX	Product(s)	Ref.
$C_7H_8O_4$-R_2			
n-$C_3H_7CH{=}C(CO_2C_2H_5)_2$ (0.16 mole)	1-$C_{10}H_7CH_2MgCl$ (0.21 mole $C_{11}H_9Cl$)	n-$C_3H_7(1$-$C_{10}H_7CH_2)CHCH(CO_2C_2H_5)_2$ (68%)	360
n-$C_3H_7CH{=}C(CO_2C_2H_5)_2$ (0.16 mole)	1-$C_{10}H_7CH_2MgCl$ (0.21 mole $C_{11}H_9Cl$) + $CdCl_2$ (0.20 mole)	n-$C_3H_7(1$-$C_{10}H_7CH_2)CHCH(CO_2C_2H_5)_2$ (77%)	360
$C_7H_9O_2$-R			
$(CH_2)_4CHCO_2C_2H_5$	n-$C_{10}H_{21}MgBr$	$(CH_2)_4CH(n$-$C_{10}H_{21})_2COH$ (yielding 42% paraffin)	453
$C_7H_9O_3$-R			
Ethyl 2-oxocyclopentaneacetate*	CH_3MgX	2-Hydroxy-2-methylcyclopentaneacetic acid γ-lactone	385
$C_7H_{10}O_2N$-R			
$NCC(C_2H_5)_2CO_2C_2H_5$	C_2H_5MgX†	$(C_2H_5)_2CO$; $(C_2H_5)_2CHCN$; $(C_2H_5)_3COH$; $(C_2H_5)_2CHCO_2C_2H_5$; $(C_2H_5)_2CHCOC(C_2H_5)_2CO_2C_2H_5$; $NCC(C_2H_5)_2C(C_2H_5)_2OH$	263
$NCC(C_2H_5)_2CO_2C_2H_5$	C_6H_5MgBr	$(C_6H_5)_2CO$; $(C_2H_5)_2CHCOC(C_2H_5)_2CO_2C_2H_5$	263
$C_7H_{10}O_4$-R_2			
$CH_3(H_3CO_2CCH_2)CH$—$(CH_2)_2CO_2CH_3$	CH_3MgI	$HO(CH_3)_2CCH_2CH(CH_3)(CH_2)_2C(CH_3)_2OH$	23
$C_7H_{11}O_2$-R			
$(CH_2)_5CHCO_2CH_3$	CH_3MgI	$(CH_2)_5CHC(CH_3)_2OH$	300

* 2-Carbethoxymethylcyclopentanone.

† X = Br, I.

TABLE VIII-III (Continued)

Ester	RMgX	Product(s)	Ref.
$C_7H_{11}O_2$-R (*cont.*)			
$(CH_2)_5CHCO_2C_2H_5$	CH_3MgI	$(CH_2)_5CH(CH_3)_2COH$	*155*
$(CH_2)_5CHCO_2C_2H_5$	C_2H_5MgBr	$(CH_2)_5CH(C_2H_5)_2COH$	*155*
$(CH_2)_5CHCO_2C_2H_5$	C_6H_5MgBr	$(CH_2)_5CH(C_6H_5)_2COH$	*155*
$(CH_2)_5CHCO_2C_2H_5$ (3 g.)	C_6H_5MgI (15 g. C_6H_5I)	$(CH_2)_5CH(C_6H_5)_2COH$ (*ca.* 2 g.); $(C_6H_5—)_2$	*376*
$(CH_2)_5CHCO_2C_2H_5$ (22.5 g.)	t-$C_4H_9C\equiv CMgBr$ (24 g. t-$C_4H_9C\equiv CH$)	$(CH_2)_5CH(t$-$C_4H_9C\equiv C)_2COH$ (70%)	*126*
$(CH_2)_5CHCO_2C_2H_5$ (31 g.)	$(CH_2)_5CHMgCl$ (100 g. $C_6H_{11}Cl$)	$[(CH_2)_5CH—]_2$ (6 g.); $[(CH_2)_5CH]_2CO$ (27 g.); $[(CH_2)_5CH]_3COH$ (*ca.* 4 g.)	*303*
$(CH_2)_5CHCO_2C_2H_5$	$(CH_2)_5CHMgBr$	$[(CH_2)_5CH]_2CO$; $[(CH_2)_5CH]_2CHOH$	*296*
$(CH_2)_5CHCO_2CH_2CH=CH_2$	C_6H_5MgBr	$(CH_2)_2CH(C_6H_5)_2COH$	*6*
$C_7H_{11}O_3$-R			
$(CH_2)_5C(OH)CO_2CH_3$	CH_3MgI (4 equiv.)	$(CH_2)_5C(OH)C(CH_3)_2OH$ (94%)	*280,413*
$(CH_2)_5C(OH)CO_2CH_3$ (20 g.)	C_6H_5MgBr (80 g. C_6H_5Br)	$(CH_2)_5C(OH)C(C_6H_5)_2OH$ (27 g.)	*280*
$C_7H_{12}O_2N$-R			
$(CH_2)_5C(NH_2)CO_2C_2H_5$	CH_3MgI (3 equiv.)	$(CH_2)_5C(NH_2)COCH_3$	*128*
$(CH_2)_5C(NH_2)CO_2C_2H_5$	CH_3MgI (5 equiv.)	$(CH_2)_5C(NH_2)C(CH_3)_2OH$; $(CH_2)_5C(NH_2)COCH_3$; 8,16-dimethyl-7,5-diazadispiro[5.2.5.2]hexadeca-7,15-diene	*128*
$(CH_2)_5C(NH_2)CO_2C_2H_5$	C_2H_5MgBr (3 equiv.)	$(CH_2)_5C(NH_2)COC_2H_5$	*128*
$(CH_2)_5C(NH_2)CO_2C_2H_5$	C_6H_5MgBr (3 equiv.)	$(CH_2)_5C(NH_2)COC_6H_5$	*128*
$C_7H_{13}O_2$-R			
n-$C_6H_{13}CO_2C_2H_5$	CH_3MgX (2 equiv.)	n-$C_6H_{13}(CH_3)_2COH$ (80–85%); corresponding olefin (*ca.* 1%)	*259*
n-$C_6H_{13}CO_2C_2H_5$	t-C_4H_9MgCl	$(n$-$C_6H_{13})_2CO$	*329*

TABLE VIII-III (Continued)

Ester	RMgX	Product(s)	Ref.
$C_7H_{13}O_2$-R (*cont.*)			
(+)-*n*-$C_3H_7CH(C_2H_5)CO_2C_2H_5$	CH_3MgI	After dehydr'n and hydrogen'n, (+)-$CH_3(C_2H_5)$(*i*-C_5H_{11})CH	*241*
$CH_3(C_2H_5)_2CCO_2C_2H_5$	CH_3MgBr	Addition (45%); enolization (25%)*	*457*
$CH_3(C_2H_5)_2CCO_2$-*n*-C_4H_9	CH_3MgBr	Addition (60%); enolization (22%)*	*457*
$C_8H_4O_3N$-R			
Ethyl α-cyano-β-(2-furyl)acrylate (40 g.)	*n*-C_3H_7MgBr (70 g. C_3H_7Br)	*n*-C_3H_7(α-C_4H_3O)CHCH(CN)$CO_2C_2H_5$ (40 g., 82%)	*264*
Ethyl α-cyano-β-(2-furyl)acrylate (20 g.)	*i*-C_4H_9MgCl (27 g. C_4H_9Cl)	*i*-C_4H_9(α-C_4H_3O)CHCH(CN)$CO_2C_2H_5$ (24 g.)	*264*
$C_8H_4O_4$-R_2			
C_6H_4-1,2-$(CO_2CH_3)_2$	C_2H_5MgI	3,3-Diethylphthalide	*382*
C_6H_5-1,2-$(CO_2CH_3)_2$	C_6H_5MgBr (large excess)	1,3,3-Triphenyl-1-phthalanol (90%)†	*145,146*
C_6H_4-1,2-$(CO_2CH_3)_2$ (18.0 g.)	C_6H_5MgBr (83.7 g. C_6H_5Br)	$C_{26}H_{18}O$, m. 192–193°‡§	*167;cf.382*
C_6H_5-1,2-$(CO_2C_2H_5)_2$	CH_3MgI (4 equiv.)	1,1-Dimethyl-3-methylenephthalan¶	*382*
C_6H_5-1,2-$(CO_2C_2H_5)_2$	C_2H_5MgX‖	3,3-Diethylphthalide	*382*

* "Grignard machine" study; according to Whitmore and Lewis (*457*), the apparent enolization of these esters is actually that of the ketones formed by reaction with the Grignard reagent (see textual discussion).

† Pérard, *Ann. chim.*, [9], 7, 344, f'tnote (1917), suggests that the product of Guyot and Catel (*145*) [and hence the corresponding product of Howell (*167*)] should be formulated as 2-$C_6H_5COC_6H_4C(C_6H_5)_2OH$.

‡ Purification by steam-distillation; recovery by distillation at reduced pressure.

§ According to Howell (*167*), this product [doubtless 10,10-diphenyl-9-anthrone—see Barnett *et al.* (*25*)] is the dehydrate of the "1,3,3-triphenyl-1-phthalanol" of Guyot and Catel (*145*), and is identical with the "1,1-diphenyl-3-phenylenephthalan" of Shibata (*382*).

¶ Possibly 2-$CH_3COC_6H_4C(CH_3)$=CH_2 [*cf.* Barnett *et al.* (*25*)].

‖ X = Br, I.

TABLE VIII-III (Continued)

Ester	RMgX	Product(s)	Ref.
$C_8H_4O_4$-R_2 *(cont.)*			
C_6H_5-1,2-$(CO_2C_2H_5)_2$ (10.0 g.)	Pyrryl-MgBr (6.7 g. pyrrole)	3-(2-Pyrroleninylidene)phthalide	*129*
C_6H_4-1,2-$(CO_2C_2H_5)_2$ (18.0 g.)	C_6H_5MgBr (83.7 g. C_6H_5Br)	$C_{26}H_{18}O$, m. 192–193° *†	*167*
C_6H_4-1,2-$(CO_2C_2H_5)_2$ (23.0 g.)	C_6H_5MgBr (125.6 g. C_6H_5Br)	1,3,3-Triphenyl-1-phthalanol‡ §	*167*
C_6H_4-1,2-$(CO_2C_2H_5)_2$	C_6H_5MgBr (4 equiv.)	10,10-Diphenyl-9-anthrone	*25;cf.382*
C_6H_4-1,2-$(CO_2C_2H_5)_2$	$C_6H_5CH_2MgCl$	3,3-Dibenzylphthalide	*382*
C_6H_4-1,2-$(CO_2$-n-$C_4H_9)_2$ (69.5 g.)	C_6H_5MgBr (39.0 g. C_6H_5Br)	2-$C_6H_5COC_6H_4CO_2$-n-C_4H_9 (yielding 7.0 g. acid; 3,3-diphenylphthalide; $(C_6H_5—)_2$ (2.0 g.)	*233*
C_6H_4-1,3-$(CO_2CH_3)_2$ (20 g.)	C_6H_5MgBr (65 g. C_6H_5Br)	C_6H_4-1,3-$[C(C_6H_5)_2OH]_2$ (40 g., crude)	*403*
C_6H_4-1,4-$(CO_2CH_3)_2$ (15 g.)	C_6H_5MgBr (50 g. C_6H_5Br)	C_6H_4-1,4-$[C(C_6H_5)_2OH]_2$ (25 g., crude)	*415,483*
$C_8H_4O_5$-R			
Diethyl furfurylidenemalonate (25 g.)	i-C_4H_9MgCl (27 g. C_4H_9Cl)	i-C_4H_9(α-C_4H_3O)$CHCH(CO_2C_2H_5)_2$ (22 g., 71%)	*264*
Diethyl furfurylidenemalonate (40 g.)	i-$C_5H_{11}MgBr$ (43 g. $C_5H_{11}Br$)	i-C_5H_{11}(α-C_4H_3O)$CHCH(CO_2C_2H_5)_2$ (45 g., 87%)	*264*
Diethyl furfurylidenemalonate (15 g.)	C_6H_5MgBr (28 g. C_6H_5Br)	C_6H_5(α-C_4H_3O)$CHCH(CO_2C_2H_5)_2$ (15 g., 77%)	*264*

* Purification by steam-distillation; recovery by distillation at reduced pressure.

† According to Howell (*167*), this product [doubtless 10,10-diphenyl-9-anthrone—see Barnett *et al.* (*25*)] is the dehydrate of the "1,3,3-triphenyl-1-phthalanol" of Guyot and Catel (*145*), and is identical with the "1,1-diphenyl-3-phenylenephthalan" of Shibata (*382*).

‡ Pérard, *Ann.chim.*, [9], 7, 344, f'tnote (1917), suggests that the product of Guyot and Catel (*145*) [and hence the corresponding product of Howell (*167*)] should be formulated as 2-$C_6H_5COC_6H_4C(C_6H_5)_2OH$.

§ Purification and recovery by crystallization.

TABLE VIII-III (Continued)

Ester	RMgX	Product(s)	Ref.
$C_8H_5O_4$-R			
3,4-CH_2O_2=$C_6H_3CO_2CH_3$	CH_3MgI (4 equiv.)	3,4-CH_2O_2=$C_6H_3C(CH_3)$=CH_2	*33*
3,4-CH_2O_2=$C_6H_3CO_2CH_3$	C_6H_5MgBr	3,4-CH_2O_2=$C_6H_3(C_6H_5)_2COH$	*62*
2-$HO_2CC_6H_4CO_2C_2H_5$	C_2H_5MgBr	3,3-Diethylphthalide	*382*
2-$HO_2CC_6H_4CO_2C_2H_5$	C_6H_5MgBr	"1,1-Diphenyl-3-phenylenephthalan"*	*382*
2-$HO_2CC_6H_4CO_2C_2H_5$	$C_6H_5CH_2MgCl$	3,3-Dibenzylphthalide; 1,1-dibenzyl-3-benzylidenephthalan†	*382*
$C_8H_6O_2Br$-R			
$C_6H_5CHBrCO_2C_2H_5$	$C_6H_5CH(CO_2Na)MgCl$‡	$C_6H_5CH(CO_2H)CH(C_6H_5)CO_2C_2H_5$ (38.4%)	*405*
$C_8H_6O_2Cl$-R			
4-$ClC_6H_4CH_2CO_2C_2H_5$	*i*-C_3H_7MgCl	4-$ClC_6H_4CH_2COCH(C_6H_5)CO_2C_2H_5$ (93%)	*183*
$C_8H_7O_2$-R			
$C_6H_5CH_2CO_2C_2H_5$	CH_3MgI	$C_6H_5CH_2(CH_3)_2COH$	*204*
$C_6H_5CH_2CO_2C_2H_5$	C_2H_5MgI	$C_6H_5CH_2(C_2H_5)_2COH$ (65%)	*204*
$C_6H_5CH_2CO_2C_2H_5$ (0.1 mole)	*i*-C_3H_7MgCl (0.15 mole)	$C_6H_5CH_2COCH(C_6H_5)CO_2C_2H_5$; C_3H_8	*183*
$C_6H_5CH_2CO_2C_2H_5$ (49.2 g., 0.3 mole)	*i*-C_3H_7MgBr (0.5 mole)	$C_6H_5CH_2COCH(C_6H_5)CO_2C_2H_5$ (39.5 g., 94%); "saturated gas"	*87*
$C_6H_5CH_2CO_2C_2H_5$	C_6H_5MgBr	$C_6H_5CH_2(C_6H_5)_2COH$ ("good yield")	*205*
$C_6H_5CH_2CO_2C_2H_5$	$C_6H_5CH_2MgCl$	$(C_6H_5CH_2)_3COH$	*205*

* Doubtless 10,10-diphenyl-9-anthrone.

† Possibly 2-$C_6H_5CH_2COC_6H_4C(CH_2C_6H_5)$=$CHC_6H_5$.

‡ In the opinion of Schlenk, Hilleman, and Rodloff, *Ann.*, *487*, 135–54 (1931), this "Grignard reagent" should be formulated as an enolate.

TABLE VIII-III (Continued)

Ester	RMgX	Product(s)	Ref.
$C_8H_7O_2$-R (*cont.*)			
$C_6H_5CH_2CO_2C_2H_5$ + 2-$CH_3C_6H_4CO_2C_2H_5$ (0.1 mole each)	$C_6H_5CH_2MgCl$ (0.2 mole)	2-$CH_3C_6H_4CO_2C_2H_5$ (72% recovery); $C_6H_5CH_2CO_2H$ (1 g.); $(C_6H_5CH_2)_3COH$ (corresponding to 71% conversion of $C_6H_5CH_2CO_2C_2H_5$)	*10*
$C_6H_5CH_2CO_2C_2H_5$	$C_6H_5CH_2MgBr$	$(C_6H_5CH_2)_3COH$	*364*
2-$CH_3C_6H_4CO_2CH_3$ (13.6 g.)	C_6H_5MgBr (31.0 g. C_6H_5Br)	2-$CH_3C_6H_4(C_6H_5)_2COH$ (11.0 g.)	*48*
2-$CH_3C_6H_4CO_2C_2H_5$	C_6H_5MgBr	2-$CH_3C_6H_4(C_6H_5)_2COH$ (39.7%); [C_6H_5(2-$CH_3C_6H_4$)COH —]$_2$ (13.6%)*	*63*
2-$CH_3C_6H_4CO_2C_2H_5$ (7.5 g.)	C_6H_5MgBr	[C_6H_5(2-$CH_3C_6H_4$)COH —]$_2$ (0.02 g., 0.26%); 2-$CH_3C_6H_4(C_6H_5)_2COH$ (1.29 g.); $C_2H_5OC(C_6H_5)_2C_6H_4$-2-CH_3 (0.77 g.)†	*63*
2-$CH_3C_6H_4CO_2C_2H_5$ (7.5 g.)	C_6H_5MgBr (16.2 g. C_6H_5Br) + excess Mg	[C_6H_5(2-$CH_3C_6H_4$)COH —]$_2$ (3.62 g., 38%); 2-$CH_3C_6H_4(C_6H_5)_2COH$ (2.92 g., 23.3%)‡	*63*
2-$CH_3C_6H_4CO_2C_2H_5$	$C_6H_5CH_2MgCl$ (excess)	*No* dibenzyl-*o*-tolylmethanol; liquid believed to be benzyl-*o*-tolyl ketone	*10*
2-$CH_3C_6H_4CO_2C_2H_5$ (6.7 g.)	2-$CH_3C_6H_4MgBr$ (16.5 g. C_7H_7Br) + Mg	[(2-$CH_3C_6H_4$)$_2$COH —]$_2$ (5.2%); (2-$CH_3C_6H_4$)$_2$CHOH (0.71 g.)	*63*
2-$CH_3C_6H_4CO_2CH_2CH{=}CH_2$ (15.0 g.)	C_6H_5MgBr (30 g. C_6H_5Br)	2-$CH_3C_6H_4(C_6H_5)_2COH$ (15.4 g.)	*4*
3-$CH_3C_6H_4CO_2CH_3$	C_6H_5MgBr	3-$CH_3C_6H_4(C_6H_5)_2COH$ (81%)	*48*
3-$CH_3C_6H_4CO_2C_2H_5$	C_6H_5MgBr	3-$CH_3C_6H_4(C_6H_5)_2COH$ (5.3 g.); (C_6H_5 —)$_2$ (1.2 g.)	*2*
4-$CH_3C_6H_4CO_2CH_3$ (13.8 g.)	C_6H_5MgBr (31.0 g. C_6H_5Br)	4-$CH_3C_6H_4(C_6H_5)_2COH$ (20.0 g.)	*484*
4-$CH_3C_6H_4CO_2CH_3$	4-$CH_3C_6H_4MgI$	(4-$CH_3C_6H_4$)$_3$COH	*293*
4-$CH_3C_6H_4CO_2C_2H_5$ (37.1 g.)	4-*t*-$C_4H_9C_6H_4MgBr$ (106.5 g. $C_{10}H_{13}Br$)	4-$CH_3C_6H_4$(4-*t*-$C_4H_9C_6H_4$)$_2$COH (24 g.)	*257*

* Addition of Et_2O-ester solution to Grignard reagent solution.

† Addition of Et_2O-ester solution to *filtered* Grignard reagent solution.

‡ Gradual addition of filtered Grignard reagent solution to stirred Et_2O-ester solution and excess Mg; one hour reflux. Reaction under N_2.

TABLE VIII-III (Continued)

Ester	RMgX	Product(s)	Ref.
$C_8H_7O_3$-R			
$C_6H_5OCH_2CO_2C_2H_5$	CH_3MgX	$C_6H_5OCH_2(CH_3)_2COH$ (70%)	*408*
$C_6H_5OCH_2CO_2C_2H_5$	C_2H_5MgBr	$C_6H_5OCH_2(C_2H_5)_2COH$	*31*
$C_6H_5OCH_2CO_2C_2H_5$	C_6H_5MgBr	$C_6H_5OCH_2(C_6H_5)_2COH$ (71%)	*408*
$C_6H_5OCH_2CO_2C_2H_5$	4-$CH_3C_6H_4MgBr$ (2 equiv.)	$C_6H_5OCH_2(4\text{-}CH_3C_6H_4)_2COH$ (65%)	*408*
2-$CH_3OC_6H_4CO_2CH_3$	CH_3MgI (2 equiv.)	2-$CH_3OC_6H_4(CH_3)_2COH$	*32*
2-$CH_3OC_6H_4CO_2CH_3$	CH_3MgI (3 equiv.)	2-$CH_3C_6H_4C(CH_3){=}CH_2$	*32*
2-$CH_3OC_6H_4CO_2CH_3$	C_6H_5MgBr	2-$CH_3OC_6H_4(C_6H_5)_2COH$	*20*
3-$CH_3OC_6H_4CO_2C_2H_5$	CH_3MgI (2 equiv.)	3-$CH_3OC_6H_4(CH_3)_2COH$	*32*
3-$CH_3OC_6H_4CO_2C_2H_5$	CH_3MgI (3 equiv.)	3-$CH_3OC_6H_4C(CH_3){=}CH_2$	*32*
4-$CH_3OC_6H_4CO_2R$*	CH_3MgI (2 or 3 equiv.)	4-$CH_3OC_6H_4C(CH_3){=}CH_2$ (*ca.* 50%); dimer	*32*
4-$CH_3OC_6H_4CO_2CH_3$	$C_6H_5CH_2MgCl$	4-$CH_3OC_6H_4(C_6H_5CH_2)_2COH$ (75%)	*208*
4-$CH_3OC_6H_4CO_2C_2H_5$	C_2H_5MgBr (3 equiv.)	4-$CH_3OC_6H_4(C_2H_5)_2COH$	*445*
2-HO-3-$CH_3C_6H_3CO_2CH_3$	CH_3MgI (4 equiv.)	2-HO-3-$CH_3C_6H_3C(CH_3){=}CH_2$	*34*
2-HO-3-$CH_3C_6H_3CO_2CH_3$	CH_3MgI (3.5 equiv.)	2-HO-3-$CH_3C_6H_3C(CH_3)_2OH$; 2-HO-3-$CH_3C_6H_3C(CH_3){=}CH_2$	*144*
2-HO-4-$CH_3C_6H_3CO_2CH_3$	CH_3MgI (3.5 equiv.)	2-HO-4-$CH_3C_6H_3C(CH_3)_2OH$; 2-HO-4-$CH_3C_6H_3C(CH_3){=}CH_2$	*144*
2-HO-5-$CH_3C_6H_3CO_2CH_3$	CH_3MgI (3.5 equiv.)	2-HO-5-$CH_3C_6H_3C(CH_3)_2OH$	*144*
$C_6H_5CH(OH)CO_2CH_3$ (3 g.)	C_6H_5MgBr (11 g. C_6H_5Br)	$C_6H_5CH(OH)C(C_6H_5)_2OH$ (4 g.)	*1*
$C_6H_5CH(OH)CO_2CH_3$ (16.6 g.)	$C_6H_5CH_2MgCl$ (63.5 g. C_7H_7Cl)	$C_6H_5CH(OH)C(CH_2C_6H_5)_2OH$ (26 g., 81%)	*312*
$C_6H_5CH(OH)CO_2C_2H_5$	C_2H_5MgBr	$C_6H_5CH(OH)C(C_2H_5)_2OH$	*419*
$C_6H_5CH(OH)CO_2C_2H_5$ (40 g.)	*n*-C_3H_7MgBr (from 90 g. bromide)	$C_6H_5CH(OH)C(n\text{-}C_3H_7)_2OH$	*420*
$C_6H_5CH(OH)CO_2C_2H_5$ (22.5 g.)	*n*-C_4H_9MgI (95.0 g. C_4H_9I)	$C_6H_5CH(OH)C(n\text{-}C_4H_9)_2OH$	*420*

*R = CH_3, C_2H_5.

TABLE VIII-III (Continued)

Ester	RMgX	Product(s)	Ref.
$C_8H_7O_3$-R (*cont.*)			
$C_6H_5CH(OH)CO_2C_2H_5$	C_6H_5MgBr (3.5 equiv.)	$C_6H_5CH(OH)C(C_6H_5)_2OH$	*420*
$C_6H_5CH(OH)CO_2C_2H_5$	$C_6H_5CH_2MgBr$	$C_6H_5CH(OH)C(CH_2C_6H_5)_2OH$ (54%)	*43*
DL-$C_6H_5CH(OH)CO_2C_2H_5$	2-$CH_3C_6H_4MgBr$ (4.5 equiv.)	Unstable oil	*362,408*
DL-$C_6H_5CH(OH)CO_2C_2H_5$	3-$CH_3C_6H_4MgBr$ (4 equiv.)	$C_6H_5CH(OH)C(C_6H_4$-3-$CH_3)_2OH$	*362*
D(−)-$C_6H_5CH(OH)CO_2C_2H_5$	*n*-C_3H_7MgBr (4 equiv.)	D(+)-$C_6H_5CH(OH)C(n$-$C_3H_7)_2OH$	*269*
D(−)-$C_6H_5CH(OH)CO_2C_2H_5$	C_6H_5MgBr	D(+)-$C_6H_5CH(OH)C(C_6H_5)_2OH$	*362*
D(−)-$C_6H_5CH(OH)CO_2C_2H_5$	4-$CH_3C_6H_4MgBr$ (5 equiv.)	D(+)-$C_6H_5CH(OH)C(C_6H_4$-*n*-$CH_3)_2OH$	*362*
L(−)-$C_6H_5CH(OH)CO_2CH_3$	CH_3MgI	L(−)-$C_6H_5CH(OH)C(CH_3)_2OH$	*278*
L(−)-$C_6H_5CH(OH)CO_2CH_3$	C_6H_5MgBr	L(+)-$C_6H_5CH(OH)C(C_6H_5)_2OH$	*278*
L(−)-$C_6H_5CH(OH)CO_2C_2H_5$	C_2H_5MgBr (3.5 equiv.)	L(−)-$C_6H_5CH(OH)C(C_6H_5)_2OH$	*269*
$C_8H_7O_4$-R			
3-CH_3O-4-$HOC_6H_3CO_2C_2H_5$	CH_3MgI (3 equiv.)	3-CH_3O-4-$HOC_6H_3C(CH_3)_2OH$; dimer	*33*
$C_8H_8O_2NS$-R			
$C_6H_5SO_2HNCH_2CO_2C_2H_5$	C_6H_5MgBr	$C_6H_5SO_2HNCH_2(C_6H_5)_2COH$ (51%)	*45*
$C_8H_9O_2ClN$-R			
$HCl\cdot HN(C_6H_5)CH_2CO_2C_2H_5$	CH_3MgBr	$C_6H_5HNCH_2(CH_3)_2COH$	*45*
$C_6H_5CH(NH_2\cdot HCl)CO_2C_2H_5$	C_2H_5MgBr	$C_6H_5CH(NH_2)C(C_2H_5)_2OH$ (65%)	*416*
$C_6H_5CH(NH_2\cdot HCl)CO_2C_2H_5$ (16.6 g.)	C_6H_5MgBr (145.0 g. C_6H_5Br)	$C_6H_5CH(NH_2)C(C_6H_5)_2OH$ (11.0 g., 49%)	*273*
$C_6H_5CH(NH_2\cdot HCl)CO_2C_2H_5$	C_6H_5MgBr	$C_6H_5CH(NH_2)C(C_6H_5)_2OH$ (72%)	*416*
$C_6H_5CH(NH_2\cdot HCl)CO_2C_2H_5$ (10.0 g.)	$C_6H_5CH_2MgCl$ (52.5 g. C_7H_7Cl)	$C_6H_5CH(NH_2)C(CH_2C_6H_5)_2OH$	*274*
$C_6H_5CH(NH_2\cdot HCl)CO_2C_2H_5$	$C_6H_5CH_2MgBr$	$C_6H_5CH(NH_2)C(CH_2C_6H_5)_2OH$ (61%)	*416*

TABLE VIII-III (Continued)

Ester	RMgX	Product(s)	Ref.
$C_8H_9O_2ClN$-R (*cont.*)			
$C_6H_5CH(NH_2{\cdot}HCl)CO_2C_2H_5$ (6.2 g.)	1-$C_{10}H_7MgBr$ (75.0 g. $C_{10}H_7Br$)	No identified product	*273*
DL-$C_6H_5CH(NH_2{\cdot}HCl)CO_2C_2H_5$ (10 g.)	CH_3MgI (59 g. CH_3I)	DL-$C_6H_5CH(NH_2)C(CH_3)_2OH$	*269;cf.273*
DL-$C_6H_5CH(NH_2{\cdot}HCl)CO_2C_2H_5$ (5 g.)	n-C_3H_7MgBr (26 g. C_3H_7Br)	DL-$C_6H_5CH(NH_2)C(n\text{-}C_3H_7)_2OH$	*269*
D-$C_6H_5CH(NH_2{\cdot}HCl)CO_2C_2H_5$ (6 g.)	C_6H_5MgBr (52 g. C_6H_5Br)	D-$C_6H_5CH(NH_2)C(C_6H_5)_2OH$ (2 g., crude)	*275*
D-$C_6H_5CH(NH_2{\cdot}HCl)CO_2C_2H_5$ (12 g.)	$C_6H_5CH_2MgCl$ (63 g. C_7H_7Cl)	D-$C_6H_5CH(NH_2)C(CH_2C_6H_5)_2OH$ (8.2 g.)	*271*
L-$C_6H_5CH(NH_2{\cdot}HCl)CO_2C_2H_5$ (10 g.)	C_2H_5MgBr (51 g. C_2H_5Br)	L-$C_6H_5CH(NH_2)C(C_2H_5)_2OH$	*269*
L-$C_6H_5CH(NH_2{\cdot}HCl)CO_2C_2H_5$ (5 g.)	n-C_3H_7MgBr (26 g. C_3H_7Br)	L-$C_6H_5CH(NH_2)C(n\text{-}C_3H_7)_2OH$	*269*
L-$C_6H_5CH(NH_2{\cdot}HCl)CO_2C_2H_5$ (5 g.)	C_6H_5MgBr (12 equiv.)	L-$C_6H_5CH(NH_2)C(C_6H_5)_2OH$ (6 g., crude)	*275*
$C_8H_9O_3$-R			
Methyl 5-isopropyl-2-furoate	CH_3MgBr (2 equiv.)	2-(2-Hydroxy-2-propyl)-5-isopropylfuran (90%)	*14*
$C_8H_{10}O_4$-R_2			
$(CH_3)_2C{=}CHCH_2CH(CO_2C_2H_5)_2$	CH_3MgBr	Recovered ester (*quant.*)	*386*
Diethyl hexahydrophthalate	CH_3MgI	Cyclohexane-1,2-bisdimethylmethanol	*465*
$C_8H_{12}O_4$-R_2			
$[{-}(CH_2)_3CO_2CH_3]_2$	C_6H_5MgBr	$[{-}(CH_2)_3C(C_6H_5)_2OH]_2$ (yielding 80–90% alkene)	*377*
$[{-}(CH_2)_3CO_2C_2H_5]_2$ (0.2 mole)	t-C_4H_9MgCl (2.5 mole)	$[{-}(CH_2)_3C(t\text{-}C_4H_9)_2OH]_2$	*336*
$C_8H_{13}O_6$-R			
"Methyl 3,4,5-trimethyl-α-ketoärabonate" (20.20 g.)	CH_3MgI (13.06 g. CH_3I)	"Methyl 3,4,5-trimethylsaccharinate" (60%)	*123*

TABLE VIII-III (Continued)

Ester	RMgX	Product(s)	Ref.
$C_8H_{15}O_2$-R			
n-$C_7H_{15}CO_2CH_3$	C_6H_5MgBr	n-$C_7H_{15}(C_6H_5)_2COH$ (yielding 80–90% alkene)	*377*
n-$C_7H_{15}CO_2C_2H_5$	n-$C_8H_{17}MgBr$	n-$C_7H_{15}(n$-$C_8H_{17})_2COH$; dehydr'n product	*339*
$CH_3(i$-$C_5H_{11})CHCO_2CH_3$	CH_3MgI	$CH_3(i$-$C_5H_{11})CHC(CH_3)_2OH$	*23*
$C_2H_5(n$-$C_4H_9)CHCO_2CH_2CH{=}CH_2$ (31.5 g.)	C_6H_5MgBr (36.6 g. C_6H_5Br)	$C_2H_5(n$-$C_4H_9)CHCO_2H$ (30%); $C_6H_5CH_2CH{=}CH_2$ (26%); $C_2H_5(n$-$C_4H_9)CHC(C_6H_5)_2OH$ (49%); $C_2H_5(n$-$C_4H_9)C{=}C(C_6H_5)_2$	*6*
D-n-$C_3H_7(i$-$C_3H_7)CHCO_2C_2H_5$	CH_3MgI	After dehydr'n and hydrogen'n D-$CH_3(n$-$C_3H_7)(i$-$C_5H_{11})CH$	*241*
$(C_2H_5)_3CCO_2C_2H_5$	CH_3MgBr	Addition (0%); enolization (0%)*	*457*
$C_9H_5O_2$-R			
$C_6H_5C{\equiv}CCO_2C_2H_5$	4-$CH_3C_6H_4MgBr$	$C_6H_5C{\equiv}C(4$-$CH_3C_6H_4)_2COH$	*100*
$C_9H_5O_3$-R			
Ethyl 2-benzofurancarboxylate	CH_3MgBr	2-Isopropenylbenzofuran (54%)	*14*
$C_9H_6O_2Br$-R			
$C_6H_5CH{=}CBrCO_2C_2H_5$	CH_3MgI	$C_6H_5CH{=}CBrC(CH_3)_2OH$	*219*
$C_6H_5CH{=}CBrCO_2C_2H_5$	C_6H_5MgBr	$(C_6H_5)_2CHCHBrCO_2C_2H_5$ (*ca.* 70%); $(C_6H_5)_2CHCHBrCOC_6H_5$	*219*
$C_9H_7O_2$-R			
$C_6H_5CH{=}CHCO_2CH_3$	CH_3MgI	[illegible]$_5CH{=}CHC(CH_3)_2OH$; [$C_6H_5CH{=}CHC(CH_3)]_2O$ (?) (<5%)	*216*
$C_6H_5CH{=}CHCO_2CH_3$	t-C_4H_9MgCl	[illegible]$CH{=}CHCO_2H$ (3%)	*154*

* "Grignard machine" study.

TABLE VIII-III (Continued)

Ester	RMgX	Product(s)	Ref.
$C_9H_7O_2$-R (*cont.*)			
$C_6H_5CH{=}CHCO_2CH_3$	C_6H_5MgBr	[illegible]$H_5)_2CHCH_2CO_2CH_3$; $(C_6H_5)_2CHCH_2COC_6H_5$*	*216,211*
$C_6H_5CH{=}CHCO_2CH_3$	C_6H_5MgBr	[illegible]$H_5)_2CHCH(CO_2CH_3)COCH_2CH(C_6H_5)_2$; [illegible]$C_6H_5)_2CHCH(COC_6H_5)COCH_2CH(C_6H_5)_2$†	*218*
$C_6H_5CH{=}CHCO_2C_6H_5$	C_6H_5MgBr (1 equiv.)	$(C_6H_5)_2CHCH(CO_2C_6H_5)COCH_2CH(C_6H_5)_2$‡	*218*
$C_6H_5CH{=}CHCO_2C_6H_5$ (22.4 g.)	C_6H_5MgBr (3 equiv.)	$(C_6H_5)_2CHCH_2CO_2C_6H_5$; $(C_6H_5)_2CHCH_2COC_6H_5$; $(C_6H_5{-}{-})_2$§	*218*
$C_6H_5CH{=}CHCO_2$-*t*-C_4H_9	CH_3MgI	No product isolated	*154*
$C_6H_5CH{=}CHCO_2$-*t*-C_4H_9	C_2H_5MgBr	No product isolated	*154*
$C_6H_5CH{=}CHCO_2$-*t*-C_4H_9 (20.4 g., 0.1 mole)	Butenyl-MgBr (0.19 mole)	No appreciable 1,4 addition	*472*
$C_6H_5CH{=}CHCO_2$-*t*-C_4H_9 (20.4 g., 0.1 mole)	*n*-C_4H_9MgBr (0.2 mole)	*n*-$C_4H_9(C_6H_5)CHCH_2CO_2$-*t*-C_4H_9 (8.8 g., 43%)	*472*
$C_6H_5CH{=}CHCO_2$-*t*-C_4H_9 (23.5 g., 0.115 mole)	C_6H_5MgBr (46.1 g., 0.23 mole C_6H_5Br)	$(C_6H_5)_2CHCH_2CO_2$-*t*-C_4H_9 (15 g., 44%)	*117*
$C_6H_5CH{=}CHCO_2$-*t*-C_4H_9 (35.0 g., 0.172 mole)	C_6H_5MgBr (5.1 g., 0.21 mole Mg)	$(C_6H_5)_2CHCH_2CO_2$-*t*-C_4H_9 (36.5 g., 76%)	*154*
$H_2C{=}C(C_6H_5)CO_2CH_3$ (4.0 g.)	CH_3MgI (14.0 g. CH_3I)	DL-$C_2H_5(C_6H_5)CHCOCH_3$ (1.8 g.)	*276*
$C_9H_7O_2Br_2$-R			
$C_6H_5CHBrCHBrCO_2C_2H_5$	C_6H_5MgBr	$(C_6H_5)_2CHCH_2CO_2C_2H_5$; $(C_6H_5)_2CHCH_2COC_6H_5$	*219*
$C_9H_7O_4$-R			
Ethyl α-acetyl-β-(2-furyl)acrylate (25 g.)	C_2H_5MgI (45 g. C_2H_5I)	$C_2H_5(\alpha\text{-}C_4H_3O)CHCH(COCH_3)CO_2C_2H_5$ (17 g.)	*264*

* Dropwise addition of dilute Et_2O-ester solution to agitated Grignard reagent solution at -10°; two hours in freezing mixture; one hour at room temperature.

† Slow addition of Grignard reagent solution to cooled Et_2O-ester solution.

‡ Slow addition of Grignard reagent solution to Et_2O-ester solution; overnight standing.

§ Slow addition of dilute Et_2O-ester solution [illegible]

TABLE VIII-III (Continued)

Ester	RMgX	Product(s)	Ref.
$C_9H_7O_4$-R (*cont.*)			
Ethyl α-acetyl-β-(2-furyl)acrylate (25 g.)	n-C_3H_7MgBr (36 g. C_3H_7Br)	n-$C_3H_7(\alpha$-$C_4H_3O)CHCH(COCH_3)CO_2C_2H_5$ (16 g., 55%)	*264*
Ethyl α-acetyl-β-(2-furyl)acrylate (20 g.)	C_6H_5MgBr (42 g. C_6H_5Br)	$C_6H_5(\alpha$-$C_4H_3O)CHCH(COCH_3)CO_2C_2H_5$ (15 g., 52%)	*264*
$C_9H_7O_5$-R			
3,4-$CH_2O_2{=}C_6H_3CH(OH)CO_2C_2H_5$	CH_3MgI (4 equiv.)	3,4-$CH_2O_2{=}C_6H_3CH(OH)C(CH_3)_2OH$	*422*
$C_9H_8O_3N$-R			
$C_6H_5COHNCH_2CO_2C_2H_5$	C_2H_5MgBr	$C_6H_5COHNCH_2C(C_2H_5)_2OH$ (76%)	*524*
$C_6H_5COHNCH_2CO_2C_2H_5$	C_2H_5MgBr	$C_6H_5COHNCH_2C(C_2H_5)_2OH$ (81%)*	*524*
$C_6H_5COHNCH_2CO_2C_2H_5$	C_6H_5MgBr	$C_6H_5COHNCH_2C(C_6H_5)_2OH$ (63%)	*524*
$C_9H_9O_2$-R			
$C_6H_5(CH_2)_2CO_2C_2H_5$	C_6H_5MgBr (2 equiv.)	$C_6H_5(CH_2)_2C(C_6H_5)_2OH$ (90%)	*224*
$C_6H_5(CH_2)_2CO_2C_2H_5$ (32 g.)	$C_6H_5CH_2MgCl$ (51 g. C_7H_7Cl)	$C_6H_5CH_2CH_2(C_6H_5CH_2)_2COH$ (25–27 g.)	*310*
$C_9H_9O_3$-R			
DL-$C_6H_5CH(OCH_3)CO_2CH_3$	C_6H_5MgBr	DL-$C_6H_5CH(OCH_3)C(C_6H_5)_2OH$	*278*
(−)-$C_6H_5CH(OCH_3)CO_2CH_3$ (5 g.)	C_6H_5MgBr (13.2 g. C_6H_5Br)	(+)-$C_6H_5CH(OCH_3)C(C_6H_5)_2OH$ (9 g., crude)	*278*
DL-$C_6H_5CH(CH_2OH)CO_2CH_3$ (8.7 g.)	CH_3MgI (34.5 g. CH_3I)	DL-$HOCH_2CH(C_6H_5)C(CH_3)_2OH$ (2.5 g.); DL-$CH_3COCH(C_2H_5)C_6H_5$	*276*
DL-$C_6H_5CH(CH_2OH)CO_2CH_3$(7.5 g.)	C_6H_5MgBr (40 g. C_6H_5Br)	DL-$C_6H_5COCH(C_6H_5)CH_2C_6H_5$ (5 g.)	*276*
(−)-$C_6H_5CH(CH_2OH)CO_2CH_3$ (4 g.)	C_6H_5MgBr (40 g. C_6H_5Br)	DL-$C_6H_5COCH(C_6H_5)CH_2C_6H_5$ (2.5 g.)	*276*
DL-$C_6H_5CH_2CH(OH)C_2H_5$ (10 g.)	C_6H_5MgBr (50 g. C_6H_5Br)	DL-$C_6H_5CH_2CH(OH)C(C_6H_5)_2OH$ (12 g.)	*270*
$CH_3CH(OC_6H_5)CO_2C_2H_5$	C_6H_5MgBr	$CH_3CH(OC_6H_5)C(C_6H_5)_2OH$	*408*
4-$C_2H_5OC_6H_4CO_2C_2H_5$ (100 g.)	CH_3MgI (30 g. Mg)	4-$C_2H_5OC_6H_4C(CH_3){=}CH_2$ (35 g.); dimer (8 g.)	*32*

* In xylene.

TABLE VIII-III (Continued)

Ester	RMgX	Product(s)	Ref.
$C_9H_9O_3$-R (*cont.*)			
4-$CH_3C_6H_4CH(OH)CO_2C_2H_5$	CH_3MgI (4 equiv.)	4-$CH_3C_6H_4CH(OH)C(CH_3)_2OH$ (60–80%)	*422*
$C_9H_9O_4$-R			
2-$CH_3OC_6H_4CH(OH)CO_2C_2H_5$	CH_3MgI (4 equiv.)	2-$CH_3OC_6H_4CH(OH)C(CH_3)_2OH$ (70–80%)	*244*
3-$CH_3OC_6H_4CH(OH)CO_2C_2H_5$	CH_3MgI (4 equiv.)	3-$CH_3OC_6H_4CH(OH)C(CH_3)_2OH$ (70–80%)	*244*
4-$CH_3OC_6H_4CH(OH)CO_2C_2H_5$ (42 g.)	C_2H_5MgBr (97 g. C_2H_5Br)	4-$CH_3OC_6H_4CH(OH)C(C_2H_5)_2OH$	*420*
4-$CH_3OC_6H_4CH(OH)CO_2C_2H_5$	*n*-C_3H_7MgBr (4 equiv.)	4-$CH_3OC_6H_4CH(OH)C(n\text{-}C_3H_7)_2OH$ (50%)	*418*
2,4-$(CH_3O)_2C_6H_3CO_2C_2H_5$	2,4-$(CH_3O)_2C_6H_3MgI$	[2,4-$(CH_3O)_2C_6H_3]_3COH$ (40%)	*198*
3,4-$(CH_3O)_2C_6H_3CO_2C_2H_5$	CH_3MgI (2.5 equiv.)	3,4-$(CH_3O)_2C_6H_3C(CH_3)_2OH$	*33*
3,4-$(CH_3O)_2C_6H_3CO_2C_2H_5$	CH_3MgI (3–4 equiv.)	3,4-$(CH_3O)_2C_6H_3C(CH_3){=}CH_2$	*33*
3,5-$(CH_3O)_2C_6H_3CO_2CH_3$ (4 g.)	C_6H_5MgBr (8 g. C_6H_5Br)	3,5-$(CH_3O)_2C_6H_3(C_6H_5)_2COH$	*199*
$C_9H_{10}O_2N$-R			
2-$(CH_3)_2NC_6H_4CO_2CH_3$ (80 g.)	C_2H_5MgBr (109 g. C_2H_5Br)	2-$(CH_3)_2NC_6H_4(C_2H_5)_2COH$	*288*
2-$(CH_3)_2NC_6H_4CO_2CH_3$ (80.0 g.)	*i*-C_3H_7MgCl (78.5 g. C_3H_7Cl)	2-$(CH_3)_2NC_6H_4(n\text{-}C_3H_7)_2COH$ (65%)	*288*
3-$(CH_3)_2NC_6H_4CO_2CH_3$	C_6H_5MgBr (1.5 equiv.)	3-$(CH_3)_2NC_6H_4(C_6H_5)_2COH$	*20*
3-$(CH_3)_2NC_6H_4CO_2CH_3$	2-$(CH_3)_2NC_6H_4MgI$	3-$(CH_3)_2NC_6H_4[2\text{-}(CH_3)_2NC_6H_4]_2COH$	*20*
Ethyl α-cyano-α-cyclohexylideneacetate (24.0 g.)	CH_3MgI (19.5 g. CH_3I)	Ethyl α-cyano-α-(1-methylcyclohexyl)acetate (45%)	*505*
Ethyl α-cyano-α-cyclohexylideneacetate (15.0 g.)	*n*-$C_{10}H_{21}MgBr$ (25.0 g. $C_{10}H_{21}Br$)	Ethyl α-cyano-α-(1-*n*-decylcylohexyl)acetate (14%)	*505*
$C_9H_{10}O_4$-R_2			
Dimethyl spiro[3.3]heptane-2,6-dicarboxylate	CH_3MgI	α,α,α′,α′,-Tetramethylspiro[3.3]heptane-2,6-dimethanol	*18*
Dimethyl spiro[3.3]heptane-2,6-dicarboxylate (13.0 g.)	C_6H_5MgBr (0.3 mole)	α,α,α′,α′,-Tetraphenylspiro[3.3]heptane-2,6-dimethanol	*18*

TABLE VIII-III (Continued)

Ester	RMgX	Product(s)	Ref.
$C_9H_{10}O_4NS$-R			
4-$CH_3C_6H_4SO_2HNCH_2CO_2C_2H_5$	C_6H_5MgBr	4-$CH_3C_6H_4SO_2HNCH_2C(C_6H_5)_2OH$ (50%)	*45*
4-$CH_3C_6H_4SO_2HNCH_2CO_2C_2H_5$	$C_6H_5CH_2MgBr$	4-$CH_3C_6H_4SO_2HNCH_2C(CH_2C_6H_5)_2OH$ (35%)	*45*
$C_9H_{11}O_2ClN$-R			
$C_6H_5CH_2CH(NH_2 \cdot HCl)CO_2C_2H_5$	C_2H_5MgBr	$C_6H_5CH_2CH(NH_2)C(C_2H_5)_2OH$	*416*
$C_6H_5CH_2CH(NH_2 \cdot HCl)CO_2C_2H_5$	C_6H_5MgBr	$C_6H_5CH_2CH(NH_2)C(C_6H_5)_2OH$ (69%)	*416,273*
$C_6H_5CH_2CH(NH_2 \cdot HCl)CO_2C_2H_5$	$C_6H_5CH_2MgBr$	$C_6H_5CH_2CH(NH_2)C(CH_2C_6H_5)_2OH$ (58%)	*416*
$C_6H_5CH(NH_2 \cdot HCl)CH_2CO_2C_2H_5$ (15.0 g.)	C_6H_5MgBr (98.0 g.)	$C_6H_5CH(NH_2)CH_2C(C_6H_5)_2OH$ (1.2 g.)	*273*
$C_9H_{11}O_3ClN$-R			
$C_6H_5CH(OH)CH(NH_2 \cdot HCl)CO_2C_2H_5$	C_6H_5MgBr	$C_6H_5CH(OH)CH(NH_2)C(C_6H_5)_2OH$ (40%)	*44*
$C_6H_5CH(OH)CH(NH_2 \cdot HCl)CO_2C_2H_5$	$C_6H_5CH_2MgBr$	$C_6H_5CH(OH)CH(NH_2)C(CH_2C_6H_5)_2OH$ (13%)	*44*
$C_9H_{14}O_4$-R_2			
$H_2C[(CH_2)_3CO_2CH_3]_2$ (32 g., 0.15 mole)	CH_3MgI (46 g. CH_3I)	$H_2C[(CH_2)_3C(CH_3)_2OH]_2$ (24 g., 75%)	*185*
$H_2C[(CH_2)_3CO_2CH_3]_2$	C_2H_5MgX	$H_2C[(CH_2)_3C(C_2H_5)_2OH]_2$	*185*
$H_2C[(CH_2)_3CO_2C_2H_5]_2$	*t*-C_4H_9MgCl	$H_2C[(CH_2)_3C(t\text{-}C_4H_9)_2OH]_2$	*336*
$C_9H_{15}O_2$-R			
$(CH_2)_5C(C_2H_5)CO_2CH_2CH{=}CH_2$ (3 g.)	C_6H_5MgBr (5 ml. C_6H_5Br)	$(CH_2)_5C(C_2H_5)C(C_6H_5)_2OH$	*6*
$C_9H_{17}O_2$-R			
n-$C_8H_{17}CO_2C_2H_5$	C_2H_5MgX (2 equiv.)	*n*-$C_8H_{17}(C_2H_5)_2COH$ (80–85%); corresponding olefin (*ca.* 1%)	*259*

TABLE VIII-III (Continued)

Ester	RMgX	Product(s)	Ref.
$C_9H_{17}O_2$-R (*cont.*)			
L-*n*-C_3H_7(*n*-C_4H_9)$CHCO_2C_2H_5$	CH_3MgI	After dehydr'n and hydrogen'n L-CH_3(*n*-C_4H_9)(*i*-C_5H_{11})CH	*241*
CH_3(*n*-C_3H_7)$_2CCO_2C_2H_5$ (26 g.)	*n*-C_3H_7MgBr (72 g. C_3H_7Br)	CH_3(*n*-C_3H_7)$_2CCH$(*n*-C_3H_7)OH (20 g.); recovered ester (5 g.); residue (2 g.); C_3H_6; C_3H_8	*238*
$C_{10}H_5O_2ClN$-R			
Ethyl 6-chloroquinaldate (13 g., 0.055 mole)	CH_3MgBr (*ca.* 0.18 mole)	2-(6-Chloro-2-quinolyl)-2-propanol (7.5 g., crude)	*15*
$C_{10}H_6O_2N$-R			
$C_6H_5CH{=}C(CN)CO_2C_2H_5$	CH_3MgI	$CH_3(C_6H_5)CHCH(CN)CO_2C_2H_5$	*220*
$C_6H_5CH{=}C(CN)CO_2C_2H_5$	*i*-C_3H_7MgBr	*i*-$C_3H_7(C_6H_5)CHCH(CN)CO_2C_2H_5$	*220*
$C_6H_5CH{=}C(CN)CO_2C_2H_5$ (20 g.)	C_6H_5MgBr	$(C_6H_5)_2CHCH(CN)CO_2C_2H_5$ (25.4 g.)	*220*
$C_6H_5CH{=}C(CN)CO_2C_2H_5$	$C_6H_5CH_2MgCl$	$C_6H_5(C_6H_5CH_2)CHCH(CN)CO_2C_2H_5$; $CH_3C_6H_5$; $(C_6H_5CH_2{-}{-})_2$	*220*
$C_6H_5CH{=}C(CN)CO_2C_2H_5$	1-$C_{10}H_7MgBr$	$C_6H_5(1\text{-}C_{10}H_7)CHCH(CN)CO_2C_2H_5$	*220*
Ethyl quinaldate	CH_3MgBr (3.3 equiv.)	2-(2-Quinolyl)-2-propanol (16 g., 86%)	*15*
Ethyl quinaldate (46.2 g., 0.23 mole)	C_6H_5MgBr (0.50 mole)	α-(2-Quinolyl)benzhydrol (47.3 g., 66%)	*97*
Ethyl cinchoninate	C_6H_5MgBr	α-(4-Quinolyl)benzhdrol; 4-benzoylquinoline	*355*
$C_{10}H_6O_4$-R_2			
$C_6H_5CH{=}C(CO_2C_2H_5)_2$	CH_3MgI	$CH_3(C_6H_5)CHCH(CO_2C_2H_5)_2$	*212*
$C_6H_5CH{=}C(CO_2C_2H_5)_2$	C_2H_5MgBr (excess)	$C_2H_5(C_6H_5)CHCH(CO_2C_2H_5)_2$ (quant.)	*356*
$C_6H_5CH{=}C(CO_2C_2H_5)_2$ (25 g.)	C_6H_5MgBr (1 equiv.)	$(C_6H_5)_2CHCH(CO_2C_2H_5)_2$ (27 g.)	*212,356*
$C_6H_5CH{=}C(CO_2C_2H_5)_2$ (32 g.)	C_6H_5MgBr (34 g. C_6H_5Br)	$(C_6H_5)_2CHCH(CO_2C_2H_5)$ (yielding 30 g. α-bromo deriv.)	*463*

TABLE VIII-III (Continued)

Ester	RMgX	Product(s)	Ref.
$C_{10}H_6O_4$-R_2 *(cont.)*			
$C_6H_5CH{=}C(CO_2C_2H_5)_2$ (6.7 g.)	C_6H_5MgBr (2 equiv.) + C_6H_5Li (excess)	1,3-Diphenyl-2-benzhydryl-1-indenol (1.5 g.)	*249*
$C_{10}H_6O_4N$-R			
Ethyl phthalimidoäcetate	C_6H_5MgBr	2-$C_6H_5COC_6H_4CONHCH_2CO_2C_2H_5$; 2-$C_6H_5COC_6H_4CONHCH_2CO_2H$; 2-$C_6H_5COC_6H_4CONHCH_2C(C_6H_5)_2OH$	*45*
$C_{10}H_8O_4$-R_2			
$[{-}(CH_2)_4CO_2CH_3]_2$	n-C_3H_7MgX	$[{-}(CH_2)_4C(n\text{-}C_3H_7)_2OH]_2$ (<5%); non-crystallizable oil	*185*
$C_{10}H_9O_2$-R			
$C_6H_5CH{=}C(CH_3)CO_2CH_3$	CH_3MgI	$C_6H_5CH{=}C(CH_3)C(CH_3)_2OH$	*213*
$C_6H_5CH{=}C(CH_3)CO_2CH_3$	C_6H_5MgBr	$(C_6H_5)_2CHCH(CH_3)COC_6H_5$	*213*
$C_6H_5CH{=}C(CH_3)CO_2CH_3$ (sl. excess)	C_6H_5MgBr	$C_6H_5CH{=}C(CH_3)COC_6H_5$; $(C_6H_5)_2CHCH(CH_3)COC_6H_5$	*213*
$C_{10}H_9O_2N_2$-R			
$CH_3CH{=}C(N{=}NC_6H_5)CO_2C_2H_5$	CH_3MgI	Unidentified products	*438*
$C_{10}H_{10}O_3N$-R			
$CH_3CH(NHCOC_6H_5)CO_2C_2H_5$	CH_3MgI (6 equiv.)	$CH_3CH(NHCOC_6H_5)C(CH_3)_2OH$ (80%)	*30*
$CH_3CH(NHCOC_6H_5)CO_2C_2H_5$	C_2H_5MgBr	$CH_3CH(NHCOC_6H_5)C(C_2H_5)_2OH$	*417*
$CH_3CH(NHCOC_6H_5)CO_2C_2H_5$	$C_6H_5CH_2MgBr$	$CH_3CH(NHCOC_6H_5)C(CH_2C_6H_5)_2OH$	*45*
$C_{10}H_{11}O_2$-R			
2,4,6-$(CH_3)_3C_6H_2CO_2CH_3$	n-C_4H_9MgBr	2,4,6-$(CH_3)_3C_6H_2CO_2H$ (25%); CH_3Br (20%)	*120*

TABLE VIII-III (Continued)

Ester	RMgX	Product(s)	Ref.
$C_{10}H_{11}O_2$-R (*cont.*)			
2,4,6-$(CH_3)_3C_6H_2CO_2CH_2CH{=}CH_2$ (33.7 g.)	C_6H_5MgBr (32 g. C_6H_5Br)	2,4,6-$(CH_3)_3C_6H_2CO_2H$ (95%); $H_2C{=}CHCH_2C_6H_5$ (13.5 g.)	*4*
2,4,6-$(CH_3)_3C_6H_2CO_2CH_2CH{=}CHCH_3$	C_6H_5MgBr	$C_6H_5CH_2CH{=}CHCH_3$ (75.5%)	*7*
2,4,6-$(CH_3)_3C_6H_2CO_2CH_2CH{=}CHCH_3$	C_6H_5MgBr	$C_6H_5CH_2CH{=}CHCH_3$ (86%)	*468*
2,4,6-$(CH_3)_3C_6H_2CO_2CH(CH_3)CH{=}CH_2$	C_6H_5MgBr	$C_6H_5CH_2CH{=}CHCH_3$ (81%)	*9*
2,4,6-$(CH_3)_3C_6H_2CO_2CH(CH_3)CH{=}CH_2$	C_6H_5MgBr	$C_6H_5CH_2CH{=}CHCH_3$ (61 ± 5%); $C_6H_5CH(CH_3)CH{=}CH_2$ (13 ± 2%)	*468*
2,4,6-$(CH_3)_3C_6H_2CO_2$-n-C_4H_9 (66.0 g.)	C_6H_5MgI (30.6 g. C_6H_5I)	2,4,6-$(CH_3)_3C_6H_2CO_2H$ (61%); n-C_4H_9I (54%); recovered ester (14.0 g.); $(C_6H_5{-})_2$ "small am't"	*129*
2,4,6-$(CH_3)_3C_6H_2CO_2$-t-C_4H_9	C_6H_5MgBr	C_6H_5-t-C_4H_9 (24%)	*9*
2,4,6-$(CH_3)_3C_6H_2CO_2$-$CH(C_2H_5)CH{=}CH_2$	C_6H_5MgBr	After hydrogen'n, $C_6H_5CH(CH_3)$-n-C_4H_9 + $C_6H_5CH(C_2H_5)$-n-C_3H_7 (totaling 61%)	*9*
2,4,6-$(CH_3)_3C_6H_2CO_2CH_2C_6H_5$	n-C_4H_9MgBr	2,4,6-$(CH_3)_3C_6H_2CO_2H$ (50%); $C_6H_5CH_2Br$*	*120*
2,4,6-$(CH_3)_3C_6H_2CO_2CH_2C_6H_5$	C_6H_5MgBr	No cleavage in Et_2O	*4*
2,4,6-$(CH_3)_3C_6H_2CO_2CH_2C_6H_5$	C_6H_5MgI	2,4,6-$(CH_3)_3C_6H_2CO_2H$ (65%); $C_6H_5CH_2I$ (70%)*	*120*
2,4,6-$(CH_3)_3C_6H_2CO_2C_6H_4$-3-CH_3	C_6H_5MgBr	3-$CH_3C_6H_4OH$ (80%); 1,4-$[2,4,6\text{-}(CH_3)_3C_6H_2CO]_2C_6H_4$	*119*
2,4,6-$(CH_3)_3C_6H_2CO_2C_6H_4$-4-CH_3	CH_3MgI	2,4,6-$(CH_3)_3C_6H_2COCH_3$ (45%); 4-$CH_3C_6H_4OH$ (76%)	*120*
2,4,6-$(CH_3)_3C_6H_2CO_2C_6H_4$-4-CH_3	C_2H_5MgBr	2,4,6-$(CH_3)_3C_6H_2COC_2H_5$ (61%); 4-$CH_3C_6H_4OH$ (54%)	*120*
2,4,6-$(CH_3)_3C_6H_2CO_2C_6H_4$-4-CH_3 (20.4 g.)	C_6H_5MgBr (28.2 g.)	1,4-$[2,4,6\text{-}(CH_3)_3C_6H_2CO]C_6H_4$ (5.0 g., 34%); 4-$CH_3C_6H_4OH$ (6.4 g., 74%)	*119*

* Twenty-four hours reflux under N_2 in Bu_2O.

TABLE VIII-III (Continued)

Ester	RMgX	Product(s)	Ref.
$C_{10}H_{11}O_2$-R (*cont.*)			
2,4,6-$(CH_3)_3C_6H_2CO_2C_6H_4$-4-CH_3	$C_6H_5CH_2MgCl$	[2,4,6-$(CH_3)_3C_6H_2CO$—]$_2$ "small am't"; 4-$CH_3C_6H_4OH$ (55%)	*120*
2,4,6-$(CH_3)_3C_6H_2CO_2C_6H_4$-4-CH_3	2-$CH_3C_6H_4MgBr$	1,4-[2,4,6-$(CH_3)_3C_6H_2CO]_2C_6H_3$-2-$CH_3$ (29%); 4-$CH_3C_6H_4OH$	*120*
2,4,6-$(CH_3)_3C_6H_2CO_2C_6H_4$-4-CH_3	3-$CH_3C_6H_4MgBr$	1,4-[2,4,6-$(CH_3)_3C_6H_2CO]_2C_6H_3$-2-$CH_3$ (11%); 4-$CH_3C_6H_4OH$	*119*
2,4,6-$(CH_3)_3C_6H_2CO_2C_6H_4$-4-CH_3	4-$CH_3C_6H_4MgBr$	2,4,6-$(CH_3)_3C_6H_3COC_6H_4$-2-(C_6H_4-4-CH_3) (13%); 4-$CH_3C_6H_4OH$ (95%)	*120*
2,4,6-$(CH_3)_3C_6H_2CO_2C_6H_4$-4-CH_3	2-$CH_3OC_6H_4MgBr$	2,4,6-$(CH_3)_3C_6H_2COC_6H_4$-2-(C_6H_4-2-OCH_3) (13%); 4-$GH_3C_6H_4OH$ (74%)	*120*
2,4,6-$(CH_3)_3C_6H_2CO_2C_6H_4$-4-CH_3	3-$CH_3OC_6H_4MgBr$	2,4,6-$(CH_3)_3C_6H_2C_6H_4$-2-(C_6H_4-3-OCH_3) (6%); 4-$CH_3C_6H_4OH$ (75%)*	*120*
2,4,6-$(CH_3)_3C_6H_2CO_2C_6H_4$-4-CH_3	3-$CH_3OC_6H_4MgBr$	1,4-[2,4,6-$(CH_3)_3C_6H_2CO]_2C_6H_3$-2-($C_6H_4$-3-$OCH_3$) (3.5%); 4-$CH_3C_6H_4OH$†	*119*
2,4,6-$(CH_3)_3C_6H_2CO_2C_6H_4$-4-CH_3	2,4,6-$(CH_3)_3C_6H_2MgBr$	[2,4,6-$(CH_3)_3C_6H_2]_2CO$ (3%); [2,4,6-$(CH_3)_3C_6H_2CO$—]$_2$ (trace); 4-$CH_3C_6H_4OH$ (85%)	*120*
2,4,6-$(CH_3)_3C_6H_2CO_2C_6H_4$-4-CH_3	1-$C_{10}H_7MgBr$	1-[2,4,6-$(CH_3)_3C_6H_2CO]C_{10}H_6$-2-$\alpha$-$C_{10}H_7$ (trace); 4-$CH_3C_6H_4OH$	*120*
2,4,6-$(CH_3)_3C_6H_2CO_2CH(C_6H_5)CH_2C_6H_5$ (5.0 g., 0.020 mole)	CH_3MgI (0.045 mole)	*trans*-(C_6H_5CH=)$_2$ (1.0 g., 30%); [$C_6H_5CH_2(C_6H_5)CH$—]$_2$ (0.3 g., 9%)	*153*
2,4,6-$(CH_3)_3C_6H_2CO_2CH(C_6H_5)CH_2C_6H_5$ (6.8 g., 0.028 mole)	C_2H_5MgBr (0.040 mole)	Mixture of *cis*- and *trans*- (C_6H_5CH=)$_2$ (1.5 g., 45%); [$C_6H_5CH_2(C_6H_5)CH$—]$_2$ (0.3 g., 8%); 2,4,6-$(CH_3)_3C_6H_2CO_2H$ (76%)	*153*

* Addition of Bu_2O-ester solution to stirred Bu_2O-Grignard reagent solution; five hours at 115° under N_2.

† Addition of Bu_2O-ester solution to stirred Bu_2O-Grignard reagent solution; two hours at 100° under N_2.

TABLE VIII-III (Continued)

Ester	RMgX	Product(s)	Ref.
$C_{10}H_{11}O_2$-R (*cont.*)			
2,4,6-$(CH_3)_3C_6H_2CO_2CH(C_6H_5)CH_2C_6H_5$ (13.0 g., 0.05 mole)	C_6H_5MgBr (0.10 mole)	*trans*-$(C_6H_5CH=)_2$ (5.5 g., 68%); *cis*-$(C_6H_5CH=)_2$ (1.1 g., 13%); 2,4,6-$(CH_3)_3C_6H_2CO_2H$ (7.3 g., 90%)	153
$C_{10}H_{11}O_3$-R			
4-$C_2H_5OC_6H_4CH_2CO_2C_2H_5$	4-$CH_3OC_6H_4MgBr$	4-$C_2H_5OC_6H_4CH_2(4\text{-}CH_3OC_6H_4)_2COH$	164
4-$C_2H_5OC_6H_4CH_2CO_2C_2H_5$ (10.4 parts)	4-$C_2H_5OC_6H_4MgBr$ (30.0 parts C_8H_9BrO)	4-$C_2H_5OC_6H_4CH_2(4\text{-}C_2H_5OC_6H_4)_2COH$	164
4-$C_2H_5OC_6H_4CH_2CO_2C_2H_5$ (10.0 g.)	4-*n*-$C_3H_7OC_6H_4MgBr$ (32.3 g. $C_9H_{11}BrO$)	4-$C_2H_5OC_6H_4CH_2(4\text{-}n\text{-}C_3H_7OC_6H_4)_2COH$	164
$HO(CH_3)(C_6H_5CH_2)CCO_2C_2H_5$ (25 g.)	C_6H_5MgBr (75 g. C_6H_5Br)	$HO(CH_3)(C_6H_5CH_2)CC(C_6H_5)_2OH$ (27 g., *ca.* 57%, crude)	420
$C_{10}H_{12}O_3N$-R			
Ethyl cryptopyrrylglyoxalate* (2.00 g.)	Cryptopyrryl-MgBr† (10.00 g. cryptopyrrole)	(5-Cryptopyrryl-CO—)$_2$ (1.35 g., 50%)	107
$C_{10}H_{12}O_4NS$-R			
4-$CH_3C_6H_4SO_2NHCH(CH_3)CO_2C_2H_5$	$C_6H_5CH_2MgBr$	4-$CH_3C_6H_4SO_2NHCH(CH_3)C(CH_2C_6H_5)_2OH$ (39%)	45
$C_{10}H_{12}O_5$-R_2			
Diethyl 2-oxo-1,3-cyclohexanediacetate (12.0 g.)	C_6H_5MgBr (7.5 g. C_6H_5Br)	Diethyl 2-hydroxy-2-phenyl-1,3-cyclohexanediacetate	78

* Ethyl (3,5-dimethyl-4-ethyl-2-pyrryl)glyoxalate.
† From 2,4-dimethyl-3-ethylpyrrole.

TABLE VIII-III (Continued)

Ester	RMgX	Product(s)	Ref.
$C_{10}H_{15}O_3$-R			
Methyl 2,2,3-trimethyl-3-formylcyclopentanecarboxylate	CH_3MgI (4 equiv.)	2,2,3-Trimethyl-3-α-hydroxyethylcyclopentanecarboxylic acid δ-lactone* (62%)†	*440*
Methyl 2,2,3-trimethyl-3-formylcyclopentanecarboxylate (43 g.)	CH_3MgI (125 g. CH_3I)	α,1,2,2-Tetramethyl-3-isopropenylcyclopentanemethanol; 1,2,4,4,8,8-hexamethyl-3-oxabicyclo[3.2.1]octane; 1,2,2-trimethyl-1-vinyl-3-isopropenylcyclopentane‡	*441*
Methyl 2,2,3-trimethyl-3-formylcyclopentanecarboxylate (50 g.)	C_2H_5MgBr (110 g. C_2H_5Br)	2,2,3-Trimethyl-3-α-hydroxypropylcyclopentanecarboxylic acid δ-lactone (40%); 2,2,3-trimethyl-3-hydroxymethylcyclopentanecarboxylic acid δ-lactone (4%)†	*440*
Methyl 2,2,3-trimethyl-3-formylcyclopentanecarboxylate (40 g.)	C_2H_5MgBr (109 g. C_2H_5Br)	α,α′,α′-Triethyl-1,2,2-trimethylcyclopentane-1,3-dimethanol; α-ethyl-1,2,2-trimethyl-3-(3-Δ^2-pentenyl)cyclopentanemethanol; 1,8,8-trimethyl-2,4,4-triethyl-3-oxabicyclo[3.2.1]octane; 1,2,2-trimethyl-1-propenyl-3-(3-Δ^2-pentenyl)cyclopentane §	*441*
Methyl 2,2,3-trimethyl-3-formylcyclopentanecarboxylate (30 g.)	C_2H_5MgBr (82 g. C_2H_5Br)	α-Ethyl-1,2,2-trimethyl-3-(3-Δ^2-pentenyl)cyclopentanemethanol; 1,8,8-trimethyl-2,4,4-triethyl-3-oxabicyclo[3.2.1]octane; 1,2,2-trimethyl-1-propenyl-3-(3-Δ^2-pentenyl)cyclopentane‡	*441*

* 4,5,8,8-Tetramethyl-3-oxabicyclo[3.2.1]octan-2-one.

† Dropwise addition of Et_2O-ester solution to agitated Grignard reagent solution; one hour reflux; twenty-four hours at room temperature.

‡ Gradual addition of xylene-ester solution to Grignard reagent solution; distillation of Et_2O; four hours reflux.

§ Slow addition of toluene-ester solution to Grignard reagent solution; distillation of Et_2O; two hours reflux.

TABLE VIII-III (Continued)

Ester	RMgX	Product(s)	Ref.
$C_{10}H_{15}O_3$-R (*cont.*)			
Methyl 2,2,3-trimethyl-3-formylcyclopentanecarboxylate	*n*-C_3H_7MgBr	2,2,3-Trimethyl-3-α-hydroxybutylcyclopentanecarboxylic acid δ-lactone; 2,2,3-trimethyl-3-hydroxymethylcyclopentanecarboxylic acid δ-lactone	*440*
Methyl 2,2,3-trimethyl-3-formylcyclopentanecarboxylate	*n*-C_4H_9MgBr	2,2,3-Trimethyl-3-α-hydroxyamylcyclopentanecarboxylic acid δ-lactone; 2,2,3-trimethyl-3-hydroxymethylcyclopentanecarboxylic acid δ-lactone	*440*
Methyl 2,2,3-trimethyl-3-formylcyclopentanecarboxylate	C_6H_5MgBr (2 equiv.)	2,2,3-Trimethyl-3-α-hydroxybenzylcyclopentanecarboxylic acid δ-lactone; $(C_6H_5—)_2$	*440*
Methyl 2,2,3-trimethyl-3-formylcyclopentanecarboxylate	$C_6H_5CH_2MgCl$	2,2,3-Trimethyl-3-α-hydroxyphenethylcyclopentanecarboxylic acid δ-lactone; unidentified oils	*440*
$C_{10}H_{16}O_4$-R_2			
$[—(CH_2)_4CO_2CH_3]_2$	C_6H_5MgBr	$[—(CH_2)_4C(C_6H_5)_2OH]_2$ (*ca.* 80%)	377
$[—(CH_2)_4CO_2C_2H_5]_2$ (130 g.)	CH_3MgBr (100 g. Mg)	$[—(CH_2)_4C(CH_3)_2OH]_2$ (70 g.)	228
$[—(CH_2)_4CO_2C_2H_5]_2$ (70 g.)	CH_3MgI (230 g. CH_3I)	$[—(CH_2)_4C(CH_3)_2OH]_2$ (92%)	337
$[—(CH_2)_4CO_2C_2H_5]_2$	C_2H_5MgBr	$[—(CH_2)_4C(C_2H_5)_2OH]_2$ (70%)	337,227
$[—(CH_2)_4CO_2C_2H_5]_2$ (50 g.)	*n*-C_4H_9MgBr (115 g. C_4H_9Br)	$[—(CH_2)_4C(n\text{-}C_4H_9)_2OH]_2$ (68%)	337
$[—(CH_2)_4CO_2C_2H_5]_2$	*t*-C_4H_9MgCl (4 equiv.)	$[—(CH_2)_4CO_2H]_2$; a hydroxy acid, m. 121°	336
$[—(CH_2)_4CO_2C_2H_5]_2$ (0.2 mole)	*t*-C_4H_9MgCl (2.5 mole)	$[—(CH_2)_4C(t\text{-}C_4H_9)_2OH]_2$; *i*-$C_4H_8$; a sat'd hydrocarbon; liquid byproducts	336
$[—(CH_2)_4CO_2C_2H_5]_2$ (34 g.)	*n*-$C_6H_{13}MgBr$ (120 g. $C_6H_{13}Br$)	$[—(CH_2)_4C(n\text{-}C_6H_{13})_2OH]_2$	337

TABLE VIII-III (Continued)

Ester	RMgX	Product(s)	Ref.
$C_{10}H_{17}O_2$-R			
Ethyl campholate*	n-C_3H_7MgX†	α-Propyl-1,2,2,3-tetramethylcyclopentane-methanol; C_3H_6; C_3H_8	*238*
$C_{10}H_{19}O_2$-R			
n-$C_9H_{19}CO_2C_2H_5$	n-C_4H_9MgBr	n-$C_9H_{19}(n$-$C_4H_9)_2COH$	*334*
L-$CH_3(n$-$C_7H_{15})CHCO_2C_2H_5$	CH_3MgI	After dehydr'n and hydrogen'n, L-$CH_3(i$-$C_3H_7)(n$-$C_7H_{15})CH$	*242*
L-n-$C_3H_7(n$-$C_5H_{11})CHCO_2C_2H_5$	CH_3MgI	After dehydr'n and hydrogen'n, L-n-$C_3H_7(i$-$C_3H_7)(n$-$C_5H_{11})CH$	*241*
$C_{11}H_7O_2$-R			
1-$C_{10}H_7CO_2C_2H_5$	CH_3MgI (2 equiv.)	1-$C_{10}H_7(CH_3)_2COH$	*88*
$C_{11}H_7O_3$-R			
5-$HOC_{10}H_6$-1-CO_2CH_3 (4 g.)	C_6H_5MgBr (14 ml. C_6H_5Br)	5-$HOC_{10}H_6$-1-$C(C_6H_5)_2OH$ (63%)	*499*
6-$HOC_{10}H_6$-1-CO_2CH_3	C_6H_5MgBr (excess)	6-$HOC_{10}H_6$-1-$C(C_6H_5)_2OH$	*499*
7-$HOC_{10}H_6$-1-CO_2CH_3	C_6H_5MgBr	7-$HOC_{10}H_6$-1-$C(C_6H_5)_2OH$ (67%)	*499*
1-$HOC_{10}H_6$-2-CO_2CH_3	CH_3MgI	1-$HOC_{10}H_6$-2-$C(CH_3){=}CH_2$ (60%)	*343*
1-$HOC_{10}H_6$-2-CO_2CH_3	C_2H_5MgI	1-$HOC_{10}H_6$-2-$C(C_2H_5)_2OH$ (*ca.* 60%)	*343*
1-$HOC_{10}H_6$-2-CO_2CH_3 (6 g.)	C_6H_5MgBr (20 g. C_6H_5Br)	1-$HOC_{10}H_6$-2-$C(C_6H_5)_2OH$ (7 g.)	*197*
1-$HOC_{10}H_6$-2-CO_2CH_3	C_6H_5MgBr	1-$HOC_{10}H_6$-2-$C(C_6H_5)_2OH$ (10%); 2-benzhydrilidene-1(2*H*)-naphthalenone	*343*
1-$HOC_{10}H_6$-2-CO_2CH_3	1-$C_{10}H_7MgBr$	2-(Di-α-naphthylmethylene)-1(2*H*)-naphthalenone	*343*
3-$HOC_{10}H_6$-2-CO_2CH_3 (5 g.)	CH_3MgI (18 g. CH_3I)	3-$HOC_{10}H_6$-2-$C(CH_3)_2OH$ (60–70%)	*225*
3-$HOC_{10}H_6$-2-CO_2CH_3 (5 g.)	C_6H_5MgBr (20 g. C_6H_5Br)	3-$HOC_{10}H_6$-2-$C(C_6H_5)_2OH$ (70–80%)	*225*

* Ethyl 1,2,2,3-tetramethylcyclopentanecarboxylate.

† X = Cl, Br.

TABLE VIII-III (Continued)

Ester	RMgX	Product(s)	Ref.
$C_{11}H_7O_3$-R (*cont.*)			
3-$HOC_{10}H_6$-2-CO_2CH_3 (5 g.)	$C_6H_5CH_2MgCl$ (18 g. C_7H_7Cl)	3-$HOC_{10}H_6$-2-$C(CH_2C_6H_5)_2OH$ (70%)	*225*
3-$HOC_{10}H_6$-2-CO_2CH_3 (10 g.)	1-$C_{10}H_7MgBr$ (55 g. $C_{10}H_7Br$)	3-$HOC_{10}H_6$-2-$C(1\text{-}C_{10}H_7)_2OH$ (30–70%)	*225*
3-$HOC_{10}H_6$-2-$CO_2C_2H_5$ (6.5 g.)	C_6H_5MgBr (30.0 g. C_6H_5Br)	3-$HOC_{10}H_6$-2-$C(C_6H_5)_2OH$ (8.0 g.)	*197*
6-$HOC_{10}H_6$-2-$CO_2C_2H_5$	C_6H_5MgBr	6-$HOC_{10}H_6$-2-$C(C_6H_5)_2OH$	*499*
8-$HOC_{10}H_6$-2-CO_2CH_3 (1.85 g.)	C_6H_5MgBr (6.6 ml. C_6H_5Br)	8-$HOC_{10}H_6$-2-$C(C_6H_5)_2OH$ (67%)	*499*
$C_{11}H_9O_2$-R			
$C_6H_5(CH{=}CH)_2CO_2CH_3$ (stable form)	C_2H_5MgBr (4 equiv.)	$C_6H_5(CH{=}CH)_2C(C_2H_5)_2OH$; unidentified products	*357*
$C_6H_5(CH{=}CH)_2CO_2CH_3$ (stable form) (28.0 g.)	C_6H_5MgBr (2.5 equiv.)	$C_6H_5CH{=}CHCH(C_6H_5)CH_2COC_6H_5$ (25.5 g.); recovered ester (9.0 g.)	*357*
$C_6H_5(CH{=}CH)_2CO_2CH_3$ (allo form)	C_6H_5MgBr (4 equiv.)	$C_6H_5CH{=}CHCH(C_6H_5)CH_2COC_6H_5$ (60%)	*357*
$C_6H_5(CH{=}CH)_2CO_2CH_3$ (stable form (14.0 g.)	$C_6H_5CH_2MgBr$	$C_6H_5(CH{=}CH)_2C(CH_2C_6H_5)_2OH$ (2.0 g., crude); $C_6H_5CH{=}CHCH(CH_2C_6H_5)CH_2COCH_2C_6H_5$ (12.5 g.); $C_6H_5CH{=}CHCH(CH_2C_6H_5)CH_2CO_2CH_3$ (1.2 g. as acid)	*357*
$C_{11}H_{13}O_3$-R			
4-*n*-$C_3H_7OC_6H_4CH_2CO_2C_2H_5$ (6.7 parts)	C_6H_5MgBr (14.1 parts C_6H_5Br)	4-*n*-$C_3H_7OC_6H_4CH_2(C_6H_5)_2COH$	*164*
$C_{11}H_{13}O_4$-R			
4-$CH_3OC_6H_4CH(OC_2H_5)CO_2C_2H_5$	C_2H_5MgBr	4-$CH_3OC_6H_4CH(OC_2H_5)C(C_2H_5)_2OH$ (yielding 60–70% 4-anisyl-3-hexanone)	*367*
$C_{12}H_8O_2N$-R			
$C_6H_5CH{=}CHCH{=}C(CN)CO_2C_2H_5$	C_2H_5MgBr (2.5 equiv.)	$C_6H_5CH{=}CHCH(C_2H_5)CH(CN)CO_2C_2H_5$ (quant.)	*250*

TABLE VIII-III (Continued)

Ester	RMgX	Product(s)	Ref.
$C_{12}H_8O_2N$-R (*cont.*)			
$C_6H_5CH{=}CHCH{=}C(CN)CO_2C_2H_5$	C_6H_5MgBr	$C_6H_5CH{=}CHCH(C_6H_5)CH(CN)CO_2C_2H_5$ (quant.)	250
$C_{12}H_8O_4$-R_2			
$C_6H_5CH{=}CHCH{=}C(CO_2CH_3)_2$	CH_3MgI	$C_6H_5CH{=}CHCH(CH_3)CH(CO_2CH_3)_2$ (76%)	352
$C_6H_5CH{=}CHCH{=}C(CO_2CH_3)_2$ (16 g.)	C_6H_5MgBr	$C_6H_5CH{=}CHCH(C_6H_5)CH(CO_2CH_3)_2$ (21 g.)	352
$C_6H_5CH{=}CHCH{=}C(CO_2CH_3)_2$	$C_6H_5CH_2MgCl$	$C_6H_5CH{=}CHCH(CH_2C_6H_5)CH(CO_2CH_3)_2$	352
$C_{12}H_9O_2$-R			
$4\text{-}CH_3C_{10}H_6\text{-}2\text{-}CO_2CH_3$	CH_3MgBr	$4\text{-}CH_3C_{10}H_6\text{-}2\text{-}C(CH_3)_2OH$	93
$C_{12}H_{10}O_4NS$-R			
$C_{10}H_7SO_2NHCH_2CO_2C_2H_5$	C_6H_5MgBr	$C_{10}H_7SO_2NHCH_2C(C_6H_5)_2OH$ (43%)	45
$C_{12}H_{11}O_2$-R			
Ethyl 4-methyl-1-naphthoate	CH_3MgI	2-(4-Methyl-1-naphthyl)-2-propanol	24
$C_{12}H_{13}O_2$-R			
Methyl 4-methyl-1,2,3,4-tetrahydro-2-naphthoate	CH_3MgBr	2-(4-Methyl-1,2,3,4-tetrahydro-2-naphthyl)-2-propanol	93
$C_{12}H_{13}O_3$-R			
$C_6H_5CO(CH_3)_2CCH_2CO_2C_2H_5$	C_6H_5MgBr	$C_{18}H_{38}O_2$, m. 146–147°; β,β-di-methyl-γ,γ-diphenyl-γ-butyrolactone (?)	523
$C_{12}H_{13}O_4N_2$-R			
$C_6H_5COHNCH_2COHNCH(CH_3)CO_2C_2H_5$	C_6H_5MgBr	$C_6H_5COHNCH_2COHNCH(CH_3)C(C_6H_5)_2OH$ (61%)	45

TABLE VIII-III (Continued)

Ester	RMgX	Product(s)	Ref.
$C_{12}H_{13}O_4N_2$-R (*cont.*)			
$C_6H_5COHNCH_2COHNCH(CH_3)CO_2C_2H_5$	$C_6H_5CH_2MgBr$	$C_6H_5COHNCH_2COHNCH(CH_3)C(CH_2C_6H_5)_2OH$	*45*
$C_{12}H_{15}O_2$-R			
$CH_3(C_2H_5)(C_6H_5CH_2)CCO_2CH_2CH{=}CH_2$ (20 g.)	C_6H_5MgBr (21 ml. C_6H_5Br)	$CH_3(C_2H_5)(C_6H_5CH_2)CCO_2H$ (14.5 g., 87%); $C_6H_5CH_2CH{=}CH_2$ (7.0 g., 70%)	*6*
$C_{12}H_{23}O_2$-R			
n-$C_{11}H_{23}CO_2CH_3$	C_6H_5MgBr	n-$C_{11}H_{23}(C_6H_5)_2COH$ (yielding 80–90% alkene)	*377*
n-$C_{11}H_{23}CO_2CH_3$	n-$C_{10}H_{21}MgBr$ (2.5 equiv.)	n-$C_{11}H_{23}(n$-$C_{10}H_{21})_2COH$	*460*
n-$C_{11}H_{23}CO_2C_2H_5$	n-C_4H_9MgCl	n-$C_{11}H_{23}(n$-$C_4H_9)_2COH$ (65%)	*326*
n-$C_{11}H_{23}CO_2C_2H_5$	s-C_4H_9MgBr	$(n$-$C_{11}H_{23})_2CO$	*327*
n-$C_{11}H_{23}CO_2C_2H_5$	t-C_4H_9MgCl	$(n$-$C_{11}H_{23})_2CO$ (30–35%)	*326,327*
n-$C_{11}H_{23}CO_2$-s-C_8H_{17}	t-C_4H_9MgCl	$(n$-$C_{11}H_{23})_2CO$; n-$C_{11}H_{23}CO_2H$	*338*
$(CH_3)(t$-$C_4H_9)(t$-$C_4H_9CH_2)CCO_2CH_3$	CH_3MgBr	$CH_3(t$-$C_4H_9)(t$-$C_4H_9CH_2)CCO_2H$ (13.0%); recovered ester (70.3%)	*454*
$C_{13}H_9O_2$-R			
2-$C_6H_5C_6H_4CO_2C_2H_5$	3-$C_6H_5C_6H_4MgBr$	2-$C_6H_5C_6H_4(3$-$C_6H_5C_6H_4)_2COH$	*81*
4-$C_6H_5C_6H_4CO_2CH_3$	C_6H_5MgBr	4-$C_6H_5C_6H_4(C_6H_5)_2COH$ (*ca.* quant.)	*372*
4-$C_6H_5C_6H_4CO_2CH_3$	4-$C_6H_5C_6H_4MgI$	$(4$-$C_6H_5C_6H_4)_3COH$ (yield depends on quality of I_2-activated Mg)	*372*
$C_{13}H_9O_3$-R			
Ethyl α-phenyl-β-2-furylacrylate (30 g.)	C_2H_5MgBr (42 g. C_2H_5Br)	$C_2H_5(\alpha$-$C_4H_3O)CHCH(C_6H_5)CO_2C_2H_5$ (30 g.)	*265*

TABLE VIII-III (Continued)

Ester	RMgX	Product(s)	Ref.
$C_{13}H_9O_3$-R (*cont.*)			
Ethyl α-phenyl-β-2-furylacrylate (30 g.)	C_6H_5MgBr (49 g. C_6H_5Br)	$C_6H_5(\alpha\text{-}C_4H_3O)CHCH(C_6H_5)CO_2C_2H_5$ (20 g.); $\alpha\text{-}C_4H_3OCH{=}C(C_6H_5)C(C_6H_5)_2OH$	*265*
Propyl α-phenyl-β-2-furylacrylate (30 g.)	C_2H_5MgBr (32 g. C_2H_5Br)	$C_2H_5(\alpha\text{-}C_4H_3O)CHCH(C_6H_5)CO_2\text{-}n\text{-}C_3H_7$ (29 g.)	*265*
Propyl α-phenyl-β-2-furylacrylate (30 g.)	C_6H_5MgBr (46 g. C_6H_5Br)	$C_6H_5(\alpha\text{-}C_4H_3O)CHCH(C_6H_5)CO_2\text{-}n\text{-}C_3H_7$ (19 g.); $\alpha\text{-}C_4H_3OCH{=}C(C_6H_5)C(C_6H_5)_2OH$ (17 g.)	*265*
Butyl α-phenyl-β-2-furylacrylate (20 g.)	C_2H_5MgBr (19 g. C_2H_5Br)	$C_2H_5(\alpha\text{-}C_4H_3O)CHCH(C_6H_5)CO_2\text{-}n\text{-}C_4H_9$ (19 g.)	*265*
Butyl α-phenyl-β-2-furylacrylate (30 g.)	C_6H_5MgBr (50 g. C_6H_5Br)	$C_6H_5(\alpha\text{-}C_4H_3O)CHCH(C_6H_5)CO_2\text{-}n\text{-}C_4H_9$ (19 g.); $\alpha\text{-}C_4H_3OCH{=}C(C_6H_5)C(C_6H_5)_2OH$ (16 g.)	*265*
Amyl α-phenyl-β-2-furylacrylate (20 g.)	C_2H_5MgBr (26 g. C_2H_5Br)	$C_2H_5(\alpha\text{-}C_4H_3O)CHCH(C_6H_5)CO_2\text{-}n\text{-}C_5H_{11}$ (19 g.)	*265*
Amyl α-phenyl-β-2-furylacrylate (30 g.)	C_6H_5MgBr (47 g. C_6H_5Br)	$C_6H_5(\alpha\text{-}C_4H_3O)CHCH(C_6H_5)CO_2\text{-}n\text{-}C_5H_{11}$ (17 g.); $\alpha\text{-}C_4H_3OCH{=}C(C_6H_5)C(C_6H_5)_2OH$ (12 g.)	*265*
$C_{13}H_{10}O_2N$-R			
2-$C_6H_5NHC_6H_4CO_2CH_3$ (30.0 g., 0.132 mole)	CH_3MgI (82.5 g., 0.6 mole CH_3I)	2-$C_6H_5NHC_6H_4\text{-}t\text{-}C_4H_9$ (10.0 g., 33%); 9,9-dimethylacridan	*506,500*
2-$C_6H_5NHC_6H_4CO_2CH_3$ (30.0 g., 0.132 mole)	C_2H_5MgI (0.3 mole)	9,9-Diethylacridan (27.0 g., 79%)	*500*
2-$C_6H_5NHC_6H_4CO_2CH_3$ (16.0 g.)	C_6H_5MgBr (51.0 g. C_6H_5Br)	9,9-Diphenylacridan	*507*
$C_{13}H_{11}O_2$-R			
2,3-$(CH_3)_2C_{10}H_5$-1-$CO_2CH_2CH{=}CH_2$ (15.1 g.)	C_6H_5MgBr (13.0 ml. C_6H_5Br)	2,3-$(CH_3)_2C_{10}H_5$-1-CO_2H (12.2 g., 97.0%); $C_6H_5CH_2CH{=}CH_2$ (6.0 g., 82.4%)	*6*
4,7-$(CH_3)_2C_{10}H_5$-1-CO_2CH_3	CH_3MgI	4,7-$(CH_3)_2C_{10}H_5$-1-$C(CH_3)_2OH$	*24*

TABLE VIII-III (Continued)

Ester	RMgX	Product(s)	Ref.
$C_{13}H_{11}O_2N_2$-R			
2-*p*-$H_2NC_6H_4NHC_6H_4CO_2CH_3$ (0.5 g.)	CH_3MgI (3.9 g. CH_3I)	2-*p*-$H_2NC_6H_4NHC_6H_4C(CH_3)_2OH$	*511*
2-*p*-$H_2NC_6H_4NHC_6H_4CO_2CH_3$ (0.5 g.)	C_2H_5MgBr (2.9 g. C_2H_5Br)	2-*p*-$H_2NC_6H_4NHC_6H_4C(C_2H_5)_2OH$	*512*
$C_{13}H_{11}O_3N_2$-R			
2-*p*-HOC_6H_4NH-5-$H_2NC_6H_3CO_2CH_3$ (0.2 g.)	C_6H_5MgBr (3.0 g. C_6H_5Br)	2-*p*-HOC_6H_4NH-5-$H_2NC_6H_3C(C_6H_5)_2OH$	*510*
$C_{13}H_{12}O_2N_3$-R			
2-*p*-$H_2NC_6H_4NH$-5-$H_2NC_6H_3CO_2CH_3$ (0.5 g.)	CH_3MgI (3.9 g. CH_3I)	2-*p*-$H_2NC_6H_4NH$-5-$H_2NC_6H_3C(CH_3)_2OH$	*511,5*
2-*p*-$H_2NC_6H_4NH$-5-$H_2NC_6H_3CO_2CH_3$ (0.5 g.)	C_2H_5MgBr (2.9 g. C_2H_5Br)	2-*p*-$H_2NC_6H_4NH$-5-$H_2NC_6H_3C(C_2H_5)_2OH$ (yielding 60% of the carbazine dihydrochloride)	*512*
2-*m*-$H_2NC_6H_4NH$-5-$C_6H_3CO_2CH_3$ (1.0 g.)	C_6H_5MgBr (7.5 g. C_6H_5Br)	2-*m*-$H_2NC_6H_4NH$-5-$H_2NC_6H_3C(C_6H_5)_2OH$	*509*
2-C_6H_5NH-3,5-$(H_2N)_2C_6H_2CO_2CH_3$ (0.2 g.)	C_6H_5MgBr (1.2 g. C_6H_5Br)	2-C_6H_5NH-3,5-$(H_2N)_2C_6H_2C(C_6H_5)_2OH$	*508*
$C_{13}H_{12}O_3N_3$-R			
2-*p*-HOC_6H_4NH-3,5-$(H_2N)_2C_6H_2CO_2CH_3$ (3.8 g.)	C_6H_5MgBr (45.0 g. C_6H_5Br)	2-*p*-HOC_6H_4NH-3,5-$(H_2N)_2C_6H_2C(C_6H_5)_2OH$	*510*
$C_{13}H_{13}O_2N_4$-R			
2-*p*-$H_2NC_6H_4NH$-3,5-$(H_2N)_2C_6H_2CO_2CH_3$	C_6H_5MgBr	2-*p*-$H_2NC_6H_4NH$-3,5-$(H_2N)_2C_6H_2C(C_6H_5)_2OH$	*510*
$C_{13}H_{15}O_2$-R			
4-$(CH_2)_5CHC_6H_4CO_2CH_3$	C_6H_5MgBr (2 equiv.)	4-$(CH_2)_5CHC_6H_4(C_6H_5)_2COH$	*477*

TABLE VIII-III (Continued)

Ester	RMgX	Product(s)	Ref.
$C_{13}H_{15}O_2$-R (*cont.*)			
4-$(CH_2)_5CHC_6H_4CO_2CH_3$ (13 g.)	4-$(CH_2)_5CHC_6H_4MgI$ (57 g. $C_{12}H_{15}I$)	$[4\text{-}(CH_2)_5CHC_6H_4]_2CO$; $[4\text{-}(CH_2)_5CHC_6H_4]_3COH$	*304*
$C_{13}H_{16}O_3N$-R			
i-$C_4H_9CH(NHCOC_6H_5)CO_2C_2H_5$	C_6H_5MgBr	*i*-$C_4H_9CH(NHCOC_6H_5)C(C_6H_5)_2OH$ (52%)	*45*
$C_{13}H_{17}O_2$-R			
2,4,6-$(C_2H_5)_3C_6H_2CO_2C_6H_4$-4-$CH_3$	C_6H_5MgBr	1,4-$[2,4,6\text{-}(C_2H_5)_3C_6H_2CO]_2C_6H_4$; 4-$CH_3C_6H_4OH$	*119*
$C_{13}H_{17}O_4$-R			
n-$C_4H_9O(4\text{-}CH_3OC_6H_4)CHCO_2$-*n*-$C_4H_9$	C_2H_5MgCl	*n*-$C_4H_9O(4\text{-}CH_3OC_6H_4)CHC(C_2H_5)_2OH$ (yielding 75% 4-anisyl-3-hexanone)	*363*
n-$C_4H_9O(4\text{-}CH_3OC_6H_4)CHCO_2$-*n*-$C_4H_9$ (1030 g.)	C_2H_5MgBr (908 g. C_2H_5Br)	*n*-$C_4H_9O(4\text{-}CH_3OC_6H_4)CHC(C_2H_5)_2OH$ (yielding 60–70% 4-anisyl-3-hexanone)	*367*
$C_{14}H_8O_4$-R_2			
(—C_6H_4-2-$CO_2CH_3)_2$	C_6H_5MgBr	5,5,7,7-Tetraphenyl-5,7-dihydrodibenz[*c*,*e*]oxepin	*370*
(—C_6H_4-3-$CO_2CH_3)_2$ (5 g.)	C_6H_5MgBr (18 g. C_6H_5Br)	[—C_6H_4-3-$C(C_6H_5)_2OH]_2$ (8 g.)	*370*
(—C_6H_4-4-$CO_2CH_3)_2$	C_6H_5MgBr (2 equiv.)	[—C_6H_4-4-$C(C_6H_5)_2OH]_2$	*432*
(—C_6H_4-4-$CO_2CH_3)_2$ (5 g.)	4-$C_6H_5C_6H_4MgI$ (30 g. $C_{12}H_9I$)	[—C_6H_4-4-$C(C_6H_4\text{-}4\text{-}C_6H_5)_2OH]_2$	*370*
$C_{14}H_9O_3$-R			
2-$C_6H_5COC_6H_4CO_2CH_3$	C_6H_5MgBr (large excess)	1,3,3-Triphenyl-1-phthalanol* (90%)	*145,146*
Ethyl 9-Hydroxy-9-fluorenecarboxylate	CH_3MgI (7–8 equiv.)	α,α-Dimethyl-β-(*o*,*o*′-biphenylene)glycol (*ca.* quant.)	*280*

* Pérard, *Ann. chim.*, [9], 7, 344, f'tnote (1917), suggests that this product should be formulated as 2-$C_6H_5COC_6H_4C(C_6H_5)_2OH$.

TABLE VIII-III (Continued)

Ester	RMgX	Product(s)	Ref.
$C_{14}H_9O_3$-R (*cont.*)			
Ethyl 9-Hydroxy-9-fluorenecarboxylate (21 g.)	C_2H_5MgBr (85 g. C_2H_5Br)	α,α-Diethyl-β-(o-o′-biphenylene)glycol (20 g.)	280
Ethyl 9-Hydroxy-9-fluorenecarboxylate (57 g.)	C_6H_5MgBr (178 g. C_6H_5Br)	α,α-Diphenyl-β-(o,o′-biphenylene)glycol (82%)	280
$C_{14}H_{11}O_2$-R			
$(C_6H_5)_2CHCO_2C_2H_5$ (17.5 g., 0.073 mole)	i-C_3H_7MgBr (0.073 mole) [+ C_6H_5COCl (14.0 g., 0.1 mole)]	$C_6H_5CO(C_6H_5)_2CCO_2C_2H_5$ (3.5 g., 14%); recovered ester	153
$(C_6H_5)_2CHCO_2C_2H_5$ (5.5 g.)	$(CH_2)_5CHMgCl$ (12.0 g. $C_6H_{11}Cl$)	Recovered ester	305
$(C_6H_5)_2CHCO_2C_2H_5$ (48 g.)	$C_6H_5CH_2MgCl$ (102 g. C_7H_7Cl)	$(C_6H_5)_2CH(C_6H_5CH_2)_2COH$ (65 g., 86%)	311
$(C_6H_5)_2CHCO_2CH_2CH{=}CH_2$ (25.0 g.)	2,4,6-$(CH_3)_3C_6H_2MgBr$ (25.0 g. $C_9H_{11}Br$)	Rec. ester (5.4 g.); 1,3,5-$(CH_3)_3C_6H_3$ (9.5 g., 63%); $H_2C{=}CHCH_2C(C_6H_5)_2CO_2H$ (11.9 g.)	514
$(C_6H_5)_2CHCO_2CH_2CH{=}CHCH_3$ (12.5 g.)	2,4,6-$(CH_3)_3C_6H_2MgBr$ (12.0 g. $C_9H_{11}Br$)	1,3,5-$(CH_3)_3C_6H_3$ (5.0 g.); $H_2C{=}CHCH(CH_3)C(C_6H_5)_2CO_2H$ (8.2 g. 65.5%)	514
$(C_6H_5)_2CHCO_2CH(CH_3)CH{=}CH_2$ (11.5 g.)	2,4,6-$(CH_3)_3C_6H_2MgBr$ (10.75 g. $C_9H_{11}Br$)	Rec. ester (0.9 g.); 1,3,5-$(CH_3)_3C_6H_3$ (4.6 g., 88.4%); $CH_3CH{=}CHCH_2C(C_6H_5)_2CO_2H$ (8.5 g., 74%)	514
2-$C_6H_5CH_2C_6H_4CO_2CH_3$	C_6H_5MgBr	2-$C_6H_5CH_2C_6H_4C(C_6H_5)_2OH$*; $[HO(C_6H_5)(2\text{-}C_6H_5CH_2C_6H_4)C—]_2$†	25
2-$C_6H_5CH_2C_6H_4CO_2C_2H_5$ (32 g.)	C_6H_5MgBr (48 g. C_6H_5Br)	2-$C_6H_5CH_2C_6H_4C(C_6H_5)_2OH$* (yielding 18 g. anthracene deriv.); $[HO(C_6H_5)(2\text{-}C_6H_5CH_2C_6H_4)C—]_2$† (15 g.)	25

* Isolated, after treatment with acetic acid, as 9,9-diphenyl-9,10-dihydroanthracene.

† In a private communication to Boyd and Hatt, *J. Chem. Soc.*, *1927*, 909, Barnett states that when filtered (*i.e.*, Mg-free) Grignard reagent solutions were used no glycols were detected.

TABLE VIII-III (Continued)

Ester	RMgX	Product(s)	Ref.
$C_{14}H_{11}O_2$-R (*cont.*)			
2-$C_6H_5CH_2C_6H_4CO_2C_2H_5$	4-$CH_3OC_6H_4MgI$	2-$C_6H_5CH_2C_6H_4(4\text{-}CH_3OC_6H_4)_2COH$	*51*
2-$C_6H_5CH_2C_6H_4CO_2C_6H_5$	C_6H_5MgBr	2-$C_6H_5CH_2C_6H_4C(C_6H_5)_2OH$* [HO($C_6H_5$)(2-$C_6H_5CH_2C_6H_4$)C—]$_2$†	*25*
$C_{14}H_{11}O_3$-R			
$(C_6H_5)_2C(OH)CO_2CH_3$ (1.0 g.)	C_6H_5MgBr (5.0 g. C_6H_5Br)	[HO$(C_6H_5)_2$C—]$_2$ (1.3 g.)	*1*
$(C_6H_5)_2C(OH)CO_2CH_3$ (10 g.)	$(CH_2)_5CHMgCl$ (60 g. $C_6H_{11}Cl$)	$(C_6H_5)_2C(OH)COCH(CH_2)_5$	*304*
$C_{14}H_{12}O_2N$-R			
2-*p*-$CH_3C_6H_4NHC_6H_4CO_2CH_3$ (15 g.)	C_6H_5MgBr (60 g. C_6H_5Br)	2-*p*-$CH_3C_6H_4NHC_6H_4C(C_6H_5)_2OH$ (75–80%)	*513*
$C_{14}H_{12}O_3N$-R			
2-*p*-$CH_3OC_6H_4NHC_6H_4CO_2CH_3$	C_6H_5MgBr	2-*p*-$CH_3OC_6H_4NHC_6H_4C(C_6H_5)_2OH$ (75%)	*513*
$C_{14}H_{19}O_3$-R			
i-$C_5H_{11}O(4\text{-}CH_3OC_6H_4)CHCO_2$-*i*-$C_5H_{11}$	C_2H_5MgBr	*i*-$C_5H_{11}O(4\text{-}CH_3OC_6H_4)CHC(C_2H_5)_2OH$ (yielding 60–70% 4-anisyl-3-hexanone)	*367*
$C_{14}H_{27}O_3$-R			
n-$C_{13}H_{27}CO_2CH_3$ (77 g., 0.32 mole)	*t*-C_4H_9MgCl (1.08 mole)	After alkaline hydrolysis, (*n*-$C_{13}H_{27})_2CO$ (27.5 g., 44%); *n*-$C_{13}H_{27}CO_2H$ (6.0 g., 8%); *t*-C_4H_9(*n*-$C_{13}H_{27}$)CHOH (37.0 g., 40%); *i*-C_4H_8 (0.09 mole); *i*-C_4H_{10} (0.17 mole)	*476*

* Isolated, after treatment with acetic acid, as 9,9-diphenyl-9,10-dihydroanthracene.

† In a private communication to Boyd and Hatt, *J. Chem. Soc.*, *1927*, 909, Barnett states that when filtered (*i.e.*, Mg-free) Grignard reagent solutions were used no glycols were detected.

TABLE VIII-III (Continued)

Ester	RMgX	Product(s)	Ref.
$C_{14}H_{27}O_3$-R (*cont.*)			
n-$C_{13}H_{27}CO_2CH_3$	n-$C_8H_{17}MgBr$ (2.5 equiv.)	n-$C_{13}H_{27}(n$-$C_8H_{17})_2COH$	*460*
n-$C_{13}H_{27}CO_2C_2H_5$ (313 g.)	CH_3MgI (380 g. CH_3I)	n-$C_{13}H_{27}(CH_3)_2COH$ (220 g.)	*330*
$C_{15}H_{11}O_2$-R			
$C_6H_5CH{=}C(C_6H_5)CO_2CH_3$ (42.0 g.)	CH_3MgI (12.7 g. Mg)	$C_6H_5CH{=}C(C_6H_5)C(CH_3)_2OH$ (21.0 g., 50%)	*210,217*
$C_6H_5CH{=}C(C_6H_5)CO_2CH_3$	C_6H_5MgBr	$(C_6H_5)_2CHCH(C_6H_5)CO_2CH_3$	*217,211*
$C_6H_5CH{=}C(C_6H_5)CO_2CH_3$	2-$CH_3C_6H_4MgBr$	C_6H_5(2-$CH_3C_6H_4$)$CHCH(C_6H_5)CO_2CH_3$	*217*
$C_6H_5CH{=}C(C_6H_5)CO_2CH_3$	1-$C_{10}H_7MgBr$	C_6H_5(1-$C_{10}H_7$)$CHCH(C_6H_5)CO_2CH_3$	*217*
$C_6H_5CH{=}C(C_6H_5)CO_2C_6H_5$	C_6H_5MgBr (excess)	$(C_6H_5)_2CHCH(C_6H_5)COC_6H_5$	*218*
$C_{15}H_{11}O_3$-R			
$(C_6H_5)_2CHCOCO_2C_2H_5$	C_6H_5MgBr (excess)	$(C_6H_5)_2CHC(OH)(C_6H_5)CO_2C_2H_5$ (8 g.; inverse add'n, 10 g.)*	*221*
$(C_6H_5)_2CHCOCO_2C_2H_5$	C_6H_5MgBr ("large excess")	$(C_6H_5)_2CHC(OH)(C_6H_5)COC_6H_5$; $(C_6H_5)_2CHC(OH)(C_6H_5)C(C_6H_5)_2OH$†	*221*
Ethyl β,β-diphenylglycidate	C_6H_5MgBr ("large excess")	$(C_6H_5)_3COH$; $(C_6H_5)_2CHCHO$; $(C_6H_5{-})_2$	*221*
Ethyl 9-xanthylacetate	C_6H_5MgBr (3 equiv.)	1,1-Diphenyl-2-(9-xanthyl)ethanol ("good yield")	*475*
$C_{15}H_{11}O_4$-R			
2-(2-$CH_3OC_6H_4CO$)$C_6H_4CO_2C_2H_5$ (20.3 g.)	4-$CH_3OC_6H_4MgI$ (46.8 g. C_7H_7IO)	2-(2-$CH_3OC_6H_4CO$)C_6H_4(4-$CH_3OC_6H_4$)$_2COH$ (22.7 g.)	*51*
2-(4-$CH_3OC_6H_4CO$)$C_6H_4CO_2CH_3$	4-$CH_3OC_6H_4MgI$	2-(4-$CH_3OC_6H_4CO$)$C_6H_4COC_6H_4$-4-OCH_3	*52*
$C_{15}H_{12}O_3N$-R			
$C_6H_5(C_6H_5CO)NCH_2CO_2C_2H_5$	CH_3MgBr	$C_6H_5(C_6H_5CO)NCH_2C(CH_3)_2OH$	*45*

* Addition of Et_2O-ester solution to ice-cooled Grignard reagent solution.

† Addition of Et_2O-ester solution to Grignard reagent solution; several days at room temperature, or three to four hours reflux.

TABLE VIII-III (Continued)

Ester	RMgX	Product(s)	Ref.
$C_{15}H_{12}O_3N$-R (*cont.*)			
$C_6H_5CONHCH(C_6H_5)CO_2C_2H_5$	C_2H_5MgBr	$C_6H_5CONHCH(C_6H_5)C(C_2H_5)_2OH$ (82%)	*417*
$C_{15}H_{13}O_2$-R			
$CH_3(C_6H_5)_2CCO_2CH_2CH{=}CH_2$ (5.07 g.)	C_6H_5MgBr (5.25 ml. C_6H_5Br)	$CH_3(C_6H_5)_2CCO_2H$ (3.8 g., 88%)	*6*
$C_6H_5(C_6H_5CH_2)CHCO_2CH_3$	$C_6H_5CH_2MgCl$ (3 equiv.)	$C_6H_5(C_6H_5CH_2)CH(C_6H_5CH_2)_2COH$	*312*
$C_{15}H_{13}O_3$-R			
$CH_3O(C_6H_5)_2CCO_2CH_3$ (70 g.)	CH_3MgI (3 equiv.)	$CH_3O(C_6H_5)_2CC(CH_3)_2OH$ (60 g.)	*280*
$HO(C_6H_5)_2CCH_2CO_2C_2H_5$	CH_3MgI	$HO(C_6H_5)_2CCH_2C(CH_3)_2OH$; $(C_6H_5)_2C{=}C{=}C(CH_3)_2$	
$HO(C_6H_5)_2CCH_2CO_2C_2H_5$	C_2H_5MgI	$HO(C_6H_5)_2CCH_2C(C_2H_5)_2OH$	*35*
$HO(C_6H_5)_2CCH_2CO_2C_2H_5$	C_6H_5MgBr	$[HO(C_6H_5)_2C]_2CH_2$	*35*
2-(4-$CH_3OC_6H_4CH_2$)$C_6H_4CO_2C_2H_5$ (23 g.)	2-$CH_3OC_6H_4MgI$ (50 g. C_7H_7IO)	2-(4-$CH_3OC_6H_4CH_2$)C_6H_4(2-$CH_3OC_6H_4$)$_2$COH (26 g.)	*51*
2-(4-$CH_3OC_6H_4CH_2$)$C_6H_4CO_2C_2H_5$ (20.3 g.)	4-$CH_3OC_6H_4MgI$ (46.8 g. C_7H_7IO)	2-(4-$CH_3OC_6H_4CH_2$)C_6H_4(4-$CH_3OC_6H_4$)$_2$COH (17 g.)	*51,53*
$C_{15}H_{15}O_2N_2$-R			
2-*p*-$(CH_3)_2NC_6H_4NHC_6H_4CO_2CH_3$ (1.35 g.)	C_6H_5MgBr (4.80 g. C_6H_5Br)	2-*p*-$(CH_3)_2NC_6H_4NHC_6H_4C(C_6H_5)_2OH$	*508*
$C_{15}H_{16}O_2N_3$-R			
2-*p*-$(CH_3)_2NC_6H_4$NH-5-$H_2NC_6H_3CO_2CH_3$ (0.5 g.)	CH_3MgI (3.9 g. CH_3I)	2-*p*-$(CH_3)_2NC_6H_4$NH-5-$H_2NC_6H_3C(CH_3)_2OH$ (yielding 70% of the carbazine dihydrochloride)	*511*
2-*p*-$(CH_3)_2NC_6H_4$NH-5-$H_2NC_6H_3CO_2CH_3$	C_2H_5MgBr	2-*p*-$(CH_3)_2NC_6H_4$NH-5-$H_2NC_6H_3C(C_2H_5)_2OH$ (yielding 65% of the carbazine dihydrochloride)	*512*

TABLE VIII-III (Continued)

Ester	RMgX	Product(s)	Ref.
$C_{15}H_{16}O_2N_3$-R (*cont.*)			
2-*p*-$(CH_3)_2NC_6H_4NH$-5-$H_2NC_6H_3CO_2CH_3$	C_6H_5MgBr (6.2 g. C_6H_5Br)	2-*p*-$(CH_3)_2NC_6H_4NH$-5-$H_2NC_6H_3C(C_6H_5)_2OH$	*508*
$C_{15}H_{25}O_2$-R			
Ethyl homoaleprate*	C_6H_5MgBr ("large excess")	$C_5H_7(CH_2)_9C(C_6H_5)_2OH$	*71*
$C_{16}H_{10}O_2N$-R			
Acitrin†	CH_3MgI	α,α-Dimethyl-2-phenyl-4-quinolinemethanol	*103*
Acitrin†	C_2H_5MgI	α,α-Diethyl-2-phenyl-4-quinolinemethanol	*111*
Acitrin†	C_6H_5MgBr	α,α,2-Triphenyl-4-quinolinemethanol; pinacol (?), m. 196°; $C_{38}H_{26}ON_2$ (?), m. 202-3°	*482*
Acitrin†	$C_6H_5CH_2MgCl$	α,α-Dibenzyl-2-phenyl-4-quinolinemethanol	*103*
Acitrin†	3-$CH_3C_6H_4MgBr$	α,α-Di-*m*-tolyl-2-phenyl-4-quinolinemethanol	*103*
$C_{16}H_{13}O_2$-R			
$(C_6H_5)_2C{=}C(CH_3)CO_2C_2H_5$ (23.0 g.)	C_6H_5MgBr (27.1 g. C_6H_5Br)	$(C_6H_5)_2C{=}C(CH_3)C(C_6H_5)_2OH$ (3.5 g.)	*41*
Methyl 1-methyl-3-phenanthrenecarboxylate	CH_3MgBr	α,α,1-Trimethyl-3-phenanthrenemethanol	*93*
Methyl 3-phenyl-1-indancarboxylate (6.7 g.)	C_6H_5MgBr (8.5 ml. C_6H_5Br)	α,α,3-Triphenyl-1-indanmethanol (3.5 g.)	*54*
$C_{16}H_{14}O_3N$-R			
$C_6H_5CONH(C_6H_5CH_2)CHCO_2C_2H_5$	C_2H_5MgBr	$C_6H_5CONH(C_6H_5CH_2)CHC(C_2H_5)OH$ (69%)	*45*

* Ethyl 10-(Δ^2-cyclopentenyl)decanoate.

† Ethyl 2-phenylcinchonimate; ethyl 2-phenyl-4-quinolinecarboxylate.

TABLE VIII-III (Continued)

Ester	RMgX	Product(s)	Ref.
$C_{16}H_{15}O_2$-R			
$CH_3(C_6H_5)_2CCH_2CO_2C_2H_5$	CH_3MgI	$CH_3(C_6H_5)_2CCH_2C(CH_3)_2OH$ (65%)	*40*
$(C_6H_5)_2CHCH(CH_3)CO_2CH_3$ (25 g.)	C_6H_5MgBr (125 ml., 2*M*)	$(C_6H_5)_2CHCH(CH_3)C(C_6H_5)_2OH$ (yielding 15 g., 43% olefin)	*209*
$C_{16}H_{15}O_3$-R			
$HO(C_6H_5)(4\text{-}CH_3C_6H_4)CCH_2CO_2C_2H_5$	C_6H_5MgBr	$HO(C_6H_5)(4\text{-}CH_3C_6H_4)CCH_2C(C_6H_5)_2OH$	*35*
$C_{16}H_{15}O_4$-R			
$HO(C_6H_5)(4\text{-}CH_3OC_6H_4)CCH_2CO_2C_2H_5$	CH_3MgI	$HO(C_6H_5)(4\text{-}CH_3OC_6H_4)CCH_2C(CH_3)_2OH$	*35*
$HO(C_6H_5)(4\text{-}CH_3OC_6H_4)CCH_2CO_2C_2H_5$	C_6H_5MgBr	$HO(C_6H_5)(4\text{-}CH_3OC_6H_4)CCH_2C(C_6H_5)_2OH$	*35*
$C_{16}H_{17}O_2$-R			
Methyl 1-methyl-1,2,3,4-tetrahydro-3-phenanthrenecarboxylate	CH_3MgBr	α,α,1-Trimethyl-1,2,3,4-tetrahydro-3-phenanthrenemethanol	*93*
$C_{16}H_{19}O_3$-R			
Methyl 2-*o*-anisyl-4,5-dimethyl-4-cyclohexene-1-carboxylate	CH_3MgI	α,α,4,5-Tetramethyl-2-*o*-anisyl-4-cyclohexene-1-methanol (91%)	*279*
$C_{16}H_{23}O_2$-R			
2,4,6-$(i\text{-}C_3H_7)_3C_6H_2CO_2C_6H_4$-4-$CH_3$	CH_3MgI	2,4,6-$(i\text{-}C_3H_7)_3C_6H_2COCH_3$ (46%); 4-$CH_3C_6H_4OH$ (78%)	*120*
2,4,6-$(i\text{-}C_3H_7)_3C_6H_2CO_2C_6H_4$-4-$CH_3$	C_2H_5MgBr	2,4,6-$(i\text{-}C_3H_7)_3C_6H_2COC_2H_5$ (43%); 4-$CH_3C_6H_4OH$	*120*
2,4,6-$(i\text{-}C_3H_7)_3C_6H_2CO_2C_6H_4$-4-$CH_3$	C_6H_5MgBr	1,4-[2,4,6-$(i\text{-}C_3H_7)_3C_6H_2CO]_2C_6H_4$; 4-$CH_3C_6H_4OH$	*119*

TABLE VIII-III (Continued)

Ester	RMgX	Product(s)	Ref.
$C_{16}H_{27}O_2$-R			
Ethyl hydnocarpate* (9 g.)	C_2H_5MgBr	$C_5H_7(CH_2)_{10}C(C_2H_5)_2OH$ (*ca.* 9 g.)	71
Ethyl hydnocarpate* (8 g.)	$H_2C{=}CHCH_2MgBr$	$C_5H_7(CH_2)_{10}C(CH_2CH{=}CH_2)_2OH$ (yielding 4–5 g. dehydrate)	71
Ethyl hydnocarpate* (9 g.)	n-C_3H_7MgBr (10 g. C_3H_7Br)	$C_5H_7(CH_2)_{10}C(n\text{-}C_3H_7)_2OH$ (*ca.* 11 g.)	71
Ethyl hydnocarpate* (50 g.)	C_6H_5MgBr (70 g. C_6H_5Br)	$C_5H_7(CH_2)_{10}C(C_6H_5)_2OH$ (yielding 55 g. olefin)	71
$C_{16}H_{31}O_2$-R			
n-$C_{15}H_{31}CO_2CH_3$	n-C_3H_7MgBr	n-$C_3H_7(n\text{-}C_{15}H_{31})CHOH$	238
n-$C_{15}H_{31}CO_2CH_3$	C_6H_5MgBr	n-$C_{15}H_{31}(C_6H_5)_2COH$ (yielding 80–90% olefin)	377
n-$C_{15}H_{31}CO_2CH_3$	n-$C_6H_{13}MgBr$ (2.5 equiv.)	n-$C_{15}H_{31}(n\text{-}C_6H_{13})_2COH$	460
n-$C_{15}H_{31}CO_2C_2H_5$	CH_3MgBr	n-$C_{15}H_{31}(CH_3)_2COH$	229
n-$C_{15}H_{31}CO_2C_2H_5$	C_2H_5MgBr	n-$C_{15}H_{31}(C_2H_5)_2COH$ (99%)	230
n-$C_{15}H_{31}CO_2C_2H_5$	n-C_3H_7MgBr	n-$C_{15}H_{31}(n\text{-}C_3H_7)_2COH$	226
n-$C_{15}H_{31}CO_2C_2H_5$	s-C_4H_9MgBr	$(n\text{-}C_{15}H_{31})_2CO$	327
n-$C_{15}H_{31}CO_2C_2H_5$ (50 g.)	t-C_4H_9MgCl (52 g. C_4H_9Cl)	$(n\text{-}C_{15}H_{31})_2CO$ (25%)	326,327
$C_{17}H_{12}O_2N$-R			
2-β-$C_{10}H_7NHC_6H_4CO_2CH_3$	C_6H_5MgBr	2-β-$C_{10}H_7NHC_6H_4C(C_6H_5)_2OH$ (75%)	513
Ethyl 2-phenyl-6-methyl-cinchoninate†	C_2H_5MgBr	α,α-Diethyl-2-phenyl-6-methyl-4-quinolinemethanol	111
$C_{17}H_{13}O_2$-R			
$C_6H_5CH{=}CHCH{=}C(C_6H_5)CO_2CH_3$	CH_3MgI (4 equiv.)	$C_6H_5CH{=}CHCH{=}C(C_6H_5)C(CH_3)_2OH$; $C_6H_5CH{=}CHCH{=}C(C_6H_5)C(CH_3){=}CH_2$	353

* Ethyl 11-(Δ^2-cyclopentenyl)undecanoate.
† Ethyl 2-phenyl-6-methyl-4-quinolinecarboxylate.

TABLE VIII-III (Continued)

Ester	RMgX	Product(s)	Ref.
$C_{17}H_{13}O_2$-R (*cont.*)			
$C_6H_5CH{=}CHC(C_6H_5){=}CHCO_2CH_3$	C_6H_5MgBr	$C_6H_5CH{=}CHC(C_6H_5){=}CHC(C_6H_5)_2OH$ (40%); oil	*214*
$C_6H_5CH{=}CHCH{=}C(C_6H_5)CO_2CH_3$	C_6H_5MgBr (3 equiv.)	$C_6H_5CH{=}CHCH(C_6H_5)CH(C_6H_5)COC_6H_5$	*353*
$C_6H_5CH{=}CHCH{=}C(C_6H_5)CO_2CH_3$	$C_6H_5CH_2MgBr$ (3 equiv.)	$C_6H_5CH{=}CHCH(CH_2C_6H_5)CH(C_6H_5)COCH_2C_6H_5$ (17%)	*353*
$C_6H_5CH{=}CHCH{=}C(C_6H_5)CO_2CH_3$	2-$CH_3C_6H_4MgBr$ (3 equiv.)	Recovered ester (as acid); C_7H_8 (65%); unidentified oil	*353*
$C_6H_5CH{=}CHCH{=}C(C_6H_5)CO_2CH_3$	1-$C_{10}H_7MgBr$ (3 equiv.)	Recovered ester (as acid); $C_{10}H_8$; tar	*353*
$C_{17}H_{15}O_4N_2$-R			
$C_6H_5CONHCH_2CONHCH(C_6H_5)$-$CO_2C_2H_5$	C_6H_5MgBr	$C_6H_5CONHCH_2CONHCH(C_6H_5)C(C_6H_5)_2OH$	*45*
$C_6H_5CONHCH_2CONHCH(C_6H_5)$-$CO_2C_2H_5$	$C_6H_5CH_2MgBr$	$C_6H_5CONHCH_2CONHCH(C_6H_5)C(CH_2C_6H_5)_2OH$	*45*
$C_{17}H_{19}O_2N_2$-R			
2-*p*-$(C_2H_5)_2NC_6H_4NHC_6H_4CO_2CH_3$ (0.2 *g.*)	C_6H_5MgBr (1.5 *g.* C_6H_5Br)	2-*p*-$(C_2H_5)_2NC_6H_4NHC_6H_4C(C_6H_5)_2OH$	*509*
$C_{17}H_{20}O_2N_3$-R			
2-*p*-$(C_2H_5)_2NC_6H_3NH5$-$H_2NC_6H_4CO_2CH_3$ (0.5 *g.*)	C_6H_5MgBr (2.2 *g.* C_6H_5Br)	2-*p*-$(C_2H_5)_2NC_6H_4NH$-5-$H_2NC_6H_3C(C_6H_5)_2OH$	*509*
$C_{18}H_{11}O_3$-R			
2-$C_6H_5\dot{C}OC_{10}H_6$-1-CO_2CH_3	CH_3MgI (*ca.* 1 equiv.)	3-Methyl-3-phenyl-6,7-benzophthalide (56%)	*106*

TABLE VIII-III (Continued)

Ester	RMgX	Product(s)	Ref.
$C_{18}H_{14}O_4$-R_2			
Diethyl γ-truxillate* (20.0 g.)	CH_3MgI (32.3 g. CH_3I)	γ-2,4-Diphenyl-3-(α-hydroxyisopropyl)-1-cyclobutanecarboxylic acid lactone; α,α,α′,α′-tetramethyl-2,4-diphenyl-1,3-cyclobutanedimethanol; 1,3-diisopropylidene-2,4-diphenylcyclobutane	*409*
$C_{18}H_{15}O_4$-R			
Monoethyl α-truxillate† (18.8 g.)	CH_3MgI (33.0 g. CH_3I)	α-2,4-Diphenyl-3-(α-hydroxyisopropyl)-1-cyclobutanecarboxylic acid ("good yield")	*409*
Monoethyl γ-truxillate† (15 g.)	C_2H_5MgBr (28 g. C_2H_5Br)	γ-2,4-Diphenyl-3-(3-hydroxy-3-amyl)-1-cyclobutanecarboxylic acid	*409*
$C_{18}H_{20}O_5$-R_2			
Dimethyl (+)β-7-methylmarrianolate‡	C_6H_5MgBr	(+)β-2′-Hydroxy-2′,2′-diphenyl-7-methyldoisynolic acid lactone§	*46*
$C_{18}H_{31}O_2$-R			
Ethyl chaulmoograte¶ (9 g.)	CH_3MgI (10 g. CH_3I)	$C_5H_7(CH_2)_{12}C(CH_3)_2OH$ (90%)	*71*
Ethyl chaulmoograte¶	1-$C_{10}H_7MgBr$ (3 equiv.)	$C_5H_7(CH_2)_{11}CH{=}C(1\text{-}C_{10}H_7)_2$	*71*
$C_{18}H_{32}O_4$-R_2			
$[\text{—}(CH_2)_8CO_2CH_3]_2$	C_6H_5MgBr	$[\text{—}(CH_2)_8C(C_6H_5)_2OH]_2$ (*ca.* 80%)	*377*

* Diethyl 2,4-diphenyl-1,3-cyclobutanedicarboxylate.

† 2,4-Diphenyl-3-carbethoxy-1-cyclobutanecarboxylic acid.

‡ 1-Carbomethoxymethyl-2-carbomethoxy-7-methoxy-1,2,3,4,4a,9,10,10a-octahydrophenanthrene.

§ 1-Oxo-3,3-diphenyl-8-methoxy-3,4,4a,4b,5,6,10b,11,12,12a-decahydro-1-phenanthro[2,1-c]pyran.

¶ Ethyl 13-(Δ^2-cyclopentenyl)tridecanoate.

TABLE VIII-III (Continued)

Ester	RMgX	Product(s)	Ref.
$C_{18}H_{32}O_4$-R_2 (*cont.*)			
[—$(CH_2)_8CO_2C_2H_5]_2$	CH_3MgBr	[—$(CH_2)_8C(CH_3)_2OH]_2$	*228*
$C_{18}H_{33}O_2$-R			
$CH_3(CH_2)_7CH{=}CH(CH_2)_7CO_2CH_3$ (296 g.)	n-C_4H_9MgBr (685 g. C_4H_9Br)	$C_{17}H_{33}(n$-$C_4H_9)_2COH$	*460*
$C_{18}H_{35}O_2$-R			
n-$C_{17}H_{35}CO_2CH_3$	CH_3MgI	n-$C_{17}H_{35}(CH_3)_2COH$	*283*
n-$C_{17}H_{35}CO_2CH_3$	C_6H_5MgBr	n-$C_{17}H_{35}(C_6H_5)_2COH$ (yielding 80–90% olefin)	*377*
n-$C_{17}H_{35}CO_2C_2H_5$ (0.1 mole)	2,4,6-$(CH_3)_3C_6H_2MgBr$ (0.1 mole)	n-$C_{17}H_{35}CO(n$-$C_{16}H_{33})CHCO_2C_2H_5$ (27%)	*396*
$C_{19}H_{13}O_3$-R			
2-o-$CH_3C_6H_4COC_{10}H_6$-1-CO_2CH_3	CH_3MgI (*ca.* 1 equiv.)	3-Methyl-3-o-tolyl-6,7-benzophthalide (51%, on basis of ester consumed)	*106*
$C_{19}H_{13}O_5Br$-R_2			
Dimethyl 2-benzoyl-3-(3-bromo-4-methoxyphenyl)-1,1-cyclopropanedicarboxylate	C_2H_5MgBr	Dimethyl 2-(α-hydroxy-α-phenylpropyl)-3-(3-bromo-4-methoxyphenyl)-1,1-cyclopropanedicarboxylate (2 isomers, m. 135° and 161°)	*215*
Dimethyl 2-benzoyl-3-(3-bromo-4-methoxyphenyl)-1,1-cyclopropanedicarboxylate	C_6H_5MgBr (4 equiv.)	Dimethyl α-benzoyl-β-phenyl-β-(3-bromo-4-methoxyphenyl)ethylmalonate (30%)*	*215*
Dimethyl 2-benzoyl-3-(3-bromo-4-methoxyphenyl)-1,1-cyclopropanedicarboxylate	C_6H_5MgBr	Methyl 1,2-dibenzoyl-3-(3-bromo-4-methoxyphenyl)-1-cyclopropanecarboxylate†	*215*

* Gradual addition of powdered ester to agitated, ice-cold Grignard reagent solution.

† Gradual addition of Grignard reagent solution to agitated C_6H_6-ester solution at 35°.

TABLE VIII-III (Continued)

Ester	RMgX	Product(s)	Ref.
$C_{20}H_{11}O_3$-R			
Methyl 2-phenyl-9-oxo-1-fluorenecarboxylate (3.1 g.)	C_6H_5MgBr (15.6 g. C_6H_5Br)	1-Benzoyl-2-phenyl-9-fluorenone (1.0 g.)	*449*
$C_{20}H_{13}O_3$-R			
Methyl 2-(9-xanthyl)benzoate (6.0 g.)	C_6H_5MgBr (9.0 g. C_6H_5Br)	2-(9-Xanthyl)triphenylmethanol (4.5 g.)	*484*
$C_{20}H_{15}O_2$-R			
$(C_6H_5)_3CCO_2CH_2CH{=}CH_2$ (3.8 g.)	C_6H_5MgBr (2.6 g. C_6H_5Br)	$(C_6H_5)_3CCO_2H$ (3.1 g., 93%)	*6*
2-$[(C_6H_5)_2CH]C_6H_4CO_2CH_3$ (5.0 g.)	CH_3MgI (5.9 g. CH_3I)	2-$[(C_6H_5)_2CH]C_6H_4C(CH_3)_2OH$*	*65*
2-$[(C_6H_5)_2CH]C_6H_4CO_2CH_3$	C_6H_5MgBr	2-$[(C_6H_5)_2CH]C_6H_4C(C_6H_5)_2OCH_3$	*148*
2-$[(C_6H_5)_2CH]C_6H_4CO_2CH_3$	C_6H_5MgBr (2 equiv.)	2-$[(C_6H_5)_2CH]C_6H_4C(C_6H_5)_2OH$	*25*
$C_{20}H_{17}O_5N$-R_2			
Diethyl 1-methyl-2,6-diphenyl-4-oxo-3,5-pyridinedicarboxylate (3.1 g.)	C_2H_5MgI (1.2 g. C_2H_5I)	Diethyl 1-methyl-2,6-diphenyl-4-hydroxy-4-ethyl-3,5-pyridinedicarboxylate (3.0 g.)	*485*
Diethyl 1-methyl-2,6-diphenyl-4-oxo-3,5-pyridinedicarboxylate (3.0 g.)	*n*-C_3H_7MgBr (1.0 g. C_3H_7Br)	Diethyl 1-methyl-2,6-diphenyl-4-hydroxy-4-*n*-propyl-3,5-pyridinedicarboxylate (3.1 g.)	*485*
Diethyl 1-methyl-2,6-diphenyl-4-oxo-3,5-pyridinedicarboxylate (3.0 g.)	*n*-C_4H_9MgBr	Diethyl 1-methyl-2,6-diphenyl-4-hydroxy-4-*n*-butyl-3,5-pyridinedicarboxylate (3.1 g.)	*485*
Diethyl 1-methyl-2,6-diphenyl-4-oxo-3,5-pyridinedicarboxylate (6.0 g.)	C_6H_5MgBr (2.4 g. C_6H_5Br)	Diethyl 1-methyl-2,4,6-triphenyl-4-hydroxy-3,5-pyridinedicarboxylate (6.5 g.)	*485*

* Isolated, after $AlCl_3$ cyclization, as 9,9-dimethyl-10-phenyl-9,10-dihydroanthracene (0.75 g., 16%).

TABLE VIII-III (Continued)

Ester	RMgX	Product(s)	Ref.
$C_{20}H_{19}O_5$-R			
$CH_3CO_2(C_2H_5O)C=C[CH(C_6H_5)_2]CO_2C_2H_5$	C_6H_5MgBr (2 equiv.)	$(C_6H_5)_2CHCH(CO_2C_2H_5)_2$; $CH_3(C_6H_5)_2COH$	*212*
$C_{20}H_{21}O_3$-R			
$C_2H_5(4\text{-}CH_3OC_6H_4)C=C(C_2H_5)C_6H_4\text{-}3\text{-}CO_2CH_3$	CH_3MgI (1.33 equiv.)	$C_2H_5(4\text{-}CH_3OC_6H_4)C=C(C_2H_5)C_6H_4\text{-}3\text{-}COCH_3$	*483*
$C_{21}H_{17}O_3$-R			
$(C_6H_5)_2CHC(OH)(C_6H_5)CO_2C_2H_5$	C_6H_5MgBr ("large excess")	$(C_6H_5)_2CHC(OH)(C_6H_5)COC_6H_5$; $(C_6H_5)_2CHC(OH)(C_6H_5)C(C_6H_5)_2OH$	*221*
$C_{21}H_{19}O_5N$-R_2			
Diethyl 1-ethyl-2,6-diphenyl-4-oxo-3,5-pyridinedicarboxylate (0.007 mole)	C_2H_5MgI (0.0075 mole)	Diethyl 1,4-diethyl-2,6-diphenyl-4-hydroxy-3,5-piperidinedicarboxylate (2.0 g.)	*380*
Diethyl 1-ethyl-2,6-diphenyl-4-oxo-3,5-pyridinedicarboxylate (0.01 mole)	C_6H_5MgBr (0.01 mole)	Diethyl 1-ethyl-2,4,6-triphenyl-4-hydroxy-3,5-piperidinedicarboxylate (2.5 g.)	*380*
$C_{21}H_{35}O_3$-R			
Methyl 3(α),11(α)-dihydroxy-bisnorcholanate (22.5 g., 0.06 mole)	C_6H_5MgBr (1.2 mole)	3(α),11(α)-Dihydroxytrischolanyldiphenylmethanol (yielding 18.4 g. crude olefin); recovered ester (as acid, 1.6 g., 7%)	*247*
$C_{22}H_{13}O_3$-R			
Methyl 4-(1-oxo-3-phenyl-2-indenyl)benzoate	C_6H_5MgBr (excess)	1,3-Diphenyl-2-(4-α-hydroxybenzhydrylphenyl)-1-indenol	*208*

TABLE VIII-III (Continued)

Ester	RMgX	Product(s)	Ref.
$C_{22}H_{33}O_3$-R			
Methyl 3-hydroxy-Δ^5-bisnorcholenate (12 g.)	C_6H_5MgBr (49 g. C_6H_5Br)	3-Hydroxy-Δ^5-ternorcholenyldiphenylmethanol (*ca.* 11 g.)	*406*
$C_{22}H_{34}O_2Cl$-R			
Methyl 3-chlorobisnorallocholanate	C_6H_5MgBr	3-Chloroternorallocholanyldiphenylmethanol	*253,254*
$C_{22}H_{35}O_2$-R			
Ethyl α-bisnorcholanate	CH_3MgI	Ternorcholanyldimethylmethanol	*465*
$C_{22}H_{35}O_4$-R			
Methyl bisnordesoxycholate	C_6H_5MgBr (16 equiv.)	3,12-Dihydroxyternorcholanyldiphenylmethanol	*165*
Methyl 3(α),12(α)-dihydroxy-bisnorcholanate (4.5 g.)	C_6H_5MgBr	(3α),12(α)-Dihydroxy-20-pregnyldiphenylmethanol (5.1 g.)	*394*
Methyl 3(α),12(β)-dihydroxy-bisnorcholanate (18 g.)	C_6H_5MgBr (69 ml. C_6H_5Br)	3(α),12(β)-Dihydroxy-20-pregnyldiphenylmethanol (22.3 g.)	*351,394*
Methyl 3(α),12(α)-dihydroxy-isobisnorcholanate (0.5 g.)	C_6H_5MgBr	3(α),12(α)-Dihydroxy-20-isopregnyldiphenylmethanol (440 mg.)	*394*
Methyl 3(α),12(β)-dihydroxy-isobisnorcholanate (440 mg.)	C_6H_5MgBr (2.5 ml. C_6H_5Br)	3(α),12(β)-Dihydroxy-20-isopregnyldiphenylmethanol (430 mg.)	*394*
$C_{22}H_{35}O_5$-R			
Methyl bisnorcholanate	CH_3MgI	3,7,12-Trihydroxyternorcholanyldimethylmethanol	*313*
Methyl bisnorcholanate (4.1 g.)	C_6H_5MgBr (28.0 g. C_6H_5Br)	3,7,12-Trihydroxyternorcholanyldiphenylmethanol (3.8 g.)	*290*
$C_{22}H_{41}O_2$-R			
$CH_3(CH_2)_7CH{=}CH(CH_2)_{11}CO_2C_2H_5$ (40 g.)	C_6H_5MgBr (3 equiv.)	$CH_3(CH_2)_7CH{=}CH(CH_2)_{10}CH{=}C(C_6H_5)_2$ (25 g.)	72

TABLE VIII-III (Continued)

Ester	RMgX	Product(s)	Ref.
$C_{22}H_{43}O_2$-R			
n-$C_{21}H_{43}CO_2C_2H_5$	CH_3MgBr (2 equiv.)	n-$C_{21}H_{43}(CH_3)_2COH$	*229*
$C_{23}H_{35}O_4$-R			
Methyl 3-acetoxyetiocholanate (1.35 g.)	C_6H_5MgBr (12.60 g. C_6H_5Br)	3-Hydroxynoretiocholanyldiphenylmethanol (1.80 g.)	*92*
$C_{23}H_{36}O_2Cl$-R			
Methyl 3-chloronorallocholanate	C_6H_5MgBr	3-Chlorobisnorallocholanyldiphenylmethanol	*253,254*
$C_{23}H_{36}O_3$-R			
Methyl 3-methoxybisnor-5-cholenate (1.6 g.)	C_6H_5MgBr (6.7 g. C_6H_5Br)	3-Methoxyternor-5-cholenyldiphenylmethanol (1.8 g., 85%)	*359*
Methyl 6-methoxybisnorisocholenate (1.45 g.)	C_6H_5MgBr (6.08 g. C_6H_5Br)	6-Methoxyternorisocholenyldiphenylmethanol (1.12 g.)	*359*
$C_{23}H_{37}O_2$-R			
Ethyl norcholanate	CH_3MgI	Bisnorcholanyldimethylmethanol	*465*
Ethyl norcholanate	C_6H_5MgBr	Bisnorcholanyldiphenylmethanol	*465*
$C_{23}H_{37}O_3$-R			
Methyl norlithocholate	CH_3MgI	3-Hydroxybisnorcholanyldimethylmethanol	*354*
Methyl 3-hydroxyallocholanate (3.8 g.)	C_6H_5MgBr (23.0 g. C_6H_5Br)	3-Hydroxynorallocholanyldiphenylmethanol (5.0 g., crude)	*92*
Methyl 3(α),11(α)-dihydroxynorcholanate (22.1 g., 0.056 mole)	C_6H_5MgBr (1.48 mole)	3(α),11(α)-Dihydroxybisnorcholanyldiphenylmethanol (26.4 g., crude)	*247*
$C_{23}H_{37}O_4$-R			
Methyl nordesoxycholate	C_6H_5MgBr (16 equiv.)	3,12-Dihydroxybisnorcholanyldiphenylmethanol	*165*

TABLE VIII-III (Continued)

Ester	RMgX	Product(s)	Ref.
$C_{23}H_{37}O_4$-R (*cont.*)			
Methyl norhydrodesoxycholate (5 g., 0.105 mole)	C_6H_5MgBr (1.68 mole)	3(α),6(β)-Dihydroxybisnorcholanyldiphenylmethanol (74%)	*289*
$C_{23}H_{37}O_5$-R			
Methyl norcholate (5 g.)	CH_3MgBr (15 g. CH_3Br)	3,7,12-Trihydroxybisnorcholanyldimethylmethanol (4 g.)	*290*
Methyl norcholate	CH_3MgI	3,7,12-Trihydroxybisnorcholanyldimethylmethanol	*313*
$C_{23}H_{40}O_4$-R			
Methyl chenodesoxycholate (5.0 g.)	CH_3MgI	"Tertiary carbinol" (2.5 g.)	*180*
$C_{24}H_{28}O_4$-R_2			
$H_3CO_2CCH_2[CH{=}C(CH_3)CH{=}CH]_4CH_2CO_2CH_3$ (1 g.)	CH_3MgI (60 equiv.)	$HO(CH_3)_2CCH_2[CH{=}C(CH_3)CH{=}CH]_4CH_2C(CH_3)_2OH$	*195*
$C_{24}H_{37}O_3$-R			
Methyl 3-hydroxy-5-cholenate (5.5 g.)	C_6H_5MgBr (excess)	3-Hydroxy-5-norcholenyldiphenylmethanol (3.4 g.)	*358*
$C_{24}H_{37}O_4$-R			
Methyl 3-acetoxybisnorallocholanate (8.6 g.)	C_6H_5MgBr (55.0 g. C_6H_5Br)	3-Hydroxyternorcholanyldiphenylmethanol (12.2 g.)	*92*
$C_{24}H_{38}O_2Cl$-R			
Methyl 3-chloroallocholanate (27 g.)	C_6H_5MgBr (0.27 mole)	3-Chloronorallocholanyldiphenylmethanol (27 g.)	*253,254*

TABLE VIII-III (Continued)

Ester	RMgX	Product(s)	Ref.
$C_{24}H_{38}O_2Cl$-R (*cont.*)			
Methyl *trans*(?)-3-chloroallocholanate (1.2 g.)	C_6H_5MgBr (1.5 g. C_6H_5Br)	Carbinol, isolated, after oxidation as *trans*(?)-3-chloronorallocholanic acid	*26*
$C_{24}H_{39}O_2$-R			
Ethyl cholanate	CH_3MgI	Norcholanyldimethylmethanol (*ca.* quant.)	*465*
$C_{24}H_{39}O_3$-R			
Methyl lithocholate (3.9 g., 0.01 mole)	CH_3MgI (8.5 g., 0.06 mole CH_3I)	3-Hydroxynorcholanyldimethylmethanol (*ca.* 3.0 g.)	*354*
Methyl 3(α),11(α)-dihydroxycholanate (20 g., 0.05 mole)	C_6H_5MgBr (1.0 mole)	3(α),11(α)-Dihydroxynorcholanyldiphenylmethanol (22.4 g., crude); recovered ester (as acid, 3.2 g., 15%); 3(α),11(α)-dihydroxynorcholanyl phenyl ketone	*247*
$C_{24}H_{39}O_4$-R			
Methyl desoxycholate	C_6H_5MgBr (16 equiv.)	3,12-Dihydroxynorcholanyldiphenylmethanol (yielding 74% dehydrate)	*165*
Methyl hyodesoxycholate (1 kg.)	C_6H_5MgBr (39 moles)	3(α),6(β)-Dihydroxynorcholanyldiphenylmethanol (1035 g., crude)	*289*
$C_{24}H_{39}O_5$-R			
Methyl cholate (45 g.)	CH_3MgBr (*ca.* 105 g. CH_3Br)	3,7,12-Trihydroxynorcholanyldimethylmethanol (*ca.* 40 g.)	*290*
Methyl cholate	CH_3MgI	3,7,12-Trihydroxynorcholanyldimethylmethanol	*313*
Methyl cholate (50 g.)	C_6H_5MgBr (280 g. C_6H_5Br)	3,7,12-Trihydroxynorcholanyldiphenylmethanol (42 g.)	*290*

TABLE VIII-III (Continued)

Ester	RMgX	Product(s)	Ref.
$C_{25}H_{39}O_3$-R			
Methyl 3-methoxy-5-cholenate (2.0 g.)	C_6H_5MgBr (excess)	3-Methoxy-5-norcholenyldiphenylmethanol (2.26 g., 96%)	358
Methyl 6(α)-methoxyisocholenate (2.69 g.)	C_6H_5MgBr (11.00 g. C_6H_5Br)	6(α)-Methoxynorisocholenyldiphenylmethanol (1.97 g., 57%)	358
$C_{25}H_{39}O_4$-R			
Methyl 3-acetoxynorallocholanate (18 g.)	C_6H_5MgBr (103 g. C_6H_5Br)	3-Hydroxynorcholanic acid (1 g.); 3-hydroxybisnorallocholanyldiphenylmethanol (27 g.)	92
$C_{25}H_{41}O_5$-R			
Methyl 25-homocholate (1062 mg.)	CH_3MgI	3,7,12,25-Tetrahydroxycholestane (252 mg.)	325
$C_{26}H_{17}O_2$-R			
Ethyl 9,9-diphenyl-4-fluorenecarboxylate	C_6H_5MgBr	α,α,9,9-Tetraphenyl-4-fluorenemethanol	397
$C_{26}H_{19}O_2$-R			
$2\text{-}(C_6H_5)_2CHC_6H_4C_6H_4\text{-}2\text{-}CO_2CH_3$	C_6H_5MgBr	$2\text{-}(C_6H_5)_2CHC_6H_4C_6H_4\text{-}2\text{-}C(C_6H_5)_2OH$	397
$C_{28}H_{45}O_2$-R			
Methyl 5-cholestene-3-carboxylate (200 mg.)	CH_3MgI	α,α-Dimethyl-5-cholestene-3-methanol (200 mg.)	22
$C_{28}H_{52}O_4$-R_2			
$[\text{—}(CH_2)_{13}CO_2CH_3]_2$	C_6H_5MgBr	$[\text{—}(CH_2)_{13}C(C_6H_5)_2OH]_2$ (yielding 80–90% olefin)	377

REFERENCES FOR TABLE VIII-III

(*1*) Acree, *Ber.*, *37*, 2753–64 (1904).
(*2*) Acree, *Am. Chem. J.*, *33*, 180–95 (1905).
(*3*) Alessandri, *Atti accad. Lincei*, [5], *24,II*, 194–9 (1915); *Chem. Zentr.*, *1916,I*, 1072.
(*4*) Arnold, Bank, and Liggett, *J. Am. Chem. Soc.*, *63*, 3444–6 (1941).
(*5*) Bradbury and Linnell, *Quart. J. Pharm. Pharmacol.*, *11*, 240–51 (1938).
(*6*) Arnold and Liggett, *J. Am. Chem. Soc.*, *64*, 2875–7 (1942).
(*7*) Arnold and Liggett, *J. Am. Chem. Soc.*, *67*, 337–8 (1945).
(*8*) Arnold, Liggett, and Searles, *J. Am. Chem. Soc.*, *70*, 3938 (1948).
(*9*) Arnold and Searles, *J. Am. Chem. Soc.*, *71*, 2021–3 (1949).
(*10*) Austin and Johnson, *J. Am. Chem. Soc.*, *54*, 647–60 (1932).
(*11*) Bachman, *J. Am. Chem. Soc.*, *55*, 4279–84 (1933).
(*12*) Bachman, *Organic Syntheses*, *16*, 41–3 (1936); Coll. Vol. II, 323–5 (1943).
(*13*) Bachman and Finholt, *J. Am. Chem. Soc.*, *70*, 622–4 (1948).
(*14*) Bachman and Heisey, *J. Am. Chem. Soc.*, *71*, 1985–8 (1949).
(*15*) Bachman and Micucci, *J. Am. Chem. Soc.*, *70*, 2381–4 (1948).
(*16*) Bachmann and Cockerill, *J. Am. Chem. Soc.*, *55*, 2932–4 (1933).
(*17*) Bachmann and Hetzner, *Organic Syntheses*, *23*, 98–100 (1934).
(*18*) Backer and Kemper, *Rec. trav. chim.*, *57*, 1249–58 (1938).
(*19*) Backer, Strating, and Cool, *Rec. trav. chim.*, *58*, 778–84 (1939).
(*20*) Baeyer, *Ann.*, *354*, 152–204 (1907).
(*21*) Baeyer, *Ann.*, *372*, 80–151 (1910).
(*22*) Baker and Squire, *J. Am. Chem. Soc.*, *70*, 1487–90 (1948).
(*23*) Barbier and Locquin, *Compt. rend.*, *156*, 1443–6 (1913); *Chem. Zentr.*, *1913,II*, 27; *Chem. Abstr.*, 7, 3110 (1913).
(*24*) Barnett and Cook, *J. Chem. Soc.*, *1933*, 22–4.
(*25*) Barnett, Cook, and Nixon, *J. Chem. Soc.*, *1927*, 504–12.
(*26*) Barr, Heilbron, and Spring, *J. Chem. Soc.*, *1936*, 737–8.
(*27*) Barr and Ladouceur, *Can. J. Research*, *27B*, 61–6 (1949).
(*28*) Barré, *Compt. rend.*, *184*, 825–6 (1927).
(*29*) Barré, *Ann. chim.*, [10], 9, 204–75 (1927).
(*30*) Barrow and Ferguson, *J. Chem. Soc.*, *1935*, 410–8.
(*31*) Béhal and Sommelet, *Compt. rend.*, *138*, 89–92 (1904); *Chem. Zentr.*, *1904,I*, 504.
(*32*) Béhal and Tiffeneau, *Bull. soc. chim.*, [4], 3, 314–21 (1908).
(*33*) Béhal and Tiffeneau, *Bull. soc. chim.*, [4], 3, 732–6 (1908).
(*34*) Béhal and Tiffeneau, *Bull. soc. chim.*, [4], 7, 330–2 (1910).
(*35*) Berberianu, *Bul. soc. romane stiin.*, *22*, 11–25 (1914); *Chem. Abstr.*, 8, 1423 (1914).
(*36*) Bergmann, *J. Org. Chem.*, 4, 1–13 (1939).
(*37*) Bergmann and Bondi, *J. Am. Chem. Soc.*, *58*, 1814 (1936).
(*38*) Bergmann and Hartrott, *J. Chem. Soc.*, *1935*, 1218–9.
(*39*) Bergmann and Israelashivili, *J. Am. Chem. Soc.*, *68*, 1–5 (1946).
(*40*) Bergmann, Taubadel, and Weiss, *Ber.*, *64B*, 1493–501 (1931).
(*41*) Bergmann and Weiss, *Ann.*, *480*, 64–75 (1930).
(*42*) Bert, *Compt. rend.*, *186*, 699–700 (1928).
(*43*) Bettzieche and Ehrlich, *Z. physiol. Chem.*, *160*, 256–62 (1926); *Chem. Abstr.*, *21*, 567 (1927).
(*44*) Bettzieche and Menger, *Z. psysiol. Chem.*, *172*, 56–63 (1927); *Chem. Abstr.*, *22*, 583 (1928).
(*45*) Bettzieche, Menger, and Wolf, *Z. physiol. Chem.*, *160*, 270–300 (1926); *Chem. Abstr.*, *21*, 568 (1927).

(46) Billeter and Miescher, *Helv. Chim. Acta*, *31*, 1302–18 (1948).
(47) Birch and Robinson, *J. Chem. Soc.*, *1942*, 488–97.
(48) Bistrzycki and Gyr, *Ber.*, *37*, 1245–53 (1904).
(49) Blaise and Courtot, *Compt. rend.*, *140*, 370–2 (1905); *Chem. Zentr.*, *1905,I*, 726.
(50) Blicke and Blake, *J. Am. Chem. Soc.*, *53*, 1015–25 (1931).
(51) Blicke and Patelski, *J. Am. Chem. Soc.*, *60*, 2638–41 (1938).
(52) Blicke and Weinkauff, *J. Am. Chem. Soc.*, *54*, 1454–9 (1932).
(53) Blicke and Weinkauff, *J. Am. Chem. Soc.*, *54*, 1460–4 (1932).
(54) Blum-Bergmann, *Ann.*, *484*, 26–51 (1930).
(55) Bodroux, *Compt. rend.*, *138*, 92–4 (1904); *Chem. Zentr.*, *1904,I*, 509.
(56) Bodroux, *Compt. rend.*, *138*, 700–1 (1904); *Chem. Zentr.*, *1904,I*, 1077.
(57) Bodroux, *Bull. soc. chim.*, [3], *31*, 585–8 (1904).
(58) Bodroux and Thomassin, *Bull. soc. chim.*, [5], *6*, 1411–6 (1939).
(59) Böeseken and Wildschut, *Rec. trav. chim.*, *51*, 168–73 (1932).
(60) Bousset and Vaugin, *Bull. soc. chim.*, [4], *47*, 986–1003 (1930).
(61) Bouvet, *Bull. soc. chim.*, [4], *17*, 202–16 (1915).
(62) Bowden, Harris, and Roberts, *J. Chem. Soc.*, *1939*, 302–8.
(63) Boyd and Hatt, *J. Chem. Soc.*, *1927*, 898–910.
(64) Boyle, McKenzie, and Mitchell, *Ber.*, *70B*, 2153–60 (1937).
(65) Bradsher and Smith, *J. Am. Chem. Soc.*, *65*, 1643–5 (1943).
(66) Bruylants, *Bull. acad. roy. Belg.*, *1908*, 1011–84; *Chem. Zentr.*, *1909,I*, 1859.
(67) Bruylants, *Bull. acad. roy. Belg.*, *1909*, 276–82; *Chem. Zentr.*, *1909,II*, 797.
(68) Bruylants, *Bull. soc. chim. Belg.*, *33*, 529–31 (1924).
(69) Butenandt, Mamoli, and Heusner, *Ber.*, *72B*, 1614–7 (1939).
(70) Butenandt and Schmidt-Thomé, *Ber.*, *72B*, 182–7 (1939).
(71) Buu-Hoï, *Ann. chim.*, [11], *19*, 446–58 (1944).
(72) Buu-Hoï and Janicaud, *Bull. soc. chim.*, [5], *13*, 147–8 (1946).
(73) Cagniant and Deluzarche, *Compt. rend.*, *224*, 473–4 (1947); *Chem. Abstr.*, *41*, 5100 (1947).
(74) Calingaert and Soroos, *J. Am. Chem. Soc.*, *58*, 635–6 (1936).
(75) Campbell and Campbell, *J. Am. Chem. Soc.*, *60*, 1372–6 (1938).
(76) Carothers and Hill, *J. Am. Chem. Soc.*, *54*, 1588–90 (1932).
(77) Cason, Adams, Bennett, and Register, *J. Am. Chem. Soc.*, *66*, 1764–7 (1944).
(78) Chatterjee, Bose, and Roy, *J. Indian Chem. Soc.*, *24*, 169–72 (1947); *Chem. Abstr.*, *43*, 2613 (1949).
(79) Chonin, *J. Russ. Phys.-Chem. Soc.*, *41*, 327–44 (1909); *Chem. Zentr.*, *1909, II*, 587.
(80) Church, Whitmore, and McGrew, *J. Am. Chem. Soc.*, *56*, 176–84 (1934).
(81) Clarkson and Gomberg, *J. Am. Chem. Soc.*, *52*, 2881–91 (1930).
(82) Clément, *Compt. rend.*, *198*, 665–7 (1937).
(83) Clément, *Compt. rend.*, *202*, 425–7 (1936); *Chem. Abstr.*, *30*, 2932 (1936).
(84) Clément, *Compt. rend.*, *207*, 864–6 (1938); *Chem. Abstr.*, *33*, 7747 (1939).
(85) Clément, *Ann. chim.*, [11], *13*, 243–316 (1940).
(86) Coleman and Craig, *Organic Syntheses*, *15*, 11–3 (1935); *Coll. Vol. II*, *179–81 (1943)*.
(87) Conant and Blatt, *J. Am. Chem. Soc.*, *51*, 1227–36 (1929).
(88) Cook, *J. Chem. Soc.*, *1932*, 456–72.
(89) Courtot, *Bull. soc. chim.*, [3], *35*, 969–88 (1906).
(90) Couturier, *Compt. rend.*, *202*, 1994–6 (1936); *Chem. Abstr.*, *30*, 6725 (1936).
(91) Dalebroux and Wuyts, *Bull. soc. chim. Belg.*, *20*, 156–8 (1906).
(92) Dalmer, von Werder, Honigmann, and Heyns, *Ber.*, *68B*, 1814–25 (1935).
(93) Darzens and Levy, *Compt. rend.*, *201*, 152–4 (1935); *Chem. Abstr.*, *29*, 6593 (1935).

(94) Davies and Kipping, *J. Chem. Soc.*, 99, 296–301 (1911).
(95) Dillon and Lucas, *J. Am. Chem. Soc.*, 50, 1711–4 (1928).
(96) Dilthey and Last, *Ber.*, 37, 2639–41 (1904).
(97) Dirstine and Bergstrom, *J. Org. Chem.*, 11, 55–9 (1946).
(98) Dornfeld and Coleman, *Organic Syntheses*, 28, 83–7 (1948).
(99) Dow Chemical Co., British Patent 618,638, Feb. 24, 1949; *Chem. Abstr.*, 43, P5806 (1949).
(100) Dufraisse and Monier, *Compt. rend.*, 196, 1325–9 (1933); *Chem. Abstr.*, 27, 3471 (1933).
(101) Edgar, Calingaert, and Marker, *J. Am. Chem. Soc.*, 51, 1483–91 (1929).
(102) Egorowa, *J. Russ. Phys.-Chem. Soc.*, 41, 1454–68 (1909); *Chem. Zentr.*, *1910,I*, 1003.
(103) Feist, Awe, Kuklinski, and Völksen, *Arch. Pharm.*, 276, 271–9 (1938); *Chem. Abstr.*, 32, 6651 (1938).
(104) Fieser and Hershberg, *J. Am. Chem. Soc.*, 59, 2331–5 (1937).
(105) Fieser and Heymann, *J. Am. Chem. Soc.*, 64, 376–82 (1942).
(106) Fieser and Newman, *J. Am. Chem. Soc.*, 58, 2376–82 (1936).
(107) Fischer, Baumgartner, and Plotz, *Ann.*, 493, 1–19 (1932).
(108) Fischer and Hess, *Ber.*, 45, 912–5 (1912).
(109) Földi and Demjén, *Ber.*, 74B, 930–4 (1941).
(110) Fourneau and Tiffeneau, *Compt. rend.*, 145, 437–9 (1907); *Chem. Zentr.*, *1907,II*, 1320.
(111) Fourneau, Tréfouel, Tréfouel, and Benoit, *Ann. inst. Pasteur*, 44, 719–51 (1930); *Chem. Abstr.*, 26, 1592 (1932).
(112) Frank, Arvan, Richter, and Vannemann, *J. Am. Chem. Soc.*, 66, 4–6 (1944).
(113) Frankland and Twiss, *J. Chem. Soc.*, 85, 1666–7 (1904).
(114) French and Smith, *J. Am. Chem. Soc.*, 67, 1949–50 (1945).
(115) Friedr. Bayer & Co., German Patent 157,573, Nov. 28, 1904; *Friedländer*, 8, 156–7 (1905–7).
(116) Fröschl, Zellner, and Zak, *Monatsh.*, 55, 25–46 (1930).
(117) Frostick, Baumgarten, and Hauser, *J. Am. Chem. Soc.*, 66, 305 (1944).
(118) Frumina, *Bull. acad. roy. Belg.*, *1909*, 1151–7; *Chem. Zentr.*, *1910,I*, 1001.
(119) Fuson, Bottorff, Foster, and Speck, *J. Am. Chem. Soc.*, 64, 2573–6 (1942).
(120) Fuson, Bottorff, and Speck, *J. Am. Chem. Soc.*, 64, 1450–3 (1942).
(121) Fuson and Rachlin, *J. Am. Chem. Soc.*, 64, 1567–71 (1942).
(122) Fuson and Ward, *J. Am. Chem. Soc.*, 68, 521–2 (1946).
(123) Gakhokidze, *J. Gen. Chem.* (U.S.S.R.), 11, 109–16 (1941); *Chem. Abstr.*, 35, 5464 (1941).
(124) Gattermann, *Ann.*, 393, 215–34 (1912).
(125) Gattermann and Maffezzoli, *Ber.*, 36, 4152–3 (1903).
(126) Gillespie and Marvell, *J. Am. Chem. Soc.*, 52, 3368–76 (1930).
(127) Gilman and Franz, *Rec. trav. chim.*, 51, 991–5 (1932).
(128) Godchot and Cauquil, *Compt. rend.*, 200, 1479–81 (1935); *Chem. Abstr.*, 29, 7940 (1935).
(129) Godnew, *Ber.*, 68B, 422–3 (1935).
(130) Golovchanskaya, *J. Gen. Chem.* (U.S.S.R.), 16, 1243–7 (1946); *Chem. Abstr.*, 41, 3082 (1947).
(131) Gomberg and Van Slyke, *J. Am. Chem. Soc.*, 33, 531–49 (1911).
(132) Graf, *J. prakt. Chem.*, [2], *146, 88–104 (1936).*
(133) Grard, *Compt. rend.*, 189, 541–3 (1929).
(134) Greenwood and Gortner, *J. Org. Chem.*, 6, 401–9 (1941).
(135) Grignard, *Compt. rend.*, 132, 336–8 (1901); *Chem. Zentr.*, *1901,I*, 612.
(136) Grignard, *Ann. Univ. Lyon*, N.S., 6, 1–116 (1901); *Chem. Zentr.*, *1901,II*, 622.
(137) Grignard, *Compt. rend.*, 134, 849–51 (1902); *Chem. Zentr.*, *1902,I*, 1197.

(138) Grignard, *Compt. rend.*, *135*, 627–30 (1902); *Chem. Zentr.*, *1902,II*, 1359.
(139) Grignard, *Ann. chim.*, [7], *27*, 548–74 (1902).
(140) Grignard and Vignon, *Compt. rend.*, *144*, 1358–60 (1907); *Chem. Zentr.*, *1907,II*, 681.
(141) Gripenberg and Lindahl, *Acta Chem. Scand.*, 3, 256–8 (1949); *Chem. Abstr.*, *43*, 7928 (1949).
(142) Grishkevich-Trokhimovskiĭ, *J. Russ. Phys.-Chem. Soc.*, *43*, 204–7 (1912); *Chem. Abstr.*, *6*, 223 (1912).
(143) Grishkevich-Trokhimovskiĭ, *J. Russ. Phys.-Chem. Soc.*, *43*, 803–6 (1912); *Chem. Abstr.*, *6*, 477 (1912).
(144) Guillaumin, *Bull. soc. chim.*, [4], 7, 374–83 (1910).
(145) Guyot and Catel, *Compt. rend.*, *140*, 254–6 (1905); *Chem. Zentr.*, *1905,I*, 679.
(146) Guyot and Catel, *Bull. soc. chim.*, [3], *35*, 551–62 (1906).
(147) Hale, McNally, and Pater, *Am. Chem. J.*, *35*, 67–78 (1906);
(148) Haller and Guyot, *Bull. soc. chim.*, [3], *31*, 979–85 (1904).
(149) Halse, *J. prakt. Chem.*, [2], *89*, 451–65 (1914).
(150) Hamel, *Bull. soc. chim.*, [4], *29*, 390–402 (1921).
(151) Harries and Turk, *Ann.*, *343*, 360–9 (1905).
(152) Harries and Weil, *Ann.*, *343*, 362–9 (1905).
(153) Hauser, Saperstein, and Shivers, *J. Am. Chem. Soc.*, *70*, 606–8 (1948).
(154) Hauser, Yost, and Ringler, *J. Org. Chem.*, *14*, 261–71 (1949).
(155) Hell and Schaal, *Ber.*, *40*, 4162–6 (1907).
(156) Hennion and Raley, *J. Am. Chem. Soc.*, *70*, 865–6 (1948).
(157) Henry, *Compt. rend.*, *142*, 1023–4 (1906); *Chem. Zentr.*, *1906,II*, 15.
(158) Henry, *Compt. rend.*, *143*, 1221–5 (1906); *Chem. Zentr.*, *1907,I*, 708.
(159) Henry, *Compt. rend.*, *144*, 308–13 (1907); *Chem. Zentr.*, *1907,I*, 1102.
(160) Henry, *Bull. soc. chim. Belg.*, *20*, 152–6 (1906).
(161) Henry and Dewael, *Bull. acad. roy. Belg., Classe sci.*, *1908*, 857–63; *Chem. Zentr.*, *1909,I*, 1854.
(162) Henze, Allen, and Leslie, *J. Org. Chem.*, 7, 326–35 (1942).
(163) Hepworth, *J. Chem. Soc.*, *115*, 1203–10 (1919).
(164) Hey and Carter, British Patent 586,493, March 20, 1947; *Chem. Abstr.*, *42*, P1967 (1948).
(165) Hoehn and Mason, *J. Am. Chem. Soc.*, *60*, 1493–7 (1938).
(166) Houben, *Ber.*, *36*, 3087–9 (1903).
(167) Howell, *J. Am. Chem. Soc.*, *42*, 2333–7 (1920).
(168) Hudson, *J. Chem. Soc.*, *1946*, 76–8.
(169) Hurd and Bonner, *J. Am. Chem. Soc.*, *67*, 1972–7 (1945).
(170) Hurd, Jones, and Blunck, *J. Am. Chem. Soc.*, *57*, 2033–6 (1935).
(171) Huston, Jackson, and Spero, *J. Am. Chem. Soc.*, *63*, 1459–60 (1941).
(172) Ingraffia, *Gazz. chim. ital.*, *63*, 584–91 (1933); *Chem. Abstr.*, *28*, 1342 (1934).
(173) Iotsitch, *J. Russ. Phys.-Chem. Soc.*, *35*, 1269–75 (1905); *Bull. soc. chim.*, [3], *34*, 181 (1905).
(174) Iotsitch, *J. Russ. Phys.-Chem. Soc.*, *35*, 553–4 (1903); *Bull. soc. chim.*, [3], *32*, 719 (1904).
(175) Iotsitch, *J. Russ. Phys.-Chem. Soc.*, *36*, 1551–3 (1904); *Bull. soc. chim.*, [3], *36*, 179 (1906).
(176) Iotsitch, *J. Russ. Phys.-Chem. Soc.*, *42*, 1490–1 (1910); *Bull. soc. chim.*, [4], *10*, 1294 (1911);
(177) Iotsitch, Breitfous, Roudolf, Stassevitch, Kondyref, and Fomine, *J. Russ. Phys.-Chem. Soc.*, *39*, 652–7 (1907); *Bull. soc. chim.*, [4], *6*, 98 (1909).
(178) Iotsitch and Lebedef, *J. Russ. Phys.-Chem. Soc.*, *42*, 1494–5 (1910); *Bull. soc. chim.*, [4], *10*, 1294 (1911).

(179) Iotsitch and Lebedef, *J. Russ. Phys.-Chem. Soc.*, *42*, 1495 (1910); *Bull. soc. chim.*, [4], *10*, 1294 (1911).
(180) Isihara, *J. Biochem.* (Japan), *27*, 265–77 (1938); *Chem. Abstr.*, *33*, 4265 (1939).
(181) Ivanoff, *Compt. rend.*, *193*, 773–6 (1931); *Chem. Abstr.*, *26*, 963 (1932).
(182) Ivanov and Ivanov, *Ber.*, *77B*, 180–5 (1944).
(183) Ivanoff and Spassoff, *Bull. soc. chim.*, [4], *49*, 375–7 (1931).
(184) Ivanoff and Spassoff, *Bull. soc. chim.*, [5], *2*, 816–24 (1935).
(185) Johnston and Quayle, *J. Am. Chem. Soc.*, *70*, 479–82 (1948).
(186) Julian, Cole, and Diemer, *J. Am. Chem. Soc.*, *67*, 1721–3 (1945).
(187) Julian, Cole, and Meyer, *J. Am. Chem. Soc.*, *67*, 1724–7 (1945).
(188) Kanao and Inagawa, *J. Pharm. Soc., Japan*, *48*, 66–8 (1928); *Chem. Zentr.*, *1928,II*, 50.
(189) Kanao and Inagawa, *J. Pharm. Soc. Japan*, *48*, 238–52 (1928); *Chem. Abstr.*, *22*, 2923 (1928).
(190) Kanao and Shinozuka, *J. Pharm. Soc. Japan*, *50*, 148–52 (1930); *Chem. Zentr.*, *1931,I*, 1743.
(191) Kanao and Yaguchi, *J. Pharm. Soc. Japan*, *48*, 252–8 (1928); *Chem. Zentr.*, *1928,II*, 51; *Chem. Abstr.*, *22*, 2937 (1928).
(192) Kanao and Yaguchi, *J. Pharm. Soc. Japan*, *48*, 358–66 (1928); *Chem. Zentr.*, *1928,II*, 52; *Chem. Abstr.*, *22*, 3407 (1928).
(193) Kapfhammer and Matthes, *Z. physiol. Chem.*, *223*, 43–52 (1933); *Chem. Abstr.*, *28*, 2353 (1934); *Chem. Zentr.*, *1934,I*, 2759.
(194) Karasev, *J. Gen. Chem.* (U.S.S.R.), *7*, 179–84 (1937); *Chem. Abstr.*, *31*, 4268 (1937).
(195) Karrer and Rubel, *Helv. Chim. Acta*, *17*, 773–4 (1934).
(196) Karvonen, *Suomen Kemistilehti*, *3*, 101–11 (1930); *Chem. Zentr.*, *1931,I*, 3344.
(197) Kauffmann and Egner, *Ber.*, *46*, 3779–88 (1913).
(198) Kauffmann and Kieser, *Ber.*, *45*, 2333–7 (1912).
(199) Kauffmann and Kieser, *Ber.*, *46*, 3788–801 (1913).
(200) Kharasch and Clapp, *J. Org. Chem.*, *3*, 355–60 (1938).
(201) Kirrmann, *Ann. chim.*, [10], *11*, 223–86 (1929).
(202) Kishner and Amosow, *J. Russ. Phys.-Chem. Soc.*, *37*, 517–20 (1905); *Chem. Zentr.*, *1905,II*, 816.
(203) Kislovskaya, *J. Russ. Phys.-Chem. Soc.*, *45*, 1975–9 (1914); *Chem. Abstr.*, *8*, 1421 (1914).
(204) Klages, *Ber.*, *37*, 1721–6 (1904).
(205) Klages and Heilmann, *Ber.*, *37*, 1447–57 (1904).
(206) Kliegl, *Ber.*, *38*, 84–7 (1905).
(207) Kling, *Bull. soc. chim.*, [3], *31*, 16–9 (1904).
(208) Koelsch, *J. Am. Chem. Soc.*, *58*, 1331–3 (1935).
(209) Koelsch, *J. Am. Chem. Soc.*, *65*, 1639–40 (1943).
(210) Koelsch and Johnson, *J. Am. Chem. Soc.*, *65*, 565–7 (1943).
(211) Kohler, *Am. Chem. J.*, *31*, 642–61 (1904).
(212) Kohler, *Am. Chem. J.*, *34*, 132–47 (1906).
(213) Kohler, *Am. Chem. J.*, *36*, 529–38 (1906).
(214) Kohler and Butler, *J. Am. Chem. Soc.*, *48*, 1036–48 (1926).
(215) Kohler and Conant, *J. Am. Chem. Soc.*, *39*, 1699–715 (1917).
(216) Kohler and Heritage, *Am. Chem. J.*, *33*, 21–35 (1905).
(217) Kohler and Heritage, *Am. Chem. J.*, *33*, 153–64 (1905).
(218) Kohler and Heritage, *Am. Chem. J.*, *34*, 568–80 (1906).
(219) Kohler and Johnstin, *Am. Chem. J.*, *33*, 35–45 (1905).
(220) Kohler and Reimer, *Am. Chem. J.*, *33*, 333–56 (1905).

(*221*) Kohler, Richtmyer, and Hester, *J. Am. Chem. Soc.*, *53*, 205–21 (1931).
(*222*) Kovache, *Ann. chim.*, [9], *10*, 184–248 (1918).
(*223*) Kritchevsky, *J. Am. Chem. Soc.*, *65*, 487 (1943).
(*224*) LaGrave, *Ann. chim.*, [10], *8*, 363–446 (1927).
(*225*) Lammer, *Monatsh.*, *35*, 171–88 (1914).
(*226*) Landa, Cech, and Sliva, *Collection Czechoslov. Chem. Commun.*, *5*, 204–10 (1933); *Chem. Abstr.*, *27*, 4211 (1933).
(*227*) Landa and Habada, *Collection Czechoslov. Chem. Commun.*, *8*, 473–6 (1936); *Chem. Abstr.*, *31*, 1757 (1937).
(*228*) Landa and Kejvan, *Collection Czechoslov. Chem. Commun.*, *3*, 367–76 (1931); *Chem. Abstr.*, *26*, 77 (1932).
(*229*) Landa and Riedl, *Collection Czechoslov. Chem. Commun.*, *2*, 520–30 (1930); *Chem. Zentr.*, *1931*,*I*, 2454; *Chem. Abstr.*, *25*, 67 (1931).
(*230*) Landa and Sliva, *Collection Czechoslov. Chem. Commun.*, *4*, 538–42 (1932); *Chem. Abstr.*, *27*, 1611 (1933).
(*231*) Lapkin, *J. Gen. Chem.* (U.S.S.R.), *16*, 721–8 (1936); *Chem. Abstr.*, *41*, 1218 (1947).
(*232*) Lapkin, *J. Gen. Chem.* (U.S.S.R.), *16*, 729–34 (1946); *Chem. Abstr.*, *41*, 1218 (1947).
(*233*) Lapkin, *J. Gen. Chem.* (U.S.S.R.), *17*, 1339–50 (1947); *Chem. Abstr.*, *42*, 4978 (1948).
(*234*) Lapkin and Lyubimova, *J. Gen. Chem.* (U.S.S.R.), *18*, 701–9 (1948); *Chem. Abstr.*, *43*, 188 (1949).
(*235*) Lapkin, Shklyaev, and Shklyaeva, *J. Gen. Chem.* (U.S.S.R.), *10*, 1449–52 (1940); *Chem. Abstr.*, *35*, 2479 (1941).
(*236*) Lapkin, Shklyaeva, Koryakina, and Vinokurova, *J. Gen. Chem.* (U.S.S.R.), *17*, 1332–8 (1947); *Chem. Abstr.*, *42*, 4978 (1948).
(*237*) Lemaire, *Bull. acad. roy. Belg.*, *1909*, 83–159; *Rec. trav. chim.*, *29*, 22–84 (1910); *Chem. Zentr.*, *1909*,*I*, 1982; *Chem. Abstr.*, *4*, 1483 (1910).
(*238*) Leroide, *Ann. chim.*, [9], *16*, 354–410 (1921).
(*239*) Lespieau, *Bull. soc. chim.*, [5], *6*, 947–9 (1939).
(*240*) Letellier, *Compt. rend.*, *146*, 343–5 (1908); *Chem. Zentr.*, *1908*,*I*, 1378.
(*241*) Levene and Marker, *J. Biol. Chem.*, *95*, 1–24 (1932).
(*242*) Levene and Marker, *J. Biol. Chem.*, *100*, 769–73 (1933).
(*243*) Levene and Marker, *J. Biol. Chem.*, *101*, 413–8 (1933).
(*244*) Lévy and Pernot, *Bull. soc. chim.*, [4], *49*, 1721–30 (1931).
(*245*) Liang, *Bull. soc. chim.*, [4], *53*, 33–41 (1933).
(*246*) Loder and Whitmore, *J. Am. Chem. Soc.*, *57*, 2727 (1935).
(*247*) Long, Marshall, and Gallagher, *J. Biol. Chem.*, *165*, 197–209 (1946).
(*248*) Lund, *J. Am. Chem. Soc.*, *49*, 1346–60 (1927).
(*249*) Lüttringhaus and Sholtis, *Ann.*, *557*, 70–82 (1945).
(*250*) MacLeod, *Am. Chem. J.*, *44*, 331–52 (1910).
(*251*) Malengreau, *Bull. acad. roy. Belg.*, *Classe sci.*, *1906*, 802–10; *Chem. Zentr.*, *1907*,*I*, 1398; *Chem. Abstr.*, *1*, 1970 (1907).
(*252*) Maman, *Compt. rend.*, *198*, 1323–5 (1934).
(*253*) Marker, Kamm, Jones, Wittle, Oakwood, and Crooks, *J. Am. Chem. Soc.*, *59*, 768 (1937).
(*254*) Marker, Kamm, McGinty, Jones, Wittle, Oakwood, and Crooks, *J. Am. Chem. Soc.*, *59*, 1367–8 (1937).
(*255*) Marvel, Dietz, and Himel, *J. Org. Chem.*, *7*, 392–6 (1942).
(*256*) Marvel, Ginsberg, and Mueller, *J. Am. Chem. Soc.*, *61*, 77–8 (1939).
(*257*) Marvel, Kaplan, and Himel, *J. Am. Chem. Soc.*, *63*, 1892–6 (1941).
(*258*) Moyer and Marvel, *Organic Syntheses*, *11*, 98–100 (1931); Coll. Vol. II, 602–4 (1943).

(259) Masson, *Compt. rend.*, *132*, 483-5 (1901); *Chem. Zentr.*, *1901,I*, 725.
(260) Masson, *Compt. rend.*, *135*, 533-4 (1902); *J. Chem. Soc.*, *84,I*, 28 (1903).
(261) Mavrodin, *Compt. rend.*, *183*, 1504-6 (1929).
(262) Mavrodin, *Compt. rend.*, *191*, 1064-6 (1930).
(263) Mavrodin, *Compt. rend.*, *192*, 363-5 (1931).
(264) Maxim and Georgescu, *Bull. soc. chim.*, [5], 3, 1114-24 (1936).
(265) Maxim and Stancovici, *Bull. soc. chim.*, [5], 3, 1319-23 (1936).
(266) May and Mosettig, *J. Org. Chem.*, *13*, 459-64 (1948).
(267) Mazurewitsch, *J. Russ. Phys.-Chem. Soc.*, *42*, 1582-9 (1910); *Chem. Zentr.*, *1911,I*, 1500.
(268) McKenzie and Duff, *Ber.*, *60B*, 1335-41 (1927).
(269) McKenzie and Lesslie, *Ber.*, *62B*, 288-95 (1929).
(270) McKenzie, Martin, and Rule, *J. Chem. Soc.*, *105*, 1583-91 (1914).
(271) McKenzie and Mills, *Ber.*, *62B*, 284-8 (1929).
(272) McKenzie, Mills, and Myles, *Ber.*, *63B*, 904-11 (1930).
(273) McKenzie and Richardson, *J. Chem. Soc.*, *123*, 79-91 (1923).
(274) McKenzie, Roger, and Wills, *J. Chem. Soc.*, *1926*, 779-91.
(275) McKenzie and Wills, *J. Chem. Soc.*, *127*, 283-95 (1925).
(276) McKenzie and Winton, *J. Chem. Soc.*, *1940*, 840-4.
(278) McKenzie and Wren, *J. Chem. Soc.*, *97*, 473-86 (1910).
(279) McPhee and Ball, *J. Am. Chem. Soc.*, *66*, 1636-50 (1944).
(280) Meerwein, *Ann.*, *396*, 200-63 (1913).
(281) Meerwein, *Ann.*, *419*, 121-75 (1919).
(282) Meerwein and Unkel, *Ann.*, *376*, 152-63 (1910).
(283) Messer, *Chem. News*, *138*, 292-3 (1929).
(284) Michiels, *Bull. soc. chim. Belg.*, *27*, 25-6 (1913).
(285) Midzuch, *J. Gen. Chem.* (U.S.S.R.), *16*, 147-4 (1946); *Chem. Abstr.*, *41*, 5508 (1947).
(286) Mikhailov and Blokhina, *J. Gen. Chem.* (U.S.S.R.), *13*, 609-15 (1943); *Chem. Abstr.*, *39*, 702 (1945).
(287) Miller and Bachman, *J. Am. Chem. Soc.*, *57*, 766-71 (1935).
(288) Mills and Dazeley, *J. Chem. Soc.*, *1939*, 460-3.
(289) Moffett, Stafford, Linsk, and Hoehn, *J. Am. Chem. Soc.*, *68*, 1857-60 (1946).
(290) Morsman, Steiger, and Reichstein, *Helv. Chim. Acta*, *20*, 3-16 (1937).
(291) Morton and Peakes, *J. Am. Chem. Soc.*, *55*, 2110-2 (1933).
(292) Moskalenko, *J. Russ. Phys.-Chem. Soc.*, *44*, 1862-5 (1912); *Chem. Zentr.*, *1913,I*, 1408.
(293) Mothwurf, *Ber.*, *37*, 3153-63 (1904).
(294) Moureu and Barrett, *Bull. soc. chim.*, [4], *29*, 993-1006 (1921).
(295) Mousseron and Granger, *Compt. rend.*, *217*, 483-5 (1943); *Chem. Abstr.*, *39*, 2066 (1945).
(296) Mousseron and Granger, *Bull. soc. chim.*, [5], *13*, 251-6 (1946).
(297) Mousseron and Jacquier, *Compt. rend.*, *226*, 256-8 (1948); *Chem. Abstr.*, *42*, 3734 (1948).
(298) Muset, *Bull. acad. roy. Belg.*, *Classe sci.*, *1906*, 775-89; *Chem. Abstr.*, *1*, 1969 (1907).
(299) Nametkin and Gabriadze, *J. Gen. Chem.* (U.S.S.R.), *13*, 560-8 (1943); *Chem. Abstr.*, *39*, 1142 (1945).
(300) Nametkin and Volodina, *J. Gen. Chem.* (U.S.S.R.), *17*, 325-34 (1947); *Chem. Abstr.*, *42*, 527 (1948).
(301) Naylor, *J. Chem. Soc.*, *1947*, 1106-8.
(302) Nazarov and Elizarova, *Bull. acad. sci. U.R.S.S.*, *Classe sci. chim.*, *1940*, 189-94; *Chem. Abstr.*, *36*, 741 (1942).
(303) Neunhoeffer, *Ann.*, *509*, 115-30 (1934).

(304) Neunhoeffer, *Ann.*, *526*, 58–65 (1936).
(305) Neunhoeffer and Nerdel, *Ann.*, *526*, 47–58 (1936).
(306) Neunhoeffer and Schluter, *Ann.*, *526*, 65–71 (1936).
(307) Norris and Cortese, *J. Am. Chem. Soc.*, *49*, 2640–50 (1927).
(308) Ochiai and Ichikawa, *J. Pharm. Soc. Japan*, 58, 632–6 (1938); *Chem. Abstr.*, *32*, 8427 (1938).
(309) Oparin, *J. Russ. Phys.-Chem. Soc.*, *61*, 2011–5 (1929); *Chem. Zentr.*, *1930*, *I*, 3556; *Chem. Abstr.*, *24*, 4785 (1930).
(310) Orechoff and Konowaloff, *Ber.*, *45*, 861–5 (1912).
(311) Orékhoff, *Bull. soc. chim.*, [4], *25*, 108–11 (1919).
(312) Orékhoff, *Bull. soc. chim.*, [4], *25*, 111–5 (1919).
(313) Organon, British Patent 495,156, Nov. 8, 1938; *Chem. Abstr.*, *33*, P2534 (1939).
(314) Paal, *Ber.*, *49*, 1583–97 (1916).
(315) Paal and Hornstein, *Ber.*, *39*, 1361–4 (1906).
(316) Paal and Kinscher, *Ber.*, *44*, 1343–55 (1911).
(317) Paal and Weidenkaff, *Ber.*, *38*, 1686–91 (1905).
(318) Paal and Weidenkaff, *Ber.*, *39*, 810–3 (1906).
(319) Paal and Weidenkaff, *Ber.*, *39*, 2062–3 (1906).
(320) Paal and Weidenkaff, *Ber.*, *39*, 4344–6 (1906).
(321) Paal and Zahn, *Ber.*, *40*, 1819–21 (1907).
(322) Paloma, *Ber.*, *42*, 1299–302 (1909).
(323) Paloma and Kaski, *Ber.*, *72B*, 317–8 (1939).
(324) Paloma and Kaski, *Suomen Kemistilehti*, *17B*, 7–9 (1944); *Chem. Abstr.*, *40*, 6414 (1946).
(325) Pearlman, *J. Am. Chem. Soc.*, *69*, 1475–6 (1947).
(326) Pétroff, Karasseff, and Tschelzowa, *Compt. rend. acad. sci. U.R.S.S.*, [N.S.], *4*, 31–5 (1935); *Bull. soc. chim.*, [5], *3*, 169–76 (1936); *Chem. Abstr.*, *30*, 2915 (1936).
(327) Petrov, *Sci. Records Gorky State Univ.*, 7, 3–9 (1939); *Chem. Abstr.*, *35*, 435 (1941).
(328) Petrov, *Doklady Akad. Nauk S.S.S.R.*, *63*, 41–4 (1948); *Chem. Abstr.*, *43*, 2604 (1949).
(329) Petrov, Belyaeva, and Kukanova, *Sci. Records Gorky State Univ.*, No. 7, 14–6 (1939); *Khim. Referat. Zhur.*, *1940*, No. 10–11, 20; *Chem. Abstr.*, *37*, 1379 (1943).
(330) Petrov and Chel'tsova, *J. Gen. Chem.* (U.S.S.R.), *12*, 87–94 (1942); *Chem. Abstr.*, *37*, 1993 (1943).
(331) Petrov and Kaplan, *Doklädy Akad. Nauk S.S.S.R.*, *64*, 683–5 (1949); *Chem. Abstr.*, *43*, 5368 (1949).
(332) Petrov, Koptev, and Kaplan, *Bull. acad. sci. U.R.S.S.*, *Classe. sci. chim.*, *1944*, 152–5; *Chem. Abstr.*, *39*, 1617 (1945).
(333) Petrov and Kurbskiĭ, *J. Gen. Chem.* (U.S.S.R.), *14*, 492–4 (1944); *Chem. Abstr.*, *39*, 4600 (1945).
(334) Petrov, Lapteva, and Pchelkina, *J. Gen. Chem.* (U.S.S.R.), *14*, 495–7 (1944); *Chem. Abstr.*, *39*, 4598 (1945).
(335) Petrov and Malinovskiĭ, *Sci. Records Gorky State Univ.*, No. 7, 9–14 (1939); *Khim. Referat. Zhur.*, *1940*, No. 10–11, 20; *Chem. Abstr.*, *37*, 1378 (1943).
(336) Petrov and Sanin, *J. Gen. Chem.* (U.S.S.R.), *8*, 195–8 (1938); *Chem. Abstr.*, *32*, 5376 (1938).
(337) Petrov and Sanin, *J. Gen. Chem.* (U.S.S.R.), *9*, 2129–37 (1939); *Chem. Abstr.*, *34*, 4054 (1940).
(338) Petrov and Sokolova, *J. Gen. Chem.* (U.S.S.R.), *8*, 199–206 (1938); *Chem. Abstr.*, *32*, 5376 (1938).

(339) Petrov and Vittikh, *Bull. acad. sci. U.R.S.S., Classe sci. chim., 1944*, 152-5; *Chem. Abstr.*, 39, 1618 (1945).
(340) Petyunin, *Trudy Moskov. Med. Inst., 1940*, No. 16, 7-12; *Khim. Referat. Zhur., 4*, No. 9, 58 (1941); *Chem. Abstr., 38*, 950 (1944).
(341) Petyunin, *Trudy Molotov. Med. Inst., 1940*, No. 16, 13-16; *Khim. Referat. Zhur., 4*, No. 9, 58 (1941); *Chem. Abstr., 38*, 2636 (1944).
(342) Pogorjelsky, *J. Russ. Phys.-Chem. Soc.*, 35, 882-96 (1904); *Chem. Zentr., 1904,I*, 578.
(343) Preissecker, *Monatsh*, 35, 889-908 (1914).
(344) Proost and Wibaut, *Rec. trav. chim., 59*, 971-7 (1940).
(345) Purdie and Arup, *J. Chem. Soc.*, 97, 1524-36 (1910).
(346) Purdie and Arup, *J. Chem. Soc.*, 97, 1537-46 (1910).
(347) Purdie and Young, *J. Chem. Soc.*, 97, 1524-36 (1910).
(348) Putochin, *Ber., 59B*, 1987-98 (1926).
(349) Quelet, *Bull. soc. chim.*, [4], *45*, 255-74 (1929).
(350) Quilico and Freri, *Gazz. chim. ital.*, 76, 87-107 (1946); *Chem. Abstr., 41*, 383 (1947).
(351) Reichstein and von Artz, *Helv. Chim. Acta, 23*, 747-53 (1940).
(352) Reimer, *Am. Chem. J.*, 38, 227-37 (1907).
(353) Reimer and Reynolds, *Am. Chem. J., 40*, 428-44 (1908).
(354) Reindel and Niederlander, *Ber., 68B*, 1969-73 (1935).
(355) Remfrey and Decker, *Ber., 41*, 1007-9 (1908).
(356) Reynolds, *Am. Chem. J., 44*, 305-31 (1910).
(357) Reynolds, *Am. Chem. J., 46*, 198-211 (1911).
(358) Riegel, Dunker, and Thomas, *J. Am. Chem. Soc., 64*, 2115-20 (1942).
(359) Riegel and Meyer, *J. Am. Chem. Soc.*, 68, 1097-9 (1946).
(360) Riegel, Siegel, and Lilienfeld, *J. Am. Chem. Soc., 68*, 984-5 (1946).
(361) Rivière, *Ann. chim.*, [12], *1*, 157-231 (1946).
(362) Roger and McKay, *J. Chem. Soc., 1931*, 2229-38.
(363) Rubin, Kozlowski, and Salmon, *J. Am. Chem. Soc.*, 67, 192-3 (1945).
(364) Sachs and Loevy, *Ber., 36*, 3236 (1903).
(365) Sah, *J. Am. Chem. Soc., 64*, 1487-8 (1942).
(366) Sah, *J. Chinese Chem. Soc.*, 13, 89-95 (1946); *Chem. Abstr.*, 41, 5869 (1947).
(367) Salmon and Rubin, U. S. Patent 2,393,570, Jan. 22, 1946; *Chem. Abstr.*, 40, P3572 (1946).
(368) Savard and Hösögüt, *Rev. faculté sci. univ. Istanbul*, [N.S.], 3, 164-73 (1938); *Chem. Abstr.*, 32, 5795 (1938).
(369) Scheibler and Schmidt, *Ber., 67B*, 1514-8 (1934).
(370) Schlenk and Brauns, *Ber., 48*, 716-28 (1915).
(371) Schlenk and Ochs, *Ber., 48*, 676-80 (1915).
(372) Schlenk and Weickel, *Ann., 368*, 295-304 (1909).
(373) Schmidlin, *Ber., 43*, 1137-44 (1910).
(374) Schmidlin and Huber, *Ber., 43*, 2824-37 (1910).
(375) Schmidlin and Massini, *Ber., 42*, 2377-92 (1909).
(376) Schmidlin and von Escher, *Ber., 41*, 447-50 (1908).
(377) Schmidt and Hartmann, *Ber., 74B*, 1325-32 (1941).
(378) Schorigin, *Ber., 40*, 3111-8 (1907).
(379) Schreiner, *J. prakt. Chem.*, [2], 82, 292-6 (1910).
(380) Sen and Sidhu, *J. Indian Chem. Soc., 25*, 433-6 (1948); *Chem. Abstr.*, 43, 4674 (1949).
(381) Shamshurin, *J. Gen. Chem.* (U.S.S.R.), *13*, 569-72 (1943); *Chem. Abstr.*, 39, 700 (1945).
(382) Shibata, *J. Chem. Soc.*, 95, 1449-56 (1909).

(383) Shine and Turner, *Nature*, *158*, 170 (1946).
(384) Shivers, Hudson, and Hauser, *J. Am. Chem. Soc.*, *65*, 2051-3 (1943).
(385) Ghosh, *Science and Culture*, 3, 120-1 (1937); *Chem. Abstr.*, *32*, 145 (1938).
(386) Simon, Kaufmann, and Schinz, *Helv. Chim. Acta*, *29*, 1133-44 (1946).
(387) Slavjanov, *J. Russ. Phys.-Chem. Soc.*, 39, 140-60 (1907); *Chem. Abstr.*, *1*, 2077 (1907).
(388) Smith, *J. Chem. Soc.*, *1946*, 572-3.
(389) Smith and Bayliss, *J. Org. Chem.*, 6, 437-42 (1941).
(390) Smith and Hoehn, *J. Am. Chem. Soc.*, 63, 1176-8 (1941).
(391) Smith and Nichols, *J. Org. Chem.*, 6, 489-506 (1941).
(392) Sobecki, *Ber.*, *41*, 4103-10 (1908).
(393) Sommelet and Hamel, *Bull. soc. chim.*, [4], *29*, 545-53 (1921).
(394) Sorkin and Reichstein, *Helv. Chim. Acta*, *28*, 875-91 (1945).
(395) Speck and Bost, *J. Org. Chem.*, *11*, 788-94 (1946).
(396) Spielman and Schmidt, *J. Am. Chem. Soc.*, *59*, 2009-10 (1937).
(397) Ssergejew, *J. Russ. Phys.-Chem. Soc.*, *61*, 1421-49 (1929); *Chem. Zentr.*, *1930,II*, 391.
(398) Stadnikoff, *Ber.*, *47*, 2133-42 (1914).
(399) Iotsitch, *J. Russ. Phys.-Chem. Soc.*, *34*, 100-2 (1902); *Bull. soc. chim.*, [3], *28*, 922 (1902).
(400) Stadnikow, *J. Russ. Phys.-Chem. Soc.*, *47*, 2037-44 (1916); *Chem. Zentr.*, *1916,II*, 388.
(401) Stadnikow, *J. Russ. Phys.-Chem. Soc.*, *47*, 2115-20 (1916); *Chem. Zentr.*, *1916,II*, 388.
(402) Stadnikoff, *Ber.*, *57B*, 1-8 (1924).
(403) Stark and Garben, *Ber.*, *46*, 659-66 (1913).
(404) Stas, *Bull. soc. chim. Belg.*, *34*, 188-90 (1925).
(405) Stefanova, *Annuaire univ. Sofia, Faculté phys.-math.*, *40*, Livre 2, 147-66 (1943-44); *Chem. Abstr.*, *42*, 4156 (1948).
(406) Steiger and Reichstein, *Helv. Chim. Acta*, *20*, 1040-54 (1937).
(407) Stevens, *J. Am. Chem. Soc.*, *54*, 3732-8 (1932).
(408) Stoermer, *Ber.*, *39*, 2288-306 (1906).
(409) Stoermer, Stroh, and Albert, *Ber.*, *68B*, 2102-11 (1935).
(410) Süsskind, *Ber.*, *39*, 225-6 (1906).
(411) Sweet and Marvel, *J. Am. Chem. Soc.*, *54*, 1184-90 (1932).
(412) Tarbell and Lindstrom, *J. Am. Chem. Soc.*, *68*, 1930-2 (1946).
(413) Tarbouriech, *Compt. rend.*, *149*, 604-6 (1909); *Chem. Zentr.*, *1909,II*, 1869.
(414) Theunis, *Bull. acad. roy. Belg.*, [5], *12*, 785-96 (1926); *Chem. Zentr.*, *1927,I*, 889.
(415) Thiele and Balhorn, *Ber.*, *37*, 1463-70 (1904).
(416) Thomas and Bettzieche, *Z. physiol. Chem.*, *140*, 244-60 (1924); *Chem. Abstr.*, *19*, 635 (1925).
(417) Thomas and Bettzieche, *Z. physiol. Chem.*, *140*, 261-72 (1924); *Chem. Abstr.*, *19*, 636 (1925).
(418) Tiffeneau, Lévy, and Weill, *Bull. soc. chim.*, [4], *49*, 1709-21 (1931).
(419) Tiffeneau and Dorlencourt, *Compt. rend.*, *143*, 126-8 (1906); *Chem. Zentr.*, *1906,II*, 670.
(420) Tiffeneau and Lévy, *Bull. soc. chim.*, [4],*33*, 735-59 (1923).
(421) Tiffeneau and Lévy, *Bull. soc. chim.*, [4], *33*, 759-79 (1923).
(422) Tiffeneau and Lévy, *Bull. soc. chim.*, [4], *49*, 1738-53 (1931).
(423) Tiffeneau, Oryekhov, and Lévy, *Bull. soc. chim.*, [4], *49*, 1840-6 (1931).
(424) Tissier and Grignard, *Compt. rend.*, *132*, 1182-4 (1901); *Chem. Zentr.*, *1901,I*, 1357.
(425) Treibs, *Ber.*, *65B*, 1324-9 (1932).

(426) Trotman, *J. Chem. Soc.*, *127*, 88–95 (1925).
(427) Tschelinzeff and Terentjeff, *Ber.*, *47*, 2647–52 (1914).
(428) Tschelinzeff and Terentjeff, *Ber.*, *47*, 2652–4 (1914).
(429) Tschitschibabin, *Ber.*, *37*, 186–8 (1904).
(430) Tschitschibabin, *Ber.*, *37*, 850–3 (1904).
(431) Tschitschibabin, *Ber.*, *38*, 561–6 (1905).
(432) Tschitschibabin, *Ber.*, *40*, 1810–9 (1907).
(433) Tuot and Guyard, *Bull. soc. chim.*, [5], *14*, 1087–96 (1947).
(434) Ullmann and Munzhuber, *Ber.*, *36*, 404–10 (1903).
(435) Ushakov and Kucherov, *J. Gen. Chem.* (U.S.S.R.), *14*, 1080–6 (1944); *Chem. Abstr.*, *40*, 7185 (1946).
(436) Valeur, *Compt. rend.*, *132*, 833–4 (1901); *Chem. Zentr.*, *1901*,*I*, 999.
(437) Valeur, *Bull. soc. chim.*, [3], *29*, 683–9 (1903).
(438) van Alphen, *Rec. trav. chim.*, *64*, 109–14 (1945).
(439) van Keersbilck, *Bull. soc. chim. Belg.*, *38*, 205–11 (1929).
(440) Vène, *Ann. chim.*, [11], *10*, 194–279 (1938).
(441) Vène, *Bull. soc. chim.*, [5], 6, 692–7 (1939).
(442) Viquier, *Compt. rend.*, *152*, 1490–3 (1911); *Chem. Abstr.*, *5*, 3409 (1911).
(443) Viquier, *Compt. rend.*, *153*, 955–7 (1911); *Chem. Zentr.*, *1912*,*I*, 20.
(444) Vorländer, Osterburg, and Meye, *Ber.*, *56B*, 1136–44 (1923).
(445) Weill, *Bull. soc. chim.*, [4], *49*, 1795–806 (1931).
(446) Weizmann and Bergmann, *J. Chem. Soc.*, *1936*, 401–2.
(447) Weizmann and Bergmann, *J. Am. Chem. Soc.*, *60*, 2647–50 (1938).
(448) Weizmann, Bergmann, and Berlin, *J. Am. Chem. Soc.*, *60*, 1331–4 (1938).
(449) Weizmann, Bergmann, and Haskelberg, *J. Chem. Soc.*, *1939*, 391–7.
(450) White, Rose, Calingaert, and Soroos, *J. Research Natl. Bur. Standards*, *22*, 315–9 (1939).
(451) Whitmore, *Rec. trav. chim.*, *57*, 562–8 (1938).
(452) Whitmore and Badertscher, *J. Am. Chem. Soc.*, *55*, 1559–67 (1933).
(453) Whitmore, Cosby, Sloatman, and Clarke, *J. Am. Chem. Soc.*, *64*, 1801–3 (1942).
(454) Whitmore and Forster, *J. Am. Chem. Soc.*, *64*, 2966–8 (1942).
(455) Whitmore and Krueger, *J. Am. Chem. Soc.*, *55*, 1528–35 (1933).
(456) Whitmore and Lewis, *J. Am. Chem. Soc.*, *64*, 1618–9 (1942).
(457) Whitmore and Lewis, *J. Am. Chem. Soc.*, *64*, 2964–6 (1942).
(458) Whitmore, Popkin, Whitaker, Mattil, and Zech, *J. Am. Chem. Soc.*, *60*, 2458–62 (1938).
(459) Whitmore and Sloat, *J. Am. Chem. Soc.*, *64*, 2966–8 (1942).
(460) Whitmore, Sutherland, and Cosby, *J. Am. Chem. Soc.*, *64*, 1360–4 (1942).
(461) Whitmore and Williams, *J. Am. Chem. Soc.*, *55*, 406–11 (1933).
(462) Whitmore and Woodburn, *J. Am. Chem. Soc.*, *55*, 361–5 (1933).
(463) Wideqvist, *Arkiv Kemi, Mineral. Geol.*, *B20*, No. 7, 7 pp. (1945); *Chem. Abstr.*, *41*, 4453 (1947).
(464) Wideqvist, *Arkiv. Kemi, Mineral. Geol.*, *B23*, No. 4, 6 pp. (1946); *Chem. Abstr.*, *41*, 1615 (1947).
(465) Wieland, Schlichting, and Jacobi, *Z. physiol. Chem.*, *161*, 80–115 (1926); *Chem. Abstr.*, *21*, 590 (1927).
(466) Wieland, Schlichting, and von Langsdorf, *Z. physiol. Chem.*, *161*, 74–9 (1926); *Chem. Abstr.*, *21*, 590 (1927).
(467) Willcox and Brunel, *J. Am. Chem. Soc.*, *38*, 1821–41 (1916).
(468) Wilson, Roberts, and Young, *J. Am. Chem. Soc.*, *71*, 2019–20 (1949).
(469) Wohl and Bernreuther, *Ann.*, *481*, 1–29 (1930).
(470) Wohl and Mylo, *Ber.*, *45*, 323–49 (1912).
(471) Wood and Comley, *J. Soc. Chem. Ind.*, *42*, 429–32T (1923).

(472) Young and Roberts, *J. Am. Chem. Soc.*, *68*, 649–52 (1946).
(473) Zal'kind and Pletz, *Trans. Leningrad Chem.-Tech. Inst.*, *1*, 57–60 (1934); *Chem. Abstr.*, *29*, 2908 (1935).
(474) Zelinsky and Kravts, *J. Russ. Phys.-Chem. Soc.*, *39*, 1170 (1908); *Chem. Abstr.*, *2*, 1266 (1908).
(475) Ziegler, *Ann.*, *434*, 34–78 (1923).
(476) Zook, McAleer, and Horwin, *J. Am. Chem. Soc.*, *68*, 2404 (1946).
(477) Zugrăvescu and Zugrăvescu, *Bul. soc. chim. România*, *19A*, 85–92 (1937); *Chem. Abstr.*, *33*, 4228 (1939).
(478) Gilman, Kirby, Fothergill, and Harris, *Proc. Iowa Acad. Sci.*, *34*, 221–2 (1927); *Chem. Abstr.*, *22*, 4504 (1928).
(479) Paal and Hornstein, *Ber.*, *39*, 2823–7 (1906).
(480) Paal and Weidenkaff, *Ber.*, *39*, 2827–33 (1906).
(481) Lapkin and Golovkova, *J. Gen. Chem.* (U.S.S.R.), *18*, 485–95 (1948); *Chem. Abstr.*, *42*, 7273 (1948).
(482) Feist, Awe, and Kuklinski, *Arch. Pharm.*, *276*, 420–31 (1938); *Chem. Abstr.*, *33*, 1327 (1939).
(483) Ullmann and Schlaepfer, *Ber.*, *37*, 2001–8 (1904).
(484) Ullmann and Tcherniak, *Ber.*, *38*, 4110–1 (1905).
(485) Zaher, Sen, and Sidhu, *J. Indian Chem. Soc.*, *24*, 293–5 (1949); *Chem. Abstr.*, *42*, 5912 (1948).
(486) Linnell and Roushdi, *Quart. J. Pharm. Pharmacol.*, *14*, 270–80 (1941); *Chem. Abstr.*, *36*, 2544 (1942).
(487) Bistrzycki and Gyr, *Ber.*, *37*, 655–64 (1904).
(488) Oddo, *Gazz. chim. ital.*, *41*,*I*, 273–94 (1911); *Chem. Abstr.*, *5*, 2639 (1911).
(489) Lewis, *J. Chem. Education*, *7*, 856–8 (1930).
(490) Fields, Leaffer, and Rohan, *Science*, *109*, 35, (1949); *Chem. Abstr.*, *43*, 9045 (1949).
(491) Iotsitch and Kochélef, *J. Russ. Phys.-Chem. Soc.*, *42*, 1492 (1910); *Bull. soc. chim.*, [4], *10*, 1308 (1911).
(492) Iotsitch and Kochélef, *J. Russ. Phys.-Chem. Soc.*, *42*, 1082 (1910); *Bull. soc. chim.*, [4], *10*, 1148 (1911).
(493) Grignard, *Ann. chim.*, [7], *24*, 433–90 (1901).
(494) Grignard and Liang, *Bull. soc. chim.*, [4], *49*, 858–9 (1931).
(495) Iotsitch and Orelkine, *J. Russ. Phys.-Chem. Soc.*, *42*, 1082 (1910); *Bull. soc. chim.*, [4], *10*, 1148 (1911).
(496) Temnikova and Veksler, *J. Gen. Chem.* (U.S.S.R.), *11*, 3–8 (1941); *Chem. Abstr.*, *35*, 5459 (1941).
(497) Temnikova and Veksler, *J. Gen. Chem.* (U.S.S.R.), *19*, 1318–23 (1949); *Chem. Abstr.*, *44*, 1056 (1950).
(498) Petrov and Ol'dekop, *J. Gen. Chem.* (U.S.S.R.), 18, 859–64 (1948); *Chem. Abstr.*, *43*, 107 (1949).
(499) Anderson and Thomas, *J. Am. Chem. Soc.*, *65*, 234–8 (1943).
(500) Semon and Craig, *J. Am. Chem. Soc.*, *58*,1278–82 (1936).
(501) Mizuch, *J. Gen. Chem.* (U.S.S.R.), *16*, 1471–4 (1946); *Chem. Zentr.*, *1947*,*I*, 989; *Chem. Abstr.*, *43*, 3819 (1949).
(502) Grard, *Ann. chim.*, [10], *13*, 336–81 (1930).
(503) Barré and Repentigny, *Can. J. Research*, *27B*, 716–20 (1949).
(504) Arnold, Buckley, and Richter, *J. Am. Chem. Soc.*, *69*, 2322–5 (1947).
(505) Birch and Robinson, *J. Chem. Soc.*, *1943*, 501–2.
(506) Craig, *J. Am. Chem. Soc.*, *57*, 195–8 (1935).
(507) Baeyer and Villiger, *Ber.*, *37*, 3191–210 (1904).
(508) Goldstein and Piolino, *Helv. Chim. Acta*, *10*, 334–8 (1927).
(509) Goldstein and Simo, *Helv. Chim. Acta*, *10*, 607–10 (1927).

(*510*) Goldstein and Vaymatchar, *Helv. Chim. Acta, 11*, 245–9 (1928).
(*511*) Goldstein and Kopp, *Helv. Chim. Acta, 11*, 478–86 (1928).
(*512*) Goldstein and Kopp, *Helv. Chim. Acta, 11*, 486–95 (1928).
(*513*) Goldstein and Kopp, *Helv. Chim. Acta, 27*, 616–9 (1944).
(*514*) Arnold and Searles, *J. Am. Chem. Soc., 71*, 1150–1 (1959).
(*515*) McBee, Pierce, and Higgins, *J. Am. Chem. Soc., 74*, 1736–7 (1952).
(*516*) Kohler and Larsen, *J. Am. Chem. Soc., 57*, 1448–52 (1935).
(*517*) Chelintzev and Karmanov, *J. Russ. Phys.-Chem. Soc., 47*, 161–9 (1915); *Chem. Abstr., 9*, 1472 (1915).
(*518*) Salzberg and Marvel, *J. Am. Chem. Soc., 50*, 1737–44 (1928).
(*519*) Davis and Marvel, *J. Am. Chem. Soc., 53*, 3840–51 (1931).
(*520*) Steinkopf and Schmitt, *Ann., 533*, 264–9 (1938).
(*521*) Inhoffen, Bohlman, and Reinefeld, *Chem. Ber., 82*, 313–6 (1949).
(*522*) Gaertner, *J. Am. Chem. Soc., 74*, 766–7 (1952).
(*523*) Haller and Ramart-Lucas, *Compt. rend., 159*, 143–9 (1914); *Chem. Abstr., 8*, 3437 (1914).
(*524*) Thomas and Bettzieche, *Z. physiol. Chem., 140*, 279–98 (1924); *Chem. Abstr., 19*, 636 (1925).

TABLE VIII-IV

REACTIONS OF GRIGNARD REAGENTS WITH LACTONES AND LACTIDES

Lactone or Lactide	RMgX	Product(s)	Ref.
$C_3H_4O_2$			
β-Propiolactone (1 mole)	CH_3MgI (1 mole)	$(C_3H_4O_2)_x$ (3 g., 4.2%); $ICH_2CH_2CO_2H$ (87 g., 43.5%); $CH_3COCH{=}CH_2$ (13 g., crude)	22
β-Propiolactone (72 g., 1 mole)	C_6H_5MgBr (1 mole)	$(C_3H_4O_2)_x$ (6.5 g., 9.6%); $BrCH_2CH_2CO_2H$ (64 g., 43.0%); $H_2C{=}CHCOC_6H_5$ (21.2%)*	22
β-Propiolactone (72 g., 1 mole)	C_6H_5MgBr (1 mole)	$(C_3H_4O_2)_x$ (31 g., 43.1%); $BrCH_2CH_2CO_2H$ (44 g., 28.7%); $H_2C{=}CHCOC_6H_5$ †	22
β-Propiolactone (72 g., 1 mole)	$(C_6H_5)_2Mg$ (from 1 mole C_6H_5MgBr)	$(C_3H_4O_2)_x$ (84 g.); $H_2C{=}CHCOC_6H_5$ (12 g., crude)	22
β-Propiolactone (1 mole)	$C_6H_5CH_2MgCl$ (1 mole)	$(C_3H_4O_2)_x$ (16.1 g., 22.4%); $ClCH_2CH_2CO_2H$ (17.5 g., 16.1%); $C_6H_5(CH_2)_3CO_2H$ (53.2 g., 32.4%)	22
$C_4H_6O_2$			
γ-Butyrolactone	CH_3MgI	$HO(CH_3)_2CCH_2CH_2CH_2OH$	28
γ-Butyrolactone (7.5 g.)	C_6H_5MgBr (13.7 g. C_6H_5Br)	$HO(C_6H_5)_2CCH_2CH_2CH_2OH$ (2.0 g.)	59
$C_5H_8O_2$			
γ-Valerolactone	CH_3MgI	$HO(CH_3)_2CCH_2CH_2CH(CH_3)OH$	32
$C_6H_8O_4$			
Lactide ‡	C_6H_5MgBr	$HO(C_6H_5)_2CCH(CH_3)OH$	39

* Gradual (1.25 hrs.) addition of Et_2O-lactone solution to Grignard reagent solution at −6 to 0°.

† Addition of Grignard reagent solution to Et_2O-lactone solution at −35 to −28°.

‡ Dilactylic anhydride.

TABLE VIII-IV (Continued)

Lactone or Lactide	RMgX	Product(s)	Ref.
$C_6H_{10}O_3$			
α-Hydroxy-β,β-dimethyl-γ-butyrolactone (684.6 mg.)	CH_3MgI (3.0 ml. CH_3I)	$HO(CH_3)_2CCH(OH)C(CH_3)_2CH_2OH$ (850.0 mg.)	53
α-Hydroxy-β,β-dimethyl γ-butyrolactone (400.0 mg.)	C_6H_5MgBr (5.8 g. C_6H_5Br)	$HO(C_6H_5)_2CCH(OH)C(CH_3)_2CH_2OH$ (870.0 mg.)	53
2,2,5-Trimethyl-1,3-dioxolan-4-one	t-C_4H_9MgCl	i-$C_3H_7OCH(CH_3)CO_2H$ (20%)	17
$C_7H_{10}O_2$			
2-Methylene-4-hydroxy-4-methylpentanoic acid lactone (or 2,4-dimethyl-4-hydroxy-2-pentenoic acid lactone) (25 g.)	CH_3MgI (2.5 equiv.)	$HO(CH_3)_2CCH_2C(=CH_2)C(C_6H_5)_2OH$ [or $HO(CH_3)_2CCH=C(CH_3)C(C_6H_5)_2OH$] (30 g., crude)	31
$C_7H_{12}O_3$			
α,γ-Dihydroxy-α,γ-dimethylvaleric acid γ-lactone	CH_3MgI (3 equiv.)	$HO(CH_3)_2CCH_2C(OH)(CH_3)C(CH_3)_2OH$	30
α,γ-Dihydroxy-α,γ-dimethylvaleric acid γ-lactone	C_6H_5MgBr (3 equiv.)	2,2,4-Trimethyl-4-hydroxy-5-5-diphenyltetrahydrofuran	30
α,γ-Dihydroxy-α,γ-dimethyl valeric acid γ-lactone	C_6H_5MgBr	$HO(CH_3)_2CCH_2C(OH)(CH_3)C(C_6H_5)_2OH$	31
2,2,5,5-Tetramethyl-1,3-dioxolan-4-one	t-C_4H_9MgCl	i-$C_3H_7OC(CH_3)_2CO_2H$ (50%)	17
$C_7H_{13}O_2N$			
α-Amino-α,γ-dimethyl-γ-hydroxyvaleric acid γ-lactone	CH_3MgI (3 equiv.)	$HO(CH_3)_2CCH_2C(NH_2)(CH_3)C(CH_3)_2OH$	30
α-Amino-α,γ-dimethyl-γ-hydroxyvaleric acid γ-lactone	C_6H_5MgBr (3 equiv.)	$HO(CH_3)_2CCH_2C(NH_2)(CH_3)C(C_6H_5)_2OH$	30
$C_8H_6O_2$			
Phthalide	CH_3MgBr (3 equiv.)	2-$HOCH_2C_6H_4C(CH_3)_2OH$	36

TABLE VIII-IV (Continued)

Lactone or Lactide	RMgX	Product(s)	Ref.
$C_8H_6O_2$ (*cont.*)			
Phthalide	C_2H_5MgBr	2-$HOCH_2C_6H_4C(C_2H_5)_2OH$	36
Phthalide	*i*-C_3H_7MgX	2-$HOCH_2C_6H_4C$(*i*-$C_3H_7)_2OH$	36
Phthalide (6.7 g.)	C_6H_5MgBr (27.3 g. C_6H_5Br)	2-$HOCH_2C_6H_4C(C_6H_5)_2OH$ (7.3 g.)	47,65
Phthalide	$C_6H_5CH_2MgCl$ (3 equiv.)	2-$HOCH_2C_6H_4C(CH_2C_6H_5)_2OH$	36
$C_9H_6O_2$			
Coumarin (30 g.)	CH_3MgI (65 g. CH_3I)	2,2-Dimethyl-1,2-benzopyran (26 g., 80%)	29
Coumarin	CH_3MgI	2-Methyl-1-benzopyrylium iodide	14
Coumarin	CH_3MgI	2-$HOC_6H_4CH{=}CHC(CH_3)_2OH$; 2,2-dimethyl-1,2-benzopyran	49
Coumarin (0.125 mole)	CH_3MgX (0.4 mole CH_3X)	2,2-Dimethyl-1,2-benzopyran (59%)	48
Coumarin (50 g.)	C_2H_5MgBr (80 g. C_6H_5Br)	2,2-Diethyl-1,2-benzopyran (31 g., 48.8%)	29
Coumarin (25 g.)	C_2H_5MgBr (40 g. C_2H_5Br)	2-$HOC_6H_4CH{=}CHC(C_2H_5)_2OH$ (32 g., crude)	49
Coumarin (0.125 mole)	C_2H_5MgX (0.4 mole C_2H_5X)	2,2-Diethyl-1,2-benzopyran (64%)	48
Coumarin (0.125 mole)	*n*-C_3H_7MgX (0.4 mole C_3H_7X)	2,2-Di-*n*-propyl-1,2-benzopyran (68%)	48
Coumarin (24 g.)	*i*-C_3H_7MgBr (41 g. C_3H_7Br)	Unidentified products	29
Coumarin (22 g.)	*n*-C_4H_9MgBr (45.2 g. C_4H_9Br)	2-$HOC_6H_5CH{=}CHC$(*n*-$C_4H_9)_2OH$; 2,2-di-*n*-butyl-1,2-benzopyran (17–18 g.)	49
Coumarin (0.125 mole)	*n*-C_4H_9MgX (0.4 mole C_4H_9X)	2,2-Di-*n*-butyl-1,2-benzopyran (70%)	48
Coumarin (0.125 mole)	*n*-$C_5H_{11}MgX$ (0.4 mole $C_5H_{11}X$)	2,2-Di-*n*-amyl-1,2-benzopyran (77.3%)	48
Coumarin (30 g.)	C_6H_5MgBr (65 g. C_6H_5Br)	2,4-Diphenyl-2-chromanol* (10 g.)	29
Coumarin (40 g.)	C_6H_5MgBr (90 g. C_6H_5Br)	2,4-Diphenyl-2-chromanol (45%); 2,2-diphenyl-1,2-benzopyran (35%)	34
Coumarin	C_6H_5MgBr (+ fuming HCl)	2-Phenyl-1-benzopyrylium chloride	14
Coumarin (0.125 mole)	*n*-$C_6H_{13}MgX$ (0.4 mole $C_6H_{13}X$)	2,2-Di-*n*-hexyl-1,2-benzopyran (83%)	48
Coumarin (30 g.)	$C_6H_5CH_2MgCl$ (80 g. C_7H_7Cl)	$CH_3C_6H_5$; $(C_6H_5CH_2-)_2$; 2-$HOC_6H_4CH{=}CHCOCH_2C_6H_5$ (47 g.)	29

* Originally reported by Houben (*29*) as 2-$HOC_6H_4CH{=}CHC(C_6H_5)_2OH$; *cf.*, however, Lowenbein, *et al.* (*34*).

TABLE VIII-IV (Continued)

Lactone or Lactide	RMgX	Product(s)	Ref.
$C_9H_6O_2$ (*cont.*)			
Coumarin (0.125 mole)	n-$C_7H_{15}MgX$	2,2-Di-n-heptyl-1,2-benzopyran (91.5%)	*48*
Coumarin (10 g.)	1-$C_{10}H_7MgBr$ (32.5 g. $C_{10}H_7Br$)	2,4-Di-α-naphthyl-2-chromanol	*34,29*
Isocoumarin (21 g., 0.14 mole)	C_6H_5MgBr (0.13 mole) (+ 70% $HClO_4$)	1-Phenyl-2-benzopyrilium perchlorate (9 g., 21%)	*66*
$C_9H_6O_3$			
4-Hydroxycoumarin (5 g.)	C_6H_5MgBr (14.5 g. C_6H_5Br)	2,2-Diphenyl-4-hydroxy-1,2-benzopyran	*26*
$C_9H_7O_2N$			
2-Methyl-3,1,4-benzoxaz-4-one (30 g.)	C_6H_5MgBr (32.3 g. C_6H_5Br)	2-$CH_3CONHC_6H_4(C_6H_5)_2COH$ (10 g., 23%)	*33*
2-Methyl-3,1,4-benzoxaz-4-one (10 g.)	C_6H_5MgBr (9.7 g. C_6H_5Br)	$C_6H_5COC_6H_4$-2-$NHCOCH_3$ (5.2 g., 33%)	*33*
2-Methyl-3,1,4-benzoxaz-4-one	$C_6H_5CH_2MgCl$	Unidentified oily product	*33*
2-Methyl-3,1,4-benzoxaz-4-one	2-$CH_3C_6H_4MgBr$	o-$CH_3C_6H_4COC_6H_4$-2-$NHCOCH_3$ (43%)	*33*
2-Methyl-3,1,4-Benzoxaz-4-one	3-$CH_3C_6H_4MgBr$ (*ca.* 1 equiv.)	m-$CH_3C_6H_4COC_6H_4$-2-$NHCOCH_3$ (10% overall yield of amine upon hydrolysis)	*33*
2-Methyl-3,1,4-benzoxaz-4-one (15 g.)	1-$C_{10}H_7MgBr$	α-$C_{10}H_7COC_6H_4$-2-$NHCOCH_3$ (2.4 g.); 2-$CH_3CONHC_6H_4$(α-$C_{10}H_7)_2COH$ (?) (1.2 g.)	*33*
2-Methyl-3,1,4-benzoxaz-4-one (15.0 g.)	1-$C_{10}H_7MgBr$ (17.7 g. $C_{10}H_7Br$)	α-$C_{10}H_7COC_6H_4$-2-$NHCOCH_3$ (11.6 g., 47%)	*33*
2-Methyl-3,1,4-benzoxaz-4-one (7.8 g.)	2-$C_{10}H_7MgBr$ (10.0 g. $C_{10}H_7Br$)	β-$C_{10}H_7COC_6H_4$-2-$NHCOCH_3$ (yielding 1 g., 8.3% 2-$C_{10}H_7COC_6H_4$-2-NH_2 upon hydrolysis)	*33*
2-Methyl-3,1,4-benzoxaz-4-one (15.0 g.)	2-$CH_3C_{10}H_6$-1-MgBr (19.6 g. $C_{11}H_9Br$)	2-$CH_3C_{10}H_6$-1-COC_6H_4-2-$NHCOCH_3$ (9.5 g., 34%)	*33*
$C_9H_8O_2$			
3,4-Dihydrocoumarin (5 g.)	C_2H_5MgBr (7.4 g. C_2H_5Br)	2-$HOC_6H_4CH_2CH_2(C_2H_5)_2COH$ (6 g.)	*51*

TABLE VIII-IV (Continued)

Lactone or Lactide	RMgX	Product(s)	Ref.
$C_9H_8O_2$ (*cont.*)			
3,4-Dihydrocoumarin (5 g.)	*n*-C_3H_7MgCl (7.8 g. C_3H_7Cl)	2-$HOC_6H_4CH_2CH_2$(*n*-C_3H_7)$_2COH$ (6.15 g.)	*51*
3,4-Dihydrocoumarin (14.8 g.)	*n*-C_4H_9MgBr (28.0 g. C_4H_9Br)	2-$HOC_6H_4CH_2CH_2$(*n*-C_4H_9)$_2COH$ (25 g.)	*49*
3-Methylphthalide (5.5 g.)	CH_3MgI (17.8 g. CH_3I)	1-Methylene-3-methylphthalan	*38*
$C_{10}H_8O_2$			
3-Methylcoumarin (10 g.)	C_6H_5MgBr (3 equiv.)	2,4-Diphenyl-3-methyl-2-chromanol	*26*
4-Methylcoumarin (10 g.)	C_6H_5MgBr (30 g. C_6H_5Br)	2,2-Diphenyl-4-methyl-1,2-benzopyran	*26*
$C_{10}H_8O_3$			
4-Methoxycoumarin (5 g.)	C_6H_5MgBr (14 g. C_6H_5Br)	2,2-Diphenyl-4-methoxy-1,2-benzopyran (7 g.)	*26*
4-Methoxycoumarin	4-$CH_3OC_6H_4MgBr$	2,2-Di-*p*-anisyl-4-methoxy-1,2-benzopyran	*26*
$C_{10}H_{10}O_2$			
3,3-Dimethyl phthalide	C_6H_5MgBr (12 g. C_6H_5Br)	2-$C_6H_5COC_6H_4C(CH_3)_2OH$, or the corresponding hydroxyphthalan (9.7 g.)	*11*
$C_{10}H_{14}O_3$			
α-(5-Methyl-2-furylidene)-γ-valerolactone*	CH_3MgI	$C_{12}H_{20}O_2$ †	*32*
$C_{11}H_{10}O_2$			
4,6-Dimethylcoumarin	C_6H_5MgBr	2,4-Diphenyl-4,6-dimethyl-2-chromanol	*34*
4,6-Dimethylcoumarin (5 g.)	C_6H_5MgBr	2,2-Diphenyl-4,6-dimethyl-1,2-benzopyran, m. 126°	*26*

* Divalerolactone.

† Described as the anhydride corresponding to the expected glycol.

TABLE VIII-IV (Continued)

Lactone or Lactide	RMgX	Product(s)	Ref.
$C_{11}H_{10}O_2$ (*cont.*)			
4,7-Dimethylcoumarin	C_6H_5MgBr	2,4-Diphenyl-4,7-dimethyl-2-chromanol	*34*
4,7-Dimethylcoumarin	C_6H_5MgBr	2-HO-4-$CH_3C_6H_3C(CH_3)$=$CHC(C_6H_5)_2OH$ (10%); 2,2-Diphenyl-4,7-dimethyl-1,2-benzopyran (75%)	*26*
5,7-Dimethylcoumarin	C_6H_5MgBr	2,4-Diphenyl-5,7-dimethyl-2-chromanol	*34*
$C_{11}H_{11}O_3Br$			
2,2-Dimethyl-5-*p*-bromophenyl-1,3-dioxolan-4-one	*t*-C_4H_9MgCl	*i*-$C_3H_7OCH(C_6H_4$-*p*-$Br)CO_2H$ (71%)	*17*
$C_{11}H_{12}O_3$			
2,2-Dimethyl-5-phenyl-1,3-dioxolan-4-one (38.4 g.)	*t*-C_4H_9MgCl (55.8 g. C_4H_9Cl)	*i*-$C_3H_7OCH(C_6H_5)CO_2H$ (22 g., 57%); *i*-C_4H_8	*17*
2,2-Dimethyl-5-phenyl-1,3-dioxolan-4-one (76.8 g.)	*t*-C_4H_9MgCl (92 g. C_4H_9Cl)	*i*-$C_3H_7OCH(C_6H_5)CO_2H$ (34 g., 45%); *i*-C_4H_8 [recovered as $(CH_3)_2CBrCH_2Br$, 20 g., 24%]	*17*
2,2-Dimethyl-5-phenyl-1,3-dioxolan-4-one	C_6H_5MgBr	$HO(C_6H_5)_2CCH(C_6H_5)OH$ (66%)	*15,17*
2,2-Dimethyl-5-phenyl-1,3-dioxolan-4-one (96 g.)	2-$CH_3C_6H_4MgBr$ (342 g. C_7H_7Br)	HO(2-$CH_3C_6H_4)_2CCH(C_6H_5)OH$ (30.5 g.)	*17*
2,2-Dimethyl-5-phenyl-1,3-dioxolan-4-one	2,4,6-$(CH_3)_3C_6H_2MgBr$	"Intractable oil"	*17*
$C_{11}H_{14}O_8$			
Triacetyl-α-arabonic acid lactone	C_6H_5MgBr (11 equiv.)	$HO(C_6H_5)_2C[CH(OH)]_3CH_2OH$ (1,1-Diphenyl-α-arabitol) (15–16%); $CH_3(C_6H_5)_2COH$	*41*
Triacetyl-α-arabonic acid lactone (4.5 parts)	$C_6H_5CH_2MgCl$ (25.3 parts C_7H_7Cl)	$HO(C_6H_5CH_2)_2C[CH(OH)]_3CH_2OH$ (1,1-Dibenzyl-α-arabitol) (*ca.* 15%); $CH_3(C_6H_5CH_2)_2COH$	*41*
Triacetyl-α-arabonic acid lactone	4-$CH_3C_6H_5MgBr$ (11 equiv.)	HO(4-$CH_3C_6H_4)_2C[CH(OH)]_3CH_2OH$ (1,1-Di-*p*-tolyl-α-arabitol) (15%); CH_3(4-$CH_3C_6H_4)_2COH$	*41*

TABLE VIII-IV (Continued)

Lactone or Lactide	RMgX	Product(s)	Ref.
$C_{12}H_{12}O_3$			
3,4-Dimethyl-7-methoxycoumarin* (10 g.)	C_6H_5MgBr (2 equiv.) (+ CONCHCl)	2-Phenyl-3,4-dimethyl-7-methoxybenzopyrylium chloride (quant.)	*27*
$C_{12}H_{12}O_4$			
4-Carbomethoxymethyl-3,4-dihydrocoumarin (2.1 g.)	C_6H_5MgBr (excess)	$2\text{-}HOC_6H_4CH[CH_2C(C_6H_5)_2OH]_2$	*18*
$C_{12}H_{12}O_5$			
3,5,7-Trimethoxycoumarin (1.5 g.)	C_6H_5MgBr (3 g. C_6H_5Br) (+ 20% HCl)	2-Phenyl-3,5,7-trimethoxy-1-benzopyrylium chloride (1.3 g., including 13.3% H_2O)	*60*
3,5,7-Trimethoxycoumarin (1 g.)	$4\text{-}CH_3OC_6H_4MgBr$ (3.75 g.) C_6H_5Br (+ 20% HCl)	2-*p*-Anisyl-3,5,7-trimethoxy-1-benzopyrylium chloride (0.8–1.0 g., *ca.* 60%)	*61*
3,5,7-Trimethoxycoumarin (0.9 g.)	$2,4\text{-}(CH_3O)_2C_6H_3MgI$ (3 g. $C_8H_9IO_2$) (+ 20% HCl)	2-(2,4-Dimethoxyphenyl)-3,5,7-trimethoxy-1-benzopyrilium chloride (0.8 g., >50%)	*60*
3,5,7-Trimethoxycoumarin (0.3 g.)	$3,4\text{-}(CH_3O)_2C_6H_3MgI$ (3.3 g. $C_8H_9IO_2$) (+ 20% HCl)	2-(3,4-Dimethoxyphenyl)-3,5,7-trimethoxy-1-benzopyrylium chloride	*61*
$C_{12}H_{13}O_3$			
5,7,8-Trimethyl-6-hydroxy-3,4-dihydrocoumarin (1.33 g.)	CH_3MgI (4.00 g. CH_3I)	2,2,5,7,8-Pentamethyl-6-hydroxychroman and corresponding carbinol	*50,62*
5,7,8-Trimethyl-6-hydroxy-3,4-dihydrocoumarin (1.33 g.)	CH_3MgI (0.62 g. Mg)	2-Methyl-4-(2,5-dihydroxy-3,4,6-trimethylphenyl)butanol-2; 2,2,5,7,8-pentamethyl-6-hydroxychroman	*51*
$C_{12}H_{14}O_3$			
2,2-Dimethyl-5-*p*-tolyl-1,3-dioxolan-4-one	$t\text{-}C_4H_9MgCl$	$i\text{-}C_3H_7OCH(C_6H_4\text{-}p\text{-}CH_3)CO_2H$ (66%)	*17*

* Heilbron and Zaki (*27*) erroneously reported this compound as the isomeric 2,3-dimethyl-7-methoxychromone. See: Canter, Curd, and Robertson, *J. Chem. Soc.*, *1931*, 1255–65; Hamer, Heilbron, Reade, and Walls, *ibid.*, *1932*, 251–60.

TABLE VIII-IV (Continued)

Lactone or Lactide	RMgX	Product(s)	Ref.
$C_{12}H_{14}O_4$			
3,3-Diethylphthalide	C_6H_5MgBr	2-$C_6H_5COC_6H_4C(C_2H_5)_2OH$, or the corresponding hydroxyphthalan	*11*
$C_{13}H_8O_2$			
6-Dibenzo[*b*,*d*]pyrone	C_6H_5MgBr	6-Phenyldibenzo[*b*,*d*]pyrylium hydroxide	*13*
$C_{13}H_8O_3$			
3-Hydroxy-6-dibenzo[*b*,*d*]pyrone (10 g.)	CH_3MgI (48 g. CH_3I)	3-Hydroxy-6,6-dimethyl-6-dibenzo[*b*,*d*]pyran (4.3 g., 40%)	7
$C_{13}H_9O_2N$			
2-Methyl-4-naphth[2.3-*d*][1.3]oxazin-4-one (15 g.)	C_6H_5MgBr	2-$CH_3CONHC_{10}H_6$-3-$C(C_6H_5)_2OH$ (?) (1.2 g.); 2-$CH_3CONHC_{10}H_6$-3-COC_6H_5 (8 g., 39%)	*33*
2-Methyl-4-naphth[2.3-*d*][1.3]oxazin-4-one (15 g.)	$C_6H_5CH_2MgCl$	2-$CH_3CONHC_{10}H_6$-3-$C(CH_2C_6H_5)_2OH$ ("very small yield")	*33*
2-Methyl-4-naphth[2.3-*d*][1.3]oxazin-4-one	$C_6H_5CH_2MgCl$	3-CH_3CONH-2-$C_{10}H_6(C_6H_5CH_2)_2COH$ (small am't); no ketone	*33*
2-Methyl-4-naphth[2.3-*d*][1.3]oxazin-4-one	2-$C_{10}H_7MgBr$	2-$CH_3CONHC_{10}H_6$-3-CO-2-$C_{10}H_7$	*33*
2-Methyl-4-naphth[2.3-*d*][1.3]oxazin-4-one	2-$C_{10}H_7MgBr$	2-(β-$C_{10}H_7CO$)-3-$CH_3CONHC_{10}H_6$	*33*
$C_{13}H_{10}O_3N$			
3-Methyl-10-hydroxy-1,2,3,4-tetrahydropyridino[3,4-*c*]benzo-[*e*]pyran-5-one (5 g.)	CH_3MgI (10.5 ml. CH_3I)	3,5,5-Trimethyl-10-hydroxy-1,2,3,4-tetrahydropyridino[3,4-*c*]benzo[*e*]pyran (0.5 g.)	*10*

TABLE VIII-IV (Continued)

Lactone or Lactide	RMgX	Product(s)	Ref.
$C_{13}H_{10}O_3N$ (*cont.*)			
3-Methyl-8-hydroxy-1,2,3,4-tetrahydropyridino[3,4-*c*]benzo[*e*]pyran-5-one (4.2 g.)	CH_3MgI (8 ml. CH_3I)	3,5,5-Trimethyl-8-hydroxy-1,2,3,4-tetrahydropyridino[3,4-*c*]benzo[*e*]pyran (1.8 g.)	*10*
$C_{13}H_{12}O_4$			
4,7-Dimethyl-5-acetoxycoumarin	CH_3MgI (excess)	2,2,4,7-Tetramethyl-5-hydroxy-1,2-benzopyran	*44*
$C_{14}H_{10}O_2$			
3-Phenylphthalide (excess)	C_6H_5MgBr	2-[$C_6H_5CH(OH)$]$C_6H_4C(C_6H_5)_2OH$	*23,24*
3-Phenylphthalide	C_6H_5MgBr (excess)	1,3-Diphenylphthalan-1-ol	*23,24*
3-Phenylphthalide (6.3 g.)	C_6H_5MgBr (9.6 g. C_6H_5Br)	1,3-Diphenylphthalan-1-ol	*47*
3-Phenylphthalide (10 g.)	$C_6H_5CH_2MgCl$ (7 g. C_7H_7Cl)	1-Phenyl-3-benzylidenephthalan (5.3 g.)	*55*
3-Phenylphthalide	4-$CH_3C_6H_4MgBr$	1-*p*-Tolyl-3-phenylphthalan-1-ol	*30*
$C_{14}H_{12}O_3N$			
3,8-Dimethyl-10-hydroxy-1,2,3,4-tetrahydropyridino[3,4-*c*]benzo[*e*]pyran-5-one (4.9 g.) (5-Hydroxy-7-methyl-*N*-methyltetrahydropyrido[3,4-*d*]coumarin	CH_3MgI (11 ml. CH_3I)	3,5,5,8-Tetramethyl-10-hydroxy-1,2,3,4-tetrahydropyridino[3,4-*c*]benzo[*e*]pyran	*10*
$C_{14}H_{14}O_3$			
1-Hydroxy-3-methyl-7,8,9,10-tetrahydro-6-dibenzo[*b,d*]pyrone (1.5 g.)	CH_3MgI (6 ml. CH_3I)	1-Hydroxy-3,6,6-trimethyl-7,8,9,10-tetrahydro-6-dibenzo[*b,d*]pyran (1.0 g., 63%) (after HBr dehydration)	*2*
$C_{14}H_{14}O_4$			
1,3-Dihydroxy-9-methyl-7,8,9,10-tetrahydro-6-dibenzo[*b,d*]pyrone	CH_3MgI (excess)	1,3-Dihydroxy-6,6,9-trimethyl-7,8,9,10-tetrahydro-6-dibenzo[*b,d*]pyran	*44*

TABLE VIII-IV (Continued)

Lactone or Lactide	RMgX	Product(s)	Ref.
$C_{14}H_{18}O_3$			
2,2-Dimethyl-5-mesityl-1,3-dioxolan-4-one	t-C_4H_9MgCl	i-$C_3H_7OCH(Mes)CO_2H$ (80%)	*17*
2,2-Dimethyl-5-mesityl-1,3-dioxolan-4-one (50 g.)	C_6H_5MgBr (4 equiv.)	$HO(C_6H_5)_2CCH(Mes)OH$ (?) [yielding $(C_6H_5)_2CHCOMes$ on AcH-HCl reflux]	*16*
$C_{14}H_{18}O_{10}$			
Tetraäcetyl-D-glucuronic acid γ-lactone (3 g.)	C_6H_5MgBr (12 equiv.)	$(C_6H_5)_2C(OH)(CHOH)_4CH_2OH$ (1,1-Diphenyl-D-sorbitol) (10–12%); $CH_3(C_6H_5)_2COH$	*40*
Tetraäcetyl-D-glucuronic acid γ-lactone	C_6H_5MgBr (13 equiv.)	$(C_6H_5)_2C(OH)(CHOH)_4CH_2OH$ (1,1-Diphenyl-D-sorbitol) (25%); $CH_3(C_6H_5)_2COH$	*40*
Tetraäcetyl-D-glucuronic acid γ-lactone (5.5 g.)	$C_6H_5CH_2MgCl$ (30 g. C_7H_7Cl)	$(C_6H_5CH_2)_2C(OH)(CHOH)_4CH_2OH$ (1,1-Dibenzyl-D-sorbitol) (0.83–1.24 g. crude); $CH_3(C_6H_5CH_2)_2COH$	*42*
Tetraäcetyl-D-glucuronic acid γ-lactone (5.5 g.)	4-$CH_3C_6H_4MgBr$ (13 equiv.)	$(4$-$CH_3C_6H_4)_2C(OH)(CHOH)_4CH_2OH$ (1,1-Di-p-tolyl-D-sorbitol) (0.5–0.8 g., crude; 0.45–0.61 g., 8–10%, pure); $CH_3(4$-$CH_3C_6H_4)_2COH$	*42*
Tetraäcetyl-D-galactonic acid γ-lactone (10 g.)	C_6H_5MgBr (14 equiv.)	$(C_6H_5)_2C(OH)(CHOH)_4CH_2OH$ (1,1-Diphenyl-dulcitol) (30%); $CH_3(C_6H_5)_2COH$	*43,42*
Tetraäcetyl-D-galactonic acid γ-lactone (5 g.)	4-$CH_3C_6H_4MgBr$ (14 equiv.)	$(4$-$CH_3C_6H_4)_2C(OH)(CHOH)_4CH_2OH$ (1,1-Di-p-tolyldulcitol) (10–20%); $CH_3(4$-$CH_3C_6H_4)_2COH$	*42*
$C_{15}H_{10}O_2$			
3-Benzylidenephthalide (44.5 g., 0.2 mole)	C_6H_5MgBr (78.5 g. C_6H_5Br)	2,3-Diphenyl-1-indenone (34–40 g., 60–71%)	*9,57*
3-Benzylidenephthalide (30 g.)	$C_6H_5CH_2MgCl$ (24 g. C_7H_7Cl)	2-Phenyl-3-benzyl-1-indenone (26%); 1,1-dibenzyl-3-benzylidenephthalan; 1,3-dibenzylidenephthalan	*56,54*

TABLE VIII-IV (Continued)

Lactone or Lactide	RMgX	Product(s)	Ref.
$C_{15}H_{10}O_2$ (*cont.*)			
3-Benzylidenephthalide (6.5 g.)	2-$CH_3C_6H_4MgBr$ (5 g. C_7H_7Br)	2-Phenyl-3-*o*-tolyl-1-indenone (3.1 g.)	57
3-Benzylidenephthalide (4.15 g.)	1-$C_{10}H_7MgBr$ (5.15 g. $C_{10}H_7Br$)	2-Phenyl-3-α-naphthyl-1-indenone (2.2 g.)	57
3-Phenylcoumarin (40 g.)	C_6H_5MgBr (100 g. C_6H_5Br)	2,3,4-Triphenyl-2-chromanol (70%)	35
3-Phenylcoumarin (25 g.)	1-$C_{10}H_7MgBr$ (14 g. $C_{10}H_7Br$)	2,4-Di-α-naphthyl-3-phenyl-1,4-benzopyran (23 g., 69%)	35
3-Phenyl-2,1-benzopyrone* (23 g.)	$C_6H_5CH_2MgCl$ (16 g. C_7H_7Cl)	1-$C_6H_5COCH_2C_6H_4$-2-$COCH_2C_6H_5$ (18 g.)	58
$C_{15}H_{10}O_3$			
1-Methyl-3-hydroxy-6-dibenzo-[*b*,*d*]pyrone (7 g.)	CH_3MgI (31 g. CH_3I)	1,6,6-Trimethyl-3-hydroxy-6-dibenzo[*b*,*d*]pyran (5.5 g., 75%)	7
$C_{15}H_{12}O_2$			
3-*o*-Tolylphthalide	C_6H_5MgBr (large excess)	2-[*o*-$CH_3C_6H_4CH(OH)$]$C_6H_4C(C_6H_5)_2OH$	25
3-*o*-Tolylphthalide	4-$CH_3C_6H_4MgBr$ (large excess)	2-[*o*-$CH_3C_6H_4CH(OH)$]$C_6H_4C(C_6H_4$-*p*-$CH_3)_2OH$	25
3-*p*-Tolylphthalide (50 g.)	C_6H_5MgBr (8 g. Mg)	1-Phenyl-3-*p*-tolylphthalen-1-ol	25
3-*p*-Tolylphthalide	C_6H_5MgBr (1.5 equiv.)	1-Phenyl-3-*p*-tolylisobenzofuran	25
3-*p*-Tolylphthalide (10.0 g.)	$C_6H_6CH_2MgCl$ (5.3 g. C_7H_7Cl)	1-*p*-Tolyl-3-benzylidenephthalan (50%)	55
3-*p*-Tolylphthalide	4-$CH_3C_6H_4MgBr$	1,3-Di-*p*-tolylphthalan-1-ol; 1,3-di-*p*-tolylisobenzofuran	25
$C_{15}H_{14}O_4$			
2-Acetoxy-7,8,9,10-tetrahydro-6-dibenzo[*b*,*d*]pyrone	CH_3MgI (excess)	2-Hydroxy-6,6-dimethyl-7,8,9,10-tetrahydro-6-dibenzo[*b*,*d*]pyran (60%)	21
3-Acetoxy-7,8,9,10-tetrahydro-6-dibenzo[*b*,*d*]pyrone (28 g.)	CH_3MgI (100 g. CH_3I)	3-Hydroxy-6,6-dimethyl-7,8,9,10-tetrahydro-6-dibenzo[*b*,*d*]pyran (14 g.)	21
7-Methyl-9-acetoxy-2,3-dihydrobenzo[*b*]cyclopenta[*d*]pyran 4-(1*H*)-one	CH_3MgI (excess)	4,4,7-Trimethyl-1,2,3,4-tetrahydrobenzo-[*b*]cyclopenta[*d*]pyran-9-ol	44

* Isobenzophthalide.

TABLE VIII-IV (Continued)

Lactone or Lactide	RMgX	Product(s)	Ref.
$C_{15}H_{16}O_2$			
8,9-Dimethyl-6a,7,10,10a-tetrahydro-6-dibenzo[*b*,*d*]pyrone	CH_3MgI	1,2-Dimethyl-4-(*o*-hydroxyphenyl)-5-(α-hydroxyisopropyl)-1-cyclohexene (85%)	*37*
$C_{15}H_{16}O_3$			
1-Hydroxy-3,9-dimethyl-7,8,9,10-tetrahydro-6-dibenzo[*b*,*d*]pyrone (4.5 g.)	CH_3MgI (12 ml. CH_3I)	1-Hydroxy-3,6,6,9-tetramethyl-7,8,9,10-tetrahydro-6-dibenzo[*b*,*d*]pyran (3.7 g., 77%) (after HBr dehydration)	*2*
$C_{16}H_{16}O_4$			
1-Acetoxy-3-methyl-7,8,9,10-tetrahydro-6-dibenzo[*b*,*d*]pyrone	CH_3MgI (excess)	1-Hydroxy-3,6,6-trimethyl-7,8,9,10-tetrahydro-6-dibenzo[*b*,*d*]pyran (60%)	*21*
2-Acetoxy-9-methyl-7,8,9,10-tetrahydro-6-dibenzo[*b*,*d*]pyrone (5.0 g.)	CH_3MgI (22.5 g. CH_3I)	2-Hydroxy-6,6,9-trimethyl-7,8,9,10-tetrahydro-6-dibenzo[*b*,*d*]pyran (4 g.)	*20*
3-Acetoxy-9-methyl-7,8,9,10-tetrahydro-6-dibenzo[*b*,*d*]pyrone	CH_3MgI (excess)	3-Hydroxy-6,6,9-trimethyl-7,8,9,10-tetrahydro-6-dibenzo[*b*,*d*]pyran	*21*
$C_{16}H_{18}O_3$			
1-Hydroxy-3-ethyl-9-methyl-7,8,9,10-tetrahydro-6-dibenzo[*b*,*d*]pyrone	CH_3MgI (excess)	1-Hydroxy-3-ethyl-6,6,9-trimethyl-7,8,9,10-tetrahydro-6-dibenzo[*b*,*d*]pyran	*63*
$C_{17}H_{18}O_4$			
1-Acetoxy-3,9-dimethyl-7,8,9,10-tetrahydro-6-dibenzo[*b*,*d*]pyrone	CH_3MgI (excess)	1-Hydroxy-3,6,6,9-tetramethyl-7,8,9,10-tetrahydro-6-dibenzo[*b*,*d*]pyran	*21*
1-Acetoxy-3,9-dimethyl-7,8,9,10-tetrahydro-6-dibenzo[*b*,*d*]pyrone	*n*-C_3H_7MgX (excess)	1-Hydroxy-3,9-dimethyl-6,6-di-*n*-propyl-7,8,9,10-tetrahydro-6-dibenzo[*b*,*d*]pyran	*63*

TABLE VIII-IV (Continued)

Lactone or Lactide	RMgX	Product(s)	Ref.
$C_{17}H_{18}O_4$ (*cont.*)			
1-Acetoxy-3,9-dimethyl-7,8,9,10-tetrahydro-6-dibenzo[*b,d*]pyrone	*n*-C_4H_9MgX (excess)	1-Hydroxy-3,9-dimethyl-6,6-di-*n*-butyl-7,8,9,10-tetrahydro-6-dibenzo[*b,d*]pyran	63
$C_{17}H_{20}O_3$			
1-Hydroxy-3-*n*-propyl-9-methyl-7,8,9,10-tetrahydro-6-dibenzo[*b,d*]pyrone	CH_3MgI (excess)	1-Hydroxy-3-*n*-propyl-6,6,9-trimethyl-7,8,9,10-tetrahydro-6-dibenzo[*b,d*]pyran (85.6%)	6,63
$C_{17}H_{20}O_4$			
3-*n*-Butyl-4,7-dimethyl-5-acetoxycoumarin	CH_3MgI	2,2,4,7-Tetramethyl-3-*n*-butyl-5-hydroxy-1,2-benzopyran	63
4-Methyl-5-acetoxy-7-*n*-amylcoumarin	CH_3MgI (excess)	2,2,4-Trimethyl-5-hydroxy-7-*n*-amyl-1,2-benzopyran	44
$C_{18}H_{12}O_2$			
3-α-Naphthylphthalide (5.0 g.)	1-$C_{10}H_7MgBr$ (8.3 g. $C_{10}H_7Br$)	1,3-Di-α-naphthylisobenzofuran (3.5 g., 46%)	46
$C_{18}H_{20}O_3N$			
3-Methyl-8-isoamyl-10-hydroxy-1,2,3,4-tetrahydropyridino-[3,4-*c*]benzo[*e*]pyran-5-one (5 g.)	CH_3MgI (7.5 ml. CH_3I)	3,5,5-Trimethyl-8-isoamyl-10-hydroxy-1,2,3,4-tetrahydropyridino[3,4-*c*]benzo[*e*]pyran	10
$C_{18}H_{22}O_3$			
1-Hydroxy-3-*n*-amyl-7,8,9,10-tetrahydro-6-dibenzo[*b,d*]pyrone	CH_3MgI (excess)	1-Hydroxy-3-*n*-amyl-6,6-dimethyl-7,8,9,10-tetrahydro-6-dibenzo[*b,d*]pyran (71.5)	8
1-Hydroxy-3-*n*-butyl-9-methyl-7,8,9,10-tetrahydro-6-dibenzo[*b,d*]pyrone	CH_3MgI (excess)	1-Hydroxy-3-*n*-butyl-6,6,9-trimethyl-7,8,9,10-tetrahydro-6-dibenzo[*b,d*]pyran (80%)	8,63

TABLE VIII-IV (Continued)

Lactone or Lactide	RMgX	Product(s)	Ref.
$C_{19}H_{14}O_2$			
3-*o*-Tolyl-1,3-naphtho[1.8-*cd*]-pyrone (4.0 g.)	$C_6H_5CH_2MgCl$ (2.3 g. C_7H_7Cl)	1-Benzylidene-3-*o*-tolyl-1,3-naphtho[1.8-*cd*]-pyran (50%)	55
$C_{19}H_{20}O_3$			
1-Hydroxy-3-*n*-amyl-9-methyl-6-dibenzo[*b,d*]pyrone (3.6 g.)	CH_3MgI (8.0 ml. CH_3I)	1-Hydroxy-3-*n*-amyl-6,6,9-trimethyl-6-dibenzo[*b,d*]pyran (Cannabinol) (2.8 g., 75%) (after $MgSO_4$ dehydration)	3
1-Hydroxy-3-diethylmethyl-9-methyl-6-dibenzo[*b,d*]pyrone	CH_3MgI (excess)	1-Hydroxy-3-diethylmethyl-6,6,9-trimethyl-6-dibenzo[*b,d*]pyran (after $MgSO_4$ dehydration)	3
1-*n*-Amyl-3-hydroxy-9-methyl-6-dibenzo[*b,d*]pyrone (8.3 g.)	CH_3MgI (49.0 g. CH_3I)	1-*n*-Amyl-3-hydroxy-6,6,9-trimethyl-6-dibenzo[*b,d*]pyran	7
2-*n*-Amyl-3-hydroxy-9-methyl-6-dibenzo[*b,d*]pyrone (6.9 g.)	CH_3MgI (24.0 ml. CH_3I)	2-*n*-Amyl-3-hydroxy-6,6,9-trimethyl-6-dibenzo[*b,d*]pyran (6.0 g., 85%) (after $MgSO_4$ dehydration)	4
3-Hydroxy-4-*n*-amyl-9-methyl-6-dibenzo[*b,d*]pyrone (1.7 g.)	CH_3MgI (9.8 g. CH_3I)	3-Hydroxy-4-*n*-amyl-6,6,9-trimethyl-6-dibenzo[*b,d*]pyran (1.3 g.) (after $MgSO_4$ dehydration)	4
$C_{19}H_{22}O_4$			
7-*n*-Amyl-9-acetoxy-2,3-dihydrobenzo[*b*]cyclopenta[*d*]pyran-4(1*H*)-one	CH_3MgI (excess)	4,4-Dimethyl-7-*n*-amyl-9-hydroxy-1,2,3,4-tetrahydrobenzo[*b*]cyclopenta[*d*]pyran	44
$C_{19}H_{24}O_3$			
1-Hydroxy-3-*n*-amyl-8-methyl-7,8,9,10-tetrahydro-6-dibenzo[*b,d*]pyrone	CH_3MgI (excess)	1-Hydroxy-3-*n*-amyl-6,6,9-trimethyl-7,8,9,10-tetrahydro-6-dibenzo[*b,d*]pyran (80%)	8,63

TABLE VIII-IV (Continued)

Lactone or Lactide	RMgX	Product(s)	Ref.
$C_{19}H_{24}O_3$ (*cont.*)			
DL-1-Hydroxy-3-*n*-amyl-9-methyl-7,8,9,10-tetrahydro-6-dibenzo[*b,d*]pyrone* (9 g.)	CH_3MgI (22.5 g. CH_3I)	DL-1-Hydroxy-3-*n*-amyl-6,6,9-trimethyl-7,8,9,10-tetrahydro-6-dibenzo[*b,d*]pyran (Tetrahydrocannabinol) (7.3 g., 78%)	2
1-Hydroxy-3-*n*-amyl-9-methyl-7,8,9,10-tetrahydro-6-dibenzo[*b,d*]pyrone	C_2H_5MgBr (excess)	1-Hydroxy-3-*n*-amyl-6,6-diethyl-9-methyl-7,8,9,10-tetrahydro-6-dibenzo[*b,d*]pyran (77%)	8
1-Hydroxy-3-*n*-amyl-9-methyl-7,8,9,10-tetrahydro-6-dibenzo[*b,d*]pyrone	*n*-C_3H_7MgBr (excess)	1-Hydroxy-3-*n*-amyl-6,6-di-*n*-propyl-9-methyl-7,8,9,10-tetrahydro-6-dibenzo[*b,d*]pyran (77.5%)	8
1-Hydroxy-3-*n*-amyl-10-methyl-7,8,9,10-tetrahydro-6-dibenzo[*b,d*]pyrone	CH_3MgI (excess)	1-Hydroxy-3-*n*-amyl-6,6,10-trimethyl-7,8,9,10-tetrahydro-6-dibenzo[*b,d*]pyran (71%)	8,63
1-Hydroxy-3-*i*-amyl-9-methyl-7,8,9,10-tetrahydro-6-dibenzo[*b,d*]pyrone	CH_3MgI (excess)	1-Hydroxy-3-*i*-amyl-6,6,9-trimethyl-7,8,9,10-tetrahydro-6-dibenzo[*b,d*]pyran	63
1-Hydroxy-3-(1-methylbutyl)-9-methyl-7,8,9,10-tetrahydro-6-dibenzo[*b,d*]pyrone	CH_3MgI (12 equiv.)	1-Hydroxy-3-(1-methylbutyl)-6,6,9-trimethyl-7,8,9,10-tetrahydro-6-dibenzo[*b,d*]pyran (73%)	5
$C_{20}H_{14}O_2$			
3,3-Diphenylphthalide† (20 g.)	C_6H_5MgBr (30 g. C_6H_5Br)	1,2-[$HO(C_6H_5)_2C]_2C_6H_4$ (*ca.* 18 g.)	45,64
3,3-Diphenylphthalide†	4-$CH_3C_6H_4MgBr$	1-*p*-Tolyl-3,3-diphenylphthalan-1-ol	25

* The D and L compounds were treated separately in a similar manner by Adams, Smith, and Loewe, *J. Am. Chem. Soc.*, 64, 2087-9 (1942), with similar results.

† Phthalophenone.

TABLE VIII-IV (Continued)

Lactone or Lactide	RMgX	Product(s)	Ref.
$C_{20}H_{22}O_3$			
1-Methoxy-4-*n*-amyl-9-methyl-6-dibenzo[*b,d*]pyrone (2.1 g.)	CH_3MgI (8.0 ml. CH_3I)	1-Methoxy-4-*n*-amyl-6,6,9-trimethyl-6-dibenzo[*b,d*]pyran (1.85 g., 84%) (after $MgSO_4$ dehydration)	*1*
1-Methoxy-4-*n*-amyl-9-methyl-6-dibenzo[*b,d*]pyrone (1.36 g.)	CH_3MgI (2.60 ml. CH_3I)	2-(α-Methyl-α-hydroxyethyl)-5-methyl-2′-hydroxy-3′-*n*-amyl-6′-methoxybiphenyl (1.2 g., 80%)	*1*
$C_{20}H_{24}O_4$			
1-Acetoxy-3-*n*-amyl-7,8,9,10-tetrahydro-6-dibenzo[*b,d*]pyrone	CH_3MgI (excess)	1-Hydroxy-3-*n*-amyl-6,6-dimethyl-7,8,9,10-tetrahydro-6-dibenzo[*b,d*]pyran	*44*
$C_{20}H_{26}O_3$			
1-Hydroxy-3-*n*-hexyl-9-methyl-7,8,9,10-tetrahydro-6-dibenzo[*b,d*]pyrone	CH_3MgI (excess)	1-Hydroxy-3-*n*-hexyl-6,6,9-trimethyl-7,8,9,10-tetrahydro-6-dibenzo[*b,d*]pyran (80.7%)	*6,63*
1-Hydroxy-3-*i*-hexyl-9-methyl-7,8,9,10-tetrahydro-6-dibenzo[*b,d*]pyrone	CH_3MgI (excess)	1-Hydroxy-3-*i*-hexyl-6,6,9-trimethyl-7,8,9,10-tetrahydro[*b,d*]pyran	*63*
1-Hydroxy-3-(1-methylpentyl)-9-methyl-7,8,9,10-tetrahydro-6-dibenzo[*b,d*]pyrone	CH_3MgI (12 equiv.)	1-Hydroxy-3-(1-methylpentyl)-6,6,9-trimethyl-7,8,9,10-tetrahydro-6-dibenzo[*b,d*]pyran (70%)	*5*
1-Hydroxy-3-(1-ethylbutyl)-9-methyl-7,8,9,10-tetrahydro-6-dibenzo[*b,d*]pyrone	CH_3MgI (12 equiv.)	1-Hydroxy-3-(1-ethylbutyl)-6,6,9-trimethyl-7,8,9,10-tetrahydro-6-dibenzo[*b,d*]pyran (76%)	*5*
$C_{21}H_{26}O_4$			
1-Acetoxy-3-*n*-amyl-9-methyl-7,8,9,10-tetrahydro-6-dibenzo[*b,d*]pyrone	CH_3MgI (excess)	1-Hydroxy-3-*n*-amyl-6,6,9-trimethyl-7,8,9,10-tetrahydro-6-dibenzo[*b,d*]pyran (Tetrahydrocannabinol)	*21*

TABLE VIII-IV (Continued)

Lactone or Lactide	RMgX	Product(s)	Ref.
$C_{21}H_{26}O_4$ (*cont.*)			
1-Acetoxy-3-*n*-amyl-9-methyl-7,8,9,10-tetrahydro-6-dibenzo[*b,d*]pyrone	C_2H_5MgBr (excess)	1-Hydroxy-3-*n*-amyl-6,6-diethyl-9-methyl-7,8,9,10-tetrahydro-6-dibenzo[*b,d*]pyran	63
2-Acetoxy-3-*n*-amyl-9-methyl-7,8,9,10-tetrahydro-6-dibenzo[*b,d*]pyrone (0.25 g.)	CH_3MgI (0.25 g. Mg)	2-Hydroxy-3-*n*-amyl-6,6,9-trimethyl-7,8,9,10-tetrahydro-6-dibenzo[*b,d*]pyran	44
2-Acetoxy-5-*n*-amyl-9-methyl-7,8,9,10-tetrahydro-6-dibenzo[*b,d*]pyrone	CH_3MgI (excess)	2-Hydroxy-5-*n*-amyl-6,6,9-trimethyl-7,8,9,10-tetrahydro-6-dibenzo[*b,d*]pyran	20
$C_{21}H_{28}O_3$			
1-Hydroxy-3-*n*-heptyl-9-methyl-7,8,9,10-tetrahydro-6-dibenzo[*b,d*]pyrone	CH_3MgI (excess)	1-Hydroxy-3-*n*-heptyl-6,6,9-trimethyl-7,8,9,10-tetrahydro-6-dibenzo[*b,d*]pyran (70%)	6,63
1-Hydroxy-3-(1-methylhexyl)-9-methyl-7,8,9,10-tetrahydro-6-dibenzo[*b,d*]pyrone	CH_3MgI (12 equiv.)	1-Hydroxy-3-(1-methylhexyl)-6,6,9-trimethyl-7,8,9,10-tetrahydro-6-dibenzo[*b,d*]pyran (74%)	5
$C_{21}H_{28}O_4$			
3-*n*-Butyl-4-methyl-5-acetoxy-7-*n*-amylcoumarin	CH_3MgI	2,2,4-Trimethyl-3-*n*-butyl-5-hydroxy-7-*n*-amyl-1,2-benzopyran	63
$C_{22}H_{14}O_2$			
3-α-Naphthyl-1,3-naphtho-[1.8-*cd*]pyrone	$C_6H_5CH_2MgCl$ (2.3 g. C_7H_7Cl)	1-Benzylidene-3-α-naphthyl-1,3-naphtho-[1.8-*cd*]pyran (60%)	55
$C_{22}H_{30}O_3$			
1-Hydroxy-3-*n*-octyl-9-methyl-7,8,9,10-tetrahydro-6-dibenzo[*b,d*]pyrone	CH_3MgI (excess)	1-Hydroxy-3-*n*-octyl-6,6,9-trimethyl-7,8,9,10-tetrahydro-6-dibenzo[*b,d*]pyran (93.2%)	6

TABLE VIII-IV (Continued)

Lactone or Lactide	RMgX	Product(s)	Ref.
$C_{22}H_{30}O_3$ *(cont.)*			
1-Hydroxy-3-(1-methylheptyl)-9-methyl-7,8,9,10-tetrahydro-6-dibenzo[*b,d*]pyrone	CH_3MgI (12 equiv.)	1-Hydroxy-3-(1-methylheptyl)-6,6,9-trimethyl-7,8,9,10-tetrahydro-6-dibenzo[*b,d*]pyran (56%)	*5*
1-Hydroxy-3-(1-*n*-propylpentyl)-9-methyl-7,8,9,10-tetrahydro-6-dibenzo[*b,d*]pyrone	CH_3MgI (12 equiv.)	1-Hydroxy-3-(1-*n*-propylpentyl)-6,6,9-trimethyl-7,8,9,10-tetrahydro-6-dibenzo[*b,d*]pyran (60%)	*5*
$C_{24}H_{16}O_2$			
3,3-Diphenyl-1,3-naphtho-[1.8-*cd*]pyrone	C_2H_5MgBr (2-fold excess)	1-Ethyl-3,3-diphenyl-1,3-naphtho[1.8-*cd*]pyran-1-ol	*19*
3,3-Diphenyl-1,3-naphtho-[1.8-*cd*]pyrone (10 g.)	*i*-C_3H_7MgBr (2-fold excess)	1-Isopropyl-3,3-diphenyl-1,3-naphtho-[1.8-*cd*]pyran-1-ol	*19*
3,3-Diphenyl-1,3-naphtho-[1.8-*cd*]pyrone	*n*-C_4H_9MgBr (2-fold excess)	1-*n*-Butyl-3,3-diphenyl-1,3-naphtho-[1.8-*cd*]pyran-1-ol	*19*
3,3-Diphenyl-1,3-naphtho-[1.8-*cd*]pyrone	*s*-C_4H_9MgBr (2-fold excess)	1-*s*-Butyl-3,3-diphenyl-1,3-naphtho-[1.8-*cd*]pyran-1-ol	*19*
$C_{26}H_{18}O_2$			
7,7-Diphenyldiphenide	C_6H_5MgBr	5-Benzoyl-9,9-diphenylfluorene	*52*
$C_{26}H_{26}O_3$			
1-α-Toloxy-2-*n*-amyl-9-methyl-6-dibenzo[*b,d*]pyrone (1.5 g.)	CH_3MgI (6.0 ml. CH_3I)	2-(α-Methyl-α-hydroxyethyl)-5-methyl-2′-hydroxy-5′-*n*-amyl-6′-α-toloxybiphenyl (1.2 g., 74%)	*1*
1-α-Toloxy-4-*n*-amyl-9-methyl-6-dibenzo[*b,d*]pyrone (1 g.)	CH_3MgI (3 ml. CH_3I)	1-α-Toloxy-4-*n*-amyl-6,6,9-trimethyl-6-dibenzo[*b,d*]pyran (0.9 g., 85%) (after $MgSO_4$ dehydration)	*1*

TABLE VIII-IV (Continued)

Lactone or Lactide	RMgX	Product(s)	Ref.
$C_{26}H_{26}O_3$ (*cont.*)			
1-α-Toloxy-4-*n*-amyl-9-methyl-6-dibenzo[*b*,*d*]pyrone	CH_3MgI	2-(α-Methyl-α-hydroxyethyl)-5-methyl-2′-hydroxy-3′-*n*-amyl-6′-α-toloxybiphenyl	*1*
$C_{26}H_{40}O_4$			
3(β)-Acetoxy-17-hydroxy-allocholanic acid lactone-(24→17)	CH_3MgI	3(β),17,24-Trihydroxy-24,24-dimethyl-allocholane	*12*

REFERENCES FOR TABLE VIII-IV

(1) Adams and Baker, *J. Am. Chem. Soc.*, *62*, 2208–15 (1940).
(2) Adams and Baker, *J. Am. Chem. Soc.*, *62*, 2405–8 (1940).
(3) Adams, Baker, and Wearn, *J. Am. Chem. Soc.*, *62*, 2204–7 (1940).
(4) Adams, Cain, and Baker, *J. Am. Chem. Soc.*, *62*, 2201–4 (1940).
(5) Adams, Chen, and Loewe, *J. Am. Chem. Soc.*, *67*, 1534–7 (1945).
(6) Adams, Loewe, Jelinek, and Wolff, *J. Am. Chem. Soc.*, *63*, 1971–3 (1941).
(7) Adams, Pease, Clark, and Baker, *J. Am. Chem. Soc.*, *62*, 2197–200 (1940).
(8) Adams, Smith, and Loewe, *J. Am. Chem. Soc.*, *63*, 1973–6 (1941).
(9) Allen, Gates, and Van Allan, *Organic Syntheses*, *27*, 31–2 (1947).
(10) Anker and Cook, *J. Chem. Soc.*, *1946*, 58–60.
(11) Barnett, Cook, and Nixon, *J. Chem. Soc.*, *1927*, 504–12.
(12) Billeter and Miescher, *Helv. Chim. Acta*, *32*, 564–73 (1949).
(13) Decker and Felser, *Ber.*, *41*, 3755–7 (1908).
(14) Decker and von Fellenberg, *Ann.*, *356*, 281–342 (1907).
(15) Freudenberg, Todd, and Seidler, *Ann.*, *501*, 199–219 (1933).
(16) Fuson, Armstrong, Fisher, Rabjohn, Ullyot, and Wallace, *J. Am. Chem. Soc.*, *68*, 343 (1946).
(17) Fuson and Rachlin, *J. Am. Chem. Soc.*, *64*, 1567–71 (1942).
(18) Geissman, *J. Am. Chem. Soc.*, *62*, 1363–7 (1940).
(19) Geissman and Morris, *J. Am. Chem. Soc.*, *63*, 1111–4 (1941).
(20) Ghosh, Pascal, and Todd, *J. Chem. Soc.*, *1940*, 1118–21.
(21) Ghosh, Todd, and Wilkinson, *J. Chem. Soc.*, *1940*, 1121–5.
(22) Gresham, Jansen, Shaver, and Bankert, *J. Am. Chem. Soc.*, *71*, 2807–8 (1949).
(23) Guyot and Catel, *Compt. rend.*, *140*, 1348–50 (1905); *Chem. Zentr.*, *1905,II*, 137.
(24) Guyot and Catel, *Bull. soc. chim.*, [3], *35*, 1124–35 (1906).
(25) Guyot and Vallette, *Ann. chim.*, [8], *23*, 363–97 (1911).
(26) Heilbron and Hill, *J. Chem. Soc.*, *1927*, 2005–13.
(27) Heilbron and Zaki, *J. Chem. Soc.*, *1926*, 1902–6.
(28) Henry, *Compt. rend.*, *143*, 1221–5 (1906); *Chem. Zentr.*, *1907,I*, 708.
(29) Houben, *Ber.*, *37*, 489–502 (1904).
(30) Kohn, *Monatsh.*, *34*, 1729–40 (1913).
(31) Kohn and Ostersetzer, *Monatsh.*, *37*, 37–51 (1916).
(32) Losanitsch, *Compt. rend.*, *153*, 390–2 (1911); *Chem. Zentr.*, *1911,II*, 1118.
(33) Lothrop and Goodwin, *J. Am. Chem. Soc.*, *65*, 363–7 (1943).
(34) Löwenbein, Pongrácz, and Spiess, *Ber.*, *57B*, 1517–26 (1924).
(35) Löwenbein and Rosenbaum, *Ann.*, *448*, 223–48 (1926).
(36) Ludwig, *Ber.*, *40*, 3060–5 (1907).
(37) McPhee and Ball, *J. Am. Chem. Soc.*, *66*, 1636–40 (1944).
(38) Mermod and Simonis, *Ber.*, *41*, 982–5 (1908).
(39) Neuberg and Ohle, *Biochem. Z.*, *127*, 327–39 (1922); *Chem. Zentr.*, *1922,I*, 1333.
(40) Paal and Hörnstein, *Ber.*, *39*, 1361–4 (1906).
(41) Paal and Kinscher, *Ber.*, *44*, 1343–55 (1911).
(42) Paal, Küster, and Roth, *Ber.*, *49*, 1583–97 (1916).
(43) Paal and Weidenkaff, *Ber.*, *39*, 2827–33 (1906).
(44) Russell, Todd, Wilkinson, Macdonald, and Wolfe, *J. Chem. Soc.*, *1941*, 169–72.
(45) Schlenk and Brauns, *Ber.*, *48* 716–28 (1915).
(46) Seer and Dischendorfer, *Monatsh.*, *34*, 1493–502 (1914).
(47) Seidel, *Ber.*, *61B*, 2267–76 (1928).
(48) Shriner and Sharp, *J. Org. Chem.*, *4*, 575–82 (1939).

(49) Smith and Ruoff, *J. Am. Chem. Soc.*, *62*, 145–8 (1940).
(50) Smith, Ungnade, Hoehn, and Wawzonek, *J. Org. Chem.*, *4*, 304–10 (1939).
(51) Smith, Ungnade, and Prichard, *J. Org. Chem.*, *4*, 358–62 (1939).
(52) Ssergejew, *J. Russ. Phys.-Chem. Soc.*, *61*, 1421–49 (1929); *Chem. Zentr.*, *1930,II*, 391.
(53) Stiller, Kereszetesy, and Finkelstein, *J. Am. Chem. Soc.*, *62*, 1779–84 (1940).
(54) Weiss and Alberti, *Monatsh.*, *59*, 220–7 (1932).
(55) Weiss and Fastmann, *Monatsh.*, *47*, 727–32 (1926).
(56) Weiss, Grobstein, and Sauermann, *Ber.*, *59B*, 301–6 (1926).
(57) Weiss and Sauermann, *Ber.*, *58B*, 2736–40 (1925).
(58) Weiss and Sonnenschein, *Ber.*, *58B*, 1043–7 (1925).
(59) Weizmann and Bergmann, *J. Am. Chem. Soc.*, *60*, 2647–50 (1938).
(60) Willstätter and Schmidt, *Ber.*, *57B*, 1945–50 (1924).
(61) Willstätter, Zechmeister, and Kindler, *Ber.*, *57B*, 1938–44 (1924).
(62) John, Günther, and Schmeil, *Ber.*, *71B*, 2637–49 (1938).
(63) Russell, Todd, Wilkinson, Macdonald, and Woolfe, *J. Chem. Soc.*, *1941*, 826–9.
(64) Guyot and Catel, *Bull. soc. chim.*, [3], *35*, 551–62 (1906).
(65) Guyot and Catel, *Bull. soc. chim.*, [3], *35*, 567–71 (1906).
(66) Shriner, Johnston, and Kaslow, *J. Org. Chem.*, *14*, 204–9 (1949).

CHAPTER IX

Reactions of Grignard Reagents with Carbonyl Halides

SPECULATIONS ON THE ("NORMAL") REACTION MECHANISM

The reaction of an acid chloride of the type RCOCl with two equivalents of a Grignard reagent to yield a tertiary alcohol was first reported by Tissier and Grignard,[1] who proposed a two-stage reaction mechanism analogous to that previously suggested by Grignard[2] for the similar reaction of a carboxylic ester with a Grignard reagent (see Chapter VIII).

$$\mathrm{RCOCl + R'MgX \rightarrow RC(OMgX)(R')(Cl)}$$

$$\mathrm{RC(OMgX)(R')(Cl) + R'MgX \rightarrow RC(OMgX)(R')(R') + MgXCl}$$

Courtot[3] has suggested the alternatives:

$$\mathrm{RCOCl + R'MgX \rightarrow RCOR' + MgXCl}$$

or

$$\mathrm{RCOCl + R'MgX \rightarrow RC(OMgX)(R')(Cl) \xrightarrow{H_2O} RC(OH)(R')(Cl) + MgXOH}$$

$$\mathrm{\rightarrow RCOR' + HCl + MgXOH}$$

These, of course, do not describe exhaustively the reaction mechanism possibilities. Either of Courtot's alternatives might involve the initial formation of a Werner complex, presumably through the carbonyl oxygen atom, but conceivably, in the first case at least, through the acyl halogen atom. A Werner complex of either kind might then rearrange to form ketone and magnesium halide.

$$\mathrm{(X)(R)C{=}O:Mg(X')(R') \rightarrow (R')(R)C{=}O:Mg(X')(X)}$$

$$\mathrm{(O{=})(R)C{-}X:Mg(X')(R') \rightarrow (R')(R)C{=}O:Mg(X')(X)}$$

---

[1]Tissier and Grignard, *Compt. rend.*, *132*, 683-5 (1901); *J. Chem. Soc.*, *80,I*, 316 (1901); *Chem. Zentr.*, *1901,I*, 930.

[2]Grignard, *Compt. rend.*, *132*, 336-8 (1901); *J. Chem. Soc.*, *80,I*, 250(1901); *Ann. chim.*, [7], *24*, 433-90 (1901).

[3]Courtot, "Le magnesium en chimie organique," Nancy, *1926*, p. 191.

In either case the reaction would be second-order, and either the first step (complex formation) or the second step (rearrangement) might be rate-determining.

Courtot's second alternative would be most likely to take place through Werner complex formation at the carbonyl oxygen atom and subsequent rearrangement.

$$\begin{matrix} X \\ R \end{matrix}\!\!>\!C{=}O:Mg\!<\!\!\begin{matrix} X' \\ R' \end{matrix} \rightarrow X{-}\overset{\displaystyle R}{\underset{\displaystyle R'}{C}}{-}OMgX'$$

In this case also the reaction would be second-order, and either complex formation or complex rearrangement might be the rate-determining step.

It may be noted in passing that the persistence of a derivative of the type postulated seems highly improbable. Even if a rearrangement of this type took place in preference to one of the type previously discussed, it would almost certainly be followed by further rearrangement (either monomolecular or bimolecular to form a ketone-magnesium halide complex.

There remains for consideration the possibility that the reaction is in fact third-order, requiring for completion the reaction of a second molecule of Grignard reagent with a Werner or some other type of intermediate complex.

$$RCOX{\cdot}R'MgX' + R'MgX' \rightarrow RR'CO{\cdot}MgXX' + R'MgX'$$

Unfortunately, the rapidity with which aryl halides and Grignard reagents interact discourages attempts at investigation of the reaction kinetics by the classical experimental methods. Moreover, the probability of further reaction of the initial product with excess Grignard reagent eliminates the possibility of applying one of the routine checks on reaction order (except in the cases of "hindered" acyl halides, which are not necessarily typical). However, the fact that ketone may be formed by the slow addition of Grignard reagent solution to an excess of acyl halide solution suggests that the reaction is not third-order in the sense here implied.

Commenting upon the very slow reaction between methylmagnesium chloride and the supposedly "hindered" 2,4,6-trichlorobenzoyl chloride, Fuson[4] says: "This reaction between 2,4,6-trichlorobenzoyl chloride and methylmagnesium chloride is interesting because it shows the effect of steric hindrance on a reaction which may be either additive or metathetical. In view of the fact that reactions of the former type are generally much more greatly affected by steric factors than are those known to be of the latter type, the results here reported suggest that the primary reaction between RMgX and an acid chloride is one of addition."

---

[4]Fuson, Bertetti, and Ross, *J. Am. Chem. Soc.*, *54*, 4380–3 (f'tnote, p. 4381) (1932).

If by a "metathetical"* reaction is meant one of the type,

$$RCO^{+} + Cl^{-} + R^{-} + MgX^{+} \rightarrow RCOR' + Cl^{-} + MgX^{+}$$

the improbability of such a reaction in a medium of the low dielectric constant of ether is obvious. If anything else is meant the distinction between a metathetical reaction and an additive reaction becomes rather equivocal.

It is doubtful that the formation of a Werner complex of either of the types here suggested would be greatly inhibited sterically by the *ortho* chlorine atoms of 2,4,6-trichlorobenzoyl chloride. However, the subsequent rearrangement, involving addition of the Grignard reagent organic ion to the carbonyl carbon atom would be subject to steric hindrance. If the 2,4,6-trichlorobenzoyl chloride reaction may be regarded as typical it would seem that rearrangement rather than complex formation must be the rate-determining step. According to Swain[5] this is probably the case in nitrile reactions (see section on Reaction Mechanism in Chapter X.)

By means of competitive reactions in the presence of acetophenone and benzophenone, Entemann and Johnson[6] have determined that the order of reactivity toward phenylmagnesium bromide of the benzoyl halides is the reverse of that encountered in hydrolytic,[7] alcoholytic,[8] phenolytic,[9] and Friedel-Crafts[10] reactions. That is, the fluoride is more reactive than the chloride, which is, in turn, more reactive than the bromide.

Without supporting argument or elucidative discussion, they state: "The order of activity of the three acid halides, benzoyl fluoride, chloride, and bromide, is of particular interest because of its bearing upon the mechanism of the action of Grignard reagents upon acid derivatives. Either one of two reactions may occur in the initial stage of the reaction: addition to the carbonyl group (I) or direct replacement of the halogen atom (II). If the reaction follows the second mechanism, one would expect the acid fluoride to be the least reactive of the halides. Since the acid fluoride is actually found to be the most reactive, it is obvious that the reaction occurs through addition to the carbonyl group and not through a metathetical reaction of the halogen atom."

This line of reasoning depends upon a gratuitous assumption concerning the mechanism of the rate-determining step of the "metathetical" reaction. An *ion-ion* exchange might be expected to give rise to the

---

*Actually, the term metathetical is primarily stoichiometric in significance. It can be regarded as having mechanistic connotations only in so far as it eliminates certain reaction mechanisms from consideration.

[5]Swain, *J. Am. Chem. Soc.*, *69*, 2306–9 (1947).

[6]Entemann and Johnson, *J. Am. Chem. Soc.*, *55*, 2900–3 (1933).

[7]Staudinger and Anthes, *Ber.*, *46*, 1417–26 (1913); Karve and Dole, *J. Univ. Bombay*, 7, Pt. 3, 108–25 (1938); *Chem. Abstr.*, *33*, 5269 (1939).

[8]Dann, Davies, Hambly, Paul, and Semmens, *J. Chem. Soc.*, *1933*, 15–21; Leimu, *Ber.*, *70B*, 1040–53 (1937).

[9]Bernoulli and St. Goar, *Helv. Chim. Acta*, 9, 730–65 (1926).

[10]Calloway, *J. Am. Chem. Soc.*, *59*, 1474–9 (1937).

halide reactivity order experimentally observed. For reasons already suggested monomolecular or solvolytic ionization of the reactants as a prelude to reaction appears impossible. Ionic exchange must therefore be preceded by some sort of addition-complex formation, though *not necessarily* by carbonyl double-bond addition. It may or may not be significant in this connection that the order of reactivity of acyl halides toward the organozinc, -cadmium, and -mercury compounds (which do not undergo carbonyl double bond addition, or which do so very slowly indeed) is said to be the reverse of that toward Grignard reagents.[11] Even mercuric chloride is known to form complexes with carbonyl compounds.[12]

On the whole it appears most probable that the "normal" reaction includes (1) acyl halide-Grignard reagent Werner complex formation and (2) a rate-determining *ionic* rearrangement of the complex, and that the reaction product is a ketone-magnesium halide Werner complex.

On this basis it may be predicted that, when investigated, the order of reactivity of the acyl halides in the "abnormal" coupling reaction will be found to be the reverse of that established for the "normal" ketone-formation reaction.

PREPARATION OF KETONES BY GRIGNARD-HALIDE INTERACTION

Grignard's two-stage reaction formulation, together with the reported isolation of ketones as products of many carbonyl chloride-Grignard reagent interactions (see Table IX-II), suggests that the first stage of the reaction might be employed as a method of ketone preparation. For that purpose low operating temperatures, reverse addition (*i.e.,* addition of the Grignard reagent to the acid chloride or its solution), and the use of an excess of the acid chloride are obviously indicated. The reaction has indeed been so employed by, among others: Gilman *et al.*,[13] Helferich and Malkomes,[14] Darzens and Rost,[15] Acree,[16] Schmidlin,[17] Karrer,[18] and Whitmore and Badertscher[19] (see Table IX-II).

Often, however, the reactivity differential between the acid chloride chlorine and the ketone carbonyl group either favors the carbonyl group or is too small to make this a satisfactory method of ketone preparation. Even in favorable cases and under optimum experimental conditions the yields are usually indifferent (*i.e.,* of the order of 40–60 percent).

---

[11] Gilman, "Organic Chemistry," 2nd ed., Chapter 5, pp. 501–2, *1943*.

[12] See, *e.g.:* Marini-Bettolo and Paolini, *Gazz. chim. ital.*, *75*, 78–86 (1945); *Chem. Abstr.*, *41*, 3444 (1947).

[13] Gilman, Fothergill, and Parker, *Rec. trav. chim.*, *48*, 748–51 (1929).

[14] Helferich and Malkomes, *Ber.*, *55B*, 702–8 (1922).

[15] Darzens and Rost, *Compt. rend.*, *153*, 772–5 (1911); *Chem. Zentr.*, *1911,II*, 1860.

[16] Acree, *Ber.*, *37*, 625–8 (1904).

[15] Schmidlin and Massini, *Ber.*, *42*, 2377–92 (1909); Schmidlin, *ibid.*, *43*, 1137–44 (1910).

[18] Karrer, *Ber.*, *50*, 1499–508 (1917).

[19] Whitmore and Badertscher, *J. Am. Chem. Soc.*, *55*, 1559–67 (1933).

As good, or better, yields might reasonably be expected in the special cases in which the intermediate ketone is both readily enolizable and relatively inert toward enolate addition. The reaction of phenylmesitylacetyl chloride with mesitylmagnesium bromide, reported by Fuson *et al.*,[20] probably represents such a case. These authors, using equimolecular quantities of acid chloride and Grignard reagent, and employing reverse addition, reported a 34 percent yield of ketone, but with recovery of 27.5 percent acid chloride (as the acid). Paradoxically, the normal order of addition of acid chloride to an *excess* of Grignard reagent (to supply the loss through enolization) should improve the yield of ketone. Upon slow addition of 2,4,6-tribromobenzoyl chloride to 2.2 equivalents of methylmagnesium iodide,* Fuson[21] obtained a 46 percent yield of the acetophenone derivative.

It may be noted in passing that, for reasons not altogether obvious, the pyrryl and indolyl Grignard reagents appear to have a tendency to terminate reaction with acyl halides (as with esters, *q.v.*) at the first stage, forming ketones.

When applicable, however, the organozinc halides or the diorganocadmium compounds give superior results.

KETONE PREPARATION WITH THE AID OF ZINC AND CADMIUM SALTS

Although this topic does not fall strictly within the announced scope of the present work, the preparations concerned are (from the standpoint of procedure) essentially Grignard preparations,† and they have now been shown to constitute so useful a supplement to the ordinary Grignard reactions that they are included for the convenience of the reader.

The use of organocadmium compounds for the preparation of ketones from acid chlorides was first recommended by Gilman and Nelson.[22] Optimum experimental conditions have been investigated by Cason,[23] who has also reviewed the field.[24]

The advantages claimed for the use of organocadmium compounds are: that they are readily prepared from Grignard reagents and the relatively economical, nonhygroscopic cadmium chloride; that the preparation and subsequent reaction can be carried out in ether solution (although ben-

---

[20]Fuson, Armstrong, Kneisley and Shenk, *J. Am. Chem. Soc.*, *66*, 1414–6 (1944).

*For this purpose the bromide would be preferable because it has little or no "coupling" action.

[21]Fuson, Van Campen, and Wolf, *J. Am. Chem. Soc.*, *60*, 2269–72 (1938).

†Organocadmium compounds may be prepared from organolithium compounds as well as from Grignard reagents, but there is no advantage to be derived from the use of the lithium compounds except in the relatively rare cases in which the Grignard reagent can be prepared only with great difficulty or in very poor yield.

[22]Gilman and Nelson, *Rec. trav. chim.*, *55*, 518–30 (1936).

[23]Cason, *J. Am. Chem. Soc.*, *68*, 2078–81 (1946).

[24]Cason, *Chem. Revs.*, *40*, 15–32 (1947).

zene, or toluene, is the preferred solvent for acid chloride reactions); that, although they react readily with acid chlorides and acid anhydrides, they are very unreactive toward other functional groups (including the carbonyl) that react more or less readily with Grignard reagents. The R_2Cd and RCdX compounds appear to be equally satisfactory but the former are most often used as requiring less cadmium chloride.

The organozinc compounds are similar in chemical properties to the corresponding organocadmium compounds but, notwithstanding the recommendation of Blaise,[25] who gives no experimental details, are alleged to be comparatively disadvantageous because of: the greater difficulty of preparation; the undesirability of using ether as a solvent in acid chloride reactions (because of ether cleavage and ester formation); and the greater reactivity of the zinc compounds, particularly toward carbonyl groups. The earlier investigators[26] employed organozinc iodides prepared by the action of organic iodides on zinc or a zinc-copper couple. It is possible, however, to affect the preparation by a method analogous to that commonly employed for the preparation of organocadmium compounds, namely, by the addition of anhydrous zinc chloride to a Grignard reagent solution, a method which has been used with good success by Jones[27] and others.

In general the organomagnesium iodides are unsatisfactory for the preparation of organocadmium compounds and their subsequent reaction with acid chlorides (Gilman and Nelson, *loc. cit.*;[22] Cason, *loc. cit.*[23,24]), and Cason reports that in general the bromides give better yields than the corresponding chlorides. Secondary alkylmagnesium halides with the possible exception of isopropyl, do not give satisfactory results, even at low temperatures.

The experimental procedure recommended by Cason (*loc. cit.*[23]) is described in an illustrative example as follows. "A Grignard reagent was prepared from excess methyl bromide and 4.9 g. (0.2 mole) of magnesium in 100 ml. of ether. To the ice-cold solution was added, during five minutes, 19.6 g. of cadmium chloride; then the mixture was stirred under reflux until a negative Gilman test was obtained (fifteen to twenty minutes). Ether was distilled rapidly from the stirred mixture by heating on a steam-bath until distillation became slow and a nearly dry residue remained. After addition of 65 ml. of benzene, distillation was continued until an additional 25 ml. of distillate had been collected. There was then added 120 ml. of benzene, the stirred solution was heated to boiling and there was added without external heating 24.9 g. (0.1 mole) of ω-carbethoxynonoyl chloride in 30 ml. of benzene as rapidly (two minutes) as

[25]Blaise, *Bull. soc. chim.*, [4], 9, I–XXVI (1911).

[26]See, for example: Blaise, *loc. cit.*[25]; Mauthner, *J. prakt. Chem.*, [2], *103*, 391–6 (1921); Michael, *J. Am. Chem. Soc.*, *41*, 393–424 (1919); Ruzicka and Stoll, *Helv. Chim. Acta*, *10*, 692–4 (1927).

[27]Jones, *J. Am. Chem. Soc.*, *69*, 2350–4 (1947).

consistent with control of the exothermic reaction. Heating under reflux with stirring was continued for ten minutes, at which time the stirrer was stopped by the mass of precipitate. Ten minutes later the reaction was worked up as previously described;[28] yield of ethyl 10-ketohendecanoate, b.p. 147.5–149.5° (4 mm.), 19.4 g. (83.7 percent). The distillation residue weighed 2.7 g."

An analogous preparation with the aid of zinc chloride is described by by Jones (*loc. cit.*[27]) as follows. "A solution of 110 g. (0.33 mole) of octadecyl bromide, b.p. 182–183° (2.5 mm.), m.p. 28.5°; in 400 ml. of anhydrous ether was added in the usual way to 15 g. of magnesium turnings in 100 ml. of ether. Titration of the resulting Grignard solution showed it to be 0.58 molar (about 85 percent yield).

"In a 1-liter, three-necked flask provided with a stirrer, reflux condenser and dropping funnel, were placed 38 g. (0.27 mole) of freshly-fused, powdered zinc chloride and 100 ml. of anhydrous ether. To this was added (by means of a 100-ml. pipet) 470 ml. (0.27 mole) of the octadecylmagnesium bromide solution. After the initial reaction, the mixture was stirred and heated for two hours during which time ether was allowed to distill until the volume had been reduced to about 300 ml. With continued stirring a solution of 54 g. (0.20 mole) of ω-carbethoxyundecanoyl chloride in 100 ml. of dry benzene was added during fifteen minutes. The viscous mixture was stirred and heated under reflux for three hours and then hydrolyzed with 500 ml. of 2 *N* hydrochloric acid solution. One liter of hot benzene was added. The aqueous layer was separated, and the warm benzene solution was washed with 400 ml. of hot dilute hydrochloric acid and two 400-ml. portions of hot (80–70°) water. The benzene solution was evaporated to about 100 ml., treated with 30 ml. of 12 *N* sodium hydroxide solution and 50 ml. of ethanol and digested on the steam-bath for two hours during which time most of the remaining solvent evaporated. The resulting white solid was thoroughly washed by suspension in two 500-ml. portions of warm benzene, air-dried, and then washed by suspension in two 500-ml. portions of water. Finally it was suspended in 500 ml. of 2 *N* hydrochloric acid solution and digested on the steam-bath for two hours. The 12-ketotriacontanoic acid was collected, air-dried and recrystallized from benzene." [Yield, 79 percent.]

Data on some representative examples of preparations of this kind are collected in Table IX-I.

---

[28]Cason and Prout, *J. Am. Chem. Soc.*, *66*, 46–50 (1944). "The organometallic complex was decomposed with ice and sulfuric acid, and the water layer was separated and extracted twice with benzene. The benzene extracts were washed with water, 5 percent sodium carbonate solution, water, and saturated sodium chloride solution, then filtered through a layer of anhydrous sodium sulfate. After the solvent had been flashed off, the residue was distilled through an 18-inch Podbielniak-type column."

TABLE IX-I

PREPARATION OF KETONES FROM ACID HALIDES WITH THE AID OF CADMIUM OR ZINC SALTS

Halide	RMgX	Cd or Zn Salt	% Yield Ketone	Ref.
$C_2H_2OCl_2$				
$ClCH_2COCl$ (0.78 mole)	n-C_4H_9MgBr (0.775 mole Mg)	$CdCl_2$ (0.44 mole)	26.0	*1*
$ClCH_2COCl$ (0.28 mole)	n-C_4H_9MgBr (0.35 mole C_4H_9Br)	$CdCl_2$ (0.188 mole)	50.8	*2*
$ClCH_2COCl$	n-$C_5H_{29}MgBr$	$CdCl_2$	24.0	*1*
$ClCH_2COCl$	n-$C_{12}H_{25}MgBr$	$CdCl_2$	18.0	*1*
$ClCH_2COCl$ (0.05 mole)	n-$C_{14}H_{29}MgBr$ (0.063 mole $C_{14}H_{29}Br$)	$CdCl_2$	33.0	*2*
$ClCH_2COCl$	n-$C_{14}H_{20}MgBr$	$CdCl_2$	14.5	*1*
C_2H_3OCl				
CH_3COCl	C_2H_5MgBr	$CdCl_2$	46.0	*3*
CH_3COCl	C_2H_5MgBr	$CdBr_2$	50.0	*3*
CH_3COCl	n-C_4H_9MgBr	$CdCl_2$	74.0	*3*
CH_3COCl	t-C_4H_9MgBr	$CdBr_2$	17.0	*3*
CH_3COCl	C_6H_5MgBr	$CdCl_2$	83.0	*3*
CH_3COCl	C_6H_5MgBr	$CdBr_2$	61.0	*3*
CH_3COCl	$C_6H_5CH_2MgCl$	$CdCl_2$	18.0	*3*
$C_3H_4OCl_2$				
$CH_3CHClCOCl$ (0.173 mole)	n-C_4H_9MgBr (0.216 mole C_4H_9Br)	$CdCl_2$	42.7	*2*
$CH_3CHClCOCl$ (15.4 g.)	n-$C_{12}H_{25}MgBr$ (33.1 g. $C_{12}H_{25}Br$)	$CdCl_2$	13.0, crude	*1*
C_3H_5OCl				
C_2H_5COCl	C_6H_5MgBr	$CdCl_2$	76.0	*3*
C_2H_5COCl (14.8 g.)	C_6H_5MgBr (32.4 g. C_6H_5Br)	$CdCl_2$ (19.5 g.)	80.8	*2*

TABLE IX-I (Continued)

Halide	RMgX	Cd or Zn Salt	% Yield Ketone	Ref.
C_4H_7OCl				
n-C_3H_7COCl	i-C_3H_7MgBr	$CdBr_2$	60.0	3
$C_5H_3O_2Cl$				
2-Furoyl chloride	C_2H_5MgBr	$CdCl_2$	61.0	3
$C_5H_7O_3Cl$				
$H_3CO_2CCH_2CH_2COCl$	n-C_4H_9MgCl	$CdCl_2$	62.8	2
$H_3CO_2CCH_2CH_2COCl$	n-C_4H_9MgBr	$CdCl_2$	76.6	2
$H_3CO_2CCH_2CH_2COCl$	n-C_4H_9MgI	$CdCl_2$	44.7	2
$H_3CO_2CCH_2CH_2COCl$ (0.16 mole)	i-$C_5H_{11}MgBr$ (0.2 mole $C_5H_{11}Br$)	$CdCl_2$ (0.17 mole)	78.7	2,4,5
$H_3CO_2CCH_2CH_2COCl$ (0.8 mole)	i-$C_5H_{11}MgBr$ (1.0 mole $C_5H_{11}Br$)	$CdCl_2$ (0.535 mole)	73–75	6
$H_3CO_2CCH_2CH_2COCl$	$CH_3(C_2H_5)CHCH_2MgBr$	$CdCl_2$	60.0	5
$H_3CO_2CCH_2CH_2COCl$ (33.8 g.)	$CH_3(n$-$C_3H_7)CHMgBr$ (0.3 mole $C_5H_{11}Br$)	$CdCl_2$ (29.3 g.)	21.5	5,2
C_6H_3OClBr				
5-Bromonicotinyl chloride	CH_3MgBr	$CdCl_2$	25.0	7
C_6H_4OClN				
Nicotinyl chloride (70.0 g., 0.494 mole)	n-C_3H_7MgBr (73.8 g., 0.60 mole C_3H_7Br)	$CdCl_2$ (55.0 g., 0.30 mole)	30.0	38
C_6H_5OClS				
2-Methyl-3-thiophenecarbonyl chloride (62.4 g.)	CH_3MgI (11.40 g. CH_3I)	$CdCl_2$ (8.25 g.)	49.0	36

TABLE IX-I (Continued)

Halide	RMgX	Cd or Zn Salt	% Yield Ketone	Ref.
$C_6H_9O_3Cl$				
$H_3CO_2C(CH_2)_3COCl$	n-$C_{10}H_{21}C^*H_2MgBr$	$CdCl_2$	47.5	35
C_7H_5OCl				
C_6H_5COCl	CH_3MgBr	$CdCl_2$	85.0	3
C_6H_5COCl	C_2H_5MgBr	$CdCl_2$	50.0	3
C_6H_5COCl (0.21 mole)	C_2H_5MgBr (0.3 mole C_2H_5Br)	$CdCl_2$	84.4	2
C_6H_5COCl	C_6H_5MgBr	$CdCl_2$	57.0	3
$C_7H_{11}O_3Cl$				
$H_3CO_2C(CH_2)_4COCl$ (130 g.)	i-$C_5H_{11}MgBr$ (22 g. Mg)	$CdCl_2$ (89 g.)	54.6*	8
C_8H_7OCl				
3-$CH_3C_6H_4COCl$	CH_3MgBr	$CdCl_2$	83.0	3
$C_8H_7O_2Cl$				
4-$CH_3OC_6H_4COCl$ (0.21 mole)	CH_3MgBr (0.3 mole)	$CdCl_2$ (0.16 mole)	84.0	3
$C_8H_{11}OCl$				
1-Cyclohexenylacetyl chloride (30 g.)	1-$C_{10}H_7MgBr$ (90 g. $C_{10}H_7Br$)	$ZnCl_2$ (85 ml. sat'd Et_2O sol'n)	61.3, crude	10
$C_8H_{13}O_3Cl$				
$H_5C_2O_2C(CH_2)_4COCl$	CH_3MgBr	$CdCl_2$	76.0	6,5,9
$C_8H_{15}OCl$				
$CH_3(C_2H_5)(n$-$C_3H_7)CCOCl$	CH_3MgBr	$CdCl_2$	47.0	11

* Recovered in the form of 65 g. of the acid, i-$C_5H_{11}CO(CH_2)_4CO_2H$.

TABLE IX-I (Continued)

Halide	RMgX	Cd or Zn Salt	% Yield Ketone	Ref.
C_9H_7OCl				
$C_6H_5CH{=}CHCOCl$ (0.16 mole)	C_6H_5MgBr (0.16 mole)	$CdCl_2$ (0.16 mole)	44.0	*12*
C_9H_8OClBr				
4-$BrC_6H_4CH_2CH_2COCl$ (25 g. acid)	C_6H_5MgBr (0.45 mole)	$ZnCl_2$ (27 g., 0.2 mole)	?	*37*
C_9H_9OCl				
(+)-$CH_3(C_6H_5)CHCOCl$ (7.3 g. acid)	CH_3MgBr (1.5 g. Mg)	$CdCl_2$ (4.5 g.)	78.0	*13*
$C_9H_9O_3Cl$				
2,3-$(CH_3O)_2C_6H_3COCl$	CH_3MgBr	$CdCl_2$	71.0	*14*
3,5-$(CH_3O)_2C_6H_3COCl$	CH_3MgBr	$CdCl_2$	84.0	*14*
$C_{10}H_{11}OCl$				
2,4,6-$(CH_3)_3C_6H_2COCl$ (10 g.)	2-$CH_3C_{10}H_6$-1-MgBr (10 g. $C_{11}H_9Br$)	$CdCl_2$	9.6	*15*
$C_{10}H_{11}O_2Cl$				
$C_6H_5O(CH_2)_3COCl$ (41.5 g.)	CH_3MgBr (7.3 g. Mg)	$CdCl_2$ (29.3 g.)	78.0	*16*
$C_{11}H_6OCl_2$				
6-$ClC_{10}H_6$-1-COCl (0.39 mole)	CH_3MgBr	$CdCl_2$ [0.30 mole $(CH_3)_2Cd$]	?	*32*
$C_{11}H_{10}OCl$				
1,2,3,4-Tetrahydronaphthalene-1-carboxylic acid chloride (0.24 mole)	CH_3MgBr (0.48 mole)	$CdCl_2$ (48 g.)	65.0	*17*

TABLE IX-I (Continued)

Halide	RMgX	Cd or Zn Salt	% Yield Ketone	Ref.
$C_{11}H_{13}OCl$				
2,3,5,6-$(CH_3)_4C_6HCOCl$ (6.0 g.)	4-*t*-$C_4H_9C_6H_4MgBr$ (9.6 g. $C_{10}H_{13}Br$)	$CdCl_2$ (4.4 g.)	20.0	33
$C_{11}H_{19}O_3Cl$				
$H_5C_2O_2C(CH_2)_7COCl$	CH_3MgBr	$CdCl_2$	64.0	9
$H_5C_2O_2C(CH_2)_7COCl$ (0.72 mole)	$CH_3(n\text{-}C_8H_{17})CHMgBr$ (1.27 mole $C_{10}H_{21}Br$)	$ZnCl_2$ (1.0 mole)	55.0	18
$C_{12}H_{12}OCl$				
1-(1,2,3,4-Tetrahydronaphthyl)acetyl chloride	CH_3MgBr	$CdCl_2$	69.0	17
$C_{12}H_{21}O_3Cl$				
$H_5C_2O_2C(CH_2)_8COCl$ (0.1 mole)	CH_3MgBr (0.2 mole Mg)	$CdCl_2$ (19.6 g.)	83.7	2,5,6
$H_5C_2O_2C(CH_2)_8COCl$	*i*-$C_5H_{11}MgBr$	$CdCl_2$	85.0	5,6
$H_5C_2O_2C(CH_2)_8COCl$ (26.4 g.)	*i*-$C_9H_{19}MgBr$ (22 g. $C_9H_{19}Br$)	$CdCl_2$	46.0	4
$H_5C_2O_2C(CH_2)_8COCl$	$CH_3(C_2H_5)CH(CH_2)_5MgBr$	$CdCl_2$	76.5	5,6
$H_5C_2O_2C(CH_2)_8COCl$ (8.4 g.)	$CH_3(n\text{-}C_3H_7)CH(CH_2)_4MgBr$ (10 g. $C_9H_{19}Br$)	$CdCl_2$	65.0	19
$H_5C_2O_2C(CH_2)_8COCl$	$CH_3(n\text{-}C_6H_{13})CH(CH_2)_3MgBr$	$CdCl_2$	77.0	6
$H_5C_2O_2C(CH_2)_8COCl$ (6.0 g.)	*n*-$C_{12}H_{25}MgBr$ (7.5 g. $C_{12}H_{25}Br$)	$ZnCl_2$ (4.1 g.)	62.0*	20
$H_5C_2O_2C(CH_2)_8COCl$	*n*-$C_{14}H_{29}MgBr$	$ZnCl_2$	?	20
$H_5C_2O_2C(CH_2)_8COCl$ (10.8 g.)	$CH_3(n\text{-}C_{10}H_{21})CH(CH_2)_3MgBr$ (15.0 g. $C_{15}H_{31}Br$)	$CdCl_2$	77.8	19
$H_5C_2O_2C(CH_2)_8COCl$	*n*-$C_{18}H_{37}MgBr$	$ZnCl_2$	77.0	21

* Product isolated as the acid, *n*-$C_{12}H_{25}CO(CH_2)_8CO_2H$, 62.0% yield.

TABLE IX-I (Continued)

Halide	RMgX	Cd or Zn Salt	% Yield Ketone	Ref.
$C_{13}H_{17}OCl$				
2,6-$(CH_3)_2$-4-*t*-$C_4H_9C_6H_4COCl$	CH_3MgBr	$CdCl_2$	34.0	*22*
$C_{13}H_{23}O_3Cl$				
$H_5C_2O_2C(CH_2)_9COCl$	*n*-$C_{18}H_{37}MgBr$	$ZnCl_2$	92.0	*21*
$CH_3CO_2(CH_2)_{10}COCl$ (0.19 mole)	*n*-$C_{18}H_{37}MgBr$ (0.24 mole)	$ZnCl_2$ (0.30 mole)	88.0	*21*
$C_{14}H_{25}O_3Cl$				
$H_5C_2O_2C(CH_2)_{10}COCl$ (0.20 mole)	*n*-$C_{18}H_{37}MgBr$ (0.27 mole)	$ZnCl_2$ (0.27 mole)	79.0	*21*
$C_{15}H_{17}O_3Cl$				
4-(*p*-Acetoxyphenyl)hexahydrobenzoyl chloride (12.0 g. acid)	C_2H_5MgBr (0.334 g. Mg)	$CdCl_2$ (1.34 g.)	63.0	*23*
4-(*p*-Acetoxyphenyl)hexahydrobenzoyl chloride (2.70 g. acid)	*n*-C_3H_7MgBr (0.76 g. Mg)	$CdCl_2$ (3.04 g.)	75.0	*23*
$C_{15}H_{27}O_3Cl$				
$H_5C_2O_2C(CH_2)_{11}COCl$	*n*-$C_{18}H_{37}MgBr$	$ZnCl_2$	89.0	*21*
$C_{16}H_{29}O_3Cl$				
$H_5C_2O_2C(CH_2)_{12}COCl$	*n*-$C_{18}H_{37}MgBr$	$ZnCl_2$	76.0	*21*
$C_{17}H_{23}OCl$				
$RC(CH_3)=CHCH=CHCOCl$* (6.70 g.)	CH_3MgBr (0.96 g. Mg)	$CdCl_2$ (3.68 g.)	45.0	*34*
$C_{17}H_{31}O_3Cl$				
$H_5C_2O_2C(CH_2)_{13}COCl$	*n*-$C_{18}H_{37}MgBr$	$ZnCl_2$	83.0	*21*

*R = β-(2,6,6-trimethyl-1-cyclohexenyl)vinyl.

TABLE IX-I (Continued)

Halide	RMgX	Cd or Zn Salt	% Yield Ketone	Ref.
$C_{18}H_{33}O_3Cl$				
$H_5C_2O_2C(CH_2)_{14}COCl$	n-$C_{18}H_{37}MgBr$	$ZnCl_2$	77.0	*21*
$C_{18}H_{35}OCl$				
n-$C_{17}H_{35}COCl$ (0.06 mole)	C_2H_5MgBr (0.08 mole C_2H_5Br)	$CdCl_2$ (0.043 mole)	62.0	*24,3*
n-$C_{17}H_{35}COCl$ (1.41 mole)	$C_6H_5(CH_2)_2MgBr$ (1.76 mole C_8H_9Br)	$CdCl_2$ (0.936 mole)	65.5	*24*
$C_{19}H_{35}O_3Cl$				
$H_5C_2O_2C(CH_2)_{15}COCl$	n-$C_{18}H_{37}MgBr$	$ZnCl_2$	80.0	*21*
$C_{24}H_{35}O_2Cl$				
3-Oxo-4-etiocholenic acid chloride (595 mg. Na salt)	$C^{14}H_3MgBr$ (6 ml. CH_3OH + 0.599 mmole $C^{14}H_3OH$)	$CdCl_2$ (1.4 mmole)	29.2*	*26*
$C_{24}H_{35}O_3Cl$				
3-Acetoxy-5-bisnorcholenic acid chloride (4.0 g.)	CH_3MgX (X = Br, I) (1.3 g. Mg)	$CdCl_2$ (5.0 g.)	95.0	*25*
3-Acetoxy-5-bisnorcholenic acid chloride	C_2H_5MgBr	$CdCl_2$	93.5	*25*
3-Acetoxy-5-bisnorcholenic acid choloride (25 g. acid)	i-$C_5H_{11}MgBr$ (8 g. Mg)	$CdCl_2$ (38 g.)	91.2	*25*
3-Acetoxy-5-bisnorcholenic acid chloride (18 g.)	C_6H_5MgBr (32 g. C_6H_5Br)	$CdCl_2$ (28 g.)	97.9	*25*
3-Acetoxy-5-bisnorcholenic acid chloride	C_6H_5MgBr	$ZnCl_2$	88.4	*25*
3-Acetoxy-5-bisnorcholenic acid chloride (6 g.)	2,4,6-$(CH_3)_3C_6H_2MgBr$ (3 g. Mg)	$CdCl_2$ (11 g.)	45.8	*25*
$C_{24}H_{35}O_5Cl$				
3,12-Diformoxybisnorcholanic acid chloride (0.02 mole acid)	C_6H_5MgBr (1.95 g. Mg)	$CdCl_2$ (8.8 g.)	81.0	*27*

* Based on $C^{14}H_3OH$ used for preparation of $C^{14}H_3Br$.

TABLE IX-I (Continued)

Halide	RMgX	Cd or Zn Salt	% Yield Ketone	Ref.
$C_{24}H_{39}OCl$				
Cholanic acid chloride	C_6H_5MgBr	$CdCl_2$	?	27
$C_{24}H_{39}O_3Cl$				
3-Formoxynorcholanic acid chloride	C_6H_5MgBr	$CdCl_2$	?	27
$C_{24}H_{39}O_4Cl$				
Cholic acid chloride	C_6H_5MgBr	$CdCl_2$	70-75	28
$C_{25}H_{37}O_3Cl$				
3(β)-Formoxy-5-cholenic acid chloride	C_6H_5MgBr	$CdCl_2$	?	27
$C_{25}H_{37}O_4Cl$				
3-Formoxy-12-oxocholanic acid chloride	C_6H_5MgBr	$CdCl_2$	?	27
$C_{25}H_{39}O_3Cl$				
3-Formoxycholanic acid chloride	C_6H_5MgBr	$CdCl_2$	?	27
$C_{26}H_{39}O_3Cl$				
3-Acetoxy-5-cholenic acid chloride (25.0 g. acid)	i-C_3H_7MgBr (14.65 g. Mg)	$CdBr_2$ (88.0 g.)	?	29
3-Acetoxy-5-etiocholenic acid chloride (1.82 g. acid)	$C^{14}H_3MgI$ (726 mg. $C^{14}H_3I$)	$CdBr_2$ (1.2 g.)	50.6,* crude	30
3(β)-Acetoxy-5-etiocholenic acid chloride	CH_3MgBr	$CdCl_2$	31.0	26
3(β)-Acetoxy-5-etiocholenic acid chloride	i-$C_5H_{11}MgBr$	$CdCl_2$	?	31
$C_{26}H_{41}O_3Cl$				
3(β)-Acetoxyetioallocholanic acid chloride	i-$C_5H_{11}MgBr$	$CdCl_2$	?	31

* Based on $C^{14}H_3I$ used.

REFERENCES FOR TABLE IX-I

(1) Bunnett and Tarbell, *J. Am. Chem. Soc.*, *67*, 1944–6 (1945).
(2) Cason, *J. Am. Chem. Soc.*, *68*, 2078–81 (1946).
(3) Gilman and Nelson, *Rec. trav. chim.*, *55*, 518–30 (1936).
(4) Cason, *J. Am. Chem. Soc.*, *64*, 1106–10 (1942).
(5) Cason and Prout, *J. Am. Chem. Soc.*, *66*, 46–50 (1944).
(6) Cason and Prout, *Organic Syntheses*, *28*, 75–80 (1948).
(7) Bachman and Micucci, *J. Am. Chem. Soc.*, *70*, 2381–4 (1948).
(8) Wilson, *J. Am. Chem. Soc.*, *67*, 2161–2 (1945).
(9) McKennis and du Vigneaud, *J. Am. Chem. Soc.*, *68*, 832–5 (1946).
(10) Kon and Woolman, *J. Chem. Soc.*, *1939*, 794–800.
(11) Lester and Proffitt, *J. Am. Chem. Soc.*, *71*, 1877–8 (1949).
(12) Nightingale and Wadsworth, *J. Am. Chem. Soc.*, *67*, 416–8 (1945).
(13) Campbell and Kenyon, *J. Chem. Soc.*, *1946*, 25–7.
(14) Woodruff, *J. Am. Chem. Soc.*, *64*, 2859–62 (1942).
(15) Fuson, McKusick, and Spangler, *J. Am. Chem. Soc.*, *67*, 597–601 (1945).
(16) Brown and Partridge, *J. Am. Chem Soc.*, *67*, 1423–4 (1945).
(17) Newman and O'Leary, *J. Am. Chem. Soc.*, *68*, 258–61 (1946).
(18) Schmidt and Shirley, *J. Am. Chem. Soc.*, *71*, 3804–6 (1949).
(19) Cason, Adams, Bennett, and Register, *J. Am. Chem. Soc.*, *66*, 1764–7 (1944).
(20) Schneider and Spielman, *J. Biol. Chem.*, *142*, 345–54 (1942).
(21) Jones, *J. Am. Chem. Soc.*, *69*, 2350–4 (1947).
(22) Fuson, Mills, Klose, and Carpenter, *J. Org. Chem.*, *12*, 587–95 (1947).
(23) Johnson and Offenhauer, *J. Am. Chem. Soc.*, *67*, 1045–9 (1945).
(24) Sherk, Augur, and Soffer, *J. Am. Chem. Soc.*, *67*, 2239–40 (1945).
(25) Cole and Julian, *J. Am. Chem. Soc.*, *67*, 1369–75 (1945).
(26) Riegel and Prout, *J. Org. Chem.*, *13*, 933–6 (1948).
(27) Hoehn and Moffett, *J. Am. Chem. Soc.*, *67*, 740–3 (1945).
(28) Jacobsen, *J. Am. Chem. Soc.*, *66*, 662 (1944).
(29) Riegel and Kaye, *J. Am. Chem. Soc.*, *67*, 723–4 (1945).
(30) MacPhillamy and Scholz, *J. Biol. Chem.*, *178*, 37–40 (1949).
(31) Billeter and Miescher, *Helv. Chim. Acta*, *32*, 564–73 (1949).
(32) Jacobs, Winstein, Henderson, Bond, Ralls, Seymour, and Florsheim, *J. Org. Chem.*, *11*, 229–38 (1946).
(33) Fuson and McKusick, *J. Am. Chem. Soc.*, *65*, 60–4 (1943).
(34) Heilbron, Jones, and O'Sullivan, *J. Chem. Soc.*, *1946*, 866–9.
(35) Dauben, *J. Am. Chem. Soc.*, *70*, 1376–8 (1948).
(36) Gaertner, *J. Am. Chem. Soc.*, *73*, 3934–7 (1951).
(37) Johnson, Jacobs, and Schwartz, *J. Am. Chem. Soc.*, *60*, 1885–9 (1938).
(38) Frank and Weatherbee, *J. Am. Chem. Soc.*, *70*, 3482–3 (1948).

REDUCTION OF ACID HALIDES BY GRIGNARD REAGENTS

Unlike the corresponding carboxylic esters (*q.v.*, Chapter VIII) some carbonyl chlorides are reduced, in part, by Grignard reagents to the corresponding primary alcohols. Such reductions are always accompanied by the production of a secondary alcohol identical with the reduction product of the ketone which might be expected as the product of the first stage of reaction of the Grignard reagent with the carbonyl chloride. Reductions of this kind are effected by Grignard reagents of the same type responsible for the reduction of aldehydes and ketones (*q.v.*, Chapter VI), and olefin is formed in amount corresponding to two equivalents of Grignard reagent for each equivalent of acid chloride reduced to primary alcohol plus one equivalent of Grignard reagent for each equivalent of secondary alcohol produced.[29] These facts suggest that the primary and secondary alcohols may have, as Whitmore *et al.*[30] maintain, in part at least, a common origin. For example, isobutylmagnesium bromide, an efficient reducing agent, may react with a readily reducible acid chloride in in part as follows.

$$RCOCl + i\text{-}C_4H_9MgBr \longrightarrow RCHO + MgBrCl + i\text{-}C_4H_8$$

$$RCHO + i\text{-}C_4H_9MgBr \longrightarrow RCH_2OMgBr + i\text{-}C_4H_8$$

$$RCHO + i\text{-}C_4H_9MgBr \longrightarrow i\text{-}C_4H_9RCHOMgBr$$

A test of the consistency of this hypothesis with known facts (though not, of course, a conclusive proof of its validity) is to be found in a comparison of the reactions of isobutyryl chloride with *t*-butylmagnesium chloride, reported by Whitmore,[31] on the one hand, and of isobutyraldehyde with the same Grignard reagent, reported by Faworsky[32] and by Whitmore and Houk,[33] on the other.

$$i\text{-}C_3H_7COCl \text{ (1.5 mole)} + t\text{-}C_4H_9MgCl \text{ (4.2 moles)} \longrightarrow i\text{-}C_4H_9OH \text{ (20\%)} + i\text{-}C_3H_7(t\text{-}C_4H_9)CHOH \text{ (63\%)} \quad \text{(Ref. 31)}$$

$$i\text{-}C_3H_7CHO + t\text{-}C_4H_9MgCl \longrightarrow i\text{-}C_4H_9OH \text{ (50\%)} + i\text{-}C_3H_7(t\text{-}C_4H_9)CHOH \text{ (25\%)} + i\text{-}C_3H_7CH(OH)C(CH_3)_2CHO \text{ (ca. 25\%)} \quad \text{(Ref. 32)}$$

$$i\text{-}C_3H_7CHO + t\text{-}C_4H_9MgCl \longrightarrow i\text{-}C_4H_9OH \text{ (35\%)} + i\text{-}C_3H_7(t\text{-}C_4H_9)CHOH \text{ (35\%)} + \text{solid, m. } 51\text{–}52^\circ \text{ (7.5\%)} \quad \text{(Ref. 33)}$$

A further comparison may be made between the reactions of *t*-butylmagnesium chloride with trimethylacetyl chloride, reported by Whitmore

[29] Greenwood, Whitmore, and Crooks, *J. Am. Chem. Soc.*, *60*, 2028–30 (1938).

[30] Whitmore, Whitaker, Mosher, Breivik, Wheeler, Miner, Sutherland, Wagner, Clapper, Lewis, Lux, and Popkin, *J. Am. Chem. Soc.*, *63*, 643–54 (1941).

[31] Whitmore, *Rec. trav. chim.*, *57*, 562–8 (1938).

[32] Faworsky, *J. prakt. Chem.*, [2], 88, 641–98 (1913).

[33] Whitmore and Houk, *J. Am. Chem. Soc.*, *54*, 3714–8 (1932).

(*loc. cit.*[31]), on the one hand, and trimethylacetaldehyde, reported by Conant *et al.*,[34] on the other.

$t\text{-}C_4H_9COCl$ (1.1 mole) + $t\text{-}C_4H_9MgCl$ (3.9 moles) $\rightarrow$
$t\text{-}C_4H_9CH_2OH$ (94%) + $(t\text{-}C_4H_9)_2CHOH$ (1.5%) + $i\text{-}C_4H_8$ (2 moles)

$t\text{-}C_4H_9CHO$ (0.2 mole) + $t\text{-}C_4H_9MgCl$ $\rightarrow$ $t\text{-}C_4H_9CH_2OH$ (0.13 mole)

Whitmore *et al.* (*loc. cit.*[30]) have made additional comparisons of the reactions of related acyl chlorides and aldehydes with *t*-amylmagnesium chloride, and of a related acyl chloride, aldehyde, and ketone with *t*-butylmagnesium chloride.

$(C_2H_5)_2CHCOCl$ (1 mole) + $t\text{-}C_5H_{11}MgCl$ (3.15 moles) $\rightarrow$
$(C_2H_5)_2CHCH_2OH$ (75%) + $(C_2H_5)_2CH(t\text{-}C_5H_{11})CHOH$ (7.8%)

$(C_2H_5)_2CHCHO$ (0.4 mole) + $t\text{-}C_5H_{11}MgCl$ (0.5 mole) $\rightarrow$
$(C_2H_5)_2CHCH_2OH$ (67%) + $(C_2H_5)_2CH(t\text{-}C_5H_{11})CHOH$ (21%)

$CH_3(t\text{-}C_4H_9)(t\text{-}C_4H_9CH_2)CCOCl$ (0.435 mole)
+ $t\text{-}C_5H_{11}MgCl$ (1.19 mole) $\rightarrow$ $CH_3(t\text{-}C_4H_9)(t\text{-}C_4H_9CH_2)CCH_2OH$ (19%)
+ $CH_3(t\text{-}C_4H_9)(t\text{-}C_4H_9CH_2)CCHO$ (78%)

$CH_3(t\text{-}C_4H_9)(t\text{-}C_4H_9CH_2)CCHO$ (0.2 mole) + $t\text{-}C_5H_{11}MgCl$ (0.4 mole) $\rightarrow$
$CH_3(t\text{-}C_4H_9)(t\text{-}C_4H_9CH_2)CCH_2OH$ (90%)

$(C_2H_5)_2CHCOCl$ (1 mole) + $t\text{-}C_4H_9MgCl$ (3.7 moles) $\rightarrow$
$(C_2H_5)_2CHCH_2OH$ (21.3%) + $(C_2H_5)_2CH(t\text{-}C_4H_9)CHOH$ (51.3%)

$(C_2H_5)_2CHCHO$ (0.25 mole) + $t\text{-}C_4H_9MgCl$ (0.31 mole) $\rightarrow$
$(C_2H_5)_2CHCH_2OH$ (14.9%) + $(C_2H_5)_2CH(t\text{-}C_4H_9)CHOH$ (55.8%)

$(C_2H_5)_2CHCO\text{-}t\text{-}C_4H_9$ (0.5 mole) + $t\text{-}C_4H_9MgCl$ (0.8 mole) $\rightarrow$
recovered ketone (45%) + $(C_2H_5)_2CH(t\text{-}C_4H_9)CHOH$ (38%)

The isolation of traces (*ca.* 1 percent) of aldehydes from the trimethylacetyl and *t*-butylacetyl chloride reactions with *t*-butylmagnesium chloride, and of relatively high yields (67.0 percent, 62.5 percent) of aldehyde from the reactions of methyl-*t*-butylneopentylacetyl chloride with *t*-butyl- and *t*-amylmagnesium chlorides, by Whitmore *et al.* (*loc. cit.*[30]) is also in accord with the reaction scheme proposed.

There remains, of course, the possibility (in some cases the strong probability) that secondary alcohol is formed, at least in part, by the reduction of intermediate ketone in the manner already discussed (see Grignard Reductions of Aldehydes and Ketones, Chapter VI). This mode of secondary alcohol formation seems especially probable in such reactions as those of *t*-butylacetyl chloride with isopropyl- and isobutylmagnesium bromides, reported by Whitmore and Forster.[35]

---

[34]Conant, Webb, and Mendum, *J. Am. Chem. Soc.*, *51*, 1246–55 (1929).
[35]Whitmore and Forster, *J. Am. Chem. Soc.*, *64*, 2966–8 (1942).

$t\text{-}C_4H_9CH_2COCl$ (1 mole) + $i\text{-}C_3H_7MgBr$ (4 moles) $\longrightarrow$

$$i\text{-}C_4H_9COCH_2\text{-}t\text{-}C_4H_9\ (32.7\%) + i\text{-}C_3H_7(t\text{-}C_4H_9CH_2)CHOH\ (26.7\%)$$

$t\text{-}C_4H_9CH_2COCl$ (0.5 mole) + $i\text{-}C_4H_9MgBr$ (1.45 mole) $\longrightarrow$

$$i\text{-}C_4H_9COCH_2\text{-}t\text{-}C_4H_9\ (20.1\%) + i\text{-}C_4H_9(t\text{-}C_4H_9CH_2)CHOH\ (48.9\%)$$
$$+\ t\text{-}C_4H_9CH_2(i\text{-}C_4H_9)_2COH\ (13.8\%)$$

When reactions in which reduction occurs are conducted under conditions involving the presence (even temporary) of an excess of acid chloride, the reduction products are, of course, recovered in whole or in part as esters.

$$RCH_2OMgX + RCOCl \longrightarrow RCO_2CH_2R + MgXCl$$
$$RR'CHOMgX + RCOCl \longrightarrow RCO_2CHRR' + MgXCl$$

ESTER FORMATION THROUGH ETHER CLEAVAGE

Whitmore and Wheeler[36] have reported ethyl acetate as a byproduct of the reactions of acetyl chloride with several Grignard reagents in ethereal solution. It is well known that acid chlorides (and anhydrides) cleave ethers in the presence of suitable metallic halide catalysts, notably zinc chloride.[37] It has been shown by Whitmore and Wheeler (*loc. cit.*[36]) that acetyl chloride cleaves ethyl ether in the presence of anhydrous magnesium chloride.

A different type of ether cleavage has been observed by Jacobs *et al.*,[38] who report that both benzoyl bromide and benzoyl chloride react with phenoxyethynylmagnesium bromide to give phenyl benzoate (principally) and phenol as the only identifiable products.

COUPLING

A "coupling" reaction formally similar to those which have been observed with some aralkyl halides, (*q.v.*, Chapter XVI) has been reported by Fuson and Corse.[39] Mesitoyl chloride reacts with methylmagnesium iodide to yield both acetomesitylene and bimesitoyl (2,2′,4,4′,6,6′-hexamethylbenzil).

$$2,4,6\text{-}(CH_3)_3C_6H_2COCl \xrightarrow{CH_3MgI} 2,4,6\text{-}(CH_3)_3C_6H_2COCH_3$$
$$+\ [2,4,6\text{-}(CH_3)_3C_6H_2CO\text{—}]_2$$

Such reactions would appear to be most credibly explicable as consequences of the ability of some organomagnesium halides (especially iodides) to undergo homolytic as well as ionic scission.

[36] Whitmore and Wheeler, *J. Am. Chem. Soc.*, *60*, 2899–900 (1938).
[37] See, *e.g.*: Meerwein and Maier-Huser, *J. prakt. Chem.*, [2], *134*, 51–81 (1932).
[38] Jacobs, Cramer, and Weiss, *J. Am. Chem. Soc.*, *62*, 1849–54 (1940).
[39] Fuson and Corse, *J. Am. Chem. Soc.*, *60*, 2063–6 (1938).

$$RCOCl + CH_3MgI \longrightarrow MgICl + RCO\cdot + CH_3\cdot$$
$$2\ RCO\cdot \longrightarrow (RCO-)_2$$

Support for this view is to be found in the magnesious iodide reduction of *o*-toluyl chloride, reported by Fuson and Rachlin.[39.1] The equation relating the simple stoichiometric facts may be expanded to incorporate the theoretical interpretation as follows:

$$Mg\ (6.0\ g.) + I_2\ (30.6\ g.) \rightleftharpoons \cdot MgI$$
$$2\text{-}CH_3C_6H_4COCl\ (20.0\ g.) + \cdot MgI \longrightarrow 2\text{-}CH_3C_6H_4CO\cdot + MgICl$$
$$2\ 2\text{-}CH_3C_6H_4CO\cdot \longrightarrow (2\text{-}CH_3C_6H_4CO-)_2\ (34\%)$$

This type of reaction has been further studied by Kharasch *et al.*,[40] who found that, whereas methylmagnesium bromide reacts with mesitoyl chloride to yield 87 percent acetomesitylene with negligible quantities (*ca.* 1 percent) of the benzil derivative, the addition of "catalytic" quantities of cobaltous chloride to the reaction mixture under the same conditions reduces the yield of ketone to 35 percent and increases the yield of benzil derivative to 31 percent. The suggested reaction scheme is:

(1) $CH_3MgBr + CoCl_2 \longrightarrow CH_3CoCl + MgBrCl$

(2) $CH_3CoCl \longrightarrow CH_3\cdot + CoCl\cdot$

(3) $RCOCl + CoCl\cdot \longrightarrow RCO\cdot + CoCl_2$

(4) $2\ RCO\cdot \longrightarrow (RCO-)_2$

The gaseous byproduct was reported, though apparently not experimentally identified, by Fuson and Corse (*loc. cit.*[39]) as ethane. Kharasch *et al.* (*loc. cit.*[40]) found the gaseous product to consist of methane, ethane, and ethylene, with ethane present in greater quantity than ethylene. The methane is attributed in part to the enolization of acetomesitylene and in part to attack of methyl radicals on ether.

$$2,4,6\text{-}(CH_3)_3C_6H_2COCH_3 + CH_3MgX \longrightarrow [2,4,6\text{-}(CH_3)_3C_6H_2COCH_2]^- MgX^+ + CH_4$$

$$CH_3(C_2H_5O)CH_2 + CH_3\cdot \longrightarrow CH_3(C_2H_5O)CH\cdot + CH_4$$

Ethane and ethylene would presumably be produced in equimolecular proportions by decomposition of the free radicals produced by the attack of methyl radicals on ether. The excess of ethane may be due to the attack of methyl radicals on the Grignard reagent.

$$CH_3MgX + CH_3\cdot \longrightarrow C_2H_6 + \cdot MgX$$

In a similar experiment employing mesitoyl chloride, phenylmagnesium bromide, and cobaltous chloride, Kharasch *et al.* (*loc. cit.*[40]) obtained a 21 percent yield of a product attributable to reductive dimerization of the

[39.1] Fuson and Rachlin, *J. Am. Chem. Soc.*, 68, 343 (1946).
[40] Kharasch, Morrison, and Urry, *J. Am. Chem. Soc.*, 66, 368–71 (1944).

ketone formed in the first stage of the "normal" carbonyl halide-Grignard reagent reaction.*

HEXAARYLETHANE FORMATION

Schmidlin[41] found that, although phenylmagnesium bromide reacts "normally" with triphenylacetyl chloride to give the tertiary alcohol in 41 percent yield, phenylmagnesium iodide, under similar conditions, yields only a trace of the alcohol, with hexaphenylethane (or triphenylmethyl peroxide) as the isolable solid product, together with carbon monoxide corresponding to 86 percent of the acid chloride used. Probably this reaction is similar to that which leads to benzil formation, differing from it only by reason of the relative stabilities of the intermediate acyl free radicals formed.

$$(C_6H_5)_3CCOCl + C_6H_5MgI \longrightarrow (C_6H_5)_3CCO\cdot + MgClI + C_6H_5\cdot$$

$$2\,(C_6H_5)_3CCO\cdot \longrightarrow 2\,CO + [(C_6H_5)_3C—]_2$$

KETONE ENOLIZATION AND *C*-ACYLATION

The production of dibenzoylmethane derivatives in yields as high as 50 percent has been effected by Fuson *et al.*[42] through the interaction of methylmagnesium halides with 2,4,6-tribromo- and 2,4,6-trichlorobenzoyl chlorides.

$$2,4,6\text{-}Br_3C_6H_2COCl + CH_3MgBr\ (2\ equiv.) \longrightarrow$$
$$2,4,6\text{-}Br_3C_6H_2COCH_3\ (16\%) + (2,4,6\text{-}Br_3C_6H_2CO)_2CH_2\ (38\%)$$

$$2,4,6\text{-}Cl_3C_6H_2COCl + CH_3MgX\ (1\text{–}2\ equiv.) \longrightarrow$$
$$(2,4,6\text{-}Cl_3C_6H_2CO)_2CH\ (30\text{–}50\%)$$

$$(X = Cl, Br, I)$$

In view of the behavior of acetomesitylene, which reacts quantitatively with methyl Grignard reagents to form an enolate that undergoes *C*-acylation, and otherwise behaves like a true Grignard reagent of the formula $2,4,6\text{-}(CH_3)_3C_6H_2COCH_2MgX$, these reactions are readily interpretable as follows:

---

*This product, originally reported as the pinacol,

$$\{HO(C_6H_5)[2,4,6\text{-}(CH_3)_3C_6H_2]C—\}_2,$$

has since been shown by Fuson and Hornberger, *J. Org. Chem.*, *16*, 631–6 (1951), to be mesityl 2′-(mesitylhydroxymethyl)-2-biphenylyl ketone,

$$2,4,6\text{-}(CH_3)_3C_6H_2COC_6H_4\text{-}2\text{-}C_6H_4\text{-}2\text{-}CH(OH)C_6H_2\text{-}2,4,6\text{-}(CH_3)_3.$$

For a discussion of its probable mode of formation, see Magnesious Halide Reduction, Chapter VI.

[41] Schmidlin, *Ber.*, *43*, 1137–44 (1910).

[42] *(a)* Ross and Fuson, *J. Am. Chem. Soc.*, *59*, 1508–10 (1937); *(b)* Fuson, Van Campen, and Wolf, *ibid.*, *60*, 2269–72 (1938).

$$2,4,6\text{-}X_3C_6H_2COCl + CH_3MgX' \longrightarrow 2,4,6\text{-}X_3C_6H_2COCH_3 + MgX'Cl$$

$$2,4,6\text{-}X_3C_6H_2COCH_3 + CH_3MgX' \longrightarrow [2,4,6\text{-}X_3C_6H_2COCH_2]^-MgX'^+ + CH_4$$

$$2,4,6\text{-}X_3C_6H_2COCl + [2,4,6\text{-}X_3C_6H_2COCH_2]^-MgX'^+ \longrightarrow (2,4,6\text{-}X_3C_6H_2CO)_2CH_2 + MgX'Cl$$

Fuson found, in fact, that the iodomagnesium enolate of the trichloroacetophenone reacts with the trichlorobenzoyl chloride to give the dibenzoylmethane.

When, however, the chloride is added slowly to an excess of Grignard reagent the monoketone is obtained without diketone formation.

$$2,4,6\text{-}Br_3C_6H_2COCl + CH_3MgI \text{ (2.2 equiv.)} \longrightarrow 2,4,6\text{-}Br_3C_6H_2COCH_3 \text{ (46\%)}$$

Another instance of enolate *C*-acylation has been reported by Whitmore and Lewis.[43]

$$(C_2H_5)_3CCOCl + CH_3MgBr \longrightarrow CH_3COC(C_2H_5)_3 \text{ (34\%)} + [(C_2H_5)_3CCO]_2CH_2 \text{ (32\%)} + CH_4$$

OTHER "ABNORMAL" REACTIONS

Petrov and Roslova[44] have reported 3-pentanone as among the products of the reaction of propionyl chloride with *t*-butylmagnesium chloride. The available abstract contains no details regarding the conditions of reaction save that three hours warming on the water-bath was involved. If this product has been correctly characterized, it is probably attributable to the same cause as the analagous ketone formation in ester reactions (*q.v.*, Chapter VIII). Ester formed through ether cleavage might undergo Claisen condensation; decarbethoxylation of the keto ester thus derived would yield the ketone reported.

$$C_2H_5COCl \xrightarrow[MgX_2]{(C_2H_5)_2O} C_2H_5CO_2C_2H_5 \xrightarrow{RMgX} CH_3(C_2H_5CO)CHCO_2C_2H_5 \longrightarrow (C_2H_5)_2CO$$

The formation of 1-naphthoic anhydride during the reaction of 1-naphthoyl chloride with 7-isopropyl-4-indanylmagnesium bromide has been observed by Bruce.[45] The mode of formation of the anhydride has not been demonstrated, but, if acid salt were formed under the reaction conditions (say, from contaminant free acid), the anhydride would be among the expected products.

$$1\text{-}C_{10}H_7CO_2MgBr + 1\text{-}C_{10}H_7COCl \longrightarrow (1\text{-}C_{10}H_7CO)_2O + MgBrCl$$

Whitmore and Wheeler[46] have discovered mesityl oxide and isobutane among the products of reaction of acetyl chloride with *t*-butylmagnesium

[43] Whitmore and Lewis, *J. Am. Chem. Soc.*, *64*, 1618–9 (1942).

[44] Petrov and Roslova, *J. Gen. Chem.*, (U.S.S.R.), *10*, 973–6 (1940); *Chem. Abstr.*, *35*, 2467 (1941).

[45] Bruce, *J. Am. Chem. Soc.*, *60*, 2277 (1938); Bruce and Todd, *ibid.*, *61*, 157–61 (1939).

[46] Whitmore and Wheeler, *J. Am. Chem. Soc.*, *60*, 2899–900 (1938).

chloride. Whitmore points out that Karasev[47] has reported acetone and acetone condensates as products of the reaction of ethyl acetate with *t*-butylmagnesium chloride, and suggests that some of the ethyl acetate formed by acetyl chloride cleavage of ether may be converted to mesityl oxide. Alternatively, he suggests that isobutylene may condense with acetyl chloride in the presence of magnesium chloride. The isobutane is attributed to the enolization of mesityl oxide and pinacolin.

$$CH_3COCl\ (\text{excess}) + t\text{-}C_4H_9MgCl \longrightarrow CH_3COCl + CH_3CO\text{-}t\text{-}C_4H_9\ (17.4\%)$$
$$+ CH_3CO_2CH(CH_3)\text{-}t\text{-}C_4H_9\ (8\%) + CH_3CO_2H$$
$$+ (CH_3)_2C{=}CHCOCH_3\ (6.6\%) + i\text{-}C_4H_{10}\ (23.6\%) + i\text{-}C_4H_8\ (6.6\%) + CO$$

The formation of *o*-tolyl derivatives in the reactions of benzylmagnesium chloride with acetyl chloride and with chloroformic esters have been reported by Whitmore and Sloat[48] and by Austin and Johnson,[49] respectively. Whereas such reactions are illustrative of an idiosyncracy of the benzyl Grignard reagents, and are affected only secondarily by the co-reactant, they are discussed under the topic, Allylic Rearrangements in Grignard Reactions (*q.v.*, Chapter XVII).

α-HALO CARBONYL HALIDES

The few reported reactions of Grignard reagents with α-halo carbonyl chlorides are those which one would be led to expect by the corresponding reactions of α-halo ketones (*q.v.*, Chapter VI).

For example, McKenzie and Boyle[50] record that the reaction of phenylmagnesium bromide (or iodide) with α-chlorodiphenylacetyl chloride, and subsequent hydrolysis of the Grignard complex, leads to triphenylvinyl alcohol.

$$(C_6H_5)_2CClCOCl \xrightarrow{C_6H_5MgX} (C_6H_5)_2CClCOC_6H_5 \xrightarrow{C_6H_5MgX}$$
$$(C_6H_5)_2C{=}C(C_6H_5)OMgX \xrightarrow{H_2O} (C_6H_5)_2C{=}C(C_6H_5)OH$$

The reactions of bromoacetyl bromide and chloroacetyl chloride with methylmagnesium halides, reported by Huston *et al.*,[51] and that of chloroacetyl chloride with phenylmagnesium bromide, reported by Boyle *et al.*,[52] yield products identical with, or analogous to, that obtained by Henry[53] in the reaction of chloroacetone with methylmagnesium bromide, and are adequately accounted for by extension of the reaction series proposed by Henry.

---

[47]Karasev, *J. Gen. Chem.* (U.S.S.R.), 7, 179–84 (1937); *Chem. Abstr.*, *31*, 4268 (1937).

[48]Whitmore and Sloat, *J. Am. Chem. Soc.*, *64*, 2968–70 (1942).

[49]Austin and Johnson, *J. Am. Chem. Soc.*, *54*, 647–60 (1932).

[50]McKenzie and Boyle, *J. Chem. Soc.*, *119*, 1131–40 (1921).

[51]Huston, Jackson, and Spero, *J. Am. Chem. Soc.*, *63*, 1459–60 (1941).

[52]Boyle, McKenzie, and Mitchell, *Ber.*, *70B*, 2153–60 (1937).

[53]Henry, *Compt. rend.*, *145*, 21–25 (1907); *Chem. Zentr.*, *1907,II*, 889; *Chem. Abstr.*, *1*, 2682 (1907).

$$XCH_2COX \xrightarrow{RMgX'} XCH_2COR \xrightarrow{RMgX'} XCH_2CR_2OMgX' \rightarrow H_2C\underset{O}{\diagdown\!\!\diagup}CR_2 \rightarrow$$

$$R_2CHCHO \xrightarrow{RMgX'} R_2CHCHROMgX' \xrightarrow{H_2O} R_2CHCHROH$$

α,β-UNSATURATED CARBONYL HALIDES

The α,β-unsaturated carbonyl halides have been but little investigated. Their reactions with Grignard reagents, however, appear to resemble those of the corresponding α,β-unsaturated esters (*q.v.*, Chapter VIII), and to be foreshadowed in part by the reactions of the α,β-unsaturated ketones (*q.v.*, Chapter VI) which may be postulated as possible intermediates.

Kohler and Heritage[54] brought about the reaction of cinnamoyl chloride with phenylmagnesium bromide in dilute ethereal solution at −20° under conditions not specified in detail. The viscous liquid product "obtained in the usual way," was first extracted by steam-distillation to remove traces of bromobenzene and biphenyl, and was then extracted with hot water, which removed a small amount of cinnamic acid. The residue was then submitted to alkaline hydrolysis. The alkali-insoluble fraction proved to be chiefly α,β-diphenylpropiophenone. Acidification of the alkaline filtrate precipitated cinnamic and α,β-diphenylpropionic acids, which were separated by fractional crystallization.

Kohler accounted for the production of α,β-diphenylpropionic acid and a part of the cinnamic acid as follows:

$$C_6H_5CH{=}CHCOCl \xrightarrow{C_6H_5MgBr}$$

$$(C_6H_5)_2CHCH{=}CClOMgBr \xrightarrow{C_6H_5CH{=}CHCOCl}$$

$$(C_6H_5)_2CHCH{=}CClO_2CCH{=}CHC_6H_5 \xrightarrow{KOH}$$

$$(C_6H_5)_2CHCH_2CO_2K + C_6H_5CH{=}CHCO_2K$$

α,β-Diphenylpropiophenone and the remainder of the cinnamic acid were attributed to the following reaction sequence:

$$C_6H_5CH{=}CHCOCl \xrightarrow{2\ C_6H_5MgBr}$$

$$(C_6H_5)_2CHCH{=}C(C_6H_5)OMgBr \xrightarrow{C_6H_5CH{=}CHCOCl}$$

$$(C_6H_5)_2CHCH{=}C(C_6H_5)O_2CCH{=}CHC_6H_5 \xrightarrow{KOH}$$

$$(C_6H_5)_2CHCH_2COC_6H_5 + C_6H_5CH{=}CHCO_2K$$

An explanation of α,β-diphenylpropionic acid production at least as credible as that proposed by Kohler would be:

$$C_6H_5CH{=}CHCOCl \xrightarrow{C_6H_5MgBr} (C_6H_5)_2CHCH{=}CO + MgBrCl$$

$$(C_6H_5)_2CHCH{=}CO \xrightarrow{H_2O} (C_6H_5)_2CHCH_2CO_2H$$

Being non-volatile with steam and virtually water-insoluble, the propionic acid would appear in the alkaline hydrolysate.

---

[54] Kohler and Heritage, *Am. Chem. J.*, 33, 21–35 (1905).

In the presence of excess Grignard reagent the ketene would be converted to the enolate of α,β-diphenylpropiophenone.

$$(C_6H_5)_2CHCH{=\!=}CO \xrightarrow{C_6H_5MgBr} (C_6H_5)_2CHCH{=\!=}C(C_6H_5)OMgBr$$

Incidentally, on the basis of the experimental evidence presented, this enolate (structurally identical with that produced by the 1,4-addition of phenylmagnesium bromide to benzalacetophenone) need not necessarily undergo *O*-acylation upon further reaction with acid chloride. *C*-Acylation would yield a ketone of a type readily cloven by alkali to form the same products that would be expected to result from hydrolysis of the ester.[55]

$$[(C_6H_5)_2CHCHCOC_6H_5]^- MgBr^+ \xrightarrow{C_6H_5CH{=\!=}CHCOCl}$$
$$(C_6H_5)_2CHCH(COC_6H_5)COCH{=\!=}CHC_6H_5 \xrightarrow{KOH}$$
$$(C_6H_5)_2CHCH_2COC_6H_5 + C_6H_5CH{=\!=}CHCO_2K$$

This carbonyl chloride-Grignard reagent reaction, and others like it would repay further study.

Ivanoff and Nicoloff[56] have studied the reaction of cinnamoyl chloride with the "Grignard reagent"* derived from sodium phenylacetate. Ketone formation (and decarboxylation), together with some 1,4-addition to the unsaturated ketone, are reported.

$$C_6H_5CH{=\!=}CHCOCl + C_6H_5CH(CO_2Na)MgX \longrightarrow$$
$$C_6H_5CH_2COCH{=\!=}CHC_6H_5 + C_6H_5CH_2COCH_2CH(C_6H_5)CH(C_6H_5)CO_2H$$

CARBONYL HALIDES OTHER THAN THOSE OF THE TYPE RCOX

Phosgene has been used by Grignard[57] and others (see Table IX-II) to prepare tertiary alcohols in which all three carbinol substituents are supplied by the Grignard reagent.

$$COCl_2 + 3\ RMgX \longrightarrow R_3COMgX + 2\ MgXCl$$

The chloroformic esters are at once esters and acyl chlorides. Whereas the carbonyl chlorine is the more reactive of the two functional groups, esters may be prepared by the addition of one equivalent of Grignard reagent to a chloroformic ester solution.

$$ROCOCl + R'MgX \longrightarrow R'CO_2R + MgXCl$$

When an excess of Grignard reagent is used a tertiary alcohol is formed.

$$ROCOCl + 3\ R'MgX \longrightarrow R'_3COMgX + MgXOR + MgXCl$$

For this reason chloroformic ester reactions are included in both the ester (Table VIII-III) and carbonyl halide (Table IX-II) tabulations.

---

[55] See: Kohler and Peterson, *J. Am. Chem. Soc.*, *55*, 1073-82 (1933).

[56] Ivanoff and Nicoloff, *Bull. soc. chim.*, [4], *51*, 1331-7 (1932).

*It has been suggested by Schlenk, Hillemann, and Rodloff, *Ann.*, *487*, 135-54 (1931), that this compound should be formulated as an enolate.

[57] Grignard, *Compt. rend.*, *136*, 815-7 (1903); *Chem. Zentr.*, *1903,I*, 1077.

TABLE IX-II

REACTIONS OF GRIGNARD REAGENTS WITH CARBONYL HALIDES

Halide	RMgX	Product(s)	Ref.
$COCl_2$			
$COCl_2$	n-C_3H_7MgBr (3 equiv.)	n-$(C_3H_7)_2CHOH$; $(n$-$C_3H_7)_3COH$	*1*
$COCl_2$	Pyrryl-MgBr	2-Pyrryl ketone (28.5%)	*130,94,95*
$COCl_2$ (25 ml. 20% sol'n)	2-Methylpyrryl-MgBr (8 g. C_5H_7N)	Bis(5-methyl-2-pyrryl) ketone (5–6 g.)	*94*
$COCl_2$	i-$C_5H_{11}MgBr$ (2 equiv.)	$(i$-$C_5H_{11})_2C{=}CH$-i-C_4H_9	*1*
$COCl_2$	i-$C_5H_{11}MgBr$ (3 equiv.)	$(i$-$C_5H_{11})_2CHOH$; $(i$-$C_5H_{11})_3COH$	*1*
$COCl_2$	C_6H_5MgBr (3 equiv.)	$(C_6H_5)_3COH$ (50%)	*2*
$COCl_2$ (15 ml. 20% sol'n)	2-Ethylpyrryl-MgBr (5.7 g. C_6H_9N)	Bis(5-ethyl-2-pyrryl) ketone (*ca.* 60%)	*94*
$COCl_2$ (25 ml. 20% sol'n)	2,3-Dimethylpyrryl-MgBr (9.5 g. C_6H_9N)	Bis(4,5-dimethyl-2-pyrryl) ketone	*94*
$COCl_2$	$C_6H_5CH_2MgBr$ (2 equiv.)	$(C_6H_5CH_2)_3COH$ (35–40%)	*2*
$COCl_2$	4-$CH_3C_6H_4MgBr$ (3 equiv.)	$(4$-$CH_3C_6H_4)_3COH$ ("moderate yield")	*2*
$COCl_2$	2-Methyl-4-ethylpyrryl-MgBr	Bis(3-ethyl-5-methyl-2-pyrryl) ketone (30–35%)	*94*
$COCl_2$ (25 ml. 20% sol'n)	Xanthopyrryl-MgBr (10 g. $C_7H_{11}N$)	Bis(3-methyl-5-ethyl-2-pyrryl) ketone (7.0–7.5 g.)	*94*
$COCl_2$	2,3,4-Trimethylpyrryl-MgBr (12 g. $C_7H_{11}N$)	Bis(3,4,5-trimethyl-2-pyrryl) ketone (10–11 g.)	*94*
$COCl_2$ (1.22 g.)	Indolyl-MgBr (2.50 g. C_8H_7N)	3-Indolyl ketone	*96*
$COCl_2$	$C_6H_5CH(CO_2Na)MgCl$* (2 equiv.)	$(C_6H_5CH_2CO)_2O$ (78.1%); $C_6H_5CH_2CO_2H$ (15.6%); CO_2; CO	*97*
$COCl_2$	2-Methyl-3-carbethoxypyrryl-MgBr (1.5 g. $C_8H_{11}NO_2$)	Bis(4-carbethoxy-5-methyl-2-pyrryl) ketone (15–20%)	*94*
$COCl_2$	2,4-Diethylpyrryl-MgBr (10 g. $C_8H_{13}N$)	Bis(3,5-diethyl-2-pyrryl) ketone (4–6 g.)	*94*

*In the opinion of Schlenk, Hilleman, and Rodloff, *Ann.*, *487*, 135–54 (1931), this "Grignard reagent" should be formulated as an enolate.

TABLE IX-II (Continued)

Halide	RMgX	Product(s)	Ref.
$COCl_2$ (*cont.*)			
$COCl_2$	2-Methylindolyl-MgBr	Bis (α-methyl-β-indolyl) ketone	*96*
$COCl_2$ (15 ml. 20% sol'n)	2-Methyl-3,4-diethylpyrryl-MgBr	Bis (3,4-diethyl-5-methyl-2-pyrryl) ketone	*94*
$COCl_2$	2,4-Dimethyl-3-*n*-propylpyrryl-MgBr	Bis(3,5-dimethyl-4-*n*-propyl-2-pyrryl) ketone	*94*
$COCl_2$	2,3-Diethyl-4-methylpyrryl-MgBr (4.2 g. $C_9H_{15}N$)	Bis (3-methyl-4,5-diethyl-2-pyrryl) ketone (2.5 g.)	*94*
$COCl_2$	2,3,4-Triethylpyrryl-MgBr (1.6 g. $C_{10}H_{17}N$)	Bis(3,4-5-triethyl-2-pyrryl) ketone (20–25%)	*94*
$COCl_2$ (25 ml. 20% sol'n)	2,3-Diethyl-4-*n*-propylpyrryl-MgBr (13 g. $C_{11}H_{19}N$)	Bis(3-*n*-propyl-4,5-diethyl-2-pyrryl) ketone	*94*
$COCl_2$ (5 ml.)	2,4,6-$(C_6H_5)_3C_6H_2MgBr$ (50 g. $C_{24}H_{17}Br$)	$[2,4,6\text{-}(C_6H_5)_3C_6H_2\text{—}]_2$ (8 g.); $[2,4,6\text{-}(C_6H_5)_3C_6H_2]_2CO$ (6 g.); 2,4,6-$(C_6H_5)_3C_6H_3$	*3*
C_2OCl_4			
Cl_3CCOCl	C_2H_5MgBr	$Cl_3C(C_2H_5)CHOH$	*98*
$C_2O_2Cl_2$			
$(\text{—}COCl)_2$	Cryptopyrryl-MgBr (10.0 g. $C_8H_{13}N$)	1,2-Bis (3,5-dimethyl-4-ethyl-2-pyrryl)-1,2-ethanedione	*99*
$(\text{—}COCl)_2$ (0.6 g.)	$C_6H_5C\equiv CMgBr$ (3.1 g. C_8H_6)	$C_{34}H_{22}O_2$ (0.1 g.)	*103*
$C_2H_2OCl_2$			
$ClCH_2COCl$	CH_3MgBr (3 equiv.)	$CH_3(i\text{-}C_3H_7)CHOH$	*5*
$ClCH_2COCl$	CH_3MgBr (4 equiv.)	$CH_3(i\text{-}C_3H_7)CHOH$ (51%)	*4*
$ClCH_2COCl$	CH_3MgI (4 equiv.)	$CH_3(i\text{-}C_3H_7)CHOH$ (48%)	*4*
$ClCH_2COCl$	Pyrryl-MgBr	2-Chloroäcetylpyrrole	*100*

TABLE IX-II (Continued)

Halide	RMgX	Product(s)	Ref.
$C_2H_2OCl_2$ (*cont.*)			
$ClCH_2COCl$ (28 g.)	C_6H_5MgBr (230 g. C_6H_5Br)	$(C_6H_5)_2CHCH(OH)C_6H_5$ (36 g.); $ClCH_2C(C_6H_5)_2OH$ (0.3 g.)	*6*
$ClCH_2COCl$	Indolyl-MgBr	3-Chloroäcetylindole; 2-chloroäcetylindole (?)	*7*
$ClCH_2COCl$ (5.6 g.)	3-Methylindolyl-MgBr (6.5 g. C_9H_9N)	2-Chloroäcetyl-3-methylindole	*7*
$C_2H_2OBr_2$			
$BrCH_2COBr$	CH_3MgBr (4 equiv.)	$CH_3(i\text{-}C_3H_7)CHOH$ (21%)	*4*
$BrCH_2COBr$	CH_3MgI (4 equiv.)	$CH_3(i\text{-}C_3H_7)CHOH$ (16%)	*4*
C_2H_3OCl			
CH_3COCl	CH_3MgI	$(CH_3)_3COH$	*8*
CH_3COCl	Pyrryl-MgI (1 equiv.)	2-Acetylpyrrole (50–60%)	*9*
CH_3COCl (2 moles)	$n\text{-}C_4H_9MgBr$ (5 moles C_4H_9Br)	$CH_3(n\text{-}C_4H_9)_2COH$; $CH_3(n\text{-}C_4H_9)CHOH$ (13%); $n\text{-}C_4H_9OH$; C_2H_5OH (8%)	*10,11*
CH_3COCl (236 g.)	$t\text{-}C_4H_9MgCl$ (2.26 moles)	$CH_3CO\text{-}t\text{-}C_4H_9$((40.7%)	*12,13*
CH_3COCl (3.2 moles)	$t\text{-}C_4H_9MgCl$ (2.46 moles)	$CH_3CO_2CH(CH_3)\text{-}t\text{-}C_4H_9$ (8%); $CH_3CO\text{-}t\text{-}C_4H_9$ (17%); $CH_3CO_2C_2H_5$ (9%); $i\text{-}C_4H_8$ (6.6%); $CH_3COCH=C(CH_3)_2$ (6.6%); $i\text{-}C_4H_{10}$ (23.6%); CO	*14,11*
CH_3COCl* (345 g. 4.4 moles)	$t\text{-}C_4H_9MgCl$ (2.72 moles)	$CH_3CO\text{-}t\text{-}C_4H_9$ (10%); $CH_3CO_2\text{-}n\text{-}C_4H_9$ (2%); $CH_3COCH=C(CH_3)_2$ (5%); $CH_3CO_2CH(CH_3)\text{-}t\text{-}C_4H_9$ (11%); $i\text{-}C_4H_8$ (0.356 mole); $i\text{-}C_4H_{10}$ (0.522 mole); CO (0.005 mole)	*90*
CH_3COCl	$(CH_3)_3SiCH_2MgCl$	$(CH_3)_2CO$; unidentified products	*101*
CH_3COCl (1 mole)	2-Thenyl-MgCl (0.246 mole)	2-Methyl-2-acetylthiophene (31–34%)	*133*

*Reaction in $n\text{-}Bu_2O$ solution.

TABLE IX-II (Continued)

Halide	RMgX	Product(s)	Ref.
C_2H_3OCl (*cont.*)			
CH_3COCl (308 g.)	$CH_3(i\text{-}C_3H_7)CHMgBr$ (412 g.)	$CH_3COCH(CH_3)\text{-}i\text{-}C_3H_7$ (55 g., 9.3%)	*15*
CH_3COCl (2.2 moles)	$t\text{-}C_5H_{11}MgCl$ (1.97 mole)	$CH_3CO\text{-}t\text{-}C_5H_{11}$ (< 66.5 g.)	*12*
CH_3COCl (3.1 moles)	$t\text{-}C_5H_{11}MgCl$ (1.99 mole)	$CH_3CO\text{-}t\text{-}C_5H_{11}$ (96.6 g.)	*12*
CH_3COCl	$t\text{-}C_5H_{11}MgCl$	$CH_3CO_2C_2H_5$ (4%); $CH_3CO\text{-}t\text{-}C_5H_{11}$ (9%); $CH_3COC(CH_3){=}C(CH_3)_2$ (9%)	*90*
CH_3COCl	C_6H_5MgBr	$C_6H_5CH{=}CH_2$	*16*
CH_3COCl	C_6H_5MgBr (2.5 equiv.)	$CH_3(C_6H_5)_2COH$ (39%)	*17*
CH_3COCl	2-Pyridylmethyl-MgX*	2-Pyridylacetone	*131*
CH_3COCl	2,5-Dimethylpyrryl-MgI	2,5-Dimethyl-3-acetylpyrrole (86%)	*18*
CH_3COCl	$RC{\equiv}CMgX$†	$CH_3COC{\equiv}CR$† (8–15% for chlorides and bromides; 0% for iodides)	*102*
CH_3COCl	$CH_3(C_2H_5)_2CMgCl$	$CH_3COC(C_2H_5)_2CH_3$ (18%)	*12*
CH_3COCl	$2,6\text{-}Cl_2C_6H_3CH_2MgCl$	$CH_3COC_6H_2\text{-}3,5\text{-}Cl_2\text{-}4\text{-}CH_3$	*27*
CH_3COCl	$2\text{-}ClC_6H_4CH_2MgCl$	$CH_3COC_6H_3\text{-}2\text{-}CH_3\text{-}3\text{-}Cl$	*27*
CH_3COCl (excess)	$C_6H_5CH_2MgCl$	$CH_3COC_6H_4\text{-}2\text{-}CH_3$ (18%)	*19,27*
CH_3COCl (52 g.)	$2\text{-}CH_3C_6H_4MgBr$ (114 g. C_7H_7Br)	$CH_3COC_6H_4\text{-}2\text{-}CH_3$ (30%)	*26*
CH_3COCl	$n\text{-}C_4H_9(CH_3)_2CMgCl$	$CH_3COC(CH_3)_2\text{-}n\text{-}C_4H_9$ (9%)	*12*
CH_3COCl (0.05, 0.075, and 0.10 mole)	$C_6H_5CH(CO_2Na)MgX$‡ (0.10 mole)	$CH_3COCH_2C_6H_5$ (54%, 48%, and 42%); $CH_3C[CH(C_6H_5)CO_2H]_2OH$ (25%, 19.8%, and 25%)	*20*
CH_3COCl (28 ml.)	2-Thianaphthenylmethyl-MgCl (0.0277 mole)	2-Methyl-3-acetylthianaphthene (1.51 g., 29%)	*129*
CH_3COCl (15.7 g.)	$2,4,6\text{-}(CH_3)_3C_6H_2MgBr$ (40 g. $C_9H_{11}Br$)	$CH_3COC_6H_2\text{-}2,4,6\text{-}(CH_3)_3$ (10%)	*26*

*X = Br, I.

†R = $n\text{-}C_4H_9$, $n\text{-}C_5H_{11}$; X = Cl, Br, I.

‡In the opinion of Schlenk, Hilleman, and Rodloff, *Ann.*, *487*, 135–54 (1931), this "Grignard reagent" should be formulated as an enolate.

TABLE IX-II (Continued)

Halide	RMgX	Product(s)	Ref.
C_2H_3OCl (*cont.*)			
CH_3COCL (19.5 g.)	1-$C_{10}H_7MgBr$ (52 g. $C_{10}H_7Br$)	CH_3CO-1-$C_{10}H_7$ (50%)	*26*
CH_3COCl	1-$C_{10}H_7CH_2MgCl$	1-$C_{10}H_7CH{=}C(CH_3)CH_2$-1-$C_{10}H_7$	*21*
CH_3COCl (5 g.)	2-$C_{10}H_7CH_2MgBr$ (9 g. $C_{11}H_9Br$)	2-$C_{10}H_7CH{=}C(CH_3)CH_2$-2-$C_{10}H_7$ (4.5 g.)	*21*
CH_3COCl	$(CH_3)_5C_6MgBr$	$CH_3COC_6(CH_3)_5$ (38%)	*22,23*
CH_3COCl (0.5 mole)	9-Fluorenyl-MgBr (0.11 mole)	9-Acetylfluorene (50%)	*24*
CH_3COCl (0.5 mole)	9-Phenanthryl-MgBr (0.11 mole)	9-Acetylphenanthrene (27%)	*24*
CH_3COCl	$(C_6H_5)_3CMgCl$	"Passive"	*25*
CH_3COCl (1.6 g.)	2,4,6-$(C_6H_5)_3C_6H_2$-MgBr (7.7 g. $C_{24}H_{17}Br$)	$CH_3COC_6H_2$-2,4,6-$(C_6H_5)_3$	*3*
$C_2H_3O_2Cl$			
CH_3OCOCl (9.4 g.)	Pyrryl-MgBr (6.7 g. C_4H_5N)	Methyl 2-pyrrolecarboxylate (85–90%)	*100*
CH_3OCOCl (10 g.)	2,6-$Cl_2C_6H_3CH_2MgCl$	2,6-$Cl_2C_6H_3CH_2CO_2H$; unidentified fraction	*27*
CH_3OCOCl (excess)	2-$ClC_6H_4CH_2MgCl$ (0.032 mole)	2-$ClC_6H_4CH_2CO_2H$	*27*
CH_3OCOCl (10 g.)	$C_6H_5CH_2MgCl$ (0.07 mole)	2-$CH_3C_6H_4CO_2CH_3$ (equiv. 1 g. acid); $C_6H_5CH_2CO_2H$ (trace)	*27*
CH_3OCOCl (9.45 g.)	*t*-$C_4H_9(C_6H_5)$(*t*-$C_4H_9C{\equiv}C)CMgBr$ (30.7 g., $C_{17}H_{23}Br$)	*t*-$C_4H_9(C_6H_5)C{=}C{=}C$(*t*-$C_4H_9)CO_2CH_3$ (18.5 g., 64%)	*132*
CH_3OCOCl	$(C_6H_5)_3CMgBr$	$(C_6H_5)_3CCO_2CH_3$ (66%)	*28*
C_3H_4OClBr			
$CH_3CHBrCOCl$	Pyrryl-MgX	"Bromopropionylpyrrole"	*107*
C_3H_5OCl			
C_2H_5COCl	Pyrryl-MgBr	2-Propionylpyrrole (50%)	*29*
C_2H_5COCl	Pyrryl-MgI	2-Propionylpyrrole (50–60%)	*9*

TABLE IX-II (Continued)

Halide	RMgX	Product(s)	Ref.
C_3H_5OCl (*cont.*)			
C_2H_5COCl	t-C_4H_9MgCl	$(C_2H_5)_2CO$; C_2H_5CO-t-C_4H_9; n-C_3H_7OH; $C_2H_5CO_2H$; $C_2H_5CO_2CH(C_2H_5)_2$; $C_2H_5CO_2CH(C_2H_5)$-t-C_4H_9	*31*
C_2H_5COCl	C_6H_5MgBr (2 equiv.)	$C_2H_5(C_6H_5)_2COH$ (57%)	*17*
C_2H_5COCl	2,5-Dimethylpyrryl-MgX	2,5-Dimethyl-3-propionylpyrrole	*18*
$C_3H_5O_2Cl$			
C_2H_5OCOCl	2-Furyl-MgI (1 equiv.)	Ethyl furoate	*30*
C_2H_5OCOCl (1 mole)	2-Thenyl-MgCl (0.179 mole)	2-Methyl-3-thiophenecarboxylic acid (17.85 g., 72%)	*133*
C_2H_5OCOCl	t-$C_5H_{11}MgCl$ (1 equiv.)	t-$C_5H_{11}CO_2C_2H_5$ (46%)	*12*
C_2H_5OCOCl	2,4-Dimethylpyrryl-MgX	Ethyl 3,5-dimethyl-2-pyrrolecarboxylate	*104*
C_2H_5OCOCl (50 g.)	$C_6H_5CH_2MgCl$ (50 g. C_7H_7Cl)	$C_6H_5CH_2CO_2C_2H_5$ (28 g., 43%); $(C_6H_5CH_2)_3COH$ (6 g.)	*32*
C_2H_5OCOCl	$C_6H_5CH_2MgCl$ (1 equiv.)	2-$CH_3C_6H_4CO_2H$; $C_6H_5CH_2CO_2H$; $(C_6H_5CH_2)_3COH$	*27,33*
C_2H_5OCOCl (1.07 mole)	n-$C_4H_9(CH_3)_2CMgCl$ (0.99 mole)	n-$C_4H_9(CH_3)_2CCO_2C_2H_5$ (47.1 g.)	*12*
C_2H_5OCOCl	$C_6H_5CH(CO_2Na)MgCl$*	$C_6H_5CH(CO_2H)CO_2C_2H_5$ (73%)	*97*
C_2H_5OCOCl (3.0 g.)	$(C_8H_9NO_2MgBr)MgBr$†	Ethyl 3-methyl-4-(β-carboxyethyl)-2-pyrrolecarboxylate (45%)	*105*
C_2H_5OCOCl (33 ml.)	3-Thianaphthenylmethyl-MgCl (0.164 mole)	3-Methyl-2-thianaphthenecarboxylic acid (13.6 g., 43%)	*134*
C_2H_5OCOCl (2.6 g.)	$(C_9H_{11}NO_2MgBr)MgBr$‡	Ethyl 3-(β-carboxyethyl)-4,5-dimethyl-2-pyrrolecarboxylate (45%)	*105*

*In the opinion of Schlenk, Hilleman, and Rodloff, *Ann.*, *487*, 135–54 (1931), this "Grignard reagent" should be formulated as an enolate.

†From 2.2 g. "opsopyrrolecarboxylic acid."

‡From 2.0 g. "hemopyrrolecarboxylic acid."

TABLE IX-II (Continued)

Halide	RMgX	Product(s)	Ref.
$C_3H_5O_2Cl$ (*cont.*)			
C_2H_5OCOCl	2-Phenylpyrryl-MgBr	Ethyl 5-phenylpyrrole-2-carboxylate	*34*
C_2H_5OCOCl (10 g.)	$C_{10}H_{17}MgCl$* (0.1 mole)	Recovered ester (55%); $(C_{10}H_{17})CO_2C_2H_5$ (33%); $(C_{10}H_{17})CH_2OH$ (12%); bornylene	*106*
C_2H_5OCOCl (69 g.)	Bornyl-MgCl† (0.5 mole)	$(C_{10}H_{17})CO_2C_2H_5$ (95%)	*106*
C_2H_5OCOCl (20 g.)	Isobornyl-MgCl‡ (0.136 mole)	$(C_{10}H_{17})CH_2OH$ (0.039 mole); bornylene	*106*
C_2H_5OCOCl (4 g.)	9-Phenanthryl-MgBr (6.45 g. $C_{14}H_9Br$)	Ethyl phenanthrene-9-carboxylate (> 50%)	*35*
C_2H_5OCOCl	$(C_6H_5)_3CMgBr$	$(C_6H_5)_3CCO_2C_2H_5$ (72%)	*28*
$C_4H_4O_2Cl_2$			
$(—CH_2COCl)_2$	$C_6H_5CH(CO_2Na)MgCl$§ (2 equiv.)	$(—CH_2CO_2H)_2$ (74%); $(C_6H_5CH_2CO)_2O$ (40.7%); $C_6H_5CH_2CO_2H$ (40.4%)	*97*
$C_4H_5O_2Cl$			
CH_3COCH_2COCl (12% excess)	n-C_4H_9MgBr (1 mole)	CH_3COCH_2CO-n-C_4H_9 (1.4 g., 10%)	*36*
CH_3COCH_2COCl (35 g.)	n-$C_7H_{15}MgBr$ (46 g. $C_7H_{15}Br$)	CH_3COCH_2CO-n-C_7H_{15} (16%)	*36*
CH_3COCH_2COCl	n-$C_8H_{17}MgBr$	CH_3COCH_2CO-n-C_8H_{17} (16%)	*36*
CH_3COCH_2COCl	$CH_3(n$-$C_6H_{13})CHMgBr$	$CH_3COCH_2COCH(CH_3)$-n-C_6H_{13} (6%); n-C_8H_{18} (60%)	*36*

*From (+)-α-pinene hydrochloride; Rivière *(106)* concludes that this Grignard reagent is an equimolecular mixture of bornyl- and isobornylmagnesium chlorides.

†Prepared by refluxing in xylene for three hours at *ca.* 140° the Grignard reagent from (+)-α-pinene hydrochloride.

‡Prepared by partial (*ca.* 66%) carbonation of the Grignard reagent from (+)-α-pinene hydrochloride, which removes the more reactive bornylmagnesium chloride.

§In the opinion of Schlenk, Hilleman, and Rodloff, *Ann.*, *487*, 135–54 (1931), this "Grignard reagent" should be formulated as an enolate.

TABLE IX-II (Continued)

Halide	RMgX	Product (s)	Ref.
$C_4H_5O_3Cl$			
$H_5C_2O_2CCOCl$	RMgX* (2 equiv.)	$H_5C_2O_2CCR_2OH$* (35–40%)	37
$H_5C_2O_2CCOCl$	CH_3MgI (1 equiv.)	$HO(CH_3)_2CCO_2C_2H_5$; $H_5C_2O_2CCO_2C(CH_3)_2CO_2C_2H_5$	38
$H_5C_2O_2CCOCl$ (1 mole)	C_2H_5MgI (1 mole)	$HO(C_2H_5)_2CCO_2C_2H_5$ (19 g.); $H_5C_2O_2CCO_2C(C_2H_5)_2CO_2C_2H_5$ (58 g.)	38
$H_5C_2O_2CCOCl$	Pyrryl-MgBr (1 equiv.)	Ethyl 2-pyrroleglyoxalate (91%)	108
$H_5C_2O_2CCOCl$	2,5-Dimethylpyrryl-MgI	Ethyl 2,5-dimethyl-3-pyrroleglyoxalate	18
$H_5C_2O_2CCOCl$ (0.25 mole)	$4-CH_3C_6H_4MgBr$ (0.50 mole)	$HO(4-CH_3C_6H_4)_2CCO_2C_2H_5$ (equiv. to 27 g. acid)	38
$H_5C_2O_2CCOCl$ (6.8 g.)	Indolyl-MgBr (5.2 g. C_8H_7N)	Ethyl 3-indoleglyoxalate	109
$H_5C_2O_2CCOCl$	$C_6H_5CH(CO_2Na)MgCl$†	$C_6H_5CH_2COCO_2C_2H_5$	97
C_4H_7OCl			
$n-C_3H_7COCl$	Pyrryl-MgI	2-Butyrylpyrrole (50–60%)	9
$n-C_3H_7COCl$ (1 mole)	$t-C_4H_9MgCl$ (4 moles)	$i-C_4H_8$ (0.94 mole); $n-C_4H_9OH$ (9%); $n-C_3H_7(t-C_4H_9)CHOH$ (71%)	11
$n-C_3H_7COCl$ (0.98 mole)	$t-C_4H_9MgCl$ (4 moles)	$(t-C_4H_9—)_2$ (20 g.); $n-C_4H_9OH$ (6.5 g., 9%); $n-C_3H_7(t-C_4H_9)CHOH$ (90.8 g., 71%); $i-C_4H_8$ (94% on basis of $t-C_4H_9Cl$)	39
$n-C_3H_7COCl$ (200 g.)	$t-C_4H_9MgCl$ (1.86 mole)	$n-C_3H_7CO-t-C_4H_9$ (21%); $n-C_3H_7CO_2-n-C_4H_9$ (11.6%); $n-C_3H_7CO_2CH(n-C_3H_7)-t-C_4H_9$ (36.8%)	90
$n-C_3H_7COCl$	C_6H_5MgBr (2.5 equiv.)	$C_2H_5CH{=}C(C_6H_5)_2$ (84%)	17

*R = CH_3, C_2H_5, $i-C_5H_{11}$, C_6H_5, $4-CH_3C_6H_4$.

†In the opinion of Schlenk, Hilleman, and Rodloff, *Ann.*, *487*, 135–54 (1931), this "Grignard reagent" should be formulated as an enolate.

TABLE IX-II (Continued)

Halide	RMgX	Product (s)	Ref.
C_4H_7OCl (*cont.*)			
i-C_3H_7COCl	CH_3MgCl (1 equiv.)	CH_3CO-i-C_3H_7 (7.6%); i-$C_3H_7(CH_3)_2COH$	40,123
i-C_3H_7COCl	n-C_3H_7MgCl (1 equiv.)	n-C_3H_7CO-i-C_3H_7 (7.6%); i-$C_3H_7(CH_3)_2COH$	40,123
i-C_3H_7COCl	i-C_3H_7MgCl (1 equiv.)	$(i$-$C_3H_7)_2CO$; C_3H_6; $(i$-$C_3H_7)_2CHOH$; $(i$-$C_3H_7)_3COH$	40,123
i-C_3H_7COCl (0.84 mole)	t-C_4H_9MgCl (4.2 moles)	$(t$-C_4H_9—$)_2$ (2.2 g.); i-C_4H_9OH (12.5 g.); i-$C_3H_7(t$-$C_4H_9)CHOH$ (82.0 g.); i-C_4H_8 (*ca.* 1.3 mole)	39,11
i-C_3H_7COCl	t-C_4H_9MgCl (1 equiv.)	i-C_3H_7CO-t-C_4H_9 (35%); i-$C_3H_7(t$-$C_4H_9)_2COH$	40,123
i-C_3H_7COCl* (20 moles)	t-C_4H_9MgCl (20 moles)	i-C_3H_7CO-t-C_4H_9 (87%); i-$C_3H_7CO_2$-i-C_4H_9 (5%); i-C_3H_7CHO (0.1%); i-C_4H_9OH (2%)	41
i-C_3H_7COCl (1.86 mole)	t-C_4H_9MgCl (1.86 mole)	i-C_3H_7CO-t-C_4H_9 (19%, crude); i-$C_3H_7(t$-$C_4H_9)CHOH$ (17.7%); i-$C_3H_7CO_2CH(i$-$C_3H_7)$-t-C_4H_9 (45%)	90
i-C_3H_7COCl (160 g., 1.5 mole)	t-$C_5H_{11}MgCl$ (1.3 mole)	i-$C_3H_7CO_2$-i-C_4H_9 (44%)	90
i-C_3H_7COCl	C_6H_5MgX (1 equiv.)	i-$C_3H_7COC_6H_5$ (21%)	40
i-C_3H_7COCl	2-$CH_3C_6H_4MgBr$ (1 equiv.)	i-$C_3H_7COC_6H_4$-2-CH_3 (67%); i-$C_3H_7(2$-$CH_3C_6H_4)_2COH$	40,123
i-C_3H_7COCl	2-$CH_3OC_6H_4MgX$ (1 equiv.)	i-$C_3H_7COC_6H_4$-2-OCH_3 (63%)	40,123
i-C_3H_7COCl (0.1 mole)	$C_6H_5CH(CO_2Na)MgX$† (0.2 mole)	i-$C_3H_7COCH_2C_6H_5$ (10.7 g., 66%); i-$C_3H_7C[CH(C_6H_5)CO_2H]_2OH$ (5 g., 14.6%)	20

*Reaction at 14–17° in copper vessel; reverse order of addition.

†In the opinion of Schlenk, Hilleman, and Rodloff, *Ann.*, *487*, 135–54 (1931), this "Grignard reagent" should be formulated as an enolate.

TABLE IX-II (Continued)

Halide	RMgX	Product(s)	Ref.
C_4H_7OCl (*cont.*)			
i-C_3H_7COCl	2,6-$(CH_3)_2C_6H_3MgX$ (1 equiv.)	*i*-$C_3H_7COC_6H_3$-2,6-$(CH_3)_2$ (65%)	*40,123*
i-C_3H_7COCl	1-$C_{10}H_7MgBr$ (1 equiv.)	*i*-C_3H_7CO-1-$C_{10}H_7$ (63%)	*40,123*
i-C_3H_7COCl	9-Phenanthryl-MgX (1 equiv.)	9-Isobutyrylphenanthrene (61%)	*40*
$C_4H_7O_2Cl$			
n-C_3H_7OCOCl	Pyrryl-MgBr	*n*-Propyl 2-pyrrolecarboxylate (85–90%)	*100*
C_5H_3OClS			
2-Thenoyl chloride	Pyrryl-MgBr	2-Thienyl 2-pyrryl ketone	*87*
2-Thenoyl chloride	Indolyl-MgBr	2-Thienyl 3-indolyl ketone	*87*
C_5H_4OClN			
2-Pyrrolecarbonyl chloride	Pyrryl-MgBr	2-Pyrryl ketone (11%)	*130,108*
$C_5H_7O_3Cl$			
$H_5C_2O_2CCH_2COCl$	Pyrryl-MgBr	Ethyl β-oxo-2-pyrrolepropionate	*100*
C_5H_9OCl			
i-C_4H_9COCl (0.1 mole)	$C_6H_5CH(CO_2Na)MgX$* (0.2 and 0.1 mole)	*i*-$C_4H_9COCH_2C_6H_5$ (66% and 48%); *i*-$C_4H_9C[CH(C_6H_5)CO_2H]_2OH$ (7% and 6%)	*20*
t-C_4H_9COCl (2.54 moles)	C_2H_5MgBr (6.1 moles)	*t*-$C_4H_9(C_2H_5)_2COH$ (26.1%); $C_2H_5(t\text{-}C_4H_9)CHOH$ (60.0%)	*43*

*In the opinion of Schlenk, Hilleman, and Rodloff, *Ann.*, *487*, 135–54 (1931), this "Grignard reagent" should be formulated as an enolate.

TABLE IX-II (Continued)

Halide	RMgX	Product(s)	Ref.
C_5H_9OCl (*cont.*)			
t-C_4H_9COCl (1.5 mole)	C_2H_5MgBr (5 moles C_2H_5Br)	t-$C_4H_9(C_2H_5)_2COH$ (20%); $C_2H_5(t$-$C_4H_9)CHOH$ (69%); C_2H_5OH; residue (10 g.)	*45*
t-C_4H_9COCl (1.5 mole)	n-C_3H_7MgBr (4.5 moles C_3H_7Br)	t-$C_4H_9CH_2OH$ (20%); n-C_3H_7OH; n-$C_3H_7(t$-$C_4H_9)CHOH$ (76%)	*45*
t-C_4H_9COCl (1.5 mole)	i-C_3H_7MgBr (4.5 moles)	i-C_3H_7OH; t-$C_4H_9CH_2OH$ (23%); i-$C_3H_7(t$-$C_4H_9)CHOH$ (53%)	*45*
t-C_4H_9COCl (*ca.* 1 mole)	n-C_4H_9MgBr (4 moles C_4H_9Br)	t-$C_4H_9CH_2OH$ (27–28%); n-$C_4H_9(t$-$C_4H_9)CHOH$ (69–71%)	*10,11,45*
t-C_4H_9COCl (1.5 mole)	i-C_4H_9MgBr (4.5 moles)	i-C_4H_9OH; t-$C_4H_9CH_2OH$ (61%); i-$C_4H_9(t$-$C_4H_9)CHOH$ (26%)	*45*
t-C_4H_9COCl (55.8 g., 0.465 mole)	i-C_4H_9MgI (0.98 mole)	t-$C_4H_9CH_2OH$ (74%)	*90*
t-C_4H_9COCl (302 g., 2.5 moles)	t-C_4H_9MgCl (7.0 moles)	t-$C_4H_9CH_2OH$; $(t$-$C_4H_9)_2CO$; t-C_4H_9CHO (1%)	*90*
t-C_4H_9COCl* (966.5 g.)	t-C_4H_9MgCl (1.5 mole)	$(t$-$C_4H_9)_2CO$ (67.4 g., 32%); mixture $(t$-$C_4H_9)_2CO$ and t-$C_4H_9CO_2CH_2$-t-C_4H_9 (?) (50.3 g.); t-$C_4H_9CO_2CH_2$-t-C_4H_9 (14.1 g.); $(t$-$C_4H_9CO)_2O$ (15.3 g.); i-C_4H_8 (17% on basis of G.r.).	*39*
t-C_4H_9COCl† (1.1 mole)	t-C_4H_9MgCl (3.9 moles)	$(t$-C_4H_9 —$)_2$ (6 g., crude); t-$C_4H_9CH_2OH$ 88 g., 94%); $(t$-$C_4H_9)_2CHOH$ (1.8 g., 1.5%); i-C_4H_8 (*ca.* 2 moles)	*39,11*
t-C_4H_9COCl (0.22 mole)	t-C_4H_9MgCl (1.1 mole)	i-C_4H_8 (0.27 mole); t-$C_4H_9CH_2OH$ (45%); t-$C_4H_9CO_2CH_2$-t-C_4H_9 (45%)	*11*

*Slow (17 hours) addition of filtered Grignard solution to Et_2O-chloride solution at $-10°$; warming to $50°$.
†Gradual (4.5 hours) addition of chloride to filtered Grignard solution at *ca.* $40°$; overnight standing.

TABLE IX-II (Continued)

Halide	RMgX	Product(s)	Ref.
C_5H_9OCl (*cont.*)			
t-C_4H_9COCl (8 moles)	*t*-C_4H_9MgCl (1.5 mole)	*i*-C_4H_8 (17%); *t*-$C_4H_9CO_2CH_2$-*t*-C_4H_9 (8%); (*t*-$C_4H_9)_2CO$ (32%); *t*-$C_4H_9CO_2H$ (6.2 moles)	*11*
t-C_4H_9COCl (1.5 mole)	*n*-$C_5H_{11}MgBr$ (4.5 moles $C_5H_{11}Br$)	*t*-$C_4H_9CH_2OH$ (20%); *t*-C_4H_9(*n*-C_5H_{11})CHOH (75%)	*45*
t-C_4H_9COCl (1.5 mole)	*i*-$C_5H_{11}MgBr$ (4.5 moles)	*i*-$C_5H_{11}OH$; $C_{16}H_{32}$ (7%); *t*-$C_4H_9CH_2OH$ (15%); *t*-C_4H_9(*i*-C_5H_{11})CHOH (71%)	*45*
t-C_4H_9COCl (0.5 mole)	*t*-$C_5H_{11}MgCl$ (1.17 mole)	*t*-$C_4H_9CH_2OH$ (97.5%)	*90*
t-C_4H_9COCl (129 g.)	C_6H_5MgBr (1050 ml., 1.6*N*)	*t*-$C_4H_9COC_6H_5$ (116 g., 67%)	*132*
$C_5H_9O_2Cl$			
i-C_4H_9OCOCl	Pyrryl-MgBr	Isobutyl 2-pyrrolecarboxylate (85–90%)	*100*
C_6H_3OClBr			
5-Bromonicotinyl chloride	CH_3MgBr	3-Acetyl-5-bromopyridine (15%)	*110*
5-Bromonicotinyl chloride	CH_3MgI (3.5 equiv.)	2-(5-Bromo-3-pyridyl)-2-propanol	*110*
$C_6H_3OCl_2$			
5-Chloronicotinyl chloride (20.0 g., 0.12 mole)	CH_3MgI (3.5 equiv.)	2-(5-Chloro-3-pyridyl)-2-propanol (14.2 g., 73%)	*110*
$C_6H_8O_2Cl_2$			
(—$CH_2CH_2COCl)_2$	$C_6H_5CH(CO_2Na)MgCl$* (2 equiv.)	(—$CH_2CH_2CO_2H)_2$ (82.2%); $(C_6H_5CH_2CO)_2O$ (16.6%); $C_6H_5CH_2CO_2H$ (58.0%)	*97*

*In the opinion of Schlenk, Hilleman, and Rodloff, *Ann.*, *487*, 135–54 (1931), this "Grignard reagent" should be formulated as an enolate.

TABLE IX-II (Continued)

Halide	RMgX	Product(s)	Ref.
C_6H_9OCl			
$H_2C{=}CH(CH_2)_3COCl$ (30 g.)	CH_3MgI (33 g. CH_3I)	$CH_3CO(CH_2)_3CH{=}CH_2$ (48%)	48
$C_6H_9O_3Cl$			
$H_5C_2O_2C(CH_2)_2COCl$	$C_6H_5CH(CO_2Na)MgCl$*	$H_5C_2O_2C(CH_2)_2COCH_2C_6H_5$	97
$C_6H_{11}OCl$			
i-$C_5H_{11}COCl$	t-C_4H_9MgCl (1 equiv.)	$(i$-$C_5H_{11})_2CO$; i-$C_5H_{11}CO_2$-i-C_6H_{13}	31
t-$C_4H_9CH_2COCl$[†] (1.3 mole)	C_2H_5MgBr (5 moles C_2H_5Br)	t-$C_4H_9CH_2(C_2H_5)_2COH$ (118.5 g., crude); C_2H_5OH	44
t-$C_4H_9CH_2COCl$[‡] (1.86 mole)	C_2H_5MgBr (1.84 mole)	t-$C_4H_9CH_2CO_2C_2H_5$; t-$C_4H_9CH_2CO_2CH(C_2H_5)CH_2$-$t$-$C_4H_9$ (7%); t-$C_4H_9CH_2COC_2H_5$ (51%); t-$C_4H_9CH_2(C_2H_5)_2COH$ (?); t-$C_4H_9CH_2CO_2H$	46
t-$C_4H_9CH_2COCl$[§] (1.7 mole)	n-C_3H_7MgBr (4.5 moles)	n-C_3H_7OH; n-$C_3H_7(t$-$C_4H_9CH_2)CHOH$ (24.4%); t-$C_4H_9CH_2(n$-$C_3H_7)_2COH$	44
t-$C_4H_9CH_2COCl$[¶] (1.94 mole)	n-C_3H_7MgBr (1.85 mole)	t-$C_4H_9CH_2CO_2C_2H_5$; t-$C_4H_9CH_2CO$-n-C_3H_7 (36.7%); t-$C_4H_9CH_2CO_2$-$CH(n$-$C_3H_7)CH_2$-t-C_4H_9 (20%); t-$C_4H_9CH_2CO_2H$; $C_{12}H_{24}$	46

*In the opinion of Schlenk, Hilleman, and Rodloff, *Ann.*, *487*, 135–54 (1931), this "Grignard reagent" should be formulated as an enolate.

†Gradual (1.25 hour) addition of chloride to Grignard solution.

‡Gradual (50 minutes) addition of filtered Grignard solution to Et_2O-chloride solution; overnight standing.

§Gradual (1.7 hour) addition of chloride to Grignard solution.

¶Gradual (45 minutes) addition of filtered Grignard solution to Et_2O-chloride solution; overnight standing.

TABLE IX-II (Continued)

Halide	RMgX	Product(s)	Ref.
$C_6H_{11}OCl$ (*cont.*)			
t-$C_4H_9CH_2COCl$ (1 mole)	i-C_3H_7MgBr (4 moles)	t-$C_4H_9CH_2CO$-i-C_3H_7 (32.7%); i-C_3H_7(t-$C_4H_9CH_2$)CHOH (26.7%)	43
t-$C_4H_9CH_2COCl$* (1.7 mole)	n-C_4H_9MgBr (4.5 moles)	n-C_4H_9(t-$C_4H_9CH_2$)CHOH (54.9 g., 20.5%); t-$C_4H_9CH_2$-(n-C_4H_9)$_2$COH; n-C_4H_9OH	44
t-$C_4H_9CH_2COCl$† (2.18 moles)	n-C_4H_9MgBr (2.01 moles)	t-$C_4H_9CH_2CO_2C_2H_5$; t-$C_4H_9CH_2CO$-n-C_4H_9 (34%); t-$C_4H_9CH_2CO_2CH$-(n-C_4H_9)CH_2-t-C_2H_9 (23%); t-$C_4H_9CH_2CO_2H$	46
t-$C_4H_9CH_2COCl$ (0.5 mole)	i-C_4H_9MgBr (1.45 mole)	t-$C_4H_9CH_2CO$-i-C_4H_9 (15.7 g., 20.1%); i-C_4H_9(t-$C_4H_9CH_2$)CHOH (38.6 g., 48.9%); t-$C_4H_9CH_2$(i-C_4H_9)$_2$COH (14.7 g., 13.8%)	46
t-$C_4H_9CH_2COCl$ (134.5 g.,1 mole)	t-C_4H_9MgCl (2.87 moles)	t-$C_4H_9CH_2CH_2OH$ (5.0%); t-C_4H_9(t-$C_4H_9CH_2$)CHOH (48.5%)	90
t-$C_4H_9CH_2COCl$‡ (2.5 moles)	t-C_4H_9MgCl (5.4 moles)	t-C_4H_9(t-$C_4H_9CH_2$)CHOH (282.3 g., 71%); t-$C_4H_9CH_2CH_2OH$ (1%); t-$C_4H_9CH_2CO_2CH$(t-C_4H_9)CH_2-t-C_4H_9 (5%)	47
t-$C_4H_9CH_2COCl$§ (0.95 mole)	t-C_4H_9MgCl (1.0 mole)	t-$C_4H_9CH_2CO$-t-C_4H_9 (75.4 g., 51%); t-$C_4H_9CH_2CO_2CH$(t-C_4H_9)CH_2-t-C_4H_9 (17%)	44

*Gradual (1.5 hour) addition of chloride to Grignard solution.
†Gradual (80 minutes) addition of filtered Grignard solution to Et_2O-chloride solution; overnight standing.
‡Slow (3 days) addition of Et_2O-chloride solution to Grignard solution; four days reflux.
§Slow (36 hours) addition of filtered Grignard solution to Et_2O-chloride solution.

TABLE IX-II (Continued)

Halide	RMgX	Product(s)	Ref.
$C_6H_{11}OCl$ (*cont.*)			
t-$C_4H_9CH_2COCl$* (1.5 mole)	*n*-$C_5H_{11}MgBr$ (4.1 moles)	*n*-C_5H_{11}(*t*-$C_4H_9CH_2$)CHOH (19.3%); $C_{16}H_{32}$ (0.71 mole); *n*-$C_5H_{11}OH$	44
t-$C_4H_9CH_2COCl$† (2.0 moles)	*n*-$C_5H_{11}MgBr$ (1.9 mole)	*t*-$C_4H_9CH_2CO$-*n*-C_5H_{11} (29%); *t*-$C_4H_9CH_2CO_2CH$(*n*-C_5H_{11})CH_2-*t*-C_4H_9 (21%); $C_{16}H_{32}$; *t*-$C_4H_9CH_2CO_2C_2H_5$; *t*-$C_4H_9CH_2CO_2H$	46
t-$C_4H_9CH_2COCl$ (102.8 g., 0.85 mole)	*t*-$C_4H_9CH_2MgCl$ (1.13 mole)	(*t*-$C_4H_9CH_2)_2CO$ (87%); *t*-$C_4H_9CH_2OH$	90
$(C_2H_5)_2CHCOCl$ (134.5 g., 1 mole)	*t*-C_4H_9MgCl (2.12 moles, 0.98*M*)	$(C_2H_5)_2CHCH_2OH$ (18.6%); *t*-$C_4H_9[(C_2H_5)_2CH]CHOH$ (68.6%)	90
$(C_2H_5)_2CHCOCl$ (134.5 g., 1 mole)	*t*-C_4H_9MgCl (2.12 moles, 2.06*M*)	$(C_2H_5)_2CHCH_2OH$ (24.6%); *t*-$C_4H_9[(C_2H_5)_2CH]CHOH$ (63.0%)	90
$(C_2H_5)_2CHCOCl$ (134.5 g., 1 mole)	*t*-C_4H_9MgCl (2.12 moles, 3.78*M*)	$(C_2H_5)_2CHCH_2OH$ (28.7%); *t*-$C_4H_9[(C_2H_5)_2CH]CHOH$ (45.0%)	90
$(C_2H_5)_2CHCOCl$ (134.5 g., 1 mole)	*t*-C_4H_9MgCl (2.56 moles, 1.07*M*)	$(C_2H_5)_2CHCH_2OH$ (20.0%); *t*-$C_4H_9[(C_2H_5)_2CH]CHOH$ (63.3%)	90
$(C_2H_5)_2CHCOCl$ (134.5 g., 1 mole)	*t*-C_4H_9MgCl (2.56 moles, 2.17*M*)	$(C_2H_5)_2CHCH_2OH$ (25.3%); *t*-$C_4H_9[(C_2H_5)_2CH]CHOH$ (60.5%)	90
$(C_2H_5)_2CHCOCl$ (134.5 g., 1 mole)	*t*-C_4H_9MgCl (2.56 moles, 3.95*M*)	$(C_2H_5)_2CHCH_2OH$ (30.0%); *t*-$C_4H_9[(C_2H_5)_2CH]CHOH$ (43.2%)	90
$(C_2H_5)_2CHCOCl$ (134.5 g., 1 mole)	*t*-C_4H_9MgCl (3.70 moles, 1.85*M*)	$(C_2H_5)_2CHCH_2OH$ (21.7 g.); *t*-$C_4H_9[(C_2H_5)_2CH]CHOH$ (88.3 g.); (*t*-C_4H_9—$)_2$ (21.7 g.)	90
$(C_2H_5)_2CHCOCl$ (134.5 g., 1 mole)	*t*-$C_5H_{11}MgCl$ (3.15 moles, 1.90*M*)	$(C_2H_5)_2CHCH_2OH$ (74.5%); *t*-$C_5H_{11}[(C_2H_5)_2CH]CHOH$ (7.8%)	90

*Gradual (1.3 hour) addition of chloride to Grignard solution.

†Gradual (50 minutes) addition of filtered Grignard solution to Et_2O-chloride solution.

TABLE IX-II (Continued)

Halide	RMgX	Product(s)	Ref.
$C_6H_{11}OCl$ (*cont.*)			
t-$C_5H_{11}COCl$ (1 mole)	i-C_3H_7MgBr (4.16 moles)	t-$C_5H_{11}CH_2OH$ (30 g., 29.4%); i-C_3H_7(t-C_5H_{11})CHOH (76 g., 49.3%)	*43*
$C_6H_{11}OBr$			
$(C_2H_5)_2CHCOBr$ (1.24 mole)	t-C_4H_9MgCl (3.03 moles)	$(C_2H_5)_2CHCH_2OH$ (27.7%); t-$C_4H_9[(C_2H_5)_2CH]CHOH$ (60.0%)	*90*
$C_6H_{11}OI$			
$(C_2H_5)_2CHCOI$ (277 g., crude)	t-C_4H_9MgCl (3.27 moles)	$(C_2H_5)_2CHCH_2OH$ (12%); t-$C_4H_9[(C_2H_5)_2CH]CHOH$ (36%); high-boiling material	*90*
$C_7H_2OClBr_3$			
2,4,6-$Br_3C_6H_2COCl$ (5 g.)	CH_3MgI (75 ml., 2.2*M*)	2,4,6-$Br_3C_6H_2COCH_3$ (2.2 g., 46%)	*49*
2,4,6-$Br_3C_6H_2COCl$	CH_3MgBr (2 equiv.)	(2,4,6-$Br_3C_6H_2CO)_2CH_2$ (38%); 2,4,6-$Br_3C_6H_2COCH_3$ (16%)	*49*
$C_7H_2OCl_4$			
2,4,6-$Cl_3C_6H_2COCl$	CH_3MgX* (1–2 equiv).	(2,4,6-$Cl_3C_6H_2CO)_2CH_2$ (30–50%)	*50,49*
2,4,6-$Cl_3C_6H_2COCl$ (12.3 g.)	CH_3MgCl (25 ml., 2*M*)	2,4,6-$Cl_3C_6H_2COCH_3$ (50%)	*111*
C_7H_4OClBr			
4-BrC_6H_4COCl (0.1 mole)	$C_6H_5CH(CO_2Na)MgX$† (0.2 mole)	4-$BrC_6H_4COCH_2C_6H_5$ (16 g., 58%); 4-$BrC_6H_4C[CH(C_6H_5)CO_2H]_2OH$ (6.2 g., 14%)	*20*

*X = Cl, Br, I.

†In the opinion of Schlenk, Hilleman, and Rodloff, *Ann.*, *487*, 135–54 (1931), this "Grignard reagent" should be formulated as an enolate.

TABLE IX-II (Continued)

Halide	RMgX	Product(s)	Ref.
$C_7H_4O_3Cl_2S$			
2-$ClO_2SC_6H_4$-1-COCl (10 g.)	C_6H_5MgBr (3.5 equiv.)	2-$C_6H_5O_2SC_6H_4$-1-$C(C_6H_5)_2OH$	*51*
C_7H_5OCl			
C_6H_5COCl	CH_3MgI	$C_6H_5(CH_3)_2COH$	*8*
C_6H_5COCl	C_2H_5MgBr (2.5 equiv.)	$C_6H_5(C_2H_5)_2COH$ (93%)	*17*
C_6H_5COCl	*n*-C_3H_7MgBr (2.5 equiv.)	$C_6H_5(n\text{-}C_3H_7)_2COH$ (81%)	*17*
C_6H_5COCl	Pyrryl-MgI	2-Benzoylpyrrole (*ca.* 80%)	*9*
C_6H_5COCl	C_6H_5MgX* (1 equiv.)	$(C_6H_5)_2CO$ (Cl, 48%; Br, 55%; I, 68.5%); $(C_6H_5)_3COH$	*52*
C_6H_5COCl (0.5 mole)	C_6H_5MgBr (0.5 mole)	$(C_6H_5)_2CO$ (29%); $(C_6H_5)_3COH$ (38%); $(C_6H_5—)_2$ (5.4%)	*17*
C_6H_5COCl (0.17 mole)	C_6H_5MgBr (0.5 mole)	$(C_6H_5)_2CO$ (91.5%); $(C_6H_5—)_2$ (7%)	*17*
C_6H_5COCl (0.5 mole)	C_6H_5MgBr (0.3 mole)	$(C_6H_5)_2CO$ (45.2%); $(C_6H_5)_3COH$ (32.6%); $(C_6H_5—)_2$ (10.8%)	*17*
C_6H_5COCl	$C_6H_5OC{\equiv}CMgBr$ (?)	$(C_6H_5CO_2C_6H_5$ (38%); C_6H_5OH (10%); tar	*42*
C_6H_5COCl (0.1, 0.1, and 0.075 mole)	$C_6H_5CH(CO_2Na)MgX$† (0.2, 0.1, and 0.1 mole)	$C_6H_5COCH_2C_6H_5$ (75%, 48%, and 60%); $C_6H_5C[CH(C_6H_5)CO_2H]_2OH$ (16%, 17%, and 18%)	*20*
C_6H_5COCl	4-$CH_3C_6H_4SO_2CH(MgBr)_2$	4-$CH_3C_6H_4SO_2CH(COC_6H_5)_2$	*128*
C_6H_5COCl	2,3-$(CH_3)_2C_6H_3MgBr$	2,3-$(CH_3)_2C_6H_3COC_6H_5$	*88*
C_6H_5COCl	1-$C_{10}H_7MgBr$	C_6H_5CO-1-$C_{10}H_7$	*53*
C_6H_5COCl	$(CH_3)_5C_6MgBr$	$C_6H_5COC_6(CH_3)_5$ (35%)	*54*
C_6H_5COCl	$(CH_3)_5C_6MgBr$	$C_6H_5COC_6(CH_3)_5$ (5%)	*22,23*
C_6H_5COCl	2,5-Diphenyl-3-furyl-MgBr	2,5-Diphenyl-3-benzoylfuran (32%)	*125*

*X = Cl, Br, I.

†In the opinion of Schlenk, Hilleman, and Rodloff, *Ann.*, *487*, 135–54 (1931), this "Grignard reagent" should be formulated as an enolate.

TABLE IX-II (Continued)

Halide	RMgX	Product(s)	Ref.
C_7H_5OCl (*cont.*)			
C_6H_5COCl	$(C_6H_5SO_2)_2C(MgBr)_2$	$(C_6H_5SO_2)_2CHCOC_6H_5$	*126*
C_6H_5COCl	$(4\text{-}CH_3C_6H_4SO_2)_2CHMgBr$	$(4\text{-}CH_3C_6H_4SO_2)_2CHCOC_6H_5$ (81%)	*127*
C_6H_5COCl (2 ml.)	α-Phenyl-β-o-biphenylenevinyl-MgBr (5 g. $C_{20}H_{13}Br$)	α-Phenyl-β-o-biphenyleneacrylophenone	*56*
C_6H_5COCl (4 ml.)	$(C_6H_5)_2C{=}C(C_6H_5)MgBr$ (10 g. $C_{20}H_{15}Br$)	$C_6H_5COC(C_6H_5){=}C(C_6H_5)_2$ (5 g.)	*55*
C_6H_5COCl	$2,4,6\text{-}(C_6H_5)_3C_6H_2MgBr$	$C_6H_5COC_6H_2\text{-}2,4,6\text{-}(C_6H_5)_3$ (60%)	*3*
C_7H_5OBr			
C_6H_5COBr (0.2 mole)	C_6H_5MgCl (0.5 mole)	$(C_6H_5)_3COH$ (51 g., 98%, crude)	*17*
C_6H_5COBr	$C_6H_5OC{\equiv}CMgBr$	$C_6H_5CO_2C_6H_5$ (26%); C_6H_5OH (2%); tar	*42*
C_7H_9OCl			
1-Cyclohexenecarboxylic acid chloride	$(CH_2)_5CHMgBr$	Cyclohexyl 1-cyclohexenyl ketone (40–60%)*	*57*
$C_7H_{10}O_3ClBr$			
$C_2H_5CBr(CO_2C_2H_5)COCl$ (8.0 g.)	C_6H_5MgBr (13.0 g. C_6H_5Br)	$C_6H_5COC(C_2H_5){=}C(C_6H_5)_2$ (0.1 g.)	*112*
$C_7H_{11}OCl$			
$(CH_2)_5CHCOCl$	CH_3MgI	$(CH_2)_5CHCOCH_3$ (40–60%)*	*57*
$(CH_2)_5CHCOCl$	$n\text{-}C_3H_7MgBr$	$(CH_2)_5CHCO\text{-}n\text{-}C_3H_7$ (40–60%)*	*57*
$(CH_2)_5CHCOCl$	$n\text{-}C_3H_7MgBr$	$(CH_2)_5CHCO\text{-}n\text{-}C_3H_7$ (80%); $n\text{-}C_3H_7OH$; $n\text{-}C_4H_9CH(CH_2)_5$	*113*

* Yields of 40–60% are reported for a series of reactions investigated.

TABLE IX-II (Continued)

Halide	RMgX	Product(s)	Ref.
$C_7H_{11}OCl$ (*cont.*)			
$(CH_2)_5CHCOCl$	$(CH_2)_5CHMgBr$	$[(CH_2)_5CH]_2CO$ (60–70%); $[(CH_2)_5CH]_2CH_2$; $(CH_2)_5CHOH$; cyclohexene	*113*
$(CH_2)_4C(CH_3)COCl$ (29.2 g.)	CH_3MgI (34.1 g. CH_3I)	$(CH_2)_4C(CH_3)COCH_3$ (15 g.); $(CH_2)_4C(CH_3)CO_2H$ (8 g.)	*58*
$C_7H_{13}OCl$			
t-$C_4H_9(CH_2)_2COCl$ (126 g., 0.85 mole)	t-C_4H_9MgCl (3.3 moles)	t-$C_4H_9(CH_2)_3OH$ (13.5%); t-$C_4H_9[t$-$C_4H_9(CH_2)_2]CHOH$ (67.0%)	*90*
$CH_3(C_2H_5)_2CCOCl$ (37.1 g.)	CH_3MgBr (excess)	$CH_3(C_2H_5)_2CCOCH_3$ (15.3 g., 48%)	*59*
$CH_3(t$-$C_4H_9)CHCOCl$	C_2H_5MgBr	$CH_3(t$-$C_4H_9)CHCOC_2H_5$	*13*
$C_8H_4O_2ClN$			
Benzoxazole-2-carboxylic acid chloride (4 g.)	C_6H_5MgBr	Diphenyl-2-benzoxazolylcarbinol (0.3 g.); 2-benzoxazolylcarbinol	*60*
$C_8H_4O_2Cl_2$			
C_6H_4-1,2-$(COCl)_2$	2,4-Dimethylpyrryl-MgX	3,3-Bis(3,5-dimethyl-2-pyrryl)phthalide	*114*
C_6H_4-1,2-$(COCl)_2$	$C_6H_5CH(CO_2Na)MgCl$*	C_6H_4-1,2-$(CO_2H)_2$ (71.0%); $(C_6H_5CH_2CO)_2O$ (39.4%); $C_6H_5CH_2CO_2H$ (58.8%)	*97*
$C_8H_5OClBr_2$			
2,6-Br_2-4-$CH_3C_6H_2COCl$ (32 g.)	CH_3MgI (9-fold excess)	2,6-Br_2-4-$CH_3C_6H_2COCH_3$	*49*

*In the opinion of Schlenk, Hilleman, and Rodloff, *Ann.*, *487*, 135–54 (1931), this "Grignard reagent" should be formulated as an enolate.

TABLE IX-II (Continued)

Halide	RMgX	Product(s)	Ref.
$C_8H_6OCl_2$			
$C_6H_5CHClCOCl$* (34 g.)	C_6H_5MgBr (170 g. C_6H_5Br)	$(C_6H_5)_2CHC(C_6H_5)_2OH$ (14.5 g.)	*6*
$C_6H_5CHClCOCl$† (15 g.)	C_6H_5MgBr (75 g. C_6H_5Br)	$(C_6H_5)_2CHCOC_6H_5$ (3 g.)	*6*
C_8H_7OCl			
$C_6H_5CH_2COCl$ (247 g., 1.6 mole)	t-C_4H_9MgCl (3.14 moles)	$C_6H_5(CH_2)_2OH$ (9.2%); t-$C_4H_9(C_6H_5CH_2)CHOH$ (14.9%); $C_6H_5CH_2CO_2CH(t$-$C_4H_9)CH_2C_6H_5$ (20.0%)	*90*
$C_6H_5CH_2COCl$ (0.1 mole)	$C_6H_5CH(CO_2Na)MgX$‡ (0.1 mole)	$(C_6H_5CH_2)_2CO$ (16 g., 77%); $C_6H_5CH_2C[CH(C_6H_5)CO_2H]_2OH$ (4.2 g., 22%)	*20*
$C_6H_5CH_2COCl$ (10 g.)	2,6-$(CH_3)_2$-4-$CH_3OC_6H_2MgBr$ (1.32 g. Mg)	$C_6H_5CH_2COC_6H_2$-2,6-$(CH_3)_2$-4-OCH_3	*63*
2-$CH_3C_6H_4COCl$	2,3,5,6-$(CH_3)_4C_6HMgBr$	2,3,5,6-$(CH_3)_4C_6HCOC_6H_4$-2-CH_3	*115*
4-$CH_3C_6H_4COCl$	2,3,5,6-$(CH_3)_4C_6HMgBr$	2,3,5,6-$(CH_3)_4C_6HCOC_6H_4$-4-CH_3	*115*
$C_8H_{11}OCl$			
1-Cyclohexenylacetyl chloride	CH_3MgI	1-Acetonylcyclohexene (40–60%)§	*57*
$C_8H_{15}OCl$			
$CH_3(t$-$C_4H_9CH_2)CHCOCl$ (110 g., 0.67 mole)	t-C_4H_9MgCl (2.7 moles)	$CH_3(t$-$C_4H_9CH_2)CHCH_2OH$ (21%); t-$C_4H_9[CH_3(t$-$C_4H_9CH_2)CH]CHOH$ (67%); gas	*90*

*Gradual (0.5 hour) addition of Et_2O-chloride solution to Grignard solution; 5.5 hours reflux.

†Slow (1.5 hour) addition of Grignard solution to Et_2O-chloride solution.

‡In the opinion of Schlenk, Hilleman, and Rodloff, *Ann.*, *487*, 135–54 (1931), this "Grignard reagent" should be formulated as an enolate.

§Yields of 40–60% are reported for a series of reactions investigated.

TABLE IX-II (Continued)

Halide	RMgX	Product(s)	Ref.
$C_8H_{15}OCl$ (*cont.*)			
$C_2H_5(n\text{-}C_4H_9)CHCOCl$ (162 g., 1 mole)	$t\text{-}C_4H_9MgCl$ (4.25 moles)	$C_2H_5(n\text{-}C_4H_9)CHCH_2OH$ (29.6%); $t\text{-}C_4H_9[C_2H_5(n\text{-}C_4H_9)CH]CHOH$ (64.0%)	*90*
$C_2H_5(n\text{-}C_4H_9)CHCOCl$ (162.5 g., 1 mole)	$t\text{-}C_5H_{11}MgCl$ (2.56 moles)	$C_2H_5(n\text{-}C_4H_9)CHCH_2OH$ (74.5%); $t\text{-}C_5H_{11}[C_2H_5(n\text{-}C_4H_9)CH]CHOH$ (15.7%)	*90*
$(C_2H_5)_3CCOCl$ (157 g.)	CH_3MgBr (2 moles)	CH_4 (*ca.* 0.5 mole); $(C_2H_5)_3CCOCH_3$ (45.6 g., 34%); $[(C_2H_5)_3CCO]_2CH_2$ (39.9 g., 32%)	*62*
$(C_2H_5)_3CCOCl$ (0.3 mole)	$i\text{-}C_4H_9MgBr$ (1.0 mole)	$(C_2H_5)_3CCH_2OH$ (16 g., 40%); $(C_2H_5)_3CCO\text{-}i\text{-}C_4H_9$ (24.4 g., 43%)	*59*
$(C_2H_5)_3CCOCl$ (144 g., 0.88 mole)	$t\text{-}C_4H_9MgCl$ (2 moles)	$(C_2H_5)_3CCH_2OH$ (89.5%)	*90*
C_9H_7OCl			
$C_6H_5CH{=}CHCOCl$	C_6H_5MgBr	$(C_6H_5)_2CHCH{=}C(C_6H_5)O_2CCH{=}CHC_6H_5$ $(C_6H_5)_2CHCH{=}CClO_2CCH{=}CHC_6H_5$	*61*
$C_6H_5CH{=}CHCOCl$ (0.1 mole)	$C_6H_5CH(CO_2Na)MgX$* (0.2 mole)	$C_6H_5CH{=}CHCOCH_2C_6H_5$; $C_6H_5CH_2COCH(C_6H_5)CH(C_6H_5)CO_2H$	*20*
$C_9H_7O_3Cl$			
$2\text{-}CH_3CO_2C_6H_4COCl$	Indolyl-MgX	3-Salicyloylindole	*116*
$2\text{-}CH_3CO_2C_6H_4COCl$	2-Methylindolyl-MgBr (1 equiv.)	2-Methyl-3-acetylindole; $2\text{-}HOC_6H_4CO_2H$; 2-(α-methyl-β-indolyl)phenyl α-methyl-β-indolyl ketone hydrobromide; 1,3-*o*-phenylene-2-methyl-4-(1*H*)-quinolone hydrobromide	*64*

*In the opinion of Schlenk, Hilleman, and Rodloff, *Ann.*, *487*, 135–54 (1931), this "Grignard reagent" should be formulated as an enolate.

TABLE IX-II (Continued)

Halide	RMgX	Product(s)	Ref.
$C_9H_7O_3Cl$ (*cont.*)			
2-$CH_3CO_2C_6H_4COCl$	2-Methylindolyl-MgBr (2 equiv.)	2-Methyl-3-acetylindole; 2-methyl-3-salicyloylindole; unidentified dark-red product.	*64*
2-$CH_3CO_2C_6H_4COCl$	3-Methylindolyl-MgX	*N*-Salicyloylskatole	*116*
$C_9H_8O_2ClN$			
$C_6H_5CONHCH_2COCl$	C_2H_5MgBr	$C_6H_5CONHCH_2C(C_2H_5)_2OH$ (46%)	*65*
C_9H_9OCl			
$C_6H_5CH_2CH_2COCl$ (0.1 mole)	$C_6H_5CH(CO_2Na)MgX$* (0.2 mole)	$C_6H_5CH_2CH_2COCH_2C_6H_5$ (17 g., 76%); $C_6H_5CH_2CH_2C[CH(C_6H_5)CO_2H]_2OH$ (6.2 g., 15%)	*20*
$C_9H_{13}OCl$			
2-Methyl-1-cyclohexenylacetyl chloride	CH_3MgI	1-Acetonyl-2-methylcyclohexene (40–60%)†	*57*
3-Methyl-1-cyclohexenylacetyl chloride	CH_3MgI	1-Acetonyl-3-methylcyclohexene (40–60%)†	*57*
$C_9H_{15}OCl$			
3-Methylcyclohexylacetyl chloride	CH_3MgI	1-Acetonyl-3-methylcyclohexane (40–60%)†	*57*
4-Methylcyclohexylacetyl chloride	CH_3MgI	1-Acetonyl-4-methylcyclohexane (40–60%)†	*57*

*In the opinion of Schlenk, Hilleman, and Rodloff, *Ann.*, *487*, 135–54 (1931), this "Grignard reagent" should be formulated as an enolate.

†Yields of 40–60% are reported for a series of reactions investigated.

TABLE IX-II (Continued)

Halide	RMgX	Product(s)	Ref.
$C_{10}H_6OClN$			
Cinchoninyl chloride (8 g. hydrochloride)	Pyrryl-MgI (5.2 g. pyrrole)	2-Pyrryl 4-quinolyl ketone	67
$C_{10}H_9O_2Cl$			
$4\text{-}CH_3OC_6H_4CH{=}CHCOCl$	$C_2H_5O_2CCH_2Br$ + Mg	$4\text{-}CH_3OC_6H_4CH{=}CHCOCH(COCH_3)\text{-}CO_2C_2H_5$; $4\text{-}CH_3OC_6H_4CH{=}CHCO_2\text{-}C_2H_5$; yellow comp'd, m.p. 176–177°	69
$C_{10}H_{10}OClBr$			
$2,4,6\text{-}(CH_3)_3\text{-}3\text{-}BrC_6HCOCl$ (13.0 g.)	$2,4,6\text{-}(CH_3)_3C_6H_2CH_2MgCl$ (8.4 g. $C_{10}H_{13}Cl$)	$2,4,6\text{-}(CH_3)_3\text{-}3\text{-}BrC_6HCOCH_2C_6H_2\text{-}2,4,6\text{-}(CH_3)_3$ (8.0 g., 45%)	117
$C_{10}H_{11}OCl$			
$2,4,6\text{-}(CH_3)_3C_6H_2COCl$	CH_3MgBr	$2,4,6\text{-}(CH_3)_3C_6H_2COCH_3$ (87%); $[2,4,6\text{-}(CH_3)_3C_6H_2CO—]_2$ (1%)*	66
$2,4,6\text{-}(CH_3)_3C_6H_2COCl$ (10.95 g.)	CH_3MgI (23.7 g. CH_3I)	$2,4,6\text{-}(CH_3)_3C_6H_2COCH_3$ (35%); $[2,4,6\text{-}(CH_3)_3C_6H_2CO—]_2$ (39%)*	68
$2,4,6\text{-}(CH_3)_3C_6H_2COCl$	CH_3MgI	$2,4,6\text{-}(CH_3)_3C_6H_2COCH_3$ (25%); $[2,4,6\text{-}(CH_3)_3C_6H_2CO—]_2$ (50%)*	66
$2,4,6\text{-}(CH_3)_3C_6H_2COCl$	CH_3MgI	$2,4,6\text{-}(CH_3)_3C_6H_2COCH_3$ (88%)†	68
$2,4,6\text{-}(CH_3)_3C_6H_2COCl$	CH_3MgI	$2,4,6\text{-}(CH_3)_3C_6H_2COCH_3$ (83%)†	66
$2,4,6\text{-}(CH_3)_3C_6H_2COCl$ (72 g.)	$2\text{-}CH_3OC_6H_4MgBr$ (85 g. C_7H_7BrO)	$2,4,6\text{-}(CH_3)_3C_6H_2COC_6H_4\text{-}2\text{-}OCH_3$ (30 g.)	70
$2,4,6\text{-}(CH_3)_3C_6H_2COCl$ (59 g.)	$4\text{-}CH_3OC_6H_4MgBr$ (72 g. C_7H_7BrO)	$2,4,6\text{-}(CH_3)_3C_6H_2COC_6H_4\text{-}4\text{-}OCH_3$ (28 g.)	118
$2,4,6\text{-}(CH_3)_3C_6H_2COCl$ (173 g.)	$2,4,6\text{-}(CH_3)_3C_6H_2MgBr$ (280 g. $C_9H_{11}Br$)	$[2,4,6\text{-}(CH_3)_3C_6H_2]_2CO$ (149 g.)	71

*Addition of Grignard solution to Et_2O-chloride solution.
†Addition of Et_2O-chloride solution to Grignard solution.

TABLE IX-II (Continued).

Halide	RMgX	Product(s)	Ref.
$C_{10}H_{11}OCl$ (*cont.*)			
2,4,6-$(CH_3)_3C_6H_2COCl$ (24 g.)	4-$C_6H_5C_6H_4MgI$ (40 g. $C_{12}H_9I$)	2,4,6-$(CH_3)_3C_6H_2COC_6H_4$-4-C_6H_5 (32 g., 80%)	72
$C_{10}H_{11}O_4Cl$			
3,4,5-$(CH_3O)_3C_6H_2COCl$ (29.0 g.)	2,3,5,6-$(CH_3)_4C_6HMgBr$ (27.7 g. $C_{10}H_{13}Br$)	3,4,5-$(CH_3O)_3C_6H_2COC_6H$-2,3,5,6-$(CH_3)_4$ (6.8 g., 16%)	*118*
$C_{10}H_{15}OCl$			
? -Methyl-?-*n*-butyl-1-cyclohenylacetyl chloride	CH_3MgI	1-Acetonyl-?-methyl-?-*n*-butyl-cyclohexene (40–60%)*	57
$C_{10}H_{16}O_2Cl_2$			
$[—(CH_2)_4COCl]_2$ (0.13 mole)	*n*-$C_6H_{13}MgBr$ (0.11 mole)	*n*-$C_6H_{13}CO(CH_2)_8CO_2H$ (28%); diketone (1 g.)	73
$[—(CH_2)_4COCl]_2$ (31 g.)	*i*-$C_6H_{13}MgBr$ (0.11 mole)	*i*-$C_6H_{13}CO(CH_2)_8CO_2H$ (7.4 g., 24%)	73
$[—(CH_2)_4COCl]_2$	$C_6H_5CH(CO_2Na)MgCl$† (2 equiv.)	$[—(CH_2)_4CO_2H]_2$ (87.3%); $(C_6H_5CH_2CO)_2O$ (15.8%); $C_6H_5CH_2CO_2H$ (60.2%)	97
$[—(CH_2)_4COCl]_2$	*n*-$C_8H_{17}MgBr$	*n*-$C_8H_{17}CO(CH_2)_8CO_2H$ (12%)	73
$[—(CH_2)_4COCl]_2$ (31 g.)	*i*-$C_8H_{17}MgBr$	*i*-$C_8H_{17}CO(CH_2)_8CO_2H$ (3.8 g., 11%)	73
$C_{11}H_7OCl$			
1-$C_{10}H_7COCl$ (18.5 g.)	1-$C_{10}H_7MgBr$ (20.0 g. $C_{10}H_7Br$)	$(1\text{-}C_{10}H_7)_2CO$	74
1-$C_{10}H_7COCl$ (17 g.)	1-$C_{10}H_7MgBr$ (60 g. $C_{10}H_7Br$)	$(1\text{-}C_{10}H_7)_3COH$ (5–14 g.)	74

*Yields of 40–60% are reported for a series of reactions investigated.

†In the opinion of Schlenk, Hilleman, and Rodloff, *Ann.*, *487*, 135–54 (1931), this "Grignard reagent" should be formulated as an enolate.

TABLE IX-II (Continued)

Halide	RMgX	Product (s)	Ref.
$C_{11}H_7OCl$ (*cont.*)			
1-$C_{10}H_7COCl$ (15.5 g.)	7-Methyl-4-indanyl-MgBr (10.0 g. $C_{10}H_{11}Br$)	7-Methyl-4-indanyl 1-naphthyl ketone	*119*
1-$C_{10}H_7COCl$ (15 g.)	7-Isopropyl-4-indanyl-MgBr (10 g. $C_{12}H_{15}Br$)	(1-$C_{10}H_7CO)_2O$ (3 g.); 1-isopropylindan (2 g.); 7-isopropyl-4-indanyl 1-naphthyl ketone (7.3 g., 55.5%)	*75*
2-$C_{10}H_7COCl$ (17 g.)	1-$C_{10}H_7MgBr$ (60 g. $C_{10}H_7Br$)	2-$C_{10}H_7$(1-$C_{10}H_7)_2COH$ (20 g., crude)	*76*
2-$C_{10}H_7COCl$	2-$C_{10}H_7MgBr$	(2-$C_{10}H_7)_3CH$; (2-$C_{10}H_7)_3COH$	*77*
2-$C_{10}H_7COCl$ (15.5 g.)	7-Methyl-4-indanyl-MgBr (10.0 g. $C_{10}H_{11}Br$)	7-Methyl-4-indanyl 2-naphthyl ketone (6.1 g., 45%)	*119*
$C_{11}H_8O_2Cl$			
6-Methoxy-4-quinolinecarboxylic acid chloride (8.8 g. hydrochloride)	Pyrryl-MgI (5.0 g. pyrrole)	2-Pyrryl 6-methoxy-4-quinolinyl ketone	*67*
6-Methoxy-4-quinolinecarboxylic acid chloride (7 g. hydrochloride)	3,5-Dimethylpyrryl-MgI (6 g. dimethylpyrrole)	3,5-Dimethyl-2-pyrryl 6-methoxy-4-quinolinyl ketone	*67*
$C_{11}H_{13}OCl$			
2,3,5,6-$(CH_3)_4C_6HCOCl$ (30.0 g.)	2-$CH_3OC_6H_4MgBr$ (26.0 g. C_7H_7BrO)	2,3,5,6-$(CH_3)_4C_6HCOC_6H_4$-2-OCH_3 (10.4 g.); 2,3,5,6-$(CH_3)_4C_6HCO_2H$ (7.0 g.)	*118*
2,3,5,6-$(CH_3)_4C_6HCOCl$ (0.02 mole)	2,4,6-$(CH_3)_3C_6H_2MgBr$ (0.02 mole $C_9H_{11}Br$)	2,3,5,6-$(CH_3)_4C_6HCOC_6H_2$-2,4,6-$(CH_3)_3$	*81*
2,3,5,6-$(CH_3)_4C_6HCOCl$ (0.02 mole)	2,6-$(CH_3)_2$-4-*i*-$C_4H_9C_6H_2MgBr$ (1 equiv.)	2,3,5,6-$(CH_3)_4C_6HCOC_6H_2$-2,6-$(CH_3)_2$-4-*i*-C_4H_9	*81*
2,3,5,6-$(CH_3)_4C_6HCOCl$ (8.4 g.)	2-$C_6H_5CH_2C_6H_4MgBr$ (13.6 g. $C_{13}H_{11}Br$)	2,3,5,6-$(CH_3)_4C_6HCOC_6H_4$-2-$CH_2C_6H_5$ (6.9 g., 49%)	*124*

TABLE IX-II (Continued)

Halide	RMgX	Product(s)	Ref.
$C_{11}H_{17}OCl$			
Camphane-2-carboxylic acid chloride	i-$C_3H_7MgX + FeCl_3$ (1%)	Isopropyl bornyl ketone (40%)	*82*
Camphane-2-carboxylic acid chloride	n-$C_4H_9MgX + FeCl_3$ (1%)	n-Butyl bornyl ketone (66%)	*82*
Camphane-2-carboxylic acid chloride	t-$C_4H_9MgX + FeCl_3$ (1%)	t-Butyl bornyl ketone (36%)	*82*
Camphane-2-carboxylic acid chloride	$C_6H_5MgX + FeCl_3$ (1%)	Phenyl bornyl ketone (80%)	*82*
Camphane-2-carboxylic acid chloride	1-$C_{10}H_7MgBr + FeCl_3$ (1%)	1-Naphthyl bornyl ketone (70%)	*82*
Camphane-2-carboxylic acid chloride	Bornyl-MgCl + $FeCl_3$ (1%)	Dibornyl ketone	*82*
$C_{11}H_{13}OCl$			
$CH_3(t$-$C_4H_9)(t$-$C_4H_9CH_2)CCOCl$ (271 g.)	CH_3MgBr (4 moles)	$CH_3(t$-$C_4H_9)(t$-$C_4H_9CH_2)CCOCH_3$ (223.5 g., 91%)	*78*
$CH_3(t$-$C_4H_9)(t$-$C_4H_9CH_2)CCOCl$ (70.2 g.)	C_2H_5MgBr (87.2 g. C_2H_5Br)	$CH_3(t$-$C_4H_9)(t$-$C_4H_9CH_2)CCOC_2H_5$ (53.6 g., 79%)	*78*
$CH_3(t$-$C_4H_9)(t$-$C_4H_9CH_2)CCOCl$ (218 g.)	i-C_3H_7MgBr (2 moles C_3H_7Br)	$CH_3(t$-$C_4H_9)(t$-$C_4H_9CH_2)CCO$-i-C_3H_7 (130.5 g., 58%)	*78*
$C_{12}H_9OCl$			
2-$CH_3C_{10}H_6$-1-COCl (50 g.)	CH_3MgI (110 g. CH_3I)	1-$CH_3COC_{10}H_6$-2-CH_3 (40 g., 89%)	*79*
2-$CH_3C_{10}H_6$-1-COCl (15 g.)	C_2H_5MgBr	1-$C_2H_5COC_{10}H_6$-2-CH_3 (13.5 g., 95%)	*79*
$C_{12}H_9O_2Cl$			
2-$CH_3OC_{10}H_6$-1-COCl	C_2H_5MgBr	1-$C_2H_5COC_{10}H_6$-2-OCH_3	*120*

TABLE IX-II (Continued)

Halide	RMgX	Product(s)	Ref.
$C_{12}H_{10}O_2Cl$			
6-Ethoxy-4-quinolinecarboxylic acid chloride (9.0 g. hydrochloride)	Pyrryl-MgI (5.2 g. pyrrole)	2-Pyrryl 6-ethoxy-4-quinolinyl ketone	67
$C_{12}H_{21}O_3Cl$			
$H_5C_2O_2C(CH_2)_8COCl$ (0.1 mole)	i-C_4H_9MgBr (*ca.* 0.1 mole)	i-$C_4H_9CO(CH_2)_8CO_2C_2H_5$ (43–47%)	73
$C_{12}H_{23}OCl$			
n-$C_{11}H_{23}COCl$ (0.75 mole)	t-C_4H_9MgCl (2.40 mole)	n-$C_{12}H_{25}OH$ (13.7%); t-$C_4H_9(n$-$C_{11}H_{23})CHOH$ (67.0%)	90
n-$C_{11}H_{23}COCl$ (0.50 mole)	t-$C_5H_{11}MgCl$ (1.22 mole)	n-$C_{12}H_{25}OH$ (54.8%); t-$C_5H_{11}(n$-$C_{11}H_{23})CHOH$ (17.7%)	90
$(t$-$C_4H_9CH_2)_2CHCOCl$* (1 mole)	CH_3MgBr (2.4 moles)	$(t$-$C_4H_9CH_2)_2CHCOCH_3$ (142.6 g., 72%); CH_4	80
$(t$-$C_4H_9CH_2)_2CHCOCl$† (1 mole)	CH_3MgBr (2 moles)	$(t$-$C_4H_9CH_2)_2CHCOCH_3$ (65 g., 33%); $(t$-$C_4H_9CH_2CO)_2CH_2$ (106 g., 56%)	80
$(t$-$C_4H_9CH_2)_2CHCOCl$* (0.5 mole)	C_2H_5MgBr (1.24 mole)	$(t$-$C_4H_9CH_2)_2CHCOC_2H_5$ (81 g., 76%); $(t$-$C_4H_9CH_2CO)_2CHCH_3$ (10 g., 10%)	80
$(t$-$C_4H_9CH_2)_2CHCOCl$ (152 g., 0.7 mole)	t-C_4H_9MgCl (2.3 mole)	$(t$-$C_4H_9CH_2)_2CHCH_2OH$ (60%); t-$C_4H_9[(t$-$C_4H_9CH_2)_2CH]CHOH$ (17%)	90
$(t$-$C_4H_9CH_2)_2CHCOCl$† (0.5 mole)	C_6H_5MgBr (0.48 mole)	$(t$-$C_4H_9CH_2)_2CHCOC_6H_5$ (110 g.)	80
$(t$-$C_4H_9CH_2)_2CHCOCl$ (0.25 mole)	2-$CH_3C_6H_4MgBr$ (0.21 mole)	$(t$-$C_4H_9CH_2)_2CHCOC_6H_4$-2-CH_3 (33 g., crude)	80
$(t$-$C_4H_9CH_2)_2CHCOCl$ (0.125 mole)	4-$CH_3C_6H_4MgBr$ (0.112 mole)	$(t$-$C_4H_9CH_2)_2CHCOC_6H_4$-4-CH_3 (26.3 g., 85%)	80

*Addition of chloride to Grignard reagent solution.
†Addition of Grignard reagent solution to chloride.

TABLE IX-II (Continued)

Halide	RMgX	Product(s)	Ref.
$C_{12}H_{23}OCl$ (*cont.*)			
$CH_3(t\text{-}C_4H_9)(t\text{-}C_4H_9CH_2)CCOCl$ (218 g., 1 mole)	$t\text{-}C_4H_9MgCl$ (3 moles)	$CH_3(t\text{-}C_4H_9)(t\text{-}C_4H_9CH_2)CCH_2OH$ (19.7%); $CH_3(t\text{-}C_4H_9)(t\text{-}C_4H_9CH_2)CCHO$ (62.5%)	*90*
$CH_3(t\text{-}C_4H_9)(t\text{-}C_4H_9CH_2)CCOCl$ (0.435 mole)	$t\text{-}C_5H_{11}MgCl$ (1.19 mole)	$CH_3(t\text{-}C_4H_9)(t\text{-}C_4H_9CH_2)CCH_2OH$ (19%); $CH_3(t\text{-}C_4H_9)(t\text{-}C_4H_9CH_2)CCHO$ (78%)	*90*
$C_{13}H_{10}OClN$			
$(C_6H_5)_2NCOCl$	RMgX*	$RCON(C_6H_5)_2$	*121*
$C_{13}H_{11}OCl$			
$2\text{-}C_2H_5C_{10}H_6\text{-}1\text{-}COCl$ (12.0 g.)	C_2H_5MgBr (16.4 g. C_2H_5Br)	$1\text{-}C_2H_5COC_{10}H_6\text{-}2\text{-}C_2H_5$ (86%)	*120*
$C_{13}H_{17}OCl$			
$2,4,6\text{-}(C_2H_5)_3C_6H_2COCl$ (28.3 g.)	CH_3MgI (200 ml., 1.35 *M*)	$2,4,6\text{-}(C_2H_5)_3C_6H_2COCH_3$ (9.8 g., 38.4%); $[2,4,6\text{-}(C_2H_5)_3C_6H_2CO\text{—}]_2$ (7.75 g., 32.5%)	*68*
$C_{14}H_9OCl$			
Fluorene-4-carbonyl chloride (16.6 g.)	C_6H_5MgBr (6.8 ml. C_6H_5Br)	Fluorene-4-carboxylic acid (4.84 g.); 4-benzoylfluorene (9.81 g.)	*122*
$C_{14}H_{10}OCl_2$			
$(C_6H_5)_2CClCOCl$ (40 g.)	C_6H_5MgBr (144 g. C_6H_5Br)	$(C_6H_5)_2C{=}C(C_6H_5)OH$ (58%); $(C_6H_5\text{—})_2$ (13.3 g.)†	*83*
$(C_6H_5)_2CClCOCl$ (40 g.)	C_6H_5MgBr (85 g. C_6H_5Br)	$C_{34}H_{26}O_2$, m.p. 256.5–257.5° (4.5 g.); $(C_6H_5\text{—})_2$ (12.8 g.); resin (37 g.)‡	*83*

*RMgX = C_2H_5MgI, $n\text{-}C_3H_7MgBr$, C_6H_5MgBr.

†Gradual addition of Et_2O-chloride solution to Grignard reagent solution.

‡Gradual addition of Grignard reagent solution to Et_2O-chloride solution.

TABLE IX-II (Continued)

Halide	RMgX	Product(s)	Ref.
$C_{14}H_{10}OCl_2$ (*cont.*)			
$(C_6H_5)_2CClCOCl$ (13 g.)	C_6H_5MgI (35 g. C_6H_5I)	Resin.*	83
$(C_6H_5)_2CClCOCl$ (13 g.)	C_6H_5MgI (60 g. C_6H_5I)	$(C_6H_5)_2C{=}C(C_6H_5)OH$ (8.1 g., crude)†	83
$C_{14}H_{11}OCl$			
$(C_6H_5)_2CHCOCl$ (1.3 mole)	t-C_4H_9MgCl (3.4 moles)	$(C_6H_5)_2CHCH_2OH$ (67.5%)	90
$C_{14}H_{27}OCl$			
$(n$-$C_4H_9)_3CCOCl$ (119 g., 0.48 mole)	t-C_4H_9MgCl (1.5 mole)	$(n$-$C_4H_9)_3CCH_2OH$ (88.5%)	90
$C_{15}H_{12}O_2ClN$			
$C_6H_5CONHCH(C_6H_5)COCl$	C_2H_5MgBr	$C_6H_5CONHCH(C_6H_5)C(C_2H_5)_2OH$ (37%)	65
$C_{16}H_{23}OCl$			
2,4,6-$(i$-$C_3H_7)_3C_6H_2COCl$ (26.6 g.)	2,4,6-$(i$-$C_3H_7)_3C_6H_2MgBr$ (30.0 g. $C_{15}H_{23}Br$)	$[2,4,6$-$(i$-$C_3H_7)_3C_6H_2]_2CO$	91
$C_{17}H_{17}OCl$			
2,4,6-$(CH_3)_3C_6H_2(C_6H_5)CHCOCl$ (10 g.)	CH_3MgI (7.25 g. CH_3I)	2,4,6-$(CH_3)_3C_6H_2(C_6H_5)CHCO_2H$ (1.1 g.); 2,4,6-$(CH_3)_3C_6H_2(C_6H_5)CHCOCH_3$ (<50%); 2,4,6-$(CH_3)_3C_6H_2(C_6H_5)C{=}C(CH_3)_2$	84
2,4,6-$(CH_3)_3C_6H_2(C_6H_5)CHCOCl$ (0.08 mole)	2,4,6-$(CH_3)_3C_6H_2MgBr$ (0.08 mole)	2,4,6-$(CH_3)_3C_6H_2COCH(C_6H_5)C_6H_2$-2,4,6-$(CH_3)_3$ (10 g.); 2,4,6-$(CH_3)_3C_6H_2(C_6H_5)$-$CHCO_2H$ (6 g.)	89

*Gradual addition of Et_2O-chloride solution to Grignard reagent solution.
†Gradual addition of Grignard reagent solution to Et_2O-chloride solution.

TABLE IX-II (Continued)

Halide	RMgX	Product(s)	Ref.
$C_{17}H_{25}OCl$			
2,4,6-(i-C_3H_7)$_3C_6H_2CH_2COCl$	2,4,6-(i-C_3H_7)$_3C_6H_2MgBr$	2,4,6-(i-C_3H_7)$_3C_6H_2COCH_2C_6H_2$-2,4,6-(i-C_3H_7)$_3$	91
$C_{18}H_{14}O_2Cl_2$			
α-Truxillyl chloride*	C_6H_5MgBr	No crystalline product	92
$C_{20}H_{15}OCl$			
$(C_6H_5)_3CCOCl$ (7 g.)	C_2H_5MgI (20 g. C_2H_5I)	$(C_6H_5)_3CCOC_2H_5$ (2.5 g.); C_2H_4	85
$(C_6H_5)_3CCOCl$ (7 g.)	C_6H_5MgBr (20 g. C_6H_5Br)	$(C_6H_5)_3CC(C_6H_5)_2OH$ (4 g.)	85
$(C_6H_5)_3CCOCl$† (17 g.)	C_6H_5MgI (40 g. C_6H_5I)	CO (86.4%); $[(C_6H_5)_3C—]_2$ (4.8 g.); $(C_6H_5)_3CC(C_6H_5)_2OH$ (trace)	85
$(C_6H_5)_3CCOCl$‡ (15 g.)	C_6H_5MgI (21 g. C_6H_5I)	$[(C_6H_5)_3C]_2O_2$ (0.7 g.); CO; $(C_6H_5)_3COH$ (4.4 g.); $(C_6H_5)_3CH$ (3.5 g.)	85
$C_{20}H_{23}OCl$			
$[2,4,6-(CH_3)_3C_6H_2]_2CHCOCl$ (22.7 g.)	C_6H_5MgBr (7.85 g. C_6H_5Br)	$[2,4,6-(CH_3)_3C_6H_2]_2CHCO_2C_2H_5$; $[2,4,6-(CH_3)_3C_6H_2]_2CHCOC_6H_5$; tar	84
$C_{24}H_{35}O_3Cl$			
3-Acetoxy-5-bisnorcholenic acid chloride (from 5 g. acid)	CH_3MgBr (5 g. Mg)	3-Hydroxy-5-ternorcholenyldimethylcarbinol (4.6 g.)	86
$C_{28}H_{45}OCl$			
5-Cholestene-3-carbonyl chloride (from 2.84 g. acid)	CH_3MgI (0.02 mole CH_3I)	α-(3-Cholesteryl)ethanol	93

*2,4-Diphenylcyclobutane-1,3-dicarbonyl chloride.

†Addition of powdered chloride to Grignard solution at room temperature; two days standing.

‡Reaction in boiling Et_2O.

REFERENCES FOR TABLE IX-II.

(*1*) Grignard, *Compt. rend.*, *136*, 815–7 (1903); *Chem. Zentr.*, *1903,I*, 1077.
(*2*) Sachs and Loevy, *Ber.*, *36*, 1588–90 (1903).
(*3*) Kohler and Blanchard, *J. Am. Chem. Soc.*, *57*, 367–71 (1935).
(*4*) Huston, Jackson, and Spero, *J. Am. Chem. Soc.*, *63*, 1459–60 (1941).
(*5*) Henry, *Compt. rend.*, *145*, 21–5 (1907); *Chem. Zentr.*, *1907,II*, 889.
(*6*) Boyle, McKenzie, and Mitchell, *Ber.*, *70B*, 2153–60 (1937).
(*7*) Mingoia, *Gazz. chim. ital.*, *61*, 646–50 (1931); *Chem. Abstr.*, *26*, 1279 (1932).
(*8*) Tissier and Grignard, *Compt. rend.*, *132*, 336–8 (1901); *Chem. Zentr.*, *1901,I*, 930; *J. Chem. Soc.*, *80,I*, 316 (1901).
(*9*) Oddo, *Ber.*, *43*, 1015–21 (1910).
(*10*) Whitmore, Popkin, Whitaker, Mattil, and Zech, *J. Am. Chem. Soc.*, *60*, 2458–62 (1938).
(*11*) Whitmore, *Rec. trav. chim.*, *57*, 562–8 (1938).
(*12*) Whitmore and Badertscher, *J. Am. Chem. Soc.*, *55*, 1559–67 (1933).
(*13*) Whitmore and Block, *J. Am. Chem. Soc.*, *64*, 1619–21 (1942).
(*14*) Whitmore and Wheeler, *J. Am. Chem. Soc.*, *60*, 2899–900 (1938).
(*15*) Huston and Guile, *J. Am. Chem. Soc.*, *61*, 69–71 (1939).
(*16*) Tissier and Grignard, *Compt. rend.*, *132*, 1182–4 (1901); *Chem. Zentr.*, *1901,I*, 1357.
(*17*) Gilman, Fothergill, and Parker, *Rec. trav. chim.*, *48*, 748–51 (1929).
(*18*) Oddo and Acuto, *Gazz. chim. ital.*, *65*, 1029–36 (1935); *Chem. Abstr.*, *30*, 4857 (1936).
(*19*) Whitmore and Sloat, *J. Am. Chem. Soc.*, *64*, 2968–70 (1942).
(*20*) Ivanoff and Nicoloff, *Bull. soc. chim.*, [4], *51*, 1331–7 (1932).
(*21*) Campbell, Anderson, and Gilmore, *J. Chem. Soc.*, *1940*, 819–21.
(*22*) Savard and Hösögüt, *Rev. faculté sci. univ. Istanbul*, [N.S.], *3*, 164–73 (1938); *Chem. Abstr.*, *32*, 5795 (1938).
(*23*) Clément, *Ann. chim.*, [11], *13*, 243–316 (1940).
(*24*) Miller and Bachman, *J. Am. Chem. Soc.*, *57*, 766–71 (1935).
(*25*) Schmidlin and Hodgson, *Ber.*, *41*, 430–7 (1908).
(*26*) Lapkin and Lyubimova, *Zhur. Obschei Khim.*, *19*, 707–16 (1949); *Chem. Abstr.*, *44*, 1058 (1950); *J. Gen. Chem.* (U.S.S.R.), *19*, 677–88 (1949); *Chem. Abstr.*, *44*, 6391 (1950).
(*27*) Austin and Johnson, *J. Am. Chem. Soc.*, *54*, 647–60 (1932).
(*28*) Bachmann and Cockerill, *J. Am. Chem. Soc.*, *55*, 2932–4 (1933).
(*29*) Hess, *Ber.*, *46*, 3113–25 (1913).
(*30*) Gilman and Franz, *Rec. trav. chim.*, *51*, 991–5 (1932).
(*31*) Petrov and Roslova, *J. Gen. Chem.* (U.S.S.R.), *10*, 993–6 (1940); *Chem. Abstr.*, *35*, 2467 (1941).
(*32*) Houben, *Ber.*, *36*, 3087–9 (1903).
(*33*) Gilman, Kirby, Fothergill, and Harris, *Proc. Iowa Acad. Sci.*, *34*, 221–2 (1927); *Chem. Abstr.*, *22*, 4504 (1922).
(*34*) Blicke, Warzynski, Faust, and Gearien, *J. Am. Chem. Soc.*, *66*, 1675–7 (1944).
(*35*) Bachmann, *J. Am. Chem. Soc.*, *56*, 1363–7 (1934).
(*36*) Hurd and Kelso, *J. Am. Chem. Soc.*, *62*, 2184–7 (1940).
(*37*) Grignard, *Compt. rend.*, *136*, 1200–1 (1903); *Chem. Zentr.*, *1903,II*, 22.
(*38*) Grignard, *Bull. soc. chim.*, [3], *29*, 948–53 (1903).
(*39*) Greenwood, Whitmore, and Crooks, *J. Am. Chem. Soc.*, *60*, 2028–30 (1938).
(*40*) Vavon and Décombe, *Bull. soc. chim.*, [5], *11*, 363–5 (1944).
(*41*) Stehman, Cook, and Whitmore, *J. Am. Chem. Soc.*, *71*, 1509–10 (1949).
(*42*) Jacobs, Cramer, and Weiss, *J. Am. Chem. Soc.*, *62*, 1849–54 (1940).
(*43*) Whitmore and Forster, *J. Am. Chem. Soc.*, *64*, 2966–8 (1942).

(44) Whitmore, Popkin, Whitaker, Mattil, and Zech, *J. Am. Chem. Soc.*, *60*, 2462–4 (1938).
(45) Whitmore, Meyer, Pedlow, and Popkin, *J. Am. Chem. Soc.*, *60*, 2788–9 (1938).
(46) Whitmore, Whitaker, Mattil, and Popkin, *J. Am. Chem. Soc.*, *60*, 2790–2 (1938).
(47) Whitmore and Heyd, *J. Am. Chem. Soc.*, *60*, 2030–1 (1938).
(48) Helferich and Malkomes, *Ber.*, *55B*, 702–8 (1922).
(49) Fuson, Van Campen, and Wolf, *J. Am. Chem. Soc.*, *60*, 2269–72 (1938).
(50) Ross and Fuson, *J. Am. Chem. Soc.*, *59*, 1508–10 (1937).
(51) Cobb, *Am. Chem. J.*, *35*, 486–508 (1906).
(52) Gilman and Mayhue, *Rec. trav. chim.*, *51*, 47–50 (1932).
(53) Acree, *Ber.*, *37*, 625–8 (1904).
(54) Clément, *Compt. rend.*, *202*, 425–7 (1936); *Chem. Abstr.*, *30*, 2932 (1936).
(55) Koelsch, *J. Am. Chem. Soc.*, *54*, 2045–8 (1932).
(56) Koelsch, *J. Am. Chem. Soc.*, *54*, 3384–9 (1932).
(57) Darzens and Rost, *Compt. rend.*, *153*, 772–5 (1911); *Chem. Zentr.*, *1911,II*, 1860.
(58) Meerwein, *Ann.*, *417*, 255–77 (1918).
(59) Whitmore and Lewis, *J. Am. Chem. Soc.*, *64*, 2964–6 (1942).
(60) Skraup and Moser, *Ber.*, *55B*, 1080–101 (1922).
(61) Kohler and Heritage, *Am. Chem. J.*, *33*, 21–35 (1905).
(62) Whitmore and Lewis, *J. Am. Chem. Soc.*, *64*, 1618–9 (1942).
(63) Fuson and Hoch, *J. Am. Chem. Soc.*, *71*, 1585–6 (1949).
(64) Toffoli, *Gazz. chim. ital.*, *64*, 364–71 (1934); *Chem. Abstr.*, *28*, 6437 (1934).
(65) Thomas and Bettzieche, *Z. physiol. Chem.*, *140*, 279–98 (1924); *Chem. Abstr.*, *19*, 636 (1925).
(66) Kharasch, Morrison, and Urry, *J. Am. Chem. Soc.*, *66*, 368–71 (1944).
(67) Karrer, *Ber.*, *50*, 1499–508 (1917).
(68) Fuson and Corse, *J. Am. Chem. Soc.*, *60*, 2063–6 (1938).
(69) Macierewicz, *Roczniki Chem.*, *22*, 93–5 (1948); *Chem. Abstr.*, *43*, 2973 (1949).
(70) Fuson and Speck, *J. Am. Chem. Soc.*, *64*, 2446–8 (1942).
(71) Kohler and Baltzly, *J. Am. Chem. Soc.*, *54*, 4015–26 (1932).
(72) Fuson, Armstrong, and Speck, *J. Org. Chem.*, *7*, 297–302 (1942).
(73) Fordyce and Johnson, *J. Am. Chem. Soc.*, *55*, 3368–72 (1933).
(74) Schmidlin and Massini, *Ber.*, *42*, 2377–92 (1909).
(75) Bruce and Todd, *J. Am. Chem. Soc.*, *61*, 157–61 (1939).
(76) Schmidlin and Massini, *Ber.*, *42*, 2392–404 (1909).
(77) Schmidlin and Huber, *Ber.*, *43*, 2824–37 (1910).
(78) Whitmore and Randall, *J. Am. Chem. Soc.*, *64*, 1242–6 (1942).
(79) Adams and Binder, *J. Am. Chem. Soc.*, *63*, 2773–6 (1941).
(80) Whitmore and Lester, *J. Am. Chem. Soc.*, *64*, 1247–51 (1942).
(81) Fuson and Tull, *J. Am. Chem. Soc.*, *71*, 2542–6 (1949).
(82) Quesnel and Tatibouet, *Bull. soc. chim.*, [5], *14*, 1079–80 (1947).
(83) McKenzie and Boyle, *J. Chem. Soc.*, *119*, 1131–40 (1921).
(84) Fuson, Armstrong, Chadwick, Kneisley, Rowland, Shenk, and Soper, *J. Am. Chem. Soc.*, *67*, 386–93 (1945).
(85) Schmidlin, *Ber.*, *43*, 1137–44 (1910).
(86) Julian, Cole, Meyer, and Herness, *J. Am. Chem. Soc.*, *67*, 1375–81 (1945).
(87) Buu-Hoï and Nguyen-Hoán, *Rec. trav. chim.*, *68*, 5–33 (1949).
(88) Grunert, Nichol, and Sandin, *J. Am. Chem. Soc.*, *69*, 2254–6 (1947).
(89) Fuson, Armstrong, Kneisley, and Shenk, *J. Am. Chem. Soc.*, *66*, 1464–6 (1944).
(90) Whitmore, Whitaker, Mosher, Breivik, Wheeler, Miner, Sutherland, Wagner, Clapper, Lewis, Lux, and Popkin, *J. Am. Chem. Soc.*, *63*, 643–54 (1941).

(91) Fuson, Chadwick, and Ward, *J. Am. Chem. Soc.*, 68, 389–93 (1946).
(92) Adler, *Sitzber. Abhandl. naturforsch. Ges. Rostock*, 7, 3–20 (1938–9); *Chem. Abstr.*, 37, 345 (1934).
(93) Baker and Squire, *J. Am. Chem. Soc.*, 70, 1487–90 (1948).
(94) Fischer and Orth, *Ann.*, 502, 237–64 (1933).
(95) Ghigi and Scaramelli, *Boll. sci. facoltà chim. ind. univ. Bologna*, 4, 83–5 (1943); *Chem. Abstr.*, 42, 3389 (1948).
(96) Oddo and Mingoia, *Gazz. chim. ital.*, 57, 473–9 (1927); *Chem. Abstr.*, 22, 77 (1928).
(97) Stefanova, *Annuaire univ. Sofia, Faculté phys.-math.*, 40, Livre 2, 147–66 (1943–44); *Chem. Abstr.*, 42, 4156 (1948).
(98) Jacob, *Bull. soc. chim.*, [5], 7, 581–6 (1940).
(99) Fischer, Baumgartner, and Plotz, *Ann.*, 493, 1–19 (1932).
(100) Oddo and Moschini, *Gazz. chim. ital.*, 42,II, 244–56 (1912); *Chem. Abstr.*, 6, 3425 (1912).
(101) Whitmore, Sommer, Gold, and Van Strien, *J. Am. Chem. Soc.*, 69, 1551 (1947).
(102) Kroeger and Nieuwland, *J. Am. Chem. Soc.*, 58, 1861–3 (1936).
(103) Hess and Weltzien, *Ber.*, 54B, 2511–21 (1921).
(104) Ingraffia, *Gazz. chim. ital.*, 63, 584–91 (1933); *Chem. Abstr.*, 28, 1342 (1934).
(105) Fischer and Hussong, *Ann.*, 492, 128–55 (1932).
(106) Rivière, *Ann. chim.*, [12], 1, 157–231 (1946).
(107) Sanna, *Rend. seminario facoltà sci. univ. Cagliari*, 4, 59–61 (1934); *Chem. Abstr.*, 29, 1815 (1935).
(108) Oddo, *Gazz. chim. ital.*, 50,II, 258–68 (1920); *Chem. Abstr.*, 15, 2096 (1921).
(109) Oddo and Albanese, *Gazz. chim. ital.*, 57, 827–35 (1927); *Chem. Abstr.*, 22, 1775 (1928).
(110) Bachman and Micucci, *J. Am. Chem. Soc.*, 70, 2381–4 (1948).
(111) Fuson, Bertetti, and Ross, *J. Am. Chem. Soc.*, 54, 4380–3 (1932).
(112) Hurd, Jones, and Blunck, *J. Am. Chem. Soc.*, 57, 2033–6 (1935).
(113) Mousseron and Granger, *Bull. soc. chim.*, [5], 13, 251–6 (1946).
(114) Ingraffia, *Gazz. chim. ital.*, 64, 289–94 (1934); *Chem. Abstr.*, 28, 5437 (1934).
(115) Fuson, McKusick, and Mills, *J. Org. Chem.*, 11, 60–6 (1946).
(116) Toffoli, *Gazz. chim. ital.*, 65, 459–61 (1935); *Chem. Abstr.*, 30, 455 (1936).
(117) Fuson, Lindsey, and Welldon, *J. Am. Chem. Soc.*, 64, 2888–91 (1942).
(118) Fuson and Gaertner, *J. Org. Chem.*, 13, 496–501 (1948).
(119) Fieser and Seligman, *J. Am. Chem. Soc.*, 57, 942–6 (1935).
(120) Fuson and Chadwick, *J. Org. Chem.*, 13, 484–8 (1948).
(121) Meyer, *J. prakt. Chem.*, [2], 82, 521–38 (1910).
(122) Bachmann and Brockway, *J. Org. Chem.*, 13, 394–9 (1948).
(123) Vavon and Décombe, *Compt. rend.*, 214, 360–2 (1942); *Chem. Abstr.*, 37, 3733 (1943).
(124) Fuson and McKusick, *J. Am. Chem. Soc.*, 65, 60–4 (1943).
(125) Lutz and Smith, *J. Am. Chem. Soc.*, 63, 1148–50 (1941).
(126) Kohler and Tishler, *J. Am. Chem. Soc.*, 57, 217–24 (1935).
(127) Kohler and Potter, *J. Am. Chem. Soc.*, 58, 2166–70 (1936).
(128) Kohler and Potter, *J. Am. Chem. Soc.*, 57, 1316–21 (1935).
(129) Gaertner, *J. Am. Chem. Soc.*, 74, 766–7 (1952).
(130) Chelintzev and Skvortzov, *J. Russ. Phys.-Chem. Soc.*, 47, 170–6 (1915); *Chem. Abstr.*, 9, 1472 (1915).
(131) Gilman and Towle, *Rec. trav. chim.*, 69, 428–32 (1950).
(132) Ford, Thompson, and Marvel, *J. Am. Chem. Soc.*, 57, 2619–23 (1935).
(133) Gaertner, *J. Am. Chem. Soc.*, 73, 3934–7 (1951)

CHAPTER X

Reactions of Grignard Reagents with Nitriles and Other Cyano Compounds

THE "NORMAL" REACTION AND ITS PROBABLE MECHANISM

The reactions of Grignard reagents with nitriles were first investigated by Blaise,[1] who found that in ethereal solution organomagnesium iodides react to form compounds of the general formula $RR'C{=}NMgI \cdot Et_2O$, which upon acid hydrolysis yield the corresponding ketones (RR'CO).

Moureu and Mignonac[2] have shown that, in some cases at least, the ketimines may be liberated from the Grignard reaction products by sufficiently mild hydrolytic procedure (as with aqueous ammonium chloride at $-15°$), and isolated as hydrochlorides by treatment of the dried ethereal solutions with dry hydrogen chloride. To this extent the product obtained (whether ketone or ketimine) depends upon the recovery procedure adopted. However, some ketimines are so susceptible to hydrolysis that they are difficult to isolate from aqueous Grignard hydrolysates,* whereas others are so stable that rather vigorous secondary hydrolysis is necessary to obtain the ketones.

By means of competition experiments,† Gilman[3] has determined that the radical order of reactivity of various benzonitriles toward phenylmagnesium bromide is: $p\text{-}ClC_6H_4 > C_6H_5 > (m\text{-}CH_3C_6H_4,\ p\text{-}CH_3C_6H_4) > o\text{-}$

---

[1] Blaise, *Compt. rend.*, *132*, 38 (1901); *J. Chem. Soc.*, *80,I*, 133 (1901); *Chem. Zentr.*, *1901,I*, 298; *Compt. rend.*, *133*, 1217–8 (1901); *J. Chem. Soc.*, *82,I*, 164 (1902); *Chem. Zentr.*, *1902,I*, 299.

[2] Moureu and Mignonac, *Compt. rend.*, *156*, 1801–6 (1913); *Chem. Zentr.*, *1913,II*, 497.

* In such cases, however, the ketimine (or its hydrochloride) may often be isolated by application of the liquid ammonia solvolysis method developed independently by Cornell [*J. Am. Chem. Soc.*, *50*, 3311–8 (1928)] and Cloke [Cloke and Van Wyck, *Thesis*, Rensselaer Polytechnic Institute, *1927*; Cloke, *J. Am. Chem. Soc.*, *62*, 117–9 (1940); Cloke, Baer, Robbins, and Smith, *ibid.*, *67*, 2155–8 (1945)].

† These experiments were conducted with the aid of the Michler's ketone color test. This test is not reliable in the presence of appreciable quantities of relatively reactive Grignard reagent co-reactants—specifically those more reactive than Michler's ketone itself (see Chapter III, Estimation and Detection of Grignard Reagents). For comparison of the relatively unreactive benzonitriles the test is probably altogether satisfactory.

[3] Gilman and Lichtenwalter, *Rec. trav. chim.*, *55*, 588–90 (1936).

$CH_3C_6H_4 > p\text{-}(CH_3)_2NC_6H_4$. Excepting the slightly displaced *o*-tolunitrile, for which some small "ortho effect" might be expected in reactions of this kind, the order of decreasing reactivity is the order of increasing radical "electronegativity" as assigned by Kharasch *et al.*[4]

In a similar manner Gilman[5] has determined the relative reactivities of various Grignard reagents toward benzonitrile. Ignoring the atypical allyl and phenylethynyl radicals, the radical order of decreasing reactivity is:

$$2,4,6\text{-}(CH_3)_3C_6H_2 > p\text{-}CH_3C_6H_4 > C_6H_5 > C_2H_5 > n\text{-}C_3H_7 > i\text{-}C_3H_7 > n\text{-}C_4H_9 > s\text{-}C_4H_9 > t\text{-}C_4H_9$$

In so far as the members of the series are common, this is the reverse of the order of reactivity toward benzophenone, as determined by Kharasch and Weinhouse.[6]

Swain[7] has studied the kinetics of the reaction between *n*-butylmagnesium bromide and benzonitrile, and has found the reaction to be homogeneous and second order. The rate constants at 0° and at 25° are, respectively, $5.8 \pm 0.9 \times 10^{-5}$ and $3.7 \pm 0.6 \times 10^{-4}$ l. mole^{-1} sec.$^{-1}$, corresponding to an activation energy of 12.0 ± 1.0 kcal.

Concerning the probable mechanism of the reaction Swain says:

"The second-order kinetics of the reaction between *n*-butylmagnesium bromide and benzonitrile eliminates from consideration a mechanism involving a unimolecular or solvolytic ionization of the organometallic reagent to a carbanion as the rate-determining step.

"Formation of a complex between reagent and addend seems to be eliminated as the rate-determining step by the whole series of relative reactivity of different nitriles obtained by Gilman. For example benzonitrile reacts faster with phenylmagnesium bromide than does *p*-tolunitrile, although the latter would be expected to be more nucleophilic and to form a stronger complex from a consideration of inductive effects.

"A rate-determining reaction of a complex with a second molecule of Grignard reagent is eliminated because it would require the kinetics to be second order in the reagent alone and third order over-all.

"Direct reaction of Grignard reagent with nitrile is unlikely, because then we should expect the aliphatic reagents to react faster than phenyl Grignard. Ethylsodium will react with benzene to give phenylsodium and

---

[4] For a discussion of the relative electronegativities of organic radicals see: Kharasch and Reinmuth, *J. Chem. Education*, *5*, 404–18 (1928); *8*, 1703–48 (1931); Kharasch, Reinmuth, and Mayo, *ibid.*, *11*, 82–96 (1934); *13*, 7–19 (1936). The electronegativity of the *p*-dimethylaminophenyl radical cannot be evaluated directly by the Kharasch method (because of salt formation), but for a variety of chemical reasons it is estimated as highly electronegative. Complications arising from tertiary amine-Grignard reagent complex formation may affect quantitatively, but apparently do not alter qualitatively, the character of the radical.

[5] Gilman, St. John, St. John, and Lichtenwalter, *Rec. trav. chim.*, *55*, 577–85 (1936).

[6] Kharasch and Weinhouse, *J. Org. Chem.*, *1*, 209–30 (1936).

[7] Swain, *J. Am. Chem. Soc.*, *69*, 2306–9 (1947).

ethane, demonstrating that the 'salts' of ethane (considered as a very weak acid) are less stable at equilibrium than the 'salts' of benzene. In many reactions, including metalation, cleavage of ether, and reaction with benzophenone, it is furthermore found that ethylmagnesium or *n*-butylmagnesium bromide reacts faster than phenylmagnesium bromide. However, here, in the nitrile reaction, we have the opposite series of reactivity of different Grignard reagents.

"The following mechanism, on the other hand, is consistent with the kinetic order and all reported series of relative reactivity. A complex between reagent and addend* is formed rapidly and reversibly, though very possibly in low concentration at equilibrium relative to the total concentration of Grignard reagent. The rate-determining step consists of an *intramolecular* rearrangement of the complex, in which the radical attached to the metal migrates, with its pair of electrons, to the nitrile carbon. The rearrangement may be pictured as follows.

$$Et_2O \longrightarrow \overset{\ominus}{Mg}(X) : R \;\; \ddot{N}{=}\overset{\oplus}{C}{-}Ph \longrightarrow (Et_2O)_2Mg(X){-}N{=}C(Ph)R$$

"There is evidence for this mechanism in the fact that the series of decreasing relative reactivities with benzonitrile of Grignard reagents with different organic radicals is the same, as far as the data overlaps, as the series of decreasing migration aptitudes of these same radicals in the pinacol rearrangement,[8] which is believed to proceed by intramolecular shift of the radical with its electron pair."

PREPARATIVE PROCEDURES

It is known from general experience and from competition experiments[9] that nitriles (RCN) are, in general, less reactive toward Grignard reagents than are the corresponding RCHO, R_2CO, RNCO, RCOX, and RCO_2R' compounds. Preparative procedures, therefore, often involve prolonged heating, or the use of high-boiling solvents, or both. However, the reaction rates for individual nitrile-Grignard reagent pairs vary widely, and some reactions are even described as "vigorous." As might be predicted by theoretical extension of Gilman's[10] limited relative reactivity

*(*Footnote inserted by present authors*)—Direct evidence of complex formation was obtained by Kohler, *Am. Chem. J.*, 35, 386–404 (1906), in the case of the interaction of the non-"acidic" α-phenylcinnamonitrile with ethylmagnesium bromide. "The primary product is always a dark-red substance that is soluble in ether, but insoluble in ligroïn, from which it separates as a paste. On treatment with water it gives ethane, unchanged nitrile, and magnesium salts. It is, therefore, a double compound containing the nitrile in place of ether."

[8] Bennett and Chapman, *Annual Reports on the Progress of Chemistry*, 27, 118 (1930).

[9] See, *e.g.*: Entemann and Johnson, *J. Am. Chem. Soc.*, 55, 2900–3 (1933).

[10] Gilman and Lichtenwalter, *Rec. trav. chim.*, 55, 588–90 (1936).

series, the aliphatic nitriles (with less "electronegative" radicals), are, in general, more reactive toward Grignard reagents than are the aromatic nitriles (with more "electronegative" radicals). Descriptions of some representative illustrative preparations are here assembled.

Kaufmann *et al.*[11] have prepared several quinolyl and isoquinolyl ketones in relatively good yields. Their procedure for methylmagnesium iodide and 2-cyanoquinoline is described as follows. Methylmagnesium iodide solution (2.25 equivalents*) is dropped slowly into a well-cooled benzene-ether solution of 2-cyanoquinoline. The reaction is unusually energetic. The reaction product separates as a light-yellow granular precipitate. Without warming, the product is separated from the liquid and is decomposed with water and ammonium chloride. By steam distillation the ketone is isolated as a colorless oil which soon crystallizes. The yield is 79%.

Moureu and Mignonac[12] employed several modifications of method in the preparation of their ketimine hydrochlorides, but the following will serve for example. To a solution of phenylmagnesium bromide, prepared from 4.8 g. of magnesium and 32 g. of bromobenzene in about 85 ml. of ethyl ether, is added 15 g. of benzonitrile dissolved in its own volume of ethyl ether. A white powder appears, and the reaction mixture is refluxed for eight hours. The solid reaction-product mixture is separated and washed thoroughly with four portions of ether. Re-suspended in ether it is treated at -10° with a mixture of crushed ice and ammonium chloride. The ether layer is thoroughly dried over anhydrous sodium sulfate, and is then saturated (while agitated and cooled) with dry hydrogen chloride. The precipitated ketimine hydrochloride is separated by centrifugation and is then washed several times with ether. The reported yield is 27 g. (85.2%).

Several ketones have been prepared by Shriner and Turner[13] by the reaction of phenylmagnesium bromide with alkyl nitriles. Except for isocapronitrile (yield, 50%), the yields range from 70% (for acetonitrile) to 91% (for propionitrile). They describe a typical procedure as follows.

"The phenylmagnesium bromide is prepared in the usual way from 25 g. of magnesium turnings and 160 g. of bromobenzene in 300 ml. of dry ether. A solution of 0.25 mole of the nitrile in 100 ml. of dry ether is run in slowly with stirring during a period of fifteen minutes. The solution is stirred for an hour longer and allowed to stand overnight. The mixture is poured onto 500 g. of ice and 300 ml. of concentrated hydrochloric acid. The water layer, which contains the hydrochloride of the ketimine, is separated from the ether layer and refluxed vigorously for one hour. The solution is cooled and extracted with four 200-ml. por-

---

[11] Kaufmann, Dandliker, and Burkhardt, *Ber.*, *46*, 2929–35 (1913).

* One equivalent of Grignard reagent forms a tertiary-amine complex with the quinolyl nitrogen atom; the other reacts with the cyano group.

[12] Moureu and Mignonac, *Ann. chim.*, [9], *14*, 322–59 (1920).

[13] Shriner and Turner, *J. Am. Chem. Soc.*, *52*, 1267–9 (1930).

tions of ether. The ether extract is dried over anhydrous calcium chloride and the ether is distilled from a water-bath. The residue is transferred to a small modified Claisen flask and vacuum-distilled."

Some ketimine hydrochlorides are not only surprisingly resistant to acid hydrolysis but relatively insoluble in cold water. Examples are those prepared from *o*-chlorobenzonitrile and 8-methyl-1-naphthylmagnesium bromide by Fieser and Seligman,[14] and from 4-cyano-7-isopropylhydrindene and α-naphthylmagnesium bromide by Bruce and Todd.[15]

"The Grignard reagent from 66 g. of 1-bromo-8-methylnaphthalene was mixed with 26 g. of *o*-chlorobenzonitrile in benzene, and after refluxing for sixteen hours, dilute hydrochloric acid was added, and the crystalline ketimine hydrochloride was collected and washed with cold water, alcohol, and ether; yield, 60 g. (63%). This salt, which is moderately soluble in hot water, was recovered after refluxing with hydrochloric acid at various concentrations."[14]

"To the Grignard reagent prepared from 22 g. of α-bromonaphthalene, 3 g. of magnesium and 80 ml. of ether, was added 50 ml. of benzene and 13 g. of 4-cyano-7-isopropylhydrindene. After the reaction mixture was heated overnight it was poured on 100 g. of ice with 50 ml. of hydrochloric acid. After two hours 25 g. of the ketimine hydrochloride, a yellow, crystalline solid, was collected on a filter. A sample crystallized from 70% acetic acid melted at 262° with decomposition; yield, 100%."[15]

A method of preparing more water-sensitive ketimine salts is described by Cloke,[16] whose procedure may be summarized as follows. Ethylmagnesium bromide was first prepared in the usual manner from 42.3 g. of ethyl bromide, 9 g. of magnesium and 150 ml. of anhydrous ether. To this ethereal solution 10.35 g. of isopropyl cyanide in three times its volume of ether was added slowly from a dropping funnel. The material was then boiled gently for about twelve hours, when it was transferred to a separatory funnel, from which it was added slowly to about 300 ml. of liquid ammonia in a 500-ml. Dewar flask, which was then connected with a five-foot lime tower. From time to time during a twenty-hour period the mixture was agitated to disintegrate lumps. At this point 200 ml. of dry ether was added, and the solution was filtered through a Buchner funnel in a moisture-proof apparatus. After removal of residual ammonia with a stream of dry air the solution was somewhat diluted with ether and treated with dry hydrogen chloride. Purification was effected by solution in a mixture of acetic acid (*ca.* 50 ml.) and acetic anhydride (*ca.* 5 ml.) and reprecipitation with dry ether; yield, 10 g. (48.5%).

The preparation of a series of alkyl α-naphthyl ketones in yields ranging from 37 percent to 63 percent is described by Nunn and Henze[17] as follows.

---

[14] Fieser and Seligman, *J. Am. Chem. Soc.*, *61*, 136–42 (1939).
[15] Bruce and Todd, *J. Am. Chem. Soc.*, *61*, 157–61 (1939).
[16] Cloke, *J. Am. Chem. Soc.*, *62*, 117–9 (1940).
[17] Nunn and Henze, *J. Org. Chem.*, *12*, 540–2 (1947).

"To a Grignard reagent prepared from magnesium turnings (0.21 g.-atom) and an alkyl bromide (0.22 mole) in 250 ml. of anhydrous ether, α-naphthonitrile (0.20 mole) in 300 ml. of anhydrous toluene was added over a period of one hour with continuous stirring. The ether was removed by distillation, and the toluene solution was refluxed for five hours. After cooling, the ketimine was obtained by hydrolysis of the toluene solution with 100 ml. of saturated ammonium chloride and chipped ice. The aqueous layer was then separated from the toluene solution and extracted once with ether. The ether and toluene extracts were combined and extracted twice with 100-ml. portions of dilute sulfuric acid. These two acid extracts were combined, extracted once with ether, and heated at reflux temperature for two hours, cooled, and extracted twice with an ether-benzene mixture. The ether-benzene extracts were washed with water, twice with saturated sodium bicarbonate solution, and twice with saturated sodium chloride solution. The ether-benzene layer was then concentrated and distilled under diminished pressure."

t-ALKYLAMINE (OR TERTIARY ALCOHOL) FORMATION

For the most part the initial product of reaction between a nitrile and a Grignard reagent displays little or no tendency to react further with the Grignard reagent. Apparently the halomagnesium ketimine derivatives are, in general, for solubility or other reasons, less reactive than the parent nitriles. In a few instances, however, products which cannot be readily accounted for in any other manner have been reported. In all such cases the product of the Grignard reaction itself is presumably a compound of the general formula $RR'_2CN(MgX)_2$. The products isolated after hydrolysis are, in some cases, *t*-alkylamines, and in others, tertiary alcohols.

$$RR'_2CN(MgX)_2 \xrightarrow{2\ H_2O} RR'_2CNH_2 + MgX_2 + Mg(OH)_2$$

$$RR'_2CN(MgX)_2 \xrightarrow{3\ H_2O} RR'_2COH + MgX_2 + Mg(OH)_2 + NH_3$$

The isolation of 3-amino-3-γ-quinolylpentane as one of the byproducts in the intended preparation of 4-propionylquinoline from 4-cyanoquinoline and ethylmagnesium iodide was reported by Rabe and Pasternack.[18]

4-Cyanoquinoline (0.3 mole) + C_2H_5MgI (0.6 mole) $\xrightarrow{H_2O}$ 4-propionylquinoline (COC_2H_5) (5 g.) + 4-ethylquinoline (C_2H_5) (10 g.) + 4-quinolyl-$H_2NC(C_2H_5)_2$

[18] Rabe and Pasternack, *Ber.*, 46, 1026–32 (1913).

Allen and Henze,[19] attempting the preparation of alkoxymethyl ketones, rediscovered this reaction, and (evidently regarding it as new) employed it to prepare in excellent yields some otherwise difficultly accessible alkoxymethyldialkylamines.

$$CH_3OCH_2CN + H_2C{=}CHCH_2MgBr \text{ (2 equiv.)} \xrightarrow{H_2O} CH_3OCH_2(H_2C{=}CHCH_2)_2CNH_2 \text{ (65.6\%)}$$

$$C_2H_5OCH_2CN \text{ (100 g.)} + H_2C{=}CHCH_2MgBr \text{ (from 370 g. bromide)} \xrightarrow{H_2O} C_2H_5OCH_2(H_2C{=}CHCH_2)_2CNH_2 \text{ (156.6 g., 78.7\%)}$$

$$C_2H_5OCH_2CN + n\text{-}C_3H_7MgBr \text{ (2 equiv.)} \xrightarrow{H_2O} C_2H_5OCH_2(n\text{-}C_3H_7)_2CNH_2 \text{ (98.9\%)}$$

$$C_2H_5OCH_2CN \text{ (49.5 g.)} + n\text{-}C_3H_7MgBr \text{ (from 86.3 g. bromide)} + H_2C{=}CHCH_2MgBr \text{ (from 100 g. bromide)} \xrightarrow{H_2O} H_2C{=}CHCH_2(n\text{-}C_3H_7)(C_2H_5OCH_2)CNH_2 \text{ (60.7\%)}$$

The stepwise reaction, leading to the formation of a potentially optically active amine, would seem to leave little doubt that the course of the reaction is as represented.

Baerts[20] has detected small quantities (*ca.* 1%) of tertiary alcohols among the products of the reactions of propio- and butyronitriles with ethylmagnesium bromide. A similar report is made by Bruylants and Mathus[21] concerning the reaction of low-boiling α-butenonitrile (1-cyanopropene) with ethylmagnesium bromide. In the reaction of *n*-butylmagnesium bromide with valeronitrile, conducted in methylal, Bourgom[22] actually found the tertiary alcohol to be the major product.

$$n\text{-}C_4H_9CN \text{ (1 mole)} + n\text{-}C_4H_9MgBr \text{ (1 mole)} \xrightarrow{H_2O} (n\text{-}C_4H_9)_3COH \text{ (38 g.)} + (n\text{-}C_4H_9)_2CO \text{ (27 g.)} + \text{gas (2.5 l.)} + \text{black residue}$$

KETENIMINATE FORMATION

Nitriles with labile hydrogen atoms attached to the *alpha* carbon atom are capable of undergoing with Grignard reagents a reaction analogous to a ketone enolization (*q.v.*, Chapter VI). Bruylants,[23] in discussing the reactions of acetonitrile with aliphatic Grignard reagents, postulates that the nitrile reacts primarily as a "pseudo-acid."

$$H_2C{=}C{=}NH + RMgX \longrightarrow H_2C{=}C{=}NMgX + RH$$

If the nitrile is in fact in equilibrium with a "pseudo-acidic" tautomer the reaction suggested would undoubtedly take place. It seems alto-

[19] Allen and Henze, *J. Am. Chem. Soc.*, *61*, 1790-4 (1939).

[20] Baerts, *Bull. soc. chim. Belg.*, *31*, 184-92, 421-6 (1922).

[21] Bruylants and Mathus, *Bull. acad. roy. Belg.*, *Classe sci.*, [5], *11*, 636-53 (1925); *Chem. Zentr.*, *1926*,*I*, 3145.

[22] Bourgom, *Bull. soc. chim. Belg.*, *33*, 101-15 (1924).

[23] Bruylants, *Bull. acad. roy. Belg.*, *Classe sci.*, [5], 8, 7-23 (1922); *Chem. Zentr.*, *1923*,*I*, 85.

gether possible (indeed, highly probable), however, that keteniminate formation may take place (similarly to analogous enolate formation) by attack of the Grignard reagent upon the normal cyano form of the molecule.

$$H_3C—C{\equiv}N : MgXR \longrightarrow H_2C{=}C{=}NMgX + RH$$

If this is in fact the case, then the complex decomposition leading to keteniminate formation is competitive with the complex rearrangement leading to "normal" addition-product formation. In view of the established relative reactivities of Grignard reagents toward benzonitrile (in the "normal" reaction) it is of interest in this connection, though, of course, not critically conclusive, that phenylmagnesium bromide is reported as reacting with acetonitrile to give moderate to fairly good yields of the "normal" product (acetophenone),[24] whereas the aliphatic Grignard reagents yield no normal product at all [Bruylants (*loc. cit.*[23]), Mignonac and Hoffmann[25]].

Amide formation. According to Mignonac and Hoffmann (*loc. cit.*[25]), the initial product (other than ethane) of the reaction of acetonitrile with ethylmagnesium bromide, upon treatment with water at 0°, yields acetamide.

$$H_2C{=}C{=}NMgBr \xrightarrow{2\ H_2O} \left[H_2C{=}C\begin{matrix} OH \\ NH_2 \end{matrix} \right] \longrightarrow CH_3CONH_2$$

The presence, subsequent to hydrolysis, of phenylacetamide among the products of the reaction of phenylacetonitrile with methylmagnesium bromide[26] may be similarly explained.*

Condensation and polymerization. Rondou (*loc. cit.*[26]) attributes the formation of the dimer of phenylacetonitrile to the interaction of two molecules of keteniminate.

$$2\ C_6H_5CH{=}C{=}NMgBR \longrightarrow C_6H_5CH{=}C[N(MgBr)_2]CH(CN)C_6H_5$$

$$\xrightarrow{2\ H_2O} C_6H_5CH_2C({=}NH)CH(CN)C_6H_5{}^{\dagger} + MgBr_2 + Mg(OH)_2$$

However, on the basis of analogy with the ketolization reaction, it seems more probable that the condensation involves one molecule of keteniminate and one molecule of nitrile, as Bruylants (*loc. cit.*[23]) has assumed in the case of acetonitrile.

[24] Shriner and Turner, *J. Am. Chem. Soc.*, *52*, 1267–9 (1930); Troger and Beck, *J. prakt. Chem.*, [2], *87*, 289–311 (1913); Bary, *Bull. soc. chim. Belg.*, *31*, 397–410 (1922).

[25] Mignonac and Hoffmann, *Compt. rend.*, *191*, 718–20 (1930).

[26] Rondou, *Bull. soc. chim. Belg.*, *31*, 231–41 (1922).

*It is, of course, probable that in many cases simple hydrolysis, without the addition of water, may regenerate the nitrile.

$$RR'C{=}C{=}NMgBr \xrightarrow{H_2O} RR'CHCN + MgXOH$$

†The assignment of structure of the dimer is made on the basis of its identity with the dimer of von Meyer, *J. prakt. Chem.*, *52*, 81–117 (1895), obtained by the action of sodium on the nitrile, and shown to yield an isoöxime identical with that obtained from α-cyanodesoxybenzoïn [$C_6H_5CH_2COCH(CN)C_6H_5$].

$$H_2C{=}C{=}NMgBr + CH_3C{\equiv}N \rightarrow CH_3C({=}NMgBr)CH_2CN$$

The trimer of phenylacetonitrile is formulated by Rondou (*loc. cit.*[26]) as 2,4-diamino-3,5-diphenyl-6-benzylpyridine, and is assumed by him to result from the reaction of two molecules of keteniminate with one of nitrile. It would seem, however, quite as logical to attribute its formation to successive condensations of a molecule of keteniminate with a molecule of nitrile, and of the secondary keteniminate thus formed with a second molecule of nitrile, followed by ring closure, either before or during hydrolysis.

$$C_6H_5CH{=}C{=}NMgBr \xrightarrow{C_6H_5CH_2CN} C_6H_5CH_2C({=}NMgBr)CH(C_6H_5)CN$$

$$\rightarrow C_6H_5CH_2C({=}NH)C(C_6H_5){=}C{=}NMgBr$$

$$\xrightarrow{C_6H_5CH_2CN} C_6H_5CH_2C({=}NH)CH(C_6H_5)C({=}NMgBr)CH(C_6H_5)CN$$

[Structural formulas: a ring with C(=NH) at top, H/C with H_5C_6 and C_6H_5/C–H, $C_6H_5CH_2$–C, C≡N, and N–H at bottom $\rightarrow$ pyridine ring with NH_2 at top, H_5C_6–C, C–C_6H_5, $C_6H_5CH_2$–C, C–NH_2, N]

Bruylants (*loc. cit.*[23]) has isolated from among the reaction products of acetonitrile with an aliphatic Grignard reagent two compounds which he characterizes as 2-hydroxy-4,6-dimethyl-5-cyanopyridine and 2-amino-4,6-dimethyl-5-cyanopyridine, respectively. He accounts for their formation as follows.

$$H_2C{=}C{=}NMgBr + CH_3{-}C{\equiv}N \rightarrow CH_3C({=}NMgBr)CH_2CN \xrightarrow{H_2O}$$

$$CH_3C({=}NH)CH_2CN \rightarrow CH_3C(NH_2){=}CHCN \xrightarrow{H_2O} CH_3C(OH){=}CHCN$$

$$2\ CH_3C(OH){=}CHCN \xrightarrow{-H_2O} CH_3{-}C_5N(ring: CH{-}C(OH){=}N{-}C(CH_3){=}C(CN))$$

[Structural formula: ring with CH–C(OH), N, C=C bearing CN and CH_3, and CH_3–C]

$$CH_3C(OH){=}CHCN + CH_3C(NH_2){=}CHCN$$

$$\xrightarrow{-H_2O} CH_3{-}C_5N(ring: CH{-}C(NH_2){=}N{-}C(CH_3){=}C(CN))$$

[Structural formula: ring with CH–C(NH_2), N, C=C bearing CN and CH_3, and CH_3–C]

The formation of various other nitrile condensation products may be accounted for in accordance with the principles outlined.

At first glance it might appear that the foregoing discussion does not elucidate the Grignard condensations of the crotononitriles ($CH_3CH{=}CHCN$). Although the crotononitriles are the more stable of the butenonitrile isomers (96–100% at equilibrium),[27] the interconversion of the α,β- and β,γ-unsaturated nitrile isomers in the presence of suitable catalysts is rather rapid.[28] To account for the Grignard condensation of the crotononitriles it is sufficient to make only three rather probable assumptions: (1) that at equilibrium at ordinary temperatures there is a finite concentration of the β,γ-unsaturated isomer; (2) that the Grignard reagent (or some component of the Grignard reagent solution) is a suitable catalyst for the interconversion of isomers; and (3) that keteniminate formation is rapid as compared with "normal" addition. However, not all of even these rather probable assumptions may be necessary. It is conceivable, at least, that the Grignard reagent is capable of effecting a direct conversion of α,β-unsaturated isomer to keteniminate, thus bypassing β,γ-unsaturated isomer formation entirely.

$$CH_3CH{=}CH{-}C{\equiv}N:MgXR \longrightarrow H_2C{=}CH{-}CH{=}C{=}NMgX + RH$$

In that case it would be necessary to assume only that the nitrile-keteniminate conversion is rapid as compared with "normal" addition.

It may be noted in passing that, according to Bruylants and Gevaert,[29] the dimeric condensation product of the reaction of ethylmagnesium bromide with crotononitrile is identical with that similarly obtained from allyl cyanide and with that obtained by von Meyer[29.1] by the treatment of allyl cyanide with sodium or with sodium ethoxide.

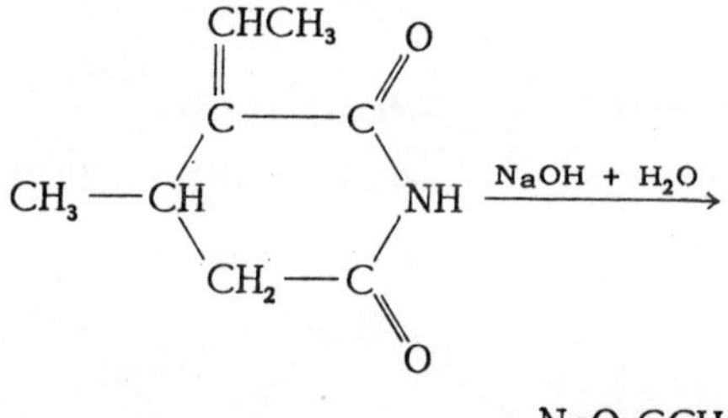

```
         CHCH3   O
          ||    //
          C----C
         /      \
CH3 --CH         NH   --NaOH + H2O-->
         \      /
          CH2--C
                \\
                 O
```

$$NaO_2CCH_2CH(CH_3)C({=}CHCH_3)CO_2Na + NH_3$$

CYANO GROUP DISPLACEMENT

Replacement by organic radical of Grignard reagent. The ability of the cyano group to behave, under certain conditions, as a "pseudo-halogen" is illustrated by the Grignard reactions of some nitriles.

---

[27] Letch and Linstead, *J. Chem. Soc.*, *1932*, 443–56.

[28] Ingold, Salas, and Wilson, *J. Chem. Soc.*, *1936*, 1328–34.

[29] Bruylants and Gevaert, *Bull. acad. roy. Belg., Classe es sciences*, [5], 9, 27–37 (1923); *Chem. Zentr.*, *1923,III*, 1263.

[29.1] von Meyer, *J. prakt. Chem.*, *52*, 81–117 (1895).

$$RCN + R'MgX \longrightarrow RR' + MgXCN$$

Although this type of reaction has not been exhaustively investigated, it appears to be fairly general for α-amino[30] and α,α-disubstituted cyanohydrins.[31] It must also be the initial step in the formation of tertiary alcohols from benzoyl cyanide[32] and from cyanoformic ester.[33]

$$C_6H_5COCN \xrightarrow{RMgX} C_6H_5COR + MgXCN \xrightarrow{RMgX} R_2(C_6H_5)COMgX$$

$$H_5C_2O_2CCN \xrightarrow{RMgX} H_5C_2O_2CR + MgXCN \xrightarrow{2\ RMgX} R_3COMgX + MgXOC_2H_5$$

The range of cyano compounds represented in the foregoing summary is scarcely broad enough to justify any very dogmatic generalizations, yet two characteristics are common to the radicals attached to the cyano group—$(CH_2)_5NCH_2$, $(CH_3)_2NCH_2$, $C_6H_5NHCH_2$, $R(CH_2)_5NCH$, $R(CH_3)_2NCH$, $RR'(CH_2)_5NC$, $RR'(CH_3)_2NC$, $RR'(HO)C$, C_6H_5CO, $H_2C_5O_2C$. (1) All would be estimated as rather weakly "electronegative" in the Kharasch sense. (2) None are capable of any considerable degree of resonance stabilization as free radicals. It may reasonably be assumed, therefore, that in all these cases the radical-cyano bond has a rather high degree of ionic character, with the negative end of the dipole at the cyano group.

The behavior of 1-cyanohydrastinine (Stevens *et al.*, *loc. cit.*[30d,e]) may be explained on the grounds of its constitutional similarity to the α-amino nitriles already discussed, as may that of 9,10-dimethyl-10-cyano-9,10-dihydroacridine (Stevens *et al.*, *loc. cit.*[30]) if the principle of vinylology be invoked.

[Structure: 1-cyanohydrastinine — H_2C(O)(O) methylenedioxy benzene ring fused with CH_2–CH_2–N–CH_3 and CH–CN] $\xrightarrow{CH_3MgI}$ [Structure: same ring system with CH–CH_3]

---

[30] (*a*) Christiaen, *Bull. soc. chim. Belg.*, *33*, 483–90 (1924); (*b*) Bruylants, *Bull. acad. roy. Belg.*, *Classe sci.*, [5], *11*, 261–80 (1925); *Chem. Zentr.*, *1926*,*I*, 874; (*c*) Velghe, *ibid.*, [5], *11*, 301–8 (1925); *Chem. Zentr.*, *1926*,*I*, 875; (*d*) Stevens, Cowan, and MacKinnon, *J. Chem. Soc.*, *1931*, 2568–72; (*e*) Thomson and Stevens, *ibid.*, *1932*, 2607–12.

[31] Guerden, *Bull. acad. roy. Belg.*, *Classe sci.*, [5], *11*, 701–10 (1925); *Chem. Zentr.*, *1926*,*I*, 3146.

[32] Adams, Bramlet, and Tendick, *J. Am. Chem. Soc.*, *42*, 2369–74 (1920); de Coster, *Bull. acad. roy. Belg.*, *Classe sci.*, [5], *11*, 661–5 (1925); *Chem. Zentr.*, *1926*,*I*, 3146.

[33] Bruylants, *Bull. acad. roy. Belg.*, *Classe sci.*, [5], *10*, 392–5 (1924); *Chem. Zentr.*, *1924*,*II*, 2457; McKenzie and Duff, *Ber.*, *60B*, 1335–41 (1927).

$$\text{9-cyano-9-methyl-10-methylacridan} \xrightarrow{CH_3MgI} \text{9,9-dimethyl-10-methylacridan}$$

The formally similar behavior of 4-cyanoquinoline, is, perhaps, somewhat different. Rabe and Pasternack[34] regarded it as an example of a special type of 1,4-addition reaction.

$$\text{4-cyanoquinoline} \xrightarrow{RMgX} \text{(1-MgX-4-R-4-cyano-1,4-dihydroquinoline)} \longrightarrow \text{4-R-quinoline} + MgXCN$$

Vinylologists, however, will detect here an analogy with the cyanogen reactions (*q.v.*).

Somewhat resembling these reactions formally, and analogous to the methoxyl group displacements previously discussed (see Chapter VI, Cleavages Involving 1,6-Addition), are the reactions of 4-cyanobenzoyldurene* reported by Fuson *et al.*[35]

Coupling. A few examples of a reaction analogous (formally, at least) to the coupling reactions of aralkyl halides (*q.v.*, Chapter XVI) have been reported.[36]

$$(a)\quad H_2C{=}CHCH_2CN \xrightarrow{C_2H_5MgBr} C_6H_{10} + CH_3CH{=}CHCN \text{ (2 isomers)} + (H_2C{=}CHCH_2CN)_2 + \text{other polymerization products}$$

$$(b,1)\quad (CH_3)_2N(CH_3)_2CCN \xrightarrow{CH_3MgBr} [(CH_3)_2N(CH_3)_2C{-}]_2$$

$$(b,2)\quad (CH_3)_2N(CH_3)_2CCN \xrightarrow{C_2H_5MgBr} [(CH_3)_2N(CH_3)_2C{-}]_2 + (CH_3)_2NC(CH_3)_2C_2H_5$$

$$(b,3)\quad (CH_3)_2N(CH_3)_2CCN \xrightarrow{n\text{-}C_3H_7MgBr} [(CH_3)_2N(CH_3)_2C{-}]_2 \text{ (very little)} + (CH_3)_2NC(CH_3)_2\text{-}n\text{-}C_3H_7 \text{ (20\%)}$$

---

[34] Rabe and Pasternack, *Ber.*, *46*, 1026–32 (1913).

* The corresponding 3-cyano compound reacts "normally" to form diketones. The 2-cyano isomer forms 1,1-disubstituted 3-durylpseudoisoindoles. (See Table VI-XVIII, **$C_{18}H_{17}ON$** and Table X-I, **$C_{18}H_{17}NO$**.)

[35] Fuson, Emmons, and Tull, *J. Org. Chem.*, *16*, 648–54 (1951).

[36] (*a*) Bruylants and Gevaert, *Bull. acad. roy. Belg.*, *Classe sci.*, [5], 9, 27–37 (1923); *Chem. Zentr.*, *1923,III*, 1263; (*b*) Velghe, *ibid.*, [5], *11*, 301–8 (1925); *Chem. Zentr.*, *1926,I*, 875; (*c*) Christiaen, *Bull. soc. chim. Belg.*, *33*, 483–90 (1924).

(*c*,1) $C_6H_5NH(C_6H_5)CHCN \xrightarrow{C_2H_5MgBr} [C_6H_5NH(C_6H_5)CH—]_2$ (30%) + gas

(*c*,2) $C_6H_5NH(C_6H_5)CHCN \xrightarrow{C_6H_5MgBr} [C_6H_5NH(C_6H_5)CH—]_2$ (25%)
$+ C_6H_5CH{=}NC_6H_5 + C_6H_5NH_2$

Unfortunately no attention has been paid to the fate of the organic radicals of the Grignard reagents. If these reactions are indeed similar to the halide coupling reactions one may describe the overall process as:

$$2\ RCN + 2\ R'MgX \longrightarrow R_2 + 2\ R'\cdot + 2\ MgXCN$$

When the Grignard reagent is methyl it would be converted almost quantitatively to the corresponding hydrocarbon by the capture of a hydrogen atom from the solvent.

$$R'\cdot + (C_2H_5)_2O \longrightarrow R'H + CH_3(C_2H_5O)CH\cdot$$

Ethyl and propyl radicals, while they might react to a very slight extent in this way, would, for the most part, disproportionate

$$2\ R'\cdot \longrightarrow R'_{(+H)} + R'_{(-H)}$$

The fact that reaction *c*,1 is reported as evolving "gas" cannot be regarded as confirmatory of the reaction scheme proposed, for this reaction is undoubtedly complicated by keteniminate formation.

Moreover, it is to be noted that none of the Grignard reagents involved in the examples cited is of the type that shows a tendency toward homolytic dissociation. If these are, like the halide coupling reactions, free-radical chain-reactions they must, in the instances cited, be attributed to the influence of metallic impurities in the magnesium employed for Grignard reagent preparation or to other (unrecognized) free-radical chain-initiating factors.

Reductive displacement. In view of the extremely limited data available concerning reactions in which the cyano group of the nitrile is replaced by a hydrogen atom (*i.e.*, by the MgX group of the Grignard reagent), any attempt at their elucidation must be regarded as speculative and tentative. In the most clear-cut example reported,[37] that of the reaction of triphenylmethyl cyanide with benzylmagnesium chloride, a 70 per-cent yield of triphenylmethane is recorded. Some bibenzyl was also isolated, but no evidence is advanced that this had any other source than the Wurtz side-reaction which accompanies the preparation of the Grignard reagent.

By theoretical extension of the relative reactivity studies of Gilman *et al.*,[38] it would appear that the Werner complex of the nitrile and Grignard reagent in question must be of an exceptionally unreactive type (as regards the "normal" addition reaction), for both the radical R of the nitrile

---

[37] Ramart-Lucas and Salmon-Legagneur, *Bull. soc. chim.*, [4], *43*, 321–9 (1928).

[38] Gilman and Lichtenwalter, *Rec. trav. chim.*, *55*, 588–90 (1936); Gilman, St. John, St. John, and Lichtenwalter, *ibid.*, *55*, 577–85 (1936).

(RCN) and the radical R′ of the Grignard reagent (R′MgX) are weakly electronegative (the former extremely so). Moreover, both radicals (especially the former) are capable of a considerable degree of resonance stabilization. On this basis one might confidently predict that at relatively low temperatures (*e.g.*, that of boiling ether) the type of complex rearrangement leading to "normal" addition would take place extremely slowly or not at all. One might then consider the probability of a competitive rearrangement, and the possibility that such a rearrangement might differ from the essentially ionic rearrangement leading to exchange of the organic radical of the Grignard reagent for the cyano group of the nitrile. A type of rearrangement that accounts for the major product reported, and which seems not unlikely in view of the outlined characteristics of the complex components may be crudely represented (without implication as to mechanistic detail) as follows.

$$(C_6H_5)_3C{-}C{\equiv}N : \underset{Cl}{\overset{CH_2C_6H_5}{Mg}} \longrightarrow \left[(C_6H_5)_3C \cdots C \equiv N : Mg{-}Cl \;\; (\text{with dotted links } (C_6H_5)_3C \cdots Mg \text{ and } C \cdots CH_2C_6H_5) \right]$$

$$\longrightarrow (C_6H_5)_3C{-}\underset{Cl}{Mg} : N{\equiv}C{-}CH_2C_6H_5 \xrightarrow{H_2O} (C_6H_5)_3CH + MgClOH + C_6H_5CH_2CN$$

The process represented is a radical rearrangement, although the actual liberation of free radicals into the solution is not implied. Perhaps it should be represented as an equilibrium, but the high yield of triphenylmethane liberated upon hydrolysis indicates that the equilibrium, if it exists, is substantically toward the right. The prehydrolysis product postulated is identical with the Werner complex which might be expected to result from the combination triphenylmethylmagnesium chloride and phenylacetonitrile—another presumably exceptionally unreactive complex (as regards "normal" addition). Unfortunately, no one has as yet applied the critical test of adding an equivalent of a suitable Grignard reagent co-reactant to such a reaction mixture, nor has anyone investigated the products of reaction in higher-boiling solvents.

Benzyldiphenylmethyl cyanide is reported to react similarly with benzylmagnesium chloride (Ramart-Lucas, *loc. cit.*[37]).

The reactions of dimethyl- and dibenzylmalononitriles with phenylmagnesium bromide have been studied by Erickson and Barnett.[39] They call attention to the formal similarity between these reactions and the Grignard cleavage reactions of disubstituted malonic esters,[40] α-oxido ketones and glycidic esters,[41] and of β-diketones.[42] They propose reaction

[39] Erickson and Barnett, *J. Am. Chem. Soc.*, *57*, 560–2 (1935).

[40] Leroide, *Ann. chim.*, [9], *16*, 354–410 (1921).

[41] Kohler, Richtmyer, and Hester, *J. Am. Chem. Soc.*, *53*, 205–21 (1931).

[42] Kohler and Erickson, *J. Am. Chem. Soc.*, *53*, 2301–9 (1931).

schemes in which the initial products are "normal" cyano-Grignard reagent addition products which either rearrange or react further with the Grignard reagent.

Although the radicals $NC(C_6H_5CH_2)_2C$ and $NC(CH_3)_2C$ are probably neither so weakly "electronegative" nor capable of so high a degree of resonance stabilization as the radicals $(C_6H_5)_3C$ and $C_6H_5CH_2(C_6H_5)_2C$, they unquestionably share those characteristics to some extent.

Dimethylmalononitrile, with the less weakly "electronegative" radical $NC(CH_3)_2C$, reacts in part "normally" when added to an excess of ethereal Grignard reagent at ordinary temperatures.

$$(CH_3)_2C(CN)_2 \xrightarrow{2\ C_6H_5MgBr} \xrightarrow{2\ H_2O} (CH_3)_2C(COC_6H_5)_2$$

However, some benzophenone is also found, so there must be some simultaneous cleavage.

When one equivalent of ethereal Grignard solution is combined (by reverse addition) with one equivalent of ethereal nitrile at $-15°$, only the cleavage products, $(CH_3)_2CHCN$ and C_6H_5CN, are isolated upon hydrolysis.

Dibenzylmalononitrile, with the more weakly electronegative radical $NC(C_6H_5CH_2)_2C$, gives only cleavage products, or their further reaction products, both in ether and in the higher-boiling benzene.

$$(C_6H_5CH_2)_2C(CN)_2 + C_6H_5MgBr \xrightarrow{Et_2O} (C_6H_5CH_2)_2CHCN + (C_6H_5)_2CO$$

$$(C_6H_5CH_2)_2C(CN)_2 + C_6H_5MgBr \xrightarrow{C_6H_6} (C_6H_5CH_2)_2CHCOC_6H_5 + (C_6H_5)_2CO$$

A scheme similar to that proposed for the triphenylmethyl cyanide reaction would account adequately for these phenomena. In the former case the rearrangement of a complex of one relatively unreactive Grignard reagent with a relatively unreactive nitrile to form the complex of another relatively unreactive Grignard reagent with another relatively unreactive nitrile was postulated. In the present instance the rearrangement would convert the complex of a relatively reactive Grignard reagent with a relatively unreactive nitrile to the complex of a relatively unreactive Grignard reagent with a relatively reactive nitrile.

$$NC(C_6H_5CH_2)_2C—C{\equiv}N : \underset{}{\overset{C_6H_5}{\overset{|}{Mg}}}—Br \rightarrow$$

$$\left[NC(C_6H_5CH_2)_2C \cdots C{\equiv}N : Mg—Br \quad (\text{with dashed bonds } C_6H_5 \cdots C \text{ and } NC(C_6H_5CH_2)_2C \cdots Mg) \right]$$

$$\rightarrow NC(C_6H_5CH_2)_2C—\underset{\underset{Br}{|}}{Mg} : N{\equiv}C—C_6H_5$$

In the presence of excess Grignard reagent new complexes would be formed.

$$NC(C_6H_5CH_2)_2C—\underset{\underset{Br}{|}}{Mg} : N\equiv C—C_6H_5 + 2\ C_6H_5MgBr \longrightarrow$$

$$C_6H_5—\underset{\underset{Br}{|}}{Mg} : N\equiv C—C_6H_5 + C_6H_5—\underset{\underset{Br}{|}}{Mg} : N\equiv C—C(CH_2C_6H_5)_2MgBr$$

Although this is potentially an equilibrium process, which would, of course, include also the etherate of the Grignard reagent, at ordinary temperatures the relatively reactive $C_6H_5BrMg : NCC_6H_5$ complex would be removed by "normal" addition-reaction rearrangement to form the ketiminate of benzophenone. At higher temperatures the other (less reactive) complex might also react, as it evidently does in boiling benzene.

$$Br(C_6H_5)Mg : N\equiv C—C(CH_2C_6H_5)_2MgBr \longrightarrow$$

$$Br—Mg—N{=}C(C_6H_5)—C(CH_2C_6H_5)_2MgBr$$

$$\xrightarrow{H_2O} C_6H_5COCH(CH_2C_6H_5)_2 + MgBr_2 + Mg(OH)_2 + NH_3$$

α,β-UNSATURATED NITRILES

Like some of the α,β-unsaturated aldehydes and esters, some of the α,β-unsaturated nitriles undergo 1,4-addition of the Grignard reagent to the conjugated system. The number of examples of reactions of Grignard reagents with α,β-unsaturated nitriles is so limited as to discourage generalization. Indeed, in some of the few cases available for consideration it is a question whether one has to do with 1,4-addition to an α-cyano α,β-unsaturated ester or to an α-carbalkoxy α,β-unsaturated nitrile.

$$C_6H_5CH{=}C(CO_2C_2H_5)CN \xrightarrow{RMgX^*} C_6H_5CHRCH(CO_2C_2H_5)CN$$

(Kohler and Reimer[43])

$$C_6H_5CH{=}CHCH{=}C(CO_2C_2H_5)CN \xrightarrow{RMgBr^\dagger}$$

$$C_6H_5CH{=}CHCHRCH(CO_2C_2H_5)CN$$

(MacLeod[44])

Unequivocal examples of 1,4-addition to α,β-unsaturated nitriles are reported, however, by Kohler[45] and by Maxim and Aldea.[46]

$$C_6H_5CH{=}C(C_6H_5)CN \xrightarrow{RMgBr^\dagger} C_6H_5CHRCH(C_6H_5)CN$$

```
HC——CH                                      HC——CH
||   ||                      RMgX‡          ||   ||
HC    C—CH=C(C6H5)CN        ——————→         HC    C—CHRCH(C6H5)CN
  \  /                                        \  /
   O                                           O
```

* R = CH_3, i-C_3H_7, C_6H_5, $C_6H_5CH_2$, $C_6H_5C\equiv C$, α-$C_{10}H_7$.

[43] Kohler and Reimer, *Am. Chem. J.*, 33, 333–56 (1905).

† R = C_2H_5, C_6H_5.

[44] MacLeod, *Am. Chem. J.*, 44, 331–52 (1910).

[45] Kohler, *Am. Chem. J.*, 35, 386–404 (1906).

[46] Maxim and Aldea, *Bull. soc. chim.*, [5], 2, 582–91 (1935); [5], 3, 1329–34 (1936).

‡ R = CH_3, C_2H_5, n-C_3H_7, i-C_4H_9, i-C_5H_{11}, $C_6H_5CH_2$, p-$CH_3C_6H_4$.

It may be noted that in all the examples cited as undergoing 1,4-addition the nitriles are α-substituted. Presumably, aside from any electronic influence it may exert, the *alpha* substituent presents some degree of steric hindrance to 1,2-addition. That this may be a necessary, but is not always a sufficient, condition for 1,4-addition is indicated by the reported 1,2-addition of phenylmagnesium bromide to α,2,4,6-tetramethyl-β-methoxycinnamonitrile.[47] In this case steric hindrance to 1,4-addition is presumably considerably greater than that to 1,2-addition. β-Methoxy-2,4,6-trimethylcinnamonitrile is also reported to undergo 1,2-addition (Fuson *et al.*, *loc. cit.*[47]), as are cinnamonitrile and β-phenylcinnamonitrile (Kohler, *loc. cit.*[45]).

CYANOHYDRINS

For the most part cyanohydrins are reported as reacting "normally" with Grignard reagents, although the yields obtained are seldom stated, and in most cases it may be inferred that no attempt at the isolation and identification of byproducts was made. One equivalent of Grignard reagent is first consumed by the highly "active" hydrogen of the hydroxyl group; a second equivalent then reacts with the relatively inert nitrile group. Yarnall and Wallis[48] have taken advantage of this marked differential in functional reactivities to spare less readily accessible Grignard reagents.

$$HOCH_2CN + CH_3MgI \longrightarrow IMgOCH_2CN + CH_4$$

```
                   H2C——CH2                  H2C——CH2
IMgOCH2CN +         |    |         →          |    |
                   H2C   CHCH3               H2C   CHCH3
                     \  /                      \  /
                      CH                        CH
                      |                         |
                     MgCl              IMgOCH2C=NMgCl
```

The cleavage reactions of nitriles of the types $R_2C(OH)CN$ and $RR'C(OH)CN$, reported by Guerden,[49] have already been discussed. That at least some nitriles of this kind also react "normally" to some extent is evidenced by the reported reactions of α-hydroxyisobutyronitrile and α-hydroxyisovaleronitrile with methylmagnesium halides (Gauthier;[50] see also Guerden, *loc. cit.*[49]).

Weissberger and Glass[51] report a cyanohydrin reaction which at first glance appears to involve a rather peculiar rearrangement. The reaction scheme which they propose, however, appears to account satisfactorily for the product isolated.*

---

[47] Fuson, Ullyot, Stedman, and Tawney, *J. Am. Chem. Soc.*, *60*, 1447–50 (1938).

[48] Yarnall and Wallis, *J. Org. Chem.*, *4*, 284–8 (1939).

[49] Guerden, *Bull. acad. roy. Belg.*, *Classe sci.*, [5], *11*, 701–10 (1925); *Chem. Zentr.*, *1926,I*, 3146.

[50] Gauthier, *Compt. rend.*, *152*, 1100–2 (1911); *Chem. Zentr.*, *1911,I*, 1809.

[51] Weissberger and Glass, *J. Am. Chem. Soc.*, *64*, 1724–7 (1942).

* Mes = mesityl = $2,4,6\text{-}(CH_3)_3C_6H_2—$.

$$\text{Mes-CH(OH)CN} \xrightarrow{C_6H_5MgBr} \text{Mes-CH(OMgBr)C(=NMgBr)}C_6H_5$$
$$\xrightarrow{H_2O} \text{Mes-C(OH)=C(NH}_2)C_6H_5$$
$$\longrightarrow \text{Mes-COCH(NH}_2)C_6H_5$$

α-HALO NITRILES

The reactions of α-halo nitriles with Grignard reagents have been but little investigated. Although the "normal" reaction of a nitrile with a Grignard reagent apparently differs in mechanism from the "normal" reaction of a ketone with a Grignard reagent, there are (as has already been noted) marked analogies between some of the "abnormal" reactions of the two types of compounds. On this ground one might regard as possibilities (by analogy with the corresponding α-halo ketone reactions, *q.v.*, the following reactions of α-halo nitriles.

(1) $RR'XCCN + R''MgX' \rightarrow RR'XCCR''{=}NMgX'$

(2) $RXCHCN + R'MgX' \rightarrow RXC{=}C{=}NMgX' + R'H$

(3) $RXCHCN + R'MgX' \rightarrow RHC{=}C{=}NMgX' + R'X$

(4) $RR'XCCN + R''MgX' \rightarrow RR'R''CCN + MgXX'$

The nature of the predominating reaction might be expected to vary with: (1) the *alpha* halogen involved, (2) the structure of the α-halo nitrile, and (3) the Grignard reagent involved. Although no extensive or very thorough studies have been made, there is evidence that reactions of the first three types occur.

Mathus[52] has reported a very small yield (1.5%) of phenacyl chloride from the reaction of phenylmagnesium bromide with chloroacetonitrile. The isolation of 1,1-diethyl-2-alkylethylenimines as products of the reactions of α-chloronitriles with ethylmagnesium bromide[53] strongly suggests a reaction sequence in which the first step is a "normal" addition at the cyano triple bond.

$$RCHClCN \xrightarrow{C_2H_5MgBr} RCHClCN : MgBrC_2H_5 \longrightarrow RCHClC(C_2H_5){=}NMgBr$$
$$\xrightarrow{C_2H_5MgBr} RCHClC(C_2H_5)_2N(MgBr)_2 \longrightarrow RCH{-}C(C_2H_5)_2\ (\text{ring closed through } N{-}MgBr) + MgBrCl$$
$$\xrightarrow{H_2O} RCH{-}C(C_2H_5)_2\ (\text{ring closed through } N{-}H) + MgBrCl + MgBrOH$$

[52] Mathus, *Bull. soc. chim. Belg.*, 34, 285–9 (1925).

[53] de Boosere, *Bull. soc. chim. Belg.*, 32, 25–51 (1923); Theunis, *Bull. acad. roy. Belg., Classe sci.*, [5], 12, 185–96 (1926).

The reports that alkanes are evolved when aliphatic Grignard reagents react with chloroacetonitrile (Mathus, *loc. cit.*[52]), and that the principle products of the reactions of Grignard reagents with chloroacetonitrile are always polymers, resins, or tars (Mathus, *loc. cit.*,[52] Tröger and Beck[54]) are indicative that reaction 2 takes place. Perhaps the occurrence of crotononitrile and crotononitrile polymers among the products of reaction of ethylmagnesium bromide with α-chlorobutyronitrile (de Boosere, *loc. cit.*[53]) might also be so interpreted.

$$CH_3CH_2CHClCN \xrightarrow{C_2H_5MgBr} CH_3CH_2CHClCN : MgBrC_2H_5 \longrightarrow$$
$$CH_3CH_2CCl{=}C{=}NMgBr + C_2H_6 \longrightarrow CH_3CH{=}CHCN + MgBrCl$$

Evidence of the occurrence of reaction 3 is found in the Grignard and Barbier reactions of iodoäcetonitrile, which acts as a fairly good iodinating agent.[55]

$$ICH_2CN + C_6H_5MgBr \longrightarrow C_6H_5I \quad (60\%)$$
$$ICH_2CN + C_6H_5(CH_2)_3MgBr \longrightarrow C_6H_5(CH_2)_3I \quad (65\%)$$
$$ICH_2CN + Br(CH_2)_3CHBrCHBrCH_3 + Mg \longrightarrow I(CH_2)_3CH{=}CHCH_3 \quad (50\%)$$
$$ICH_2CN + Br(CH_2)_5CHBrCHBrCH_3 + Mg \longrightarrow I(CH_2)_3CH{=}CHCH_3 \quad (65\%)$$

Except for the indolyl Grignard reagents,[56] which are singularly unreactive toward cyano groups, evidence for the occurrence of reaction 4 is lacking.

$$ClCH_2CN + C_8H_6NMgI \longrightarrow \text{(indole: CH}{=}C{-}CH_2CN\text{, N–H)} \quad (ca.\ 47\%)$$

$$ClCH_2CN + 6\text{-}(CH_3O)C_8H_5NMgI \longrightarrow CH_3O{-}\text{(indole: CH}{=}C{-}CH_2CN\text{, N–H)} \quad (52\%)$$

Possibly these are simple alkyl halide replacement reactions, which the corresponding α-halo ketone reactions are not (see α-Halo Ketones and Aldehydes, Chapter VI).

CYANOGEN

The reaction of cyanogen with a Grignard reagent was first investigated by Blaise,[57] who, using an excess of Grignard reagent, obtained a

[54] Tröger and Beck, *J. prakt. Chem.*, [2], 87, 289–311 (1911).

[55] von Braun, Deutsch, and Schmatloch, *Ber.*, *45*, 1246–63 (1912).

[56] Majima and Hoshino, *Ber.*, *58B*, 2042–6 (1925); Akabori and Saito, *ibid.*, *63B*, 2245–8 (1930).

[57] Blaise, *Compt. rend.*, *132*, 38 (1901); *J. Chem. Soc.*, *80,I*, 133 (1901); *Chem. Zentr.*, *1901,I*, 298.

ketone. Blaise represented the reaction as a "normal" addition, followed by a cleavage reaction.

$$(\text{-CN})_2 + \text{EtMgI} \longrightarrow \text{NCC(Et)}{=}\text{NMgI} \xrightarrow{\text{EtMgI}} \text{Et}_2\text{C}{=}\text{NMgI} + \text{MgICN}$$

Grignard[58] showed that, when the amount of Grignard reagent is limited to one equivalent and reverse addition is employed, the major product is a nitrile. Grignard also assumed that the first step in the reaction is a "normal" addition, and postulated rearrangement and cleavage in the presence of water.

$$(\text{CN})\text{C}{\equiv}\text{N} + \text{RMgX} \longrightarrow (\text{CN}){-}\overset{\text{R}}{\overset{|}{\text{C}}}{=}\text{NMgX}$$

$$(\text{CN}){-}\overset{\text{R}}{\overset{|}{\text{C}}}{=}\text{NMgX} \xrightarrow{\text{H}_2\text{O}} \text{Mg}\begin{matrix}\diagup\text{X}\\ \diagdown(\text{CN})\end{matrix} + \text{RC}{\equiv}\text{N}$$

He raised, but did not answer the questions, what part water might play in this process, and why the seemingly more probably hydrolytic reaction does not take place.

$$(\text{CN}){-}\overset{\text{R}}{\overset{|}{\text{C}}}{=}\text{NMgX} \xrightarrow{\text{H}_2\text{O}} \text{Mg}\begin{matrix}\diagup\text{X}\\ \diagdown\text{OH}\end{matrix} + (\text{CN}){-}\overset{\text{R}}{\overset{|}{\text{C}}}{=}\text{NH} \xrightarrow{\text{H}_2\text{O}} \text{RCOCN} + \text{NH}_3$$

On the whole, it appears more probable that the initial reaction involves cleavage and rearrangement, and that ketone formation is attributable to reaction of excess Grignard reagent with the initial product (nitrile complex).

$$\text{NC}{-}\text{C}{\equiv}\text{N}:\overset{\text{R}}{\overset{|}{\text{Mg}}}{-}\text{X} \longrightarrow \text{R}{-}\text{C}{\equiv}\text{N}:\overset{\text{CN}}{\overset{|}{\text{Mg}}}{-}\text{X} \xrightarrow{\text{RMgX}}$$

$$\text{R}{-}\text{C}{\equiv}\text{N}:\overset{\text{R}}{\overset{|}{\text{Mg}}}{-}\text{X} + \text{MgXCN} \longrightarrow \text{R}_2\text{C}{=}\text{NMgX} \xrightarrow{\text{H}_2\text{O}}$$

$$\text{R}_2\text{C}{=}\text{NH} + \text{MgXOH} \xrightarrow{\text{H}_2\text{O}} \text{R}_2\text{CO} + \text{NH}_3$$

However, in the case of cyanogen there would be no means of distinguishing between a pseudo-addition accompanied by cleavage and rearrangement and a true cleavage reaction.

$$\text{NC}{-}\text{C}{\equiv}\text{N}:\overset{\text{R}}{\overset{|}{\text{Mg}}}{-}\text{X} \longrightarrow \left[\text{NC}\cdots\text{C}{\equiv}\text{N}:\overset{\text{R}}{\overset{\vdots}{\text{Mg}}}{-}\text{X}\right] \longrightarrow \text{R}{-}\text{C}{\equiv}\text{N}:\overset{\text{CN}}{\overset{|}{\text{Mg}}}{-}\text{X}$$

[58] Grignard, Bellet, and Courtot, *Ann. chim.*, [9], *12*, 364–93 (1919).

Indeed, in view of the behavior of cyanogen chloride (*q.v.*), it is conceivable that some Grignard reagents might follow one path and some the other.

CYANOGEN HALIDES

With aromatic Grignard reagents (*i.e.*, with Grignard reagents that are relatively reactive toward nitriles in general), cyanogen chloride reacts to yield nitriles (or ketones) as the major products, with traces or very small amounts of chlorides.[59] Phenethylmagnesium bromide, the only reported reagent that may be taken as reasonably representative of the primary aliphatic Grignard reagents, is also said to give a fair yield (63 percent) of nitrile. The cycloalkyl and secondary alkyl Grignard reagents, on the other hand, yield the chlorides predominantly, with a little of the nitriles as byproducts.[60] This suggests a pseudo-addition for the more reactive Grignard reagents and a true cleavage reaction for the less reactive.

$$\mathrm{Cl{-}C{\equiv}N:\underset{\displaystyle |}{\overset{\displaystyle R}{Mg}}{-}X \longrightarrow R{-}C{\equiv}N:\overset{\displaystyle Cl}{Mg}{-}X}$$

$$\mathrm{Cl{-}C{\equiv}N:\overset{\displaystyle R'}{Mg}{-}X \longrightarrow R'Cl + MgXCN}$$

Exceptions to the implied generalization that the Grignard reagents more reactive toward nitriles in general react with cyanogen chloride to yield nitriles, whereas the less reactive Grignard reagents yield chlorides are found in the indolylmagnesium halides,[61] and the phenylethynylmagnesium halides (Grignard *et al.*, *loc. cit.*[60]). Although these reagents are extremely unreactive toward nitriles in general, they react with cyanogen chloride to yield the nitriles. However, in view of the differences between the ordinary Grignard reagents, on the one hand, and those derived from the nitrogen heterocycles (*q.v.*, Chapter II) and from the acetylenes, on the other, it is altogether possible that the latter react by a mechanism different from either of those here suggested.

Both cyanogen bromide and cyanogen iodide are predominantly halogenating agents, although the former sometimes yields a little nitrile (and/or ketone) as a byproduct.[60,62]

---

[59] Grignard, *Compt. rend.*, *152*, 388-90 (1911); *Chem. Abstr.*, *5*, 1589 (1911); Grignard, Bellet, and Courtot, *Ann. chim.*, [9], *4*, 28-57 (1915); Willemart, *ibid.*, [10], *12*, 345-423 (1929).

[60] Grignard and Bellet, *Compt. rend.*, *158*, 457-61 (1914); *Chem. Abstr.*, *8*, 1565 (1914); Grignard and Kashichi Ono, *Bull. soc. chim.*, [4], *39*, 1589-94 (1926); Grignard, Bellet, and Courtot, *loc. cit.*[58]

[61] Majima, Shigematsu, and Rokkaku, *Ber.*, *57B*, 1453-6 (1924).

[62] Grignard and Courtot, *Bull. soc. chim.*, [4], *17*, 228-31 (1915); Grignard and Perrichon, *Ann. chim.*, [10], *5*, 5-36 (1926).

According to Coleman and Leeper,[63] di-*n*-butylmagnesium reacts with cyanogen chloride to yield somewhat less nitrile and somewhat more chloride than does *n*-butylmagnesium bromide.

CYANAMIDES

The reactions of cyanamides with Grignard reagents have been little studied. The "normal" reaction is amidine formation.

$$RR'NCN + R''MgX \longrightarrow R''C({=}NMgX)NRR' \xrightarrow{H_2O} R''C({=}NH)NRR' + MgXOH$$

Busch and Hobein[64] obtained very poor yields of amidines from phenylcyanamide (carbanilinonitrile) and phenyl- and α-naphthylmagnesium bromides, employing a procedure which was perhaps not too well-adapted to the isolation of amidines.

Good yields of amidine hydrochlorides are reported by Adams and Beebe[65] as resulting from the treatment of dibenzylcyanamide with ethyl-, phenyl-, and *p*-tolylmagnesium bromides.

Vuylsteke[66] obtained the amidine, in unspecified yield, from dimethylcyanamide and phenylmagnesium bromide. Benzylmagnesium chloride yielded very little amidine, together with dimethylamine, toluene, and phenylmalononitrile. Vuylsteke accounted for the latter products by successive cleavage and condensation reactions.

$$(CH_3)_2NCN \xrightarrow{C_6H_5CH_2MgCl} (CH_3)_2NMgCl + C_6H_5CHCN \xrightarrow{C_6H_5CH_2MgCl}$$

$$C_6H_5CH_3 + C_6H_5CH(MgCl)CN \xrightarrow{(CH_3)_2NCN} (CH_3)_2NMgCl + C_6H_5CH(CN)_2$$

Ethylmagnesium bromide yielded no isolable product other than ethane. Vuylsteke suggests:

$$(CH_3)_2NCN \xrightarrow{C_2H_5MgBr} (CH_3)_2NMgBr + C_2H_5CN \xrightarrow{C_2H_5MgBr} C_2H_6 + CH_3CH{=}C{=}NMgBr$$

On the basis of the very limited data available one might hazard the prediction that, with proper experimental procedure, the amidines of aromatic acids are probably preparable in satisfactory yields by this method, but that those of aliphatic acids are not.

---

[63] Coleman and Leeper, *Proc. Iowa Acad. Sci.*, *47*, 201-5 (1940); *Chem. Abstr.*, *35*, 7374 (1941).

[64] Busch and Hobein, *Ber.*, *40*, 4296-8 (1907).

[65] Adams and Beebe, *J. Am. Chem. Soc.*, *38*, 2768-72 (1916).

[66] Vuylsteke, *Bull. acad. roy. Belg.*, *Classe sci.*, [5], *12*, 534-44 (1926); *Chem. Zentr.*, *1927*,*I*, 888.

TABLE X-I

REACTIONS OF GRIGNARD REAGENTS WITH CYANO COMPOUNDS

Cyano Comp'd	RMgX	Product(s)	Ref.
CNBr			
BrCN	$(\equiv CMgBr)_2$	$(\equiv CBr)_2$	*177; cf. 178*
BrCN (7.5 g.)	C_2H_5MgBr (15.5 g. C_2H_5I)	$(C_2H_5CN)_3$	*179*
BrCN (0.75 mole)	C_6H_5MgBr (1.0 mole)	C_6H_5Br (80%); C_6H_5CN (trace); $(C_6H_5)_2CO$ (5%)	*180,181,182*
BrCN (sl. excess)	$RC\equiv CMgBr$*	$RC\equiv CBr$ (72–78%)	*183*
BrCN	$C_6H_5C\equiv CMgBr$	$C_6H_5C\equiv CBr$ (80%); $C_6H_5C\equiv CCN$ (trace)	*182*
BrCN	$R'C\equiv CMgBr$†	$R'C\equiv CBr$ (64–68%)	*183*
BrCN	1-Indenyl-MgBr	1-Bromoindene	*181,182*
BrCN	$1-C_{10}H_7C\equiv CMgBr$	$1-C_{10}H_7C\equiv CBr$ (not isolable)	*183*
CNCl			
ClCN (7.5 g.)	$i-C_3H_7MgBr$ (0.1 mole)	$i-C_3H_7CN$ (9%); $i-C_3H_7Cl$ (67%)	*186*
ClCN	$n-C_4H_9MgBr$	More $n-C_4H_9CN$ and less $n-C_4H_9Cl$ than for $(n-C_4H_9)_2Mg$	*188*
ClCN	$(n-C_4H_9)_2Mg$	Less $n-C_4H_9CN$ and more $n-C_4H_9Cl$ than for $n-C_4H_9MgBr$	*188*
ClCN	Cyclopentadienyl-MgBr	$(C_5H_5CN)_2$	*182,184*
ClCN	$(C_2H_5)_2CHMgBr$	$(C_2H_5)_2CHCN$ (8%); $(C_2H_5)_2CHCl$ (70%)	*186*
ClCN	C_6H_5MgBr	C_6H_5CN (80%); C_6H_5Cl (4%)	*180,182*
ClCN	C_6H_5MgBr (2.5 equiv.)	$(C_6H_5)_2C{=}NH\cdot HCl$ (equiv. to 80% ketone)	*187*
ClCN	C_6H_5MgBr	"*sym*-Phenyldichlorotriazine" ‡	*189*
ClCN (8 g.)	C_6H_5MgBr (0.125 mole) + $2,4-(CH_3)_2C_6H_3MgBr$ (0.167 mole)	$C_6H_5[2,4-(CH_3)_2C_6H_3]C{=}NH\cdot HCl$ (equiv. to 55% ketone)	*187*

* R = $n-C_3H_7$, $n-C_5H_{11}$, $(CH_2)_5CH$, $n-C_9H_{19}$.

† R′ = $C_6H_5CH_2$, $4-CH_3C_6H_4$, "*p*-cresyl," $C_6H_5CH_2CH_2$, $2,4-(CH_3)_2C_6H_3$.

‡ With less Et_2O the product was "diphenylchlorotriazine."

TABLE X-I (Continued)

Cyano Comp'd	RMgX	Product(s)	Ref.
CNCl (*cont.*)			
ClCN	C_6H_5MgBr + 1-$C_{10}H_7MgBr$	C_6H_5(1-$C_{10}H_7$)C=NH·HCl (equiv. to 55% ketone)	*187*
ClCN	$(CH_2)_5CHMgBr$	$(CH_2)_5CHCN$ (*ca.* 5%); $(CH_2)_5CHCl$ (60%)	*182*
ClCN	2-$CH_3C_6H_4MgBr$	2-$CH_3C_6H_4CN$ (50%)	*182*
ClCN	2-$CH_3C_6H_4MgBr$ (3 equiv. C_7H_7Br)	(2-$CH_3C_6H_4$)$_2$C=NH·HCl (equiv. to 73% ketone)	*187*
ClCN	3-$CH_3C_6H_4MgBr$	3-$CH_3C_6H_4CN$ (60%)	*182*
ClCN	4-$CH_3C_6H_4MgBr$	4-$CH_3C_6H_4CN$ (60%)	*182*
ClCN	4-$CH_3C_6H_4MgBr$ (3 equiv. C_7H_7Br)	(4-$CH_3C_6H_4$)$_2$C=N·HCl (equiv. to 80% ketone)	*187*
ClCN	4-$CH_3OC_6H_4MgBr$	4-$CH_3OC_6H_4CN$ (58%); 4-$CH_3OC_6H_4Cl$ ("a little")	*180,182*
ClCN	*n*-$C_5H_{11}C\equiv CMgBr$	*n*-$C_5H_{11}C\equiv CCN$ (67%)	*181,182*
ClCN	$C_6H_5C\equiv CMgBr$	$C_6H_5C\equiv CCN$ (61%); $C_6H_5C\equiv CCl$ (trace)	*181,182*
ClCN (7 g.)	Indolyl-MgI (13.3 g. indole)	3-Cyanoindole	*190*
ClCN	$C_6H_5(CH_2)_2MgBr$	$C_6H_5(CH_2)_2CN$ (63%)	*180,182*
ClCN	$CH_3(C_6H_5)CHMgBr$	$CH_3(C_6H_5)CHCN$ (10%); $CH_3(C_6H_5)CHCl$ (47%)	*186*
ClCN	2,4-$(CH_3)_2C_6H_3MgBr$	2,4-$(CH_3)_2C_6H_3CN$ (40%); 2,4-$(CH_3)_2C_6H_3Cl$ ("a little"); 1,3-$(CH_3)_2C_6H_4$ (30%)	*182*
ClCN	2,4-$(CH_3)_2C_6H_3MgBr$ (0.167 mole) + C_6H_5MgBr (0.125 mole)	C_6H_5[2,4-$(CH_3)_2C_6H_3$]C=NH·HCl (equiv. to 55% ketone)	*187*
ClCN	2,5-$(CH_3O)_2C_6H_3MgBr$	2,5-$(CH_3O)_2C_6H_3CN$ (90%)	*182*
ClCN	$(CH_2)_5CHC\equiv CMgBr$	$(CH_2)_5CHC\equiv CCN$ (67%)*	*183*
ClCN	*p*-Cresyl-C≡CMgBr	*p*-Cresyl-C≡CCN*	*183*
ClCN	2-Methylindolyl-MgI	2-Methyl-3-cyanoindole	*190*

* Ketone was also formed when excess Grignard reagent was used.

TABLE X-I (Continued)

Cyano Comp'd	RMgX	Product(s)	Ref.
CNCl (*cont.*)			
ClCN	$C_2H_5(C_6H_5)CHMgBr$	$C_2H_5(C_6H_5)CHCN$ (8%); $C_2H_5(C_6H_5)CHCl$ (42%)	*186*
ClCN	2,4,6-$(CH_3)_3C_6H_2MgBr$	2,4,6-$(CH_3)_3C_6H_2CN$ (40%); 2,4,6-$(CH_3)_3C_6H_2Cl$ (15%); 1,3,5-$(CH_3)_3C_6H_3$ (20%)	*182*
ClCN	$(n\text{-}C_4H_9)_2CHMgBr$	$(n\text{-}C_4H_9)_2CHCN$ ("a little"); $(n\text{-}C_4H_9)_2CHCl$ (68%)	*186*
ClCN	1-$C_{10}H_7MgBr$	1-$C_{10}H_7CN$ (65%); 1-$C_{10}H_7Cl$	*180,182*
ClCN	1-$C_{10}H_7MgBr$ (3 equiv. $C_{10}H_7Br$)	$(1\text{-}C_{10}H_7)_2C{=}NH \cdot HCl$ (equiv. to 55% ketone)	*187*
ClCN (11.8 g.)	1-$C_{10}H_7MgBr$ (95 g. $C_{10}H_7Br$)	After H_2SO_4 hydrolysis: $(1\text{-}C_{10}H_7)_2CO$ (58 g., 67%)	*185*
ClCN	1-$C_{10}H_7MgBr$ + C_6H_5MgBr	$C_6H_5(1\text{-}C_{10}H_7C{=}NH \cdot HCl$ (equiv. to 55% ketone)	*187*
ClCN	*m*-Xylyl-$C{\equiv}CMgBr$	*m*-Xylyl-$C{\equiv}CCN$ (65–66%)*	*183*
ClCN	$n\text{-}C_8H_{17}C{\equiv}CMgBr$	$n\text{-}C_8H_{17}C{\equiv}CCN$ (70%)*	*183*
ClCN	2-CH_3-4-CH_3O-5-i-$C_3H_7C_6H_2MgBr$	2-CH_3-4-CH_3O-5-i-$C_3H_7C_6H_3CN$ (55%)	*182*
ClCN	$(C_6H_5)_2CHMgBr$	$(C_6H_5)_2CHCN$ (8%); $(C_6H_5)_2CHCl$ (42%); $[(C_6H_5)_2CH-]_2$ (5%)	*186*
CNI			
ICN (53 g.)	C_6H_5MgBr (0.5 mole)	C_6H_5I (64%); unchanged ICN	*180,182*
C_2NF_3			
F_3CCN (0.5 mole F_3CCONH_2)	$C_6H_5CH_2MgCl$ (0.63 mole C_7H_7Cl)	$F_3CCOCH_2C_6H_5$ (36 g., 38.4%)	*192*

* Ketone was also formed when excess Grignard reagent was used.

TABLE X-I (Continued)

Cyano Comp'd	RMgX	Product(s)	Ref.
C_2N_2			
$(-CN)_2$	$(\equiv CMgBr)_2$	$HC\equiv CH$	*181,187*
$(-CN)_2$	C_2H_5MgI	$(C_2H_5)_2CO$	*1*
$(-CN)_2$	*i*-$C_5H_{11}MgBr$	*i*-$C_5H_{11}CN$ (62%)	*180,187*
$(-CN)_2$	C_6H_5MgBr	C_6H_5CN (75%)	*180,187*
$(-CN)_2$	$(CH_2)_5CHMgBr$	$(CH_2)_5CHCN$ (50%)	*187,191*
$(-CN)_2$	2-Methylcyclohexyl-MgBr	1-Cyano-2-methylcyclohexane (40%)	*187,191*
$(-CN)_2$	3-Methylcyclohexyl-MgCl	*cis*- and *trans*-1-Cyano-3-methylcyclohexane	*2,13*
$(-CN)_2$	3-Methylcyclohexyl-MgBr	1-Cyano-3-methylcyclohexane (60%)	*187,191*
$(-CN)_2$	4-Methylcyclohexyl-MgBr	1-Cyano-4-methylcyclohexane (40%)	*187,191*
$(-CN)_2$	$C_6H_5C\equiv CMgBr$	$C_6H_5C\equiv CCN$ (*ca.* 60%)	*187*
$(-CN)_2$	$C_6H_5(CH_2)_3MgBr$	$C_6H_5(CH_2)_3CN$ (65–70%)	*180,187*
$(-CN)_2$	$C_{10}H_{17}MgCl$*	$C_{10}H_{17}CN$, m.p. 155–158° (35%); camphane (35%); bicamphanyl; C_2H_5CN†	*187*
C_2H_2NCl			
$ClCH_2CN$	RMgX‡	RH; "polymer"	*3*
$ClCH_2CN$	C_6H_5MgBr	Black resin	*4*
$ClCH_2CN$ (75 g.)	C_6H_5MgBr (195 g. C_6H_5Br)	$C_6H_5COCH_2OH$; $C_6H_5COCH_2Cl$ (1.5%); $(C_6H_5-)_2$; tar	*3*
$ClCH_2CN$	C_6H_5MgBr (2 equiv.)	"Polymer"	*3*
$ClCH_2CN$	Indolyl-MgI	3-Indolylacetonitrile (47–51%)	*11*
$ClCH_2CN$ (6.1 g.)	6-Methoxyindolyl-MgI (11.7 g. 6-methoxyindole)	6-Methoxy-3-indolylacetonitrile (7.4 g., 52%)	*194*

* From "pinene hydrochloride."
† From C_2H_5MgBr used as activator in Grignard reagent preparation.
‡ R is aliphatic.

TABLE X-I (Continued)

Cyano Comp'd	RMgX	Product(s)	Ref.
C_2H_2NI			
ICH_2CN	C_6H_5MgBr	C_6H_5I (60%)	*5*
ICH_2CN	$Br(CH_2)_3CHBrCHBrCH_3$ + Mg	$I(CH_2)_3CH{=}CHCH_3$ (50%)	*5*
ICH_2CN	$Br(CH_2)_5CHBrCH_2Br$ + Mg	$I(CH_2)_5CH{=}CH_2$ (65%)	*5*
ICH_2CN	$C_6H_5(CH_2)_3MgBr$	$C_6H_5(CH_2)_3I$ (65%)	*5*
C_2H_3N			
CH_3CN	RMgBr*	$CH_3C({=}NH)CH_2CN$; CH_3COCH_2CN; 2,4-dimethyl-3-cyano-6-hydroxypyridine (principal product); 2,4-dimethyl-3-cyano-6-aminopyridine; RH	*6*
CH_3CN	C_2H_5MgBr	CH_3CONH_2; C_2H_6	*7*
CH_3CN	Thiophthenyl-MgI†	Methyl thiophthenyl ketone†	*14*
CH_3CN	n-$C_5H_{11}MgBr$ (1.1 equiv.)	CH_3CO-n-C_5H_{11} (14%) cond'n prod. (40%)	*60*
CH_3CN (49 g., 1.2 mole)	$CH_3O(CH_2)_4MgCl$ (159 g., 1.2 mole $C_5H_{11}ClO$)	$CH_3CO(CH_2)_4OCH_3$ (35 g., 22.5%)	*232*
CH_3CN	C_6H_5MgBr (1.2 equiv.)	$CH_3COC_6H_5$(45%); 2,4-dimethyl-3-cyano-6-aminopyridine	*8*
CH_3CN (0.25 mole)	C_6H_5MgBr (160 g. C_6H_5Br)	$CH_3COC_6H_5$ (21 g., 70%)	*9,4*
CH_3CN	C_6H_5MgBr (1.1 equiv.)	$CH_3COC_6H_5$ (33%)	*59*
CH_3CN	C_6H_5MgBr (3.0 equiv.)	$CH_3COC_6H_5$ (70%)	*59*
CH_3CN	C_6H_5MgBr (1.1 equiv.)	$CH_3COC_6H_5$ (37%); cond'n prod. (*ca.* 50%)	*60*
CH_3CN (0.25 mole)	n-$C_4H_9C{\equiv}CMgBr$ (21 g. n-$C_4H_9C{\equiv}CH$)	n-$C_4H_9C{\equiv}CH$ (19.5 g.)	*195*
CH_3CN	$C_6H_5CH_2MgCl$	$CH_3COCH_2C_6H_5$ (15.8%); C_7H_8	*10*
CH_3CN (0.25 mole)	$C_6H_5C{\equiv}CMgBr$ (0.25 mole)	$C_6H_5C{\equiv}CH$ (20 g.)	*195*

*R = CH_3, C_2H_5.

†Orientation unknown.

TABLE X-I (Continued)

Cyano Comp'd	RMgX	Product(s)	Ref.
C_2H_3N (*cont.*)			
CH_3CN	Indolyl-MgBr	Recovered CH_3CN (*ca.* 100%)	*11*
CH_3CN	2,5-$(CH_3)_2C_6H_3MgBr$	$CH_3COC_6H_3$-2,5-$(CH_3)_2$ ("poor yield")	*198*
CH_3CN	1-$C_{10}H_7MgBr$	1-$CH_3COC_{10}H_7$	*15*
CH_3CN (5 g.)	ω-Camphenyl-MgBr (21.5 g.)	ω-Acetylcamphene* (3.8 g., 10.7%)	*12*
C_2H_3NO			
$HOCH_2CN$ (0.1 mole)	CH_3MgI (1 equiv.) + $(CH_2)_4CHMgCl$ (1 equiv.)	CH_4; $HOCH_2COCH(CH_2)_4$ (isolated as 3,5-dinitrobenzoate; 3.8 g.)	*16*
$HOCH_2CN$ (0.1 mole)	CH_3MgI (1 equiv.) + 2-Methylcyclopentyl-MgCl (1 equiv.)	CH_4; hydroxymethyl 2-methylcyclopentyl ketone (isolated as 3,5-dinitrobenzoate)	*16*
$HOCH_2CN$ (4.0 ml.)	CH_3MgI (4.8 ml. CH_3I) + $(CH_2)_5CHMgCl$ (9.2 ml. $C_6H_{11}Cl$)	CH_4; $HOCH_2COCH(CH_2)_5$ (isolated as 3,5-dinitrobenzoate; 7.8 g., crude)	*16*
$HOCH_2CN$	$C_6H_5CH_2MgCl$	$HOCH_2COCH_2C_6H_5$; $HOCH_2C(CH_2C_6H_5)_2OH$	*196*
$C_3H_2N_2$			
$H_2C(CN)_2$ (6.6 g.)	C_6H_5MgBr (6.1 g. Mg)	Recovered $H_2C(CN)_2$ (6.1 g.)	*17*
C_3H_5N			
C_2H_5CN	CH_3MgI (1 equiv.) + C_6H_5MgBr (1 equiv.)	$C_2H_5COC_6H_5$	*18*
C_2H_5CN	CH_3MgI (1 equiv.) + $C_6H_5CH_2MgCl$ (1 equiv.)	$C_2H_5COCH_3$; $C_2H_5COCH_2C_6H_5$	*18*
C_2H_5CN	CH_3MgI (1 equiv.)	$C_2H_5COCH_3$ (21%); $C_2H_5(C_2H_5CO)CHCN$ (28%)	*60*
C_2H_5CN	C_2H_5MgBr (sl. excess)	$(C_2H_5CN)_3$ (*ca.* 8–10%); $(C_2H_5)_2CO$ (*ca.* 35%); C_2H_6 (5.9 l. per mole nitrile); $(C_2H_5)_3COH$ ("small am't"); $(C_2H_5CN)_2$ (*ca.* 20–25%)	*19*

TABLE X-I (Continued)

Cyano Comp'd	RMgX	Product(s)	Ref.
C_3H_5N (*cont.*)			
C_2H_5CN	C_2H_5MgBr (1.1 equiv.)	$(C_2H_5)_2CO$ (23%)	*59*
C_2H_5CN	*t*-C_4H_9MgCl (1.1 equiv.)	C_2H_5CO-*t*-C_4H_9 (5%); $C_2H_5(C_2H_5CO)CHCN$ (20%)	*60*
C_2H_5CN (61 g., 1.1 mole)	$CH_3O(CH_2)_3MgCl$ (147 g., 1.36 mole C_4H_9ClO)	$C_2H_5CO(CH_2)_3OCH_3$ (76 g., 54%)	*232*
C_2H_5CN	*n*-$C_5H_{11}MgBr$ (1.1 equiv.)	C_2H_5CO-*n*-C_5H_{11} (61%); cond'n prod. (*ca.* 5%)	*60*
C_2H_5CN	$CH_2(CH_2CH_2MgCl)_2$	C_2H_5CO-*n*-C_5H_{11} (60%); $H_2C(CH_2CH_2COC_2H_5)_2$ (20%)	*20*
C_2H_5CN	C_6H_5MgBr (excess)	$C_2H_5COC_6H_5$ (*ca.* 80%); recovered C_2H_5CN (4–5%)	*8*
C_2H_5CN (0.25 mole)	C_6H_5MgBr (160 g. C_6H_5Br)	$C_2H_5COC_6H_5$ (31 g., 91%)	*9*
C_2H_5CN	C_6H_5MgBr (1.1 equiv.)	$C_2H_5COC_6H_5$ (83%)	*59,60*
C_2H_5CN	C_6H_5MgBr (3.0 equiv.)	$C_2H_5COC_6H_5$ (91%)	*59*
C_3H_5NO			
CH_3OCH_2CN (142 g., 2 moles)	C_2H_5MgBr (372 g., 3 moles C_2H_5Br)	$CH_3OCH_2COC_2H_5$ (120 g., 59%)	*232*
CH_3OCH_2CN (35 g.)	C_2H_5MgI (1.5 equiv.)	$CH_3OCH_2COC_2H_5$ (35 g., 70%)	*21*
CH_3OCH_2CN	RMgX*	CH_3OCH_2COR	*197*
CH_3OCH_2CN	$H_2C{=}CHCH_2MgBr$ (2 equiv.)	$CH_3OCH_2(H_2C{=}CHCH_2)_2CNH_2$ (65.6%)	*22*
CH_3OCH_2CN (20 g.)	*n*-C_3H_7MgI (60 g. C_3H_7I)	CH_3OCH_2CO-*n*-C_3H_7 (25 g.)	*21*
CH_3OCH_2CN (70 g.)	$CH_3O(CH_2)_3MgI$ (200 g. C_4H_9IO)	$CH_3OCH_2CO(CH_2)_3OCH_3$	*23*
CH_3OCH_2CN (21.3 g., 0.3 mole)	C_6H_5MgBr (56.5 g., 0.36 mole C_6H_5Br)	$CH_3OCH_2COC_6H_5$ (32–35 g., 71–78%)	*237,238*
CH_3OCH_2CN	$C_6H_5CH_2MgCl$	$CH_3OCH_2COCH_2C_6H_5$	*196*
$CH_3CH(OH)CN$	C_2H_5MgBr	$CH_3CH(OH)COC_2H_5$	*24*

* R = C_2H_5, *n*-C_3H_7, *n*-C_4H_9, *i*-C_5H_{11}.

TABLE X-I (Continued)

Cyano Comp'd	RMgX	Product(s)	Ref.
$C_3H_6N_2$			
$(CH_3)_2NCN$	C_2H_5MgBr	No product identified	25
$(CH_3)_2NCN$	C_6H_5MgBr	$(CH_3)_2NC(=NH)C_6H_5$	25
$(CH_3)_2NCN$	$C_6H_5CH_2MgCl$	$(CH_3)_2NH$; $CH_3C_6H_5$; $C_6H_6CH_2C(=NH)N(CH_3)_2$ (very little); $C_6H_5CH_2CN$	25
$C_4H_2N_2S$			
5-Cyanothiazole (30 g.)	$CH_3O(CH_2)_3MgBr$ (75 g. C_4H_9BrO)	5-Thiazolyl 3-methoxypropyl ketone (18 g.)	*199*
5-Cyanothiazole (11 g.)	C_6H_5MgBr (30 g. C_6H_5Br)	5-Benzoylthiazole (15 g.)	*199*
C_4H_5N			
$H_2C=CHCH_2CN$	C_2H_5MgBr	C_6H_{10}; $CH_3CH=CHCN$ (2 isomers); $(H_2C=CHCH_2CN)_2$; other cond'n products	26
$CH_3CH=CHCN$ (low-boiling isomer)	C_2H_5MgBr (2 equiv.)	$(CH_3CH=CHCN)_3$ (*ca.* 60%); $(C_2H_5)_2C(OH)CH=CHCH_3$ ("small yield")	27
$(CH_2)_2CHCN$	CH_3MgBr	$(CH_2)_2CHCOCH_3$	28,29
$(CH_2)_2CHCN$	C_2H_5MgBr	$(CH_2)_2CHCOC_2H_5$	28,29
$(CH_2)_2CHCN$	n-C_3H_7MgBr	$(CH_2)_2CHCO$-n-C_3H_7	29
$(CH_2)_2CHCN$	i-C_3H_7MgBr	$(CH_2)_2CHCO$-i-C_3H_7	28,29
$(CH_2)_2CHCN$	$(CH_2)_2CHCH_2MgBr$	$(CH_2)_2CHCOCH_2CH(CH_2)_2$	30
$(CH_2)_2CHCN$	n-C_4H_9MgBr	$(CH_2)_2CHCO$-n-C_4H_9	29
$(CH_2)_2CHCN$	i-C_4H_9MgBr	$(CH_2)_2CHCO$-i-C_4H_9	29
$(CH_2)_2CHCN$	n-$C_5H_{11}MgBr$	$(CH_2)_2CHCO$-n-C_5H_{11}	29
$(CH_2)_2CHCN$	i-$C_5H_{11}MgBr$	$(CH_2)_2CHCO$-i-C_5H_{11}	30
$(CH_2)_2CHCN$	C_6H_5MgBr (sl. excess)	$(CH_2)_2CHCOC_6H_5$ (85%)	31,8,29

TABLE X-I (Continued)

Cyano Comp'd	RMgX	Product(s)	Ref.
C_4H_5N (*cont.*)			
$(CH_2)_2CHCN$ (26.8 g.)	C_6H_5MgBr (94.2 g. C_6H_5Br)	$(CH_2)_2CHC(=NH)C_6H_5$ (isolated as hydrochloride)	32,8
$(CH_2)_2CHCN$	i-$C_6H_{13}MgBr$	$(CH_2)_2CHCO$-i-C_6H_{13}	30
$(CH_2)_2CHCN$	$C_6H_5CH_2MgCl$	$(CH_2)_2CHCOCH_2C_6H_5$	29
$(CH_2)_2CHCN$ (15 g.)	2-$CH_3C_6H_4MgBr$ (32 g. C_7H_7Br)	$(CH_2)_2CHC(=NH)C_6H_4$-2-CH_3	33
$(CH_2)_2CHCN$ (5 g.)	3-$CH_3C_6H_4MgBr$ (43 g. C_7H_7Br)	$(CH_2)_2CHC(=NH)C_6H_4$-3-CH_3	33
$(CH_2)_2CHCN$ (9.75 g.)	4-$CH_3C_6H_4MgBr$ (34.9 g. C_7H_5Br)	$(CH_2)_2CHC(=NH)C_6H_4$-4-CH_3 (11.7 g., crude)	33
$(CH_2)_2CHCN$ (5 g.)	1-$C_{10}H_7MgBr$ (52 g. $C_{10}H_7Br$)	$(CH_2)_2CHC(=NH)$-1-$C_{10}H_7$ ("poor yield")	33
$C_4H_5NO_2$			
$H_5C_2O_2CCN$ (0.33 mole)	C_2H_5MgBr (1 mole)	$(C_2H_5)_3COH$ (24 g.); $C_2H_5COC(C_2H_5)_2OH$ (17 g.)	35
$H_5C_2O_2CCN$ (6 g.)	C_6H_5MgBr (34 g. C_6H_5Br)	$(C_6H_5)_3COH$ (3 g.); $(C_6H_5-)_2$	36
$H_3CO_2CCH_2CN$ (38 g.)	C_2H_5MgI (156 g. C_2H_5I)	$H_3CO_2CCH=C(NH_2)C_2H_5$ (22 g.)	200
C_4H_6NBr			
$BrCH_2CH_2CH_2CN$	C_2H_5MgBr	n-$C_3H_7COC_2H_5$; $BrCH_2CH_2CH_2COC_2H_5$; n-$C_5H_{11}COC_2H_5$	28
C_4H_6NCl			
$ClCH_2CH_2CH_2CN$	CH_3MgX	2-Methylpyrroline (10–23%)	34
$ClCH_2CH_2CH_2CN$ (1 mole)	C_2H_5MgBr (1 mole)	C_2H_6; $(CH_2)_2CHCOC_2H_5$ (23–25%); $C_2H_5COCH_2CH_2CH_2Cl$ (14–17%); other products (1%)	37
$ClCH_2CH_2CH_2CN$ (1 mole)	C_2H_5MgBr (2 moles)	C_2H_6; $(CH_2)_2CHCOC_2H_5$ (28–30%); $C_2H_5COCH_2CH_2CH_2Cl$ (27–31%); $[(CH_2)_2CHCN]_x$; other products (2%)	37

TABLE X-I (Continued)

Cyano Comp'd	RMgX	Product(s)	Ref.
C_4H_6NCl (*cont.*)			
$ClCH_2CH_2CH_2CN$	C_2H_5MgBr (+ dry HCl)	$(CH_2)_2CHC(C_2H_5)=NH\cdot HCl$; $ClCH_2CH_2CH_2COC_2H_5$	37
$ClCH_2CH_2CH_2CN$	C_2H_5MgX	2-Ethylpyrroline (38–40%)	34,32
$ClCH_2CH_2CH_2CN$ (15 g.)	C_2H_5MgBr (38 g. C_2H_5Br)	2-Ethylpyrroline (46%)	38,39
$ClCH_2CH_2CH_2CN$	n-C_3H_7MgX	2-n-Propylpyrroline (51%)	34
$ClCH_2CH_2CH_2CN$ (30 g.)	Pyrryl-MgBr (22 g. C_4H_4N)	2-α-Pyrrylpyrroline (45%)	43
$ClCH_2CH_2CH_2CN$ (12 g.)	2-Thienyl-MgI (24.3 g. C_4H_3IS)	2-(2-Thienyl)pyrroline (4.8 g., 27.5%)	41
$ClCH_2CH_2CH_2CN$	n-C_4H_9MgX	2-n-Butylpyrroline (66%)	34
$ClCH_2CH_2CH_2CN$ (15 g.)	C_6H_5MgBr (56 g. C_6H_5Br)	2-Phenylpyrroline (55%)	38,39,40
$ClCH_2CH_2CH_2CN$	C_6H_5MgBr	$ClCH_2CH_2CH_2C(=NH)C_6H_5$; $ClCH_2CH_2CH_2COC_6H_5$	32
$ClCH_2CH_2CH_2CN$	$(CH_2)_5CHMgX$	2-Cyclohexylpyrroline	39
$ClCH_2CH_2CH_2CN$ (15 g.)	$C_6H_5CH_2MgCl$ (45 g. C_7H_7Cl)	2-Benzylpyrroline (13%)	38,39
$ClCH_2CH_2CH_2CN$	$C_6H_5CH_2MgX$	2-Benzylpyrroline (45–67%)	34
$ClCH_2CH_2CH_2CN$ (15.5 g.)	2-$CH_3C_6H_4MgBr$ (34.9 g. C_7H_7Br)	2-o-Tolylpyrroline (12.6 g.)	33
$ClCH_2CH_2CH_2CN$ (13 g.)	3-$CH_3C_6H_4MgBr$ (34.9 g. C_7H_7Br)	2-m-Tolylpyrroline (9.8 g.)	33
$ClCH_2CH_2CH_2CN$ (15 g.)	4-$CH_3C_6H_4MgBr$ (51.3 g. C_7H_7Br)	2-o-Tolylpyrroline (6.3 g.)	33,39
$ClCH_2CH_2CH_2CN$ (10.4 g.)	2,4,6-$(CH_3)_3C_6H_2MgBr$ (24.9 g. $C_9H_{11}Br$)	2-Mesitylpyrroline (7.4 g., 39.6%)	41
$CH_3CHClCH_2CN$*	C_2H_5MgBr (1 equiv.)	$CH_3CH=CHCN$ (52%); tar (6–7%); $CH_3CHClCH_2COC_2H_5$ (2%); polymer (30%); C_2H_6	37
$CH_3CHClCH_2CN$*	C_2H_5MgBr (2 equiv.)	$(CH_3CH=CHCN)_3$; tar (10%); C_2H_6	37
$CH_3CHClCH_2CN$†	C_2H_5MgBr (1 equiv.)	$CH_3CH=CHCN$; tar (40%); C_2H_6; hexadiene	37

* Addition of Et_2O-nitrile solution to Grignard solution; 24 hours standing.
† Addition of Et_2O-nitrile solution to Grignard solution.

TABLE X-I (Continued)

Cyano Comp'd	RMgX	Product(s)	Ref.
C_4H_6NCl (*cont.*)			
$CH_3CHClCH_2CN$*	C_2H_5MgBr (2 equiv.)	$CH_3CH{=}CHCN$; tar (20%); C_2H_6; 1,1,2-triethylethyleneamine	37
C_4H_7N			
n-C_3H_7CN	C_2H_5MgBr (1.2 equiv.)	*n*-$C_3H_7COC_2H_5$ (*ca.* 40%); *n*-$C_3H_7(C_2H_5)_2COH$ (*ca.* 1%); (*n*-$C_3H_7CN)_3$ (*ca.* 25%); (*n*-$C_3H_7CN)_2$ (*ca.* 8–10%); tar	44
n-C_3H_7CN (0.33 mole)	C_6H_5MgBr (0.5 mole)	*n*-$C_3H_7COC_6H_5$ (90%)	8
n-C_3H_7CN (0.25 mole)	C_6H_5MgBr (1 mole)	*n*-$C_3H_7COC_6H_5$ (77%)	9
n-C_3H_7CN	C_6H_5MgBr (1.1 equiv.)	*n*-$C_3H_7COC_6H_5$ (82%)	59
n-C_3H_7CN	C_6H_5MgBr (3.0 equiv.)	*n*-$C_3H_7COC_6H_5$ (77%)	59
n-C_3H_7CN	$C_6H_5CH_2MgCl$	*n*-$C_3H_7COCH_2C_6H_5$	45
C_4H_7NO			
$CH_3CH(OCH_3)CN$	CH_3MgBr	$CH_3CH(OCH_3)COCH_3$ (37%)	42
$CH_3CH(OCH_3)CN$ (24 g.)	CH_3MgI (60 g. CH_3I)	$CH_3CH(OCH_3)COCH_3$ (19 g., 65%)	21
$CH_3CH(OCH_3)CN$ (22.1 g.)	CH_3MgI (39 g. CH_3I)	$CH_3CH(OCH_3)COCH_3$ (12 g., 45%)	48,49
$CH_3CH(OCH_3)CN$	C_2H_5MgBr	$CH_3CH(OCH_3)COC_2H_5$ (22%)	42
$CH_3CH(OCH_3)CN$ (17 g.)	C_2H_5MgI (50 g. C_2H_5I)	$CH_3CH(OCH_3)COC_2H_5$ (17 g.)	21
$CH_3CH(OCH_3)CN$	*n*-C_3H_7MgBr	$CH_3CH(OCH_3)CO$-*n*-C_3H_7 (35%)	42
$CH_3CH(OCH_3)CN$ (17 g.)	*n*-C_3H_7MgBr (37 g. C_3H_7Br)	$CH_3CH(OCH_3)CO$-*n*-C_3H_7 (19 g., 73%)	201
$CH_3CH(OCH_3)CN$	*i*-C_3H_7MgBr	$CH_3CH(OCH_3)CO$-*i*-C_3H_7 (13%)	42
$CH_3CH(OCH_3)CN$	*n*-C_4H_9MgBr	$CH_3CH(OCH_3)CO$-*n*-C_4H_9 (63%)	42
$CH_3CH(OCH_3)CN$	*i*-C_4H_9MgBr	$CH_3CH(OCH_3)CO$-*i*-C_4H_9 (21%)	42
$CH_3CH(OCH_3)CN$	*s*-C_4H_9MgBr	$CH_3CH(OCH_3)CO$-*s*-C_4H_9 (43%)	42

* Addition of Et_2O-nitrile solution to Grignard solution.

TABLE X-I (Continued)

Cyano Comp'd	RMgX	Product(s)	Ref.
C_4H_7NO (*cont.*)			
$CH_3CH(OCH_3)CN$	t-C_4H_9MgCl*	$CH_3CH(OCH_3)CO$-t-C_4H_9 (14%)	*42*
$CH_3CH(OCH_3)CN$	n-$C_5H_{11}MgBr$	$CH_3CH(OCH_3)CO$-n-C_5H_{11} (36%)	*42*
$CH_3CH(OCH_3)CN$	i-$C_5H_{11}MgBr$	$CH_3CH(OCH_3)CO$-i-C_5H_{11} (29%)	*42*
$C_2H_5OCH_2CN$ (43 g.)	CH_3MgI (0.5 mole)	$H_5C_2OCH_2COCH_3$ (28 g.)	*46,21*
$C_2H_5OCH_2CN$	C_2H_5MgI	$H_5C_2OCH_2COC_2H_5$ (70%)	*46,47,21*
$C_2H_5OCH_2CN$ (100 g.)	$H_2C{=}CHCH_2MgBr$ (370 g. C_3H_5Br)	$H_5C_2OCH_2(H_2C{=}CHCH_2)_2CNH_2$ (156.6 g., 78.7%)	*22*
$C_2H_5OCH_2CN$ (49.5 g.)	$H_2C{=}CHCH_2MgBr$ (100 g. C_3H_5Br) + n-C_3H_7MgBr (86.3 g. C_3H_7Br)	$H_2C{=}CHCH_2(n$-$C_3H_7)(H_5C_2OCH_2)CNH_2$ (60.7%)	*22*
$C_2H_5OCH_2CN$	n-C_3H_7MgBr (2 equiv.)	$H_5C_2OCH_2(n$-$C_3H_7)_2CNH_2$ (98.9%)	*22*
$C_2H_5OCH_2CN$	n-C_3H_7MgI (1.5 equiv.)	$C_2H_5OCH_2CO$-n-C_3H_7	*21*
$C_2H_5OCH_2CN$	n-C_3H_7MgX	$C_2H_5OCH_2CO$-n-C_3H_7	*47*
$C_2H_5OCH_2CN$	n-$C_5H_{11}MgX$	$C_2H_5OCH_2CO$-n-C_5H_{11}	*47*
$C_2H_5OCH_2CN$	C_6H_5MgBr	$C_2H_5OCH_2COC_6H_5$	*46,47,48*
$C_2H_5OCH_2CN$	$C_6H_5CH_2MgCl$	$C_2H_5OCH_2COCH_2C_6H_5$	*196*
$HO(CH_3)_2CCN$	CH_3MgI	$(CH_3)_2C(OH)COCH_3$	*24*
$HO(CH_3)_2CCN$	C_2H_5MgBr	$(CH_3)_2C(OH)COC_2H_5$	*24*
$HO(CH_3)_2CCN$	C_2H_5MgBr	t-$C_5H_{11}OH$ (principal product); $(CH_3)_2C(OH)COC_2H_5$ (7%)	*69*
$HO(CH_3)_2CCN$ (43 g.)	$C_6H_5(CH_3)_2CMgCl$ (155 g. $C_9H_{11}Cl$)	$HO(CH_3)_2CCOC(CH_3)_2C_6H_5$	*202*
$C_4H_8N_2$			
$(CH_3)_2NCH_2CN$	CH_3MgI (2 equiv.)	$(CH_3)_2NC_2H_5$ (4%); $(CH_3)_2NCH_2COCH_3$ (50%)	*18*
$(CH_3)_2NCH_2CN$	C_2H_5MgBr (2 equiv.)	$(CH_3)_2N$-n-C_3H_7 (60%)	*18*
$(CH_3)_2NCH_2CN$	$HC{\equiv}CMgBr$ (2 equiv.)	No reaction	*18*

* No ketone was obtained with t-C_4H_9MgBr or t-C_4H_9MgI.

TABLE X-I (Continued)

Cyano Comp'd	RMgX	Product(s)	Ref.
$C_4H_8N_2$ (*cont.*)			
$(CH_3)_2NCH_2CN$	n-C_3H_7MgBr (2 equiv.)	$(CH_3)_2N$-n-C_4H_9 (58%)	*18*
$(CH_3)_2NCHCN$	C_6H_5MgBr (2 equiv.)	$(CH_3)_2NCH_2COC_6H_5$ (78%)	*18*
$(CH_3)_2NCH_2CN$	$C_6H_5CH_2MgCl$ (2 equiv.)	$(CH_3)_2NCH_2COCH_2C_6H_5$ ($>$50%)	*18*
C_5H_3NO			
2-Furonitrile	CH_3MgX	2-Acetylfuran	*56*
2-Furonitrile	C_2H_5MgX	2-Propionylfuran	*56*
2-Furonitrile	n-C_3H_7MgX	2-Butyrylfuran	*56*
2-Furonitrile	i-C_4H_9MgX	2-Isovalerylfuran	*56*
2-Furonitrile	i-$C_5H_{11}MgX$	2-Isocaproylfuran	*56*
2-Furonitrile	C_6H_5MgX	2-Benzoylfuran	*56*
$C_5H_3N_2ClO$			
3-Methyl-4-chloro-5-cyano-isoxazole (35 g.)	CH_3MgI (40 g. CH_3I)	3-Methyl-4-chloro-5-acetylisoxazole	*203*
$C_5H_6N_2$			
$H_2C(CH_2CN)_2$	RMgX* (1 equiv.)	$C_{10}H_{11}N_3O$	*51,26*
$H_2C(CH_2CN)_2$	C_2H_5MgBr (4 equiv.)	$C_2H_5CO(CH_2)_3CN$ (?) (small amount); C_2H_6	*51,26*
$H_2C(CH_2CN)_2$	C_2H_5MgBr	$H_2C(CH_2COC_2H_5)_2$ (trace)	*52*
$H_2C(CH_2CN)_2$ (60 g.)	C_6H_5MgBr (200 g. C_6H_5Br)	$NC(CH_2)_3C(=NH \cdot HBr)C_6H_5$ (75 g., crude)	*53*
$H_2C(CH_2CN)_2$	$C_6H_5CH_2MgCl$ (2 equiv.)	2-Imino-6,6-dibenzylpiperidine	*54*
$(CH_3)_2C(CN)_2$ (6.4 g.)	C_6H_5MgBr (8.3 g. Mg)	$(CH_3)_2C(COC_6H_5)_2$ (4.8 g.); $(C_6H_5)_2CO$ (1.3 g.)	*17*
$(CH_3)_2C(CN)_2$ (6 g.)	C_6H_5MgBr (2 g. Mg)	C_6H_5CN (5.1 g.); i-C_3H_7CN (1.1 g.)	*17*

*R = CH_3, C_2H_5, n-C_3H_7.

TABLE X-I (Continued)

Cyano Comp'd	RMgX	Product(s)	Ref.
C_5H_7N			
$(CH_3)_2C{=}CHCN$ (5 g.)	$C_{10}H_{17}MgBr$*	Zingiborone (1.2 g.)	*58*
$C_5H_7NO_2$			
$H_5C_2O_2CCH_2CN$	C_2H_5MgBr (4 equiv.)	$HO(C_2H_5)_2CCH_2CN$; $H_5C_2O_2CCH_2COC_2H_5$; $H_5C_2O_2CCH_2C({=}NH)C_2H_5$; C_2H_6	*55*
$H_5C_2O_2CCH_2CN$	C_2H_5MgI	$H_5C_2O_2CCH_2COC_2H_5$	*61,1*
$H_5C_2O_2CCH_2CN$	C_2H_5MgI	$(C_2H_5CO)_2CHC_2H_5$ (25–30%)	*62*
$H_5C_2O_2CCH_2CN$	n-C_3H_7MgX	$H_5C_2O_2CCH_2CO$-n-C_3H_7	*61*
$H_5C_2O_2CCH_2CN$	C_6H_5MgBr	$(C_6H_5CO)_2CHC_2H_5$ (60%)	*62*
C_5H_8NCl			
n-$C_3H_7CHClCN$ (1 mole)	C_2H_5MgBr (2 moles)	1,1-Diethyl-2-n-propyl ethylenimine (main product); $(n$-$C_3H_7CHClCN)_2$; C_2H_6 (24.5 l.)	*63*
C_5H_9N			
n-C_4H_9CN (1 mole)	n-C_4H_9MgBr (1 mole)	$(n$-$C_4H_9)_3COH$ (38 g.); $(n$-$C_4H_9)_2CO$ (27 g.); gas (2.5 l.); black residue	*64*
n-C_4H_9CN (0.25 mole)	C_6H_5MgBr (160 g. C_6H_5Br)	n-$C_4H_9COC_6H_5$ (32 g., 79%)	*9*
n-C_4H_9CN	C_6H_5MgBr (1.1 equiv.)	n-$C_4H_9COC_6H_5$ (83%)	*59*
n-C_4H_9CN	C_6H_5MgBr (3.0 equiv.)	n-$C_4H_9COC_6H_5$ (79%)	*59*
i-C_4H_9CN	n-C_3H_7MgX	i-C_4H_9CO-n-C_3H_7	*45*
i-C_4H_9CN (20 g.)	ω-Camphenyl-MgBr (50 g. $C_{10}H_{15}Br$)	ω-Isovalerylcamphene	*12*
t-C_4H_9CN	C_6H_5MgBr (1.5 equiv.) (+ HCl)	t-$C_4H_9(C_6H_5)C{=}NH \cdot HCl$; t-$C_4H_9COC_6H_5$ (totaling the equiv. of 72% ketone)	*65,66*

* From 8 g. of 1-bromo-2-(4-methyl-3-cyclohexen-1-yl)propane.

TABLE X-I (Continued)

Cyano Comp'd	RMgX	Product(s)	Ref.
C_5H_9NO			
$C_2H_5OCH(CH_3)CN$ (17 g.)	CH_3MgI (40 g. CH_3I)	$C_2H_5OCH(CH_3)COCH_3$ (14 g.)	*21*
$C_2H_5OCH(CH_3)CN$ (14 g.)	C_2H_5MgI (35 g. C_2H_5I)	$C_2H_5OCH(CH_3)COC_2H_5$ (13 g.)	*21*
n-$C_3H_7OCH_2CN$	CH_3MgI (1.5 equiv.)	n-$C_3H_7OCH_2COCH_3$	*21*
i-$C_3H_7OCH_2CN$	$H_2C=CHCH_2MgBr$ (2 equiv.)	i-$C_3H_7OCH_2C(CH_2CH=CH_2)_2NH_2$ (66.3%)	*22*
$HO(CH_3)(C_2H_5)CCN$	CH_3MgBr	$CH_3COC_2H_5$; t-$C_5H_{11}OH$ (74%); $CH_3(C_2H_5)C(OH)COCH_3$	*69*
$HO(CH_3)(C_2H_5)CCN$	CH_3MgI	$CH_3(C_2H_5)C(OH)COCH_3$	*24*
$HO(CH_3)(C_2H_5)CCN$	C_6H_5MgBr	$CH_3(C_2H_5)(C_6H_5)COH$ (72%)	*69*
i-$C_3H_7CH(OH)CN$	C_2H_5MgBr	i-$C_3H_7CH(OH)COC_2H_5$	*24*
i-$C_3H_7CH(OH)CN$	i-C_3H_7MgI	i-$C_3H_7CH(OH)CO$-i-C_3H_7	*24*
$HO(CH_3)_2CCH_2CN$	CH_3MgBr	$(CH_3)_2C=CHCOCH_3$ + $(CH_3)_2C(OH)CH_2COCH_3$ (totaling *ca.* 50%)	*57*
$C_5H_{10}N_2$			
$(CH_3)_2NCH(CH_3)CN$	CH_3MgI (2 equiv.)	$(CH_3)_2N$-i-C_3H_7 (14%); $(CH_3)_2NCH(CH_3)COCH_3$ (50%)	*18*
$(CH_3)_2NCH(CH_3)CN$	C_2H_5MgI (2 equiv.)	$(CH_3)_2N$-s-C_4H_9 (13%); $(CH_3)_2NCH(CH_3)COC_2H_5$ (50%)	*18*
$(CH_3)_2NCH(CH_3)CN$	n-C_3H_7MgBr (2 equiv.)	$(CH_3)_2NCH(CH_3)CO$-n-C_3H_7 (67%)	*18*
$(CH_3)_2NCH(CH_3)CN$	C_6H_5MgBr (2 equiv.)	$(CH_3)_2NCH(CH_3)C_6H_5$ (78%)	*18*
$(CH_3)_2NCH(CH_3)CN$	$(CH_2)_5CHMgCl$ (2 equiv.)	$(CH_3)_2NCH(CH_3)COCH(CH_2)_5$ (64%)	*18*
$(CH_3)_2NCH(CH_3)CN$	$C_6H_5CH_2MgCl$ (2 equiv.)	$(CH_3)_2NCH(CH_3)CH_2C_6H_5$ (76%)	*18*
$C_6H_4N_2$			
Picolinonitrile (40 g.)	$C_2H_5O(CH_2)_3MgBr$ (64 g. $C_5H_{11}BrO$)	1-Pyridyl 3-ethoxypropyl ketone (62%)	*43*
Nicotinonitrile (0.5 mole)	CH_3MgI (2.0 mole)	3-Acetylpyridine (0.13 mole)	*235*
Nicotinonitrile (46.8 g., 0.45 mole)	n-C_3H_7MgBr (221 g., 1.80 moles C_3H_7Br)	3-Butyryl-4-n-propylpyridine (18.6 g., 22%)	*235*

TABLE X-I (Continued)

Cyano Comp'd	RMgX	Product(s)	Ref.
$C_6H_4N_2$ (*cont.*)			
Nicotinonitrile (45 g.)	$C_2H_5O(CH_2)_3MgBr$ (60 g. $C_5H_{11}BrO$)	1-Pyridyl 3-ethoxypropyl ketone (47%)	*43*
$C_6H_5NO_2$			
Furfural cyanohydrin	C_6H_5MgX	Isobenzofuroïn	*67*
$C_6H_8N_2$			
$(-CH_2CH_2CN)_2$ (0.25 mole)	C_2H_5MgBr (excess)	1-Imino-2-cyanocyclopentane; C_2H_6; $(-CH_2CH_2COC_2H_5)_2$	*204*
$(-CH_2CH_2CN)_2$	C_6H_5MgBr	$(-CH_2CH_2COC_6H_5)_2$ (35%)	*204*
$(-CH_2CH_2CN)_2$	$C_6H_5CH_2MgCl$	$(-CH_2CH_2COCH_2C_6H_5)_2$ (15%)	*204*
$C_6H_{10}NCl$			
i-$C_4H_9CHClCN$	C_2H_5MgBr	1,1-Diethyl-2-isobutylethylenimine (main product)	*63*
$C_6H_{11}N$			
n-$C_5H_{11}CN$	CH_3MgI (1.1 equiv.)	*n*-$C_5H_{11}COCH_3$ (40%); *n*-C_5H_{11}(*n*-$C_5H_{11}CO$)CHCN (>20%)	*60*
n-$C_5H_{11}CN$ (0.25 mole)	C_6H_5MgBr (160 g. C_6H_5Br)	*n*-$C_5H_{11}COC_6H_5$ (36.5 g., 83%)	*9*
n-$C_5H_{11}CN$	C_6H_5MgBr (1.1 equiv.)	*n*-$C_5H_{11}COC_6H_5$ (89%)	*59,60*
n-$C_5H_{11}CN$	C_6H_5MgBr (3.0 equiv.)	*n*-$C_5H_{11}COC_6H_5$ (83%)	*59*
i-$C_5H_{11}CN$ (0.25 mole)	C_6H_5MgBr (160 g. C_6H_5Br)	*i*-$C_5H_{11}COC_6H_5$ (22 g., 50%)	*9,45*
i-$C_5H_{11}CN$	$C_6H_5CH_2MgCl$	*i*-$C_5H_{11}COCH_2C_6H_5$	*45*
$C_6H_{11}NO$			
$C_2H_5O(CH_2)_3CN$	C_2H_5MgBr (2 equiv.)	$C_2H_5O(CH_2)_3COC_2H_5$ (5%); gas; residue; $[C_2H_5O(CH_2)_3CN]_2$	*68*
n-$C_3H_7OCH(CH_3)CN$ (10 g.)	CH_3MgI (30 g. CH_3I)	*n*-$C_3H_7OCH(CH_3)COCH_3$ (7 g.)	*21*

TABLE X-I (Continued)

Cyano Comp'd	RMgX	Product(s)	Ref.
$C_6H_{11}NO$ (*cont.*)			
i-$C_4H_9OCH_2CN$	CH_3MgI (1.5 equiv.)	*i*-$C_4H_9OCH_2COCH_3$	*21*
$CH_3(n\text{-}C_3H_7)C(OH)CN$	C_6H_5MgBr	$CH_3(n\text{-}C_3H_7)(C_6H_5)COH$ (64%)	*69*
$C_6H_{12}N_2$			
$(CH_3)_2N(CH_3)_2CCN$	CH_3MgBr	$[(CH_3)_2N(CH_3)_2C—]_2$	*70*
$(CH_3)_2N(CH_3)_2CCN$	C_2H_5MgBr	$(CH_3)_2NC(CH_3)_2C_2H_5$; $[(CH_3)_2N(CH_3)_2C—]_2$	*70*
$(CH_3)_2N(CH_3)_2CCN$	*n*-C_3H_7MgBr	$(CH_3)_2NC(CH_3)_2$-*n*-C_3H_7 (20%); $[(CH_3)_2N(CH_3)_2C—]_2$ (very little)	*70*
$C_7H_3NCl_2$			
2,4-$Cl_2C_6H_3CN$ (188 g., 1.1 mole)	CH_3MgI (3.4 moles)	2,4-$Cl_2C_6H_3COCH_3$ (25%)	*205*
2,5-$Cl_2C_6H_3CN$	CH_3MgI	2,5-$Cl_2C_6H_3COCH_3$ (11.7 g., 83.5%)	*205*
C_7H_4NBr			
2-BrC_6H_4CN (12 g.)	4-$CH_3C_6H_4MgBr$ (17 g. C_7H_7Br)	2-$BrC_6H_4C(=NH)C_6H_4$-4-CH_3 (isolated as ketone; 15 g., 83%)	*71*
2-BrC_6H_4CN (12 g.)	4-$CH_3OC_6H_4MgBr$ (19 g. C_7H_7BrO)	2-$BrC_6H_4COC_6H_4$-4-OCH_3 (13 g., 69%)	*71*
4-BrC_6H_4CN (18.2 g., 0.1 mole)	$C_6H_5CH_2CH_2MgBr$ (0.1 mole)	4-$BrC_6H_4COCH_2CH_2C_6H_5$	*236*
C_7H_4NCl			
2-ClC_6H_4CN (26 g.)	8-$CH_3C_{10}H_6$-1-MgBr (66 g. $C_{11}H_9Br$)	8-$CH_3C_{10}H_6$-1-$C(=NH \cdot HCl)C_6H_4$-2-Cl (60 g., 63%)	*72*
C_7H_5N			
C_6H_5CN	CH_3MgBr	$C_6H_5COCH_3$ (80–89%); 2,4,6-triphenylpyridine (5%)	*73,74*

TABLE X-I (Continued)

Cyano Comp'd	RMgX	Product(s)	Ref.
C_7H_5N (*cont.*)			
C_6H_5CN (15 g.)	C_2H_5MgBr (23 g. C_2H_5Br)	$C_6H_5C(=NH)C_2H_5$ (15 g., crude; 10 g., dist'd); higher-boiling material (3 g.)	75
C_6H_5CN	C_2H_5MgI	$C_6H_5COC_2H_5$ (80%)	45,73,74
C_6H_5CN	RMgX*	$C_6H_5C(R)=NH \cdot HCl$ (60–92%)	76
C_6H_5CN (15 g.)	*n*-C_3H_7MgBr (25 g. C_3H_7Br)	$C_6H_5C(=NH)$-*n*-C_3H_7 (13 g., crude; 9 g., dist'd); higher-boiling material (3 g.)	75
C_6H_5CN (15 g.)	*i*-C_3H_7MgBr (25 g. C_3H_7Br)	$C_6H_5C(=NH)$-*i*-C_3H_7 (13 g. crude; 5.8 g., dist'd); higher-boiling material (7 g.)	75
C_6H_5CN (15 g.)	*i*-C_4H_9MgBr (29 g. C_4H_9Br)	$C_6H_5C(=NH)$-*i*-C_4H_9 (15.4 g., crude; 12 g., dist'd); higher-boiling material (2 g.)	75
C_6H_5CN (6 g.)	*t*-C_4H_9MgCl (12 g. C_4H_9Cl)	C_6H_5CO-*t*-C_4H_9 (7–8 g.)	206,207
C_6H_5CN (15 g.)	C_6H_5MgBr (32 g. C_6H_5Br)	$(C_6H_5)_2C=NH$ (21 g.)	75,76,8
C_6H_5CN (15 g.)	$(CH_2)_5CHMgCl$ (25 g. $C_6H_{11}Cl$)	$C_6H_5C(=NH)CH(CH_2)_5$ (10.2 g., crude; 3 g., dist'd); $C_6H_5COCH(CH_2)_5$ (1.167 g.)	75
C_6H_5CN (12 g.)	$C_6H_5CH_2MgCl$ (28 g. C_7H_7Cl)	$C_6H_5C(=NH)CH_2C_6H_5$ (15 g., crude); $C_6H_5COCH_2C_6H_5$ (1.23 g.)	75,73,74,77
C_6H_5CN	2-$CH_3C_6H_4MgBr$	$C_6H_5COC_6H_4$-2-CH_3	81
C_6H_5CN	$(C_2H_5)_2N(CH_2)_3Cl$ + Mg	$C_6H_5CO(CH_2)_3N(C_2H_5)_2$	208
C_6H_5CN (0.05 mole)	$C_6H_5C \equiv CMgBr$ (0.072 mole)	2,4,6-Triphenyl-2,5-endo-(2′-phenylethylene)-2,3,4,5-tetrahydropyrimidine (0.23 mole, 40%)	216
C_6H_5CN (15 g.)	1-$C_{10}H_7MgBr$ (42 g. $C_{10}H_7Br$)	$C_6H_5C(=NH)$-1-$C_{10}H_7$ (21 g.)	75
C_6H_5CN (20.6 g.)	1-$C_{10}H_7MgBr$ (49.6 g. $C_{10}H_7Br$)	C_6H_5CO-1-$C_{10}H_7$	239
C_6H_5CN (20 g.)	5,6,7,8-Tetrahydronaphthyl-1-MgI (39 g. $C_{10}H_{11}I$)	1-Benzoyl-5,6,7,8-tetrahydronaphthalene (7.7 g., 22%)	209
C_6H_5CN (1.2 equiv.)	ω-Camphenyl-MgBr	ω-Benzoylcamphene	12
C_6H_5CN (26 ml.)	6-$CH_3OC_{10}H_6$-2-MgBr (47.4 g. $C_{11}H_9BrO$)	C_6H_5CO-2-$C_{10}H_6$-6-OCH_3 (45%)	175,176

* R = C_2H_5; *n*-C_3H_7; *i*-C_4H_9; C_6H_5; $(CH_2)_5CH$; 2-$CH_3C_6H_4$; 4-$CH_3C_6H_4$; 1-$C_{10}H_7$.

TABLE X-I (Continued)

Cyano Comp'd	RMgX	Product(s)	Ref.
C_7H_5N (*cont.*)			
C_6H_5CN	6-$C_2H_5OC_{10}H_6$-2-MgBr	C_6H_5CO-2-$C_{10}H_6$-6-OC_2H_5 (30%)	*175*
C_6H_5CN (0.03 mole)	*n*-$C_{12}H_{25}MgBr$ (0.025 mole)	C_6H_5CO-*n*-$C_{12}H_{25}$ (>57%)	*78*
C_6H_5CN (1.25 g.)	9-Anthryl-MgBr (2.57 g. $C_{14}H_9Br$)	α-9-Anthryl-α-phenylmethyleneimine (2.45 g., 87%)	*167*
C_6H_5CN (3.2 g.)	9-Phenanthryl-MgBr	9-Benzoylphenanthrene (4.6 g., 65%)	*79*
C_6H_5CN	$C_6H_5(2\text{-}CH_3C_6H_4)CHMgCl$	"A complex hydrocarbon" only	*80*
C_6H_5CN	2,5-Diphenyl-3-furyl-MgBr	2,5-Diphenyl-3-benzoylfuran ("very poor yield")	*233*
$C_7H_6N_2$			
C_6H_5NHCN (5 g.)	C_6H_5MgBr (13 g. C_6H_5Br)	$C_6H_5NHC(=NH)C_6H_5$ (1 g., crude)	*82*
C_6H_5NHCN (5 g.)	1-$C_{10}H_7MgBr$	$C_6H_5NHC(=NH)$-1-$C_{10}H_7$ (trace)	*82*
C_7H_8NCl			
1-Chloro-2-cyanocyclohexene	CH_3MgI	1-Chloro-2-acetylcyclohexene	*211*
1-Chloro-6-cyanocyclohexene	CH_3MgI	Violent reaction; nitrile recovered	*13*
C_7H_9N			
1-Cyanocyclohexene (20.0 g.)	C_2H_5MgBr (30.0 g. C_2H_5Br)	Ethyl 1-cyclohexenyl ketone (2.5 g., crude)	*168*
1-Cyanocyclohexene	C_2H_5MgI	Ethyl 1-cyclohexenyl ketone	*13*
1-Cyanocyclohexene (20 g.)	$C_6H_5CH_2MgCl$ (30 g. C_7H_7Cl)	Benzyl 1-cyclohexenyl ketone (6–7 g., crude)	*168*
3-Cyanocyclohexene	C_2H_5MgI	No ketonic product	*13*
$C_7H_{12}N_2$			
$CH_3CH=CHCH[N(CH_3)_2]CN$	C_6H_5MgBr	$CH_3CH=CHCH[N(CH_3)_2]C_6H_5$	*83*
$(CH_2)_5NCH_2CN$	CH_3MgI (2 equiv.)	$(CH_2)_5NC_2H_5$ (50%)	*18*

TABLE X-I (Continued)

Cyano Comp'd	RMgX	Product(s)	Ref.
$C_7H_{13}NO$			
i-$C_5H_{11}OCH_2CN$	CH_3MgI (1.5 equiv.)	i-$C_5H_{11}OCH_2COCH_3$	*21*
$C_7H_{13}NO_2$			
$C_2H_5OCH_2CH(OC_2H_5)CN$ (23.3 g.)	n-C_3H_7MgBr (22 ml. C_3H_7Br)	$C_2H_5OCH_2CH(OC_2H_5)C(=NH)$-$n$-$C_3H_7$ (yielding 6.4 g., 21% ketone)	*201*
$C_7H_{14}N_2$			
$(CH_3)_2N(n\text{-}C_3H_7)CHCN$	CH_3MgI (2 equiv.)	$(CH_3)_2N(n\text{-}C_3H_7)CHCOCH_3$ (53%)	*18*
$(CH_3)_2N(CH_3)(C_2H_5)CCN$	C_2H_5MgX	$(CH_3)_2NC(C_2H_5)_2CH_3$; $[(CH_3)_2N(CH_3)(C_2H_5)C-]_2$ (?)	*83*
$(CH_3)_2N(CH_3)(C_2H_5)CCN$	C_6H_5MgBr	$(CH_3)_2NC(CH_3)(C_2H_5)C_6H_5$	*83*
$(CH_3)_2N(CH_3)(C_2H_5)CCN$	$C_6H_5CH_2MgBr$	$(CH_3)_2NC(CH_3)(C_2H_5)CH_2C_6H_5$	*83*
$C_8H_4N_2$			
C_6H_4-1,2-$(CN)_2$ (15 g.)	C_6H_5MgBr (46 g. C_6H_5Br)	3-Phenylpseudoïsoïndolone anil	*84*
C_6H_4-1,2-$(CN)_2$ (10 g.)	$C_6H_5CH_2MgCl$ (2.5 equiv.)	1,1-Dibenzyl-3-aminopseudoïsoïndole (acid hydr., 1 g.; NH_4Cl hydr., 6.5 g.)	*85*
C_8H_5NO			
C_6H_5COCN	C_2H_5MgBr	$C_6H_5COC(=NH\cdot HCN)C_2H_5$; $C_6H_5(C_2H_5)_2COH$	*86*
C_6H_5COCN	C_6H_5MgBr	$(C_6H_5)_3COH$	*86*
C_6H_5COCN	C_6H_5MgBr (1 equiv.)	$(C_6H_5)_2CO$; C_6H_5COOH; $(C_6H_5)_3CCN$ (all yields poor)	*87*
C_6H_5COCN (32.5 g.)	C_6H_5MgBr (78.0 g. C_6H_5Br)	$(C_6H_5)_3COH$; $(C_6H_5)_3CH$	*87*
C_6H_5COCN	$C_6H_5CH_2MgCl$	$C_6H_5(C_6H_5CH_2)_2COH$	*86*

TABLE X-I (Continued)

Cyano Comp'd	RMgX	Product(s)	Ref.
$C_8H_5NO_2$			
2,3-$CH_2O_2C_6H_3CN$ (8.5 g.)	C_2H_5MgBr	2,3-$CH_2O_2C_6H_3COC_2H_5$ (1.4 g.); 2,3-$CH_2O_2C_6H_3C(=NH)C_2H_5$ (8.1 g.)	*212*
3,4-$CH_2O_2C_6H_3CN$ (9.85 g.)	C_2H_5MgBr	Recovered nitrile (2.3 g.); 3,4-$CH_2O_2C_6H_3C(=NH)C_2H_5$ (9.4 g.)	*212*
C_8H_6NCl			
$C_6H_5CHClCN$ (15 g.)	C_6H_5MgBr (48 g. C_6H_5Br)	$C_6H_5CH_2COC_6H_5$ (2 g.); $C_6H_5CH_2(C_6H_5)C{=}NH \cdot HCl$	*88*
C_8H_6NClO			
4-$ClC_6H_4CH(OH)CN$	$C_6H_5CH_2MgCl$	4-$ClC_6H_4CH(OH)COCH_2C_6H_5$	*89*
C_8H_7N			
$C_6H_5CH_2CN$ (1 mole)	CH_3MgBr (1 mole)	CH_4 (20 l.); recovered nitrile; $C_6H_5CH_2COCH_3$; $C_6H_5CH_2CONH_2$; $C_6H_5CH_2C(=NH)CH(C_6H_5)CN$ (50%); $(G_6H_5CH_2CN)_3$* (10%)	*90*
$C_6H_5CH_2CN$	CH_3MgI (1.1 equiv.)	$C_6H_5CH_2COCH_3$ (8%); $C_6H_5(C_6H_5CH_2CO)CHCN$ (71%)	*60*
$C_6H_5CH_2CN$	C_2H_5MgBr (1.1 equiv.)	Recovered nitrile (10%); $C_6H_5(C_6H_5CH_2CO)CHCN$ (51%); cond'n prod. (36%)	*60*
$C_6H_5CH_2CN$	*i*-C_3H_7MgBr (1.1 equiv.)	Recovered nitrile (9%); $C_6H_5(C_6H_5CH_2CO)CHCN$ (64%); cond'n prod. (*ca.* 15%)	*60*

* Rondou (*90*) attributes to this trimer the constitution 2,4-diamino-3,5-diphenyl-6-benzylpyridine.

TABLE X-I (Continued)

Cyano Comp'd	RMgX	Product(s)	Ref.
C_8H_7N (*cont.*)			
$C_6H_5CH_2CN$	*n*-C_4H_9MgBr (1.1 equiv.)	Recovered nitrile (24%); $C_6H_5(C_6H_5CH_2CO)CHCN$ (23%); cond'n prod. (46%)	*60*
$C_6H_5CH_2CN$	*t*-C_4H_9MgCl (1.1 equiv.)	$C_6H_5(C_6H_5CH_2CO)CHCN$ (80%)	*60*
$C_6H_5CH_2CN$	*n*-$C_5H_{11}MgBr$ (1.1 equiv.)	$C_6H_5(C_6H_5CH_2CO)CHCN$ (51%); cond'n prod. (31%)	*60*
$C_6H_5CH_2CN$	C_6H_5MgBr (1.1 equiv.)	$C_6H_5CH_2COC_6H_5$; $(C_6H_5-)_2$	*4*
$C_6H_5CH_2CN$	C_6H_5MgBr (1 equiv.)	Recovered nitrile (1-2%); $C_6H_5CH_2COC_6H_5$ (10%); $C_6H_5CH_2C(=NH)CH(C_6H_5)CN$ (30%); $(C_6H_5CH_2CN)_3$* (35%); $(C_6H_5-)_2$; C_6H_6, C_6H_5Br, C_6H_6OH	*8*
$C_6H_5CH_2CN$	C_6H_5MgBr (1.1 equiv.)	$C_6H_5CH_2COC_6H_5$ (33%); $C_6H_5(C_6H_5CH_2CO)CHCN$ (15%); cond'n prod. (36%)	*60*
$C_6H_5CH_2CN$	2,4,6-$(CH_3)_3C_6H_2MgBr$ (1.1 equiv.)	$C_6H_5(C_6H_5CH_2CO)CHCN$ (45%); cond'n prod. (43%)	*60*
2-$CH_3C_6H_4CN$	CH_3MgBr (3 equiv.)	2-$CH_3C_6H_4C(=NH)CH_3$ (35%); 2-$CH_3C_6H_4COCH_3$ (20%)	*91*
2-$CH_3C_6H_4CN$	CH_3MgI	2-$CH_3C_6H_4COCH_3$ (66%)	*238*
2-$CH_3C_6H_4CN$	CH_3MgX	2-$CH_3C_6H_4COCH_3$ ("excellent yield")	*198*
2-$CH_3C_6H_4CN$	C_2H_5MgX	2-$CH_3C_6H_4COC_2H_5$ ("excellent yield")	*198,217*
2-$CH_3C_6H_4CN$	C_2H_5MgBr (3 equiv.)	2-$CH_3C_6H_4C(=NH)C_2H_5$ (19%); 2-$CH_3C_6H_4COC_2H_5$ (9%)	*91*
2-$CH_3C_6H_4CN$	C_2H_5MgBr (3 equiv.) (+ HCl)	2-$CH_3C_6H_4C(=NH\cdot HCl)C_2H_5$ (94%)	*91*
2-$CH_3C_6H_4CN$	C_2H_5MgI	2-$CH_3C_6H_4COC_2H_5$ (17%)	*45*
2-$CH_3C_6H_4CN$ (17.5 g.)	C_6H_5MgBr (32 g. C_6H_5Br)	2-$CH_3C_6H_4C(=NH)C_6H_5$ (11 g.)	*75*

*Described as identical with the trimer of Rondou (*90*).

TABLE X-I (Continued)

Cyano Comp'd	RMgX	Product(s)	Ref.
C_8H_7N (*cont.*)			
2-$CH_3C_6H_4CN$	C_6H_5MgBr (+ HCl)	2-$CH_3C_6H_4C(=NH \cdot HCl)C_6H_5$ (85%)	*91*
2-$CH_3C_6H_4CN$	$C_6H_5CH_2MgCl$	2-$CH_3C_6H_4COCH_2C_6H_5$ (20%)	*45*
2-$CH_3C_6H_4CN$	$C_6H_5CH_2MgCl$ (+ HCl)	2-$CH_3C_6H_4C(=NH \cdot HCl)CH_2C_6H_5$ (87%)	*91*
2-$CH_3C_6H_4CN$ (23.4 g.)	1-$C_{10}H_7MgBr$ (50 g. $C_{10}H_7Br$)	2-$CH_3C_6H_4C(=NH \cdot HCl)$-1-$C_{10}H_7$ (yielding 37.8 g., 76% ketone)	*213*
2-$CH_3C_6H_4CN$ (3.2 g.)	9-Phenanthryl-MgBr	9-*o*-Toluylphenanthrene (5.2 g., 70%)	79
3-$CH_3C_6H_4CN$	CH_3MgI	3-$CH_3C_6H_4COCH_3$ (87%)	238
3-$CH_3C_6H_4CN$	CH_3MgX	3-$CH_3C_6H_4COCH_3$ ("excellent yield")	*198*
3-$CH_3C_6H_4CN$	C_2H_5MgBr	3-$CH_3C_6H_4COC_2H_5$ (76.6%)	*214*
3-$CH_3C_6H_4CN$	C_2H_5MgX	3-$CH_3C_6H_4COC_2H_5$ ("excellent yield")	*198,217*
3-$CH_3C_6H_4CN$	C_6H_5MgBr	3-$CH_3C_6H_4COC_6H_5$	*81*
3-$CH_3C_6H_4CN$	2-$CH_3C_6H_4MgBr$	3-$CH_3C_6H_4COC_6H_4$-2-CH_3	*81*
4-$CH_3C_6H_4CN$ (17 g.)	C_2H_5MgBr (23 g. C_2H_5Br)	4-$CH_3C_6H_4C(=NH)C_2H_5$ (10 g., crude; 5 g., dist'd); higher-boiling material (5 g.)	*75*
4-$CH_3C_6H_4CN$ (350 g.)	C_2H_5MgX (168 g. Mg)	4-$CH_3C_6H_4COC_2H_5$	*217*
4-$CH_3C_6H_4CN$	C_2H_5MgI	4-$CH_3C_6H_4COC_2H_5$ (46%)	*45*
4-$CH_3C_6H_4CN$	*n*-C_3H_7MgX	4-$CH_3C_6H_4CO$-*n*-C_3H_7	*45*
4-$CH_3C_6H_4CN$	*n*-C_4H_9MgX	4-$CH_3C_6H_4CO$-*n*-C_4H_9	*45*
4-$CH_3C_6H_4CN$ (17.5 g.)	C_6H_5MgBr (32 g. C_6H_5Br)	4-$CH_3C_6H_4C(=NH)C_6H_5$ (13 g.)	*75*
4-$CH_3C_6H_4CN$* (6.5 g.)	$C_6H_5CH_2MgCl$ (18 g. C_7H_7Cl)	4-$CH_3C_6H_4COCH_2C_6H_5$	*92*
4-$CH_3C_6H_4CN$† (6.5 g.)	$C_6H_5CH_2MgCl$ (14 g. C_7H_7Cl	4-$CH_3C_6H_4COCH(C_6H_5)CH_2C_6H_5$	*92*
C_8H_7NO			
2-$CH_3OC_6H_4CN$ (16.6 g.)	C_2H_5MgBr	2-$CH_3OC_6H_4C(=NH)C_2H_5$ (13 g.)	*212*
3-$CH_3OC_6H_4CN$ (13.3 g.)	C_6H_5MgBr (19 g. C_6H_5Br)	3-$CH_3OC_6H_4COC_6H_5$ (17.1 g., 77%)	*93,94*

* Gradual addition of Et_2O-nitrile solution to Grignard solution; four hours reflux; two hours at room temperature.
† Addition xylene-nitrile solution to Grignard solution; six to seven hours reflux.

TABLE X-I (Continued)

Cyano Comp'd	RMgX	Product(s)	Ref.
C_8H_7NO (*cont.*)			
3-$CH_3OC_6H_4CN$ (20 g.)	3-$CH_3C_6H_4MgBr$ (31 g. C_7H_7Br)	3-$CH_3OC_6H_4COC_6H_4$-3-CH_3 (22 g., 65%)	*93*
4-$CH_3OC_6H_4CN$ (0.03 mole)	C_6H_5MgBr (0.025 mole)	4-$CH_3OC_6H_4COC_6H_5$ ("probably >90%")	*95*
4-$CH_3OC_6H_4CN$ (26 g.)	3-$CH_3C_6H_4MgBr$ (41 g. C_7H_7Br)	4-$CH_3OC_6H_4COC_6H_4$-3-CH_3 (34.9 g., 79%)	*93*
$C_6H_5CH(OH)CN$ (66.5 g.)	CH_3MgI (213 g. CH_3I)	$C_6H_5CH(OH)COCH_3$	*97*
$C_6H_5CH(OH)CN$	C_6H_5MgX	$C_6H_5CH(OH)COC_6H_5$	*67*
(+)-$C_6H_5CH(OH)CN$ (7.5 g.)	C_6H_5MgBr (23 g. C_6H_5Br)	(−)-$C_6H_5CH(OH)COC_6H_5$ (6.18 g.)	*96*
$C_8H_7NO_2$			
4-$HOC_6H_4CH(OH)CN$	C_6H_5MgX	4-$HOC_6H_4CH(OH)COC_6H_5$	*67*
$C_8H_7NO_2S$			
$C_6H_5SO_2CH_2CN$	CH_3MgI	"Negative result"	*4*
$C_6H_5SO_2CH_2CN$	C_6H_5MgBr	"Negative result"	*4*
$C_8H_8N_2$			
$C_6H_5NHCH_2CN$	CH_3MgI (2 equiv.)	$C_6H_5NHC_2H_5$	*98*
$C_8H_{14}N_2$			
$(CH_2)_5NCH(CH_3)CN$	CH_3MgI (1 equiv.) + C_6H_5MgBr (1 equiv.)	$(CH_2)_5NCH(CH_3)C_6H_5$	*18*
$(CH_2)_5NCH(CH_3)CN$	CH_3MgI (1 equiv.) + $C_6H_5CH_2MgCl$ (1 equiv.)	$(CH_2)_5NCH(CH_3)CH_2C_6H_5$	*18*
$C_8H_{12}N$			
Active 1-Cyano-5-methyl-cyclohexene	CH_3MgX	1-Acetyl-5-methylcyclohexene	*2*
Active 1-Cyano-5-methyl-cyclohexene	C_2H_5MgX	1-Propionyl-5-methylcyclohexene	*2*

TABLE X-I (Continued)

Cyano Comp'd	RMgX	Product(s)	Ref.
$C_8H_{12}N$ (*cont.*)			
Active 1-Cyano-5-methylcyclohexene	i-C_3H_7MgX	1-Isobutyryl-5-methylcyclohexene	*2*
$C_8H_{15}NO$			
$H_5C_2O_2CC(C_2H_5)_2CN$	C_6H_5MgBr	$(C_6H_5)_2CO$; $(C_2H_5)_2CHCOC(C_2H_5)_2CO_2C_2H_5$	*99*
$(n\text{-}C_3H_7)_2C(OH)CN$	C_6H_5MgBr	$(n\text{-}C_3H_7)_2CO$; $C_6H_5(n\text{-}C_3H_7)_2COH$ (65%)	*69*
$(n\text{-}C_3H_7)_2C(OH)CN$	$C_6H_5CH_2MgCl$	$(n\text{-}C_3H_7)_2CO$; $C_6H_5CH_2(n\text{-}C_3H_7)_2COH$ (75%)	*69*
$C_8H_{17}N_3$			
$(CH_3)_2NCH_2CH_2CH[N(CH_3)_2]CN$	C_6H_5MgBr	$(CH_3)_2NCH_2CH_2CH[N(CH_3)_2]C_6H_5$	*83*
C_9H_5N			
$C_6H_5C\equiv CCN$ (0.022 mole)	C_6H_5MgBr (0.039 mole)	2,3,5-Triphenylpyrimidine (0.0013 mole, 6%)	*216*
C_9H_6NBr			
trans-2-$BrCH=CHC_6H_4CN$ (4.5 g.)	CH_3MgI (6.2 g. CH_3I)	1-Methylisoquinoline (0.4 g., 13%)	*215*
trans-2-$BrCH=CHC_6H_4CN$ (5.0 g.)	C_6H_5MgBr (7.6 g. C_6H_5Br)	1-Phenylisoquinoline (0.79 g., 15.5%)	*215*
trans-2-$BrCH=CHC_6H_4CN$ (5.0 g.)	$C_6H_5CH_2MgBr$ (8.2 g. C_7H_7Br)	1-Benzylisoquinoline (0.2 g., 4%)	*215*
$C_9H_6N_2$			
$C_6H_5CH(CN)_2$ (4 g.)	C_6H_5MgBr (3.3 g. Mg)	Recovered nitrile (3.9 g.)	*17*
$C_6H_5CH(CN)_2$ (4 g.)	C_6H_5MgBr (3.3 g. Mg)	$C_6H_5CH[C(=NH)C_6H_5]_2$ (4.1 g.); tar (small am't)	*17*

TABLE X-I (Continued)

Cyano Comp'd	RMgX	Product(s)	Ref.
C_9H_7N			
$C_6H_5CH{=}CHCN$	CH_3MgI	$C_6H_5CH{=}CHCOCH_3$ (<60%)	*100*
$C_6H_5CH{=}CHCN$	C_6H_5MgBr	$C_6H_5CH{=}CHCOC_6H_5$ (68%)*	*100*
$C_6H_5CH{=}CHCN$	C_6H_5MgBr	2,4,6-Triphenyl-2,5-endo-(2′-phenylethylene)-2,3,4,5-tetrahydropyrimidine (*ca.* 40%)†	*216*
C_9H_7NO			
$C_6H_5COCH_2CN$	CH_3MgBr (3 equiv.)	$C_6H_5COCH_2C({=}NH)CH_3$ (52%); tar	*102*
$C_6H_5COCH_2CN$	C_2H_5MgBr	$C_6H_5COCH_2COC_2H_5$	*103*
$C_6H_5COCH_2CN$	C_2H_5MgBr	Dimer (12%); $C_6H_5COCH_2C({=}NH)C_2H_5$ (25%)	*102*
$C_6H_5COCH_2CN$	$H_2C{=}CHCH_2MgBr$ (1.0–2.5 equiv.)	1.0 equiv., Recovered nitrile (40%); viscous red oil. 2.5 equiv., viscous red oil	*102*
$C_6H_5COCH_2CN$	n-C_3H_7MgBr (0.5–3.0 equiv.)	0.5 equiv., recovered nitrile (90%); 1.0 equiv., recovered nitrile (83%); 2.0 equiv., recovered nitrile (50%); dimer (10%); 3.0 equiv., dimer (60%); recovered nitrile (20%)	*102*
$C_6H_5COCH_2CN$	C_6H_5MgBr (5 equiv.)	$(C_6H_5CO)_2CH_2$	*103*
$C_9H_7NO_2$			
2,3-$(CH_2)_2O_2C_6H_3CN$ (8 g.)	C_2H_5MgBr	2,3-$(CH_2)_2O_2C_6H_3COC_2H_5$ (5.3 g.); 2,3-$(CH_2)_2O_2C_6H_3C({=}NH)C_2H_5$ (2.9 g.)	*212*

* Hydrolysis with aqueous sulfuric acid.

† Hydrolysis at *ca.* 0° with aqueous ammonium chloride.

TABLE X-I (Continued)

Cyano Comp'd	RMgX	Product(s)	Ref.
$C_9H_8NO_2Br$			
2,3-$(CH_3O)_2$-4-(or 6-)BrC_6H_2CN (25 g.)	C_2H_5MgBr	2,3-$(CH_3O)_2$-4-(or 6-)$BrC_6H_2C(=NH)C_2H_5$ (7.7 g.); 2-C_2H_5-3-CH_3O-4-(or 6-)BrC_6H_2CN (9.0 g., 36%)	*212*
C_9H_9N			
$CH_3(C_6H_5)CHCN$	C_2H_5MgBr (4 equiv.)	$CH_3(C_6H_5)CHCOC_2H_5$	*50*
$CH_3(C_6H_5)CHCN$	*n*-C_3H_7MgBr (4 equiv.)	$CH_3(C_6H_5)CHCO$-*n*-C_3H_7	*50*
$CH_3(C_6H_5)CHCN$	$C_6H_5CH_2MgCl$ (4 equiv.)	$CH_3(C_6H_5)CHCOCH_2C_6H_5$	*50*
2-$C_2H_5C_6H_4CN$	CH_3MgI	2-$C_2H_5C_6H_4COCH_3$ (62%)	*217*
2-$C_2H_5C_6H_4CN$	CH_3MgX	2-$C_2H_5C_6H_4COCH_3$ ("excellent yield")	*198*
3-$C_2H_5C_6H_4CN$	CH_3MgX	3-$C_2H_5C_6H_4COCH_3$ ("excellent yield")	*198*
2,4-$(CH_3)_2C_6H_3CN$	CH_3MgX	2,4-$(CH_3)_2C_6H_3COCH_3$	*217*
2,6-$(CH_3)_2C_6H_3CN$	CH_3MgI	No reaction	*217*
3,5-$(CH_3)_2C_6H_3CN$	CH_3MgI	3,5-$(CH_3)_2C_6H_3COCH_3$ (63%)	*217*
$C_9H_9O_2$			
2,3-$(CH_3O)_2C_6H_3CN$	CH_3MgX	2,3-$(CH_3O)_2C_6H_3COCH_3$	*218*
2,3-$(CH_3O)_2C_6H_3CN$ (10.2 g.)	CH_3MgI (9 g. CH_3I)	2,3-$(CH_3O)_2C_6H_3COCH_3$ (6.5 g.)	*219*
2,3-$(CH_3O)_2C_6H_3CN$ (23.9 g.)	C_2H_5MgBr (32 g. C_2H_5Br)	2-C_2H_5-3-$CH_3OC_6H_3CN$ (14 g., 60%); 2,3-$(CH_3O)_2C_6H_3COC_2H_5$; 2-C_2H_5-3-$CH_3OC_6H_3COC_2H_5$	*166*
2,3-$(CH_3O)_2C_6H_3CN$ (24 g.)	C_2H_5MgBr (20 g. C_2H_5Br)	2-C_2H_5-3-$CH_3OC_6H_3CN$ (14.4 g., 60%)	*212*
2,3-$(CH_3O)_2C_6H_3CN$ (49 g.)	*i*-C_3H_7MgBr (61 g. C_3H_7Br)	2-*i*-C_3H_7-3-$CH_3OC_6H_3CN$ (45 g., 81%)	*218,212*
2,3-$(CH_3O)_2C_6H_3CN$ (49 g.)	*n*-C_4H_9MgBr (69 g. C_4H_9Br)	2-*n*-C_4H_9-3-$CH_3OC_6H_4CN$ (42.7 g., 80%)	*218*

TABLE X-I (Continued)

Cyano Comp'd	RMgX	Product(s)	Ref.
$C_9H_9O_2$ (*cont.*)			
2,3-$(CH_3O)_2C_6H_3CN$ (49 g.)	*i*-C_4H_9MgBr (69 g. C_4H_9Br)	2-*i*-C_4H_9-3-$CH_3OC_6H_4CN$ (25.8 g., 45%)	*218*
2,3-$(CH_3O)_2C_6H_3CN$ (12 g.)	*t*-C_4H_9MgCl	Recovered nitrile (7.4 g.); 2,3-$(CH_3O)_2C_6H_3C({=}NH)$-*t*-C_4H_9 (4.3 g.)	*212*
2,3-$(CH_3O)_2C_6H_3CN$ (16.3 g.)	C_6H_5MgBr (15.7 g. C_6H_5Br)	2-C_6H_5-3-$CH_3OC_6H_3CN$ (6.5 g., 31%); 2,3-$(CH_3O)_2C_6H_3COC_6H_5$; 2-C_6H_5-3-$CH_3OC_6H_3COC_6H_5$	*218*
2,3-$(CH_3O)_2C_6H_3CN$ (16.3 g.)	$(CH_2)_5CHMgBr$ (29.3 g. $C_6H_{11}Br$)	2-$(CH_2)_5CH$-3-$CH_3OC_6H_3CN$ (14.6 g., 68%)	*218*
2,3-$(CH_3O)_2C_6H_3CN$ (49 g.)	*n*-$C_7H_{15}MgBr$ (72 g. $C_7H_{15}Br$)	2-C_7H_{15}-3-$CH_3OC_6H_3CN$ (40 g., 62%); 2,3-$(CH_3O)_2C_6H_3CO$-*n*-C_7H_{15}	*218*
2,3-$(CH_3O)_2C_6H_3CN$ (16.3 g.)	1-$C_{10}H_7MgBr$ (2.8 g. Mg)	2-α-$C_{10}H_7$-3-$CH_3OC_6H_3CN$ (1.7 g., 6.5%); 2-HO-3-$CH_3OC_6H_3CO$-1-$C_{10}H_7$ + 2,3-$(CH_3O)_2C_6H_3CO$-1-$C_{10}H_7$ (totalling *ca.* 35%); resin	*101*
2,3-$(CH_3O)_2C_6H_3CN$	2-$C_{10}H_7MgBr$	2-β-$C_{10}H_7$-3-$CH_3OC_6H_3CN$ (7%); 2,3-$(CH_3O)_2C_6H_3CO$-2-$C_{10}H_7$; (2-$C_{10}H_7$—$)_2$; resin	*101*
2,3-$(CH_3O)_2C_6H_3CN$	3,4-Dihydro-2-naphthyl-MgBr (42 g. $C_{10}H_9Br$)	2-β-$C_{10}H_7$-3-$CH_3OC_6H_3CN$ (26.3%); 2,3-$(CH_3O)_2C_6H_3CO$-2-$C_{10}H_7$ (4.9 g.); 3,3′,4,4′-tetrahydro-2,2′-binaphthyl (1.5 g.)	*101*
2,3-$(CH_3O)_2C_6H_3CN$ (30 g.)	$C_{10}H_{11}MgCl$*	2-(2-$C_{10}H_{11}$)-3-$CH_3OC_6H_3CN$ (32 g.)	*101*
2,5-$(CH_3O)_2C_6H_3CN$ (10.5 g.)	C_2H_5MgBr	2,5-$(CH_3O)_2C_6H_3C({=}NH)C_2H_5$ (9.5 g.)	*212*
2,6-$(CH_3O)_2C_6H_3CN$ (12 g.)	C_2H_5MgBr (16 g. C_2H_5Br)	2,6-$(CH_3O)_2C_6H_3C({=}NH)C_2H_5$ (11 g., crude); recovered nitrile (0.8 g.)	*212*
2,6-$(CH_3O)_2C_6H_3CN$ (16.3 g.)	*i*-C_4H_9MgBr (32.5 g. C_4H_9Br)	2,6-$(CH_3O)_2C_6H_3CO$-*i*-C_4H_9	*105*

* From 8 g. of Mg and 35 g. of 2-chloro-1,2,3,4-tetrahydronaphthalene.

TABLE X-I (Continued)

Cyano Comp'd	RMgX	Product(s)	Ref.
$C_9H_9O_2$ *(cont.)*			
3,4-$(CH_3O)_2C_6H_3CN$ (10 g.)	C_2H_5MgBr	3,4-$(CH_3O)_2C_6H_3C({=}NH)C_2H_5$ (5.2 g.); recovered nitrile (2.7 g.)	*212*
3,5-$(CH_3O)_2C_6H_3CN$ (3.2 g.)	*i*-C_4H_9MgBr (13 g. C_4H_9Br)	3,5-$(CH_3O)_2C_6H_3CO$-*i*-C_4H_9	*106*
3-$CH_3OC_6H_4OCH_2CN$ (48 g.)	$C_6H_5CH_2MgCl$ (94.5 g. C_7H_7Cl)	3-$CH_3OC_6H_4OCH_2COCH_2C_6H_5$	*107*
2-$CH_3OC_6H_4CH(OH)CN$	C_6H_5MgX	2-$CH_3OC_6H_4CH(OH)COC_6H_5$	*67*
2-$CH_3OC_6H_4CH(OH)CN$	4-$CH_3OC_6H_4MgX$	2-$CH_3OC_6H_4CH(OH)COC_6H_4$-4-$OCH_3$	*67*
4-$CH_3OC_6H_4CH(OH)CN$	C_6H_5MgX	4-$CH_3OC_6H_4CH(OH)COC_6H_5$	*67*
4-$CH_3OC_6H_4CH(OH)CN$ (33 g.)	$(CH_2)_4CHMgBr$ (64 g. C_5H_9Br)	4-$CH_3OC_6H_4CH(OH)COCH(CH_2)_4$ (5 g.)	*104*
4-$CH_3OC_6H_4CH(OH)CN$ (13.6 g.)	$(CH_2)_5CHMgBr$ (35 g. $C_6H_{11}Br$)	4-$CH_3OC_6H_4CH(OH)COCH(CH_2)_5$	*104*
$C_9H_{10}N_2$			
4-$(CH_3)_2NC_6H_4CN$ (0.06 mole)	C_6H_5MgBr (0.05 mole)	4-$(CH_3)_2NC_6H_5COC_6H_5$ (>60%)	*95*
$C_9H_{14}N_2$			
$(CH_2)_5NCH(CH{=}CH_2)CN$	C_6H_5MgBr	$(CH_2)_5NCH(CH{=}CH_2)C_6H_5$	*83*
$C_9H_{15}NO_2$			
$H_5C_2O_2CC(C_2H_5)_2CN$	C_2H_5MgX* (1 equiv.)	$HO(C_2H_5)_2CC(C_2H_5)_2CN$	*109*
$H_5C_2O_2CC(C_2H_5)_2CN$	C_2H_5MgX* (2 equiv.)	$(C_2H_5)_2CO$; $(C_2H_5)_2CHCN$; $(C_2H_5)_3COH$; $(C_2H_5)_2CHCO_2C_2H_5$; $(C_2H_5)_2CHCOC(C_2H_5)_2CO_2C_2H_5$; $(C_2H_5)_2C(OH)C(C_2H_5)_2CN$	*109*
$H_5C_6O_2CC(C_2H_5)_2CN$	C_6H_5MgBr	$(C_2H_5)_2CHCO_2C_2H_5$; $(C_6H_5)_2CO$; $(C_2H_5)_2CHCOC(C_2H_5)_2CO_2C_2H_5$	*99*
$C_9H_{16}N_2$			
$(CH_2)_5NC(CH_3)_2CN$	CH_3MgX (2 equiv.)	$(CH_2)_5NC(CH_3)_3$	*70*
$(CH_2)_5NC(CH_3)_2CN$	C_2H_5MgX (2 equiv.)	$(CH_2)_5NC(CH_3)_2C_2H_5$	*70*

* X = Br, I.

TABLE X-I (Continued)

Cyano Comp'd	RMgX	Product(s)	Ref.
$C_9H_{16}N_2$ *(cont.)*			
$(CH_2)_5NC(CH_3)_2CN$	*n*-C_3H_7MgX (2 equiv.)	$(CH_2)_5NC(CH_3)_2$-*n*-C_3H_7	*70*
$C_9H_{17}N$			
n-$C_8H_{17}CN$	*n*-$C_8H_{17}MgX$	(*n*-$C_8H_{17})_2CO$ (*ca.* 65%)	*20*
$C_9H_{17}NO$			
4-(4-Morpholinyl)butyronitrile	CH_3MgX	5-(4-Morpholinyl)-2-pentanone (66%)	*160*
4-(4-Morpholinyl)butyronitrile	*n*-C_3H_7MgX	7-(4-Morpholinyl)-4-heptanone (50%)	*160*
$C_{10}H_6N_2$			
2-Cyanoquinoline	CH_3MgI (2.25 equiv.)	2-Acetylquinoline (79%)	*110*
2-Cyanoquinoline (4.3 g.)	CH_3MgI (1 equiv.) + $C_6H_5CH_2MgCl$ (4.7 g. C_7H_7Cl)	2-α-Toluylquinoline (0.4 g.); 2-acetylquinoline (trace)	*110*
2-Cyanoquinoline (10 g.)	C_2H_5MgI (2.25 equiv.)	2-Propionylquinoline (8.2 g., 68%)	*110*
2-Cyanoquinoline	C_6H_5MgBr	2-Benzoylquinoline	*110*
4-Cyanoquinoline (30 g.)	CH_3MgI (70 g. CH_3I)	4-Acetylquinoline (20 g., 60%)	*110*
4-Cyanoquinoline (0.3 mole)	C_2H_5MgI (0.6 mole)	3-Amino-3-γ-quinolylpentane; 4-ethylquinoline (10 g.); 4-propionylquinoline (5 g.)	*111*
4-Cyanoquinoline (10 g.)	C_6H_5MgBr (23.6 g.)	4-Benzoylquinoline (5.5 g.)	*110,111*
4-Cyanoquinoline	$C_6H_5CH_2MgCl$ (2 equiv.)	Recovered nitrile; 4-α-toluylquinoline; 4-benzylquinoline	*111*
1-Cyanoisoquinoline (2 g.)	CH_3MgI (4.1 g.)	1-Acetylisoquinoline (1.4 g.)	*112*
1-Cyanoisoquinoline	CH_3MgI	1-Acetylisoquinoline (50%)	*113*
1-Cyanoisoquinoline	C_6H_5MgBr	1-Benzoylisoquinoline	*112*
$C_{10}H_9NO_3$			
2-CH_3CO_2-3-$CH_3OC_6H_3CN$ (19.1 g.)	C_2H_5MgBr (33 g. C_2H_5Br)	2-HO-3-$CH_3OC_6H_3COC_2H_5$; $CH_3(C_2H_5)_2COH$	*166*

TABLE X-I (Continued)

Cyano Comp'd	RMgX	Product(s)	Ref.
$C_{10}H_9NO_3$ (*cont.*)			
$(\alpha\text{-}C_4H_3O)CH{=}C(CO_2C_2H_5)CN$* (40 g.)	$n\text{-}C_3H_7MgBr$ (70 g. C_3H_7Br)	$n\text{-}C_3H_7(\alpha\text{-}C_4H_3O)CHCH(CO_2C_2H_5)CN$ (40 g., 82%)	*220*
$(\alpha\text{-}C_4H_3O)CH{=}C(CO_2C_2H_5)CN$* (20 g.)	$i\text{-}C_4H_9MgCl$ (27 g. C_4H_9Cl)	$i\text{-}C_4H_9(\alpha\text{-}C_4H_3O)CHCH(CO_2C_2H_5)CN$ (24 g.)	*220*
$C_{10}H_{11}N$			
$C_2H_5(C_6H_5)CHCN$	CH_3MgI (4 equiv.)	$C_2H_5(C_6H_5)CHCOCH_3$	*50*
$C_2H_5(C_6H_5)CHCN$	$n\text{-}C_3H_7MgBr$ (4 equiv.)	$C_2H_5(C_6H_5)CHCO\text{-}n\text{-}C_3H_7$	*50*
$C_2H_5(C_6H_5)CHCN$	$n\text{-}C_4H_9MgBr$ (4 equiv.)	$C_2H_5(C_6H_5)CHCO\text{-}n\text{-}C_4H_9$	*50*
$C_{10}H_{11}NO$			
$C_6H_5CH_2CH_2OCH_2CN$	CH_3MgI (1.5 equiv.)	$C_6H_5CH_2CH_2OCH_2COCH_3$	*114*
$2\text{-}C_2H_5\text{-}3\text{-}CH_3OC_6H_3CN$	C_2H_5MgBr	$2\text{-}C_2H_5\text{-}3\text{-}CH_3OC_6H_3COC_2H_5$	*166*
$C_{10}H_{11}NO_2$			
$2,3\text{-}(CH_3O)_2\text{-}5\text{-}CH_3C_6H_2CN$ (12 g.)	C_2H_5MgBr	$2\text{-}C_2H_5\text{-}3\text{-}CH_3O\text{-}5\text{-}CH_3C_6H_2CN$ (6.3 g., 52%); $2,3\text{-}(CH_3O)_2\text{-}5\text{-}CH_3C_6H_2C({=}NH)C_2H_5$ (4.0 g.)	*212*
$C_{10}H_{11}NO_3$			
$3,4,5\text{-}(CH_3O)_3C_6H_2CN$ (19.3 g.)	$i\text{-}C_4H_9MgBr$ (34.2 g. C_4H_9Br)	$3,4,5\text{-}(CH_3O)_3C_6H_2CO\text{-}i\text{-}C_4H_9$ (6.5 g.); $3,5\text{-}(CH_3O)_2\text{-}4\text{-}HOC_6H_2CO\text{-}i\text{-}C_4H_9$ (?); $3,5\text{-}(CH_3O)_2\text{-}4\text{-}i\text{-}C_4H_9C_6H_2CO\text{-}i\text{-}C_4H_9$ (?)	*106*
$3,4,5\text{-}(CH_3O)_3C_6H_2CN$ (19.3 g.)	$i\text{-}C_4H_9MgBr$ (2.5 equiv.)	$3,4,5\text{-}(CH_3O)_3C_6H_2CO\text{-}i\text{-}C_4H_9$ (3.8 g.); $3,5\text{-}(CH_3O)_2\text{-}4\text{-}HOC_6H_2CO\text{-}i\text{-}C_4H_9$ (4.5 g.)	*106*

* $(\alpha\text{-}C_4H_3O)$ = 2-furyl.

TABLE X-I (Continued)

Cyano Comp'd	RMgX	Product(s)	Ref.
$C_{10}H_{11}NO_3$ (*cont.*)			
3,4,5-$(CH_3O)_3C_6H_2CN$ (19.3 g.)	*i*-C_4H_9MgBr (4 equiv.)	3,4,5-$(CH_3O)_3C_6H_2CO$-*i*-C_4H_9 (1.5 g.); 3,5-$(CH_3O)_2$-4-HOC_6H_2CO-*i*-C_4H_9 (10.0 g.); 3,5-$(CH_3O)_2$-4-*i*-$C_4H_9C_6H_2CO$-*i*-C_4H_9 (7.7 g., crude)	*106*
$C_{10}H_{11}NS$			
$C_6H_5S(CH_2)_3CN$	C_6H_5MgBr	$C_6H_5S(CH_2)_3COC_6H_5$	*116*
$C_{10}H_{12}N$			
4-Methyl-7-cyanoindan (120 g.)	1-$C_{10}H_7MgBr$ (195 g. $C_{10}H_7Br$)	4-Methyl-7-α-naphthoylindan ketimine hydrochloride (yielding 194 g., 89% ketone)	*221*
$C_{10}H_{12}N_2$			
$C_2H_5(C_6H_5)NCH_2CN$	CH_3MgI (2 equiv.)	$C_2H_5(C_6H_5)NCH_2COCH_3$	*98*
$(CH_3)_2NCH(C_6H_5)CN$	CH_3MgI (2 equiv.)	$(CH_3)_2NCH(C_6H_5)CH_3$	*98*
$(CH_3)_2NCH(C_6H_5)CN$	C_6H_5MgBr (2 equiv.)	$(CH_3)_2NCH(C_6H_5)_2$	*98*
$(CH_3)_2NCH(C_6H_5)CN$	$C_6H_5CH_2MgCl$ (2 equiv.)	$(CH_3)_2NCH(C_6H_5)CH_2C_6H_5$	*98*
$C_{10}H_{18}N_2$			
$(CH_2)_5N(CH_3)(C_2H_5)CCN$	C_2H_5MgX	$(CH_2)_5NC(C_2H_5)_2CH_3$	*83*
$(CH_2)_5N(CH_3)(C_2H_5)CCN$	C_6H_5MgX	$(CH_2)_5NC(CH_3)(C_2H_5)C_6H_5$	*83*
$(CH_2)_5N(CH_3)(C_2H_5)CCN$	$C_6H_5CH_2MgX$	$(CH_2)_5NC(CH_3)(C_2H_5)CH_2C_6H_5$	*83*
$C_{10}H_{19}N$			
n-$C_9H_{19}CN$	*n*-$C_7H_{15}MgX$	*n*-$C_9H_{19}CO$-*n*-C_7H_{15} (*ca.* 65%)	*20*
n-$C_9H_{19}CN$	*n*-$C_8H_{17}MgX$	*n*-$C_9H_{19}CO$-*n*-C_8H_{17} (*ca.* 65%)	*20*

TABLE X-I (Continued)

Cyano Comp'd	RMgX	Product(s)	Ref.
$C_{10}H_{19}NO$			
n-$C_8H_{17}OCH_2CN$	CH_3MgI (excess)	n-$C_8H_{17}OCH_2COCH_3$	*114*
$C_{11}H_7N$			
1-$C_{10}H_7CN$ (0.20 mole)	RMgBr (0.22 mole RBr)	1-$C_{10}H_7C(=NH)R$*	*222*
1-$C_{10}H_7CN$ (86.4 g.)	C_2H_5MgBr (80 g. C_2H_5Br)	1-$C_{10}H_7C(=NH)C_2H_5$ (yielding 90 g., 89% ketone)	*223,214*
1-$C_{10}H_7CN$	4-ClC_6H_4MgBr	4-ClC_6H_4(1-$C_{10}H_7$)$C{=}NH \cdot HCl$	*117*
1-$C_{10}H_7CN$	2-$CH_3OC_6H_4MgBr$	2-$CH_3OC_6H_4CO$-1-$C_{10}H_7$ (87%)	*118*
1-$C_{10}H_7CN$ (17 g.)	4-(7-Methylindanyl)-MgBr (22 g. $C_{10}H_{11}Br$)	4-α-Naphthoyl-7-methylindan ketimine hydrochloride (yielding 14.6 g., 49% ketone)	*213*
1-$C_{10}H_7CN$ (15 g.)	1-$C_{10}H_7MgBr$ (30 g. $C_{10}H_7Br$)	(1-$C_{10}H_7$)$_2C{=}NH$ (20.7 g.)	*119*
2-$C_{10}H_7CN$	C_2H_5MgBr	2-$C_{10}H_7COC_2H_5$ (67%)	*214*
2-$C_{10}H_7CN$	C_2H_5MgI (1.5 equiv.)	C_2H_5CO-2-$C_{10}H_7$ (95%)	*120*
2-$C_{10}H_7CN$	2-ClC_6H_4MgBr	2-ClC_6H_4(2-$C_{10}H_7$)$C{=}NH \cdot HCl$	*121*
2-$C_{10}H_7CN$ (5 g.)	4-ClC_6H_4MgBr (7.5 g. C_6H_4BrCl)	4-ClC_6H_4(2-$C_{10}H_7$)$C{=}NH \cdot HCl$ (yielding 7 g., 81% ketone)	*117*
2-$C_{10}H_7CN$ (10 g.)	C_6H_5MgBr (15 g. C_6H_5Br)	2-$C_{10}H_7COC_6H_5$ (70%)	*174,176*
2-$C_{10}H_7CN$	2-$CH_3OC_6H_4MgBr$	2-$CH_3OC_6H_4CO$-2-$C_{10}H_7$ (74%)	*118*
2-$C_{10}H_7CN$ (15 g.)	1-$C_{10}H_7MgBr$ (30 g. $C_{10}H_7Br$)	1-$C_{10}H_7$(2-$C_{10}H_7$)$C{=}NH$ (21.5 g.)	*119*
2-$C_{10}H_7CN$ (15 g.)	2-$C_{10}H_7MgBr$ (30 g. $C_{10}H_7Br$)	(2-$C_{10}H_7$)$_2C{=}NH$ (22.3 g.)	*119*
2-$C_{10}H_7CN$ (33 g.)	2-$CH_3C_{10}H_6$-1-MgBr (54 g. $C_{11}H_9Br$)	2-$C_{10}H_7C(=NH \cdot HCl)$-1-$C_{10}H_6$-2-$CH_3$ (78 g.)	*213*

* The ketimines were converted to the corresponding ketones in the indicated yields for R =: CH_3, 52%; C_2H_5, 37%; n-C_3H_7, 63%; i-C_3H_7, 39%; n-C_4H_9, 46%; i-C_4H_9, 48%; n-C_5H_{11}, 44%; i-C_5H_{11}, 51%; C_6H_5, 55%; $(CH_2)_5CH$, 37%; n-C_6H_{13}, 35%.

TABLE X-I (Continued)

Cyano Comp'd	RMgX	Product(s)	Ref.
$C_{11}H_8N_2O$			
4-Cyano-6-methoxyquinoline (10 g.)	CH_3MgI (19.3 g. CH_3I)	4-Acetyl-6-methoxyquinoline	*110*
6-Methoxy-8-cyanoquinoline (18 g.)	CH_3MgBr (5 g. Mg)	6-Methoxy-8-acetoquinoline (16 g., 79%)	*225*
6-Methoxy-8-cyanoquinoline	C_2H_5MgI	6-Methoxy-8-propionylquinoline	*122*
$C_{11}H_9N$			
1-Methyl-5-cyanonaphthalene	CH_3MgI (2 ml. CH_3I)	1-Methyl-5-acetylnaphthalene (2.5 g.)	*124*
$C_{11}H_{10}N_2$			
2-Cyano-3,3-dimethyl-3-pseudoindole (10 g.)	CH_3MgI (1.6 g. Mg)	2-Acetyl-3,3-dimethyl-3-pseudoindole	*125*
2-Cyano-3,3-dimethyl-3-pseudoindole (10 g.)	C_6H_5MgBr (3 g. C_6H_5Br)	2-Benzimino-3,3-dimethyl-3-pseudoindole	*125*
$C_{11}H_{11}N$			
4-Methyl-7-cyanoindan (2.8 g.)	5-$BrC_{10}H_6$-2-MgBr (5 g. $C_{10}H_6Br_2$)	4-Methyl-7-(5-bromo-2-naphthoyl)indan (3.2 g., 50%)	*226*
4-Methyl-7-cyanoindan (2.0 g.)	6-$ClC_{10}H_6$-2-MgBr (3 g. $C_{10}H_6BrCl$)	4-Methyl-7-(6-chloro-2-naphthoyl)indan (2.5 g., 63%)	*226*
4-Methyl-7-cyanoindan (8.5 g.)	6-$CH_3OC_{10}H_6$-1-MgI (15 g. $C_{10}H_9IO$)	4-Methyl-7-(6-methoxy-1-naphthoylindan (63%)	*226*
4-Cyano-7-methylindan	1-$C_{10}H_7MgBr$	4-(1-Naphthoyl)-7-methylindan (83%)	*126*
2-Cyano-5,6,7,8-tetrahydronaphthalene	C_6H_5MgBr	2-Benzoyl-5,6,7,8-tetrahydronaphthalene (76%)	*209*
$C_{11}H_{11}NO_2$			
2-$H_2C{=}CHCH_2O$-3-$CH_3OC_6H_3CN$ (38 g.)	C_2H_5MgBr (22 g. C_2H_5Br)	2-C_2H_5-3-$CH_3OC_6H_3CN$ (4.1 g.); recovered nitrile (16.3 g.)	*166*

TABLE X-I (Continued)

Cyano Comp'd	RMgX	Product(s)	Ref.
$C_{11}H_{12}NCl$			
$ClCH_2CH_2C(CH_3)(C_6H_5)CN$	C_6H_5MgBr (*ca.* 3 equiv.)	2,3-Diphenyl-3-methyl-Δ^1-pyrroline (78%)	*123*
$C_{11}H_{13}N$			
n-$C_3H_7(C_6H_5)CHCN$	CH_3MgI (4 equiv.)	n-$C_3H_7(C_6H_5)CHCOCH_3$	*50*
n-$C_3H_7(C_6H_5)CHCN$	C_2H_5MgBr (4 equiv.)	n-$C_3H_7(C_6H_5)CHCOC_2H_5$	*50*
n-$C_3H_7(C_6H_5)CHCN$	n-C_4H_9MgBr (4 equiv.)	n-$C_3H_7(C_6H_5)CHCO$-n-C_4H_9	*50*
$CH_3(C_2H_5)(C_6H_5)CCN$	C_6H_5MgBr (1.25 equiv.)	$CH_3(C_2H_5)(C_6H_5)CCOC_6H_5$ (55%)	*66*
$CH_3(C_2H_5)(C_6H_5)CCN$	C_6H_5MgBr	$CH_3(C_2H_5)(C_6H_5)CCOC_6H_5$ ("excellent yield")	*65*
$C_{11}H_{13}NO$			
$C_2H_5(C_6H_5CH_2O)CHCN$	C_2H_5MgBr	$C_6H_5CH_2NHC(C_2H_5)_2CH(OH)C_2H_5$	*229*
$C_2H_5(C_6H_5CH_2O)CHCN$	C_6H_5MgBr	$C_6H_5CH_2NHC(C_6H_5)_2CH(OH)C_2H_5$	*229*
2,4,6-$(CH_3)_3C_6H_2CH(OH)CN$ (0.1 mole)	C_6H_5MgBr (0.5 mole C_6H_5Br)	2,4,6-$(CH_3)_3C_6H_2COCH(NH_2 \cdot HCl)C_6H_5$ (16 g., 55%)	*127*
$C_{11}H_{13}NO_2$			
2,6-$(C_2H_5O)_2C_6H_3CN$	RMgX*	Unchanged nitrile	*92*
3,5-$(CH_3O)_2C_6H_3CH(CH_3)CN$ (41.5 g.)	n-$C_3H_7CH(CH_3)CH_2MgBr$ (98.5 g. $C_6H_{13}Br$)	3,5-$(CH_3O)_2C_6H_3CH(CH_3)COCH_2CH(CH_3)$-$n$-$C_3H_7$ (30 g., 52%)	*128*
$C_{11}H_{14}N_2$			
$(CH_3)_2NCH(CH_2C_6H_5)CN$	C_6H_5MgBr (2 equiv.)	$(CH_3)_2NCH(C_6H_5)CH_2C_6H_5$	*98*
$C_{11}H_{15}NO_2$			
Ethyl α-cyano-α-cyclohexylidene-acetate (24.0 g.)	CH_3MgI (19.5 g. CH_3I)	Ethyl α-cyano-α-(1-methylcyclohexyl)acetate (45%)	*224*

* R = CH_3, C_2H_5, C_6H_5, $C_6H_5CH_2$.

TABLE X-I (Continued)

Cyano Comp'd	RMgX	Product(s)	Ref.
$C_{11}H_{15}NO_2$ (*cont.*)			
Ethyl α-cyano-α-cyclohexylideneacetate (15.0 g.)	n-$C_{10}H_{21}MgBr$ (25.0 g. $C_{10}H_{21}Br$)	Ethyl α-cyano-α-(1-n-decylcyclohexyl)acetate (14%)	*224*
$C_{11}H_{21}N$			
n-$C_{10}H_{21}CN$	C_2H_5MgBr	n-$C_{10}H_{21}COC_2H_5$ ("poor yield")	*230*
n-$C_{10}H_{21}CN$	n-$C_6H_{13}MgX$	n-$C_{10}H_{21}CO$-n-C_6H_{13} (*ca.* 65%)	*20*
$C_{12}H_9N$			
1-$C_{10}H_7CH_2CN$ (30 g., 0.18 mole)	C_2H_5MgBr (18.5 g., 0.17 mole C_2H_5Br)	1-$C_{10}H_7CH_2COC_2H_5$ (5.3 g., 0.027 mole, 16%); polymeric material	*234*
1-Methyl-7-cyanonaphthalene (3.3 g.)	CH_3MgI (4.3 g. CH_3I)	1-Methyl-7-acetylnaphthalene	*129*
$C_{12}H_9NO$			
2-$CH_3OC_{10}H_6$-1-CN (11 g.)	C_2H_5MgBr (14 g. C_2H_5Br)	2-$CH_3OC_{10}H_7$ (2 g.); 2-$HOC_{10}H_7$ (1.7 g.); 2-$CH_3OC_{10}H_6$-1-C(=NH)C_2H_5 (isolated as ketone, 1.7 ml.); recovered nitrile (1.0 g.)	*231*
2-$CH_3OC_{10}H_6$-1-CN (11 g.)	$C_6H_5CH_2MgCl$ (16 ml. C_7H_7Cl)	2-$CH_3OC_{10}H_6$-1-C(=NH · HCl)$CH_2C_6H_5$; recovered nitrile (2.3 g.)	*231*
$C_{12}H_{10}N_2O$			
4-Cyano-6-ethoxyquinoline	CH_3MgI (2.5 equiv.)	4-Acetyl-6-ethoxyquinoline (80%)	*130*
4-Cyano-6-ethoxyquinoline	C_2H_5MgI (2.5 equiv.)	4-Propionyl-6-ethoxyquinoline	*130*
$C_{12}H_{11}NO_2$			
$C_6H_5CH=C(CO_2C_2H_5)CN$	CH_3MgI	$C_6H_5CH(CH_3)CH(CO_2C_2H_5)CN$	*131*

TABLE X-I (Continued)

Cyano Comp'd	RMgX	Product(s)	Ref.
$C_{12}H_{11}NO_2$ (*cont.*)			
$C_6H_5CH{=}C(CO_2C_2H_5)CN$	i-C_3H_7MgBr	$C_6H_5CH(i\text{-}C_3H_7)CH(CO_2C_2H_5)CN$	*131*
$C_6H_5CH{=}C(CO_2C_2H_5)CN$ (20 g.)	C_6H_5MgBr (2.75 g. Mg)	$(C_6H_5)_2CHCH(CO_2C_2H_5)CN$ (25.4 g.)	*131*
$C_6H_5CH{=}C(CO_2C_2H_5)CN$	$C_6H_5CH_2MgCl$	$C_6H_5CH_2CH(C_6H_5)CH(CO_2C_2H_5)CN$ (isolated, after hydrolysis, as the corresponding malonamic acid)	*131*
$C_6H_5CH{=}C(CO_2C_2H_5)CN$	$C_6H_5C{\equiv}CMgBr$	$C_6H_5C{\equiv}CCH(C_6H_5)CH(CO_2C_2H_5)CN$ ("excellent yield")	*131*
$C_6H_5CH{=}C(CO_2C_2H_5)CN$	1-$C_{10}H_7MgBr$	$C_6H_5(1\text{-}C_{10}H_7)CHCH(CO_2C_2H_5)CN$	*131*
$C_{12}H_{12}N_2O_2$			
1-Cyanohydrohydrastinine	CH_3MgI (2 equiv.)	1-Methylhydrohydrastinine	*98*
$C_{12}H_{14}NCl$			
$ClCH_2CH_2C(C_2H_5)(C_6H_5)CN$ (20.8 g.)	C_6H_5MgBr (50 g. C_6H_5Br)	2,3-Diphenyl-3-ethyl-Δ^1-pyrroline (70%)	*123*
$C_{12}H_{15}N$			
$C_6H_5(C_2H_5)_2CCN$	C_6H_5MgBr	$C_6H_5(C_2H_5)_2CCOC_6H_5$	*65*
$C_6H_5(C_2H_5)_2CCN$	C_6H_5MgBr (1.25 equiv.) (+ HBr)	$C_6H_5(C_2H_5)_2CC({=}NH \cdot HBr)C_6H_5$	*66*
$C_{12}H_{21}N$			
$H_2C{=}CH(CH_2)_9CN$ (24.5 g.)	CH_3MgI (14 g. Mg)	$CH_3CO(CH_2)_9CH{=}CH_2$ (19 g.)	*133*
$C_{12}H_{23}N$			
n-$C_{11}H_{23}CN$	n-C_4H_9MgBr (sl. excess)	n-C_4H_9CO-n-$C_{11}H_{23}$ (68%)	*134*
n-$C_{11}H_{23}CN$	n-$C_5H_{11}MgX$	n-$C_{11}H_{23}CO$-n-C_5H_{11} (*ca.* 65%)	*20*
n-$C_{11}H_{23}CN$ (1.5–2 moles)	C_6H_5MgBr (sl. excess)	n-$C_{11}H_{23}COC_6H_5$ (75–90%)*	*163*

* Range of yields claimed for series of nitriles treated.

TABLE X-I (Continued)

Cyano Comp'd	RMgX	Product(s)	Ref.
$C_{12}H_{23}N$ (*cont.*)			
n-$C_{11}H_{23}CN$	n-$C_6H_{13}MgX$	n-$C_{11}H_{23}CO$-n-C_5H_{11} (*ca.* 65%)	*20*
n-$C_{11}H_{23}CN$ (293 g., 1.61 mole)	9-Phenanthryl-MgBr (508 g., 1.98 mole $C_{14}H_9Br$)	Hendecyl 9-phenanthryl ketone (465 g., 80%)	*228*
$C_{13}H_9N$			
2-$C_6H_5C_6H_4CN$	C_6H_5MgBr	$C_6H_5COC_6H_4$-2-C_6H_5 (76%)	*135*
$C_{13}H_9NO$			
α-Phenyl-β-(2-furyl)acrylonitrile	CH_3MgI	α-Phenyl-β-(2-furyl)butyronitrile (80%)	*227*
α-Phenyl-β-(2-furyl)acrylonitrile (20 g.)	C_2H_5MgBr (25 g. C_2H_5Br)	α-Phenyl-β-(2-furyl)valeronitrile (20 g.)	*136*
α-Phenyl-β-(2-furyl)acrylonitrile	n-C_3H_7MgBr	α-Phenyl-β-(2-furyl)capronitrile (80%)	*136*
α-Phenyl-β-(2-furyl)acrylonitrile (25 g.)	i-C_4H_9MgCl (27 g. C_4H_9Cl)	α-Phenyl-β-(2-furyl)-γ-methylcapronitrile (25 g.)	*136*
α-Phenyl-β-(2-furyl)acrylonitrile	i-$C_5H_{11}MgBr$	α-Phenyl-β-(2-furyl)-δ-methylenanthonitrile (33%)	*227*
α-Phenyl-β-(2-furyl)acrylonitrile	$C_6H_5CH_2MgCl$	α,γ-Diphenyl-β-(2-furyl)butyronitrile (80%)	*227*
α-Phenyl-β-(2-furyl)acrylonitrile	4-$CH_3C_6H_4MgBr$	α-Phenyl-β-(2-furyl)-β-4-tolylpropionitrile (20%)	*227*
$C_{13}H_{14}N_2O$			
1-Benzyl-5-methyl-5-cyano-2-pyrrolidone (6 g.)	CH_3MgI (9.95 g. CH_3I)	1-Benzyl-5-methyl-5-acetyl-2-pyrrolidone	*137*
1-Benzyl-5-methyl-5-cyano-2-pyrrolidone (6 g.)	C_2H_5MgI (10.9 g. C_2H_5I)	1-Benzyl-5-methyl-5-propionyl-2-pyrrolidone (3.4 g.)	*137*
1-Benzyl-5-methyl-5-cyano-2-pyrrolidone	C_6H_5MgBr	1-Benzyl-5-methyl-5-benzoyl-2-pyrrolidone	*137*

TABLE X-I (Continued)

Cyano Comp'd	RMgX	Product(s)	Ref.
$C_{13}H_{15}N$			
4-Cyano-7-isopropylindan (13 g.)	1-$C_{10}H_7MgBr$ (22 g. $C_{10}H_7Br$)	4-(7-Isopropyl)hydrindenyl-1-naphthyl ketimine hydrochloride (25 g., 100%)	*138*
$C_{13}H_{15}NO$			
2,4,6-$(CH_3)_3C_6H_2(CH_3O)C{=}CHCN$	C_6H_5MgBr (*ca.* 1 to *ca.* 4 equiv.)*	2,4,6-$(CH_3)_3C_6H_2(CH_3O)C{=}CHC({=}NH \cdot HBr)C_6H_5$; 2,4,6-$(CH_3)_3C_6H_2(CH_3O)C{=}CHCOC_6H_5$; 2,4,6-$(CH_3)_3C_6H_2COCH_2COC_6H_5$; 2,4,6-$(CH_3)_3C_6H_2COCH_2C({=}NH)C_6H_5$; recovered nitrile	*108*
$C_{13}H_{16}NCl$			
$ClCH_2CH_2C(n\text{-}C_3H_7)(C_6H_5)CN$	C_6H_5MgBr (*ca.* 3 equiv.)	2,3-Diphenyl-2-*n*-propyl-Δ^1-pyrroline (58%)	*123*
$C_{13}H_{16}N_2$			
$(CH_2)_5NCH(C_6H_5)CN$ (70 g.)	C_2H_5MgBr (17 g. Mg)	$(CH_2)_5NCH(C_2H_5)C_6H_5$ (59 g., 80%)	*140*
$(CH_2)_5NCH(C_6H_5)CN$ (50 g.)	C_6H_5MgBr (78.5 g. C_6H_5Br)	$(CH_2)_5NCH(C_6H_5)_2$ (52 g., 83%)	*140*
$(CH_2)_5NCH(C_6H_5)CN$ (40 g.)	$C_6H_5CH_2MgCl$ (50 g. C_7H_7Cl)	$(CH_2)_5NCH(C_6H_5)CH_2C_6H_5$ (60%)	*140*
$C_{13}H_{25}N$			
$n\text{-}C_{12}H_{25}CN$ (430 g.)	$n\text{-}C_3H_7MgCl$	$n\text{-}C_{12}H_{25}CO\text{-}n\text{-}C_3H_7$ (265 g., 50%)	*141*
$n\text{-}C_{12}H_{25}CN$	$n\text{-}C_4H_9MgX$	$n\text{-}C_{12}H_{25}CO\text{-}n\text{-}C_4H_9$ (*ca.* 65%)	*20*
$n\text{-}C_{12}H_{25}CN$	$n\text{-}C_5H_{11}MgX$	$n\text{-}C_{12}H_{25}CO\text{-}n\text{-}C_5H_{11}$ (*ca.* 65%)	*20*
$C_{14}H_8N_2$			
9,10-Dicyanoanthracene	CH_3MgI	No reaction	*142*
9,10-Dicyanoanthracene	C_2H_5MgBr	Reaction with one cyano group	*142*

* Nine experiments.

TABLE X-I (Continued)

Cyano Comp'd	RMgX	Product(s)	Ref.
$C_{14}H_8N_2$ (*cont.*)			
9,10-Dicyanoanthracene	C_6H_5MgBr	No reaction	*142*
$C_{14}H_9N$			
1-Cyanofluorene (13.27 g.)	C_6H_5MgBr	1-Benzoylfluorene (7.78 g.)	*209*
4-Cyanofluorene (5 g.)	C_6H_5MgBr (4.4 ml. C_6H_5Br)	4-Benzoylfluorene (3.64 g., 56%)	*209*
$C_{14}H_{11}N$			
2-$C_6H_5CH_2C_6H_4CN$ (11.0 g.)	C_6H_5MgBr (13.4 g. C_6H_5Br)	2-$C_6H_5CH_2C_6H_4C(=NH)C_6H_5$	*143*
2-$C_6H_5CH_2C_6H_4CN$ (10.0 g.)	C_6H_5MgBr (8.5 g. C_6H_5Br)	2-$C_6H_5CH_2C_6H_4COC_6H_5$ (12.5 g.)	*162*
$(C_6H_5)_2CHCN$ (7.5 g.)	C_6H_5MgBr (15.0 g. C_6H_5Br)	$(C_6H_5)_2CHCOC_6H_5$ (2.0 g.); recovered nitrile (1.5 g.); $[NC(C_6H_5)_2C-]_2$ (very little)	88
$(C_6H_5)_2CHCN$	2-$CH_3C_6H_4MgBr$	No reaction	80
$(C_6H_5)_2CHCN$ (5 g.)	3-$CH_3C_6H_4MgBr$ (13 g. C_7H_7Br)	$(C_6H_5)_2CHCOC_6H_4$-3-CH_3	80
$(CH_2)_2C(1\text{-}C_{10}H_7)CN$ (38.6 g.)	C_6H_5MgBr (90.0 g. C_6H_5Br)	$(CH_2)_2C(1\text{-}C_{10}H_7)C=NH$	*144*
$C_{14}H_{13}NO_2$			
$C_6H_5CH=CHCH=C(CO_2C_2H_5)CN$ (1 mole)	C_2H_5MgBr (2.5 mole)	$C_6H_5CH=CHCH(C_2H_5)CH(CO_2C_2H_5)CN$ (quant.)	*145*
$C_6H_5CH=CHCH=C(CO_2C_2H_5)CN$	C_6H_5MgBr	$C_6H_5CH=CHCH(C_6H_5)CH(CO_2C_2H_5)CN$	*145*
$C_{14}H_{12}N_2$			
$C_6H_5NH(C_6H_5)CHCN$ (52 g.)	C_2H_5MgBr (12 g. Mg)	Gas (8.4 1.); $C_6H_5NH_2$; $[C_6H_5NH(C_6H_5)CH-]_2$ (30%)	*140*
$C_6H_5NH(C_6H_5)CHCN$ (52 g.)	C_6H_5MgBr (78.5 g. C_6H_5Br)	$[C_6H_5NH(C_6H_5)CH-]_2$ (25%); $C_6H_5CH=NC_6H_5$ (15 g.); $C_6H_5NH_2$	*140*

TABLE X-I (Continued)

Cyano Comp'd	RMgX	Product(s)	Ref.
$C_{14}H_{17}N$			
$C_6H_5[(CH_2)_5CH]CHCN$	C_2H_5MgBr (1 equiv.)	$C_6H_5[(CH_2)_5CH]CHCOC_2H_5$	*146*
$C_6H_5[(CH_2)_5CH]CHCN$	n-C_3H_7MgCl (1 equiv.)	$C_6H_5[(CH_2)_5CH]CHCO$-n-C_3H_7	*146*
$C_6H_5[(CH_2)_5CH]CHCN$	i-C_3H_7MgCl (1 equiv.)	$C_6H_5[(CH_2)_5CH]CHCO$-i-C_3H_7	*146*
$C_6H_5[(CH_2)_5CH]CHCN$	$C_6H_5CH_2MgCl$ (1 equiv.)	$C_6H_5[(CH_2)_5CH]COCH_2C_6H_5$	*146*
$C_{14}H_{17}NO$			
2,4,6-$(CH_3)_3C_6H_2(CH_3O)C=C(CH_3)CN$ (2.0 g.)	C_6H_5MgBr (7.3 g. C_6H_5Br)	2,4,6-$(CH_3)_3C_6H_2(CH_3O)C=C(CH_3)C(=NH \cdot HBr)C_6H_5$ (1.3 g.); 2,4,6-$(CH_3)_3C_6H_2COCH(CH_3)COC_6H_5$	*108*
$C_{14}H_{18}NCl$			
$ClCH_2CH_2C(n$-$C_4H_9)(C_6H_5)CN$	C_6H_5MgBr (*ca.* 3 equiv.)	2,3-Diphenyl-2-n-butyl-Δ^1-pyrroline (35%)	*123*
$C_{14}H_{27}N$			
n-$C_{13}H_{27}CN$	n-C_3H_7MgX	n-$C_{13}H_{27}COC_2H_5$ (*ca.* 65%)	*20*
n-$C_{13}H_{27}CN$	n-C_4H_9MgX	n-$C_{13}H_{27}CO$-n-C_4H_9 (*ca.* 65%)	*20,134*
n-$C_{13}H_{27}CN$ (1.5–2 moles)	C_6H_5MgBr (sl. excess)	n-$C_{13}H_{27}COC_6H_5$ (75–90%)*	*163*
i-$C_6H_{13}CH(CH_3)CH(CH_2CH_2OC_2H_5)CH$	CH_3MgI	i-$C_6H_{13}CH(CH_3)CH(CH_2CH_2OC_2H_5)COCH_3$	*164*
$C_{15}H_9N$			
2-Cyanophenanthrene (6 g.)	C_6H_5MgBr (7 ml. C_6H_5Br)	2-Benzoylphenanthrene (9 g., 85%)	*147*
2-Cyanophenanthrene (4.3 g.)	2-$CH_3C_6H_4MgBr$ (10 g. C_6H_5Br)	2-*o*-Toluylphenanthrene (48%)	*148*
2-Cyanophenanthrene (5 g.)	2-$CH_3C_{10}H_6$-1-MgBr (12.5 g. $C_{11}H_9Br$)	2-(2-Methyl-1-naphthoyl)phenanthrene (73%)	*148*
3-Cyanophenanthrene (6 g.)	C_6H_5MgBr (7 ml. C_6H_5Br)	3-Benzoylphenanthrene (60%)	*147*
3-Cyanophenanthrene (4.3 g.)	2-$CH_3C_6H_4MgBr$ (10 g. C_7H_7Br)	3-*o*-Toluylphenanthrene (79%)	*148*

* Range of yields claimed for series of nitriles investigated.

TABLE X-I (Continued)

Cyano Comp'd	RMgX	Product(s)	Ref.
$C_{15}H_9N$ (*cont.*)			
3-Cyanophenanthrene (5 g.)	$2\text{-}CH_3C_{10}H_6\text{-}1\text{-}MgBr$ (12.5 g. $C_{11}H_9Br$)	3-(2-Methyl-1-naphthoyl)phenanthrene (51%)	*148*
9-Cyanophenanthrene (609 g., 3 moles)	CH_3MgI (6 moles CH_3I)	9-Acetylphenanthrene (345–390 g., 52–59%)	*165*
9-Cyanophenanthrene (5.4 g.)	C_6H_5MgBr (6 g. C_6H_5Br)	9-Benzoylphenanthrene (3 g. 42%)	*79*
9-Cyanophenanthrene (1.0 g.)	C_6H_5MgBr (1.5 g. C_6H_5Br)	α-9-Anthroyl-α-phenylmethyleneimine (1.26 g., 92%)	*167*
9-Cyanophenanthrene (4.3 g.)	$2\text{-}CH_3C_6H_4MgBr$ (10 g. C_7H_7Br)	9-*o*-Toluylphenanthrene (83%)	*148*
9-Cyanophenanthrene (5 g.)	$2\text{-}CH_3C_{10}H_6\text{-}1\text{-}MgBr$ (12.5 g. $C_{11}H_9Br$)	9-(2-Methyl-1-naphthoyl)phenanthrene (65%)	*148*
$C_{15}H_{11}N$			
$C_6H_5CH{=}C(C_6H_5)CN$	C_2H_5MgBr	$C_6H_5CH(C_2H_5)CH(C_6H_5)CN$; two isomeric products (m. 115°; b. 210–212°/20 mm.)	*100*
$C_6H_5CH{=}C(C_6H_5)CN$ (41 g.)	C_2H_5MgBr (0.2 mole)	$C_6H_5CH(C_2H_5)C(C_2H_5)(C_6H_5)CN$ (isomer m. 102–103°, >24.4 g.; isomer m. 93–99°, 2.76 g.)	*149*
$C_6H_5CH{=}C(C_6H_5)CN$ (41 g.)	C_2H_5MgBr (0.4 mole)	$C_6H_5CH(C_2H_5)C(C_2H_5)(C_6H_5)CN$ (isomer m. 102–103°, 26.7 g.; isomer m. 93–99°, 2.69 g.)	*149*
$C_6H_5CH{=}C(C_6H_5)CN$	C_6H_5MgBr	$(C_6H_5)_2CHCH(C_6H_5)CN$; $C_6H_5CH{=}C(C_6H_5)COC_6H_5$ (30–40%)	*100*
$(C_6H_5)_2C{=}CHCN$	C_6H_5MgBr	$(C_6H_5)_2C{=}CHCOC_6H_5$ (68%)	*100*
$C_{15}H_{13}N$			
$C_6H_5(C_6H_5CH_2)CHCN$	CH_3MgI (4 equiv.)	$C_6H_5(C_6H_5CH_2)CHCOCH_3$	*50*
$C_6H_5(C_6H_5CH_2)CHCN$	C_2H_5MgBr (4 equiv.)	$C_6H_5(C_6H_5CH_2)CHCOC_2H_5$	*50*
$C_6H_5(2\text{-}CH_3C_6H_4)CHCN$	C_6H_5MgBr	Recovered nitrile	*80*

TABLE X-I (Continued)

Cyano Comp'd	RMgX	Product(s)	Ref.
$C_{15}H_{13}N$ (*cont.*)			
$C_6H_5(3\text{-}CH_3C_6H_4)CHCN$ (4.3 g.)	C_6H_5MgBr (15.0 g. C_6H_5Br)	$C_6H_5(3\text{-}CH_3C_6H_4)CHCOC_6H_5$	*80*
$2\text{-}C_6H_5CH_2CH_2C_6H_4CN$ (18.0 g.)	C_6H_5MgBr (14.2 ml. C_6H_5Br)	$C_6H_5COC_6H_4\text{-}2\text{-}CH_2CH_2C_6H_5$ (24.0 g.)	*162*
$2\text{-}[CH_3(C_6H_5)CH]C_6H_4CN$ (18.0 g.)	C_6H_5MgBr (14.2 ml. C_6H_5Br)	$C_6H_5COC_6H_4\text{-}2\text{-}CH(CH_3)C_6H_5$ (21.1 g.)	*162*
$2\text{-}C_6H_5CH_2O\text{-}3\text{-}CH_3OC_6H_3CN$ (23.9 g.)	C_2H_5MgBr (10.9 g. C_2H_5Br)	Recovered nitrile ("much"); $2\text{-}C_2H_5\text{-}3\text{-}CH_3OC_6H_3CN$ (2 g.); $2\text{-}HO\text{-}3\text{-}CH_3OC_6H_3COC_2H_5$ ("some"); $C_6H_5CH_2OH$	*166*
$C_{15}H_{14}N_2$			
$(C_6H_5CH_2)_2NCN$ (12 g.)	C_2H_5MgBr	$(C_6H_5CH_2)_2NC(=NH \cdot HCl)C_2H_5$ (15 g., crude)	*150*
$(C_6H_5CH_2)_2NCN$	C_6H_5MgBr	$(C_6H_5CH_2)_2NC(=NH \cdot HCl)C_6H_5$ (70%)	*150*
$(C_6H_5CH_2)_2NCN$	$4\text{-}CH_3C_6H_4MgBr$	$(C_6H_5CH_2)_2NC(=NH \cdot HCl)C_6H_4\text{-}4\text{-}CH_3$ (70%)	*150*
$C_{15}H_{29}N$			
$n\text{-}C_{14}H_{29}CN$ (493 g.)	CH_3MgBr (285 g. CH_3Br)	$n\text{-}C_{14}H_{29}COCH_3$ (40%)	*141*
$n\text{-}C_{14}H_{29}CN$	C_2H_5MgX	$n\text{-}C_{14}H_{29}COC_2H_5$ (*ca.* 65%)	*20*
$n\text{-}C_{14}H_{29}CN$	$n\text{-}C_3H_7MgX$	$n\text{-}C_{14}H_{29}CO\text{-}n\text{-}C_3H_7$ (*ca.* 65%)	*20*
$C_{16}H_{10}N_2$			
2-Phenyl-4-cyanoquinoline	C_2H_5MgBr	2-Phenyl-4-propionylquinoline	*151*
2-Phenyl-4-cyanoquinoline	C_6H_5MgBr	2-Phenyl-4-benziminoquinoline	*152*
2-Phenyl-4-cyanoquinoline	$C_6H_5CH_2MgCl$	2-Phenyl-4-α-toluylquinoline	*151*
$C_{16}H_{13}NO$			
$4\text{-}CH_3OC_6H_4CH=C(C_6H_5)CN$ (58.7 g.)	C_2H_5MgBr (0.35 mole) (+ C_2H_5I)	$4\text{-}CH_3OC_6H_4CH(C_2H_5)C(C_2H_5)(C_6H_5)CN$ (43.7 g.); liquid isomer	*149*

TABLE X-I (Continued)

Cyano Comp'd	RMgX	Product(s)	Ref.
$C_{16}H_{14}N_2$			
9-Cyano-9,10-dimethyl-9,10-dihydroacridine	CH_3MgI (2 equiv.)	9,9,10-Trimethyl-9,10-dihydroacridine	*98*
$C_{16}H_{15}N$			
2-$[C_6H_5(CH_3)_2C]C_6H_4CN$ (5.0 g.)	C_6H_5MgBr (14.2 g. C_6H_5Br)	2-$[C_6H_5(CH_3)_2C]C_6H_4C(=NH \cdot HCl)C_6H_5$ (4.55 g., 60%)	*115*
$C_{16}H_{28}N_2$			
$[-(CH_2)_7CH]_7$	C_2H_5MgBr (excess)	$[-(CH_2)_7COC_2H_5]_2$ (85%)	*132*
$C_{16}H_{31}N$			
n-$C_{15}H_{31}CN$	CH_3MgX	n-$C_{15}H_{31}COCH_3$ (*ca.* 65%)	*20*
n-$C_{15}H_{31}CN$	C_2H_5MgX	n-$C_{15}H_{31}COC_2H_5$ (*ca.* 65%)	*20*
n-$C_{15}H_{31}CN$	n-C_4H_9MgBr (sl. excess)	n-$C_{15}H_{31}CO$-n-C_4H_9	*134*
n-$C_{15}H_{31}CN$ (1.5–2 moles)	C_6H_5MgBr (sl. excess)	n-$C_{15}H_{31}COC_6H_5$ (75–90%)*	*163*
$C_{17}H_9N$			
4-Cyanofluoranthene	CH_3MgI	4-Acetylfluoranthene	*156*
$C_{17}H_{14}N_2$			
$(C_6H_5CH_2)_2C(CN)_2$ (7.0 g.)	C_6H_5MgBr (3.5 g. Mg)	$(C_6H_5CH_2)_2CHCN$ (5.1 g., 80%); $(C_6H_5)_2C=NH$ (isolated as benzophenone)	*17*
$(C_6H_5CH_2)_2C(CN)_2$ (7.0 g.)	C_6H_5MgBr (3.5 g. Mg)	$(C_6H_5CH_2)_2CHCOC_6H_5$ (3.1 g.); $(C_6H_5)_2CO$	*17*

* Range of yields claimed for series of nitriles investigated.

TABLE X-I (Continued)

Cyano Comp'd	RMgX	Product(s)	Ref.
$C_{17}H_{15}NO_2$			
$4\text{-}CH_3OC_6H_4CH{=}C(C_6H_4\text{-}4\text{-}OCH_3)CN$ (26.5 g.)	C_2H_5MgBr (0.2 mole)	$4\text{-}CH_3OC_6H_4CH(C_2H_5)C(C_2H_5)(C_6H_4\text{-}4\text{-}OCH_3)CN$ (11.4 g.); liquid isomer	*149*
$C_{17}H_{17}N$			
$C_2H_5(C_6H_5)CHCH(C_6H_5)CN$ (m. (m. 115°)	CH_3MgI	$C_2H_5CH(C_6H_5)CH(C_6H_5)COCH_3$ (two isomers; m. 56°, m. 116°)	*100*
$C_2H_5(C_6H_5)CHCH(C_6H_5)CN$ (either isomer)	C_6H_5MgBr	$C_2H_5CH(C_6H_5)CH(C_6H_5)COC_6H_5$ (two isomers; m. 92°, m. 170°)	*100*
$i\text{-}C_3H_7(C_6H_5)_2CCN$	C_6H_5MgBr	$i\text{-}C_3H_7(C_6H_5)_2CCOC_6H_5$	*65*
$i\text{-}C_3H_7(C_6H_5)_2CCN$	C_6H_5MgBr (3 equiv.) (+ HBr)	$i\text{-}C_3H_7(C_6H_5)_2CC({=}NH\cdot HBr)C_6H_5$ (30%)	*66*
$(C_2H_5)(C_6H_5)(C_6H_5CH_2)CCN$	C_6H_5MgBr	$(C_2H_5)(C_6H_5)(C_6H_5CH_2)CCOC_6H_5$	*65*
$C_2H_5(C_6H_5)(C_6H_5CH_2)CCN$	C_6H_5MgBr (1.25 equiv.) (+ HBr)	$C_2H_5(C_6H_5)(C_6H_5CH_2)CC({=}NH\cdot HBr)C_6H_5$ (65–70%)	*66*
$C_{18}H_{13}NO$			
$2\text{-}\beta\text{-}C_{10}H_7\text{-}3\text{-}CH_3OC_6H_3CN$ (13 g.)	CH_3MgI	$2\text{-}\beta\text{-}C_{10}H_7\text{-}3\text{-}CH_3OC_6H_3COCH_3$ (3.5 g.)	*101*
$C_{18}H_{14}N_2$			
α-Truxillic acid dinitrile	C_6H_5MgBr	α- and γ-1,3-Diphenyl-2,4-dibenzoylcyclobutane	*169*
δ-Truxinic acid dinitrile	C_6H_5MgBr	δ-1,2-Diphenyl-3,4-dibenzoylcyclobutane	*169*
Epitruxillic acid dinitrile	C_6H_5MgBr	No appreciable reaction	*169*
Neotruxillic acid dinitrile	C_6H_5MgBr	No appreciable reaction	*169*
$C_{18}H_{17}NO$			
$2,3,5,6\text{-}(CH_3)_4C_6HCOC_6H_4\text{-}2\text{-}CN$ (2.6 g.)	CH_3MgI (7.1 g. CH_3I)	1,1-Dimethyl-3-durylpseudoïsoïndole (2.6 g., 83%)	*193*

TABLE X-I (Continued)

Cyano Comp'd	RMgX	Product(s)	Ref.
$C_{18}H_{17}NO$ (*cont.*)			
2,3,5,6-$(CH_3)_4C_6HCOC_6H_4$-2-CN (7.9 g.)	$H_2C{=}CHCH_2MgBr$ (0.15 mole)	1,1-Diallyl-3-durylpseudoïsoïndole (7.5 g., 76%)	*193*
2,3,5,6-$(CH_3)_4C_6HCOC_6H_4$-2-CN (2.6 g.)	C_6H_5MgBr (15.7 g. C_6H_5Br)	1,1-Diphenyl-3-durylpseudoïsoïndole (2.1 g., 51%)	*193*
2,3,5,6-$(CH_3)_4C_6HCOC_6H_4$-2-CN (5.2 g.)	4-$CH_3C_6H_4MgBr$ (17.0 g. C_7H_7Br)	1,1-Di-*p*-tolyl-3-durylpseudoïsoïndole (2.6 g., 31%)	*193*
2,3,5,6-$(CH_3)_4C_6HCOC_6H_4$-2-CN (7.9 g.)	4-$CH_3OC_6H_4MgBr$ (28.0 g. C_7H_7BrO)	1,1-Di-*p*-anisyl-3-durylpseudoïsoïndole (5.0 g., 36%)	*193*
2,3,5,6-$(CH_3)_4C_6HCOC_6H_4$-2-CN (7.9 g.)	1-$C_{10}H_7MgBr$ (20.7 g. $C_{10}H_7Br$)	1,1-Di-α-naphthyl-3-durylpseudoïsoïndole (9.3 g., 65%)	*193*
2,3,5,6-$(CH_3)_4C_6HCOC_6H_4$-3-CN (1.3 g.)	*s*-C_4H_9MgBr (3.4 g. C_4H_9Br)	2,3,5,6-$(CH_3)_4C_6HCOC_6H_4$-3-CO-*s*-C_4H_9 (0.5 g., 31%)	*193*
2,3,5,6-$(CH_3)_4C_6HCOC_6H_4$-3-CN (1.3 g.)	$C_6H_5CH_2MgCl$ (3.2 g. C_7H_7Cl)	2,3,5,6-$(CH_3)_4C_6HCOC_6H_4$-3-$COCH_2C_6H_5$ (0.95 g., 53%)	*193*
2,3,5,6-$(CH_3)_4C_6HCOC_6H_4$-4-CN (2.6 g.)	CH_3MgI (7.1 g. CH_3I)	Recovered nitrile (*ca.* 50%); 2,3,5,6-$(CH_3)_4C_6HCOC_6H_4$-4-CH_3 (14%)	*193*
2,3,5,6-$(CH_3)_4C_6HCOC_6H_4$-4-CN (1.3 g.)	$C_6H_5CH_2MgCl$ (3.2 g. C_7H_7Cl)	2,3,5,6-$(CH_3)_4C_6HCOC_6H_4$-4-$CH_2C_6H_5$ (44%)	*193*
2-(1,2,3,4-Tetrahydro-2-naphthyl)-3-methoxybenzonitrile (9.3 g.)	CH_3MgI (8 g. CH_3I)	2-(1,2,3,4-Tetrahydro-2-naphthyl)-3-methoxyacetophenone (5.6 g.)	*101*
$C_{18}H_{17}NO_2$			
4-$CH_3OC_6H_4COCH(C_2H_5)C_6H_4$-4-CN (5 g.)	CH_3MgBr (5 g. Mg)	4-$CH_3OC_6H_3C(OH)(CH_3)CH(C_2H_5)C_6H_4$-4-$COCH_3$ (4 g.)	*154*
$C_{18}H_{20}N_2$			
$(CH_3)_2N(CH_2)_2C(C_6H_5)_2CN$	CH_3MgX	$(CH_3)_2N(CH_2)_2C(C_6H_5)_2COCH_3$	*160*
$(CH_3)_2N(CH_2)_2C(C_6H_5)_2CN$	C_2H_5MgBr	$(CH_3)_2N(CH_2)_2C(C_6H_5)_2COC_2H_5$ (78%)	*160,158*

TABLE X-I (Continued)

Cyano Comp'd	RMgX	Product(s)	Ref.
$C_{18}H_{20}N_2$ (*cont.*)			
D- or L-$(CH_3)_2N(CH_2)_2C(C_6H_5)_2CN$	C_2H_5MgBr	D- or L-$(CH_3)_2N(CH_2)_2C(C_6H_5)_2COC_2H_5$	*169*
$(CH_3)_2N(CH_2)_2C(C_6H_5)_2CN$	n-C_3H_7MgI	$(CH_3)_2N(CH_2)_2C(C_6H_5)_2CO$-$n$-$C_3H_7$	*158*
$(CH_3)_2N(CH_2)_2C(C_6H_5)_2CN$	i-C_3H_7MgBr	$(CH_3)_2N(CH_2)_2C(C_6H_5)_2CO$-$i$-$C_3H_7$	*158*
$(CH_3)_2N(CH_2)_2C(C_6H_5)_2$	C_6H_5MgX	$(CH_3)_2N(CH_2)_2C(C_6H_5)_2COC_6H_5$ (89%)	*160*
$C_{18}H_{35}N$			
n-$C_{17}H_{35}CN$ (1.5–2 moles)	C_6H_5MgBr (sl. excess)	n-$C_{17}H_{35}COC_6H_5$ (75–90%)*	*163*
n-$C_{17}H_{35}CN$ (530 g.)	$C_6H_5CH_2CH_2MgBr$ (420 g. C_8H_9Br)	n-$C_{17}H_{35}COCH_2CH_2C_6H_5$ (394 g., 53%)	*153*
n-$C_{17}H_{35}CN$ (531 g.)	$(CH_2)_4CH(CH_2)_3MgBr$ (440 g. $C_8H_{15}Br$)	n-$C_{17}H_{35}CO(CH_2)_3CH(CH_2)_4$ (371 g., 49%)	*153*
n-$C_{17}H_{35}CN$ (755.5 g.)	n-$C_8H_{17}MgBr$ (772 g. $C_8H_{17}Br$)	n-$C_{17}H_{35}CO$-n-C_8H_{17} (920 g., 69%)	*153*
$C_{19}H_{21}N$			
$C_2H_5(C_6H_5)CHC(C_2H_5)(C_6H_5)CN$	CH_3MgI	Recovered nitrile	*100*
$C_2H_5(C_6H_5)CHC(C_2H_5)(C_6H_5)CN$	C_6H_5MgBr	Recovered nitrile	*100*
$C_{19}H_{22}N_2$			
$(CH_3)_2NCH(CH_3)CH_2C(C_6H_5)_2CN$ (5 g.)	CH_3MgI (7.7 g. CH_3I)	$(CH_3)_2NCH(CH_3)CH_2C(C_6H_5)_2COCH_3$	*158*
(–)-$(CH_3)_2NCH(CH_3)CH_2C(C_6H_5)_2CN$	C_2H_5MgBr	(–)-$(CH_3)_2NCH(CH_3)CH_2C(C_6H_5)_2COC_2H_5$	*158*
$(CH_3)_2NCH(CH_3)CH_2C(C_6H_5)_2CN$	C_2H_5MgBr	$(CH_3)_2NCH(CH_3)CH_2C(C_6H_5)_2C(=NH)C_2H_5$	*170,171,172*
$(CH_3)_2NCH(CH_3)CH_2C(C_6H_5)_2CN$ (11.1 g.)	C_2H_5MgI (12.5 g. C_2H_5I)	$(CH_3)_2NCH(CH_3)CH_2C(C_6H_5)_2COC_2H_5$ (83%)	*161*
$(CH_3)_2NCH(CH_3)CH_2C(C_6H_5)_2CN$	n-C_3H_7MgI	$(CH_3)_2NCH(CH_3)CH_2C(C_6H_5)_2CO$-$n$-$C_3H_7$	*158*
$(CH_3)_2NCH(CH_3)CH_2C(C_6H_5)_2CN$	i-C_3H_7MgBr	$(CH_3)_2NCH(CH_3)CH_2C(C_6H_5)_2CO$-$i$-$C_3H_7$	*158*

* Range of yields claimed for series of nitriles investigated.

TABLE X-I (Continued)

Cyano Comp'd	RMgX	Product(s)	Ref.
$C_{19}H_{22}N_2$ (*cont.*)			
$(CH_3)_2NCH(CH_3)CH_2C(C_6H_5)_2CN$	n-C_4H_9MgI	$(CH_3)_2NCH(CH_3)CH_2C(C_6H_5)_2CO$-$n$-$C_4H_9$	*158*
$(CH_3)_2NCH(CH_3)CH_2C(C_6H_5)_2CN$	C_6H_5MgBr	$(CH_3)_2NCH(CH_3)CH_2C(C_6H_5)_2COC_6H_5$	*158*
$(CH_3)_2NCH(CH_3)CH_2C(C_6H_5)_2CN$	$C_6H_5CH_2MgBr$	$(CH_3)_2NCH(CH_3)CH_2C(C_6H_5)_2COCH_2C_6H_5$	*158*
$(CH_3)_2NCH_2CH(CH_3)C(C_6H_5)_2CN$ (150 g.)	C_2H_5MgBr (132 g. C_2H_5Br)	$(CH_3)_2NCH_2CH(CH_3)C(C_6H_5)_2C(=NH)C_2H_5$ (147 g., crude)	*158,170, 171,172*
$(CH_3)_2NCH_2CH(CH_3)C(C_6H_5)_2CN$ (16.6 g.)	n-C_3H_7MgBr	$HCl \cdot (CH_3)_2NCH_2CH(CH_3)C(C_6H_5)_2CO$-$n$-$C_3H_7$ (3.75 g.)	*158*
$(CH_3)_2NCH_2CH(CH_3)C(C_6H_5)_2CN$	i-C_3H_7MgBr (5 equiv.)	$(CH_3)_2NCH_2CH(CH_3)C(C_6H_5)_2CO$-$i$-$C_3H_7$	*158*
$(CH_3)_2N(CH_2)_3C(C_6H_5)_2CN$ (20 g.)	C_2H_5MgBr (22 g. C_2H_5Br)	$(CH_3)_2N(CH_2)_3C(C_6H_5)_2C(=NH)C_2H_5$	*170*
$C_{20}H_{15}N$			
$(C_6H_5)_3CCN$	$C_6H_5CH_2MgCl$ (4 equiv.)	$(C_6H_5)_3CH$ (70%); $(C_6H_5CH_2-)_2$	*66*
$C_{20}H_{22}N_2$			
$(CH_2)_4N(CH_2)_2C(C_6H_5)_2CN$	C_2H_5MgX	$(CH_2)_4N(CH_2)_2C(C_6H_5)_2CN$ (68%)	*160*
$C_{20}H_{22}N_2O$			
2,2-Diphenyl-4-(4-morpholinyl)butyronitrile	C_2H_5MgX	4,4-Diphenyl-6-(4-morpholinyl)-3-hexanone	*160*
$C_{20}H_{23}NO_2$			
4-$CH_3OC_6H_4C(OH)(C_2H_5)$-$CH(C_2H_5)C_6H_4$-4-CN (5 g.)	CH_3MgBr (2.5 g. Mg)	4-$CH_3OC_6H_4C(OH)(C_2H_5)CH(C_2H_5)C_6H_4$-4-$COCH_3$ (4.5 g.)	*154*
$C_{20}H_{24}N_2$			
$(CH_3)_2NCH(C_2H_5)CH_2C(C_6H_5)_2CN$	$C^{14}H_3CH_2MgBr$	$(CH_3)_2NCH(C_2H_5)CH_2C(C_6H_5)_2COCH_2C^{14}H_3$	*159*
$(CH_3)_2NCH(C_2H_5)CH_2C(C_6H_5)_2CN$	$CH_3C^{14}H_2MgBr$	$(CH_3)_2NCH(C_2H_5)CH_2C(C_6H_5)_2C^{14}CH_2CH_3$	*159*
$(C_2H_5)_2N(CH_2)_2C(C_6H_5)_2CN$	C_2H_5MgX	$(C_2H_5)_2N(CH_2)_2C(C_6H_5)_2COCH_3$	*160*

TABLE X-I (Continued)

Cyano Comp'd	RMgX	Product(s)	Ref.
$C_{21}H_{17}N$			
$(C_6H_5)_3CCH_2CN$ (28.3 g.)	CH_3MgI (71.0 g. CH_3I)	$CH_3[(C_6H_5)_3CCH_2]C{=}NH \cdot HCl$ (20.5 g.)	*155*
$(C_6H_5)_3CCH_2CN$ (28.3 g.)	C_2H_5MgBr (65.4 g. C_2H_5Br)	$C_2H_5[(C_6H_5)_3CCH_2]C{=}NH \cdot HCl$ (30.9 g., 88%)	*155*
$(C_6H_5)_3CCH_2CN$ (14.0 g.)	C_6H_5MgBr (39.2 g. C_6H_5Br)	$C_6H_5[(C_6H_5)_3CCH_2]C{=}NH \cdot HCl$ (12.8 g., 70%)	*155*
$C_6H_5CH_2(C_6H_5)_2CCN$	C_6H_5MgBr	Recovered nitrile (quant.)	*65*
$C_6H_5CH_2(C_6H_5)_2CCN$	$C_6H_5CH_2MgCl$ (3–5 equiv.)	$C_6H_5CH_2(C_6H_5)_2CH$	*66*
$C_{21}H_{23}NO_2$			
3-Acetoxy-17-cyano-1,3,5,16-estratetraëne	CH_3MgBr (excess)	3-Hydroxy-17-acetyl-1,3,5,16-estratetraëne	*173*
$C_{21}H_{24}N_2$			
$(CH_2)_5NCH_2CH_2C(C_6H_5)_2CN$	CH_3MgI	$(CH_2)_5NCH_2CH_2C(C_6H_5)_2COCH_3$	*158*
$(CH_2)_5NCH_2CH_2C(C_6H_5)_2CN$	C_2H_5MgX	$(CH_2)_5NCH_2CH_2C(C_6H_5)_2COC_2H_5$ (74%)	*160,158*
$(CH_2)_5NCH_2CH_2C(C_6H_5)_2CN$	n-C_3H_7MgI	$(CH_2)_5NCH_2CH_2C(C_6H_5)_2CO$-$n$-$C_3H_7$	*158*
$(CH_2)_5NCH_2CH_2C(C_6H_5)_2CN$	C_6H_5MgBr	$(CH_2)_5NCH_2CH_2C(C_6H_5)_2COC_6H_5$	*158*
2,2-Diphenyl-4-(2-methyl-4-morpholinyl)butyronitrile)	C_2H_5MgX	4,4-Diphenyl-6-(2-methyl-4-morpholinyl)-3-hexanone (65%)	*160*
2-Phenyl-2-*o*-tolyl-4-(4-morpholinyl)butyronitrile	C_2H_5MgX	4-Phenyl-4-*o*-tolyl-6-(4-morpholinyl)-3-hexanone	*160*
2-Phenyl-2-*p*-tolyl-4-(4-morpholinyl)butyronitrile	C_2H_5MgX	4-Phenyl-4-*p*-tolyl-6-(4-morpholinyl)-3-hexanone (61%)	*160*
2,2-Diphenyl-5-(4-morpholinyl)valeronitrile	C_2H_5MgX	4,4-Diphenyl-7-(4-morpholinyl)-3-heptanone (74%)	*160*

TABLE X-I (Continued)

Cyano Comp'd	RMgX	Product(s)	Ref.
$C_{21}H_{24}N_2O$			
2,2-Diphenyl-4-(4-morpholinyl)valeronitrile	C_2H_5MgI	4,4-Diphenyl-6-(4-morpholinyl)-3-heptanone (73%)	*161,210*
2,2-Diphenyl-3-methyl-4-(4-morpholinyl)butyronitrile (3.2 g.)	C_2H_5MgI (3.2 g. C_2H_5I)	3-Imino-4,4-diphenyl-6-(4-morpholinyl)-5-methylhexane (3.36 g., crude)	*161*
$C_{21}H_{26}N_2$			
$(C_2H_5)_2N(CH_2)_3C(C_6H_5)_2CN$	C_2H_5MgX	$(C_2H_5)_2N(CH_2)_3C(C_6H_5)_2COC_2H_5$ (82%)	*106*
$C_{22}H_{26}N_2$			
2,2-Diphenyl-4-(2-methyl-1-piperidyl)butyronitrile	C_2H_5MgX	4,4-Diphenyl-6-(2-methyl-1-piperidyl)-3-hexanone (60%)	*160*
2,2-Diphenyl-4-(3-methyl-1-piperidyl)butyronitrile	C_2H_5MgX	4,4-Diphenyl-6-(3-methyl-1-piperidyl)-3-hexanone (60%)	*160*
2,2-Diphenyl-4-(4-methyl-1-piperidyl)butyronitrile	C_2H_5MgX	4,4-Diphenyl-6-(4-methyl-1-piperidyl)-3-hexanone (53%)	*160*
$C_{22}H_{26}N_2O$			
2,2-Diphenyl-4-(2,6-dimethyl-4-morpholinyl)butyronitrile	C_2H_5MgX	4,4-Diphenyl-6-(2,6-dimethyl-4-morpholinyl)-3-hexanone (32%)	*160*
2,2-Diphenyl-6-(4-morpholinyl)capronitrile	C_2H_5MgX	4,4-Diphenyl-8-(4-morpholinyl)-3-octanone (79%)	*160*
$C_{22}H_{28}N_2$			
$(n\text{-}C_3H_7)_2N(CH_2)_2C(C_6H_5)_2CN$	C_2H_5MgX	$(n\text{-}C_3H_7)_2N(CH_2)_2C(C_6H_5)_2COC_2H_5$ (65%)	*160*
$C_{22}H_{29}NO_2$			
3-Acetoxy-17-cyano-5,16-androstadiene (1.8 g.)	CH_3MgBr* (5 g. Mg)	5,16-Pregnadien-3-ol-20-one (1.26 g., 75%)	*139*

* CH_3MgI gives poorer yields. Forty-eight hours reflux.

TABLE X-I (Continued)

Cyano Comp'd	RMgX	Product(s)	Ref.
$C_{22}H_{29}NO_2$ (*cont.*)			
3-Acetoxy-17-cyano-5,16-androstadiene*	CH_3MgBr	17-Cyano-5,16-androstadien-3-ol	*139*
$C_{22}H_{31}NO_2$			
3-Acetoxy-17-cyano-16-androstene (900 mg.)	CH_3MgBr (2.5 g. Mg)	*epi-allo*-16-Pregnen-3-ol-20-one (450 mg.)	*157*
$C_{23}H_{28}N_2$			
2,2-Diphenyl-4-(2,6-dimethyl-1-piperidyl)butyronitrile	C_2H_5MgX	4,4-Diphenyl-6-(2,6-dimethyl-1-piperidyl)-3-hexanone (69%)	*160*
$C_{24}H_{16}N_2$			
2,4,6-Triphenyl-3-cyanopyridine (11.6 g., 0.035 mole)	C_6H_5MgBr (0.25 mole)	2,4,6-Triphenyl-3-phenylketiminopyridine (72%)	*216*
$C_{24}H_{24}N_2$			
$CH_3(C_6H_5CH_2)N(CH_2)_2C(C_6H_5)_2CN$	C_2H_5MgX	$CH_3(C_6H_5CH_2)N(CH_2)_2C(C_6H_5)_2CN$ (60%)	*160*
$C_{24}H_{32}N_2$			
$(n\text{-}C_4H_9)_2N(CH_2)_2C(C_6H_5)_2CN$	C_2H_5MgX	$(n\text{-}C_4H_9)_2N(CH_2)_2C(C_6H_5)_2COC_2H_5$ (70%)	*160*
$C_{28}H_{28}N_2$			
$(C_6H_5CH_2)_2N(CH_2)_2C(C_6H_5)_2CN$	C_2H_5MgX	$(C_6H_5CH_2)_2N(CH_2)_2C(C_6H_5)_2COC_2H_5$ (54%)	*160*

* Short reaction time.

REFERENCES FOR TABLE X-I

(*1*) Blaise, *Compt. rend.*, *132*, 38–41 (1901); *Chem. Zentr.*, *1901,I*, 298.
(*2*) Mousseron and Winternitz, *Compt. rend.*, *217*, 428–30 (1943); *Chem. Abstr.*, *39*, 2054 (1945).
(*3*) Mathus, *Bull. soc. chim. Belg.*, *34*, 285–9 (1925).
(*4*) Tröger and Beck, *J. prakt. Chem.*, [2], *87*, 289–311 (1913).
(*5*) von Braun, Deutsch, and Schmatloch, *Ber.*, *45*, 1246–63 (1912).
(*6*) Bruylants, *Bull. acad. roy. Belg.*, [5], 8, 7–23 (1922); *Chem. Zentr.*, *1923,I*, 85.
(*7*) Mignonac and Hoffman, *Compt. rend.*, *191*, 718–20 (1930).
(*8*) Bary, *Bull. soc. chim. Belg.*, *31*, 397–410 (1922).
(*9*) Shriner and Turner, *J. Am. Chem. Soc.*, *52*, 1267–9 (1930).
(*10*) Whitmore and Sloat, *J. Am. Chem. Soc.*, *64*, 2968–70 (1942).
(*11*) Majima and Hoshino, *Ber.*, *58B*, 2042–6 (1925).
(*12*) Lipp and Quaedvlieg, *Ber.*, *62B*, 2311–22 (1929).
(*13*) Mousseron, Winternitz, Jullien, and Jacquier, *Bull. soc. chim.*, [5], *15*, 79–84 (1948).
(*14*) Challenger, Clapham, and Emmott, *J. Inst. Petroleum*, *34*, 922–9 (1948); *Chem. Abstr.*, *43*, 4666 (1949).
(*15*) Cauquil and Barrera, *Compt. rend.*, *226*, 1282–3 (1948); *Chem. Abstr.*, *42*, 5888 (1948).
(*16*) Yarnall and Wallis, *J. Org. Chem.*, *4*, 284–8 (1939).
(*17*) Erickson and Barnett, *J. Am. Chem. Soc.*, *57*, 560–2 (1935).
(*18*) Thomson and Stevens, *J. Chem. Soc.*, *1932*, 2607–12.
(*19*) Baerts, *Bull. soc. chim. Belg.*, *31*, 184–92 (1922).
(*20*) Oldham and Ubbelohde, *J. Chem. Soc.*, *1939*, 201–2.
(*21*) Gauthier, *Ann. chim.*, [8], *16*, 289–358 (1909).
(*22*) Allen and Henze, *J. Am. Chem. Soc.*, *61*, 1790–4 (1939).
(*23*) Paul, *Bull. soc. chim.*, [4], *45*, 152–4 (1929).
(*24*) Gauthier, *Compt. rend.*, *152*, 1100–2 (1911); *Chem. Zentr.*, *1911,I*, 1809.
(*25*) Vuylsteke, *Bull. acad. roy. Belg.*, [5], *12*, 535–44 (1926); *Chem. Zentr.*, *1927,I*, 888; *Chem. Abstr.*, *21*, 1108 (1927).
(*26*) Bruylants and Gevaerts, *Bull. acad. roy. Belg.*, [5], 9, 27–37 (1923); *Chem. Zentr.*, *1923,III*, 1263.
(*27*) Bruylants and Mathus, *Bull. acad. roy. Belg.*, [5], *11*, 636–53 (1925); *Chem. Zentr.*, *1926,I*, 3145.
(*28*) Bruylants, *Bull. acad. roy. Belg.*, *1908*, 1011–84; *Chem. Zentr.*, *1909,I*, 1859.
(*29*) Bruylants, *Bull. soc. chim. Belg.*, *36*, 519–32 (1927).
(*30*) Michiels, *Bull. acad. roy. Belg.*, *1912*, 10–34; *Chem. Zentr.*, *1912,I*, 1105.
(*31*) Lipp, Buchkremer, and Seeles, *Ann.*, *499*, 1–25 (1932).
(*32*) Cloke, *J. Am. Chem. Soc.*, *51*, 1174–87 (1929).
(*33*) Cloke, Baer, Robbins, and Smith, *J. Am. Chem. Soc.*, *67*, 2155–8 (1945).
(*34*) Lachmann, Dissertation, Rensselaer Pol. Inst., as cited by Cloke *et al.* (*33*), f'tnote, p. 2156.
(*35*) Bruylants, *Bull. acad. roy. Belg.*, [5], *10*, 392–5 (1924); *Chem. Zentr.*, *1924,II*, 2457.
(*36*) McKenzie and Duff, *Ber.*, *60B*, 1335–41 (1927).
(*37*) de Boosere, *Bull. soc. chim. Belg.*, *32*, 26–51 (1923).
(*38*) Craig, Bulbrook, and Hixon, *J. Am. Chem. Soc.*, *53*, 1831–5 (1931).
(*39*) Starr, Bulbrook, and Hixon, *J. Am. Chem. Soc.*, *54*, 3971–6 (1932).
(*40*) Lipp and Seeles, *Ber.*, *62B*, 2456–8 (1929).
(*41*) Kirchner and Johns, *J. Am. Chem. Soc.*, *62*, 2183–4 (1940).
(*42*) Wallace and Henze, *J. Am. Chem. Soc.*, *64*, 2882 (1942).

(43) Craig, *J. Am. Chem. Soc.*, *56*, 1144–7 (1934).
(44) Baerts, *Bull. soc. chim. Belg.*, *31*, 421–6 (1922).
(45) Blaise, *Compt. rend.*, *133*, 1217–8 (1901); *Chem. Zentr.*, *1902,I*, 299.
(46) Sommelet, *Ann. chim.*, [8], *9*, 484–574 (1906).
(47) Béhal and Sommelet, *Compt. rend.*, *138*, 89–92 (1904); *Chem. Zentr.*, *1904,I*, 504.
(48) Henze, U. S. Patent 2,460,747; *Chem. Abstr.*, *43*, P3452 (1949).
(49) Henze, Allen, and Leslie, *J. Org. Chem.*, *7*, 326–53 (1942).
(50) Lévy and Jullien, *Bull. soc. chim.*, [4], *45*, 941–50 (1929).
(51) Bruylants, *Bull. acad. roy. Belg.*, [5], *7*, 252–9 (1921); *Chem. Zentr.*, *1921,III*, 1349.
(52) Blaise, *Compt. rend.*, *173*, 313–5 (1921).
(53) Bruylants, *Bull. soc. chim. Belg.*, *32*, 307–10 (1923).
(54) Bruylants and Dewael, *Bull. acad. roy. Belg.*, [5], *12*, 464–76 (1926); *Chem. Zentr.*, *1927,I*, 887.
(55) Breckpot, *Bull. soc. chim. Belg.*, *32*, 386–97 (1923).
(56) Asahina and Murayama, *Arch. Pharm.*, *252*, 435–48 (1914); *Chem. Zentr.*, *1914,II*, 1196.
(57) Lemaire, *Rec. trav. chim.*, *29*, 22–84 (1910); *Bull. acad. roy. Belg.*, *1909*, 83–159; *Chem. Abstr.*, *4*, 1483 (1910).
(58) Mukherjee, *J. Indian Chem. Soc.*, *25*, 155–64 (1948); *Chem. Abstr.*, *43*, 2605 (1949).
(59) Hauser, Humphlett, and Weiss, *J. Am. Chem. Soc.*, *70*, 426 (1948).
(60) Hauser and Humphlett, *J. Org. Chem.*, *15*, 359–66 (1950).
(61) Blaise, *Compt. rend.*, *132*, 978–80 (1901); *Chem. Zentr.*, *1901,I*, 1195.
(62) Mavrodin, *Compt. rend.*, *188*, 1504–6 (1929).
(63) Theunis, *Bull. acad. roy. Belg.*, [5], *12*, 785–96 (1926); *Chem. Zentr.*, *1927,I*, 889.
(64) Bourgom, *Bull. soc. chim. Belg.*, *33*, 101–15 (1924).
(65) Ramart-Lucas and Salmon-Legagneur, *Compt. rend.*, *184*, 102–4 (1927).
(66) Ramart-Lucas and Salmon-Legagneur, *Bull. soc. chim.*, [4], *43*, 321–9 (1928).
(67) Asahina and Terasaka, *J. Pharm. Soc. Japan*, *1923*, No. 494, 19–21; *Chem. Zentr.*, *1923,III*, 434.
(68) Breckpot, *Bull. soc. chim. Belg.*, *33*, 490–4 (1924).
(69) Guerden, *Bull. acad. roy. Belg.*, [5], *11*, 701–10 (1925); *Chem. Zentr.*, *1926,I*, 3146.
(70) Velghe, *Bull. acad. roy. Belg.*, [5], *11*, 301–8 (1925); *Chem. Zentr.*, *1926,I*, 875.
(71) Bachmann, *J. Am. Chem. Soc.*, *54*, 1969–74 (1932).
(72) Fieser and Seligman, *J. Am. Chem. Soc.*, *61*, 136–42 (1939).
(73) Ectors, *Bull. soc. chim. Belg.*, *33*, 146–59 (1924).
(74) Ectors, *Bull. acad. roy. Belg.*, [5], *9*, 501–18 (1923); *Chem. Zentr.*, *1924,I*, 913.
(75) Moureu and Mignonac, *Ann. chim.*, [9], *14*, 322–59 (1920).
(76) Moureu and Mignonac, *Compt. rend.*, *156*, 1801–6 (1913); *Chem. Zentr.*, *1913,II*, 497.
(77) Ectors, *Bull. acad. roy. Belg.*, [5], *10*, 347–52 (1924); *Chem. Zentr.*, *1924,II*, 2463.
(78) Gilman, St. John, St. John, and Lichtenwalter, *Rec. trav. chim.*, *55*, 577–85 (1936).
(79) Bachmann, *J. Am. Chem. Soc.*, *56*, 1363–7 (1934).
(80) Roger and McKay, *J. Chem. Soc.*, *1933*, 332–6.
(81) Newman and McCleary, *J. Am. Chem. Soc.*, *63*, 1537–41 (1941).

(*82*) Busch and Hobein, *Ber.*, *40*, 4296–9 (1907).
(*83*) Bruylants, *Bull. acad. roy. Belg.*, [5], *11*, 261–80 (1925); *Chem. Zentr.*, *1926,I*, 874.
(*84*) Weiss and Schlesinger, *Monatsh.*, *48*, 451–7 (1927).
(*85*) Weiss and Freund, *Monatsh.*, *45*, 105–14 (1924).
(*86*) de Coster, *Bull. acad. roy. Belg.*, [5], *11*, 661–5 (1925).
(*87*) Adams, Bramlet, and Tendick, *J. Am. Chem. Soc.*, *42*, 2369–74 (1920).
(*88*) Smith, *Ber.*, *71B*, 634–43 (1938).
(*89*) Stevens, *J. Am. Chem. Soc.*, *61*, 1714–6 (1939).
(*90*) Rondou, *Bull. soc. chim. Belg.*, *31*, 231–41 (1922).
(*91*) Jaspers, *Bull. soc. chim. Belg.*, *34*, 182–7 (1925).
(*92*) Turner, *J. Chem. Soc.*, *107*, 1459–64 (1915).
(*93*) Bachmann and Ferguson, *J. Am. Chem. Soc.*, *56*, 2081–4 (1934).
(*94*) Bailar, *J. Am. Chem. Soc.*, *52*, 3596–603 (1930).
(*95*) Gilman and Lichtenwalter, *Rec. trav. chim.*, *55*, 561–3 (1936).
(*96*) Smith, *Ber.*, *64B*, 427–34 (1931).
(*97*) Tiffeneau and Lévy, *Bull. soc. chim.*, [4], *33*, 735–59 (1923).
(*98*) Stevens, Cowan, and MacKinnon, *J. Chem. Soc.*, *1931*, 2568–72.
(*99*) Mavrodin, *Compt. rend.*, *191*, 1064–6 (1930).
(*100*) Kohler, *Am. Chem. J.*, *35*, 386–404 (1906).
(*101*) Richtzenhain and Miedreich, *Chem. Ber.*, *81*, 92–7 (1948).
(*102*) Rehberg and Henze, *J. Am. Chem. Soc.*, *63*, 2785–9 (1941).
(*103*) Mavrodin, *Bul. soc. chim. România*, *15*, 99–106 (1933); *Chem. Abstr.*, *28*, 3396 (1934).
(*104*) Ruggli and Businger, *Helv. Chim. Acta*, *24*, 1112–26 (1941).
(*105*) Haller, *J. Am. Chem. Soc.*, *55*, 3032–5 (1933).
(*106*) Haller and Schaffer, *J. Am. Chem. Soc.*, *61*, 2175–7 (1939).
(*107*) Pfeiffer and Simons, *J. prakt. Chem.*, [2], *160*, 83–94 (1942).
(*108*) Fuson, Ullyot, Stedman, and Tawney, *J. Am. Chem. Soc.*, *60*, 1447–50 (1938).
(*109*) Mavrodin, *Compt. rend.*, *192*, 363–5 (1931).
(*110*) Kaufmann, Peyer, and Kunkler, *Ber.*, *45*, 3090–8 (1912).
(*111*) Rabe and Pasternack, *Ber.*, *46*, 1026–32 (1932).
(*112*) Kaufman, Dandliker, and Burkhardt, *Ber.*, *46*, 2929–35 (1913).
(*113*) Padbury and Lindwall, *J. Am. Chem. Soc.*, *67*, 1268–70 (1945).
(*114*) Sabetay, *Bull. soc. chim.*, [4], *45*, 534–40 (1929).
(*115*) Bradsher and Smith, *J. Am. Chem. Soc.*, *65*, 1643–5 (1943).
(*116*) Cagniant and Deluzarche, *Compt. rend.*, *223*, 677–9 (1946); *Chem. Abstr.*, *41*, 1669 (1947).
(*117*) Newman and Orchin, *J. Am. Chem. Soc.*, *60*, 586–9 (1938).
(*118*) Newman and Wise, *J. Am. Chem. Soc.*, *63*, 2109–11 (1941).
(*119*) Tschitschibabin and Korjagin, *J. Russ. Phys.-Chem. Soc.*, *45*, 1823–9 (1914); *Chem. Abstr.*, 8, 912 (1914); *Chem. Zentr.*, *1914,I*, 1658.
(*120*) Haworth, Mavin, and Sheldrick, *J. Chem. Soc.*, *1934*, 454–61.
(*121*) Newman, *J. Am. Chem. Soc.*, *60*, 1368–70 (1938).
(*122*) Strukow, *Khim. Farm. Prom.*, *1934*, No. 3, 13–14; *Chem. Abstr.*, *29*, 1821 (1935).
(*123*) Murray and Cloke, *J. Am. Chem. Soc.*, *68*, 126–9 (1946).
(*124*) Haworth and Mavin, *J. Chem. Soc.*, *1932*, 2720–3.
(*125*) Plancher and Guimelli, *Atti accad. Lincei*, [5], *18,II*, 393–7 (1910); *Chem. Zentr.*, *1910,I*, 451.
(*126*) Cagniant and Cagniant, *Bull. soc. chim.*, [5], *15*, 1012–4 (1948).
(*127*) Weissberger and Glass, *J. Am. Chem. Soc.*, *64*, 1724–7 (1942).
(*128*) Adams, Harfenist, and Loewe, *J. Am. Chem. Soc.*, *71*, 1624–8 (1949).

(129) Haworth and Sheldrick, *J. Chem. Soc.*, *1934*, 1950–2.
(130) Kaufman, Kunkler, and Peyer, *Ber.*, *46*, 57–64 (1913).
(131) Kohler and Reimer, *Am. Chem. J.*, *33*, 335–56 (1908).
(132) Meyer and Streuch, *Helv. Chim. Acta*, *20*, 1179–83 (1937).
(133) Polgar and Robinson, *J. Chem. Soc.*, *1945*, 389–95.
(134) Whitmore, Sutherland, and Cosby, *J. Am. Chem. Soc.*, *64*, 1360–4 (1942).
(135) Clarkson and Gomberg, *J. Am. Chem. Soc.*, *52*, 2881–91 (1930).
(136) Maxim and Aldea, *Bull. soc. chim.*, [5], *2*, 582–91 (1935).
(137) Kühling and Frank, *Ber.*, *42*, 3952–8 (1909).
(138) Bruce and Todd, *J. Am. Chem. Soc.*, *60*, 1447–50 (1938).
(139) Butenandt and Schmidt-Thomé, *Ber.*, *72B*, 182–7 (1939).
(140) Christiaen, *Bull. soc. chim. Belg.*, *33*, 483–90 (1924).
(141) Asinger and Eckholdt, *Ber.*, *76B*, 579–84 (1943).
(142) Dufraisse and Mathieu, *Bull. soc. chim.*, [5], *14*, 302–6 (1947).
(143) Seidel, *Ber.*, *61B*, 2267–76 (1928).
(144) Cloke and Leary, *J. Am. Chem. Soc.*, *67*, 1249–51 (1945).
(145) MacLeod, *Am. Chem. J.*, *44*, 331–52 (1910).
(146) Vasiliu and Radvan, *Bul. soc. chim. România*, *20A*, 243–50 (1938); *Chem. Abstr.*, *34*, 4058 (1940).
(147) Bachmann, *J. Am. Chem. Soc.*, *57*, 555–9 (1935).
(148) Bachmann, *J. Am. Chem. Soc.*, *57*, 1130–1 (1935).
(149) Wawzonek, *J. Am. Chem. Soc.*, *68*, 1157–9 (1946).
(150) Adams and Beebe, *J. Am. Chem. Soc.*, *38*, 2768–72 (1916).
(151) Feist, Awe, Kuklinski, and Volksen, *Arch. Pharm.*, *276*, 271–9 (1938); *Chem. Abstr.*, *32*, 6651 (1938).
(152) Feist, Awe, and Kuklinski, *Arch. Pharm.*, *276*, 420–31 (1938); *Chem. Abstr.*, *33*, 1327 (1939).
(153) Whitmore, Herr, Clarke, Rowland, and Schiessler, *J. Am. Chem. Soc.*, *67*, 2059–61 (1945).
(154) Jaeger and Robinson, *J. Chem. Soc.*, *1941*, 744–7.
(155) Garner and Hellerman, *J. Am. Chem. Soc.*, *68*, 823–5 (1946).
(156) Campbell and Easton, *J. Chem. Soc.*, *1949*, 340–5.
(157) Butenandt, Mamoli, and Heusner, *Ber.*, *72B*, 1614–7 (1939).
(158) Walton, Ofner, and Thorpe, *J. Chem. Soc.*, *1949*, 648–55.
(159) Tolbert, Christenson, Chang, and Sah, *J. Org. Chem.*, *14*, 525–9 (1949).
(160) Dupré, Elks, Hems, Speyer, and Evans, *J. Chem. Soc.*, *1949*, 500–10.
(161) Attenburrow, Elks, Hems, and Speyer, *J. Chem. Soc.*, *1949*, 510–8.
(162) Bergmann, *J. Org. Chem.*, *4*, 1–13 (1939).
(163) Whitmore, Schiessler, Rowland, and Cosby, *J. Am. Chem. Soc.*, *69*, 235–7 (1947).
(164) Dutta, *Science and Culture*, *7*, 316–7 (1941); *Chem. Abstr.*, *36*, 3156 (1942).
(165) Callen, Dornfeld, and Coleman, *Organic Syntheses*, *28*, 6–8 (1948).
(166) Richtzenhain, *Ber.*, *77B*, 1–6 (1944).
(167) Bachmann and Kloetzel, *J. Org. Chem.*, *3*, 55–61 (1938).
(168) Bergs, Wittfeld, and Wildt, *Ber.*, *67B*, 238–44 (1934).
(169) Thorpe, Walton, and Ofner, *Nature*, *160*, 605–6 (1947).
(170) Easton, Gardner, Evanick, and Stevens, *J. Am. Chem. Soc.*, *70*, 76–8 (1948).
(171) Schultz, Robb, and Sprague, *J. Am. Chem. Soc.*, *69*, 188–9 (1947).
(172) Schultz, Robb, and Sprague, *J. Am. Chem. Soc.*, *69*, 2454–9 (1947).
(173) Velluz and Muller, *Compt. rend.*, *226*, 411 (1948); *Chem. Abstr.*, *42*, 4596 (1948).
(174) Schönberg, *Ber.*, *58B*, 580–6 (1925).

(175) Anderson and Thomas, *J. Am. Chem. Soc.*, *65*, 234–8 (1943).
(176) Buu-Hoï, Nguyen-Hoán, Lecocq, and de Clercq, *Rec. trav. chim.*, *67*, 795–812 (1948).
(177) Biltz, *Ber.*, *60B*, 2413 (1927).
(178) Nekrassov, *Ber.*, *60B*, 1756–8 (1927).
(179) Meyer, *J. prakt. Chem.*, [2], *82*, 521–38 (1910).
(180) Grignard, *Compt. rend.*, *152*, 388–90 (1911); *Chem. Abstr.*, *5*, 1589 (1911).
(181) Grignard and Courtot, *Bull. soc. chim.*, [4], *17*, 228–31 (1915).
(182) Grignard, Bellet, and Courtot, *Ann. chim.*, [9], *4*, 28–57 (1915).
(183) Grignard and Perrichon, *Ann. chim.*, [10], *5*, 5–36 (1925).
(184) Grignard and Courtot, *Compt. rend.*, *158*, 1763–6 (1914); *Chem. Abstr.*, 8, 3436 (1914).
(185) Willemart, *Ann. chim.*, [10], *12*, 345–423 (1929).
(186) Grignard and Kasichi Ono, *Bull. soc. chim.*, [4], *39*, 1589–94 (1926).
(187) Grignard, Bellet, and Courtot, *Ann. chim.*, [9], *12*, 364–93 (1919).
(188) Coleman and Leeper, *Proc. Iowa Acad. Sci.*, *47*, 201–5 (1940); *Chem. Abstr.*, *35*, 7374 (1941).
(189) Ostrogovich, *Chem.-Ztg.*, *36*, 738–9 (1912); *Chem. Abstr.*, 6, 2911 (1912).
(190) Majima, Shigematsu, and Rokkaku, *Ber.*, *59B*, 1453–6 (1924).
(191) Grignard and Bellet, *Compt. rend.*, *155*, 44–6 (1912); *Chem. Abstr.*, 6, 2739 (1912).
(192) Jones, *J. Am. Chem. Soc.*, 70, 143–4 (1948).
(193) Fuson, Emmons, and Tull, *J. Org. Chem.*, *16*, 648–51 (1951).
(194) Akabori and Saito, *Ber.*, *63B*, 2245–8 (1930).
(195) Kroeger and Nieuwland, *J. Am. Chem. Soc.*, *58*, 1861–3 (1936).
(196) Darmon, *Compt. rend.*, *197*, 1328–9 (1933).
(197) Maruyama, *Sci. Papers Inst. Phys. Chem. Research* (Tokyo), *20*, 53–62 (1933); *Chem. Abstr.*, *27*, 1863 (1933).
(198) Baddeley, *J. Chem. Soc.*, *1944*, 232–6.
(199) Erlenmeyer and Marbet, *Helv. Chim. Acta*, *29*, 1946–9 (1946).
(200) Woodward and Eastman, *J. Am. Chem. Soc.*, *68*, 2229–35 (1946).
(201) Niemann, Benson, and Mead, *J. Org. Chem.*, *8*, 397–404 (1943).
(202) Khaletskiĭ, *J. Gen. Chem.* (U.S.S.R.), *15*, 524–9 (1945); *Chem. Abstr.*, *40*, 4696 (1946).
(203) Quilico, Fusco, and Rosnati, *Gazz. chim. ital.*, *76*, 87–107 (1946); *Chem. Abstr.*, *41*, 383 (1947).
(204) Compère, *Bull. soc. chim. Belg.*, *44*, 523–6 (1935).
(205) Lutz, Allison, Asburn, Bailey, Clark, Codington, Deinert, Freek, Jordan, Leake, Martin, Nicodemus, Rowlett, Shearer, Smith, and Wilson, *J. Org. Chem.*, *12*, 617–703 (1947).
(206) Willemart, *Bull. soc. chim.*, [5], *2*, 867–82 (1935).
(207) Tsatsas, *Ann. chim.*, [12], *1*, 342–94 (1946).
(208) Miescher and Marxer, U. S. Patent 2,411,664, Nov. 26, 1946; *Chem. Abstr.*, *41*, P6276 (1947).
(209) Bachmann and Brockway, *J. Org. Chem.*, *13*, 384–9 (1948).
(210) Hems and Elks, British Patent 627,280, Aug. 4, 1949; *Chem. Abstr.*, *44*, P3535 (1950).
(211) Mousseron and Jacquier, *Compt. rend.*, *226*, 256–8 (1948); *Chem. Abstr.*, *42*, 3734 (1948).
(212) Fuson, Gaertner, and Chadwick, *J. Org. Chem.*, *13*, 489–95 (1948).
(213) Bachmann, *J. Org. Chem.*, *1*, 347–53 (1936).
(214) Hartung, Munch, and Crossley, *J. Am. Chem. Soc.*, *57*, 1091–3 (1935).
(215) Davies, Kefford, and Osborne, *J. Chem. Soc.*, *1939*, 360–1.
(216) Piper and Wright, *J. Am. Chem. Soc.*, 72, 1669–74 (1950).

(217) Birch, Dean, Fidler, and Lowry, *J. Am. Chem. Soc.*, 71, 1362–9 (1949).
(218) Richtzenhain and Nippus, *Ber.*, 77B, 566–72 (1944).
(219) Baker and Smith, *J. Chem. Soc.*, 1936, 346–8.
(220) Maxim and Georgescu, *Bull. soc. chim.*, [5], 3, 1114–24 (1936).
(221) Fieser and Seligman, *J. Am. Chem. Soc.*, 58, 2482–7 (1936).
(222) Nunn and Henze, *J. Org. Chem.*, 12, 540–2 (1947).
(223) Kloetzel and Wildman, *J. Org. Chem.*, 11, 390–4 (1946).
(224) Birch and Robinson, *J. Chem. Soc.*, 1943, 501–2.
(225) Campbell, Kirwin, LaForge, and Campbell, *J. Am. Chem. Soc.*, 68, 1844–6 (1946).
(226) Fieser and Riegel, *J. Am. Chem. Soc.*, 59, 2561–5 (1937).
(227) Maxim and Aldea, *Bull. soc. chim.*, [5], 3, 1329–34 (1936).
(228) Schiessler, Rytina, and Whitmore, *J. Am. Chem. Soc.*, 70, 529–30 (1948).
(229) Kuwada and Sasagawa, *Bull. Chem. Soc. Japan*, 16, 423–7 (1941); *Chem. Abstr.*, 41, 4472 (1947).
(230) Birch and Robinson, *J. Chem. Soc.*, 1942, 488–97.
(231) Fuson and Chadwick, *J. Org. Chem.*, 13, 484–8 (1948).
(232) Elderfield, Pitt, and Wempen, *J. Am. Chem. Soc.*, 72, 1334–45 (1950).
(233) Lutz and Smith, *J. Am. Chem. Soc.*, 63, 1148–50 (1941).
(234) Gaylord and Becker, *J. Org. Chem.*, 15, 305–16 (1950).
(235) Frank and Weatherbee, *J. Am. Chem. Soc.*, 70, 3482–3 (1948).
(236) Johnson, Jacobs, and Schwartz, *J. Am. Chem. Soc.*, 60, 1885–9 (1938).
(237) Moffett and Shriner, *Organic Syntheses*, 21, 79–80 (1941).
(238) Tilford, Shelton, and Van Campen, *J. Am. Chem. Soc.*, 70, 4001–8 (1948).
(239) Blicke and Powers, *J. Am. Chem. Soc.*, 51, 3378–83 (1929).

CHAPTER XI

Reactions of Grignard Reagents with Carboxylic Anhydrides

THE "NORMAL" REACTIONS

Tissier and Grignard[1] found that the addition of ethereal solutions of acetic or benzoic anhydride to ethereal methylmagnesium iodide led to the formation of tertiary alcohols.

$$(RCO)_2O \xrightarrow{CH_3MgI} R(CH_3)_2COMgI \xrightarrow{H_2O} R(CH_3)_2COH + MgIOH$$

By employing high dilution and reverse addition, and operating at low temperature (–23°), Fournier[2] was able to show that the first step in the reaction is ketone (and acid) formation. He formulated the reaction as follows:

$$\begin{array}{l} R—C{=}O \\ \quad\;\; \diagdown \\ \qquad O \\ \quad\;\; \diagup \\ R—C{=}O \end{array} \xrightarrow{R'MgX} \begin{array}{l} \qquad O—MgX \\ \qquad\;\; | \\ R—C—R' \\ \qquad\;\; \diagdown \\ \qquad\quad O \\ \qquad\;\; \diagup \\ R—C{=}O \end{array} \xrightarrow{H_2O} MgXOH + RCO_2H + RCOR'$$

Because of the availability of competitive methods at least as satisfactory, and often more so, the reactions of acyclic carboxylic anhydrides with Grignard reagents have found little use in the preparation of ketones, although Newman[3] has had good success in the preparation of methyl ketones by operating with Dry-Ice cooling in the neighborhood of –70°, as have Brokaw and Brode.[4] Newman attributes the success of his method to increased stability and decreased solubility of the initial reaction product at low temperatures.

This method has been further studied by Newman and Smith,[5] who report that the yield of 2-hexanone from acetic anhydride and *n*-butylmagnesium bromide varies but little from 34° to –37° (48–51%), but gradually improves thereafter as the temperature is lowered to –82° (83%). The temperature effect was found to be about the same for the reactions of *t*-butylmagnesium chloride with acetic anhydride and phenylmagnesium

---

[1] Tissier and Grignard, *Compt. rend.*, *132*, 683–5 (1901); *Chem. Zentr.*, *1901*,*I*, 930.

[2] Fournier, *Bull. soc. chim.*, [3], *31*, 483 (1904); [3], *35*, 14 (1906); [4], 7, 836–40 (1910).

[3] Newman and Booth, *J. Am. Chem. Soc.*, *67*, 154 (1945); Newman and O'Leary, *ibid.*, *68*, 258–61 (1946).

[4] Brokaw and Brode, *J. Org. Chem.*, *13*, 194–9 (1948).

[5] Newman and Smith, *J. Org. Chem.*, *13*, 592–8 (1948).

bromide with benzoic anhydride. The reactions of various Grignard reagent-anhydride pairs at −70° were studied, and the method appears to have general applicability.

The use of organocadmium (or -zinc) compounds prepared from Grignard reagents, which has proved so successful in the preparation of ketones from carbonyl chlorides (*q.v.*), has been explored somewhat. According to Cason,[6] however, the symmetrical acyclic anhydrides give yields inferior to those obtainable with the corresponding acid chlorides. For the preparation of keto acids the half-ester chlorides are recommended as superior to the corresponding cyclic anhydrides, except in the case of the phthalic acid derivatives whose half-ester chlorides are unstable.[7] Examples of such preparations are, however, included in Table XI-I.

All the theoretically possible "normal" reactions of Grignard reagents with cyclic anhydrides have been observed (though not with any single anhydride), and examples are recorded in Table XI-I.

$$(1)\qquad \begin{array}{c} O \\ \| \\ C \\ / \quad \backslash \\ R \qquad O \\ \backslash \quad / \\ C \\ \| \\ O \end{array} \xrightarrow{R'MgX} R'CO-R-CO_2H$$

$$(2)\qquad \begin{array}{c} O \\ \| \\ C \\ / \quad \backslash \\ R \qquad O \\ \backslash \quad / \\ C \\ \| \\ O \end{array} \xrightarrow{2\,R'MgX} R'_2C(OH)-R-CO_2H$$

$$(3)\qquad \begin{array}{c} O \\ \| \\ C \\ / \quad \backslash \\ R \qquad O \\ \backslash \quad / \\ C \\ \| \\ O \end{array} \xrightarrow{2\,R'MgX} \begin{array}{c} R' \quad R' \\ \backslash \; / \\ C \\ / \quad \backslash \\ R \qquad O \\ \backslash \quad / \\ C \\ \| \\ O \end{array}$$

$$(4)\qquad \begin{array}{c} O \\ \| \\ C \\ / \quad \backslash \\ R \qquad O \\ \backslash \quad / \\ C \\ \| \\ O \end{array} \xrightarrow{2\,R'MgX} (R'CO)_2{=}R$$

[6] Cason, *Chem. Revs.*, *40*, 15–32 (1947).

[7] Zelinsky, *Ber.*, *30*, 1010–3 (1887).

$$\text{(5)}\quad R\begin{matrix} C{=}O \\ \diagup\ \ \diagdown \\ O \\ \diagdown\ \ \diagup \\ C{=}O \end{matrix} \xrightarrow{\cdot 3\ R'MgX} R'_2C(OH)-R-COR'$$

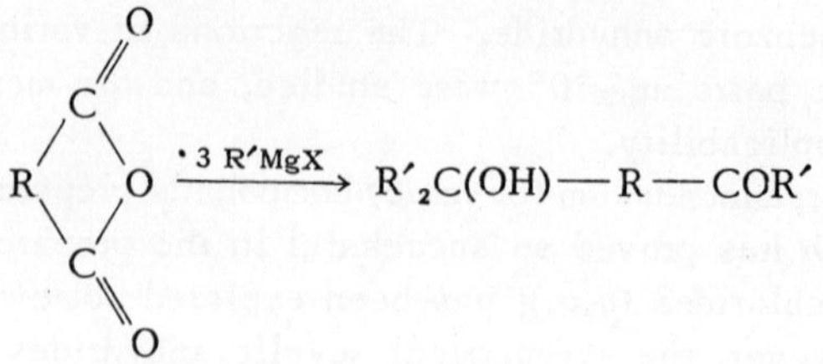

$$\text{(6)}\quad R\begin{matrix} C{=}O \\ \diagup\ \ \diagdown \\ O \\ \diagdown\ \ \diagup \\ C{=}O \end{matrix} \xrightarrow{4\ R'MgX} [R'_2C(OH)]=R$$

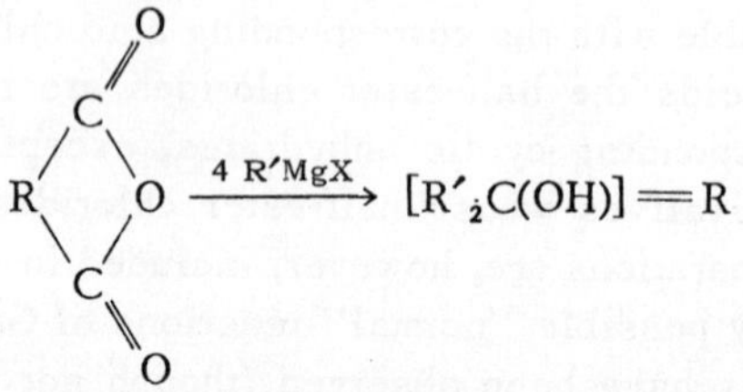

On the basis of the available data, reaction 3 appears to be by far the most common of those consuming two molecules of Grignard reagent, with reaction 2 in the runner-up position, and reaction 4 extremely rare. It is highly probable that reaction products 5 and 6 result in most cases from further reaction of the product of reaction 3.

If the reactions of thienylmagnesium iodide with methylsuccinic anhydride[8] and of phenyl- and α-naphthylmagnesium bromides with phenylsuccinic anhydride[9] may be regarded as typical (although the yields reported are low), an *alpha* substituent tends to inhibit reaction at the adjacent carbonyl group.

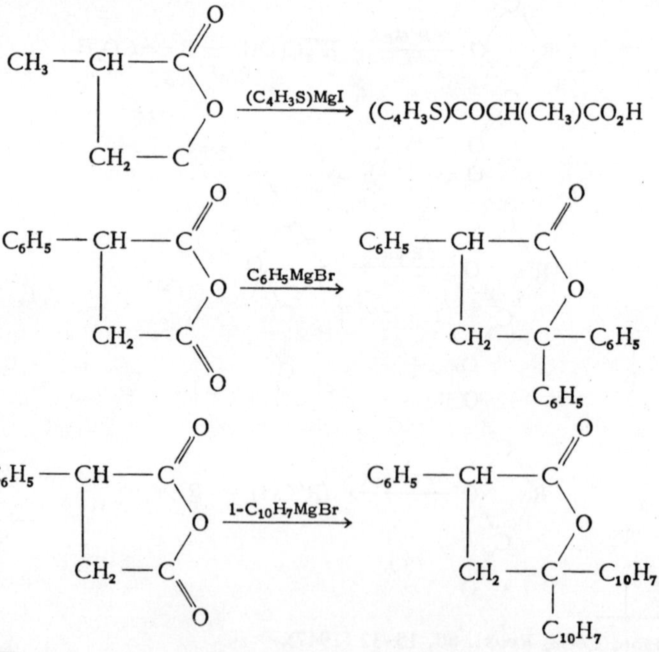

$$\begin{matrix} CH_3-CH-C{=}O \\ |\qquad\quad\diagdown \\ |\qquad\qquad O \\ |\qquad\quad\diagup \\ CH_2-C{=}O \end{matrix} \xrightarrow{(C_4H_3S)MgI} (C_4H_3S)COCH(CH_3)CO_2H \quad (27\%)$$

$$\begin{matrix} C_6H_5-CH-C{=}O \\ |\qquad\quad\diagdown \\ |\qquad\qquad O \\ |\qquad\quad\diagup \\ CH_2-C{=}O \end{matrix} \xrightarrow{C_6H_5MgBr} \begin{matrix} C_6H_5-CH-C{=}O \\ |\qquad\quad\diagdown \\ |\qquad\qquad O \\ |\qquad\quad\diagup \\ CH_2-C-C_6H_5 \\ | \\ C_6H_5 \end{matrix} \quad (7.7\%)$$

$$\begin{matrix} C_6H_5-CH-C{=}O \\ |\qquad\quad\diagdown \\ |\qquad\qquad O \\ |\qquad\quad\diagup \\ CH_2-C{=}O \end{matrix} \xrightarrow{1\text{-}C_{10}H_7MgBr} \begin{matrix} C_6H_5-CH-C{=}O \\ |\qquad\quad\diagdown \\ |\qquad\qquad O \\ |\qquad\quad\diagup \\ CH_2-C-C_{10}H_7 \\ | \\ C_{10}H_7 \end{matrix} \quad (5\%)$$

[8] Kitchin and Sandin, *J. Am. Chem. Soc.*, *67*, 1645–6 (1945).

[9] Weizmann, Blum-Bergmann, and Bergmann, *J. Chem. Soc.*, *1935*, 1370–1.

Newman[10] has made a similar observation as regards the 3-substituted phthalic anhydrides.

CH_3 ... $\xrightarrow{1\text{-}C_{10}H_7MgBr}$ CH_3, CO_2H, $COC_{10}H_7$ (52%)

+ CH_3, $COC_{10}H_7$, CO_2H (1.5%)

$\xrightarrow{4\text{-}ClC_6H_4MgBr}$ CO_2H, $COC_6H_4\text{-}4\text{-}Cl$ (31%)

+ $COC_6H_4\text{-}4\text{-}Cl$, CO_2H (10%)

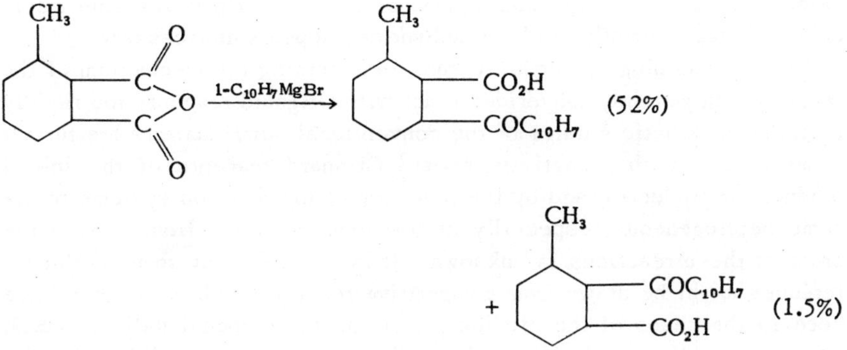

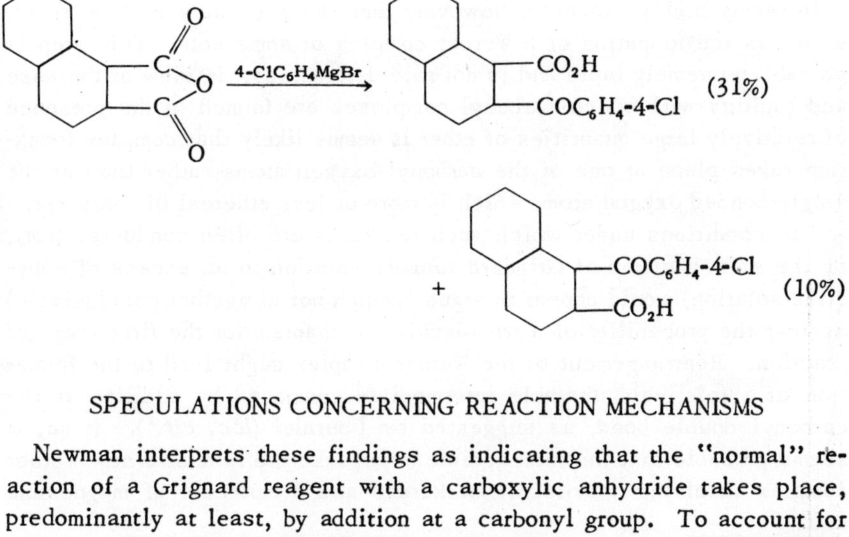

SPECULATIONS CONCERNING REACTION MECHANISMS

Newman interprets these findings as indicating that the "normal" reaction of a Grignard reagent with a carboxylic anhydride takes place, predominantly at least, by addition at a carbonyl group. To account for what he regards as the improbable ratio of isomeric reaction products in such cases, and for the reactivity of the 3,6- and 3,4,6-substituted phthalic anhydrides, Newman postulates a "metathetical"* reaction mechanism which becomes competitive with the "normal" addition reaction. This may be the correct interpretation. However, if the actual reaction mechanism is bimolecular, and resembles that of the nitriles (*q.v.*), steric hindrance, while probably appreciable, would be much less pronounced

---

[10] (*a*) Fieser and Newman, *J. Am. Chem. Soc.*, *68*, 2376–82 (1936); (*b*) Newman, *ibid.*, *59*, 1003–6 (1937); (*c*) Newman and Orchin, *ibid.*, *60*, 586–9 (1938); (*d*) Newman, *ibid.*, *60*, 1368–70 (1938); (*e*) Newman and Orchin, *ibid.*, *61*, 244–7 (1939); (*f*) Newman and McCleary, *ibid.*, *63*, 1542–4 (1941); (*g*) Newman and Wise, *ibid.*, *63*, 2109–13 (1941); (*h*) Newman and Lord, *ibid.*, *66*, 733–5 (1944). See also: (*i*) Nichol and Sandin, *ibid.*, *69*, 2256–8 (1947).

*Actually, the term metathetical is primarily stoichiometric in significance. It can be regarded as having mechanistic connotations only in so far as it eliminates certain types of reaction mechanism from consideration.

than in a trimolecular mechanism like that postulated for the ketones (*q.v.*), and, by inference, for the aldehydes, and at least some of the esters. In that case the assumption of two competitive reaction mechanisms for the partially hindered anhydrides appears unnecessary.

Actually, nothing is certainly known concerning the mechanism of the reaction. In general, anhydrides react with Grignard reagents too rapidly to permit of kinetic studies of the conventional sort. Matters are further complicated by the reactivity toward Grignard reagents of the initial product (or products), and by the tendency of the reaction systems to become heterogeneous, especially at low temperatures. Hence, even the order of these reactions is unknown. It is possible that some useful inferences might be drawn from competitive reaction studies, as they have been in the cases of the nitriles (*q.v.*) and the carbonyl halides (*q.v.*). At present, only speculation on the basis of analogy is possible.

It seems highly probable, however, that the necessary prelude to reaction is the formation of a Werner complex of some sort. This step is probably extremely rapid and is not rate-determining. In view of the ease and rapidity with which carbonyl complexes are formed in the presence of relatively large quantities of ether it seems likely that complex formation takes place at one of the carbonyl oxygen atoms rather than at the singly-bonded oxygen atom, which is more or less ethereal in character.

The conditions under which such reactions are often conducted (*i.e.*, by the slow addition of Grignard reagent solution to an excess of anhydride solution) would appear to argue (though not altogether conclusively) against the probability of a trimolecular mechanism for the first stage of reaction. Rearrangement of the Werner complex might lead to the formation of a relatively unstable intermediate compound by addition at the carbonyl double bond, as suggested by Fournier (*loc. cit.*[2]). If so, it seems probable that the intermediate might take the form of a new Werner complex involving a molecule of ketone and a molecule of magnesium salt.

```
R     O      X        R     O       X        R    O      X
 \   //  ·· /          \   //  ··  /          \  //  ·· /
  C      Mg             C.      .Mg             C      Mg
  |    /          →     :  .R'. :        →     \      |
  |  R'                 :       :              R'     |
  O                     O       O           O         O
  |    O                 ·.   .·             \\      /
   \  //                   C                   C
    C                      |                   |
    |                      R                   R
    R
```

The results of the low-temperature (–70°) studies of Newman and Smith (*loc. cit.*[5]) are consistent with a concept of this general nature. Treatment of the precipitated acetic anhydride-*n*-butylmagnesium bromide product with excess ethanol at –70° (and subsequent aqueous hydrolysis) liberates the ketone rather than butane, indicating that the product is not a simple Grignard reagent-anhydride Werner complex. At –70° the ethereal solution is ketone-free; allowed to warm to room temperature in the presence of the precipitated product, it contains all the ketone present; recooled to $-70°$ in the presence of the residual bromomagnesium acetate, it retains the ketone.

PREPARATIVE PROCEDURES

Newman's[11] method for the preparation of methyl ketones is described as follows:

"In a typical experiment, 0.2 mole of a titrated Grignard reagent was added slowly during one hour to a stirred solution of 40 g. of acetic anhydride in 100 ml. of dry ether in a 500-ml. 3-necked flask cooled by a mixture of Dry Ice and acetone in a Dewar flask. The added reagent was cooled by dripping through a tube externally cooled with Dry Ice. After stirring for two to three hours the cooling bath was removed and the mixture was treated with ammonium chloride solution. After washing out the acetic anhydride and acid with alkali the ether was fractionated and the ketones distilled.... The following Grignard reagents gave the corresponding methyl ketones in the following yields: *n*-butylmagnesium chloride, 79 percent; *n*-butylmagnesium bromide, 79 percent; *s*-butylmagnesium bromide, 78 percent; *t*-butylmagnesium chloride, 77 percent; phenylmagnesium bromide, 70 percent; benzylmagnesium chloride, 52 percent; and allylmagnesium bromide, 42 percent. With phenylmagnesium bromide and propionic anhydride a 59 percent yield of propiophenone was obtained."

The method of Bauer[12] for the preparation of 3,3-disubstituted phthalides may be summarized as follows. To a cooled ethereal solution of two molecular equivalents of Grignard reagent one molecular equivalent of finely powdered phthalic anhydride is added slowly. After completion of the addition the reaction mixture is allowed to stand for about an hour, and is then treated with water and dilute sulfuric acid, and extracted with ether. The ether is removed by distillation, and the oily residue is washed with dilute sodium carbonate solution, whereupon it solidifies. The yields claimed for the following Grignard reagents are as indicated: methyl- and ethylmagnesium iodides, 75-80 percent; phenylmagnesium bromide 70-75 percent; benzylmagnesium chloride, 60 percent.

Treating phthalic, 4-methoxyphthalic, tetrachlorophthalic, and 2,3-naphthalenedicarboxylic anhydrides with aryl Grignard reagents, Weizmann *et al.*[13] have prepared some sixteen keto acids in 70-80 percent yields. Typical procedure is described essentially as follows. The anhydride is dissolved or suspended in boiling benzene or warm *n*-butyl ether on a water-bath, and 1.1 equivalent of Grignard solution is added slowly from a dropping funnel. The mixture is boiled for two hours, and is then treated with ice and sulfuric acid. The non-aqueous layer is extracted with sodium carbonate solution, and the alkaline extract is acidified, the keto acid being thus obtained.

---

[11] Newman and Booth, *J. Am. Chem. Soc.*, 67, 154 (1945).

[12] Bauer, *Ber.*, 37, 735-7 (1904); 38, 240-1 (1905).

[13] Weizmann, Bergmann, and Bergmann, *J. Chem. Soc.*, *1935*, 1367-70.

TABLE XI-I

REACTIONS OF GRIGNARD REAGENTS WITH CARBOXYLIC ANHYDRIDES

Anhydride	RMgX	Product(s)	Ref.
$C_4O_3Br_2$			
Dibromomaleic anhydride (20.0 g.)	CH_3MgI (33.4 g. CH_3I)	3,3-Dimethyl-4,5-dibromo-2-oxa-4-cyclopenten-1-one (7-8 g., 33-38%)	*1*
$C_4H_2O_3$			
Maleic anhydride	C_2H_5MgBr	$(C_2H_5)_2C(OH)CH{=}CHCO_2H$; $CH_3CH{=}C(C_2H_5)CH{=}CHCO_2H$ (?); $C_2H_5COCH_2CH(C_2H_5)C(C_2H_5)_2OH$	*2*
Maleic anhydride	n-C_4H_9MgBr	$(n\text{-}C_4H_9)_2C(OH)CH{=}CHCO_2H$	*2*
Maleic anhydride (1.0 mole)	C_6H_5MgBr (4.5 moles C_6H_5Br)	$C_6H_5COCH_2CH(C_6H_5)COC_6H_5$ (*ca.* 10 g.); oil (*ca.* 10 g.)	*3*
Maleic anhydride (8.8 g.)	C_6H_5MgBr (15.7 g. C_6H_5Br)	$C_6H_5COCH_2CH(C_6H_5)COC_6H_5$; $C_6H_5COCH_2CH(C_6H_5)CO_2H$	*27*
Maleic anhydride	$C_6H_5CH_2MgCl$	$(C_6H_5CH_2)_2C(OH)CH{=}CHCO_2H$; $[C_6H_5CH{=}C(CH_2C_6H_5)CH{=}]_2$	*2*
$C_4H_4O_3$			
Succinic anhydride (10.0 g.)	C_2H_5MgBr (69.6 g. C_2H_5Br)	2,2,5,5-Tetraethyltetrahydrofuran (?)	*9*
Succinic anhydride (22.5 g.)	i-$C_5H_{11}MgBr$ (0.3 mole $C_5H_{11}Br$) + $CdCl_2$	i-$C_5H_{11}COCH_2CH_2CO_2H$ (11.9 g., 30.8%)	*7,6*
Succinic anhydride (0.5 equiv.)	i-$C_5H_{11}MgBr$ + $ZnCl_2$	i-$C_5H_{11}COCH_2CH_2CO_2H$ (5-10%)	*6*
Succinic anhydride (10.0 g.)	C_6H_5MgBr (17.3 g. C_6H_5Br)	$C_6H_5COCH_2CH_2CO_2H$	*8*
Succinic anhydride (10 g.)	C_6H_5MgBr (100 g. C_6H_5Br)	$[(C_6H_5)_2C(OH)CH_2{-}]_2$ (10 g., 26%)	*9*
Succinic anhydride	C_6H_5MgBr (0.5 equiv.)	$C_6H_5COCH_2CH_2CO_2H$ (50-70%)*	*10*
Succinic anhydride (0.16 mole)	C_6H_5MgBr (7.3 g., 0.3 g.-atom Mg) + $CdCl_2$ (31.2 g., 0.17 mole)	$C_6H_5COCH_2CH_2CO_2H$	*11*

* Reaction at −70°.

TABLE XI-I (Continued)

Anhydride	RMgX	Product(s)	Ref.
$C_4H_4O_3$ (*cont.*)			
Succinic anhydride (10.0 g.)	$C_6H_5CH_2MgCl$ (75.6 g. C_7H_7Cl)	$[(C_6H_5CH_2)_2C(OH)CH_2-]_2$ (12.0 g., 27%)	*9*
Succinic anhydride	$C_6H_5CH_2MgCl$	$C_6H_5CH_2COCH_2CH_2CO_2H$ (54.4%)	*12*
Succinic anhydride	$C_6H_5CH(CO_2Na)MgCl$*	$C_6H_5CH_2COCH_2CH_2CO_2H$ (64.5%)	*12*
Succinic anhydride (10.0 g.)	1-$C_{10}H_7MgBr$ (22.8 g. $C_{10}H_7Br$)	1-$C_{10}H_7COCH_2CH_2CO_2H$ (2.5 g.)	*13*
Succinic anhydride (10.0 g.)	2-$C_{10}H_7MgBr$ (22.8 g. $C_{10}H_7Br$)	2-$C_{10}H_7COCH_2CH_2CO_2H$ (4.0 g.)	*13*
$C_4H_4O_3Cl_2$			
$(ClCH_2CO)_2O$	*n*-C_4H_9MgBr (0.5 equiv.)	*n*-$C_4H_9COCH_2Cl$ (35–50%)†	*10*
$(ClCH_2CO)_2O$ (0.6 mole)	$C_6H_5CH_2MgCl$ (0.5 mole)	$ClCH_2COC_6H_4$-2-CH_3 (42%, crude)	*14*
$C_4H_6O_3$			
$(CH_3CO)_2O$	CH_3MgI	*t*-C_4H_9OH	*15*
$(CH_3CO)_2O$	C_2H_5MgBr	$CH_3COC_2H_5$ ("very little"); $CH_3(C_2H_5)_2COH$	*16*
$(CH_3CO)_2O$	Pyrazolyl-MgBr	No reaction	*17*
$(CH_3CO)_2O$ (40 g.)	$H_2C{=}CHCH_2MgBr$ (0.2 mole)	$CH_3COCH_2CH{=}CH_2$ (42%)†	*18*
$(CH_3CO)_2O$	*i*-C_3H_7MgBr	CH_3CO-*i*-C_3H_7 (45%)	*19*
$(CH_3CO)_2O$	*i*-C_3H_7MgBr (0.5 equiv.)	CH_3CO-*i*-C_3H_7 (74–78%)†	*10*
$(CH_3CO)_2O$	$H_2C{=}CHC{\equiv}CMgBr$	Product(s) explosive	*20*
$(CH_3CO)_2O$ (40 g.)	*n*-C_4H_9MgX‡ (0.2 mole)	CH_3CO-*n*-C_4H_9 (79%)†	*18*
$(CH_3CO)_2O$ (55 g., 0.54 mole	*n*-C_4H_9MgBr (0.257 mole)	CH_3CO-*n*-C_4H_9 (48–83%)§	*10*

* In the opinion of Schlenk, Hilleman, and Rodloff, *Ann.*, *487*, 135–54 (1931), this "Grignard reagent" should be formulated as an enolate.

† Reaction at −70°.

‡ X = Cl, Br.

§ Reactions at temperatures ranging from 34 to −82°; the following yields are reported for the temperatures indicated: 34°, 48%; 5°, 48%; −26°, 50%; −37°, 51%; −46°, 68%; −54°, 64%; −67°, 79%; −82°, 83%.

TABLE XI-I (Continued)

Anhydride	RMgX	Product(s)	Ref.
$C_4H_6O_3$ (*cont.*)			
$(CH_3CO)_2O$ (0.16 mole)	n-C_4H_9MgBr (7.3 g., 0.3 g.-atom Mg) + $CdCl_2$ (31.2 g., 0.17 mole)	CH_3CO-n-C_4H_9 (56%)	*11*
$(CH_3CO)_2O$	i-C_4H_9MgCl (1 equiv.)	CH_3CO-i-C_4H_9 ("very little")	*42,16*
$(CH_3CO)_2O$ (40 g.)	s-C_4H_9MgBr (0.2 mole)	CH_3CO-s-C_4H_9 (78%)*	*18*
$(CH_3CO)_2O$ (40 g.)	t-C_4H_9MgCl (0.2 mole)	CH_3CO-t-C_4H_9 (77%)*	*18*
$(CH_3CO)_2O$ (1 mole)	2-Thenyl-MgCl (0.190 mole)	2-Methyl-3-acetyllthiophene (6.52 g., 25%); 1,3-bis-(2-thienyl)-propene (?) (9.08 g., 31%)	76
$(CH_3CO)_2O$	i-$C_5H_{11}MgX$† (1 equiv.)	CH_3CO-i-C_5H_{11}; CH_3CO_2-i-C_5H_{11}	*16,42*
$(CH_3CO)_2O$	D-s-$C_4H_9CH_2MgBr$‡	D(+)-$CH_3COCH_2CH(CH_3)C_2H_5$ ("excellent yield")*	22
$(CH_3CO)_2O$	C_6H_5MgBr (0.5 equiv.)	$CH_3COC_6H_5$ (73–75%)*	*10,18*
$(CH_3CO)_2O$ (0.16 mole)	C_6H_5MgBr (7.3 g., 0.3 g.-atom Mg) + $CdCl_2$ (31.2 g., 0.17 mole)	$CH_3COC_6H_5$ (75%)	*11*
$(CH_3CO)_2O$ (0.5 mole)	n-$C_4H_9C\equiv CMgCl$ (0.25 mole)	$CH_3COC\equiv C$-n-C_4H_9 (18 g.); n-$C_4H_9C\equiv CH$ (8 g.)§	23
$(CH_3CO)_2O$ (1.0 mole)	n-$C_4H_9C\equiv CMgBr$ (0.5 mole)	$CH_3COC\equiv C$-n-C_4H_9 (20 g.); $CH_3(n$-$C_4H_9C\equiv C)_2COH$ (8 g.)¶	23
CH_3CO_2O (0.5 mole)	n-$C_4H_9C\equiv CMgX$‖ (0.25 mole)	$CH_3COC\equiv C$-n-C_4H_9 (10–20%)§	23
$(CH_3CO)_2O$	$(CH_2)_5CHMgBr$	$CH_3COCH(CH_2)_5$ (56%)	*19*
$(CH_3CO)_2O$ (25 g.)	2,6-$Cl_2C_6H_3CH_2MgCl$ (0.056 mole)	$CH_3COCH_2C_6H_3$-2,6-Cl_2	*14*

*Reaction at −70°.

†X = Cl, Br.

‡From D(+)-$CH_3(C_2H_5)CHCH_2Br$.

§Slow (two and one-half hours) addition of anhydride to stirred Grignard reagent suspension at −30 to −25°; two hours stirring at −30°; 2 hrs. stirring at −5°.

¶Slow (three hours) addition of Grignard reagent solution to stirred, ice-salt-cooled anhydride; two hours stirring.

‖X = Br, I.

TABLE XI-I (Continued)

Anhydride	RMgX	Product(s)	Ref.
$C_4H_6O_3$ *(cont.)*			
$(CH_3CO)_2O$ (0.53 mole)	$2\text{-}ClC_6H_4CH_2MgCl$ (0.07 mole)	$CH_3COC_6H_3\text{-}2\text{-}CH_3\text{-}3\text{-}Cl$	*14*
$(CH_3CO)_2O$ (1.65 mole)	$C_6H_5CH_2MgCl$ (0.55 mole)	$CH_3COC_6H_4\text{-}2\text{-}CH_3$ (30%)*	*14*
$(CH_3CO)_2O$ (40 g.)	$C_6H_5CH_2MgCl$ (0.2 mole)	$CH_3COCH_2C_6H_5$ † (52%)	*18*
$(CH_3CO)_2O$ (0.5 mole)	$n\text{-}C_5H_{11}C\equiv CMgCl$ (0.25 mole)	$CH_3COC\equiv C\text{-}n\text{-}C_5H_{11}$ (22 g.); $n\text{-}C_5H_{11}C\equiv CH$ (10 g.) ‡	*23*
$(CH_3CO)_2O$ (0.5 mole)	$n\text{-}C_5H_{11}C\equiv CMgX$ § (0.25 mole)	$CH_3COC\equiv C\text{-}n\text{-}C_5H_{11}$ (10–20%) ‡	*23*
$(CH_3CO)_2O$ (0.5 mole)	$C_6H_5C\equiv CMgCl$ (0.25 mole)	$CH_3COC\equiv CC_6H_5$ (40–45%); $CH_3(C_6H_5C\equiv C)_2COH$ ‡	*23*
$(CH_3CO)_2O$ (0.5 mole)	$C_6H_5C\equiv CMgBr$ (0.25 mole)	$CH_3COC\equiv CC_6H_5$ (3 g.); $CH_3(C_6H_5C\equiv C)_2COH$ (30 g., crude) ¶	*23*
$(CH_3CO)_2O$ (102 g.)	1-Cyclohexenylethynyl-MgBr (62 g. C_8H_{10})	1-Acetoethynylcyclohexene (36 g.)	*72,71,73*
$(CH_3CO)_2O$ (150.0 g.)	β-(1-Tetralyl)ethyl-MgCl (141.4 g. $C_{12}H_{15}Cl$)	4-(1-Tetralyl)-2-butanone 61% ǁ	*25*
$C_5H_6O_3$			
Glutaric anhydride (11.4 g.)	CH_3MgI (15.6 g. CH_3I)	$CH_3CO(CH_2)_3CO_2H$; lactone (trace); unsat'd acid (trace)**	*8*

* Other products not investigated probably include $CH_3(C_6H_5CH_2)_2COH$.

† Reaction at −70°.

‡ Slow (two and one-half hours) addition of anhydride to stirred Grignard reagent suspension at −30 to −25°; two hours stirring at −30°; 2 hrs. stirring at −5°.

§ X = Br, I.

¶ Slow (three hours) addition of Grignard reagent solution to stirred, ice-salt-cooled anhydride; two hours stirring.

ǁ Reaction at −78°.

** Slow addition of Grignard reagent solution to ice-cooled C_6H_6-anhydride solution; twenty-four hours standing.

TABLE XI-I (Continued)

Anhydride	RMgX	Product(s)	Ref.
$C_5H_6O_3$ (*cont.*)			
Glutaric anhydride (10 g.)	CH_3MgI (28 g. CH_3I)	δ-Methyl-δ-caprolactone (1.5 g.); $(CH_3)_2C{=}CHCH_2CH_2CO_2H$ (2 g.)*	*8*
Glutaric anhydride	*n*-C_4H_9MgBr + $CdCl_2$	*n*-$C_4H_9CO(CH_2)_3CO_2H$ (30.5%)	*26*
Methylsuccinic anhydride (14 g.)	2-Thienyl-MgI (25 g. CH_3I)	α-Methyl-β-(2-thenoyl)propionic acid (6.6 g., 27%)	*24*
$C_6H_6O_3$			
Dimethylmaleic anhydride (6.4 g.)	C_6H_5MgBr (17.3 g. C_6H_5Br)	$C_6H_5COCH(CH_3)C(CH_3)(C_6H_5)CO_2H$ [2 forms: m. 183–185° (3.4 g.); m. 112–114° (8.1 g.)]	*27,28*
1,2-Cyclobutanedicarboxylic anhydride (3.2 g.)	C_6H_5MgBr (24 ml. 2.1 *N*)	4,4-Diphenyl-3-oxabicyclo[3.2.0]heptan-2-one	*29*
1,2-Cyclobutanedicarboxylic anhydride (3.2 g., 0.025 mole)	C_6H_5MgBr (0.025 mole)	*trans*-2-Benzoylcyclobutanecarboxylic acid	*29*
$C_6H_{10}O_3$			
$(C_2H_5CO)_2O$	*n*-C_4H_9MgBr (0.5 equiv.)	C_2H_5CO-*n*-C_4H_9 (74%)†	*10*
$(C_2H_5CO)_2O$	*i*-C_4H_9MgCl	C_2H_5CO-*i*-C_4H_9‡	*21,16*
$(C_2H_5CO)_2O$	D-*s*-$C_4H_9CH_2MgBr$§	D(+)-$C_2H_5COCH_2CH(CH_3)C_2H_5$ ("excellent yield")†	*22*
$(C_2H_5CO)_2O$	C_6H_5MgBr	$C_2H_5COC_6H_5$ (59%)†	*18*
$(C_2H_5CO)_2O$ (0.16 mole)	C_6H_5MgBr (7.3 g., 0.3 g.-atom Mg) + $CdCl_2$ (31.2 g., 0.17 mole)	$C_2H_5COC_6H_5$ (68%)	*11*

* Gradual addition of Grignard reagent solution to C_6H_6-anhydride solution; twenty-four hours standing; heating to b.p. of C_6H_6.

† Reaction at −70°.

‡ Reaction at −20°.

§ From D(+)-$CH_3(C_2H_5)CHCH_2Br$.

TABLE XI-I (Continued)

Anhydride	RMgX	Product(s)	Ref.
$C_7H_3O_3N$			
Cinchomeronic anhydride	C_2H_5MgI	3-(γ-Hydroxy-γ-amyl)pyridine-4-carboxylic acid lactone; 4-(γ-hydroxy-γ-amyl)pyridine-3-carboxylic acid lactone ("small yields")	*30*
$C_7H_4O_4S$			
2-Sulfobenzoic anhydride	C_6H_5MgBr	$2\text{-}HO(C_6H_5)_2CC_6H_4SO_3H$; 2-α-hydroxybenzhydrylbenzenesulfonic acid lactone (*ca.* 10%)	*31*
$C_7H_{10}O_3$			
β,β-Dimethylglutaric anhydride (20.3 g.)	C_2H_5MgBr (24 g. C_2H_5Br)	$C_2H_5COCH_2C(CH_3)_2CH_2CO_2H$ (4.8 g.); β,β-dimethyl-δ-ethyl-δ-enanthylolactone	*8*
$C_8O_3Cl_4$			
Tetrachlorophthalic anhydride	CH_3MgI (2 equiv.)	3,3-Dimethyl-4,5,6,7-tetrachlorophthalide	*32*
Tetrachlorophthalic anhydride	C_2H_5MgBr (2 equiv.)	3-Ethyl-4,5,6,7-tetrachlorophthalide	*32*
Tetrachlorophthalic anhydride	$4\text{-}BrC_6H_4MgBr$ (10% excess)	3,3-Di-(*p*-bromophenyl)-4,5,6,7-tetrachlorophthalide	*33*
Tetrachlorophthalic anhydride	C_6H_5MgBr (10% excess)	$2\text{-}C_6H_5CO\text{-}3,4,5,6\text{-}Cl_4C_6CO_2H$ (70–80%)	*33*
Tetrachlorophthalic anhydride	$4\text{-}CH_3OC_6H_4MgBr$	2-(*p*-$CH_3OC_6H_4CO$)-3,4,5,6-$Cl_4C_6CO_2H$ (70–80%)	*33*
Tetrachlorophthalic anhydride	$1\text{-}C_{10}H_7MgBr$ (10% excess)	2-α-$C_{10}H_7CO$-3,4,5,6-$Cl_4C_6CO_2H$ (70–80%)	*33*
$C_8H_4O_3$			
Phthalic anhydride (0.16 mole)	CH_3MgBr (7.3 g., 0.3 g.-atom Mg) + $CdCl_2$ (31.2 g., 0.17 mole)	$2\text{-}CH_3COC_6H_4CO_2H$ (62%)	*11*

TABLE XI-I (Continued)

Anhydride	RMgX	Product(s)	Ref.
$C_8H_4O_3$ (*cont.*)			
Phthalic anhydride	CH_3MgI (2 equiv.)	3,3-Dimethylphthalide	*34,38*
Phthalic anhydride	CH_3MgI (7.3 g., 0.3 g.-atom Mg) + $CdCl_2$ (31.2 g., 0.17 mole)	2-$CH_3COC_6H_4CO_2H$ (47%)	*11*
Phthalic anhydride	C_2H_5MgBr (7.3 g., 0.3 g.-atom Mg) + $CdCl_2$ (31.2 g., 0.17 mole)	2-$C_2H_5COC_6H_4CO_2H$ (67%)	*11*
Phthalic anhydride	C_2H_5MgI (2 equiv.)	3,3-Diethylphthalide	*34,38*
Phthalic anhydride	$H_2C{=}CHCH_2Br$ + Mg	3,3-Diallylphthalide (70%)	*35*
Phthalic anhydride	*n*-C_3H_7MgBr (2 equiv.)	3,3-Di-*n*-propylphthalide	*32*
Phthalic anhydride	*i*-C_3H_7MgBr (2 equiv.)	3,3-Diisopropylphthalide	*32*
Phthalic anhydride	4-BrC_6H_4MgBr (10% excess)	2-(*p*-BrC_6H_6CO)$C_6H_4CO_2H$ (70–80%)	*33*
Phthalic anhydride	C_6H_5MgBr	2-$C_6H_5COC_6H_4CO_2H$	*47,36*
Phthalic anhydride	C_6H_5MgBr (2 equiv.)	3,3-Diphenylphthalide (70–75%); 1,2-$(C_6H_5CO)_2C_6H_4$	*37*
Phthalic anhydride (0.16 mole)	C_6H_5MgBr (7.3 g., 0.3 g.-atom Mg) + $CdCl_2$ (31.2 g., 0.17 mole)	2-$C_6H_5COC_6H_4CO_2H$ (64%)	*11*
Phthalic anhydride	$C_6H_5CH_2MgCl$ (2 equiv.)	3,3-Dibenzylphthalide (*ca.* 60%)	*37*
Phthalic anhydride (50 g.)	2-$CH_3C_6H_4MgBr$ (205 ml., 1.125 *M*)	2-(*o*-$CH_3C_6H_4CO$)$C_6H_4CO_2H$ (47 g.)	*39*
Phthalic anhydride	2-$CH_3C_6H_4MgBr$	2-(*o*-$CH_3C_6H_4CO$)$C_6H_4CO_2H$ (74%)	*40,41*
Phthalic anhydride (14 g.)	4-$CH_3C_6H_4MgBr$ (2 equiv.)	2-(*p*-$CH_3C_6H_4CO)_2C_6H_4$ (1–2 g.); 3,3-di-(*p*-tolyl)phthalide; resin	*37,32*
Phthalic anhydride	2-$CH_3OC_6H_4MgI$ (94 g. C_7H_7IO)	3,3-Di-(*o*-methoxyphenyl)phthalide	*43*
Phthalic anhydride	4-$CH_3OC_6H_4MgBr$	"Thick brown grease"	*37*
Phthalic anhydride	4-$CH_3OC_6H_4MgBr$ (10% excess)	2-(*p*-$CH_3OC_6H_4CO$)$C_6H_4CO_2H$ (70–80%)	*33*
Phthalic anhydride	4-$CH_3OC_6H_4MgI$	1,2-(*p*-$CH_3OC_6H_4CO)_2C_6H_4$	*45*
Phthalic anhydride (18.7 g.)	3-Thianaphthenyl-MgBr (27 g. C_8H_5BrS)	3-(*o*-Carboxybenzoyl)thianaphthene (16 g.)	*46*
Phthalic anhydride (21 g.)	2,3-$(CH_3)_2C_6H_3MgBr$ (30 g. C_8H_9Br)	2-[2,3-$(CH_3)_2C_6H_3CO$]$C_6H_4CO_2H$ (25 g.)	*44*
Phthalic anhydride	3,5-$(CH_3)_2C_6H_3MgBr$	2-[3,5-$(CH_3)_2C_6H_3CO$]$C_6H_4CO_2H$ (42.5%)	*40*

TABLE XI-I (Continued)

Anhydride	RMgX	Product(s)	Ref.
$C_8H_4O_3$ (*cont.*)			
Phthalic anhydride	1-$C_{10}H_7MgBr$ (10% excess)	2-α-$C_{10}H_7COC_6H_4CO_2H$ (70–80%)	*33,47*
Phthalic anhydride (0.16 mole)	1-$C_{10}H_7MgBr$ (7.3 g., 0.3 g.-atom Mg) + $CdCl_2$ (31.2 g., 0.17 mole)	2-α-$C_{10}H_7COC_6H_4CO_2H$ (57%)	*11*
Phthalic anhydride	2-$C_{10}H_7MgBr$ (10% excess)	2-β-$C_{10}H_7COC_6H_4CO_2H$ (70–80%); 3,3-di-β-naphthylphthalide	*33,47*
Phthalic anhydride (35.5 g.)	5-Tetralyl-MgBr (29.4 g. $C_{10}H_{11}Br$)	2-(5-Tetraloyl)benzoic acid (21 g., 54%)	*48*
Phthalic anhydride (0.5 mole)	$C_{10}H_{17}MgCl$* (0.5 mole)	2-($C_{10}H_{17}CO$)$C_6H_4CO_2H$ (95%)	*49*
Phthalic anhydride	4-$CH_3C_{10}H_6$-1-MgBr (10% excess)	2-(4-CH_3-1-$C_{10}H_6CO$)$C_6H_4CO_2H$	*50*
Phthalic anhydride (25 g.)	8-$CH_3C_{10}H_6$-1-MgBr (22 g. $C_{11}H_9Br$)	2-(8-CH_3-1-$C_{10}H_6CO$)$C_6H_4CO_2H$ (19 g., 66%)	*51*
Phthalic anhydride (3.5 g.)	2-$CH_3OC_{10}H_6$-1-MgBr (6.8 g. $C_{11}H_9BrO$)	2-(2-CH_3O-1-$C_{10}H_6CO$)$C_6H_4CO_2H$	*52*
Phthalic anhydride	6-$CH_3OC_{10}H_6$-2-MgBr (10% excess)	2-(6-CH_3O-2-$C_{10}H_6$)$COC_6H_4CO_2H$ (70–80%)	*33*
Phthalic anhydride	9-Phenanthryl-MgBr (10% excess)	2-(9-Phenanthroyl)benzoic acid (70–80%)	*33*
Phthalic anhydride	9-Phenanthryl-MgBr	2-(9-Phenanthroyl)benzoic acid; 3,3-bis(9-phenanthryl)phthalide	*53*
$C_8H_6O_3$			
4,5-Dihydrophthalic anhydride (7.5 g.)	$C_6H_5CH_2Cl$ (12.7 g.) + Mg (2.4 g.)	3,3-Dibenzyl-5,6-dihydrophthalide; $(C_6H_5CH_2-)_2$	*54*
$C_8H_8O_3$			
1,4,5,6-Tetrahydrophthalic anhydride	CH_3MgI	3-Methyl-3a,4,5,6-tetrahydrophthalide	*55*
1,4,5,6-Tetrahydrophthalic anhydride	C_2H_5MgX	3-Ethyl-3a,4,5,6-tetrahydrophthalide	*55*
1,4,5,6-Tetrahydrophthalic anhydride (7.6 g.)	$C_6H_5CH_2Cl$ (12.7 g.) + Mg (2.4 g.)	3,3-Dibenzyl-5,6,7,7a-tetrahydrophthalide; $(C_6H_5CH_2-)_2$	*54*

* From pinene hydrochloride.

TABLE XI-I (Continued)

Anhydride	RMgX	Product(s)	Ref.
$C_8H_{10}O_3$			
Hexahydroisophthalic anhydride (15.4 g.)	CH_3MgI (from 31.2 g. iodide)	3-Acetylcyclohexanecarboxylic acid; (5.4 g.); dimethylhexahydroisophthalide (4.2 g.); 3-isopropylidenecyclohexane-carboxylic acid	8
Hexahydroisophthalic anhydride (7.7 g.)	CH_3MgI (from 7.8 g. iodide)	3-Acetylcyclohexanecarboxylic acid (>50%)	8
$C_8H_{14}O_3$			
$(n\text{-}C_3H_7CO)_2O$	$n\text{-}C_4H_9MgBr$	$n\text{-}C_3H_7CO\text{-}n\text{-}C_4H_9$ (73%)	*10*
$(n\text{-}C_3H_7CO)_2O$	$i\text{-}C_4H_9MgCl$	$n\text{-}C_3H_7CO\text{-}i\text{-}C_4H_9$; $n\text{-}C_3H_7CO_2\text{-}i\text{-}C_4H_9$	*21,16*
$(n\text{-}C_3H_7CO)_2O$	$i\text{-}C_5H_{11}MgCl$ (1 equiv.)	$n\text{-}C_3H_7CO\text{-}i\text{-}C_5H_{11}$; $n\text{-}C_3H_7CO_2\text{-}i\text{-}C_5H_{11}$	*21,16*
$(i\text{-}C_3H_7CO)_2O$	CH_3MgBr (1 equiv.)	$CH_3CO\text{-}i\text{-}C_3H_7$	*16*
$(i\text{-}C_3H_7CO)_2O$	C_2H_5MgBr (1 equiv.)	$C_2H_5CO\text{-}i\text{-}C_3H_7$	*16*
$(i\text{-}C_3H_7CO)_2O$ (0.16 mole)	C_6H_5MgBr (7.3 g., 0.3 g.-atom Mg) + $CdCl_2$ (31.2 g., 0.17 mole)	$i\text{-}C_3H_7COC_6H_5$ (72%)	*11*
$C_9H_6O_3$			
Homophthalic anhydride*	CH_3MgX (2 equiv.)	"Dimethylhomophthalide," m. 94–95°	*60*
Homophthalic anhydride* (5.0 g.)	CH_3MgI (4.7 ml. CH_3I)	1,1-Dimethyl-2,1-benzopyran-3(4*H*)-one (1.9–2.3 g.); recovered anhydride (1.3–1.8 g.); homophthalic acid (0.4–0.6 g.); residual oil (0.6–0.8 g.); CH_4	*56*
Homophthalic anhydride*	C_6H_5MgX (2 equiv.)	"Diphenylhomophthalide," m. 160–161°	*60*
Homophthalic anhydride*	$C_6H_5CH_2MgX$ (2 equiv.)	"Debenzylhomophthalide," m. 163–164°	*60*
3-Methylphthalic anhydride (8 g.)	C_6H_5MgBr (48 ml., 1.09 *M*)	3,3-Diphenyl-7-methylphthalide (3.7%); 2-C_6H_5CO-6-$CH_3C_6H_3CO_2H$ (44%); 2-C_6H_5CO-3-$CH_3C_6H_3CO_2H$	*39*

* 2,1-Benzopyran-1,3(4*H*)-dione.

TABLE XI-I (Continued)

Anhydride	RMgX	Product(s)	Ref.
$C_9H_6O_3$ (*cont.*)			
3-Methylphthalic anhydride (5.3 g.)	C_6H_5MgBr (38 ml., 1.17 *M*)	3,3-Diphenyl-7-methylphthalide (3.5 g., 53%)	*39*
3-Methylphthalic anhydride (16 g.)	$2\text{-}CH_3C_6H_4MgBr$ (100 ml., 0.98 *M*)	2-*o*-Toluyl-6-methylbenzoic acid (11.57 g., 46.9%); 2-*o*-toluyl-3-methylbenzoic acid (1.31 g., 5.3%)	*39*
3-Methylphthalic anhydride (16.2 g.)	$1\text{-}C_{10}H_7MgBr$ (23 g. $C_{10}H_7Br$)	6-α-Naphthoyl-*o*-toluic acid (15.2 g., 52%); 2-α-naphthoyl-*m*-toluic acid (0.45 g., 1.5%)	*61*
$C_9H_6O_4$			
4-Methoxyphthalic anhydride	C_2H_5MgBr (2 equiv.)	3,3-Diethyl-6-methoxyphthalide	*62*
4-Methoxyphthalic anhydride	C_6H_5MgBr (10% excess)	$2\text{-}C_6H_5CO\text{-}4(5?)\text{-}CH_3OC_6H_3CO_2H$ (70–80%)	*33*
4-Methoxyphthalic anhydride	$1\text{-}C_{10}H_7MgBr$ (10% excess)	$2\text{-}\alpha\text{-}C_{10}H_7CO\text{-}4(5?)\text{-}CH_3OC_6H_3CO_2H$ (70–80%)	*33*
$C_9H_{12}O_3$			
Apocamphoric anhydride (16.8 g.)	CH_3MgI (15.6 g. CH_3I)	2,2-Dimethyl-3-acetyl-1-cyclopentanecarboxylic acid ("poor yield")	*63*
Apocamphoric anhydride (8.4 g.)	CH_3MgI (15.6 g. CH_3I)	4,4,8,8-Tetramethyl-3-oxabicyclo[3.2.1]-octan-2-one; 2,2-dimethyl-3-isopropylidene-1-cyclopentanecarboxylic acid	*63*
Santenic anhydride (8.4 g.)	CH_3MgI (7.8 g. CH_3I)	2,3-Dimethyl-3-acetyl-1-cyclopentanecarboxylic acid	*63*
Santenic anhydride (8.4 g.)	CH_3MgI (17.0 g. CH_3I)	"Dimethylsantolide" (*i.e.*, 1,4,4,8-tetramethyl-3-oxabicyclo[3.2.1]octan-2-one or 1,2,2,8-tetramethyl-3-oxabicyclo-[3.2.1]octan-4-one); an unsat'd acid	*63*

TABLE XI-I (Continued)

Anhydride	RMgX	Product(s)	Ref.
$C_{10}H_8O_3$			
Phenylsuccinic anhydride (8.7 g.)	C_6H_5MgBr (5.5 ml. C_6H_5Br)	α,γ,γ-Triphenyl-γ-butyrolactone (1.2 g.)	13
Phenylsuccinic anhydride (17.6 g.)	1-$C_{10}H_7MgBr$ (21.0 g. $C_{10}H_7Br$)	α-Phenyl-γ,γ-di-1-naphthyl-γ-butyrolactone; $HO_2CCH(C_6H_5)CHCO_2H$ (2 g.) (after red'n of acidic fraction with amalg. Zn)	13
3,4-Dimethylphthalic anhydride (20.0 g.)	2,3-$(CH_3)_2C_6H_3MgBr$ (20.0 g. C_8H_9Br)	2-(2,3-Dimethylbenzoyl)-3,4-dimethylbenzoic acid (2.4 g., 8%); 2-(2,3-dimethylbenzoyl)-5,6-dimethylbenzoic acid (9.0 g., 30%)	75
3,6-Dimethylphthalic anhydride	C_6H_5MgBr	2-C_6H_5CO-3,6-$(CH_3)_2C_6H_2CO_2H$ (81%)	64
3,6-Dimethylphthalic anhydride	2,4-$(CH_3)_2C_6H_3MgBr$	2-[2,4-$(CH_3)_2C_6H_3CO$]-3,6-$(CH_3)_2C_6H_2CO_2H$ (55%); recovered anhydride (31%)	64
3,6-Dimethylphthalic anhydride	2,4,6-$(CH_3)_3C_6H_2MgBr$	2-[2,4,6-$(CH_3)_3C_6H_2CO$]-3,6-$(CH_3)_2C_6H_2CO_2H$ (27%); recovered anhydride (33%)*	64
3,6-Dimethylphthalic anhydride	2,4,6-$(CH_3)_3C_6H_2MgBr$	2-[2,4,6-$(CH_3)_3C_6H_2CO$]-3,6-$(CH_3)_2C_6H_2CO_2H$ (44%); recovered anhydride (22%)†	64
$C_{10}H_8O_5$			
Hemipinic anhydride (2 g.)	C_6H_5MgBr (1.1 ml. C_6H_5Br)	2-C_6H_5CO-3,4-$(CH_3O)_2C_6H_2CO_2H$	52
Hemipinic anhydride	1-$C_{10}H_7MgBr$	2-α-$C_{10}H_7CO$-3,4-$(CH_3O)_2C_6H_2CO_2H$	52
Hemipinic anhydride	6-$CH_3OC_{10}H_6$-2-MgBr	2-(6-CH_3O-2-$C_{10}H_6CO$)3,4-$(CH_3O)_2$-$C_6H_2CO_2H$	52
$C_{10}H_{14}O_3$			
Camphoric anhydride (18.2 g.)	CH_3MgI (24.8 g. CH_3I)	3,3-Dimethylcampholide (1,4,4,8.8-pentamethyl-3-oxabicyclo[3.2.1]octan-2-one) (3 g.); camphoric acid; recovered anhydride	66

* Refluxed two hours in Et_2O. † Refluxed one hour in C_6H_6.

TABLE XI-1 (Continued)

Anhydride	RMgX	Product(s)	Ref.
$C_{10}H_{14}O_3$ (*cont.*)			
(+)-Camphoric anhydride (18.2 g.)	CH_3MgI (17.0 g. CH_3I)	2,2,3-Trimethyl-3-acetyl-1-cyclopentanecarboxylic acid	*63*
(+)-Camphoric anhydride (18.2 g.)	CH_3MgI (34.0 g. CH_3I)	2,2,3-Trimethyl-3-acetyl-1-cyclopentanecarboxylic acid; 3,3-dimethylcampholide (1,4,4,8,8-pentamethyl-3-oxabicyclo[3.2.1]octan-2-one); 1,2,2-trimethyl-3-isopropenyl-1-cyclopropanecarboxylic acid	*63*
(+)-Camphoric anhydride (18.2 g.)	$C_6H_5CH_2MgCl$ (27.9 g. C_7H_7Cl)	A dibenzylmethylenetrimethylcyclopentanecarboxylic acid and a phenylacetyltrimethylcyclopentanecarboxylic acid of undetermined constitution	*63; cf. 9*
$C_{10}H_{14}O_4$			
Cineolic anhydride (50 g.)	CH_3MgX* (16.5 g. Mg)	2,2,6-Trimethyl-6-(1-hydroxyisopropyl)tetrahydropyran-3-carboxylic acid (50 g., 27%)	*65*
Cineolic anhydride (80 g.)	C_2H_5MgBr (110 g. C_2H_5Br)	2,2,6-Trimethyl-6-(1-hydroxy-1-ethylpropyl)tetrahydropyran-3-carboxylic acid (90 g., 92%)	*65*
Cineolic anhydride (15.0 g.)	*n*-C_3H_7MgBr (23.5 g. C_3H_7Br)	2,2,6-Trimethyl-6-(1-hydroxy-1-propylbutyl)tetrahydropyran-3-carboxylic acid (6 g.); 2,2,6-trimethyl-6-(1-hydroxybutyl)tetrahydropyran-6-carboxylic acid (8 g.)	*65*
Cineolic anhydride (15.0 g.)	*i*-C_3H_7MgBr (23.5 g. C_3H_7Br)	2,2,6-Trimethyl-6-(1-hydroxyisobutyl)tetrahydropyran-3-carboxylic acid (87%)	*65*

*X = Br, I.

TABLE XI-I (Continued)

Anhydride	RMgX	Product(s)	Ref.
$C_{10}H_{14}O_4$ *(cont.)*			
Cineolic anhydride (90 g.)	C_6H_5MgBr (180 g. C_6H_5Br)	2,2,6-Trimethyl-6-(α-hydroxybenzhydryl)tetrahydropyran-3-carboxylic acid (142 g., 88%, crude)*	*65*
Cineolic anhydride (17 g.)	C_6H_5MgBr (16 g. C_6H_5Br)	Cineolic acid (5 g.); 2,2,6-trimethyl-6-(α-hydroxybenzhydryl)tetrahydropyran-3-carboxylic acid (15.5 g.)†	*65*
Cineolic anhydride (20 g.)	$(CH_2)_5CHMgBr$ (59 g. $C_6H_{11}Br$)	2,2,6-Trimethyl-6-cyclohexylhydroxymethyltetrahydropyran-3-carboxylic acid (22 g., 78%)	*65*
Cineolic anhydride (22 g.)	$C_6H_5CH_2MgCl$ (52 g. C_7H_7Cl)	2,2,6-Trimethyl-6-(1-hydroxy-2,2′-diphenylisopropyl)tetrahydropyran-3-carboxylic acid (32 g., 84%)	*65*
Cineolic anhydride (6 g.)	$4\text{-}CH_3C_6H_4MgBr$ (25.7 g. C_7H_7Br)	2,2,6-Trimethyl-6-(α-hydroxy-4,4′-dimethylbenzhydryl)tetrahydropyran-3-carboxylic acid (10 g., 88%)	*65*
Cineolic anhydride (5 g.)	$1\text{-}C_{10}H_7MgBr$ (42 g. $C_{10}H_7Br$)	2,2,6-Trimethyl-6-di-α-naphthylhydroxymethyl)tetrahydropyran-3-carboxylic acid (10 g., 88%)	*65*
$C_{10}H_{18}O_3$			
$(i\text{-}C_4H_9CO)_2O$	$i\text{-}C_4H_9MgCl$	$(i\text{-}C_4H_9)_2CO$	*21,16*
$C_{12}H_6O_3$			
1,2-Naphthalenedicarboxylic anhydride (19.8 g.)	$2\text{-}ClC_6H_4MgBr$ (21.1 g. C_6H_4BrCl)	$2\text{-}(o\text{-}ClC_6H_4CO)C_{10}H_6\text{-}1\text{-}CO_2H$ (13.3 g., 43%)	*67*

*Slow dropwise addition of Et_2O-anhydride solution to stirred Grignard reagent solution; one to two hours stirring; overnight standing.

†Addition of cooled (−15°) Grignard reagent solution to stirred Et_2O-anhydride solution at −15° to −10°.

TABLE XI-I (Continued)

Anhydride	RMgX	Product(s)	Ref.
$C_{12}H_6O_3$ (*cont.*)			
1,2-Naphthalenedicarboxylic anhydride (19.8 g.)	$4\text{-}ClC_6H_4MgBr$ (21.1 g. C_6H_4BrCl)	2-(p-ClC_6H_4CO)$C_{10}H_6$-1-CO_2H (9.7 g., 31%); 1-(p-ClC_6H_4CO)$C_{10}H_6$-2-CO_2H (2.9 g., 10%)	*68*
1,2-Naphthalenedicarboxylic anhydride	C_6H_5MgBr	2-$C_6H_5COC_{10}H_6$-1-CO_2H (30%)	*69*
1,2-Naphthalenedicarboxylic anhydride (20 g.)	$2\text{-}CH_3C_6H_4MgBr$ (19 g. C_7H_7Br)	2-(o-$CH_3C_6H_4CO$)$C_{10}H_6$-1-CO_2H (11-12.5 g., 38-43%); 1-(o-$CH_3C_6H_4CO$)$C_{10}H_6$-2-CO_2H (1 g., 3%)	*69*
1,2-Naphthalenedicarboxylic anhydride (33.3 g.)	$2\text{-}CH_3OC_6H_4MgBr$ (140 cc., 1.2 *M*)	2-(o-$CH_3OC_6H_4CO$)$C_{10}H_6$-1-CO_2H (13%); 1-(o-$CH_3OC_6H_4CO$)$C_{10}H_6$-2-CO_2H (13%); 3,3-di-(o-methoxyphenyl)-6,7-benzophthalide (17%); recovered anhydride	*70*
1,2-Naphthalenedicarboxylic anhydride (29.7 g.)	2,3-$(CH_3)_2C_6H_3MgBr$ (30.0 g. C_8H_9Br)	2-[2,3-$(CH_3)_2C_6H_3CO$]$C_{10}H_6$-1-CO_2H (10.8 g.)	*44*
1,2-Naphthalenedicarboxylic anhydride (15.0 g.)	$1\text{-}C_{10}H_7MgBr$ (20.4 g. $C_{10}H_7Br$)	2-α-$C_{10}H_7COC_{10}H_6$-1-CO_2H (11.3 g., 45.8%); 1-α $C_{10}H_7COC_{10}H_6$-2-CO_2H	*57*
2,3-Naphthalenedicarboxylic anhydride	C_6H_5MgBr (10% excess)	3-$C_6H_5COC_{10}H_6$-2-CO_2H (70-80%)	*33*
2,3-Naphthalenedicarboxylic anhydride	$4\text{-}CH_3OC_6H_4MgBr$	3-(p-$CH_3OC_6H_4CO$)$C_{10}H_6$-3-CO_2H (70-80%)	*33*
2,3-Naphthalenedicarboxylic anhydride	$1\text{-}C_{10}H_7MgBr$ (10% excess)	3-(α-$C_{10}H_7CO$)$C_{10}H_6$-2-CO_2H (70-80%)	*33*
2,3-Naphthalenedicarboxylic anhydride	$2\text{-}C_{10}H_7MgBr$ (10% excess)	3-(β-$C_{10}H_7CO$)$C_{10}H_6$-2-CO_2H (70-80%)	*33*
Naphthalic anhydride (10 g.)	$2\text{-}CH_3C_6H_4MgBr$	8-(o-$CH_3C_6H_4$)$C_{10}H_6$-1-CO_2H (70%)	*5*
Naphthalic anhydride (12 g.)	$1\text{-}C_{10}H_7MgBr$ (17 g. $C_{10}H_7Br$)	8-(α-$C_{10}H_7CO$)$C_{10}H_6$-1-CO_2H (65%)	*5*
$C_{14}H_8O_3$			
3-Phenylphthalic anhydride (5 g.)	C_6H_5MgBr (2.6 ml. C_6H_5Br)	2-C_6H_5-6-$C_6H_5COC_6H_3CO_2H$; 2-C_6H_5CO-3-$C_6H_5C_6H_3CO_2H$	*58*

TABLE XI-I (Continued)

Anhydride	RMgX	Product(s)	Ref.
$C_{14}H_8O_3$ (*cont.*)			
Diphenic anhydride	C_6H_5MgBr (2.5 equiv.)	2-[$HO(C_6H_5)_2C$]$C_6H_4C_6H_4$-2-CO_2H	*4*
$C_{14}H_{10}O_3$			
$(C_6H_5CO)_2O$	CH_3MgI	$C_6H_5(CH_3)_2COH$	*15*
$(C_6H_5CO)_2O$ (0.16 mole)	C_2H_5MgBr (7.3 g., 0.3 g.-atom Mg) + $CdCl_2$ (31.2 g., 0.17 mole)	$C_2H_5COC_6H_5$ (53%)	*11*
$(C_6H_5CO)_2O$ (0.16 mole)	*i*-C_3H_7MgBr (7.3 g., 0.3 g.-atom Mg) + $CdCl_2$ (31.2 g., 0.17 mole)	*i*-$C_3H_7COC_6H_5$ (47%)	*11*
$(C_6H_5CO)_2O$ (0.16 mole)	*i*-C_3H_7MgI (7.3 g., 0.3 g.-atom Mg) + $CdCl_2$ (31.2 g., 0.17 mole)	*i*-$C_3H_7COC_6H_5$ (33%)	*11*
$(C_6H_5CO)_2O$ (47.5 g., 0.21 mole)	*t*-C_4H_9MgCl (14.5 g. Mg) + $CdCl_2$ (56.8 g., 0.31 mole)	*t*-$C_4H_9COC_6H_5$ (40%)	*11*
$(C_6H_5CO)_2O$	C_6H_5MgBr (0.5 equiv.)	$(C_6H_5)_2CO$ (75–87%)	*10*
$(C_6H_5CO)_2O$ (16 g.)	2,5-Diphenyl-3-furyl-MgBr (19 g. $C_{16}H_{11}OBr$)	2,5-Diphenyl-3-benzoylfuran (13 g., 65%)	*74*
$C_{14}H_{12}O_3$			
3-Phenyl-1,2,3,4-tetrahydrophthalic anhydride (7.6 g.)	C_6H_5MgBr (3.5 ml. C_6H_5Br)	3,3,7-Triphenyl-3a,4,7,7a-tetrahydrophthalide; unidentified acidic products	*13*
$C_{14}H_{26}O_3$			
(*n*-$C_6H_{13}CO)_2O$	CH_3MgBr (1 equiv.)	CH_3CO-*n*-C_6H_{13}	*16*
(*n*-$C_6H_{13}CO)_2O$	C_2H_5MgBr (1 equiv.)	C_2H_5CO-*n*-C_6H_{13}; *n*-$C_6H_{13}CO_2C_2H_5$	*16*
$C_{16}H_8O_3$			
9,10-Phenanthrenedicarboxylic anhydride (0.7 g.)	C_6H_5MgBr (0.44 g. C_6H_5Br)	9-Benzoyl-10-phenanthrenecarboxylic acid	*53*

TABLE XI-I (Continued)

Anhydride	RMgX	Product(s)	Ref.
$C_{20}H_{12}O_3$			
3,6-Diphenylphthalic anhydride	4-BrC_6H_4MgBr	$2\text{-}(p\text{-BrC}_6H_4CO)\text{-}3,6\text{-}(C_6H_5)_2C_6H_2CO_2H$	58
3,6-Diphenylphthalic anhydride (6.00 g.)	C_6H_5MgBr (2.14 g. C_6H_5Br)	$2\text{-}C_6H_5CO\text{-}3,6\text{-}(C_6H_5)_2C_6H_2CO_2H$ (50%)	58
3,6-Diphenylphthalic anhydride (15 g.)	$4\text{-CH}_3OC_6H_4MgBr$ (28 g. C_7H_7BrO)	$2\text{-}(p\text{-CH}_3OC_6H_4CO)\text{-}3,6\text{-}(C_6H_5)_2C_6H_2CO_2H$	58
3,6-Diphenylphthalic anhydride (15.0 g.)	$1\text{-}C_{10}H_7MgBr$ (10.3 g. $C_{10}H_7Br$)	$2\text{-}(\alpha\text{-}C_{10}H_7CO)\text{-}3,6\text{-}(C_6H_5)_2C_6H_2CO_2H$ (50%)	58
3,6-Diphenylphthalic anhydride (15 g.)	$6\text{-CH}_3OC_{10}H_6\text{-}2\text{-MgBr}$ (15 g. $C_{11}H_9BrO$)	$2\text{-}(6\text{-CH}_3OC_{10}H_6\text{-}2\text{-CO})\text{-}3,6\text{-}(C_6H_5)_2C_6H_2CO_2H$	58
$C_{20}H_{22}O_3$			
Mesitoic anhydride (1.0 g.)	$2,4,6\text{-}(CH_3)_3C_6H_2MgBr$ (8.8 g. $C_9H_{11}Br$)	$[2,4,6\text{-}(CH_3)_3C_6H_2]_2CO$	59

REFERENCES FOR TABLE XI-I

(*1*) Diels and Reinbeck, *Ber.*, *43*, 1271–9 (1910).
(*2*) Weizmann and Bergmann, *J. Am. Chem. Soc.*, *60*, 2647–50 (1938).
(*3*) Purdie and Arup, *J. Chem. Soc.*, *97*, 1537–46 (1910).
(*4*) Ssergejew, *J. Russ. Phys.-Chem. Soc.*, *61*, 1421–49 (1929); *Chem. Zentr.*, *1930,II*, 391.
(*5*) Weiss and Fastmann, *Monatsh.*, *47*, 727–32 (1926).
(*6*) Cason, *J. Am. Chem. Soc.*, *64*, 1106–10 (1942).
(*7*) Cason and Prout, *J. Am. Chem. Soc.*, *66*, 46–50 (1944).
(*8*) Komppa and Rohrmann, *Ann.*, *509*, 259–68 (1934).
(*9*) Houben and Hahn, *Ber.*, *41*, 1580–8 (1908).
(*10*) Newman and Smith, *J. Org. Chem.*, *13*, 592–8 (1948).
(*11*) Benneville, *J. Org. Chem.*, 6, 462–6 (1941).
(*12*) Stefanova, *Annuaire univ. Sofia, Faculté phys.-math.*, *40*, Livre 2, 147–66 (1943–44); *Chem. Abstr.*, *42*, 4156 (1948).
(*13*) Weizmann, Blum-Bergmann, and Bergmann, *J. Chem. Soc.*, *1935*, 1370–1.
(*14*) Austin and Johnson, *J. Am. Chem. Soc.*, *54*, 647–60 (1932).
(*15*) Tissier and Grignard, *Compt. rend.*, *132*, 336–8 (1901); *Chem. Zentr.*, *1901,I*, 930; *J. Chem. Soc.*, *80,I*, 316 (1901).
(*16*) Fournier, *Bull. soc. chim.*, [4], 7, 836–40 (1910).
(*17*) Mingoia, *Gazz. chim. ital.*, *61*, 449–58 (1931); *Chem. Abstr.*, *26*, 453 (1932).
(*18*) Newman and Booth, *J. Am. Chem. Soc.*, *67*, 154 (1945).
(*19*) Sweet and Marvel, *J. Am. Chem. Soc.*, *54*, 1184–90 (1932).
(*20*) Nazarov and Elizarova, *Bull. acad. sci. U.R.S.S., Classe sci. chim.*, *1940*, 189–94; *Chem. Abstr.*, *36*, 741 (1942).
(*21*) Fournier, *Bull. soc. chim.*, [3], *35*, 14 (1906).
(*22*) Brokaw and Brode, *J. Org. Chem.*, *13*, 194–9 (1948).
(*23*) Kroeger and Nieuwland, *J. Am. Chem. Soc.*, *58*, 1861–3 (1936).
(*24*) Kitchin and Sandin, *J. Am. Chem. Soc.*, *67*, 1645–6 (1945).
(*25*) Newman and O'Leary, *J. Am. Chem. Soc.*, *68*, 258–61 (1946).
(*26*) Cason, *J. Am. Chem. Soc.*, *68*, 2078–81 (1946).
(*27*) Tarbell, *J. Am. Chem. Soc.*, *60*, 215–6 (1938).
(*28*) Tarbell and Weaver, *J. Am. Chem. Soc.*, *62*, 2747–50 (1940).
(*29*) Ellingboe and Fuson, *J. Am. Chem. Soc.*, *56*, 1777–9 (1934).
(*30*) Mazza, *Rend. accad. sci. fis. mat., Napoli ser. 3a*, *34*, 59–65 (1928); *Chem. Zentr.*, *1929,I*, 1826.
(*31*) Cobb, *Am. Chem. J.*, *35*, 486–508 (1906).
(*32*) Bauer, *Arch. Pharm.*, *247*, 220–5 (1909); *Chem. Zentr.*, *1909,II*, 525.
(*33*) Weizmann, Bergmann, and Bergmann, *J. Chem. Soc.*, *1935*, 1367–70.
(*34*) Bauer, *Ber.*, *37*, 735–7 (1904).
(*35*) Orlov, *J. Russ. Phys.-Chem. Soc.*, *44*, 1868–70 (1912); *Chem. Abstr.*, 7, 1174 (1913).
(*36*) Pickles and Weizmann, *Chem. News*, *90*, 276 (1904).
(*37*) Bauer, *Ber.*, *38*, 240–1 (1905).
(*38*) Vène and Gérard, *Compt. rend.*, *222*, 1115–7 (1946); *Chem. Abstr.*, *40*, 5715 (1946).
(*39*) Newman and McCleary, *J. Am. Chem. Soc.*, *63*, 1537–41 (1941).
(*40*) Fieser and Heymann, *J. Am. Chem. Soc.*, *64*, 376–82 (1942).
(*41*) Scholl and Donat, *Ber.*, *64B*, 318–21 (1931).
(*42*) Fournier, *Bull. soc. chim.*, [3], *31*, 483 (1904).
(*43*) Ferrario, *Gazz. chim. ital.*, *41,I*, 1–11 (1911); *Chem. Zentr.*, *1911,I*, 1059.
(*44*) Badger, Cook, and Goulden, *J. Chem. Soc.*, *1940*, 16–8.

(45) Blicke and Weinkauff, *J. Am. Chem. Soc.*, *54*, 1454–9 (1932).
(46) Komppa, *Kgl. Norske Vedenskab. Selskabs, Forh.*, *9*, 157–60 (1936); *Chem. Abstr.*, *31*, 7423 (1937); *Chem. Zentr.*, *1937,II*, 391.
(47) Pickles and Weizmann, *Proc. Chem. Soc.*, *20*, 201 (1904).
(48) Fieser and Hershberg, *J. Am. Chem. Soc.*, *59*, 2331–5 (1937).
(49) Bousset, *Bull. soc. chim.*, [5], *2*, 2182–7 (1935).
(50) Cook and Robinson, *J. Chem. Soc.*, *1938*, 505–13.
(51) Fieser and Seligman, *J. Am. Chem. Soc.*, *61*, 136–42 (1939).
(52) Weizmann and Bergmann, *J. Chem. Soc.*, *1936*, 567–9.
(53) Weizmann, Bergmann, and Berlin, *J. Am. Chem. Soc.*, *60*, 1331–4 (1938).
(54) Berlingozzi, *Gazz. chim. ital.*, *61*, 886–97 (1932); *Chem. Abstr.*, *26*, 2728 (1932).
(55) Berlingozzi and Mazza, *Gazz. chim. ital.*, *56*, 88–98 (1926); *Chem. Zentr.*, *1926,II*, 401.
(56) Price, Lewis, and Meister, *J. Am. Chem. Soc.*, *61*, 2760–2 (1939).
(57) Fieser and Kilmer, *J. Am. Chem. Soc.*, *61*, 862–4 (1939).
(58) Weizmann, Bergmann, and Haskelberg, *J. Chem. Soc.*, *1939*, 391–7.
(59) Fuson, Corse, and Rabjohn, *J. Am. Chem. Soc.*, *63*, 2852–3 (1941).
(60) Bauer and Wölz, *Arch. Pharm.*, *249*, 454–8 (1911); *Chem. Zentr.*, *1911,II*, 1221.
(61) Newman, *J. Am. Chem. Soc.*, *59*, 1003–6 (1937).
(62) Bauer, *Arch. Pharm.*, *249*, 450–3 (1911); *Chem. Zentr.*, *1911,II*, 1220.
(63) Komppa and Rohrmann, *Ann.*, *521*, 227–42 (1936).
(64) Newman and Lord, *J. Am. Chem. Soc.*, *66*, 733–5 (1944).
(65) Rupe and Zweidler, *Helv. Chim. Acta*, *23*, 1025–45 (1940).
(66) Komppa, *Ber.*, *41*, 1039–41 (1908).
(67) Newman, *J. Am. Chem. Soc.*, *60*, 1368–70 (1938).
(68) Newman and Orchin, *J. Am. Chem. Soc.*, *60*, 586–9 (1938).
(69) Fieser and Newman, *J. Am. Chem. Soc.*, *58*, 2376–82 (1936).
(70) Newman and Wise, *J. Am. Chem. Soc.*, *63*, 2109–11 (1941).
(71) Heilbron, *J. Chem. Soc.*, *1948*, 386–93.
(72) Heilbron, Jones, and Richardson, *J. Chem. Soc.*, *1949*, 287–93.
(73) Sobotka and Chanley, *J. Am. Chem. Soc.*, *70*, 3914–8 (1948).
(74) Lutz and Smith, *J. Am. Chem. Soc.*, *63*, 1148–50 (1941).
(75) Nichol and Sandin, *J. Am. Chem. Soc.*, *69*, 2256–8 (1947).
(76) Gaertner, *J. Am. Chem. Soc.*, *73*, 3934–7 (1951).

CHAPTER XII

Reactions of Grignard Reagents with Carboxylic Amides Imides, and Lactams

KETONE OR ALDEHYDE FORMATION (FROM AMIDES)

The amide-Grignard reagent reaction that is usually regarded as "normal" is that originally reported by Béïs,[1] which he described as follows:

$$RCONH_2 + 2\,R'MgX \rightarrow RC(OMgX)(NHMgX)R' + R'H$$

$$RC(OMgX)(NHMgX)R' + 2\,H_2O \rightarrow RC(OH)(NH_2)R' + MgX_2 + MgO$$

$$RC(OH)(NH_2)R' \rightarrow RCOR' + NH_3$$

Actually, little or nothing concerning the mechanism of the reaction is known. In general the yields obtained are not such as to recommend the reaction as a preparative method. For the amides investigated by Béïs (propionamide, butyramide, isovaleramide, and benzamide), 20–50 percent yields of ketone were obtained from methylmagnesium iodide, ethylmagnesium iodide, and ethylmagnesium bromide reactions. The yields tended to be higher for the amides of higher molecular weight. Acetamide gave meagre yields of methyl ketones, and formamide produced no aldehyde at all.

Aldehydes have, however, been obtained in varying yields from *N,N*-disubstituted formamides investigated by Bouveault[2] and others (see Table XII-I).

$$HCONR_2 \xrightarrow{R'MgX} \xrightarrow{H_2O} R'CHO + R_2NH + MgXOH$$

NITRILE FORMATION (FROM AMIDES)

Relatively few cases of nitrile formation have been reported. However, in view of the facts that nitriles might be expected to react further with an excess of Grignard reagent to yield ketimines (or the corresponding ketones) and that most investigators have made no attempt to isolate nitriles, this is scarcely surprising. It is altogether possible that in some instances the reported "normal" product (ketone) is obtained by way of the nitrile.

---

[1]Béïs, *Compt. rend.*, *137*, 575–6 (1903); *Chem. Zentr.*, *1903,II*, 1110.
[2]Bouveault, *Bull. soc. chim.*, [3], *31*, 1322–7 (1904).

On the basis of a rather small number of cases examined, Ramart *et al.*[3] have generalized as follows. With phenylmagnesium bromide, α-mono- and α,α-disubstituted acetamides react to give ketones, but α,α,α-trisubstituted acetamides give nitriles. Of the latter, those of the types $AlkAr_2CCONH_2$ and $ArAlk_2CCONH_2$ give nitriles almost exclusively; those of the type Alk_3CCONH_2 give a preponderance of ketone, but with some nitrile.

Ramart *et al.* have accounted for nitrile formation on the assumption that reaction takes place with the imido form.

$$RC\begin{matrix}\diagup OH \\ \diagdown\!\!\!\diagdown NH\end{matrix} \xrightarrow{2\ R'MgX} 2\ R'H + RC\begin{matrix}\diagup OMgX \\ \diagdown\!\!\!\diagdown NMgX\end{matrix} \rightarrow RCN + MgO + MgX_2$$

Specific examples of acetamides said to give nitriles exclusively (with phenylmagnesium bromide) are: α-methyl-α-ethyl-α-phenyl-, α,α-diethyl-α-phenyl-, and α-benzyl-α,α-diphenyl-. Fencholamide and "dimethylcampholamide" are said to react similarly. α,α-Dimethyl-α-benzylacetamide is reported to give nitrile as the principle product, together with some ketone. α,α-Dimethyl-α-ethyl- and α,α,α-trimethylacetamides gave the respective ketones chiefly, together with a little of the respective nitriles.

Bruzau[4] has also isolated nitriles as byproducts of the reactions of α-phenylpropionamide with aryl Grignard reagents, and Fries and Schimmelschmidt[5] report 2-methoxy-3-naphthonitrile as the product of the reaction of 2-methoxy-3-naphthamide with methylmagnesium iodide.

AMINE FORMATION (FROM AMIDES)

In exploring the possibilities of aldehyde preparation by reactions of Grignard reagents with *N,N*-dialkylated formamides, Bouveault (*loc. cit.*[2]) obtained, as a byproduct of the reaction of isoamylmagnesium chloride with *N,N*-dimethylformamide, some 2,8-dimethyl-5-dimethylaminononane $[(i\text{-}C_5H_{11})_2CHN(CH_3)_2]$. The available data are scarcely extensive enough to support any generalizations concerning the necessary and sufficient requirements for this type of reaction, but all instances so far reported have involved amides of the type $RCONR'_2$ in which R may be H or a hydrocarbon radical.

On the whole it seems probable that the reaction is a stepwise phenomenon of which the more significant portions may be summarized as follows:

---

[3]Ramart-Lucas, Laclôtre, and Anagnostopoulis, *Compt. rend.*, *185*, 282–4 (1927); *Chem. Zentr.*, *1927,II*, 1566; *Chem. Abstr.*, *21*, 3359 (1927).

[4]Bruzau, *Ann. chim.*, [11], *1*, 257–358 (1934).

[5]Fries and Schimmelschmidt, *Ber.*, *58B*, 2835–45 (1925).

$$RCONR'_2 \xrightarrow{R''MgX} RR''C(OMgX)NR'_2 \xrightarrow{R''MgX} RR''_2CNR'_2 + (XMg)_2O$$

If, for steric or other reasons, the final step failed of realization one might expect as product an amino alcohol. This might possibly account for the product obtained by Houben and Doescher[6] from the reaction of *N*-methylformanilide with the Grignard reagent of pinene hydrochloride.

$$HCON(CH_3)C_6H_5 \xrightarrow{C_{10}H_{17}MgCl} C_{10}H_{17}CH(OMgCl)N(CH_3)C_6H_5 \xrightarrow{H_2O} C_{10}H_{17}CH(OH)N(CH_3)C_6H_5$$

It is also conceivable that the final step might be, in some cases, a disproportionation rather than a simple metathesis. This would account for the products observed by Bouveault (*loc. cit.*[2]) in the reaction of *t*-amylmagnesium chloride with *N*,*N*-dimethylformamide.

$$HCON(CH_3)_2 \xrightarrow{t\text{-}C_5H_{11}MgCl} t\text{-}C_5H_{11}CH(OMgCl)N(CH_3)_2 \xrightarrow{t\text{-}C_5H_{11}MgCl} t\text{-}C_5H_{11}CH_2N(CH_3)_2 + (ClMg)_2O + C_5H_{10}$$

Some examples of reactant pairs which appear to follow, at least in part, the reaction sequence first suggested are: $HCON(C_2H_5)_2$, $CH_3C{\equiv}CMgBr$ (Viguier[7]); $HCON(C_2H_5)_2$, C_2H_5MgX (Maxim[8]); $HCON(C_2H_5)_2$, $n\text{-}C_3H_7MgBr$ (Maxim and Mavrodineanu[9]); $HCON(CH_3)_2$, RMgX (Maxim and Mavrodineanu[10]); $n\text{-}C_3H_7CONRR'$, R''MgX (Montagne[11]); $C_6H_5CON(C_2H_5)C_6H_5$, C_6H_5MgBr (Busch and Fleischmann[12]); $4\text{-}CH_3OC_6H_4CON(C_2H_5)_2$, RMgBr (Couturier[13]). Other examples are to be found in Table XII-I.

IMINE FORMATION (FROM AMIDES)

In a few instances imines have been reported among the products of reactions of amides with Grignard reagents. For example:

$4\text{-}CH_3OC_6H_4CONH_2 + C_2H_5MgBr \rightarrow 4\text{-}CH_3OC_6H_4COC_2H_5$ (70%) $+ 4\text{-}CH_3OC_6H_4C({=}NH)C_2H_5$ + recovered amide (Couturier, *loc. cit.*[13])

$3,4,5\text{-}(CH_3O)_3C_6H_2CONH_2$ (90 g.) + C_2H_5MgBr (144 g. C_2H_5Br) $\rightarrow$ $3,4,5\text{-}(CH_3O)_3C_6H_2COC_2H_5$ (32 g.) $+ 3,4,5\text{-}(CH_3O)_3C_6H_2C({=}NH)C_2H_5$ (17 g.) + recovered amide (30 g.) (Couturier, *loc. cit.*[13])

$C_6H_5(CH_3)_2CCONH_2 + 4\text{-}CH_3COC_6H_4MgBr \rightarrow$ $C_6H_5(CH_3)_2C({=}NH)C_6H_4\text{-}4\text{-}OCH_3$ (Bruzau[14])

---

[6]Houben and Doescher, *Ber.*, *40*, 4576–9 (1907).
[7]Viguier, *Compt. rend.*, *153*, 955–7 (1911); *Chem. Zentr.*, *1912*,*I*, 20.
[8]Maxim, *Bull. soc. chim.*, [4], *41*, 809–13 (1927).
[9]Maxim and Mavrodineanu, *Bull. soc. chim.*, [5], *2*, 591–600 (1935).
[10]Maxim and Mavrodineanu, *Bull. soc. chim.*, [5], *3*, 1084–93 (1936).
[11]Montagne, *Compt. rend.*, *183*, 216–8 (1926).
[12]Busch and Fleischmann, *Ber.*, *43*, 2553–6 (1910).
[13]Couturier, *Compt. rend.*, *205*, 800–2 (1937); *Ann. chim.*, [11], *10*, 559–629 (1938).
[14]Bruzau, *Compt. rend.*, *194*, 1662–4 (1932).

Conceivably imine formation could result in these cases from further reaction of an intermediate nitrile. It seems equally probable, however, that it might result from a reaction akin to a dehydration.

$$RCONH_2 \xrightarrow{2\ R'MgX} RR'C(OMgX)NHMgX \rightarrow RR'C{=}NH + (XMg)_2O$$

In a case reported by Montagne and Rousseau,[15] intermediate nitrile formation would be impossible, and it is necessary to assume a reaction of the "dehydration" type. Upon treatment of propionanilide with an excess of ethylmagnesium bromide they obtained as one of the products the anil of 3-pentanone (*ca.* 40 percent yield). Butyranilide reacted similarly.

An unusual case of reductive anil formation has been reported by Skraup and Moser.[16]

$$\text{(benzoxazol-2-yl)}\text{—}CONHC_6H_5 \xrightarrow[\text{(1.5 equiv.)}]{CH_3MgI} \text{(benzoxazol-2-yl)}\text{—}CH{=}NC_6H_5$$

Such a reaction appears all the more remarkable in that it is not conducted under "forced" conditions. It would probably repay further study, with due attention to the exclusion of excess magnesium.

PHTHALIDE FORMATION

Maxim and Andreescu[17] report the formation of 3,3-disubstituted phthalides by the action of Grignard reagents on *N*,*N*-diethylphthalamic acid.

$$C_6H_4(CO_2H)(CON(C_2H_5)_2) \xrightarrow{RMgX^*} C_6H_4\langle{}^{C(=O)}_{CR_2}\rangle O$$

α-HALO AMIDES

In so far as they have been studied, the reactions of the α-halo amides appear to have something in common with those of the α-halo ketones (*q.v.*). Sou Phou Ti[18] has reported the products of the reaction of excess phenylmagnesium bromide with α-bromo-*N*,*N*-diethylbutyramide as *N*,*N*-diethylbutyramide, *N*,*N*-diethylcrotonamide, *n*-propyldiphenylcarbinol, and butyrophenone (trace). He attributes dehalogenation to the action of excess magnesium, which is assumed to form a Grignard reagent that

---

[15] Montagne and Rousseau, *Compt. rend.*, *196*, 1165–7 (1933).

[16] Skraup and Moser, *Ber.*, *55B*, 1080–101 (1922).

[17] Maxim and Andreescu, *Bull. soc. chim.*, [5], *5*, 54–7 (1938).

*RMgX = n-C_3H_7MgBr, i-C_4H_9MgCl, i-$C_5H_{11}MgBr$, C_6H_5MgBr, $C_6H_5CH_2MgCl$.

[18] Sou Phou Ti, *Bull. soc. chim.*, [5], *2*, 1799–800 (1935). See also: *Chem. Abstr.*, *29*, 2519 (1935).

then reacts further with phenylmagnesium bromide. The crotonamide is supposed to result in some manner not fully explained from the combined action of water and excess magnesium on residual α-bromobutyramide.

It is unfortunate that an unnecessary complication was introduced into this study by failure to take precautions against the presence of excess magnesium. The work should be repeated with magnesium-free reagent prepared from sublimed magnesium.

If the reaction products found in the absence of metallic magnesium were the same as those reported by Sou Phou Ti (with the addition of bromobenzene) a reasonably plausible explanation might be constructed on the basis of analogy with the known behavior of α-halo ketones, *q.v.*

$$C_2H_5CHBrCON(C_2H_5)_2 + C_6H_5MgBr \rightarrow C_2H_5CH{=}C(OMgBr)N(C_2H_5)_2 + C_6H_5Br$$

$$C_2H_5CHBrCON(C_2H_5)_2 + C_2H_5CH{=}C(OMgBr)N(C_2H_5)_2 \rightarrow CH_3CH{=}CHCON(C_2H_5)_2 + n\text{-}C_3H_7COC_6H_5 + MgBr_2$$

$$n\text{-}C_3H_7COC_6H_5 + C_6H_5MgBr \rightarrow n\text{-}C_3H_7(C_6H_5)_2COMgBr$$

$$C_2H_5CHBrCON(C_2H_5)_2 + C_6H_5MgBr \rightarrow C_2H_5CHBrCOC_6H_5 + (C_2H_5)_2NMgBr$$

$$C_2H_5CHBrCOC_6H_5 + C_6H_5MgBr \rightarrow C_2H_5CH{=}C(OMgBr)C_6H_5 + C_6H_5Br$$

$$C_2H_5CH{=}C(OMgBr)N(C_2H_5)_2 + H_2O \rightarrow n\text{-}C_3H_7CON(C_2H_5)_2 + MgBrOH$$

$$n\text{-}C_3H_7(C_6H_5)_2COMgBr + H_2O \rightarrow n\text{-}C_3H_7(C_6H_5)_2COH + MgBrOH$$

$$C_2H_5CH{=}C(OMgBr)C_6H_5 + H_2O \rightarrow n\text{-}C_3H_7COC_6H_5 + MgBrOH$$

The same investigator[19] has reported the formation of an amino alcohol by the action of ethylmagnesium bromide on *N,N*-diethylchloroacetamide. The product isolated might well arise from the following reaction sequence.

$$ClCH_2CON(C_2H_5)_2 + C_2H_5MgBr \rightarrow ClCH_2COC_2H_5 + (C_2H_5)_2NMgBr$$

$$ClCH_2COC_2H_5 + C_2H_5MgBr \rightarrow ClCH_2(C_2H_5)_2COMgBr$$

$$(C_2H_5)_2NMgBr + ClCH_2(C_2H_5)COMgBr \rightarrow (C_2H_5)_2NCH_2C(C_2H_5)_2OMgBr + MgBrCl$$

$$(C_2H_5)_2NCH_2C(C_2H_5)_2OMgBr + H_2O \rightarrow (C_2H_5)_2NCH_2C(C_2H_5)_2OH + MgBrOH$$

If it be assumed that addition at the carbonyl double bond is a step in the "normal" cleavage reaction another possible reaction sequence suggests itself.

$$ClCH_2CON(C_2H_5)_2 \xrightarrow{C_2H_5MgBr} ClCH_2C(OMgBr)(C_2H_5)N(C_2H_5)_2 \rightarrow$$

$$\left[\begin{matrix} CH_2 & & N(C_2H_5)_2 \\ & C & \\ H_5C_2 & & OMgBr \end{matrix}\right]^{+}Cl^{-} \xrightarrow{C_2H_5MgBr} (C_2H_5)_2NCH_2C(C_2H_5)_2OMgBr + MgBrCl$$

[19]Sou Phou Ti, *Compt. rend.*, *192*, 1462–4 (1931).

Neither of the sequences suggested should be interpreted as implying anything concerning mechanistic detail, nor should it be inferred that still other probable sequences are inconceivable. The sole object of these speculations is to show that a product which at first glance appears unusual may be the result of reactions of well-known types.

α,β-UNSATURATED AMIDES

In an investigation of the reactions of Grignard reagents with α,β-unsaturated compounds, Kohler and Heritage[20] found that phenylmagnesium bromide reacts with *N*-ethylcinnamanilide by 1,4-addition. Having apparently overlooked this work, Maxim and Ioanid[21] repeated and extended it, obtaining nearly quantitative yields of 1,4-addition products.

$$C_6H_5CH{=}CHCONRC_6H_5 \xrightarrow{R'MgBr} \xrightarrow{H_2O} C_6H_5CHR'CH_2CONRC_6H_5{}^*$$

The reaction of methylmagnesium iodide was exceptional in that, under comparable conditions (four hours reflux in ether; twelve hours standing), considerable amounts of amide remained unchanged, the rest being converted to unsaturated methyl ketone and amine.

$$C_6H_5CH{=}CHCONRC_6H_5 \xrightarrow{CH_3MgI} \xrightarrow{H_2O} C_6H_5CH{=}CHCOCH_3 + C_6H_5NHR$$

Similar 1,4-additions to *N,N*-disubstituted cinnamamides, crotonamides, and furfurilideneacetamides have been reported by Maxim *et al.*[22] Other examples are included in Table XII-I.

AMIDE CONDENSATIONS

From the reaction of methylmagnesium iodide with *N*-phenylcrotonanalide Maxim[23] was able to isolate only about 1-2 percent of the 1,4-addition product, but obtained in about 80 percent yield a condensation product of empirical formula $C_{33}H_{34}N_2O_2$ to which he assigned the constitution $(C_6H_5)_2NCH(CH_3)CH[CON(C_6H_5)_2]CO\text{-}i\text{-}C_4H_9$. Nenitzescu[24] has repeated this work and declares that the product is actually $(C_6H_5)_2NCOCH_2CH(CH_3)CH[CON(C_6H_5)_2]\text{-}i\text{-}C_3H_7$, *i.e.*, the one which would be expected to result from 1,4-condensation of the enolate (formed by

[20]Kohler and Heritage, *Am. Chem. J.*, 33, 21-35 (1905).

[21]Maxim and Ioanid, *Bull. soc. chim. România*, *10*, 29-48 (1928); *Chem. Zentr.*, *1928,III*, 754; *Chem. Abstr.*, *22*, 4114 (1928).

*$R = CH_3, C_2H_5, C_6H_5$; $R' = C_2H_5, C_6H_5$.

[22](*a*) Maxim, *Ann. chim.*, [10], 9, 55-111 (1928); (*b*) Maxim, *Bull. soc. chim. România*, *10*, 97-115 (1928); *Chem. Zentr.*, *1929,I*, 2161; *Chem. Abstr.*, *23*, 2697 (1929); (*c*) Maxim and Ioanid, *Bull. soc. chim. România*, *12*, 28-32 (1930); *Chem. Zentr.*, *1930,II*, 3013; *Chem. Abstr.*, *25*, 488 (1931); (*d*) Maxim and Zugravescu, *Bull. soc. chim.*, [5], *1*, 1987-99 (1934); (*e*) Maxim and Stancovici, *ibid.*, [5], 3, 1319-23 (1936).

[23]Maxim, *Bull. soc. chim. România*, *11*, 123-9 (1929); *Chem. Zentr.*, *1930,I*, 2550; *Chem. Abstr.*, *24*, 2427 (1930).

[24]Nenitzescu, *Bull. soc. chim. România*, *12*, 48-57 (1930); *Chem. Zentr.*, *1930,II*, 3014; *Chem. Abstr.*, *25*, 1509 (1931).

1,4-addition of the Grignard reagent to the amide) with a second molecule of amide.

$$CH_3CH{=}CHCON(C_6H_5)_2 \xrightarrow{CH_3MgI}$$
$$(CH_3)_2CH{=}C(OMgI)N(C_6H_5)_2 \xrightarrow{CH_3CH=CHCON(C_6H_5)_2}$$
$$(CH_3)_2CHC[CH(CH_3)CH_2CON(C_6H_5)_2]{=}C(OMgI)N(C_6H_5)_2 \xrightarrow{H_2O}$$
$$i\text{-}C_3H_7CH[CON(C_6H_5)_2]CH(CH_3)CH_2CON(C_6H_5)_2$$

A somewhat different type of condensation has been reported by Montagne and Isambert[25] as resulting from the reaction of *N*-ethylbutyranilide with ethylmagnesium bromide. Apparently a part of the amide reacts "normally", forming 3-hexanone, whereas a part "enolizes". Condensation between ketone and enolate then takes place.

$$n\text{-}C_3H_7CON(C_2H_5)C_6H_5 \xrightarrow{C_2H_5MgBr} n\text{-}C_3H_7COC_2H_5 + C_2H_5(C_6H_5)NMgBr$$
$$C_2H_5CH_2CON(C_2H_5)C_6H_5 \xrightarrow{C_2H_5MgBr}$$
$$C_2H_5CH{=}C(OMgBr)N(C_2H_5)C_6H_5 + C_2H_6$$
$$n\text{-}C_3H_7COC_2H_5 + C_2H_5CH{=}C(OMgBr)N(C_2H_5)C_6H_5 \rightarrow$$
$$C_2H_5(n\text{-}C_3H_7)C(OMgBr)CH(C_2H_5)CON(C_2H_5)C_6H_5$$

UNREACTIVE AMIDES

Some amides that have been reported as unreactive toward Grignard reagents in ethereal solution are as follows: $(-CONH_2)_2$, $C_6H_5CON(C_2H_5)_2$ (McKenzie and Duff[26]); $C_6H_5CON(C_2H_5)_2$, $C_6H_4\text{-}1,2\text{-}[CON(C_2H_5)_2]_2$, $C_2H_5(C_6H_5)CHCH_2CON(C_2H_5)_2$, $(C_6H_5)_2CHCON(C_2H_5)_2$, $(C_6H_5)_2CHCH_2\text{-}CON(C_2H_5)_2$, $(C_6H_5CH_2)_2CHCON(C_2H_5)_2$ (Maxim[27]); $(C_6H_5)_2C(OH)CONH_2$ (Burton[28]); DL-$C_6H_5CH(OH)CONHC_2H_5$ (McKenzie *et al.*[29]); 3,4-$(HO)_2\text{-}C_6H_3CON(C_2H_5)_2$, 3,4,5-$(HO)_3C_6H_2CON(C_2H_5)_2$ (Couturier[30]); $HCONH\text{-}NHC_6H_5$, $CH_3CONHNHC_6H_5$, $C_6H_5CONHNHC_6H_5$ (Grammaticakis[31]). In some cases at least the apparent lack of reactivity is probably due to initial reaction of the amide as an "active hydrogen" compound, with the formation of a relatively insoluble halomagnesium derivative.

IMIDES

The published data on the reactions of Grignard reagents with imides are very meagre. Béïs[32] reported the formation of isoindolones from phthalimide. The reactions probably take the following course.

[25] Montagne and Isambert, *Compt. rend.*, *208*, 285–7 (1939); *Chem. Abstr.*, *33*, 3772 (1939).

[26] McKenzie and Duff, *Ber.*, *60B*, 1335–41 (1927).

[27] Maxim, *Compt. rend.*, *182*, 1393–5 (1926); *Ann. chim.*, [10], 9, 55–111 (1928).

[28] Burton, *J. Chem. Soc.*, *1930*, 2400.

[29] McKenzie, Martin, and Rule, *J. Chem. Soc.*, *105*, 1583–91 (1914).

[30] Couturier, *Ann. chim.*, [11], *10*, 559–629 (1938).

[31] Grammaticakis, *Compt. rend.*, *207*, 239–41 (1938); *Chem. Abstr.*, *34*, 2808 (1940).

[32] Béïs, *Compt. rend.*, *138*, 987–9 (1904); *Chem. Zentr.*, *1904,I*, 1446.

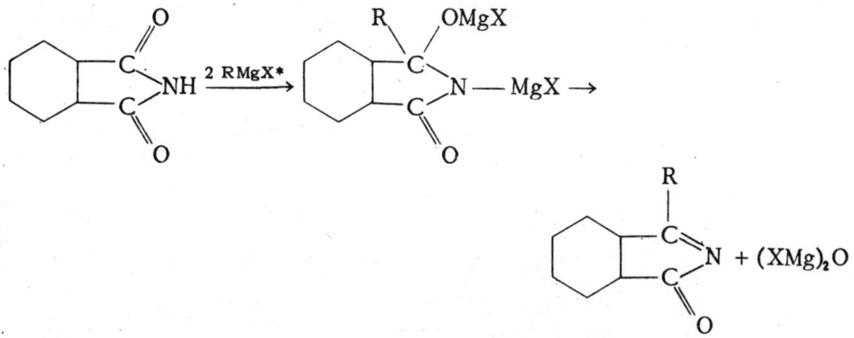

$$\xrightarrow{2\ RMgX^*} \quad N-MgX \rightarrow \quad + (XMg)_2O$$

The reaction of N,α-dimethyl-α-n-decylsuccinimide with n-decylmagnesium bromide, according to Birch and Robinson[33], also involves a dehydration, but one of a different type, which probably follows a different course.

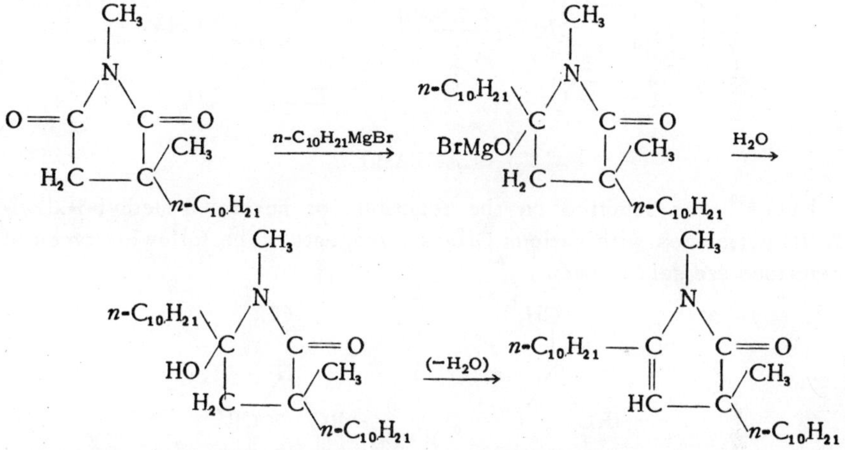

$$\xrightarrow{n\text{-}C_{10}H_{21}MgBr} \quad \xrightarrow{H_2O} \quad \xrightarrow{(-H_2O)}$$

According to Sachs and Ludwig,[34] N-ethylphthalimide reacts with Grignard reagents to form substituted phthalimidines in "good yields".

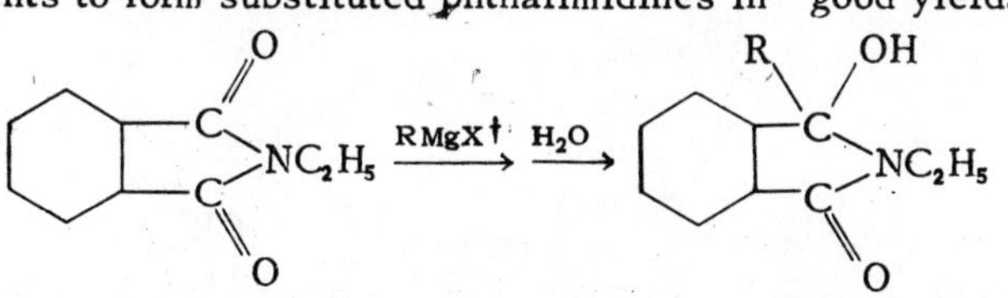

$$NC_2H_5 \xrightarrow{RMgX^{\dagger}} \xrightarrow{H_2O} NC_2H_5$$

Reactions of the same type are reported for N-methylsuccinimide (Lukeš *et al.*[35]) and N-methylglutarimide (Lukeš and Gorocholinskij[36]).

*R = C_2H_5, i-C_4H_9, i-C_5H_{11}.

[33]Birch and Robinson, *J. Chem. Soc.*, *1942*, 488–97.

[34]Sachs and Lugwig, *Ber.*, 37, 385–90 (1904).

†R = CH_3, C_2H_5, C_6H_5.

[35]Lukeš and Prelog, *Chem. Listy*, *22*, 244–51 (1928); *Chem. Abstr.*, *23*, 1408 (1929); Lukeš, *Collection Czechoslov. Chem. Commun.*, 5, 761–9 (1932); *Chem. Abstr.*, *27*, 290 (1933); Lukeš and Smolek, *Collection Czechoslov. Chem. Commun.*, 7, 482–90 (1935); *Chem. Abstr.*, *30*, 1785 (1936).

[36]Lukeš and Gorocholinskij, *Collection Czechoslov. Chem. Commun.*, 8, 223–35 (1936); *Chem. Abstr.*, *30*, 5989 (1936).

N-Alkylated saccharins have been reported to undergo ring-opening (Sachs and Ludwig, *loc. cit.*[34]; Sachs *et al.*[37]).

$$C_6H_4\langle{}^{SO_2}_{CO}\rangle NR\ddagger \xrightarrow{R'MgX^*} C_6H_4(SO_2NRMgX)(COR') \xrightarrow{R'MgX}$$

$$C_6H_4(SO_2NRMgX)(C(OMgX)R'_2) \xrightarrow{H_2O} C_6H_4(SO_2NHR)(C(OH)R'_2) + 2\ MgXOH$$

Cobb and Fuller,[38] however, report a cyclic product of the reaction of phenylmagnesium bromide with *N*-methylsaccharin.

$$C_6H_4\langle{}^{SO_2}_{CO}\rangle NCH_3 \xrightarrow{2\ C_6H_5MgBr} C_6H_4\langle{}^{SO_2}_{C(C_6H_5)_2}\rangle NCH_3$$

LACTAMS

Lukeš[39] has reported on the reactions of several 1-methyl-5-alkyl-2(3*H*)-pyrrolones with various Grignard reagents. The following types of reactions are said to occur.

(I) $$\begin{matrix} & CH_3 & \\ & N & \\ \dagger RC & & C{=}O \\ HC & — & CH_2 \end{matrix} \xrightarrow{R'MgX\dagger} \begin{matrix} & CH_3 & \\ & N & \\ RC & & CR' \\ HC & — & CH \end{matrix}$$

(II) $$\begin{matrix} & CH_3 & \\ & N & \\ \ddagger RC & & C{=}O \\ HC & — & CH_2 \end{matrix} \xrightarrow{2\ R'MgX\ddagger} \begin{matrix} & CH_3 & \\ & N & \\ RC & & CR'_2 \\ HC & — & CH_2 \end{matrix}$$

---

[37]Sachs, Wolff, and Ludwig, *Ber.*, 37, 3252–68 (1904).

*R = CH_3, C_2H_5; R′ = CH_3, C_2H_5, *i*-C_3H_7, *i*-C_5H_{11}, C_6H_5.

[38]Cobb and Fuller, *Am. Chem. J.*, 45, 605–11 (1911).

[39]Lukeš, *Collection Czechoslov. Chem. Commun.*, 4, 181–92 (1932); *Chem. Zentr.*, *1932,II*, 873; *Chem. Abstr.*, 26, 4328 (1932).

†R = CH_3, R′MgX = CH_3MgBr; R = C_2H_5, R′MgX = CH_3MgBr, C_2H_5MgBr, $C_6H_5CH_2MgCl$; R = $C_6H_5CH_2$, R′MgX = CH_3MgBr, C_2H_5MgBr, $C_6H_5CH_2MgCl$.

‡R = C_2H_5, R′MgX = C_2H_5MgBr; R = $C_6H_5CH_2$, R′MgX = CH_3MgBr.

$$\text{(III)}\quad \begin{array}{c} CH_3 \\ | \\ N \\ {}^{*}RC \diagup \quad \diagdown C{=}O \\ \| \qquad\quad | \\ HC{-}{-}CH_2 \end{array} \xrightarrow{R'MgX^{*}} RCOCH_2CH_2COR'$$

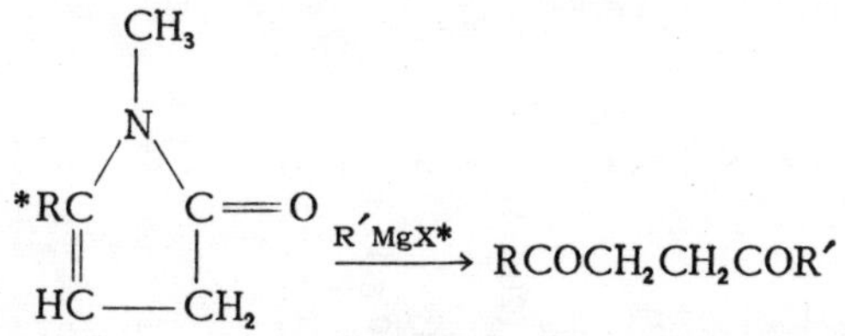

Reaction of type I consists (formally, at least) of "normal" addition at the carbonyl double bond followed by either elimination of halomagnesium hydroxide prior to hydrolysis or elimination of water subsequent to hydrolysis. Reaction of type II resembles amine formation from an acyclic amide and may well take the same course. Conceivably, however, it could consist in alkylation of a cyclic amine formed by elimination of halomagnesium hydroxide from the initial addition product. Reaction of type III might take place through some such sequence as the following.

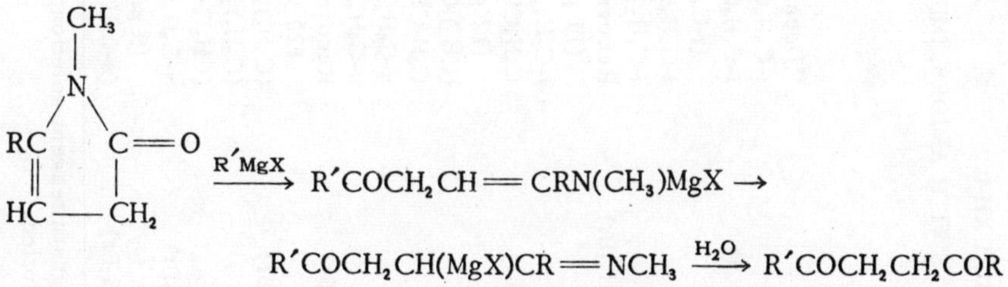

$$\begin{array}{c} CH_3 \\ | \\ N \\ RC \diagup \quad \diagdown C{=}O \\ \| \qquad\quad | \\ HC{-}{-}CH_2 \end{array} \xrightarrow{R'MgX} R'COCH_2CH{=}CRN(CH_3)MgX \rightarrow$$

$$R'COCH_2CH(MgX)CR{=}NCH_3 \xrightarrow{H_2O} R'COCH_2CH_2COR$$

Aside from the secondary rearrangement this is essentially "normal" ketone formation from an *N*,*N*-disubstituted amide. These three reaction types include all that have been reported for simple lactams and α-amino acid hydrides. Other examples are included in Table XII-I.

---

*$R = C_2H_5$; $R'MgX = C_2H_5MgBr$, $C_6H_5CH_2MgCl$.

TABLE XII-I

REACTIONS OF GRIGNARD REAGENTS WITH AMIDES, IMIDES, AND LACTAMS

Co-reactant	RMgX	Product(s)	Ref.
CHO-NRR′			
$HCONH_2$	RMgX	"Does not react like other amides"	2
$HCON(CH_3)_2$	i-C_4H_9MgCl	i-C_4H_9CHO	7
$HCON(CH_3)_2$ (20 g.)	i-C_4H_9MgCl (83 g. C_4H_9Cl)	i-C_4H_9CHO (13.0 g., 56%); (i-$C_4H_9)_2CHN(CH_3)_2$ (15 g.)	53
$HCON(CH_3)_2$	t-C_4H_9MgCl	t-C_4H_9CHO ("insignificant quantity")	7
$HCON(CH_3)_2$	i-$C_5H_{11}MgCl$	i-$C_5H_{11}CHO$; (i-$C_5H_{11})_2CHN(C_2H_5)_2$	7,6
$HCON(CH_3)_2$ (20 g.)	i-$C_5H_{11}MgBr$ (130 g. $C_5H_{11}Br$)	Recovered amide (5 g.); i-$C_5H_{11}CHO$ (11 g., 40%); (i-$C_5H_{11})_2CHN(CH_3)_2$ (20 g.)	53
$HCON(CH_3)_2$	t-$C_5H_{11}MgCl$	t-$C_5H_{11}CHO$ ("few drops")	7
$HCON(CH_3)_2$ (30 g.)	C_6H_5MgBr (140 g. C_6H_5Br)	C_6H_5CHO (15 g., 34%); $(C_6H_5)_2CHOH$ (12 g., 16%); $(C_6H_5)_2CHN(CH_3)_2$ (10 g.)	53,7
$HCON(CH_3)_2$	$(CH_2)_5CHMgCl$	$(CH_2)_5CHCHO$ ("good yield")	7
$HCON(CH_3)_2$	$C_6H_5CH_2MgCl$	$C_6H_5CH_2CHO$ ("good yield")	7
$HCON(CH_3)_2$	n-$C_8H_{17}MgCl$	n-$C_8H_{17}CHO$	7
$HCON(CH_3)_2$	n-$C_9H_{19}MgCl$	n-$C_9H_{19}CHO$	7
$HCON(C_2H_5)_2$ (50 g.)	C_2H_5MgBr (120 g. C_2H_5Br)	Recovered amide; $(C_2H_5)_2CHN(C_2H_5)_2$ (20 g., 22%)*	44
$HCON(C_2H_5)_2$ (35 g.)	C_2H_5MgBr (120 g. C_2H_5Br)	$(C_2H_5)_2CHN(C_2H_5)_2$ (25 g., 51%)†	44
$HCON(C_2H_5)_2$ (30 g.)	C_2H_5MgI (146 g. C_2H_5I)	$(C_2H_5)_2CHN(C_2H_5)_2$ (17 g., 41%)	44
$HCON(C_2H_5)_2$	$CH_3C{\equiv}CMgBr$	$(CH_3C{\equiv}C)_2CHN(C_2H_5)_2$	86
$HCON(C_2H_5)_2$ (30 g.)	n-C_3H_7MgBr (37 g. C_3H_7Br)	n-C_3H_7CHO (6 g.); (n-$C_3H_7)_2CHN(C_2H_5)_2$ (9 g.)	52
$HCON(C_2H_5)_2$ (50 g.)	n-C_3H_7MgBr (180 g. C_3H_7Br)	(n-$C_3H_7)_2CHN(C_2H_5)_2$ (30 g.)	52

*Dropwise addition of Et_2O-amide solution to cooled Et_2O-Grignard reagent solution; twelve hours standing.
†Addition of C_6H_6-amide solution to C_6H_6-Grignard reagent solution.

TABLE XII-I (Continued)

Co-reactant	RMgX	Product(s)	Ref.
CHO-NRR′ (*cont.*)			
$HCON(C_2H_5)_2$ (40 g.)	*i*-C_4H_9MgBr (69 g. C_4H_9Br)	Recovered amide; *i*-C_4H_9CHO (8 g., 23%); (*i*-$C_4H_9)_2CHN(C_2H_5)_2$ (*ca.* 17%)	44
$HCON(C_2H_5)_2$ (40 g.)	*i*-C_4H_9MgBr (140 g. C_4H_9Br)	*i*-C_4H_9CHO (10 g., 29%); (*i*-$C_4H_9)_2CHN(C_2H_5)_2$ (17 g., 22%)	44
$HCON(C_2H_5)_2$ (40 g.)	C_6H_5MgBr (140 g. C_6H_5Br)	C_6H_5CHO (25 g., 60%); $(C_6H_5)_2CHOH$ (10 g., 13%); $[(C_6H_5)_2C{=}]_2$ (12 g., 18%)	53
$HCON(C_2H_5)_2$	$C_6H_5CH_2MgCl$	$C_6H_5CH_2CHO$ ("good yield")	7
$HCON(CH_2)_5$ (40 g.)	C_2H_5MgBr (55 g. C_2H_5Br)	Recovered amide (7 g.); $(C_2H_5)_2CHN(CH_2)_5$ (16 g.); $(CH_2)_5N$ (5 g.)	52
$HCON(CH_2)_5$ (40 g.)	C_2H_5MgBr (116 g. C_2H_5Br)	$(C_2H_5)_2CHN(CH_2)_5$ (32 g.); $(CH_2)_5NH$ (3 g.); C_2H_5CHO (trace)	52
$HCON(CH_2)_5$ (30 g.)	*n*-C_3H_7MgBr (71 g. C_3H_7Br)	*n*-C_3H_7CHO (5 g.); (*n*-$C_3H_7)_2CHN(CH_2)_5$ (31 g.)	53
$HCON(CH_2)_5$ (30 g.)	*i*-C_4H_9MgCl (80 g. C_4H_9Cl)	*i*-C_4H_9CHO (4 g.); (*i*-$C_4H_9)_2CHN(CH_2)_2$ (42 g.)	53,6
$HCON(CH_2)_5$ (20 g.)	C_6H_5MgBr (88 g. C_6H_5Br)	$[(C_6H_5)_2C{=}]_2$ (22 g.); C_6H_5CHO (2 g., 11%) $(C_6H_5)_2CHN(CH_2)_5$ (27 g.)	53
$HCON(CH_2)_5$ (30 g.)	$C_6H_5CH_2MgCl$ (74 g. C_7H_7Cl)	$C_6H_5CH_2CHO$ (10 g.); $(C_6H_5CH_2)_2CHN(CH_2)_5$ (8 g.)	53
$HCONHNHC_6H_5$	C_6H_5MgBr ("large excess")	$(C_6H_5)_2CO$ (chiefly); $(C_6H_5)_2C{=}NNHC_6H_5$ ("very little"); $(C_6H_5)_2C{=}NC_6H_5$ ("very little")*	20
$HCON(CH_3)C_6H_5$ (50 g.)	C_2H_5MgBr (133 g. C_2H_5Br)	$(C_2H_5)_2CHN(CH_3)C_6H_5$ (> 20 g.); $CH_3NHC_6H_5$	52
$HCON(CH_3)C_6H_5$ (30 g.)	*i*-C_4H_9MgCl (25 g. C_4H_9Cl)	Recovered amide (10 g.); *i*-C_4H_9CHO (6 g.); (*i*-$C_4H_9)_2CHN(CH_3)C_6H_5$ (1–2 g.); $CH_3NHC_6H_5$	52

*Reaction at 116–120°, seven to twelve hours.

TABLE XII-I (Continued)

Co-reactant	RMgX	Product(s)	Ref.
CHO-NRR′ (*cont.*)			
$HCON(CH_3)C_6H_5$ (45 g.)	*i*-C_4H_9MgCl (90 g. C_4H_9Cl)	*i*-C_4H_9CHO (10 g.); (*i*-$C_4H_9)_2CHN(CH_3)C_6H_5$ (20 g.); $CH_3NHC_6H_5$	52
$HCON(CH_3)C_6H_5$ (20 g.)	C_6H_5MgBr (70 g. C_6H_5Br)	C_6H_5CHO (10 g., 64%); $(C_6H_5)_2CHOH$ (10 g., 35%); $CH_3NHC_6H_5$ (14 g.)	53
$HCON(CH_3)C_6H_5$ (0.2 mole)	C_6H_5MgBr (0.2 mole C_6H_5Br)	C_6H_5CHO (59%); $C_6H_5NHCH_3$*	75
$HCON(CH_3)C_6H_5$ (0.2 mole)	C_6H_5MgBr (0.2 mole C_6H_5Br)	C_6H_5CHO (11%); $C_6H_5NHCH_3$†	75
$HCON(CH_3)C_6H_5$ (0.37 mole)	C_6H_5MgBr (0.2 mole C_6H_5Br)	C_6H_5CHO (67%); $C_6H_5NHCH_3$‡	75
$HCON(CH_3)C_6H_5$ (0.37 mole)	C_6H_5MgBr (0.2 mole C_6H_5Br)	C_6H_5CHO (67%); $C_6H_5NHCH_3$§	75
$HCON(CH_3)C_6H_5$ (100% excess)	2-$CH_3C_6H_4MgBr$ (0.2 mole C_6H_5Br)	2-$CH_3C_6H_4CHO$ (11 g., 50%); $C_6H_5NHCH_3$	75
$HCON(CH_3)C_6H_5$ (25% excess)	3-$CH_3C_6H_4MgBr$ (0.2 mole C_7H_7Br)	3-$CH_3C_6H_4CHO$ (8 g., 33%); $C_6H_5NHCH_3$	75
$HCON(CH_3)C_6H_5$	4-$CH_3C_6H_4MgBr$	4-$CH_3C_6H_4CHO$ (9 g., 37%)	75
$HCON(CH_3)C_6H_5$	2,5-$(CH_3O)_2C_6H_3MgBr$	2,5-$(CH_3O)_2C_6H_3CHO$ (17–22%); $C_6H_5NHCH_3$; 1,4-$(CH_3O)_2C_6H_4$ (38%)	75
$HCON(CH_3)C_6H_5$	2,4,6-$(CH_3)_3C_6H_2MgBr$	2,4,6-$(CH_3)_3C_6H_2CHO$ (18.8%); $C_6H_5NHCH_3$; 2,4,6-$(CH_3)_3C_6H_3$ (40%)	75
$HCON(CH_3)C_6H_5$ (1 equiv.)	$C_{10}H_{17}MgCl$¶	$CH_3(C_6H_5)N(C_{10}H_{17})CHOH$ (yielding 23–24 g. aldehyde-bisulfite compound)	22
$HCON(CH_3)C_6H_5$ (13.5 g.)	2-$C_6H_5C_6H_4MgI$ (28 g. $C_{12}H_9I$)	2-$C_6H_5C_6H_4CHO$ (12.2 g.)	85
$HCON(C_2H_5)C_6H_5$ (50 g.)	C_2H_5MgBr (115 g. C_2H_5Br)	$(C_2H_5)_2CHN(C_2H_5)C_6H_5$ (26 g.)	52
$HCON(C_2H_5)C_6H_5$ (30 g.)	*i*-C_4H_9MgCl (22 g. C_4H_9Cl)	Recovered amide (12 g.); *i*-C_4H_9CHO (6 g.); (*i*-$C_4H_9)_2CHN(C_2H_5)C_6H_5$ (1–2 g.); $C_2H_5NHC_6H_5$ (14 g.)	52

*Slow addition of amide to stirred Grignard reagent solution; overnight standing.

†Replacement of Et_2O by $CH_3C_6H_5$; heating at 90°.

‡Normal addition.

§Reverse addition.

¶From 50 g. of pinene hydrochloride.

TABLE XII-I (Continued)

Co-reactant	RMgX	Product(s)	Ref.
CHO-NRR′ (*cont.*)			
$HCON(C_2H_5)C_6H_5$ (46 g.)	i-C_4H_9MgCl (83 g. C_4H_9Cl)	i-C_4H_9CHO (6 g.); $(i$-$C_4H_9)_2CHN(C_2H_5)C_6H_5$ (30 g.); $C_2H_5NHC_6H_5$ (5 g.)	52
$HCON(C_2H_5)C_6H_5$	C_6H_5MgBr	C_6H_5CHO	6
$HCON(C_2H_5)C_6H_5$	$(CH_2)_5CHMgCl$	$(CH_2)_5CHCHO$	6
$HCON(C_2H_5)C_6H_5$	$C_6H_5CH_2MgCl$	$C_6H_5CH_2CHO$	6
$HCON(C_6H_5)_2$ (30 g.)	C_2H_5MgBr (55 g. C_2H_5Br)	$(C_6H_5)_2NH$ (17 g.); $(C_2H_5)_2CHN(C_6H_5)_2$ (8 g.)	53
$HCON(C_6H_5)_2$ (30 g.)	i-C_4H_9MgCl (51 g. C_4H_9Cl)	i-C_4H_9CHO (5 g.); $(i$-$C_4H_9)_2CHN(C_6H_5)_2$ (12 g.); $(C_6H_5)_2NH$	52
$HCON(C_6H_5)_2$ (20 g.)	C_6H_5MgBr (50 g. C_6H_5Br)	C_6H_5CHO (1 g.); $(C_6H_5)_2CHOH$ (16 g., 88%)	53
C_2O_2-$(NRR')_2$			
$(-CONH_2)_2$ (8 g.)	C_6H_5MgBr (86 g. C_6H_5Br)	Recovered amide (7.5 g.)	57
$[-CON(C_2H_5)_2]_2$	C_2H_5MgBr (3 equiv.)	$C_2H_5COCON(C_2H_5)_2$ (70%); $(C_2H_5)_2NCH(C_2H_5)CON(C_2H_5)_2$ (20%); $(C_2H_5CO-)_2$ (trace); C_2H_4*	1
$[-CON(C_2H_5)_2]_2$	C_2H_5MgBr (3 equiv.)	$C_2H_5COCON(C_2H_5)_2$ (55%); $(C_2H_5)_2NCH(C_2H_5)CON(C_2H_5)_2$ (36%); $(C_2H_5CO-)_2$ (1%); C_2H_4†	1
$[-CON(C_2H_5)_2]_2$	C_2H_5MgBr (4 equiv.)	$C_2H_5COCON(C_2H_5)_2$ (28%); $(C_2H_5)_2NCH(C_2H_5)CON(C_2H_5)_2$ (60%); $(C_2H_5CO-)_2$ (3%); C_2H_4‡	1
$[-CON(C_2H_5)_2]_2$	C_2H_5MgI (3 equiv.)	$C_2H_5COCON(C_2H_5)_2$ (80%); $(C_2H_5)_2NCH(C_2H_5)CON(C_2H_5)_2$ (very little); C_2H_4†	1

* Four hours reflux in Et_2O.
† Ten hours at 70° in C_6H_6.
‡ Two hours agitation at 90° in $CH_3C_6H_5$ under H_2.

TABLE XII-I (Continued)

Co-reactant	RMgX	Product(s)	Ref.
C_2O_2-(NRR′)$_2$ *(cont.)*			
[—CON(C_2H_5)$_2$]$_2$	C_6H_5MgBr (4 equiv.)	(C_2H_5)$_2$NC(C_6H_5)$_2$CON(C_2H_5)$_2$ (75%)*	1
N,N′-Vinylideneoxanilide	RMgX† (2+ equiv.)	(RCO—)$_2$	80
[—CON(CH_3)C_6H_5]$_2$ (1 mole)	CH_3MgI (4 moles)	CH_3(C_6H_5)NCOCOCH$_3$	88
[—CON(CH_3)C_6H_5]$_2$ (1 mole)	C_2H_5MgBr (4 moles)	CH_3(C_6H_5)NCOCOC$_2H_5$ (27 g., crude)	88
[—CON(CH_3)C_6H_5]$_2$	4-$CH_3C_6H_4MgBr$ (4 equiv.)	CH_3(C_6H_5)NCOCOC$_6H_4$-4-CH_3	88
C_2H_2OCl-NRR′			
$ClCH_2CON(C_2H_5)_2$	C_2H_5MgBr	(C_2H_5)$_2$NCH$_2$(C_2H_5)$_2$COH	76
C_2H_3O-NRR′			
CH_3CONH_2	CH_3MgI (2+ equiv.)	(CH_3)$_2$CO (poor yield)	2
CH_3CONH_2	C_2H_5MgX‡ (2+ equiv.)	$CH_3COC_2H_5$ (poor yield)	2
CH_3CONH_2	Pyrryl-MgBr	α-Amino-α-2-pyrrylethanol	72
CH_3CONH_2	$C_6H_5CH_2MgCl$ (3 equiv.)	$CH_3COCH_2C_6H_5$ (41.3%)	82
CH_3CONH_2 (20 g., 0.33 mole)	*n*-$C_5H_{11}C{\equiv}CMgBr$ (96 g. C_7H_{12})	*n*-$C_5H_{11}C{\equiv}CH$ (90 g.)	33
$CH_3CONHC_6H_5$	C_2H_5MgBr (excess)	Butanone condens'n products and recovered amide, only	63
$CH_3CONHNHC_6H_5$	C_6H_5MgBr	2-Phenylindole (chiefly); CH_3(C_6H_5)C$=$NNHC$_6H_5$ ("a little"); $CH_3COC_6H_5$ ("a little")§	20
C_3H_5O-NRR′			
$C_2H_5CONH_2$	CH_3MgI (2+ equiv.)	$CH_3COC_2H_5$ (*ca.* 20%)	2

* One and one-half hour reflux in $CH_3C_6H_5$ under H_2.
† RMgX = CH_3MgI, C_2H_5MgBr.
‡ X = Br,I.
§ Reaction at 116–120°, 7–12 hrs.

TABLE XII-I (Continued)

Co-reactant	RMgX	Product(s)	Ref.
C_3H_5O-NRR′ (*cont.*)			
$C_2H_5CONH_2$	C_2H_5MgX* (2+ equiv.)	$(C_2H_5)_2CO$ (*ca.* 20%)	*2*
$C_2H_5CONHC_6H_5$	C_2H_5MgBr (excess)	$(C_2H_5)_2C{=}NC_6H_5$ (*ca.* 40%); unsat'd ketone, $C_{10}H_{18}O$, b. 90–93°/20 mm.; recovered amide	*63*
$C_4H_4O_2$-NR			
N-Methylsuccinimide	RMgX†	1-Methyl-5-hydroxy-5-R-2-pyrrolidone	*37*
N-Methylsuccinimide	C_6H_5MgBr	1-Methyl-5-hydroxy-5-phenyl-2-pyrrolidone; 1-methyl-2,5-diphenylpyrrole	*39,40*
$C_4H_4O_2$-(NRR′)$_2$			
$[-CH_2CON(C_2H_5)_2]_2$	C_2H_5MgBr	$C_2H_5COCH_2CH_2CON(C_2H_5)_2$ (63%); $(-CH_2COC_2H_5)_2$ (3%)	*63*
C_4H_5O-NRR′			
$CH_3CH{=}CHCON(C_2H_5)_2$	C_2H_5MgBr	$CH_3(C_2H_5)CHCH_2CON(C_2H_5)_2$ (quant.)	*46*
$CH_3CH{=}CHCON(C_2H_5)_2$	C_6H_5MgBr	$CH_3(C_6H_5)CHCH_2CON(C_2H_5)_2$ (quant.)	*46*
$CH_3CH{=}CHCON(CH_3)C_6H_5$	C_2H_5MgBr	$CH_3(C_2H_5)CHCH_2CON(CH_3)C_6H_5$ (40–50%)	*51*
$CH_3CH{=}CHCON(CH_3)C_6H_5$	C_6H_5MgBr	$CH_3(C_6H_5)CHCH_2CON(CH_3)C_6H_5$ (40–50%); $(C_6H_5-)_2$; unidentified product	*51*
$CH_3CH{=}CHCON(C_2H_5)C_6H_5$	C_2H_5MgBr	$CH_3(C_2H_5)CHCH_2CON(C_2H_5)C_6H_5$ (40–50%)	*51*
$CH_3CH{=}CHCON(C_6H_5)_2$	CH_3MgI	*i*-$C_4H_9CON(C_6H_5)_2$ (1–2%); $(C_6H_5)_2NCH(CH_3)CH[CON(C_6H_5)_2]CO$-*i*-$C_4H_9$ (?)‡ (principal product)	*47*

* X = Br, I.

† R = C_2H_5, C_6H_5, $C_6H_5CH_2$.

‡ *Cf.* Nenitzescu (*64*).

TABLE XII-I (Continued)

Co-reactant	RMgX	Product(s)	Ref.
C_4H_5O-NRR′ (*cont.*)			
$CH_3CH{=}CHCON(C_6H_5)_2$	CH_3MgI	*i*-$C_3H_7CH[CON(C_6H_5)_2]CH(CH_3)CH_2$-$CON(C_6H_5)_2$	64
$CH_3CH{=}CHCON(C_6H_5)_2$	C_2H_5MgBr	$CH_3(C_2H_5)CHCH_2CON(C_6H_5)_2$ (quant.)	46
$CH_3CH{=}CHCON(C_6H_5)_2$	C_2H_5MgBr	$CH_3(C_2H_5)CHCH{=}C(OMgBr)N(C_6H_5)_2$; $CH_3(C_2H_5)CHCH[CON(C_6H_5)_2]CH(CH_3)$-$CH_2CON(C_6H_5)_2$	65
$CH_3CH{=}CHCON(C_6H_5)_2$	C_6H_5MgBr	$CH_3(C_6H_5)CHCH_2CON(C_6H_5)_2$ (quant.)	46
C_4H_6OBr-NRR′			
$C_2H_5CHBrCON(CH_3)_2$ (44 g.)	C_6H_5MgBr (150 g. C_6H_5Br)	$C_2H_5CH[N(CH_3)_2]C(C_6H_5)_2OH$ (1 g.); *n*-$C_3H_7CON(CH_3)_2$ (4 g.); *n*-$C_3H_7COC_6H_5$; $CH_3CH{=}CHCON(CH_3)_2$; $(CH_3)_2NH$; C_6H_5Br; $(C_6H_5—)_2$	77
$C_2H_5CHBrCON(C_2H_5)_2$	C_6H_5MgBr (excess)	*n*-$C_3H_7CON(C_2H_5)_2$; *n*-$C_3H_7COC_6H_5$ (trace); $CH_3CH{=}CHCON(C_2H_5)_2$; *n*-$C_3H_7(C_6H_5)_2COH$	87
C_4H_7ON			
2-Pyrrolidone (43.5 g.)	*n*-C_3H_7MgBr (250 ml. C_3H_7Br)	2-Propylpyrrolidine; dipropylpyrrolidine + $C_{13}H_{25}N$, b.p. 125–135° (aggregating 6 g.)	42
C_4H_7O-NRR′			
n-$C_3H_7CONH_2$	CH_3MgI (2+ equiv.)	CH_3CO-*n*-C_3H_7 (> 20%, < 50%)	2
n-$C_3H_7CONHC_6H_5$	C_2H_5MgBr* (excess)	$C_2H_5(n\text{-}C_3H_7)C{=}NC_6H_5$ (*ca.* 40%); unsat'd ketone, $C_{11}H_{20}O$, b. 99–103°/14 mm.; recovered amide	63

* C_2H_5MgI gave no anil.

TABLE XII-I (Continued)

Co-reactant	RMgX	Product(s)	Ref.
C_4H_7O-NRR′ (*cont.*)			
n-$C_3H_7CONHC_6H_4$-4-CH_3	C_2H_5MgBr (excess)	C_2H_5(*n*-C_3H_7)$C{=}NC_6H_4$-4-CH_3 (*ca.* 40%)	*63*
n-$C_3H_7CON(CH_3)_2$	CH_3MgI	*n*-$C_3H_7(CH_3)_2CN(CH_3)_2$	*59*
n-$C_3H_7CON(C_2H_5)_2$	CH_3MgI	*n*-$C_3H_7(CH_3)_2CN(C_2H_5)_2$	*59*
n-$C_3H_7CON(C_2H_5)_2$ + CH_3I	CH_3MgI	*n*-$C_3H_7(CH_3)_2CN(C_2H_5)_2$; $CH_3(C_2H_5)$(*n*-C_3H_7)$CN(C_2H_5)_2$*	*60*
n-$C_3H_7CON(C_2H_5)_2$ (30 g.) + C_2H_5I (33 g.)	CH_3MgI (92 g. CH_3I)	*n*-$C_3H_7(CH_3)_2CN(C_2H_5)_2$; CH_3(*n*-C_3H_7)$_2CN(C_2H_5)_2$*	*60*
n-$C_3H_7CON(C_2H_5)_2$	C_2H_5MgBr	$(C_2H_5)_2NC(C_2H_5)_2$-*n*-C_3H_7	*59*
n-$C_3H_7CON(C_2H_5)C_6H_5$	C_2H_5MgBr	C_2H_5(*n*-C_3H_7)$C(OH)CH(C_2H_5)CON$-$(C_2H_5)C_6H_5$	*62*
n-$C_3H_7CON(C_2H_5)C_6H_5$	C_2H_5MgBr	C_2H_6; *n*-$C_3H_7(C_2H_5)_2COH$ (10–30%); $HO(C_2H_5)$(*n*-C_3H_7)$CCH(C_2H_5)CON$-$(C_2H_5)C_6H_5$; "an ethylenic dehydr'n product"	*61*
i-$C_3H_7CONH_2$	C_2H_5MgX (2+ equiv.)	C_2H_5CO-*i*-C_3H_7 (>20%, <50%)	*2*
$C_5H_3O_2$-NRR′			
N,*N*-Diethyl-2-furoämide	C_2H_5MgBr	2-Propionylfuran (80–85%)	*48*
N,*N*-Diethyl-2-furoämide	*n*-C_3H_7MgI	2-Butyrylfuran (80–85%)	*48*
N-Methyl-2-furoänilide (20 g.)	C_2H_5MgBr (29 g. C_2H_5Br)	2-Propionylfuran (4 g.); $CH_3NHC_6H_5$	*56*
N-Methyl-2-furoänilide	*i*-C_4H_9MgCl (27 g. C_4H_9Cl)	2-Isovalerylfuran (4 g.)	*56*
N-Ethyl-2-furoänilide (40 g.)	C_2H_5MgBr (51 g. C_2H_5Br)	2-Propionylfuran (13 g.)	*56*
N-Ethyl-2-furoänilide (46 g.)	*i*-C_4H_9MgCl (50 g. C_4H_9Cl)	2-Isovalerylfuran (12 g.)	*56*
N-Ethyl-2-furoänilide (40 g.)	C_6H_5MgBr (73 g. C_6H_5Br)	2-Benzoylfuran (7 g.); tertiary base, $C_{25}H_{23}ON$ (5 g.)	*56*
N-Ethyl-2-furoänilide (40 g.)	2-$CH_3C_6H_4MgBr$ (69 g. C_7H_7Br)	2-*o*-Toluylfuran (5 g.)	*56*

* Replacement of Et_2O by C_6H_6; four hours reflux.

TABLE XII-I (Continued)

Co-reactant	RMgX	Product(s)	Ref.
$C_5H_3O_2$-NRR′ (*cont.*)			
N,*N*-Diphenyl-2-furoämide (40 g.)	C_2H_5MgBr (54 g. C_2H_5Br)	2-Propionylfuran (15 g.)	56
N,*N*-Diphenyl-2-furoämide (17 g.)	*i*-C_4H_9MgCl (15 g. C_4H_9Cl)	2-Isovalerylfuran (9 g.)	56
N,*N*-Diphenyl-2-furoämide	C_6H_5MgBr (30 g. C_6H_5Br)	2-Benzoylfuran (4 g.); $(C_6H_5)_2NH$ (3 g.)	56
N,*N*-Diphenyl-2-furoämide (20 g.)	2-$CH_3C_6H_4MgBr$ (30 g. C_6H_5Br)	2-o-Toluylfuran (3 g.); $(C_6H_5)_2NH$ (5 g.); recovered amide	56
$C_5H_6O_2$-NR			
N-Methylglutarimide	RMgBr*	1-Methyl-6-hydroxy-6-alkyl-2-piperidone	38
$C_5H_6O_2$-(NRR′)$_2$			
$CH_2[CH_2CON(C_2H_5)_2]_2$	C_2H_5MgX	$CH_2(CH_2COC_2H_5)_2$ (25–30%)	4
$CH_2[CH_2CON(C_2H_5)_2]_2$	C_2H_5MgBr	$CH_2(CH_2COC_2H_5)_2$ (20–30%); $C_2H_5CO(CH_2)_3CON(C_2H_5)_2$; $C_2H_5CO(CH_2)_3C(C_2H_5)_2N(C_2H_5)_2$	5
$CH_2[CH_2CON(C_2H_5)_2]_2$	*n*-C_3H_7MgX	$CH_2(CH_2CO$-*n*-$C_3H_7)_2$ (25–30%)	4
C_5H_9O-NRR′			
t-$C_4H_9CONH_2$	C_6H_5MgBr (3 equiv.)	*t*-$C_4H_9COC_4H_5$ (chiefly); *t*-C_4H_9CN ("very little")	68
C_5H_9ON			
2-Piperidone (29 g.)	*n*-C_3H_7MgBr (164 g. C_3H_7Br)	(±)-γ-Coniceïne (7.6 g.); $C_{10}H_{22}N_2$, b.p. 118–122°/11 mm.	42
1-Methyl-2(3*H*)-pyrrolone	RMgX†	1-Methyl-2-alkyl-Δ^2-pyrroline; 1-methyl-2,2-dialkylpyrrolidine	35,40
1-Methyl-2(3*H*)-pyrrolone	C_6H_5MgBr	1-Methyl-2-phenyl-Δ^2-pyrroline	35

* R = CH_3, C_2H_5, *n*-C_3H_7, *n*-C_4H_9, *n*-C_5H_{11}, *n*-C_6H_{13}.
† R = CH_3, C_2H_5, *n*-C_3H_7.

TABLE XII-I (Continued)

Co-reactant	RMgX	Product(s)	Ref.
C_5H_9ON (*cont.*)			
1-Methyl-2(3*H*)-pyrrolone	$C_6H_5CH_2MgX$	1-Methyl-2-benzyl-Δ^2-pyrroline	*37*
$C_6H_6O_2$-NR			
N-Phenylcyclobutane-1,2-dicarboximide (5 g., 0.025 mole)	C_6H_5MgBr (0.025 mole)	*cis*-2-Benzoylcyclobutanecarboxanilide	*18*
N-Phenylcyclobutane-1,2-dicarboximide (4 g. 0.02 mole)	C_6H_5MgBr (0.04 mole)	2-(α-Hydroxybenzhydryl)cyclobutanecarboxanilide	*18*
C_6H_9ON			
1,5-Dimethyl-2(3*H*)-pyrrolone	CH_3MgBr	1,2,5-Trimethylpyrrole	*36*
$C_6H_9O_2$-NRR′			
$C_2H_5COCH_2CH_2CON(C_2H_5)_2$	C_2H_5MgBr (excess)	$(C_2H_5)_2C(OH)CH_2CH_2CON(C_2H_5)_2$ (principal product); $(—CH_2COC_2H_5)_2$ (5%); 2,2,5-triethyldihydrofuran	*63*
$C_6H_{10}O_2N_2$			
Sarcosine anhydride*	C_2H_5MgBr	1,4-Dimethyl-2,2,5,5-tetraëthylpiperazine	*91*
Sarcosine anhydride*	C_6H_5MgBr	$CH_3NHCH_2COC_6H_5$; $CH_3NHCH_2CON(CH_3)CH_2COC_6H_5$	*91*
$C_6H_{11}O$-NRR′			
t-$C_5H_{11}CONH_2$	C_6H_5MgBr (3 equiv.)	*t*-$C_5H_{11}COC_6H_5$ (chiefly); *t*-$C_5H_{11}CCN$ (very little)	*68*

* 1,4-Dimethyl-2,5-piperazinedione.

TABLE XII-I (Continued)

Co-reactant	RMgX	Product(s)	Ref.
$C_6H_{11}O_3$-NRR′			
$(C_2H_5O)_2CHCON(CH_2)_5$ (54 g.)	CH_3MgI (55 ml. CH_3I)	$(C_2H_5O)_2CHCOCH_3$ (29.4 g., 80.7%; 70–76%, pure)	83
C_7H_4OCl-NRR′			
2-$ClC_6H_4CONH_2$	2-$ClC_6H_4CH_2MgBr$ (3–4 equiv.)	2-$ClC_6H_4COCH_2C_6H_4$-2-Cl (70%)	29
2-$ClC_6H_4CONH_2$ (0.025 mole)	3-$ClC_6H_4CH_2MgBr$ (0.10 mole C_7H_6BrCl)	2-$ClC_6H_4COCH_2C_6H_4$-3-Cl (78%)	26
2-$ClC_6H_4CONH_2$	4-$ClC_6H_4CH_2MgBr$ (3–4 equiv.)	2-$ClC_6H_4COCH_2C_6H_4$-4-Cl (72%)	29
2-$ClC_6H_4CONH_2$	$C_6H_5CH_2MgCl$ (3–4 equiv.)	2-$ClC_6H_4COCH_2C_6H_5$ (71%)	29
3-$ClC_6H_4CONH_2$ (0.025 mole)	2-$ClC_6H_4CH_2MgBr$ (0.10 mole C_7H_6BrCl)	3-$ClC_6H_4COCH_2C_6H_4$-2-Cl (61%)	26
3-$ClC_6H_4CONH_2$ (0.025 mole)	3-$ClC_6H_4CH_2MgBr$ (0.10 mole C_7H_6BrCl)	3-$ClC_6H_4COCH_2C_6H_4$-3-Cl (79%)	26
3-$ClC_6H_4CONH_2$ (0.025 mole)	4-$ClC_6H_4CH_2MgBr$ (0.10 mole C_7H_6BrCl)	3-$ClC_6H_4COCH_2C_6H_4$-4-Cl (85%)	26
3-$ClC_6H_4CONH_2$	$C_6H_5CH_2MgCl$ (3–4 equiv.)	3-$ClC_6H_4COCH_2C_6H_5$ (72%)	25,26
4-$ClC_6H_4CONH_2$	2-$ClC_6H_4CH_2MgBr$ (3–4 equiv.)	4-$ClC_6H_4COCH_2C_6H_4$-2-Cl (80%)	29
4-$ClC_6H_4CONH_2$ (0.025 mole)	3-$ClC_6H_4CH_2MgBr$ (0.10 mole C_7H_6BrCl)	4-$ClC_6H_4COCH_2C_6H_4$-3-Cl (60%)	26
4-$ClC_6H_4CONH_2$	4-$ClC_6H_4CH_2MgBr$	4-$ClC_6H_4COCH_2C_6H_4$-4-Cl (74%)	29
4-$ClC_6H_4CONH_2$ (7.78 g.)	$C_6H_5CH_2MgCl$ (25.3 g. C_7H_7Cl)	4-$ClC_6H_4COCH_2C_6H_5$ (77%)	29,27
$C_7H_4O_3S$-NR			
N-Methylsaccharin	CH_3MgBr	2-$[HO(CH_3)_2C]C_6H_4SO_2NHCH_3$	71
N-Methylsaccharin	C_2H_5MgBr	2-$[HO(C_2H_5)_2C]C_6H_4SO_2NHCH_3$	71
N-Methylsaccharin	*i*-C_3H_7MgBr	2-$[HO(i\text{-}C_3H_7)_2C]C_6H_4SO_2NHCH_3$	71
N-Methylsaccharin	*i*-$C_5H_{11}MgBr$	2-$[HO(i\text{-}C_5H_{11})_2C]C_6H_4SO_2NHCH_3$	71

TABLE XII-I (Continued)

Co-reactant	RMgX	Product(s)	Ref.
$C_7H_4O_3S$-NR (*cont.*)			
N-Methylsaccharin	C_6H_5MgBr	2-[$HO(C_6H_5)_2C$]$C_6H_4SO_2NHCH_3$	71
N-Ethylsaccharin (12 g.)	CH_3MgBr* (50 g. CH_3Br)	2-[$HO(CH_3)_2C$]$C_6H_4SO_2NHC_2H_5$	71
N-Ethylsaccharin	C_2H_5MgBr	2-[$HO(C_2H_5)_2C$]$C_6H_4SO_2NHC_2H_5$ (quant.)	70,71
N-Ethylsaccharin	*i*-C_3H_7MgBr	2-[HO(*i*-$C_3H_7)_2C$]$C_6H_4SO_2NHC_2H_5$	71
N-Ethylsaccharin	*i*-$C_5H_{11}MgBr$	2-[HO(*i*-$C_5H_{11})_2C$]$C_6H_4SO_2NHC_2H_5$	71
N-Ethylsaccharin	C_6H_5MgBr (2–3 equiv.)	2-[$HO(C_6H_5)_2C$]$C_6H_4SO_2NHC_2H_5$ (*ca.* quant.)	70,71
C_7H_5O-NRR′			
$C_6H_5CONH_2$	CH_3MgI (2+ equiv.)	$CH_3COC_6H_5$ (*ca.* 50%)	2
$C_6H_5CONH_2$	C_2H_5MgBr	$C_2H_5COC_6H_5$	43
$C_6H_5CONH_2$	C_2H_5MgX† (2+ equiv.)	$C_2H_5COC_6H_5$ (*ca.* 50%)	2
$C_6H_5CONH_2$	2-$ClC_6H_4CH_2MgBr$ (3–4 equiv.)	$C_6H_5COCH_2C_6H_4$-2-Cl (73%)	29
$C_6H_5CONH_2$ (0.025 mole)	3-$ClC_6H_4CH_2MgBr$ (0.10 mole C_7H_6BrCl)	$C_6H_5COCH_2C_6H_4$-3-Cl (42%)	26
$C_6H_5CONH_2$	4-$ClC_6H_4CH_2MgBr$ (3–4 equiv.)	$C_6H_5COCH_2C_6H_4$-4-Cl (70%)	29,27
$C_6H_5CONH_2$	$C_6H_5CH_2MgCl$ (3–4 equiv.)	$C_6H_5COCH_2C_6H_5$ (77%)	25
$C_6H_5CON(C_2H_5)_2$ (55 g.)	C_2H_5MgBr (110 g. C_2H_5Br)	$C_2H_5COC_6H_5$ (13 g., 31%)‡	45
$C_6H_5CON(C_2H_5)_2$	C_2H_5MgBr	$C_2H_5COC_6H_5$ (55%)§	45
$C_6H_5CON(C_2H_5)_2$	C_2H_5MgBr	$C_2H_5COC_6H_5$ (60%)¶	45
$C_6H_5CON(C_2H_5)_2$	C_6H_5MgBr	Quant. recovery of amide‡	45
$C_6H_5CON(C_2H_5)_2$ (10 g.)	C_6H_5MgBr (22 g. C_6H_5Br)	Recovered amide (8 g.)‖	57

* The use of CH_3MgI leads to liberation of I_2 in large quantities.

† X = Br, I.

‡ Twelve hours standing in Et_2O.

§ Four hours reflux in C_6H_6, with stirring.

¶ Four hours reflux in $CH_3C_6H_5$, with stirring.

‖ Fifteen hours reflux in Et_2O.

TABLE XII-I (Continued)

Co-reactant	RMgX	Product(s)	Ref.
C_7H_5O-NRR′ (*cont.*)			
$C_6H_5CON(C_2H_5)_2$ (30 g.)	$C_6H_5CH_2MgCl$ (64 g. C_7H_7Cl)	$C_6H_5COCH_2C_6H_5$ (21%)*	*45*
$C_6H_5CON(C_2H_5)_2$	$C_6H_5CH_2MgCl$	$C_6H_5COCH_2C_6H_5$ (31%)†	*45*
$C_6H_5CON(C_2H_5)_2$	$C_6H_5CH_2MgCl$	$C_6H_5COCH_2C_6H_5$ (33%)‡	*45*
$C_6H_5CON(C_2H_5)C_6H_5$ (4 g.)	C_6H_5MgBr (7 g. C_6H_5Br)	$(C_6H_5)_3CN(C_2H_5)C_6H_5$; $(C_6H_5)_2CO$; $C_2H_5NHC_6H_5$	*12*
$C_6H_5CONHNHC_6H_5$	C_6H_5MgBr	$(C_6H_5)_2C{=}NNHC_6H_5$; $(C_6H_5)_2C{=}NC_6H_5$; $(C_6H_5)_2C{=}NH$; $(C_6H_5)_2CO$	*20*
$C_7H_5O_2$-NRR′			
2-$HOC_6H_4CONH_2$ (14 g.)	C_2H_5MgBr (68 g. C_2H_5Br)	$C_2H_5COC_6H_4$-2-OH (trace); recovered amide §	*15*
2-$HOC_6H_4CONH_2$ (14 g.)	C_2H_5MgBr (68 g. C_2H_5Br)	$C_2H_5COC_6H_4$-2-OH (5.5 g., 30%); recovered amide¶	*15*
2-$HOC_6H_4CON(C_2H_5)_2$ (30 g.)	C_2H_5MgBr (68 g. C_2H_5Br)	$C_2H_5COC_6H_4$-2-OH (10–12 g., *ca.* 45%); recovered amide (4 g.)‖	*15*
2-$HOC_6H_4CON(C_2H_5)_2$	C_2H_5MgBr	$C_2H_5COC_6H_4$-2-OH (82–84%)**	*15,14*
3-$HOC_6H_4CON(C_2H_5)_2$	C_2H_5MgBr	$C_2H_5COC_6H_4$-3-OH (10%); recovered amide**	*15*
3-$HOC_6H_4CON(C_2H_5)_2$	C_2H_5MgBr	$C_2H_5COC_6H_4$-3-OH (75%); recovered amide††	*15*

* Twelve hours standing in Et_2O.
† Four hours reflux in C_6H_6, with stirring.
‡ Four hours reflux in $CH_3C_6H_5$, with stirring.
§ Six hours reflux, twelve hours standing in Et_2O.
¶ Six hours reflux, twelve hours standing in Et_2O-C_6H_6.
‖ Five hours reflux in Et_2O.
** Six hours reflux at 60–70° in Et_2O-C_6H_6.
†† Four hours reflux in n-Bu_2O.

TABLE XII-I (Continued)

Co-reactant	RMgX	Product(s)	Ref.
$C_7H_5O_2$-NRR′ (*cont.*)			
4-$HOC_6H_4CON(C_2H_5)_2$	C_2H_5MgBr	$C_2H_5COC_6H_4$-4-OH (5%); recovered amide*	15,14
4-$HOC_6H_4CON(C_2H_5)_2$	C_2H_5MgBr	$C_2H_5COC_6H_4$-4-OH (65%); recovered amide†	15
N,N-Diethyl-β-2-furylacrylamide (20 g.)	C_2H_5MgBr (25 g. C_2H_5Br)	*N,N*-Diethyl-β-2-furylvaleramide (70%)	55
N,N-Diethyl-β-2-furylacrylamide (20 g.)	C_6H_5MgBr (36 g. C_6H_5Br)	*N,N*-Diethyl-β-2-furylhydrocinnamamide (78%)	55
N-Methyl-β-2-furylacrylanilide	C_2H_5MgBr	*N*-Methyl-β-2-furylvaleranilide (68%)	55
N-Methyl-β-2-furylacrylanilide	C_6H_5MgBr	*N*-Methyl-β-2-furylhydrocinnamanilide (70%)	55
N-Ethyl-β-2-furylacrylanilide	C_2H_5MgBr	*N*-Ethyl-β-2-furylvaleranilide	55
N-Ethyl-β-2-furylacrylanilide	C_6H_5MgBr	*N*-Ethyl-β-2-furylhydrocinnamanilide (70%)	55
N,N-Diphenyl-β-2-furylacrylamide (17 g.)	C_2H_5MgBr (19 g. C_2H_5Br)	*N,N*-Diphenyl-β-2-furylvaleramide (90%); $(C_6H_5)_2NH$	55
N,N-Diphenyl-β-2-furylacrylamide (25 g.)	*n*-C_3H_7MgBr (36 g. C_3H_7Br)	*N,N*-Diphenyl-β-2-furylcaproamide	55
N,N-Diphenyl-β-2-furylacrylamide (17 g.)	C_6H_5MgBr (21 g. C_6H_5Br)	*N,N*-Diphenyl-β-2-furylhydrocinnamamide (95%)	55
$C_7H_5O_3$-NRR′			
2,4-$(HO)_2C_6H_3CON(C_2H_5)_2$	C_2H_5MgBr (5 equiv.)	$C_2H_5COC_6H_3$-2,4-$(OH)_2$ (12%)	15,14
3,4-$(HO)_2C_6H_3CON(C_2H_5)_2$	C_2H_5MgBr (6 equiv.)	No reaction in C_6H_6; resinification in *n*-Bu_2O	15
$C_7H_5O_4$-NRR′			
3,4,5-$(HO)_3C_6H_2CON(C_2H_5)_2$	C_2H_5MgBr (6 equiv.)	No reaction in C_6H_6; resinification in *n*-Bu_2O	15

* Six hours reflux at 60–70° in Et_2O-C_6H_6.

† Four hours reflux in *n*-Bu_2O.

TABLE XII-I (Continued)

Co-reactant	RMgX	Product(s)	Ref.
$C_7H_{10}O_2$-NR			
N,β,β-Trimethylglutarimide	*n*-$C_7H_{15}MgBr$	After hydrolysis: *n*-$C_7H_{15}COCH_2C(CH_3)_2CH_2CO_2H$	3
$C_7H_{11}ON$			
1-Methyl-5-ethyl-2(3*H*)-pyrrolone	CH_3MgBr (3 equiv.)	1,2-Dimethyl-5-ethylpyrrole (38%)	36
1-Methyl-5-ethyl-2(3*H*)-pyrrolone	C_2H_5MgBr (2 equiv.)	1-Methyl-2,5-diethylpyrrole; $(C_2H_5COCH_2—)_2$; 1-methyl-2,2,5-triethyl-Δ^2-pyrroline; C_2H_6	36
1-Methyl-5-ethyl-2(3*H*)-pyrrolone	$C_6H_5CH_2MgCl$	1-Methyl-2-ethyl-5-benzylpyrrole (29%); $C_2H_5COCH_2CH_2COCH_2C_6H_5$ (71%)	36
3,3,5-Trimethyl-2-pyrrolidone	RMgX	"Did not react"	67
$C_7H_{13}ON$			
1-Methyl-2-oxo-1-azacyloheptane	CH_3MgI	1,2,2-Trimethyl-1-azacycloheptane	41
1-Methyl-2-oxo-1-azacycloheptane	C_2H_5MgBr	1-Methyl-2,2-diethyl-1-azacycloheptane	41
1-Methyl-2-oxo-1-azacycloheptane	C_6H_5MgBr	1-Methyl-2-phenyl-2-hydroxy-1-azocycloheptane (?) or 1-methylamino-6-phenylhexanone (?)	41
1-Methyl-2-oxo-1-azacycloheptane	$C_6H_5CH_2MgCl$	Methyldibenzylazacycloheptane hydrochloride	41
1-Methyl-2-oxo-1-azacycloheptane	1-$C_{10}H_7MgBr$	1-Methyl-2-α-naphthyl-1-azacycloheptane	41
$C_8H_4O_2$-NR			
Phthalimide	C_2H_5MgBr	3-Ethylisoïndolone	2
Phthalimide	*i*-C_4H_9MgX	3-Isobutylisoïndolone	2
Phthalimide	*i*-$C_5H_{11}MgX$	3-Isoamylisoïndolone	2
N-Ethylphthalimide (10 g.)	CH_3MgBr (20 g. CH_3Br)	2-Ethyl-3-hydroxy-3-methylphthalimidine ("good yield")	70

TABLE XII-I (Continued)

Co-reactant	RMgX	Product(s)	Ref.
$C_8H_4O_2$-NR (*cont.*)			
N-Ethylphthalimide	C_2H_5MgBr	2,3-Diethyl-3-hydroxyphthalimidine ("very good yield")	70
N-Ethylphthalimide	C_6H_5MgBr	2-Ethyl-3-hydroxy-3-phenylphthalimidine	70
$C_8H_4O_2$-(NRR′)$_2$			
C_6H_4-1,2-$[CON(C_2H_5)_2]_2$ (40 g.)	C_2H_5MgBr (110 g. C_2H_5Br)	3,3-Diethylphthalide (15%); 2-$C_2H_5COC_6H_4CON(C_2H_5)_2$ (10%); recovered amide	45
C_6H_4-1,2-$[CON(C_2H_5)_2]_2$	C_6H_5MgBr	No reaction	45
C_6H_4-1,3-$[CON(C_2H_5)_2]_2$ (45 g.)	C_2H_5MgBr (110 g. C_2H_5Br)	3-$C_2H_5COC_6H_4CON(C_2H_5)_2$ (20%); 1,3-$(C_2H_5CO)_2C_6H_4$ (25%); recovered amide	45
C_6H_4-1,3-$[CON(C_2H_5)_2]_2$	C_6H_5MgBr	No reaction	45
C_6H_4-1,4-$[CON(C_2H_5)_2]_2$ (40 g.)	C_2H_5MgBr (110 g. C_2H_5Br)	4-$C_2H_5COC_6H_4CON(C_2H_5)_2$ (25%); 1,4-$(C_2H_5CO)_2C_6H_4$ (30%); recovered amide	45
C_6H_4-1,4-$[CON(C_2H_5)_2]_2$	C_6H_5MgBr	No reaction	45
$C_8H_4O_2N$-NRR′			
Benzoxazole-2-carboxanilide (10 g.)	CH_3MgI (1.5 equiv.)	Benzoxazole-2-carboxaldehyde anil	73
$C_8H_5O_3$-NRR′			
2-$HO_2CC_6H_4CON(C_2H_5)_2$ (30 g.)	C_2H_5MgBr (110 g. C_2H_5Br)	3,3-Diethylphthalide (26 g., 80%)	45
2-$HO_2CC_6H_4CON(C_2H_5)_2$ (20 g.)	*n*-C_3H_7MgBr (66 g. C_3H_7Br)	3,3-Di-*n*-propylphthalide (15 g.)	49
2-$HO_2CC_6H_4CON(C_2H_5)_2$ (19 g.)	*i*-C_4H_9MgCl (53 g. C_4H_9Cl)	3,3-Diisobutylphthalide (15 g.)	49
2-$HO_2CC_6H_4CON(C_2H_5)_2$ (20 g.)	*i*-$C_5H_{11}MgBr$ (90 g. $C_5H_{11}Br$)	3,3-Diisoamylphthalide (15 g.)	49
2-$HO_2CC_6H_4CON(C_2H_5)_2$ (20 g.)	C_6H_5MgBr (94 g. C_6H_5Br)	3,3-Diphenylphthalide (16 g.)	49
2-$HO_2CC_6H_4CON(C_2H_5)_2$ (20 g.)	$C_6H_5CH_2MgCl$ (75 g. C_7H_7Cl)	3,3-Dibenzylphthalide (17 g.)	49

TABLE XII-I (Continued)

Co-reactant	RMgX	Product(s)	Ref.
C_8H_6OCl-NRR′			
DL-$C_6H_5CHClCONH_2$ (12 g.)	C_6H_5MgBr (91 g. C_6H_5Br)	$(C_6H_5)_2CHCOC_6H_5$ (small yield)	74
$C_8H_6O_2Cl$-NRR′			
3-$ClC_6H_4CH(OH)CONH_2$ (4.64 g.)	4-$CH_3OC_6H_4MgBr$ (18.70 g. C_7H_7BrO)	4-$CH_3OC_6H_4COCH(OH)C_6H_4$-3-Cl (30%)	30
4-$ClC_6H_4CH(OH)CONH_2$ (1.3 g.)	4-$(CH_3)_2NC_6H_4MgBr$ (20 g. $C_8H_{10}BrN$)	β-4-$(CH_3)_2NC_6H_4COCH(OH)C_6H_4$-4-Cl (0.5 g.)	23
C_8H_7O-NRR′			
$C_6H_5CH_2CONH_2$ (38 g.)	C_2H_5MgBr (120 g. C_2H_5Br)	Recovered amide; $C_2H_5COCH_2C_6H_5$ (39%)	45
$C_6H_5CH_2CON(C_2H_5)_2$	C_2H_5MgX*	No reaction	45
$C_6H_5CH_2CON(C_2H_5)_2$ (30 g.)	C_6H_5MgBr (60 g. C_6H_5Br)	(C_6H_5—); recovered amide; $C_6H_5COCH_2C_6H_5$ (37%)	45
$C_8H_7O_2$-NRR′			
$C_6H_5CH(OH)CONH_2$ (10.0 g.)	CH_3MgI (70.5 g. CH_3I)	$CH_3COCH(OH)C_6H_5$ (8 g., crude)	66
DL-$C_6H_5CH(OH)CONH_2$ (20.0 g.)	CH_3MgI (111.2 g. CH_3I)	DL-$C_6H_5CH(OH)COCH_3$ (3.5 g.)	84,79
$C_6H_5CH(OH)CONH_2$	C_2H_5MgBr (4 equiv.)	$C_2H_5COCH(OH)C_6H_5$ (*ca.* 40%)	79
D(−)-$C_6H_5CH(OH)CONH_2$ (15 g.)	C_2H_5MgBr (from 50 g. bromide)	D(−)-$C_6H_5CH(OH)COC_2H_5$	69
$C_6H_5CH(OH)CONH_2$ (25 g.)	C_2H_5MgI	$C_2H_5COCH(OH)C_6H_5$ (10 g.)	66
$C_6H_5CH(OH)CONH_2$	*n*-C_3H_7MgBr (4 equiv.)	*n*-$C_3H_7COCH(OH)C_6H_5$ (30%)	79
$C_6H_5CH(OH)CONH_2$	*i*-C_3H_7MgBr (4 equiv.)	*i*-$C_3H_7COCH(OH)C_6H_5$ (28–30%)	79
$C_6H_5CH(OH)CONH_2$	*n*-C_4H_9MgBr (4 equiv.)	*n*-$C_4H_9COCH(OH)C_6H_5$ (20%)	79
$C_6H_5CH(OH)CONH_2$	*i*-C_4H_9MgBr (4 equiv.)	*i*-$C_4H_9COCH(OH)C_6H_5$ (17%)	79
$C_6H_5CH(OH)CONH_2$ (15.8 g.)	C_6H_5MgBr (62 g. C_6H_5Br)	$C_6H_5COCH(OH)C_6H_5$	66
D-$C_6H_5CH(OH)CONH_2$	C_6H_5MgBr	D-$C_6H_5CH(OH)COC_6H_5$	84
$C_6H_5CH(OH)CONH_2$	$C_6H_5CH_2MgCl$	$C_6H_5CH_2COCH(OH)C_6H_5$ (30%)	79
D(−)-$C_6H_5CH(OH)CONH_2$ (8 g.)	$C_6H_5CH_2MgCl$ (32 g. C_7H_7Cl)	D(−)-$C_6H_5CH(OH)COCH_2C_6H_5$	69
DL-$C_6H_5CH(OH)CONH_2$	2-$CH_3C_6H_4MgBr$	DL-$C_6H_5CH(OH)COC_6H_4$-2-CH_3 ("very small yield")	58

* X = Br, I

TABLE XII-I (Continued)

Co-reactant	RMgX	Product(s)	Ref.
$C_8H_7O_2$-NRR′ (*cont.*)			
DL-$C_6H_5CH(OH)CONH_2$ (5 g.)	4-$CH_3C_6H_4MgBr$ (34 g. C_7H_7Br)	DL-$C_6H_5CH(OH)COC_6H_4$-4-CH_3 (0.5 g.)	*58*
$C_6H_5CH(OH)CONH_2$ (3 g.)	4-$CH_3OC_6H_4MgBr$ (22.4 g. C_7H_7BrO)	4-$CH_3OC_6H_4COCH(OH)C_6H_5$ (1.5 g.)	*24*
DL-$C_6H_5CH(OH)CONHC_2H_5$	C_6H_5MgBr	"No success"	*58*
DL-$C_6H_5CH(OH)CON(CH_2)_5$	C_6H_5MgX*	DL-$C_6H_5CH(OH)COC_6H_5$; DL-$C_6H_5CH(OH)C(C_6H_5)_2OH$	*58*
2-$CH_3OC_6H_4CONH_2$	C_2H_5MgBr	2-$CH_3OC_6H_4COC_2H_5$ (70%);	*14*
		2-$CH_3OC_6H_4C(=NH)C_2H_5$	*14*
2-$CH_3OC_6H_4CONH_2$ (22.5 g.)	C_2H_5MgBr (55 g. C_2H_5Br)	$C_2H_5COC_6H_4$-2-OCH_3 (49%); recovered amide (40–50%)†	*15*
2-$CH_3OC_6H_4CON(C_2H_5)_2$ (21 g.)	C_2H_5MgBr (24 g. C_2H_5Br)	2-$CH_3OC_6H_4(C_2H_5)_2CN(C_2H_5)_2$ (?); $C_2H_5COC_6H_4$-2-OCH_3 (84%); recovered amide‡	*15*
2-$CH_3OC_6H_4CON(C_2H_5)_2$	C_2H_5MgBr	2-$CH_3OC_6H_4COC_2H_5$ (60–80%)	*14*
4-$CH_3OC_6H_4CONH_2$ (20 g.)	C_2H_5MgBr (55 g. C_2H_5Br)	$C_2H_5C(=NH)C_6H_4$-4-OCH_3; $C_2H_5COC_6H_4$-4-OCH_3 (70%); recovered amide	*14,15, 13*
4-$CH_3OC_6H_4CONH_2$	2-$ClC_6H_4CH_2MgBr$ (3–4 equiv.)	4-$CH_3OC_6H_4COCH_2C_6H_4$-4-Cl (55%)	*25*
4-$CH_3OC_6H_4CONH_2$	3-$ClC_6H_4CH_2MgBr$ (4 equiv.)	4-$CH_3OC_6H_4COCH_2C_6H_4$-3-Cl (60%)	*30*
4-$CH_3OC_6H_4CONH_2$	4-$ClC_6H_4CH_2MgBr$ (3–4 equiv.)	4-$CH_3OC_6H_4COCH_2C_6H_4$-4-Cl (66%)	*25,28*
4-$CH_3OC_6H_4CONH_2$	$C_6H_5CH_2MgCl$ (3–4 equiv.)	4-$CH_3OC_6H_4COCH_2C_6H_5$ (70–76%)	*24,25, 27*
4-$CH_3OC_6H_4CON(C_2H_5)_2$	C_2H_5MgBr	$C_2H_5COC_6H_4$-4-OCH_3 ("very little")§	*15*

* X = Br, I.
† Four hours at 65°.
‡ Five hours at 50°.
§ Reaction in Et_2O.

TABLE XII-I (Continued)

Co-reactant	RMgX	Product(s)	Ref.
$C_8H_7O_2$-NRR′ *(cont.)*			
4-$CH_3OC_6H_4CON(C_2H_5)_2$	C_2H_5MgBr	4-$CH_3OC_6H_4COC_2H_5$ (60–80%)	*14*
4-$CH_3OC_6H_4CON(C_2H_5)_2$ (50 g.)	C_2H_5MgBr (2.2 equiv.)	4-$CH_3OC_6H_4(C_2H_5)_2CN(C_2H_5)_2$ (14 g., crude); $C_2H_5COC_6H_4$-4-OCH_3 (12 g., 30%)*	*15*
4-$CH_3OC_6H_4CON(C_2H_5)_2$ (31 g.)	C_6H_5MgBr (71 g. C_6H_5Br)	4-$CH_3OC_6H_4(C_6H_5)_2CN(C_2H_5)_2 \cdot HCl$ (11 g., 22%); C_6H_5OH; $(C_6H_5—)_2$; recovered amide	*15*
4-$CH_3OC_6H_4CON(C_2H_5)_2$	C_6H_5MgBr	4-$CH_3OC_6H_4COC_6H_5$; 4-$CH_3OC_6H_4(C_6H_5)_2CN(C_2H_5)_2$	*14*
$C_8H_{15}O_2$-NRR′			
n-$C_6H_{13}CH(OH)CONH_2$ (65 g.)	*n*-C_3H_7MgBr	*n*-$C_3H_7COCH(OH)$-*n*-C_6H_{13} (36 g.)	*66*
n-$C_6H_{13}CH(OH)CONH_2$ (20 g.)	*n*-C_4H_9MgBr (137 g. C_4H_9Br)	*n*-$C_4H_9COCH(OH)$-*n*-C_6H_{13}	*66*
C_9H_7O-NRR′			
$C_6H_5CH=CHCONH_2$	C_2H_5MgBr	Unidentified H_2O-insol., Et_2O-insol. syrup	*45*
$C_6H_5CH=CHCON(C_2H_5)_2$ (45 g.)	C_2H_5MgBr (55 g. C_2H_5Br)	$C_6H_5CH(C_2H_5)CH_2CON(C_2H_5)_2$ (80%; 82% in C_6H_6 sol'n)	*45*
$C_6H_5CH=CHCON(C_2H_5)_2$ (45 g.)	C_6H_5MgBr (80 g. C_6H_5Br)	$(C_6H_5)_2CHCH_2CON(C_2H_5)_2$ (83%)	*45*
$C_6H_5CH=CHCONRC_6H_5$†	CH_3MgI	$CH_3COCH=CHC_6H_5$; $RNHC_6H_5$; recovered amide	*50*
$C_6H_5CH=CHCON(CH_3)C_6H_5$	C_2H_5MgBr	$C_2H_5CH(C_6H_5)CH_2CON(CH_3)C_6H_5$ (quant.)	*50*
$C_6H_5CH=CHCON(CH_3)C_6H_5$	C_6H_5MgBr	$(C_6H_5)_2CHCH_2CON(CH_3)C_6H_5$ (quant.)	*50*
$C_6H_5CH=CHCON(C_2H_5)C_6H_5$	C_2H_5MgBr	$C_2H_5CH(C_6H_5)CH_2CON(C_2H_5)C_6H_5$ (quant.)	*50*
$C_6H_5CH=CHCON(C_2H_5)C_6H_5$	C_6H_5MgBr	$(C_6H_5)_2CHCH_2CON(C_2H_5)C_6H_5$ (quant.)	*50,22*

* Reaction in C_6H_6.
† R = CH_3, C_2H_5, C_6H_5.

TABLE XII - I (Continued)

Co-reactant	RMgX	Product(s)	Ref.
C_9H_7O-NRR′ (*cont.*)			
$C_6H_5CH{=}CHCON(C_6H_5)_2$	C_2H_5MgBr	$C_2H_5CH(C_6H_5)CH_2CON(C_6H_5)_2$ (quant.)	*50*
$C_6H_5CH{=}CHCON(C_6H_5)_2$	C_6H_5MgBr	$(C_6H_5)_2CHCH_2CON(C_6H_5)_2$ (quant.)	*50*
$C_9H_7O_2N$			
N-Methylisatin (0.05 mole)	C_6H_5MgBr (0.25 mole)	1-Methyl-2,3-epoxy-2,3-diphenylindoline (*ca.* 52%); 1-methyl-3,3-diphenyloxindole	*89*
C_9H_9O-NRR′			
$C_6H_5(CH_2)_2CON(C_2H_5)_2$ (30 g.)	C_2H_5MgBr (100 g. C_2H_5Br)	Recovered amide; $C_2H_5CO(CH_2)_2C_6H_5$ (12 g., 50%)	*45,43*
$C_6H_5(CH_2)_2CON(C_2H_5)_2$	C_6H_5MgBr	$C_6H_5CO(CH_2)_2C_6H_5$	*43*
$C_6H_5(CH_2)_2CON(C_2H_5)_2$ (30 g.)	C_6H_5MgBr (5 g. C_6H_5Br)	Recovered amide; $C_6H_5CO(CH_2)_2C_6H_5$ (69%)	*45*
$CH_3(C_6H_5)CHCONH_2$ (16 g.)	C_6H_5MgBr (2.5 equiv.)	$C_6H_5COCH(CH_3)C_6H_5$ (24%); $CH_3(C_6H_5)CHCN$; $(C_6H_5—)_2$	*10*
$CH_3(C_6H_5)CHCONH_2$ (27.5 g.)	4-$CH_3C_6H_4MgBr$ (2.5 equiv.)	$CH_3(C_6H_5)CHCOC_6H_4$-4-CH_3 (8.5 g.); $CH_3(C_6H_5)CHCN$; (4-$CH_3C_6H_4—)_2$; resin	*10,9*
$CH_3(C_6H_5)CHCONH_2$ (23 g.)	4-$CH_3OC_6H_4MgBr$ (2.5 equiv.)	$CH_3(C_6H_5)CHCOC_6H_4$-4-OCH_3 (7 g.); $CH_3(C_6H_5)CHCN$; (4-$CH_3OC_6H_4—)_2$	*10,9*
$C_9H_9O_2$-NRR′			
$C_6H_5CH_2OCH_2CONH_2$	$C_6H_5CH_2MgCl$	$C_6H_5CH_2OCH_2COCH_2C_6H_5$	*17*
4-$CH_3OC_6H_4CH_2CONH_2$ (1.2 g.)	3-ClC_6H_4MgI (7.2 g. C_6H_4ICl)	3-$ClC_6H_4COCH_2C_6H_4$-4-OCH_3 (20%)	*30*
4-$CH_3OC_6H_4CH_2CONH_2$ (11.0 g.)	4-ClC_6H_4MgBr (38.3 g. C_6H_4BrCl)	4-$ClC_6H_4COCH_2C_6H_4$-4-OCH_3 (23%)	*28*
4-$CH_3OC_6H_4CH_2CONH_2$ (4.13 g.)	C_6H_5MgBr (15.7 g. C_6H_5Br)	$C_6H_5COCH_2C_6H_4$-4-OCH_3 (1.85 g., 30%)	*27*
L-$C_6H_5CH(OCH_3)CONH_2$ (5.5 g.)	C_6H_5MgBr (20 g. C_6H_5Br)	$(C_6H_5—)_2$; recovered amide; $C_6H_5CH(OCH_3)COC_6H_5$ (0.35 g., crude)	*58*

TABLE XII-I (Continued)

Co-reactant	RMgX	Product(s)	Ref.
$C_9H_9O_2$-NRR′ (*cont.*)			
D-, L-, or DL-$C_6H_5CH(OH)CH_2CONH_2$	C_6H_5MgBr	"Unsuccessful"	*58*
D-$C_6H_5CH_2CH(OH)CONH_2$ (5 g.)	C_6H_5MgBr (29 g. C_6H_5Br)	D-$C_6H_5CH_2CH(OH)COC_6H_5$ (2.5 g.)	*58*
DL-$C_6H_5CH_2CH(OH)CONH_2$ (5 g.)	C_6H_5MgBr (23 g. C_6H_5Br)	DL-$C_6H_5CH_2CH(OH)COC_6H_5$ (1.5 g.); DL-$C_6H_5CH_2CH(OH)C(C_6H_5)_2OH$	*58*
$C_9H_9O_3$-NRR′			
3,4-$(CH_3O)_2C_6H_3CONH_2$	C_2H_5MgBr	3,4-$(CH_3O)_2C_6H_3COC_2H_5$ (70%); 3,4-$(CH_3O)_2C_6H_3C(=NH)C_2H_5$	*14*
3,4-$(CH_3O)_2C_6H_3CON(C_2H_5)_2$	C_2H_5MgBr (*ca.* 2 equiv.)	3,4-$(CH_3O)_2C_6H_3COC_2H_5$ (70%)	*15,14*
3,5-$(CH_3O)_2C_6H_3CONH_2$ (110 g.)	CH_3MgI (5-fold excess)	3,5-$(CH_3O)_2C_6H_3COCH_3$ (63 g., 57%)	92
3,5-$(CH_3O)_2C_6H_3CONH_2$ (0.25 mole)	C_2H_5MgBr (1 mole C_2H_5Br)	3,5-$(CH_3O)_2C_6H_3COC_2H_5$ (84%)	78
3,5-$(CH_3O)_2C_6H_3CONH_2$ (46 g.)	*n*-C_3H_7MgBr (123 g. C_3H_7Br)	3,5-$(CH_3O)_2C_6H_3CO$-*n*-C_3H_7 (88%)	78
3,5-$(CH_3O)_2C_6H_3CONH_2$	*n*-C_4H_9MgBr (4 equiv.)	3,5-$(CH_3O)_2C_6H_3CO$-*n*-C_4H_9 (80%)	78
3,5-$(CH_3O)_2C_6H_3CONH_2$	*n*-$C_5H_{11}MgBr$ (4 equiv.)	3,5-$(CH_3O)_2C_6H_3CO$-*n*-C_5H_{11} (88%)	78
3,5-$(CH_3O)_2C_6H_3CONH_2$	*n*-$C_6H_{13}MgBr$ (4 equiv.)	3,5-$(CH_3O)_2C_6H_3CO$-*n*-C_6H_{13} (85%)	78
3,5-$(CH_3O)_2C_6H_3CON(C_2H_5)_2$ (47.4 g.)	*n*-C_4H_9MgBr (31.5 g. C_4H_9Br)	Recovered amide; 3,5-$(CH_3O)_2C_6H_3CO$-*n*-C_4H_9 (18.9 g., 43%)	78
$C_9H_{11}O$-NRR′			
t-$C_4H_9CH_2CONH_2$	*n*-C_4H_9MgBr	*n*-$C_4H_9COCH_2$-*t*-C_4H_9 (77%)	*81*
t-$C_4H_9CH_2CONH_2$	*n*-$C_5H_{11}MgBr$	*n*-$C_5H_{11}COCH_2$-*t*-C_4H_9 (60%)	*81*
$C_9H_{17}ON$			
3,3-Diethyl-5-methyl-2-pyrrolidone	RMgX	"Did not react"	*67*

TABLE XII-I (Continued)

Co-reactant	RMgX	Product(s)	Ref.
$C_{10}H_6O_2N_2$			
Proline anhydride*	C_6H_5MgBr	1-(α-Pyrrolidyldiphenylmethyl)-2-benzoylpyrrolidine	*91*
$C_{10}H_9O_2N$			
N-Ethylisatin	*n*-C_4H_5MgBr (4 equiv.)	1-Ethyl-2,3-di-*n*-butyl-2,3-epoxyindoline	*90*
N-Ethylisatin	C_6H_5MgBr (5 equiv.)	1-Ethyl-2,3-diphenyl-2,3-epoxyindoline (56%); 1-methyl-3,3-diphenyloxindole (16%)	*89*
$C_{10}H_{10}ON_2$			
1,2-Dimethyl-4(1*H*)-quinazolone (8.0 g.)	C_6H_5MgBr (17.5 g. C_6H_5Br)	Product isolated after treatment with HI as 2-methyl-4-phenylquinazolinium methiodide	*21*
$C_{10}H_{11}O$-NRR′			
$C_2H_5CH(C_6H_5)CONH_2$	*n*-C_4H_9MgBr (4 equiv.)	*n*-$C_4H_9COCH(C_2H_5)C_6H_5$	*34*
$C_2H_5CH(C_6H_5)CONH_2$	*i*-C_4H_9MgBr (4 equiv.)	*i*-$C_4H_9COCH(C_2H_5)C_6H_5$	*34*
$C_2H_5CH(C_6H_5)CONH_2$	$C_6H_5CH_2MgCl$ (4 equiv.)	$C_6H_5CH_2COCH(C_2H_5)C_6H_5$	*34*
$C_2H_5CH(C_6H_5)CONH_2$	$C_6H_5(CH_2)_2MgBr$ (4 equiv.)	$C_6H_5CH_2CH_2COCH(C_2H_5)C_6H_5$	*34*
$C_6H_5(CH_3)_2CCONH_2$ (0.1 mole)	4-$CH_3OC_6H_4MgBr$ (2.5 equiv.)	$C_6H_5(CH_3)_2CC(=NH \cdot HBr)C_6H_4$-4-$OCH_3$ (*ca.* 40%)	*10,8*
$C_{10}H_{11}O_3$-NRR′			
2-CH_3-3,5-$(CH_3O)_2C_6H_2CONH_2$	CH_3MgBr	$CH_3COC_6H_2$-2-CH_3-3,5-$(OCH_3)_2$	*16*
$C_{10}H_{11}O_4$-NRR′			
3,4,5-$(CH_3O)_3C_6H_2CONH_2$ (90 g.)	C_2H_5MgBr (144 g. C_2H_5Br)	$C_2H_5C(=NH)C_6H_2$-3,4,5-$(OCH_3)_3$ (17 g.); $C_2H_5COC_6H_2$-3,4,5-$(OCH_3)_3$ (32 g.); recovered amide (30 g.)	*15,14*

* Hexahydropyrocoll.

TABLE XII-I (Continued)

Co-reactant	RMgX	Product(s)	Ref.
$C_{10}H_{11}O_4$-NRR′ (*cont.*)			
3,4,5-$(CH_3O)_3C_6H_2CON(C_2H_5)_2$	C_2H_5MgBr (*ca.* 2 equiv.)	$C_2H_5COC_6H_2$-3,4,5-$(OCH_3)_2$ (80%)	*15,14*
$C_{10}H_{12}O_2N$-NRR′			
4-$(CH_3)_2NC_6H_4CH(OH)CONH_2$ (3 g.)	4-ClC_6H_4MgBr (15 g. C_6H_4BrCl)	α-4-$ClC_6H_4COCH(OH)C_6H_4$-4-$N(CH_3)_2$ (2 g.)	*23*
$C_{10}H_{16}O_2$-$(NRR')_2$			
$[—(CH_2)_4CON(C_2H_5)_2]_2$	C_2H_5MgBr	$[—(CH_2)_4COC_2H_5]_2$; $C_2H_5CO(CH_2)_8COC_2H_5$	*93*
$C_{11}H_9O_5$-NRR′			
3,4-$(CH_3CO_2)_2C_6H_3CON(C_2H_5)_2$	C_2H_5MgBr (excess)	$CH_3(C_2H_5)_2COH$	*15,13*
$C_{11}H_{13}O$-NRR′			
$C_2H_5CH(C_6H_5)CH_2CON(C_2H_5)_2$	C_2H_5MgBr	Quant. recovery of amide	*45*
$C_6H_5CH(n\text{-}C_3H_7)CONH_2$	$i\text{-}C_4H_9MgBr$ (4 equiv.)	$i\text{-}C_4H_9COCH(n\text{-}C_3H_7)C_6H_5$	*34*
$C_6H_5CH(i\text{-}C_3H_7)CONH_2$	$n\text{-}C_4H_9MgBr$ (4 equiv.)	$n\text{-}C_4H_9COCH(i\text{-}C_3H_7)C_6H_5$	*34*
$C_6H_5CH_2(CH_3)_2CCONH_2$	C_2H_5MgBr (3 equiv.)	$C_2H_5COC(CH_3)_2CH_2C_6H_5$	*68*
$C_6H_5CH_2(CH_3)_2CCONH_2$	C_6H_5MgBr (3 equiv.)	$C_6H_5COC(CH_3)_2CH_2C_6H_5$; $C_6H_5CH_2(CH_3)_2CCN$	*68*
$CH_3(C_2H_5)(C_6H_5)CCONH_2$	C_6H_5MgBr (3 equiv.)	$CH_3(C_2H_5)(C_6H_5)CCN$	*68*
$C_{12}H_9O_3$-NRR′			
2-$CH_3OC_{10}H_6$-3-$CONH_2$	CH_3MgI	2-$CH_3OC_{10}H_6$-3-CN	*19*
$C_{12}H_{13}ON$			
1-Methyl-5-benzyl-2(3*H*)-pyrrolone	CH_3MgBr	1,2-Dimethyl-5-benzylpyrrole (19%); 1,5,5-trimethyl-2-benzyl-Δ^2-pyrroline	*36*

TABLE XII-I (Continued)

Co-reactant	RMgX	Product(s)	Ref.
$C_{12}H_{13}ON$ (*cont.*)			
1-Methyl-5-benzyl-2(3*H*)-pyrrolone	C_2H_5MgBr	1-Methyl-2-ethyl-5-benzylpyrrole (50%)	*36*
1-Methyl-5-benzyl-2(3*H*)-pyrrolone	$C_6H_5CH_2MgCl$	1-Methyl-2,5-dibenzylpyrrole	*36*
$C_{12}H_{15}O$-NRR′			
$C_6H_5CH(n\text{-}C_4H_9)CONH_2$	C_2H_5MgBr (4 equiv.)	$C_2H_5COCH(n\text{-}C_4H_9)C_6H_5$	*34*
$C_6H_5CH(n\text{-}C_4H_9)CONH_2$	$n\text{-}C_3H_7MgBr$ (4 equiv.)	$n\text{-}C_3H_7COCH(n\text{-}C_4H_9)C_6H_5$	*34*
$C_6H_5CH(i\text{-}C_4H_9)CONH_2$	$n\text{-}C_3H_7MgBr$ (4 equiv.)	$n\text{-}C_3H_7COCH(i\text{-}C_4H_9)C_6H_5$	*34*
$C_6H_5(C_2H_5)_2CCONH_2$	C_6H_5MgBr (3 equiv.)	$C_6H_5(C_2H_5)_2CCN$	*68*
$C_{13}H_9O_2$-NRR′			
$(C_4H_3O)CH{=}C(C_6H_5)CON(C_2H_5)_2$* (30 g.)	C_2H_5MgBr (37 g. C_2H_5Br)	$C_2H_5(C_4H_5O)CHCH(C_6H_5)CON(C_2H_5)_2$* (27 g.)	*54*
$(C_4H_3O)CH{=}C(C_6H_5)CON(C_2H_5)_2$* (30 g.)	C_6H_5MgBr (53 g. C_6H_5Br)	$C_6H_5(C_4H_3O)CHCH(C_6H_5)_2CON(C_2H_5)_2$* (29 g.)	*54*
$(C_4H_3O)CH{=}C(C_6H_5)CON(CH_3)C_6H_5$* (30.0 g.)	C_2H_5MgBr (30.5 g. C_2H_5Br)	$C_2H_5(C_4H_3O)CHCH(C_6H_5)CON(CH_3)C_6H_5$* (28.0 g.)	*54*
$(C_4H_3O)CH{=}C(C_6H_5)CON(CH_3)C_6H_5$* (30 g.)	C_6H_5MgBr (44 g. C_6H_5Br)	$C_6H_5(C_4H_3O)CHCH(C_6H_5)CON(CH_3)C_6H_5$*	*54*
$(C_4H_3O)CH{=}C(C_6H_5)CON(C_6H_5)_2$* (20.0 g.)	C_2H_5MgBr (14.5 g. C_2H_5Br)	$C_2H_5(C_4H_3O)CHCH(C_6H_5)CON(C_6H_5)_2$* (18.0 g.)	*54*
$(C_4H_3O)CH{=}C(C_6H_5)CON(C_6H_5)_2$* (20 g.)	C_6H_5MgBr (19 g. C_6H_5Br)	$C_6H_5(C_4H_3O)CHCH(C_6H_5)CON(C_6H_5)_2$* (19 g.)	*54*
$C_{13}H_{11}O_7$-NRR′			
$3,4,5\text{-}(CH_3CO_2)_3C_6H_2CON(C_2H_5)_2$	C_2H_5MgBr (excess)	$CH_3(C_2H_5)_2COH$	*15,13*
$C_{14}H_8ON_2Cl$			
3-*p*-Chlorophenyl-4(3*H*)-quinazolone	$C_6H_5CH_2MgCl$ (2–3 equiv.)	$2\text{-}(C_6H_5CH_2)_2CHNHC_6H_4CONHC_6H_4\text{-}4\text{-}Cl$	*31*

* (C_4H_3O) = α-furyl.

TABLE XII-I (Continued)

Co-reactant	RMgX	Product(s)	Ref.
$C_{14}H_9ON_2$			
3-Phenyl-4(3*H*)-quinazolone (20 g.)	$C_6H_5CH_2MgCl$ (2–3 equiv.)	2-$(C_6H_5CH_2)_2CHNHC_6H_4CONHC_6H_5$ (34.5 g., 94% crude)	*31*
$C_{14}H_{11}O$-NRR′			
$(C_6H_5)_2CHCONH_2$ (15 g.)	C_2H_5MgBr (30 g. C_2H_5Br)	$C_2H_5COCH(C_6H_5)_2$ (11 g., 31%)	*45,43*
$(C_6H_5)_2CHCONH_2$ (20 g.)	C_6H_5MgBr (52 g. C_6H_5Br)	$C_6H_5COCH(C_6H_5)_2$ (11 g., 42%)	*45*
$(C_6H_5)_2CHCON(C_2H_5)_2$	RMgBr*	No reaction	*45,43*
$C_{14}H_{11}O_2$-NRR′			
$(C_6H_5)_2C(OH)CONH_2$	4-$CH_3C_6H_4MgI$	Amide recovered unchanged†	*11*
$(C_6H_5)_2C(OH)CONH_2$ (4.5 g.)	4-$CH_3C_6H_4MgI$ (26.2 g. C_6H_4ICl)	$(C_6H_5)_2CHCONH_2$ (1.5 g.)‡	*11*
2-Methyl-3-phenyl-4(3*H*)-quinazolone (3.0 g.)	*n*-C_3H_7MgBr (1.6 g. C_3H_7Br)	2-Methyl-3-phenyl-4-*n*-propyl-3,4-dihydro-4-quinazolinol (2.5 g.)	*94*
2-Methyl-3-phenyl-4(3*H*)-quinazolone (3.0 g.)	*n*-C_4H_9MgBr (1.6 g. C_4H_9Br)	2-Methyl-3-phenyl-4-*n*-butyl-3,4-dihydro-4-quinazolinol (2.5 g.)	*94*
2-Methyl-3-phenyl-4(3*H*)-quinazolone (0.05 mole)	C_6H_5MgBr (0.05 mole)	2-Methyl-3,4-diphenyl-3,4-dihydro-4-quinazolinol (7.5 g.)	*94*
$C_{15}H_{13}O$-NRR′			
$(C_6H_5)_2CHCH_2CON(C_2H_5)_2$	RMgX	No reaction	*45*
$C_{15}H_{26}O_2$-NR			
N, α-Dimethyl-α-*n*-decylsuccinimide (20 g.)	*n*-$C_{10}H_{21}MgBr$ (35 g. $C_{10}H_{21}Br$)	1,3-Dimethyl-3,5-di-*n*-decyl-2(3*H*)-pyrrolone (8 g., crude)	3

* R = C_2H_5, C_6H_5.
† Eight hours reflux in Et_2O.
‡ Eight hours reflux in *n*-Am_2O.

TABLE XII-I (Continued)

Co-reactant	RMgX	Product(s)	Ref.
$C_{16}H_{15}O$-NRR′			
$C_6H_5CH_2CH_2CH(C_6H_5)CONH_2$	C_2H_5MgBr (4 equiv.)	$C_2H_5COCH(C_6H_5)CH_2CH_2C_6H_5$	34
$(C_6H_5CH_2)_2CHCONH_2$ (10 g.)	C_2H_5MgBr (25 g. C_2H_5Br)	$C_2H_5COCH(CH_2C_6H_5)_2$ (3.5 g., 32%)	45,43
$(C_6H_5CH_2)_2CHCON(C_2H_5)_2$	RMgBr*	No reaction	45,43
$C_{21}H_{17}O$-NRR′			
$C_6H_5CH_2(C_6H_5)_2CCONH_2$	C_6H_5MgBr (3 equiv.)	$C_6H_5CH_2(C_6H_5)_2CCN$	68
N,N′-Bis-(*p*-tolylsulfonyl)-dianthranilide	CH_3MgI	α,α-Dimethyl-2-(*p*-tolylsulfonamido)-benzyl alcohol	95
N,N′-Bis-(*p*-tolylsulfonyl)-dianthranilide	C_6H_5MgBr	α,α-Diphenyl-2-(*p*-tolylsulfonamido)-benzyl alcohol	95
N,N′-Bis-(*p*-tolylsulfonyl)-dianthranilide	$4-CH_3C_6H_4MgBr$	α,α-Di-*p*-tolyl-2-(*p*-tolylsulfonamido)benzyl alcohol	95

* R = C_2H_5, C_6H_5.

REFERENCES FOR TABLE XII-I

(*1*) Barré, *Ann. chim.*, [10], *9*, 204–75 (1927).
(*2*) Béïs, *Compt. rend.*, *137*, 575–6 (1930); *Chem. Zentr.*, *1903,II*, 1110.
(*3*) Birch and Robinson, *J. Chem. Soc.*, *1942*, 488–97.
(*4*) Blaise, *Compt. rend.*, *173*, 313–5 (1921).
(*5*) Blaise and Montagne, *Compt. rend.*, *180*, 1345–6 (1925).
(*6*) Bouveault, *Compt. rend.*, *137*, 987–9 (1903); *Chem. Zentr.*, *1904,I*, 257.
(*7*) Bouveault, *Bull. soc. chem.*, [3], *31*, 1322–7 (1904).
(*8*) Bruzau, *Compt. rend.*, *194*, 1662–4 (1932).
(*9*) Bruzau, *Compt. rend.*, *196*, 122–4 (1932).
(*10*) Bruzau, *Ann. chim.*, [11], *1*, 257–358 (1934).
(*11*) Burton, *J. Chem. Soc.*, *1930*, 2400.
(*12*) Busch and Fleischmann, *Ber.*, *43*, 2553–6 (1910).
(*13*) Couturier, *Compt. rend.*, *202*, 1994–6 (1936); *Chem. Abstr.*, *30*, 6725 (1936).
(*14*) Couturier, *Compt. rend.*, *205*, 800–2 (1937); *Chem. Abstr.*, *32*, 1251 (1938).
(*15*) Couturier, *Ann. chim.*, [11], *10*, 559–629 (1938).
(*16*) Cram, *J. Am. Chem. Soc.*, *70*, 440–1 (1948).
(*17*) Darmon, *Compt. rend.*, *197*, 1328–9 (1933).
(*18*) Ellingboe and Fuson, *J. Am. Chem. Soc.*, *56*, 1777–9 (1934).
(*19*) Fries and Schimmelschmidt, *Ber.*, *58B*, 2835–45 (1925).
(*20*) Grammaticakis, *Compt. rend.*, *207*, 239–41 (1938); *Chem. Abstr.*, *34*, 2808 (1940).
(*21*) Hamer, Heilbron, Reade, and Walls, *J. Chem. Soc.*, *1932*, 251–60.
(*22*) Houben and Doescher, *Ber.*, *40*, 4576–9 (1907).
(*23*) Jenkins, *J. Am. Chem. Soc.*, *53*, 3115–22 (1931).
(*24*) Jenkins, *J. Am. Chem. Soc.*, *54*, 1155–63 (1932).
(*25*) Jenkins, *J. Am. Chem. Soc.*, *55*, 703–6 (1933).
(*26*) Jenkins, *J. Am. Chem. Soc.*, *55*, 2896–9 (1933).
(*27*) Jenkins, *J. Am. Chem. Soc.*, *56*, 682–4 (1934).
(*28*) Jenkins, *J. Am. Chem. Soc.*, *56*, 1137–8 (1934).
(*29*) Jenkins and Richardson, *J. Am. Chem. Soc.*, *55*, 1618–21 (1933).
(*30*) Jenkins and Richardson, *J. Am. Chem. Soc.*, *55*, 3874–9 (1933).
(*31*) Koelsch, *J. Am. Chem. Soc.*, *67*, 1718–20 (1945).
(*32*) Kohler and Heritage, *Am. Chem. J.*, *33*, 21–35 (1905).
(*33*) Kroeger and Nieuwland, *J. Am. Chem. Soc.*, *58*, 1861–3 (1936).
(*34*) Lévy and Jullien, *Bull. soc. chim.*, [4], *45*, 941–50 (1929).
(*35*) Lukeš, *Collection Czechoslov. Chem. Commun.*, *2*, 531–44 (1930); *Chem. Abstr.*, *25*, 102 (1931).
(*36*) Lukeš, *Collection Czechoslov. Chem. Commun.*, *4*, 181–92 (1932); *Chem. Zentr.*, *1932,II*, 873; *Chem. Abstr.*, *26*, 4328 (1932).
(*37*) Lukeš, *Collection Czechoslov. Chem. Commun.*, *5*, 761–9 (1932); *Chem. Abstr.*, *27*, 290 (1933).
(*38*) Lukeš and Gorocholinskij, *Collection Czechoslov. Chem. Commun.*, *8*, 223–35 (1936); *Chem. Abstr.*, *30*, 5989 (1936).
(*39*) Lukeš and Prelog, *Chem. Listy*, *22*, 244–51 (1928); *Chem. Abstr.*, *23*, 1408 (1929).
(*40*) Lukeš and Smolek, *Collection Czechoslov. Chem. Commun.*, *7*, 482–90 (1935); *Chem. Abstr.*, *30*, 1785 (1936).
(*41*) Lukeš and Smolek, *Collection Czechoslov. Chem. Commun.*, *11*, 506–16 (1939); *Chem. Abstr.*, *34*, 7868 (1940).
(*42*) Lukeš, Šorm, and Arnold, *Collection Czechoslov. Chem. Commun.*, *12*, 641–6 (1947); *Chem. Abstr.*, *42*, 5899 (1948).
(*43*) Maxim, *Compt. rend.*, *182*, 1393–5 (1926).
(*44*) Maxim, *Bull. soc. chim.*, [4], *41*, 809–13 (1927).

(45) Maxim, *Ann. chim.*, [10], 9, 55–111 (1928).
(46) Maxim, *Bul. soc. chim. România, 10*, 97–115 (1928); *Chem. Zentr., 1929,I*, 2161.
(47) Maxim, *Bul. soc. chim. România, 11*, 123–9 (1929); *Chem. Zentr., 1930,I*, 2550.
(48) Maxim, *Bul. soc. chim. România, 12*, 33–5 (1930); *Chem. Zentr., 1930,II*. 3023.
(49) Maxim and Andreescu, *Bull. soc. chim.*, [5], 5, 54–7 (1938).
(50) Maxim and Ioanid, *Bul. soc. chim. România, 10*, 29–48 (1928); *Chem. Zentr., 1928,II*, 754.
(51) Maxim and Ioanid, *Bul. soc. chim. România, 12*, 28–32 (1930); *Chem. Zentr., 1930,II*, 3013.
(52) Maxim and Mavrodineanu, *Bull. soc. chim.*, [5], 2, 591–600 (1935).
(53) Maxim and Mavrodineanu, *Bull. soc. chim.*, [5], 3, 1084–93 (1936).
(54) Maxim and Stancovici, *Bull. soc. chim.*, [5], 3, 1319–23 (1936).
(55) Maxim and Zugrăvescu, *Bull. soc. chim.*, [5], *1*, 1087–99 (1934).
(56) Maxim, Zugrăvescu, and Fulga, *Bull. soc. chim.*, [5], 6, 1339–47 (1939).
(57) McKenzie and Duff, *Ber., 60B*, 1335–41 (1927).
(58) McKenzie, Martin, and Rule, *J. Chem. Soc., 105*, 1583–91 (1914).
(59) Montagne, *Compt. rend., 183*, 216–8 (1926).
(60) Montagne and Guilmart, *Bull. soc. chim.*, [5], *12*, 836–9 (1945).
(61) Montagne and Isambert, *Compt. rend., 203*, 331–3 (1936); *Chem. Abstr., 30*, 8210 (1936).
(62) Montagne and Isambert, *Compt. rend., 208*, 285–7 (1939); *Chem. Abstr., 33*, 3772 (1939).
(63) Montagne and Rousseau, *Compt. rend., 196*, 1165–7 (1933).
(64) Nenitzescu, *Bul. soc. chim. România, 12*, 48–57 (1930); *Chem. Zentr., 1930,II*, 3014.
(65) Nenitzescu and Cantuniari, *Bul. soc. chim. România, 14*, 62–4 (1932); *Chem. Abstr., 27*, 958 (1933).
(66) Nicolle, *Bull. soc. chim.*, [4], 39, 55–67 (1926).
(67) Ramart-Lucas and Fasal, *Compt. rend., 184*, 1253–5 (1927); *Chem. Abstr., 21*, 2472 (1927).
(68) Ramart-Lucas, Laclôtre, and Anagnostopoulos, *Compt. rend., 185*, 282–4 (1927).
(69) Roger, *Helv. Chim. Acta, 12*, 1060–7 (1929).
(70) Sachs and Ludwig, *Ber.*, 37, 385–90 (1904).
(71) Sachs, von Wolff, and Ludwig, *Ber.*, 37, 3252–68 (1904).
(72) Sanna, *Gazz. chim. ital., 64*, 857–60 (1934); *Chem. Abstr., 29*, 3336 (1935).
(73) Skraup and Moser, *Ber., 55B*, 1080–101 (1922).
(74) Smith, *Ber., 71B*, 634–43 (1938).
(75) Smith and Bayliss, *J. Org. Chem.*, 6, 437–42 (1941).
(76) Sou Phou Ti, *Compt. rend., 192*, 1462–4 (1931).
(77) Sou Phou Ti, *Bull. faculté sci. univ. franco-chinoise, Peiping*, No. 1, 1–40 (1934); *Chem. Abstr., 29*, 2519 (1935).
(78) Suter and Weston, *J. Am. Chem. Soc., 61*, 232–6 (1939).
(79) Tiffeneau and Lévy, *Bull. soc. chim.*, [4], 37, 1247–51 (1925).
(80) Tschugaeff, *Ber., 40*, 186–7 (1907).
(81) Whitmore, Popkin, Whitaker, Mattil, and Zech, *J. Am. Chem. Soc.*, 60, 2462–4 (1938).
(82) Whitmore and Sloat, *J. Am. Chem. Soc.*, 64, 2968–70 (1942).
(83) Wohl and Lange, *Ber., 41*, 3612–20 (1908).
(84) Wren, *J. Chem. Soc.*, 95, 1583–93 (1909).
(85) Zaher and Faseeh, *J. Indian Chem. Soc., 21*, 381–2 (1944).

(86) Viguier, *Compt. rend.*, *153*, 955-7 (1911); *Chem. Zentr.*, *1912,I*, 20.
(87) Sou Phou Ti, *Bull. soc. chim.*, [5], *2*, 1799-800 (1935).
(88) Adams, Bramlet, and Tendick, *J. Am. Chem. Soc.*, *42*, 2369-74 (1920).
(89) Meyers and Lindwall, *J. Am. Chem. Soc.*, *60*, 2153-5 (1938).
(90) Sumpter, *Trans. Kentucky Acad. Sci.*, *9*, 61-4 (1941); *Chem. Abstr.*, *36*, 4508 (1942).
(91) Kapfhammer and Matthes, *Z. physiol. Chem.*, *223*, 43-52 (1933); *Chem. Abstr.*, *28*, 2353 (1934); *Chem. Zentr.*, *1934,I*, 2759.
(92) Adams, Harfenist, and Loewe, *J. Am. Chem. Soc.*, *71*, 1624-8 (1949).
(93) Paraskova, *Compt. rend.*, *198*, 1701-3 (1934).
(94) Sen and Sidhu, *J. Indian Chem. Soc.*, *25*, 437-8 (1948); *Chem. Abstr.*, *43*, 4675 (1949).
(95) Mustafa and Gad, *J. Chem. Soc.*, *1949*, 384-7.

CHAPTER XIII

Reactions of Grignard Reagents with Oxides of Carbon, and with Carboxylic Acids and Their Salts.

CARBON SUBOXIDE

Carbon suboxide (C_3O_2) is essentially a bifunctional ketene. Its reaction with methylmagnesium iodide has been investigated by Billman and Smith.[1] Under the experimental conditions employed by them (addition of ethereal suboxide solution to ice-salt-cooled Grignard reagent solution to negative Grignard reagent test[2]) each molecule of suboxide reacts with only one molecule of Grignard reagent—probably because of the ether-insolubility of the initial product. The product isolated (in 24 percent yield) was 2,4,6-triacetylphloroglucinol. The reaction, therefore, may be represented as follows:

$$3\ C({=}CO)_2 + 3\ CH_3MgI \longrightarrow 3\ CH_3C(OMgI){=}C{=}CO$$

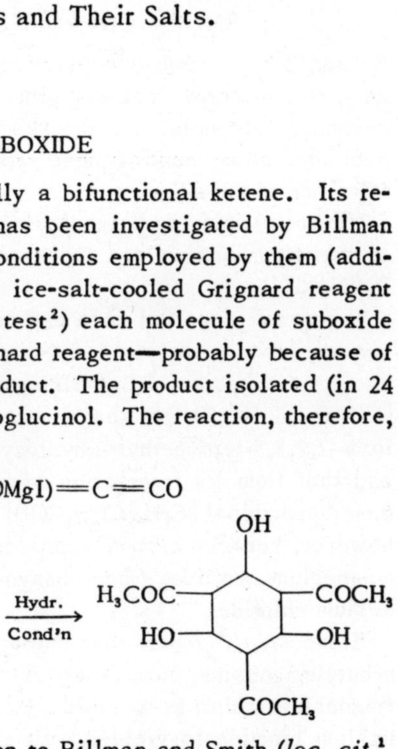

$$\xrightarrow[\text{Cond'n}]{\text{Hydr.}}$$ 2,4,6-triacetylphloroglucinol (benzene ring bearing OH, $COCH_3$, OH, $COCH_3$, OH, H_3COC)

According to a private communication to Billman and Smith (*loc. cit.*[1], f'tnote, p. 458), Reyerson and Kolbe have obtained an unidentified white product from the interaction of carbon suboxide and phenylmagnesium bromide.

More recently Billman and Smith[2.1] have reëxamined the reaction of methylmagnesium iodide with carbon suboxide, and have isolated, in addition to the major product (triacetylphloroglucinol), a small amount of dehydroacetic acid (2-acetyl-3-oxo-5-hydroxy-4-hexenoic acid δ-lactone).

From cyclohexylmagnesium bromide and carbon suboxide they have obtained the 2,4,6-triacylphloroglucinol derivative analogous to the methylmagnesium iodide product.

---

[1] Billman and Smith, *J. Am. Chem. Soc.*, *61*, 457–8 (1939).
[2] Gilman and Schulze, *J. Am. Chem. Soc.*, *47*, 2002–5 (1925).
[2.1] Billman and Smith, *J. Am. Chem. Soc.*, *74*, 3174 (1952).

CARBON MONOXIDE

In his first general review of work on organomagnesium halides and their reactions, Grignard[3] remarked that carbon monoxide is at once an unsaturated compound and a carbonyl group,* and that, if it were possible to arrest reaction at the first stage, the oxide might be expected to combine with organomagnesium halides to form aldehyde derivatives.

$$RMgX + CO \longrightarrow RCOMgX \xrightarrow{H_2O} RCHO$$

He added that unpublished experiments of his own indicated that at ordinary temperatures reaction proceeds through a second stage, yielding secondary alcohols. To the knowledge of the present authors, Grignard published no account of these experiments, and made no further published reference to the subject.

Vinay[4] claimed to have obtained tertiary alcohols from the interaction of carbon monoxide and Grignard reagents of the types R_2CHMgX and R_3CMgX.

Jegorowa[5] reported that carbon monoxide reacts with isopropylmagnesium bromide to yield 2,4-dimethyl-2-pentene [$(CH_3)_2C{=}CH$-*i*-C_3H_7] and 2,3,4-trihydroxy-2,3,4-triisopropyl-5-oxo-6-methylheptanal {*i*-C_3H_7CO-[C(OH)-*i*-$C_3H_7]_3CHO$}; that it reacts with *t*-butylmagnesium chloride to form 2,2,5,5-tetramethyl-4-hydroxy-3-hexanone [*t*-$C_4H_9COCH(OH)$-*t*-C_4H_9]; and that from its interaction with *t*-amylmagnesium chloride only ethyldimethylcarbinol [$C_2H_5(CH_3)_2COH$] was obtained. No reaction took place, however, between carbon monoxide and methylmagnesium iodide, phenylmagnesium bromide, *t*-heptylmagnesium bromide, or triphenylmethylmagnesium chloride.

Eidus *et al.*[6] report that carbon monoxide under pressure reacts with *n*-butylmagnesium bromide to yield 4-nonene (25.4 percent), with *n*-butylmagnesium chloride to yield 4-nonene (51.0 percent), with isoämylmagnesium bromide to yield 2,8-dimethyl-4-nonene (51.0 percent), and with isoämylmagnesium chloride to yield 2,8-dimethyl-4-nonene (53.6 percent).

In a private communication to Schlubach,[7] Staudinger stated that carbon monoxide either does not react with phenylmagnesium bromide, or reacts to form complicated products.

---

[3] Grignard, *Bull. soc. chim.*, [4], *13*, I–XXXVII (1926).

* In the light of present-day valence theories the fallacy of this line of reasoning is, of course, obvious.

[4] Vinay, Dissertation, Geneva, *1913*, as cited by: Gilliland and Blanchard, *J. Am. Chem. Soc.*, *48*, 410–20 (1926); Fischer and Stoffers, *Ann.*, *500*, 253–70 (1933).

[5] Jegorowa, *J. Russ. Phys.-Chem. Soc.*, *46*, 1319–32 (1914); *Chem. Zentr.*, *1915*, *I*, 1055.

[6] Eidus, Elagina, and Zelinski, *Bull. acad. sci. U.R.S.S.*, *Classe sci. chim.*, *1945*, 672–4; *Chem. Abstr.*, *42*, 5838 (1948).

[7] Schlubach, *Ber.*, *52B*, 1910–4 (1919).

Zelinsky[8] has reported the formation of aldehydes and ketones by the action of nickel carbonyl on *n*-propylmagnesium iodide. From alkylmagnesium iodides and nickel carbonyl Jones[9] obtained dark oils from which no identified products were isolated, but from the products of reaction of phenylmagnesium iodide and nickel carbonyl he was able to isolate biphenyl and benzoïn.

Gilliland and Blanchard[10] found that the finely divided nickel liberated when nickel carbonyl reacts with phenylmagnesium bromide in ethereal solution regenerates nickel carbonyl when carbon monoxide is passed into the suspension. A similar observation had been made previously by Job and Reich[11] regarding nickel liberated in the reaction of nickel chloride ($NiCl_2$) with Grignard reagents.

Gilliland and Blanchard accordingly investigated the reaction initiated by adding a small quantity of nickel carbonyl to an ethereal solution of phenylmagnesium bromide, and continued by passing carbon monoxide into the reaction mixture. From the reaction products they were able to isolate triphenylmethane, triphenylvinyl alcohol, small amounts of pentaphenylethane, and, occasionally, small amounts of tetraphenylethylene. When the experimental conditions were such that carbon monoxide absorption was slow, triphenylmethane was the predominant product; when carbon monoxide absorption was rapid triphenylvinyl alcohol predominated. The foregoing products are all soluble in ether. A red crystalline product which deposited during the course of the reaction was partially identified as an etherated basic magnesium bromide.

Gilliland and Blanchard accounted for the products identified by the following series of reactions:

(1) $>CO + C_6H_5MgBr \longrightarrow C_6H_5COMgBr$

(2) $C_6H_5COMgBr + C_6H_5MgBr \longrightarrow (C_6H_5)_2C(OMgBr)MgBr$

(3) $(C_6H_5)_2C(OMgBr)MgBr + C_6H_5MgBr \longrightarrow (C_6H_5)_3CMgBr + (BrMg)_2O$

(4) $(C_6H_5)_2C(OMgBr)MgBr + >CO \longrightarrow BrMgO(C_6H_5)_2CCOMgBr$

(5) $BrMgO(C_6H_5)_2CCOMgBr \longrightarrow (C_6H_5)_2C{=}C{=}O + (BrMg)_2O$

(6) $(C_6H_5)_2C{=}C{=}O + C_6H_5MgBr \longrightarrow (C_6H_5)_2C{=}C(C_6H_5)OMgBr$

(7) $(C_6H_5)_3CMgBr + >CO \longrightarrow (C_6H_5)_3CCOMgBr$

(8) $(C_6H_5)_3CCOMgBr + C_6H_5MgBr \longrightarrow (C_6H_5)_3CC(C_6H_5)(OMgBr)MgBr$

(9) $(C_6H_5)_3CC(C_6H_5)(OMgBr)MgBr + C_6H_5MgBr \longrightarrow$

$(C_6H_5)_3CC(C_6H_5)_2MgBr + (BrMg)_2O$

---

[8] Zelinsky, *J. Russ. Phys.-Chem. Soc.*, *36*, 339–40 (1904); as cited by Gilliland and Blanchard, *J. Am. Chem. Soc.*, *48*, 410–20 (1926).

[9] Jones, *Chem. News*, *90*, 144–5 (1904).

[10] Gilliland and Blanchard, *J. Am. Chem. Soc.*, *48*, 410–20 (1926).

[11] Job and Reich, *Compt. rend.*, *177*, 1438–41 (1923); *Chem. Abstr.*, *19*, 1851 (1925).

Job and Cassal[12] report that when small quantities of chromium chloride ($CrCl_3$) are added to an ethereal solution of phenylmagnesium bromide the resultant reaction system absorbs carbon monoxide more or less rapidly at temperatures between −15° and the boiling point of ether. (The lower temperature is that at which reaction between chromium chloride and the Grignard reagent begins.) The reaction products isolated and identified were: biphenyl, benzophenone, benzhydrol, triphenylvinyl alcohol, β-benzopinacolone, benzoïn, benzil, and triphenylmethane, together with traces of benzaldehyde, phenol, and chromium carbonyl. Roughly 50 percent of the Grignard reagent expended is thus accounted for; the remainder gives rise to resinous or tarry materials.

Job and Cassal attribute the chromium chloride activation of the carbon monoxide-phenylmagnesium bromide reaction to the formation of an intermediate chromium carbonyl compound or compounds. Chromium carbonyl itself appears to be ineffective.

The work of Fischer and Stoffers[13] raises the question whether or not there are in fact any uncatalyzed reactions of carbon monoxide with Grignard reagents. Operating in an autoclave under carbon monoxide pressures from 50 up to 180 atmospheres and at temperatures from 60° to as high as 160°, they found that carbon monoxide absorption begins at much lower temperatures and proceeds much more rapidly when small amounts of halomagnesium alcoholates (generated either by oxidation of the Grignard reagent or by addition of alcohol) are present in the system. It was found that the alcoholates do not themselves react with carbon monoxide, although they do, in some way, facilitate the Grignard reaction.

Two types of reactions were observed: (1) that characteristic for aryl- and *t*-alkylmagnesium halides, in which one molecule of carbon monoxide per molecule of Grignard reagent is absorbed; (2) that characteristic for primary alkylmagnesium halides, in which one-half molecule of carbon monoxide per molecule of Grignard reagent is absorbed. *s*-Alkylmagnesium halides undergo both types of reaction simultaneously. Fischer and Stoffers describe the two typical modes of reaction schematically as follows.

$$(1)\quad 2\,RMgBr + 2\,CO \longrightarrow 2\,RCOMgBr \longrightarrow R(BrMgO)C{=}C(OMgBr)R \longrightarrow RCOCH(OH)R$$

$$(2)\quad RCH_2MgBr + CO \longrightarrow RCH_2COMgBr \xrightarrow{RCH_2MgBr} RCH_2C(MgBr)(OMgBr)CH_2R \longrightarrow RCH{=}CHCH_2R$$

The acyloïns may be accompanied by, or even completely converted to, the corresponding "autoxidation" products (the diketones). Under the experimental conditions employed by Fischer and Stoffers, phenylmagnesium bromide yielded benzoïn (90 percent), together with small amounts

[12] Job and Cassal, *Compt. rend.*, *183*, 58–60 (1926); *Chem. Abstr.*, *20*, 2999 (1926); *Bull. soc. chim.*, [4], *41*, 814–24 (1927).

[13] Fischer and Stoffers, *Ann.*, *500*, 253–70 (1933).

of benzil; *p*-tolylmagnesium bromide behaved similarly; α-naphthylmagnesium bromide yielded only α-naphthil (63 percent); *t*-butylmagnesium bromide yielded hexamethylacetoïn (2,2,5,5-tetramethyl-4-hydroxy-3-hexanone). Ethylmagnesium bromide yielded 2-pentene (25 percent); *n*-butylmagnesium chloride, 4-nonene (65 percent); isoämylmagnesium bromide, 2,8-dimethyl-4-nonene (70 percent); benzylmagnesium chloride, 1,3-diphenylpropene (60 percent). Cyclohexylmagnesium bromide yielded cyclohexylmethylenecyclohexane (25 percent), together with dodecahydrobenzoïn and dodecahydrobenzil (aggregating 44 percent).

No reaction was effected with pyrrylmagnesium bromide (100°, 90 atmospheres), *p*-dimethylaminophenylmagnesium bromide, or ethynylenedimagnesium bromide (145°, 90 atmospheres).

CARBON DIOXIDE

It was discovered by Grignard[14] that when carbon dioxide is passed into an ethereal solution of an organomagnesium halide gas absorption takes place, with the formation of a carboxylate from which the corresponding carboxylic acid is readily liberated.

$$\mathrm{RMgX} \xrightarrow{\mathrm{CO_2}} \mathrm{RCO_2MgX} \xrightarrow{\mathrm{HX'}} \mathrm{RCO_2H} + \mathrm{MgXX'}$$

The principal side-reactions, also observed by Grignard,[15] are successive reaction of the carboxylate thus formed with one or two molecules, respectively, of excess Grignard reagent to form ketone or tertiary alcohol. For most aliphatic Grignard reagents the relative rates of the successive reactions are such that tertiary alcohol is the principal byproduct, and little or no ketone can be isolated. For some aromatic Grignard reagents (especially those that give rise to "hindered" ketones), ketone is the principal byproduct. In most cases, however, it is possible, by suitable selection of experimental conditions, to arrest reaction at the carboxylate stage, and thus to obtain a fairly satisfactory yield of carboxylic acid.

As was demonstrated by Bodroux,[16] one effective method of reaction control is operation at low temperature, which reduces both the solubility and the reactivity of the carboxylate initially formed. Bodroux found, for example, that when carbon dioxide is passed into an ethereal solution of *p*-chlorophenylmagnesium bromide at the boiling point of the solution (*ca.* 36°) the principal product is *p,p'*-dichlorobenzophenone (50 percent), the *p*-chlorobenzoic acid being obtained in only 24 percent yield. When the gas is passed into a cooled solution at 0° the yield of acid is increased

[14] Grignard, *Annales de l'Universite de Lyon*, N.S., 6, 1–116 (1901); *Chem. Zentr., 1901,II*, 622; *Ann. chim.*, [7], *24*, 433–90 (1901).

[15] Grignard, *Compt. rend.*, *138*, 152–4 (1904); *Chem. Zentr.*, *1904,I*, 577; *Bull. soc. chim.*, [3], *31*, 751–7 (1904).

[16] Bodroux, (*a*) *Compt. rend.*, *137*, 710–2 (1903); *Chem. Zentr.*, *1903,II*, 1441; (*b*) *Bull. soc. chim.*, [3], *31*, 24–30 (1904).

to 60 percent and that of the benzophenone reduced to 18 percent. When carbonation is effected by the addition of carbon dioxide snow to the reaction system at an average temperature of about −40° the yields of acid and benzophenone are 80 percent and 4 percent, respectively. Similar results were obtained with *p*-bromophenylmagnesium bromide.

Another method of control for which several procedures have been adopted is to avoid, as far as possible, the presence of excess Grignard reagent.

According to Kinney and Mayhue[17] the presence of the halomagnesium alcoholate corresponding to the Grignard reagent inhibits the reaction of the Grignard reagent with carbon dioxide and lowers the yield of acid obtainable.

Preparative procedures. The principal carbonation method variations, together with their symbolic designations as employed in column 2 of Table XIII-I, are as follows.

Method I. The classical method of Grignard (*loc. cit.*[14]), consisting in bubbling carbon dioxide gas into a Grignard reagent solution. If desired the solution may be externally cooled, or, in special cases, heated.

Method Ia. Dauben's[18] adaptation of the method of Grignard to vacuum-line technique (operation at *ca.* −20°; well suited to employment of $C^{14}O_2$).

Method Ib. The method of Ruben *et al.*,[19] in which a small volume of the gas ($C^{11}O_2$ or $C^{14}O_2$) is shaken with an excess of the Grignard reagent solution.

Method II. A modification of the method of Grignard attributed to Dr. H. T. Clarke of the Eastman Kodak Co.,[20] in which carbon dioxide is led over the surface of a stirred Grignard solution instead of directly into the solution. This method avoids clogging of the carbon dioxide delivery tube, and probably has the additional virtue of minimizing local superheating.

Method III. The method of Bodroux (*loc. cit.*[16]), in which carbon dioxide snow or Dry Ice in small pieces is gradually added to the Grignard reagent solution.

Method IV. The method of Fieser,[21] in which the Grignard reagent solution is poured or dropped onto solid carbon dioxide (usually crushed).

Method IVa. The method of Fries,[22] in which the Grignard solution is added to an ethereal suspension of solid carbon dioxide.

---

[17] Kinney and Mayhue, *J. Am. Chem. Soc.*, *53*, 190–9 (1931).

[18] Dauben, Reid, and Yankwich, *Anal. Chem.*, *19*, 828–32 (1947); Heidelberger, Brewer, and Dauben, *J. Am. Chem. Soc.*, *69*, 1389–91 (1947); Dauben, *J. Org. Chem.*, *13*, 313–6 (1948).

[19] Ruben, Allen, and Nahinskey, *J. Am. Chem. Soc.*, *64*, 3050 (1942).

[20] Gilman and Parker, *J. Am. Chem. Soc.*, *46*, 2816–22 (1924).

[21] Fieser, Holmes, and Newman, *J. Am. Chem. Soc.*, *58*, 1055 (1936).

[22] Fries and Schimmelschmidt, *Ber.*, *58B*, 2835–45 (1925). See also: Hussey, *J. Am. Chem. Soc.*, *73*, 1364–5 (1951).

TABLE XIII-I

REACTIONS OF GRIGNARD REAGENTS WITH CARBON DIOXIDE

RMgX	Method *	Product(s)	Ref.
CH_3			
CH_3MgI	I	CH_3CO_2H	*71,87*
CH_3MgI	Ib	$CH_3C^{11}O_2H$ (*ca.* 95%, based on $C^{11}O_2$)	*150*
CH_3MgI	?	$CH_3C^{13}O_2H$ or $CH_3C^{14}O_2H$	*38*
CH_3MgI	?	$CH_3C^{14}O_2H$ (94%)	*79*
CH_3MgI	Ib	$CH_3C^{14}O_2H$ (*ca.*, 95% based on $C^{14}O_2$)	*150*
C_2			
$(\equiv CMgBr)_2$	I	$(\equiv CCO_2H)_2$ (5%)	*171,91,95*
C_2H			
$HC\equiv CMgBr$	I	$HC\equiv CCO_2H$ (62%)	*77,210*
C_2H_5			
C_2H_5MgBr	I	$C_2H_5CO_2H$ (50%)	*87,172*
C_2H_5MgBr	I (−20°)	$C_2H_5CO_2H$ (72%)	*96*
C_2H_5MgBr	? (−20°)	$C_2H_5CO_2H$ (40%); $(C_2H_5)_2CO$ (20%)	*33*
C_3H_3			
$HC\equiv CCH_2MgBr$ (36 g., 0.3 C_3H_3Br)	IV	$HC\equiv CCH_2CO_2H$ + $H_2C=C=CHCO_2H$ + $CH_3C\equiv CCO_2H$ (aggregating 7 g., 28%, crude)	*221,222*
$CH_3C\equiv CMgBr$	I	$CH_3C\equiv CCO_2H$	*92*
$C_3H_4F_3$			
$F_3CCH_2CH_2MgCl$	III	$F_3CCH_2CH_2CO_2H$ (43%, crude)	*126*

* See pp. 914, 947.

TABLE XIII-I (Continued)

RMgX	Method*	Product(s)	Ref.
C_3H_5			
$H_2C{=}CHCH_2Br$ + Mg	V	$H_2C{=}CHCH_2CO_2H$ (11%)	85
$H_2C{=}CHCH_2MgBr$	VIa	$H_2C{=}CHCH_2CO_2H$ (21.7%)	59
C_3H_7			
n-C_3H_7MgBr	I (−20°, rapid)	n-$C_3H_7CO_2H$ (77%)	96
RMgBr†	I (−15 to −20°)	RCO_2H ("high yields")	178
C_4H_3			
$H_2C{=}CHC{\equiv}CMgBr$	I (0°)	$H_2C{=}CHC{\equiv}CCO_2H$	25
C_4H_3O			
2-Furyl-MgBr	?	2-Furancarboxylic acid‡	163
C_4H_3S			
2-Thienyl-MgI	I	2-Thiophenecarboxylic acid (82–100%)	157
3-Thienyl-MgBr (20 g. C_4H_3IS)	I	3-Thiophenecarboxylic acid (5 g., 42%)	223
C_4H_4N			
Pyrryl-MgBr	VIa	α-Pyrrolecarboxylic acid (32.5–42.5%)	60
Pyrryl-MgBr	VIII (250–270°)	β-Pyrrolecarboxylic acid (12%)	141
Pyrryl-MgI	I	α-Pyrrolecarboxylic acid (25–30%)	139
C_4H_5			
$C_2H_5C{\equiv}CMgBr$	?	$C_2H_5C{\equiv}CCO_2H$	36

*See pp. 914, 947.

†R = n-C_3H_7, i-C_3H_7, n-C_4H_9, i-C_4H_9.

‡Furoic acid, pyromucic acid.

TABLE XIII-I (Continued)

RMgX	Method *	Product(s)	Ref.
C_4H_7			
$H_2C{=}CHCH_2CH_2MgBr$	I	$H_2C{=}CHCH_2CH_2CO_2H$	*188*
Butenyl-MgBr	IV	$CH_3(H_2C{=}CH)CHCO_2H$ (70%)	*149*
Butenyl-MgBr †	IV	$CH_3(CH_2{=}CH)CHCO_2H$ (75%)	*113*
Butenyl-MgBr †	VI	$H_2C{=}CHCH(CH_3)CO_2H$ (63%); $(C_4H_7)_2CO$; octadienes; high-boiling residue	*113*
Dibutenyl-Mg	IV	$CH_3(H_2C{=}CH)CHCO_2H$ (37%)	*149*
C_4H_8			
$(-CH_2CH_2MgBr)_2$	?	$(CH_2)_4CO$	*187*
C_4H_9			
n-C_4H_9MgCl	I (−2°, rapid)	*n*-$C_4H_9CO_2H$ (80%)	*96*
n-C_4H_9MgBr	I (−2°, rapid)	*n*-$C_4H_9CO_2H$ (86%)	*96*
n-C_4H_9MgBr	II (0°)	*n*-$C_4H_9CO_2H$ (78.9%)	*60*
i-C_4H_9MgBr	I	*i*-$C_4H_9CO_2H$ (55%)	*72,71*
s-C_4H_9MgCl	II (−12 to −5°)	DL-$CH_3(C_2H_5)CHCO_2H$ (76–86%)	*58*
s-C_4H_9MgBr	II (<2°)	DL-$CH_3(C_2H_5)CHCO_2H$ (66–67%)	*55,124*
t-C_4H_9MgCl	II (0°)	*t*-$C_4H_9CO_2H$ (69–70%)	*145,24,65,66, 70,188*
$C_4H_{11}Si$			
$(CH_3)_3SiCH_2MgCl$	IV	$(CH_3)_3SiCH_2CO_2H$ (88%)	*167*
C_5H_4BrMgO			
$BrMgOCH_2CH{=}CHC{\equiv}CMgBr$	IX	$HOCH_2CH{=}CHC{\equiv}CCO_2H$	*84*

*See pp. 914, 947.

†From 80% crotyl, 20% α-methallyl bromides.

TABLE XIII-I (Continued)

RMgX	Method *	Product(s)	Ref.
C_5H_5O			
3-Furfuryl-MgCl (13.5 g., 0.116 mole C_5H_5ClO)	IV	3-Methyl-2-furoic acid (3.9 g., 26.8%); 3-furanacetic acid (0.25 g., 1.7%, crude)	224
C_5H_5S			
2-Thenyl-MgCl (0.141 mole)	IVa	2-Thienylacetic acid (5.82 g., 29.1%); 2-methyl-3-thiophenecarboxylic acid (3.13 g., 15.6%)	226,225
3-Thenyl-MgBr	IV	3-Methyl-2-thiophenecarboxylic acid (12.5%)†	227
C_5H_6BrMgO			
$CH_3CH(OMgBr)CH_2C{\equiv}CMgBr$	VII	$CH_3CH(OH)CH_2C{\equiv}CCO_2H$ (75%)	82
C_5H_9			
$CH_3CH{=}CHCH_2CH_2MgBr$	I	$CH_3CH{=}CHCH_2CH_2CO_2H$	184
$(CH_2)_4CHMgCl$	I	$(CH_2)_4CHCO_2H$ (55%)	203
$(CH_2)_4CHMgCl$	VII	$(CH_2)_4CHCO_2H$ (51%)	138
$(CH_2)_4CHMgBr$	III	$(CH_2)_4CHCO_2H$ (83%)	133
$(CH_2)_4CHMgBr$	IVa	$(CH_2)_4CHCO_2H$ (86%)	90
C_5H_{10}			
$H_2C(CH_2CH_2MgBr)_2$	I (?)	$(CH_2)_5CO$ (chief product); $H_2C(CH_2CH_2CO_2H)_2$	78,187
C_5H_{11}			
i-$C_5H_{11}MgX$	I	*i*-$C_5H_{11}CO_2H$ (55%)	71
t-$C_5H_{11}MgCl$	?	*t*-$C_5H_{11}CO_2H$ (60%)	24,190

*See pp. 914, 947.

†Yield based on C_5H_5BrS; Grignard reagent preparation in the conventional manner (much Wurtz product).

TABLE XIII-I (Continued)

RMgX	Method *	Product(s)	Ref.
$C_6H_3S_2$			
Thiophthenyl-MgBr	?	Thiophthenecarboxylic acid	*26*
C_6H_4			
C_6H_4-1,4-$(MgBr)_2$	I	C_6H_4-1,4-$(CO_2H)_2$	*86*
C_6H_4Br			
3-BrC_6H_4MgBr	I	3-$BrC_6H_4CO_2H$ (70%)	*94*
4-BrC_6H_4MgBr	I (36°)	4-$BrC_6H_4CO_2H$ (10%); (4-$BrC_6H_4)_2CO$ (55%)	*18*
4-BrC_6H_4MgBr	I (0°)	4-$BrC_6H_4CO_2H$ (61%); (4-$BrC_6H_4)_2CO$ (26%)	*18*
4-BrC_6H_4MgBr	III	4-$BrC_6H_4CO_2H$ (76%); (4-$BrC_6H_4)_2CO$ (6%)	*18*
4-BrC_6H_4MgBr	I	4-$BrC_6H_4CO_2H$ (70%)	*94*
C_6H_4BrMgO			
2-$BrMgOC_6H_4MgBr$	I	2-$HOC_6H_4CO_2H$ (20%)	*135*
C_6H_4Cl			
4-ClC_6H_4MgBr	I (36°)	4-$ClC_6H_4CO_2H$ (24%); (4-$ClC_6H_4)_2CO$ (50%)	*18*
4-ClC_6H_4MgBr	I (0°)	4-$ClC_6H_4CO_2H$ (64%); (4-$ClC_6H_4)_2CO$ (18%)	*18*
4-ClC_6H_4MgBr	III	4-$ClC_6H_4CO_2H$ (80%); (4-$ClC_6H_4)_2CO$ (4%)	*18*
4-XC_6H_4MgBr †	I (cold)	4-$XC_6H_4CO_2H$ (predominating); (4-$XC_6H_4)_2CO$	*16*
4-XC_6H_4MgBr †	I (36°)	(4-$XC_6H_4)_2CO$ (predominating); 4-$XC_6H_4CO_2H$	*16*
C_6H_5			
C_6H_5MgCl	I	$C_6H_5CO_2H$ (39%)	*104*

* See pp. 914, 947.
† X = Cl, Br.

TABLE XIII-I (Continued)

RMgX	Method*	Product(s)	Ref.
C_6H_5 (*cont.*)			
C_6H_5MgCl	I (?)	$C_6H_5CO_2H$; 4-$C_6H_5C_6H_4CO_2H$; 4-(*p*-$C_6H_5C_6H_4$)C_6H_4-1-CO_2H	*122*
C_6H_5MgBr	I	$C_6H_5CO_2H$ (50%)	*172,87*
C_6H_5MgBr	I (cold)	$C_6H_5CO_2H$ (88.5–91.0%)	*128*
C_6H_5MgBr	I (–20°, rapid)	$C_6H_5CO_2H$ (80%)	*96*
C_6H_5MgBr	I (ice-cooled)	$C_6H_5CO_2H$; $(C_6H_5)_3COH$	*15*
C_6H_5MgBr	I (hot)	$[(C_6H_5)_3CO-]_2$	*15*
C_6H_5MgBr	I (36°)	$C_6H_5CO_2H$ (16%); $(C_6H_5)_2CO$ (13%); $(C_6H_5)_3COH$ (32%)	*162*
C_6H_5MgBr	I (hot Et_2O, rapid)	$C_6H_5CO_2H$ (17.4%); $(C_6H_5)_2CO$ (20.2%); $(C_6H_5)_3COH$ (25.7%); $[(C_6H_5)_3CO-]_2$	*62*
C_6H_5MgBr	I (hot Et_2O, 6 hrs.)	$C_6H_5CO_2H$ (16.3%); $(C_6H_5)_3COH$ (36.9%); $(C_6H_5)_3CH$ (3.08%)	*62*
C_6H_5MgBr	I (hot C_6H_6, 10 hrs.)	$(C_6H_5)_3COH$ (46.2%); $(C_6H_5)_3CH$ (2.4%)	*62*
C_6H_5MgBr	I (hot C_6H_6, 16 hrs.)	$(C_6H_5)_3COH$ (44.5%); $(C_6H_5)_3CH$ (1.2%)	*62*
C_6H_5MgBr	I (hot C_7H_8, 4 hrs.)	$(C_6H_5)_3COH$ (41.6%); $(C_6H_5)_3CH$ (3.08%)	*62*
C_6H_5MgBr	I (hot cymene, 9 hrs.)	$(C_6H_5)_3COH$ (46.8%)	*62*
C_6H_5MgBr	Ia (–20°)	$C_6H_4C^{14}O_2H$ (85.4%)	*32*
C_6H_5MgBr	II (0°)	$C_6H_5CO_2H$ (71.5–72.5%)	*60*
C_6H_5MgBr	IVa	$C_6H_5CO_2H$ (91%)	*90*
C_6H_5MgBr	IX†	$C_6H_5CH_2OH$; $(C_6H_5)_3COH$; $(C_6H_5)_2CO$; $C_6H_5CO_2H$; C_6H_5OH	*130*
C_6H_5MgI	I	$C_6H_5CO_2H$ (60%)	*200*
C_6H_6Br			
$H_2C{=}CBr(CH_2)_2C{\equiv}CMgBr$	I	$H_2C{=}CBr(CH_2)_2C{\equiv}CCO_2H$ (40%)	*93*

* See pp. 914, 947.

† One equivalent of C_6H_5MgBr saturated with CO_2; then treated with two equivalents of C_6H_5MgBr (?) or RMgX (?).

TABLE XIII-I (Continued)

RMgX	Method *	Product(s)	Ref.
C_6H_6IO			
2,5-Dimethyl-4-iodo-3-furyl-MgI	IV	2,5-Dimethyl-4-iodo-3-furoic acid	*89*
C_6H_7S			
5-Methyl-3-thenyl-MgBr	?	2,5-Dimethyl-3-thiophenecarboxylic acid	*228*
2,5-Dimethyl-3-thienyl-MgI	I (0°)	2,5-Dimethyl-3-thiophenecarboxylic acid (40%)	*170,218*
$C_6H_8ClMgO_2$			
$[C_2H_5CH{=}CHCH(CO_2MgCl)]^-MgCl^+$	I (cold)	$C_2H_5CH{=}CHCH(CO_2H)_2$	*98*
C_6H_9			
n-$C_3H_7C{\equiv}CCH_2MgBr$ (32 g., 0.2 mole C_6H_9Br)	IV	n-$C_3H_7C{\equiv}CCH_2CO_2H$ (16%); n-$C_3H_7C(CO_2H){=}C{=}CH_2$ (38%); dimeric acid (12%); acidic residue (6%)	*229*
C_6H_9O			
$CH_3(C_2H_5O)CHC{\equiv}CMgBr$	?	$CH_3(C_2H_5O)CHC{\equiv}CCO_2H$	*69,211*
$CH_3(C_2H_5)C(OH)C{\equiv}CMgBr$	I (0°)	$CH_3(C_2H_5)C(OH)C{\equiv}CCO_2H$ (20%)	*129*
C_6H_{11}			
$CH_3CH{=}CH(CH_2)_3MgBr$	I	$CH_3CH{=}CH(CH_2)_3CO_2H$	*183*
$(CH_2)_5CHMgCl$	I	$(CH_2)_5CHCO_2H$ (55%)	*136,23,154*
$(CH_2)_5CHMgCl$	II (0°)	$(CH_2)_5CHCO_2H$ (68%)	*60,219*
$(CH_2)_5CHMgCl$	III	$(CH_2)_5CHCO_2H$ (81%)	*134*
$(CH_2)_5CHMgBr$	?	Cyclohexene; $(CH_2)_5CHOH$; $(CH_2)_5CHCH_2OH$; $[(CH_2)_5CH]_2CH_2$; $[(CH_2)_5CH]_2CHOH$	*130*

* See pp. 914, 947.

TABLE XIII-I (Continued)

RMgX	Method*	Product(s)	Ref.
C_6H_{11} (*cont.*)			
$(CH_2)_5CHMgBr$[†] (+n-C_3H_7MgBr)	?	$(CH_2)_5CHCO_2H$ (80%); $(CH_2)_5CHCH_2OH$ (20%); n-C_3H_7OH	*130*
$(CH_2)_5CHMgI$	I	$(CH_2)_5CHCO_2H$ (35%)	*199*
$(CH_2)_4C(CH_3)MgCl$ (53 g. $C_6H_{11}Cl$)	I	$(CH_2)_4C(CH_3)CO_2H$ (12 g.)	*212,176*
3-Methylcyclopentyl-MgI	I	3-Methylcyclopentanecarboxylic acid	*199*
C_6H_{12}			
$[-(CH_2)_3MgBr]_2$	I	$[-(CH_2)_3CO_2H]_2$ (poor yield)	*204*
C_6H_{13}			
t-$C_4H_9CH_2CH_2MgBr$	III	t-$C_4H_9CH_2CH_2CO_2H$ (78%)	*197*
$CH_3(C_2H_5)_2CMgCl$	II, ?	$CH_3(C_2H_5)_2CCO_2H$ (27%, 42%)	*230,189*
$C_6H_{17}OSi_2$			
$(CH_3)_3SiOSi(CH_3)_2CH_2MgCl$	IV	$(CH_3)_3SiOSi(CH_3)_2CH_2CO_2H$ (85%)	*167*
$C_7H_4F_3$			
2-$F_3CC_6H_4MgBr$	IV	2-$F_3CC_6H_4CO_2H$ (85.7%)	*105*
2-$F_3CC_6H_4MgI$	IV	2-$F_3CC_6H_4CO_2H$ (73.4%)	*105*
4-$F_3CC_6H_4MgBr$	IV	4-$F_3CC_6H_4CO_2H$ (90.0%)	*105*
$C_7H_5Cl_2$			
2,6-$Cl_2C_6H_3CH_2MgCl$	I	2,6-$Cl_2C_6H_3CH_2CO_2H$	7
C_7H_6Cl			
2-$ClC_6H_4CH_2MgCl$	I	2-$ClC_6H_3CH_2CO_2H$	7

*See pp. 914, 947.

†One equivalent of $(CH_2)_5CHMgBr$ saturated with CO_2; then treated with two equivalents of n-C_3H_7MgBr.

TABLE XIII-I (Continued)

RMgX	Method *	Product(s)	Ref.
C_7H_7			
$C_6H_5CH_2MgCl$	I	$C_6H_5CH_2CO_2H$ (60%)	*87,196,200*
$C_6H_5CH_2MgCl$	I (−20°, rapid)	$C_6H_5CH_2CO_2H$ (79%)	*96*
$C_6H_5CH_2MgCl$	IVa	$C_6H_5CH_2CO_2H$ (40%, crude)	*7*
$C_6H_5CH_2MgBr$	I	$C_6H_5CH_2CO_2H$ (10%)	*87*
2-$CH_3C_6H_4MgBr$	IVa	2-$CH_3C_6H_4CO_2H$ (62%)	*7*
C_7H_7O			
4-$CH_3OC_6H_4MgBr$	I	4-$CH_3OC_6H_4CO_2H$	*19*
4-$CH_3OC_6H_4MgBr$	IVa	4-$CH_3OC_6H_4CO_2H$ (92%)	*90*
C_7H_{11}			
n-$C_4H_9C \equiv CCH_2MgBr$	IV	*n*-$C_4H_9C \equiv CCH_2CO_2H$ (9%); *n*-$C_4H_9C(CO_2H){=}C{=}CH_2$ (41%); dimeric acid and acidic residue (7%)	*229*
C_7H_{13}			
$(CH_2)_6CHMgBr$	I	$(CH_2)_6CHCO_2H$ (40%)	*199*
$(CH_2)_5C(CH_3)MgCl$	I	1-Methylcyclohexanecarboxylic acid (25%)	*80,127*
2-Methylcyclohexyl-MgCl	I	2-Methylcyclohexanecarboxylic acid (62%)	*80,132*
3-Methylcyclohexyl-MgCl	I	3-Methylcyclohexanecarboxylic acid (63%)	*80*
3-Methylcyclohexyl-MgCl	?	3-Methylcyclohexanecarboxylic acid (2 isomers in ratio of 60A : 40B)	*131*
3-Methylcyclohexyl-MgI	I	3-Methylcyclohexanecarboxylic acid (35%)	*199*
3-Methylcyclohexyl-MgI (from "active" iodide)	?	3-Methylcyclohexanecarboxylic acid (A isomer)	*131*
4-Methylcyclohexyl-MgCl	I	4-Methylcyclohexanecarboxylic acid (52.5%)	*80*

*See pp. 914, 947.

TABLE XIII-I (Continued)

RMgX	Method *	Product(s)	Ref.
$C_7H_{13}O$			
$H_2C{=}CH[CH_3O(CH_2)_3]CHMgCl$	IVA	$H_2C{=}CH[CH_3O(CH_2)_3]CHCO_2H$ (38%)	*205*
C_7H_{14}			
$H_2C[(CH_2)_3MgBr]_2$	?	$H_2C[(CH_2)_3CO_2H]_2$	*187*
$C_7H_{14}O$			
$H_2C{=}CH[CH_3O(CH_2)_3]CHMgCl$ (22.3 g., 0.15 mole $C_7H_{14}ClO$)	IVA	$H_2C{=}CH[CH_3O(CH_2)_3]CHCO_2H$ (8.92 g., 38%)	*213*
C_7H_{15}			
$(C_2H_5)_3CMgCl$	?	$(C_2H_5)_3CCO_2H$	*193*
n-$C_4H_9(CH_3)_2CMgCl$	VII (60 mm., 0°)	*n*-$C_4H_9(CH_3)_2CCO_2H$	*189*
$C_7H_{15}O$			
$C_2H_5[CH_3O(CH_2)_3]CHMgCl$	IV	$C_2H_5[CH_3O(CH_2)_3]CHCO_2H$ (64%)	*205*
C_8H_5			
$C_6H_5C{\equiv}CMgBr$	I	$C_6H_5C{\equiv}CCO_2H$ (55%); $C_6H_5C{\equiv}CH$ (21%)	*107,173*
$C_6H_5C{\equiv}CMgBr$	I (−10 to 0°, or −40 to −30°)	Unstable, unidentified oil	*101*
$C_8H_5BrClMgO_2$			
$[2\text{-}BrC_6H_4CH(CO_2MgCl)]^-MgX^+$	I (cold)	2-$BrC_6H_4CH(CO_2H)_2$	97
$[3\text{-}BrC_6H_4CH(CO_2MgCl)]^-MgX^+$	I (cold)	3-$BrC_6H_4CH(CO_2H)_2$	97
$C_8H_5Cl_2MgO_2$			
$[2\text{-}ClC_6H_4CH(CO_2MgCl)]^-MgX^+$	I (0°)	2-$ClC_6H_4CH(CO_2H)_2$ (46.2–52.8%)	99

* See pp. 914, 947.

TABLE XIII-I (Continued)

RMgX	Method *	Product(s)	Ref.
$C_8H_5Cl_2MgO_2$ (*cont.*)			
$[3\text{-}ClC_6H_4CH(CO_2MgCl)]^-MgX^+$	I (cold)	$3\text{-}ClC_6H_4CH(CO_2H)_2$	*97*
$[4\text{-}ClC_6H_4CH(CO_2MgCl)]^-MgX^+$	I (0°)	$4\text{-}ClC_6H_4CH(CO_2H)_2$ (48.3–56.4%)	*99*
$C_8H_6ClMgO_2$			
$[C_6H_5CH(CO_2MgCl)]^-MgX^+$	I (0°)	$C_6H_5CH(CO_2H)_2$ (40–66%)†	*99*
C_8H_6N			
Indolyl-MgI	?	*N*-Indolecarboxylic acid	*142*
Indolyl-MgI	I (<0°)	β-Indolecarboxylic acid (8.6% in Et_2O; 25% in MeOPh)	*120*
C_8H_6NS			
2-Benzothiozolylmethyl-MgBr	?	2-Benzothiazoleacetic acid	*29*
C_8H_7			
$C_6H_5CH{=}CHMgBr$	?	$C_6H_5CH{=}CHCO_2H$	*173*
C_8H_9			
$C_6H_5(CH_2)_2MgBr$	I	$C_6H_5CH_2CH_2CO_2H$ (50%)	*73*
$2\text{-}CH_3C_6H_4CH_2MgBr$	II	$2\text{-}CH_3C_6H_4CH_2CO_2H$	*231*
$3\text{-}CH_3C_6H_4CH_2MgBr$	II	$2,6\text{-}(CH_3)_2C_6H_3CO_2H$ (?)	*231*; *cf. 206*

* See pp. 914, 947.

† The Grignard reagent, or, as has been suggested by Schlenk, Hilleman, and Rodloff, *Ann.*, *487*, 135–54 (1931), the enolate, is prepared by the action of an organomagnesium halide on $C_6H_5CH_2CO_2MgCl$. The overall yield of phenylmalonic acid depends upon the organomagnesium halide used. C_2H_5MgBr, 62.5%; *i*-C_3H_7MgCl, 65.6%; *i*-C_3H_7MgBr, 48.9%; *n*-C_3H_7MgCl, 45.0%; *n*-C_4H_9MgBr, 42.2%; $(CH_2)_5CHMgBr$, 40.0%; $2\text{-}CH_3C_6H_4MgBr$, 50.6%; $1\text{-}C_{10}H_7MgBr$, 53.3%; $C_6H_5CH_2MgCl$, 3.1%; CH_3MgI, negligible.

TABLE XIII-I (Continued)

RMgX	Method *	Product(s)	Ref.
C_8H_9 (*cont.*)			
4-$CH_3C_6H_4CH_2MgBr$	II	4-$CH_3C_6H_4CH_2CO_2H$ (90x%); 2,5-$(CH_3)_2C_6H_3CO_2H$ (10x%)	*231*
C_8H_9O			
$CH_3OCH_2C\equiv CCH_2CH_2C\equiv CMgI$	?	$CH_3OCH_2C\equiv CCH_2CH_2C\equiv CCO_2H$	*114*
4-$CH_3OC_6H_4CH_2MgBr$	II	4-$CH_3OC_6H_4CH_2CO_2H$	*67*
4-$C_2H_5OC_6H_4MgBr$	I	4-$C_2H_5OC_6H_4CO_2H$ ("good yield")	*19*
$C_8H_9O_2$			
3,4-$(CH_3O)_2C_6H_3MgI$	I	3,4-$(CH_3O)_2C_6H_3CO_2H$	*106*
$C_8H_9O_2S$			
$CH_3(C_6H_5SO_2)CHMgBr$	?	Acidic gum	*232*
$C_8H_{10}N$			
2-$(CH_3)_2NC_6H_4MgBr$	?	2-$(CH_3)_2NC_6H_4CO_2H$	*233*
C_8H_{13}			
n-$C_5H_{11}C\equiv CCH_2MgBr$	IV	*n*-$C_5H_{11}C\equiv CCH_2CO_2H$ (13%); *n*-$C_5H_{11}C(CO_2H){=}C{=}CH_2$ (23%); dimeric acid (3%); acidic residue (13%)	*229*
$CH_3(n\text{-}C_4H_9C\equiv C)CHMgBr$	IV	Acidic material (7.0 g., 41.6%), including *n*-$C_4H_9C(CO_2H){=}C{=}CHCH_3$ (3.4 g., 20.0%)	*234*
C_8H_{15}			
Octenyl-MgBr †	?	$H_2C{=}CH[CH_3(CH_2)_4]CHCO_2H$	*235*

*See pp. 914, 947.

† From mixture of $CH_3(CH_2)_4CH{=}CHCH_2Br$ and $H_2C{=}CH[CH_3(CH_2)_4]CHBr$.

TABLE XIII-I (Continued)

RMgX	Method*	Product(s)	Ref.
C_8H_{15} (*cont.*)			
3,5-Dimethylcyclohexyl-MgI	I	3,5-Dimethylcyclohexanecarboxylic acid (<35%)	*199*
$C_8H_{15}O$			
$[t\text{-}C_4H_9COC(CH_3)_2]^-MgBr^+$	I	$t\text{-}C_4H_9COC(CH_3)_2CO_2H$	*179*
4-(Tetrahydro-2-furyl)-2-butyl-MgBr	II	α-Methyl-γ-tetrahydro-2-furylbutyric acid (59%)	*50*
C_8H_{17}			
$t\text{-}C_4H_9(CH_3)_2CCH_2MgCl$	I (−5°)	$t\text{-}C_4H_9(CH_3)_2CCH_2CO_2H$ (59%)	*194*
$t\text{-}C_4H_9CH_2C(CH_3)_2MgCl$	?	$t\text{-}C_4H_9CH_2C(CH_3)_2CO_2H$ (34%)	*207*
$n\text{-}C_5H_{11}(CH_3)_2CMgCl$	VII (80 mm., 0°)	$n\text{-}C_5H_{11}(CH_3)_2CCO_2H$ (22%)	*189*
C_9H_7			
$C_6H_5C{\equiv}CCH_2MgBr$	I	$C_6H_5C{\equiv}CCH_2CO_2H$;	*236*
		$C_6H_5C(CO_2H){=}C{=}CH_2$ †	*236*
I-Indenyl-MgBr	I	1-Indenecarboxylic acid	*100,75*
2-Indenyl-MgBr	?	2-Indenecarboxylic acid (15%)	*144*
3-Indenyl-MgBr	I	3-Indenecarboxylic acid	*100*
C_9H_7S			
2-Thianaphthenylmethyl-MgCl	IVa	2-Methyl-3-thianaphthenecarboxylic acid (*ca.* 45%)	237
3-Thianaphthenylmethyl-MgCl (0.3 mole)	IVa	3-Methyl-2-thianaphthenecarboxylic acid (32.2 g., 56%); 3-thianaphtheneacetic acid (9.4 g., 16%)	238

* See pp. 914, 947.

† Carbonation must be carried out in absence of oxygen and peroxides; otherwise polymeric material only is obtained.

TABLE XIII-I (Continued)

RMgX	Method *	Product(s)	Ref.
$C_9H_8ClMgO_2$			
$[2\text{-}CH_3C_6H_4CH(CO_2MgCl)]^-MgX^+$	I (cold)	$2\text{-}CH_3C_6H_4CH(CO_2H)_2$	97
$[3\text{-}CH_3C_6H_4CH(CO_2MgCl)]^-MgX^+$	I (cold)	$3\text{-}CH_3C_6H_4CH(CO_2H)_2$	97
$[4\text{-}CH_3C_6H_4CH(CO_2MgCl)]^-MgX^+$	I (cold)	$4\text{-}CH_3C_6H_4CH(CO_2H)_2$	97
C_9H_8N			
2-Methylindolyl-MgBr	I (36°)	α-Methylindole-*N*-carboxylic acid; α-methylindole-β-carboxylic acid (14%)	*140*
2-Methylindolyl-MgBr	I (b.p. C_7H_8)	α-Methylindole-β-carboxylic acid (63%)	*140*
3-Methylindolyl-MgBr	I (36°)	β-Methylindole-*N*-carboxylic acid	*140*
3-Methylindolyl-MgBr	VIII (315–320°)	β-Methylindole-α-carboxylic acid (50%)	*140*
C_9H_9			
C_9H_9MgCl (from cinnamyl chloride)	?	$H_2C{=}CH(C_6H_5)CHCO_2H$	*52,51,53*
$C_6H_5CH_2CH{=}CHMgBr$	I	$C_6H_5CH_2CH{=}CHCO_2H$	*185*
$CH_3(C_6H_5)C{=}CHMgBr$	?	$CH_3(C_6H_5)C{=}CHCO_2H$ (2 isomers)	*173*
$C_6H_5CH_2C({=}CH_2)MgBr$	I	$C_6H_5CH_2C({=}CH_2)CO_2H$	*185*
$4\text{-}H_2C{=}CHCH_2C_6H_4MgBr$	I	$4\text{-}H_2C{=}CHCH_2C_6H_4CO_2H$	*146*
$4\text{-}CH_3CH{=}CHC_6H_4MgBr$	I (0°)	$4\text{-}CH_3CH{=}CHC_6H_4CO_2H$ (30%)	*146*
C_9H_{11}			
$C_6H_5(CH_2)_3MgBr$	I	$C_6H_5(CH_2)_3CO_2H$	*152,218*
$CH_3(C_6H_5)CHCH_2MgCl$	?	$CH_3(C_6H_5)CHCH_2CO_2H$	*117*
$CH_3(C_6H_5)CHCH_2MgBr$	?	$CH_3(C_6H_5)CHCH_2CO_2H$	*119*

* See pp. 914, 947.

TABLE XIII-I (Continued)

RMgX	Method *	Product(s)	Ref.
C_9H_{11} (*cont.*)			
$CH_3(C_6H_5CH_2)CHMgBr$ (22.0 g. $C_9H_{11}Br$)	IV	$CH_3(C_6H_5CH_2)CHCO_2H$ (7.6 g., 42%)	*214*
2,4,6-$(CH_3)_3C_6H_2MgBr$	I	2,4,6-$(CH_3)_3C_6H_2CO_2H$ (*ca.* quant.)	*111*
2,4,6-$(CH_3)_3C_6H_2MgBr$	I	2,4,6-$(CH_3)_3C_6H_2CO_2H$ (53.7%)	*165*
2,4,6-$(CH_3)_3C_6H_2MgBr$	II	2,4,6-$(CH_3)_3C_6H_2CO_2H$ (50%)	*54*
2,4,6-$(CH_3)_3C_6H_2MgBr$	IV	2,4,6-$(CH_3)_3C_6H_2CO_2H$ (60%)	*5*
2,4,6-$(CH_3)_3C_6H_2MgBr$	VI	2,4,6-$(CH_3)_3C_6H_2CO_2H$ (84%)	*5*
$C_9H_{11}O$			
2,6-$(CH_3)_2$-4-$CH_3OC_6H_2MgBr$	IV	2,6-$(CH_3)_2$-4-$CH_3OC_6H_2CO_2H$ (69%)	*44*
$C_9H_{13}Si$			
$C_6H_5(CH_3)_2SiCH_2MgCl$	IV	$C_6H_5(CH_3)_2SiCH_2CO_2H$ (69%)	*167*
C_9H_{15}			
n-$C_4H_9C{\equiv}C(CH_3)_2CMgBr$	IV	*n*-$C_4H_9C(CO_2H){=}C{=}C(CH_3)_2$ (4.4 g., 9.5%)	*234*
$C_9H_{18}IMgO$			
t-$C_4H_9C(CH_3)(OMgI)C(CH_3)_2MgBr$	I	*t*-$C_4H_9C(OH)(CH_3)C(CH_3)_2CO_2H$	*179*
$C_{10}H_6$			
$C_{10}H_6$-1,2-$(MgBr)_2$	I	$C_{10}H_6$-1,2-$(CO_2H)_2$ (very little)	*155*
$C_{10}H_6$-1,4-$(MgBr)_2$	I (−20°)	$C_{10}H_6$-1,4-$(CO_2H)_2$ (51%)	*155*
$C_{10}H_6$-1,5-$(MgBr)_2$	I (−18°)	$C_{10}H_6$-1,5-$(CO_2H)_2$ (*ca.* quant.)	*155*
$C_{10}H_6Br$			
4-$BrC_{10}H_6$-1-$MgBr$	I	4-$BrC_{10}H_6$-1-CO_2H (20%)	*86*

* See pp. 914, 947.

TABLE XIII-I (Continued)

RMgX	Method *	Product(s)	Ref.
$C_{10}H_6Br$ (*cont.*)			
4-$BrC_{10}H_6$-1-MgBr	I (−20°)	4-$BrC_{10}H_6$-1-CO_2H (77%)	*155*
5-$BrC_{10}H_6$-2-MgBr	I	5-$BrC_{10}H_6$-2-CO_2H	*40*
$C_{10}H_6Cl$			
4-$ClC_{10}H_6$-1-MgI	?	4-$ClC_{10}H_6$-1-CO_2H	*168*
$C_{10}H_7$			
1-$C_{10}H_7MgCl$	I	1-$C_{10}H_7CO_2H$ (16%)	*104*
1-$C_{10}H_7MgBr$	I	1-$C_{10}H_7CO_2H$ (65–70%)	*15,1,86,191*
1-$C_{10}H_7MgBr$	Ia (0°)	1-$C_{10}H_7C^{14}O_2H$ (82.4%)	*30*
1-$C_{10}H_7MgBr$	II	1-$C_{10}H_7CO_2H$ (68–70%)	*63*
1-$C_{10}H_7MgBr$	III	1-$C_{10}H_7CO_2H$ (80–90%)	*32*
1-$C_{10}H_7MgBr$	IV	1-$C_{10}H_7CO_2H$ (85%)	*39*
1-$C_{10}H_7MgBr$	IVa	1-$C_{10}H_7CO_2H$ (89%)	*90*
2-$C_{10}H_7MgBr$	I	2-$C_{10}H_7CO_2H$ (65%)	*155*
2-$C_{10}H_7MgBr$	Ia (−20°)	2-$C_{10}H_7C^{14}O_2H$ (73%)	*83*
2-$C_{10}H_7MgBr$	II	2-$C_{10}H_7CO_2H$ (62.7%, crude)	*61*
$C_{10}H_8MgO_2X$			
$[C_6H_5CH{=}CHCH(CO_2MgX)]^-MgX^+$	I (cold)	$C_6H_5CH{=}CHCH(CO_2H)_2$	*98*
$C_{10}H_9S$			
3-Methyl-2-thianaphthenyl-MgBr (22.7 g. $C_{10}H_9BrS$)	IVa	3-Methyl-2-thianaphthenecarboxylic acid (7.9 g., 41%)	*238*
$C_{10}H_{11}$			
7-Methyl-4-indanyl-MgBr	Ia (0°)	7-Methylindan-4-carboxylic acid (64%)	*30*

* See pp. 914, 947.

TABLE XIII-I (Continued)

RMgX	Method*	Product(s)	Ref.
$C_{10}H_{13}$			
$C_2H_5(C_6H_5)CHCH_2MgBr$	?	$C_2H_5(C_6H_5)CHCH_2CO_2H$	*119*
(+)-$C_2H_5(C_6H_5)CHCH_2MgCl$	?	(+)-$C_2H_5(C_6H_5)CHCH_2CO_2H$	*117*
(−)-$C_6H_5CH_2CH(CH_3)CH_2MgBr$	?	(+)-$C_6H_3CH_2CH(CH_3)CH_2CO_2H$	*118*
4-*s*-$C_4H_9C_6H_4MgBr$	IVa (?)	4-*s*-$C_4H_9C_6H_4CO_2H$ (50%)	*49*
4-*t*-$C_4H_9C_6H_4MgBr$	IVa	4-*t*-$C_4H_9C_6H_4CO_2H$ (55%)	*49*
2,3,5,6-$(CH_3)_4C_6HMgBr$	IV	2,3,5,6-$(CH_3)_4C_6HCO_2H$ (55%)	*47*
2-CH_3-5-*i*-$C_3H_7C_6H_3MgBr$	VII (<0°)	2-CH_3-5-*i*-$C_3H_7C_6H_3CO_2H$ (35–40%)	*21*
3-CH_3-6-*i*-$C_3H_7C_6H_3MgBr$	VII (<−5°)	3-CH_3-6-*i*-$C_3H_7C_6H_3CO_2H$ (*ca.* 55%, crude)	*21*
3-CH_3-6-*i*-$C_3H_7C_6H_3MgBr$	III	3-CH_3-6-*i*-$C_3H_7C_6H_3CO_2H$ (56%)	*116*
$C_{10}H_{13}O$			
2,4,6-$(CH_3)_3$-3-CH_3OC_6HMgBr	III	2,4,6-$(CH_3)_3$-3-$CH_3OC_6HCO_2H$ (43%)	*44*
$C_{10}H_{15}O$			
$(C_{10}H_{15}O)^-MgBr^+$ (from α-bromocamphor and Mg)	I (36°)	$(C_{10}H_{15}O)CO_2H$ (26%)	*121,202*
$C_{10}H_{17}$			
$C_{10}H_{17}MgCl$†	I	(±)-Camphanecarboxylic acid	*180,148,86*
Bornyl-MgCl‡	I	(+)-Camphane-2-carboxylic acid	*180,148,151*
"Bornyl-MgI"	I	Camphane-2-carboxylic acid	*201*

*See pp. 914, 947.

†From (+)-α-pinene hydrochloride; Rivière (*148*) concludes that this Grignard reagent is an equimolecular mixture of bornylmagnesium and isobornylmagnesium chlorides.

‡Prepared by refluxing in xylene (three hours at 130°) the Grignard reagent from (+)-α-pinene hydrochloride; Rivière (*148*) concludes that the reagent so obtained is substantially pure bornylmagnesium chloride.

TABLE XIII-I (Continued)

RMgX	Method *	Product(s)	Ref.
$C_{10}H_{17}$ (*cont.*)			
Isobornyl-MgCl [†]	I	(−)-Camphane-2-carboxylic acid	*180,148*
$C_{10}H_{18}$			
$C_{10}H_{18}(MgCl)_2$ [‡]	I	*p*-Menthane-1,8-dicarboxylic acid	*12*
$C_{10}H_{19}$			
$C_{10}H_{19}MgBr$ (from 3-bromo-*p*-menthane)	I	*p*-Menthane-3-carboxylic acid	*201*
$C_{10}H_{20}$			
$[-(CH_2)_5MgI]_2$	?	$[-(CH_2)_5CO_2H]_2$	*187*
$C_{10}H_{21}$			
n-$C_{10}H_{21}MgBr$	Ia (−20°)	*n*-$C_{10}H_{21}C^{14}O_2H$ (yielding 79.3% methyl ester)	*62*
$C_{11}H_9$			
1-$C_{10}H_7CH_2MgCl$	II	1-$C_{10}H_7CH_2CO_2H$ (59.4%)	*57*
2-$C_{10}H_7CH_2MgBr$	II	2-$C_{10}H_7CH_2CO_2H$	*57*
2-$CH_3C_{10}H_6$-1-MgBr	III	2-$CH_3C_{10}H_6$-1-CO_2H (72%)	*46*
$C_{11}H_9ClO$			
2,4-$(CH_3)_2$-3-Cl-6-$CH_3OC_6HC{\equiv}CMgBr$	?	2,4-$(CH_3)_2$-3-Cl-6-$CH_3OC_6HC{\equiv}CCO_2H$ (55%, crude)	*4*

* See pp. 914, 947.

† Prepared by partial (66%) carbonation of the Grignard reagent from (+)-α-pinene hydrochloride; Rivière (*148*) concludes that the residual reagent is substantially pure isobornylmagnesium chloride.

‡ From 1,8-dichloro-*p*-menthane.

TABLE XIII-I (Continued)

RMgX	Method *	Product(s)	Ref.
$C_{11}H_9O$			
2-$CH_3OC_{10}H_6$-1-MgBr	I	2-$CH_3OC_{10}H_6$-1-CO_2H (*ca.* 20%)	*17*
4-$CH_3OC_{10}H_6$-1-MgBr		4-$CH_3OC_{10}H_6$-1-CO_2H (84%)	*168*
6-$CH_3OC_{10}H_6$-2-MgBr	IVa	6-$CH_3OC_{10}H_6$-2-CO_2H (50%)	*41*
$C_{11}H_{12}ClMgO_2$			
$[4\text{-}i\text{-}C_3H_7C_6H_4CH(CO_2MgCl)]^-MgX^+$	I (cold)	4-*i*-$C_3H_7C_6H_4CH(CO_2H)_2$	*97*
$C_{11}H_{12}ClO_2$			
$[2,4\text{-}(CH_3)_2\text{-}3\text{-}Cl\text{-}6\text{-}CH_3OC_6HCOCH_2]^-MgBr^+$	VII (2–3 atm.)	2,4-$(CH_3)_2$-3-Cl-6-$CH_3OC_6HCOCH_2CO_2H$ (45%)	*3*
$C_{11}H_{13}$			
2-Phenylcyclopentyl-MgBr	?	2-Phenylcyclopentanecarboxylic acid (25%)	*186*
3-Phenylcyclopentyl-MgBr	I (cold)	3-Phenylcyclopentanecarboxylic acid (70%)	*22*
2-Methyl-5,6,7,8-tetrahydro-1-naphthyl-MgBr	I	2-Methyl-5,6,7,8-tetrahydro-1-naphthoic acid	*125*
$C_{11}H_{13}O$			
$[2,4,6\text{-}(CH_3)_3C_6H_2COCH_2]^-MgBr^+$	VII	2,4,6-$(CH_3)_3C_6H_2COCH_2CO_2H$	*45,111*
$C_{11}H_{14}$			
$H_2C[(CH_2)_3C\equiv CMgBr]_2$	I (?)	$H_2C[(CH_2)_3C\equiv CCO_2H]_2$	*114,115*
$C_{11}H_{15}$			
$C_6H_5(CH_2)_5MgBr$	?	$C_6H_5(CH_2)_5CO_2H$	*218*
t-$C_4H_9(C_6H_5)CHMgBr$ (10 g. $C_{11}H_{15}Br$)	?	*t*-$C_4H_9(C_6H_5)CHCO_2H$ (1.1 g., 13%)†	*239*

* See pp. 914, 947.

† Yield based on $C_{11}H_{15}Br$; much Wurtz product formed in preparation of Grignard reagent.

TABLE XIII-I (Continued)

RMgX	Method *	Product(s)	Ref.
$C_{11}H_{15}$ (*cont.*)			
$(CH_3)_5C_6MgBr$	I (0°)	$(CH_3)_5C_6CO_2H$ (39%); $(CH_3)_5C_6C_2H_5$	*28,27,74*
$(CH_3)_5C_6MgBr$ [from 0.2 mole $(CH_3)_5C_6Br$ + 0.2 mole C_2H_5Br + Mg]	I (0°)	$(CH_3)_5C_6Br$ (2 g.); $(CH_3)_5C_6C_2H_5$ (17 g.); $(CH_3)_5C_6CO_2H$ (15 g.); $(CH_3)_5C_6H$ (2 g.); $C_2H_5CO_2H$	*156*
$(CH_3)_5C_6Br + C_2H_5Br$ + Mg	V (0°)	$(CH_3)_5C_6CO_2H$ (39%); $(CH_3)_5C_6C_2H_5$ (48.3%)	*156*
$C_{11}H_{23}$			
n-$C_{11}H_{23}MgBr$	I (with N_2; −40°)	n-$C_{11}H_{23}C^{14}O_2H$ (57%)	*81*
$C_{12}H_7O$			
1-Dibenzofuryl-MgBr	III	1-Dibenzofurancarboxylic acid (90%)	*64,103*
4-Dibenzofuryl-MgBr (16.8 g., 0.1 mole $C_{12}H_8O$)	III	4-Dibenzofurancarboxylic acid (1.05 g., 5%)	*240*
$C_{12}H_8$			
$(—C_6H_4$-3-$MgBr)_2$	IV	$(—C_6H_4$-3-$CO_2H)_2$ (40%)	*166*
$C_{12}H_8Br$			
3-$BrC_6H_4C_6H_4$-3-MgBr	IV	3-$BrC_6H_4C_6H_4$-3-CO_2H (*ca.* 21%); $(—C_6H_4$-3-$CO_2H)_2$	*166*
$C_{12}H_8ClMgO_2$			
$[1\text{-}C_{10}H_7CH(CO_2MgCl)]^-MgX^+$	I (cold)	1-$C_{10}H_7CH(CO_2H)_2$	*97*
$[2\text{-}C_{10}H_7CH(CO_2MgCl)]^-MgX^+$	I (cold)	2-$C_{10}H_7CH(CO_2H)_2$	*97*
$C_{12}H_9$			
2-$C_6H_5C_6H_4MgI$	?	2-$C_6H_5C_6H_4C^{14}O_2H$ (60%)	*147*

* See pp. 914, 947.

TABLE XIII-I (Continued)

RMgX	Method*	Product(s)	Ref.
$C_{12}H_9$ (*cont.*)			
3-$C_6H_5C_6H_4MgBr$	IVa	3-$C_6H_5C_6H_4CO_2H$ (70% on basis of $C_{12}H_9Br$)	*198*
$C_{12}H_{11}$			
2-$C_2H_5C_{10}H_6$-1-MgBr	IV	2-$C_2H_5C_{10}H_6$-1-CO_2H (76%)	*42*
2,3-$(CH_3)_2C_{10}H_5$-1-MgBr	VI	2,3-$(CH_3)_2C_{10}H_5$-1-CO_2H (74–83%, crude)	*6*
4,7-$(CH_3)_2C_{10}H_5$-1-MgBr	?	4,7-$(CH_3)_2C_{10}H_5$-1-CO_2H	*14*
$C_{12}H_{11}O$			
6-$C_2H_5OC_{10}H_6$-2-MgBr	IVa	6-$C_2H_5OC_{10}H_6$-2-CO_2H (33%)	*88*
$C_{12}H_{14}ClO_2$			
[2,4-$(CH_3)_2$-3-Cl-6-CH_3OC_6-$HCOCHCH_3$]$^-MgBr^+$	VII (2–3 atm.)	2,4-$(CH_3)_2$-3-Cl-6-$CH_3OC_6HCOCH(CH_3)CO_2H$ (50%)	*3*
[2,4-$(CH_3)_2$-3-Cl-6-$C_2H_5OC_6$-$HCOCH_2$]$^-MgBr^+$	VII (2–3 atm.)	2,4-$(CH_3)_2$-3-Cl-6-$C_2H_5OC_6HCOCH_2CO_2H$ (55%)	*3*
$C_{12}H_{15}$			
t-$C_4H_9(C_6H_5)C{=}CHMgBr$ (in Am_2O)	?	*cis*-*t*-$C_4H_9(C_6H_5)C{=}CHCO_2H$	*174*
t-$C_4H_9(C_6H_5)C{=}CHMgBr$	I (0°)	*cis*-*t*-$C_4H_9(C_6H_5)C{=}CHCO_2H$ (37%); *trans*-*t*-$C_4H_9(C_6H_5)C{=}CHCO_2H$ (4%)	*174*
4-$(CH_2)_5CHC_6H_4MgBr$	I	4-$(CH_2)_5CHC_6H_4CO_2H$ ("poor yield")	*20,208*
4-$(CH_2)_5CHC_6H_4MgBr$	III	4-$(CH_2)_5CHC_6H_4CO_2H$ (70%)	*20,49*
4-$(CH_2)_5CHC_6H_4MgI$	VII	4-$(CH_2)_5CHC_6H_4CO_2H$ (25%)	*137*
$C_{12}H_{15}O$			
[2,4,6-$(CH_3)_3C_6H_2COCH(CH_3)$]$^-MgBr^+$	VII	2,4,6-$(CH_3)_3C_6H_2COCH(CH_3)CO_2H$	*45*

*See pp. 914, 947.

TABLE XIII-I (Continued)

RMgX	Method *	Product(s)	Ref.
$C_{12}H_{15}O_2$			
$[2,4\text{-}(CH_3)_2\text{-}6\text{-}CH_3OC_6H_2\text{-}COCHCH_3]^-MgBr^+$	VII (2–3 atm.)	$2,4\text{-}(CH_3)_2\text{-}6\text{-}CH_3OC_6H_2COCH(CH_3)CO_2H$ (30%)	3
$C_{12}H_{17}$			
$2,4,6\text{-}(C_2H_5)_3C_6H_2MgBr$	III	$2,4,6\text{-}(C_2H_5)_3C_6H_2CO_2H$ (66%)	43
$C_{12}H_{25}$			
$n\text{-}C_{12}H_{25}MgBr$	VII	$n\text{-}C_{12}H_{25}CO_2H$ (yielding 55% methyl ester)	217
$C_{13}H_9$			
9-Fluorenyl-MgBr	I	9-Fluorenecarboxylic acid	76
9-Fluorenyl-MgBr	IV + VIII	9-Fluorenecarboxylic acid (18%); fluorene (30%)	177
$C_{13}H_9O_2$			
2-Methoxy-1-dibenzofuryl-MgBr	III	2-Methoxy-1-dibenzofurancarboxylic acid (70%)	64
2-Methoxy-3-dibenzofuryl-MgBr	III	2-Methoxy-3-dibenzofurancarboxylic acid (60%)	64
$C_{13}H_{11}$			
$(C_6H_5)_2CHCl$ + Mg	V	$(C_6H_5)_2CHCO_2H$ (32.5%)	56
$C_{13}H_{11}O$			
$[2\text{-}CH_3C_{10}H_6\text{-}1\text{-}COCH_2]^-MgBr^+$	VII (3 atm., $<0°$)	$2\text{-}CH_3C_{10}H_6\text{-}1\text{-}COCH_2CO_2H$ (46%)	2,216

* See pp. 914, 947.

TABLE XIII-I (Continued)

RMgX	Method *	Product(s)	Ref.
$C_{13}H_{12}NS$			
10-Ethyl-3-phenothiazinyl-MgI	IV (?)	10-Ethyl-3-phenothiazinecarboxylic acid (76%)	*209*
$C_{13}H_{15}Br_2O_2$			
$[2,4,6\text{-}(CH_3)_3\text{-}3,5\text{-}Br_2C_6COC(CH_3)_2]^-MgBr^+$	VII	$2,4,6\text{-}(CH_3)_3\text{-}3,5\text{-}Br_2C_6COC(CH_3)_2CO_2H$	*45*
$C_{13}H_{16}ClO_2$			
$[2,4\text{-}(CH_3)_2\text{-}3\text{-}Cl\text{-}6\text{-}C_2H_5OC_6HCOCHCH_3]^-MgBr^+$	VII (2–3 atm.)	$2,4\text{-}(CH_3)_2\text{-}3\text{-}Cl\text{-}6\text{-}C_2H_5OC_6HCOCH(CH_3)CO_2H$ (41%)	*3*
$C_{13}H_{17}$			
$4\text{-}(CH_2)_5CHC_6H_4CH_2MgCl$	I	$4\text{-}(CH_2)_5CHC_6H_4CH_2CO_2H$ (55%)	*20*
$4\text{-}(CH_2)_5CHC_6H_4CH_2MgCl$	III	$4\text{-}(CH_2)_5CHC_6H_4CH_2CO_2H$ (60%)	*20*
$C_{13}H_{17}O$			
$[2,4,6\text{-}(CH_3)_3C_6H_2COC(CH_3)_2]^-MgBr^+$	VII	$2,4,6\text{-}(CH_3)_3C_6H_2COC(CH_3)_2CO_2H$ (77.4%)	*45*
$C_{13}H_{25}O$			
$[t\text{-}C_4H_9CH_2C(CH_3)(t\text{-}C_4H_9)COCH_2]^-MgBr^+$	I	$t\text{-}C_4H_9CH_2C(CH_3)(t\text{-}C_4H_9)COCH_2CO_2H$ (66%)	*195*
$[(t\text{-}C_4H_9CH_2)_2CHCOCH_2]^-MgBr^+$	I	$(t\text{-}C_4H_9CH_2)_2CHCOCH_2CO_2H$ (49%)	*192*
$C_{14}H_9$			
9-Anthryl-MgBr	I (hot)	9-Anthroic acid (72%)	*10*
9-Phenanthryl-MgBr		9-Phenanthrenecarboxylic acid (70%)	*9,164*

*See pp. 914, 947.

TABLE XIII-I (Continued)

RMgX	Method *	Product(s)	Ref.
$C_{14}H_{13}$			
2-$C_6H_5C_6H_4CH_2CH_2MgBr$ (13.5 g. $C_{14}H_{13}Br$)	II	2-$C_6H_5C_6H_4CH_2CH_2CO_2H$ (5.0 g., 45%)	*220*
$C_{14}H_{13}O$			
[2-$CH_3C_{10}H_6$-1-$COCH(CH_3)]^-MgBr^+$	VII (3 atm., <0°)	2-$CH_3C_{10}H_6$-1-$COCH(CH_3)CO_2H$ (*ca.* 46%)	*2,216*
$C_{14}H_{27}O$			
[*t*-$C_4H_9CH_2C(CH_3)$(*t*-C_4H_9)-$COCH(CH_3)]^-MgBr^+$	I	*t*-$C_4H_9CH_2C(CH_3)$(*t*-C_4H_9)$COCH(CH_3)CO_2H$ (48%)	*195*
$C_{14}H_{29}$			
n-$C_{14}H_{29}MgBr$	?	*n*-$C_{14}H_{29}CO_2H$	*218*
$C_{15}H_{29}O$			
[*t*-$C_4H_9CH_2C(CH_3)$(*t*-C_4H_9)-$COC(CH_3)_2]^-MgBr^+$	I	*t*-$C_4H_9CH_2C(CH_3)$(*t*-C_4H_9)$COC(CH_3)_2CO_2H$ (37%)	*195*
$C_{15}H_{31}$			
n-$C_{15}H_{31}MgBr$	Ia (−20°)	*n*-$C_{15}H_{31}C^{14}O_2H$ (yielding 80.4% methyl ester)	*31*
$C_{15}H_{31}O$			
i-$C_6H_{13}CH(CH_3)CH(CH_2CH_2O$-$C_2H_5)CH(CH_3)MgCl$		*i*-$C_6H_{13}CH(CH_3)CH(CH_2CH_2OC_2H_5)$-$CH(CH_3)CO_2H$	*37*
$C_{16}H_{11}O$			
2,5-Diphenyl-3-furyl-MgBr	I	2,5-Diphenylfurancarboxylic acid (80%)	*215*
$C_{16}H_{33}$			
n-$C_{16}H_{33}MgI$	I	*n*-$C_{16}H_{33}CO_2H$	*153*

* See pp. 91[illegible]-947.

TABLE XIII-I (Continued)

RMgX	Method *	Product(s)	Ref.
$C_{16}H_{33}$ (*cont.*)			
n-$C_{16}H_{33}MgBr$	VII	n-$C_{16}H_{13}CO_2H$ (yielding 32% methyl ester)	*217*
$C_{17}H_{23}$			
t-$C_4H_9(C_6H_5)(t$-$C_4H_9C{\equiv}C)CMgBr$	?	t-$C_4H_9(C_6H_5)C{=}C{=}C(CO_2H)$-$t$-$C_4H_9$	*239*
$C_{18}H_{37}$			
n-$C_{18}H_{37}MgBr$	I	n-$C_{18}H_{37}CO_2H$	*143,218*
$C_{19}H_{13}$			
Phenylbiphenylenemethyl-MgBr	I	Phenylbiphenyleneacetic acid (60%)	*8*
$C_{19}H_{15}$			
$(C_6H_5)_3CMgCl$	I	$(C_6H_5)_3CCO_2H$ (83%)	*158*
$(C_6H_5)_3CMgBr$	?	$(C_6H_5)_3CCO_2H$ (*ca.* quant.)	*68*
$C_{19}H_{19}$			
t-$C_4H_9C{\equiv}C(C_6H_5)_2CMgBr$	II	t-$C_4H_9C{\equiv}C(C_6H_5)_2CCO_2H$ (34%, crude)	*169*
$C_{19}H_{27}$			
$(t$-$C_4H_9C{\equiv}C)_3CMgBr$	II	$(t$-$C_4H_9C{\equiv}C)_3CCO_2H$	*241*
$C_{20}H_{13}$			
10-Phenyl-9-anthryl-MgBr	I	10-Phenyl-9-anthracenecarboxylic acid (40%)	*35*
α-Phenyl-β-biphenylenevinyl-MgBr	I	α-Phenyl-β-biphenyleneacrylic acid	*110*
$C_{20}H_{14}Cl$			
4-$ClC_6H_4(C_6H_5)C{=}C(C_6H_5)MgBr$	I	*cis*- and *trans*-4-$ClC_6H_4(C_6H_5)C{=}C(C_6H_5)CO_2H$	*109*

* See pp. 914, 947.

TABLE XIII-I (Continued)

RMgX	Method *	Product(s)	Ref.
$C_{20}H_{15}$			
$(C_6H_5)_2C{=}C(C_6H_5)MgBr$	I	$(C_6H_5)_2C{=}C(C_6H_5)CO_2H$ (94%)	*108*
$C_{21}H_{15}$			
$(1\text{-}C_{10}H_7)_2CHMgCl$	V	$(1\text{-}C_{10}H_7)_2CHCO_2H$ (57%)	*161*
$(2\text{-}C_{10}H_7)_2CHMgCl$	V	$(2\text{-}C_{10}H_7)_2CH_2CO_2H$ (36%)	*160*
$C_{21}H_{17}$			
$C_6H_5(4\text{-}CH_3C_6H_4)C{=}C(C_6H_5)MgBr$	I	*cis*-$C_6H_5(4\text{-}CH_3C_6H_4)C{=}C(C_6H_5)CO_2H$	*109*
$C_{21}H_{17}O$			
$C_6H_5(4\text{-}CH_3OC_6H_4)C{=}C(C_6H_5)MgBr$	I	*cis*- and *trans*-$C_6H_5(4\text{-}CH_3OC_6H_4)C{=}$ $C(C_6H_5)CO_2H$	*109*
$C_{22}H_{19}$			
$(4\text{-}CH_3C_6H_4)_2C{=}C(C_6H_5)MgBr$	I	$(4\text{-}CH_3C_6H_4)_2C{=}C(C_6H_5)CO_2H$	*109*
$C_{22}H_{19}O_2$			
$(4\text{-}CH_3OC_6H_4)_2C{=}C(C_6H_5)MgBr$	I	$(4\text{-}CH_3OC_6H_4)_2C{=}C(C_6H_5)CO_2H$	*109*
$C_{22}H_{21}$			
$(4\text{-}CH_3C_6H_4)_3CMgCl$	I (hot)	$(4\text{-}CH_3C_6H_4)_3CCO_2H$ ("very poor yield")	*159*
$C_{22}H_{45}$			
$n\text{-}C_{22}H_{45}MgBr$	?	$n\text{-}C_{22}H_{45}CO_2H$	*218*
$C_{24}H_{17}$			
$2,4,6\text{-}(C_6H_5)_3C_6H_2MgBr$	I	$2,4,6\text{-}(C_6H_5)_3C_6H_2CO_2H$ (84.1%)	*112*

* See pp. 914, 947.

TABLE XIII-I (Continued)

RMgX	Method *	Product(s)	Ref.
$C_{26}H_{16}$			
$C_{26}H_{16}(MgBr)_2$ (from 9,10-bis-*p*-bromophenylanthracene)	I (−15°)	9,10-Bis-(4-carboxyphenyl)anthracene (50%)	*34*
$C_{27}H_{45}$			
3-Cholesteryl-MgCl	II (0°)	5-Cholestene-3-carboxylic acid	*123*
3-Cholesteryl-MgCl	IVa	5-Cholestene-3-carboxylic acid (85%)	*11*

* See p. 914.

REFERENCES FOR TABLE XIII-I

(*1*) Acree, *Ber.*, *37*, 265–8 (1904).
(*2*) Adams and Binder, *J. Am. Chem. Soc.*, *63*, 2773–6 (1941).
(*3*) Adams and Gross, *J. Am. Chem. Soc.*, *64*, 1786–90 (1942).
(*4*) Adams and Ludington, *J. Am. Chem. Soc.*, *67*, 794–7 (1945).
(*5*) Arnold, Bank, and Liggett, *J. Am. Chem. Soc.*, *63*, 3444–6 (1941).
(*6*) Arnold and Liggett, *J. Am. Chem. Soc.*, *64*, 2875–7 (1942).
(*7*) Austin and Johnson, *J. Am. Chem. Soc.*, *54*, 647–60 (1932).
(*8*) Bachmann, *J. Am. Chem. Soc.*, *52*, 3287–90 (1930).
(*9*) Bachmann, *J. Am. Chem. Soc.*, *56*, 1363–7 (1934).
(*10*) Bachmann and Kloetzel, *J. Org. Chem.*, *3*, 55–61 (1938).
(*11*) Baker and Squire, *J. Am. Chem. Soc.*, *70*, 1487–90 (1948).
(*12*) Barbier and Grignard, *Compt. rend.*, *145*, 255–7 (1907); *Chem. Abstr.*, *1*, 2797 (1907).
(*13*) Barnes, *Organic Syntheses*, *21*, 77–9 (1941).
(*14*) Barnett and Cook, *J. Chem. Soc.*, *1933*, 22–4.
(*15*) Blicke, *J. Am. Chem. Soc.*, *49*, 2843–9 (1927).
(*16*) Bodroux, *Compt. rend.*, *137*, 710–2 (1903); *J. Chem. Soc.*, *86,I*, 64 (1904).
(*17*) Bodroux, *Compt. rend.*, *136*, 617–8 (1903); *J. Chem. Soc.*, *84,I*, 420 (1903).
(*18*) Bodroux, *Bull. soc. chim.*, [3], *31*, 24–30 (1904).
(*19*) Bodroux, *Bull. soc. chim.*, [3], *31*, 30–33 (1904).
(*20*) Bodroux and Thomassin, *Bull. soc. chim.*, [5], *6*, 1411–6 (1939).
(*21*) Bogert and Tuttle, *J. Am. Chem. Soc.*, *38*, 1349–68 (1916).
(*22*) Borsche and Menz, *Ber.*, *41*, 190–210 (1908).
(*23*) Bouveault, *Bull. soc. chim.*, [3], *29*, 1051–4 (1903).
(*24*) Bouveault, *Compt. rend.*, *138*, 1108–10 (1904); *J. Chem. Soc.*, *86,I*, 546 (1904).
(*25*) Carothers and Berchet, *J. Am. Chem. Soc.*, *55*, 1094–6 (1933).
(*26*) Challenger, Clapham, and Emmott, *J. Inst. Petroleum*, *34*, 922–9 (1948); *Chem. Abstr.*, *43*, 4666 (1949).
(*27*) Clément, *Compt. rend.*, *198*, 655–7 (1937).
(*28*) Clément, *Ann. chim.*, [11], *13*, 243–316 (1940).
(*29*) Courtot and Tchelitcheff, *Compt. rend.*, *217*, 201–3 (1943); *Chem. Abstr.*, *38*, 5502 (1944).
(*30*) Dauben, *J. Org. Chem.*, *13*, 313–6 (1948).
(*31*) Dauben, *J. Am. Chem. Soc.*, *70*, 1376–8 (1948).
(*32*) Dauben, Reid, and Yankwich, *Anal. Chem.*, *19*, 828–32 (1947).
(*33*) Denisenko, *J. Gen. Chem.* (U.S.S.R.), *18*, 219–21 (1948); *Chem. Abstr.*, *42*, 6744 (1948).
(*34*) Dufraisse and Margoulis-Molho, *Bull. soc. chim.*, [5], *7*, 930–3 (1940).
(*35*) Dufraisse, Velluz, and Velluz, *Bull. soc. chim.*, [5], *4*, 1260–4 (1937).
(*36*) Dupont, *Compt. rend.*, *148*, 1522–4 (1909); *Chem. Abstr.*, *3*, 2674 (1909); *Chem. Zentr.*, *1909,II*, 181.
(*37*) Dutta, *Science and Culture*, 7, 316–7 (1941); *Chem. Abstr.*, *36*, 3156 (1942).
(*38*) Fields, Leaffer, and Rohan, *Science*, *109*, 35 (1949); *Chem. Abstr.*, *43*, 9045 (1949).
(*39*) Fieser, Holmes, and Newman, *J. Am. Chem. Soc.*, *58*, 1055 (1936).
(*40*) Fieser and Riegel, *J. Am. Chem. Soc.*, *59*, 2561–5 (1937).
(*41*) Fries and Schimmelschmidt, *Ber.*, *58B*, 2835–45 (1925).
(*42*) Fuson and Chadwick, *J. Org. Chem.*, *13*, 484–8 (1948).
(*43*) Fuson and Corse, *J. Am. Chem. Soc.*, *60*, 2063–6 (1938).
(*44*) Fuson, Corse, and Welldon, *J. Am. Chem. Soc.*, *63*, 2645–8 (1941).
(*45*) Fuson, Fugate, and Fisher, *J. Am. Chem. Soc.*, *61*, 2362–5 (1939).

(46) Fuson, McKeever, and Behr, *J. Am. Chem. Soc.*, *63*, 2648–9 (1941).
(47) Fuson, McKusick, and Mills, *J. Org. Chem.*, *11*, 60–6 (1946).
(48) Fuson, Mills, Klose, and Carpenter, *J. Org. Chem.*, *12*, 587–95 (1947).
(49) Fuson and Tull, *J. Am. Chem. Soc.*, *71*, 2543–6 (1949).
(50) Gilman and Dickey, *J. Am. Chem. Soc.*, *52*, 2144–7 (1930).
(51) Gilman and Harris, *J. Am. Chem. Soc.*, *49*, 1825–8 (1927).
(52) Gilman and Harris, *J. Am. Chem. Soc.*, *53*, 3541–6 (1931).
(53) Gilman and Harris, *Rec. trav. chim.*, *50*, 1050–5 (1931).
(54) Gilman and Heck, *Ber.*, *62B*, 1379–84 (1929).
(55) Gilman and Kirby, *Organic Syntheses*, *5*, 75–7 (1925).
(56) Gilman and Kirby, *J. Am. Chem. Soc.*, *48*, 1733–6 (1926).
(57) Gilman and Kirby, *J. Am. Chem. Soc.*, *51*, 3475–8 (1929).
(58) Gilman and Kirby, *Organic Syntheses*, Coll. Vol. I, 2nd ed., pp. 361–4, *1941*.
(59) Gilman and McGlumphy, *Bull. soc. chim.*, [4], *43*, 1322–8 (1928).
(60) Gilman and Parker, *J. Am. Chem. Soc.*, *46*, 2816–22 (1924).
(61) Gilman and St. John, *Rec. trav. chim.*, *48*, 743–4 (1929).
(62) Gilman and St. John, *Rec. trav. chim.*, *49*, 1172–7 (1930).
(63) Gilman, St. John, and Schulze, *Organic Syntheses*, Coll. Vol. II, pp. 425–7, *1943*.
(64) Gilman and Van Ess, *J. Am. Chem. Soc.*, *61*, 1365–71 (1939).
(65) Gilman and Zoellner, *J. Am. Chem. Soc.*, *50*, 425–8 (1928).
(66) Gilman and Zoellner, *Rec. trav. chim.*, *47*, 1058–63 (1928).
(67) Gilman and Zoellner, *Bull. soc. chim.*, [4], *49*, 7–9 (1931).
(68) Gomberg and Bachmann, *J. Am. Chem. Soc.*, *52*, 2455–61 (1930).
(69) Grard, *Compt. rend.*, *189*, 541–3 (1929).
(70) Greenwood, Whitmore, and Crooks, *J. Am. Chem. Soc.*, *60*, 2028–30 (1938).
(71) Grignard, *Ann. Univ. Lyon*, N.S., 6, 1–116 (1901); *Chem. Zentr.*, *1901,II*, 622.
(72) Grignard, *Ann. chim.*, [7], *24*, 433–90 (1901).
(73) Grignard, *Compt. rend.*, *138*, 1048–50 (1904); *J. Chem. Soc.*, *86,I*, 494 (1904).
(74) Grignard, *Compt. rend.*, *198*, 2217–20 (1934).
(75) Grignard and Courtot, *Compt. rend.*, *152*, 272–4 (1911); *Chem. Zentr.*, *1911,I*, 885.
(76) Grignard and Courtot, *Compt. rend.*, *152*, 1493–5 (1911); *Chem. Abstr.*, *5*, 3409 (1911); *Chem. Zentr.*, *1911,II*, 148.
(77) Grignard, Lepayre, and Tchéoufaki, *Compt. rend.*, *187*, 517–20 (1928).
(78) Grignard and Vignon, *Compt. rend.*, *144*, 1358–60 (1907); *Chem. Zentr.*, *1907,II*, 681.
(79) Grosse and Weinhouse, *Science*, *104*, 402–3 (1946); *Chem. Abstr.*, *41*, 2009 (1947).
(80) Gutt, *Ber.*, *40*, 2061–70 (1907).
(81) Harwood and Ralston, *J. Org. Chem.*, *12*, 740–1 (1947).
(82) Haynes and Jones, *Nature*, *155*, 730 (1945).
(83) Heidelberger, Brewer, and Dauben, *J. Am. Chem. Soc.*, *69*, 1389–91 (1947).
(84) Heilbron, Jones, and Sondheimer, *J. Chem. Soc.*, *1947*, 1586–90.
(85) Houben, *Ber.*, *36*, 2897–900 (1903).
(86) Houben, *Ber.*, *38*, 3796–801 (1905).
(87) Houben and Kesselkaul, *Ber.*, *35*, 2519–23 (1902).
(88) Hudson, *J. Chem. Soc.*, *1946*, 76–8.
(89) Hurd and Wilkinson, *J. Am. Chem. Soc.*, *70*, 739–41 (1948).
(90) Hussey, *J. Am. Chem. Soc.*, *73*, 1364–5 (1951).
(91) Iotsitch, *J. Russ. Phys.-Chem. Soc.*, *34*, 242–4 (1902); *Bull. soc. chim.*, [3], *30*, 210 (1903).

(92) Iotsitch, *J. Russ. Phys.-Chem. Soc.*, *35*, 431–2 (1903); *Bull. soc. chim.*, [3], *32*, 552 (1904).
(93) Iotsitch, *J. Russ. Phys.-Chem. Soc.*, *35*, 1269–75 (1903); *Bull. soc. chim.*, [3], *34*, 181 (1905).
(94) Iotsitch, *J. Russ. Phys.-Chem. Soc.*, *36*, 8–9 (1904); *Bull. soc. chim.*, [3], *34*, 204 (1905).
(95) Iotsitch, *J. Russ. Phys.-Chem. Soc.*, *36*, 1545–51 (1904); *Bull. soc. chim.*, [3], *36*, 177 (1906).
(96) Ivanoff, *Bull. soc. chim.*, [4], *37*, 287–96 (1925).
(97) Ivanoff and Pchénitchny, *Bull. soc. chim.*, [5], *1*, 223–33 (1934).
(98) Ivanoff and Pchénitchny, *Bull. soc. chim.*, [5], *1*, 233–5 (1934).
(99) Ivanoff and Spassoff, *Bull. soc. chim.*, [4], *49*, 19–23 (1931).
(100) Jacobi, *J. prakt. Chem.*, [2], *129*, 55–96 (1931).
(101) Jacobs, Cramer, and Weiss, *J. Am. Chem. Soc.*, *62*, 1849–54 (1940).
(102) Jacobs, Winstein, Henderson, Bond, Ralls, Seymour, and Florsheim, *J. Org. Chem.*, *11*, 229–38 (1946).
(103) Jacoby, Hayes, and Van Ess, *Proc. Iowa Acad. Sci.*, *43*, 204–5 (1936); *Chem. Abstr.*, *32*, 4160 (1938).
(104) Jezierski, *Roczniki Chem.*, *20*, 47–53 (1946); *Chem. Abstr.*, *42*, 1910 (1948).
(105) Jones, *J. Am. Chem. Soc.*, *69*, 2346–50 (1947).
(106) Kauffmann, *Ber.*, *45*, 2333–7 (1912).
(107) Kharasch, Lambert, and Urry, *J. Org. Chem.*, *10*, 298–306 (1945).
(108) Koelsch, *J. Am. Chem. Soc.*, *54*, 2045–8 (1932).
(109) Koelsch, *J. Am. Chem. Soc.*, *54*, 2487–93 (1932).
(110) Koelsch, *J. Am. Chem. Soc.*, *54*, 3384–9 (1932).
(111) Kohler and Baltzly, *J. Am. Chem. Soc.*, *54*, 4015–26 (1932).
(112) Kohler and Blanchard, *J. Am. Chem. Soc.*, *57*, 367–71 (1935).
(113) Lane, Roberts, and Young, *J. Am. Chem. Soc.*, *66*, 543–5 (1944).
(114) Lespieau, *Compt. rend.*, *157*, 1439–40 (1913); *Chem. Zentr.*, *1914,I*, 339.
(115) Lespieau, *Bull. soc. chim.*, [4], *43*, 1189–93 (1928).
(116) Lester and Bailey, *J. Am. Chem. Soc.*, *68*, 375–6 (1946).
(117) Levene and Marker, *J. Biol. Chem.*, *93*, 749–74 (1931).
(118) Levene and Marker, *J. Biol. Chem.*, *110*, 299–309 (1935).
(119) Levene and Marker, *J. Biol. Chem.*, *110*, 329–42 (1935).
(120) Majima and Kotake, *Ber.*, *55B*, 3859–72 (1922).
(121) Malmgren, *Ber.*, *36*, 2608–42 (1903).
(122) Manske and Ledingham, *Can. J. Research*, *27*, 158–60 (1949).
(123) Marker, Oakwood, and Crooks, *J. Am. Chem. Soc.*, *58*, 481–3 (1936).
(124) Marvel, Blomquist, and Vaughn, *J. Am. Chem. Soc.*, *50*, 2810–2 (1928).
(125) Mayer, Schafer, and Rosenblack, *Arch. Pharm.*, *267*, 571–84 (1929); *Chem. Zentr.*, *1929,II*, 3009.
(126) McBee and Truchan, *J. Am. Chem. Soc.*, *70*, 2910–1 (1948).
(127) Meerwein, *Ann.*, *417*, 255–77 (1918).
(128) Meyer and Tögel, *Ann.*, *347*, 55–70 (1906).
(129) Mikhant'ev, *J. Gen. Chem.* (U.S.S.R.), *15*, 641–2 (1945); *Chem. Abstr.*, *40*, 5697 (1946).
(130) Mousseron and Granger, *Bull. soc. chim.*, [5], *13*, 251–6 (1946).
(131) Mousseron, Granger, Bourrel, Cellier, Jullien, Canals, and Cabanes, *Bull. soc. chim.*, [5], *14*, 605–15 (1947).
(132) Mousseron and Winternitz, *Bull. soc. chim.*, [5], *12*, 70–1 (1945).
(133) Nametkin and Gabriadze, *J. Gen. Chem.* (U.S.S.R.), *13*, 560–8 (1943); *Chem. Abstr.*, *39*, 1142 (1945).
(134) Nametkin and Volodina, *J. Gen. Chem.* (U.S.S.R.), *17*, 325–34 (1947); *Chem. Abstr.*, *42*, 527 (1948).

(135) Nesmeyanov and Pecherskaya, *Bull. acad. sci. U.R.S.S., Classe sci. chim., 1943*, 317–8; *Chem. Abstr.*, 38, 5492 (1944).
(136) Neunhoeffer, *Ann.*, *509*, 115–30 (1934).
(137) Neunhoeffer, *Ann.*, *526*, 58–65 (1936).
(138) Neunhoeffer and Schlüter, *Ann.*, *526*, 65–71 (1936).
(139) Oddo, *Gazz. chim. ital.*, *39,I*, 649–59 (1909); *Chem. Zentr.*, *1909,II*, 914.
(140) Oddo, *Gazz. chim. ital.*, *42,I*, 346–52 (1912); *Chem. Abstr.*, 6, 2234 (1912).
(141) Oddo and Moschini, *Gazz. chim. ital.*, *42,II*, 244–56 (1912); *Chem. Abstr.*, 6, 3425 (1912).
(142) Oddo and Sessa, *Gazz. chim. ital.*, *41,I*, 234–48 (1911); *Chem. Abstr.*, 5, 2638 (1911).
(143) Oskerk, *J. Russ. Phys.-Chem. Soc.*, *46*, 411–6 (1914); *Chem. Abstr.*, 8, 3185 (1914).
(144) Porter and Suter, *J. Am. Chem. Soc.*, *57*, 2022–6 (1935).
(145) Puntambeker and Zoellner, *Organic Syntheses*, Coll. Vol. I, 2nd ed., pp. 524–6, *1941*.
(146) Quelet, *Bull. soc. chim.*, [4], *45*, 255–74 (1929).
(147) Ray and Geiser, *Science*, *109*, 200 (1949); *Chem. Abstr.*, *43*, 3917 (1949).
(148) Rivière, *Ann. chim.*, [12], *1*, 157–231 (1946).
(149) Roberts and Young, *J. Am. Chem. Soc.*, *67*, 148–50 (1945).
(150) Ruben, Allen, and Nahinskey, *J. Am. Soc.*, *64*, 3050 (1942).
(151) Rupe and Hirschmann, *Helv. Chim. Acta*, *11*, 1180–200 (1928).
(152) Rupe and Proske, *Ber.*, *43*, 1231–4 (1910).
(153) Ruttan, *Original Commun., 8th Int. Congr. Appl. Chem.*, *25*, 431–42 (1913); *Chem. Zentr.*, *1913,I*, 2108.
(154) Sabatier and Mailhe, *Ann. chim.*, [8], *10*, 527–71 (1907).
(155) Salkind, *Ber.*, *67B*, 1031–6 (1934).
(156) Savard and Hösögüt, *Rev. faculte sci. univ. Istanbul*, [N.S.], 3, 164–73 (1938); *Chem. Abstr.*, *32*, 5795 (1938).
(157) Schlenk and Ochs, *Ber.*, *48*, 676–80 (1915).
(158) Schmidlin, *Ber.*, *39*, 628–36 (1906).
(159) Schmidlin and Hodgson, *Ber.*, *41*, 438–47 (1908).
(160) Schmidlin and Huber, *Ber.*, *43*, 2824–37 (1910).
(161) Schmidlin and Massini, *Ber.*, *42*, 2377–92 (1909).
(162) Schroeter, *Ber.*, *40*, 1584–5 (1907).
(163) Shepard, Winslow, and Johnson, *J. Am. Chem. Soc.*, *52*, 2083–90 (1930).
(164) Shoppee, *J. Chem. Soc.*, *1933*, 37–45.
(165) Smith and Byrkit, *J. Am. Chem. Soc.*, *55*, 4305–8 (1933).
(166) Snyder, Weaver, and Marshall, *J. Am. Chem. Soc.*, *71*, 289–91 (1949).
(167) Sommer, Gold, Goldberg, and Marans, *J. Am. Chem. Soc.*, *71*, 1509 (1949).
(168) Spaeth, Geissman, and Jacobs, *J. Org. Chem.*, *11*, 399–404 (1946).
(169) Stampfli and Marvel, *J. Am. Chem. Soc.*, *53*, 4057–63 (1931).
(170) Steinkopf, Poulsson, and Herdey, *Ann.*, *536*, 128–34 (1938).
(171) Straus, Kollek, and Hauptmann, *Ber.*, *63B*, 1886–99 (1930).
(172) Thorp and Kamm, *J. Am. Chem. Soc.*, *36*, 1022–8 (1914).
(173) Tiffeneau, *Compt. rend.*, *135*, 1346–8 (1902); *J. Chem. Soc.*, *84,I*, 241 (1903); *Chem. Zentr.*, *1903,I*, 328.
(174) Tsatsas, *Compt. rend.*, *220*, 662–4 (1945); *Chem. Abstr.*, *40*, 4699 (1946).
(175) Tsatsas, *Ann. chim.*, [12], *1*, 342–94 (1946).
(176) Tschitschibabin, *J. Russ. Phys.-Chem. Soc.*, *45*, 184–8 (1913); *Chem. Zentr.*, *1913,I*, 2028.
(177) Tucker and Whalley, *J. Chem. Soc.*, *1949*, 50–5.
(178) Tuot, *Compt. rend.*, *208*, 1026–8 (1939); *Chem. Abstr.*, *33*, 6794 (1939).
(179) Umnowa, *J. Russ. Phys.-Chem. Soc.*, *44*, 1395–406 (1912); *Chem. Zentr.*, *1913,I*, 1402.

(*180*) Vavon and Rivière, *Compt. rend.*, *213*, 1016–8 (1941).
(*181*) Vavon and Rivière, *Compt. rend.*, *220*, 286–8 (1945).
(*182*) von Braun and Deutsch, *Ber.*, *44*, 3699–706 (1911).
(*183*) von Braun and Kirschbaum, *Ber.*, *44*, 1039–48 (1911).
(*184*) von Braun and Kirschbaum, *Ber.*, *52B*, 1713–6 (1919).
(*185*) von Braun and Kühn, *Ber.*, *58B*, 2168–73 (1925).
(*186*) von Braun and Kühn, *Ber.*, *60B*, 2557–66 (1927).
(*187*) von Braun and Sobecki, *Ber.*, *44*, 1918–31 (1911).
(*188*) Whitmore, *Rec. trav. chim.*, *57*, 562–8 (1938).
(*189*) Whitmore and Badertscher, *J. Am. Chem. Soc.*, *55*, 1559–67 (1933).
(*190*) Whitmore and Forster, *J. Am. Chem. Soc.*, *64*, 2966–8 (1942).
(*191*) Whitmore and Fox, *J. Am. Chem. Soc.*, *51*, 3363–7 (1929).
(*192*) Whitmore and Lester, *J. Am. Chem. Soc.*, *64*, 1251–3 (1942).
(*193*) Whitmore and Lewis, *J. Am. Chem. Soc.*, *64*, 1618–9 (1942).
(*194*) Whitmore, Marker, and Plambeck, *J. Am. Chem. Soc.*, *63*, 1626–30 (1941).
(*195*) Whitmore and Randall, *J. Am. Chem. Soc.*, *64*, 1242–6 (1942).
(*196*) Whitmore and Sloat, *J. Am. Chem. Soc.*, *64*, 2968–70 (1942).
(*197*) Whitmore, Whitaker, Mosher, Breivik, Wheeler, Miner, Sutherland, Wagner, Clapper, Lewis, Lux, and Popkin, *J. Am. Chem. Soc.*, *63*, 643–54 (1941).
(*198*) Woods and Reed, *J. Am. Chem. Soc.*, *71*, 1348–50 (1949).
(*199*) Zelinsky, *Ber.*, *35*, 2687–92 (1902).
(*200*) Zelinsky, *Ber.*, *35*, 2692–4 (1902).
(*201*) Zelinsky, *Ber.*, *35*, 4415–9 (1902).
(*202*) Zelinsky, *Ber.*, *36*, 208–9 (1903).
(*203*) Zelinsky, *Ber.*, *41*, 2627–8 (1908).
(*204*) Zelinsky and Gutt, *Ber.*, *40*, 3049–50 (1907).
(*205*) Letsinger and Schnizer, *J. Org. Chem.*, *16*, 704–7 (1951).
(*206*) Moser and Sause, *J. Org. Chem.*, *15*, 631–3 (1950).
(*207*) Whitmore, Wheeler, and Surmatis, *J. Am. Chem. Soc.*, *63*, 3237 (1941).
(*208*) Truffault, *Compt. rend.*, *207*, 676–8 (1938); *Chem. Abstr.*, *33*, 2886 (1939).
(*209*) Gilman, Van Ess, and Shirley, *J. Am. Chem. Soc.*, *66*, 1214–6 (1944).
(*210*) Grignard, Lepayre, and Tchéoufaki, *Bull. soc. chim.*, [4], *43*, 931–2 (1928).
(*211*) Grard, *Ann. chim.*, [10], *13*, 336–81 (1930).
(*212*) Meerwein, *Ann.*, *405*, 129–75 (1914).
(*213*) Letsinger and Schnizer, *J. Org. Chem.*, *16*, 704–7 (1951).
(*214*) Newman, *J. Am. Chem. Soc.*, *62*, 2295–300 (1940).
(*215*) Lutz and Smith, *J. Am. Chem. Soc.*, *63*, 1148–50 (1941).
(*216*) Adams and Binder, *J. Am. Chem. Soc.*, *63*, 1459–60 (1941).
(*217*) Cason and Winans, *J. Org. Chem.*, *15*, 139–47 (1950).
(*218*) Smith and Fuzek, *J. Am. Chem. Soc.*, *72*, 3454–8 (1950).
(*219*) Hiers and Adams, *J. Am. Chem. Soc.*, *48*, 2385–95 (1926).
(*220*) Dice, Watkins, and Schuman, *J. Am. Chem. Soc.*, *72*, 1738–40 (1950).
(*221*) Wotiz, Matthews, and Lieb, *J. Am. Chem. Soc.*, *73*, 5503–4 (1951).
(*222*) Prevost, Gaudemar, and Honigberg, *Compt. rend.*, *230*, 1186–8 (1950); *Chem. Abstr.*, *45*, 1497 (1951).
(*223*) Steinkopf and Schmitt, *Ann.*, *533*, 264–9 (1938).
(*224*) Sherman and Amstutz, *J. Am. Chem. Soc.*, *72*, 2195–9 (1950).
(*225*) Gaertner, *J. Am. Chem. Soc.*, *72*, 4326–7 (1950).
(*226*) Gaertner, *J. Am. Chem. Soc.*, *73*, 3934–7 (1951).
(*227*) Campaigne and LeSuer, *J. Am. Chem. Soc.*, *70*, 1555–8 (1948).
(*228*) Lecocq and Buu-Hoï, *Compt. rend.*, *224*, 658–9 (1947); *Chem. Abstr.*, *41*, 4791 (1947).
(*229*) Wotiz, *J. Am. Chem. Soc.*, *72*, 1639–42 (1950).
(*230*) Davis and Marvel, *J. Am. Chem. Soc.*, *53*, 3840–51 (1931).
(*231*) Mousseron and Du, *Bull. soc. chim.*, [5], *15*, 91–6 (1948).

(232) Gilman and Webb, *J. Am. Chem. Soc.*, *71*, 4062–6 (1949).
(233) Challenger and Miller, *J. Chem. Soc.*, *1938*, 849–9.
(234) Wotiz and Palchak, *J. Am. Chem. Soc.*, *73*, 1971–2 (1951).
(235) Bateman, Cunneen, and Koch, *Nature*, *164*, 242 (1949).
(236) Lappin, *J. Am. Chem. Soc.*, *71*, 3966–8 (1949).
(237) Gaertner, *J. Am. Chem. Soc.*, *74*, 766–7 (1952).
(238) Gaertner, *J. Am. Chem. Soc.*, *74*, 2185–8 (1952).
(239) Ford, Thompson, and Marvel, *J. Am. Chem. Soc.*, *57*, 2619–23 (1933).
(240) Gilman and Haubein, *J. Am. Chem. Soc.*, *67*, 1033–4 (1945).
(241) Salzberg and Marvel, *J. Am. Chem. Soc.*, *50*, 1737–44 (1928).

Method V. The method of Houben[23] (reminiscent of the Barbier synthesis of alcohols), in which an alkyl halide is gradually added to magnesium covered with ether while carbon dioxide is passed into the ether.

Method VI. The method of Arnold,[24] whereby a Grignard reagent solution is slowly dropped into ether through which carbon dioxide is passed.

Method VIa. The method of Gilman,[25] whereby a Grignard reagent solution is sprayed into an atmosphere of carbon dioxide.

Method VII. The method of Bogert,[26] in which a Grignard reagent solution is treated with carbon dioxide under pressure, with provisions for cooling if necessary.

Method VIII. The method of Oddo,[27] in which an ether-free Grignard reagent is heated (>250°) in a stream of carbon dioxide.

Miscellaneous methods (*IX*), including that of Heilbron *et al.*[27.1], in which the Grignard reagent is combined with a benzene-solid carbon dioxide suspension in an autoclave, which is then sealed and is allowed to stand at room temperature for about a day (*i.e.*, twenty-two hours).

Miscellaneous uses of the carbonation reaction. In addition to its preparative use, which is summarized in Table XIII-I, the carbonation reaction has been used for various diagnostic purposes. For example, Spencer and Stokes[28] have used it to demonstrate the preparation of a Grignard reagent from iodobenzene and magnesium without the aid of ether. Their method, differing somewhat from any of those heretofore described, consisted in triturating the Grignard reagent in a mortar with solid carbon dioxide and a little added ether.

Carbonation has also served to furnish a rough estimate of yields in Grignard reagent preparations (see Chapter II. The Preparation of Grignard Reagents, Table II-VI.) for which purpose it is obviously ill-adapted to general use.

---

[23] Houben, *Ber.*, *36*, 2897–900 (1903).
[24] Arnold, Bank, and Liggett, *J. Am. Chem. Soc.*, *63*, 3444–6 (1941).
[25] Gilman and Parker, *J. Am. Chem. Soc.*, *46*, 2816–22 (1924).
[26] Bogert and Tuttle, *J. Am. Chem. Soc.*, *38*, 1349–68 (1916).
[27] Oddo and Moschini, *Gazz. chim. ital.*, *42,II*, 244–56 (1912); *Chem. Abstr.*, 6, 3425 (1912).
[27.1] Heilbron, Jones, and Sondheimer, *J. Chem. Soc.*, *1947*, 1586–90.
[28] Spencer and Stokes, *J. Chem. Soc.*, 93, 68–72 (1908).

Gilman and Jones[29] have employed the carbonation reaction to investigate the possibility of functional exchange (*q.v.*, Chapter XVI) between organomagnesium halides and organic halides, as have Kharasch and Fuchs.[30]

St. John and St. John[31] have carbonated the mixtures of Grignard reagents resulting from the treatment of magnesium with mixtures of organic halides, and have so arrived at a rough estimate of the relative reactivities of various halides toward magnesium.

Ivanoff *et al.*[32] have employed carbonation to determine to what extent phenylacetic and related acids undergo reaction 1, to form a Grignard reagent (or enolate[33]), as distinguished from the "normal" reaction 2a. The products of reaction 1 undergo reaction 3 to form phenylmalonic or related acids.

(1) $$RCH_2CO_2MgCl + R'MgX \longrightarrow R'H + [RCH(CO_2MgCl)]^-MgX^+$$

(2a) $$RCH_2CO_2MgCl + R'MgX \longrightarrow RCH_2COR' + ClMgOMgX$$

(2b) $$RCH_2COR' + [RCH(CO_2MgCl)]^-MgX^+ \longrightarrow RCH_2C(OMgX)(R')C(CO_2MgCl)R$$

(3) $$[RCH(CO_2MgCl)]^-MgX^+ \xrightarrow{CO_2} RCH(CO_2MgCl)(CO_2MgX)$$

Taking advantage of the relative rates of carbonation of bornyl- and isobornylmagnesium chlorides, Rivière[34] has employed partial carbonation (*ca.* 66 percent) to remove bornylmagnesium chloride from the mixture of Grignard reagents prepared from pinene hydrochloride, leaving nearly pure isobornylmagnesium chloride.

It is now well-known that there are definite limitations on the use of carbonation as a means toward determination of structure. For instance carbonation cannot be depended upon to distinguish between halomagnesium enolates and true organomagnesium compounds.[35] Several enolate carbonations are recorded in Table XIII-I. Other limitations of the method are discussed in Chapter XVII. Allylic Rearrangements (*q.v.*).

CARBOXYLIC ACIDS AND THEIR SALTS

As was noted in the preceding discussion of carbon dioxide reactions, Grignard (*loc. cit.*[15]) observed that the carboxylates initially formed

[29] Gilman and Jones, *J. Am. Chem. Soc.*, *51*, 2840–3 (1929).

[30] Kharasch and Fuchs, *J. Org. Chem.*, *10*, 292–7 (1945).

[31] St. John and St. John, *Rec. trav. chim.*, *55*, 585–8 (1936).

[32] Ivanoff and Spassoff, *Bull. soc. chim.*, [4], *49*, 19–23, 371–5 (1931); Ivanoff and Pchénitchny, *ibid.*, [5], *1*, 223–33, 233–5 (1934).

[33] See: Schlenk, Hilleman, and Rodloff, *Ann.*, *487*, 135–54 (1931).

[34] Rivière, *Ann. chim.*, [12], *1*, 157–231 (1946).

[35] See, *e.g.*, Kohler and Tishler, *J. Am. Chem. Soc.*, *54*, 1594–600 (1932).

undergo further successive reactions with Grignard reagents to form ketone complexes and tertiary alcoholates. The available data indicate that only in very special cases have these reactions any preparative potentialities. In general the esters may be expected to furnish better yields of tertiary alcohols than the corresponding acids, whereas the acid chlorides may be expected to furnish superior yields of ketones, particularly if one of the special techniques, such as low-temperature operation or cadmium chloride addition, is employed. Perhaps for this reason, the reactions of carboxylic acids and their salts with Grignard reagents have been the object of relatively little study and practically no theoretical investigation. Representative data are collected in Table XIII-II.

Of special interest, however, are the reactions of phenylacetic and related acids (or their salts) with Grignard reagents. Grignard[36] observed that when an ethereal solution of ethylmagnesium bromide (1.5 equivalent) is added to an ethereal suspension of chloromagnesium phenylacetate at 0° an "active hydrogen" displacement occurs with the liberation of ethane.

$$C_6H_5CH_2CO_2MgCl + C_2H_5MgBr \longrightarrow C_6H_5CH(MgBr)CO_2MgCl + C_2H_6$$

Schlenk *et al.*[37] suggest that this reaction should be regarded as a special case of enolization (*q.v.*), and there is much to recommend that point of view, for the resulting magnesium compound behaves in practically all respects like the enolate of acetomesitylene, as the extensive studies of Ivanoff *et al.*[38] have shown.

However, as Ivanoff *et al.* have demonstrated, the enolization reaction is, for some Grignard reagents, at least, competitive with "normal" ketone formation. From reactions of phenyl-, *p*-bromophenyl-, *m*-tolyl- and *p*-tolylmagnesium bromides with chloromagnesium phenylacetate, Ivanoff and Spassoff (*loc. cit.*[38b]) have isolated products which must result from condensation of enolate with ketone.

$$\text{(I)}\quad C_6H_5CH_2CO_2MgCl + C_6H_5MgBr \longrightarrow C_6H_5CH_2COC_6H_5 + BrMgOMgCl$$

$$\text{(II)}\quad C_6H_5CH_2CO_2MgCl + C_6H_5MgBr \longrightarrow [C_6H_5CH(CO_2MgCl)]^-MgBr^+ + C_6H_6$$

$$\text{(III)}\quad C_6H_5CH_2COC_6H_5 + [C_6H_5CH(CO_2MgCl)]^-MgBr^+ \longrightarrow C_6H_5(C_6H_5CH_2)C(OMgBr)CH(CO_2MgCl)C_6H_5 \xrightarrow{2\ H_2O} C_6H_5(C_6H_5CH_2)C(OH)CH(CO_2H)C_6H_5 + MgClOH + MgBrOH$$

---

[36] Grignard, *Bull. soc. chim.*, [3], *31*, 751–7 (1904).

[37] Schlenk, Hilleman, and Rodloff, *Ann.*, *487*, 135–54 (1931).

[38] Ivanoff and Spassoff, (*a*) *Bull. soc. chim.*, [4], *49*, 19–23 (1931); (*b*) [4], *49*, 371–5 (1931); (*c*) [4], *49*, 375–7 (1931); (*d*) [4], *49*, 377–9 (1931); (*e*) [4], *51*, 619–22 (1932); (*f*) Ivanoff, Mihova, and Christova, *ibid.*, [4], *51*, 1321–5 (1932); (*g*) Ivanoff and Nicoloff, *ibid.*, [4], *51*, 1325–31, 1331–7 (1932); (*h*) Ivanoff and Pchénitchny, *ibid.*, [5], *1*, 223–33, 233–5 (1934).

The rates of both the enolization reaction and the "normal" reaction vary with the Grignard reagent employed. Ivanoff and Spassoff (*loc. cit.*[38e]) have measured the rates of gas evolution in the reactions of several aliphatic organomagnesium halides with chloromagnesium phenylacetate and have found them to increase in the order: CH_3MgI, i-C_4H_9MgBr, s-C_4H_9MgBr, n-C_3H_7MgBr, C_2H_5MgBr, i-C_3H_7MgBr.

It has also been shown by Ivanoff and Pchénitchny (*loc. cit.*[38h]) that 3-hexenoïc and styrylacetic acids undergo reactions similar to those of the phenylacetic acids.

According to the observations of McKenzie *et al.*,[39] the α-halo phenylacetic acids react in part like alkyl halides, undergoing coupling to a considerable degree. For example,

$$(-)\text{-}C_6H_5CHClCO_2H + C_6H_5MgBr \longrightarrow \beta\text{-}[C_6H_5CH(CO_2H)\text{—}]_2$$
$$+ (+)\text{-}[C_6H_5CH(CO_2H)\text{—}]_2 + (C_6H_5)_2CHCO_2H$$
$$+ (+)\text{-}C_6H_5CH(OH)C(C_6H_5)_2OH$$

Quite possibly "reductive enolization" (*q.v.*, Chapter VI) is involved in such reactions.

---

[39] McKenzie, Drew, and Martin, *J. Chem. Soc.*, *107*, 26–32 (1915).

TABLE XIII-II

REACTIONS OF GRIGNARD REAGENTS WITH CARBOXYLIC ACIDS AND THEIR SALTS

Acid (or Salt)	RMgX	Product(s)	Ref.
CHO_2			
HCO_2H (10.9 g.)	$C_6H_5CH_2MgCl$ (60 g. C_7H_7Cl)	$C_6H_5CH_2CHO$ (5.3 g.)	*1,2*
C_2O_4			
$(-CO_2H)_2$ (15 g.)	C_6H_5MgBr (105 g. C_6H_5Br)	$C_6H_5COCO_2H$ (trace)	*21*
$C_2HO_2Cl_2$			
Cl_2CHCO_2H (10.0 g.)	C_6H_5MgBr (73.0 g. C_6H_5Br)	$C_6H_5CH(OH)C(C_6H_5)_2OH$ (8.6 g.)	*22*
$C_2H_3O_2$			
CH_3CO_2H	CH_3MgX (3.3 equiv.)	t-C_4H_9OH (4%)	3
CH_3CO_2K	CH_3MgI	t-C_4H_9OH	4
CH_3CO_2H	C_2H_5MgX (3.3 equiv.)	$CH_3(C_2H_5)_2COH$ (32%)	3
CH_3CO_2K	C_2H_5MgBr	$CH_3(C_2H_5)_2COH$	4
$CH_3CO_2NH_4$	C_2H_5MgBr	$CH_3(C_2H_5)_2COH$	4
CH_3CO_2Na (42 g.)	i-C_4H_9MgBr (69 g. C_4H_9Br)	CH_3CO-i-C_4H_9 (25 g., crude)	6
CH_3CO_2Na	t-C_4H_9MgCl	$(CH_3)_2CO$; CH_3CO-t-C_4H_9	5
CH_3CO_2H	n-$C_5H_{11}MgX$ (3.3 equiv.)	$CH_3(n$-$C_5H_{11})_2COH$ (40–60%)*; CH_3CO-n-C_5H_{11} (10–20%)*	3
CH_3CO_2Na (42 g.)	i-$C_5H_{11}MgI$ (99 g. $C_5H_{11}I$)	CH_3CO-i-C_5H_{11} (29 g., crude)	6
CH_3CO_2K	C_6H_5MgBr	$CH_3(C_6H_5)_2COH$	4
CH_3CO_2Na (42 g.)	C_6H_5MgBr (79 g. C_6H_5Br)	$CH_3COC_6H_5$ (30 g., crude)	6
$C_3H_5O_2$			
$C_2H_5CO_2Na$ (48 g.)	C_2H_5MgBr (55 g. C_2H_5Br)	$(C_2H_5)_2CO$ (21 g., crude)	6

* These are the ranges of yields reported for a series of reactions.

TABLE XIII-II (Continued)

Acid (or Salt)	RMgX	Product(s)	Ref.
$C_3H_5O_2$ (*cont.*)			
$C_2H_5CO_2H$	n-$C_5H_{11}MgX$ (3.3 equiv.)	$C_2H_5(n$-$C_5H_{11})_2COH$ (40–60%);* C_2H_5CO-n-C_5H_{11} (10–20%)*	3
$C_4H_4O_3Cl_3$			
DL-$Cl_3CCH(OH)CH_2CO_2H$† (20 g.)	C_6H_5MgBr (75 g. C_6H_5Br)	DL-$Cl_3CCH(OH)CH_2C(C_6H_5)_2OH$ (6 g.)	22
$C_4H_7O_2$			
n-$C_3H_7CO_2H$	CH_3MgX (3.3 equiv.)	n-$C_3H_7(CH_3)_2COH$ (40–60%);* CH_3CO-n-C_3H_7 (10–20%)*	3
n-$C_3H_7CO_2H$	C_2H_5MgX	n-$C_3H_7(C_2H_5)_2COH$ (40–60%);* C_2H_5CO-n-C_3H_7 (10–20%)*	3
n-$C_3H_7CO_2Na$	C_2H_5MgBr	C_2H_5CO-n-C_3H_7 ($\lesssim$25%)	5
n-$C_3H_7CO_2Na$	i-C_3H_7MgBr	$(n$-$C_3H_7)_2CO$	5
n-$C_3H_7CO_2Na$	n-C_4H_9MgBr	n-C_3H_7CO-n-C_4H_9 ($\lesssim$25%)	5
n-$C_3H_7CO_2H$	s-C_4H_9MgBr (3.3 equiv.)	n-C_3H_7CO-s-C_4H_9 (<15%); n-$C_3H_7(s$-$C_4H_9)_2COH$ (<1.%)	3
n-$C_3H_7CO_2Na$	t-C_4H_9MgCl	$(n$-$C_3H_7)_2CO$	5
n-$C_3H_7CO_2H$	t-C_4H_9MgBr (3.3 equiv.)	n-C_3H_7CO-t-C_4H_9 (<2%); n-$C_3H_7(t$-$C_4H_9)_2COH$ (<1%)	3
n-$C_3H_7CO_2H$	n-$C_5H_{11}MgX$ (3.3 equiv.)	n-$C_3H_7(n$-$C_5H_{11})_2COH$ (40–60%);* n-C_3H_7CO-n-C_5H_{11} (10–20%)*	3
n-$C_3H_7CO_2Na$	C_6H_5MgBr	n-$C_3H_7COC_6H_5$ ($\lesssim$25%)	5
i-$C_3H_7CO_2H$	CH_3MgBr	i-$C_3H_7(CH_3)_2COH$	9
i-$C_3H_7CO_2H$	C_2H_5MgX (3.3 equiv.)	i-$C_3H_7(C_2H_5)_2COH$ (53%); C_2H_5CO-i-C_3H_7	3
i-$C_3H_7CO_2H$	C_2H_5MgX (3.3 equiv.)	i-$C_3H_7(C_2H_5)_2COH$ (70%); C_2H_5CO-i-C_3H_7	3

* These are the ranges of yields reported for a series of reactions.

† When the *levo* acid was so treated, no crystalline product was isolated.

TABLE XIII-II (Continued)

Acid (or Salt)	RMgX	Product(s)	Ref.
$C_4H_7O_2$ (*cont.*)			
i-$C_3H_7CO_2H$	n-$C_5H_{11}MgX$ (3.3 equiv.)	i-$C_3H_7(n$-$C_5H_{11})_2COH$ (40–60%);* i-C_3H_7CO-n-C_5H_{11} (10–20%)*	3
$C_5H_4O_3$			
2-Furoic acid (12 g.)	n-C_3H_7MgI (9 g. Mg)	2-n-Butyrylfuran; 1,1-di-α-furyl-1-butanol	19
2-Furoic acid (12 g.)	i-C_4H_9MgI (90 g. C_4H_9I)	2-Isovalerylfuran, 1,1-di-α-furyl-3-methyl-1-butanol; i-$C_4H_9CH=CHCH_2COCO$-i-C_4H_9	19
2-Furoic acid	i-$C_5H_{11}MgI$	2-Isocaproylfuran, 1,1-di-α-furyl-4-methyl-1-pentanol; i-$C_5H_{11}CH=CHCH_2COCO$-i-C_5H_{11}	19
$C_5H_9O_2$			
n-$C_4H_9CO_2H$	CH_3MgX (3.3 equiv.)	n-$C_4H_9(CH_3)_2COH$ (40–60%);* CH_3CO-n-C_4H_9 (10–20%)*	3
n-$C_4H_9CO_2H$	C_2H_5MgX (3.3 equiv.)	n-$C_4H_9(C_2H_5)_2COH$ (40–60%);* C_2H_5CO-n-C_4H_9 (10–20%)*	3
n-$C_4H_9CO_2H$	n-C_4H_9MgX (3.3 equiv.)	$(n$-$C_4H_9)_3COH$ (40–60%);* $(n$-$C_4H_9)_2CO$ (10–20%)*	3
n-$C_4H_9CO_2H$	n-$C_5H_{11}MgX$ (3.3 equiv.)	n-$C_4H_9(n$-$C_5H_{11})_2COH$ (40–60%);* n-C_4H_9CO-n-C_5H_{11} (10–20%)*	3
i-$C_4H_9CO_2Na$	C_2H_5MgBr	C_2H_5CO-i-C_4H_9 ($\overline{<}$25%)	5
i-$C_4H_9CO_2H$	C_2H_5MgX (3.3 equiv.)	i-$C_4H_9(C_2H_5)_2COH$ (40–60%);* C_2H_5CO-i-C_4H_9 (10–20%)*	3
i-$C_4H_9CO_2H$	n-$C_5H_{11}MgX$ (3.3 equiv.)	i-$C_4H_9(n$-$C_5H_{11})_2COH$ (40–60%);* i-C_4H_9CO-n-C_5H_{11} (10–20%)*	3
i-$C_4H_9CO_2MgBr$	i-$C_5H_{11}MgBr$	i-$C_4H_9(i$-$C_5H_{11})_2COH$	7

* These are the ranges of yields reported for a series of reactions.

TABLE XIII-II (Continued)

Acid (or Salt)	RMgX	Product(s)	Ref.
$C_6H_9O_2$			
$C_2H_5CH{=}CHCH_2CO_2H$ (9 g.)	C_6H_5MgBr (37.2 g. C_6H_5)	$C_6H_5(C_2H_5CH{=}CHCH_2)C(OH)CH(CH{=}CHC_2H_5)CO_2H$ (4.5 g. crude)	8
$C_2H_5CH{=}CHCH_2CO_2H$ (11.4 g.)	4-$CH_3C_6H_4MgBr$ (51.3 g. C_7H_7Br)	4-$CH_3C_6H_4(C_2H_5CH{=}CHCH_2)C(OH)CH(CH{=}CHC_2H_5)CO_2H$ (5.5 g., crude)	8
$C_6H_{11}O_2$			
n-$C_5H_{11}CO_2H$	C_2H_5MgX (3.3 equiv.)	n-$C_5H_{11}(C_2H_5)_2COH$ (40–60%);* C_2H_5CO-n-C_5H_{11} (10–20%)*	3
n-$C_5H_{11}CO_2H$	n-$C_5H_{11}MgX$ (3.3 equiv.)	$(n$-$C_5H_{11})_3COH$ (40–60%);* $(n$-$C_5H_{11})_2CO$ (10–20%)*	3
i-$C_5H_{11}CO_2MgBr$ (from 1 mole i-$C_5H_{11}MgBr$)	C_2H_5MgBr (1.5 equiv.)	i-$C_5H_{11}(C_2H_5)_2COH$ (40–45 g.)	7
$C_7H_5O_2$			
$C_6H_5CO_2Na$	CH_3MgBr	$C_6H_5(CH_3)_2COH$	4
$C_6H_5CO_2H$	CH_3MgI	$C_6H_5(CH_3)_2COH$	9
$C_6H_5CO_2MgBr$	C_2H_5MgBr	$C_6H_5(C_2H_5)_2COH$	7
$C_6H_5CO_2H$	C_2H_5MgBr	$C_6H_5(C_2H_5)_2COH$	9
$C_6H_5CO_2Na$	C_2H_5MgI	$C_6H_5(C_2H_5)_2COH$	4
$(C_6H_5CO_2)_2Mg$	C_6H_5MgBr	$(C_6H_5)_2CO$ (35%)	10
$C_8H_2O_4Br_2$			
4,5-$Br_2C_6H_2$-1,2-$(CO_2H)_2$	C_2H_5MgBr (*ca.* 8 equiv.)	3,3-Diethyl-5,6-dibromophthalide; 2-C_2H_5CO-4,5-$Br_2C_6H_2CO_2H$	11

* These are the ranges of yields reported for a series of reactions.

TABLE XIII-II (Continued)

Acid (or Salt)	RMgX	Product(s)	Ref.
$C_8H_4O_4$			
C_6H_4-1,2-$(CO_2H)_2$ (5 g.)	C_2H_5MgBr (30 g., 8 equiv., C_2H_5Br)	3,3-Diethylphthalide (1.5 g.); 2-$C_2H_5COC_6H_4CO_2H$ (1 g.)	*11*
C_6H_4-1,2-$(CO_2H)_2$	*n*-C_3H_7MgBr (*ca.* 8 equiv.)	3,3-Di-*n*-propylphthalide; 2-*n*-$C_3H_7COC_6H_4CO_2H$	*11*
$C_8H_6O_2Br$			
3-$BrC_6H_4CH_2CO_2MgCl$ (0.05 mole acid)	C_6H_5MgBr (0.15 mole C_6H_5Br)	C_6H_5(3-$BrC_6H_5CH_2$)C(OH)CH(C_6H_4-3-Br)CO_2H (4.4 g., crude)	*12*
3-$BrC_6H_4CH_2CO_2MgCl$ (9.5 g. acid)	3-$CH_3C_6H_4MgBr$ (22.5 g. C_7H_7Br)	3-$CH_3C_6H_4$(3-$BrC_6H_4CH_2$)C(OH)CH(C_6H_4-3-Br)CO_2H (4.5 g., crude)	*12*
3-$BrC_6H_4CH_2CO_2MgCl$ (4.6 g. acid)	4-$CH_3C_6H_4MgBr$ (5.1 g. C_7H_7Br)	4-$CH_3C_6H_4$(3-$BrC_6H_4CH_2$)C(OH)CH(C_6H_4-3-Br)CO_2H	*12*
DL-$C_6H_5CHBrCO_2H$ (12.5 g.)	C_6H_5MgBr (37 g., 4 equiv., C_6H_5Br)	$C_6H_5CH(OH)C(C_6H_5)_2OH$; $(C_6H_5)_2CHCO_2H$; β-$[C_6H_5CH(CO_2H)-]_2$ (1.9 g.); α-$[C_6H_5CH(CO_2H)-]_2$ (1.8 g.)	*13*
$C_8H_6O_2Cl$			
3-$ClC_6H_4CH_2CO_2MgCl$ (0.1 mole 3-$ClC_6H_4CH_2Cl$)	C_6H_5MgBr (0.15 mole C_6H_5Br)	C_6H_5(3-$ClC_6H_4CH_2$)C(OH)CH(C_6H_4-3-Cl)CO_2H	*12*
4-$ClC_6H_4CH_2CO_2MgCl$	4-BrC_6H_4MgBr	4-BrC_6H_4(4-$ClC_6H_4CH_2$)C(OH)CH(C_6H_4-4-Cl)CO_2H ("good yield")	*14*
4-$ClC_6H_4CH_2CO_2MgCl$ (0.1 mole 4-$ClC_6H_4CH_2Cl$)	C_6H_5MgBr (0.2 mole)	C_6H_5(4-$ClC_6H_4CH_2$)C(OH)CH(C_6H_4-4-Cl)CO_2H (10 g., 49.8%); 4-$ClC_6H_4CH_2(C_6H_5)_2COH$ (?) (8.5 g.)	*14*
4-$ClC_6H_4CH_2CO_2MgCl$	3-$CH_3C_6H_4MgCl$	3-$CH_3C_6H_4$(4-$ClC_6H_4CH_2$)C(OH)CH(C_6H_4-4-Cl)CO_2H (13.4 g., 64.5%)	*14*
4-$ClC_6H_4CH_2CO_2MgCl$	4-$CH_3C_6H_4MgCl$	4-$CH_3C_6H_4$(4-$ClC_6H_4CH_2$)C(OH)CH(C_6H_4-4-Cl)CO_2H (13.2 g., 63.5%)	*14*

TABLE XIII-II (Continued)

Acid (or Salt)	RMgX	Product(s)	Ref.
$C_8H_6O_2Cl$ (*cont.*)			
DL-$C_6H_5CHClCO_2H$	CH_3MgI (4 equiv.)	β-$[C_6H_5CH(CO_2H)—]_2$; α-$[C_6H_5CH(CO_2H)—]_2$; $C_6H_5CH(OH)CO_2H$; recovered acid	*13*
DL-$C_6H_5CHClCO_2H$	C_6H_5MgBr	$C_6H_5CH(OH)C(C_6H_5)_2OH$ (10–20%); β-$[C_6H_5CH(CO_2H)—]_2$ (5–13%); α-$[C_6H_5CH(CO_2H)—]_2$ (0–1%); $(C_6H_5)_2CHCO_2H$ (1–8%)	*13*
(–)-$C_6H_5CHClCO_2H$ (30 g.)	C_6H_5MgBr (111 g., 4 equiv., C_6H_5Br)	(+)-$C_6H_5CH(OH)C(C_6H_5)_2OH$ (2.2 g., crude; 1.6 g., pure); $(C_6H_5)_2CHCO_2H$ (3.1 g.); β-$[C_6H_5CH(CO_2H)—]_2$ (1 g.); (+)-$[C_6H_5CH(CO_2H)—]_2$ (0.2 g.)	*13*
$C_8H_7O_2$			
$C_6H_5CH_2CO_2MgCl$	C_2H_5MgBr (1.5 equiv.)	$C_6H_5CH(MgBr)CO_2MgCl$; C_2H_6	7
$C_6H_5CH_2CO_2MgCl$ (0.1 mole)	C_6H_5MgBr (0.15 mole)	$C_6H_5(C_6H_5CH_2)C(OH)CH(C_6H_5)CO_2H$ (20.2 g., 61%)	*14*
$C_6H_5CH_2CO_2MgCl$ (0.1 mole)	3-$CH_3C_6H_4MgBr$ (0.15 mole)	3-$CH_3C_6H_4(C_6H_5CH_2)C(OH)CH(C_6H_5)CO_2H$ ("good yield")	*14*
$C_6H_5CH_2CO_2MgCl$ (0.1 mole)	4-$CH_3C_6H_4MgBr$ (0.15 mole)	4-$CH_3C_6H_4(C_6H_5CH_2)C(OH)CH(C_6H_5)CO_2H$ (62.5%)	*14*
$C_8H_7O_3$			
DL-$C_6H_5CH(OH)CO_2^-H_2N(CH_2)_5^+$	C_6H_5MgX * (3–8 equiv.)	DL-$C_6H_5CH(OH)COC_6H_5$; DL-$C_6H_5CH(OH)C(C_6H_5)_2OH$; recovered acid; $(C_6H_5—)_2$	*23*
$C_8H_8O_2N$			
$C_6H_5CH(NH_2)CO_2H$	C_6H_5MgBr (4 equiv.)	Recovered acid	*15*

* X = Br, I.

TABLE XIII-II (Continued)

Acid (or Salt)	RMgX	Product(s)	Ref.
$C_8H_{15}O_2$			
$C_2H_5(n\text{-}C_4H_9)CHCO_2H$ (0.3 mole)	$t\text{-}C_5H_{11}MgCl$ (1.0 mole)	Recovered acid (99%)	*20*
$C_9H_9O_2$			
$2\text{-}CH_3C_6H_4CH_2CO_2MgCl$ (10 g. acid)	C_6H_5MgBr (28 g. C_6H_5Br)	$C_6H_5(2\text{-}CH_3C_6H_4CH_2)C(OH)CH(C_6H_4\text{-}2\text{-}CH_3)CO_2H$ (9.1 g., crude)	*12*
$2\text{-}CH_3C_6H_4CH_2CO_2MgCl$ (10 g. acid)	$3\text{-}CH_3C_6H_4MgBr$ (28 g. C_7H_7Br)	$3\text{-}CH_3C_6H_4(2\text{-}CH_3C_6H_4CH_2)C(OH)CH(C_6H_4\text{-}2\text{-}CH_3)CO_2H$ (8 g., crude)	*12*
$2\text{-}CH_3C_6H_4CH_2CO_2MgCl$ (10 g. acid)	$4\text{-}CH_3C_6H_4MgBr$ (28 g. C_7H_7Br)	$4\text{-}CH_3C_6H_4(2\text{-}CH_3C_6H_4CH_2)C(OH)CH(C_6H_4\text{-}2\text{-}CH_3)CO_2H$ (8.8 g., crude)	*12*
$3\text{-}CH_3C_6H_4CH_2CO_2MgCl$ (0.1 mole $3\text{-}CH_3C_6H_4CH_2Cl$)	C_6H_5MgBr (0.15 mole C_6H_5Br)	$C_6H_5(3\text{-}CH_3C_6H_4CH_2)C(OH)CH(C_6H_4\text{-}3\text{-}CH_3)CO_2H$ (10.2 g., crude)	*12*
$3\text{-}CH_3C_6H_4CH_2CO_2MgCl$ (0.1 mole $3\text{-}CH_3C_6H_4CH_2Cl$)	$3\text{-}CH_3C_6H_4MgBr$ (0.15 mole C_7H_7Br)	$3\text{-}CH_3C_6H_4(3\text{-}CH_3C_6H_4CH_2)C(OH)CH(C_6H_4\text{-}3\text{-}CH_3)CO_2H$ (9.8 g., crude)	*12*
$3\text{-}CH_3C_6H_4CH_2CO_2MgCl$ (0.1 mole $3\text{-}CH_3C_6H_4CH_2Cl$)	$4\text{-}CH_3C_6H_4MgBr$ (0.15 mole C_7H_7Br)	$4\text{-}CH_3C_6H_4(3\text{-}CH_3C_6H_4CH_2)C(OH)CH(C_6H_4\text{-}3\text{-}CH_3)CO_2H$ (9.5 g., crude)	*12*
$4\text{-}CH_3C_6H_4CH_2CO_2MgCl$ (0.1 mole $4\text{-}CH_3C_6H_4CH_2Cl$)	C_6H_5MgBr	$C_6H_5(4\text{-}CH_3C_6H_4CH_2)C(OH)CH(C_6H_4\text{-}4\text{-}CH_3)CO_2H$ (7.3 g., crude)	*12*
$4\text{-}CH_3C_6H_4CH_2CO_2MgCl$ (0.1 mole $4\text{-}CH_3C_6H_4CH_2Cl$)	$3\text{-}CH_3C_6H_4MgBr$ (0.15 mole C_7H_7Br)	$3\text{-}CH_3C_6H_4(4\text{-}CH_3C_6H_4CH_2)C(OH)CH(C_6H_4\text{-}4\text{-}CH_3)CO_2H$ (5.8 g., crude)	*12*
$4\text{-}CH_3C_6H_4CH_2CO_2MgCl$ (0.1 mole $4\text{-}CH_3C_6H_4CH_2Cl$)	$4\text{-}CH_3C_6H_4MgBr$ (0.15 mole C_7H_7Br)	$4\text{-}CH_3C_6H_4(4\text{-}CH_3C_6H_4CH_2)C(OH)CH(C_6H_4\text{-}4\text{-}CH_3)CO_2H$ (5.8 g., crude)	*12*
$C_9H_{10}O_2N$			
DL-$C_6H_5CH_2CH(NH_2)CO_2H$ (3 g.)	C_6H_5MgBr (34 g., 12 equiv., C_6H_5Br)	DL-$C_6H_5CH_2CH(NH_2)C(C_6H_5)_2OH$ (4 g., crude; 2.4 g., pure)	*16*
(+)-$C_6H_5CH_2CH(NH_2)CO_2H$ (3 g.)	C_6H_5MgBr (34 g., 12 equiv., C_6H_5Br)	(+)-$C_6H_5CH_2CH(NH_2)C(C_6H_5)_2OH$ (4.2 g., crude)	*16*

TABLE XIII-II (Continued)

Acid (or Salt)	RMgX	Product(s)	Ref.
$C_9H_{10}O_2N$ (*cont.*)			
$CH_3(C_6H_5)C(NH_2)CO_2H$ (6 g.)	C_6H_5MgBr (71 g., 12 equiv., C_6H_5Br)	$CH_3(C_6H_5)C(NH_2)C(C_6H_5)_2OH$ (5 g., crude; 2 g., pure)	*16*
$C_{10}H_8O_6$			
3,4-$(CH_3O)_2C_6H_2$-1,2-$(CO_2H)_2$ (6.9 g.)	C_2H_5MgBr (*ca.* 8 equiv.)	3,3-Diethyl-4,5-dimethoxyphthalide; 3,3-diethyl-6,7-dimethoxyphthalide; 2-C_2H_5CO-3,4-$(CH_3O)_2C_6H_2CO_2H$; 2,3-$(CH_3O)_2$-6-$C_2H_5COC_6H_2CO_2H$	*11*
$C_{10}H_9O_2$			
$C_6H_5CH{=}CHCH_2CO_2H$ (5 g.)	C_6H_5MgBr (12 g. C_6H_5Br)	$C_6H_5(C_6H_5CH{=}CHCH_2)C(OH)CH(CH{=}CHC_6H_5)CO_2H$ (4.9 g., crude)	*8*
$C_6H_5CH{=}CHCH_2CO_2H$ (5 g.)	3-$CH_3C_6H_4MgBr$ (13.2 g. C_7H_7Br)	3-$CH_3C_6H_4(C_6H_5CH{=}CHCH_2)C(OH)CH(CH{=}CHC_6H_5)CO_2H$ (4.7 g., crude)	*8*
$C_6H_5CH{=}CHCH_2CO_2H$ (2.5 g.)	4-$CH_3C_6H_4MgBr$ (6.6 g. C_7H_7Br)	4-$CH_3C_6H_4(C_6H_5CH{=}CHCH_2)C(OH)CH(CH{=}CHC_6H_5)CO_2H$ (2.2 g., crude)	*8*
$C_{10}H_9O_4$			
2-$H_5C_2O_2CC_6H_4CO_2H$	C_2H_5MgBr	3,3-Diethylphthalide	*17*
2-$H_5C_2O_2CC_6H_4CO_2H$	C_6H_5MgBr (4 equiv.)	"1,1-Diphenyl-3-phenylenephthalan"	*17*
2-$H_5C_2O_2CC_6H_4CO_2H$	$C_6H_5CH_2MgCl$	3,3-Dibenzylphthalide; 1,1-dibenzyl-3-benzylidenephthalan	*17*
$C_{11}H_{13}O_2$			
4-*i*-$C_3H_7C_6H_4CH_2CO_2MgCl$ (10.5 g. 4-*i*-$C_3H_7C_6H_4CH_2Cl$)	C_6H_5MgBr (14.5 g. C_6H_5Br)	C_6H_5(4-*i*-$C_3H_7C_6H_4CH_2$)$C(OH)CH(C_6H_4$-4-*i*-$C_3H_7)CO_2H$ (10.6 g., crude)	*12*
4-*i*-$C_3H_7C_6H_4CH_2CO_2MgCl$ (0.05 mole 4-*i*-$C_3H_7C_6H_4CH_2Cl$)	3-$CH_3C_6H_4MgBr$ (0.075 mole C_7H_7Br)	3-$CH_3C_6H_4$(4-*i*-$C_3H_7C_6H_4CH_2$)$C(OH)CH(C_6H_4$-4-*i*-$C_3H_7)CO_2H$ ("good yield")	*12*

TABLE XIII-II (Continued)

Acid (or Salt)	RMgX	Product(s)	Ref.
$C_{11}H_{13}O_2$ (*cont.*)			
4-*i*-$C_3H_7C_6H_4CH_2CO_2MgCl$	4-$CH_3C_6H_4MgBr$	4-$CH_3C_6H_4$(4-*i*-$C_3H_7C_6H_4CH_2$)C(OH)CH(C_6H_4-4-*i*-C_3H_7)CO_2H	*12*
$C_{11}H_{14}O_2N$			
2-$(C_2H_5)_2NC_6H_4CO_2H$ (30 g.)	C_2H_5MgBr (110 g. C_2H_5Br)	3,3-Diethylphthalide (26 g.)	*18*
$C_{12}H_9O_2$			
2-$C_{10}H_7CH_2CO_2MgCl$ (9 g. acid)	C_6H_5MgBr (23 g. C_6H_5Br)	C_6H_5(β-$C_{10}H_7CH_2$)C(OH)CH(β-$C_{10}H_7$)CO_2H (8.8 g., crude)	*12*
$C_{12}H_{14}O_3N$			
2-$(C_2H_5)_2NOCC_6H_4CO_2H$ (30 g.)	C_2H_5MgBr (110 g. C_2H_5Br)	3,3-Diethylphthalide (26 g., 80%)	*18*
$C_{12}H_{17}O_2$			
β-(1,3,3-Trimethyl-2-cyclohexenyl)acrylic acid	CH_3MgBr	$(C_9H_{15})CH{=}CHC(CH_3)_2OH$	*9*
Sodium β-(1,3,3-trimethyl-2-cyclohexenyl)acrylate	CH_3MgBr	$(C_9H_{15})CH{=}CHC(CH_3)_2OH$	*4*
$C_{12}H_{23}O_2$			
n-$C_{11}H_{23}CO_2Na$	C_2H_5MgBr	C_2H_5CO-*n*-$C_{11}H_{23}$ ($\overline{<}$25%)	*5*

REFERENCES FOR TABLE XIII-II

(*1*) Houben, *Chem.-Ztg.*, *29*, 667 (1905); *J. Chem. Soc.*, *88,I*, 600 (1905).
(*2*) Zelinsky, *Chem.-Ztg.*, *28*, 303 (1904).
(*3*) Huston and Bailey, *J. Am. Chem. Soc.*, *68*, 1382–3 (1946).
(*4*) Friedr. Baeyer & Co., German Patent 166,899, Nov. 13, 1905; *Friedlaender*, 8, 1294–5 (1905–1907).
(*5*) Petrov and Sokolova, *J. Gen. Chem.* (U.S.S.R.), 8, 199–206 (1938); *Chem. Abstr.*, *32*, 5376 (1938).
(*6*) Salkind and Beburischwili, *Ber.*, *42*, 4500–3 (1909).
(*7*) Grignard, *Bull. soc. chim.*, [3], *31*, 751–7 (1904); *Compt. rend.*, *138*, 152–4 (1904); *J. Chem. Soc.*, *86,I*, 213 (1904).
(*8*) Ivanoff and Pchénitchny, *Bull. soc. chim.*, [5], *1*, 233–5 (1934).
(*9*) Friedr. Baeyer & Co., German Patent 166,898, Nov. 13, 1905; *Friedlaender*, 8, 1292–3 (1905–1907).
(*10*) Ivanoff, *Compt. rend.*, *186*, 442–4 (1928); *Chem. Abstr.*, *22*, 3159 (1928).
(*11*) Simonis and Arand, *Ber.*, *42*, 3721–8 (1909).
(*12*) Ivanoff and Pchénitchny, *Bull. soc. chim.*, [5], *1*, 223–33 (1934).
(*13*) McKenzie, Drew, and Martin, *J. Chem. Soc.*, *107*, 26–32 (1915).
(*14*) Ivanoff and Spassoff, *Bull. soc. chim.*, [4], *49*, 371–5 (1931).
(*15*) McKenzie and Richardson, *J. Chem. Soc.*, *123*, 79–91 (1923).
(*16*) McKenzie and Wills, *J. Chem. Soc.*, *127*, 283–95 (1925).
(*17*) Shibata, *J. Chem. Soc.*, *95*, 1449–56 (1909).
(*18*) Maxim, *Ann. chim.*, [10], *9*, 55–111 (1928).
(*19*) Kuznetsov, *J. Gen. Chem.* (U.S.S.R.), *12*, 631–7 (1942). *Chem. Abstr.*, *38*, 1494 (1944).
(*20*) Whitmore, Whitaker, Mosher, Breivik, Wheeler, Miner, Sutherland, Wagner, Clapper, Lewis, Lux, and Popkin, *J. Am. Chem. Soc.*, *63*, 643–54 (1941).
(*21*) McKenzie and Duff, *Ber.*, *60B*, 1335–41 (1927).
(*22*) Boyle, McKenzie, and Mitchell, *Ber.*, *70B*, 2153–60 (1937).
(*23*) McKenzie, Martin, and Rule, *J. Chem. Soc.*, *105*, 1583–91 (1914).

CHAPTER XIV

Reactions of Grignard Reagents with Epoxides*

ETHYLENE OXIDE

The reactions of ethylene oxide with alkylmagnesium bromides were first investigated by Blaise,[1] who concluded that the addition of the reagent to the oxide takes place in two ways, forming RCH_2CH_2OMgBr and $BrCH_2CH_2OMgR$, respectively, with the latter predominating.

Whereas this finding appeared to have a bearing on the Grignard-Baeyer controversy concerning the nature and constitution of Grignard reagent-ether oxonium complexes (see Chapter IV), it was naturally reinvestigated by Grignard.[2] Operating at a temperature of about $-15°$, Grignard added a precooled ether-ethylene oxide solution to a refrigerated ethereal solution of ethylmagnesium bromide. The system was allowed to warm slowly to room temperature, and then to stand for about twenty-four hours. Finally, ether, together with any excess ethylene oxide, was removed by water-bath distillation. Near the completion of the distillation a vigorous exothermic reaction took place. Upon hydrolytic treatment of the product Grignard was able to isolate *n*-butyl alcohol equivalent to about 83 percent of the ethylene oxide used.

Grignard conceived of the reaction as taking place in two "phases": (1) the formation of an oxonium complex analogous to the ether complex previously postulated, and (2) thermal rearrangement of the complex.

$$\begin{array}{l} H_2C \\ \; | \\ H_2C \end{array} \!\!>\! O \!<\! \begin{array}{l} R \\ \\ MgX \end{array} \xrightarrow{\Delta} \begin{array}{l} H_2C - R \\ \;\;| \\ H_2C - OMgX \end{array}$$

Although at that time unaware of the phenomenon now known as the Schlenk equilibrium (see Chapter IV), Grignard attributed bromohydrin formation to reaction of the epoxide with magnesium bromide (arising from the Wurtz side-reaction in the preparation of the Grignard reagent). He accounted for the observation of Blaise on the assumption that under the conditions employed the Grignard reagent-oxide reaction had been substantially arrested in the "first phase."

*The Grignard and other reactions of epoxides have been reviewed by Winstein and Henderson in Chapter I (pp. 1–60), Volume I of Elderfield's "Heterocyclic Compounds," John Wiley & Sons, Inc., New York, *1950*. See also: "The Reaction between Grignard Reagents and the Oxirane Ring," Gaylord and Becker, *Chem. Revs.*, *49*, 413–533 (1950).

[1] Blaise, *Compt. rend.*, *134*, 551–3 (1902); *J. Chem. Soc.*, *82,I*, 357 (1902).

[2] Grignard, *Bull. soc. chim.*, [3], *29*, 944–8 (1903).

Meisenheimer[3] formulated Grignard's initial product as a Werner complex:

$$\begin{array}{c} \quad\quad\quad\quad Br \quad\quad\quad\quad \\ H_2C \quad\quad | \quad\quad C_2H_5 \\ |\rangle O\cdots Mg\cdots O\langle \\ H_2C \quad\quad | \quad\quad C_2H_5 \\ \quad\quad\quad\quad C_2H_5 \quad\quad\quad\quad \end{array}$$

A crystalline precipitate formed at *ca.* $-20°$, however, gave bromine and and magnesium analyses corresponding to $C_2H_5MgBr{\cdot}C_2H_4O{\cdot}1/4\,(C_2H_5)_2O$. His general conclusions were in substantial agreement with those of Grignard.

Ribas and Tapia[4] have shown that even at $-21°$ magnesium bromide reacts readily with epoxides in ethereal solution as described by Grignard (*loc. cit.*[2]),

$$(CH_2)_2O \xrightarrow{MgBr_2} BrCH_2CH_2OMgBr$$

the products being identical with those obtained by treatment of the corresponding bromohydrins with one equivalent of ethylmagnesium bromide.

$$BrCH_2CH_2OH \xrightarrow{C_2H_5MgBr} BrCH_2CH_2OMgBr + C_2H_6$$

They interpret Grignard's first reaction stage as consisting in the formation of insoluble and relatively unreactive $BrCH_2CH_2OMgBr$ by interaction of ethylene oxide with magnesium bromide arising from the Schlenk equilibrium. This product is capable of reacting with a second molecule of ethylene oxide to form a product to which they ascribe the formula $(BrCH_2CH_2O)_2Mg$.

Huston and Agett[5] have found that the initial product of the reaction of ethylmagnesium bromide with ethylene oxide has the empirical formula $C_4H_8Br_2MgO_2$. However, upon hydrolysis, half the bromine present appears in ionic form. Perhaps, as Cottle and Hollyday[6] have suggested, this material is actually a complex of one molecule of ethylene oxide-magnesium bromide reaction product with an additional molecule of ethylene oxide: $BrCH_2CH_2OMgBr{\cdot}O(CH_2)_2$. According to Huston and Agett, neither the Grignard reagent itself nor the dialkylmagnesium compound react appreciably with ethylene oxide until all the magnesium bromide present has reacted. They therefore represent the "normal" reaction of an alkylmagnesium bromide with ethylene oxide as follows:

(1) $2\,RMgBr \rightleftharpoons MgBr_2 + R_2Mg$

(2) $MgBr_2 + 2\,(CH_2)_2O \rightarrow C_4H_8Br_2MgO_2$

(3) $C_4H_8Br_2MgO_2 + R_2Mg \rightarrow (RCH_2CH_2O)_2Mg + MgBr_2$

(4) $(RCH_2CH_2O)_2Mg + 2\,H_2O \rightarrow 2\,RCH_2CH_2OH + Mg(OH)_2$

---

[3]Meisenheimer, *Ann.*, *442*, 180–210 (1925).

[4]Ribas and Tapia, *Anales. soc. españ. fís. quím.*, *28*, 636–44 (1930); *30*, 778–91, 944–70 (1932); *Chem. Abstr.*, *24*, 4265 (1930); *27*, 1323, 1864 (1933).

[5]Huston and Agett, *J. Org. Chem.*, *6*, 123–33 (1941).

[6]Cottle and Hollyday, *J. Org. Chem.*, *12*, 510–6 (1947).

In support of the reaction scheme proposed they cite the additional observations that: (a) $C_4H_8Br_2MgO_2$ from magnesium bromide and ethylene oxide, when suspended in an ethereal solution of ethylmagnesium bromide and heated, gives an excellent yield of *n*-butyl alcohol; (b) $C_4H_8Br_2MgO_2$ from *n*-propylmagnesium bromide and ethylene oxide, when suspended in ethereal di-*n*-amylmagnesium and heated, yields *n*-heptyl alcohol; (c) $C_4H_8Br_2MgO_2$ from *n*-amylmagnesium bromide and ethylene oxide, suspended in di-*n*-propylmagnesium and heated, yields *n*-amyl alcohol; (d) dialkylmagnesium compounds, prepared by the dioxane precipitation method, react at room temperature with two equivalents of ethylene oxide to give good yields of alcohol.

Huston and Langham[7] have observed that when ethylmagnesium chloride is allowed to react with two molecular equivalents of ethylene oxide in cold ethereal solution, calculation of the yields of *n*-butyl alcohol (*ca.* 80 percent) and ethylene chlorohydrin (*ca.* 70 percent) must be based upon the stoichiometrical equations,

$$2\,(CH_2)_2O + MgCl_2 \rightarrow (ClCH_2CH_2O)_2Mg \text{ and}$$
$$2\,(CH_2)_2O + (C_2H_5)_2Mg \rightarrow (n\text{-}C_4H_9O)_2Mg$$

if they are not to aggregate considerably more than 100 percent.

Taken in conjunction with Grignard's[8] earlier observation that β-chloroethoxymagnesium bromide, upon prolonged reflux in ethereal Grignard reagent solutions, or upon heating with Grignard reagents at higher temperatures, reacts to form alcohols according to the equation

$$ClCH_2CH_2OMgBr + RMgX \rightarrow RCH_2CH_2OMgBr + MgXCl$$

these facts seem to afford a fair qualitative picture of the course of ethylene oxide reactions, although the details of reaction mechanism are still obscure.

However, as in the case of the enolization reactions (see Chapter VI, Enolate Formation by Grignard Reagents), it should be possible to recognize some useful analogies between aqueous and Grignard reactions. Brønsted *et al.*[9] conclude from the results of kinetic studies that, in the presence of aqueous hydrochloric acid, ethylene oxide disappears by four different paths:

$$(5) \quad (CH_2)_2O + H_2O \rightarrow (HOCH_2—)_2,$$
$$(6) \quad (CH_2)_2O + H_2O + H_3O^+ \rightarrow (HOCH_2—)_2 + H_3O^+,$$
$$(7) \quad (CH_2)_2O + H_2O + Cl^- \rightarrow HOCH_2CH_2Cl + OH^-,$$
$$(8) \quad (CH_2)_2O + H_3O^+ + Cl^- \rightarrow HOCH_2CH_2Cl + H_2O.$$

Reaction 6 is much more rapid than reaction 5, and reaction 8 is much more rapid than reaction 7. In other words, the epoxide ring-opening is acid-catalyzed.

---

[7]Huston and Langham, *J. Org. Chem.*, *12*, 90–5 (1947).

[8]Grignard, *Compt. rend.*, *141*, 44–6 (1905); *J. Chem. Soc.*, *88*,*I*, 593 (1905); *Bull. soc. chim.*, [3], *33*, 918–9 (1905); *Ann. chim.*, [8], *10*, 23–40 (1905).

[9]Brønsted, Kilpatrick, and Kilpatrick, *J. Am. Chem. Soc.*, *51*, 428–61 (1929).

In magnesium halide cleavage of the epoxide ring (with halohydrinate formation), among the (Lewis) acids present or potentially available are MgX_2 and MgX^+. The formal analogy between equations 8 and 9 (or 10) is obvious.

(9) $(CH_2)_2O + MgX^+ + X^- \rightarrow XMgOCH_2CH_2X$

(10) $(CH_2)_2O + MgX_2 \cdot MgX^+ + X^- \rightarrow XMgCH_2CH_2X + MgX_2$

However, because actual ionic dissociation in media of such low dielectric constants as ethereal epoxide solutions must be very slight indeed, there is strong incentive to seek a plausible concerted reaction mechanism which does not necessarily presuppose material ionic dissociation prior to reaction.* A hypothetical quasi six-membered ring transition state analogous to some of those previously proposed for other reactions might be invoked to that end.

```
      X                    .X.                       X
 H2    \             H2.·     ·.               H2/
   /C   Mg—X           /C       Mg—X             /C     Mg—X
H2C\ |    ··     → H2C\ :       :       →  H2C\          |
   O    X             O.       .X               O       X
  ·· /                  ·.   .·                  \
   Mg                    Mg                        Mg
   |                     |                         |
   X                     X                         X
```

A similar reaction scheme involving XCH_2CH_2OMgX or combinations of XCH_2CH_2OMgX and MgX_2 would account for the high yields of halohydrins obtained in magnesium halide epoxide ring cleavages.

```
      X                              .X.
 H2    \                       H2.·     ·.
   /C   Mg—OCH2CH2X              /C       Mg—OCH2CH2X
H2C\ |    ··             →  H2C\ :        :                →
   O    X                       O.       .X
  ·· /                            ·.   .·
   Mg                              Mg
   |                               |
   OCH2CH2X                        OCH2CH2X

                                           X
                                      H2/
                                        /C      Mg—OCH2CH2X
                                   H2C\          |
                                        O       X
                                         \
                                          Mg
                                          |
                                          OCH2CH2X
```

Extensions of this concept to the postulation of reaction schemes for the formation of alcohols from ethylene oxide and diorganomagnesium compounds, and for the formation of mixtures of halohydrins and alcohols

*There are also stereochemical reasons (to be discussed later) for postulating an intermediate of some structural stability.

from ethylene oxide and the mixture of components commonly designated by the convenient but fictional simplification RMgX are obvious. It should again be emphasized, however, that all such representations are over-simplifications designed merely to outline the minimum essentials of more complicated systems.

It may also be pointed out that, whereas the acids which facilitate epoxide ring-opening by coördination with the epoxide oxygen are themselves consumed in the resultant transformations, these processes are not "acid-catalyzed" in the classical sense of the term. Perhaps it might be said with propriety that the epoxide is "acid-activated," or that the reaction is "acid-induced" or "acid-expedited."

EPOXIDE ISOMERIZATION

Reactions yielding alcohols in which both the hydroxyl group and the organic radical of the Grignard reagent are attached to the same carbon atom were early observed by Tiffeneau[10,11,12], and by Henry.[13]

$$(H_3C)(H_5C_6)C\overset{O}{—}CH_2 \xrightarrow{C_6H_5MgBr} CH_3(C_6H_5)CHCH(OH)C_6H_5 \quad \text{(Ref. 10)}$$

$$(H_3C)(H_5C_2)C\overset{O}{—}CH_2 \xrightarrow{C_2H_5MgBr} CH_3(C_2H_5)CHCH(OH)C_2H_5 \quad \text{(Ref. 11)}$$

$$(H)(H_5C_6)C\overset{O}{—}CH_2 \xrightarrow{RMgX} C_6H_5CH_2CHROH \quad \text{(Ref. 12)}$$

$$(H_3C)(H_3C)C\overset{O}{—}CH_2 \xrightarrow{CH_3MgBr} CH_3(i\text{-}C_3H_7)CHOH \quad \text{(Ref. 13)}$$

$$(H)(H_3C)C\overset{O}{—}C(H)(CH_3) \xrightarrow{CH_3MgBr} C_2H_5(CH_3)_2COH\ (44\%)$$

$$+\ CH_3(i\text{-}C_3H_7)CHOH\ (7\%) \quad \text{(Ref. 13)}$$

Other examples are recorded in Table XIV-I.

The only plausible explanation for these reactions would appear to be that offered by Henry (*loc. cit.*[13]); namely, that the epoxides are isomerized to the corresponding aldehydes (or ketones), and react as such.

Of the numerous reported instances of the magnesium (or zinc) halide isomerization of epoxides, the following examples may serve as representative.

---

[10] Tiffeneau, *Compt. rend.*, *140*, 1458–60 (1905); *Chem. Zentr.*, *1905,II*, 235.

[11] Fourneau and Tiffeneau, *Compt. rend.*, *145*, 437–9 (1907); *Chem. Zentr.*, *1907,II*, 1320.

[12] Tiffeneau and Fourneau, *Compt. rend.*, *146*, 677–9 (1908); *Chem. Zentr.*, *1908,I*, 1776.

[13] Henry, *Compt. rend.*, *145*, (*a*) 21–5, (*b*) 154–6, (*c*) 406–8 (1907); *Chem. Zentr.*, *1907,II*, 1320; *J. Chem. Soc.*, *92,I*, 745 (1907).

$$\underset{H_5C_6}{\overset{H}{>}}C\underset{O}{\frown}C\underset{CH=CH_2}{\overset{CH_3}{<}} \xrightarrow{MgBr_2} CH_3(H_2C=CH)(C_6H_5)CCHO \quad \text{(Ref. 14)}$$

$$\underset{H_5C_6}{\overset{H}{>}}C\underset{O}{\frown}C\underset{CH_3}{\overset{CH_3}{<}} \xrightarrow{MgBr_2} C_6H_5(CH_3)_2CCHO\ (90\%)$$

$$+ CH_3COCH(CH_3)C_6H_5 \text{ ("a little")} \quad \text{(Ref. 15)}$$

$$\underset{H_3C}{\overset{H_3C}{>}}C\underset{O}{\frown}C\underset{CH=CH_2}{\overset{H}{<}} \xrightarrow{MgBr_2} H_2C=CH(CH_3)_2CCHO \quad \text{(Ref. 16)}$$

$$\underset{H_5C_6}{\overset{H}{>}}C\underset{O}{\frown}C\underset{CH=CH_2}{\overset{H}{<}} \xrightarrow{MgBr_2} CH_3CH=C(C_6H_5)CHO^* \quad \text{(Ref. 17)}$$

$$\underset{H_5C_6}{\overset{H}{>}}C\underset{O}{\frown}C\underset{C_6H_9}{\overset{H}{<}} \xrightarrow{MgBr_2} C_6H_5(C_6H_9)CHCHO^{\dagger} \quad \text{(Ref. 18)}$$

$$\underset{H_5C_6}{\overset{H}{>}}C\underset{O}{\frown}C\underset{CH(CH_2)_5}{\overset{H}{<}} \xrightarrow{MgBr_2} C_6H_5CH_2COCH(CH_2)_5 \quad \text{(Ref. 18)}$$

$$(CH_2)_5C\underset{O}{\frown}CH_2 \xrightarrow[\text{or } ZnCl_2]{MgBr_2} (CH_2)_5CHCHO \quad \text{(Ref. 19)}$$

Cyclohexene oxide $\xrightarrow{MgBr_2}$ $(CH_2)_4CHCHO$ (Refs. *20, 21*)

Indene oxide $\xrightarrow{MgBr_2}$ 2-Indanone (Ref. *22*)

1,2-Dihydronaphthalene oxide $\xrightarrow{MgBr_2}$ β-Tetralone (Ref. *22*)

1,4-Dihydronaphthalene oxide $\xrightarrow{MgBr_2}$ 2-Indancarboxaldehyde + β-tetralone (Ref. *22*)

α-Pinene oxide $\xrightarrow{ZnBr_2}$ Campholenic aldehyde (62.5%) (Ref. *23*)

---

[14] Deux, *Compt. rend.*, *206*, 1017–9 (1938); *Chem. Abstr.*, *32*, 4965 (1938).

[15] Poctivas and Tchoubar, *Compt. rend.*, *205*, 287–8 (1937); *Chem. Abstr.*, *31*, 7853 (1937).

[16] Deux, *Compt. rend.*, *209*, 920–1 (1938); *Chem. Abstr.*, *33*, 1660 (1939).

*The product reported is "phenylcrotonaldehyde," which implies a double-bond shift as well as a hydrobenzoïn-type rearrangement. The isocrotonaldehydes are apparently unstable.

[17] Deux, *Compt. rend.*, *211*, 441–3 (1940); *Chem. Abstr.*, *36*, 1307 (1942).

†C_6H_9 = 1-cyclohexenyl.

[18] Tiffeneau and Kuriaki, *Compt. rend.*, *209*, 465–8 (1939); *Chem. Abstr.*, *34*, 731 (1940).

[19] Tiffeneau, Weill, and Tchoubar, *Compt. rend.*, *205*, 54–6 (1937); *Chem. Abstr.*, *31*, 7409 (1937).

[20] Bedos, *Compt. rend.*, *189*, 255–7 (1929); *Chem. Abstr.*, *24*, 76 (1930).

[21] Clemo and Ormston, *J. Chem. Soc.*, *1933*, 362.

[22] Tchoubar, *Compt. rend.*, *214*, 117–9 (1942); *Chem. Abstr.*, 37, 3427 (1943).

[23] Ritter and Russel, *J. Am. Chem. Soc.*, 58, 291–3 (1936).

$$\text{Nopinene oxide}^{*} \xrightarrow[\text{or } ZnCl_2]{ZnBr_2} \text{Dihydromyrtenal} \qquad \text{(Ref. 24)}$$

$$\text{Camphene oxide} \xrightarrow{ZnBr_2} \text{Campholenaldehyde (80\%)} \qquad \text{(Ref. 24)}$$

All these reactions appear to be truly acid-catalyzed in the Lewis sense, although it may be necessary to supply one equivalent or more of catalyst because of complex formation between product and catalyst.

It is commonly assumed: (*a*) that the simpler epoxides (*e.g.*, ethylene oxide, α-epichlorohydrin, and propylene oxide) have little or no tendency to rearrange, and (*b*) that rearrangement of the more complex epoxides is effected solely or principally by the MgX_2 component of the Grignard reagent. From a practical quantitative standpoint these assumptions are not seriously in error. As implying fundamental distinctions of kind rather than of degree, however, they are to be taken *cum grano salis*. In illustration, Cottle and Hollyday (*loc. cit.*[6]), in a preparation involving fairly large quantities of ethylene oxide (11.33 moles) and di-*n*-butylmagnesium (4.20 moles), isolated, in addition to a 43.5 percent yield of 1-hexanol (the "normal" product), an 0.8 percent yield of 2-hexanol, which must have had its origin in isomerization of the oxide to acetaldehyde.

Although the mechanisms of the epoxide reactions are not actually known, it would seem reasonable to suppose that, if the addition reactions (halohydrinate and alcoholate formation) are trimolecular, the isomerization reactions are probably bimolecular. This supposition is consistent with the observation of Kharasch and Clapp[25] that the predominant product of the interaction of styrene oxide with phenylmagnesium bromide depends upon the order of reagent addition. When the oxide is added gradually to the Grignard reagent, so that most of the reaction takes place in the presence of an excess of Grignard reagent, the "normal" addition reaction (presumably requiring two molecules of Grignard reagent components per molecule of oxide) yields the predominant product, 2,2-diphenylethanol. When, however, the reverse addition is employed, so that most of the reaction takes place in the presence of an excess of oxide, the major product is the alcohol (1,2-diphenylethanol) arising from the presumably bimolecular isomerization.†

FACTORS INFLUENCING DIRECTION OF RING-OPENING

Both the addition reactions (halohydrinate and alcoholate formation) and the isomerization reactions (aldehyde or ketone formation) involve the opening of the oxirane ring. For the unsymmetrical epoxides it be-

* β-Pinene oxide.

[24]Arbuzov, *J. Gen. Chem.* (U.S.S.R.), 9, 255–71 (1939); *Chem. Abstr.*, 33, 6280 (1939).

[25]Kharasch and Clapp, *J. Org. Chem.*, 3, 355–60 (1938).

†It may be noted that in this particular instance the product in question could conceivably arise from a "normal" addition reaction in which the direction of ring-opening is reversed. It is difficult, however, to conjure up any plausible explanation as to how reversal of the order of reagent addition could reverse the direction of ring-opening.

comes a matter of some interest to determine whether or not the direction of ring opening can be accounted for on acceptable theoretical grounds that permit extension to the confident prediction of behavior in cases as yet unknown. Because the two types of reactions are fundamentally dissimilar it is necessary to consider them separately.

Ring-Opening in Isomerizations. For the sake of simplicity, and because of the greater abundance of relevant experimental evidence this discussion is limited to rearrangements of the hydrobenzoïn type.* Upon a purely statistical basis it might be concluded that the tendency is for the rearrangement, whenever possible, to take a course leading to aldehyde formation in preference to ketone formation. At best such a generalization would be empirical, and it encounters at least one glaring exception in the magnesium bromide isomerization of α-phenyl-β-cyclohexylethylene oxide to form cyclohexyl benzyl ketone rather than phenylcyclohexylacetaldehyde (Ref. *18*).

Attempts have been made to relate the courses of such rearrangements to the relative migratory aptitudes of the transient groups, or to the converse property—the relative "affinities" of the non-transient groups. It has been estimated that relative migratory aptitudes run in the order: $C_6H_5 > H_2C{=}CH > H > CH_3 >$ higher alkyl groups. Deux (*loc. cit.*[14]) states that the "affinities" of the methyl and vinyl groups are superior to that of the phenyl group, and thus seeks to account for the magnesium bromide isomerization of 3-methyl-3,4-epoxy-4-phenyl-1-butene to form 2-methyl-2-phenyl-3-butenal rather than 4-phenyl-1-penten-3-one or 3-phenyl-4-penten-2-one.

The present authors believe, however, that the most promising approach to a solution of this problem is by way of a variation of the Whitmore mechanism[26] for the pinacol, hydrobenzoïn, and related intramolecular rearrangements.[27] Although it seems probable that the processes involved in such rearrangements may be simultaneous rather than successive, it is convenient for expository purposes to divide them into stages.

The first, and primarily directive, stage in the (Lewis) acid-catalyzed rearrangement of an epoxide may be conceived of as the scission of one of the carbon-oxygen bonds of the oxirane ring.

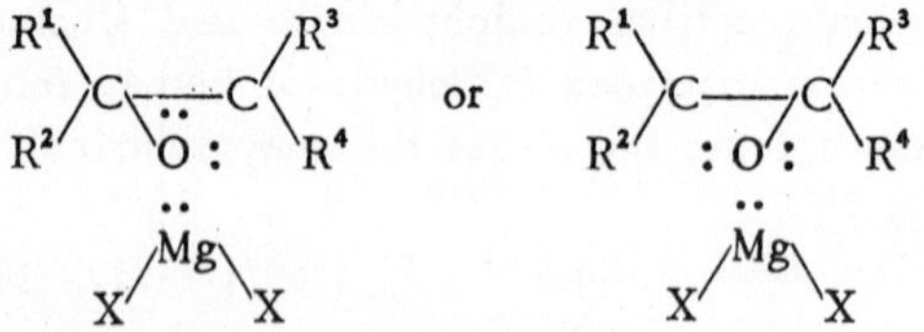

```
R¹        R³               R¹        R³
  \      /                   \      /
   C----C          or         C----C
  / \  .. \                  /        \
R²   O :   R⁴              R²   : O :  R⁴
     ..                           ..
     Mg                           Mg
    /  \                         /  \
   X    X                       X    X
```

*See: Porter, "Molecular Rearrangements," A.C.S. Monograph Series, The Chemical Catalog Co., Inc., New York, *1928*, pp. 106*ff*.

[26]Whitmore, *J. Am. Chem. Soc.*, *54*, 3274–83 (1932).

[27]For an excellent and well-documented discussion of the mechanims of such rearrangements see: Wheland, "Advanced Organic Chemistry," John Wiley & Sons, Inc., New York, 2nd ed., *1949*, pp. 475*ff*.

At this stage the *alpha* carbon atom (that from which the oxygen atom is detached) would remain with an "open sextet" of valence electrons. According to the Kharasch "electronegativity" theory,[28] the relatively electron-deficient carbon atom of the oxirane ring should become the *alpha* carbon atom. When as many as two of the R groups are hydrogen atoms and the other two are *gem* hydrocarbon radicals, or when one R group is a hydrogen atom and the other three are identical hydrocarbon radicals, no difficulty need be experienced in predicting the direction of ring-opening.

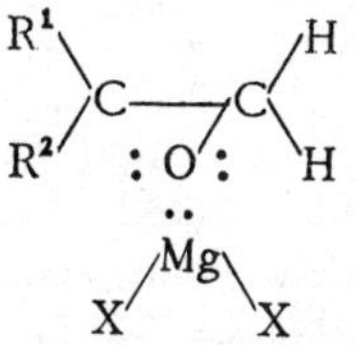

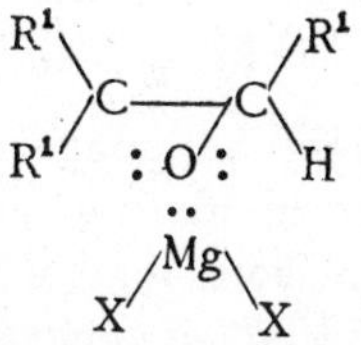

```
R¹\        /H          R¹\        /R¹
   >C——C<                 >C——C<
R²/ :O: \H             R¹/ :O: \H
     ··                      ··
     Mg                      Mg
   X/  \X                  X/  \X
```

In the case of the unsymmetrically α,β-disubstituted oxirane, that carbon atom which bears the more "electronegative" substituent will become the *alpha* carbon atom; *i.e.*, if R^1 is more "electronegative" than R^2, the following diagrams will apply to the formation of the preponderant product.

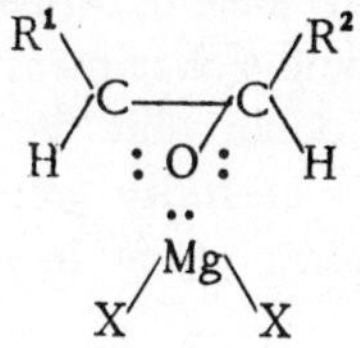

```
R¹\        /R²            R¹\        /H
   >C——C<          or        >C——C<
H/  :O: \H                H/  :O: \R²
     ··                         ··
     Mg                         Mg
   X/  \X                     X/  \X
```

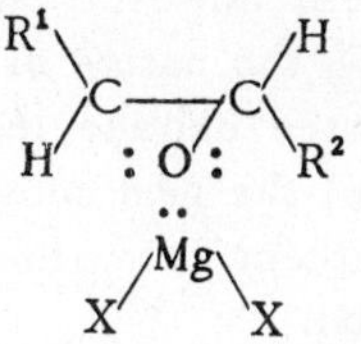

When R^1 and R^2 differ but little in "electronegativity" the product ratio may approach 50 : 50, but as the disparity in relative "electronegativities" increases it should approach 100 : 0. An abbreviated series of radicals in the order of decreasing "electronegativity" on the Kharasch scale follows: p-$CH_3OC_6H_4$ > p-$CH_3C_6H_4$ > C_6H_5 > $H_2C{=}CH$* > CH_3 > C_2H_5 > i-C_3H_7 > $C_6H_5CH_2$ > t-C_4H_9.

That upon the primary electronic effect thus hypothesized there may be superimposed a relatively minor secondary effect is suggested by the case of the heterotrisubstituted oxirane 1-phenyl-2-methyl-1,2-epoxypropane. Although it might be inferred from the above "electronegativity" series that one phenyl radical is slightly more effective than two methyl

[28] Concerning the electronegativity theory and the relative electronegativities of organic radicals, see: Kharasch and Reinmuth, *J. Chem. Education*, *5*, 404–18 (1928); *8*, 1703–48 (1931); Kharasch, Reinmuth, and Mayo, *ibid.*, *11*, 82–96 (1934); *13*, 7–19 (1936).

*The relative "electronegativities" of groups capable of associating a proton cannot be determined experimentally by the Kharasch technique [see Kharasch and Swartz, *J. Org. Chem.*, *3*, 405–8 (1938)]. A considerable variety of qualitative chemical evidence, however, suggests that the vinyl radical is probably very close to, but slightly lower than, the phenyl radical in "electronegativity."

radicals (i-C_3H_7 > $C_6H_5CH_2$) in decreasing the electron density about a substituted carbon atom, this epoxide when treated with magnesium bromide yields about 90 percent of α-methyl-α-phenylpropionaldehyde and only a little 3-phenylbutanone (Ref. *15*).

$$\begin{array}{c} C_6H_5 \quad\quad CH_3 \\ \diagdown C \overset{\cdot\cdot}{—} C \diagup \\ H \diagup \; \diagdown \ddot{O} : \diagup \; \diagdown CH_3 \\ \vdots \\ Mg \\ X \diagup \quad \diagdown X \end{array}$$

Although it might be suggested that the methyl radical is a more potent substituent in olefinic and closely related systems than in the methane series, a more logical explanation would seem to be that the rearrangement is in fact a concerted coincidence, rather than a series, of processes, and that, whereas the substituent effect of a phenyl radical differs but little from that of two methyl radicals, the potential migratory aptitude of the phenyl group is considerably greater than that of a methyl group.

In many cases, however, as in that of 3-methyl-4-phenyl-3,4-epoxybutene (Ref. *14*), the nature of the individual substituent radicals of the heterotrisubstituted oxirane leaves little doubt that the aggregate substituent effect of the *gem* substituents is materially greater than that of the lone substituent, and ring-opening takes place in the readily predictable direction.

$$\begin{array}{c} C_6H_5 \quad\quad CH{=}CH_2 \\ \diagdown C \overset{\cdot\cdot}{—} C \diagup \\ H \diagup \; \diagdown \ddot{O} : \diagup \; \diagdown CH_3 \\ \vdots \\ Mg \\ X \diagup \quad \diagdown X \end{array}$$

That which we have arbitrarily chosen to call the second stage of the reaction is directed in part (but only in part) by the property which we have chosen to call the "potential migratory aptitude" of the transitive group. Here a definitive statement is in order. It is obvious from the foregoing discussion of the so-called first stage of the epoxide rearrangement that any attempt to establish an order of relative group migratory aptitudes by merely observing which group migrates in these or analogous (*e.g.*, pinacol, hydrobenzoïn) rearrangements is foredoomed to encounter the most embarrassing inconsistencies. Superficially it might appear that having duly regarded the so-called first stage of the reaction, and having thus automatically eliminated from consideration half of the potential migrants, it might be possible to establish an order of migratory aptitudes by observing, in a sufficient number of cases, which of two remaining eligible groups actually does migrate. Analogous observations have been made in the closely related rearrangements of symmetrical pinacols of the type [ArAr′C(OH)—]$_2$, notably by Bachmann.[29]

It is true that in this manner much more self-consistent orderings of groups can be attained, and that upon them much more reliable predictions of group behavior can be based. It is to the property (or, to be more precise, the combination of properties) involved that Wheland has chosen to apply the term "intrinsic migratory aptitude." In the opinion of the present authors this choice is unfortunate because the migratory behavior of a group in such rearrangements is dependent on properties not exclusively its own. A better term would be "effective migratory aptitude" (with reference to a specific reaction).

To particularize, a group migration involves both a "take-off" and a "landing." It is only for the first of these that aptitude can be related to an intrinsic property of the migratory group. Whereas these rearrangements involve the transfer of a pair of electrons from the *beta* to the *alpha* carbon atom, it follows that the group which has the greater tendency to accompany the electron pair is the more "electronegative" of the two potential migrants. It is to this tendency that the present authors would have preferred to apply the term "intrinsic migratory aptitude"; for second choice, they adopt the term "potential migratory aptitude."

However, *effective* migratory aptitude entails facility in both "take-off" and "landing." The latter is determined by what may be loosely called the relative "sizes" of the migrant and the "landing-field." In more conventional, though less specific, language, the course of such a process is so strongly influenced by steric factors that energetic factors are often reduced to a secondary (and sometimes a negligible) rôle. This accounts for the relatively high effective migratory aptitude of hydrogen (which must have a relatively low potential migratory aptitude), and for the relatively low effective migratory aptitudes of the *m*- and *o*-anisyl groups (which must have nearly as high potential migratory aptitudes as has the *p*-anisyl group).

Parenthetically, the working hypothesis proposed implies that if steric screening of the "landing-field" could be eliminated or minimized the *effective* migratory aptitude of a group (with respect to the test reaction) would equal or approximate its true *potential* migratory aptitude. The prescribed condition is met, or closely approached, in rearrangements of carbonium ions of the types $[RR'R''CO]^+$ and $[RR'_2CO]^+$, generated in the acid-catalyzed decompositions of tertiary aralkyl hydroperoxides, and the course of rearrangement is consistent with the implication stated, as has been demonstrated by Kharasch *et al.*[30]

---

[29] Bachmann and Moser, *J. Am. Chem. Soc.*, *54*, 1124–33 (1932); Bachmann and Ferguson, *ibid.*, *56*, 2081–4 (1934). See also: Wheland, *op. cit.*,[27] p. 515; Adkins, Chapter 13 of Volume I of Gilman's "Organic Chemistry," John Wiley & Sons, Inc., New York, 2nd ed., *1943*, p. 1067; Wallis, Chapter 12 of Volume I of Gilman's "Organic Chemistry," p. 969.

[30] Kharasch, Fono, Nudenberg, and Poshkus, *J. Org. Chem.*, *15*, 775–81 (1951).

For example:

$$o\text{-}CH_3C_6H_4(C_6H_5)_2COOH \xrightarrow[HAc]{H^+} H_2O + [o\text{-}CH_3C_6H_4(C_6H_5)_2CO]^+$$

$$[o\text{-}CH_3C_6H_4(C_6H_5)_2CO]^+ \longrightarrow [o\text{-}CH_3C_6H_4O(C_6H_5)_2C]^+$$

$$[o\text{-}CH_3C_6H_4O(C_6H_5)_2C]^+ + o\text{-}CH_3C_6H_4(C_6H_5)_2COOH \rightarrow$$
$$o\text{-}CH_3C_6H_4OH\ (80\%) + (C_6H_5)_2CO\ (56\%) + [o\text{-}CH_3C_6H_4(C_6H_5)_2CO]^+$$

and

$$o\text{-}CH_3OC_6H_4(C_6H_5)_2COOH \xrightarrow[HAc]{H^+} H_2O + [o\text{-}CH_3OC_6H_4(C_6H_5)_2CO]^+$$

$$[o\text{-}CH_3OC_6H_4(C_6H_5)_2CO]^+ \longrightarrow [o\text{-}CH_3C_6H_4O(C_6H_5)_2C]^+$$

$$[o\text{-}CH_3OC_6H_4O(C_6H_5)_2C]^+ + o\text{-}CH_3OC_6H_4(C_6H_5)_2COOH \rightarrow$$
$$o\text{-}CH_3OC_6H_4OH\ (60\%) + (C_6H_5)_2CO\ (75\%) + o\text{-}CH_3OC_6H_4COC_6H_5\ (10\%)$$
$$+ [o\text{-}CH_3OC_6H_4(C_6H_5)_2CO]^+$$

All such working hypotheses relating to relative migratory aptitudes implicitly presuppose that the preferred migration shall yield a stable, or readily stabilizable, product or intermediate. When this is not the case, the less-favored migration may yield a stable product that is superficially misleading [*cf.* Kharasch *et al.*[31] concerning the dehydration-rearrangement of $HO(C_6H_5)_2CC(CH_3)_2C_6H_5$].

Incidentally, it may here be noted that rearrangements of the general 1,2 carbon-to-carbon type under discussion all presumably involve a Walden inversion of the *alpha* carbon atom. In one case of semipinacolic deamination the *vic* amino alcohol and corresponding ketone have been shown to be of opposite configurations.[32]

$$(-)\text{-}HO(C_6H_5)_2CCH(NH_2)CH_3 \xrightarrow{HNO_2} (+)\text{-}C_6H_5COCH(CH_3)C_6H_5$$

This retention of optical activity (with inversion) argues strongly in favor of a reaction mechanism involving a concerted coincidence of processes rather than a more or less disconnected sequence of processes. Such a mechanism might be schematically represented as follows.

$$R^1R^2C\overset{O(:MgX_2)}{—}CR^3R^4 \rightarrow R^1R^2C\cdots(R^3)\cdots O(:MgX_2)\cdots C—R^4 \rightarrow R^1—\underset{R^2}{\overset{R^3}{C}}—\underset{O:MgX_2}{\overset{}{C}}—R^4$$

To the further confusion of lovers of the simple solution and the easy generalization it has recently been realized (and demonstrated) that compounds in which both the *alpha* and the *beta* carbon atoms are asymmetric may undergo stereospecific rearrangement (at least in some degree).

[31] Kharasch, Poshkus, Fono, and Nudenberg, *J. Org. Chem.*, *16*, 1458–70 (1951).
[32] Bernstein and Whitmore, *J. Am. Chem. Soc.*, *61*, 1324–6 (1939).

This has been demonstrated for the semipinacolic deaminations of the racemic *alpha* and *beta* forms of several *vic* amino alcohols by Curtin *et al.*,[33] *e.g.*:

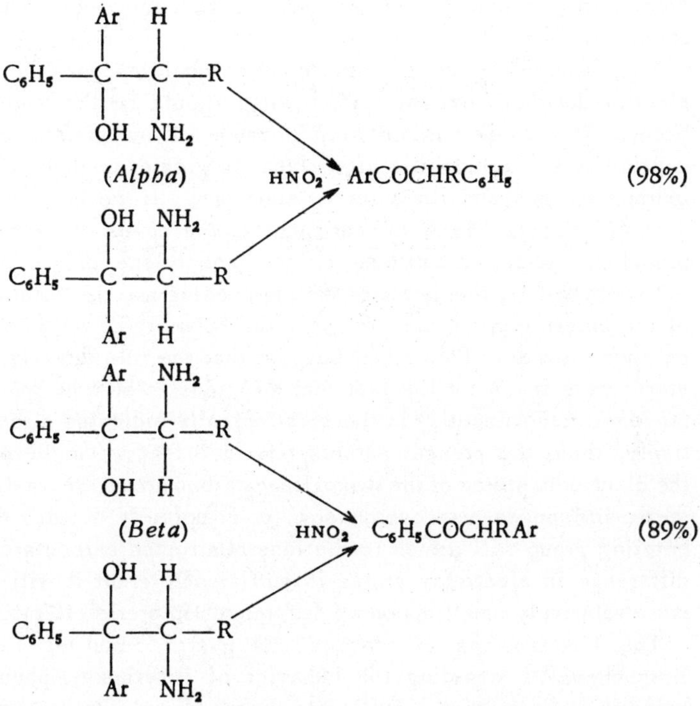

$$\begin{array}{c} \text{Ar}\quad \text{H} \\ | \qquad | \\ C_6H_5-\text{C}-\text{C}-\text{R} \\ | \qquad | \\ \text{OH}\quad NH_2 \end{array}$$

(*Alpha*) $\xrightarrow{HNO_2}$ $ArCOCHRC_6H_5$ (98%)

$$\begin{array}{c} \text{OH}\quad NH_2 \\ | \qquad | \\ C_6H_5-\text{C}-\text{C}-\text{R} \\ | \qquad | \\ \text{Ar}\quad \text{H} \end{array}$$

$$\begin{array}{c} \text{Ar}\quad NH_2 \\ | \qquad | \\ C_6H_5-\text{C}-\text{C}-\text{R} \\ | \qquad | \\ \text{OH}\quad \text{H} \end{array}$$

(*Beta*) $\xrightarrow{HNO_2}$ $C_6H_5COCHRAr$ (89%)

$$\begin{array}{c} \text{OH}\quad \text{H} \\ | \qquad | \\ C_6H_5-\text{C}-\text{C}-\text{R} \\ | \qquad | \\ \text{Ar}\quad NH_2 \end{array}$$

At the present writing a significant degree of stereospecificity in the Grignard isomerizations of epoxides has not been demonstrated. Alexander,[34] however, has shown that there is at least perceptible stereospecificity in the closely related phosphoric acid-catalyzed isomerizations of the *cis*- and *trans*-β-butylene oxides, as well as in the analogous rearrangements of the related *meso*- and DL-2,3-butanediols and the *erythro*- and *threo*-3-chloro-2-butanols.

$$trans\text{-}\beta\text{-Butylene oxide} \xrightarrow{H^+} CH_3COC_2H_5\ (26.3\text{–}33.0\%) + i\text{-}C_3H_7CHO\ (8.6\text{–}11.0\%)$$

$$cis\text{-}\beta\text{-Butylene oxide} \xrightarrow{H^+} CH_3COC_2H_5\ (53.8\%) + i\text{-}C_3H_7CHO\ (4.1\%)$$

Ring-Opening in Additions. The reader who has followed the foregoing discussion of the Grignard isomerizations of epoxides has perceived that in non-stereospecific cases the task of predicting the course of a reaction is considerably simplified by the fact that (except in readily recognizable border-line instances) the question of the direction

[33]Pollak and Curtin, *J. Am. Chem. Soc.*, 72, 961–5 (1950); Curtin and Pollak, *ibid.*, 73, 992–4 (1951); Curtin, Harris, and Pollak, *ibid.*, 73, 3453–4 (1951).
[34]Alexander and Dittmer, *J. Am. Chem. Soc.*, 73, 1665–8 (1951).

of ring-opening may be treated independently of the question of the natures of the migratory group and of the locus of its ultimate attachment. Unfortunately no such simplification is possible in attempts to predict the courses of the Grignard addition reactions of unsymmetrical epoxides.

From a purely electronic standpoint it would appear that the relatively electron-deficient oxirane carbon atom should be the more disposed to become the *alpha* carbon, both because of its greater potential susceptibility to nucleophilic attack and its greater tendency to release the oxirane oxygen and its octet of electrons. However, the experimental data (see Table XIV-I) indicate that in the cases of α-epichlorohydrin, propylene oxide, α-butylene oxide, isobutylene oxide, and 2-methyl-2,3-epoxybutane, the direction of ring-opening and the point of attachment of the entering group are precisely the opposite of those to be expected on such grounds. This might suggest that the true directive influence is steric were it not for the fact that additions to styrene oxide take place (at least predominantly) in the electronically-indicated direction. Tentatively, then, the present authors conclude that when the differences in the electronic states of the two oxirane carbon atoms are small or moderate, steric influences may overshadow (or completely negate) them, and the entering group will attach to the less obstructed carbon atom. When the difference in electronic states is sufficiently great it will tend to overcome relatively small opposing differences in steric effect.

The observations of Stevens and Pratt[34.1] and of Temnikova and Kropacheva[34.2] regarding the behavior of 1-methoxy-1-phenyl-1,2-epoxypropane indicate that a sufficient degree of polarity in the oxirane ring system may overcome a relatively high degree of steric inhibition.

$$(H_3CO)(H_5C_6)C\overset{O}{—}CH(CH_3) \xrightarrow{CH_3MgI} H_5C_6—C(OCH_3)(CH_3)—CH(CH_3)(OH) \quad (85\%)$$

$$(H_3CO)(H_5C_6)C\overset{O}{—}CH(CH_3) \xrightarrow{C_6H_5MgBr} H_5C_6—C(OCH_3)(C_6H_5)—CH(CH_3)(OH) \quad (88\%)$$

It goes without saying, of course, that the foregoing discussion relates to *predominant* rather than *exclusive* product formation. Undoubtedly, sufficiently skillful and careful reëxamination of many of the reactions recorded in Table XIV-I would reveal the formation of two addition products where only one is now reported.

[34.1] Stevens and Pratt, Abstracts of Papers, 119th Meeting, A.C.S., Cleveland, Ohio, April, 1951, p. 92M.

[34.2] Temnikova and Kropacheva, *J. Gen. Chem.* (U.S.S.R.), *21*, 183–6 (1951); *Chem. Abstr.*, *45*, 7046 (1951).

It may not be amiss to reïterate the fact that the steric effect reflects a composite of the properties of the *alpha* oxirane carbon atom (with its substituents) and the entering group. If the existent data are in fact as reliable as they appear, 3,4-epoxy-1-butene, in its reactions with diethylmagnesium[35] and 1-naphthylmagnesium bromide,[36] respectively, provides an interesting and cogent illustration. Although both Grignard reagents participate to some extent in "1,4-addition"[35,36b] (*q.v.*), the former, with the relatively small entering group, follows the electronically-indicated course in "normal" addition, whereas the latter, with the relatively large entering group, follows the sterically-indicated course.*

```
       H    CH=CH2                         H    CH=CH2
       |    |                              |    |
   H—C——C—H                            H—C——C—H
       \ . . :                             \    \
        O    C2H5                           O    C2H5
        :    :            →                 |                      (53.4%)
H5C2—Mg    Mg—C2H5                  H5C2—Mg    Mg—C2H5
        . .                                    /
       C2H5                                  C2H5

       H    CH=CH2                         H    CH=CH2
       |    |                              |    |
   H—C——C—H                            H—C——C—H
     . .   /                               /    /
  H7C10    O                          H7C10    O
     :     :              →                    |                   (55–58%)
Br—Mg    Mg—Br                        Br—Mg    Mg—Br
       . .                                 \
      C10H7                               C10H7
```

1,4-ADDITION

Addition reactions formally analogous to the 1,4-addition reactions of α,β-unsaturated ketones (*q.v.*) have been reported for 3,4-epoxy-1-butene with: ethylmagnesium bromide (31 percent) and diethylmagnesium (17 percent);[35] for methylmagnesium iodide (36 percent), phenylmagnesium bromide (38 percent), cyclohexylmagnesium chloride (34 percent), 2-ethoxyphenylmagnesium bromide (15 percent), and 1-naphthylmagnesium bromide (30 percent);[36b] and for 2-thienylmagnesium bromide (26 percent).[37]

---

[35] Freedman and Becker, *J. Org. Chem.*, *16*, 1701–11 (1951).

[36] (*a*) Gaylord and Becker, *J. Org. Chem.*, *15*, 305–16 (1950); (*b*) Semeniuk and Jenkins, *J. Am. Pharm. Assoc.*, *Sci. Ed.*, *37*, 118–21 (1948); *Chem. Abstr.*, *42*, 5410 (1948).

*It should be noted in passing that the two studies cited[36a,b] are not strictly comparable with each other, nor with the study on styrene oxide,[25] by reason of the limited ether-solubility of α-naphthylmagnesium bromide. A better choice of reaction medium or of Grignard reagent should yield data of higher critical value.

[37] Gmitter and Benton, *J. Am. Chem. Soc.*, *72*, 4586–9 (1950).

By analogy it might be postulated that, whereas the ordinary additions are probably trimolecular, the 1,4-additions are probably bimolecular.

```
H2C——CH              H2C——CH               H2C——CH
  \  / \               \  ..\                \    \\
   O    CH              O.   .CH              O    CH
   ..   ||     →        :    :|       →       |    |
X—Mg    CH2          X—Mg    CH2           X—Mg    CH2
    \                    . .  .                    /
     R                    .R.                     R
```

It would be interesting to learn whether or not the proportion of 1,4-addition could be materially altered by reversal of the order of reagent addition, and also whether or not cuprous chloride would facilitate the 1,4-addition as it does in the case of the α,β-unsaturated ketones.

PREPARATIVE PROCEDURES

Only the reactions of ethylene oxide with Grignard reagents may be said to have been developed into a general preparative method. The preparation of octanol, here described, has been employed by Vaughn *et al.*[38] for several other alkanols: hexanol (59 percent), heptanol (58 percent), nonanol (55 percent), decanol (52 percent). A somewhat similar method which does not employ liquid-ammonia cooling is described by Dreger[39] for hexanol (60–62 percent).

"A solution of 330 g. of hexyl bromide in 700 ml. of ether was added in the usual manner to 48 g. of magnesium turnings contained in a 2-liter 3-necked flask fitted with dropping funnel, mercury-sealed stirrer, and reflux condenser. As soon as the reaction was completed (thirty to forty-five minutes) the flask was placed in an ice-salt bath, and the reflux condenser was replaced by a liquid-ammonia-cooled spiral condenser.[40] The dropping funnel was replaced by an inlet tube reaching almost to the surface of the liquid, and 95 g. of ethylene oxide was added as rapidly (forty-five to sixty minutes) as the vigorous refluxing permitted. The cooling bath was removed, and, after refluxing ceased, 250 to 275 ml. of ether was removed by distillation from a water-bath. Three hundred thirty ml. of dry benzene was added, and the distillation was continued without interruption of stirring until the temperature of the effluent vapor reached 65°. The mixture was then refluxed for one hour, and was hydrolyzed with ice-cold 10% sulfuric acid. The benzene layer was separated and washed twice with 10% sodium hydroxide solution. The benzene was removed by distillation, and the residue was fractionated under reduced pressure. The yield was 185 g. (71%) of material boiling at 105° at fifteen mm."

---

[38] Vaughn, Spahr, and Nieuwland, *J. Am. Chem. Soc.*, 55, 4206–9 (1933).
[39] Dreger, *Organic Syntheses*, 6, 54–7 (1926); Coll. Vol. I, 1st ed., 298–301 (1932); 2nd ed., 306–8 (1941).
[40] Vaughn and Pozzi, *J. Chem. Education*, 8, 2433–4 (1931).

A slightly different technique, employed by Bachman and Thomas[41] in the preparation of 2-*m*-anisylethanol is described as follows.

"A solution of 46.8 g. of *m*-iodoanisole and 21.8 g. of ethyl bromide in 75 ml. of ether was added in portions to 10.7 g. of ground magnesium and 125 ml. of ether in a three-necked flask equipped with condenser, dropping funnel and mercury-seal stirrer. When the addition was complete (about forty-five minutes), 100 ml. of benzene was added, and the mixture was refluxed for an hour. Another 100 ml. of benzene was then added, and refluxing was continued for four or five hours. The mixture was cooled to 5°, and ethylene oxide gas, after being passed first over soda lime and then [over] potassium hydroxide pellets, was led to within an inch of the surface of the stirred mixture. When 30 g. of ethylene oxide had been added, the entire contents of the flask set to a gelatinous solid. After standing for two hours (or overnight), the mixture was refluxed for three or four hours, during which time most of the solid disappeared. The mixture was cooled to 5°, and, after addition of 6 g. more of ethylene oxide, gelation again occurred. After standing an hour, the mixture was refluxed for an hour and a half, then cooled, hydrolyzed, and worked up in the usual manner.

"The product was fractionated under reduced pressure. A forerun up to 110° was discarded, and the main fraction was collected from 110–150° at 12 mm.; most of it boiled within the range 143–150°. The yield of β-*m*-anisylethyl alcohol suitable for conversion to the bromide was 25.8 g. (85%)."

---

[41] Bachman and Thomas, *J. Am. Chem. Soc.*, *64*, 94–7 (1942).

TABLE XIV-I

REACTIONS OF GRIGNARD REAGENTS WITH EPOXIDES

Epoxide	RMgX	Product(s)	Ref.
C_2H_4O			
$(CH_2)_2O$	C_2H_5MgCl (1.0 equiv.)	n-C_4H_9OH (54.6%); $ClCH_2CH_2OH$ (22%)*	*71*
$(CH_2)_2O$	C_2H_5MgCl (1.0 equiv.)	n-C_4H_9OH (45.9%); $ClCH_2CH_2OH$ (16.4%)†	*71*
$(CH_2)_2O$	C_2H_5MgCl (0.5 equiv.)	n-C_4H_9OH (80.3%); $ClCH_2CH_2OH$ (69.4%)‡	*71*
$(CH_2)_2O$	RMgBr§	RCH_2CH_2OH;§ $BrCH_2CH_2OH$	*12*
$(CH_2)_2O$ (15 g.)	C_2H_5MgBr (0.5 equiv.)	n-C_4H_9OH (82.6%)	*53,58,95*
$(CH_2)_2O$	C_2H_5MgBr (1.0 equiv.)	n-C_4H_9OH (79%);¶ $BrCH_2CH_2OH$ (11%)‖	*68*
$(CH_2)_2O$	C_2H_5MgBr (1.0 equiv.)	n-C_4H_9OH (72%);¶ $BrCH_2CH_2OH$ (45%)‖	*68*
$(CH_2)_2O$	$CH_3C{\equiv}CMgBr$	$CH_3C{\equiv}CCH_2CH_2OH$ (95%)	*76*
$(CH_2)_2O$	n-C_3H_7MgCl (1.0 equiv.)	n-$C_5H_{11}OH$ (39.5%); $ClCH_2CH_2OH$ (31.5%)*	*71*
$(CH_2)_2O$	n-C_3H_7MgCl (1.0 equiv.)	n-$C_5H_{11}OH$ (49.9%); $ClCH_2CH_2OH$ (32.0%)†	*71*
$(CH_2)_2O$	n-C_3H_7MgCl (0.5 equiv.)	n-$C_5H_{11}OH$ (66.4%); $ClCH_2CH_2OH$ (54.0%)‡	*71*
$(CH_2)_2O$	n-C_3H_7MgBr (1.0 equiv.)	n-$C_5H_{11}OH$ (76%)¶ $BrCH_2CH_2OH$ (6%)‖	*68*
$(CH_2)_2O$	n-C_3H_7MgBr (0.5 equiv.)	n-$C_5H_{11}OH$ (75%);¶ $BrCH_2CH_2OH$ (43%)‖	*68*
$(CH_2)_2O$ (132 g.)	i-C_3H_7MgCl (236 g. C_3H_7Cl)	i-$C_5H_{11}OH$ (160 g., 60%)	*137*
$(CH_2)_2O$	i-C_3H_7MgCl (1.0 equiv.)	i-$C_5H_{11}OH$ (34.5%); $ClCH_2CH_2OH$ (35.1%)*	*71*
$(CH_2)_2O$	i-C_3H_7MgCl (1.0 equiv.)	i-$C_5H_{11}OH$ (46.5%); $ClCH_2CH_2OH$ (19.5%)†	*71*
$(CH_2)_2O$	i-C_3H_7MgCl (0.5 equiv.)	i-$C_5H_{11}OH$ (54.8%); $ClCH_2CH_2OH$ (58.0%)‡	*71*

*Slow addition of Dry Ice-cooled Et_2O-epoxide solution to ice-salt-cooled Grignard reagent solution; one hour stirring without cooling under N_2.

†Slow addition of Dry Ice-cooled Et_2O-epoxide solution to ice-salt-cooled Grignard reagent solution; partial distillation of Et_2O; addition of C_6H_6; six hours reflux under N_2.

‡Slow addition of Dry Ice-cooled Et_2O-epoxide solution to ice-salt-cooled Grignard reagent solution under N_2. Yields are calculated on the basis of the postulated reactions: $R_2Mg + 2\ (CH_2)_2O \longrightarrow (RCH_2CH_2O)_2Mg$ and $MgCl_2 + 2\ (CH_2)_2O \longrightarrow (ClCH_2CH_2O)_2Mg$.

§According to Grignard (*53*), R = C_2H_5.

¶Yield of alcohol calculated on the basis of $(CH_2)_2O$.

‖Yield of halohydrin calculated on the basis of halide (RX) used in preparation of the Grignard reagent (RMgX).

TABLE XIV-I (Continued)

Epoxide	RMgX	Product(s)	Ref.
C_2H_4O (*cont.*)			
$(CH_2)_2O$	i-C_3H_7MgBr	i-$C_5H_{11}OH$ (30%)	*102,34*
$(CH_2)_2O$	i-C_3H_7MgBr (1.0 equiv.)	i-$C_5H_{11}OH$ (74%);* $BrCH_2CH_2OH$ (7%)†	*68*
$(CH_2)_2O$	i-C_3H_7MgBr (0.5 equiv.)	i-$C_5H_{11}OH$ (70%);* $BrCH_2CH_2OH$ (45%)†	*68*
$(CH_2)_2O$	$H_2C{=}CHC{\equiv}CMgBr$	$H_2C{=}CHC{\equiv}CCH_2CH_2OH$ (20%); $BrCH_2CH_2OH$ (55%)	*97*
$(CH_2)_2O$ (44.0 g., 1 mole)	2-Thienyl-MgBr (81.5 g., 0.5 mole C_4H_3BrS)	2-Thiopheneëthanol (33.6 g., 53%)	*193*
$(CH_2)_2O$ (20.0 g.)	$C_2H_5C{\equiv}CMgBr$ (15.0 g. C_4H_6)	$C_2H_5C{\equiv}CCH_2CH_2OH$ (7.6 g.); $BrCH_2CH_2OH$ (14.0 g.)	*127*
$(CH_2)_2O$	n-C_4H_9MgCl (1.0 equiv.)	n-$C_6H_{13}OH$ (39.0%); $ClCH_2CH_2OH$ (25.5%)‡	*71*
$(CH_2)_2O$	n-C_4H_9MgCl (1.0 equiv.)	n-$C_6H_{13}OH$ (45.8%); $ClCH_2CH_2OH$ (36.8%)§	*71*
$(CH_2)_2O$	n-C_4H_9MgCl (0.5 equiv.)	n-$C_6H_{13}OH$ (69.6%); $ClCH_2CH_2OH$ (60.1%)¶	*71*
$(CH_2)_2O$ (278 g.)	n-C_4H_9MgBr (822 g. C_4H_9Br)	n-$C_6H_{13}OH$ (368–380 g., 60–62%)	*31,26,102, 134*
$(CH_2)_2O$	n-C_4H_9MgBr (1.0 equiv.)	n-$C_6H_{13}OH$ (70%);* $BrCH_2CH_2OH$ (5%)†	*68*
$(CH_2)_2O$	n-C_4H_9MgBr (0.5 equiv.)	n-$C_6H_{13}OH$ (71%);* $BrCH_2CH_2OH$ (41%)†	*68*
$(CH_2)_2O$ (500 g., 11.33 moles)	$(n$-$C_4H_9)_2Mg$ (4.2 moles)	n-$C_6H_{13}OH$ (373 g., 43.5%); $CH_3(n$-$C_4H_9)CHOH$ (7 g.)	*26*

*Yield of alcohol calculated on the basis of $(CH_2)_2O$.

†Yield of halohydrin calculated on the basis of halide (RX) used in preparation of the Grignard reagent (RMgX).

‡Slow addition of Dry Ice-cooled Et_2O-epoxide solution to ice-salt-cooled Grignard reagent solution; one hour stirring without cooling under N_2.

§Slow addition of Dry Ice-cooled Et_2O-epoxide solution to ice-salt-cooled Grignard reagent solution; partial distillation of Et_2O; addition of C_6H_6; six hours reflux under N_2.

¶Slow addition of Dry Ice-cooled Et_2O-epoxide solution to ice-salt-cooled Grignard reagent solution under N_2. Yields are calculated on the basis of the postulated reactions: $R_2Mg + 2\ (CH_2)_2O \rightarrow (RCH_2CH_2O)_2Mg$ and $MgCl_2 + 2\ (CH_2)_2O \rightarrow (ClCH_2CH_2O)_2Mg$.

TABLE XIV-I (Continued)

Epoxide	RMgX	Product(s)	Ref.
C_2H_4O (*cont.*)			
$(CH_2)_2O$	*i*-C_4H_9MgCl (1.0 equiv.)	*i*-$C_6H_{13}OH$ (23.6%); $Cl_2CH_2CH_2OH$ (34.6%)*	*71*
$(CH_2)_2O$	*i*-C_4H_9MgCl (1.0 equiv.)	*i*-$C_6H_{13}OH$ (29.8%); $ClCH_2CH_2OH$ (25.0%)†	*71*
$(CH_2)_2O$	*i*-C_4H_9MgCl (0.5 equiv.)	*i*-$C_6H_{13}OH$ (35.2%); $ClCH_2CH_2OH$ (60.4%)‡	*71*
$(CH_2)_2O$	*i*-C_4H_9MgBr	*i*-$C_6H_{13}OH$ (30–40%)	*34,102,183*
$(CH_2)_2O$	*i*-C_4H_9MgBr (1.0 equiv.)	*i*-$C_6H_{13}OH$ (64%);§ $BrCH_2CH_2OH$ (3%)¶	*68*
$(CH_2)_2O$	*i*-C_4H_9MgBr (0.5 equiv.)	*i*-$C_6H_{13}OH$ (69%);§ $BrCH_2CH_2OH$ (41%)¶	*68*
$(CH_2)_2O$	*s*-C_4H_9MgCl (1.0 equiv.)	*s*-$C_4H_9CH_2CH_2OH$ (25.6%); $ClCH_2CH_2OH$ (30.9%)*	*71*
$(CH_2)_2O$	*s*-C_2H_9MgCl	*s*-$C_4H_9CH_2CH_2OH$ (35.1%); $ClCH_2CH_2OH$ (23.9%)†	*71*
$(CH_2)_2O$	*s*-C_4H_9MgCl (0.5 equiv.)	*s*-$C_4H_9CH_2CH_2OH$ (40.9%); $ClCH_2CH_2OH$ (61.5%)‡	*71*
$(CH_2)_2O$	*s*-C_4H_9MgBr	*s*-$C_4H_9CH_2CH_2OH$ (36%)	*102*
$(CH_2)_2O$	*s*-C_4H_9MgBr (1.0 equiv.)	*s*-$C_4H_9CH_2CH_2OH$ (65%);§ $BrCH_2CH_2OH$ (9%)¶	*68*
$(CH_2)_2O$	*s*-C_4H_9MgBr (0.5 equiv.)	*s*-$C_4H_9CH_2CH_2OH$ (65%);§ $BrCH_2CH_2OH$ (51%)¶	*68*
$(CH_2)_2O$ (15 g.)	*t*-C_4H_9MgCl (31 g. C_4H_9Cl)	*t*-$C_4H_9CH_2CH_2OH$ (13.2%)	*91*

*Slow addition of Dry Ice-cooled Et_2O-epoxide solution to ice-salt-cooled Grignard reagent solution; one hour stirring without cooling under N_2.

†Slow addition of Dry Ice-cooled Et_2O-epoxide solution to ice-salt-cooled Grignard reagent solution; partial distillation of Et_2O; addition of C_6H_6; six hours reflux under N_2.

‡Slow addition of Dry Ice-cooled Et_2O-epoxide solution to ice-salt-cooled Grignard reagent solution under N_2. Yields are calculated on the basis of the postulated reactions: $R_2Mg + 2\ (CH_2)_2O \longrightarrow (RCH_2CH_2O)_2Mg$ and $MgCl_2 + 2\ (CH_2)_2O \longrightarrow (ClCH_2CH_2O)_2Mg$.

§Yield of alcohol calculated on the basis of $(CH_2)_2O$.

¶Yield of halohydrin calculated on the basis of halide (RX) used in preparation of the Grignard reagent (RMgX).

TABLE XIV-I (Continued)

Epoxide	RMgX	Product(s)	Ref.
C_2H_4O (*cont.*)			
$(CH_2)_2O$	t-C_4H_9MgCl (1.0 equiv.)	t-$C_4H_9CH_2CH_2OH$ (0.0%); $ClCH_2CH_2OH$ (21.3%)*	*71*
$(CH_2)_2O$	t-C_4H_9MgCl (1.0 equiv.)	t-$C_4H_9CH_2CH_2OH$ (0.0%); $ClCH_2CH_2OH$ (23.3%)†	*71*
$(CH_2)_2O$	t-C_4H_9MgCl (0.5 equiv.)	t-$C_4H_9CH_2CH_2OH$ (0.0%); $ClCH_2CH_2OH$ (48.1%)‡	*71*
$(CH_2)_2O$	t-C_4H_9MgBr (1.0 equiv.)	$BrCH_2CH_2OH$ (60%)§	*68*
$(CH_2)_2O$	t-C_4H_9MgBr (0.5 equiv.)	t-$C_4H_9CH_2CH_2OH$ (9%);¶ $BrCH_2CH_2OH$ (50%)§	*68*
$(CH_2)_2O$ (10 moles)	$(CH_3)_3SiCH_2MgCl$ (5 moles $C_4H_{11}ClSi$)	$(CH_3)_3Si(CH_2)_3OH$ (468 g., 3.57 moles)	*188*
$(CH_2)_2O$ (52 g.)	$H_2C{=}C(CH_3)C{\equiv}CMgBr$ (109 g. C_2H_5Br)	$H_2C{=}C(CH_3)C{\equiv}CCH_2CH_2OH$ (25 g.); $BrCH_2CH_2OH$ (51 g.)	*97*
$(CH_2)_2O$ (26.4 g., 0.6 mole)	2-Thenyl-MgBr (0.241 mole)	2-Methyl-3-thiopheneëthanol (13.5 g., 39%)	*194*
$(CH_2)_2O$	n-$C_3H_7C{\equiv}CMgBr$	n-$C_3H_7C{\equiv}CCH_2CH_2OH$ (*ca.* 30%)	*195*
$(CH_2)_2O$	$(CH_2)_4CHMgCl$	$(CH_2)_4CHCH_2CH_2OH$ (27%)	*177*
$(CH_2)_2O$	n-$C_5H_{11}MgBr$	n-$C_7H_{15}OH$ (58%)	*134*
$(CH_2)_2O$	n-$C_5H_{11}MgBr$ (1.0 equiv.)	n-$C_7H_{15}OH$ (69%);¶ $BrCH_2CH_2OH$ (10%)§	*68*
$(CH_2)_2O$	n-$C_5H_{11}MgBr$ (0.5 equiv.)	n-$C_7H_{15}OH$ (60%);¶ $BrCH_2CH_2OH$ (40%)§	*68*

*Slow addition of Dry Ice-cooled Et_2O-epoxide solution to ice-salt-cooled Grignard reagent solution; one hour stirring without cooling under N_2.

†Slow addition of Dry Ice-cooled Et_2O-epoxide solution to ice-salt-cooled Grignard reagent solution; partial distillation of Et_2O; addition of C_6H_6; six hours reflux under N_2.

‡Slow addition of Dry Ice-cooled Et_2O-epoxide solution to ice-salt-cooled Grignard reagent solution under N_2. Yields are calculated on the basis of the postulated reactions: $R_2Mg + 2\,(CH_2)_2O \longrightarrow (RCH_2CH_2O)_2Mg$ and $MgCl_2 + 2\,(CH_2)_2O \longrightarrow (ClCH_2CH_2O)_2Mg$.

§Yield of halohydrin calculated on the basis of halide (RX) used in preparation of the Grignard reagent (RMgX).

¶Yield of alcohol calculated on the basis of $(CH_2)_2O$.

TABLE XIV-I (Continued)

Epoxide	RMgX	Product(s)	Ref.
C_2H_4O (*cont.*)			
$(CH_2)_2O$ (17 g.)	i-$C_5H_{11}MgBr$ (0.5 equiv.)	i-$C_7H_{15}OH$ (75%)	*53,52*
$(CH_2)_2O$	i-$C_5H_{11}MgBr$ (1.0 equiv.)	i-$C_7H_{15}OH$ (59%);* $BrCH_2CH_2OH$ (4%)†	*68*
$(CH_2)_2O$	i-$C_5H_{11}MgBr$ (0.5 equiv.)	i-$C_7H_{15}OH$ (56%);* $BrCH_2CH_2OH$ (41%)†	*68*
$(CH_2)_2O$	s-$C_4H_9CH_2MgBr$ (1.0 equiv.)	s-$C_4H_9(CH_2)_3OH$ (58%);* $BrCH_2CH_2OH$ (9%)†	*68*
$(CH_2)_2O$	s-$C_4H_9CH_2MgBr$ (0.5 equiv.)	s-$C_4H_9(CH_2)_3OH$ (53%);* $BrCH_2CH_2OH$ (35%)†	*68*
$(CH_2)_2O$ (15 g.)	t-$C_4H_9CH_2MgBr$ (30 g. $C_5H_{11}Br$)	t-$C_4H_9(CH_2)_3OH$ (30%)	*91*
$(CH_2)_2O$	$CH_3(n$-$C_3H_7)CHMgBr$	$CH_3(n$-$C_3H_7)CHCH_2CH_2OH$ (28%)	*21,102*
$(CH_2)_2O$	$CH_3(n$-$C_3H_7)CHMgBr$ (1.0 equiv.)	$CH_3(n$-$C_3H_7)CHCH_2CH_2OH$ (63%);* $BrCH_2CH_2OH$ (5%)†	*68*
$(CH_2)_2O$	$CH_3(n$-$C_3H_7)CHMgBr$ (0.5 equiv.)	$CH_3(n$-$C_3H_7)CHCH_2CH_2OH$ (50%);* $BrCH_2CH_2OH$ (44%)†	*68*
$(CH_2)_2O$	$CH_3(i$-$C_3H_7)CHMgBr$ (1.0 equiv.)	$CH_3(i$-$C_3H_7)CHCH_2CH_2OH$ (40%);* $BrCH_2CH_2OH$ (10%)†	*68*
$(CH_2)_2O$	$CH_3(i$-$C_3H_7)CHMgBr$ (0.5 equiv.)	$CH_3(i$-$C_3H_7)CHCH_2CH_2OH$ (46%);* $BrCH_2CH_2OH$ (41%)†	*68*
$(CH_2)_2O$	t-$C_5H_{11}MgCl$ (1.0 equiv.)	$ClCH_2CH_2OH$ (39%)†	*68*
$(CH_2)_2O$	t-$C_5H_{11}MgCl$ (0.5 equiv.)	$ClCH_2CH_2OH$ (35%)†	*68*
$(CH_2)_2O$	t-$C_5H_{11}MgBr$ (1.0 equiv.)	$BrCH_2CH_2OH$ (48%)†	*68*
$(CH_2)_2O$	t-$C_5H_{11}MgBr$ (0.5 equiv.)	$BrCH_2CH_2OH$ (42%)†	*68*
$(CH_2)_2O$ (50 g.)	$CH_3OCH_2CH(CH_3)CH_2MgCl$ (1 mole $C_5H_{11}ClO$)	$CH_3(CH_3OCH_2)CH(CH_2)_3OH$ (98 g., 74%)	*158*
$(CH_2)_2O$	C_6H_5MgCl	$C_6H_5CH_2CH_2OH$ (*ca.* 75%)	*184,117, 169*

* Yield of alcohol calculated on the basis of $(CH_2)_2O$.

† Yield of halohydrin calculated on the basis of halide (RX) used in preparation of the Grignard reagent (RMgX).

TABLE XIV-I (Continued)

Epoxide	RMgX	Product(s)	Ref.
C_2H_4O *(cont.)*			
$(CH_2)_2O$ (99 g.)	C_6H_5MgCl* (72 g. Mg)	$C_6H_5CH_2CH_2OH$ (185 g.); 4-$C_6H_5C_6H_4CH_2CH_2OH$; 4-(4-$C_6H_5C_6H_4$)$C_6H_4CH_2CH_2OH$; 1,4-$(C_6H_5)_2C_6H_4$; $(C_6H_5-)_2$	*92*
$(CH_2)_2O$	C_6H_5MgBr	$C_6H_5CH_2CH_2OH$	*140,167, 187*
$(CH_2)_2O$	C_6H_5MgBr (1.0 equiv.)	$C_6H_5CH_2CH_2OH$ (58%);† $BrCH_2CH_4OH$ (42%)‡	*68*
$(CH_2)_2O$	C_6H_5MgBr (0.5 equiv.)	$C_6H_5CH_2CH_2OH$ (55%);† $BrCH_2CH_2OH$ (50%)‡	*68*
$(CH_2)_2O$	2-Pyridylmethyl-MgX§	3-(2-Pyridyl)-1-propanol	*196*
$(CH_2)_2O$	*n*-$C_4H_9C\equiv CMgBr$	*n*-$C_4H_9C\equiv CH$ (*ca.* 34%); $BrCH_2CH_2OH$ (*ca.* 58%); *n*-$C_4H_9C\equiv CCH_2CH_2OH$ (*ca.* 40%)¶	*155*
$(CH_2)_2O$ (70 g.)	$(CH_2)_5CHMgBr$ (163 g. $C_6H_{11}Br$)	$(CH_2)_5CHCH_2CH_2OH$ (56 g., 53%)	*63,168*
$(CH_2)_2O$	$(CH_2)_5CHMgBr$ (1.0 equiv.)	$(CH_2)_5CHCH_2CH_2OH$ (50%);† $BrCH_2CH_2OH$ (8%)‡	*68*
$(CH_2)_2O$	$(CH_2)_5CHMgBr$ (0.5 equiv.)	$(CH_2)_5CHCH_2CH_2OH$ (45%);† $BrCH_2CH_2OH$ (42%)‡	*68*
$(CH_2)_2O$ (95 g.)	*n*-$C_6H_{13}MgBr$ (330 g. $C_6H_{13}Br$)	*n*-$C_8H_{17}OH$ (185 g., 71%)	*134*
$(CH_2)_2O$	*n*-$C_6H_{13}MgBr$ (1.0 equiv.)	*n*-$C_8H_{17}OH$ (49%);† $BrCH_2CH_2OH$ (4%)‡	*68*
$(CH_2)_2O$	*n*-$C_6H_{13}MgBr$ (0.5 equiv.)	*n*-$C_8H_{17}OH$ (47%);† $BrCH_2CH_2OH$ (30%)‡	*68*
$(CH_2)_2O$	*i*-$C_6H_{13}MgBr$	*i*-$C_8H_{17}OH$ (60–65%)	*34*

* This Grignard reagent was prepared from Mg (72 g.) and C_6H_5Cl (1000 g.) without solvent other than the excess halide.

†Yield of alcohol calculated on the basis of $(CH_2)_2O$.

‡Yield of halohydrin calculated on the basis of halide (RX) used in preparation of the Grignard reagent (RMgX).

§X = Br, I.

¶Calculated on basis of Grignard reagent (RMgX) reacting.

TABLE XIV-I (Continued)

Epoxide	RMgX	Product(s)	Ref.
C_2H_4O (*cont.*)			
$(CH_2)_2O$ (132 g.)	t-$C_4H_9CH_2CH_2MgCl$ (362 g., $C_6H_{13}Cl$)	t-$C_4H_9(CH_2)_4OH$ (260 g., 67%)	*186*
$(CH_2)_2O$	$CH_3(n$-$C_4H_9)CHMgBr$ (1.0 equiv.)	$CH_3(n$-$C_4H_9)CHCH_2CH_2OH$ (43%);* $BrCH_2CH_2OH$ (6%)†	*68*
$(CH_2)_2O$	$CH_3(n$-$C_4H_9)CHMgBr$ (0.5 equiv.)	$CH_3(n$-$C_4H_9)CHCH_2CH_2OH$ (40%);* $BrCH_2CH_2OH$ (47%)†	*68*
$(CH_2)_2O$	n-$C_3H_7(CH_3)_2CMgBr$ (1.0 equiv.)	$BrCH_2CH_2OH$ (48%)†	*68*
$(CH_2)_2O$	n-$C_3H_7(CH_3)_2CMgBr$ (0.5 equiv.)	$BrCH_2CH_2OH$ (42%)†	*68*
$(CH_2)_2O$ (200 ml.)	$(CH_3)_3Si(CH_2)_3MgBr$ (390 g. $C_6H_{15}BrSi$)	$(CH_3)_3Si(CH_2)_5OH$ (206 g., 64%)	*188*
$(CH_2)_2O$	3-$F_3CC_6H_4MgBr$ (101.0 g., 0.45 mole $C_7H_4BrF_3$)	3-$F_3CC_6H_4CH_2CH_2OH$ (57.4 g., 67%)	*2,191*
$(CH_2)_2O$ (63 ml.)	2-$BrC_6H_4CH_2MgBr$ (160 g. $C_7H_6Br_2$)	2-$BrC_6H_4CH_2CH_2OH$ (47%); (2-$BrC_6H_4CH_2$—$)_2$; (2-$HOCH_2CH_2$-$C_6H_4CH_2$—$)_2$	*147*
$(CH_2)_2O$ (35.0 g.)	3-F-4-$CH_3OC_6H_3MgBr$ (79.5 g. C_7H_6BrFO)	3-F-4-$CH_3OC_6H_3CH_2CH_2OH$ (35.0 g., 44%)	*35*
$(CH_2)_2O$ (excess)	$C_6H_5CH_2MgCl$ (0.5 mole)	Oil (32.5 g., 47.8%, yielding upon oxid'n *ca.* equal wts. $C_6H_5CO_2H$ and 1,4-$(HO_2C)_2C_6H_4$	*164*
$(CH_2)_2O$	$C_6H_5CH_2MgCl$ (1.0 equiv.)	$C_6H_5(CH_2)_3OH$ (73%);* $ClCH_2CH_2OH$ (3%)†	*68*
$(CH_2)_2O$	$C_6H_5CH_2MgCl$ (0.5 equiv.)	$C_6H_5(CH_2)_3OH$ (79%);* $ClCH_2CH_2OH$ (6%)	*68*
$(CH_2)_2O$	4-$CH_3C_6H_4MgBr$	4-$CH_3C_6H_4CH_2CH_2OH$ (55%)	*55,140,187*
$(CH_2)_2O$ (44 g.)	2-$CH_3OC_6H_4MgBr$ (100 g. C_7H_7BrO)	2-$CH_3OC_6H_4CH_2CH_2OH$ (54.5 g., 67%)	*94*
$(CH_2)_2O$ (35 g.)	3-$CH_3OC_6H_4MgBr$ (120 g. C_7H_7BrO)	3-$CH_3OC_6H_4CH_2CH_2OH$ (60 g.)	*96,162*
$(CH_2)_2O$ (36.0 g.)	3-$CH_3OC_6H_4MgI$ (46.8 g. C_7H_7IO)	3-$CH_3OC_6H_4CH_2CH_2OH$ (25.8 g., 85%)	*3*
$(CH_2)_2O$	4-$CH_3OC_6H_4MgBr$ (70 g. C_7H_7BrO)	4-$CH_3C_6H_4CH_2CH_2OH$ (11 g.)	*66,140,187*

* Yield of alcohol calculated on the basis of $(CH_2)_2O$.

† Yield of halohydrin calculated on the basis of halide (RX) used in preparation of the Grignard reagent (RMgX).

TABLE XIV-I (Continued)

Epoxide	RMgX	Product(s)	Ref.
C_2H_4O (*cont.*)			
$(CH_2)_2O$ (1.5 equiv.)	n-$C_5H_{11}C{\equiv}CMgBr$	n-$C_5H_{11}C{\equiv}CCH_2CH_2OH$ (*ca.* 40%)	*33,28,4*
$(CH_2)_2O$ (90 g.)	n-$C_5H_{11}C{\equiv}CMgBr$ (192 g., 2 moles C_7H_{12})	n-$C_5H_{11}C{\equiv}CH$ (65 g.); $BrCH_2CH_2OH$ (95 g.); n-$C_5H_{11}C{\equiv}CCH_2CH_2OH$ (60 g.)	*155*
$(CH_2)_2O$ (excess)	n-$C_7H_{15}MgBr$ (179 g. $C_7H_{15}Br$)	n-$C_9H_{19}OH$ (95 g., 65%)	*93,134,90*
$(CH_2)_2O$	$CH_3(n$-$C_3H_7)CHCH_2CH_2MgBr$	$CH_3(n$-$C_3H_7)CH(CH_2)_4OH$ (65%)	*21*
$(CH_2)_2O$ (1.5 equiv.)	$C_6H_5C{\equiv}CMgBr$	$C_6H_5C{\equiv}CCH_2CH_2OH$ (*ca.* 40%)	*33,28,107*
$(CH_2)_2O$	$C_6H_5C{\equiv}CMgBr$	$C_6H_5C{\equiv}CH$ (*ca.* 34%); $BrCH_2CH_2OH$ (*ca.* 58%); $C_6H_5C{\equiv}CCH_2CH_2OH$ (*ca.* 40%)	*155*
$(CH_2)_2O$ (2.2 g.)	Indolyl-MgX (5.5 g. C_8H_7N)	2-(β-Indolyl)ethanol (52%)	*104; cf. 67*
$(CH_2)_2O$	2-$CH_3C_6H_4CH_2MgBr$	2,3-$(CH_3)_2C_6H_3CH_2CH_2OH$ (10x%); 3,4-$(CH_3)_2C_6H_3CH_2CH_2OH$ (90x%)	*175*
$(CH_2)_2O$	3-$CH_3C_6H_4CH_2MgBr$	3-$CH_3C_6H_4(CH_2)_3OH$ (45%)	*175*
$(CH_2)_2O$	4-$CH_3C_6H_4CH_2MgBr$	4-$CH_3C_6H_4(CH_2)_3OH$ (80x%); 2,3-$(CH_3)_2C_6H_3CH_2CH_2OH$ (20x%)	*175*
$(CH_2)_2O$ (4.5 ml.)	2,3-$(CH_3)_2C_6H_3MgBr$ (19.0 g. C_8H_9Br)	2,3-$(CH_3)_2C_6H_3CH_2CH_2OH$	*113*
$(CH_2)_2O$ (100 g., 3.15 moles)	2-$CH_3OCH_2C_6H_4MgBr$ (145 g. C_8H_9BrO)	2-$CH_3OCH_2C_6H_4CH_2CH_2OH$ (64 g., 53%)	*65*
$(CH_2)_2O$	2-CH_3O-4-$CH_3C_6H_3MgBr$	2-CH_3O-4-$CH_3C_6H_3CH_2CH_2OH$	*140*
$(CH_2)_2O$ (25 g.)	2-CH_3O-5-$CH_3C_6H_3MgBr$ (86 g. C_8H_9BrO)	2-CH_3O-5-$CH_3C_6H_3CH_2CH_2OH$	*25*
$(CH_2)_2O$ (1.5 equiv.)	n-$C_6H_{13}C{\equiv}CMgBr$	n-$C_6H_{13}C{\equiv}CCH_2CH_2OH$ (*ca.* 40%)	*33*
$(CH_2)_2O$	$(CH_2)_5CHCH_2CH_2MgBr$	$(CH_2)_5CH(CH_2)_4OH$ (47–53%)	*168*
$(CH_2)_2O$	$(CH_3)_2C{=}CHCH_2CH_2CH(CH_3)MgBr$	$(CH_3)_2C{=}CHCH_2CH_2CH(CH_3)CH_2CH_2OH$	*129*
$(CH_2)_2O$	n-$C_8H_{17}MgBr$	n-$C_{10}H_{21}OH$ (52%)	*134*
$(CH_2)_2O$ (10 ml.)	3-Thianaphthenylmethyl-MgCl (0.0405 mole)	3-(3-Thianaphthenyl)-1-propanol + 3-methyl-2-thianaphtheneëthanol (aggregating 2.76 g., 35%)	*197*
$(CH_2)_2O$	$C_6H_5(CH_2)_3MgBr$ (2 equiv.)	$C_6H_5(CH_2)_5OH$ (68%)	*189,185*
$(CH_2)_2O$ (6 g.)	3-i-$C_3H_7C_6H_4MgBr$ (20 g. $C_9H_{11}Br$)	3-i-$C_3H_7C_6H_4CH_2CH_2OH$ (8 g.)	*54,13*

TABLE XIV-I (Continued)

Epoxide	RMgX	Product(s)	Ref.
C_2H_4O (*cont.*)			
$(CH_2)_2O$ (9.0 g.)	2,3,4-$(CH_3)_3C_6H_2MgBr$ (11.2 g. $C_9H_{11}Br$)	2,3,4-$(CH_3)_3C_6H_2CH_2CH_2OH$	*119*
$(CH_2)_2O$ (60. g., 1.36 mole)	2-$C_2H_5OCH_2C_6H_4MgBr$ (100 g., 0.46 mole $C_9H_{11}BrO$)	2-$C_2H_5OCH_2C_6H_4CH_2CH_2OH$ (29 g., 35%)	*64*
$(CH_2)_2O$	1-$C_{10}H_7MgBr$	1-$C_{10}H_7CH_2CH_2OH$ (75%)	*99,124,154*
$(CH_2)_2O$ (5.5 g.)	2-$C_{10}H_7MgBr$ (21.0 g. $C_{10}H_7Br$)	2-$C_{10}H_7CH_2CH_2OH$ (11.6 g., 68%)	*182,124*
$(CH_2)_2O$ (0.75 mole)	$C_{10}H_{17}MgCl$* (0.5 mole)	$C_{10}H_{17}CH_2CH_2OH$†	*14*
$(CH_2)_2O$	$(CH_2)_5CH(CH_2)_4MgBr$	$(CH_2)_5CH(CH_2)_6OH$ (37%)	*168*
$(CH_2)_2O$ (18.5 ml.)	4-$CH_3OC_{10}H_6$-1-MgBr (70.0 g. $C_{11}H_9BrO$)	4-$CH_3OC_{10}H_6$-1-CH_2CH_2OH (22.0 g.)	*108*
$(CH_2)_2O$ (7.5 g.)	6-$CH_3OC_{10}H_6$-1-MgI (34.0 g. $C_{11}H_9IO$)	6-$CH_3OC_{10}H_6$-1-CH_2CH_2OH (12.5 g.)	*153*
$(CH_2)_2O$	4-$(CH_2)_4CHC_6H_4MgBr$	4-$(CH_2)_4CHC_6H_4CH_2CH_2OH$	*19*
$(CH_2)_2O$ (30 g.)	2-CH_3-4-*t*-$C_4H_9C_6H_3MgBr$ (115 g. $C_{11}H_{15}Br$)	2-CH_3-4-*t*-$C_4H_9C_6H_3CH_2CH_2OH$ (60 g.)	*17*
$(CH_2)_2O$	2-CH_3O-5-*t*-$C_4H_9C_6H_3MgBr$ (120 g. $C_{11}H_{15}BrO$)	2-CH_3O-5-*t*-$C_4H_9C_6H_3CH_2CH_2OH$ (50 g.)	*17*
$(CH_2)_2O$ (82.5 g.)	2,4,5-$(CH_3)_3$-3,6-$(CH_3O)_2C_6MgBr$ (55.0 g. $C_{11}H_{15}BrO_2$)	2,4,5-$(CH_3)_3$-3,6-$(CH_3O)_2C_6CH_2CH_2OH$ (29.4 g., 62%)	*122,120*
$(CH_2)_2O$ (8.0 g.)	2-$C_6H_5C_6H_4MgI$ (20.0 g. $C_{12}H_9I$)	2-$C_6H_5C_6H_4CH_2CH_2OH$ (10.5 g., 76%)	*156*
$(CH_2)_2O$ (25 g.)	3-Acenaphthenyl-MgI (40 g. $C_{12}H_9I$)	2-(3-Acenapthenyl)ethanol	*23*
$(CH_2)_2O$ (100.0 g., 2.28 moles)	4-$C_6H_5OC_6H_4MgBr$ (294.0 g., 1.18 mole $C_{12}H_9BrO$)	4-$C_6H_5OC_6H_4CH_2CH_2OH$ (133.4 g., 52%)	*162*
$(CH_2)_2O$ (1.9 g.)	4-CH_3O-6-$CH_3C_{10}H_5$-1-MgBr (8.8 g.)	4-CH_3O-6-$CH_3C_{10}H_5$-1-CH_2CH_2OH (4.6 g.)	*86*
$(CH_2)_2O$ (30 g.)	4-$(CH_2)_5CHC_6H_4MgBr$ (145 g. $C_{12}H_{15}Br$)	4-$(CH_2)_5CHC_6H_4CH_2CH_2OH$ (50 g.)	*18*

* From "pinene hydrochloride."

† "β-Camphanylethanol;" recovered as the acid phthalate (62 g.).

TABLE XIV-I (Continued)

Epoxide	RMgX	Product(s)	Ref.
C_2H_4O (*cont.*)			
$(CH_2)_2O$ (10.0 g.)	9-Phenanthryl-MgBr (48.5 g. $C_{14}H_9Br$)	$(C_{14}H_9)CH_2CH_2OH$ (15–21 g.)	*148,178*
$(CH_2)_2O$ (30 g.)	2-$C_6H_5C_6H_4CH_2CH_2MgBr$ (33 g. $C_{14}H_{13}Br$)	2-$C_6H_5C_6H_4(CH_2)_4OH$ (11 g.)	*156*
$(CH_2)_2O$ (1.5 equiv.)	*n*-$C_{11}H_{23}CH(CH_3)(CH_2)_3MgCl$ (57 g., 0.22 mole $C_{16}H_{33}Cl$)	$CH_3(n\text{-}C_{11}H_{23})CH(CH_2)_5OH$ (38.9 g., 66%)	*150*
$C_3H_3OCl_3$			
1,2-Epoxy-3,3,3-trichloropropane (21.0 g., 0.13 mole)	CH_3MgI (0.13 mole)	$Cl_3CCH(OH)CH_2I$ (22.2 g., 59%)	*163*
C_3H_5OCl			
α-Epichlorohydrin	CH_3MgI	$ClCH_2CH(OH)CH_2I$ (*ca.* quant.)	82
α-Epichlorohydrin	C_2H_5MgBr (0.5 equiv.)	$ClCH_2(n\text{-}C_3H_7)CHOH$ (80%)	32,73;*cf.* 60
α-Epichlorohydrin (92.5 g., 1 mole)	C_2H_5MgBr (109.0 g., 1 mole C_2H_5Br)	$ClCH_2(n\text{-}C_3H_7)CHOH$ (20–23 g., 16–19%); $ClCH_2CH(OH)CH_2Br$ (*ca.*, 100 g.)	83,75
α-Epichlorohydrin (0.82–0.91 mole)	C_2H_5MgBr (1 equiv.)	$ClCH_2(n\text{-}C_3H_7)CHOH$ (4.5–13.0%); $ClCH_2CH(OH)CH_2Br$ (41–61%); $(CH_2)_2CHOH$ (0.0–4.5 g.); C_2H_4;C_2H_6, tar (0.0–8.6 g.)*	89
α-Epichlorohydrin (1.35 mole)	C_2H_5MgBr (0.9 mole)	$ClCH_2(n\text{-}C_3H_7)CHOH$ (35%); $ClCH_2CH(OH)CH_2Br$ (78%)	89
α-Epichlorohydrin	C_2H_5MgBr†	$(CH_2)_2CHOH$ (6.0%)‡	*125*
α-Epichlorohydrin (1.66 mole) + $MgBr_2$ (1.66 mole)	C_2H_5MgBr (5 moles) + $FeCl_3$ (0.0015 mole)	$(CH_2)_2CHOH$ (31%); gas	*125*

*The results of three experiments, conducted under varying conditions, are summarized. Compare with reactions of $ClCH_2CH(OMgBr)CH_2Br$ with C_2H_5MgBr, Table XVI-I (**$C_3H_5Br_2ClMgO$**).

†From pure sublimed magnesium.

‡Compare with the reaction of $ClCH_2CH(OH)CH_2Br$ with C_2H_5MgBr, Table XVI-I (**C_3H_6BrClO**).

TABLE XVI-I (Continued)

Epoxide	RMgX	Product(s)	Ref.
C_3H_5OCl (*cont.*)			
α-Epichlorohydrin (1 mole) + $MgBr_2$ (1 mole)	C_2H_5MgBr (3 moles) + $FeCl_3$ (0.0014 mole)	$(CH_2)_2CHOH$ (43%); gas	*125*
α-Epichlorohydrin (1.1 mole)	$(C_2H_5)_2Mg$ (0.548 mole)	$ClCH_2(n\text{-}C_3H_7)CHOH$ (70–83%)	89
α-Epichlorohydrin (44 g.)	$n\text{-}C_3H_7MgI$ (1 equiv.)	$ClCH_2(n\text{-}C_4H_9)CHOH$* (2.5 g., 3.9%)	84
α-Epichlorohydrin (42 g.)	$i\text{-}C_3H_7MgBr$ (1 equiv.)	No chlorohydrin isolated	84
α-Epichlorohydrin	$i\text{-}C_3H_7MgI$ (1 equiv.)	No chlorohydrin isolated	84
α-Epichlorohydrin (46.2 g.)	$n\text{-}C_4H_9MgCl$ (1 equiv.)	$ClCH_2(n\text{-}C_5H_{11})CHOH$ (12.0 g., 16%)	84
α-Epichlorohydrin (38.8 g.)	$s\text{-}C_4H_9MgCl$ (1 equiv.)	$ClCH_2(s\text{-}C_4H_9CH_2)CHOH$* (3.8 g., 9%)	84
α-Epichlorohydrin (23.0 g.)	$t\text{-}C_4H_9MgCl$ (1 equiv.)	No chlorohydrin isolated	84
α-Epichlorohydrin (39.8 g.)	$n\text{-}C_5H_{11}MgCl$ (1 equiv.)	$ClCH_2(n\text{-}C_6H_{13})CHOH$* (12.0 g., 29.8%)	84
α-Epichlorohydrin (29.4 g.)	$(C_2H_5)_2CHMgCl$ (1 equiv.)	$ClCH_2[(C_2H_5)_2CHCH_2]CHOH$* (5.7 g., 10.9%)	84
α-Epichlorohydrin (25.9 g.)	C_6H_5MgBr (1 equiv.)	$ClCH_2(C_6H_5CH_2)CHOH$ (8.7 g., 18.2%)	*84,161*
α-Epichlorohydrin (46.2 g.)	C_6H_5MgBr (78.5 g. C_6H_5Br)	$ClCH_2(C_6H_5CH_2)CHOH$ (30.0 g.); $ClCH_2CH(OH)CH_2Br$	*37,75,180*
α-Epichlorohydrin (46 g.)	C_6H_5MgBr (78 g. C_6H_5Br)	$CH_3(C_6H_5)C{=}CHC_6H_5$ (10 g.); $ClCH_2CH(OH)CH_2Br$ (23 g.)	*128*
α-Epichlorohydrin	C_6H_5MgI	$ClCH_2(C_6H_5)CHCH_2OH$†	*110*
α-Epichlorohydrin (40.6 g.)	$(CH_2)_5CHMgCl$ (1 equiv.)	$ClCH_2[(CH_2)_5CHCH_2]CHOH$ (11.9 g., 15.3%)	84
α-Epichlorohydrin	$3\text{-}F_3CC_6H_4MgBr$	$3\text{-}F_3CC_6H_4CH_2CH(OH)CH_2Cl$ (70%)	*191*
α-Epichlorohydrin (62 g.)	$C_6H_5CH_2MgCl$ (84 g. C_7H_7Cl)	$ClCH_2(C_6H_5CH_2CH_2)CHOH$ (70 g.); $ClCH_2CH(OH)CH_2Br$ (28 g.)	*37,180*
α-Epichlorohydrin (31.0 g.)	$C_6H_5CH_2MgCl$ (1 equiv.)	$ClCH_2(C_6H_5CH_2CH_2)CHOH$* (19.7 g., 32.0%); tar (7.8 g.)	84

* Structure assumed.

† The structure assigned is undoubtedly erroneous; the general formula for the products claimed should be $ClCH_2(RCH_2)CHOH$ rather than $R(ClCH_2)CHCH_2OH$.

TABLE XIV-I (Continued)

Epoxide	RMgX	Product(s)	Ref.
C_3H_5OCl (*cont.*)			
α-Epichlorohydrin	2-$CH_3OC_6H_4MgBr$	$ClCH_2(2\text{-}CH_3OC_6H_4CH_2)CHOH$ (25–30%)	*101*
α-Epichlorohydrin (60 g.)	4-$CH_3OC_6H_4MgBr$ (125 g. C_7H_7BrO)	$ClCH_2(4\text{-}CH_3OC_6H_4CH_2)CHOH$ (36 g.); $ClCH_2CH(OH)CH_2Br$	*37,180,161*
α-Epichlorohydrin (24.0 g.)	$(CH_2)_5CHCH_2MgCl$ (1 equiv.)	$ClCH_2[(CH_2)_5CHCH_2CH_2]CHOH$ (14.7 g., 29.9%)	*84*
α-Epichlorohydrin	$C_6H_5C{\equiv}CMgBr$	$ClCH_2(C_6H_5C{\equiv}CCH_2)CHOH$; $ClCH_2CH(OH)CH_2Br$; $(C_6H_5C{\equiv}C—)_2$; $C_6H_5C{\equiv}CH$	*74*
α-Epichlorohydrin (28.0 g.)	$C_6H_5CH_2CH_2MgCl$ (1 equiv.)	$ClCH_2[C_6H_5(CH_2)_3]CHOH$* (7.9 g., 12.8%)	*84*
α-Epichlorohydrin (5.7 g.)	$(CH_2)_5CHCH(CH_3)MgCl$ (1 equiv.)	No chlorohydrin isolated	*84*
α-Epichlorohydrin (20.0 g.)	$C_6H_5(CH_2)_3MgCl$	$ClCH_2[C_6H_5(CH_2)_4]CHOH$* (11.5 g., 25.0%)	*84*
α-Epichlorohydrin (180 g.)	1-$C_{10}H_7MgBr$ (207 g. $C_{10}H_7Br$)	$ClCH_2(1\text{-}C_{10}H_7CH_2)CHOH$ (*ca.* 100 g.)	*161*
α-Epichlorohydrin	4-$CH_3OC_{10}H_6$-1-$MgBr$	$ClCH_2(4\text{-}CH_3OC_{10}H_6\text{-}1\text{-}CH_2)CHOH$	*161*
C_3H_5OBr			
α-Epibromohydrin	C_2H_5MgBr	$(BrCH_2)_2CHOH$	*75*
C_3H_6O			
Propylene oxide (0.40 mole)	$(CH_3)_2Mg$ (0.17 mole)	$CH_3(C_2H_5)CHOH$ (7.0 g., 28%)	*51*
Propylene oxide	C_2H_5MgCl (1.0 equiv.)	$CH_3(n\text{-}C_3H_7)CHOH$ (40%); $CH_3CH(OH)CH_2Cl$ (35%)†	*72*
Propylene oxide	C_2H_5MgCl (1.0 equiv.)	$CH_3(n\text{-}C_3H_7)CHOH$ (42%); $CH_3CH(OH)CH_2Cl$ (40%)‡	*72*

* Structure assumed.

† Dropwise addition of Et_2O-oxide solution to stirred Grignard reagent solution; one hour stirring; overnight standing.

‡ Dropwise addition of Et_2O-oxide solution to stirred Grignard reagent solution; one hour stirring; overnight standing; distillation of *ca.* half of Et_2O; addition of two volumes of C_6H_6; distillation to b.p. 75°; seven hours reflux with stirring; overnight standing.

TABLE XIV-I (Continued)

Epoxide	RMgX	Product(s)	Ref.
C_3H_6O (*cont.*)			
Propylene oxide	C_2H_5MgCl (0.5 equiv.)	$CH_3(n\text{-}C_3H_7)CHOH$ (56%); $CH_3CH(OH)CH_2Cl$ (73%)*	72
Propylene oxide	C_2H_5MgBr	$CH_3(n\text{-}C_3H_7)CHOH$ (60%)	60
Propylene oxide (45 g.)	C_2H_5MgBr (1.0 equiv.)	$CH_3(n\text{-}C_3H_7)CHOH$ (8 g., 11.7%); $(C_2H_5)_2CHOH$	103
Propylene oxide	C_2H_5MgBr (1.0 equiv.)	$CH_3(n\text{-}C_3H_7)CHOH$ (13%); $CH_3CH(OH)CH_2Br$	69
Propylene oxide	C_2H_5MgBr (0.5 equiv.)	$CH_3(n\text{-}C_3H_7)CHOH$ (54%); $CH_3CH(OH)CH_2Br$ (76%)	69
Propylene oxide (25.2 g.)	$(C_2H_5)_2Mg$ (0.47 equiv.)	$CH_3(n\text{-}C_3H_7)CHOH$ (9.0 g., 23%)	103
Propylene oxide	$n\text{-}C_3H_7MgCl$ (1.0 equiv.)	$CH_3(n\text{-}C_4H_9)CHOH$ (28%); $CH_3CH(OH)CH_2Cl$ (50%)†	72
Propylene oxide	$n\text{-}C_3H_7MgCl$ (1.0 equiv.)	$CH_3(n\text{-}C_4H_9)CHOH$ (31%); $CH_3CH(OH)CH_2Cl$ (35%)‡	72
Propylene oxide	$n\text{-}C_3H_7MgCl$ (0.5 equiv.)	$CH_3(n\text{-}C_4H_9)CHOH$ (63%); $CH_3CH(OH)CH_2Cl$ (64%)*	72
Propylene oxide	$n\text{-}C_3H_7MgBr$ (1.0 equiv.)	$CH_3(n\text{-}C_4H_9)CHOH$ (4%); $CH_3CH(OH)CH_2Br$ (69%)	69
Propylene oxide	$n\text{-}C_3H_7MgBr$ (0.5 equiv.)	$CH_3(n\text{-}C_4H_9)CHOH$ (51%); $CH_3CH(OH)CH_2Br$ (74%)	69
(+)-Propylene oxide	$n\text{-}C_3H_7MgBr$	(−)-$CH_3(n\text{-}C_4H_9)CHOH$	87
Propylene oxide	$i\text{-}C_3H_7MgCl$ (1.0 equiv.)	$CH_3(i\text{-}C_4H_9)CHOH$ (23%); $CH_3CH(OH)CH_2Cl$ (55%)†	72

* Dropwise addition of Et_2O-oxide solution to stirred Grignard reagent solution; one hour stirring; several days standing (to negative Michler's ketone test).

† Dropwise addition of Et_2O-oxide solution to stirred Grignard reagent solution; one hour stirring; overnight standing.

‡ Dropwise addition of Et_2O-oxide solution to stirred Grignard reagent solution; one hour stirring; overnight standing; distillation of *ca.* half of Et_2O; addition of two volumes of C_6H_6; distillation to b.p. 75°; seven hours reflux with stirring; overnight standing.

TABLE XIV-I (Continued)

Epoxide	RMgX	Product(s)	Ref.
C_3H_6O (*cont.*)			
Propylene oxide	i-C_3H_7MgCl (1.0 equiv.)	$CH_3(i$-$C_4H_9)CHOH$ (30%); $CH_3CH(OH)CH_2Cl$ (53%)*	72
Propylene oxide	i-C_3H_7MgCl (0.5 equiv.)	$CH_3(i$-$C_4H_9)CHOH$ (46%); $CH_3CH(OH)CH_2Cl$ (81%)†	72
Propylene oxide	i-C_3H_7MgBr (1.0 equiv.)	$CH_3(i$-$C_4H_9)CHOH$ (7%); $CH_3CH(OH)CH_2Br$ (50%)	69
Propylene oxide	i-C_3H_7MgBr (0.5 equiv.)	$CH_3(i$-$C_4H_9)CHOH$ (38%); $CH_3CH(OH)CH_2Cl$ (76%)	69
(+)-Propylene oxide	i-C_3H_7MgBr	(−)-$CH_3(i$-$C_4H_9)CHOH$	88
Propylene oxide (116 g., 2 moles)	2-Thienyl-MgBr (163 g., 1 mole C_4H_3BrS)	1-(2-Thienyl)-2-propanol (84.5 g., 60%)	193
Propylene oxide (30 g.)	Pyrryl-MgBr (34 g. C_4H_5N)	1-α-Pyrryl-2-propanol	62
Propylene oxide	n-C_4H_9MgCl (1.0 equiv.)	$CH_3(n$-$C_5H_{11})CHOH$ (41%); $CH_3CH(OH)CH_2Cl$ (52%)‡	72
Propylene oxide	n-C_4H_9MgCl (1.0 equiv.)	$CH_3(n$-$C_5H_{11})CHOH$ (58%); $CH_3CH(OH)CH_2Cl$ (28%)*	72
Propylene oxide	n-C_4H_9MgCl (0.5 equiv.)	$CH_3(n$-$C_5H_{11})CHOH$ (59%); $CH_3CH(OH)CH_2Cl$ (77%)†	72
Propylene oxide (12 g.)	n-C_4H_9MgBr (28 g. C_4H_9Br)	$CH_3(n$-$C_5H_{11})CHOH$ (30%);	91
Propylene oxide	n-C_4H_9MgBr (1.0 equiv.)	$CH_3(n$-$C_5H_{11})CHOH$ (5%); $CH_3CH(OH)CH_2Br$ (67%)	69
Propylene oxide	n-C_4H_9MgBr (0.5 equiv.)	$CH_3(n$-$C_5H_{11})CHOH$ (56%); $CH_3CH(OH)CH_2Br$ (70%)	69

* Dropwise addition of Et_2O-oxide solution to stirred Grignard reagent solution; one hour stirring; overnight standing; distillation of *ca.* half of Et_2O; addition of two volumes of C_6H_6; distillation to b.p. 75°; seven hours reflux with stirring; overnight standing.

† Dropwise addition of Et_2O-oxide solution to stirred Grignard reagent solution; one hour stirring; several days standing (to negative Michler's ketone test).

‡ Dropwise addition of Et_2O-oxide solution to stirred Grignard reagent solution; one hour stirring; overnight standing.

TABLE XIV-I (Continued)

Epoxide	RMgX	Product(s)	Ref.
C_3H_6O (*cont.*)			
Propylene oxide	*i*-C_4H_9MgCl (1.0 equiv.)	CH_3(*i*-C_5H_{11})CHOH (19%); $CH_3CH(OH)CH_2Cl$ (58%)*	72
Propylene oxide	*i*-C_4H_9MgCl (1.0 equiv.)	CH_3(*i*-C_5H_{11})CHOH (40%); $CH_3CH(OH)CH_2Cl$ (19%)†	72
Propylene oxide	*i*-C_4H_9MgCl (0.5 equiv.)	CH_3(*i*-C_5H_{11})CHOH (62%); $CH_3CH(OH)CH_2Cl$ (73%)‡	72
Propylene oxide (12 g.)	*i*-C_4H_9MgBr (28 g. C_4H_9Br)	CH_3(*i*-C_5H_{11})CHOH (20%)	91
Propylene oxide	*i*-C_4H_9MgBr (1.0 equiv.)	CH_3(*i*-C_5H_{11})CHOH (4%); $CH_3CH(OH)CH_2Br$ (64%)	69
Propylene oxide	*i*-C_4H_9MgBr (0.5 equiv.)	CH_3(*i*-C_5H_{11})CHOH (15%); $CH_3CH(OH)CH_2Br$ (28%)	69
Propylene oxide	*s*-C_4H_9MgCl (1.0 equiv.)	CH_3(*s*-$C_4H_9CH_2$)CHOH (10%); $CH_3CH(OH)CH_2Cl$ (54%)*	72
Propylene oxide	*s*-C_4H_9MgCl (1.0 equiv.)	CH_3(*s*-$C_4H_9CH_2$)CHOH (16%); $CH_3CH(OH)CH_2Cl$ (24%)†	72
Propylene oxide	*s*-C_4H_9MgCl (0.5 equiv.)	CH_3(*s*-$C_4H_9CH_2$)CHOH (30%); $CH_3CH(OH)CH_2Cl$ (69%)‡	72
Propylene oxide	*s*-C_4H_9MgBr (1.0 equiv.)	CH_3(*s*-$C_4H_9CH_2$)CHOH (4%); $CH_3CH(OH)CH_2Br$ (62%)	69
Propylene oxide	*s*-C_4H_9MgBr (0.5 equiv.)	CH_3(*s*-$C_4H_9CH_2$)CHOH (31%); $CH_3CH(OH)CH_2Br$ (62%)	69
Propylene oxide (220 g.)	*t*-C_4H_9MgCl (150 g. Mg)	C_2H_5(*t*-C_4H_9)CHOH (11%)	126

* Dropwise addition of Et_2O-oxide solution to stirred Grignard reagent solution; one hour stirring; overnight standing.

† Dropwise addition of Et_2O-oxide solution to stirred Grignard reagent solution; one hour stirring; overnight standing; distillation of *ca.* half of Et_2O; addition of two volumes of C_6H_6; distillation to b.p. 75°; seven hours reflux with stirring; overnight standing.

‡ Dropwise addition of Et_2O-oxide solution to stirred Grignard reagent solution; one hour stirring; several days standing (to negative Michler's ketone test).

TABLE XIV-I (Continued)

Epoxide	RMgX	Product(s)	Ref.
C_3H_6O (*cont.*)			
Propylene oxide	t-C_4H_9MgCl (1.0 equiv.)	$CH_3(t\text{-}C_4H_9CH_2)CHOH$ (0%); $CH_3CH(OH)CH_2Cl$ (65%)*	*72*
Propylene oxide	t-C_4H_9MgCl (1.0 equiv.)	$CH_3(t\text{-}C_4H_9CH_2)CHOH$ (25%); $CH_3CH(OH)CH_2Cl$ (3%)†	*72*
Propylene oxide	t-C_4H_9MgCl (0.5 equiv.)	$CH_3(t\text{-}C_4H_9CH_2)CHOH$ (15%); $CH_3CH(OH)CH_2Cl$ (61%)‡	*72*
Propylene oxide	t-C_4H_9MgBr (1.0 equiv.)	$CH_3(t\text{-}C_4H_9CH_2)CHOH$ (4%); $CH_3CH(OH)CH_2Br$ (62%)	*69*
Propylene oxide	t-C_4H_9MgBr (0.5 equiv.)	$CH_3(t\text{-}C_4H_9CH_2)CHOH$ (15%); $CH_3CH(OH)CH_2Br$ (52%)	*69*
Propylene oxide (180 g.)	C_6H_5MgBr (471 g. C_6H_5Br)	$CH_3(C_6H_5CH_2)CHOH$ (244 g., 60%)	*98*
Propylene oxide	C_6H_5MgBr (1.0 equiv.)	$CH_3(C_6H_5CH_2)CHOH$ (47%); $CH_3CH(OH)CH_2Br$ (39%)	*69*
Propylene oxide	C_6H_5MgBr (0.5 equiv.)	$CH_3(C_6H_5CH_2)CHOH$ (67%); $CH_3CH(OH)CH_2Br$ (74%)	*69*
(+)-Propylene oxide	C_6H_5MgBr	(−)-$CH_3(C_6H_5CH_2)CHOH$	*87*
Propylene oxide	3-$F_3CC_6H_4MgBr$	$CH_3(3\text{-}F_3CC_6H_4CH_2)CHOH$ + 3-$F_3CC_6H_4CH(CH_3)CH_2OH$ (aggregating 43%)	*191*
Propylene oxide	2-$CH_3C_6H_4MgBr$	$CH_3(2\text{-}CH_3C_6H_4CH_2)CHOH$ (55%)	*100*
Propylene oxide	3-$CH_3C_6H_4MgBr$	$CH_3(3\text{-}CH_3C_6H_4CH_2)CHOH$	*116*
Propylene oxide (88.0 g., 1.5 mole)	4-$CH_3C_6H_4MgBr$ (256.5 g., 1.5 mole C_7H_7Br)	$CH_3(4\text{-}CH_3C_6H_4CH_2)CHOH$ (87.1 g.)	*116*

* Dropwise addition of Et_2O-oxide solution to stirred Grignard reagent solution; one hour stirring; overnight standing.

† Dropwise addition of Et_2O-oxide solution to stirred Grignard reagent solution; one hour stirring; overnight standing; distillation of *ca.* half of Et_2O; addition of two volumes of C_6H_6; distillation to b.p. 75°; seven hours reflux with stirring; overnight standing.

‡ Dropwise addition of Et_2O-oxide solution to stirred Grignard reagent solution; one hour stirring; several days standing (to negative Michler's ketone test).

TABLE XIV-I (Continued)

Epoxide	RMgX	Product(s)	Ref.
C_3H_6O (*cont.*)			
Propylene oxide	2,4,6-$(CH_3)_3C_6H_2MgBr$ (1 equiv.)	$CH_3[2,4,6\text{-}(CH_3)_3C_6H_2CH_2]CHOH$ (58%); $CH_3CH(OH)CH_2Br$ (35%)	*69*
C_4H_6O			
3,4-Epoxy-1-butene	CH_3MgBr	$C_2H_5CH{=}CHCH_2OH$; $CH_3(H_2C{=}CH)CHCH_2OH$	*181*
3,4-Epoxy-1-butene	CH_3MgI	$C_2H_5CH{=}CHCH_2OH$ (35.7%)	*115*
3,4-Epoxy-1-butene (60.0 g., 0.855 mole)	C_2H_5MgBr (0.859 mole)	$C_2H_5(H_2C{=}CHCH_2)CHOH$ (16.1 g., 0.161 mole, 18.9%); $C_2H_5(H_2C{=}CH)CHCH_2OH$ (20.1 g., 0.201 mole, 23.5%); *n*-$C_3H_7CH{=}CHCH_2OH$ (26.8 g., 0.268 mole, 31.4%)	*38*
3,4-Epoxy-1-butene (106.0 g., 1.52 mole)	$(C_2H_5)_2Mg$ (0.76 mole)	$C_2H_5(H_2C{=}CH)CHCH_2OH$ (41.2 g., 53.4%); *n*-$C_3H_7CH{=}CHCH_2OH$ (13.1 g., 16.9%)	*38*
3,4-Epoxy-1-butene (52 g., 0.72 mole)	2-Thienyl-MgBr (135 g., 0.83 mole C_4H_3BrS)	$(\alpha\text{-}C_4H_3S)CH_2CH{=}CHCH_2OH$ (40 g., 26%)	*42*
3,4-Epoxy-1-butene	C_6H_5MgBr	$C_6H_5CH_2CH{=}CHCH_2OH$ (38.0%)	*115*
3,4-Epoxy-1-butene	$(CH_2)_5CHMgCl$	$(CH_2)_5CHCH_2CH{=}CHCH_2OH$ (34.0%)	*115*
3,4-Epoxy-1-butene	2-$C_2H_5OC_6H_4MgBr$	2-$C_2H_5OC_6H_4CH_2CH{=}CHCH_2OH$ (14.7%)	*115*
3,4-Epoxy-1-butene	1-$C_{10}H_7MgBr$	1-$C_{10}H_7CH_2CH{=}CHCH_2OH$ (30.2%)	*115;cf. 41*
3,4-Epoxy-1-butene (17.5 g., 0.25 mole)	1-$C_{10}H_7MgBr$ (51.8 g., 0.25 mole $C_{10}H_7Br$)	$H_2C{=}CH(1\text{-}C_{10}H_7CH_2)CHOH$ (27.2–28.6 g., 0.137–0.145 mole, 55–58%)	*41*
C_4H_8O			
(+)-α-Butylene oxide	*n*-C_3H_7MgBr	(−)-$C_2H_5(n\text{-}C_4H_9)CHOH$	88
(+)-α-Butylene oxide	*i*-C_3H_7MgBr	(−)-$C_2H_5(i\text{-}C_4H_9)CHOH$	88
β-Butylene oxide	CH_3MgBr (1.0 equiv.)	$CH_3(i\text{-}C_3H_7)CHOH$ (7%); $C_2H_5(CH_3)_2COH$ (44%)	27,59

TABLE XIV-I (Continued)

Epoxide	RMgX	Product(s)	Ref.
C_4H_8O *(cont.)*			
β-Butylene oxide (0.20 mole)	$(CH_3)_2Mg$ (0.105 mole)	$CH_3(i\text{-}C_3H_7)CHOH$ (6.1 g., 35%)	*27*
β-Butylene oxide	C_2H_5MgCl (1.0 equiv.)	$CH_3(s\text{-}C_4H_9)CHOH$ (27%); $CH_3(C_2H_5)_2COH$ (30%)	*27*
β-Butylene oxide	C_2H_5MgBr (1.0 equiv.)	$CH_3(s\text{-}C_4H_9)CHOH$ (2%); $CH_3(C_2H_5)_2COH$ (31%)	*27*
β-Butylene oxide	C_2H_5MgI (1.0 equiv.)	$CH_3(s\text{-}C_4H_9)CHOH$ (trace); $CH_3(C_2H_5)_2COH$ (27%)	*27*
β-Butylene oxide (0.62 mole)	$(C_2H_5)_2Mg$ (0.62 mole)	$CH_3(s\text{-}C_4H_9)CHOH$ (50 g., 79%)	*27*
cis-β-Butylene oxide (14.0 g.)	C_2H_5MgBr (1.0 equiv.)	$CH_3(C_2H_5)_2COH$ (3.5 g., 17.5%)	*103*
cis-β-Butylene oxide (19.0 g.)	$(C_2H_5)_2Mg$ (0.4 equiv.)	$CH_3(s\text{-}C_4H_9)CHOH$ (16.5 g., 61.0%)	*103*
trans-β-Butylene oxide (15.0 g.)	C_2H_5MgBr (1.0 equiv.)	$CH_3(C_2H_5)_2COH$ (10.5 g., 49.0%)	*103*
trans-β-Butylene oxide (21.0 g.)	$(C_2H_5)_2Mg$ (0.4 equiv.)	$CH_3(s\text{-}C_4H_9)CHOH$ (6.5 g., 21.8%)	*103*
Isobutylene oxide	CH_3MgBr	$CH_3(i\text{-}C_3H_7)CHOH$ (80.0%)	*57,58*
Isobutylene oxide	CH_3MgBr (2.0 equiv.)	$CH_3(i\text{-}C_3H_7)CHOH$ (40.8%); $BrCH_2C(CH_3)_2OH$ (40.2%)	*70*
Isobutylene oxide	$(CH_3)_2Mg$ (1.0 equiv.)	$C_2H_5(CH_3)_2COH$	*70*
Isobutylene oxide (135 g.)	C_2H_5MgBr (1.0 equiv.)	$C_2H_5(i\text{-}C_3H_7)CHOH$ (39 g., 21%)	*103*
Isobutylene oxide	C_2H_5MgBr (0.5 equiv.)	$C_2H_5(i\text{-}C_3H_7)CHOH$ (13.2%); $n\text{-}C_3H_7(CH_3)_2COH$ (17.9%); $(C_4H_8O)_3$ (14.0%); $BrCH_2C(CH_3)_2OH$ (51.2%)	*70*
Isobutylene oxide	C_2H_5MgBr (1.0 equiv.)	$C_2H_5(i\text{-}C_3H_7)CHOH$ (42.2%); $BrCH_2C(CH_3)_2OH$ (28.3%)	*70*
Isobutylene oxide	C_2H_5MgBr (2.0 equiv.)	$C_2H_5(i\text{-}C_3H_7)CHOH$ (51.4%); $BrCH_2C(CH_3)_2OH$ (40.4%)	*70*
Isobutylene oxide (29.0 g.)	$(C_2H_5)_2Mg$ (0.37 equiv.)	$n\text{-}C_3H_7(CH_3)_2COH$ (11.3 g., 27.5%)	*103*
Isobutylene oxide	$(C_2H_5)_2Mg$ (1.0 equiv.)	$n\text{-}C_3H_7(CH_3)_2COH$ (35.0%)	*70*
Isobutylene oxide	$n\text{-}C_3H_7MgBr$ (0.5 equiv.)	$n\text{-}C_3H_7(i\text{-}C_3H_7)CHOH$ (12.8%); $n\text{-}C_4H_9(CH_3)_2COH$ (15.2%); $(C_4H_8O)_3$ (28.0%); $BrCH_2C(CH_3)_2OH$ (57.2%)	*70*

TABLE XIV-I (Continued)

Epoxide	RMgX	Product(s)	Ref.
C_4H_8O (*cont.*)			
Isobutylene oxide	n-C_3H_7MgBr (1.0 equiv.)	n-C_3H_7(i-C_3H_7)CHOH (39.4%); $BrCH_2C(CH_3)_2OH$ (30.5%)	*70*
Isobutylene oxide	n-C_3H_7MgBr (2.0 equiv.)	n-C_3H_7(i-C_3H_7)CHOH (44.5%); $BrCH_2C(CH_3)_2OH$ (23.0%)	*70*
Isobutylene oxide	(n-$C_3H_7)_2Mg$ (1.0 equiv.)	n-$C_4H_9(CH_3)_2COH$ (25.5%)	*70*
Isobutylene oxide	i-C_3H_7MgBr (2.0 equiv.)	(i-$C_3H_7)_2CHOH$ (21.5%); $BrCH_2C(CH_3)_2OH$ (60.0%)	*70*
Isobutylene oxide	n-C_4H_9MgBr (2.0 equiv.)	n-C_4H_9(i-C_3H_7)CHOH (20.1%); $BrCH_2C(CH_3)_2OH$ (41.0%)	*70*
Isobutylene oxide	(n-$C_4H_9)_2Mg$	n-$C_5H_{11}(CH_3)_2COH$ (11.5%)	*70*
Isobutylene oxide	t-C_4H_9MgBr (2.0 equiv.)	i-C_3H_7(t-C_4H_9)CHOH (0.0%); $BrCH_2(CH_3)_2OH$ (56.0%)	*70*
Isobutylene oxide	(t-$C_4H_9)_2Mg$	t-$C_4H_9CH_2(CH_3)_2COH$ (6.0%)	*70*
$C_4H_8O_2$			
1,2-Epoxy-3-methoxypropane	C_6H_5MgBr	$CH_3OCH_2(C_6H_5CH_2)CHOH$; $BrCH_2(CH_3OCH)_2CHOH$	*109*
C_5H_8O			
Cyclopentene oxide	CH_3MgI (2.0 equiv.)	*cis*-2-Methylcyclopentanol ("good yield")	*46*
Cyclopentene oxide (3.9 g.)	CH_3MgI (2.0 equiv.)	2-Iodocyclopentanol	*141*
C_5H_8OBr			
1-Bromo-2,3-epoxypentane (33 g.)	C_2H_5MgBr (30 g. C_2H_5Br)	$BrCH_2(C_2H_5CHBr)CHOH$ (20 g.)	*30,29*
1-Bromo-2,3-epoxypentane (33 g.)	C_6H_5MgBr (38 g. C_6H_5Br)	$BrCH_2(C_2H_5CHBr)CHOH$ (14 g.); unidentified products (12 g.)	*30,29*

TABLE XIV-I (Continued)

Epoxide	RMgX	Product(s)	Ref.
$C_5H_{10}O$			
2,3-Epoxypentane	C_2H_5MgBr	$CH_3[(C_2H_5)_2CH]CHOH$	*36*
1,2-Epoxy-2-methylbutane	C_2H_5MgBr	$C_2H_5(s\text{-}C_4H_9)CHOH$	*36*
1,2-Epoxy-3-methylbutane (17 g.)	C_2H_5MgBr (22 g. C_2H_5Br)	$n\text{-}C_3H_7(i\text{-}C_3H_7)CHOH$ (63%)	*174*
1,2-Epoxy-3-methylbutane	$n\text{-}C_3H_7MgBr$	$i\text{-}C_3H_7(n\text{-}C_4H_9)CHOH$ (38%)	*174*
1,2-Epoxy-3-methylbutane	$i\text{-}C_3H_7MgBr$	$i\text{-}C_3H_7(i\text{-}C_4H_9)CHOH$ (41%)	*174*
2,3-Epoxy-2-methylbutane	CH_3MgBr	$i\text{-}C_3H_7(CH_3)_2COH$	*56,61*
2,3-Epoxy-2-methylbutane (40 g.)	C_2H_5MgBr (1.0 equiv.)	$CH_3(C_2H_5)(i\text{-}C_3H_7)COH$ (27 g., 50%)	*103*
2,3-Epoxy-2-methylbutane (25.8 g.)	$(C_2H_5)_2Mg$ (0.4 equiv.)	$s\text{-}C_4H_9(CH_3)_2COH$ (7.0 g., 21%)	*103*
C_6H_8O			
3,4-Epoxycyclohexene	C_2H_5MgBr	2-Cyclopentene-1-carboxaldehyde; 3-cyclohexen-1-one	*132*
4,5-Epoxycyclohexene	C_2H_5MgBr	3-Cyclopentene-1-carboxaldehyde; 3-cyclohexen-1-one	*132*
$C_6H_{10}O$			
1-Methylcyclopentene oxide	CH_3MgI	1,2-Dimethylcyclopentanol* (40%)	*151*
Cyclohexene oxide	CH_3MgBr	$(CH_2)_4CHCH_2OH$; $CH_3COCH(CH_2)_4$ (20–25%)	*10*
Cyclohexene oxide (26 g.)	CH_3MgI (80 g. CH_3I)	$(CH_2)_4CHCH(CH_3)OH$† (63%)	*48,43*
Cyclohexene oxide	$(CH_3)_2Mg$	*trans*-2-Methylcyclohexanol	7
Cyclohexene oxide	C_2H_5MgBr	$(CH_2)_4CHCH_2OH$ and $C_2H_5COCH(CH_2)_4$ (aggregating 55%)	*10;cf. 142*

* This product is said to be stereoisomeric with that obtained by van Rysselberge, *Bull. acad. roy. Belg., Classe sci.*, [5], *12*, 171–92 (1926), through the reaction of 2-methylcyclopentanone with CH_3MgI.

† Erroneously reported by Godchot and Bedos (*48,43*) as *cis*-2-methylcyclohexanol; *cf.* Vavon and Mitchovitch (*137*); Godchot, Bedos, and Cauquil (*166*).

TABLE XIV-I (Continued)

Epoxide	RMgX	Product(s)	Ref.
$C_6H_{10}O$ (*cont.*)			
Cyclohexene oxide (18.5 g.)	$(C_2H_5)_2Mg$ (180 ml., 1.04*N*)	*trans*-2-Methylcyclohexanol (10.0 g., 42%)	7
Cyclohexene oxide (24.5 g., 0.25 mole)	$H_2C{=}CHCH_2MgBr$ (0.75 mole C_3H_5Br)	2-Allylcyclohexanol* (22.5 g., 64%); 2-bromocyclohexanol (?)	*172*
Cyclohexene oxide	C_6H_5MgBr	2-Bromocyclohexanol (chief product); 2-phenylcyclohexanol	8,*142*,*143*; *cf*. *24*
Cyclohexene oxide	C_6H_5MgBr	$(CH_2)_4CH(C_6H_5)CHOH$	*24*
Cyclohexene oxide	$(CH_2)_5CHMgCl$	$(CH_2)_4CH[(CH_2)_5CH]CHOH$	*136*; *cf*. 9, *144*
Cyclohexene oxide (35.0 g.)	$C_6H_5CH_2MgCl$ (47.5 ml. C_7H_7Cl)	2-Benzylcyclohexanol† (34.0 g., 50%); stereoisomeric 2-chlorocyclohexanols (10.0 g.)	*24*
Cyclohexene oxide (19.8 g.)	$C_6H_5CH_2CH_2MgBr$ (74.0 g. C_8H_9Br)	$(CH_2)_4CH(C_6H_5CH_2CH_2)CHOH$‡ (37.3 g., 91.5%)	*39*
$C_6H_{10}O_2$			
1,2,5,6-Diepoxyhexane (4.4 g.)	CH_3MgI (2.4 equiv. CH_3I)	1,6-Diiodo-2,5-dihydroxyhexane, m. 116–117° (0.4 g.); stereoisomer, m. 94–95° (4.8 g.)	*110*
$C_6H_{12}O$			
2,3-Epoxy-2,3-dimethylbutane (50 g.)	C_2H_5MgBr (1.0 equiv.)	$CH_3(C_2H_5)(t\text{-}C_4H_9)COH$ (25 g., 38%)	*103*

* The identity of the product was established by hydrogenation to 2-propylcyclohexanol, followed by oxidation to 2-propylcyclohexanone, which was compared with an authentic specimen directly and through the oximes, semicarbazones, and 2,4-dinitrophenylhydrazones.

† The identity of the product was established by oxidation to the ketone and comparison of the semicarbazone with that of an authentic specimen (from α-benzylpimelic acid).

‡ Erroneously reported by Fulton and Robinson (*39*) as 2-phenethylcyclohexanol; *cf*., however, Cook *et al*. (*24*) and Robinson (*112*).

TABLE XIV-I (Continued)

Epoxide	RMgX	Product(s)	Ref.
$C_6H_{12}O$ (*cont.*)			
2,3-Epoxy-2,3-dimethylbutane (20 g.)	$(C_2H_5)_2Mg$ (0.4 equiv.)	$C_2H_5(CH_3)_2C(CH_3)_2COH$ (9 g., 34.6%)	*103*
$C_7H_{12}O$			
1,2-Epoxy-4-methylcyclohexane (26 g.)	CH_3MgI (80 g. CH_3I)	"cis"-2,5-Dimethoxycyclohexanol,* allophanate m. 157–158° (64%)	*49,44*
1,2-Epoxy-4-methylcyclohexane	i-C_3H_7MgBr	Menthol,* allophanate m. 177°	*146,145*
Cycloheptene oxide	CH_3MgI	1-Methylcycloheptanol†	*47*
C_8H_8O			
Styrene oxide	CH_3MgBr	$CH_3(C_6H_5CH_2)CHOH$	*131; cf. 36*
Styrene oxide	CH_3MgI (1 equiv.)	$CH_3(C_6H_5CH_2)CHOH$ (51–53%)	*51*
Styrene oxide (0.25 mole)	$(CH_3)_2Mg$ (0.13 mole)	$CH_3(C_6H_5)CHCH_2OH$ (60%)	*51*
Styrene oxide	C_2H_5MgBr	$C_2H_5(C_6H_5CH_2)CHOH$	*131*
Styrene oxide	C_6H_5MgBr (1 or 2 equiv.)	$(C_6H_5)_2CHCH_2OH$‡	*81*
Styrene oxide	C_6H_5MgBr	$C_6H_5(C_6H_5CH_2)CHOH$§	*81*
Styrene oxide	4-$CH_3OC_6H_4MgBr$	C_6H_4(4-$CH_3OC_6H_4$)$CHCH_2OH$; C_6H_4(4-$CH_3OC_6H_4$)$C{=}CH_2$‡	*81*
Styrene oxide	4-$CH_3OC_6H_4MgBr$	4-$CH_3OC_6H_4CH{=}CHC_6H_5$§	*81*
$C_9H_{10}O$			
α-Methylstyrene oxide (25.0 g.)	t-C_4H_9MgCl (20.0 g. C_4H_9Cl)	t-$C_4H_9[CH_3(C_6H_5)CH]CHOH$ (10.5 g.); (t-C_4H_9 —$)_2$ (14.0 g.)	*80*

*It is altogether possible that the constitutional assignment is in error, and that the product is in fact a cyclopentylcarbinol.

†Gaylord and Becker, *Chem. Revs.*, *49*, 488*f* (1951), question the constitution assigned to this product. To say the least, the identification seems inadequate.

‡Slow addition of oxide to stirred Grignard reagent solution; one hour reflux.

§Slow addition of Grignard reagent solution to stirred, ice-cooled Et_2O-oxide solution; one hour reflux.

TABLE XIV-I (Continued)

Epoxide	RMgX	Product(s)	Ref.
$C_9H_{10}O$ (*cont.*)			
α-Methylstyrene oxide	C_6H_5MgBr	$C_6H_5[CH_3(C_6H_5)CH]CHOH$	*130*
$C_9H_{10}O_2$			
Phenylglycide* (14.5 g.)	C_6H_5MgBr (16.0 g. C_6H_5Br)	$C_6H_5CH_2(C_6H_5OCH_2)CHOH$ (16.5 g., 75%)	*15*
$C_9H_{14}O_4$			
3,4-Isopropylidene-1,2,5,6-dianhydromannitol (3.7 g.)	CH_3MgI (3 ml., 2.4 equiv. CH_3I)	1,6-Diiodo-3,4-isopropylidene-1,6-dideoxymannitol (4.9 g., 54%)	*110*
$C_9H_{16}O_4$			
4,6-Dimethyl-α-methyl-2,3-anhydroalloside (14.5 g.)	CH_3MgI (12.7 g. CH_3I)	4,6-Dimethyl-α-methyl-3-iodo-3-deoxyglucoside (1.38 g., 5.8%); (after acetylation of residue): 3-acetyl-4,6-dimethyl-α-methyl-2-iodo-2-deoxyglucoside; 2-acetyl-4,6-dimethyl-α-methyl-3-deoxyglucoside (?) (2.45 g., 15.9%)	*176*
$C_{10}H_{12}O$			
1-Phenyl-2-methyl-1,2-epoxypropane	C_2H_5MgBr	$C_6H_5[C_2H_5(CH_3)_2C]CHOH$; $C_2H_5(C_6H_5)CHC(CH_3)_2OH$	*105*
$C_{10}H_{12}O_2$			
1-Methoxy-1-phenyl-1,2-epoxypropane	CH_3MgI	$CH_3(CH_3O)(C_6H_5)CCH(OH)CH_3$ (85%)	*190*
1-Methoxy-1-phenyl-1,2-epoxypropane	C_6H_5MgBr	$CH_3O(C_6H_5)_2CCH(OH)CH_3$ (88%)	*190,192*

* 1-Phenyl-3-hydroxy-1,2-epoxypropane.

TABLE XIV-I (Continued)

Epoxide	RMgX	Product(s)	Ref.
$C_{10}H_{16}O$			
α-Pinene oxide* (35 g.)	CH_3MgI (36 g. CH_3I)	α-2,2,3-Tetramethyl-Δ^3-cyclopentene-ethanol (29 g.)	*111,1; cf. 106*
α-Pinene oxide*	C_2H_5MgX (1.0 equiv.)	α-Ethyl-2,2,3-trimethyl-Δ^3-cyclopentene-ethanol (*ca.* 70%)	*111; cf. 106*
α-Pinene oxide*	*n*-C_3H_7MgX (1.0 equiv.)	α-*n*-Propyl-2,2,3-trimethyl-Δ^3-cyclopenteneëthanol (*ca.* 70%)	*111;cf. 106*
α-Pinene oxide*	*n*-C_4H_9MgX (1.0 equiv.)	α-*n*-Butyl-2,2,3-trimethyl-Δ^3-cyclopenteneëthanol (*ca.* 70%)	*111; cf. 106*
α-Pinene oxide*	*i*-C_4H_9MgX (1.0 equiv.)	α-Isobutyl-2,2,3-trimethyl-Δ^3-cyclopenteneëthanol (*ca.* 70%)	*111,1; cf. 106*
α-Pinene oxide*	C_6H_5MgBr (1.0 equiv.)	α-Phenyl-2,2,3-trimethyl-Δ^3-cyclopentene-ethanol (*ca.* 70%)	*111,1; cf. 106*
β-Pinene oxide†	RMgX	RH; "a monocyclic primary alcohol"‡	*179*
$C_{11}H_{14}O$			
1-(1-Cyclohexenyl)-3-methyl-3,4-epoxy-1-butyne (8.1 g., 0.05 mole)	C_2H_5MgBr (0.075 mole)	4-Methyl-9-(1-cyclohexenyl)-5-hexyn-3-ol (6.0 g., 40%)	*123*
1-(1-Cyclohexenyl)-3-methyl-3,4-epoxy-1-butyne (48.0 g., 0.3 mole)	$CH_3OCH_2CH{=}C(CH_3)C{\equiv}CMgBr$ (0.3 mole)	1-(1-Cyclohexenyl)-3,7-dimethyl-9-methoxy-7-nonen-1,5-diyn-4-ol (7.7 g., 10%)	*123*
$C_{14}H_{12}O$			
Stilbene oxide (8.0 g.)	CH_3MgBr (8.0 g. CH_3Br)	α-$C_6H_5[CH_3(C_6H_5)CH]CHOH$ (*ca.* 5%); *trans*-$(C_6H_5CH{=})_2$	*170,79*

* 2,3-Epoxy-2,6,6-trimethylbicyclo[3.1.1]heptane.
† 2-Methylene-6,6-dimethylbicyclo[3.1.1]heptane oxide.
‡ According to Gaylord and Becker, *Chem. Revs.*, *49*, 497 (1950), this product is probably a derivative of dihydromyrtenal.

TABLE XIV-I (Continued)

Epoxide	RMgX	Product(s)	Ref.
$C_{14}H_{12}O$ (*cont.*)			
Stilbene oxide	CH_3MgI	Complex mixture	*170*
Stilbene oxide	C_2H_5MgBr	β-$C_6H_5[C_2H_5(C_6H_5)CH]CHOH$,* m. 82° (25%)	*170,79*
Stilbene oxide (8.0 g.)	$C_6H_5CH_2MgCl$	β-$C_6H_5[C_6H_5(C_6H_5CH_2)CH]CHOH$, m. 87° (8.0 g., 50%); *trans*-$(C_6H_5CH=)_2$ (3.0 g.)	*170,79*
Isostilbene oxide	CH_3MgBr	α-$C_6H_5[CH_3(C_6H_5)CH]CHOH$; *trans*-$(C_6H_5CH=)_2$	*170*
Isostilbene oxide	CH_3MgI	*trans*-$(C_6H_5CH=)_2$; unidentified products	*170*
Isostilbene oxide	C_2H_5MgBr	α-$C_6H_5[C_2H_5(C_6H_5)CH]CHOH$†	*170*
Isostilbene oxide (5.0 g.)	$C_6H_5CH_2MgCl$	α-$C_6H_5[C_6H_5(C_6H_5CH_2)CH]CHOH$, m. 92° (3.5 g., 50%)	*170,79*
$C_{14}H_{16}O_4$			
4,6-Benzylidene-α-methyl-2,3-anhydroalloside (7.0 g.)	CH_3MgI (5.0 g. CH_3I)	4,6-Benzylidene-α-methyl-3-iodo-3-deoxyglucoside (13.6 g., 80%)	*176*
$C_{15}H_{11}O_2Cl$			
α-(2-Chlorophenyl)-β-benzoylethylene oxide (15.0 g.)	C_6H_5MgBr (2.8 g. Mg)	Recovered oxidoketone (2.0 g.); 1,1-diphenyl-2,3-epoxy-3-o-chlorophenyl-1-propanol (13.5 g.)	*171*
$C_{15}H_{12}O_2$			
Benzylideneacetophenone oxide (35 g.)	C_2H_5MgBr (5.0 equiv.)	$C_6H_5(C_2H_5)_2COH$ (17 g., 66%); gum	85

* Identical with that obtained by reduction of $C_2H_5(C_6H_5)CHCOC_6H_5$.
† Identical with that obtained from $C_2H_5(C_6H_5)CHCHO + C_6H_5MgBr$.

TABLE XIV-I (Continued)

Epoxide	RMgX	Product(s)	Ref.
$C_{15}H_{12}O_2$ (*cont.*)			
Benzylideneacetophenone oxide (34 g.)	C_6H_5MgBr (47 g. C_6H_5Br)	1,1,3-Triphenyl-2,3-epoxy-1-propanol (22 g.)	*85*
Benzylideneacetophenone oxide	C_6H_5MgBr (5.0 equiv.)	$(C_6H_5)_3COH$ (*ca.* 70%); gum	*85*
$C_{15}H_{24}O$			
Copaene oxide* (7.30 g.)	CH_3MgI (3.0 equiv.)	2,8,9-Trimethyl-5-isopropyltricyclo[$4.4.0.0^{2,4}$]decan-8-ol (6.43 g., 82%, crude)	*16*
Cadinene monoxide† (44.5 g.)	CH_3MgCl (excess)	After Se dehydrogen'n: "monomethylcadalene"‡	*20*
$C_{15}H_{24}O_2$			
Cadinene dioxide§ (35.5 g.)	CH_3MgCl (36.0 g. Mg)	After Se dehydrogen'n: "dimethylcadalene"¶ (0.6 g., crude)	*20*
$C_{16}H_{10}O_3$			
Benzylidene-*p*-methoxyacetophenone oxide (5.0 g.)	C_6H_5MgBr (10.5 ml. C_6H_5Br)	$HO(C_6H_5)(4\text{-}CH_3OC_6H_4)CCH(C_6H_5)CH(C_6H_5)OH$ (3.0 g.)	*11*
$C_{16}H_{14}O_3$			
α-Phenyl-β-*p*-anisoylethylene oxide (15.0 g.)	C_6H_5MgBr (1 equiv.)	Recovered oxidoketone (7.5 g.); $(C_6H_5)_2CHCH(OH)C(OH)(C_6H_5)C_6H_4\text{-}4\text{-}OCH_3$, m. 132° (12.0 g.)‖	*149*

* 1,8-Dimethyl-5-isopropyl-8,9-epoxytricyclo[$4.4.0.0^{2,4}$]decane.

† 1,6-Dimethyl-1,2-epoxy-4-isopropyl-1,2,3,4,4a,5,8,8a-octahydronaphthalene.

‡ 1,2,6-Trimethyl-4-isopropylnaphthalene.

§ 1,6-Dimethyl-1,2,6,7-diepoxy-4-isopropyltetralin.

¶ 1,2,6,7-Tetramethyl-4-isopropylnaphthalene.

‖ Inverse addition at −15°; half-hour stirring.

TABLE XIV-I (Continued)

Epoxide	RMgX	Product(s)	Ref.
$C_{16}H_{14}O_3$ *(cont.)*			
α-Phenyl-β-*p*-anisoylethylene oxide (15.0 g.)	C_6H_5MgBr (4 equiv.)	$(C_6H_5)_2CHCH(OH)C(OH)(C_6H_5)C_6H_4$-4-$OCH_3$, m. 132° (23.5 g.)*	*149*
$C_{17}H_{16}O_3$			
Ethyl β,β-diphenylglycidate†	C_6H_5MgBr ("large excess")	$(C_6H_5)_3COH$; $(C_6H_5)_2CHCHO$; $(C_6H_5—)_2$	*85*
$C_{18}H_{21}O_2N$			
Desoxycodeïne-C (10.0 g.)	CH_3MgI (120 ml., 1.0 *M*)	Methyldihydrodesoxycodeïne (5.7 g., 55%)	*118*
Desoxycodeïne-C (11.0 g.)	C_2H_5MgI (240% excess)	α-Ethyldihydrodesoxycodeïne (3.5 g.)	*118*
Desoxycodeïne-C (5.5 g.)	C_6H_5MgBr (70 ml., 1.0 *M*)	Phenyldihydrodesoxycodeïne (5.2 g.); recovered oxide (0.8 g.)	*118*
Desoxycodeïne-C (6.8 g.)	$(CH_2)_5CHMgCl$ (150 ml., 0.6 *M*)	Cyclohexyldihydrodesoxycodeïne (isolated as perchlorate, 6.8 g.)	*118*
$C_{19}H_{30}O_3$			
Δ^5-3(β),17(α)-Androstanediol 5,6-oxide (0.06 g.)	CH_3MgI (1.5 g. CH_3I)	6-Methylandrostane-3,5,17-triol	*173*
$C_{21}H_{16}O_2$			
Benzylidene-*p*-phenylacetophenone oxide (10.0 g.)	C_6H_5MgBr (20 ml. C_6H_5Br)	$[HO(C_6H_5)(4\text{-}C_6H_5C_6H_4)C—]_2$; $HO(C_6H_5)$-$(4\text{-}C_6H_5C_6H_4)CCH(C_6H_5)CH(C_6H_5)OH$	*11*
α,β-Epoxy-β,β-diphenylpropiophenone	C_2H_5MgI (excess)	$(C_6H_5)_2CHCHO$	*85*
α,β-Epoxy-β-*p*-biphenylylpropiophenone (5.0 g.)	C_6H_5MgBr (12.0 g. C_6H_5Br)	4-$C_6H_5C_6H_4(C_6H_5)_2COH$ (2.8 g.); gum	*5*

* Normal addition; one hour reflux.

† Ethyl α,β-epoxy-β-β-diphenylpropionate; according to Kohler *et al.* (*85*), the supposed glycidate investigated by Bardon and Ramart (*6*) was in fact the isomeric glyoxylate, $(C_6H_5)_2CHCOCO_2C_2H_5$.

TABLE XIV-I (Continued)

Epoxide	RMgX	Product(s)	Ref.
$C_{21}H_{16}O_2$ (*cont.*)			
α,β-Epoxy-β-*p*-biphenylylpropiophenone (5.0 g.)	$C_6H_5MgBr + Mg + MgBr_2$	$[HO(C_6H_5)(4\text{-}C_6H_5C_6H_4)C—]_2$ (2.0 g.)	*5*
α,β-Epoxy-β,β-diphenylpropiophenone	C_6H_5MgBr (excess)	$(C_6H_5)_2CHCHO$; $(C_6H_5)_2CHOH$	*85*
1,3,3-Triphenyl-2,3-epoxy-1-propanol	CH_3MgI (1.25 equiv.)	C_6H_5CHO; $(C_6H_5)_2CHCHO$; $(C_6H_5)_2CHCOCH(C_6H_5)OH$ (?)	*85*
1,1,3-Triphenyl-2,3-epoxy-1-propanol	C_6H_5MgBr (excess)	$(C_6H_5)_3COH$	*85*
1,3,3-Triphenyl-2,3-epoxy-1-propanol	C_6H_5MgBr (excess)	$(C_6H_5)_2CHCHO$; $(C_6H_5)_2CHOH$; $(C_6H_5—)_2$	*5*
$C_{21}H_{17}O_2Cl$			
1,1-Diphenyl-2,3-epoxy-3-*o*-chlorophenyl-1-propanol	C_2H_5MgBr	$C_2H_5(C_6H_5)_2COH$*	*171*
$C_{21}H_{24}O_2$			
α-Mesityl-α-mesitoylethylene oxide	CH_3MgI	$2,4,6\text{-}(CH_3)_3C_6H_2COC[C_6H_2\text{-}2,4,6\text{-}(CH_3)_3]{=}CH_2$ (*ca.* quant.)	*40*
α-Mesityl-α-mesitoylethylene oxide	C_2H_5MgBr	$2,4,6\text{-}(CH_3)_3C_6H_2COC[C_6H_2\text{-}2,4,6\text{-}(CH_3)_3]{=}CH_2$ (*ca.* quant.)	*40*
α-Mesityl-α-mesitoylethylene oxide	C_6H_5MgBr	$2,4,6\text{-}(CH_3)_3C_6H_2COC[C_6H_2\text{-}2,4,6\text{-}(CH_3)_3]{=}CH_2$ (*ca.* quant.)	*40*
α-Mesityl-β-mesitoylethylene oxide	C_2H_5MgBr	$2,4,6\text{-}(CH_3)_3C_6H_2CH(C_2H_5)CH(OH)COC_6H_2\text{-}2,4,6\text{-}(CH_3)_3$ (?)	*40*

*The formation of this product is interpreted as arising from cleavage of the propoxide initially formed: $ROMgBr \rightarrow (C_6H_5)_2CO + C_6H_5CH{=}CHOMgBr$.

TABLE XIV-I (Continued)

Epoxide	RMgX	Product(s)	Ref.
$C_{21}H_{34}O_4$			
3(β),20,21-Pregnanetriol 5,6-oxide	CH_3MgBr	6-Methyl-3(β),5,20,21-pregnanetetrol	*157*
$C_{21}H_{36}O_3$			
Methyl 1,4a,7-trimethyl-7,8-epoxy-8a-ethylperhydro-1-phenanthrene-carboxylate (4.0 g.)	CH_3MgI (40.0 g. CH_3I)	1,4a,7,8-Tetramethyl-1-(α-hydroxy-isopropyl)-8a-ethylperhydro-7-phenanthrol	*114*
$C_{22}H_{18}O_3$			
α,β-Epoxy-β-anisyl-*p*-phenylpropiophenone	$C_6H_5MgBr + Mg + MgBr_2$	No benzpinacol isolated	*5*
$C_{22}H_{20}O_3$			
1,3-Diphenyl-1-*p*-anisyl-2,3-epoxy-1-propanol (2.0 g.)	C_6H_5MgBr (3 equiv.)	$(C_6H_5)_2CHCH(OH)C(OH)(C_6H_5)C_6H_4$-4-$OCH_3$ (2.5 g.)	*149*
$C_{22}H_{26}O_2$			
α-Mesityl-α-isoduroylethylene oxide	CH_3MgI	2,3,4,6-$(CH_3)_4C_6HCOC[C_6H_2$-2,4,6-$(CH_3)_3]{=}CH_2$	*40*
α-Mesityl-α-duroylethylene oxide	CH_3MgI	2,3,5,6-$(CH_3)_4C_6HCOC[C_6H_2$-2,4,6-$(CH_3)_3]{=}CH_2$	*40*
$C_{24}H_{22}O_2$			
α,β-Diphenyl-α-mesitoylethylene oxide	CH_3MgI	2,4,6-$(CH_3)_3C_6H_2COC(C_6H_5){=}CHC_6H_5$	*40*
$C_{25}H_{24}O_2$			
α,β-Diphenyl-α-duroylethylene oxide	CH_3MgI	2,3,5,6-$(CH_3)_4C_6HCOC(C_6H_5){=}CHC_6H_5$	*40*

TABLE XIV-I (Continued)

Epoxide	RMgX	Product(s)	Ref.
$C_{27}H_{46}O_2$			
Cholesterol α-oxide	CH_3MgI	6-Methyl-3,5-cholestanediol* (60%)	*133*
Cholesterol α-oxide	CH_3MgI	6-Methylcholesterol†	*133*
Cholesterol α-oxide	CH_3MgI	6(β)-Methylcholestane-3(β),5(α)-diol (40%)	*159; cf. 152*
Cholesterol α-oxide	C_6H_5MgBr	6-Oxo-3-cholestanol‡	*22*
Cholesterol β-oxide	CH_3MgI	5(α)-Methyl-3(β),6(β)-cholestanediol	*160,152*
$C_{28}H_{22}O$			
9,10-Epoxy-9,10-dibenzyl-9,10-dihydrophenanthrene (5 g.)	C_2H_5MgBr (4 g. C_2H_5Br)	9,10-Dibenzyl-10-ethyl-9-phenanthrol	*139*
$C_{40}H_{56}O$			
β-Carotene monoëpoxide	CH_3MgI (excess)	Mutatochrome	77
$C_{40}H_{56}O_2$			
β-Carotene diëpoxide	CH_3MgI (excess)	Aurochrome	77
$C_{40}H_{56}O_4$			
Violoxanthin	CH_3MgI (excess)	Auroxanthin	77

* Five hours reflux in C_6H_6.
† Seven hours reflux in C_6H_6.
‡ Two hours reflux in C_6H_6.

REFERENCES FOR TABLE XIV-I

(1) Arbuzov, *J. Gen. Chem.* (U.S.S.R.), 9, 249–54 (1939); *Chem. Abstr.*, 33, 6279 (1939).
(2) Bachman and Lewis, *J. Am. Chem. Soc.*, 69, 2022–5 (1947).
(3) Bachman and Thomas, *J. Am. Chem. Soc.*, 64, 94–7 (1942).
(4) Bachman, *J. Am. Chem. Soc.*, 57, 382–3 (1935).
(5) Bachmann and Wiselogle, *J. Am. Chem. Soc.*, 56, 1559–60 (1934).
(6) Bardon and Ramart, *Compt. rend.*, 183, 214–6 (1926).
(7) Bartlett and Berry, *J. Am. Chem. Soc.*, 56, 2683–5 (1934).
(8) Bedos, *Bull. soc. chim.*, [4], 39, 292–305 (1926).
(9) Bedos, *Bull. soc. chim.*, [4], 39, 473–87 (1926).
(10) Bedos, *Compt. rend.*, 228, 1441–3 (1949); *Chem. Abstr.*, 43, 7431 (1949).
(11) Bergmann and Wolff, *J. Am. Chem. Soc.*, 54, 1644–7 (1932).
(12) Blaise, *Compt. rend.*, 134, 551–3 (1902); *Chem. Zentr.*, 1902,I, 856.
(13) Bogert and Sterling, *Science*, 87, 196, 234 (1938); *Chem. Abstr.*, 32, 4147 (1938).
(14) Bousset, *Bull. soc. chim.*, [5], 1, 1305–8 (1934).
(15) Boyd and Vineall, *J. Chem. Soc.*, 1929, 1622.
(16) Briggs and Taylor, *J. Chem. Soc.*, 1947, 1338–9.
(17) Buu-Hoï and Cagniant, *Bull. soc. chim.*, [5], 11, 349–54 (1944).
(18) Buu-Hoï, Cagniant, and Mentzer, *Bull. soc. chim.*, [5], 11, 127–36 (1944).
(19) Cagniant and Deluzarche, *Compt. rend.*, 224, 473–4 (1947); *Chem. Abstr.*, 41, 5100 (1947).
(20) Campbell and Soffer, *J. Am. Chem. Soc.*, 64, 417–25 (1943).
(21) Cason, Adams, Bennett, and Register, *J. Am. Chem. Soc.*, 66, 1764–7 (1944).
(22) Chinaeva and Ushakov, *J. Gen. Chem.* (U.S.S.R.), 11, 335–8 (1941); *Chem. Abstr.*, 35, 5903 (1941).
(23) Cook, Haslewood, and Robinson, *J. Chem. Soc.*, 1935, 667–71.
(24) Cook, Hewett, and Lawrence, *J. Chem. Soc.*, 1936, 71–80.
(25) Cook and Robinson, *J. Chem. Soc.*, 1938, 505–13.
(26) Cottle and Hollyday, *J. Org. Chem.*, 12, 510–6 (1947).
(27) Cottle and Powell, *J. Am. Chem. Soc.*, 58, 2267–72 (1936).
(28) Danehy, Vogt, and Nieuwland, *J. Am. Chem. Soc.*, 56, 2790 (1934).
(29) Delaby, *Compt. rend.*, 176, 1153–6 (1923).
(30) Delaby, *Ann. chim.*, [9], 20, 33–81 (1923).
(31) Dreger, *Organic Syntheses*, 6, 54–7 (1926); Coll. Vol. **I**, 1st ed., 298–301 (1932); 2nd ed., 306–8 (1941).
(32) Elderfield, Craig, Lauer, Arnold, Gensler, Head, Bembry, Mighton, Tinker, Galbreath, Holley, Goldman, Maynard, and Pincus, *J. Am. Chem. Soc.*, 68, 1516–23 (1946).
(33) Faucounau, *Compt. rend.*, 199, 605–7 (1934); *Chem. Abstr.*, 28, 7245 (1934).
(34) Fordyce and Johnson, *J. Am. Chem. Soc.*, 55, 3368–72 (1933).
(35) Fosdick, Fancher, and Urbach, *J. Am. Chem. Soc.*, 68, 840–3 (1946).
(36) Fourneau and Tiffeneau, *Compt. rend.*, 145, 437–9 (1907); *Chem. Zentr.*, 1907,II, 1320.
(37) Fourneau and Tiffeneau, *Bull. soc. chim.*, [4], 1, 1227–33 (1907).
(38) Freedman and Becker, *J. Org. Chem.*, 16, 1701–11 (1951).
(39) Fulton and Robinson, *J. Chem. Soc.*, 1933, 1463–6.
(40) Fuson, Byers, Sperati, Foster, and Warfield, *J. Org. Chem.*, 10, 69–75 (1945).
(41) Gaylord and Becker, *J. Org. Chem.*, 15, 305–16 (1950).
(42) Gmitter and Benton, *J. Am. Chem. Soc.*, 72, 4586–9 (1950).
(43) Godchot and Bedos, *Compt. rend.*, 174, 461–4 (1922).
(44) Godchot and Bedos, *Compt. rend.*, 175, 1411–5 (1922).
(45) Godchot and Bedos, *Compt. rend.*, 180, 751–4 (1925).
(46) Godchot and Bedos, *Compt. rend.*, 182, 393–5 (1926).

(47) Godchot and Bedos, *Compt. rend.*, *184*, 208–10 (1927).
(48) Godchot and Bedos, *Bull. soc. chim.*, [4], *37*, 1451–66 (1925).
(49) Godchot and Bedos, *Bull. soc. chim.*, [4], *37*, 1637–51 (1925).
(50) Godchot and Bedos, *Bull. soc. chim.*, [4], *43*, 521–2 (1928).
(51) Golumbic and Cottle, *J. Am. Chem. Soc.*, *61*, 996–1000 (1939).
(52) Grignard, *Bull. soc. chim.*, [3], *29*, 944–8 (1903).
(53) Grignard, *Compt. rend.*, *136*, 1260–2 (1903); *Chem. Zentr.*, *1903,I*, 105.
(54) Haworth and Barker, *J. Chem. Soc.*, *1939*, 1299–303.
(55) Haworth, Mavin, and Sheldrick, *J. Chem. Soc.*, *1934*, 454–61.
(56) Henry, *Compt. rend.*, *144*, 308–13 (1907); *Chem. Zentr.*, *1907,I*, 1102.
(57) Henry, *Compt. rend.*, *145*, 21–5 (1907); *Chem. Zentr.*, *1907,II*, 889.
(58) Henry, *Compt. rend.*, *145*, 154–6 (1907); *J. Chem. Soc.*, *92,I*, 745 (1907).
(59) Henry, *Compt. rend.*, *145*, 406–8 (1907); *Chem. Zentr.*, *1907,II*, 1320.
(60) Henry, *Compt. rend.*, *145*, 453–6 (1907); *Chem. Zentr.*, *1907,II*, 1320.
(61) Henry, *Bull. acad. roy. Belg., Classe sci.*, *1907*, 162–89; *Chem. Zentr.*, *1907,II*, 445.
(62) Hess, *Ber.*, *46*, 3113–25 (1913).
(63) Hiers and Adams, *J. Am. Chem. Soc.*, *48*, 1089–93 (1926).
(64) Holliman and Mann, *J. Chem. Soc.*, *1942*, 737–4.
(65) Holliman and Mann, *J. Chem. Soc.*, *1947*, 1634–42.
(66) Horeau and Jacques, *Bull. soc. chim.*, [5], *13*, 382–5 (1946).
(67) Hoshino and Shimodaira, *Ann.*, *520*, 19–30 (1935).
(68) Huston and Agett, *J. Org. Chem.*, *6*, 123–33 (1941).
(69) Huston and Bostwick, *J. Org. Chem.*, *13*, 331–8 (1948).
(70) Huston and Brault, *J. Org. Chem.*, *15*, 1211–8 (1950).
(71) Huston and Langham, *J. Org. Chem.*, *12*, 90–5 (1947).
(72) Huston and Tiefenthal, *J. Org. Chem.*, *16*, 673–8 (1951).
(73) Iotsitch, *J. Russ. Phys.-Chem. Soc.*, *34*, 96–8 (1902); *Bull. soc. chim.*, [3], *28*, 920 (1902).
(74) Iotsitch, *J. Russ. Phys.-Chem. Soc.*, *35*, 554–5 (1903); *Bull. soc. chim.*, [3], *32*, 740 (1904).
(75) Iotsitch, *J. Russ. Phys.-Chem. Soc.*, *36*, 6–8 (1904); *Bull. soc. chim.*, [3], *34*, 185 (1905).
(76) Iotsitch, Bréitfous, Roudolf, Stassévitch, Elmanovitch, Kondyref, and Fomine, *J. Russ. Phys.-Chem. Soc.*, *39*, 652–7 (1907); *Bull. soc. chim.*, [4], *6*, 98 (1909).
(77) Karrer, Jucker, and Steinlein, *Helv. Chim. Acta*, *29*, 233–6 (1946).
(78) Kayser, *Compt. rend.*, *196*, 1127–9 (1933).
(79) Kayser, *Compt. rend.*, *199*, 1424–7 (1934).
(80) Khaletzkiĭ, *J. Gen. Chem.* (U.S.S.R.), *6*, 1–14 (1936); *Chem. Abstr.*, *30*, 4844 (1936).
(81) Kharasch and Clapp, *J. Org. Chem.*, *3*, 355–60 (1938).
(82) Kling, *Bull. soc. chim.*, [3], *31*, 14–6 (1904).
(83) Koelsch and McElvain, *J. Am. Chem. Soc.*, *51*, 3390–4 (1929).
(84) Koelsch and McElvain, *J. Am. Chem. Soc.*, *52*, 1164–9 (1930).
(85) Kohler, Richtmyer, and Hester, *J. Am. Chem. Soc.*, *53*, 205–21 (1931).
(86) Kon and Woolman, *J. Chem. Soc.*, *1939*, 794–800.
(87) Levene and Walti, *J. Biol. Chem.*, *90*, 81–8 (1931); *Chem. Abstr.*, *25*, 1818 (1931).
(88) Levene and Walti, *J. Biol. Chem.*, *94*, 367–73 (1931).
(89) Magrane and Cottle, *J. Am. Chem. Soc.*, *64*, 484–7 (1942).
(90) Mair, *Bur. Standards J. Research*, *9*, 457–72 (1922).
(91) Malinovskiĭ, Volkova, and Morozova, *J. Gen. Chem.* (U.S.S.R.), *19*, 114–7 (1949); *Chem. Abstr.*, *43*, 6155 (1949).
(92) Manske and Ledingham, *Can. J. Research*, *27*, 158–60 (1949).

(93) Marvel, Blomquist, and Vaughn, *J. Am. Chem. Soc.*, *50*, 2810–2 (1928).
(94) Marvel and Hein, *J. Am. Chem. Soc.*, *70*, 1895–8 (1948).
(95) Meisenheimer, *Ann.*, *442*, 180–210 (1925).
(96) Natelson and Gottfried, *J. Am. Chem. Soc.*, *61*, 1001–2 (1939).
(97) Nazarov and Elizarova, *Bull. acad. sci. U.R.S.S., Classe sci. chim.*, *1940*, 189–94; *Chem. Abstr.*, *36*, 741 (1942).
(98) Newman, *J. Am. Chem. Soc.*, *62*, 2295–300 (1940).
(99) Newman, *J. Org. Chem.*, *9*, 518–28 (1944).
(100) Newman, Magerlein, and Wheatley, *J. Am. Chem. Soc.*, *68*, 2112–5 (1946).
(101) Normant, *Compt. rend.*, *219*, 163–4 (1944); *Chem. Abstr.*, *40*, 4041 (1946).
(102) Norris and Cortese, *J. Am. Chem. Soc.*, *49*, 2640–50 (1927).
(103) Norton and Hass, *J. Am. Chem. Soc.*, *58*, 2147–50 (1936).
(104) Oddo and Cambieri, *Gazz. chim. ital.*, *69*, 19–24 (1939); *Chem. Abstr.*, *33*, 4239 (1939).
(105) Poctivas and Tchoubar, *Compt. rend.*, *205*, 287–8 (1937); *Chem. Abstr.*, *31*, 7853 (1937).
(106) Prilezhaev and Vershuk, *J. Russ. Phys.-Chem. Soc.*, *61*, 473–82 (1929); *Chem. Abstr.*, *23*, 4463 (1929).
(107) Quelet and Golse, *Compt. rend.*, *224*, 661–3 (1947); *Chem. Abstr.*, *41*, 4779 (1947).
(108) Rajagopalan, *J. Indian Chem. Soc.*, *17*, 567–72 (1940).
(109) Ribas, *Anales soc. españ. fís. quím.*, *26*, 122–32 (1928); *Chem. Zentr.*, *1928,II*, 40.
(110) Wiggins and Wood, *J. Chem. Soc.*, *1950*, 1566–75.
(111) Ritter and Russell, *J. Am. Chem. Soc.*, *58*, 291–3 (1936).
(112) Robinson, *J. Chem. Soc.*, *1936*, 80.
(113) Ruzicka, Ehmann, and Morgeli, *Helv. Chim. Acta*, *16*, 314–26 (1933).
(114) Ruzicka and Sternbach, *Helv. Chim. Acta*, *23*, 124–31 (1940).
(115) Semeniuk and Jenkins, *J. Am. Pharm. Assoc., Sci. Ed.*, *37*, 118–21 (1948); *Chem. Abstr.*, *42*, 5410 (1948).
(116) Sharefkin and Ritter, *J. Am. Chem. Soc.*, *63*, 1478–9 (1941).
(117) Shoruigin and Isagulyantz, *Trans. VI Mendeleev Congr. Theoret. Applied Chem. 1932*, *2*, Pt. 1, 973–80 (1935); *Chem. Abstr.*, *30*, 4157 (1936).
(118) Small and Yuen, *J. Am. Chem. Soc.*, *58*, 192–6 (1936).
(119) Smith and Agre, *J. Am. Chem. Soc.*, *60*, 648–52 (1938).
(120) Smith and Miller, *J. Am. Chem. Soc.*, *64*, 440–5 (1942).
(121) Smith and Miller, U. S. Patent 2,372,132, March 20, 1945; *Chem. Abstr.*, *39*, P4894 (1945).
(122) Smith, Wawzonek, and Miller, *J. Org. Chem.*, *6*, 229–35 (1941).
(123) Sobotka and Chanley, *J. Am. Chem. Soc.*, *70*, 3914–8 (1948).
(124) Sontag, *Ann. chim.*, [11], *1*, 359–438 (1934).
(125) Stahl and Cottle, *J. Am. Chem. Soc.*, *65*, 1782–3 (1943).
(126) Stevens and McCoubrey, *J. Am. Chem. Soc.*, *63*, 2847–8 (1941).
(127) Stoll and Rouvé, *Helv. Chim. Acta*, *21*, 1542–7 (1938).
(128) Tapia and Hernández, *Anales. soc. españ. fís. quím.*, *28*, 691–3 (1930); *Chem. Zentr.*, *1930,II*, 1697.
(129) Taub, Wingler, and Schulemann, German Patent 423,544, Jan. 9, 1926; *Chem. Zentr.*, *1926,I*, 3635.
(130) Tiffeneau, *Compt. rend.*, *140*, 1458–60 (1905); *Chem. Zentr.*, *1905,II*, 235.
(131) Tiffeneau and Fourneau, *Compt. rend.*, *146*, 697–9 (1908); *Chem. Zentr.*, *1908,I*, 1776.
(132) Tiffeneau and Tchoubar, *Compt. rend.*, *212*, 581–5 (1941); *Chem. Zentr.*, *1942,I*, 610; *Chem. Abstr.*, *37*, 2720 (1943).
(133) Ushakov and Madaeva, *J. Gen. Chem.* (U.S.S.R.), *9*, 436–41 (1939); *Chem. Abstr.*, *33*, 9309 (1939).

(*134*) Vaughn, Spahr, and Nieuwland, *J. Am. Chem. Soc.*, *55*, 4207–9 (1933).
(*135*) Vavon and Mitchovitch, *Bull. soc. chim.*, [4], *37*, 1451–66 (1925).
(*136*) Vavon and Mitchovitch, *Compt. rend.*, *186*, 702–5 (1928); *Chem. Abstr.*, *22*, 2552 (1928).
(*137*) Veibel, Lundqvist, Andersen, and Frederiksen, *Bull. soc. chim.*, [5], *6*, 990–8 (1939).
(*138*) Zincke and Schwabe, *Ber.*, *41*, 897–902 (1908).
(*139*) Zincke and Tropp, *Ann.*, *362*, 242–59 (1908).
(*140*) Altwegg, U. S. Patent 1,315,619, Sept. 9, 1919; *Chem. Abstr.*, *13*, P2883 (1919).
(*141*) Turner, *J. Am. Chem. Soc.*, *72*, 878–82 (1950).
(*142*) Bedos, *Bull. soc. chim.*, [4], *33*, 163–4 (1923).
(*143*) Bedos, *Compt. rend.*, *177*, 111–3 (1923); *Chem. Abstr.*, *17*, 3177 (1923).
(*144*) Bedos, *Compt. rend.*, *177*, 958–60 (1923); *Chem. Abstr.*, *18*, 532 (1924).
(*145*) Bedos, *Compt. rend.*, *181*, 117–9 (1925); *Chem. Abstr.*, *19*, 3266 (1925).
(*146*) Bedos, *Bull. soc. chim.*, [4], *39*, 674–90 (1926).
(*147*) Beeby and Mann, *J. Chem. Soc.*, *1951*, 411–5.
(*148*) Bergmann and Blum-Bergmann, *J. Am. Chem. Soc.*, *58*, 1678–81 (1936).
(*149*) Bickel, *J. Am. Chem. Soc.*, *59*, 325–8 (1937).
(*150*) Cason and Winans, *J. Org. Chem.*, *15*, 139–47 (1950).
(*151*) Chavanne and de Vogel, *Bull. soc. chim. Belg.*, *37*, 141–52 (1928).
(*152*) Chuman, *J. Chem. Soc. Japan, Pure Chem. Sect.*, *70*, 253–7 (1949); *Chem. Abstr.*, *45*, 6651 (1951).
(*153*) Cohen, Cook, Hewett, and Girard, *J. Chem. Soc.*, *1934*, 653–8.
(*154*) Cook and Hewett, *J. Chem. Soc.*, *1933*, 1098–111.
(*155*) Danehy, Vogt, and Nieuwland, *J. Am. Chem. Soc.*, *57*, 2327 (1935).
(*156*) Dice, Watkins, and Schuman, *J. Am. Chem. Soc.*, *72*, 1738–40 (1950).
(*157*) Ehrenstein, *J. Org. Chem.*, *8*, 83–94 (1943).
(*158*) Elderfield, Pitt, and Wempen, *J. Am. Chem. Soc.*, *72*, 1334–45 (1950).
(*159*) Fieser and Rigaudy, *J. Am. Chem. Soc.*, *73*, 4660–2 (1951).
(*160*) Urishibara and Chuman, *Bull. soc. chim. Japan*, *22*, 69–74 (1949); *Chem. Abstr.*, *44*, 1124 (1950).
(*161*) Fourneau, Tréfouel, and Tréfouel, *Bull. soc. chim.*, [4], *43*, 454–8 (1928).
(*162*) Frank, Adams, Allen, Gander, and Smith, *J. Am. Chem. Soc.*, *68*, 1365–8 (1946).
(*163*) Gilman and Abbott, *J. Org. Chem.*, *8*, 224–9 (1943).
(*164*) Gilman and Kirby, *J. Am. Chem. Soc.*, *54*, 345–55 (1932).
(*165*) Godchot and Bedos, *Bull. soc. chim.*, [4], *33*, 162–3 (1923).
(*166*) Godchot, Bedos, and Cauquil, *Bull. soc. chim.*, [4], *43*, 521–2 (1928).
(*167*) Harlow and Britton, U. S. Patent 1,591,125, July 6, 1926; *Chem. Abstr.*, *20*, P3171 (1926).
(*168*) Hiers and Adams, *J. Am. Chem. Soc.*, *48*, 2385–95 (1926).
(*169*) I. G. Farbenindustrie A.-G., French Patent 807,632, Jan. 1, 1937; *Chem. Zentr.*, *1937,I*, 4022.
(*170*) Kayser, *Ann. chim.*, [11], *6*, 145–248 (1936).
(*171*) Kohler and Bickel, *J. Am. Chem. Soc.*, *57*, 1099–101 (1935).
(*172*) Letsinger, Traynham, and Bobko, *J. Am. Chem. Soc.*, *74*, 399–401 (1952).
(*173*) Madaeva, Ushakov, and Kosheleva, *J. Gen. Chem.* (U.S.S.R.), *10*, 213–6 (1940); *Chem. Zentr.*, *1940,II*, 1298; *Chem. Abstr.*, *34*, 7292 (1940).
(*174*) Malinovskiĭ and Konevichev, *J. Gen. Chem.* (U.S.S.R.), *18*, 1833–5 (1948); *Chem. Abstr.*, *43*, 3776 (1949).
(*175*) Mousseron and Du, *Bull. soc. chim.*, [5], *15*, 91–6 (1948).
(*176*) Newth, Richards, and Wiggins, *J. Chem. Soc.*, *1950*, 2356–64.
(*177*) Plate, Shafran, and Batuev, *J. Gen. Chem.* (U.S.S.R.), *20*, 472–8 (1950); *Chem. Abstr.*, *44*, 7785 (1950).
(*178*) Price and Halpern, *J. Am. Chem. Soc.*, *73*, 818–20 (1951).

(*179*) Prilezhaev and Prokopchuk, *J. Gen. Chem.* (U.S.S.R.), *3*, 865–8 (1933); *Chem. Abstr.*, *28*, 6133 (1934).
(*180*) Riedel A.-G., German Patent 183,361, Feb. 25, 1907; *Friedlaender*, 8, 1041–2 (1905–1907); *Chem. Zentr.*, *1907,I*, 1607.
(*181*) Rothman and Becker, Unpublished results, as cited by Gaylord and Becker, *Chem. Revs.*, *49*, 413–533 (1951).
(*182*) Ruzicka, Ehmann, Goldberg, and Hösli, *Helv. Chim. Acta*, *16*, 833–41 (1933).
(*183*) Schinz and Simon, *Helv. Chim. Acta*, *28*, 774–80 (1945).
(*184*) Schorigin, Issaguljanz, Gussewa, Ossipowa, and Poljakowa, *Ber.*, *64B*, 2584–90 (1931).
(*185*) Smith and Fuzek, *J. Am. Chem. Soc.*, *72*, 3454–8 (1950).
(*186*) Sobotka and Stynler, *J. Am. Chem. Soc.*, *72*, 5139–43 (1950).
(*187*) Soc. chim. usines Rhone, British Patent 122,630, Jan. 3, 1919; *Chem. Abstr.*, *13*, P1715 (1919).
(*188*) Sommer, Van Strien, and Whitmore, *J. Am. Chem. Soc.*, *71*, 3056–60 (1949).
(*189*) Truce and Wise, *J. Am. Chem. Soc.*, *72*, 2300 (1950).
(*190*) Stevens and Pratt, Abstracts of Papers, 119th Meeting, A.C.S., Cleveland, Ohio, April, 1951, p. 92M.
(*191*) Szmant, Anzenberger, and Hartle, *J. Am. Chem. Soc.*, *72*, 1419–20 (1950).
(*192*) Temnikova and Kropacheva, *J. Gen. Chem.* (U.S.S.R.), *21*, 183–6 (1951); *Chem. Abstr.*, *45*, 7046 (1951).
(*193*) Blicke and Burckhalter, *J. Am. Chem. Soc.*, *64*, 477–80 (1942).
(*194*) Gaertner, *J. Am. Chem. Soc.*, *73*, 3934–7 (1951).
(*195*) Newman and Wotiz, *J. Am. Chem. Soc.*, *71*, 1292–7 (1949).
(*196*) Gilman and Towle, *Rec. trav. chim.*, *69*, 428–32 (1950).
(*197*) Gaertner, *J. Am. Chem. Soc.*, *74*, 2185–8 (1952).

CHAPTER XV

Reactions of Grignard Reagents with Ethers, Acetals, and Ketals

CLEAVAGES OF ACYCLIC ETHERS

In the attempt to prepare an organomagnesium bromide from β-bromoethoxybenzene Grignard[1] obtained only ethylene, phenol, and a trace of 1,4-diphenoxybutane. The attempt to condense this bromide with *n*-amylmagnesium bromide was similarly unsuccessful, and likewise resulted in the production of phenol. With benzylmagnesium chloride the attempt was only partially successful, resulting in the production of considerable phenol. Grignard reported *n*-amyl alcohol and benzyl alcohol, respectively, as co-products of these reactions, but any of these alcohols detected must have been due to oxygen contamination (see Chapter XX).

Grignard[2] believed that the Grignard reagent of β-bromoethoxybenzene is formed but immediately undergoes an ether-cleavage reaction with unchanged bromide. It is at least equally probable, however, that this reaction is a special case of internal Wurtz reaction (analogous to that undergone by ethylene bromide), with the phenoxy group playing the rôle of a "pseudohalogen" (see Chapter II, Limitations of the Classical Method).

$$BrCH_2CH_2Br + Mg \longrightarrow C_2H_4 + MgBr_2$$

$$C_6H_5OCH_2CH_2Br + Mg \longrightarrow C_2H_4 + C_6H_5OMgBr$$

Grignard (*loc. cit.*[2]) showed, however, that such ethers as phenetole, estragole (4-methoxyallylbenzene), and 3,4-dimethoxyallylbenzene undergo cleavage when heated to a sufficiently high temperature with ethylmagnesium bromide, yielding the corresponding phenols. He regarded this phenomenon as constituting additional support for his ether-complex theory and for the constitution assigned by him to the Grignard reagent-ether complexes (see Chapter IV). In general the cleavage of a phenolic ether by an aliphatic Grignard reagent was characterized by him as follows:

$$C_6H_5OR + R'MgX \longrightarrow \overset{H_5C_6}{\underset{R}{}}\!\!>\!O\!<\!\!\overset{R'}{\underset{MgX}{}} \xrightarrow{\Delta} C_6H_5OMgX + (R + R')$$

$$(R + R') \longrightarrow \text{Disproportionation products}$$

---

[1] Grignard, *Compt. rend.*, *138*, 1048–50 (1904); *Chem. Zentr.*, *1904,I*, 1493.
[2] Grignard, *Compt. rend.*, *151*, 322–5 (1910); *Chem. Zentr.*, *1910,II*, 1048.

Stadnikoff (Stadnikow, Stadnikov)[3] carried out a series of studies on the reactions of aliphatic Grignard reagents with the alkyl ethers of benzhydrol. In all cases symmetrical tetraphenylethane was reported as one of the principal products.* Stadnikoff, like Grignard, believed that the intermediate product in such reactions is an ether-Grignard reagent complex, but maintained that actual cleavage of the ether takes place during the process of hydrolysis.

Tschelinzew[4] showed, however, that cleavage products of the ethyl ethers of benzyl alcohol and benzhydrol, treated with *n*-propylmagnesium iodide, are present prior to hydrolysis.

It may be mentioned in passing, incidentally, that a byproduct observed by Zeile and Meyer[5] as arising from the treatment of 3-triphenylmethoxypropyne with ethylmagnesium bromide is readily explicable as the result of an ether cleavage.

$$\underset{(12.5\ g.)}{(C_6H_5)_3COCH_2C{\equiv}CH} + C_2H_5MgBr \xrightarrow{H_2O}$$

$$\underset{(principally)}{(C_6H_5)_3COCH_2C{\equiv}CH} + \underset{(1.6\ g.)}{(C_6H_5)_3COCH_2C{\equiv}CC(C_6H_5)_3}$$

$$2\ (C_6H_5)_3COCH_2C{\equiv}CMgBr \longrightarrow$$

$$(C_6H_5)_3COCH_2C{\equiv}CC(C_6H_5)_3 + BrMgOCH_2C{\equiv}CMgBr$$

The question, of course, arises as to which of the components of the Schlenk equilibrium is the effective one (or the most effective one). Schönberg and Moubasher[6] propose that the cleavage is effected by the magnesium halide present.

Some qualitative evidence may be advanced in support of this hypothesis. Gilman and Schulze[7] had found that, although a refluxing ethyl ethereal solution of benzyl phenyl ether appears to be stable toward anhydrous magnesium bromide, cleavage takes place slowly in a higher-boiling benzene solution. Grignard and Ritz[8] have shown that anisole

---

[3] (*a*) Stadnikoff, *Ber.*, *44*, 1157–60 (1911); (*b*) Stadnikov, *J. Russ. Phys.-Chem. Soc.*, *43*, 1244–57 (1911); *Chem. Abstr.*, *6*, 1434 (1912); (*c*) Stadnikow, *J. Russ. Phys.-Chem. Soc.*, *44*, 1219–47 (1912); *Chem. Zentr.*, *1913,I*, *21*; *Chem. Abstr.*, 7, 983 (1913); (*d*) Stadnikoff, *J. prakt. Chem.*, [2], *88*, 1–20 (1913); (*e*) Stadnikoff and Kusmina-Aron, *ibid.*, [2], *88*, 20–5 (1913); (*f*) Stadnikoff, *Ber.*, *46*, 2496–503 (1913); (*g*) Stadnikow, *J. Russ. Phys.-Chem. Soc.*, *45*, 1391–414 (1913); *Chem. Zentr.*, *1913,II*, 2120.

*Like the hexaphenylethane of Gomberg and Kamm,[13] tetraphenylethane is undoubtedly the product of a "coupling" reaction (*q.v.*, Chapter XVI). In this case the source is probably benzhydryl halide, originating in magnesium halide cleavage of the benzhydryl ether.

[4] Tschelinzew and Pawlow, *J. Russ. Phys.-Chem. Soc.*, *45*, 289–300 (1913); *Chem. Zentr.*, *1913,I*, 1962; *Chem. Abstr.*, 7, 2227 (1913); *J. Chem. Soc.*, *104,I*, 461 (1913).

[5] Zeile and Meyer, *Ber.*, *75B*, 356–62 (1942).

[6] Schönberg and Moubasher, *J. Chem. Soc.*, *1944*, 462–3.

[7] Gilman and Schulze, *Rec. trav. chim.*, *47*, 752–60 (1928).

[8] Grignard and Ritz, *Bull. soc. chim.*, [5], 3, 1181–4 (1936).

undergoes cleavage when heated with magnesium iodide. Moreover, it would seem that one of the simplest and most plausible ways of accounting for symmetrical tetraphenylethane as a major product of Stadnikoff's (*loc. cit.*[3]) benzhydryl ether cleavages would be to assume that benzhydryl halide is formed by magnesium halide cleavage of the ether and then undergoes a "coupling" reaction (*q.v.*, Chapter XVI). Schönberg and Moubasher (*loc. cit.*[6]) confirmed the observation of Grignard and Ritz (*loc. cit.*[8]), and showed that magnesium bromide behaves similarly, though less effectively.*

It may be further conceded that the products, other than ROH, resulting from the reaction of an unsymmetrical ether (ROR′) with a Grignard reagent (R″MgX) are in general (qualitatively) those which might be expected to result from one or more of the possible reactions of the Grignard reagent with the corresponding halide, R′X (see Chapter XVI).

(*a*) $R'X + R''MgX \longrightarrow R'R''$

(*b*) $R'X + R''MgX \longrightarrow R'_{(-H)} + R''_{(+H)}$

(*c*) $2\,R'X + 2\,R''MgX \longrightarrow R'_2 + (2\,R''\cdot)$

Insofar as data are available for quantitative comparisons, however, the case for the Schönberg and Moubasher hypothesis does not appear quite so persuasive. There is, for example, no sufficient evidence that ethers *in general* react preferentially with the magnesium halide constituent of the Grignard reagent. Indeed, the observations of Schönberg and Moubasher (*loc. cit.*[6]) on the reaction of allyl phenyl ether with magnesium bromide and of Lüttringhaus *et al.* on the reactions of the same ether with phenylmagnesium bromide[9] and diphenylmagnesium[10] indicate that, for some reactant combinations at least, the reverse may be true.

$$H_2C{=}CHCH_2OC_6H_5 + MgBr_2 \xrightarrow[5\ hrs.]{95^\circ} C_6H_5OH\ (9\%) + H_2C{=}CHCH_2Br$$

$$H_2C{=}CHCH_2OC_6H_5 + C_6H_5MgBr \xrightarrow[7\ hrs.]{70^\circ} C_6H_5OH\ (71\%) + H_2C{=}CHCH_2C_6H_5\ (63\%)$$

$$H_2C{=}CHCH_2OC_6H_5 + (C_6H_5)_2Mg \xrightarrow[6\ hrs.]{75^\circ} C_6H_5OH\ (76\%) + H_2C{=}CHCH_2C_6H_5\ (67\%)$$

For a comparison of the products of reactions of Grignard reagents with ethers, on the one hand, and with halides corresponding to the ethers, on the other, data are fragmentary and inconclusive. Stadnikow (*loc. cit.*[3f,g]) reports that, under conditions not precisely described, methylmagnesium iodide reacts with *n*-butyl benzhydryl ether to give a 42 percent yield of symmetrical tetraphenylethane (with 42 percent ether recovery). Späth[11] reports that when benzhydryl bromide is added slowly

* Conceivably this is a solubility rather than a reactivity effect.

[9] Lüttringhaus, von Sääf, and Hauschild, *Ber.*, *71B*, 1673–81 (1938).

[10] Lüttringhaus, Wagner-von Sääf, Sucker, and Borth, *Ann.*, *557*, 46–69 (1945).

[11] Späth, *Monatsh.*, *34*, 1965–2014 (1913).

to an ethereal solution of methylmagnesium bromide an 85 percent yield of the condensation product (1,1-diphenylethane) was obtained, together with a small amount of coupling product (*sym.*-tetraphenylethane). However, in view of the fact that methylmagnesium iodide is an excellent coupling reagent, whereas methylmagnesium bromide is not,[12] the discrepancy is probably more apparent than real. According to Späth, benzhydryl bromide with ethylmagnesium bromide gives a 30 percent yield of the condensation product (1,1-diphenylpropane), but only 15.7 percent with ethylmagnesium iodide. Unfortunately the relative amounts of coupling product for the two cases cannot be compared because the value given for the bromide is an obvious misprint. The value for the iodide corresponds to 74 percent.

According to Gomberg and Kamm[13] treatment of triphenylmethyl chloride with phenylmagnesium bromide by the usual procedure leads to maximum yields of 5 percent of the condensation product (tetraphenylmethane), the major product being that resulting from coupling (hexaphenylethane). When heated to 200° with phenylmagnesium bromide, however, phenyl triphenylmethyl ether yields 15 to 20 percent of tetraphenylmethane. (The experimental conditions, of course, are not comparable.[14])

At best the Schönberg and Moubasher hypothesis merits a Scottish verdict—"not proven." If one may properly draw any conclusions from the very special case of the epoxides (*q.v.*, Chapter XIV), it seems possible, even probable, that some ethers may react preferentially with magnesium halide and others with the Grignard reagent itself. It has been definitely established that ethylene oxide reacts preferentially with magnesium bromide in the presence of ethylmagnesium bromide,[15] for example. This cannot be true of 1-phenyl-2-methyl-1,2-epoxybutane, however, for the products of reaction of ethylmagnesium bromide with that epoxide are not those which would be formed by further reaction of the magnesium bromide cleavage products with ethylmagnesium bromide or diethylmagnesium.[16]

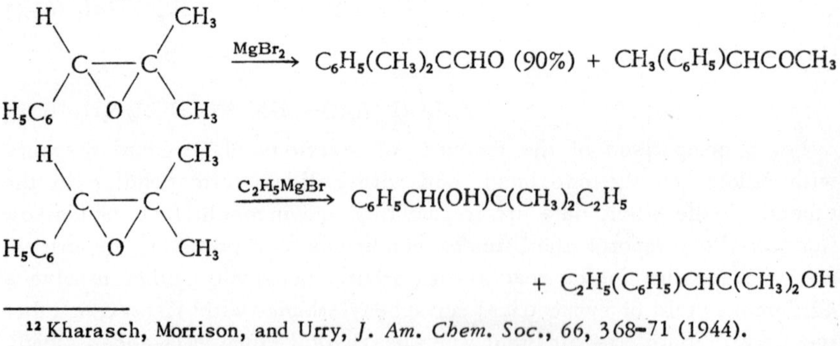

$$\underset{H_5C_6}{\overset{H}{>}}C\overset{O}{—}C\underset{CH_3}{\overset{CH_3}{<}} \xrightarrow{MgBr_2} C_6H_5(CH_3)_2CCHO\ (90\%) + CH_3(C_6H_5)CHCOCH_3$$

$$\underset{H_5C_6}{\overset{H}{>}}C\overset{O}{—}C\underset{CH_3}{\overset{CH_3}{<}} \xrightarrow{C_2H_5MgBr} C_6H_5CH(OH)C(CH_3)_2C_2H_5$$

$$+\ C_2H_5(C_6H_5)CHC(CH_3)_2OH$$

---

[12] Kharasch, Morrison, and Urry, *J. Am. Chem. Soc.*, *66*, 368–71 (1944).

[13] Gomberg and Kamm, *J. Am. Chem. Soc.*, *39*, 2009–15 (1917).

[14] *Cf.* Schoepfle and Trepp, *J. Am. Chem. Soc.*, *58*, 791–4 (1936).

[15] Huston and Agett, *J. Org. Chem.*, 6, 123–33 (1941).

[16] Poctivas and Tchoubar, *Compt. rend.*, *205*, 287–8 (1937); *Chem. Abstr.*, *31*, 7853 (1937).

TABLE XV-I

REACTIONS OF GRIGNARD REAGENTS ($R''MgX$) WITH ACYCLIC ETHERS (ROR')

(In general, R is adjudged more "electronegative" than R'.)

ROR'	R''MgX (or MgX_2)	Temp. (Time)	Product(s)	Ref.
$2,6\text{-}(CH_3O)_2C_6H_3OCH_3$	CH_3MgI	b. C_7H_8	ROH	*1*
$2\text{-}CH_3O\text{-}5\text{-}CH_3CH{=}CHC_6H_3OCH_2C_6H_5$	CH_3MgI *	—	ROH	*2*
$2\text{-}CH_3O\text{-}5\text{-}CH_3CH{=}CHC_6H_3OCH_2CH{=}CH_2$	CH_3MgI *	—	ROH	*2*
$2\text{-}CH_3O\text{-}5\text{-}CH_3CH{=}CHC_6H_3OCH(CH_2)_5$	CH_3MgI *	—	ROH	*2*
$2\text{-}CH_3O\text{-}5\text{-}CH_3CH{=}CHC_6H_3O\text{-}i\text{-}C_3H_7$	CH_3MgI *	—	ROH	*2*
$3\text{-}R'''O\text{-}4\text{-}CH_3CH{=}CHC_6H_3OCH_3$ †	CH_3MgI	—	ROH	*3*
$3\text{-}n\text{-}C_3H_7\text{-}4\text{-}CH_3CH{=}CHC_6H_3OCH_3$	CH_3MgI	—	ROH	*3*
$3\text{-}C_2H_5\text{-}4\text{-}CH_3CH{=}CHC_6H_3OCH_3$	CH_3MgI	b. xylene (2 hrs.)	ROH	*3*
$4\text{-}CH_3OC_6H_4OCH_3$	R''MgX	200°	ROH	*4, cf. 5*
$4\text{-}CH_3OC_6H_4OCH_3$	R''MgX	—	ROH	*4*
$4\text{-}CH_3OC_6H_4OCH_2(\alpha\text{-}C_4H_3O)$ ‡	$n\text{-}C_4H_9MgCl$	b. C_6H_6	ROH (69%) + R'R'' (15%) + rearr.§ (20%)	*6*
$4\text{-}C_2H_5OC_6H_4OCH_3$	R''MgX	200–230°	ROH	*4*
$4\text{-}C_2H_5OC_6H_4OCH_3$	R''MgX	—	ROH	*4*
$4\text{-}n\text{-}C_3H_7OC_6H_4OCH_3$	R''MgX	—	ROH	*4*
$4\text{-}n\text{-}C_4H_9OC_6H_4OCH_3$	R''MgX	—	ROH	*4*
$4\text{-}R'''SeC_6H_4OCH_3$ ¶	CH_3MgI	—	ROH (62–78%)¶	*7*
$2\text{-}C_6H_5OC_6H_4OC_2H_5$	R''MgX	—	ROH	*8*

* Similar, but "less satisfactory" results were obtained with C_2H_5MgBr.

† R''' = "$CH_2OC_2H_5$, $CH_2O\text{-}n\text{-}C_3H_7$, etc."

‡ $(\alpha\text{-}C_4H_3O)$ = 2-furyl.

§ The rearrangement product is 2-α-furylmethyl-4-methoxyphenol.

¶ R''' = CH_3 (78.2%); C_2H_5 (62.4%); $n\text{-}C_3H_7$ (76.0%); $i\text{-}C_3H_7$ (74.5%); $n\text{-}C_4H_9$ (76.0%); $i\text{-}C_4H_9$ (74.0%); $n\text{-}C_6H_{13}$ (74.0%).

TABLE XV-I (Continued)

ROR′	R″MgX (or MgX_2)	Temp. (Time)	Product(s)	Ref.
2-$C_6H_5OC_6H_4O$-*n*-C_3H_7	R″MgX	—	ROH	*8*
2-$CH_3OC_6H_4OCH_3$	CH_3MgI	160–170°	ROH (85%)	*9*
2-$CH_3OC_6H_4OCH_2C_6H_5$	R″MgX	—	ROH	*8*
2-$CH_3OC_6H_4OCH_2CH=CH_2$	*n*-C_4H_9MgBr	60° (14 hrs.)	ROH (87%) + R′R″ (36%)	*10*
2-$CH_3OC_6H_4OCH_2$(α-C_4H_3O) *	*n*-C_4H_9MgCl	b. C_6H_6	ROH (74%) + R′R″ (63%) + rearr. † (14%)	*6*
2-$C_2H_5OC_6H_4OCH_3$	R″MgX	—	ROH	*8*
2-$C_2H_5OC_6H_4OC_2H_5$	R″MgX	—	ROH	*8*
2-$C_2H_5OC_6H_4OCH_2C_6H_5$	R″MgX	—	ROH	*8*
2-*n*-$C_3H_7OC_6H_4OCH_3$	R″MgX	—	ROH	*8*
2-*n*-$C_4H_9OC_6H_4OCH_3$	R″MgX	—	ROH	*8*
2-*n*-$C_4H_9OC_6H_4OC_2H_5$	R″MgX	—	ROH	*8*
2-$HOC_6H_4OCH_3$	CH_3MgI	155–160° (2 hrs.)	ROH (+ ROR′)	*9*
2-R‴$SeC_6H_4OCH_3$ ‡	CH_3MgI	—	ROH (30–69%) ‡	*7*
4-$CH_3CH=CHC_6H_4OCH_3$	C_2H_5MgI	—	ROH (+ polymer?)	*11*
4-$CH_3CH=CHC_6H_4OCH_3$	*n*-C_3H_7MgI	—	ROH (+ polymer?)	*11*
4-$H_2C=CHCH_2C_6H_4OCH_3$	CH_3MgI	160–170°	ROH (59%)	*12, cf. 13*
4-$H_2C=CHCH_2C_6H_4OCH_3$	C_2H_5MgBr	—	ROH + gases	*14,13*
4-$H_2C=CHCH_2C_6H_4OC_2H_5$	C_2H_5MgI	—	ROH + gas	*9*
$C_6H_5OC_6H_5$	C_2H_5MgI	170–190° (15 hrs.)	ROH (31%) + rearr. § (6.5%)	*9*
$C_6H_5OCH_3$	CH_3MgBr	—	ROH + gases	*13*
$C_6H_5OCH_3$	CH_3MgI	200–220° (8 hrs.)	ROH (85%) + "C_2H_6"	*5, cf. 13*
$C_6H_5OCH_3$	$MgBr_2$	200–220° (1 hr.)	ROH (≪66%)	*15*
$C_6H_5OCH_3$	MgI_2	200–220° (1 hr.)	ROH (66%)	*15, cf. 13*

* (α-C_4H_3O) = 2-furyl.

† The rearrangement product is 2-methoxy-6-α-furylmethylphenol.

‡ R‴ = CH_3 (65%); C_2H_5 (69%); *n*-C_3H_7 (49%); *i*-C_3H_7 (53%); *n*-C_4H_9 (63%); *i*-C_4H_9 (45%); *i*-C_5H_{11} (50%); *n*-C_6H_{13} (30%).

§ The rearrangement product is 2-biphenylol (2-phenylphenol).

TABLE XV-I (Continued)

ROR′	R″MgX (or MgX_2)	Temp. (Time)	Product(s)	Ref.
$C_6H_5OCH_3$	C_2H_5MgX	—	ROH + gases	*13*
$C_6H_5OCH_3$	*i*-C_3H_7MgI	—	ROH + gases	*13*
$C_6H_5OCH_3$	*n*-C_4H_9MgI	—	ROH + gases	*13*
$C_6H_5OCH_3$	*i*-$C_5H_{11}MgI$	130–140°	ROH (78%) + RR″ (?)	*9*
$C_6H_5OC_2H_5$	CH_3MgBr	—	ROH (16%) + gases + tar	*13*
$C_6H_5OC_2H_5$	CH_3MgI	230° (1 hr.)	ROH (85%) + "C_3H_8"	*5, cf. 13*
$C_6H_5OC_2H_5$	C_2H_5MgX	—	ROH + gases	*13*
$C_6H_5OC_2H_5$	*n*-C_4H_9MgI	—	ROH + gases	*13*
$C_6H_5OCH_2CH_2Br$	$C_6H_5CH_2MgCl$	—	ROH + R″OH (?)* + $C_6H_5O(CH_2)_3C_6H_5$	*16*
$C_6H_5OCH_2CH_2Br$	*n*-$C_5H_{11}MgBr$	—	ROH + R″OH (?)*	*16*
$C_6H_5OCH_2CH_2Br$	C_6H_5MgBr	145°	$C_6H_5OCH_2CH_2C_6H_5$	*16*
$C_6H_5OCH_2C_6H_5$	$MgBr_2$	b. Et_2O (46 hrs.)	"No change"	*26*
$C_6H_5OCH_2C_6H_5$ (0.2 mole)	$MgBr_2$	b. C_6H_6 (24 hrs.)	Rec. ROR′ (7.3 g.) + R′Br (5.0 g.) + ROH (12.0 g.) + h.-b. residue (15.0 g.)	*26*
$C_6H_5OCH_2C_6H_5$	C_2H_5MgBr	170–190° (15 hrs.)	ROH (49%) + R′R″ (50%) + rec. ROR′	*9*
$C_6H_5OCH_2C_6H_5$	*n*-C_4H_9MgBr	80° (16 hrs.)	Rec. ROR′ (91%)	*10*
$C_6H_5OCH_2CH=CH_2$	$MgBr_2$	95° (5 hrs.)	ROH (9%) + R′Br	*15*
$C_6H_5OCH_2CH=CH_2$	*n*-C_4H_9MgCl	79° (5 hrs.)	ROH (74%)	*10*
$C_6H_5OCH_2CH=CH_2$	*n*-C_4H_9MgBr	17° (3 hrs.)	ROH (<2%)	*17*
$C_6H_5OCH_2CH=CH_2$	*n*-C_4H_9MgBr	17° (40 hrs.)	ROH (12%)	*17*
$C_6H_5OCH_2CH=CH_2$	*n*-C_4H_9MgBr	17° (140 hrs.)	ROH (43%)	*17*
$C_6H_5OCH_2CH=CH_2$	*n*-C_4H_9MgBr	34° (3 hrs.)	ROH (<2%)	*17*
$C_6H_5OCH_2CH=CH_2$	*n*-C_4H_9MgBr	34° (40 hrs.)	ROH (61%)	*17*
$C_6H_5OCH_2CH=CH_2$	*n*-C_4H_9MgBr	34° (140 hrs.)	ROH (58%)	*17*
$C_6H_5OCH_2CH=CH_2$	*n*-C_4H_9MgBr	61–72° (4–6 hrs.)	ROH (51.0–86.5%) + R′R″	*10*
$C_6H_5OCH_2CH=CH_2$	*n*-C_4H_9MgI	70–72° (5 hrs.)	ROH (53%)	*10*
$C_6H_5OCH_2CH=CH_2$	*n*-$C_{12}H_{25}MgBr$	75° (6 hrs.)	ROH (71%) + R′R″ (43%)	*10*

*If this alcohol was indeed present among the reaction products, it must have arisen from oxygen contamination (see Chapter XX).

TABLE XV-I (Continued)

ROR′	R″MgX (or MgX_2)	Temp. (Time)	Product(s)	Ref.
$C_6H_5OCH_2CH{=}CH_2$	C_6H_5MgBr	20° (210 hrs.)	ROH (63%)	*17*
$C_6H_5OCH_2CH{=}CH_2$	C_6H_5MgBr	70° (7 hrs.)	ROH (71%) + R′R″ (63%)	*10*
$C_6H_5OCH_2CH{=}CH_2$	C_6H_5MgI	70° (6 hrs.)	ROH (60%)	*10*
$C_6H_5OCH_2CH{=}CH_2$	$(C_6H_5)_2Mg$	75° (6 hrs.)	ROH (76%) + R′R″ (67%)	*18*
$C_6H_5OCH_2(\alpha\text{-}C_4H_3O)$ *	*n*-C_4H_9MgCl	b. C_6H_6	ROH (60%) + R′R″ (46%) + rearr.† (31%)	*6*
$C_6H_5OCH_2(\alpha\text{-}C_4H_3O)$ *	*n*-C_4H_9MgBr	*ca.* 70° (*ca.* 5 hrs.)	ROH (40%) + R′R″ (31%) + rearr.† (44%).	*6*
$C_6H_5OC(C_6H_5)_3$	C_6H_5MgBr	b. Et_2O	$(R'O—)_2$ (46%)	*19*
$C_6H_5OC(C_6H_5)_3$	C_6H_5MgBr	200°	R′R″ (15–20%) + R″H	*19*
$CH_3OCH_2C_6H_5$	C_6H_5MgBr	170–180° (6 hrs.)	Rec. ROR′ (62%) + R′R″ (14%)	*9*
$CH_3OC(C_6H_5)_3$	C_6H_5MgBr	200°	R′R″ (12%) + R″H	*19*
$C_2H_5OCH_2C_6H_5$	CH_3MgBr	160–180° (8 hrs.)	R′R″ (39.6%) + R'_2O (11%)	*9*
$C_2H_5OCH_2C_6H_5$	*n*-C_3H_7MgI	—	R′R″ + R'_2	*20*
$C_2H_5OCH(CH_3)$-*i*-C_4H_9	CH_3MgI	170–190° (40 hrs.)	R′R″ (12.4%)	*9*
$C_2H_5OCH(C_6H_5)_2$	*n*-C_3H_7MgI	—	R′R″ + R'_2	*20*
$C_2H_5OC(C_6H_5)_3$ (14.4 g.)	*n*-C_3H_7MgI	b. Et_2O (10 min.)	Rec. ROR′ (1.5 g.) + R′H (7.0 g.)	*27*
$C_2H_5OC(C_6H_5)_3$	*i*-C_4H_9MgI	—	R′H	*28*
$C_2H_5OC(C_6H_5)_3$	C_6H_5MgBr	200°	R′R″ (8–12%) + RH	*19*
n-$C_3H_7OCH(C_6H_5)_2$	*n*-C_3H_7MgI	—	R'_2 + gases	*21,24*
n-$C_3H_7OCH(C_6H_5)_2$	*i*-C_4H_9MgI	—	R'_2	*28*
n-$C_4H_9OCH(C_6H_5)_2$	CH_3MgI	—	Rec. ROR′ (42%) + R'_2 (42%) + R″H (39%)	*22,23*
n-$C_4H_9OCH(C_6H_5)_2$	C_2H_5MgI	—	Rec. ROR′ (50%) + R'_2 (23%) + R′R″ (39%) + ROH (24%) + R″H (21%) + $R''_{(-H)}$	*22,23*

* $(\alpha\text{-}C_4H_3O)$ = 2-furyl.

† The rearrangement product is 2-α-furylmethylphenol.

TABLE XV-I (Continued)

ROR′	R″MgX (or MgX_2)	Temp. (Time)	Product(s)	Ref.
n-$C_4H_9OCH(C_6H_5)_2$	n-C_3H_7MgI	—	Rec. ROR′ (46%) + R'_2 (24%) + R′OR″ (16%) + ROH (16%) + R″H (22%) + $R''_{(-H)}$ (5%)	23,24,25
i-$C_5H_{11}O$-i-C_5H_{11}	CH_3MgI	200–215° (2.5 da.)	ROH (?)	9
i-$C_5H_{11}OCH(C_6H_5)_2$	n-C_3H_7MgI	—	Rec. ROR′ + R″H	23
n-$C_8H_{17}OCH_2CH{=}CH_2$	C_6H_5MgBr	75° (6 hrs.)	ROH (70.5%) + R′R″ (85.0%)	18
$C_6H_5CH_2OCH_2C_6H_5$	CH_3MgI	160–170° (12 hrs.)	ROH (60%) + R′R″ (55%)	9

REFERENCES FOR TABLE XV-I

(*1*) Hurd and Winberg, *J. Am. Chem. Soc.*, *64*, 2085–6 (1942).
(*2*) Hirao, *J. Chem. Soc. Japan*, *54*, 991–5 (1933); *Chem. Abstr.*, *28*, 471 (1934).
(*3*) Hirao, *J. Chem. Soc. Japan*, *52*, 263–9 (1931); *Chem. Abstr.*, *26*, 5084 (1932).
(*4*) Hirao, *J. Chem. Soc. Japan*, *54*, 97–102 (1933); *Chem. Abstr.*, *27*, 2944 (1933).
(*5*) Simonis and Remmert, *Ber.*, *47*, 269–71 (1914).
(*6*) Normant, *Bull. soc. chim.*, [5], 7, 371–4 (1940).
(*7*) Keimatsu, Yokata, and Satoda, *J. Pharm. Soc. Japan*, *53*, 994–1046 (1933); *Chem. Abstr.*, *29*, 7300 (1935).
(*8*) Hirao, *J. Chem. Soc., Japan*, *53*, 488–96 (1932); *Chem. Abstr.*, *27*, 276 (1933).
(*9*) Späth, *Monatsh.*, *35*, 319–32 (1914).
(*10*) Lüttringhaus, von Sääf, and Hauschild, *Ber.*, *71B*, 1673–81 (1938).
(*11*) Serini and Steinruck, *Naturwiss.*, *25*, 682–3 (1937); *Chem. Abstr.*, *32*, 2953 (1938).
(*12*) Zemplin and Gerecs, *Ber.*, *70B*, 1098–101 (1937).
(*13*) Grignard and Ritz, *Bull. soc. chim.*, [5], 3, 1181–4 (1936).
(*14*) Grignard, *Compt. rend.*, *151*, 322–5 (1910); *Chem. Zentr.*, *1910,II*, 1048.
(*15*) Schönberg and Moubasher, *J. Chem. Soc.*, *1944*, 462–3.
(*16*) Grignard, *Compt. rend.*, *138*, 1048–50 (1904); *Chem. Zentr.*, *1904,I*, 1493.
(*17*) Lüttringhaus and von Sääf, *Angew. Chem.*, *51*, 915–20 (1938).
(*18*) Lüttringhaus, Wagner-von Sääf, Sucker, and Borth,. *Ann.*, *557*, 46–69 (1945).
(*19*) Gomberg and Kamm, *J. Am. Chem. Soc.*, *39*, 2009–15 (1917).
(*20*) Tschelinzew and Pawlow, *J. Russ. Phys.-Chem. Soc.*, *45*, 289–300 (1913); *Chem. Zentr.*, *1913,I*, 1962; *Chem. Abstr.*, 7, 2227 (1913).
(*21*) Stadnikow, *J. Russ. Phys.-Chem. Soc.*, *44*, 1219–47 (1912); *Chem. Zentr.*, *1913,I*, 21.
(*22*) Stadnikow, *J. Russ. Phys.-Chem. Soc.*, *45*, 1391–44 (1913); *Chem. Zentr.*, *1913,II*, 2120.
(*23*) Stadnikoff, *Ber.*, *46*, 2496–503 (1913).
(*24*) Stadnikoff, *J. prakt. Chem.*, [2], 88, 1–20 (1913).
(*25*) Stadnikoff and Kusmina-Aron, *J. prakt. Chem.*, [2], 88, 20–5 (1913).
(*26*) Gilman and Schulze, *Rec. trav. chim.*, *47*, 752–60 (1928).
(*27*) Stadnikoff, *Ber.*, *44*, 1157–60 (1911).
(*28*) Stadnikow, *J. Russ. Phys.-Chem. Soc.*, *43*, 1244–57 (1911); *Chem. Abstr.*, 6, 1434 (1912).

Speculations on the mechanism of ether cleavage. If, for the moment, the Schönberg and Moubasher hypothesis be set aside, and it be presumed tentatively that ether cleavage is, in general, effected by the Grignard reagent itself, then it may be stated empirically that the direction of cleavage of an unsymmetrical ether follows the general rule for the cleavage of unsymmetrical ethers by polar reagents. This is most economically stated in the form of an equation in which R represents a radical more "electronegative"[17] than R′, and A is the positive and B the negative constituent of the polar reagent:

$$ROR' + A^+B^- \longrightarrow ROA + R'B$$

[17] For a discussion of the relative "electronegativities" of organic radicals see: Kharasch and Reinmuth, *J. Chem. Education*, *5*, 404–18 (1928); 8, 1703–48 (1931); Kharasch, Reinmuth, and Mayo, *ibid.*, *11*, 82–96 (1934); *13*, 7–19 (1936).

For the special case of the Grignard reagent (R″MgX) the rule may be stated more specifically:

$$ROR' + R''MgX \longrightarrow ROMgX + (R' + R'')$$

The product resulting from the interaction of R′ with R″ depends upon the natures of the specific radicals (or, rather, ions) involved:

(*a*) $R' + R'' \longrightarrow R'R''$

(*b*) $R' + R'' \longrightarrow R'_{(-H)} + R''_{(+H)}$

As a subsidiary rule it may be stated that when R is very strongly "electronegative" and R′ is very weakly "electronegative" the ether is much more susceptible to cleavage than when both R and R′ are strongly or even moderately "electronegative."

What might at first glance appear to constitute a minor inconsistency with the general spirit of the stated rules crops up in the cleavages of the methyl alkyl ethers of the diphenols. Invariably the methyl group (the most "electronegative" of the alkyl groups) is removed in preference to the other alkyl group,[18] *e.g.*,

$$AlkOC_6H_4OCH_3 \xrightarrow{R''MgX} AlkOC_6H_4OMgX$$

However, this inconsistency may be more apparent than real. There is some reason to believe that a hydroxyphenyl group is markedly more "electronegative" than a methoxyphenyl group. Whereas the hydrogen atom is considerably less "electronegative" than any of the alkyl groups, it would seem to follow that the alkoxyphenyl groups in general are intermediate in "electronegativity" between the hydroxyphenyl and the methoxyphenyl groups. It may be, therefore, that in general the $AlkOC_6H_4O$—CH_3 bonds are more polar (and hence more susceptible to cleavage) than the $CH_3OC_6H_4O$—Alk bonds.

In view of the relatively low rates of ether cleavage by Grignard reagents there would appear to be no reason why satisfactory kinetic studies could not be made directly with intelligently selected reactant pairs. To the knowledge of the present authors, however, no such studies have as yet been made. Present speculations on mechanism must, therefore, be based on *a priori* reasoning and extension by analogy of what is known about other polar ether cleavages.

The known properties of ethereal Grignard reagent solutions (see Chapter IV) make it seem a reasonable assumption that the inevitable prelude to ether-Grignard reagent reaction is the formation of Werner complexes of one or more of the following types:

$$\begin{matrix}R \\ R'\end{matrix}\!\!>O:Mg\!<\!\!\begin{matrix}X \\ X\end{matrix} \qquad \begin{matrix}R \\ R'\end{matrix}\!\!>O:Mg\!<\!\!\begin{matrix}R'' \\ X\end{matrix} \qquad \begin{matrix}R \\ R'\end{matrix}\!\!>O:Mg\!<\!\!\begin{matrix}R'' \\ R''\end{matrix}$$

[18] Hirao, *J. Chem. Soc. Japan*, 52, 263-9 (1931); 54, 97-102, 991-5 (1933); *Chem. Abstr.*, 26, 5084 (1932); 27, 2944 (1933); 28, 471 (1934); *Bull. Chem. Soc. Japan*, 11, 179-84 (1936); *Chem. Abstr.*, 30, 5953 (1936).

Under suitably selected experimental conditions kinetic studies could determine whether cleavage takes place through thermal rearrangement of such a complex or through attack of a second molecule of one of the Grignard reagent components upon the complex.

In view of the relative stability of most ethereal carbon-to-oxygen bonds, one would be inclined to regard favorably the latter possibility as affording opportunity for a concerted "push-pull" mechanism which would presumably have a relatively low energy of activation. Kinetic studies of the supposedly analogous hydrogen bromide cleavage of ethyl ether by Mayo *et al.*[19] reveal that in toluene or chlorobenzene (and presumably in excess ethyl ether) the reaction is third-order (*i.e.*, first-order with respect to ether, and second-order with respect to hydrogen bromide).

A mechanism consistent with similar kinetics for the Grignard reagent cleavage could be formulated in terms of the familiar quasi six-membered ring transition state.

$$\begin{array}{ccccc} \begin{array}{ccc} & R' & \\ R{-}O & & R'' \\ \cdot\cdot & & | \\ X{-}Mg & & Mg{-}X \\ & R'' & \end{array} & \longrightarrow & \begin{array}{ccc} & R' & \\ R{-}O & \vdots & R'' \\ \vdots & & \vdots \\ X{-}Mg & \vdots & Mg{-}X \\ & R'' & \end{array} & \longrightarrow & \begin{array}{ccc} & R' & \\ R{-}O & & R'' \\ | & & | \\ X{-}Mg & & Mg{-}X \\ & R'' & \end{array} \end{array}$$

There would seem to be no compelling reason to adopt the six-membered ring transition state for the particular type of cleavage illustrated. However, any concerted "push-pull" mechanism would imply a Walden inversion of the oxygen-linked carbon atom of R′. Such inversion has not been demonstrated for any Grignard ether cleavage, but has been shown to occur in that portion of the chloroacetyl iodide cleavage of (+)-*s*-hexyl methyl ether that leads to the production of 2-iodohexane (Stevens[20]).

$$(+)\text{-}\,C(H)(OCH_3)(H_3C)(n\text{-}C_4H_9) \xrightarrow{(ClCH_2COI)} \begin{cases} (-)\text{-}\,C(H)(I)(H_3C)(n\text{-}C_4H_9) & (28.8\%) \\ (+)\text{-}\,C(H)(OCOCH_2Cl)(H_3C)(n\text{-}C_4H_9) & (52.4\%) \end{cases}$$

(More precisely, it has been demonstrated that there is a retention of optical activity with presumable inversion.)

In the more general convention commonly employed the postulated mechanism might be formulated as follows:

---

[19] Mayo, Hardy, and Schultz, *J. Am. Chem. Soc.*, 63, 426–36 (1941). Concerning the hydrogen bromide cleavage of optically active methyl *s*-butyl ether, see: Burwell, Elkin, and Maury, *J. Am. Chem. Soc.*, 73, 2428–31 (1951).

[20] Stevens, *J. Am. Chem. Soc.*, 62, 1801–2 (1940).

$$\left[\begin{matrix} X \\ R'' \end{matrix} \!\!>\! Mg : R'' \right]^- + \left[R'\!-\!\overset{\overset{R}{|}}{O} : MgX \right]^+ \longrightarrow \begin{matrix} X \\ R'' \end{matrix}\!\!>\! Mg : R'' \cdots R' \cdots \overset{\overset{R}{|}}{O} : MgX$$

$$\longrightarrow \begin{matrix} X \\ R'' \end{matrix}\!\!>\! Mg + R''\!-\!R' + \overset{\overset{R}{|}}{O}\!-\!MgX$$

Obviously the magnesium halide cleavages might be formulated in either of the ways suggested.

As regards the cleavages in which R′ and R″ disproportionate rather than combine, however, a special significance might attach to the six-membered ring method of formulation. Conceivably, such cleavages could be bimolecular. By way of illustration (with $R' = R^1CH_2CH_2$):

$$\begin{matrix} & H_2 & \\ & C & \\ R-O & & CH-R^1 \\ \cdot\cdot & & | \\ X-Mg & & H \\ \backslash & & \\ R'' & & \end{matrix} \longrightarrow \begin{matrix} & H_2 & \\ & C & \\ R-O & & CH-R^1 \\ \vdots & & \\ X-Mg & & H \\ & R'' & \end{matrix} \longrightarrow \begin{matrix} & H_2 & \\ & C & \\ & & \| \\ R-O & & CH-R^1 \\ | & & \\ X-Mg & & H \\ & & / \\ & & R'' \end{matrix}$$

Under suitable experimental conditions such a reaction would, of course, display second-order kinetics, and the disproportionation would be strictly a one-way affair.

$$R'' + R' \longrightarrow R''_{(+H)} + R'_{(-H)}$$

Unfortunately, the data presently available can scarcely be accepted as constituting sufficient grounds for either acceptance or rejection of this formulation.

With the allylic ethers also, there is the possibility of a bimolecular reaction.

$$\begin{matrix} & H_2 & \\ & C & \\ R-O & & CH \\ \cdot\cdot & & \| \\ X-Mg & & CH-R^1 \\ \backslash & & \\ R'' & & \end{matrix} \longrightarrow \begin{matrix} & H_2 & \\ & C & \\ R-O & & CH \\ \vdots & & \vdots| \\ X-Mg & & CH-R^1 \\ & R'' & \end{matrix} \longrightarrow \begin{matrix} & H_2 & \\ & C & \\ & & \| \\ R-O & & CH \\ | & & | \\ X-Mg & & CH-R^1 \\ & & / \\ & & R'' \end{matrix}$$

It is altogether possible that allylic ethers undergo both bimolecular and trimolecular cleavages.

REDUCTIVE (FREE-RADICAL) CLEAVAGE OF ETHERS

Although nothing in the presently available data appears to prohibit treatment of the Grignard reagent cleavages of ethers as special cases of solvolysis in which the Grignard reagent plays the rôle of a polar "solvent," there are certain aspects of the *res gestae* which tend to raise the question whether these reactions may not, in part at least, involve free-radical processes. (1) In general, these reactions proceed very slowly (if at all) at the boiling point of ethyl ether;* usually they are conducted in the temperature range 160–200°. (2) It has been reported by, *inter alios*, Grignard and Ritz[21] that the organomagnesium iodides are more effective ether-cleavage reagents than the corresponding bromides or chlorides. (3) Stadnikoff (*loc. cit.*[3]) found considerable quantities of symmetrical tetraphenylethane (bibenzhydryl) among the products of Grignard reagent cleavages of benzhydryl ethers—unmistakable evidence of a free-radical process of some sort (though not necessarily one directly associated with the ether-cleavage stage of the reaction).

For these reasons Kharasch and Huang[22] undertook to investigate the effect upon the cleavage reaction of an experimental device known to produce free radicals from Grignard reagents at relatively low temperatures, namely, the addition to the reaction system of certain metallic halides, notably cobaltous chloride.

The procedure adopted was to add the metallic halide in small portions at intervals over a period of three to four hours to an ethyl ether solution of the Grignard reagent containing the ether under investigation. After the addition had been completed the reaction mixture was heated for about thirty minutes to the boiling point of ethyl ether and was then allowed to cool. Under the experimental conditions described neither the Grignard reagents nor any of the metallic halides tested (save aluminum chloride) effected appreciable cleavage of any of the ethers investigated. The results of the combined action of Grignard reagents and metallic halides on ethers are summarized in Table XV-II. In many respects they are strikingly similar to those observed in the hydrogenolysis of ethers in the presence of Raney nickel.[23]

---

*This may not be altogether a temperature effect. Ethyl ether (one of the more basic ethers) would probably be a very poor solvent for ether cleavage studies even at high temperatures under pressure. The equilibrium

$$\mathrm{Et_2O : \overset{\displaystyle X}{\underset{\displaystyle R''}{Mg}} : OEt_2 \rightleftharpoons Et_2O : \overset{\displaystyle X}{\underset{\displaystyle R''}{Mg}} : O\langle^{R}_{R'}}$$

would probably tend, in most cases, to lie far toward the left, especially if ethyl ether were present in excess. [Concerning the solvent effect in Grignard reactions, *cf.*: Lewis and Wright, *J. Am. Chem. Soc.*, *74*, 1253–7 (1952).]

[21] Grignard and Ritz, *Bull. soc. chim.*, [5], 3, 1181–4 (1936).

[22] Kharasch and Huang, *J. Org. Chem.*, *17*, 669–77. (1952).

[23] Adkins, "Reactions of Hydrogen with Organic Compounds with Copper-Chromic Oxide and Nickel Catalysts," The University of Wisconsin Press, Madison, Wis., *1937*, pp. 73–5.

TABLE XV-II

REACTIONS OF ETHERS (1 MOLE) WITH ETHYL ETHEREAL GRIGNARD REAGENT SOLUTIONS IN THE PRESENCE OF METALLIC HALIDES AT OR NEAR ROOM TEMPERATURE

ROR′ (1 Mole)	R″MgX (Moles)	Halide (Moles)	% Cleavage *
4-$CH_3OC_6H_4OC_6H_5$	*n*-C_4H_9MgBr (6)	$CoCl_2$ (2.5)	33 †
4-$CH_3OC_6H_4O$-*i*-C_3H_7	*n*-C_4H_9MgBr (4)	$CoCl_2$ (2.0)	0
4-$CH_3OC_6H_4OCH_2C_6H_5$	*i*-C_3H_7MgBr (4)	$CoCl_2$ (2.0)	82
4-$CH_3OC_6H_4OCH_2C_6H_5$	C_6H_5MgBr (4)	$CoCl_2$ (2.0)	10
1-$C_{10}H_7OC_6H_5$	*n*-C_4H_9MgBr (6)	$CoCl_2$ (2.5)	52 ‡
1-$C_{10}H_7OC_2H_5$	*n*-C_4H_9MgBr (4)	$CoCl_2$ (2.0)	0
1-$C_{10}H_7OCH_2C_6H_5$	CH_3MgBr (4)	$CoCl_2$ (2.0)	31
1-$C_{10}H_7OCH_2C_6H_5$	*n*-C_4H_9MgBr (2)	$CoCl_2$ (1.1)	40
1-$C_{10}H_7OCH_2C_6H_5$	*n*-C_4H_9MgBr (4)	$CoCl_2$ (2.0)	81
2-$C_{10}H_7OCH_2C_6H_5$	*n*-C_4H_9MgBr (2)	$CoCl_2$ (1.1)	35
$C_6H_5OC_6H_5$	C_2H_5MgBr (4)	$CoCl_2$ (2.0)	42
$C_6H_5OC_6H_5$	*n*-C_4H_9MgBr (4)	$CoCl_2$ (2.0)	43
$C_6H_5OC_6H_5$	*n*-C_4H_9MgBr (6)	$CoCl_2$ (2.5)	72
$C_6H_5OC_6H_5$	*t*-C_4H_9MgBr (4)	$CoCl_2$ (2.0)	58
$C_6H_5OCH_3$	*n*-C_4H_9MgBr (4)	$CoCl_2$ (2.0)	0
$C_6H_5OC_2H_5$	*n*-C_4H_9MgBr (4)	$CoCl_2$ (2.0)	0
C_6H_5O-*i*-C_3H_7	*n*-C_4H_9MgBr (4)	$CoCl_2$ (2.0)	5
$C_6H_5OCH_2CH=CH_2$	*n*-C_4H_9MgBr (1.2)	$CoCl_2$ (0.01)	89
$C_6H_5OCH_2C_6H_5$	C_6H_5MgBr (4)	$CoCl_2$ (2.0)	<8 §
$C_6H_5OCH_2C_6H_5$	CH_3MgBr (4)	$CoCl_2$ (2.0)	35
$C_6H_5OCH_2C_6H_5$	C_2H_5MgBr (2)	$CoCl_2$ (0.3)	9
$C_6H_5OCH_2C_6H_5$	C_2H_5MgBr (2)	$CoCl_2$ (2.0)	18

* Except where otherwise noted the phenolic (or alcoholic) product is ROH.
† The phenolic product is chiefly phenol.
‡ The phenolic product is 36% phenol, 16% 1-naphthol.
§ After correction for phenol formed by oxygenation of the Grignard reagent.

TABLE XV-II (Continued)

ROR′ (1 Mole)	R″MgX (Moles)	Halide (Moles)	% Cleavage *
$C_6H_5OCH_2C_6H_5$	C_2H_5MgBr (4)	$CoCl_2$ (2.0)	48
$C_6H_5OCH_2C_6H_5$	C_2H_5MgBr (2)	$FeCl_3$ (0.3)	8
$C_6H_5OCH_2C_6H_5$	*i*-C_3H_7MgBr (4)	$CoCl_2$ (2.0)	80
$C_6H_5OCH_2C_6H_5$	*n*-C_4H_9MgBr (4)	$CoCl_2$ (2.0)	86
$C_6H_5OCH_2C_6H_5$	*n*-C_4H_9MgBr (4)	$NiCl_2$ (2.0)	68
$C_6H_5OCH_2C_6H_5$	*n*-C_4H_9MgBr (4)	$FeCl_3$ (2.0)	65
$C_6H_5OCH_2C_6H_5$	*n*-C_4H_9MgBr (4)	$CuCl_2$ (2.0)	10
$C_6H_5OCH_2C_6H_5$	*n*-C_4H_9MgBr (4)	Cu_2Br_2 (2.0)	0
$C_6H_5OCH_2C_6H_5$	*n*-C_4H_9MgBr (4)	$MnCl_2$ (2.0)	0
$C_6H_5OCH_2C_6H_5$	*n*-C_4H_9MgBr (4)	$AlCl_3$ (2.0)	3 †
$C_6H_5OCH_2C_6H_5$	*s*-C_4H_9MgBr (2)	$CoCl_2$ (1.0)	66
$C_6H_5OCH_2C_6H_5$	*s*-C_4H_9MgBr (4)	$CoCl_2$ (2.0)	82
$C_6H_5OCH_2C_6H_5$	*t*-C_4H_9MgBr (4)	$CoCl_2$ (2.0)	92
$C_6H_5OCH_2CH_2C_6H_5$	*n*-C_4H_9MgBr (4)	$CoCl_2$ (2.0)	49
$CH_3OCH_2C_6H_5$	*n*-C_4H_9MgBr (4)	$CoCl_2$ (2.0)	90
$(C_6H_5CH_2)_2O$	*n*-C_4H_9MgBr (4)	$CoCl_2$ (2.0)	88

* Except where otherwise noted the phenolic (or alcoholic) product is ROH.

† Under the experimental conditions here employed, aluminum chloride in the absence of a Grignard reagent effects *ca.* 25% ether cleavage.

Under the experimental conditions described alkyl benzyl, aryl benzyl, aryl allyl, and diaryl ethers undergo cleavage in ethyl ether solution at room temperature. Although phenyl phenethyl ether may be regarded as an exception, the phenyl alkyl ethers in general do not undergo cleavage under these conditions; it may be, however, that they are otherwise hydrogenated. Isosafrole is converted principally to dihydrosafrole, with very little opening of the methylenedioxy ring.

The products of the cleavage of phenyl benzyl ether are phenol and toluene; those of phenyl allyl ether, phenol and propylene. In general it would appear that such cleavages are reductive, with the free radical of the Grignard reagent supplying the reducing hydrogen atom. The data at hand do not justify the formulation of a detailed reaction mechanism, but the essential features of the processes involved may be indicated by some such scheme as the following:

$$R''MgX + CoX_2 \longrightarrow R''CoX + MgX_2$$

$$R''CoX \longrightarrow R''\cdot + \cdot CoX$$

$$ROR' + R''\cdot \longrightarrow R'_{(+H)} + R''_{(-H)} + RO\cdot$$

Insofar as methyl or phenyl Grignard reagents are effective in bringing about such cleavages, they probably operate indirectly by attacking the ethyl ether present, with the production of ethyl radicals. The gases from the methylmagnesium bromide cleavage of phenyl benzyl ether include methane, ethylene, and ethane.

It would appear, therefore, that most of the Grignard reagent cleavages of ethers hitherto reported are probably ionic "solvolysis" reactions, rather than free-radical processes.

PREPARATIVE PROCEDURES

With a few exceptions, such as Gomberg's (*loc. cit.*[13]) preparation of tetraphenylmethane, the Grignard cleavages of ethers have found preparative use chiefly in the deälkylation (usually demethylation) of "protected" aromatic hydroxyl groups which for one reason or another do not lend themselves to satisfactory treatment with hydrogen iodide, hydrogen bromide, or concentrated alkali. Incidentally, for some reason not altogether obvious, the aromatic benzyl ethers seem to offer little or no special advantages, being nearly as stable toward Grignard reagents as the corresponding methyl ethers. A common procedure is to add the ether to be deälkylated to an excess of an ethyl ethereal solution of methylmagnesium iodide, to remove the ethyl ether by distillation, and then to bring the reaction mixture to the desired temperature (usually 160–200°) by means of an oil-bath for the required length of time (often only until the desired bath temperature is reached; sometimes four to six hours).

Among those who have made use of the Grignard cleavage in the preparation of synthetic estrogens are: Zajic and Wesseley,[24] Linnell and

[24]Zajic and Wesseley, German Patent 701,402, Dec. 12, 1944; *Chem. Abstr.*, 35, P7661 (1941).

Shaikmahamud,[25] Hobday and Short,[26] Menzer and Urbain,[27] Hudson,[28,29] Wilds and McCormack,[30] Wessely and Prillinger,[31] Sisido and Nozaki,[32] Ungnade and Tucker,[33] and Mousseron and Winternitz.[34]

A reaction which would appear to have some preparative potentialities, although yields are not stated, is described by Robinson and Robinson.[35] This consists in the cleavage of dialkylaminomethyl *n*-butyl ethers by Grignard reagents. The reaction is said to take place vigorously when an ethereal Grignard reagent solution is added dropwise to an ethereal dialkylamino ether solution. (The amino ethers are prepared by condensing secondary amines with formaldehyde and *n*-butyl alcohol.)

$$n\text{-}C_4H_9OCH_2N(C_2H_5)_2 \xrightarrow{H_2C{=}CHCH_2MgCl} H_2C{=}CHCH_2CH_2N(C_2H_5)_2 + n\text{-}C_4H_9OH$$

$$n\text{-}C_4H_9OCH_2N(CH_2)_5 \xrightarrow{n\text{-}C_4H_9MgI} n\text{-}C_5H_{11}N(CH_2)_5 + n\text{-}C_4H_9OH$$

$$n\text{-}C_4H_9OCH_2N(C_2H_5)_2 \xrightarrow{C_6H_5CH_2MgCl} C_6H_5CH_2CH_2N(C_2H_5)_2 + n\text{-}C_4H_9OH$$

$$n\text{-}C_4H_9OCH_2N(C_2H_5)_2 \xrightarrow{1\text{-}C_{10}H_7MgBr} 1\text{-}C_{10}H_7CH_2N(C_2H_5)_2 + n\text{-}C_4H_9OH$$

$$(n\text{-}C_4H_9OCH_2)_2NCH_3 \xrightarrow{CH_3MgI} (C_2H_5)_2NCH_3 + n\text{-}C_4H_9OH$$

Apparently little use has been made of this reaction, though an additional example is reported by Massie.[36]

$$n\text{-}C_4H_9OCH_2N(n\text{-}C_4H_9)_2 \xrightarrow{n\text{-}C_{12}H_{25}MgBr} n\text{-}C_{13}H_{27}N(n\text{-}C_4H_9)_2 \quad (52\%)$$

It is probable that the reaction mechanism of this cleavage differs somewhat from that of the cleavages previously discussed.

Somewhat similar imino ether cleavages have been reported by Monier-Williams.[36.1]

$$C_6H_5N{=}CHOC_2H_5 \xrightarrow{C_6H_5MgBr} C_6H_5N{=}CHC_6H_5\ (46\%) + C_2H_5OH$$

$$C_6H_5N{=}CHOC_2H_5 \xrightarrow{2\text{-}CH_3C_6H_4MgBr} C_6H_5N{=}CHC_6H_4\text{-}2\text{-}CH_3\ (54\%) + C_2H_5OH$$

$$C_6H_5N{=}CHOC_2H_5 \xrightarrow{1\text{-}C_{10}H_7MgBr} C_6H_5N{=}CH\text{-}1\text{-}C_{10}H_7\ (48\%) + C_2H_5OH$$

$$C_6H_5N{=}CHOC_2H_5 \xrightarrow{2\text{-}C_{10}H_7MgBr} C_6H_5N{=}CH\text{-}2\text{-}C_{10}H_7\ (36\%) + C_2H_5OH$$

---

[25] Linnell and Shaikmahamud, *Quart. J. Pharm. Pharmacol.*, *15*, 384–8 (1942).
[26] Hobday and Short, *J. Chem. Soc.*, *1943*, 609–12.
[27] Menzer and Urbain, *Compt. rend.*, *215*, 554–6 (1942); *Bull. soc. chim.*, [5], *10*, 353–6 (1943); *Chem. Abstr.*, *38*, 2645 (1944).
[28] Hudson and Walton, *J. Chem. Soc.*, *1946*, 85–7.
[29] Hudson, *J. Chem. Soc.*, *1946*, 754–5.
[30] Wilds and McCormack, *J. Am. Chem. Soc.*, *70*, 884–5, 4127–32 (1948).
[31] Wessely and Prillinger, *Ber.*, *72B*, 629–33 (1939).
[32] Sisido and Nozaki, *J. Am. Chem. Soc.*, *70*, 776–8 (1948).
[33] Ungnade and Tucker, *J. Am. Chem. Soc.*, *71*, 2584–5 (1949).
[34] Mousseron and Winternitz, *Bull. soc. chim.*, [5], *15*, 567–70 (1948).
[35] Robinson and Robinson, *J. Chem. Soc.*, *123*, 532–43 (1923).
[36] Massie, *Iowa State Coll. J. Sci.*, *21*, 41–5 (1946); *Chem. Abstr.*, *41*, 3043 (1947).
[36.1] Monier-Williams, *J. Chem. Soc.*, *89*, 273–80 (1906).

CLEAVAGES OF CYCLIC ETHERS

Whereas the "normal" reaction of a Grignard reagent with an epoxide may be regarded as constituting a special case of ether cleavage, these reactions present so many unique features that they have been discussed separately (see Chapter XIV).

Derick and Bissell[37] removed the ether from an ethereal mixture of *n*-propylmagnesium bromide and trimethylene oxide, and, upon further heating, observed a violent reaction. From the residue only traces of 1-hexanol could be isolated. When, however, the ether was partially replaced by benzene and the resultant mixture was refluxed at 70° for four hours, 1-hexanol was obtained in 43 percent yield.

Noller and Adams[38] refluxed an ethereal mixture of cyclopentylmagnesium bromide and trimethylene oxide for four hours, partially replaced the ether by benzene, and continued the reflux at 70° for three hours. They obtained a very poor yield of 3-cyclopentyl-1-propanol (3 g., 0.023 mole alcohol from 29 g., 0.5 mole oxide).

Upon combining trimethylene oxide with an ethereal solution of ethylmagnesium bromide and allowing the system to stand overnight, Bermejo and Aranda[39] obtained a precipitate. The precipitate was warmed on a water-bath at 80° for a half-hour, and the residue was hydrolyzed. The products were 1-pentanol (30 percent) and trimethylene bromohydrin (34 percent).

More recently, Searles[40] has investigated the general applicability of the preparation of alcohols by treatment of trimethylene oxide with Grignard reagents and organolithium compounds. In general, the procedure employed was to add, with stirring, a solution of trimethylene oxide in three volumes of anhydrous ethyl ether to a cold ethereal solution of the Grignard reagent or organolithium compound. After an initial mildly exothermic reaction, during which a white precipitate generally separated, the mixture was refluxed for one hour. Benzene (150–200 ml.) was then added; the ether was removed by distillation through a Vigreux column; and the mixture was refluxed four hours, after which it was cooled and hydrolyzed with saturated ammonium chloride solution.

The procedure was modified for the reactions of the cyclohexyl, isopropyl, and *t*-butyl Grignard reagents and of anhydrous magnesium bromide in that the reaction mixture was allowed to stand at room temperature under an atmosphere of nitrogen for twenty-four hours before benzene was added, and the benzene mixture was refluxed only two hours after removal of ether. The results of the Grignard reactions are summarized in Table XV-III.

[37] Derick and Bissell, *J. Am. Chem. Soc.*, *38*, 2484 (1916).

[38] Noller and Adams, *J. Am. Chem. Soc.*, *48*, 1080–9 (1926).

[39] Bermejo and Aranda, *Anales soc. españ. fis. quim.*, *27*, 798–800 (1929); *Chem. Zentr.*, *1930*,*I*, 2382.

[40] Searles, *J. Am. Chem. Soc.*, *73*, 124–5 (1951).

TABLE XV-III

REACTIONS OF SOME GRIGNARD REAGENTS WITH TRIMETHYLENE OXIDE

RMgX (Mole)	Mole $(CH_2)_3O$	Product(s)
i-C_3H_7MgBr (0.25)	0.20	i-$C_3H_7(CH_2)_3OH$ (28%); $Br(CH_2)_3OH$ (12%)
t-C_4H_9MgCl (0.25)	0.18	t-$C_4H_9(CH_2)_3OH$ (?); $Cl(CH_2)_3OH$ (37%)
C_6H_5MgBr (0.20)	0.18	$C_6H_5(CH_2)_3OH$ (84%); $Br(CH_2)_3OH$ (4%)
$(CH_2)_5CHMgBr$ (0.30)	0.20	$(CH_2)_5CH(CH_2)_3OH$ (28%); $Br(CH_2)_3OH$ (40%)
$C_6H_5CH_2MgCl$ (0.20)	0.13	$C_6H_5(CH_2)_4OH$ (83%)
1-$C_{10}H_7MgBr$ (0.30)	0.18	1-$C_{10}H_7(CH_2)_3OH$ (80%)
2-$C_{10}H_7MgBr$ (0.18)	0.18	2-$C_{10}H_7(CH_2)_3OH$ (60%)

Hirao[41] has reported Grignard cleavage of the methylenedioxy rings of safrole and isosafrole.

$H_2C{=}CHCH_2$— (ring) —O—CH_2—O— $\xrightarrow{CH_3MgI}$

$H_2C{=}CHCH_2$— (ring) —OC_2H_5, OH (much) + $H_2C{=}CHCH_2$— (ring) —OH, OC_2H_5 (little)

$H_2C{=}CHCH_2$— (ring) —O—CH_2—O— (16.4 g.) $\xrightarrow[130^\circ,\ 40\ \text{min.}]{C_6H_5MgBr}$

$H_2C{=}CHCH_2$— (ring) —OH, OH (4.4 g.)

+ $H_2C{=}CHCH_2$— (ring) —$OCH_2C_6H_5$, OH (1.1 g.)

$CH_3CH{=}CH$— (ring) —O—CH_2—O— $\xrightarrow{CH_3MgI}$

$CH_3CH{=}CH$— (ring) —OH, OC_2H_5

[41] Hirao, *J. Chem. Soc. Japan*, *52*, 153–4, 525–8 (1931); *54*, 499–504, 505–9 (1933); *Chem. Abstr.*, *25*, 5156 (1931); *26*, 5058 (1932); *27*, 5730, 5731 (1933).

$$CH_3CH{=}CH{-}C_6H_3(-O-)_2CH_2 \xrightarrow{C_6H_5MgBr}$$

$$CH_3CH{=}CH{-}C_6H_3(OH)(OH)$$

$$+\ CH_3CH{=}CH{-}C_6H_3(OH)(OCH_2C_6H_5)$$

$$+\ CH_3CH{=}CH{-}C_6H_3(OCH_2C_6H_5)(OH)$$

In the absence of more detailed experimental data one can scarcely draw any valid conclusions on the preferred direction of ring opening. According to Hirao,[42] however, the corresponding dimethyl and diethyl ethers yield a preponderance of the *p*-hydroxy compounds.

$$H_2C{=}CHCH_2{-}C_6H_3(OCH_3)(OCH_3) \xrightarrow{CH_3MgI}$$

$$H_2C{=}CHCH_2{-}C_6H_3(OH)(OCH_3)\ \text{(much)} \; + \; H_2C{=}CHCH_2{-}C_6H_3(OCH_3)(OH)\ \text{(little)}$$

$$H_2C{=}CHCH_2{-}C_6H_3(OC_2H_5)(OC_2H_5) \xrightarrow{CH_3MgI}$$

$$H_2C{=}CHCH_2{-}C_6H_3(OH)(OC_2H_5)\ \text{(much)} \; + \; H_2C{=}CHCH_2{-}C_6H_3(OC_2H_5)(OH)\ \text{(little)}$$

$$CH_3CH{=}CH{-}C_6H_3(OC_2H_5)(OC_2H_5) \xrightarrow{CH_3MgI}$$

$$CH_3CH{=}CH{-}C_6H_3(OH)(OC_2H_5)\ \text{(much)} \; + \; CH_3CH{=}CH{-}C_6H_3(OC_2H_5)(OH)\ \text{(little)}$$

[42] Hirao, *J. Chem. Soc., Japan*, 52, 519–24, 525–8 (1931); *Chem. Abstr.*, 26, 5085 (1932).

The opening of a tetramethylene oxide ring has been reported by Paul[43] who refluxed an ethereal Grignard solution prepared from 100 g. of α-bromomethyltetrahydrofuran for five hours and isolated 26 g. of 4-penten-1-ol.

Cleavages of the furan ring have been observed by Kuznetsov.[44]

$$\begin{array}{l} HC\text{---}CH \\ \|\qquad\| \\ HC\quad C\text{---}CHO \\ \quad\diagdown\diagup \\ \quad\; O \end{array} \xrightarrow[\text{xylene reflux}]{RMgX} \begin{array}{l} HC\text{---}CH \\ \|\qquad\| \\ HC\quad C\text{---}CHROH \\ \quad\diagdown\diagup \\ \quad\; O \end{array} + RCH{=}CHCH_2COCHROH$$

$(R = C_2H_5,\ n\text{-}C_3H_7,\ i\text{-}C_4H_9,$ "amyl")

$$\begin{array}{l} HC\text{---}CH \\ \|\qquad\| \\ HC\quad C\text{---}CH_2OH \\ \quad\diagdown\diagup \\ \quad\; O \end{array} \xrightarrow{n\text{-}C_3H_7MgI} \begin{array}{l} HC\text{---}CH \\ \|\qquad\| \\ HC\quad C\text{-}n\text{-}C_4H_9 \\ \quad\diagdown\diagup \\ \quad\; O \end{array} + n\text{-}C_3H_7CH{=}CHCH_2COCH_2OH$$

Lutz and Reveley[45] have observed similar cleavages, accompanied by 1,4-addition to a "hindered" α,β-unsaturated ketone. They formulate the reaction of 2-methyl-3-mesitoyl-4-phenyl-5-mesitylfuran with methylmagnesium iodide (5 equiv.) upon two and three-tenths hours reflux in isopropyl ether as follows:

$$\underset{(9.7\text{ g.})}{\begin{array}{l} H_5C_6\text{---}C\text{---}C\text{---}COMes \\ \qquad\quad\|\qquad\| \\ Mes\text{---}C\quad C\text{---}CH_3 \\ \qquad\quad\diagdown\diagup \\ \qquad\quad\; O \end{array}} \xrightarrow{CH_3MgI} \left[\begin{array}{l} \qquad\qquad\qquad\qquad OMgI \\ \qquad\qquad\qquad\qquad | \\ H_5C_6\text{---}C\text{---}C{=}C\text{---}Mes \\ \qquad\quad\|\qquad |\diagup CH_3 \\ Mes\text{---}C\quad C \\ \qquad\quad\diagdown\diagup\;\diagdown CH_3 \\ \qquad\quad\; O \end{array}\right] \xrightarrow{CH_3MgI}$$

$$\begin{array}{l} \qquad\qquad\qquad\quad OMgI \\ \qquad\qquad\qquad\quad | \\ H_5C_6\text{---}C\text{---}C{=}C\text{---}Mes \\ \qquad\quad\|\quad\; | \\ Mes\text{---}C\quad C(CH_3)_3 \\ \qquad\quad | \\ \qquad\; OMgI \end{array} \xrightarrow{H_2O} \underset{(5.85\text{ g.})}{MesCOCH(C_6H_5)CH(t\text{-}C_4H_9)COMes}$$

---

[43] Paul, *Bull. soc. chim.*, [4], 53, 417-26 (1933).

[44] Kuznetsov, (*a*) *J. Gen. Chem.* (U.S.S.R.), *9*, 2263-8 (1939); *Chem. Abstr.*, *34*, 5052 (1940); (*b*) *J. Gen. Chem.* (U.S.S.R.), *16*, 187-92 (1946); *Chem. Abstr.*, *41*, 443 (1947).

[45] Lutz and Reveley, *J. Am. Chem. Soc.*, *63*, 3178-80, 3180-9 (1941).

Cherbuliez and Araqui[46] report that thebaïne and desoxycodeïne react with Grignard reagents with rupture of the oxide rings. Small *et al.*[47] have also studied the reactions of thebaïne (and various more or less related compounds) with Grignard reagents. The reaction of thebaïne with phenylmagnesium bromide is tentatively formulated as follows:

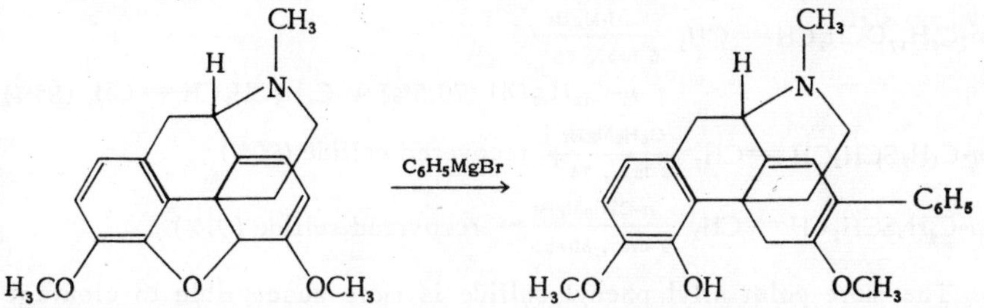

Ring-opening reactions which have features in common with the amino ether cleavages reported by Robinson and Robinson (*loc. cit.*[35]) are described by Senkus.[48] These involve oxazolidines and 1-aza-3,7-dioxabicyclo[3.3.0]octanes.

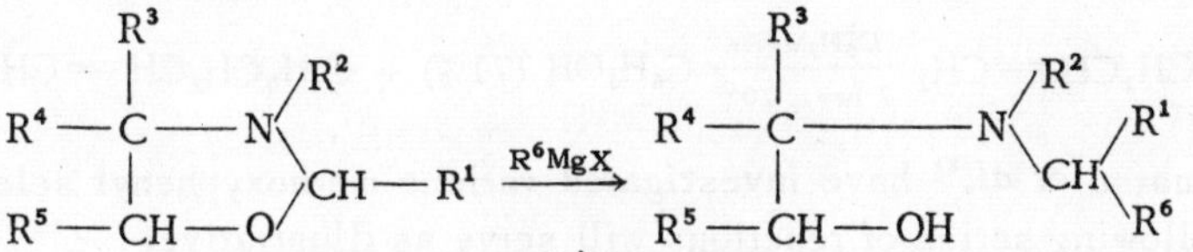

(70–96%)

(R^6MgX = CH_3MgI, C_2H_5MgBr, *i*-C_3H_7MgCl; *i*-C_3H_7MgBr gives only 35% cleavage product, together with reduction.)

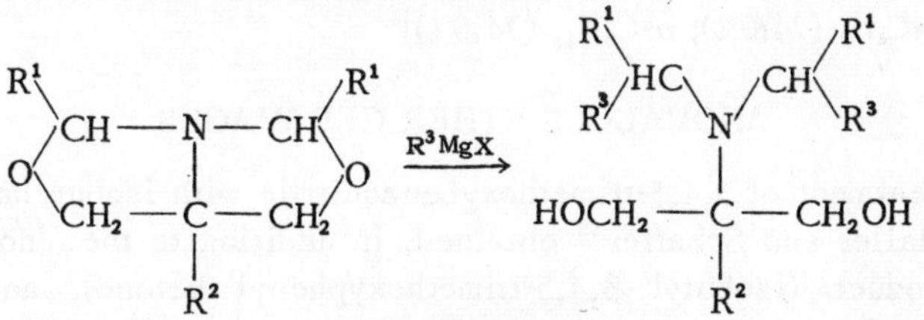

(50–82%)

(R^3MgX = C_2H_5MgCl, *n*-C_3H_7MgCl, *n*-C_4H_9MgCl, C_6H_5MgBr)
The relatively mild reaction conditions comprise the addition of an ethereal solution of the cyclic ether to the Grignard solution at the rate of gentle reflux, followed by twenty-four hours standing.

THIO AND SELENO ETHERS

Insofar as one may judge from the very limited data available the thio and seleno ethers are markedly more resistant to Grignard cleavage than are their oxygen analogs.

---

[46] Cherbuliez and Araqui, *Helv. Chim. Acta*, *26*, 2251–2 (1943).

[47] Small, Sargent, and Bralley, *J. Org. Chem.*, *12*, 839–68 (1947). (This article contains numerous references to previous work.)

[48] Senkus, *J. Am. Chem. Soc.*, *67*, 1515–9 (1945); *Chem. Abstr.*, *41*, P2431 (1947).

According to Lüttringhaus *et al.*,[49] allyl *n*-octyl ether undergoes almost complete cleavage upon six hours treatment with phenylmagnesium bromide at 75°, whereas the structurally similar allyl *n*-butyl sulfide is substantially unaffected by nine hours treatment with phenyl- or *n*-butylmagnesium bromide.

$$n\text{-}C_8H_{17}OCH_2CH{=}CH_2 \xrightarrow[6\text{ hrs., }75^\circ]{C_6H_5MgBr} n\text{-}C_{18}H_{17}OH\ (70.5\%) + C_6H_5CH_2CH{=}CH_2\ (85\%)$$

$$n\text{-}C_4H_9SCH_2CH{=}CH_2 \xrightarrow[9\text{ hrs., }74^\circ]{C_6H_5MgBr} \text{recovered sulfide (90\%)}$$

$$n\text{-}C_4H_9SCH_2CH{=}CH_2 \xrightarrow[9\text{ hrs., }80\text{–}86^\circ]{n\text{-}C_4H_9MgBr} \text{recovered sulfide (91\%)}$$

The more polar allyl phenyl sulfide is more susceptible to cleavage (Lüttringhaus *et al.*, *loc. cit.*[49]), but apparently less so than the corresponding ether (Lüttringhaus *et al.*[50]).

$$C_6H_5SCH_2CH{=}CH_2 \xrightarrow[6\text{ hrs., }78^\circ]{C_6H_5MgBr} C_6H_5SH\ (35\%) + C_6H_5CH_2CH{=}CH_2\ (48\%)$$

$$C_6H_5OCH_2CH{=}CH_2 \xrightarrow[7\text{ hrs., }70^\circ]{C_6H_5MgBr} C_6H_5OH\ (71\%) + C_6H_5CH_2CH{=}CH\ (63\%)$$

Keimatsu *et al.*[51] have investigated various methoxyphenyl selenides. The following series of reactions will serve as illustrative.

$$4\text{-}CH_3OC_6H_4SeR \xrightarrow{R'MgI} 4\text{-}IMgOC_6H_4SeR\ (62.4\text{–}78.2\%)$$

[R = CH_3 (78.2%); C_2H_5(62.4%); n-C_3H_7 (76.0%); i-C_3H_7 (74.5%); n-C_4H_9 (76.0%); i-C_4H_9 (74.0%); n-C_6H_{13} (74.0%)]

ANOMALOUS ETHER CLEAVAGES

Upon treatment of 3,4,5-trimethoxybenzonitrile with isobutylmagnesium bromide Haller and Schaffer[52] obtained, in addition to the "normal" reaction product (isobutyl 3,4,5-trimethoxyphenyl ketone), an ordinary ether-cleavage product (isobutyl 3,5-dimethoxy-4-hydroxyphenyl ketone) and a neutral ketone which they tentatively identified as isobutyl 3,5-dimethoxy-4-isobutylphenyl ketone. Hurd and Winberg,[53] who repeated and extended this study, found that when reaction is effected by prolonged heating at 40° only the "normal" product is obtained, but that when the reaction is conducted with an excess of Grignard reagent at about 110° two "abnormal" products are obtained in addition to the "normal" product. The identification of the first of the "abnormal" products by Haller and Schaffer (*loc. cit.*[52]) as isobutyl 3,5-dimethoxy-4-

[49] Lüttringhaus, Wagner-von Sääf, Sucker, and Borth, *Ann.*, 557, 46–69 (1945).

[50] Lüttringhaus, von Sääf, and Hauschild, *Ber.*, *71B*, 1673–81 (1938).

[51] Keimatsu, Yokata, and Sotada, *J. Pharm. Soc. Japan*, 53, 994–1046 (1933); *Chem. Abstr.*, *29*, 7300 (1935).

[52] Haller and Schaffer, *J. Am. Chem. Soc.*, *61*, 2175–7 (1939).

[53] Hurd and Winberg, *J. Am. Chem. Soc.*, *64*, 2085–6 (1942).

hydroxyphenyl ketone was confirmed by its oxidation to 2,6-dimethoxy-1,4-benzoquinone. The second, although not positively identified, is believed by Hurd and Winberg to have the constitution attributed to it by Haller and Schaffer.

If this identification is correct we have to do here with an anomalous type of ether cleavage which violates the general rule concerning the direction of cleavage of unsymmetrical ethers. It would appear that the most plausible explanation involves 1,6-addition to a conjugated system—possibly O═C—C═C—C═C, but more probably N≡C—C═C—C═C. It has been well-established that among conjugated carbonyl systems, which have been rather extensively investigated (see Chapter VI), 1,6-additions occur, and 1,4-additions involving aromatic rings are well-known. Among conjugated nitrile systems, which have been comparatively little studied (see Chapter X), unequivocal examples of 1,4-addition have nevertheless been observed. It therefore requires but little extension of known facts to postulate some such reaction as:

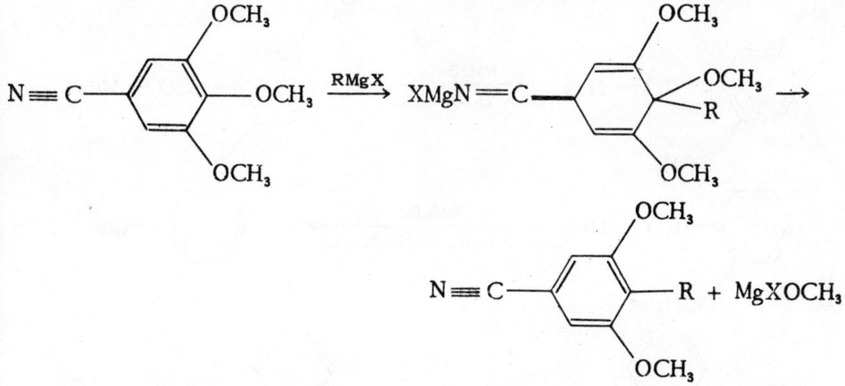

OCH_3 / N≡C—(ring)—OCH_3 / OCH_3 $\xrightarrow{RMgX}$ XMgN═C═(ring)$<^{OCH_3}_{R}$ (with OCH_3, OCH_3) →

OCH_3 / N≡C—(ring)—R + $MgXOCH_3$ / OCH_3

Similar reactions which presumably involve 1,4-addition have been reported by Richtzenhain[54] and confirmed by Fuson *et al.*[55] For example:

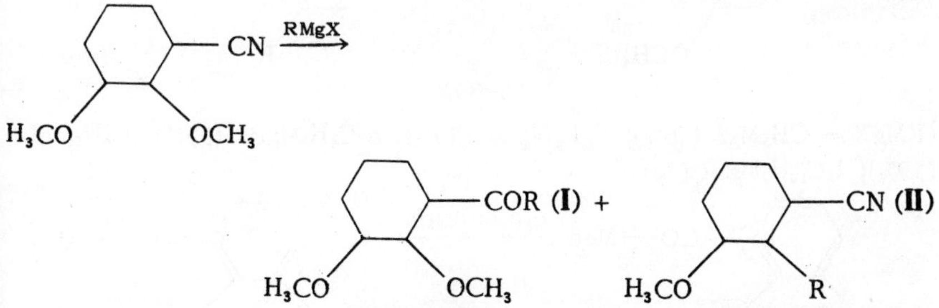

(ring)—CN with H_3CO, OCH_3 $\xrightarrow{RMgX}$

(ring)—COR (**I**) with H_3CO, OCH_3 (very little) + (ring)—CN (**II**) with H_3CO, R (good yield)

[R = C_2H_5 (**II**, 60%); *i*-C_3H_7 (**II**, 81%); *n*-C_4H_9 (**II**, 80%); *i*-C_4H_9 (**II**, 45%); $(CH_2)_5CH$ (**II**, 68%); *n*-C_7H_{15} (**II**, 62%)]

---

[54] Richtzenhain, *Ber.*, *77B*, 1–6 (1944); Richtzenhain and Nippus, *ibid.*, *77B*, 566–72 (1944).

[55] Fuson, Gaertner, and Chadwick, *J. Org. Chem.*, *13*, 489–95 (1948).

Incidentally, the foregoing exemplary reactions (Richtzenhain and Nippus, *loc. cit.*[54]) are carried out under relatively mild conditions. An ethereal solution of the nitrile is added slowly to an ethereal solution of the Grignard reagent. After subsidence of the fairly vigorous reaction the mixture is allowed to stand for four hours and is then treated in the appropriate manner for recovery of the products.

According to Fuson *et al.* (*loc. cit.*[55]), demethoxylation of an *o*-methoxybenzonitrile takes place readily only when there is a second methoxy group in the *meta* (3) position. It was also found by Fuson and Chadwick[56] that ethylmagnesium bromide and benzylmagnesium chloride react "normally" with 2-methoxy-1-naphthonitrile, *i.e.*, without replacement of the methoxy group.

Demethoxylations, similarly attributable to 1,4- and 1,6-additions to "hindered" conjugated carbonyl systems have been reported by Fuson and Speck,[57] Fuson and Gaertner,[58] Fuson and Tull,[59] Fuson and Shealy,[60] and Fuson and Hornberger.[61] For example:

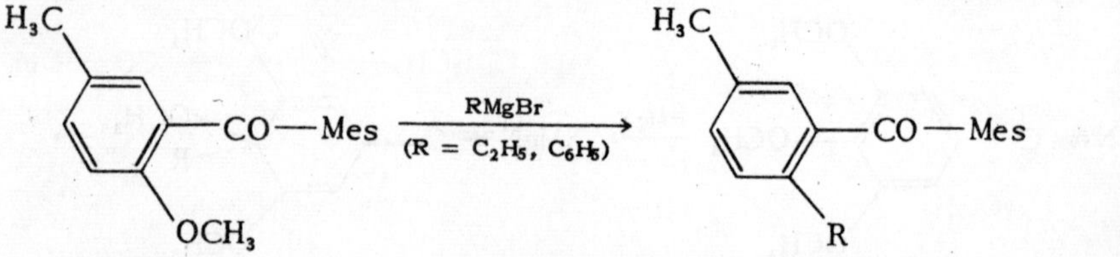

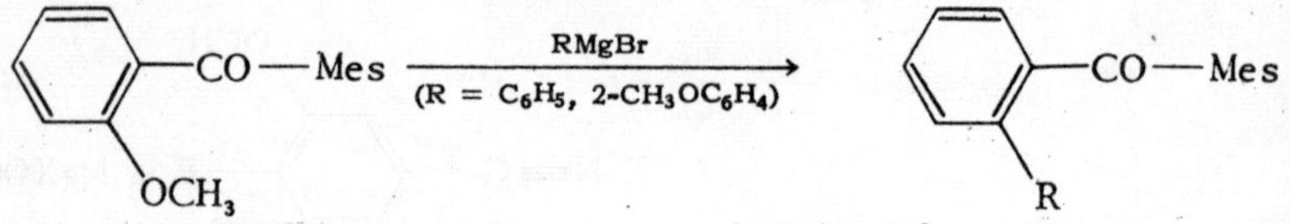

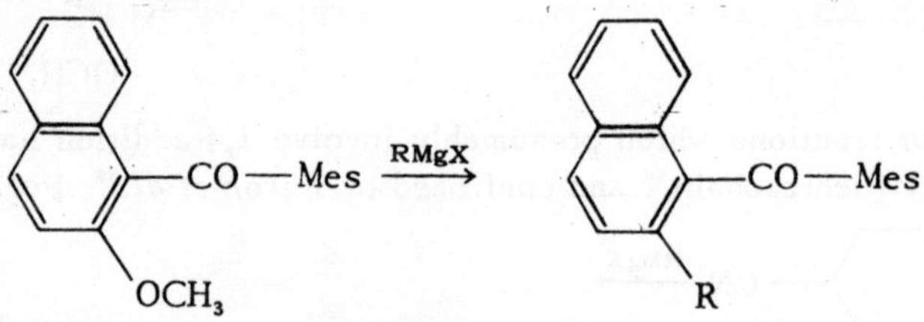

H_3C; CO—Mes; OCH_3 $\xrightarrow[(R\ =\ C_2H_5,\ C_6H_5)]{RMgBr}$ H_3C; CO—Mes; R

CO—Mes; OCH_3 $\xrightarrow[(R\ =\ C_6H_5,\ 2\text{-}CH_3OC_6H_4)]{RMgBr}$ CO—Mes; R

CO—Mes; OCH_3 $\xrightarrow{RMgX}$ CO—Mes; R

(55–80%)

[RMgX = CH_3MgI (56%); C_2H_5MgBr (80%); *n*-C_4H_9MgBr (55%); C_6H_5MgBr (59%); 1-$C_{10}H_7MgBr$ (76%)]

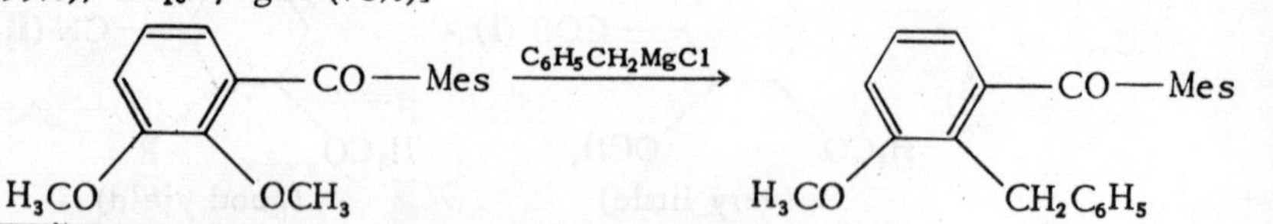

CO—Mes; H_3CO; OCH_3 $\xrightarrow{C_6H_5CH_2MgCl}$ CO—Mes; H_3CO; $CH_2C_6H_5$

[56] Fuson and Chadwick, *J. Org. Chem.*, *13*, 484–8 (1948).
[57] Fuson and Speck, *J. Am. Chem. Soc.*, *64*, 2446–8 (1942).
[58] Fuson and Gaertner, *J. Org. Chem.*, *13*, 496–501 (1948).
[59] Fuson and Tull, *J. Am. Chem. Soc.*, *71*, 2543–6 (1949).
[60] Fuson and Shealy, *J. Org. Chem.*, *16*, 643–7 (1951).
[61] Fuson and Hornberger, *J. Org. Chem.*, *16*, 631–6 (1951).

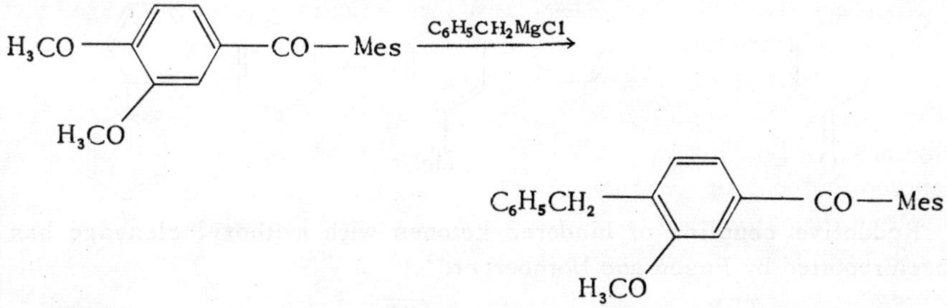

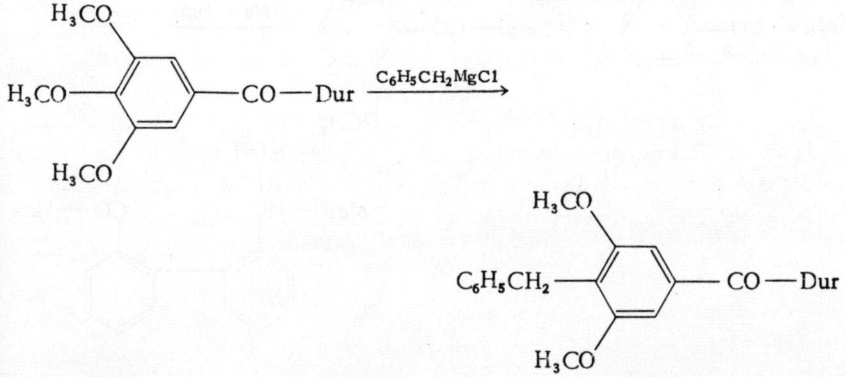

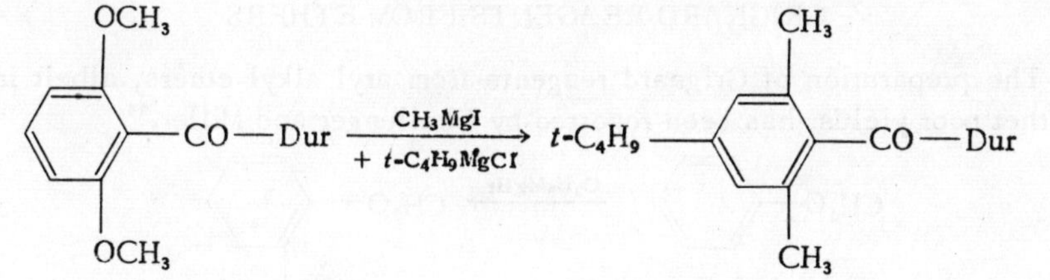

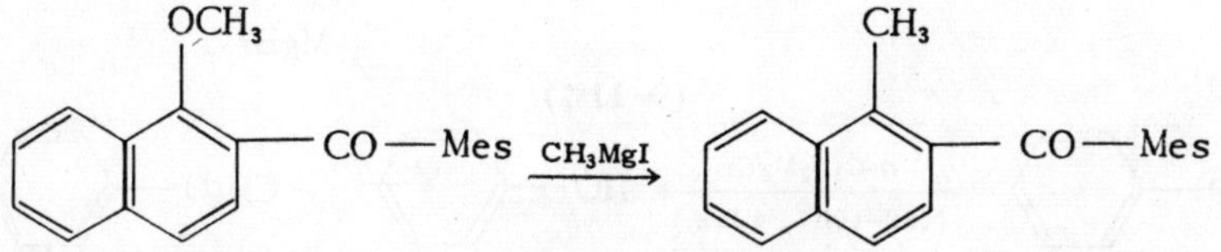

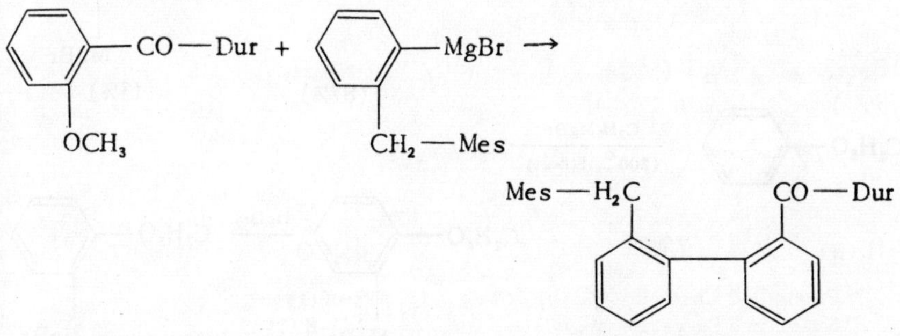

A similar demethoxylation of 3-methoxy-2-cyclohexen-1-one is reported by Woods and Reed.[62]

[62] Woods and Reed, *J. Am. Chem. Soc.*, *71*, 1348–54 (1949).

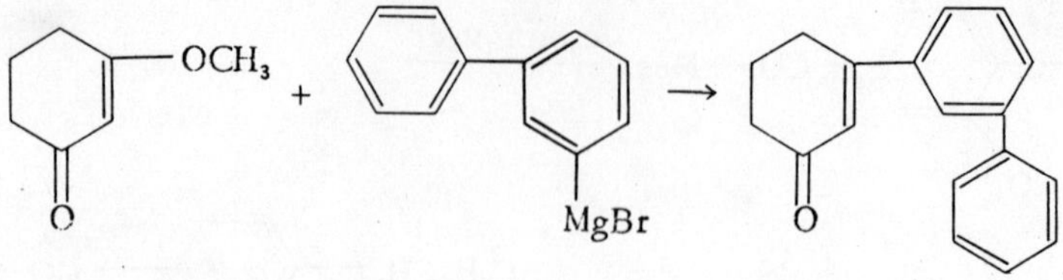
OCH$_3$
+
MgBr
O
O

Reductive coupling of hindered ketones with methoxyl cleavage has been reported by Fuson and Hornberger.[63]

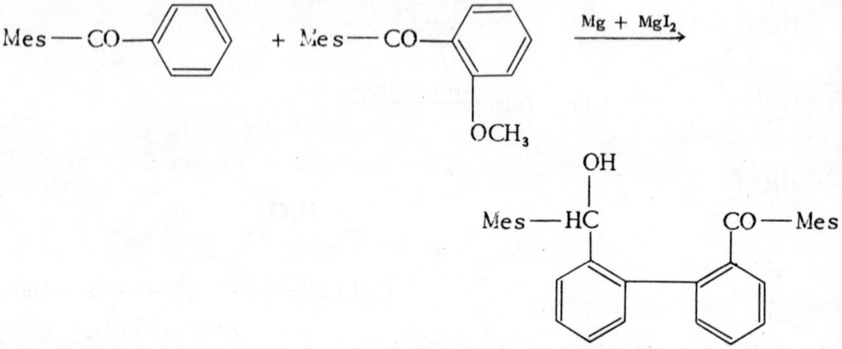
Mes—CO—
+ Mes—CO—
OCH$_3$
Mg + MgI$_2$
OH
Mes—HC
CO—Mes

GRIGNARD REAGENTS FROM ETHERS

The preparation of Grignard reagents from aryl alkyl ethers, albeit in rather poor yields, has been reported by Challenger and Miller.[64]

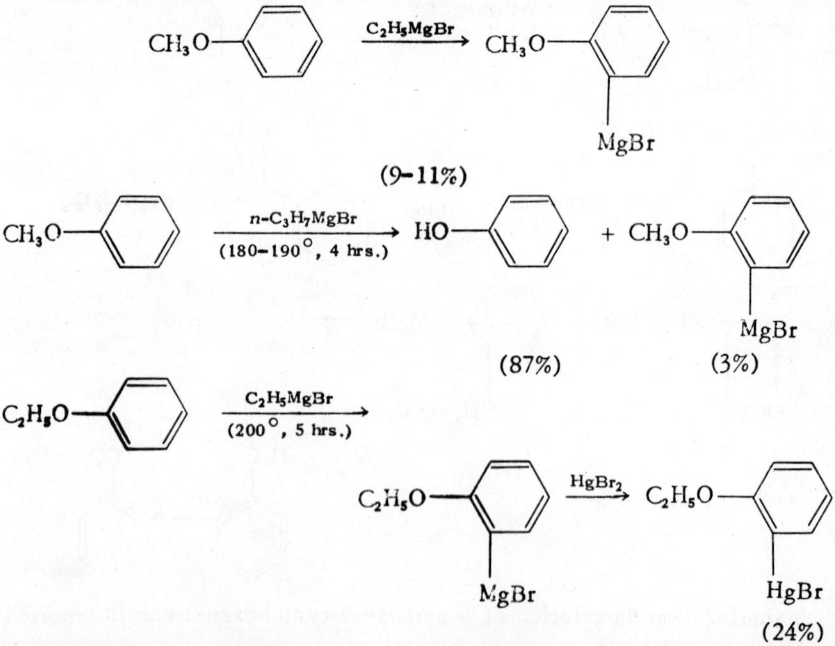
CH$_3$O—
C$_2$H$_5$MgBr
CH$_3$O—
MgBr
(9–11%)
CH$_3$O—
n-C$_3$H$_7$MgBr
(180–190°, 4 hrs.)
HO—
+ CH$_3$O—
MgBr
(87%)
(3%)
C$_2$H$_5$O—
C$_2$H$_5$MgBr
(200°, 5 hrs.)
C$_2$H$_5$O—
MgBr
HgBr$_2$
C$_2$H$_5$O—
HgBr
(24%)

[63] Fuson and Hornberger, *J. Org. Chem.*, 16, 637–42 (1951).
[64] Challenger and Miller, *J. Chem. Soc.*, 1938, 894–9.

A similar reaction of dibenzofuran has been observed by Gilman and Haubein.[65]

$$\text{Dibenzofuran} \xrightarrow{C_2H_5MgBr} \text{4-dibenzofuryl-MgBr} \xrightarrow{CO_2} \text{4-dibenzofuryl-}CO_2H \ (5\%)$$

ACETALS AND KETALS

Apparently the reactions of acetals and ketals with Grignard reagents, as constituting a possible method for the synthesis of ethers, were first investigated by Späth,[66] although nearly simultaneous independent studies were made by Tschitschibabin and Jelgasin.[67]

Nothing of any theoretical significance has been reported in this field, but it appears fairly evident that these reactions, like those of the ortho esters, which are discussed elsewhere (see Chapter VIII), represent special cases of ether cleavage. Obviously *gem* alkoxy groups are mutually activating with respect to this reaction.

Representative data are assembled in Table XV-IV. In addition it is reported by Levina *et al.*[68] that the only isolable product of the reaction of the ethyl ketal of cyclohexanone with methylmagnesium iodide is cyclohexanol, and by Nazarov[69] that the "cyclic acetal" of $CH_3COC(CH_3)_2OH$ does not react with methylmagnesium iodide.

---

[65] Gilman and Haubein, *J. Am. Chem. Soc.*, 67, 1033–4 (1945).

[66] Concerning priority claim see: Späth, *Ber.*, 47, 766–8 (1914).

[67] Tschitschibabin and Jelgasin, *Ber.*, 47, 48–50, 1843–52 (1914).

[68] Levina, Kulikov, and Parshikov, *J. Gen. Chem.* (U.S.S.R.), *11*, 567–72 (1941); *Chem. Abstr.*, 35, 6931 (1941).

[69] Nazarov, *Bull. acad. sci. U.R.S.S., Classe sci. chim.*, *1940*, 195–202; *Chem. Abstr.*, 36, 742 (1942).

TABLE XV-IV

REACTIONS OF GRIGNARD REAGENTS ($R'''MgX$) WITH ACETALS [$RCH(OR'')_2$] AND KETALS [$RR'C(OR'')_2$]

Acetal or Ketal	R'''MgX	Temp. (Time)	Product(s)	Ref.
$H_2C(OCH_3)_2$	C_6H_5MgI	120–130° (2 hrs.)	$C_6H_5CH_2OCH_3$ (15%)	*1*
$H_2C(OCH_3)_2$	$C_6H_5CH_2MgCl$	*ca.* 95° (2 hrs.)	$C_6H_5CH_2CH_2OH + C_6H_5CH_3 + (C_6H_5CH_2-)_2$	*2*
$H_2C(OCH_3)_2$	$C_6H_5CH_2MgCl$	*ca.* 100° (8 hrs.)	$C_6H_5CH_3 + (C_6H_5CH_2-)_2$	*2*
$H_2C(OCH_3)_2$	$C_6H_5CH_2MgCl$	150° (1 hr.)	$C_6H_5CH_3 + C_6H_5CH_2CH_2OCH_3$	*2*
$H_2C(OC_2H_5)_2$	n-$C_4H_9C{\equiv}CMgBr$	95° (1 hr.)	n-$C_4H_9C{\equiv}CCH_2OC_2H_5$ (31–35%)	*3*
$H_2C(OC_2H_5)_2$	$C_6H_5CH_2MgCl$	150°	$C_6H_5CH_3 + (C_6H_5CH_2)_2CH_2$	*2*
$H_2C(OC_2H_5)_2$	4-$CH_3OC_6H_4MgI$	*ca.* 120° (14 hrs.)	4-$CH_3OC_6H_4CH_2OC_2H_5$ (14%)	*1*
$H_2C(OC_2H_5)_2$	3,4-$(CH_3)_2C_6H_3MgI$	120–130° (4 hrs.)	3,4-$(CH_3)_2C_6H_3CH_2OC_2H_5$ (13%)	*1*
$H_2C(O$-n-$C_3H_7)_2$	$({\equiv}CMgBr_2)$	95° (1 hr.)	$({\equiv}CCH_2OC_2H_5)_2$ (31–35%)	*3*
$H_2C(O$-n-$C_3H_7)_2$	n-$C_4H_9C{\equiv}CMgBr$	95° (1 hr.)	n-$C_4H_9C{\equiv}CCH_2O$-n-C_3H_7 (31–35%)	*3*
$H_2C(O$-i-$C_4H_9)_2$	$C_6H_5CH_2MgCl$	125°	$(C_6H_5CH_2)_2CH_2$ (trace)	*2*
$BrCH_2CH(OC_2H_5)_2$	C_6H_5MgBr	110° (6 hrs.)	$BrCH_2(C_6H_5)CHOC_2H_5$ (22%) + $C_6H_5(C_6H_5CH_2)CHOC_2H_5$	*4*
$BrCH_2CH(OC_2H_5)_2$	4-$CH_3C_6H_4MgBr$	100° (12 hrs.)	$BrCH_2$(4-$CH_3C_6H_4)CHOC_2H_5$ + 4-$CH_3C_6H_4$(4-$CH_3C_6H_4CH_2)CHOC_2H_5$ (11%)	*4*
$ClCH_2CH(OC_2H_5)_2$	4-ClC_6H_4MgBr	Room temp.	$ClCH_2$(4-$ClC_6H_4)CHOC_2H_5$ (65%)	*4*
$ClCH_2CH(OC_2H_5)_2$	4-ClC_6H_4MgBr	120–130° (0.5 hr.)	(4-$ClC_6H_4C{=})_2$ (53%, crude)	*4*
$ClCH_2CH(OC_2H_5)_2$	C_6H_5MgBr	120° (1.5 hr.)	$C_6H_5(C_6H_5CH_2)CHOC_2H_5$ (31%) + $(C_6H_5CH{=})_2$	*4*
$ClCH_2CH(OC_2H_5)_2$	2-$CH_3C_6H_4MgBr$	120–130°	(2-$CH_3C_6H_4CH{=})_2$ + 2-$CH_3C_6H_4$(2-$CH_3C_6H_4CH_2)CHOC_2H_5$	*4*
$ClCH_2CH(OC_2H_5)_2$	4-$CH_3C_6H_4MgBr$	Room temp.	$ClCH_2$(4-$CH_3C_6H_4)CHOH$ (50%)	*4*
$ClCH_2CH(OC_2H_5)_2$	3,4-$(CH_3)_2C_6H_3MgBr$	115° (0.5 hr.)	3,4-$(CH_3)_2C_6H_3$[3,4-$(CH_3)_2C_6H_3CH_2$]-$CHOC_2H_5$ (17.5%)	*4*
$CH_3CH(OC_2H_5)_2$	$({\equiv}CMgBr)_2$	95° (1 hr.)	$[{\equiv}CCH(OC_2H_5)CH_3]_2$ (46–49%)	*3*
$CH_3CH(OC_2H_5)_2$	$HC{\equiv}CMgBr$	95° (1 hr.)	$CH_3(HC{\equiv}C)CHOC_2H_5$ (46–49%)	*3*

TABLE XV-IV (Continued)

Acetal or Ketal	R‴MgX	Temp. (Time)	Product(s)	Ref.
$CH_3CH(OC_2H_5)_2$	i-C_4H_9MgBr	*ca.* 95°	$CH_3(i$-$C_4H_9)CHOC_2H_5$	*2*
$CH_3CH(OC_2H_5)_2$	i-$C_5H_{11}MgBr$	100° (16 hrs.)	$CH_3(i$-$C_5H_{11})CHOC_2H_5$ (27%)	*1*
$CH_3CH(OC_2H_5)_2$	C_6H_5MgBr	100–150° (1 hr.)	$CH_3(C_6H_5)CHOC_2H_5$ (55%)	*1*
$CH_3CH(OC_2H_5)_2$	C_6H_5MgBr	*ca.* 95°	$CH_3(C_6H_5)CHOC_2H_5$ (50%)	*2*
$CH_3CH(OC_2H_5)_2$	$C_6H_5CH_2MgCl$	*ca.* 95°	$CH_3(C_6H_5CH_2)CHOC_2H_5$	*2*
$CH_3CH(OC_2H_5)_2$	n-$C_5H_{11}C\equiv CMgBr$	95° (1 hr.)	$CH_3(n$-$C_5H_{11}C\equiv C)CHOC_2H_5$ (46–49%)	*3*
$CH_3CH(OC_2H_5)_2$	4-Methylcyclohexyl-MgBr	*ca.* 95°	1-Ethoxy-1-(4-methylcyclohexyl)-ethane	*2*
$HC\equiv CCH(OC_2H_5)_2$	CH_3MgBr	"hot"	$CH_3(HC\equiv C)CHOC_2H_5$	*6,14*
$HC\equiv CCH(OC_2H_5)_2$	C_2H_5MgBr	b. Et_2O (several hrs.)	$C_2H_5(HC\equiv C)CHOC_2H_5$	*14,13*
$HC\equiv CCH(OC_2H_5)_2$	C_6H_5MgBr	b. Et_2O (several hrs.)	$C_6H_5(HC\equiv C)CHOC_2H_5$	*14,13*
$ClCH_2CHBrCH(OCH_3)_2$	n-C_3H_7MgBr	"cold"	$ClCH_2CHBr(n$-$C_3H_7)CHOCH_3$	*5*
$ClCH_2CHBrCH(OCH_3)_2$	n-C_4H_9MgBr	"cold"	$ClCH_2CHBr(n$-$C_4H_9)CHOCH_3$	*5*
$C_2H_5CH(OC_2H_5)_2$	n-$C_4H_9C\equiv CMgBr$	95° (1 hr.)	$C_2H_5(n$-$C_4H_9C\equiv C)CHOC_2H_5$ (46–49%)	*3*
$C_2H_5OCH_2CH(OC_2H_5)_2$	C_6H_5MgBr	100–200° (1 hr.)	$C_2H_5OCH_2(C_6H_5)CHOC_2H_5$ (40%)	*1*
$C_6H_5CH(OC_2H_5)_2$	$HC\equiv CMgBr$	95° (1 hr.)	$HC\equiv C(C_6H_5)CHOC_2H_5$ (66%)	*3*
$C_6H_5CH(OC_2H_5)_2$	C_6H_5MgBr	*ca.* 95°	$(C_6H_5)_2CHOC_2H_5$ (trace) + $(C_6H_5)_3CH$	*7*
$C_6H_5CH(OC_2H_5)_2$	n-$C_4H_9C\equiv CMgBr$	95° (1 hr.)	$C_6H_5(n$-$C_4H_9C\equiv C)CHOC_2H_5$ (66%)	*3*
n-$C_4H_9C\equiv CCH(OC_2H_5)_2$	n-$C_4H_9C\equiv CMgBr$	95° (1 hr.)	$(n$-$C_4H_9C\equiv C)_2CHOC_2H_5$ (66%)	*3*
n-$C_6H_{13}CH(OC_2H_5)_2$	C_2H_5MgBr	—	$C_2H_5(n$-$C_6H_{13})CHOC_2H_5$ + n-$C_6H_{13}(C_2H_5)_2CH$	*8*
n-$C_6H_{13}CH(OC_2H_5)_2$	i-$C_5H_{11}MgCl$	—	i-$C_5H_{11}(n$-$C_6H_{13})CHOC_2H_5$ + n-$C_6H_{13}(i$-$C_5H_{11})_2CH$	*8*
n-$C_6H_{13}CH(OC_2H_5)_2$	C_6H_5MgBr	—	$C_6H_5(n$-$C_6H_{13})CHOC_2H_5$ + n-$C_6H_{13}(C_6H_5)_2CH$	*8*
n-$C_6H_{13}CH(OC_2H_5)_2$	$C_6H_5CH_2MgCl$	—	n-$C_6H_{13}(C_6H_5CH_2)CHOC_2H_5$ + n-$C_6H_{13}(C_6H_5CH_2)_2CH$	*8*
n-$C_6H_{13}CH(OC_2H_5)_2$	1-$C_{10}H_7MgBr$	—	n-$C_6H_{13}(1$-$C_{10}H_7)CHOC_2H_5$	*8*
$(C_6H_5)_2CClCH(OC_2H_5)_2$	C_6H_5MgBr	180°	C_6H_5Cl (10%) + $(C_6H_5)_2CH_2$ (36%) + $(C_6H_5)_2CHCO_2H$ (52%)	*9*

TABLE XV-IV (Continued)

Acetal or Ketal	R'''MgX	Temp. (Time)	Product(s)	Ref.
$C_9H_{15}CH{=}CHCHOCH_2CH(OC_2H_5)_2$ *	CH_3MgI	—	$CH_3(C_9H_{15}CH{=}CHCHOCH_2)CHOC_2H_5$ *	*10*
$(CH_3)_2C(OC_2H_5)_2$	i-C_4H_9MgBr	—	i-$C_4H_9(CH_3)_2COC_2H_5$ (10–15%)	*2*
$(CH_3)_2C(OC_2H_5)_2$	C_6H_5MgBr	Dist'n Et_2O	$C_6H_5(CH_3)_2COC_2H_5$ (7%)	*11*
$(CH_3)_2C(OC_2H_5)_2$	$(CH_2)_5CHMgCl$	—	$(CH_2)_5CH(CH_3)_2COC_2H_5$ (7%)	*11*
$CH_3(C_6H_5)C(OC_2H_5)_2$	n-C_3H_7MgCl	80–90°	$CH_3(n\text{-}C_3H_7)(C_6H_5)COC_2H_5$ (59%)	*1*
$C_6H_5(C_6H_5CH{=}CH)C(OCH_3)_2$	C_6H_5MgBr	Dist'n Et_2O	$C_6H_5CH{=}CH(C_6H_5)_2COCH_3$ (57%)	*12*

* C_9H_{15} = 2,6,6-trimethyl-1-cyclohexenyl.

REFERENCES FOR TABLE XV-IV

(*1*) Späth, *Monatsh.*, *35*, 319–32 (1914).
(*2*) Tschitschibabin and Jelgasin, *Ber.*, *47*, 1843–52 (1914).
(*3*) Kranzfelder and Vogt, *J. Am. Chem. Soc.*, *60*, 1714–6 (1938).
(*4*) Späth, *Monatsh.*, *35*, 463–74 (1914).
(*5*) Quelet and Pineau, *Compt. rend.*, *222*, 1237–8 (1946); *Chem. Abstr.*, *40*, 5397 (1946).
(*6*) Grard, *Compt. rend.*, *189*, 541–3 (1929).
(*7*) Tschitschibabin and Jelgasin, *Ber.*, *47*, 48–50 (1914).
(*8*) Grinberg, *Soobschenie o Nauch.-Issledovatel. Rabote Kiev. Ind. Inst.*, *2*, 30–2 (1940); *Khim. Referat. Zhur.*, *4*, No. 2, 41 (1941); *Chem. Abstr.*, *37*, 2077 (1943).
(*9*) Scheibler and Schmidt, *Ber.*, *67B*, 1514–8 (1934).
(*10*) Shantz, *J. Am. Chem. Soc.*, *68*, 2553–7 (1946).
(*11*) Levina, Kulikov, and Parshikov, *J. Gen. Chem.* (U.S.S.R.), *11*, 567–72 (1941); *Chem. Abstr.*, *35*, 6931 (1941).
(*12*) Straus and Ehrenstein, *Ann.*, *442*, 93–118 (1925).
(*13*) Grard, *Compt. rend.*, *189*, 925–7 (1929); *Chem. Abstr.*, *24*, 2719 (1930).
(*14*) Grard, *Ann. chim.*, [10], *13*, 336–81 (1930).

CHAPTER XVI

Reactions of Grignard Reagents with Alkyl, Aralkyl, and Cycloalkyl Halides

EARLY STUDIES

It was early observed by Grignard and others[1] that the formation of an organomagnesium halide from an organic halide and metallic magnesium is accompanied by side-reactions, among them the formation of Wurtz products. Houben[2] suggested that the Wurtz products might arise in part at least from the reaction

$$RX + RMgX \rightarrow R_2 + MgX_2$$

and investigated this possibility to the extent of studying the reaction of benzyl chloride with methylmagnesium iodide. For reasons that will appear, Houben's reagent-pair was not an optimum selection for the purpose in mind; neither, however, did it represent the worst possible selection. Under the experimental conditions employed by him yields of 25 percent or less of ethylbenzene were realized.

The reaction was used by several investigators[3] for the preparation of ethers of higher carbon content from α-halo ethers, evidently in extension of the method of Henty:[4]

$$2\ ROCH_2Cl + R'_2Zn \rightarrow 2\ ROCH_2R' + ZnCl_2$$

Grignard[5] was able to prepare phenyl phenethyl ether in *ca.* 83 percent yield from β-bromophenetole and phenylmagnesium bromide, but found that with the same bromo ether isoamylmagnesium bromide or benzylmagnesium chloride gave rise principally to ether cleavage. Henry[6] reported

[1]See, *e.g.*: Tissier and Grignard, *Compt. rend.*, *132*, 683-5 (1901); *J. Chem. Soc.*, *80,I*, 316 (1901); *Chem. Zentr.*, *1901,I*, 999; Tschelinzew, *J. Russ. Phys.-Chem. Soc.*, *36*, 549-54 (1903); *Chem. Zentr.*, *1904,II*, 183; Tiffeneau, *Compt. rend.*, *139*, 481-2 (1904); *Chem. Zentr.*, *1904,II*, 1038.

[2]Houben, *Ber.*, *36*, 3083-6 (1903).

[3]Hamonet, *Compt. rend.*, *138*, 813-4, 975-7, 1609-12 (1904); *J. Chem. Soc.*, *86,I*, 401, 467, 705 (1904); Houben and Führer, *Ber.*, *40*, 4990-5000 (1907); Zeltner and Tarassoff, *ibid.*, *43*, 941-5 (1910); Lespieau and Bresch, *Compt. rend.*, *156*, 712 (1913); *Chem. Abstr.*, 7, 2213 (1913).

[4]Henry, *Compt. rend.*, *113*, 368-70 (1892); *J. Chem. Soc.*, *62*, 27 (1892).

[5]Grignard, *Compt. rend.*, *138*, 1048-50 (1904); *J. Chem. Soc.*, *86,I*, 494 (1904).

[6]Henry, *Rec. trav. chim.*, *26*, 106-15 (1906).

the preparation of hexamethylethane in *ca.* 33 percent yield from pentamethylethyl bromide and methylmagnesium bromide. Gomberg and Cone[7] obtained poor yields (5–10 percent) of tetraphenylmethane from the reaction of triphenylmethyl chloride with phenylmagnesium bromide but nearly quantitative yields of unsymmetrical tetraphenylethane from the reaction of the same chloride with benzylmagnesium chloride.

Grignard[8] also reported the preparation of various alcohols by the reactions of organomagnesium halides with halohydrins, *e.g.*:*

$$HOCH_2CH_2Cl + ArMgBr \rightarrow ArCH_2CH_2OH \ (ca.\ 80\%)$$

However, there is reasonable doubt that α,β-halohydrin reactions are, in general, simple halide-Grignard reagent reactions—a point which will be discussed further.

Späth[9] was the first to undertake a truly systematic study of the reactions of Grignard reagents with alkyl halides (see Table XVI-I, reference *212*). Unlike Abegg,[10] who had proposed an ionic theory of Grignard reagent reactions, Späth concluded that these reactions are essentially free-radical processes, of which the first stage may be represented as follows:

$$RMgX + R'X' \rightarrow MgXX' + R\cdot + R'\cdot$$

He accounted for the final products observed as resulting from the various possible reactions of the free radicals:

(1) $R\cdot + R'\cdot \rightarrow RR'$

(2) $R\cdot + R\cdot \rightarrow R_2$

(3) $R\cdot + R'\cdot \rightarrow R_{(-H)} + R'H$

(4) $R\cdot + R\cdot \rightarrow R_{(-H)} + RH$

(5) $R_{(-H)} + R'\cdot + R''\cdot \rightarrow R'R_{(-H)}R''$

Equation 5 was invoked to account for the supposed production of 1,2,3-triphenylpropane (actually 1-phenyl-2-*p*-benzylphenylethane[11]) in the reaction of benzyl chloride with methylmagnesium iodide. To these Späth might well have added:

(3a) $R\cdot + R'\cdot \rightarrow R_{(+H)} + R'_{(-H)}$

(3b) $R'\cdot + R'\cdot \rightarrow R'_{(-H)} + R'_{(+H)}$

(4a) $R'\cdot + R'\cdot \rightarrow R'_2$

---

[7]Gomberg and Cone, *Ber.*, *39*, 1461–70 (1906).

[8]Grignard, *Compt. rend.*, *141*, 44–6 (1905); *J. Chem. Soc.*, *88,I*, 593 (1905); *Ann. chim.*, [8], *10*, 23–40 (1905).

*Ar = C_6H_5, 2-$CH_3C_6H_4$, 4-$CH_3OC_6H_4$, 1-$C_{10}H_7$.

[9]Späth, *Monatsh.*, *34*, 1965–2014 (1913).

[10]Abegg, *Ber.*, *38*, 4112–6 (1905).

[11]See: Fuson, *J. Am. Chem. Soc.*, *48*, 2937–42 (1926).

Of the supposed free-radical reactions the first was the only one at that time regarded as having preparative value. Empirically, Späth generalized that alkyl halides (except the methyl) give poor yields according to equation 1. Somewhat better yields are obtained in such reactions with phenylmagnesium bromide than with alkylmagnesium halides. Favorable results (with respect to equation 1) may be expected when the carbon atom attached to the halogen atom is made more "positive" by suitable substitution (as in the α-halo ethers, the chlorohydrins, and the arylated methyl halides). The use of iodides, either as Grignard reagent coreactants or as starting materials for the preparation of Grignard reagents, in general, is to be avoided. To these may be added the observation, since made by many others (see Table XVI-I), that allyl and structurally related bromides and chlorides usually react with Grignard reagents to give excellent yields of alkenes.

SPECULATIONS CONCERNING REACTION MECHANISMS

Reconsideration of Späth's data in the light of a materially enhanced knowledge of reaction mechanisms in general and of the reactions of free radicals in solution in particular, combined with consideration of the wealth of additional data since contributed by others, leads to the conclusion that no single reaction mechanism accounts adequately for the initial step of all types of reactions observed. In attempting to assign reasonably probable reaction mechanisms to various types of reaction it is necessary to take into consideration the natures of the reactants, the reaction conditions imposed, and the products obtained.

The "normal" reaction. As a point of departure one may well choose for consideration the type of reaction which, on the basis of common usage, has the best claim to designation as the "normal" reaction. Such a reaction is usually conducted in ethereal solution under relatively mild conditions (between room temperature and the boiling point of ethyl ether) and results in a good yield (~70 percent) of "condensation" product (RR′). Among the reactions listed in Table XVI-I which fulfill these conditions are most of the reactions of allyl halides and many of the reactions of α-halo ethers and mono-, di-, and triarylmethyl halides. In general, the halides (R′X′) which give good yields of "condensation" products (RR′) under mild experimental conditions have two characteristics in common: (1) a relatively polar carbon-halogen bond (which is to say that the radical R′ is rather weakly "electronegative"[12]); and (2) relatively high resistance to loss of a *beta* hydrogen atom.

It seems highly improbable, even on *a priori* grounds, that these are free-radical reactions. For one thing, a free-radical process would seem

[12]For a discussion of the relative "electronegativities" of organic radicals see: Kharasch and Reinmuth, *J. Chem. Education*, 5, 404–18 (1928); 8, 1703–48 (1931); Kharasch, Reinmuth, and Mayo, *ibid.*, *11*, 82–96 (1934); *13*, 7–19 (1936).

to require a more nearly statistical distribution of products among RR′, R_2, and R'_2 (or the corresponding disproportionation products, $R_{(-H)}$, $R_{(+H)}$, $R'_{(-H)}$, $R'_{(+H)}$. For another, present knowledge of the behavior of free radicals in solution would lead to the prediction that such relatively reactive radicals as the methyl or phenyl would attack such a relatively good hydrogen donor as ethyl ether long before they had opportunity to encounter, and react with, other free radicals.

Moreover it is now well-known that when reaction conditions that give rise to the production of free radicals from Grignard reagents are deliberately induced (as by the addition to the system of cobaltous halides) the ensuing reaction takes a course quite other than the "normal" one (see section on "Coupling" Reactions; see also Chapter V).

On the whole it appears more profitable to treat the "normal" condensation of a Grignard reagent with an organic halide as a special case of solvolysis in which the Grignard reagent plays the rôle usually assigned to a polar solvent. In view of the present somewhat controversial status of the general solvolysis theory,* it might appear that the principal incentive to such a decision is a disposition to embrace familiar uncertainties in preference to flying to others unknown. Nevertheless this course would appear to place the problem in its proper classification and to offer the best prospects for an ultimate satisfactory solution. Quite possibly it will eventually be found that no single mechanism is adequate to account for all examples of "normal" condensation.

On *a priori* grounds, a working hypothesis embodying a concerted "push-pull" mechanism of the kind proposed by Swain has obviously attractive features. Incidentally, such a mechanism could be (though it need not necessarily be) formulated in terms of a quasi six-membered ring transision state.

```
    X'                  X'                X'
   /  :              :    :                 \
R'     Mg—X         R'      Mg—X      R'     Mg—X
       |        →   :       :     →   |
R      R            R       R         R      R
 \                    :   :                 /
  Mg                   Mg                 Mg
  |                    |                  |
  X                    X                  X
```

Superficially, at least, it would appear, however, that, for an irreversible solvolysis, such a process would require retention of optical activity (with inversion of configuration) when an optically active halide is one of the reactants.

---

*Any attempt to incorporate into this discussion an adequate critical review of present solvolysis theories would be inordinately space-consumptive. The reader unfamiliar with this field may find a fair summary of divergent views, with numerous leading references, in articles by Swain, *J. Am. Chem. Soc.*, 70, 1119–28 (1948), and Winstein, Grunwald, and Jones, *ibid.*, 73, 2700–7 (1951).

Unfortunately, this point has not been extensively investigated. There is, nevertheless, the testimony of Letsinger and Traynham[13] to the effect that benzylmagnesium chloride reacts with (–)-2-bromobutane ($[\alpha]_D^{25}$ – 16.80) to give a 17 percent yield of 1-phenyl-2-methylbutane ($[\alpha]_D^{25}$ + 0.64), on which basis it is estimated that approximately 91 percent of the assymmetry of the alkyl group is lost in the condensation reaction. This observation in itself, however, is not sufficient to eliminate from consideration a concerted "push-pull" mechanism, or even an S_N2 mechanism, unless it can be demonstrated that, under the reaction conditions imposed, (1) halogen exchange between the alkyl halide and the MgX_2 component of the Grignard reagent is negligible or very slow as compared to the "normal" condensation reaction, or/and (2) that the first portion of the corresponding R_2Mg reaction (during which the concentration of the MgX_2 component of the Grignard reagent is negligibly small) results in substantially the same degree of racemization. It may or may not be significant in this connection that in the analogous reaction of benzylsodium with (+)-2-bromobutane the degree of racemization is much smaller (≤ 26 percent.)[14]

In the special cases of the reactions of allylic Grignard reagents with alkyl halides, or of ordinary Grignard reagents with allylic halides, there is the possibility that a special second-order reaction mechanism may supersede in whole or in part the mechanism (or mechanisms) prevailing in ordinary condensations.

```
     CH2              CH2              CH2
    //               /: :             /   \
  HC      R'       HC     R'        HC     R'
  |       |    →   |:     :    →    ||
  H2C     X'       H2C.   .X'       H2C    X'
     \               . .                  /
      Mg              Mg               Mg
      |               |                |
      X               X                X

     CH2              CH2              CH2
    //               /: :             /   \
  HC      R        HC     R         HC     R
  |       |    →   |:     :    →    ||
  H2C     Mg—X     H2C.   .Mg—X     H2C    Mg—X
     \               . .                  /
      X'·             X'               X'
```

The first of these suggested reaction schemes would also seem to imply a retention of optical activity (with inversion) when the alkyl halide is optically active, although there would still be the possibility of halide racemization through halogen exchange already suggested. It may or may not be significant in this connection that both allylmagnesium bromide and allylsodium react with 2-bromoöctane to give good yields of 4-methyl-

[13]Letsinger and Traynham, *J. Am. Chem. Soc.*, 72, 849–52 (1950).

[14]Letsinger, *J. Am. Chem. Soc.*, 70, 406–9 (1948).

1-decene in the formation of which relatively little (13–21 percent) racemization has taken place (Letsinger and Traynham, *loc. cit.*[13]).

$$(+)\text{-}CH_3(n\text{-}C_6H_{13})CHBr,\ [\alpha]_D^{25} + 30.03 + H_2C{=}CHCH_2MgBr \rightarrow CH_3(H_2C{=}CHCH_2)(n\text{-}C_6H_{13})CH,\ [\alpha]_D^{25} + 4.79\ (78\%)$$

$$(-)\text{-}CH_3(n\text{-}C_6H_{13})CHBr,\ [\alpha]_D^{25} - 29.55 + H_2C{=}CHCH_2Na \rightarrow CH_3(H_2C{=}CHCH_2)(n\text{-}C_6H_{13})CH,\ [\alpha]_D^{25} - 4.73\ (83\%)$$

Concerning the allylic Grignard reagents, there arises the question whether or not there is any such thing as structure, in the sense ordinarily understood by the organic chemist, in a system involving a resonant anion. This point is discussed in more detail in connection with the allylic rearrangements (*q.v.*, Chapter XVII).

As regards the triarylmethyl halides (and probably some of the less arylated methyl halides) it seems probable that the "normal" Grignard reaction is predominantly of the S_N1 type. The addition of an ethyl ethereal solution of magnesium bromide (or zinc chloride) to an ethereal or ether-benzene solution of triphenylmethyl chloride causes an immediate color-development which has been attributed to the formation of a quinonoid addition compound.[15] It seems likely that the "addition compound" is an ion-pair resulting from ionization in the sense:

$$(C_6H_5)_3CCl + MgBr_2 \rightarrow (C_6H_5)_3C^+MgBr_2Cl^-$$

The carbonium ion is a resonance-stabilized structure to which the following forms (and others like them) make contributions:

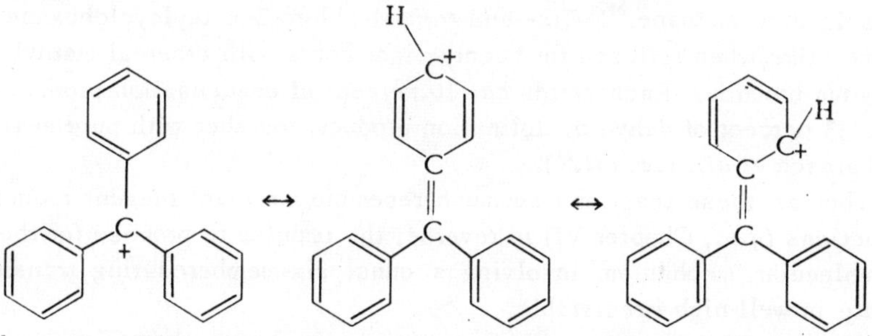

The poor yields (5–10 percent) of tetraphenylmethane obtained when triphenylmethyl chloride or bromide is treated with ethereal phenylmagnesium bromide[16,17,18,19,20] have sometimes been attributed to steric hindrance, and no doubt steric effects do play a part in inhibition of the "normal" condensation, but due consideration should also be given to the relatively high activation energy necessary to establish a covalent linkage between a resonance-stabilized carbonium ion corresponding to a

[15]Schoepfle and Trepp, *J. Am. Chem. Soc.*, *58*, 791–4 (1936).
[16]Gilman and Jones, *J. Am. Chem. Soc.*, *51*, 2840–3 (1929).
[17]Gomberg and Cone, *Ber.*, 39, 1461–70 (1906).
[18]Gomberg and Kamm, *J. Am. Chem. Soc.*, 39, 2009–15 (1917).
[19]Meyer, *J. prakt. Chem.*, [2], 82, 521–38 (1910).
[20]Freund, *Ber.*, 39, 2237–8 (1906).

very weakly "electronegative" radical and a carbanion corresponding to a strongly "electronegative" radical. The methyl and benzyl Grignard reagents, admittedly somewhat less subject to steric influence than the phenyl, but also with carbanions corresponding to radicals considerably less "electronegative" than the phenyl, give excellent yields of the respective "normal" condensation products with triarylmethyl chlorides.[17,10,21]

Somewhat better yields (21–29 percent) of tetraphenylmethane are obtained when the phenylmagnesium bromide-triphenylmethyl chloride reaction is conducted in benzene solution (or suspension).[22] The principal competing reaction under these conditions is a *para* condensation leading to the formation of diphenyl-*p*-biphenylylmethane. Doubtless the analogous *ortho* condensation would encounter prohibitive steric hindrance. When *para* condensation is "blocked," as in 4,4′,4″-tribomo- and 4,4′,4″-trichlorotriphenylmethyl chloride the yields of tetraärylmethanes obtained with phenylmagnesium bromide may approach 50 percent.[22]

Dehydrohalogenation and dehalogenation. When the radical R′ of a halide R′X′ contains a highly reactive *beta* hydrogen atom, or when a *beta* hydrogen atom is available and the condensation reaction, for steric or other reasons, is very slow, dehydrohalogenation of the halide may compete with, or completely outrun, the condensation reaction. Thus, when treated with methylmagnesium bromide in boiling ethyl ethereal solution, isobornyl chloride is 90 percent dehydrochlorinated in an hour, no appreciable condensation having taken place in the meanwhile. The evolved gas is pure methane.[23] *Cis*- and *trans*-1-chloro-2-methylcyclohexane behave alike when refluxed for twenty-eight hours with ethereal methylmagnesium bromide. Each yields *ca.* 10 percent of condensation product and *ca.* 33 percent of dehydrochlorination product, together with pure methane (Kharasch *et al.*, *loc. cit.*[23]).

Whereas these reactions so much resemble Grignard reagent reduction reactions (*q.v.*, Chapter VI) in reverse, the impulse to propose for them a bimolecular mechanism involving a quasi six-membered ring transition state is well-nigh irresistable.

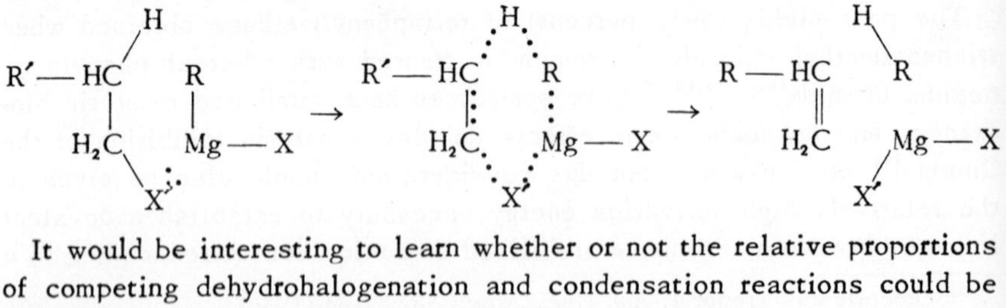

```
        H                            .H.                          H
       /                            :   :                          \
R′—HC      R               R′—HC        R               R—HC        R
   |       |         →         |:       :        →         ||
  H₂C     Mg—X                H₂C.     .Mg—X              H₂C      Mg—X
     \   :                       .   .                             /
      X′                          X′                              X′
```

It would be interesting to learn whether or not the relative proportions of competing dehydrohalogenation and condensation reactions could be

[21] Späth, *Monatsh.*, 34, 1695–2014 (1913).
[22] Schoepfle and Trepp, *J. Am. Chem. Soc.*, 58, 791–4 (1936).
[23] Kharasch, Engelmann, and Urry, *J. Am. Chem. Soc.*, 66, 365–7 (1944).

altered by loading the system with magnesium halide, as is the case with competing carbonyl reduction and addition reactions (*q.v.*, Chapter VI). Such an experiment would probably have the best chance of returning an affirmative answer if slow inverse addition were employed and if the reaction medium were incapable of forming magnesium complexes. For example, a benzene suspension of phenylmagnesium and magnesium bromides might be combined, by slow dropwise addition, with a refluxing suspension of magnesium bromide in benzene-ethyl bromide solution.* The scales, thus weighted in favor of a trimolecular (as opposed to a bimolecular) process, might register an improvement in the yield of the condensation product.

Whatever the mechanism of the dehydrohalogenation reactions, it is probable that the related process of dehalogenation (in the case of adjacent dihalides) is similar. As a tentative working hypothesis the following scheme is suggested.

$$\begin{matrix} & X' & & \\ & / & & \\ R'\text{—}HC & & R & \\ | & & | & \\ R''\text{—}HC & & Mg\text{—}X & \\ & \backslash \dot{:} & & \\ & X' & & \end{matrix} \rightarrow \begin{matrix} & X' & \\ R'\text{—}HC & \vdots & R \\ \vdots & & \vdots \\ R''\text{—}HC & \vdots & Mg\text{—}X \\ & X' & \end{matrix} \rightarrow \begin{matrix} X' & & \\ & \backslash & \\ R'\text{—}HC & & R \\ \| & & \\ R''\text{—}HC & & Mg\text{—}X \\ & / & \\ X' & & \end{matrix}$$

CONDENSATIONS WITH ACETYLENIC GRIGNARD REAGENTS

The acetylenic Grignard reagents, which are atypical in many respects, exhibit peculiarities in their behavior toward allyl bromide. Nieuwland *et al.*[24] have reported that, in general, the 1-alkynylmagnesium bromides, when prepared with magnesium of high purity, are totally inert toward allyl bromide, one of the more reactive alkyl halides with respect to Grignard condensation. For example, no reaction between 1-hexynylmagnesium bromide and allyl bromide took place in an ethyl ethereal solution intermittently stirred at room temperature for twenty-three days. Similar inertia characterized benzene or amyl ethereal solutions refluxed for two to twelve hours. When, however, 2 g. of cuprous chloride per mole of Grignard reagent was added to an ethyl ethereal solution, condensation proceeded rapidly, resulting in an 88 percent yield of "normal" product. Cuprous bromide and cuprous cyanide also proved effective catalysts, as did the cupric halides (which are immediately reduced to cuprous compounds by most Grignard reagents).

Grignard and Lepayre,[25] on the other hand, have reported the "normal" condensation, with 70 percent yield, of phenylethynylmagnesium bromide

---

*A Soxhlet extractor operated under a nitrogen atmosphere would provide a convenient means of Grignard reagent addition. This device has been employed by Schoepfle and Trepp, *J. Am. Chem. Soc.*, *58*, 791–4 (1936).

[24] Danehy, Killian, and Nieuwland, *J. Am. Chem. Soc.*, *58*, 611–2 (1926).

[25] Grignard and Lepayre, *Bull. soc. chim.*, [4], *43*, 141–2 (1928); *Compt. rend.*, *192*, 250–3 (1931); *Chem. Abstr.*, *25*, 2421 (1931).

with allyl bromide. The inference is, however, that their magnesium contained traces of copper.

Whereas cuprous halides are well-known to form complexes with both olefinic and acetylenic compounds (see section on 1,4-Addition, Chapter VI), these condensations by themselves would raise the question whether cuprous catalysis is effected through activation of the unsaturated halide, of the acetylenic Grignard reagent, or both. Ostensibly uncatalyzed "normal" condensations of various acetylenic Grignard reagents with α-halo ethers and other halides have been reported (see Table XVI-I), but chiefly by European investigators, who, for the most part, have operated with magnesium of a lower degree of purity than that available to American investigators of recent years. If these condensations prove, on further investigation, to have been copper-catalyzed then copper catalysis must be attributed primarily to activation of the acetylenic Grignard reagent.

Another peculiarity of the acetylenic Grignard reagents is to be found in their condensations with the corresponding acetylenic iodides, reported by Grignard and Tcheoufaki.[26] The interaction of an alkylmagnesium bromide and an acetylenic bromide consists in a functional exchange[27,28] (see Acetylenic Hydrocarbons, p. 70).

$$RMgBr + R'C{\equiv}CBr \rightarrow RBr + R'C{\equiv}CMgBr$$

The analogous interaction of a 1-alkynylmagnesium bromide and the corresponding 1-alkynyl bromide would result in no observable net change unless "tagged" bromine were employed. According to Grignard and Tcheoufaki, however, the reactions of phenylethynyl- and 1-heptynylmagnesium iodides with the corresponding acetylenic iodides yield condensation products.

$$C_6H_5C{\equiv}CMgI + C_6H_5C{\equiv}CI \rightarrow (C_6H_5C{\equiv}C{-})_2 + MgI_2$$

$$n\text{-}C_5H_{11}C{\equiv}CMgI + n\text{-}C_5H_{11}C{\equiv}CI \rightarrow (n\text{-}C_5H_{11}C{\equiv}C{-})_2 + MgI_2$$

On the basis of the presently available evidence it is uncertain whether or not such condensations are peculiar to the acetylenic iodides. Neither is it evident whether or not such condensations are copper-catalyzed.

"COUPLING" REACTIONS

Paradoxically enough the "coupling" reactions of Grignard reagents with organic (chiefly aralkyl) halides have been the subjects of more intensive study, and are in some respects better understood theoretically, than the so-called "normal" condensation reactions. Some of our ideas concerning the "normal" reactions are drawn by inference from the ways in which they differ from the "coupling" reactions.

---

[26] Grignard and Tcheoufaki, *Bull. soc. chim.*, [4], 43, 42-3 (1928).

[27] Iotsitch, *J. Russ. Phys.-Chem. Soc.*, 36, 1545-51 (1904); *Bull. soc. chim.*, [3], 36, 177 (1906).

[28] Kharasch, Lambert, and Urry, *J. Org. Chem.*, *10*, 298-306 (1945).

For reasons which will appear in the ensuing discussion the "coupling" reactions are adjudged to be free-radical processes; they are characterized by dimerization of the radical of the organic halide. Usually the principal product resulting from the attempt to condense phenylmagnesium bromide with triphenylmethyl chloride in ethyl ethereal solution is that of the "coupling" reaction (hexaphenylethane).[29,30]

All coupling reactions have in common the characteristic that the relatively weakly "electronegative" radical of the organic halide is unreactive toward the solvent (and other reaction-system components) and that it either shows relatively little tendency to disproportionate or is structurally incapable of disproportionation. Such reactions may, however, be divided into two general classes.

Of the first class, the reaction of triphenylmethyl chloride with phenylmagnesium bromide to form hexaphenylethane (already discussed) is representative. According to the hypothesis proposed this is, in a sense, a "hindered" reaction. Because of the difficulty of "normal" combination of a positive ion derived from a very weakly "electronegative" radical (of the organic halide) and a negative ion derived from a strongly "electronegative" radical (of the Grignard reagent) the reaction takes an alternative course. The reaction of α-naphthylmagnesium bromide with di-α-naphthylmethyl chloride[31] constitutes another example.

In the second class of "coupling" reactions there may be said to be a predisposition toward the free-radical mechanism in that the Grignard reagent or the alkyl halide, or both, have some tendency toward homolytic dissociation. In reactions of this class the radical of the organic halide need not be so weakly "electronegative," nor need the radical of the Grignard reagent be strongly "electronegative." Organomagnesium iodides are most effective, and in some cases will effect "coupling" when the corresponding bromides or chlorides show little or no tendency to do so. Methylmagnesium iodide is ordinarily the preferred reagent.

The reaction of methylmagnesium iodide with benzyl chloride will serve as illustrative. This reaction was first investigated by Houben,[32] who did not, however, report the "coupling" product, and later by Späth,[33] who isolated some 24 percent of bibenzyl in addition to a 35 percent yield of the "normal" product (ethylbenzene).* More recently it has been studied in some detail by Fuson.[34] Under the experimental conditions

[29]Meyer, *J. prakt. Chem.*, [2], *82*, 521-38 (1910).

[30]Gomberg and Kamm, *J. Am. Chem. Soc.*, *39*, 2009-15 (1917).

[31]Schmidlin and Massini, *Ber.*, *42*, 2377-92 (1909).

[32]Houben, *Ber.*, *36*, 3083-6 (1903).

[33]Späth, *Monatsh.*, *34*, 1695-2014 (1913).

*Späth[33] believed that he had also isolated small amounts of 1,2,3-triphenylpropane, and proposed a mechanism to account for its formation. However, it has been shown by Fuson[34] that this byproduct is actually 4-benzylbibenzyl, formed by the condensation of excess benzyl chloride with the "coupling" product (bibenzyl).

[34]Fuson, *J. Am. Chem. Soc.*, *48*, 2681-9, 2937-42 (1926).

employed by him the reaction resulted in a 23–27 percent yield of "normal" product (ethylbenzene), a 31–33 percent yield of "coupling" product (bibenzyl), and a gas which he characterized as ethane (33–35 percent). The identification of the gas was made upon the basis of the volume contraction upon combustion in a Hempel burette, and the further volume contraction upon carbon dioxide absorption. From what is now known of the behavior of free methyl radicals in ethereal solution, however, it would appear that the gas identification must be partially in error. Under such conditions methyl radicals do not dimerize, although some ethane may be formed by attack of the radicals on the methyl Grignard reagent. For the most part, however, the methyl radicals react with ethyl ether; the gaseous products are methane, ethane, and ethylene. Similar reactions of various benzyl halide derivatives have been reported by Fuson *et al.*[35] Other examples are to be found in Table XVI-I.

A rather interesting special case of "coupling" is that of the sterically "hindered" mesitoyl chloride with methylmagnesium iodide.[36] When the chloride is added to the Grignard reagent an excellent yield (88 percent) of acetomesitylene is obtained, but when the reversed addition is employed (as is usually recommended for the preparation of ketones from acid halides) the yield of acetomesitylene is greatly reduced (35 percent) and a considerable quantity (39 percent) of bimesitoyl is obtained.

INDUCED "COUPLING" REACTIONS

The hypothesis that "coupling" is a free-radical reaction suggests that suitable experimental devices might be invoked to induce "coupling" reactions that ordinarily would not occur spontaneously. The possible potentialities of magnesious iodide in this connection naturally come to mind. As the basis for a critical experiment designed to furnish an unequivocal answer to a theoretical question this device is somewhat lacking in appeal, for the necessary experimental conditions rather closely approximate those of the Wurtz reaction, which would result in the same product. As a practical expedient, however, this device has not been entirely overlooked, for a Japanese patent[37] describes the "coupling" of anethole hydrochloride with magnesium iodide and metallic magnesium. Presumably the significant reactions are:

$$Mg + MgI_2 \rightleftharpoons \cdot MgI$$

$$C_2H_5(4\text{-}CH_3OC_6H_4)CHCl + \cdot MgI \rightarrow C_2H_5(4\text{-}CH_3OC_6H_4)CH\cdot + MgICl$$

$$2\ C_2H_5(4\text{-}CH_3OC_6H_4)CH\cdot \rightarrow [C_2H_5(4\text{-}CH_3OC_6H_4)CH —]_2$$

---

[35]Fuson, *J. Am. Chem. Soc.*, *48*, 830–6, 2681–9 (1926); Fuson and Ross, *ibid.*, *55*, 720–3 (1933); Fuson, Denton, and Kneisley, *ibid.*, *63*, 2652–3 (1941); Fuson, Horning, Ward, Rowland, and Marsh, *ibid.*, *64*, 30–3 (1942); Fuson, Kneisley, Rabjohn, and Ward, *ibid.*, *68*, 533 (1946).

[36]Fuson and Corse, *J. Am. Chem. Soc.*, *60*, 2063–6 (1938).

[37]Aoyama Scientific Research Inst., Inc., *Japanese Patent*, 162,577, March, 7, 1944; *Chem. Abstr.*, *42*, P4200 (1948). Concerning a similar magnesium (possibly $Mg\text{-}MgBr_2$) coupling see: Docken and Spielman, *J. Am. Chem. Soc.*, *62*, 2163–4 (1940).

In the available abstract the yield is not stated. In view of the source, the lack of experimental detail, and the non-critical nature of the experiment, no theoretical significance should be attributed to this report. It is of interest chiefly because of the working hypothesis implied.

Oldham and Ubbelohde,[38] describe "a modified Grignard reaction in the synthesis of hydrocarbons." The method consists in the preparation of a Grignard reagent from a long-chain normal alkyl halide and magnesium in the usual manner. The Grignard reagent is then treated by successive alternate additions of iodine and metallic magnesium, with cooling during iodine additions and reflux prior and subsequent to magnesium additions. In a specific example the Grignard reagent was prepared from 20.3 g. of hexadecyl iodide and 2.1 g. of magnesium in 80 ml. of ether. Five additions of iodine (7.5, 5.8, 4.3, 3.2, and 2.4 g.) were made, alternating with five additions of magnesium (1.4, 1.1, 0.8, 0.6, and 0.4 g.). A yield of 70 percent of dotriacontane was obtained. As might be expected, this was accompanied by some disproportionation products.

It would appear that the significant portion of this process may be entirely analogous to that already outlined.

$$n\text{-}C_{16}H_{33}I + \cdot MgI \rightarrow n\text{-}C_{16}H_{33}\cdot + MgI_2$$

$$2\ n\text{-}C_{16}H_{33}\cdot \rightarrow n\text{-}C_{32}H_{66}$$

If so, the preliminary formation of a Grignard reagent and its subsequent decomposition with iodine serves the useful purpose of building up a working concentration of magnesium iodide in the system. Equally satisfactory results might be attainable by a simpler procedure.

It seems likely that other supposed "iodine coupling" reactions effected in the presence of residual magnesium (*e.g.*, that of 1-bromo-1-piperonylethane, described by Lieberman *et al.*[39]) owe their success at least in part to the action of magnesious iodide.

However, although the observations cited are consistent with the hypothesis that magnesious iodide (and probably magnesious bromide) may serve to induce "coupling" reactions, they cannot be said to prove anything. All are susceptible of alternative interpretation.

A more convincing demonstration of induced coupling is that of anethole hydrobromide by phenylmagnesium bromide in the presence of 5 mole percent of cobaltous chloride to yield up to 42 percent of hexestrol dimethyl ether.[40] The rôle of cobaltous chloride in the free-radical chain reaction leading to "coupling" may be described as follows:

(1) $$C_6H_5MgBr + CoCl_2 \rightarrow C_6H_5CoCl + MgBrCl$$

(2) $$2\ C_6H_5CoCl \rightarrow (C_6H_5)_2 + 2 \cdot CoCl^*$$

[38]Oldham and Ubbelohde, *J. Chem. Soc.*, *1938*, 201–6.

[39]Lieberman, Mueller, and Stiller, *J. Am. Chem. Soc.*, *69*, 1540–1 (1947).

[40]Kharasch and Kleiman, *J. Am. Chem. Soc.*, *65*, 491–3 (1943).

*It is probable that some cobaltous subchloride free radicals are also generated by the process

(2a) $$C_6H_5CoCl \rightarrow C_6H_5\cdot + \cdot CoCl,$$

(3) $C_2H_5(4\text{-}CH_3OC_6H_4)CHBr + \cdot CoCl \rightarrow$

$$C_2H_5(4\text{-}CH_3OC_6H_4CH\cdot + CoClBr$$

(4) $2\ C_2H_5(4\text{-}CH_3OC_6H_4)CH\cdot \rightarrow [C_2H_5(4\text{-}CH_3OC_6H_4)CH—]_2$

A similar induced "coupling" reaction has been carried out with methylmagnesium bromide, cobaltous chloride, and cinnamyl chloride.[41] Without cobaltous chloride these reactants yield 89 percent of "normal" condensation product and 6 percent of "coupling" products; in the presence of 5 mole percent of cobaltous chloride, 12 percent of "normal" product and a total of 70 percent of "coupling" products are formed. Nickel chloride ($NiCl_2$) and chromic chloride ($CrCl_3$) are similarly, though somewhat less, effective.

The reactions of methylmagnesium bromide with isobornyl chloride and with *cis*- or *trans*-1-chloro-2-methylcyclohexane lead principally to dehydrochlorination of the chlorides, with formation of methane. When, however, cobaltous chloride is added to the respective reaction systems, the reactions take a different course, leading to the formation of "coupling" and disproportionation products, together with a gaseous mixture consisting of methane, ethane, and ethylene.[42]

$$i\text{-}C_{10}H_{17}Cl \xrightarrow[+\ CoCl_2]{CH_3MgBr} (C_{10}H_{17})_2\ (31\%)$$
$$+\ C_{10}H_{16}\ (44\%) + C_{10}H_{18}\ (19\%) + CH_4 + C_2H_6 + C_2H_4$$

$$trans\text{-}C_7H_{13}Cl \xrightarrow[+\ CoCl_2]{CH_3MgBr} (C_7H_{13})_2\ (27\%)$$
$$+\ C_7H_{12}\ (23\%) + C_7H_{14}\ (28\%) + CH_4 + C_2H_6 + C_2H_4$$

$$cis\text{-}C_7H_{13}Cl \xrightarrow[+\ CoCl_2]{CH_3MgBr} (C_7H_{13})_2\ (22\%)$$
$$+\ C_7H_{12}\ (31\%) + C_7H_{14}\ (34\%) + CH_4 + C_2H_6 + C_2H_4$$

The effects of cobaltous chloride addition on these reactions are interpreted on the basis of a free-radical chain reaction:

(1) $CH_3MgBr + CoCl_2 \rightarrow CH_3CoCl + MgClBr$

(2) $2\ CH_3CoCl \rightarrow C_2H_6 + 2\ \cdot CoCl$; or

(2a) $CH_3CoCl \rightarrow CH_3\cdot + \cdot CoCl$

(3) $R'Cl + \cdot CoCl \rightarrow R'\cdot + CoCl_2$

(4) $2\ R'\cdot \rightarrow R_{(+H)} + R'_{(-H)}$

(5) $2\ R'\cdot \rightarrow R'_2$

(6) $CH_3\cdot + Et_2O \rightarrow CH_4 + C_2H_6 + C_2H_4$

Altogether it appears fairly evident that, in the absence of metallic addenda or impurities, reactions conducted under mild experimental con-

---

especially in reactions conducted at higher temperatures, but the relatively high yields of biphenyl resulting from reactions of this kind indicate that process 2 must be the predominant reaction [see *e.g.*; Kharasch and Fields, *J. Am. Chem. Soc.*, 63, 2316–20 (1941); Kharasch, Lewis, and Reynolds, *ibid.*, 65, 493–5 (1943)].

[41] Kharasch, Lambert, and Urry, *J. Org. Chem.*, *10*, 298–306 (1945).

[42] Kharasch, Engelmann, and Urry, *J. Am. Chem. Soc.*, *66*, 365–7 (1944).

ditions and leading to formation of the "normal" addition product, RR′, or of one-way disproportionation products in the sense $R'_{(-H)} + R_{(+H)}$, or both, are *not* free-radical reactions.

On the other hand "forced" reactions of relatively unreactive halides probably are, and "coupling" reactions certainly are.

It is interesting to note that by use of a suitably chosen intermediary organic halide a process of this kind may be extended one step farther to effect the "coupling" of hydrocarbon residues. Of several examples studied, the interaction of methylmagnesium bromide, cobaltous chloride, methyl bromide, and cumene (isopropylbenzene) in the presence of ethyl ether will serve as illustrative.[43]

(1) $CH_3MgBr + CoCl_2 \rightarrow CH_3CoCl + MgBrCl$

(2) $2\ CH_3CoCl \rightarrow C_2H_6 + 2 \cdot CoCl$

(3) $CH_3Br + \cdot CoCl \rightarrow \cdot CH_3 + CoClBr$

(4) $C_6H_5(CH_3)_2CH + \cdot CH_3 \rightarrow C_6H_5(CH_3)_2C\cdot + CH_4$

(5) $2\ C_6H_5(CH_3)_2C\cdot \rightarrow [C_6H_5(CH_3)_2C—]_2$

Some of the methyl radicals formed are removed by reaction with the ethyl ether present.

(6) $\cdot CH_3 + (C_2H_5)_2O \rightarrow CH_4 + C_2H_4 + C_2H_6$

Attempts to conduct the reaction in the total absence of ethyl ether were unsuccessful, probably because of the insolubility of the metallic reactants.

"FORCED" REACTIONS

The study just cited (Kharasch and Urry[43]) incidentally throws some light on the probable mechanism of "forced" Grignard reactions. Although there was no appreciable reaction between methylmagnesium bromide, an alkyl bromide, and cumene at 100° in the absence of cobaltous chloride, under the same conditions, ethylmagnesium bromide, *n*-propylmagnesium bromide, and isopropylmagnesium bromide all reacted. These reactions are explicable as consequences of (induced) thermal dissociation of the Grignard reagent.

(1) $i\text{-}C_3H_7MgBr \rightarrow i\text{-}C_3H_7\cdot + \cdot MgBr$

(2) $i\text{-}C_3H_7Br + \cdot MgBr \rightarrow i\text{-}C_3H_7\cdot + MgBr_2$

(3) $C_6H_5(CH_3)CH + i\text{-}C_3H_7\cdot \rightarrow C_6H_5(CH_3)_2C\cdot + C_3H_8$

(4) $2\ C_6H_5(CH_3)_2C\cdot \rightarrow [C_6H_5(CH_3)_2C—]_2$

Because the less reactive isopropyl free radicals are more selective in their action than the more reactive methyl radicals, there is relatively little loss of free radicals through attack upon the ether present. There is, however, some loss through disproportionation.

---

[43] Kharasch and Urry, *J. Org. Chem.*, 13, 101-9 (1948).

Upon *a priori* grounds it might be predicted that, of corresponding organometallic halides, the iodides should be the most, and the chlorides the least, susceptible to thermal dissociation in the manner just described. With the halogen remaining the same the Grignard reagents with the less electronegative organic radicals should be the more susceptible, and those with the more electronegative radicals the less susceptible, to thermal dissociation. It may be concluded that "forced" reactions in general are predominantly free-radical reactions.

For some reactant pairs there is a considerable amount of free-radical dissociation even under the experimental conditions often employed for the supposedly "normal" reactions. A conspicuous example is the reaction of ethylmagnesium bromide with cyclohexyl bromide at the boiling point of the ethereal reaction system (*ca.* 40°). During reaction under these conditions there is steady evolution of gas (54 percent ethane; 46 percent ethylene). A mixture of cyclohexane and cyclohexene (*ca.* 35 percent unsaturated) may be isolated from the reaction mixture.[44,*]

FUNCTIONAL EXCHANGE

The suggestion that a functional exchange between Grignard reagent and organic halide, in the sense

$$RMgX + R'X' \rightarrow R'MgX + RX'$$

might take place was made by Urion[45] in explanation of the *modus operandi* of Grignard's "entrainment" method for the preparation of organomagnesium halides[46] (*q.v.*, Chapter II). This idea had previously occurred to Gilman and Jones,[47] who had investigated the following Grignard reagent-organic halide pairs with negative results: benzylmagnesium chloride, bromobenzene; phenylmagnesium bromide, benzyl chloride; triphenylmethylmagnesium chloride, bromobenzene; benzylmagnesium chloride, triphenylmethyl chloride; phenylmagnesium bromide, triphenylmethyl chloride. Ether-benzene or ether-toluene solutions of the respective reagent pairs were refluxed for about three hours, and were then cooled, carbonated, and hydrolyzed. In no case investigated could any carboxylic acid other than that corresponding to the Grignard reagent originally present be detected.

In a similar study conducted at lower temperature (−5 to 0°), Kharasch and Fuchs (*loc. cit.*[44]) could detect no functional exchange between: *n*-butylmagnesium bromide and bromobenzene; *n*-butylmagnesium bromide and *p*-anisyl bromide; methylmagnesium bromide and *p*-biphenylyl bromide; methylmagnesium bromide and 9-chlorofluorene; phenylmagnesium bromide

---

[44] Kharasch and Fuchs, *J. Org. Chem.*, *10*, 292–7 (1945).

*In this study[44] ordinary reagent-grade magnesium was used in preparation of the Grignard reagent. Conceivably, the use of sublimed magnesium might have led to different results.

[45] Urion, *Compt. rend.*, *198*, 1244–6 (1934).

[46] Grignard, *Compt. rend.*, *198*, 625–8 (1934).

[47] Gilman and Jones, *J. Am. Chem. Soc.*, *51*, 2840–3 (1929).

and *n*-butyl bromide; and *n*-butylmagnesium bromide and 1-bromo-1,2,2-triphenylethene.

Kharasch and Fuchs (*loc. cit.*[44]) have confirmed in part Urion's (*loc. cit.*[45]) report that cyclohexyl bromide exchanges with ethylmagnesium bromide, but have found that the amount of exchange when the reactants are combined in ethereal solution and the ether is removed by distillation is by no means so great as Urion had supposed. The 40 percent yield of cyclohexane supposedly isolated by Urion upon hydrolysis of the residue so obtained is actually a mixture of cyclohexane and cyclohexene, of which only the relatively small excess of the former over the latter may be attributed to functional exchange. Urion either overlooked or ignored the simultaneous evolution of ethane and ethylene.

The apparent examples of exchange between α-halo ketones and Grignard reagents may be dismissed as special cases of enolate formation in which the enolate is of the kind that behaves like a true Grignard reagent, as does the enolate of acetomesitylene (see α-Halo Ketones, Chapter VI). Such, for instance, are Umnowa's[48] successive reactions of phenylmagnesium bromide and carbon dioxide with α,α′-dibromoisobutyrone:

$$(CH_3)_2BrCCOCBr(CH_3)_2 \xrightarrow{2\ C_6H_5MgBr} [C_6H_5(CH_3)_2CCOC(CH_3)_2]^- MgBr^+ \xrightarrow{CO_2}$$

$$C_6H_5(CH_3)_2CCOC(CH_3)_2CO_2MgBr \xrightarrow{H_2O} C_6H_5(CH_3)_2CCOC(CH_3)_2CO_2H$$

Wuyts'[49] report of the reaction of α-bromocamphor with phenylmagnesium bromide omits experimental detail, but probably should be similarly classified.

The reaction of methylmagnesium bromide with phenylethynylbromide to yield a Grignard reagent[50] is analogous to the corresponding reaction with phenylacetylene.

$$C_6H_5C{\equiv}CH + CH_3MgBr \rightarrow C_6H_5C{\equiv}CMgBr + CH_4$$

$$C_6H_5C{\equiv}CBr + CH_3MgBr \rightarrow C_6H_5C{\equiv}CMgBr + CH_3Br$$

The reaction of methylmagnesium iodide with 2,5-dimethyl-3,4-diiodofuran to form a Grignard reagent[51] is also reminiscent of the preparation of a Grignard reagent from 2,5-dimethylpyrrole.[52]

```
      HC——CH                                              HC——C-i-C3H7
      ‖    ‖       RMgX                i-C3H7I            ‖    ‖
H3C—C      C—CH3  ————→  (C6H8N)MgX  ————————→      H3C—C      C—CH3
     \    /                                              \    /
       N                                                   N
       H                                                   H
```

[48]Umnowa, *J. Russ. Phys.-Chem. Soc.*, *45*, 881–4 (1913); *Chem. Zentr.*, *1913,II*, 1478.

[49]Wuyts, *Compt. rend.*, *199*, 1317–9 (1934).

[50]Kharasch, Lambert, and Urry, *J. Org. Chem.*, *10*, 298–306 (1945).

[51]Hurd and Wilkinson, *J. Am. Chem. Soc.*, *70*, 739–41 (1948).

[52]Plancher and Tanzi, *Atti acad. Lincei*, [5], *23,II*, 412–7 (1914); *Chem. Zentr.*, *1915,I*, 743; *Chem. Abstr.*, *9*, 1477 (1915).

$$\text{3-iodo-4-iodo-2,5-dimethylfuran (IC—CI, H_3C—C, C—CH_3, O)} \xrightarrow{CH_3MgI} \text{(IC—CMgI, H_3C—C, C—CH_3, O)} \xrightarrow{CO_2} \text{(IC—C—CO_2H, H_3C—C, C—CH_3, O)}$$

It is quite possible, of course, that this is a free-radical reaction, especially in view of the halide and the Grignard reagent involved. It would be of some interest to know, however, whether or not 2,5-dimethylfuran behaves toward Grignard reagents as though it had an "active" hydrogen atom.

On the basis of the rather limited evidence available one is tempted to generalize tentatively that when an "active hydrogen" compound reacts with a Grignard reagent to form a hydrocarbon and a new Grignard reagent (or pseudo-Grignard reagent) the corresponding halide may reasonably be expected to react with the Grignard reagent to form a new halide and a new Grignard reagent (or pseudo-Grignard reagent).

The fact that 1,2,4,5-tetrabromobenzene and 1,2,4,5-tetraphenylbenzene are the isolable products of the reaction of phenylmagnesium bromide with hexabromobenzene[53] suggests that one or more types of exchange, *e.g.*,

$$C_6Br_6 \xrightarrow{2\ C_6H_5MgBr} 1,4\text{-}(MgBr)_2\text{-}2,3,5,6\text{-}Br_4C_6 + 2\ C_6H_5Br$$

$$1,4\text{-}Br_2\text{-}2,3,5,6\text{-}(C_6H_5)_4C_6 \xrightarrow{2\ C_6H_5MgBr} 1,4\text{-}(MgBr)_2\text{-}2,3,5,6\text{-}(C_6H_5)_4C_6 + 2\ C_6H_5Br$$

may take place in this reaction.*

The reported products of reaction of Grignard reagents with hexachloroethane (C_2Cl_4, $C_2H_2Cl_4$, C_2HCl_5, 1,1,1,2-$Cl_4C_2H_2$, 1,1,2,2-$Cl_4C_2H_2$)[54] also strongly suggest exchange, although experimental details are lacking.

[53] Geissman and Mallatt, *J. Am. Chem. Soc.*, *61*, 1788–90 (1939). See also: Dilthey and Hurtig, *Ber.*, *67B*, 495–6, 2004–7 (1934).

*Carbonation or other suitable treatment of the reaction mixture might supply more cogent evidence on this point than simple hydrolysis.

[54] Korschak, *J. Gen. Chem.* (U.S.S.R.), 9, 1153–4 (1939); *Chem. Abstr.*, *34*, 1303 (1940); *Chem. Zentr.*, *1940,I*, 196.

Prévost[55] has invoked the concept of exchange to account for the small amounts of "coupling" products obtained in the reaction of ethylmagnesium bromide with cinnamyl bromide, which he attributes to the reaction:

$$C_6H_5CH{=}CHCH_2MgBr + C_6H_5CH{=}CHCH_2Br \rightarrow$$
$$(C_6H_5CH{=}CHCH_2{-})_2 + C_6H_5CH{=}CHCH_2CH(C_6H_5)CH{=}CH_2$$

In view of the foregoing discussion of "coupling" reactions this assumption scarcely seems necessary, but the isolation of small amounts of allylbenzene and propenylbenzene indicates that some exchange does in fact take place, and the "coupling" products may well arise in part from the reaction proposed by Prévost.

On the basis of the evidence available it would appear that functional exchange between an organic halide and an organomagnesium halide is a relatively rare reaction, and that when the organic halide involved is not one corresponding to an "active hydrogen" compound, the exchange takes place through a free-radical mechanism.

This idea is supported by observations on induced exchange reactions. All the reagent pairs investigated by Kharasch and Fuchs (*loc. cit.*[44]) with negative results showed appreciable exchange in the presence of small amounts of cobaltous chloride. For example 1-bromo-1,2,2-triphenylethene, when treated with *n*-butylmagnesium bromide in the presence of 4 mole percent of cobaltous chloride, carbonated, and subjected to hydrolysis, yielded 14 percent of triphenylacrylic acid. The explanation suggested is:

(1) $n\text{-}C_4H_9MgBr + CoCl_2 \rightarrow n\text{-}C_4H_9CoCl + MgBrCl$

(2) $2\ n\text{-}C_4H_9CoCl \rightarrow C_4H_{10} + C_4H_8 + 2\ \cdot CoCl$

(3) $(C_6H_5)_2C{=}(C_6H_5)CBr + \cdot CoCl \rightarrow (C_6H_5)_2C{=}(C_6H_5)C\cdot + CoClBr$

(4) $(C_6H_5)_2C{=}(C_6H_5)C\cdot + n\text{-}C_4H_9MgBr \rightarrow$
$(C_6H_5)_2C{=}(C_6H_5)CMgBr + \cdot C_4H_9$

(5) $(C_6H_5)_2C{=}(C_6H_5)CBr + \cdot C_4H_9 \rightarrow (C_6H_5)_2C{=}(C_6H_5)C\cdot + n\text{-}C_4H_9Br$

That the exchange reactions of halides corresponding to "active hydrogen" compounds differ from the free-radical exchange reactions is indicated by the behavior of phenylethynyl bromide with methylmagnesium bromide. In the absence of cobaltous chloride exchange occurs spontaneously, and, upon subsequent hydrolysis, an 89 percent yield of phenylacetylene is obtained. Carbonation prior to hydrolysis leads to a 55 percent yield of phenylpropiolic acid. When the reaction is carried out in the presence of 5 mole percent of cobaltous chloride a 62 percent yield of 1-propynylbenzene is obtained, together with some tar (Kharasch, Lambert, and Urry, *loc. cit.*[50]). The mechanism of the free-radical reaction in this case invites further investigation.

[55]Prevost, *Bull. soc. chim.*, [4], 49, 1372-81 (1931).

Functional exchanges induced by traces of ferric chloride have been reported by Vavon and Mottez[56] in what appears to have been intended as a preliminary announcement, for no experimental details are given.

$$C_6H_5Br + 2\,C_2H_5MgBr + FeCl_3 \rightarrow C_6H_5MgBr + MgBr_2 + C_2H_4 + C_2H_6$$

$$C_6H_5Br + CH_3MgBr + FeCl_3 \rightarrow C_6H_5CH_3\ (10\%)$$

$$1\text{-}C_{10}H_7Br + CH_3MgBr + FeCl_3 \rightarrow 1\text{-}C_{10}H_7CH_3\ (50\%)$$

$$2\text{-}C_{10}H_7Br + CH_3MgBr + FeCl_3 \rightarrow 2\text{-}C_{10}H_7CH_3\ (22\%)$$

$$\text{9-Bromoanthracene} + CH_3MgBr + FeCl_3 \rightarrow \text{9-Methylanthracene (70\%)}$$

THE HALOHYDRINS*

There is nothing in the reported reactions of ethylene chlorohydrin with Grignard reagents to suggest that they are other than the "normal" reactions of an alkyl halide (see Table XVI-I, **C_2H_5ClO**). However, halohydrin reactions that are obviously more complicated are not far to seek. For example, Cottle and Hollyday[57] have found that the reaction of ethylene bromohydrin with *n*-butylmagnesium bromide yields, in addition to *n*-hexanol (the "normal" product), a relatively small amount of 2-hexanol.

$$\underset{(650\text{ g.})}{HOCH_2CH_2Br} + \underset{(1430\text{ g. }C_4H_9Br)}{n\text{-}C_4H_9MgBr} \rightarrow \underset{(268\text{ g., }50.6\%)}{n\text{-}C_6H_{13}OH} + \underset{(30\text{ g., }5.7\%)}{CH_3(n\text{-}C_4H_9)CHOH}$$

The reaction of 2-chlorocyclohexanol (configuration not specified) with methylmagnesium iodide is reported by Godchot *et al.*[58] to yield 1-cyclopentylethanol.†

$$\text{2-chlorocyclohexanol (OH, Cl)} \xrightarrow{CH_3MgI} \text{cyclopentyl-}CH(CH_3)OH\ (ca.\ 50\%)$$

Further, Golumbic and Cottle[59] report that the two isomeric styrene iodohydrins and styrene oxide all yield the same secondary alcohol (1-phenyl-2-propanol) when treated with methylmagnesium iodide.

$$C_6H_5CHICH_2OH \xrightarrow{CH_3MgI} CH_3(C_6H_5CH_2)CHOH\ (10\%)$$

$$C_6H_5CH(OH)CH_2I \xrightarrow{CH_3MgI} CH_3(C_6H_5CH_2)CHOH\ (15\%)$$

$$C_6H_5CH\text{—}CH_2\ (\text{—O—}) \xrightarrow{CH_3MgI} CH_3(C_6H_5CH_2)CHOH\ (51\%)$$

---

[56] Vavon and Mottez, *Bull. soc. chim.*, [5], *11*, 196 (1944).

*The general chemistry of halohydrins, including Grignard reaction rearrangements, has been reviewed by Tiffeneau, *Bull. soc. chim.*, [5], *12*, 453–76 (1945).

[57] Cottle and Hollyday, *J. Org. Chem.*, *12*, 510–6 (1947).

[58] Godchot, Bedos, and Cauquil, *Bull. soc. chim.*, [4], *43*, 521–2 (1928).

†The use of methylmagnesium bromide or chloride, prepared from sublimed magnesium, in this and similar experiments would eliminate any possible suspicion that the reaction might be of the radical, rather than the ionic, type.

[59] Golumbic and Cottle, *J. Am. Chem. Soc.*, *61*, 996–1000 (1939).

Tiffeneau[60] had early suggested that the apparently "abnormal" products arising from the reactions of Grignard reagents with some α-halo ketones might be attributed to the conversion of the halohydrinates itially formed by "normal" addition of Grignard reagents at carbonyl double bonds to epoxides and the further reaction of the epoxides with excess Grignard reagent. As regards the behavior of some halohydrins (*e.g.*, the iodohydrins of Golumbic and Cottle), this is a fairly plausible hypothesis. As regards some other halohydrin reactions, however, it constitutes an assumption which appears to be neither necessary nor altogether sufficient.

It does not seem adequate, for example, to the elucidation of stereospecific effects in halohydrinate and related rearrangements subsequently observed by Tiffeneau and his collaborators.[61] To cite but one instance, the iodomagnesium derivative of *cis*-1-methyl-2-chlorocyclohexanol, upon heating, is converted to 2-methylcyclohexanone; the corresponding *trans* isomer is converted to acetylcyclopentane. The similarity of these transformations to the familiar pinacol-pinacolone rearrangements is fairly obvious and has been recognized by Tiffeneau.

The most satisfactory general analysis of the subject has been made by Geissman and Akawie,[62] who have also investigated the thermal transformations of the halomagnesium derivatives of the *cis-trans* stereoisomers of some 2-halo-1-indanols. The *cis* isomers are converted principally, and in rather good yields (*ca.* 70 percent), to the 1-indanones; the *trans* isomers also yield a little (*ca.* 7 percent) of the 1-indanones, but are converted chiefly to tarry or resinous materials.

Geissman and Akawie propose that two types (**A** and **B**) of halohydrinate transformation are possible. With minor modifications in notation, these may be represented as follows.

$$\text{(A)}\quad R'\!-\!\underset{\underset{\underset{X}{|}}{O-MgX}}{\overset{R}{\overset{|}{C}}}\!-\!\underset{X}{\overset{|}{\underset{|}{C}}}\!- \;\rightarrow\; R'\!-\!\underset{\vdots\,O\cdots MgX'\cdots X\,\vdots}{\overset{R}{\overset{\cdot\cdot}{C}}}\!-\!C\!- \;\rightarrow\; R'\!-\!\underset{\underset{\underset{X\;\;X}{MgX_2}}{O:}}{\overset{\|}{C}}\!-\!\overset{R}{\overset{|}{\underset{|}{C}}}\!-$$

[60]Tiffeneau, *Bull. soc. chim.*, [3], *29*, 1156-8 (1903).

[61]See, e.g.: (*a*) Tiffeneau and Tchoubar, *Compt. rend.*, *198*, 941-3 (1934); *Chem. Abstr.*, *28*, 3385 (1934); (*b*) Tiffeneau and Tchoubar, *Compt. rend.*, *199*, 360-2 (1934); *Chem. Abstr.*, *28*, 6704 (1934); (*c*) Tiffeneau and Tchoubar, *Compt. rend.*, *199*, 1624-6 (1934); *Chem. Abstr.*, *29*, 2515 (1935); (*d*) Tiffeneau and Tchoubar, *Compt. rend.*, *202*, 1931-4 (1936); *Chem. Abstr.*, *8179* (1936); (*e*) Tiffeneau and Vaissiere, *Compt. rend.*, *209*, 449-53 (1939); *Chem. Abstr.*, *34*, 386 (1940); (*f*) Tchoubar, *Compt. rend.*, *212*, 195-7 (1941); *Chem. Abstr.*, *36*, 6143 (1942); (*g*) Tiffeneau, Tchoubar, and LeTellier, *Compt. rend.*, *216*, 856-60 (1943); *Chem. Abstr.*, 38, 4584 (1944). This work has been reviewed by: (*h*) Tiffeneau, *Bull. soc. chim.*, [5], *12*, 621-7 (1945).

[62]Geissman and Akawie, *J. Am. Chem. Soc.*, *73*, 1993-8 (1951).

$$\text{(B)}\quad \begin{array}{c} \text{R}\ \ \text{X} \\ |\ \ \ | \\ \text{R}'\text{—C——C—} \\ |\ \ \ | \\ \text{O} \\ \diagdown \\ \text{Mg} \\ | \\ \text{X} \end{array} \rightarrow \begin{array}{c} \text{R}\ \ \text{X} \\ |\ \ \vdots \\ \text{R}'\text{—C}\cdots\text{C}'\text{—} \\ \diagdown\ \ \therefore \\ \text{O} \\ \vdots \\ \text{X}'\text{—Mg} \end{array} \rightarrow \begin{array}{c} \text{R} \\ |\ \ \ | \\ \text{R}'\text{—C——C—} \\ \diagdown\ \diagup \\ \text{O} \\ \cdot\cdot \\ \text{X}'\text{—Mg}^{+} \end{array} + \text{X}^{-}$$

It is specified that in epoxide formation (**B**) expulsion of the X^- ion is probably facilitated by "solvation."

"Course **A** should be favored when the halogen atom is secondary or tertiary rather than primary; when the migrating R group can participate in the process and contribute to the resonance stabilization of the transition state; and when the relative disposition of X and OMgX′ is [or can be] *cis*. Course **B** should be favored when X and OMgX′ are *trans*; or, if these are or can be *cis*, when the halogen atom is primary and the migrating R group has a low migratory aptitude (*i.e.*, contributes little to resonance stabilization of the transition state).

"When the halogen atom is secondary or tertiary, course **A** seems always to be followed; but when it is primary the nature of the groups R and R′ directs the course of the rearrangement, as illustrated by the examples **C** and **D**." [See Table VI-XVIII, C_2H_5OCl.]

$$\text{(C)}\quad CH_3COCH_2Cl + RMgX' \rightarrow CH_3\text{—}\underset{\underset{OMgX'}{|}}{\overset{\overset{R}{|}}{C}}\text{—}CH_2Cl \rightarrow$$

$$\left[CH_3\text{—}\overset{\overset{R}{|}}{C}\underset{\diagdown O \diagup}{\text{——}}CH_2 \right] \rightarrow CH_3\text{—}\overset{\overset{R}{|}}{CH}\text{—}CHO \xrightarrow{RMgX'} CH_3CHRCHROH$$

$$(R = CH_3,\ C_2H_5,\ i\text{-}C_5H_{11},\ C_6H_5CH_2)$$

$$\text{(D)}\quad CH_3COCH_2Cl + C_6H_5MgBr \rightarrow CH_3\text{—}\underset{\underset{OMgBr}{|}}{\overset{\overset{C_6H_5}{|}}{C}}\text{—}CH_2Cl \rightarrow CH_3COCH_2C_6H_5$$

Although the existing data (see Tables VI-XVIII, VI-XIX, and XVI-I) can scarcely be construed as constituting a critical confirmative test of the working hypothesis proposed, they are at least interpretable in complete consistency with it.

TABLE XVI-I

REACTIONS OF GRIGNARD REAGENTS WITH ALKYL, ARALKYL, AND CYCLOALKYL HALIDES

Halide	RMgX	Product(s)	Ref.
CCl_4			
CCl_4	C_2H_5MgBr (4 equiv.)	CH_4 (1 part); C_2H_4 (4 parts)	*21*
CCl_4	C_6H_5MgBr	$[(C_6H_5)_3CO-]_2$ (30%); $(C_6H_5)_3COH$ (6%); $[(C_6H_5)_3C-]_2$	*21*
$CHCl_3$			
$CHCl_3$	C_2H_5MgBr	CH_4; C_2H_4; traces of $(C_2H_5)_3CH$ and C_2H_5Br; (*no* C_2H_2)	*21*
$CHCl_3$ (10.3 g.)	C_6H_5MgBr (40.0 g. C_6H_5Br)	$(C_6H_5)_3CH$ (70–80%, crude)	*186*
$CHBr_3$			
$CHBr_3$	C_2H_5MgBr	CH_2Br_2; CH_3Br; C_2H_5Br; CH_4; C_2H_4; C_2H_6	*163*
$CHBr_3$	C_6H_5MgBr	$[(C_6H_5)_2CH-]_2$; C_6H_5Br; [*no* $(C_6H_5)_3CH$]	*20*
CHI_3			
CHI_3	C_2H_5MgBr	CH_2I_2; CH_3I; C_2H_5Br; C_2H_5I; CH_4; C_2H_2; C_2H_6	*163*
CHI_3	C_6H_5MgBr	$[(C_6H_5)_2CH-]_2$; $(C_6H_5-)_2$; [*no* $(C_6H_6)_3CH$]	*163*
CH_2I_2			
CH_2I_2	$C_6H_5C\equiv CMgBr$	$(C_6H_5C\equiv C)_2CH_2$ (8–10%)	*88,89*
CH_3I			
CH_3I	CH_3MgI	C_2H_6 (> 51.6%)	*212*
CH_3I	CH_3MgI (excess)	C_2H_3 (> 21%)	*60*
CH_3I	*t*-C_4H_9MgI	$C(CH_3)_4$ (15–20%)	*55*

TABLE XVI-I (Continued)

Halide	RMgX	Product(s)	Ref.
CH_3I (*cont.*)			
CH_3I	n-$C_5H_{11}C \equiv CMgBr$	No reaction*	*281*
CH_3I	3-CH_3-5-$CH_3OC_6H_3MgBr$	1,3-$(CH_3)_2$-5-$CH_3OC_6H_3$	*48*
CH_3I	2-Methylindolyl-MgI	2,3-Dimethylindole; 1,3,3-trimethylindolenine	*105*
CH_3I	3-Methylindolyl-MgI	3,3-Dimethylindolenine (40%); 1,3-dimethylindole ("a little")	*105*
CH_3I (7.5 g.)	9-Anthryl-MgBr (2.57 g. $C_{14}H_9Br$)	9-Methylanthracene (0.80 g., 41%)	*11*
CH_3I	9-Phenanthryl-MgBr	9-Methylphenanthrene (73%)	*9*
CH_3I	$(C_6H_5)_3CMgBr$	$(C_6H_5)_3CCH_3$ (98%)	*10*
CH_3I	$(C_6H_5)_3CMgBr$	$(C_6H_5)_3CCH_3$ (93%)	*10*
C_2Cl_4			
C_2Cl_4 (1 equiv.)	C_2H_5MgBr (4 equiv.)	C_2H_2; C_2H_4; C_2H_6	*22*
C_2Cl_6			
C_2Cl_6	RMgX	R_2	*190*
C_2Cl_6	C_2H_5MgBr	C_2H_4; C_2H_6; C_2HCl_5; C_2Cl_4; 1,1,1,2-$Cl_4C_2H_2$; 1,1,2,2-$Cl_4C_2H_2$	*129,22*
C_2Cl_6	C_6H_5MgBr	C_6H_6; $(C_6H_5—)_2$; C_2HCl_5; C_2Cl_4; 1,1,1,2-$Cl_4C_2H_2$; 1,1,2,2-$Cl_4C_2H_2$	*129*
C_2Cl_6	4-$CH_3C_6H_4MgBr$	$CH_3C_6H_5$; (4-$CH_3C_6H_4$—$)_2$; C_2HCl_5; C_2Cl_4; 1,1,1,2-$Cl_4C_2H_2$; 1,1,2,2-$Cl_4C_2H_2$	*129*
C_2Cl_6	1-$C_{10}H_7MgBr$	$C_{10}H_8$; (1-$C_{10}H_7$—$)_2$; C_2HCl_5; C_2Cl_4; 1,1,1,2-$Cl_4C_2H_2$; 1,1,2,2-$Cl_4C_2H_2$	*129*

* Several weeks reflux in ethyl ethereal solution.

TABLE XVI-I (Continued)

Halide	RMgX	Product(s)	Ref.
C_2H_2ClN			
$NCCH_2Cl$*	Indolyl-MgI (1 equiv.)	3-Indolylacetonitrile (*ca.* 47%)†	*149*
$NCCH_2Cl$* (1 equiv.)	Indoyl-MgI (7.8 g. C_8H_7N)	3-Indolylacetonitrile (5.3 g.)‡	*149*
$NCCH_2Cl$* (6.1 g.)	6-Methoxyindolyl-MgI (11.7 g. C_9H_9NO)	6-Methoxy-3-indolylacetonitrile (7.4 g., 52%)	*1*
$C_2H_2Cl_2O$			
$ClOCCH_2Cl$§ (28 g.)	C_6H_5MgBr (230 g. C_6H_5Br)	$(C_6H_5)_2CHCH(OH)C_6H_5$ (36 g.); $ClCH_2C(C_6H_5)_2OH$ (0.3 g.)	*26*
$C_2H_2Cl_2O_2$			
HO_2CCHCl_2¶ (10 g.)	C_6H_5MgBr (73 g. C_6H_5Br)	$HO(C_6H_5)_2CCH(OH)C_6H_5$ (8.6 g.)	*26*
$C_2H_2Cl_4$			
$(-CHCl_2)_2$	C_2H_5MgBr (4 equiv.)	C_2H_2; C_2H_4; C_2H_6	*22*
$(-CHCl_2)_2$	C_6H_5MgBr	$(C_6H_5-)_2$; $[(C_6H_5)_2CH-]_2$	*22*
$C_2H_3ClO_2$			
HO_2CCH_2Cl¶	1-$C_{10}H_7MgBr$ (2 equiv.)	1-$C_{10}H_7CH_2CO_2H$	*244*

*It is altogether possible that this reaction has more in common with those of the α-halo ketones (*q.v.*, Chapter VI) than with those of the simple alkyl halides. See also α-Halo Nitriles, Chapter X.

†Reaction in Et_2O; two hours reflux.

‡Dropwise addition of anisole-halide solution to cold anisole-Grignard reagent solution; twenty minutes at 60–70°.

§It is altogether possible that this reaction has more in common with those of the α-halo ketones (*q.v.*, Chapter VI) than with those of the simple alkyl halides. See also α-Halo Carbonyl Halides, Chapter IX.

¶It is altogether possible that this reaction has more in common with those of the α-halo ketones (*q.v.*, Chapter VI) than with those of the simple alkyl halides.

TABLE XVI-I (Continued)

Halide	RMgX	Product(s)	Ref.
$C_2H_4ClBrMgO$			
$BrMgOCH_2CH_2Cl$ (42.0 g. C_2H_5ClO)	$C_6H_5CH_2MgCl$ (126.0 g. C_7H_7Cl)	$C_6H_5(CH_2)_3OH$ (43.6 g., 64%)	*266*
$BrMgOCH_2CH_2Cl$	$2,4\text{-}(CH_3)_2C_6H_3MgBr$	$2,4\text{-}(CH_3)_2C_6H_3CH_2CH_2OH$	*189*
$BrMgOCH_2CH_2Cl$	$2\text{-}C_{10}H_7MgBr$	"Unsatisfactory"	*258*
$C_2H_4Cl_2$			
CH_3CHCl_2	C_2H_5MgX*	C_2H_2; C_2H_4; C_2H_6	*22*
$C_2H_4Cl_2O$			
$O(CH_2Cl)_2$	$(\equiv CMgX)_2$	1,6-Dioxacyclodeca-3,8-diyne	*139*
$O(CH_2Cl)_2$ (22.8 g.)	C_2H_5MgBr (21.8 g. C_2H_5Br) + C_6H_5MgBr (31.0 g. C_6H_5Br)	*n*-$C_3H_7OCH_2C_6H_5$ (45–50%)	*249*
$O(CH_2Cl)_2$ (0.5 mole)	C_6H_5MgBr (1.0 mole C_6H_5Br)	$(C_6H_5CH_2)_2O$ (*ca.* 90%, crude; 56%, pure)	*249*
$O(CH_2Cl)_2$	$C_6H_5CH_2MgCl$	$(C_6H_5CH_2CH_2)_2O$ (*ca.* 80%, crude; 40–44%, pure)	*249*
$O(CH_2Cl)_2$	$4\text{-}CH_3C_6H_4MgBr$	$(4\text{-}CH_3C_6H_4CH_2)_2O$ (61%)	*249*
$O(CH_2Cl)_2$	$1\text{-}C_{10}H_7MgBr$	$(1\text{-}C_{10}H_7CH_2)_2O$ (35–40%)	*249*
$C_2H_4Br_2O$			
$O(CH_2Br)_2$ (20.4 g.)	*i*-C_4H_9MgBr (27.4 g. C_4H_9Br)	$(i\text{-}C_5H_{11})_2O$ (80%, crude; 25%, pure)	*249*
$O(CH_2Br)_2$ (0.5 mole)	C_6H_5MgBr (1.0 mole C_6H_5Br)	$(C_6H_5CH_2)_2O$ (*ca.* 90%, crude; 56%, pure)	*249*
C_2H_5ClO			
$HOCH_2CH_2Cl$	C_6H_5MgCl	$C_6H_5CH_2CH_2OH$ (53%)	*260*
$HOCH_2CH_2Cl$	$ArMgBr$†	$ArCH_2CH_2OH$† (*ca.* 80%)	*86,87,211, 271, 272*

* X = Cl, Br.

† Ar = C_6H_5, $2\text{-}CH_3C_6H_4$, $4\text{-}CH_3C_6H_4$, $4\text{-}CH_3OC_6H_4$, $1\text{-}C_{10}H_7$.

TABLE XVI-I (Continued)

Halide	RMgX	Product(s)	Ref.
C_2H_5ClO (*cont.*)			
$HOCH_2CH_2Cl$	ArMgBr*	$ArCH_2CH_2OH$*	*18*
$HOCH_2CH_2Cl$	ArMgBr†	$ArCH_2CH_2OH$† (20–24%)	*206*
$HOCH_2CH_2Cl$	$ArCH_2MgCl$‡	$Ar(CH_2)_3OH$‡	*18*
$HOCH_2CH_2Cl$	$C_6H_5O(CH_2)_5MgI$	$C_6H_5O(CH_2)_7OH$	*227*
$HOCH_2CH_2Cl$ (22.4 ml.)	9-Phenanthyl-MgBr (48.5 g. $C_{14}H_9Br$)	$C_{14}H_9CH_2CH_2OH$ (40–50 g.)	*262*
CH_3OCH_2Cl	$(\equiv CMgBr)_2$	$(\equiv CCH_2OCH_3)_2$	*49,134, 143*
CH_3OCH_2Cl	$H_2C{=}CBrCH_2CH_2MgBr$	$H_2C{=}CBr(CH_2)_3OCH_3$	*142*
CH_3OCH_2Cl	n-C_4H_9MgBr	n-$C_5H_{11}OCH_3$ (67%)	*84*
CH_3OCH_2Cl	$H_2C(CH_2CH_2MgBr)_2$	$CH_3O(CH_2)_7OCH_3$ (45%)	*47*
CH_3OCH_2Cl	$Br(CH_2)_5Br$ + Mg	$CH_3O(CH_2)_5CH_3$; $CH_3O(CH_2)_7OCH_3$; $CH_3O(CH_2)_{12}OCH_3$; high-boiling products	
CH_3OCH_2Cl	$(-CH_2C\equiv CMgBr)_2$	$(-CH_2C\equiv CCH_2OCH_3)_2$	*134*
CH_3OCH_2Cl (0.1 mole)	$C_6H_5CH_2MgCl$ (0.1 mole C_7H_7Cl)	$C_6H_5CH_2CH_2OCH_3$ (88x%); 2-$CH_3C_6H_4CH_2OCH_3$ (5x%); 4-$CH_3C_6H_4CH_2OCH_3$ (7x%)	*263*
CH_3OCH_2Cl (0.1 mole)	$C_6H_5CH_2MgBr$ (0.1 mole C_7H_7Br)	$C_6H_5CH_2CH_2OCH_3$ (79x%); 2-$CH_3C_6H_4CH_2OCH_3$ (13x%); 4-$CH_3C_6H_4CH_2OCH_3$ (8x%)	*263*
CH_3OCH_2Cl (0.1 mole)	$C_6H_5CH_2MgI$ (0.1 mole C_7H_7I)	$C_6H_5CH_2CH_2OCH_3$ (84x%); 2-$CH_3C_6H_4CH_2OCH_3$ (7x%); 4-$CH_3C_6H_4CH_2OCH_3$ (9x%)	*263*
CH_3OCH_2Cl	2-$CH_3C_6H_4CH_2MgBr$	2,3-$(CH_3)_2C_6H_3CH_2OCH_3$ (90x%)	*270*

* Ar = C_6H_5, 2-$CH_3C_6H_4$, 4-$CH_3C_6H_4$, 2,4-$(CH_3)_2C_6H_3$, 2,5-$(CH_3)_2C_6H_3$, 4-i-$C_3H_7C_6H_4$, 2-CH_3-5-i-$C_3H_7C_6H_3$.

† Ar = 2-$CH_3C_6H_4$, 3-$CH_3C_6H_4$, 4-$CH_3C_6H_4$.

‡ Ar = C_6H_5, 4-$CH_3C_6H_4$, 2,4-$(CH_3)_2C_6H_3$, 2,5-$(CH_3)_2C_6H_3$, 4-i-$C_3H_7C_6H_4$, 2-CH_3-4-i-$C_3H_7C_6H_3$, 4-$C_2H_5C_6H_4$, 4-n-$C_3H_7C_6H_4$, 4-n-$C_4H_9C_6H_4$, 4-t-$C_4H_9C_6H_4$, 4-t-$C_5H_{11}C_6H_4$, 2,4,5-$(CH_3)_3C_6H_2$, 2-CH_3-5-i-$C_3H_7C_6H_3$.

TABLE XVI-I (Continued)

Halide	RMgX	Product(s)	Ref.
C_2H_5ClO (*cont.*)			
CH_3OCH_2Cl	$3\text{-}CH_3C_6H_4CH_2MgBr$	$3\text{-}CH_3C_6H_4(CH_2)_2OCH_3$	*270*
CH_3OCH_2Cl	$4\text{-}CH_3C_6H_4CH_2MgBr$	$4\text{-}CH_3C_6H_4(CH_2)_2OCH_3$ (80*x*%); 2,5-$(CH_3)_2C_6H_3CH_2OCH_3$ (20*x*%)	*270*
CH_3OCH_2Cl (15.0 g.)	$R(CH_2)_2CH(CH_3)(CH_2)_2MgBr$* (40.0 g. $C_{15}H_{29}Br$)	$[R(CH_2)_2CH(CH_3)(CH_2)_2—]_2$* (6.8 g., crude); $R(CH_2)_2CH(CH_3)(CH_2)_3OCH_3$* (11.5 g., crude)	*116*
CH_3OCH_2Cl	$(C_6H_5)_3CMgBr$	$(C_6H_5)_3CCH_2OCH_3$ (70%)	*10*
C_2H_5Br			
C_2H_5Br	$(\equiv CMgBr)_2$	$(\equiv CC_2H_5)_2$ (20%)	*219*
C_2H_5Br	C_2H_5MgBr	$C_2H_4 + C_2H_6$ (in equimol. prop'n)	*212*
C_2H_5Br	$C_6H_5MgBr + FeCl_3$ (trace)	$C_2H_5C_6H_5$ (50–60%)	*282,225*
C_2H_5Br	$4\text{-}CH_3OC_6H_4MgBr + FeCl_3$ (trace)	$C_2H_5C_6H_4\text{-}4\text{-}OCH_3$ (50–60%)	*282,225*
C_2H_5Br	$(CH_3)_5C_6MgCl$	$(CH_3)_5C_6C_2H_5$ (40%)	*37*
C_2H_5Br (0.2 mole)	$(CH_3)_5C_6Br$ (0.2 mole) + Mg (10 g.)	$(CH_3)_5C_6C_2H_5$ (19 g.); $(CH_3)_5C_6H$ (2 g.)	*192*
C_2H_5Br	9-Anthryl-MgBr + $FeCl_3$ (trace)	9-Ethylanthracene (50–60%)	*282*
C_2H_5Br	$(C_6H_5)_3CMgBr$	$(C_6H_5)_3CC_2H_5$ (73%)	*10*
C_2H_5BrO			
$HOCH_2CH_2Br$ (650 g., 5.2 moles)	$n\text{-}C_4H_9MgBr$ (1,430 g., 10.42 moles C_4H_9Br)	$n\text{-}C_6H_{13}OH$ (268 g., 50.6%);	*39*
		$CH_3(n\text{-}C_4H_9)CHOH$ (30 g.)†	*39*
$HOCH_2CH_2Br$ (5 moles)	$n\text{-}C_4H_9MgBr$ (10 moles C_4H_9Br)	$n\text{-}C_6H_{13}OH$ (184 g., 38%); $CH_3(n\text{-}C_4H_9)CHOH$ (54.6 g.)‡	*39*

* R = 2,2,6-trimethylcyclohexyl.

† Dropwise addition of bromohydrin to ethereal Grignard reagent solution; five hours reflux.

‡ One and one-half hour reflux at 35°; partial replacement of ether by benzene; heating to 65°.

TABLE XVI-I (Continued)

Halide	RMgX	Product(s)	Ref.
C_2H_5BrO (*cont.*)			
CH_3OCH_2Br	CH_3OCH_2MgBr	$(-CH_2OCH_3)_2$	*95*
CH_3OCH_2Br	C_6H_5MgBr	$CH_3OCH_2C_6H_5$ (< 60–65%)	*94*
CH_3OCH_2Br	$C_6H_5CH_2MgCl$	$C_6H_5CH_2CH_2OCH_3$ (< 60–65%)	*94*
CH_3OCH_2Br (0.1 mole)	$C_6H_5CH_2MgCl$ (0.1 mole C_7H_7Cl)	$C_6H_5CH_2CH_2OCH_3$ (78x–79x%); 2-$CH_3C_6H_4CH_2OCH_3$ (12x–14x%); 4-$CH_3C_6H_4CH_2OCH_3$ (7x–10x%)	*263*
C_2H_5I			
C_2H_5I	n-C_3H_7MgI	Alkenes, comprising 47.1% C_2H_4, 52.9% C_3H_6; alkanes, comprising C_2H_6, C_3H_8, and traces of n-C_4H_{10} and n-C_5H_{12}	*212*
C_2H_5IO			
CH_3OCH_2I (0.1 mole)	$C_6H_5CH_2MgCl$ (0.1 mole C_7H_7Cl)	$C_6H_5CH_2CH_2OCH_3$ (88x%); 2-$CH_3C_6H_4CH_2OCH_3$ (6x%); 4-$CH_3C_6H_4CH_2OCH_3$ (6x%)	*263*
$C_3Cl_3N_3$			
Cyanuric chloride*	C_6H_5MgBr	2-Chloro-4,6-diphenyl-1,3,5-triazine; 2,4-dichloro-6-phenyl-1,3,5-triazine	*276*
$C_3Br_3N_3$			
Cyanuric bromide† (7.5 g.)	C_2H_5MgI (15.5 g. C_2H_5I)	2,4,6-Triethyl-1,3,5-triazine (yielding $C_2H_5CO_2H$ upon hydrolysis)	*277*

* 2,4,6-Trichloro-1,3,5-triazine. Although this reaction has the formal appearance of that of a simple cycloalkyl halide, it is probably nothing of the sort.

† 2,4,6-Tribromo-1,3,5-triazine.

TABLE XVI-I (Continued)

Halide	RMgX	Product(s)	Ref.
C_3HCl_5			
C_3HCl_5 (b.p. 70–71°/ 12.5 mm.) (1 equiv.)	CH_3MgI (1 equiv.)	C_2H_6; $Cl_2C{=}CHCl$ (?)	*183*
C_3HCl_7			
C_3HCl_7 (30 g.)	CH_3MgI (35.5 g. CH_3I)	CH_4 (equiv. to 1 active H); C_3HCl_5	*182*
C_3HCl_7 (23 g.)	CH_3MgI (3 equiv.)	C_3HCl_5, b.p. 70–71°/12.5 mm. (10.7 g.); CH_4; C_2H_6; high-boiling products	*182,183, 29*
C_3HCl_7	C_2H_5MgI	n-C_4H_{10}; C_3HCl (?)	*183*
C_3H_3Br			
$HC{\equiv}CCH_2Br$	RMgX	"Complex products"*	*284*
$HC{\equiv}CCH_2Br$	RMgX	$H_2C{\equiv}CCH_2R$ (chiefly); $H_2C{=}C{=}CH_2R$†	*284*
$C_3H_4ClF_3$			
$F_3CCH_2CH_2Cl$	C_2H_5MgBr	No reaction	*99*
C_3H_4ClN			
$NCCH_2CH_2Cl$ (13.8 g.)	Indolyl-MgI (18.0 g. C_8H_7N)	3-β-Indolylpropionitrile (16.8 g.)	*149*
$C_3H_4Cl_2$			
$H_2C{=}CHCHCl_2$	CH_3MgBr	CH_4; C_2H_6; $C_2H_5CH{=}CHCl$; $C_2H_5CH{=}CHCH_3$; $H_2C{=}CHCH(CH_3)_2$; $CH_3(H_2CCH{=}CH)_2CH_3$; high-boiling hydrocarbons	*290*

* At the boiling point of ethyl ethereal solution.
† At −15°.

TABLE XVI-I (Continued)

Halide	RMgX	Product(s)	Ref.
$C_3H_4Cl_2$ (*cont.*)			
$H_2C=CHCHCl_2$	n-C_3H_7MgBr	n-$C_4H_9CH=CHCl$ (*ca.* 25%); n-$C_3H_7CH=CH$-n-C_4H_9; $C_{12}H_{22}$ (30%); C_6H_{14}	*291*
$H_2C=CHCHCl_2$	i-C_3H_7MgBr	C_3H_8; C_6H_{14}; i-$C_4H_9CH=CHCl$; i-$C_4H_9CH=CH$-i-C_3H_7; $H_2C=CHCH$-(i-C_3H_7)$_2$; i-$C_3H_7(H_2CCH=CH)_2$-i-C_3H_7; high-boiling hydrocarbons	*290*
$H_2C=CHCHCl_2$	n-C_4H_9MgBr	C_4H_{10}; C_8H_8; n-$C_5H_{11}CH=CHCl$; n-$C_5H_{11}CH=CH$-n-C_4H_9; $H_2C=CHCH$-(n-C_4H_9)$_2$; n-$C_4H_9(H_2CCH=CH)_2$-n-C_4H_9; high-boiling hydrocarbons	*290*
$H_2C=CHCHCl_2$	C_6H_5MgBr	$C_6H_5CH_2CH=CHCl$ ("poor yield"); considerable tar	*126*
$ClCH=CHCH_2Cl$	CH_3MgBr	CH_4; C_2H_6; $C_2H_5CH=CHCl$; $C_2H_5CH=CHCH_3$; $H_2C=CHCH(CH_3)_2$; CH_3-$(H_2CCH=CH)_2CH_3$; high-boiling hydrocarbons	*290*
$ClCH=CHCH_2Cl$	n-C_3H_7MgBr	n-$C_4H_9CH=CHCl$ ("very little"); C_6H_{14}; n-$C_3H_7CH=CH$-n-C_4H_9; $C_{12}H_{22}$ (30%)	*291*
$ClCH=CHCH_2Cl$	i-C_3H_7MgBr	C_3H_8; C_6H_{14}; i-$C_4H_9CH=CHCl$; i-$C_4H_9CH=CH$-i-C_3H_7; $H_2C=CHCH$(i-C_3H_7)$_2$; i-$C_3H_7(H_2CCH=CH)_2$-i-C_3H_7; high-boiling hydrocarbons	*290*
$ClCH=CHCH_2Cl$	n-C_4H_9MgBr	C_4H_{10}; C_8H_{18}; n-$C_5H_{11}CH=CHCl$; n-$C_5H_{11}CH=CH$-n-C_4H_9; $H_2C=CHCH$(n-C_4H_9)$_2$; n-$C_4H_9(H_2CCH=CH)_2$-n-C_4H_9; high-boiling hydrocarbons	*290*

TABLE XVI-I (Continued)

Halides	RMgX	Product(s)	Ref.
$C_3H_4Cl_2$ *(cont)*			
$ClCH{=}CHCH_2Cl$	$4\text{-}BrC_6H_4MgBr$	$4\text{-}BrC_6H_4CH_2CH{=}CHCl$ ("high yield")	*17*
$ClCH{=}CHCH_2Cl$	C_6H_5MgBr	$C_6H_5CH_2CH{=}CHCl$ (*ca.* quant.)	*17*
$ClCH{=}CHCH_2Cl$	$2\text{-}CH_3C_6H_4MgBr$	$2\text{-}CH_3C_6H_5CH_2CH{=}CHCl$ ("high yield")	*17*
$ClCH{=}CHCH_2Cl$	$4\text{-}CH_3C_6H_4MgBr$	$4\text{-}CH_3C_6H_4CH_2CH{=}CHCl$ ("high yield")	*17*
$ClCH{=}CHCH_2Cl$	$4\text{-}CH_3OC_6H_4MgBr$	$4\text{-}CH_3OC_6H_4CH_2CH{=}CHCl$ ("high yield")	*17*
$ClCH{=}CHCH_2Cl$	$4\text{-}i\text{-}C_3H_7C_6H_4MgBr$	$4\text{-}i\text{-}C_3H_7C_6H_4CH_2CH{=}CHCl$ ("high yield")	*17*
$ClCH{=}CHCH_2Cl$	$2\text{-}CH_3\text{-}5\text{-}i\text{-}C_3H_7C_6H_3MgBr$	$2\text{-}CH_3\text{-}5\text{-}i\text{-}C_3H_7C_6H_3CH_2CH{=}CHCl$ ("high yield")	*17*
$C_3H_4Br_2$			
$H_2C{=}CBrCH_2Br$	CH_3MgBr	$H_2C{=}CBrC_2H_5$	*140,124*
$H_2C{=}CBrCH_2Br$	C_2H_5MgBr	$H_2C{=}CBr\text{-}n\text{-}C_3H_7$	*135,25*
$H_2C{=}CBrCH_2Br$	$n\text{-}C_3H_7MgBr$	$H_2C{=}CBr\text{-}n\text{-}C_4H_9$	*25*
$H_2C{=}CBrCH_2Br$	$i\text{-}C_3H_7MgBr$	$H_2C{=}CBr\text{-}i\text{-}C_4H_9$	*136*
$H_2C{=}CBrCH_2Br$	$n\text{-}C_4H_9MgBr$	$H_2C{=}CBr\text{-}n\text{-}C_5H_{11}$	*124*
$H_2C{=}CBrCH_2Br$	$t\text{-}C_4H_9MgCl$	$H_2C{=}CBrCH_2\text{-}t\text{-}C_4H_9$ (45–62%)	*165*
$H_2C{=}CBrCH_2Br$	C_6H_5MgBr	$H_2C{=}CBrCH_2C_6H_5$	*136,25*
$H_2C{=}CBrCH_2Br$	$(CH_2)_5CHMgBr$	$H_2C{=}CBrCH_2CH(CH_2)_5$	*136,25*
$H_2C{=}CBrCH_2Br$	$H_2C[(CH_2)_3MgBr]_2$	$[H_2C{=}CBr(CH_2)_4]_2CH_2$; $[H_2C{=}CBr(CH_2)_8{-}]_2$	*137*
$BrCH{=}CHCH_2Br$	CH_3MgBr	CH_4; C_2H_6 (*ca.* 3%); $(H_2C{=}CH{-})_2$ (5%); "bromobutene," b. 92–94°; "octadiene," b. 118–120°; $C_{10}H_{18}$ (?), b_{12} 70–80°	*283,291*
$BrCH{=}CHCH_2Br$	C_2H_5MgBr (excess)	"Heptene," b. 94–96° (30%)	*283,291*
$BrCH{=}CHCH_2Br$ (excess)	C_2H_5MgBr	$BrCH{=}CH\text{-}n\text{-}C_3H_8$	*283,291*
$BrCH{=}CHCH_2Br$	$n\text{-}C_3H_7MgBr$	C_6H_{14} (5%); $n\text{-}C_3H_7CH{=}CH\text{-}n\text{-}C_4H_9$ (47%); $C_{12}H_{22}$, b_{13} 83–88°	*283,291*

TABLE XVI-I (Continued)

Halide	RMgX	Product(s)	Ref.
$C_3H_4Br_2$ (*cont*)			
$BrCH{=}CHCH_2Br$	C_6H_5MgBr	$BrCH{=}CHCH_2C_6H_5$ (50%)	*291,292*
C_3H_4ICl			
$ClCH{=}CHCH_2I$	n-C_3H_7MgBr	n-$C_4H_9CH{=}CHCl$ (?)*; unidentified products	*126*
C_3H_5Cl			
$H_2C{=}CHCH_2Cl$ (153 g.)	C_2H_5MgBr (240 g. C_2H_5Br)	$H_2C{=}CH$-n-C_3H_7 (40–50%)	*117*
$H_2C{=}CHCH_2Cl$ (153 g.)	n-C_3H_7MgBr (246 g. C_3H_7Br)	$H_2C{=}CH$-n-C_4H_9 (40–50%)	*117*
$H_2C{=}CHCH_2Cl$	Butenyl-MgBr (*ca.* 1 equiv.)	$(H_2C{=}CHCH_2)_2CH_2$ (< 4%); $H_2C{=}CHCH(CH_3)CH_2CH{=}CH_2$ (> 48%)	*245*
$H_2C{=}CHCH_2Cl$ (153 g.)	n-C_4H_9MgBr (275 g. C_4H_9Br)	$H_2C{=}CH$-n-C_5H_{11} (47%)	*117*
$H_2C{=}CHCH_2Cl$	n-$C_5H_{11}MgCl$	$H_2C{=}CH$-n-C_6H_{13} (80%)	*98,38*
$H_2C{=}CHCH_2Cl$	i-$C_5H_{11}MgCl$	$H_2C{=}CH$-i-C_6H_{13} (60%)	*98*
$H_2C{=}CHCH_2Cl$	C_6H_5MgBr	$H_2C{=}CHCH_2C_6H_5$ (*ca.* 82%)	*103*
$H_2C{=}CHCH_2Cl$ (76.5 g.)	n-$C_8H_{17}MgBr$ (193.0 g. $C_8H_{17}Br$)	$H_2C{=}CH$-n-C_9H_{19} (51%)	*117*
$C_3H_5ClBr_2MgO$			
$BrCH_2CH(OMgBr)CH_2$†	C_2H_5MgBr	$(CH_2)_2CHOH$; $ClCH_2CH(OH)CH_2Br$ (13–53%); tar; C_2H_4; C_2H_6	*148*
C_3H_5Br			
$H_2C{=}CHCH_2Br$	$C^{14}H_3MgI$	$H_2C{=}CHCH_2C^{14}H_3$ (63%)	*185*
$H_2C{=}CHCH_2Br$	$HC{\equiv}CMgBr$	$H_2C{=}CHCH_2C{\equiv}CH$ (75%)	*90,196*

* Not positively identified; small yield if any.

† From α-epichlorohydrin + $MgBr_2$ (expts. 1–6) or $ClCH_2CH(OH)CH_2Br$ + C_2H_5MgBr (expts. 7–11).

TABLE XVI-I (Continued)

Halide	RMgX	Product(s)	Ref.
C_3H_5Br (*cont.*)			
$H_2C{=}CHCH_2Br$	C_2H_5MgBr	$H_2C{=}CH$-*n*-C_3H_7 (94%)	*123,112, 53,242 133*
$H_2C{=}CHCH_2Br$	*n*-C_3H_7MgBr	$H_2C{=}CH$-*n*-C_4H_9 (77%)	*242,27*
$H_2C{=}CHCH_2Br$	$H_2C{=}CHC{\equiv}CMgBr$ + CuCl	$H_2C{=}CHC{\equiv}CCH_2CH{=}CH_2$ ("high yield")	*43*
$H_2C{=}CHCH_2Br$	Pyrryl-MgBr	2-Allylpyrrole + 2,5-diallylpyrrole (*ca.* equal parts)	*250*
$H_2C{=}CHCH_2Br$ (86.5 g.)	Butenyl-MgBr (141.0 g. C_4H_7Br)	$H_2C{=}CHCH(CH_3)CH_2CH{=}CH_2$ (34.6 g., 50%)	*147*
$H_2C{=}CHCH_2Br$ (10–15% excess)	Butenyl-MgBr (0.6 mole)	$(H_2C{=}CHCH_2)_2CH_2$ (34%); $H_2C{=}CHCH(CH_3)CH_2CH{=}CH_2$ (34%)	*245*
$H_2C{=}CHCH_2Br$ (67 g.)	3-Tetrahydrofuryl-MgBr (75 g. C_4H_7BrO)	$H_2C{=}CHCH_2CH_2OH$ (6 g.); 3-allyltetrahydrofuran (3.5 g.); recovered starting material (40 g.)	*246*
$H_2C{=}CHCH_2Br$	$(-CH_2CH_2MgI)_2$	$[-(CH_2)_3CH{=}CH_2]_2$	*227*
$H_2C{=}CHCH_2Br$	*n*-C_4H_9MgBr	$H_2C{=}CH$-*n*-C_5H_{11} (90%)	*242,232*
$H_2C{=}CHCH_2Br$	*n*-C_4H_9MgBr	C_7H_{14} (b.p. 88.0–88.5°); C_7H_{14} (b.p. 90.5–90.8°). (Total heptenes, 59%)	*103*
$H_2C{=}CHCH_2Br$	*i*-C_4H_9MgBr	$H_2C{=}CH$-*i*-C_5H_{11} (21%)	*160,27, 227*
$H_2C{=}CHCH_2Br$	*t*-C_4H_9MgCl	$H_2C{=}CH$-*t*-C_4H_9 (85%)	*238,160*
$H_2C{=}CHCH_2Br$ (745 g.)	$(CH_2)_4CHMgBr$ (915 g. C_5H_9Br)	$H_2C{=}CHCH_2CH(CH_2)_4$ (510 g., 75%)	*237*
$H_2C{=}CHCH_2Br$	$Br(CH_2)_5Br$ + Mg	$[H_2C{=}CH(CH_2)_3]_2CH_2$; $[H_2C{=}CH(CH_2)_6-]_2$	*184*
$H_2C{=}CHCH_2Br$	$H_2C(CH_2CH_2MgI)_2$	$[H_2C{=}CH(CH_2)_3]_2CH_2$	*227*
$H_2C{=}CHCH_2Br$	*n*-$C_5H_{11}MgBr$	$H_2C{=}CH$-*n*-C_6H_{13} (89%)	*242,123, 233*

TABLE XVI-I (Continued)

Halide	RMgX	Product(s)	Ref.
C_3H_5Br (*cont.*)			
$H_2C{=}CHCH_2Br$	i-$C_5H_{11}MgBr$	$H_2C{=}CH$-i-C_6H_{13} ("good yield"); "a decane"	*227*
$H_2C{=}CHCH_2Br$	s-$C_4H_9CH_2MgBr$*	$H_2C{=}CHCH_2CH_2$-s-C_4H_9	*226*
$H_2C{=}CHCH_2Br$	4-BrC_6H_4MgBr	$H_2C{=}CHCH_2C_6H_4$-4-Br (70%)	*176*
$H_2C{=}CHCH_2Br$	C_6H_5MgBr	$H_2C{=}CHCH_2C_6H_5$ (86–88%)	*147,103, 221*
$H_2C{=}CHCH_2Br$	n-$C_4H_9C{\equiv}CMgBr$	No reaction†	*43*
$H_2C{=}CHCH_2Br$	n-$C_4H_9C{\equiv}CMgBr$ + CuCl‡	$H_2C{=}CHCH_2C{\equiv}C$-n-C_4H_9 (88%)	*43*
$H_2C{=}CHCH_2Br$	$(CH_2)_5CHMgBr$	$H_2C{=}CHCH_2CH(CH_2)_5$ (42%)	*227*
$H_2C{=}CHCH_2Br$	n-$C_6H_{13}MgBr$	$H_2C{=}CH$-n-C_7H_{15} (85%)	*242,200*
$H_2C{=}CHCH_2Br$	4-$BrC_6H_4CH_2MgCl$	$H_2C{=}CH(CH_2)_2C_6H_4$-4-Br (70%)	*178,177*
$H_2C{=}CHCH_2Br$	$C_6H_5CH_2MgCl$	$H_2C{=}CH(CH_2)_2C_6H_5$	*23*
$H_2C{=}CHCH_2Br$	$C_6H_5CH_2MgBr$	$H_2C{=}CH(CH_2)_2C_6H_5$ (77%)	*130*
$H_2C{=}CHCH_2Br$ (40 g.)	2-$CH_3C_6H_4MgBr$ (56 g. C_7H_7Br)	$H_2C{=}CHCH_2C_6H_4$-2-CH_3 (70%)	*108*
$H_2C{=}CHCH_2Br$	2-$CH_3C_6H_4MgI$	$H_2C{=}CHCH_2C_6H_4$-2-CH_3 (65%)	*104*
$H_2C{=}CHCH_2Br$ (120 g.)	4-$CH_3C_6H_4MgBr$ (168 g. C_7H_7Br)	$H_2C{=}CHCH_2C_6H_4$-4-CH_3 (97 g., 75%); $(4$-$CH_3C_6H_4{-})_2$ (4 g.)	*108*
$H_2C{=}CHCH_2Br$ (121 g., 1 mole)	4-$CH_3OC_6H_4MgBr$ (187 g., 1 mole C_7H_7BrO)	$H_2C{=}CHCH_2C_6H_4$-4-OCH_3 (120 g., 81%)	*278,221*
$H_2C{=}CHCH_2Br$	n-$C_5H_{11}C{\equiv}CMgBr$	$H_2C{=}CHCH_2C{\equiv}C$-n-C_5H_{11}	*89*

* From D(–)-2-methyl-1-butanol.

† No reaction took place in ether with intermittent stirring at room temperature for twenty-three days; refluxing in benzene or n-amyl ether for two to twelve hours was also ineffective. This behavior was common to the 1-alkynylmagnesium halides in general.

‡ With 2 g. of catalyst per mole of Grignard reagent, reaction proceeded in ether solution at room temperature. Cuprous bromide and cuprous cyanide were also effective, as were the cupric halides (which are immediately reduced to the cuprous compounds by most Grignard reagents); copper bronze proved ineffective.

TABLE XVI-I (Continued)

Halide	RMgX	Product(s)	Ref.
C_3H_5Br (*cont.*)			
$H_2C{=}CHCH_2Br$	$n\text{-}C_5H_{11}C{\equiv}CMgBr + CuCl$	$H_2C{=}CHCH_2C{\equiv}C\text{-}n\text{-}C_5H_{11}$ ("high yield")	43
$H_2C{=}CHCH_2Br$	$n\text{-}C_7H_{15}MgX$	$H_2C{=}CH\text{-}n\text{-}C_8H_{17}$ (*ca.* 50%)	200
$H_2C{=}CHCH_2Br$	$C_6H_5C{\equiv}CMgBr$	$H_2C{=}CHCH_2C{\equiv}CC_6H_5$ (70%)	88,89
$H_2C{=}CHCH_2Br$	$C_6H_5C{\equiv}CMgBr + CuCl$	$H_2C{=}CHCH_2C{\equiv}CC_6H_5$ ("high yield")	43
$H_2C{=}CHCH_2Br$	$C_6H_5CH_2CH_2MgBr$	$H_2C{=}CH(CH_2)_3C_6H_5$ (70%)	227
$H_2C{=}CHCH_2Br$	$4\text{-}C_2H_5OC_6H_4MgBr$	$H_2C{=}CHCH_2C_6H_4\text{-}4\text{-}OC_2H_5$ (66.5%)	279
$H_2C{=}CHCH_2Br$	$n\text{-}C_8H_{17}MgX$	$H_2C{=}CH\text{-}n\text{-}C_9H_{19}$ (65%); $C_{16}H_{34}$	227,200
$H_2C{=}CHCH_2Br$	$C_6H_5(CH_2)_3MgBr$	$H_2C{=}CH(CH_2)_4C_6H_5$ (87%)	130,227
$H_2C{=}CHCH_2Br$	$n\text{-}C_9H_{19}MgX$	$H_2C{=}CH\text{-}n\text{-}C_{10}H_{21}$ (*ca.* 50%)	200
$H_2C{=}CHCH_2Br$	$C_6H_5O(CH_2)_4MgI$	$H_2C{=}CH(CH_2)_5OC_6H_5$ (50%)	227
$H_2C{=}CHCH_2Br$	$n\text{-}C_{10}H_{21}MgBr$	$H_2C{=}CH\text{-}n\text{-}C_{11}H_{23}$ (77%)	130,200
$H_2C{=}CHCH_2Br$	$C_6H_5(CH_2)_5MgBr$	$H_2C{=}CH(CH_2)_6C_6H_5$ (55%)	227
$H_2C{=}CHCH_2Br$	$(CH_3)_5C_6MgCl$	$H_2C{=}CHCH_2C_6(CH_3)_5$ (40–50%)	37
$H_2C{=}CHCH_2Br$	$(CH_3)_5C_6Br + Mg$	$H_2C{=}CHCH_2C_6(CH_3)_5$	192
$H_2C{=}CHCH_2Br$	$C_6H_5O(CH_2)_5MgI$	$H_2C{=}CH(CH_2)_6OC_6H_5$ (*ca.* 50%)	227
$H_2C{=}CHCH_2Br$ (19.7 g.)	$2\text{-}C_6H_5C_6H_4MgBr$ (32.0 g. $C_{12}H_9Br$)	$H_2C{=}CHCH_2C_6H_4\text{-}2\text{-}C_6H_5$ (16.0 g., 60%)	259
$H_2C{=}CHCH_2Br$	$n\text{-}C_{12}H_{25}MgBr$	$H_2C{=}CH\text{-}n\text{-}C_{13}H_{27}$ (67%)	130,200
$H_2C{=}CHCH_2Br$	2-Methoxy-1-dibenzofuryl-MgBr	1-Allyl-2-methoxydibenzofuran (74%)	73
$H_2C{=}CHCH_2Br$	2-Methoxy-3-dibenzofuryl-MgBr	2-Methoxy-3-allyldibenzofuran (60%)	73
$H_2C{=}CHCH_2Br$ (12.1 g.)	9-Phenanthryl-MgBr (25.7 ml. $C_{14}H_9Br$)	9-Allylphenanthrene (13.0 g.)	13
$H_2C{=}CHCH_2Br$	$n\text{-}C_{14}H_{29}MgBr$	$H_2C{=}CH\text{-}n\text{-}C_{15}H_{31}$ (43%)	130,200
$H_2C{=}CHCH_2Br$	$n\text{-}C_{16}H_{33}MgBr$	$H_2C{=}CH\text{-}n\text{-}C_{17}H_{35}$ (56%)	130
$H_2C{=}CHCH_2Br$	$n\text{-}C_{18}H_{37}MgX$	$H_2C{=}CH\text{-}n\text{-}C_{19}H_{39}$ (*ca.* 50%)	200
$H_2C{=}CHCH_2Br$	$(C_6H_5)_3CMgBr$	$H_2C{=}CHCH_2C(C_6H_5)_3$ (88%)	10
C_3H_5I			
$H_2C{=}CHCH_2I$	$i\text{-}C_4H_9MgCl$	$H_2C{=}CH\text{-}i\text{-}C_5H_{11}$ (50%); $(H_2C{=}CHCH_2{-})_2$; $(i\text{-}C_4H_9{-})_2$	5

TABLE XVI-I (Continued)

Halide	RMgX	Product(s)	Ref.
C_3H_5I (*cont.*)			
$H_2C{=}CHCH_2I$	$C_6H_5CH_2MgCl$	$H_2C{=}CHCH_2CH_2C_6H_5$ (65%)	5
$C_3H_6ClBrMgO$			
$BrMgO(CH_2)_3Cl$ (49 g. C_3H_7ClO)	$C_6H_5CH_2MgCl$	$C_6H_5(CH_2)_4OH$ (37 g., 50%)	266
$BrMgO(CH_2)_3Cl$	$C_6H_5CH_2CH_2MgBr$	$C_6H_5(CH_2)_5OH$ (36%)	266
$BrMgO(CH_2)_3Cl$	$C_6H_5(CH_2)_3MgBr$	$C_6H_5(CH_2)_6OH$ (33%)	266
$BrMgO(CH_2)_3Cl$	$C_6H_5(CH_2)_4MgBr$	$C_6H_5(CH_2)_7OH$ (21%)	266
C_3H_6ClBrO			
$BrCH_2CH(OH)CH_2Cl$	C_2H_5MgBr*	$(CH_2)_2CHOH$ (6.3%)	253
$C_3H_6Br_2$			
$Br(CH_2)_3Br$	C_6H_4-1,4-$(MgBr)_2$	(C_6H_4)-1,2-$[(CH_2)_3Br]_2$; $(4\text{-}CH_3C_6H_4CH_2)_2CH_2$	207
C_3H_7ClO			
$C_2H_5OCH_2Cl$	$C_6H_5CH_2MgCl$	$C_6H_5CH_2CH_2OC_2H_5$ (53x%); 2-$CH_3C_6H_4CH_2OC_2H_5$ (16x%); 4-$CH_3C_6H_4CH_2OC_2H_5$ (31x%)	72
$C_2H_5OCH_2Cl$ (0.1 mole)	$C_6H_5CH_2MgCl$ (0.1 mole C_7H_7Cl)	$C_6H_5CH_2CH_2OC_2H_5$ (92x%); 2-$CH_3C_6H_4CH_2OC_2H_5$ (2x%); 4-$CH_3C_6H_4CH_2OC_2H_5$ (6x%)	263
$C_2H_5OCH_2Cl$	$(n\text{-}C_3H_7)_2CHMgBr$	$C_2H_5OCH_2CH(n\text{-}C_3H_7)_2$	2
$CH_3(CH_3O)CHCl$ (0.1 mole)	$C_6H_5CH_2MgCl$ (0.1 mole C_7H_7Cl)	$C_6H_5CH_2CH(CH_3)OCH_3$ (99.0x%); 2-$CH_3C_6H_4CH(CH_3)OCH_3$ 0.8x%); 4-$CH_3C_6H_4CH(CH_3)OCH_3$ (0.2x%)	263

* From pure sublimed magnesium.

TABLE XVI-I (Continued)

Halide	RMgX	Product(s)	Ref.
$C_3H_7ClO_2$			
$HOCH_2CH(OH)CH_2Cl$	C_2H_5MgBr	CH_3COCH_2OH	*273,272*
$HOCH_2CH(OH)CH_2Cl$	*i*-$C_5H_{11}MgBr$	$HO(CH_3)(i\text{-}C_5H_{11})CCH_2OH$	*86,87, 211,cf. 272*
$HOCH_2CH(OH)CH_2Cl$	C_6H_5MgBr	$HO(CH_3)(C_6H_5)CCH_2OH$ (chiefly); $C_6H_5CH_2CH(OH)CH_2OH$ (a little)	*86,87, 211,cf. 272*
$HOCH_2CH(OH)CH_2Cl$	$C_6H_5CH_2MgCl$	$C_6H_5CH_2CH_2CH(OH)CH_2OH$*	*272*
C_3H_7Br			
n-C_3H_7Br	C_6H_5MgBr + $FeCl_3$ (trace)	*n*-$C_3H_7C_6H_5$ (50–60%)	*282,225*
n-C_3H_7Br	$C_6H_5CH_2MgBr$ + $FeCl_3$ (trace)	*n*-$C_4H_9C_6H_5$	*225*
n-C_3H_7Br	2-$C_{10}H_7MgBr$ + $FeCl_3$ (trace)	2-*n*-$C_3H_7C_{10}H_7$	*225*
n-C_3H_7Br	9-Fluorenyl-MgBr	No reaction in boiling xylene	*155*
n-C_3H_7Br	9-Phenanthryl-MgBr	9-*n*-Propylphenanthrene (47%)	*155*
n-C_3H_7Br	$(C_6H_5)_3CMgBr$	*n*-$C_3H_7C(C_6H_5)_3$ (41%)	*10*
i-C_3H_7Br	C_6H_5MgBr + $FeCl_3$ (trace)	*i*-$C_3H_7C_6H_5$ (50–60%)	*282,225*
i-C_3H_7Br	$C_6H_5CH_2MgBr$ + $FeCl_3$ (trace)	*i*-$C_4H_9C_6H_5$	*225*
i-C_3H_7Br	1-$C_{10}H_7MgBr$ + $FeCl_3$ (trace)	1-*i*-$C_3H_7C_{10}H_7$ (50–60%)	*282*
C_3H_7BrO			
$CH_3CH(OH)CH_2Br$	$(C_2H_5)_2Mg$	$CH_3CH(OH)$-*n*-C_3H_7	*110*
C_3H_7I			
n-C_3H_7I	CH_3MgI	C_3H_6; saturated gases	*212*

*Probably an erroneous assignment of structure.

TABLE XVI-I (Continued)

Halide	RMgX	Product(s)	Ref.
C_3H_7I (*cont.*)			
n-C_3H_7I	C_2H_5MgI	Alkenes, comprising 45.8% C_2H_4, 54.2% C_3H_6; alkanes, comprising 66% C_2H_6, 34% C_3H_8	*212*
$C_4H_4Cl_4O_2$			
2,2,3,3-Tetrachloro-1,4-dioxane (0.1 mole)	*n*-C_4H_9MgBr (excess)	C_4H_{10} (0.13 mole); C_4H_8 (0.12 mole); unidentified unsat'd Cl comp'ds	*217*
2,2,3,3-Tetrachloro-1,4-dioxane (9.1 g., 0.04 mole)	C_6H_5MgBr (0.25 mole)	2-Chloro-2,3,3-triphenyl-1,4-dioxane (10.5 g., 71%)	*217*
$C_4H_4Br_2$			
($\equiv CCH_2Br$) (4.0 g.)	C_2H_5MgBr (1.4 g. Mg)	($\equiv C$-*n*-C_3H_7)$_2$ (1.2 g., crude)	*256*
C_4H_5Cl			
$H_2C{=}C{=}CHCH_2Cl$	CH_3MgCl	$H_2C{=}C(CH_3)CH{=}CH_2$ (14.7%)	*35,33*
$H_2C{=}C{=}CHCH_2Cl$	CH_3MgI	$H_2C{=}C(CH_3)CH{=}CH_2$ (23.5%)	*35,33*
$H_2C{=}C{=}CHCH_2Cl$	*n*-C_4H_9MgBr	$H_2C{=}C$(*n*-C_4H_9)$CH{=}CH_2$ (13.1%)	*35,33*
$H_2C{=}C{=}CHCH_2Cl$	C_6H_5MgBr	$H_2C{=}C{=}CHCH_2C_6H_5$ (4.0–7.2%); $H_2C{=}C(C_6H_5)CH{=}CH_2$ (8.4–9.2%); $[H_2C{=}C(C_6H_5)CH{=}CH_2]_2$ (25.3–26.7%)	*35,33*
$H_2C{=}C{=}CHCH_2Cl$	$C_6H_5CH_2MgCl$	$H_2C{=}C{=}CHCH_2CH_2C_6H_5$	*33*
$H_2C{=}C{=}CHCH_2Cl$	*n*-$C_7H_{15}MgBr$	$H_2C{=}C$(*n*-C_7H_{15})$CH{=}CH_2$ (21.0%)	*35,33*
$C_4H_5Cl_3$			
$Cl_2C{=}C(CH_3)CH_2Cl$	CH_3MgBr (5 equiv.)	Recovered trichloride; 1,1-dichloro-2,4,4,5-tetramethyl-1,5-hexadiene; 2,3,6,7-tetramethyl-2,6-octadiene; C_2H_6	*125*

TABLE XVI-I (Continued)

Halide	RMgX	Product(s)	Ref.
C_4H_6ClN			
$NC(CH_2)_3Cl$*			
$CH_3(NCCH_2)CHCl$*			
$C_4H_6Cl_2$			
$ClCH{=}CHCH_2CH_2Cl$ (37 g.)	CH_3MgBr (75 g. CH_3Br)	$(C_2H_5CH{=})_2$ (24%); $(H_2C{=}CH{-})_2$ (50%)	*146*
$ClCH{=}CHCH_2CH_2Cl$	4-*i*-$C_3H_7C_6H_4MgBr$	$ClCH{=}CH(CH_2)_2C_6H_4$-4-*i*-C_3H_7 ("high yield")	*17*
$H_2C{=}CHCHClCH_2Cl$ (41 g.)	CH_3MgBr (75 g. CH_3Br)	$(C_2H_5CH{=})_2$ (4.5 g.); $(CH_3CHCl{-})_2$ (18.0 g.)	*146*
$H_2C{=}C(CH_2Cl)_2$	C_6H_5MgBr	$H_2C{=}C(CH_2Cl)CH_2C_6H_5$	*24*
$C_4H_6Cl_2O$			
2,3-Dichlorotetrahydrofuran	RMgX† (2 equiv.)	2-R-3-Chlorotetrahydrofuran	*161*
$C_4H_6Cl_2O_2$			
2,3-Dichloro-1,4-dioxane	CH_3MgBr	Dihydro-*p*-dioxin (68%); 2,3-Dimethyl-1,4-dioxane (3%); gases: 94% C_2H_6; 5.4% CH_4; 0.6% C_2H_4	*215,214*
2,3-Dichloro-1,4-dioxane	C_2H_5MgBr	Dihydro-*p*-dioxin (54%); 2,3-Diethyl-1,4-dioxane (2%)	*215,214*
2,3-Dichloro-1,4-dioxane	$H_2C{=}CHCH_2MgBr$	2,3-Diallyl-1,4-dioxane (18%); 1,3-hexadiene	*215*
2,3-Dichloro-1,4-dioxane	*n*-C_4H_9MgBr	2,3-Di-*n*-butyl-1,4-dioxane (2%)	*215,214*
2,3-Dichloro-1,4-dioxane	*n*-C_4H_9MgBr + $ZnCl_2$	2,3-Di-*n*-butyl-1,4-dioxane (37%)	*215*
2,3-Dichloro-1,4-dioxane	*n*-C_4H_9MgBr + $CdCl_2$	2,3-Di-*n*-butyl-1,4-dioxane (44%)	*215*

* See Table X-I, **C_4H_6NCl**.

† R = CH_3, C_2H_5, *n*-C_3H_7, *n*-C_4H_9, C_6H_5.

TABLE XVI-I (Continued)

Halide	RMgX	Product(s)	Ref.
$C_4H_6Cl_2O_2$ *(cont.)*			
2,3-Dichloro-1,4-dioxane	$4\text{-}ClC_6H_4MgBr$	2,3-Di-*p*-chlorophenyl-1,4-dioxane (49%)	*215,36*
2,3-Dichloro-1,4-dioxane	C_6H_5MgBr	2,3-Diphenyl-1,4-dioxane (80%)	*215*
2,3-Dichloro-1,4-dioxane	$C_6H_5CH_2MgBr$	2,3-Dibenzyl-1,4-dioxane (22%)	*215*
2,3-Dichloro-1,4-dioxane	$2\text{-}CH_3C_6H_4MgBr$	2,3-Di-*o*-tolyl-1,4-dioxane (61%)	*215*
2,3-Dichloro-1,4-dioxane	$3\text{-}CH_3C_6H_4MgBr$	2,3-Di-*m*-tolyl-1,4-dioxane (51%)	*215*
2,3-Dichloro-1,4-dioxane	$4\text{-}CH_3C_6H_4MgBr$	2,3-Di-*p*-tolyl-1,4-dioxane (72%)	*215*
2,3-Dichloro-1,4-dioxane	$4\text{-}CH_3OC_6H_4MgBr$	2,3-Di-*p*-anisyl-1,4-dioxane (67%)	*215*
2,3-Dichloro-1,4-dioxane	$1\text{-}C_{10}H_7MgBr$ (4 equiv.)	2,3-Di-α-naphthyl-1,4-dioxane (53%)	*215*
C_4H_6BrN			
$NC(CH_2)_3Br$*			
$C_4H_6Br_2$			
$(=CHCH_2Br)_2$ (60 g.)	CH_3MgI (188 g. CH_3I)	$(=CHC_2H_5)_2$ (10–12%); $C_4H_6Br_4$, m. 117°	*146*
$BrCH=C(CH_3)CH_2Br$	C_2H_5MgBr	C_8H_{16} (30%); $C_6H_{11}Br$; $C_{10}H_{17}Br$	*291*
C_4H_7Cl			
$CH_3CH=CHCH_2Cl$	$H_2C=CHCH_2MgCl$	$(H_2C=CHCH_2)_2CH_2$ (> 50.8%); $H_2C=CHCH(CH_3)CH_2CH=CH_2$ (<3.2%)	*245*
$CH_3CH=CH_2Cl$ (110 g.)	$H_2C=CHCH_2MgBr$ (150 g. C_3H_5Br)	$CH_3CH=CHCH_2CH_2CH=CH_2$ (62.6 g., 53.5%)	*147*
$CH_3CH=CHCH_2Cl$	Butenyl-MgBr	$(CH_3CH=CHCH_2—)_2$ (8.6%); $H_2C=CHCH(CH_3)CH_2CH=CHCH_3$ (59.0%); $[H_2C=CHCH(CH_3)—]_2$ (5.0%)	*245*

* See Table X-I, **C_4H_6NBr**.

TABLE XVI-I (Continued)

Halide	RMgX	Product(s)	Ref.
C_4H_7Cl (*cont.*)			
$CH_3CH=CHCH_2Cl$	n-C_4H_9MgCl	$CH_3CH=CH$-n-C_5H_{11} (60%); $H_2C=CHCH(CH_3)$-n-C_4H_9 (10%)	38
$CH_3CH=CHCH_2Cl$	C_6H_5MgBr	$CH_3CH=CHCH_2C_6H_5$ (46 ± 3%); $H_2C=C(CH_3)CH_2C_6H_5$ (14 ± 2%)	243
$CH_3CH=CHCH_2Cl$ + $CH_3(H_2C=CH)CHCl$	n-C_4H_9MgCl	$H_2C=CHCH(CH_3)CH_2CH=CHCH_3$ (6x%); $H_2C=CHCH(CH_3)$-n-C_4H_9 (9x%); $CH_3CH=CH$-n-C_5H_{11} (85x%)	98
$CH_3CH=CHCH_2Cl$ (41%) + $CH_3(H_2C=CH)CHCl$ (59%)	C_6H_5MgBr	$CH_3CH=CHCH_2C_6H_5$ (81 ± 3x%); $CH_3(H_2C=CH)CHC_6H_5$ (19 ± 2x%)	243
$CH_3(H_2C=CH)CHCl$	$H_2C=CHCH_2MgCl$ (*ca.* 1 equiv.)	$(H_2C=CHCH_2)_2CH_2$ (42.4%); $H_2C=CHCH(CH_3)CH_2CH=CH_2$ (13.2%)	245
$CH_3(H_2C=CH)CHCl$ (0.38 mole)	Butenyl-MgBr (0.38 mole)	$(CH_3CH=CHCH_2—)_2$ (2.3%); $H_2C=CHCH(CH_3)CH_2CH_2CH=CH_2$ (65.4%); $[H_2C=CHCH(CH_3)—]_2$ (8.4%)	245
$CH_3(H_2C=CH)CHCl$	C_6H_5MgBr	$CH_3CH=CHCH_2C_6H_5$ (52 ± 4%); $CH_3(H_2C=CH)CHC_6H_5$ (14 ± 2%)	243
$H_2C=C(CH_3)CH_2Cl$	n-C_4H_9MgCl	$H_2C=C(CH_3)$-n-C_5H_{11}; $(CH_3)_2C=CH$-n-C_4H_9*	98
$H_2C=C(CH_3)CH_2Cl$	C_6H_5MgBr	$H_2C=C(CH_3)CH_2C_6H_5$	24
$H_2C=C(CH_3)CH_2Cl$ (36.5 kg.)	C_6H_5MgBr (404 moles C_6H_5Br)	$H_2C=C(CH_3)CH_2C_6H_5$ + $(CH_3)_2C=CHC_6H_5$ (totalling 45–53%)	30
$C_4H_7ClO_2$			
2-Chloro-1,4-dioxane	C_6H_5MgBr	2-Phenyl-1,4-dioxane (49%)	214

* This product is attributed to rearrangement of the primary product; the extent of rearrangement is said to depend upon the temperature of reaction and of the recovery operations.

TABLE XVI-I (Continued)

Halide	RMgX	Product(s)	Ref.
C_4H_7Br			
$CH_3CH{=}CHCH_2Br$ (60 g.)	C_6H_5MgBr (79 g. C_6H_5Br)	$CH_3CH{=}CHCH_2C_6H_5$ (34%)	*285*
$CH_3CH{=}CHCH_2Br$	$C_6H_5CH_2CH_2MgBr$	$H_2C{=}CHCH(CH_3)CH_2CH_2C_6H_5$	*285*
Butenyl bromide* (10–15% excess)	Butenyl-MgBr (0.6 mole)	$(CH_3CH{=}CHCH_2-)_2$ (5.8%); $H_2C{=}CHCH(CH_3)CH_2CH{=}CHCH_3$ (51.0%); $[H_2C{=}CHCH(CH_3)-]_2$ (1.2%)	*245*
$CH_3(H_2C{=}CH)CHBr$ (10–15% excess)	Butenyl-MgBr (0.6 mole)	$(CH_3CH{=}CHCH_2-)_2$ (37.5%); $H_2C{=}CHCH(CH_3)CH_2CH{=}CHCH_3$ (26.3%); $[H_2C{=}CHCH(CH_3)-]_2$ (11.3%)	*245*
$CH_3(H_2C{=}CH)CHBr$ + $CH_3CH{=}CHCH_2Br$[†] (107 g.)	$(CH_2)_4CHMgCl$ (82 g. C_5H_9Cl)	$CH_3(H_2C{=}CH)CHCH(CH_2)_4$ (8.3 g.); *cis*- and *trans*-$CH_3CH{=}CHCH_2CH(CH_2)_4$ (5.4 g.)	*170*
$CH_3(H_2C{=}CH)CHBr$	$C_6H_5CH_2CH_2MgBr$	$CH_3CH{=}CH(CH_2)_3C_6H_5$	*285*
$C_4H_7Br_2ClO$			
$ClCH_2CH_2OCHBrCH_2Br$	C_2H_5MgBr (*ca.* 1 equiv.)	$ClCH_2CH_2OCH(CH_2Br)C_2H_5$ (81%)	*40,216*
$ClCH_2CHBr(CH_3O)CHBr$	n-C_3H_7MgBr	$ClCH_2CHBrCH(OCH_3)$-n-C_3H_7	*181*
$ClCH_2CHBr(CH_3O)CHBr$	n-C_4H_9Br	$ClCH_2CHBrCH(OCH_2)$-n-C_4H_9	*181*
$C_4H_8Cl_2O$			
$ClCH_2(C_2H_5O)CHCl$	$(\equiv CMgX)_2$[‡]	$[ClCH_2(C_2H_5O)CHC\equiv]_2$	*141*
$ClCH_2(C_2H_5O)CHCl$ (100 g.)	C_2H_5MgBr (120 g. C_2H_5Br)	$ClCH_2(C_2H_5O)CHC_2H_5$ (*ca.* 70 g.)	*107*
$ClCH_2(C_2H_5O)CHCl$ (70 g.)	i-C_4H_9MgBr (70 g. C_4H_9Br)	$ClCH_2(C_2H_5O)CH$-i-C_4H_9 (50 g., crude)	*107*

* Comprising 87 percent crotyl bromide, $CH_3CH{=}CHCH_2Br$, and 13 percent α-methallyl bromide, $CH_3(H_2C{=}CH)CHBr$.

† From the addition of hydrogen bromide to 1,3-butadiene.

‡ Lespieau and Bresch (*141*) describe the Grignard reagent employed as $HC\equiv CMgX$, but in view of the reported product and of the known difficulty of preparing the monomagnesium reagent this appears improbable.

TABLE XVI-I (Continued)

Halide	RMgX	Product(s)	Ref.
$C_4H_8Cl_2O$ (*cont.*)			
$ClCH_2(C_2H_5O)CHCl$ (80 g.)	$i\text{-}C_5H_{11}MgBr$ (100 g. $C_5H_{11}Br$)	$ClCH_2(C_2H_5O)CH\text{-}i\text{-}C_5H_{11}$ (75 g.)	*107*
$ClCH_2(C_2H_5O)CHCl$ (115 g.)	C_6H_5MgBr (150 g. C_6H_5Br)	$ClCH_2(C_2H_5O)CHC_6H_5$ (97 g.)	*107*
$ClCH_2(C_2H_5O)CHCl$ (75 g.)	$C_6H_5CH_2MgCl$ (100 g. C_7H_7Cl)	$ClCH_2(C_2H_5O)CHCH_2C_6H_5$ (54 g.)	*107*
$ClCH_2(C_2H_5O)CHCl$	$C_6H_5C{\equiv}CMgBr$	$ClCH_2(C_2H_5O)CHC{\equiv}CC_6H_5$	*113*
$ClCH_2(C_2H_5O)CHCl$ (90 g.)	$1\text{-}C_{10}H_7MgBr$ (150 g. $C_{10}H_7Br$)	$ClCH_2(C_2H_5O)CH\text{-}1\text{-}C_{10}H_7$ (74 g.)	*107*
$C_4H_8Br_2O$			
$BrCH_2(C_2H_5O)CHBr$	CH_3MgBr (slight excess)	$BrCH_2(C_2H_5O)CHCH_3$ (77.4%)*	*218*
$BrCH_2(C_2H_5O)CHBr$	CH_3MgBr (10–30%) excess)	$BrCH_2(C_2H_5O)CHCH_3$ (71%)†	*202*
$BrCH_2(C_2H_5O)CHBr$	$({\equiv}CMgX)_2$	$BrCH_2(C_2H_5O)CHC{\equiv}CH$; $[BrCH_2(C_2H_5O)CHC{\equiv}]_2$	*144*
$BrCH_2(C_2H_5O)CHBr$	C_2H_5MgBr (slight excess)	$BrCH_2(C_2H_5O)CHC_2H_5$ (60–75%)	*218,51, 202*
$BrCH_2(C_2H_5O)CHBr$	$H_2C{=}CHCH_2MgBr$ (slight excess)	$BrCH_2(C_2H_5O)CHCH_2CH{=}CH_2$ (48–50%)	*205*
$BrCH_2(C_2H_5O)CHBr$	$n\text{-}C_3H_7MgBr$ (slight excess)	$BrCH_2(C_2H_5O)CH\text{-}n\text{-}C_3H_7$ (66.5%)	*218,51*
$BrCH_2(C_2H_5O)CHBr$	$i\text{-}C_3H_7MgBr$ (slight excess)	$BrCH_2(C_2H_5O)CH\text{-}i\text{-}C_3H_7$ (30.0%)	*218*
$BrCH_2(C_2H_5O)CHBr$	$n\text{-}C_4H_9MgBr$ (slight excess)	$BrCH_2(C_2H_5O)CH\text{-}n\text{-}C_4H_9$ (70.0%)	*218,51, 202,231*
$BrCH_2(C_2H_5O)CHBr$	$i\text{-}C_4H_9MgBr$ (slight excess)	$BrCH_2(C_2H_5O)CH\text{-}i\text{-}C_4H_9$ (46–48%)	*51,202*
$BrCH_2(C_2H_5O)CHBr$	$s\text{-}C_4H_9MgBr$ (10–30% excess)	$BrCH_2(C_2H_5O)CH\text{-}s\text{-}C_4H_9$ (30%)	*202*
$BrCH_2(C_2H_5O)CHBr$	$n\text{-}C_3H_7C{\equiv}CMgBr$	$BrCH_2(C_2H_5O)CHC{\equiv}C\text{-}n\text{-}C_3H_7$ (80%)	*6*
$BrCH_2(C_2H_5O)CHBr$	$n\text{-}C_5H_{11}MgBr$	$BrCH_2(C_2H_5O)CH\text{-}n\text{-}C_5H_{11}$ (61–66%)	*210*
$BrCH_2(C_2H_5O)CHBr$	$i\text{-}C_5H_{11}MgBr$	$BrCH_2(C_2H_5O)CH\text{-}i\text{-}C_5H_{11}$ (55–60%)	*210,218, 51*
$BrCH_2(C_2H_5O)CHBr$	$s\text{-}C_4H_9CH_2MgBr$	$BrCH_2(C_2H_5O)CHCH_2\text{-}s\text{-}C_4H_9$ (60%)	*210*

* Dropwise addition of Grignard reagent solution to ice-cooled, agitated Et_2O-bromide solution.
† Slow addition of Et_2O-bromide solution to ice-cooled, stirred Grignard reagent solution; ten to fifteen hours stirring.

TABLE XVI-I (Continued)

Halide	RMgX	Product(s)	Ref.
$C_4H_8Br_2O$ (*cont.*)			
$BrCH_2(C_2H_5O)CHBr$	$CH_3(n\text{-}C_3H_7)CHMgBr$	$BrCH_2(C_2H_5O)CHCH(CH_3)\text{-}n\text{-}C_3H_7$ (22–36%)	*210*
$BrCH_2(C_2H_5O)CHBr$	C_6H_5MgBr	$BrCH_2(C_2H_5O)CHC_6H_5$ (90%)	*234*
$BrCH_2(C_2H_5O)CHBr$	$n\text{-}C_4H_9C{\equiv}CMgBr$	$BrCH_2(C_2H_5O)CHC{\equiv}C\text{-}n\text{-}C_4H_9$ (86%)	*6*
$BrCH_2(C_2H_5O)CHBr$	$n\text{-}C_5H_{11}C{\equiv}CMgBr$	$BrCH_2(C_2H_5O)CHC{\equiv}C\text{-}n\text{-}C_5H_{11}$ (84%)	*6*
$BrCH_2(C_2H_5O)CHBr$	$C_6H_5C{\equiv}CMgBr$	$BrCH_2(C_2H_5O)CHC{\equiv}CC_6H_5$ (60%)	*180,78, 179*
$BrCH_2(C_2H_5O)CHBr$	$n\text{-}C_6H_{13}C{\equiv}CMgBr$	$BrCH_2(C_2H_5O)CHC{\equiv}C\text{-}n\text{-}C_6H_{13}$ (85%)	*6*
$BrCH_2(C_2H_5O)CHBr$	$n\text{-}C_8H_{17}C{\equiv}CMgBr$	$BrCH_2(C_2H_5O)CHC{\equiv}C\text{-}n\text{-}C_8H_{17}$ (81%)	*6*
$BrCH_2(C_2H_5O)CHBr$ (0.72 mole)	$4\text{-}C_6H_5CH_2CH_2C_6H_4MgBr$ (0.71 mole)	$BrCH_2(C_2H_5O)CHC_6H_4\text{-}4\text{-}CH_2CH_2C_6H_5$ (53%)*	*254*
$BrCH_2(C_2H_5O)CHBr$ (0.1 mole)	$4\text{-}C_6H_5CH_2CH_2C_6H_4MgBr$ (0.1 mole $C_{14}H_{13}Br$)	$BrCH_2(C_2H_5O)CHC_6H_4\text{-}4\text{-}CH_2CH_2C_6H_5$ (31%)†	*254*
C_4H_9Cl			
$t\text{-}C_4H_9Cl$	CH_3MgCl	$C(CH_3)_4$ (42–50%)	*236*
$t\text{-}C_4H_9Cl$ (400 g.)	C_2H_5MgBr (654 g. C_2H_5Br) + CuI (20 g.)	$t\text{-}C_4H_9C_2H_5$ (11%)	*150*
$t\text{-}C_4H_9Cl$	$n\text{-}C_3H_7MgBr$ + CuI	$t\text{-}C_4H_9\text{-}n\text{-}C_3H_7$ (21%)	*150*
$t\text{-}C_4H_9Cl$ (4 moles)	$n\text{-}C_3H_7MgBr$ (4 moles C_3H_7Br) + $HgCl_2$ (30 g.)	$t\text{-}C_4H_9\text{-}n\text{-}C_3H_7$ (21%); C_8H_{18}; C_6H_{14}; olefins	*52; cf. 241*
$t\text{-}C_4H_9Cl$	$n\text{-}C_4H_9MgBr$ + CuI	$t\text{-}C_4H_9\text{-}n\text{-}C_4H_9$ (14%)	*150*
$t\text{-}C_4H_9Cl$ (5.5 moles) + $t\text{-}C_4H_9I$ (0.5 mole)	$t\text{-}C_4H_9MgCl$ (6.0 moles) + CuCl (20 g.)	$(t\text{-}C_4H_9\text{—})_2$ (122 g.)	*150*
$t\text{-}C_4H_9Cl$	$t\text{-}C_4H_9MgBr$	$(t\text{-}C_4H_9\text{—})_2$ (4%)	*240*
$t\text{-}C_4H_9Cl$	$n\text{-}C_5H_{11}MgBr$ + CuI	$t\text{-}C_4H_9\text{-}n\text{-}C_5H_{11}$ (17%)	*150*

* Slow addition of Grignard reagent solution to bromide; forty-eight hours stirring.
† Slow addition of bromide to Grignard reagent solution; twenty-two hours stirring.

TABLE XVI-I (Continued)

Halide	RMgX	Product(s)	Ref.
C_4H_9Cl (*cont.*)			
t-C_4H_9Cl (40 g.)	2,4-$(CH_3)_2C_6H_3MgI$ (53 g. C_8H_9I)	*t*-$C_4H_9C_6H_3$-2,4-$(CH_3)_2$ (2.5 g.)	*209*
C_4H_9ClO			
n-$C_3H_7OCH_2Cl$ (0.1 mole)	$C_6H_5CH_2MgCl$ (0.1 mole C_7H_7Cl)	$C_6H_5CH_2CH_2O$-*n*-C_3H_7 (95.0*x*%); 2-$CH_3C_6H_4CH_2O$-*n*-C_3H_7 (2.5*x*%); 4-$CH_3C_6H_4CH_2O$-*n*-C_3H_7 (2.5*x*%)	*263*
$CH_3(C_2H_5O)CHCl$	$C_6H_5C\equiv CMgBr$	$CH_3(C_2H_5O)CHC\equiv CC_6H_5$ (50%)	*180*
$C_4H_9ClO_2$			
$CH_3OCH_2CH(OH)CH_2Cl$	C_6H_5MgBr	$CH_3OCH_2CH(OH)CH_2C_6H_5$	*187*
C_4H_9Br			
n-C_4H_9Br	$HC\equiv CMgBr$	*n*-$C_4H_9C\equiv CH$ (72%)	*90,196, 219*
n-C_4H_9Br	$C_6H_5MgBr + FeCl_3$ (trace)	*n*-$C_4H_9C_6H_5$ (50–60%)	*282,225*
n-C_4H_9Br	$C_6H_5CH_2MgBr + FeCl_3$ (trace)	*n*-$C_5H_{11}C_6H_5$	*225*
n-C_4H_9Br	1-$C_{10}H_7MgBr + FeCl_3$ (trace)	1-*n*-$C_4H_9C_{10}H_7$ (50–60%)	*282*
n-C_4H_9Br	9-Fluorenyl-MgBr	No reaction*	*155*
n-C_4H_9Br	9-Phenanthryl-MgBr	9-*n*-Butylphenanthrene (52%)	*155*
i-C_4H_9Br	C_6H_5MgBr	*i*-$C_4H_9C_6H_5$ (20%); $(C_6H_5—)_2$	*212*
i-C_4H_9Br	$C_6H_5MgBr + FeCl_3$ (trace)	*i*-$C_4H_9C_6H_5$	*282,225*
(−)-*s*-C_4H_9Br, $[\alpha]_D^{25}$ − 16.80 (21.2 g., 0.155 mole)	$C_6H_5CH_2MgCl$ (76.0 g., 0.600 mole C_7H_7Cl)	*s*-$C_4H_9CH_2C_6H_5$, $[\alpha]_D^{25}$ + 0.64 (3.8 g., 17%)	*286*
s-C_4H_9Br (46 g.)	$C_6H_5CH_2MgCl$ (50 g. C_7H_7Cl)	*s*-$C_4H_9CH_2C_6H_5$ (5 g., 10%)	*261*
t-C_4H_9Br	CH_3MgI	$(CH_3)_2C=CH_2$ (38.7%); CH_4; $C(CH_3)_4$; $(t\text{-}C_4H_9—)_2$	*212*

* Five hours reflux in xylene.

TABLE XVI-I (Continued)

Halide	RMgX	Product(s)	Ref.
C_4H_9Br (*cont.*)			
t-C_4H_9Br	CH_3MgI	$C(CH_3)_4$ (18.2%)	*236*
t-C_4H_9Br	C_6H_5MgBr	*t*-$C_4H_9C_6H_5$ (33%); $(CH_3)_2C{=}CH_2$; $(C_6H_5-)_2$	*212*
t-C_4H_9Br	$C_6H_5CH_2MgCl$	*t*-$C_4H_9CH_2C_6H_5$ (*ca.* 30%); $(C_6H_5CH_2-)_2$	*31*
t-C_4H_9Br	3-CH_3-5-$CH_3OC_6H_3MgBr$	*t*-$C_4H_9C_6H_3$-3-CH_3-5-OCH_3	*48*
t-C_4H_9Br	1-$C_{10}H_7MgBr$	1-*t*-$C_4H_9C_{10}H_7$ ("a little"); (1,1′-$C_{10}H_7-)_2$; $C_{10}H_8$	*212*
t-C_4H_9Br	$(C_6H_5)_3CMgBr$	$(C_6H_5)_3CH$ (73%)	*10*
C_4H_9BrO			
$CH_3CH(OH)CH(CH_3)Br$	CH_3MgI (2 equiv.)	"Hexene"* b. 69–70° (13%)	*79*
$CH_3CH(OH)CH(CH_3)Br$ (0.65 mole)	C_2H_5MgBr (1.30 mole)	$CH_3COC_2H_5$ (1.0 g.); *n*-$C_3H_7(CH_3)_2COH$ (17.4 g., 26%); $CH_3(C_2H_5)_2COH$ (0.6 g.)	*41*
C_4H_9I			
t-C_4H_9I	CH_3MgI	$C(CH_3)_4$ (15–20%)	*55*
t-C_4H_9I	$C_6H_5CH_2MgCl$	*t*-$C_4H_9CH_2C_6H_5$ (30%); $(C_6H_5CH_2-)_2$	*31*
t-C_4H_9I	3-CH_3-5-$CH_3OC_6H_3MgBr$	*t*-$C_4H_9C_6H_3$-3-CH_3-5-OCH_3	*48*
$C_4H_{10}ClN$			
$(CH_3)_2NCH_2CH_2Cl$ (330 g., 2.44 moles)	$H_2C{=}CHCH_2MgCl$ (230 g. C_3H_5Cl)	$(CH_3)_2N(CH_2)_3CH{=}CH_2$ (85%)	*119*

* In a personal communication from D. L. Cottle to Gaylord and Becker, *Chem. Revs.*, *49*, 471 (1950), it is stated that this product has been identified as 3-methyl-2-pentene.

TABLE XVI-I (Continued)

Halide	RMgX	Product(s)	Ref.
C_5H_5IO			
2-Iodomethylfuran* (from 6 g. $C_4H_6O_2$)	*n*-C_3H_7MgI (65 g. C_3H_7I)	2-*n*-Butylfuran	*132*
2-Iodomethylfuran* (from 6 g. $C_4H_6O_2$)	*i*-C_4H_9MgI (70 g. C_4H_9I)	2-Isoamylfuran	*132*
2-Iodomethylfuran*	*i*-$C_5H_{11}MgI$	2-Isohexylfuran	*132*
C_5H_7Cl			
3-Chlorocyclopentene (8.7 moles)	CH_3MgCl (12 moles)	3-Methylcyclopentene (23.7%)†	*42*
3-Chlorocyclopentene (8.5 moles)	C_2H_5MgCl (12 moles)	3-Ethylcyclopentene (48.3%)†	*42*
3-Chlorocyclopentene (3.0 moles)	C_2H_5MgBr (3.7 moles)	3-Ethylcyclopentene (42.7%)‡	*42,228*
3-Chlorocyclopentene (14.1 moles)	*n*-C_3H_7MgCl (20 moles)	3-*n*-Propylcyclopentene (47.5%)†	*42*
3-Chlorocyclopentene (7.34 moles)	*n*-C_3H_7MgBr (8 moles)	3-*n*-Propylcyclopentene (37.9%)‡	*42*
3-Chlorocyclopentene (8.95 moles)	*n*-C_3H_7MgBr (11 moles)	3-*n*-Propylcyclopentene (15.6%)§	*42*
3-Chlorocyclopentene (9.32 moles)	*n*-C_3H_7MgBr (12 moles)	3-*n*-Propylcyclopentene (41.1%)†	*42*
3-Chlorocyclopentene (14.6 moles)	*n*-C_3H_7MgBr (18 moles)	3-*n*-Propylcyclopentene (17.8%)¶	*42*
3-Chlorocyclopentene (9.2 moles)	*i*-C_3H_7MgCl (12 moles)	3-Isopropylcyclopentene (27.6%)†	*42*
3-Chlorocyclopentene (3.7 moles)	*i*-C_3H_7MgBr (3.7 moles)	3-Isopropylcyclopentene (20.0%)‡	*42*
3-Chlorocyclopentene (3.1 moles)	*n*-C_4H_9MgBr (5 moles)	3-*n*-Butylcyclopentene (46.3%)‡	*42*
3-Chlorocyclopentene (3.1 moles)	*i*-C_4H_9MgBr (5 moles)	3-Isobutylcyclopentene (39.0%)‡	*42*
3-Chlorocyclopentene (13.7 moles)	*s*-C_4H_9MgBr (18 moles)	3-*s*-Butylcyclopentene (23.7%)†	*42*

* The alcohol was added to an excess of RMgI with which it presumably reacted as follows:

$$(C_4H_3O)CH_2OH \xrightarrow{RMgI} (C_4H_3O)CH_2OMgI + RH \xrightarrow{MgI_2} (C_4H_3O)CH_2I + MgO + MgI_2.$$

† Normal order of addition; copper reaction vessel.
‡ Normal order of addition; glass reaction vessel.
§ Reverse order of addition; copper reaction vessel.
¶ Normal order of addition; steel reaction vessel.

TABLE XVI-I (Continued)

Halide	RMgX	Product(s)	Ref.
C_5H_7Cl (*cont.*)			
3-Chlorocyclopentene (14.2 moles)	t-C_4H_9MgBr (18 moles)	3-*t*-Butylcyclopentene (2.0%)*	*42*
3-Chlorocyclopentene	$(CH_2)_4CHMgBr$	3-Cyclopentylcyclopentene (*ca.* 60%)	*228*
3-Chlorocyclopentene	n-$C_5H_{11}MgBr$	3-*n*-Amylcyclohexene (43%)	*171*
3-Chlorocyclopentene	i-$C_5H_{11}MgBr$	3-Isoamylcyclopentene (60%)	*228*
3-Chlorocyclopentene	C_6H_5MgBr	3-Cyclopentenylbenzene (75%)	*229*
3-Chlorocyclopentene	$(CH_2)_5CHMgBr$	3-Cyclopentenylcyclohexane (*ca.* 60%)	*228*
3-Chlorocyclopentene	n-$C_6H_{13}MgBr$	3-*n*-Hexylcyclopentene (38%)	*171*
3-Chlorocyclopentene	3-Ethylcyclopentylyl-MgBr	1-Ethyl-3-(3-cyclopentenyl)cyclopentane (34%)	*230*
3-Chlorocyclopentene	n-$C_7H_{15}MgBr$	3-*n*-Heptylcyclopentene (50%)	*230*
3-Chlorocyclopentene	3-Bicyclopentyl-MgBr	"Quatercyclopentyl" (12%); 3-(3-Cyclopentenyl)bicyclopentyl (20%)	*230*
3-Chlorocyclopentene	n-$C_{12}H_{25}MgCl$	3-*n*-Dodecylcyclopentene (*ca.* 50%)	*228*
C_5H_7I			
n-$C_3H_7C\equiv CI$	n-$C_3H_7C\equiv CMgI$	$(n$-$C_3H_7C\equiv C—)_2$ (*ca.* 60%)	*91*
$C_5H_8Cl_2O$			
2,3-Dichlorotetrahydropyran	n-C_4H_9MgCl	2-*n*-Butyl-3-chlorotetrahydropyran (70%)	*169,168*
2,3-Dichlorotetrahydropyran	C_6H_5MgBr	2-Phenyl-3-chlorotetrahydropyran (70%)	*168*
$C_5H_8Br_2O$			
2,3-Dibromotetrahydropyran	C_2H_5MgX	2-Ethyl-3-bromotetrahydropyran (<75%)†	*167*
2,3-Dibromotetrahydropyran	C_6H_5MgX	2-Phenyl-3-bromotetrahydropyran (<75%)†	*167*

* Normal order of addition; copper reaction vessel.

† Yields are reported to be somewhat less for the dibromo compound than in corresponding reactions of the monobromo derivative (*i.e.*, *ca.* 75–85%).

TABLE XVI-I (Continued)

Halide	RMgX	Product(s)	Ref.
C_5H_9Cl			
$CH_3(CH_3CH{=}CH)CHCl$	n-C_3H_7MgCl	$CH_3(CH_3CH{=}CH)CH$-n-C_3H_7	98
C_5H_9Br			
$C_2H_5CH{=}CHCH_2Br$	C_2H_5MgBr (slight excess)	$C_2H_5CH{=}CH$-n-C_3H_7 (1 part); $(C_2H_5)_2CHCH{=}CH_2$ (3–4 parts)*	174,172
$C_2H_5CH{=}CHCH_2Br$	C_6H_5MgBr (slight excess)	$C_2H_5CH{=}CHCH_2C_6H_5$ (1 part); $C_2H_5(C_6H_5)CHCH{=}CH_2$ (2–3 parts)†	174
$CH_3(CH_3CH{=}CH)CHBr$	CH_3MgBr	$CH_3CH{=}CH(CH_3)_2CH$ (57%)	160
$CH_3(CH_3CH{=}CH)CHBr$	n-C_3H_7MgBr	$CH_3(CH_3CH{=}CH)CH$-n-C_3H_7 (27%)	160
$CH_3(CH_3CH{=}CH)CHBr$	n-C_4H_9MgBr	$CH_3(CH_3CH{=}CH)CH$-n-C_4H_9 (28%)	160
$CH_3(CH_3CH{=}CH)CHBr$	i-C_4H_9MgBr	$CH_3(CH_3CH{=}CH)CH$-i-C_4H_9 (36%)	160
$CH_3(CH_3CH{=}CH)CHBr$	s-C_4H_9MgBr	$CH_3(CH_3CH{=}CH)CH$-s-C_4H_9 (8%)	160
$CH_3(CH_3CH{=}CH)CHBr$	t-C_4H_9MgCl	$CH_3(CH_3CH{=}CH)CH$-t-C_4H_9 (5%)	160
$CH_3(CH_3CH{=}CH)CHBr$	$(CH_2)_4CHMgBr$	$CH_3(CH_3CH{=}CH)CHCH(CH_2)_4$ (15%)	160
C_5H_9BrO			
2-Bromotetrahydropyran	C_2H_5MgX	2-Ethyltetrahydropyran (75–85%)	167
2-Bromotetrahydropyran	n-C_3H_7MgX	2-*n*Propyltetrahydropyran (75–85%)	167
2-Bromotetrahydropyran	C_6H_5MgX .	2-Phenyltetrahydropyran (75–85%)	167
$C_5H_{10}Br_2O$			
$BrCH_2(n$-$C_3H_7O)CHBr$	CH_3MgBr (slight excess)	$BrCH_2(n$-$C_3H_7O)CHCH_3$ (61%)	51
$BrCH_2(n$-$C_3H_7O)CHBr$	C_2H_5MgBr (slight excess)	$BrCH_2(n$-$C_3H_7O)CHC_2H_5$ (73%)	51
$BrCH_2(n$-$C_3H_7O)CHBr$	n-C_3H_7MgBr (slight excess)	$BrCH_2(n$-$C_3H_7O)CH$-n-C_3H_7 (70%)	51
$BrCH_2(n$-$C_3H_7O)CHBr$	i-C_3H_7MgBr (slight excess)	$BrCH_2(n$-$C_3H_7O)CH$-i-C_3H_7 (34%)	51

* Total yield, based on bromide, *ca.* 80%.

† The total yield is reported as "excellent".

TABLE XVI-I (Continued)

Halide	RMgX	Product(s)	Ref.
$C_5H_{10}Br_2O$ (*cont.*)			
$BrCH_2(n\text{-}C_3H_7O)CHBr$	$n\text{-}C_4H_9MgBr$ (slight excess)	$BrCH_2(n\text{-}C_3H_7O)CH\text{-}n\text{-}C_4H_9$ (81%)	*51*
$BrCH_2(n\text{-}C_3H_7O)CHBr$	$i\text{-}C_5H_{11}MgBr$ (slight excess)	$BrCH_2(n\text{-}C_3H_7O)CH\text{-}i\text{-}C_5H_{11}$ (58%)	*51*
$BrCH_2(n\text{-}C_3H_7O)CHBr$	C_6H_5MgBr (slight excess)	$BrCH_2(n\text{-}C_3H_7O)CHC_6H_5$ (72%)	*51*
$BrCH_2(CH_3)(C_2H_5O)CBr$	$n\text{-}C_4H_9MgBr$	$BrCH_2(CH_3)(C_2H_5O)C\text{-}n\text{-}C_4H_9$ (35%)	*210*
$BrCH_2(CH_3)(C_2H_5O)CBr$	$i\text{-}C_4H_9MgBr$	$BrCH_2(CH_3)(C_2H_5O)C\text{-}i\text{-}C_4H_9$ (42%)	*210*
$BrCH_2(CH_3)(C_2H_5O)CBr$	$s\text{-}C_4H_9MgBr$	$BrCH_2(CH_3)(C_2H_5O)\text{-}s\text{-}C_4H_9$ (21–25%)	*210*
$CH_3CHBr(C_2H_5O)CHBr$	$H_2C{=}CHCH_2MgBr$ (slight excess)	$CH_3CHBr(C_2H_5O)CHCH_2CH{=}CH_2$ (38–43%)	*205*
$CH_3CHBr(C_2H_5O)CHBr$	$n\text{-}C_3H_7MgBr$ (10–30% excess)	$CH_3CHBr(C_2H_5O)CH\text{-}n\text{-}C_3H_7$ (60%)	*202*
$CH_3CHBr(C_2H_5O)CHBr$	$i\text{-}C_3H_7MgBr$ (10–30% excess)	$CH_3CHBr(C_2H_5O)CH\text{-}i\text{-}C_3H_7$ (55%)	*202*
$CH_3CHBr(C_2H_5O)CHBr$	$n\text{-}C_4H_9MgBr$	$CH_3CHBr(C_2H_5O)CH\text{-}n\text{-}C_4H_9$ (69%)	*210*
$CH_3CHBr(C_2H_5O)CHBr$	$i\text{-}C_4H_9MgBr$	$CH_3CHBr(C_2H_5O)CH\text{-}i\text{-}C_4H_9$ (49%)	*210*
$CH_3CHBr(C_2H_5O)CHBr$	$s\text{-}C_4H_9MgBr$	$CH_3CHBr(C_2H_5O)CH\text{-}s\text{-}C_4H_9$ (31%)	*210*
$C_2H_5CHBr(CH_3O)CHBr$	C_2H_5MgBr (10–30% excess)	$C_2H_5CHBr(CH_3O)CHC_2H_5$ (68%)	*202*
$C_5H_{11}Cl$			
$t\text{-}C_5H_{11}Cl$ (6 moles)	C_2H_5MgBr (9 moles) + $HgCl_2$ (30 g.)	$t\text{-}C_5H_{11}C_2H_5$ (13–27%); $C_{10}H_{22}$; C_4H_{10}; olefins	*52; cf. 241*
$t\text{-}C_5H_{11}Cl$	C_2H_5MgBr + CuI	$t\text{-}C_5H_{11}C_2H_5$ (22%)	*150*
$t\text{-}C_5H_{11}Cl$	$n\text{-}C_3H_7Br$	$t\text{-}C_5H_{11}\text{-}n\text{-}C_3H_7$ (15%); $C_{10}H_{22}$; unidentified gases	*212*
$t\text{-}C_5H_{11}Cl$	$n\text{-}C_3H_7MgBr$ + CuI	$t\text{-}C_5H_{11}\text{-}n\text{-}C_3H_7$ (17%)	*150*
$t\text{-}C_5H_{11}Cl$	$n\text{-}C_4H_9MgBr$ + CuI	$t\text{-}C_5H_{11}\text{-}n\text{-}C_4H_9$ (16%)	*150*
$t\text{-}C_5H_{11}Cl$	$n\text{-}C_5H_{11}MgBr$ + CuI	$t\text{-}C_5H_{11}\text{-}n\text{-}C_5H_{11}$ (11%)	*150*
$C_5H_{11}ClO$			
$n\text{-}C_4H_9OCH_2Cl$ (0.29 mole)	Butenyl-MgBr (0.29 mole)	$n\text{-}C_4H_9OCH_2CH(CH_3)CH{=}CH_2$ (29.3 g., 70%); octadienes	*245*

TABLE XVI-I (Continued)

Halide	RMgX	Product(s)	Ref.
$C_5H_{11}ClO$ (*cont.*)			
n-$C_3H_7CH(OH)CH_2Cl$ (0.32 mole)	C_2H_5MgBr (0.636 mole)	Recovered chlorohydrin; $(n\text{-}C_3H_7)_2CHOH$	*148*
$CH_3(HO)CH(CH_3)_2CCl$	CH_3MgBr	i-$C_3H_7(CH_3)_2COH$	*100*
n-$C_3H_7(CH_3O)CHCl$ (0.1 mole)	$C_6H_5CH_2MgCl$ (0.1 mole C_7H_7Cl)	$C_6H_5CH_2CH(OCH_3)$-n-C_3H_7 (98x%); $2\text{-}CH_3C_6H_4CH(OCH_3)$-$n$-$C_3H_7$ (2x%)	*263*
$C_5H_{11}Br$			
i-$C_5H_{11}Br$	i-$C_5H_{11}MgBr$	$(i\text{-}C_5H_{11}—)_2$ (9%);* $CH_3CH{=}C(CH_3)_2$; C_5H_{10}	*212*
$(C_2H_5)_2CHBr$	$(C_2H_5)_2CHMgBr$	$[(C_2H_5)CH{=}]_2$ (15%)†; unidentified gases	*212*
$(C_2H_5)_2CHBr$	C_6H_5MgBr	$(C_2H_5)_2CHC_6H_5$ (51%); $(C_6H_5—)_2$	*212*
t-$C_5H_{11}Br$	n-C_3H_7MgBr	t-C_5H_{11}-n-C_3H_7 (*ca.* 15%); $C_{10}H_{22}$	*212*
t-$C_5H_{11}Br$ (353 g.)	n-$C_4H_9C{\equiv}CMgBr$ (246 g. C_6H_{10})	t-$C_5H_{11}C{\equiv}C$-n-C_4H_9 (13 g., 3%)	*287*
$C_5H_{11}I$			
$(C_2H_5)_2CHI$	C_6H_5MgBr	$(C_2H_5)_2CHC_6H_5$ (5.4%); C_6H_6; $C_{10}H_{22}$; $(C_6H_5—)_2$	*212*
C_6Cl_6			
C_6Cl_6	RMgX‡	No reaction	*50*
C_6Br_6			
C_6Br_6	CH_3MgI	$(CH_3)_6C_6$	*50*

* Späth (*212*) did not attempt to distinguish between the 2,7-dimethyloctane formed during the preparation of the Grignard reagent and that (if any) formed subsequently.

† Späth (*212*) did not attempt to distinguish between the 3,4-diethylhexane formed during the preparation of the Grignard reagent and that (if any) formed subsequently.

‡ RMgX = CH_3MgI, C_6H_5Br.

TABLE XVI-I (Continued)

Halide	RMgX	Product(s)	Ref.
C_6Br_6 (*cont.*)			
C_6Br_6 (10 g.)	C_6H_5MgBr (8.07 equiv.)	1,2,4,5-$(C_6H_5)_4C_6H_2$ (0.50 g.); 1,2,4,5-$Br_4C_6H_2$ (0.20 g.)*	*70,46,50*
C_6I_6			
C_6I_6	CH_3MgI	Mostly tar; trace $(CH_3)_6C_6$	*50*
C_6I_6	C_6H_5MgBr	1,2,4,5-$(C_6H_5)_4C_6H_2$†	*50*
$C_6H_4Cl_2$			
C_6H_4-1,2-Cl_2 (1.5 g.)	4-$CH_3OC_6H_4MgBr$ (5.6 g. C_7H_7BrO)	1,2-(*p*-$CH_3OC_6H_4)_2C_6H_4$ (*ca.* 50 mg.)	*280*
C_6H_5Br			
C_6H_5Br	CH_3MgBr + $FeCl_3$ (trace)	$C_6H_5CH_3$ (10%)	*282*
C_6H_5Br	C_2H_5MgBr (2 equiv.) + $FeCl_3$ (trace)	C_6H_5MgBr; $MgBr_2$; C_2H_6; C_2H_4	*282*
C_6H_5Br	C_6H_5MgBr	C_6H_5Br; $(C_6H_5—)_2$ (13%)‡	*212*
C_6H_5I			
C_6H_5I (41 g.)	C_6H_5MgI (41 g. C_6H_5I)	$(C_6H_5—)_2$ (2.5 g.)§	*131*

*Comparable yields of tetrabromoterephthalic acid were obtained upon carbonation of the reaction mixture and subsequent hydrolysis.

†This product is reported by Durand and Wai-Hsun (*50*) as $(C_6H_5)_6C$; *cf.*, however, Geissman and Mallat (*70*) and Dilthey and Hurtig (*46*).

‡Spăth did not attempt to distinguish between the biphenyl formed in the preparation of the Grignard reagent and that (if any) formed subsequently. In control experiments conducted in connection with a study of the effects of metallic halides on the reactions of aryl Grignard reagents with organic halides, Kharasch and Fields, *J. Am. Chem. Soc.*, *63*, 2316–20 (1941), found 6–8 percent of biphenyl in phenylmagnesium bromide preparations.

§See footnote to preceding entry.

TABLE XVI-I (Continued)

Halide	RMgX	Product(s)	Ref.
$C_6H_6Cl_2$			
4-$ClC_6H_4CH_2Cl$ (3.5 g.)	$C_6H_5CH_2(C_{12}H_8=)CC(=C_{12}H_8)MgCl$*†	4-$ClC_6H_4CH_2(C_{12}H_8=)CC(=C_{12}H_8)$-$CH_2C_6H_5$* (1.69 g.)	66
$C_6H_8Br_2$			
$(-HC=CHCH_2Br)_2$	C_2H_5MgBr	*n*-$C_3H_7CH=CHCH(C_2H_5)CH=CH_2$; (*n*-$C_3H_7CH=CH-)_2$; $[H_2C=CH(C_2H_5)CH-]_2$; C_2H_5(*n*-$C_3H_7)CHCH=CHCH=CH_2$ (?); $BrCH_2(C_2H_5)CHCH=CHCH=CH_2$ (?); + unidentified products	293
C_6H_9Cl			
$CH_3C\equiv C(CH_3)_2CCl$ (40 g.)	CH_3MgBr (52 g. CH_3Br)	$[(CH_3)_2C=]_2C$ (50%)	248
$CH_3C\equiv C(CH_3)_2CCl$ (40 g.)	C_6H_5MgBr (50 g. C_6H_5Br)	$(CH_3)_2C=C=C(CH_3)C_6H_5$ (40%)	248
3-Chlorocyclohexene	CH_3MgBr	3-Methylcyclohexene	257
3-Chlorocyclohexene	C_2H_5MgBr	3-Ethylcyclohexene (15%); 3,3′-bicyclohexenyl (75%)	16
3-Chlorocyclohexene	RMgBr‡	3-R-cyclohexene (*ca.* 70%);§ RH; bicyclohexenyl; 1,3-cyclohexadiene	288
C_6H_9X			
3-Halocyclohexene	RMgX¶	3-R-cyclohexene	15

* $(C_{12}H_8=)$ = *o*-biphenylene.

† The Grignard reagent was prepared by the addition of $C_6H_5CH_2MgCl$ to 3.28 g. of $[(C_{12}H_8=)C=]_2$.

‡ R = CH_3, C_2H_5, *n*-C_3H_7, *i*-C_3H_7, *n*-C_4H_9, C_6H_5, $C_6H_5CH_2$.

§ At -12° or 0°; at higher temperatures the proportion of "normal" product decreases and those of the byproducts increase.

¶ R = CH_3, C_2H_5, C_6H_5.

TABLE XVI-I (Continued)

Halide	RMgX	Product(s)	Ref.
$C_6H_{10}Br_2$			
1,2-Dibromocyclohexane	n-C_3H_5MgBr	Cyclohexene; n-C_6H_{13}	*159*
1,2-Dibromocyclohexane	$(CH_2)_5CHMgCl$	Cyclohexene; bicyclohexyl (?)*	*159*
$C_6H_{11}ClO$			
$CH_3O(CH_2)_2CH{=}CHCH_2Cl$ (30 g.)	C_6H_5MgBr (35 g. C_6H_5Br)	$CH_3OCH_2CH_2CH(C_6H_5)CH{=}CH_2$ (7.7 g.); $CH_3OCH_2CH_2CH{=}CHCH_2C_6H_5$ (17.0 g.)	*175*
$CH_3OCH_2CH_2(H_2C{=}CH)CHCl$ (30 g.)	C_6H_5MgBr (35 g. C_6H_5Br)	$CH_3OCH_2CH_2CH(C_6H_5)CH{=}CH_2$ (8.8 g.); $CH_3OCH_2CH_2CH{=}CHCH_2C_6H_5$ (15.5 g.)	*175*
$CH_3OCH_2CH{=}C(CH_3)CH_2Cl$	$R(CH_3)(BrMgO)CC{\equiv}CMgBr$†	$CH_3OCH_2CH{=}C(CH_3)CH_2C{\equiv}CC(OH)(CH_3)R$†	*164*
2-Chlorocyclohexanol (27 g.)	CH_3MgI (60 g. CH_3I)	$(CH_2)_4CHCH(OH)CH_3$‡ (24 g., *ca.* 50%)	*247*
2-Chlorocyclohexanol	$(CH_2)_5CHMgCl$	$(CH_2)_4CH[(CH_2)_5CH]CHOH$	*224*
2-Chlorocyclohexanol	$C_6H_5CH_2MgCl$	$(CH_2)_4CH(C_6H_5CH_2)CHOH$	*269*
$C_6H_{12}ClN$			
2-Chlorocyclohexylamine	C_2H_5MgBr	Recovered chloride (quant.)§	*156*
2-Chlorocyclohexylamine	C_2H_5MgBr	$(CH_2)_5CO$ (*ca.* quant.)¶	*156*
$C_6H_{12}Cl_3N$			
$N(CH_2CH_2Cl)_3$ (1 mole)	$H_2C{=}CHCH_2MgCl$ (3 moles)	$N[(CH_2)_3CH{=}CH_2]_3$ (90%)	*119*

* The reaction is said to be analogous to that with n-C_3H_7MgBr.

† R = β-(2,6,6-Trimethyl-1-cyclohexenyl)vinyl.

‡ This product was originally reported by Godchot and Bedos (*75*) as a mixture of *cis*- and *trans*-2-methylcyclohexanols.

§ Combination in Et_2O solution.

¶ Combination in Et_2O solution; distillation of Et_2O; fusion of residue.

TABLE XVI-I (Continued)

Halide	RMgX	Product(s)	Ref.
$C_6H_{12}Br_2O$			
$BrCH_2(n\text{-}C_4H_9O)CHBr$	$i\text{-}C_5H_{11}MgBr$ (slight excess)	$BrCH_2(n\text{-}C_4H_9O)CH\text{-}i\text{-}C_5H_{11}$ (65%)	51
$C_2H_5CHBr(C_2H_5O)CHBr$	$H_2C{=}CHCH_2MgBr$ (slight excess)	$C_2H_5CHBr(C_2H_5O)CHCH_2CH{=}CH_2$ (37–45%)	205
$C_2H_5CHBr(C_2H_5O)CHBr$	$n\text{-}C_3H_7MgBr$	$C_2H_5CHBr(C_2H_5O)CH\text{-}n\text{-}C_3H_7$ (30–32%)	210
$C_2H_5CHBr(C_2H_5O)CHBr$	$i\text{-}C_3H_7MgBr$	$C_2H_5CHBr(C_2H_5O)CH\text{-}i\text{-}C_3H_7$ (20–35%)	210
$(CH_3)_2CBr(C_2H_5O)CHBr$	C_2H_5MgBr (10–30% excess)	$(CH_3)_2CBr(C_2H_5O)CHC_2H_5$ (49%)	202
$BrCH_2(C_2H_5)(C_2H_5O)CBr$	C_2H_5MgBr (10–30% excess)	$BrCH_2(C_2H_5O)C(C_2H_5)_2$ (55%)	202
$BrCH_2(C_2H_5)(C_2H_5O)CBr$	$n\text{-}C_8H_7MgBr$	$BrCH_2(C_2H_5)(C_2H_5O)C\text{-}n\text{-}C_3H_7$ (30%)	210
$BrCH_2(C_2H_5)(C_2H_5O)CBr$	$i\text{-}C_3H_7MgBr$	$BrCH_2(C_2H_5)(C_2H_5O)C\text{-}i\text{-}C_3H_7$ (42%)	210
$CH_3(CH_3CHBr)(C_2H_5O)CBr$	C_2H_5MgBr	$CH_3(CH_3CHBr)(C_2H_5O)CC_2H_5$ (40%)	210
$CH_3(CH_3CHBr)(C_2H_5O)CBr$	$n\text{-}C_3H_7MgBr$	$CH_3(CH_3CHBr)(C_2H_5O)C\text{-}n\text{-}C_3H_7$ (26%)	210
$CH_3(CH_3CHBr)(C_2H_5O)CBr$	$i\text{-}C_3H_7MgBr$	$CH_3(CH_3CHBr)(C_2H_5O)C\text{-}i\text{-}C_3H_7$ (22%)	210
$C_6H_{13}Cl$			
$i\text{-}C_3H_7(CH_3)_2CCl$	CH_3MgCl	$i\text{-}C_3H_7C(CH_3)_3$	194
$C_6H_{13}Br$			
$n\text{-}C_3H_7(CH_3)_2CBr$	CH_3MgI	"Impracticable"	45
$C_6H_{13}BrO$			
$n\text{-}C_5H_{11}OCH_2Br$	C_2H_5MgBr	$n\text{-}C_5H_{11}O\text{-}n\text{-}C_3H_7$ (60–65%)	94
$n\text{-}C_5H_{11}OCH_2Br$	$n\text{-}C_5H_{11}O(CH_2)_3MgI$	$[n\text{-}C_5H_{11}O(CH_2)_2\text{—}]_2$	95,97
$n\text{-}C_5H_{11}OCH_2Br$	$n\text{-}C_5H_{11}O(CH_2)_4MgI$	$[n\text{-}C_5H_{11}O(CH_2)_2]_2CH_2$	95,96,97
$C_6H_{14}ClN$			
$(C_2H_5)_2N(CH_2)_2Cl$	$H_2C{=}CHCH_2MgCl$	$(C_2H_5)_2N(CH_2)_3CH{=}CH_2$ (85%)	119,120
$(C_2H_5)_2N(CH_2)_2Cl$	$H_2C{=}C(CH_3)CH_2MgCl$	$(C_2H_5)_2N(CH_2)_3C(CH_3){=}CH_2$ (75–80%)	119

TABLE XVI-I (Continued)

Halide	RMgX	Product(s)	Ref.
$C_7H_5Cl_3$			
$4\text{-}ClC_6H_4CHCl_2$ (31.5 g.)	CH_3MgCl	$CH_3(4\text{-}ClC_6H_4)CHCHClC_6H_4\text{-}4\text{-}Cl$; (7.3 g., crude); $[CH_3(4\text{-}ClC_6H_4)CH—]_2$; $4\text{-}ClC_6H_4\text{-}i\text{-}C_3H_7$	*54*
$C_6H_5CCl_3$	CH_3MgCl (0.2 *M* sol'n)	$(C_6H_5CCl_2—)_2$	*67*
$C_6H_5CCl_3$	CH_3MgCl (2.0 *M* sol'n)	$(C_6H_5CCl=)_2$* (22%)	*67*
$C_6H_5CCl_3$	C_2H_5MgBr	$(C_6H_5CCl_2—)_2$; $(C_6H_5CCl=)_2$	*191*
$C_6H_5CCl_3$	C_6H_5MgBr	$(C_6H_5CCl_2—)_2$; $(C_6H_5CCl=)_2$; $[C_6H_5(C_6H_5CCl_2)CCl—]_2$	*191*
$C_7H_6Cl_2$			
$C_6H_5CHCl_2$ (25 g.)	CH_3MgCl	$CH_3(C_6H_5)CHCHClC_6H_5$ (5 g., crude); $[CH_3(C_6H_5)CH—]_2$ (2 forms); $C_6H_5\text{-}i\text{-}C_3H_7$	*54*
$C_6H_5CHCl_2$ (25 g.)	CH_3MgI (60 g. CH_3I)	$(C_6H_5CHCl—)_2$ (4.3 g., crude); brown oil	*67*
$C_6H_5CHCl_2$	C_6H_5MgBr	$(C_6H_5CHCl—)_2$; $(C_6H_5—)_2$; $(C_6H_5)_3CH$	*67*
$C_6H_5CHCl_2$ (20.6 g.)	C_6H_5MgBr (40.0 g. C_6H_5Br)	$(C_6H_5)_3CH$ (*ca.* 21%); $[(C_6H_5)_2CH—]_2$ (0.7 g.)	*186*
C_7H_7Cl			
$C_6H_5CH_2Cl$ (25 g.)	CH_3MgI (30 g. CH_3I)	$C_6H_5C_2H_5$ (5 g., 23.8%)†	*106*
$C_6H_5CH_2Cl$ (25 g.)	CH_3MgI (30 g. CH_3I)	$C_6H_5C_2H_5$ (*ca.* 25%)‡	*106*
$C_6H_5CH_2Cl$	CH_3MgI	$4\text{-}C_6H_5CH_2C_6H_4CH_2CH_2C_6H_5$§; $C_6H_5C_2H_5$ (37%); $(C_6H_5CH_2—)_2$ (24%)¶	*212*

* *Cis* and *trans* isomers in the approximate ratio of 1:5.

† Dropwise addition of chloride to Grignard reagent solution; distillation of Et_2O.

‡ Addition of chloride to Grignard reagent solution; addition of C_7H_8; distillation of Et_2O; one hour reflux.

§ Späth (*212*) reported this product as 1,2,3-triphenylpropane; *cf.*, however, Fuson, *J. Am. Chem. Soc.*, *48*, 2937–42 (1926).

¶ Five hours reflux in Et_2O.

TABLE XVI-I (Continued)

Halide	RMgX	Product(s)	Ref.
C_7H_7Cl (*cont.*)			
$C_6H_5CH_2Cl$	CH_3MgI (excess)	$C_6H_5C_2H_5$ (23–27%); $(C_6H_5CH_2—)_2$ (31–33%); C_2H_6 (33–35%)*	*60*
$C_6H_5CH_2Cl$	C_2H_5MgBr	C_6H_5-*n*-C_3H_7 (70%); $(C_6H_5CH_2—)_2$; C_2H_6; C_2H_4	*19*
$C_6H_5CH_2Cl$	*n*-C_3H_7MgBr	C_6H_5-*n*-C_4H_9 (26%)	*19*
$C_6H_5CH_2Cl$	*n*-C_4H_9MgBr	C_6H_5-*n*-C_5H_{11} (47%)	*19*
$C_6H_5CH_2Cl$ (46 g.)	*s*-C_4H_9MgBr (50 g. C_4H_9Br)	$C_6H_5CH_2$-*s*-C_4H_9 (9.8 g., 18%)	*261*
$C_6H_5CH_2Cl$	$C_6H_5CH_2MgCl$	$(C_6H_5CH_2—)_2$ (67.6%)†	*239*
$C_6H_5CH_2Cl$	2-Methylindolyl-MgI	2-Methyl-3-benzylindole; 2-methyl-3,3-dibenzylindolenine	*105*
$C_6H_5CH_2Cl$	$(C_6H_5)_3CMgBr$	$C_6H_5CH_2C(C_6H_5)_3$ (90%)	*10*
$C_6H_5CH_2Cl$ (2.78 g.)	4-$ClC_6H_4CH_2(C_{12}H_8{=})C$-$C({=}C_{12}H_8)MgCl$‡§	4-$ClC_6H_4CH_2(C_{12}H_8{=})CC$-$({=}C_{12}H_8)CH_2C_6H_5$‡ (0.37 g., 7%)	*66*
$C_6H_5CH_2Cl$ (3.00 g.)	$C_6H_5CH_2(C_{12}H_8{=})C$-$C({=}C_{12}H_8)MgCl$‡¶	$[C_6H_5CH_2(C_{12}H_8{=})C—]_2$‡	*66*
C_7H_7Br			
$C_6H_5CH_2Br$	CH_3MgI (excess)	$C_6H_5C_2H_5$ (20–23%); $(C_6H_5CH_2—)_2$ (34–37%); C_2H_6 (36–38%)	*60*
$C_6H_5CH_2Br$	$HC{\equiv}CMgBr$	$C_6H_5CH_2C{\equiv}CH$ (70%); $(C_6H_5CH_2C{\equiv})_2$ (8%); C_2H_2 (12%)	*90,196, 219*

* Slow dropwise addition of chloride to ethereal Grignard reagent solution at 40–50°.

† Whitmore and Sloat (*239*) do not distinguish between the bibenzyl formed during the preparation of the Grignard reagent and that formed subsequently.

‡ $(C_{12}H_8{=})$ = *o*-biphenylene.

§ The Grignard reagent was prepared by the addition of 4-$ClC_6H_4CH_2MgCl$ to 3.28 g. of $[(C_{12}H_8{=})C{=}]_2$.

¶ The Grignard reagent was prepared by the addition of $C_6H_5CH_2MgCl$ to 3.28 g. of $[(C_{12}H_8{=})C{=}]_2$.

TABLE XVI-I (Continued)

Halide	RMgX	Product(s)	Ref.
C_7H_7Br (*cont.*)			
$C_6H_5CH_2Br$	9-Fluorenyl-MgBr	$(C_6H_5CH_2—)_2$ (53%); 9,9′-bifluorenyl (85%)	*155*
C_7H_7I			
$C_6H_5CH_2I$	CH_3MgI (excess)	$C_6H_5C_2H_5$ (10%); $(C_6H_5CH_2—)_2$ ([illegible]%); C_2H_6 (40%)	*60*
$C_6H_5CH_2I$	C_2H_5MgI	C_6H_5-*n*-C_3H_7 (10.5%); 4-$C_6H_5CH_2C_6H_4CH_2CH_2C_6H_5$*	*212*
$C_7H_{11}Cl$			
3-Chloro-5-methylcyclohexene	CH_3MgI	3,5-Dimethylcyclohexene	*158*
$C_7H_{11}Br$			
1-Methyl-6-bromocyclohexene	CH_3MgBr	1,6-Dimethylcyclohexene	*93*
$C_7H_{11}I$			
n-$C_5H_{11}C{\equiv}CI$	*n*-$C_5H_{11}C{\equiv}CMgI$	(*n*-$C_5H_{11}C{\equiv}C—)_2$	*91*
$C_7H_{13}Cl$			
cis-1-Chloro-2-methylcyclohexane	CH_3MgBr	46% reaction; 1,2-dimethylcyclohexane (10%); methylcyclohexene (33%); CH_4	*118*
trans-1-Chloro-2-methylcyclohexane	CH_3MgBr	49% reaction; 1,2-dimethylcyclohexane (10%); methylcyclohexene (34%); CH_4	*118*
$C_7H_{13}ClO$			
$C_2H_5OCH_2CH_2CH{=}CHCH_2Cl$ (40.0 g.)	C_2H_5MgBr (37.0 g. C_2H_5Br)	Recovered $C_7H_{13}ClO$ (7.4 g.); $C_2H_5OCH_2CH_2CH{=}CH$-*n*-C_3H_7 (16.8 g.); $H_2C{=}CH(C_2H_5OCH_2CH_2)$-$(C_2H_5OCH_2CH_2CH{=}CHCH_2)CH$ (7.1 g.)	*289*

* Spä̈th (*212*) reported this product as 1,2,3-triphenylpropane; *cf.*, however, Fuson, *J. Am. Chem. Soc.*, *48*, 2937–42 (1926).

TABLE XVI-I (Continued)

Halide	RMgX	Product(s)	Ref.
$C_7H_{13}ClO$ (*cont.*)			
$C_2H_5OCH_2CH_2CH{=}CHCH_2Cl$ (30.0 g.)	*n*-C_4H_9MgBr (35.9 g. C_4H_9Br)	Recovered $C_7H_{13}ClO$ (3.6 g.); $C_2H_5OCH_2CH_2CH{=}CH$-*n*-C_5H_{11} (18.7 g.); $H_2C{=}CH(C_2H_5OCH_2CH_2)$-$(C_2H_5OCH_2CH_2CH{=}CHCH_2)CH$ (5.5 g.)	289
$H_2C{=}CH(C_2H_5OCH_2CH_2)CHCl$ (40.0 g.)	C_2H_5MgBr (37.0 C_2H_5Br)	Recovered $C_7H_{13}ClO$ (2.0 g.); $C_2H_5OCH_2CH_2CH{=}CH$-*n*-C_3H_7 (18.9 g.); $H_2C{=}CH(C_2H_5OCH_2CH_2)$-$(C_2H_5OCH_2CH_2CH{=}CHCH_2)CH$ (8.2 g.)	289
$H_2C{=}CH(C_2H_5OCH_2CH_2)CHCl$ (30.0 g.)	*n*-C_4H_9MgBr (35.9 g. C_4H_9Br)	Recovered $C_7H_{13}ClO$ (3.4 g.); $C_2H_5OCH_2CH_2CH{=}CH$-*n*-C_5H_{11} (18.3 g.) $H_2C{=}CH(C_2H_5OCH_2CH_2)$-$(C_2H_5OCH_2CH_2CH{=}CHCH_2)CH$ (6.3 g.)	289
2-Chloro-3-methylcyclohexanol	*i*-C_3H_7MgBr	"Menthol" (allophanate, m 133°)	265
2-Chloro-5-methylcyclohexanol, $b._{14}$ 95–97° (40 g.)	CH_3MgI (80 g. CH_3I)	2,5-Dimethylcyclohexanol* (60%)	76,74
2-Chloro-5-methylcyclohexanol, $b._{14}$ 103–105° (40 g.)	CH_3MgI (80 g. CH_3I)	2,5-Dimethylcyclohexanol (2 forms) (50%)	76,74
2-Chloro-5-methylcyclohexanol, "liquid isomer"	CH_3MgI	2,5-Dimethylcyclohexanone (semicarbazone, m. 155°)	268
2-Chloro-5-methylcyclohexanol, "solid isomer"	CH_3MgI	2,5-Dimethylcyclohexanone (semicarbazone, m. 122°)	268
2-Chloro-5-methylcyclohexanol, b_{14} 95–97°	*i*-C_3H_7MgBr	Isomeric menthols (allophanates, m. 133° and 177°)	267
2-Chloro-5-methylcyclohexanol, b_{14} 103–105°	*i*-C_3H_7MgBr	Isomeric menthols (allophanates, m. 133° and 177°)	267
2-Chlorocycloheptanol	CH_3MgI (2 equiv.)	$(CH_2)_5CHCH(CH_3)OH$ (chiefly); $(CH_2)_5C{=}CHCH_3$	77,264,4

* Two stereoisomers; the allophanates melt, respectively, at 125° and 157–158°.

TABLE XVI-I (Continued)

Halide	RMgX	Product(s)	Ref.
$C_7H_{13}ClO$ (*cont.*)			
2-Chlorocycloheptanol	C_2H_5MgBr	$(CH_2)_5CHCH(C_2H_5)OH$	*4*
2-Chlorocycloheptanol	C_6H_5MgBr	$(CH_2)_5CHCH(C_6H_5)OH$	*264,4*
$C_7H_{13}Br$			
$(CH_3)_2C{=}CHC(CH_3)_2Br$	i-C_3H_7MgBr	$(CH_3)_2C{=}CH(CH_3)_2C$-i-C_3H_7 (25%)	*145*
$(CH_3)_2C{=}CHC(CH_3)_2Br$	n-C_4H_9MgBr (excess)	$(CH_3)_2C{=}CHC(CH_3)_2$-n-C_4H_9 (30%)	*255*
$(CH_3)_2C{=}CHC(CH_3)_2Br$	i-C_4H_9MgBr	$(CH_3)_2C{=}CHC(CH_3)_2$-i-C_4H_9 (30%)	*255*
$(CH_3)_2C{=}CHC(CH_3)_2Br$	i-$C_5H_{11}MgBr$	$(CH_3)_2C{=}CH(CH_3)_2C$-i-C_5H_{11} (30%)	*145*
$(CH_3)_2C{=}CHC(CH_3)_2Br$	C_6H_5MgBr	$(CH_3)_2C{=}CH(CH_3)_2CC_6H_5$ (26%)	*145*
$C_7H_{14}ClN$			
1-Chloro-2-methylaminocyclohexane	C_2H_5MgBr	$(CH_2)_5CO$; CH_3NH_2	*156*
1-Chloro-2-amino-4-methylcyclohexane	C_2H_5MgBr	3-Methylcyclohexanone	*156*
2-Chloro-2-methylcyclohexylamine	C_2H_5MgBr	2-Methylcyclohexanone	*156*
$C_7H_{15}Cl$			
t-$C_4H_9(CH_3)_2CCl$	CH_3MgCl	$(t$-C_4H_9—$)_2$ (48%)	*32*
$C_7H_{15}Br$			
t-$C_4H_9(CH_3)_2CBr$ (16 g.)	CH_3MgBr	$(t$-C_4H_9—$)_2$ (3 g.)	*101*
C_8H_5Br			
$C_6H_5C{\equiv}CBr$ (18 g., 0.097 mole)	CH_3MgBr (0.16 mole)	$C_6H_5C{\equiv}CH$ (8.8 g., 89%); CH_3Br	*121*
C_8H_5I			
$C_6H_5C{\equiv}CI$	$C_6H_5C{\equiv}CMgI$	$(C_6H_5C{\equiv}C$—$)_2$	*91*

TABLE XVI-I (Continued)

Halide	RMgX	Product(s)	Ref.
$C_8H_6Cl_2O$			
$ClOC(C_6H_5)CHCl$ (34 g.)	C_6H_5MgBr (170 g. C_6H_5Br)	$HO(C_6H_5)_2CCH(C_6H_5)_2$ (14.5 g.)*	*26*
$ClOC(C_6H_5)CHCl$ (15 g.)	C_6H_5MgBr (75 g. C_6H_5Br)	$C_6H_5COCH(C_6H_5)_2$ (3 g.)†	*26*
C_8H_6BrN			
$2\text{-}NCC_6H_4CH_2Br$	CH_3MgI	$(2\text{-}NCC_6H_4CH_2—)_2$ (40%)	*59*
$2\text{-}NCC_6H_4CH_2Br$	C_2H_5MgI	$(2\text{-}NCC_6H_4CH_2—)_2$ (42.5%)	*59*
C_8H_6IN			
$2\text{-}NCC_6H_4CH_2I$‡	CH_3MgI	$(2\text{-}NCC_6H_4CH_2—)_2$ (25%)	*59*
$2\text{-}NCC_6H_4CH_2I$	C_2H_5MgI	$(2\text{-}NCC_6H_4CH_2—)_2$ (25%)	*59*
$C_8H_7ClO_2$			
DL-$HO_2C(C_6H_5)CHCl$	CH_3MgI (4 equiv.)§	β-$[HO_2C(C_6H_5)CH—]_2$; α-$[HO_2C(C_6H_5)CH—]_2$; $C_6H_5CH(OH)CO_2H$; recovered acid	*152*
DL-$HO_2C(C_6H_5)CHCl$	C_6H_5MgBr (4 equiv.)	$HO(C_6H_5)_2CCH(OH)C_6H_5$ (10–20%); $(C_6H_5)_2CHCO_2H$ (1–8%); β-$[HO_2C(C_6H_5)CH—]_2$ (5–13%); α-$[HO_2C(C_6H_5)CH—]_2$ (1%)	*152*
L(−)-$HO_2C(C_6H_5)CHCl$ (30 g.)	C_6H_5MgBr (4 equiv.)	D(−)-$HO(C_6H_5)_2CCH(OH)C_6H_5$ (1.6 g.); β-$[HO_2C(C_6H_5)CH—]_2$ (1.0 g.); $(C_6H_5)_2CHCO_2H$ (3.1 g.); α-$[HO_2C(C_6H_5)CH—]_2$ (0.2 g.)	*152*

* Gradual (half-hour) addition of Et_2O-chloride solution to Grignard reagent solution; five and one-half hours reflux.

† Slow (one and one-half hour) addition of Grignard reagent solution to Et_2O-chloride solution.

‡ The *para* isomer yielded an amorphous product containing halogen but no nitrogen.

§ Experiments employing two, three, six, and seven equivalents of Grignard reagent were also carried out.

TABLE XVI-I (Continued)

Halide	RMgX	Product(s)	Ref.
C_8H_7Br			
$C_6H_5CH=CHBr$	CH_3MgI	$C_6H_5CH=CHCH_3$ ("poor yield")	*220,221*
$C_8H_7BrO_2$			
DL-$HO_2C(C_6H_5)CHBr$ (12.5 g.)	C_6H_5MgBr (4 equiv.)	β-$[HO_2C(C_6H_5)CH—]_2$ (1.9 g.); α-$[HO_2C(C_6H_5)CH—]_2$ (1.8 g.); $(C_6H_5)_2CHCO_2H$; $(C_6H_5—)_2$; C_6H_5OH; $HO(C_6H_5)_2CCH(OH)C_6H_5$	*152*
C_8H_9ClO			
3-$CH_3OC_6H_4CH_2Cl$	*n*-C_4H_9MgCl	3-$CH_3OC_6H_4$-*n*-C_5H_{11} (17%)	*3*
C_8H_9BrO			
$C_6H_5OCH_2CH_2Br$	*n*-$C_5H_{11}MgBr$	C_6H_5OH; *n*-$C_5H_{11}OH$	*85*
$C_6H_5OCH_2CH_2Br$	C_6H_5MgBr	$C_6H_5OCH_2CH_2C_6H_5$ (83%); C_6H_5OH	*85*
$C_6H_5OCH_2CH_2Br$	$C_6H_5CH_2MgCl$	$C_6H_5O(CH_2)_3C_6H_5$ ("a little"); C_6H_5OH; $C_6H_5CH_2OH$	*85*
2-$CH_3OC_6H_4CH_2Br$	C_2H_5MgCl	2-$CH_3OC_6H_4$-*n*-C_3H_7 (34.5%); (2-$CH_3OC_6H_4CH_2—)_2$; 2-$CH_3OC_6H_4CH_3$	*212*
2-$CH_3OC_6H_4CH_2Br$	C_2H_5MgBr	2-$CH_3OC_6H_4$-*n*-C_3H_7 (32.6%); 2-$CH_3OC_6H_4CH_3$; (2-$CH_3OC_6H_4CH_2—)_2$	*212*
2-$CH_3OC_6H_5CH_2Br$	C_2H_5MgI	2-$CH_3OC_6H_4$-*n*-C_3H_7 (9.7%); (2-$CH_3OC_6H_4CO_2—)_2$	*212*
2-$CH_3OC_6H_4CH_2Br$	C_6H_5MgBr	2-$CH_3OC_6H_4CH_2C_6H_5$ (60%)	*212*
3-$CH_3OC_6H_4CH_2Br$	CH_3MgBr	C_2H_6 (67.6%); 3-$CH_3OC_6H_4C_2H_5$ (34.1%)	*212*
4-$CH_3OC_6H_4CH_2Br$	CH_3MgBr	4-$CH_3OC_6H_4C_2H_5$ (90%)	*212*
4-$CH_3OC_6H_4CH_2Br$	CH_3MgI	4-$CH_3OC_6H_4C_2H_5$ (13.5%); (4-$CH_3OC_6H_5CH_2—)_2$	*212*

TABLE XVI-I (Continued)

Halide	RMgX	Product(s)	Ref.
C_8H_9BrO (*cont.*)			
4-$CH_3OC_6H_4CH_2Br$	C_2H_5MgCl	4-$CH_3OC_6H_4$-*n*-C_3H_7 (88%); (4-$CH_3OC_6H_4CH_2$—$)_2$	*212*
4-$CH_3OC_6H_4CH_2Br$	C_2H_5MgBr	4-$CH_3OC_6H_4$-*n*-C_3H_7 (85%); (4-$CH_3OC_6H_4CH_2$—$)_2$	*212*
4-$CH_3OC_6H_5CH_2Br$	C_2H_5MgI	4-$CH_3OC_6H_4$-*n*-C_3H_7 (26.8%); (4-$CH_3OC_6H_4CH_2$—$)_2$ ("a little")	*212*
4-$CH_3OC_6H_4CH_2Br$	*n*-C_3H_7MgBr	4-$CH_3OC_6H_4$-*n*-C_4H_9 (68.3%); (4-$CH_3OC_6H_4CH_2$—$)_2$ ("a little")	*212*
4-$CH_3OC_6H_4CH_2Br$	*i*-C_3H_7MgCl	4-$CH_3OC_6H_4$-*i*-C_4H_9 (30.6%); (4-$CH_3OC_6H_4CH_2$—$)_2$ ("a little"); 4-$CH_2OC_6H_4CH_3$ (?)	*212*
4-$CH_3OC_6H_4CH_2Br$	*i*-C_3H_7MgBr	4-$CH_3OC_6H_4$-*i*-C_4H_9 (29.8%); (4-$CH_3OC_6H_4CH_2$—$)_2$ ("a little"); 4-$CH_3OC_6H_4CH_3$	*212*
4-$CH_3OC_6H_4CH_2Br$	*i*-C_4H_9MgBr	4-$CH_3OC_6H_4$-*i*-C_5H_{11} (50%); (4-$CH_3OC_6H_4CH_2$—$)_2$ ("a little")	*212*
4-$CH_3OC_6H_4CH_2Br$	*t*-C_4H_9MgCl	4-$CH_3OC_6H_4CH_2C(CH_3)_3$ (24.9%); (4-$CH_3OC_6H_4CH_2$—$)_2$; 4-$CH_3OC_6H_4CH_3$	*212*
4-$CH_3OC_6H_4CH_2Br$	*i*-$C_5H_{11}MgBr$	4-$CH_3OC_6H_4$-*i*-C_6H_{13} (50%); (*i*-C_5H_{11}—$)_2$; (4-$CH_3OC_6H_4CH_2$—$)_2$	*212*
4-$CH_3OC_6H_4CH_2Br$	$(C_2H_5)_2CHMgBr$	4-$CH_3OC_6H_4CH_2CH(C_2H_5)_2$ (50%); (4-$CH_3OC_6H_4CH_2$—$)_2$	*212*
4-$CH_3OC_6H_4CH_2Br$	$(C_2H_5)_2CHMgI$	4-$CH_3OC_6H_4CH_2CH(C_2H_5)_2$ ("a little"); $[(C_2H_5)_2CH$ —$]_2$	*212*
4-$CH_3OC_6H_4CH_2Br$	C_6H_5MgBr	4-$CH_3OC_6H_4CH_2C_6H_5$ (60%)	*212*
4-$CH_3OC_6H_4CH_2Br$	C_6H_5MgI	4-$CH_3OC_6H_4CH_2C_6H_5$ ("a little"); (4-$CH_3OC_6H_4CH_2$—$)_2$ (?)	*212*

TABLE XVI-I (Continued)

Halide	RMgX	Product(s)	Ref.
C_8H_9IO			
$C_6H_5CH(OH)CH_2I$	CH_3MgI (2 equiv.)	Recovered iodide (85%)*	79
$C_6H_5CH(OH)CH_2I$	CH_3MgI (2 equiv.)	$CH_3(C_6H_5CH_2)CHOH$ (42%)†	79
$HOCH_2(C_6H_5)CHI$	CH_3MgI (2 equiv.)	$CH_3(C_6H_5CH_2)CHOH$ (9.8%); recovered iodide (6.4%)*	79
$HOCH_2(C_6H_5)CHI$	CH_3MgI (2 equiv.)	$CH_3(C_6H_5CH_2)CHOH$ (56%)†	79
$C_8H_{10}Br_2O$			
$C_8H_{10}Br_2O$‡	C_2H_5MgBr	$CH_3COC_6H_5$	*157*
$C_8H_{12}Br_2O$			
$C_8H_{12}Br_2O$§	C_2H_5MgBr	C_6H_5OH	*157*
$C_8H_{13}Cl$			
$CH_3(C_2H_5)(C_2H_5C{\equiv}C)CCl$	CH_3MgBr	$C_2H_5C{\equiv}C\text{-}t\text{-}C_5H_{11}$ (66%)	287
$CH_3(C_2H_5)(C_2H_5C{\equiv}C)CCl$	C_2H_5MgBr	$C_2H_5C{\equiv}CC(C_2H_5)_2CH_3$ (61%)	287
$C_8H_{14}ClO$			
1,4-Dimethyl-3-chlorocyclohexanol	C_2H_5MgBr	1-Acetyl-3-methylcyclopentane; 2,4-dimethylcyclohexanone	222
$C_8H_{15}Cl$			
1-Chloro-1,3-dimethylcyclopentane (308 parts)	CH_3MgI (356 parts CH_3I)	1,1,3-Trimethylcyclopentane (19.3%)	*153*

* Addition of iodide to cooled, stirred Grignard reagent solution; spontaneous warming to room temperature.

† Addition of Et_2O-iodide solution to cooled, stirred Grignard reagent solution; spontaneous warming to room temperature; distillation of Et_2O on water-bath.

‡ The dibromo derivative obtained upon treatment of 1-acetylcyclohexene with *N*-bromosuccinimide.

§ The dibromo derivative obtained upon treatment of 3-ethoxycyclohexene with *N*-bromosuccinimide.

TABLE XVI-I (Continued)

Halide	RMgX	Product(s)	Ref.
$C_8H_{16}Cl_2O$			
$Cl(CH_3)_2C(i\text{-}C_4H_9O)CHCl$	CH_3MgBr (excess)	$(CH_3)_2C{=}C(O\text{-}i\text{-}C_4H_9)CH_3$	*100,102*
$C_8H_{16}Br_2O$			
$C_2H_5CHBr(n\text{-}C_4H_9O)CHBr$	$n\text{-}C_6H_{13}MgBr$	$C_2H_5CHBr(n\text{-}C_4H_9O)CH\text{-}n\text{-}C_6H_{13}$	*122*
$C_8H_{17}Br$			
$CH_3(n\text{-}C_6H_{13})CHBr$	C_2H_5MgBr	$CH_3(n\text{-}C_6H_{13})CHC_2H_5$ (7.9%); C_2H_6 (53.8%); C_2H_4 (38.3%)*	*212*
$CH_3(n\text{-}C_6H_{13})CHBr$	C_2H_5MgBr	C_8H_{16} (21.2%); $(s\text{-}C_8H_{17}-)_2$†	*212*
(+)-$CH_3(n\text{-}C_6H_{13})CHBr$, $[\alpha]_D^{24}$ + 30.03‡ (13.5 g., 0.070 mole)	$H_2C{=}CHCH_2MgBr$ (60.5 g., 0.50 mole C_3H_7Br)	$CH_3(n\text{-}C_6H_{13})CHCH_2CH{=}CH_2$, $[\alpha]_D^{25}$ + 4.79§	*286*
$CH_3(n\text{-}C_6H_{13})CHBr$	$n\text{-}C_3H_7MgBr$	C_8H_{18} (22.1%); C_8H_{16} (18.0%); $C_{16}H_{34}$ (29.0%)	*212*
$CH_3(n\text{-}C_6H_{13})CHBr$	$t\text{-}C_4H_9MgCl$	$CH_3(n\text{-}C_6H_{13})CH\text{-}t\text{-}C_4H_9$ (3.0%); $[CH_3(n\text{-}C_6H_{13})CH-]_2$ (14.0%); C_8H_{16} (18.6%); C_8H_{18} (24.1%)	*212*
$C_8H_{17}I$			
$CH_3(n\text{-}C_6H_{13})CHI$	CH_3MgI	$n\text{-}C_6H_{13}(CH_3)_2CH$ (37.4%); CH_4 ("much"); C_2H_6 ("little")	*212*

* Addition of bromide to concentrated Grignard reagent solution; several hours at 100–105°.

† Addition of bromide to cooled concentrated Grignard reagent solution; three and one-half hours reflux.

‡ The highest reported rotation for the pure enantiomorph is $[\alpha]_D^{25}$ + 34.3; it is estimated that the upper limit of the specific rotation is $[\alpha]_D$ + 38.1.

§ It is calculated that the specific rotation for the pure enantiomorph should be $[\alpha]_D$ + 7.0.

TABLE XVI-I (Continued)

Halide	RMgX	Product(s)	Ref.
C_9H_9Cl			
$C_6H_5CH=CHCH_2Cl$ (20 g., 0.13 mole)	CH_3MgBr (0.23 mole)	$C_6H_5CH=CHC_2H_5$ (89%); $(C_6H_5CH=CHCH_2-)_2$ (1%); $C_6H_5CH=CHCH_2CH(C_6H_5)CH=CH_2$ (5%)	*121*
C_9H_9ClO			
$C_6H_5COCH_2CH_2Cl$	C_6H_5MgBr	$C_6H_5COCH_2CH_2C_6H_5$	*235*
C_9H_9Br			
$C_6H_5CH=CHCH_2Br$	C_2H_5MgBr	$C_6H_5CH=CH$-*n*-C_3H_7 (*ca.* 50%); $C_2H_5(C_6H_5)CHCH=CH_2$ (*ca.* 25%)*	*174*
$C_6H_5CH=CHCH_2Br$ (1.5 mole)	C_2H_5MgBr (1.5 mole)	C_2H_5Br (14.0%); $C_6H_5CH=CHCH_3$ (2.5%); $C_6H_5CH_2CH=CH_2$ (2.5%); $(C_6H_5CH=CHCH_2-)_2$ (4.5%); $C_6H_5CH=CHCH_2CH(C_6H_5)CH=CH_2$ (4.5%); C_2H_6 (10.0%); $C_2H_5(C_6H_5)CHCH=CH_2$ (23.0%); $C_6H_5CH=CH$-*n*-C_3H_7 (50.0%); cond'n products (3.0%)†	*173*
$C_9H_{10}ClBrMgO$			
$CH_3(C_6H_5)(BrMgO)CCH_2Cl$	C_6H_5MgBr	$CH_3(C_6H_5)C=CHC_6H_5$	*221*
$C_9H_{11}ClO_2$			
2,3-$(CH_3O)_2C_6H_3CH_2Cl$ (0.08 mole)	*n*-$C_{14}H_{29}MgBr$ (0.25 mole $C_{14}H_{29}Br$)	2,3-$(CH_3O)_2C_6H_3$-*n*-$C_{15}H_{31}$ (25%); *n*-$C_{28}H_{58}$ (*ca.* 5 g.)	*151*

* Slow addition of Et_2O-bromide solution to Grignard reagent solution; several hours reflux.

† Addition of bromide to Grignard reagent solution; twelve hours at room temperature.

TABLE XVI-I (Continued)

Halide	RMgX	Product(s)	Ref.
$C_9H_{11}ClO_2$ (*cont.*)			
2,3-$(CH_3O)_2C_6H_3CH_2Cl$ (14.9 g.)	*n*-$C_{14}H_{29}MgBr$ (69.3 g. $C_{14}H_{29}Br$)	2,3-$(CH_3O)_2C_6H_3$-*n*-$C_{15}H_{31}$ (2.0 g., 7.2%); *n*-$C_{28}H_{58}$ (10.5 g.); [2,3-$(CH_3O)_2C_6H_3CH_2$—]$_2$ (1.0 g.)	151
$C_9H_{11}Br$			
$C_2H_5(C_6H_5)CHBr$	C_2H_5MgBr	$C_6H_5(C_2H_5)_2CH$ (22%); [$C_2H_5(C_6H_5)CH$—]$_2$	212
$C_9H_{15}Cl$			
n-$C_4H_9C{\equiv}C(CH_3)_2CCl$	CH_3MgBr	*n*-$C_4H_9C{\equiv}C$-*t*-C_4H_9 (74%)	287
n-$C_4H_9C{\equiv}C(CH_3)_2CCl$ (79.3 g., 0.5 mole)	C_2H_5MgBr (70.0 g. C_2H_5Br)	*n*-$C_4H_9C{\equiv}C$-*t*-C_5H_{11} (60%)	287
$C_9H_{17}Cl$			
i-$C_4H_9CH{=}CH(CH_3)_2CCl$ + *i*-$C_3H_7[(CH_3)_2C{=}CH]CHCl$	CH_3MgCl	*i*-$C_4H_9CH{=}CH$-*t*-C_4H_9 (1 part); *i*-$C_3H_7[(CH_3)_2C{=}CH]CHCH_3$ (5 parts)	98
$C_9H_{17}ClO$			
n-$C_4H_9OCH_2CH_2CH{=}CHCH_2Cl$ (40.0 g.)	*n*-C_4H_9MgBr (40.3 g. C_4H_9Br)	Recovered $C_9H_{17}ClO$ (5.2 g.); *n*-$C_4H_9OCH_2CH_2CH{=}CH$-*n*-C_5H_{11} (19.6 g.); $H_2C{=}CH$(*n*-$C_4H_9OCH_2CH_2$)(*n*-$C_4H_9OCH_2CH_2CH{=}CHCH_2$)CH (7.4 g.)	289
n-$C_4H_9OCH_2CH_2CH{=}CHCH_2Cl$ (40.0 g.)	C_6H_5MgBr (49.8 g. C_6H_5Br)	Recovered $C_9H_{17}ClO$ (5.0 g.); C_6H_6 (2.7 g.); *n*-$C_4H_9OCH_2CH_2CH{=}CHCH_2C_6H_5$ (32.6 g.)	289
$H_2C{=}CH$(*n*-$C_4H_9OCH_2CH_2$)CHCl (40.0 g.)	*n*-C_4H_9MgBr (40.3 g. C_4H_9Br)	Recovered $C_9H_{17}ClO$ (5.5 g.); *n*-$C_4H_9OCH_2CH_2CH{=}CH$-*n*-C_5H_{11} (19.8 g.); $H_2C{=}CH$(*n*-$C_4H_9OCH_2CH_2$)(*n*-$C_4H_9OCH_2CH_2CH{=}CHCH_2$)CH (7.4 g.)	289

TABLE XVI-I (Continued)

Halide	RMgX	Product(s)	Ref.
$C_9H_{17}ClO$ (*cont.*)			
$H_2C{=}CH(n\text{-}C_4H_9OCH_2CH_2)CHCl$ (40.0 g.)	C_6H_5MgBr (49.8 g. C_6H_5Br)	Recovered $C_9H_{17}ClO$ (5.8 g.); C_6H_6 (2.0 g.); $n\text{-}C_4H_9OCH_2CH_2CH{=}CHCH_2C_6H_5$ (33.3 g.)	*289*
$C_{10}H_7Br$			
$1\text{-}C_{10}H_7Br$	CH_3MgBr + $FeCl_3$ (trace)	$1\text{-}C_{10}H_7CH_3$ (50%)	*282*
$2\text{-}C_{10}H_7Br$	CH_3MgBr + $FeCl_3$ (trace)	$2\text{-}C_{10}H_7CH_3$ (22%)	*282*
$C_{10}H_{13}Cl$			
$4\text{-}i\text{-}C_3H_7C_6H_4CH_2Cl$	C_2H_5MgBr	$4\text{-}i\text{-}C_3H_7C_6H_4\text{-}n\text{-}C_3H_7$ (50%)	*19*
$2,4,6\text{-}(CH_3)_3C_6H_2CH_2Cl$	CH_3MgI	$[2,4,6\text{-}(CH_3)_3C_6H_2CH_2\text{—}]_2$ (86%)	*64*
$2,4,6\text{-}(CH_3)_3C_6H_2CH_2Cl$	$2\text{-}[2,4,6\text{-}(CH_3)_3C_6H_2CH_2]C_6H_4MgBr$	$1,2\text{-}[2,4,6\text{-}(CH_3)_3C_6H_2CH_2]_2C_6H_4$	*64,68*
$C_{10}H_{13}Br$			
$C_6H_5CH_2(CH_3)_2CBr$	$C_2H_5CH_2MgCl$ (2 equiv.)	$C_6H_5CH{=}C(CH_3)_2$; $(CH_3)_2C(CH_2C_6H_5)_2$	*223*
$CH_3(C_2H_5)(C_6H_5)CBr$	CH_3MgBr	$C_2H_5(C_6H_5)C(CH_3)_2$ (36%)	*212*
$C_{10}H_{17}Cl$			
$CH_3(C_2H_5)(n\text{-}C_4H_9C{\equiv}C)CCl$	CH_3MgBr	$n\text{-}C_4H_9C{\equiv}C\text{-}t\text{-}C_5H_{11}$ (73%)	*287*
Bornyl chloride	CH_3MgBr	5% reaction during 28 hrs. reflux	*118*
Iosbornyl chloride	CH_3MgBr	90% reaction during 1 hr. reflux: bornylene (90%); CH_4	*118*
(+)-α-Pinene hydrochloride	$C_{10}H_{17}MgCl$*	Camphane (39.5%); bornylene (39.5%); bibornyl (21.0%)	*188*

* From (+)-α-pinene hydrochloride; Rivière (*188*) concludes that this Grignard reagent is an equimolecular mixture of bornyl- and isobornylmagnesium chlorides.

TABLE XVI-I (Continued)

Halide	RMgX	Product(s)	Ref.
$C_{10}H_{17}Cl$ (*cont.*)			
(+)-α-Pinene hydrochloride	"Isomerized" $C_{10}H_{17}MgCl$*	Camphane (17.5%); bornylene (17.5%); bibornyl (65.0%)	*188*
$C_{10}H_{19}Cl$			
$CH_3(C_2H_5)(n\text{-}C_5H_{11}C\equiv C)CCl$	CH_3MgBr	$n\text{-}C_5H_{11}C\equiv C\text{-}t\text{-}C_5H_{11}$ (72%)	287
1-Chloromethoxy-4-*n*-propylcyclohexane (9.5 g.)	CH_3MgI (8.0 g. CH_3I)	1-Ethoxy-4-*n*-propylcyclohexane (8.5 g., 82%)	*69*
$C_{10}H_{19}Br_2Cl$			
$Cl(CH_2)_7CHBr(CH_3O)CHBr$	$n\text{-}C_8H_{17}MgBr$ (*ca.* 1.3 equiv.)	$Cl(CH_2)_7CHBr(CH_3O)CH\text{-}n\text{-}C_8H_{17}$	*12*
$C_{11}H_9Br$			
$1\text{-}C_{10}H_7CH_2Br$	$1\text{-}C_{10}H_7MgBr$	$(1\text{-}C_{10}H_7\text{—})_2$	*197*
$C_{11}H_{12}Cl_2$			
$2,4,6\text{-}(CH_3)_3C_6H_2CHCl_2$ (30.0 g.)	CH_3MgI	$[2,4,6\text{-}(CH_3)_3C_6H_2CH=]_2$ (5.8 g.)	*63*
$C_{11}H_{15}ClO_7$			
Triacetyl-D-xylosyl chloride	C_6H_5MgX (*ca.* 10 equiv.)	$CH_3(C_6H_5)_2COH$ (100%, crude); after re-acetylation, triacetyl-D-xylopryanosyl-benzene (86.6%, crude: 25.0% α, 75.0% β)	*109*
Triacetyl-D-xylosyl chloride	$4\text{-}CH_3C_6H_4MgX$ (*ca.* 10 equiv.)	$CH_3(4\text{-}CH_3C_6H_4)_2COH$ (100% crude); after re-acetylation, triacetyl-D-xylopyranosyl-toluene (82.3%, crude: 14.0% α, 86.0% β)	*109*

* Prepared by refluxing in xylene (three hours at 130°) the Grignard reagent from (+)-α-pinene hydrochloride; Rivière (*188*) concludes that the reagent so obtained is substantially pure bornylmagnesium chloride.

TABLE XVI-I (Continued)

Halide	RMgX	Product(s)	Ref.
$C_{11}H_{15}Br$			
$CH_3(C_2H_5)(C_6H_5CH_2)CBr$	C_2H_5MgBr (excess)	Mixture of sat'd and unsat'd h.c., probably $CH_3(C_2H_5)(C_6H_5CH_2)CH + CH_3(C_2H_5)C{=}CHC_6H_5$; C_2H_4; C_2H_6; $MgBr_2$	*223*
$C_{11}H_{17}Br$			
$C_{11}H_{17}Br$*	CH_3MgI	$C_{11}H_{17}CH_3$†	*157*
$C_{12}H_{17}Cl$			
2,6-$(CH_3)_2$-4-*i*-$C_3H_7C_6H_2CH_2Cl$	CH_3MgI	[2,6-$(CH_3)_2$-4-*i*-$C_3H_7C_6H_2CH_2$—]$_2$ (85%); 2,6-$(CH_3)_2$-4-*i*-$C_3H_7C_6H_2C_2H_5$ ("a little")	64
$C_{13}H_9Cl$			
9-Chlorofluorene	C_2H_5MgI	9-Ethylfluorene (65%); 9,9′-bifluorenyl (20%)	*155*
9-Chlorofluorene	*n*-C_4H_9MgBr	9,9′-Bifluorenyl (95%)	*155*
9-Chlorofluorene	*n*-$C_5H_{11}MgBr$	9,9′-Bifluorenyl (95%)	*155*
9-Chlorofluorene	C_6H_5MgBr	9,9′-Bifluorenyl (*ca.* quant.)	*155*
9-Chlorofluorene	$(CH_2)_5CHMgBr$	9,9′-Bifluorenyl (93%)‡§	*155*
9-Chlorofluorene	$(CH_2)_5CHMgBr$	9,9′-Bifluorenyl (70%); 9-cyclohexylfluorene (25%)§¶	*155*

* The monobromo derivative obtained by treating 2-methyl-1,4,4a,5,6,7,8,8a-octahydronaphthalene with *N*-bromosuccinimide.

† A dimethyl derivative of 1,4,4a,5,6,7,8,8a-octahydronaphthalene.

‡ Addition of chloride to ethereal Grignard reagent solution.

§ According to Miller and Bachman (*155*), the "normal" reaction is attributable to RMgX and the coupling reaction to R_2Mg. The Schlenk equilibrium is presumed to be relatively favorable to R_2Mg in ethyl ether solution and to RMgX in benzene.

¶ Addition of chloride to benzene-Grignard reagent solution.

TABLE XVI-I (Continued)

Halide	RMgX	Product(s)	Ref.
$C_{13}H_9Cl_3$			
$(4\text{-}ClC_6H_4)_2CHCl$ (0.11 mole)	CH_3MgBr (0.12 mole)	$(4\text{-}ClC_6H_4)_2CHCH_3$ (95%)	*92*
$C_{13}H_9Br$			
9-Bromofluorene	9-Phenanthryl-MgBr	9-(9-Fluorenyl)phenanthrene (50%)	*9*
9-Bromofluorene	$(C_6H_5)_3CMgBr$	9-Triphenylmethylfluorene (99%)	*8*
$C_{13}H_{11}Br$			
$(C_6H_5)_2CHBr$	CH_3MgBr	$(C_6H_5)_2CHCH_3$ (85%); $[(C_6H_5)_2CH—]_2$	*212*
$(C_6H_5)_2CHBr$ (5 g.)	C_2H_5MgBr	$(C_6H_5)_2CHC_2H_5$ (1.2 g., 30%); $[(C_6H_5)_2CH—]_2$	*212*
$(C_6H_5)_2CHBr$ (3.8 g.)	C_2H_5MgI	$(C_6H_5)_2CHC_2H_5$ (0.5 g., 15.7%); $[(C_6H_5)_2CH—]_2$ (1.9 g., 73%)	*212*
$(C_6H_5)_2CHBr$	$(C_6H_5SO_2)_2C(MgBr)_2$	$(C_6H_5SO_2)_2CHCH(C_6H_5)_2$	*254*
$(C_6H_5)_2CHBr$	9-Anthryl-MgBr	9-Benzhydrylanthracene (10%)	*11*
$(C_6H_5)_2CHBr$	9-Phenylanthryl-MgBr	9-Benzhydrylphenanthrene (72%)	*9*
$(C_6H_5)_2CHBr$ (27.8 g.)	$(C_6H_5)_3CMgBr$ (32.3 g. $C_{19}H_{15}Br$)	$(C_6H_5)_3CCH(C_6H_5)_2$ (37 g.)	*8*
$C_{13}H_{19}Cl$			
$2,6\text{-}(CH_3)_2\text{-}4\text{-}t\text{-}C_4H_9C_6H_2CH_2Cl$	CH_3MgI	$[2,6\text{-}(CH_3)_2\text{-}4\text{-}t\text{-}C_4H_9C_6H_2CH_2—]_2$ (85%)	*64*
$C_{14}H_9Br$			
9-Bromoanthracene	$CH_3MgBr + FeCl_3$ (trace)	9-Methylanthracene (70%)	*282*
$C_{14}H_{10}Cl$			
$(C_6H_5Cl_2C—)_2$ (0.7 g.)	CH_3MgCl (excess 2*M*)	$(C_6H_5ClC=)_2$ (2 isomers, 0.2 g.)	*67*
$C_{14}H_{12}Br_2$			
$(C_6H_5CHBr—)_2$ (17 g.)	C_6H_5MgBr (5 g. Mg)	$(C_6H_5CH=)_2$ (8 g.); $(C_6H_5—)_2$ (7.8 g.)	*128*

TABLE XVI-I (Continued)

Halide	RMgX	Product(s)	Ref.
$C_{14}H_{13}ClO$			
$C_6H_5(4\text{-}CH_3OC_6H_4)CHCl$	$(C_6H_5)_3CMgBr$	$C_6H_5(4\text{-}CH_3OC_6H_4)CHC(C_6H_5)_3$ (70%)	*8*
$C_{14}H_{13}Br$			
$C_6H_5(4\text{-}CH_3C_6H_4)CHBr$	$(C_6H_5)_3CMgBr$	$C_6H_5(4\text{-}CH_3C_6H_4)CHC(C_6H_5)_3$ (80%)	*8*
$C_{14}H_{19}ClO_9$			
Tetraäcetyl-α-D-glucosyl chloride	$i\text{-}C_3H_7MgX$ (*ca.* 12 equiv.)	$CH_3(i\text{-}C_3H_7)_2COH$ (50.8%, crude); unidentified syrup mixture	*109*
Tetraäcetyl-α-D-glucosyl chloride	$n\text{-}C_4H_9MgX$ (*ca.* 12 equiv.)	$CH_3(n\text{-}C_4H_9)_2COH$ (95.6%, crude); after reäcetylation, 1-tetraäcetyl-D-glucopyranosylbutane (59.4%, crude)	*109*
Tetraäcetyl-α-D-glucosyl chloride (0.0136 mole)	C_6H_5MgBr (0.165 mole C_6H_5Br)	$CH_3(C_6H_5)_2COH$ (100%, crude); after reäcetylation, tetraäcetyl-D-glucopyranosylbenzene (82.0%, crude; 28.4% α, 71.6% β)	*109*
Tetraäcetyl-α-D-glucosyl chloride	$C_6H_5CH_2MgX$ (*ca.* 12 equiv.)	$CH_3(C_6H_5CH_2)_2COH$ (100%, crude); unidentified syrup mixture)	*109*
Tetraäcetyl-α-D-glucosyl chloride	$4\text{-}CH_3C_6H_4MgBr$ (*ca.* 12 equiv.)	$CH_3(4\text{-}CH_3C_6H_4)_2COH$ (98.5%, crude); after reäcetylation, 4-(tetraäcetyl-D-glucopyranosyl)toluene (75% crude; 26.6% α, 73.4% β)	*109*
Tetraäcetyl-α-D-glucosyl chloride	$1\text{-}C_{10}H_7MgX$ (*ca.* 12 equiv.)	$CH_3(1\text{-}C_{10}H_7)_2COH$ (66%, crude); after reäcetylation, 1-tetraäcetyl-D-glucopyranosylnaphthalene (65.0%, crude; 33.3% α, 66.7% β)	*109*
Tetraäcetylfructosyl chloride (3 g.)	C_2H_5MgI (25 g. C_2H_5I)	$C_{14}H_9ClO_9\cdot(C_2H_5MgI)_2$ (regenerating original chloride upon hydrolysis)	*58*

TABLE XVI-I (Continued)

Halide	RMgX	Product(s)	Ref.
$C_{14}H_{19}BrO_9$			
Tetraäcetylglucosyl bromide	CH_3MgI (2 equiv.)	$C_{14}H_{19}BrO_9 \cdot (CH_3MgI)_2$ (regenerating original bromide upon hydrolysis)	*56*
Tetraäcetyl-α-D-glucosyl bromide (0.0122 mole)	C_6H_5MgBr (0.0911 mole) + 4-$CH_3C_6H_4$-MgBr (0.0425 mole)	Tetraäcetyl-D-glucopyranosylbenzene (A) + 4-(tetraäcetyl-D-glucopyranosyl)-toluene (B) (3.38 g. total crude: 90% A, 10% B)	*109*
$C_{14}H_{21}ClO$			
4-*i*-$C_3H_7C_6H_4CH_2CH(CH_3)$-CH_2OCH_2Cl	RMgX*	4-*i*-$C_3H_7C_6H_4CH_2CH(CH_3)CH_2OCH_2R$*	*166*
$C_{14}H_{27}ClO$			
1,1,3-Trimethyl-2-(γ-chloromethoxy-*n*-butyl)cyclohexane†	C_2H_5MgI	1,1,3-Trimethyl-2-(γ-propoxy-*n*-butyl)-cyclohexane ("poor yield")	*115*
1,1,3-Trimethyl-2-(γ-chloromethoxy-*n*-butyl)-cyclohexane†	*i*-C_3H_7MgBr	1,1,3-Trimethyl-2-(γ-isobutoxy-*n*-butyl)cyclohexane ("poor yield")	*115*
$C_{15}H_{12}Cl_2$			
$C_6H_5(C_6H_5CCl{=}CH)CHCl$ (30 g.)	C_6H_5MgBr (30 g. C_6H_5Br)	$C_6H_5CCl{=}CH(C_6H_5)_2CH$ (80–85%)	*213*
$C_{15}H_{13}Cl$			
$(C_6H_5)_2C{=}CHCH_2Cl$	C_6H_5MgBr (5.3 ml. C_6H_5Br)	$(C_6H_5)_2C{=}CHCH_2C_6H_5$	*235*
$C_{15}H_{15}ClO_2$			
$(4\text{-}CH_3OC_6H_4)_2CHCl$	$(C_6H_5)_3CMgCl$	$(4\text{-}CH_3OC_6H_4)_2CHC(C_6H_5)_3$ (40%)	8

* R = CH_3, C_2H_5, *n*-C_3H_7, *n*-C_4H_9.
† Chloromethyl ether of tetrahydroïonol.

TABLE XVI-I (Continued)

Halide	RMgX	Product(s)	Ref.
$C_{15}H_{15}Br$			
$(4\text{-}CH_3C_6H_4)_2CHBr$	$(C_6H_5)_3CMgBr$	$(4\text{-}CH_3C_6H_4)_2CHC(C_6H_5)_3$ (71%)	*8*
$C_{15}H_{15}BrO_2$			
$(4\text{-}CH_3OC_6H_4)_2CHBr$	$(C_6H_5)_3CMgBr$	$(4\text{-}CH_3OC_6H_4)_2CHC(C_6H_5)_3$ (40%)	*8*
$C_{16}H_{15}BrO_2$			
$4\text{-}[2,4,6\text{-}(CH_3)_3C_6H_2CO]C_6H_4Br$ (10 g.)	C_6H_5MgBr (0.5 g. C_6H_5Br) + Mg (1.0 g.)	$\{4\text{-}[2,4,6\text{-}(CH_3)_3C_6H_2CO]C_6H_4—\}_2$ (2.0 g.)*	*61*
$C_{16}H_{17}Br$			
$CH_3(C_6H_5CH_2)_2CBr$ (40 g.)	C_2H_5MgBr	$[CH_3(C_6H_5CH_2)_2C—]_2$ (0.5 g.); $CH_3(C_6H_5CH_2)_2CH$; $CH_3(C_6H_5CH_2)C=CHC_6H_5$ (?); C_2H_6; C_2H_4	*223*
$CH_3(C_6H_5CH_2)_2CBr$	$C_6H_5CH_2MgCl$ (4 equiv.)	$(C_6H_5CH_2)_3CCH_3$; "olefin" (chief product)	*223*
$C_{16}H_{24}Cl_2$			
$2,4,6\text{-}(i\text{-}C_3H_7)_3C_6H_2CHCl_2$	CH_3MgI	$[2,4,6\text{-}(i\text{-}C_3H_7)_3C_6H_2CHCl—]_2$ (2 isomers)	*62*
$C_{16}H_{25}Cl$			
$2,4,6\text{-}(i\text{-}C_3H_7)_3C_6H_2CH_2Cl$	CH_3MgI	$[2,4,6\text{-}(i\text{-}C_3H_7)_3C_6H_2CH_2—]_2$ (63%)	*65*
$C_{16}H_{33}I$			
$n\text{-}C_{16}H_{33}I$	CH_3MgI	$C_{17}H_{36}$; $C_{16}H_{32}$; C_2H_6; CH_4	*212*
$C_{17}H_{13}Br$			
$C_6H_5(1\text{-}C_{10}H_7)CHBr$	$(C_6H_5)_3CMgBr$	$C_6H_5(1\text{-}C_{10}H_7)CHC(C_6H_5)_3$ (72%)	*8*

* This reaction probably has more in common with the magnesious halide ketone reductions (*q.v.*, Chapter VI) than with the halide coupling reactions which it formally resembles.

TABLE XVI-I (Continued)

Halide	RMgX	Product(s)	Ref.
$C_{17}H_{19}Br$			
$C_2H_5(C_6H_5CH_2)_2CBr$	C_6H_5MgBr	Unsat'd hydrocarbon (chief product)	*44*
$C_{18}H_{20}ClO_2N$			
α-Chlorocodide (8 g.)	CH_3MgI (75 ml. 1*M*)	Desoxycodeïne-A (5.5 g.); gas (largely unsat'd); iodocodide (white form)	*208*
α-Chlorocodide (3 g.)	C_2H_5MgI	Desoxycodeïne-A (2.0 g., crude); iodocodide (white form, 0.1 g.)	*208*
β-Chlorocodide	Alk-MgX	No reaction	*208*
Iodocodide, white form (1.0 g.)	CH_3MgI (25 ml. 1*M*)	Desoxycodeïne-A (0.4 g.); recovered iodide (0.3 g.)	*208*
$C_{18}H_{21}ClO_2$			
$(C_2H_5O)_2CH(C_6H_5)_2CCl$ (7.6 g.)	C_6H_5MgBr (0.6 g. Mg)	$(C_6H_5)_2CHCO_2H$ (3.3 g.); $(C_6H_5)_2CH_2$ (2.8 g.)	*193*
$C_{19}H_{12}ClBr_3$			
$(4\text{-}BrC_6H_4)_3CCl$	C_6H_5MgBr	$(4\text{-}BrC_6H_4)_3CC_6H_5$ (43–45%)	*204*
$(4\text{-}BrC_6H_4)_3CCl$	$C_6H_5CH_2MgCl$	$(4\text{-}BrC_6H_4)_3CCH_2C_6H_5$ (quant.)	80
$C_{19}H_{12}Cl_4$			
$2\text{-}ClC_6H_4(4\text{-}ClC_6H_4)_2CCl$	$C_6H_5CH_2MgCl$	$2\text{-}ClC_6H_4(4\text{-}ClC_6H_4)_2CCH_2C_6H_5$ (*quant.*)	80
$(4\text{-}ClC_6H_4)_3CCl$	C_6H_5MgBr	$(4\text{-}ClC_6H_4)_3CC_6H_5$ (38–49%)	*204*
$C_{19}H_{13}Cl$			
9-Chloro-9-phenylfluorene (21 g.)	C_6H_5MgBr (15 ml. C_6H_5Br)	9,9-Diphenylfluorene (5.3 g., 23%); 9,9′-diphenyl-9,9′-bifluorenyl (4.8 g., 26%); gum	8,7,*201*

TABLE XVI-I (Continued)

Halide	RMgX	Product(s)	Ref.
$C_{19}H_{13}Cl$ (*cont.*)			
9-Chloro-9-phenylfluorene	$C_6H_5CH_2MgCl$	9-Phenyl-9-benzylfluorene	*81*
$C_{19}H_{13}Br$			
9-Bromo-9-phenylfluorene	$(C_6H_5)_3CMgBr$	9,9′-Diphenyl-9,9′-bifluorenyl (98%); $[(C_6H_5)_3C—]_2$	*8*
$C_{19}H_{14}Cl_2$			
$4\text{-}ClC_6H_4(C_6H_5)_2CCl$	C_6H_5MgBr	$4\text{-}ClC_6H_4(C_6H_5)_3C$ (10%); $4\text{-}ClC_6H_4(4\text{-}C_6H_5C_6H_4)(C_6H_5)CH$ (28%); $C_6H_5(4\text{-}C_6H_5C_6H_4)_2CH$ (9%)	*203*
$4\text{-}ClC_6H_4(C_6H_5)_2CCl$	$C_6H_5CH_2MgCl$ (3 equiv.)	$4\text{-}ClC_6H_4(C_6H_5)_2CCH_2C_6H_5$ (quant.)	*80*
$C_{19}H_{14}BrCl$			
$4\text{-}ClC_6H_4(C_6H_5)_2CBr$	C_6H_5MgBr	$4\text{-}ClC_6H_4(C_6H_5)_3C$ (9%); $4\text{-}ClC_6H_4(4\text{-}C_6H_5C_6H_4)(C_6H_5)CH$ (27%); $C_6H_5(4\text{-}C_6H_5C_6H_4)_2CH$ (17%)	*203*
$C_{19}H_{15}Cl$			
$(C_6H_5)_3CCl$	CH_3MgBr	$(C_6H_5)_3CCH_3$ (95%)	*212*
$(C_6H_5)_3CCl$	CH_3MgI	$(C_6H_5)_3CCH_3$ (70%)	*81,80*
$(C_6H_5)_3CCl$	C_2H_5MgBr	$(C_6H_5)_3CC_2H_5$	*81,80*
$(C_6H_5)_3CCl$ (27 g.)	C_2H_5MgI (33 g. C_2H_5I)	$(C_6H_5)_3CC_2H_5$ (20.0 g.); $(C_6H_5)_3CH$ (4.5 g.); $[(C_6H_5)_3CO—]_2$ (0.3 g.); C_2H_4 (428 ml.)	*81*
$(C_6H_5)_3CCl$ (25 g.)	$n\text{-}C_3H_7MgBr$ (20 g. C_3H_7Br)	$(C_6H_5)_3CH$ (5.3 g.); $(C_6H_5)_3C\text{-}n\text{-}C_3H_7$; C_3H_6	*81*
$(C_6H_5)_3CCl$ (25 g.)	$i\text{-}C_3H_7MgBr$ (18 g. C_3H_7Br)	$(C_6H_5)_3CH$ (7.0 g.); $(C_6H_5)_3C\text{-}i\text{-}C_3H_7$ (6.0 g.)	*81*
$(C_6H_5)_3CCl$ (10 g.)	$H_2C{=}CHC{\equiv}CMgBr$ (slight excess)	$(C_6H_5)_3CC{\equiv}CCH{=}CH_2$ (7.5 g.)	*34*
$(C_6H_5)_3CCl$	$i\text{-}C_5H_{11}MgBr$	$(C_6H_5)_3C\text{-}i\text{-}C_5H_{11}$	*81*

TABLE XVI-I (Continued)

Halide	RMgX	Product(s)	Ref.
$C_{19}H_{15}Cl$ (*cont.*)			
$(C_6H_5)_3CCl$	C_6H_5MgBr	$(C_6H_5)_4C$ (0.5–5.0%); $[(C_6H_5)_3C—]_2$ (chiefly)	*83,154*
$(C_6H_5)_3CCl$	C_6H_5MgBr	$(C_6H_5)_4C$ (5–10%); $(C_6H_5)_3CH$; $(C_6H_5)_3COH$; $[(C_6H_5)_3CO—]_2$	80
$(C_6H_5)_3CCl$ (20 g., 0.072 mole)	C_6H_5MgBr (0.25 mole)	$(C_6H_5)_4C$ (0.2 g., 0.63%); $4\text{-}C_6H_5C_6H_4(C_6H_5)_2CH$ (10.9 g., 47.4%)	*71*
$(C_6H_5)_3CCl$	C_6H_5MgBr	$(C_6H_5)_4C$ (21–29%); $4\text{-}C_6H_5C_6H_4(C_6H_5)_2CH$ (13–35%); $(C_6H_5)_3CH$ (2–14%); $C_6H_5(4\text{-}C_6H_5C_6H_4)_2CH$ (2.5–3.5%); $4\text{-}C_6H_5C_6H_4(C_6H_5)_3C$ (0.5–0.8%); $(4\text{-}C_6H_5C_6H_4)_3CH$ (trace)*	*204*
$(C_6H_5)_3CCl$ (20 g.)	C_6H_5MgI (50 g. C_6H_5I)	$[(C_6H_5)_3C—]_2$; $(C_6H_5—)_2$	*195*
$(C_6H_5)_3CCl$	$4\text{-}ClC_6H_4CH_2MgCl$	$(C_6H_5)_3CC_6H_4\text{-}4\text{-}Cl$	*154*
$(C_6H_5)_3CCl$ (14 g.)	$C_6H_5CH_2MgCl$ (1.3 equiv. C_7H_7Cl)	$(C_6H_5)_3CCH_2C_6H_5$ (14.5 g.)	*80,154*
$C_{19}H_{15}Br$			
$(C_6H_5)_3CBr$	C_6H_5MgBr	$(C_6H_5)_4C$ ("a little"); $[(C_6H_5)_3C—]_2$ ("more")	57
$(C_6H_5)_3CBr$	C_6H_5MgBr	$(C_6H_5)_4C$ (5.0–7.5%); $4\text{-}C_6H_5C_6H_4(C_6H_5)_2CH$ (50–77%)	204
$C_6H_5(4\text{-}C_6H_5C_6H_4)CHBr$	$(C_6H_5)_3CMgBr$	$C_6H_5(4\text{-}C_6H_5C_6H_4)CHC(C_6H_5)_3$ (70%)	8
$C_{19}H_{15}I$			
$(C_6H_5)_3CI$	C_6H_5MgBr	$(C_6H_5)_4C$; $4\text{-}C_6H_5C_6H_4(C_6H_5)_2CH$†	*204*

* The results of eight experiments are here summarized; other experiments under various conditions and in various solvents are described in the same article (*204*).

† The same products as for the corresponding bromide or chloride, but in lower yields.

TABLE XVI-I (Continued)

Halide	RMgX	Product(s)	Ref.
$C_{20}H_{17}ClO$			
4-$CH_3OC_6H_4(C_6H_5)_2CCl$	CH_3MgI	4-$CH_3OC_6H_4(C_6H_5)_2CCH_3$	*114*
4-$CH_3OC_6H_4(C_6H_5)_2CCl$ (3.9 g.)	C_6H_5MgBr (3 equiv.)	$(C_6H_5)_3CC_6H_4$-4-OCH_3 (0.185 g., 4.5%)	*82*
$C_{20}H_{17}BrO$			
2-$CH_3OC_6H_4(C_6H_5)_2CBr$ (6.16 g.)	C_6H_5MgBr (3 equiv.)	2-$CH_3OC_6H_4(C_6H_5)_3C$ (2.67 g., 38%)	*82*
$C_{21}H_{15}Cl$			
(1-$C_{10}H_7)_2CHCl$	C_6H_5MgI	[(1-$C_{10}H_7)_2CH$ —]$_2$	*197*
(1-$C_{10}H_7)_2CHCl$ (3 g.)	1-$C_{10}H_7MgBr$ (4 g. $C_{10}H_7Br$)	[(1-$C_{10}H_7)_2CH$ —]$_2$ (1 g.)	*197*
$C_{21}H_{17}Cl$			
$C_6H_5[(C_6H_5)_2C=CH]CHCl$ (2.0 g.)	C_6H_5MgBr (1.2 g. C_6H_5Br)	$(C_6H_5)_2C=CHCH(C_6H_5)_2$; {$C_6H_5[(C_6H_5)_2C=CH]CH$ —}$_2$ (trace)	*213*
$C_{21}H_{17}Br$			
$(C_6H_5)_2C=C(C_6H_5)CH_2Br$	C_6H_5MgBr	$(C_6H_5)_2C=C(C_6H_5)CH_2C_6H_5$; $(C_6H_5)_2CHC(C_6H_5)=CHC_6H_5$; [$(C_6H_5)_2C=C(C_6H_5)CH_2$ —]$_2$	*14*
$C_{21}H_{19}ClO_2$			
2,4-$(CH_3O)_2C_6H_3(C_6H_5)_2CCl$ (6.77 g.)	C_6H_5MgBr (3 equiv.)	2,4-$(CH_3O)_2C_6H_3(C_6H_5)_3C$ (3.2 g., 52.6%)	*82*
2,5-$(CH_3O)_2C_6H_3(C_6H_5)_2CCl$ (9.35 g.)	C_6H_5MgI (3 equiv.)	2,5-$(CH_3O)_2C_6H_3(C_6H_5)_3C$ (6.1 g., 58%)	*82*
2,5-$(CH_3O)_2C_6H_3(C_6H_5)_2CCl$ (6.77 g.)	1-$C_{10}H_7MgBr$ (3 equiv.)	2,5-$(CH_3O)_2C_6H_3$(1-$C_{10}H_7)(C_6H_5)_2C$ (3.53 g., 41%)	*82*
3,4-$(CH_3O)_2C_6H_3(C_6H_5)_2CCl$ (6.77 g.)	C_6H_5MgBr (3 equiv.)	3,4-$(CH_3O)_2C_6H_3(C_6H_5)_3C$ (2.34 g., 30%)	*82*

TABLE XVI-I (Continued)

Halide	RMgX	Product(s)	Ref.
$C_{21}H_{19}BrO_2$			
2,5-$(CH_3O)_2C_6H_3(C_6H_5)_2CBr$ (7.66 g.)	C_6H_5MgBr (3 equiv.)	2,5-$(CH_3O)_2C_6H_3(C_6H_5)_3C$ (4.4 g., 58%)	*82*
2,5-$(CH_3O)_2C_6H_3(C_6H_5)_2CBr$ (7.66 g.)	C_6H_5MgI (3 equiv.)	2,5-$(CH_3O)_2C_6H_3(C_6H_5)_3C$ (1.28 g., 17%)	*82*
$C_{22}H_{19}ClO_2$			
2-Chloro-2,3,3-triphenyl-1,4-dioxane	CH_3MgI	No reaction	*217*
$C_{22}H_{21}Cl$			
$(4-CH_3C_6H_4)_3CCl$	C_6H_5MgBr	$(4-CH_3C_6H_4)_3CC_6H_5$ (31–41%)	*204*
$C_{22}H_{21}Br$			
$(C_6H_5CH_2)_3CBr$	C_2H_5MgBr (excess)	$(C_6H_5CH_2)_2C=CHC_6H_5$; $[(C_6H_5CH_2)_3C-]_2$; gas	*223*
$(C_6H_5CH_2)_3CBr$	$C_6H_5CH_2MgCl$ (excess)	$(C_6H_5CH_2)_4C$ (5%); $(C_6H_5CH_2)_2C=CHC_6H_5$ (chief product)	*223*
$C_{24}H_{17}Br$			
2,4,6-$(C_6H_5)_3C_6H_2Br$	2,4,6-$(C_6H_5)_3C_6H_2MgBr$	*No* $[2,4,6-(C_6H_5)_3C_6H_2-]_2$	*127*
$C_{24}H_{19}ClO$			
4-CH_3O-1-$C_{10}H_6(C_6H_5)_2CCl$	CH_3MgI	4-CH_3O-1-$C_{10}H_6(C_6H_5)_2CCH_3$	*114*
$C_{25}H_{19}Br$			
$(4-C_6H_5C_6H_4)_2CHBr$	$(C_6H_5)_3CMgBr$	$(4-C_6H_5C_6H_4)_2CHC(C_6H_5)_3$ (90%)	8

TABLE XVI-I (Continued)

Halide	RMgX	Product(s)	Ref.
$C_{26}H_{20}Cl_2$			
$[(C_6H_5)_2CCl—]_2$	C_6H_5MgX*	$[(C_6H_5)_2C=]_2$; $4\text{-}C_6H_5C_6H_4(C_6H_5)C=C(C_6H_5)_2$	*162*
$[(C_6H_5)_2CCl—]_2$	RMgX†	$[(C_6H_5)_2C=]_2$	*198*
$C_{26}H_{35}ClO_{17}$			
Heptaäcetyllactosyl chloride	C_6H_5MgX (*ca.* 18 equiv.)	$CH_3(C_6H_5)_2COH$ (95.4%, crude); after reäcetylation, heptaäcetyllactosylbenzene (69.4%, crude: 41.0% α, 59.0% β)	*109*
$C_{26}H_{35}BrO_{17}$			
Heptaäcetyllactosyl bromide (5 g.)	CH_3MgI (25 g. CH_3I)	$C_{26}H_{35}BrO_{17}\cdot 2CH_3MgI$ (regenerating original bromide upon hydrolysis)	*58*
$C_{27}H_{47}ClO$			
5-Chloro-3(β),6(β)-cholestanediol	CH_3MgI	5(α)-Methyl-3(β),6(β)-cholestanediol	*274,275*

* X = Br, I.

† RMgX = C_2H_5MgBr, C_6H_5MgBr, C_6H_5MgI.

REFERENCES FOR TABLE XVI-I

(*1*) Akabori and Saito, *Ber.*, *63B*, 2245–8 (1930).
(*2*) Allen and Henze, *J. Am. Chem. Soc.*, *61*, 1790–4 (1939).
(*3*) Alles, Icke, and Feigen, *J. Am. Chem. Soc.*, *64*, 2031–5 (1942).
(*4*) Godchot and Cauquil, *Compt. rend.*, *186*, 955–7 (1928).
(*5*) André, *Ann. chim.*, [8], *29*, 540–96 (1913).
(*6*) Anzilotti and Vogt, *J. Am. Chem. Soc.*, *61*, 572–3 (1939).
(*7*) Bachmann, *J. Am. Chem. Soc.*, *52*, 3287–90 (1930).
(*8*) Bachmann, *J. Am. Chem. Soc.*, *55*, 2135–9 (1933).
(*9*) Bachmann, *J. Am. Chem. Soc.*, *56*, 1363–7 (1934).
(*10*) Bachmann and Cockerill, *J. Am. Chem. Soc.*, *55*, 2932–4 (1933).
(*11*) Bachmann and Kloetzel, *J. Org. Chem.*, *3*, 55–61 (1938).
(*12*) Bannerot and Bonner, *J. Am. Chem. Soc.*, *56*, 1563–5 (1934).
(*13*) Bergmann and Bergmann, *J. Am. Chem. Soc.*, *59*, 1443–50 (1937).
(*14*) Bergmann and Weiss, *Ber.*, *64B*, 1485–93 (1931).
(*15*) Berlande, *Compt. rend.*, *212*, 437–9 (1941); *Chem. Abstr.*, *37*, 2720 (1943).
(*16*) Berlande, *Compt. rend.*, *213*, 484–6 (1941); *Chem. Abstr.*, *37*, 2720 (1943).
(*17*) Bert, *Compt. rend.*, *180*, 1504–6 (1925).
(*18*) Bert, *Compt. rend.*, *186*, 373–5 (1928).
(*19*) Bert, *Compt. rend.*, *186*, 587–8 (1928).
(*20*) Binaghi, *Gazz. chim. ital.*, *52,II*, 132–8 (1922); *Chem. Zentr.*, *1923,I*, 1435; *Chem. Abstr.*, *17*, 1425 (1923).
(*21*) Binaghi, *Gazz. chim. ital.*, *53*, 879–87 (1923); *Chem. Zentr.*, *1924,II*, 2356; *Chem. Abstr.*, *18*, 1488 (1924).
(*22*) Binaghi, *Gazz. chim. ital.*, *57*, 669–75 (1927); *Chem. Zentr.*, *1928,I*, 908.
(*23*) Bogert and Davidson, *J. Am. Chem. Soc.*, *56*, 185–90 (1934).
(*24*) Bordwell, Suter, and Webber, *J. Am. Chem. Soc.*, *67*, 827–32 (1945).
(*25*) Bourguel, *Compt. rend.*, *177*, 688–90 (1923).
(*26*) Boyle, McKenzie, and Mitchell, *Ber.*, *70B*, 2153–60 (1937).
(*27*) Brooks and Humphrey, *J. Am. Chem. Soc.*, *40*, 822–56 (1918).
(*28*) Bruylants, *Bull. acad. roy. Belg.*, *1908*, 1011–84; *Chem. Zentr.*, *1909,I*, 1859.
(*29*) Brückner, *Österr. Chem.-Ztg.*, *41*, 363 (1938); *Chem. Zentr.*, *1939,I*, 918.
(*30*) Buess, Karabinos, Kunz, and Gibbons, *Natl. Advisory Comm. Aeronaut., Tech. Note*, No.*1021*, 8 pp. (1946); *Chem. Abstr.*, *41*, 4113 (1947).
(*31*) Bygdén, *Ber.*, *45*, 3479–83 (1912).
(*32*) Calingaert, Soroos, Hnizda, and Shapiro, *J. Am. Chem. Soc.*, *66*, 1389–94 (1944).
(*33*) Carothers, U. S. Patent 2,072,867, March 9, 1937; *Chem. Abstr.*, *31*, P3335 (1937).
(*34*) Carothers and Berchet, *J. Am. Chem. Soc.*, *55*, 1094–6 (1933).
(*35*) Carothers and Berchet, *J. Am. Chem. Soc.*, *55*, 2813–7 (1933).
(*36*) Christ and Summerbell, *J. Am. Chem. Soc.*, *55*, 4547 (1933).
(*37*) Clément and Savard, *Compt. rend.*, *204*, 1742–3 (1937); *Chem. Abstr.*, *31*, 7044 (1937).
(*38*) Cleveland, *J. Chem. Phys.*, *11*, 1–6 (1943).
(*39*) Cottle and Hollyday, *J. Org. Chem.*, *12*, 510–6 (1947).
(*40*) Cottle, Jeltsch, Stoudt, and Walters, *J. Org. Chem.*, *11*, 286–91 (1946).
(*41*) Cottle and Powell, *J. Am. Chem. Soc.*, *58*, 2267–72 (1936).
(*42*) Crane, Boord, and Henne, *J. Am. Chem. Soc.*, *67*, 1237–9 (1945).
(*43*) Danehy, Killian, and Nieuwland, *J. Am. Chem. Soc.*, *58*, 611–2 (1936).
(*44*) Davies and Kipping, *J. Chem. Soc.*, *99*, 296–301 (1911).
(*45*) Deschamps, *J. Am. Chem. Soc.*, *42*, 2670–3 (1920).
(*46*) Dilthey and Hurtig, *Ber.*, *67B*, 495–6, 2004–7 (1934).

(47) Dionneau, *Ann. Chim.*, [9], 3, 194–268 (1915).
(48) Dubinin, *J. Gen. Chem.* (U.S.S.R.), 7, 2183–7 (1937); *Chem. Abstr.*, 32, 516 (1938).
(49) Dupont, *Ann. chim.*, [8], 30, 485–587 (1913).
(50) Durand and Waï-Hsun, *Compt. rend.*, 191, 1460–3 (1930).
(51) Dykstra, Lewis, and Boord, *J. Am. Chem. Soc.*, 52, 3396–404 (1930).
(52) Edgar, Calingaert, and Marker, *J. Am. Chem. Soc.*, 51, 1483–91 (1929).
(53) Elderfield, Craig, Lauer, Arnold, Gensler, Head, Bembry, Mighton, Tinker, Galbreath, Holley, Goldman, Maynard, and Picus, *J. Am. Chem. Soc.*, 68, 1516–23 (1943).
(54) Ellingboe and Fuson, *J. Am. Chem. Soc.*, 55, 2960–6 (1933).
(55) Ferrario and Fagetti, *Gazz. chim. ital.*, 38,*II*, 630–4 (1908); *Chem. Zentr.*, *1909*,*I*, 436.
(56) Fischer and Hess, *Ber.*, 45, 912–5 (1912).
(57) Freund, *Ber.*, 39, 2237–8 (1906).
(58) Fröschl, Zellner, and Zak., *Monatsh.*, 55, 25–46 (1930).
(59) Fuson, *J. Am. Chem. Soc.*, 48, 830–6 (1926).
(60) Fuson, *J. Am. Chem. Soc.*, 48, 2681–9 (1926).
(61) Fuson and Armstrong, *J. Am. Chem. Soc.*, 63, 2650–2 (1941).
(62) Fuson, Chadwick, and Ward, *J. Am. Chem. Soc.*, 68, 389–93 (1946).
(63) Fuson, Denton, and Best, *J. Org. Chem.*, 8, 64–72 (1943).
(64) Fuson, Denton, and Kneisley, *J. Am. Chem. Soc.*, 63, 2652–3 (1941).
(65) Fuson, Kneisley, Rabjohn, and Ward, *J. Am. Chem. Soc.*, 68, 533 (1946).
(66) Fuson and Porter, *J. Am. Chem. Soc.*, 70, 895–7 (1948).
(67) Fuson and Ross, *J. Am. Chem. Soc.*, 55, 720–3 (1933).
(68) Fuson, Speck, and Hatchard, *J. Org. Chem.*, 10, 55–61 (1945).
(69) Gauthier, *Ann. chim.*, [11], 20, 581–659 (1945).
(70) Geissman and Mallatt, *J. Am. Chem. Soc.*, 61, 1788–9 (1939).
(71) Gilman and Jones, *J. Am. Chem. Soc.*, 51, 2840–3 (1929).
(72) Gilman and Kirby, *J. Am. Chem. Soc.*, 54, 345–55 (1932).
(73) Gilman and Van Ess, *J. Am. Chem. Soc.*, 61, 1365–71 (1939).
(74) Godchot and Bedos, *Compt. rend.*, 178, 1184–6 (1924).
(75) Godchot and Bedos, *Bull. soc. chim.*, [4], 37, 1451–66 (1925).
(76) Godchot and Bedos, *Bull. soc. chim.*, [4], 37, 1637–51 (1925).
(77) Godchot and Cauquil, *Compt. rend.*, 186, 375–7 (1928).
(78) Golse, *Ann. chim.*, [12], 3, 527–69 (1948).
(79) Golumbic and Cottle, *J. Am. Chem. Soc.*, 61, 996–1000 (1939).
(80) Gomberg and Cone, *Ber.*, 39, 1461–70 (1906).
(81) Gomberg and Cone, *Ber.*, 39, 2957–70 (1906).
(82) Gomberg and Forrester, *J. Am. Chem. Soc.*, 47, 2373–91 (1925).
(83) Gomberg and Kamm, *J. Am. Chem. Soc.*, 39, 2009–15 (1917).
(84) Grédy, *Bull. soc. chim.*, [5], 3, 1093–101 (1936).
(85) Grignard, *Compt. rend.*, 138, 1048–50 (1904); *J. Chem. Soc.*, 86,*I*, 494 (1904).
(86) Grignard, *Compt. rend.*, 141, 44–6 (1905); *J. Chem. Soc.*, 88,*I*, 593 (1905).
(87) Grignard, *Ann. chim.*, [8], 10, 23–40 (1905).
(88) Grignard and Lepayre, *Bull. soc. chim.*, [4], 43, 141–2 (1928).
(89) Grignard and Lepayre, *Compt. rend.*, 192, 250–3 (1931); *Chem. Abstr.*, 25, 2421 (1931).
(90) Grignard, Lepayre, and Tchéoufaki, *Compt. rend.*, 187, 517–20 (1928).
(91) Grignard and Tchéoufaki, *Bull. soc. chim.*, [4], 43, 42–3 (1928).
(92) Grummit, Buck, and Becker, *J. Am. Chem. Soc.*, 67, 2265–6 (1945).
(93) Guillemonat, *Ann. chim.*, [11], 11, 143–211 (1939).
(94) Hamonet, *Compt. rend.*, 138, 813–4 (1904); *J. Chem. Soc.*, 86,*I*, 401 (1904); *Chem. Zentr.*, *1904*,*I*, 1195.

(95) Hamonet, *Compt. rend.*, *138*, 975–7 (1904); *J. Chem. Soc.*, *86,I*, 467 (1904); *Chem. Zentr.*, *1904,I*, 1400.
(96) Hamonet, *Compt. rend.*, *138*, 1609–12 (1904); *J. Chem. Soc.*, *86,I*, 705 (1904).
(97) Hamonet, *Bull. soc. chim.*, [3], 33, 528–9 (1905).
(98) Henne, Chanan, and Turk, *J. Am. Chem. Soc.*, *63*, 3474–6 (1941).
(99) Henne and Whaley, *J. Am. Chem. Soc.*, *64*, 1157–9 (1942).
(100) Henry, *Compt. rend.*, *144*, 308–13 (1907); *Chem. Zentr.*, *1907,I*, 1102.
(101) Henry, *Rec. trav. chim.*, *26*, 106–15 (1907).
(102) Henry, *Bull. acad. roy. Belg.*, *Classe sci.*, *1907*, 162–89; *Chem. Zentr.*, *1907,II*, 445.
(103) Hershberg, *Helv. Chim. Acta*, *17*, 351–8 (1934).
(104) Hill, Short, and Stromberg, *J. Chem. Soc.*, *1937*, 937–41.
(105) Hoshino, *Abstr. Japan. Chem. Lit.*, 6, 390–1 (1932); *Chem. Abstr.*, *27*, 291 (1933).
(106) Houben, *Ber.*, *36*, 3083–6 (1903).
(107) Houben and Führer, *Ber.*, *40*, 4990–5000 (1907).
(108) Hurd and Bollman, *J. Am. Chem. Soc.*, *56*, 447–9 (1934).
(109) Hurd and Bonner, *J. Am. Chem. Soc.*, *67*, 1972–7 (1945).
(110) Huston and Bostwick, *J. Org. Chem.*, *13*, 331–8 (1948).
(111) Huston, Jackson, and Spero, *J. Am. Chem. Soc.*, *63*, 1459–60 (1941).
(112) Hyman and Wagner, *J. Am. Chem. Soc.*, *52*, 4345–9 (1930).
(113) Iotsitch, *J. Russ. Phys.-Chem. Soc.*, 38, 920–1 (1906); *Bull. soc. chim.*, [4], *4*, 1558 (1908).
(114) Julian and Gist, *J. Am. Chem. Soc.*, *57*, 2030–2 (1935).
(115) Kandel, *Ann. chim.*, [11], *11*, 73–142 (1939).
(116) Karrer, Salomon, Morf, and Walker, *Helv. Chim. Acta*, *15*, 878–89 (1932).
(117) Kazanskiĭ, Liberman, Plate, Rosengart, and Tarasova, *J. Gen. Chem.* (U.S.S.R.), *17*, 1503–10 (1947); *Chem. Abstr.*, *42*, 2225 (1948).
(118) Kharasch, Engelmann, and Urry, *J. Am. Chem. Soc.*, *66*, 365–7 (1944).
(119) Kharasch and Fuchs, *J. Org. Chem.*, *9*, 359–72 (1944).
(120) Kharasch and Fuchs, U. S. Patent 2,409,287, Oct. 15, 1946; *Chem. Abstr.*, *41*, P990 (1947).
(121) Kharasch, Lambert, and Urry, *J. Org. Chem.*, *10*, 298–306 (1945).
(122) Kinney and Spliethoff, *J. Org. Chem.*, *14*, 71–8 (1949).
(123) Kirrmann, *Bull. soc. chim.*, [4], 39, 988–91 (1926).
(124) Kirrmann, *Bull. soc. chim.*, [4], *41*, 316–23 (1927).
(125) Kirrmann and Jacob, *Bull. soc. chim.*, [5], 7, 586–93 (1940).
(126) Kirrmann, Pacaud, and Dosque, *Bull. soc. chim.*, [5], *1*, 860–71 (1934).
(127) Kohler and Blanchard, *J. Am. Chem. Soc.*, 57, 367–71 (1935).
(128) Kohler and Johnstin, *Am. Chem. J.*, 33, 35–45 (1905).
(129) Korschak, *J. Gen. Chem.* (U.S.S.R.), 9, 1153–4 (1939); *Chem. Zentr.*, *1940,I*, 196; *Chem. Abstr.*, *34*, 1303 (1940).
(130) Kozacik and Reid, *J. Am. Chem. Soc.*, *60*, 2436–8 (1938).
(131) Krizewsky and Turner, *J. Chem. Soc.*, *115*, 559–61 (1919).
(132) Kuznetsov, *J. Gen. Chem.* (U.S.S.R.), *16*, 187–91 (1946); *Chem. Abstr.*, *41*, 443 (1947).
(133) Leendertse, *Rec. trav. chim.*, 53, 715–24 (1934).
(134) Lespieau, *Ann. chim.*, [9], *2*, 280–92 (1914).
(135) Lespieau, *Compt. rend.*, *170*, 1584–5 (1920).
(136) Lespieau, *Bull. soc. chim.*, [4], *29*, 528–35 (1921).
(137) Lespieau, *Bull. soc. chim.*, [4], *43*, 1189–93 (1928).
(138) Lespieau, *Compt. rend.*, *187*, 605–7 (1928); *Chem. Abstr.*, *23*, 817 (1929).
(139) Lespieau, *Compt. rend.*, *188*, 502–3 (1929); *Brit. Chem. Abstr.*, *1929A*, 421.
(140) Lespieau, *Compt. rend.*, *188*, 998–1000 (1929).

(*141*) Lespieau and Bresch, *Compt. rend.*, *156*, 710–2 (1913); *Chem. Abstr.*, 7, 2213 (1913).
(*142*) Lespieau and Deluchat, *Compt. rend.*, *183*, 889–91 (1926); *Chem. Zentr.*, *1927,I*, 260.
(*143*) Lespieau and Dupont, *Bull. soc. chim.*, [4], *1*, 4 (1907).
(*144*) Lespieau and Guillemonat, *Compt. rend.*, *195*, 245–7 (1932).
(*145*) Levina, Faĭnzil'berg, and Shusherina, *J. Gen. Chem.* (U.S.S.R.), *18*, 1775–80 (1948); *Chem. Abstr.*, *43*, 3344 (1949).
(*146*) Levina, Skvarchenko, Kagan, and Treshchova, *J. Gen. Chem.* (U.S.S.R.), *18*, 62–8 (1949); *Chem. Abstr.*, *43*, 6152 (1949).
(*147*) Levy and Cope, *J. Am. Chem. Soc.*, *66*, 1684–8 (1944).
(*148*) Magrane and Cottle, *J. Am. Chem. Soc.*, *64*, 484–7 (1942).
(*149*) Majima and Hoshino, *Ber.*, *58B*, 2042–6 (1925).
(*150*) Marker and Oakwood, *J. Am. Chem. Soc.*, *60*, 2598 (1938).
(*151*) Mason, *J. Am. Chem. Soc.*, *67*, 1538–40 (1945).
(*152*) McKenzie, Drew, and Martin, *J. Chem. Soc.*, *107*, 26–32 (1915).
(*153*) McKinley, U. S. Patent 2,415,599, Feb. 11, 1947; *Chem. Abstr.*, *41*, P3123 (1947).
(*154*) Meyer, *J. prakt. Chem.*, [2], 82, 521–38 (1910).
(*155*) Miller and Bachman, *J. Am. Chem. Soc.*, *57*, 766–71 (1935).
(*156*) Mousseron, *Bull. soc. chim.*, [5], *12*, 73 (1945); *Chem. Abstr.*, *40*, 845 (1946).
(*157*) Mousseron and Manon, *Compt. rend.*, *227*, 533–4 (1948); *Chem. Abstr.*, *43*, 2173 (1949).
(*158*) Mousseron and Winternitz, *Bull. soc. chim.*, [5], *12*, 71–2 (1945).
(*159*) Mousseron and Winternitz, *Bull. soc. chim.*, [5], *13*, 604–10 (1946).
(*160*) Mulliken, Wakeman and Gerry, *J. Am. Chem. Soc.*, *57*, 1605–7 (1935).
(*161*) Normant, *Ind. parfum.*, 3, 136–8 (1948); *Chem. Abstr.*, *42*, 7237 (1948).
(*162*) Norris, Thomas, and Brown, *Ber.*, *43*, 2940–59 (1910).
(*163*) Oddo and Binaghi, *Gazz. chim. ital.*, *51,II*, 330–7 (1921); *Chem. Zentr.*, *1922,I*, 1025; *Chem. Abstr.*, *16*, 1392 (1922).
(*164*) Oroshnik, *J. Am. Chem. Soc.*, *67*, 1627–8 (1945).
(*165*) Ozanne and Marvel, *J. Am. Chem. Soc.*, *52*, 5267–72 (1930).
(*166*) Palfray, Sabetay, and Reynaud, *Compt. rend.*, *224*, 939–41 (1947); *Chem. Abstr.*, *41*, 4785 (1947).
(*167*) Paul, *Compt. rend.*, *198*, 1246–8 (1934).
(*168*) Paul, *Compt. rend.*, *218*, 122–4 (1944); *Chem. Abstr.*, *40*, 2447 (1946).
(*169*) Paul and Riobé, *Compt. rend.*, *224*, 474–6 (1947); *Chem. Abstr.*, *41*, 4771 (1947).
(*170*) Plate, Sterligov, and Bazhulin, *J. Gen. Chem.* (U.S.S.R.), *14*, 955–9 (1944); *Chem. Abstr.*, 39, 4594 (1945).
(*171*) Platé, *Compt. rend. acad. sci. U.R.S.S., Classe sci. chim.*, *24*, 257–62 (1939); *Chem. Abstr.*, 34, 994 (1940).
(*172*) Prévost, *Compt. rend.*, *187*, 946–8 (1928).
(*173*) Prévost, *Bull. soc. chim.*, [4], *49*, 1372–81 (1931).
(*174*) Prévost and Daujat, *Bull. soc. chim.*, [4], *47*, 588–94 (1930).
(*175*) Pudovic and Arbuzov, *Bull. acad. sci. U.R.S.S., Classe sci. chim.*, *1948*, 246–9; *Chem. Abstr.*, *42*, 4973 (1948).
(*176*) Quelet, *Compt. rend.*, *182*, 1283–5 (1926).
(*177*) Quelet, *Compt. rend.*, *184*, 888–90 (1927).
(*178*) Quelet, *Bull. soc. chim.*, [4], *45*, 75–97 (1929).
(*179*) Quelet and Golse, *Compt. rend.*, *224*, 661–3 (1947); *Chem. Abstr.*, *41*, 4779 (1947).
(*180*) Quelet and Golse, *Bull. soc. chim.*, [5], *14*, 313–6 (1947).

(181) Quelet and Pineau, *Compt. rend.*, *222*, 1237–8 (1946); *Chem. Abstr.*, *40*, 5397 (1946).
(182) Rebek and Mandrino, *Österr. Chem.-Ztg.*, *41*, 49–52 (1938); *Chem. Zentr.*, *1938,II*, 1204; *Chem. Abstr.*, *32*, 3755 (1938).
(183) Rebek and Mandrino, *Österr. Chem.-Ztg.*, *41*, 363–4 (1939); *Chem. Zentr.*, *1939,I*, 919.
(184) Reformatsky, Grischkewitsch-Frochimosky, and Semenzow, *Ber.*, *44*, 1885–6 (1911).
(185) Regier and Blue, *J. Org. Chem.*, *14*, 505–8 (1949).
(186) Reychler, *Bull. soc. chim.*, [3], *35*, 737–40 (1906).
(187) Ribas, *Anales soc. españ. fís. quím.*, *26*, 122–32 (1928); *Chem. Zentr.*, *1928,II*, 40.
(188) Rivière, *Ann. chim.*, [12], *1*, 157–231 (1946).
(189) Ruzicka, Ehmann, and Morgell, *Helv. Chim. Acta*, *16*, 314–26 (1933).
(190) Korshak and Kozarenko, *Doklady Akad. Nauk S.S.S.R.*, 76, 685–7 (1951); *Chem. Abstr.*, *45*, 8435 (1951).
(191) Sanna, *Rend. seminar. facoltà sci. univ. Cagliari*, *5*, 76–81 (1935); *Chem. Zentr.*, *1937,II*, 2345; *Chem. Abstr.*, 33, 5833 (1939).
(192) Savard and Hösögüt, *Rev. faculté sci. univ. Istanbul*, [N.S.], 3, 164–73 (1938); *Chem. Abstr.*, *32*, 5795 (1938).
(193) Scheibler and Schmidt, *Ber.*, *67B*, 1514–8 (1934).
(194) Schmerling and Ipatieff, U. S. Patent 2,404,927, July 30, 1946; *Chem. Abstr.*, *40*, P6494 (1946).
(195) Schmidlin, *Ber.*, *43*, 1137–44 (1910).
(196) Grignard, Lepayre, and Tchéoufaki, *Bull. soc. chim.*, [4], *43*, 931–2 (1928).
(197) Schmidlin and Massini, *Ber.*, *42*, 2377–92 (1909).
(198) Schmidlin and von Escher, *Ber.*, *43*, 1153–61 (1910).
(199) Schmidt and Hartmann, *Ber.*, *74B*, 1325–32 (1941).
(200) Schmidt, Schoeller, and Eberlein, *Ber.*, *74B*, 1313–24 (1941).
(201) Schmidt-Nickels, *Ber.*, *62B*, 917–9 (1929).
(202) Schmitt and Boord, *J. Am. Chem. Soc.*, *54*, 751–61 (1932).
(203) Schoepfle and Trepp, *J. Am. Chem. Soc.*, *54*, 4059–65 (1932).
(204) Schoepfle and Trepp, *J. Am. Chem. Soc.*, *58*, 791–4 (1936).
(205) Shoemaker and Boord, *J. Am. Chem. Soc.*, *53*, 1505–12 (1931).
(206) Shoesmith and Connor, *J. Chem. Soc.*, *1927*, 1768–72.
(207) Sirks, *Rec. trav. chim.*, *65*, 850–8 (1946).
(208) Small and Cohen, *J. Am. Chem. Soc.*, *53*, 2214–26 (1931).
(209) Smith and Perry, *J. Am. Chem. Soc.*, *61*, 1411–2 (1939).
(210) Soday and Boord, *J. Am. Chem. Soc.*, *55*, 3293–302 (1933).
(211) Grignard, *Bull. soc. chim.*, [3], *33*, 918–9 (1905).
(212) Späth, *Monatsh.*, *34*, 1965–2014 (1913).
(213) Straus and Ehrenstein, *Ann.*, *442*, 93–118 (1925).
(214) Summerbell and Bauer, *J. Am. Chem. Soc.*, *57*, 2364–8 (1935).
(215) Summerbell and Bauer, *J. Am. Chem. Soc.*, *58*, 759–61 (1936).
(216) Summerbell and Umhoefer, *J. Am. Chem. Soc.*, *61*, 3016 (1939).
(217) Summerbell, Umhoeffer, and Lappin, *J. Am. Chem. Soc.*, *69*, 1352–4 (1947).
(218) Swallen and Boord, *J. Am. Chem. Soc.*, *52*, 651–60 (1930).
(219) Tchéoufaki, *Contrib. Inst. Chem. Natl. Acad. Peiping*, *1*, 127–52 (1934); *Chem. Zentr.*, *1937,II*, 2982.
(220) Tiffeneau, *Bull. soc. chim.*, [3], *29*, 1156–8 (1903).
(221) Tiffeneau, *Compt. rend.*, *139*, 481–2 (1904); *Chem. Zentr.*, *1904,II*, 1038.
(222) Tiffeneau, Ditz, and Tchoubar, *Compt. rend.*, *198*, 1039–41 (1934); *Chem. Abstr.*, *28*, 3720 (1934).
(223) Trotman, *J. Chem. Soc.*, *127*, 88–95 (1925).
(224) Vavon and Mitchovitch, *Compt. rend.*, *186*, 702–5 (1928).

(225) Vavon and Mottez, *Compt. rend.*, *218*, 557-9 (1944); *Chem. Abstr.*, *39*, 2739 (1945).
(226) Velick and English, *J. Biol. Chem.*, *160*, 473-80 (1945).
(227) von Braun, Deutsch, and Schmatloch, *Ber.*, *45*, 1246-63 (1912).
(228) von Braun, Kamp, and Kopp, *Ber.*, *70B*, 1750-60 (1937).
(229) von Braun and Kühn, *Ber.*, *60B*, 2551-7 (1927).
(230) von Braun and Reitz-Kopp, *Ber.*, *74B*, 1105-10 (1941).
(231) Waterman and de Kok, *Rec. trav. chim.*, *52*, 251-6 (1933).
(232) Waterman and de Kok, *Rec. trav. chim.*, *52*, 298-302 (1933).
(233) Waterman and de Kok, *Rec. trav. chim.*, *53*, 725-9 (1934).
(234) Waterman and de Kok, *Rec. trav. chim.*, *53*, 1133-8 (1934).
(235) Weizmann and Bergmann, *J. Chem. Soc.*, *1936*, 401-2.
(236) Whitmore and Fleming, *J. Am. Chem. Soc.*, *55*, 3803-6 (1933).
(237) Whitmore, Herr, Clarke, Rowland, and Schiessler, *J. Am. Chem. Soc.*, *67*, 2059-61 (1945).
(238) Whitmore and Homeyer, *J. Am. Chem. Soc.*, *55*, 4555-9 (1933).
(239) Whitmore and Sloat, *J. Am. Chem. Soc.*, *64*, 2968-70 (1942).
(240) Whitmore, Stehman, and Herndon, *J. Am. Chem. Soc.*, *55*, 3807-9 (1933).
(241) Wibaut, Hoog, Langedijk, Overhoff, and Smittenberg, *Rec. trav. chim.*, *58*, 329-77 (1939).
(242) Wilkinson, *J. Chem. Soc.*, *1931*, 3057-62.
(243) Wilson, Roberts, and Young, *J. Am. Chem. Soc.*, *71*, 2019-20 (1949).
(244) Witman, U. S. Patent 2,290,401, July 21, 1943; *Chem. Abstr.*, *37*, P388 (1943).
(245) Young, Roberts, and Wax, *J. Am. Chem. Soc.*, *67*, 841-3 (1945).
(246) Yur'ev, Voronkov, Gragerov, and Kondrat'eva, *J. Gen. Chem.* (U.S.S.R.), *18*, 1804-10 (1948); *Chem. Abstr.*, *43*, 3818 (1949).
(247) Godchot, Bedos, and Cauquil, *Bull. soc. chim.*, [4], *43*, 521-2 (1928).
(248) Zakharova, *J. Gen. Chem.* (U.S.S.R.), *17*, 1277-85 (1947); *Chem. Abstr.*, *42*, 3722 (1948).
(249) Zeltner and Tarassoff, *Ber.*, *43*, 941-5 (1910).
(250) Hess, *Ber.*, *46*, 3125-9 (1913).
(251) Hoshino and Shimodaira, *Ann.*, *520*, 19-30 (1935).
(252) Mousseron and Winternitz, *Compt. rend.*, *221*, 701-3 (1945); *Chem. Abstr.*, *41*, 101 (1947).
(253) Stahl and Cottle, *J. Am. Chem. Soc.*, *65*, 1782-3 (1943).
(254) Lutz, Allison, Ashburn, Bailey, Clark, Codington, Deinet, Freek, Jordan, Leake, Martin, Nicodemus, Rowlett, Shearer, Smith, and Wilson, *J. Org. Chem.*, *12*, 617-703 (1947).
(255) Levina and Egorova, *J. Gen. Chem.* (U.S.S.R.), *16*, 821-4 (1946); *Chem. Abstr.*, *41*, 1596 (1947).
(256) Johnson, *J. Chem. Soc.*, *1946*, 1009-14.
(257) Mousseron, Winternitz, and Combes, *Compt. rend.*, *223*, 909-11 (1946); *Chem. Abstr.*, *41*, 1622 (1947).
(258) Sontag, *Ann. chim.*, [11], *1*, 359-438 (1934).
(259) Dice, Watkins, and Schuman, *J. Am. Chem. Soc.*, *72*, 1738-40 (1950).
(260) Schorigin, Issaguljanz, Gussewa, Ossipowa, and Poljakowa, *Ber.*, *64B*, 2584-90 (1931).
(261) Glattfeld and Cameron, *J. Am. Chem. Soc.*, *49*, 1043-8 (1927).
(262) Bergmann and Blum-Bergmann, *J. Am. Chem. Soc.*, *58*, 1678-81 (1936).
(263) Malm and Summers, *J. Am. Chem. Soc.*, *73*, 362-3 (1951).
(264) Godchot and Cauquil, *Bull. soc. chim.*, [4], *43*, 520-1 (1928).
(265) Bedos, *Compt. rend.*, *181*, 117-9 (1925); *Chem. Abstr.*, *19*, 3266 (1925).
(266) Conant and Kirner, *J. Am. Chem. Soc.*, *46*, 232-52 (1924).
(267) Bedos, *Bull. soc. chim.*, [4], *39*, 674-90 (1926).

(268) Godchot and Bedos, *Compt. rend.*, *178*, 1374–5 (1924).
(269) Cook, Hewett, and Lawrence, *J. Chem. Soc.*, *1936*, 71–80.
(270) Mousseron and Du, *Bull. soc. chim.*, [5], *15*, 91–6 (1948).
(271) Grignard, French Patent 348,957, Nov. 10, 1904; *J. Soc. Chem. Ind.*, *24*, 559 (1905).
(272) Grignard, German Patent 164,883, Nov. 16, 1905; *Chem. Zentr.*, *1905,II*, 1751.
(273) Grignard, *Bull. soc. chim.*, [4], *1*, 247–8 (1907).
(274) Urushibara and Chuman, *Bull. Chem. Soc. Japan*, *22*, 69–74 (1949); *Chem. Abstr.*, *44*, 1124 (1950).
(275) Chuman, *J. Chem. Soc. Japan, Pure Chem. Sect.*, *70*, 253–7 (1949); *Chem. Abstr.*, *45*, 6651 (1951).
(276) Ostrogovich, *Chem.-Ztg.*, 36, 738–9 (1912); *Chem. Zentr.*, *1912,II*, 607.
(277) Meyer and Nabe, *J. prakt. Chem.*, [2], *82*, 521–38 (1910).
(278) van der Zanden, *Rec. trav. chim.*, *57*, 233–47 (1938).
(279) van der Zanden, *Rec. trav. chim.*, *58*, 181–92 (1939).
(280) van der Zanden and de Vries, *Rec. trav. chim.*, *69*, 569–73 (1950).
(281) Thorne, Hennion, and Nieuwland, *J. Am. Chem. Soc.*, *58*, 796–7 (1936).
(282) Vavon and Mottez, *Bull. soc. chim.*, [5], *11*, 196 (1944).
(283) Kirrmann, *Compt. rend.*, *182*, 1629–31 (1926); *Chem. Abstr.*, *20*, 3155 (1926).
(284) Prévost, Gaudemar, and Honigberg, *Compt. rend.*, *230*, 1186–8 (1950); *Chem. Abstr.*, *45*, 1497 (1951).
(285) Lawrence and Shelton, *Ind. Eng. Chem.*, *42*, 136–40 (1950).
(286) Letsinger and Traynham, *J. Am. Chem. Soc.*, *72*, 849–52 (1950).
(287) Campbell and Eby, *J. Am. Chem. Soc.*, *62*, 1798–800 (1940).
(288) Berlande, *Bull. soc. chim.*, [5], *9*, 641–2, 642–4, 644–53 (1942).
(289) Pudovik, and Vinokurova, *J. Gen. Chem.* (U.S.S.R.), *19*, 1882–90 (1949); *Chem. Abstr.*, *44*, 1896 (1950).
(290) Pourrat, *Compt. rend.*, *228*, 1031–3 (1949).
(291) Kirrmann, *Bull. soc. chim.*, [4], *47*, 834–47 (1930).
(292) von Braun and Kühn, *Ber.*, *58B*, 2168–73 (1925).
(293) Prévost, *Bull. soc. chim.*, [4], *49*, 1372–81 (1931).

CHAPTER XVII

Allylic Rearrangements in Grignard Reactions *

The so-called allylic rearrangements of Grignard reagents have been observed in connection with the reactions of Grignard reagents prepared from halides of two general classes: (1) arylmethyl halides, and (2) substituted allyl halides, of which the butenyl halides have been most extensively studied. In reality the two types of reaction have little in common, and their co-classification must be regarded as based chiefly on formal considerations. For that reason the two kinds of reactions, although included in one chapter in deference to popular classification, are discussed separately.

"ABNORMAL" REACTIONS OF ARYLMETHYLMAGNESIUM HALIDES

Although Grignard[1] had erroneously reported the product of the reaction of benzylmagnesium chloride with "trioxymethylene" as phenethyl alcohol, Tiffeneau and Delange[2] showed that the major product of the reaction is *o*-tolylmethanol. At the time they made the sapient comment, apparently rather generally ignored by subsequent investigators other than Tschitschibabin,[3] and Johnson[4] that "this particular condensation is of the same type as that whereby the primary aromatic alcohols are obtained from formaldehyde and arylhydroxylamines or sodium phenoxides."

In Table XVII-I are summarized most of the reported "abnormal" reactions of benzylmagnesium chloride and some of its analogs. No attempt

* For discussions of the general subject of allylic rearrangements see: Wheland, "Advanced Organic Chemistry," John Wiley & Sons, Inc., New York, 2nd ed., *1949*, pp. 535–44; Young, "Allylic rearrangements during the synthesis of organic compounds," *Record of Chemical Progress*, *11*, 129–35 (1950); Young, "Organic reaction mechanisms with allylic compounds," *J. Chem. Education*, *27*, 357–64 (1950); Prévost, "La transposition allylique. Généralites. Essais d'interprétation théorique," *Bull. soc. chim.*, [5], *18*, C 1–9 (1951). For a review of allylic Grignard reactions see: Kirrmann, "Le rôle des organo-magnésiens dans la transposition allylique," *Bull. soc. chim.*, [5], *18*, C 9–13 (1951).

[1] Grignard, *Bull. soc. chim.*, [3], *29*, 953–4 (1903).

[2] Tiffeneau and Delange, *Compt. rend.*, *137*, 573–5 (1903); *J. Chem. Soc.*, *86*,*I*, 48 (1904).

[3] Tschitschibabin, *Ber.*, *42*, 3469–79 (1909).

[4] Johnson, *J. Am. Chem. Soc.*, *55*, 3029–32 (1933).

TABLE XVII-I

SOME REACTIONS OF BENZYL GRIGNARD REAGENTS AND THEIR ANALOGS

[A plus sign (+) indicates that a product is reported but that the yield is not stated; a plus sign with asterisk (+*) indicates the principal product of the reaction; a plus sign with dagger (+†) indicates a product reported to be present in small amount; a plus sign with two-handled dagger (+‡) indicates a product reported to be present in trace amount.]

RMgX	Co-reactant	"Normal" Product	"Abnormal" Product(s)		Ref.
		(%)	Ortho (%)	Para (%)	
$(\beta\text{-}C_4H_3O)CH_2MgCl$ §	CO_2	1.7	26.8	...	*16*
$(\beta\text{-}C_4H_3O)CH_2MgCl$ §	HCHO	...	33.4	...	*16*
$(\alpha\text{-}C_4H_3S)CH_2MgCl$ ¶	CO_2	29.1	15.6	...	*18,17*
$(\alpha\text{-}C_4H_3S)CH_2MgCl$ ¶	$ClCO_2C_2H_5$	0	72	...	*18,17*
$(\alpha\text{-}C_4H_3S)CH_2MgCl$ ¶	HCHO	...	49	...	*18*
$(\alpha\text{-}C_4H_3S)CH_2MgCl$ ¶	CH_3COCl	...	31–34	...	*18*
$(\alpha\text{-}C_4H_3S)CH_2MgCl$ ¶	$(CH_2)_2O$	...	39	...	*18*
$(\alpha\text{-}C_4H_3S)CH_2MgCl$ ¶	$(CH_3CO)_2O$	...	25 ‖	...	*18*
$(\beta\text{-}C_4H_3S)CH_2MgBr$ **	CO_2	...	12.5 ††	...	*19*
$(\alpha\text{-}C_5H_4N)CH_2MgX$ ‡‡	CH_3COCl	+	...	...	*20*
$(\alpha\text{-}C_5H_4N)CH_2MgX$ ‡‡	$(CH_2)_2O$	+	...	...	*20*
$(\alpha\text{-}C_5H_5S)CH_2MgBr$ §§	CO_2	...	+	...	*21*
$2,6\text{-}Cl_2C_6H_3CH_2MgCl$	CO_2	+	...	...	*10*
$2,6\text{-}Cl_2C_6H_3CH_2MgCl$	$ClCO_2CH_3$	+	...	...	*10*

§ $\beta\text{-}C_4H_3O$ = 3-furyl; the "*ortho*" product is the α (2) derivative.

¶ $\alpha\text{-}C_4H_3S$ = 2-thienyl; the "*ortho*" product is the β (3) derivative.

‖ A product believed to be 1,3-bis-(2-thienyl)propene is also reported (31.0%).

** $\beta\text{-}C_4H_3S$ = 3-thienyl; the "*ortho*" product is the α (2) derivative.

†† This is the overall yield based on $(\beta\text{-}C_4H_3S)CH_2Cl$; the method employed for the preparation of the Grignard reagent leads chiefly to Wurtz product.

‡‡ $\alpha\text{-}C_5H_4N$ = 2-pyridyl; X = Br, I.

§§ $\alpha\text{-}C_5H_5S$ = 5-methyl-2-thienyl; the "*ortho*" product is the β (3) derivative.

TABLE XVII-I (Continued)

RMgX	Co-reactant	"Normal" Product (%)	"Abnormal" Product(s) Ortho (%)	"Abnormal" Product(s) Para (%)	Ref.
$2,6\text{-}Cl_2C_6H_3CH_2MgCl$	CH_3COCl	...	...	+	*10*
$2,6\text{-}Cl_2C_6H_3CH_2MgCl$	$(CH_3CO)_2O$	+	...	...	*10*
$2\text{-}ClC_6H_4CH_2MgCl$	CO_2	+	...	...	*10*
$2\text{-}ClC_6H_4CH_2MgCl$	$ClCO_2CH_3$	+	...	...	*10*
$2\text{-}ClC_6H_4CH_2MgCl$	CH_3COCl	...	+	...	*10*
$2\text{-}ClC_6H_4CH_2MgCl$	$(CH_3CO)_2O$	...	+	...	*10*
$C_6H_5CH_2MgCl$	Br_2	63	...	...	*9*
$C_6H_5CH_2MgCl$	SO_2	+	...	...	*28*
$C_6H_5CH_2MgCl$	$(C_2H_5)_2SO_4$	$+^{*}$	0	0.4–5.0	*14*
$C_6H_5CH_2MgCl$	H_2NCl	92	0	...	*11*
$C_6H_5CH_2MgCl$	CO_2	+	...	...	*1,9*
$C_6H_5CH_2MgCl$	CO_2	40	0	...	*10*
$C_6H_5CH_2MgCl$	$ClCO_2CH_3$	$+^{\ddagger}$	$+^{*}$	...	*10*
$C_6H_5CH_2MgCl$	$ClCO_2C_2H_5$	+	+	...	*5,6,10*
$C_6H_5CH_2MgCl$	$ClCO_2C_2H_5$	$+^{*}$	*ca.* 20	$+^{\ddagger}$ (?)	*9*
$C_6H_5CH_2MgCl$	$(C_2H_5O)_2CO$	+	...	...	*10*
$C_6H_5CH_2MgCl$	$HCO_2C_2H_5$	$+^{*}$	+	+	*9*
$C_6H_5CH_2MgCl$	$HCHO$	...	40	...	*23,1*
$C_6H_5CH_2MgCl$	$(HCHO)_x$	+	42	...	*22*
$C_6H_5CH_2MgCl$	CH_3COCl	$+^{*}$	$+^{\dagger}$	...	*9*
$C_6H_5CH_2MgCl$	CH_3COCl	...	18	...	*15*
$C_6H_5CH_2MgCl$	CH_3COCl	...	24	...	*10*
$C_6H_5CH_2MgCl$	$(CH_2)_2O$	+	...	+	*5,9*
$C_6H_5CH_2MgCl$	CH_3CHO	+	+	...	*13*
$C_6H_5CH_2MgCl$	CH_3CHO	32	$29^{\S}$	...	*23*
$C_6H_5CH_2MgCl$	$(CH_3CHO)_x$	+	...	...	*1*
$C_6H_5CH_2MgCl$	CH_3OCH_2Cl	$+^{*}$	+	+	*7; cf. 8*

§The "abnormal" product reported is the glycol, $1\text{-}HOCHR'\text{-}2\text{-}HOCHR'CH_2C_6H_4$.

TABLE XVII-I (Continued)

RMgX	Co-reactant	"Normal" Product	"Abnormal" Product(s)		Ref.
		(%)	Ortho (%)	Para (%)	
$C_6H_5CH_2MgCl$	CH_3OCH_2Cl	88*x*	5*x*	7*x*	*24*
$C_6H_5CH_2MgCl$	CH_3OCH_2Br	78*x*–79*x*	12*x*–14*x*	7*x*–10*x*	*24*
$C_6H_5CH_2MgCl$	CH_3OCH_2I	88*x*	6*x*	6*x*	*24*
$C_6H_5CH_2MgCl$	C_2H_5CHO	35	62 §	...	*23*
$C_6H_5CH_2MgCl$	$(CH_3)_2CO$	+	...	...	*1*
$C_6H_5CH_2MgCl$	$C_2H_5OCH_2Cl$	53*x*	16*x*	31*x*	*9*; *cf*. *8*
$C_6H_5CH_2MgCl$	$C_2H_5OCH_2Cl$	92*x*	2*x*	6*x*	*24*
$C_6H_5CH_2MgCl$	$CH_3(CH_3O)CHCl$	99.0*x*	0.8*x*	0.2*x*	*24*
$C_6H_5CH_2MgCl$	$(ClCH_2CO)_2O$	...	*ca*. 42	...	*10*
$C_6H_5CH_2MgCl$	$(CH_3CO)_2O$	+	*ca*. 30	...	*10*
$C_6H_5CH_2MgCl$	*n*-C_3H_7CHO	+	+	...	*13*
$C_6H_5CH_2MgCl$	*n*-C_3H_7CHO	40	33 §	...	*23*
$C_6H_5CH_2MgCl$	*i*-C_3H_7CHO	75	13 §	...	*23*
$C_6H_5CH_2MgCl$	*n*-$C_3H_7OCH_2Cl$	95.0*x*	2.5*x*	2.5*x*	*24*
$C_6H_5CH_2MgCl$	*n*-$C_3H_7(CH_3O)CHCl$	98*x*	2*x*	0	*24*
$C_6H_5CH_2MgCl$	C_6H_5CN	+	...	...	*9*
$C_6H_5CH_2MgCl$	C_6H_5COCl	+	+	...	*10*
$C_6H_5CH_2MgCl$	C_6H_5CHO	+	...	...	*2*
$C_6H_5CH_2MgCl$	C_6H_5CHO	+*	+†	+‡	*3*
$C_6H_5CH_2MgCl$ ¶	C_6H_5CHO	90	...	...	*4*
$C_6H_5CH_2MgCl$ ‖	C_6H_5CHO	40*x*	60*x***	...	*4*

§ The "abnormal" product reported is the glycol, 1-HOCHR′-2-HOCHR′$CH_2C_6H_4$.

¶ Slow dropwise addition of aldehyde to Grignard reagent solution.

‖ Slow addition of Grignard reagent solution to ethereal aldehyde solution.

** The product reported is 1,3-diphenylisochroman. See also: García-Banús and Medrano, *Anales soc. españ. fís. quím.*, *21*, 436–63 (1923); *Chem. Abstr.*, *18*, 2144 (1924); García-Banús, *Anales soc. españ. fís. quím.*, *26*, 372–98 (1928); *Chem. Abstr.*, *23*, 2178 (1929).

TABLE XVII-I (Continued)

RMgX	Co-reactant	"Normal" Product (%)	"Abnormal" Product(s) Ortho (%)	"Abnormal" Product(s) Para (%)	Ref.
$C_6H_5CH_2MgCl$ §	C_6H_5CHO	84.7	1.7 ¶	...	*25*
$C_6H_5CH_2MgCl$ ‖	C_6H_5CHO	43.7	17.6 ¶	...	*25*
$C_6H_5CH_2MgCl$	$C_6H_5CH_2Cl$	65	...	...	*9*
$C_6H_5CH_2MgCl$	n-$C_6H_{13}CHO$	55	14**	...	*23*
$C_6H_5CH_2MgCl$	$ClCH_2COC_6H_5$	+	...	...	*9*
$C_6H_5CH_2MgCl$	$C_6H_5CH_2CO_2C_2H_5$	71	...	...	*10*
$C_6H_5CH_2MgCl$	$C_2H_5(n$-$C_4H_9)CHCHO$	66	6**	...	*23*
$C_6H_5CH_2MgCl$	Citronellal ††	+	+**	...	*12*; *cf.* *26,27*
$C_6H_5CH_2MgCl$	$(C_6H_5)_2NCOCl$	+	...	...	*9*
$C_6H_5CH_2MgBr$	CH_3OCH_2Cl	79*x*	13*x*	8*x*	*24*
$C_6H_5CH_2MgI$	CH_3OCH_2Cl	84*x*	7*x*	9*x*	*24*
2-$CH_3C_6H_4CH_2MgBr$	SO_2	+	...	...	*28*
2-$CH_3C_6H_4CH_2MgBr$	CO_2	+	...	...	*28*
2-$CH_3C_6H_4CH_2MgBr$	$(HCHO)_x$	1.5	28.5	...	*28*
2-$CH_3C_6H_4CH_2MgBr$	$(CH_2)_2O$	...	10*x*	90*x*	*28*
2-$CH_3C_6H_4CH_2MgBr$	CH_3OCH_2Cl	...	90*x*	...	*28*
2-$CH_3C_6H_4CH_2MgBr$	$(CH_3)_2CO$	+	...	...	*29*
3-$CH_3C_6H_4CH_2MgBr$	SO_2	+*	+‡ (?)	...	*28*
3-$CH_3C_6H_4CH_2MgBr$	CO_2	+†	64‡‡	...	*31*; *cf.* *28*

§Slow dropwise addition of aldehyde to Grignard reagent solution.

¶The product reported is 1,3-diphenylisochroman. See also: García-Banús and Medrano, *Anales soc. españ. fís. quím.*, *21*, 436–63 (1923); *Chem. Abstr.*, *18*, 2144 (1924); **García-Banús**, *Anales soc. españ. fís. quím.*, *26*, 372–98 (1928); *Chem. Abstr.*, *23*, 2178 (1929).

‖Slow addition of Grignard reagent solution to ethereal aldehyde solution.

**The "abnormal" product reported is the glycol, 1-HOCHR′-2-HOCHR′$CH_2C_6H_4$.

††Probably a mixture of $H_2C{=}C(CH_3)(CH_2)_3CH(CH_3)CH_2CHO$ and $(CH_3)_2C{=}CHCH_2CH_2CH(CH_3)CH_2CHO$.

‡‡Although Mousseron and Du (*28*) have reported the *ortho*-rearrangement product as 2,6-dimethylbenzoic acid, Moser and Sause (*31*) have shown that it is actually the more probable 2,4-dimethylbenzoic acid. Upon purely geometrical grounds this could, of course, be a *para*-rearrangement product, but that seems highly improbable.

TABLE XVII-I (Continued)

RMgX	Co-reactant	"Normal" Product	"Abnormal" Product(s)		Ref.
		(%)	Ortho (%)	Para (%)	
$3\text{-}CH_3C_6H_4CH_2MgBr$	$(HCHO)_x$	+	...	...	*29*
$3\text{-}CH_3C_6H_4CH_2MgBr$	CH_3CHO	+	...	...	*29*
$3\text{-}CH_3C_6H_4CH_2MgBr$	$(CH_2)_2O$	45	...	...	*28*
$3\text{-}CH_3C_6H_4CH_2MgBr$	CH_3OCH_2Cl	+	...	...	*28*
$3\text{-}CH_3C_6H_4CH_2MgBr$	$(CH_3)_2CO$	+	...	...	*28*
$4\text{-}CH_3C_6H_4CH_2MgBr$	SO_2	+	...	...	*28*
$4\text{-}CH_3C_6H_4CH_2MgBr$	CO_2	90*x*	10*x*	...	*28*
$4\text{-}CH_3C_6H_4CH_2MgBr$	$(HCHO)_x$	7.5	22.5	...	*28*
$4\text{-}CH_3C_6H_4CH_2MgBr$	$(CH_2)_2O$	80*x*	20*x*	...	*28*
$CH_3(C_6H_5)CHMgCl$	$(HCHO)_x$	+	...	...	*28*
$(\alpha\text{-}C_8H_5S)CH_2MgCl$ §	CO_2	...	*ca.* 45	...	*32*
$(\alpha\text{-}C_8H_5S)CH_2MgCl$ §	$HCHO$	...	35	...	*32*
$(\alpha\text{-}C_8H_5S)CH_2MgCl$ §	CH_3COCl	...	29	...	*32*
$(\alpha\text{-}C_8H_5S)CH_2MgCl$ §	$C_6H_5CO_2C_2H_5$	...	23	...	*32*
$(\alpha\text{-}C_8H_5S)CH_2MgCl$ §	$C_6H_5COC_6H\text{-}2,3,5,6\text{-}(CH_3)_4$	31	...	...	*32*
$(\beta\text{-}C_8H_5S)CH_2MgCl$ ¶	CO_2	16	56	...	*33*
$(\beta\text{-}C_8H_5S)CH_2MgCl$ ¶	$ClCO_2C_2H_5$	...	43	...	*33*
$(\beta\text{-}C_8H_5S)CH_2MgCl$ ¶	$HCHO$	+	18	...	*33*
$(\beta\text{-}C_8H_5S)CH_2MgCl$ ¶	$(CH_2)_2O$	+	+	...	*33*
$(\beta\text{-}C_8H_5S)CH_2MgCl$ ¶	$(C_6H_5)_2CO$	19	...	...	*33*
$(\beta\text{-}C_8H_5S)CH_2MgCl$ ¶	$C_6H_5COC_6H\text{-}2,3,5,6\text{-}(CH_3)_4$	20	...	...	*33*
$3,5\text{-}(CH_3)_2C_6H_3CH_2MgBr$	$(HCHO)_x$	...	+	...	*33*
$1\text{-}C_{10}H_7CH_2MgCl$	H_2NCl	47	0	...	*11*
$1\text{-}C_{10}H_7CH_2MgCl$	CO_2	59.4	...	...	*6*
$1\text{-}C_{10}H_7CH_2MgCl$	$HCHO$	+	...	...	*28*

§ $\alpha\text{-}C_8H_5S$ = 2-thianaphthenyl; the "*ortho*" product is the β (3) derivative.
¶ $\beta\text{-}C_8H_5S$ = 3-thianaphthenyl; the "*ortho*" product is the α (2) derivative.

TABLE XVII-I (Continued)

RMgX	Co-reactant	"Normal" Product (%)	"Abnormal" Product(s) Ortho (%)	Para (%)	Ref.
1-$C_{10}H_7CH_2MgCl$	HCHO	...	+‡	...	*6*
1-$C_{10}H_7CH_2MgCl$	$(HCHO)_x$	45.6	...	...	*28*
1-$C_{10}H_7CH_2MgCl$	$ClCO_2C_2H_5$	...	41	...	*5,6*
1-$C_{10}H_7CH_2MgCl$	$(CH_3)_2SO_4$	55	...	...	*6*
1-$C_{10}H_7CH_2MgCl$	C_6H_5NCO	36	...	...	*6*
2-$C_{10}H_7CH_2MgCl$	$(HCHO)_x$	+	...	...	*28*
2-$C_{10}H_7CH_2MgBr$	CO_2	+	...	...	*6*
2-$C_{10}H_7CH_2MgBr$	HCHO	+	?	...	*34*

REFERENCES FOR TABLE XVII-I

(*1*) Tiffeneau and Delange, *Compt. rend.*, *137*, 573–5 (1903); *J. Chem. Soc.*, *86*,*I*, 48 (1904).
(*2*) Hell, *Ber.*, *37*, 453–8 (1904).
(*3*) Tschitschibabin, *Ber.*, *42*, 3469–79 (1909).
(*4*) Schmidlin and García-Banús, *Ber.*, *45*, 3193–203 (1912).
(*5*) Gilman, Kirby, Fothergill, and Harris, *Proc. Iowa Acad. Sci.*, *34*, 221–2 (1927); *Chem. Abstr.*, *22*, 4504 (1928).
(*6*) Gilman and Kirby, *J. Am. Chem. Soc.*, *51*, 3475–8 (1929).
(*7*) Bottomley, Lapworth, and Walton, *J. Chem. Soc.*, *1930*, 2215–6.
(*8*) Baeyer & Co., German Patent 154,658 (1903); *Chem. Zentr.*, *1904*,*II*, 1355; *Friedländer*, 7, 758 (1905).
(*9*) Gilman and Kirby, *J. Am. Chem. Soc.*, *54*, 345–55 (1932).
(*10*) Austin and Johnson, *J. Am. Chem. Soc.*, *54*, 647–60 (1932).
(*11*) Coleman and Forrester, *J. Am. Chem. Soc.*, *58*, 27–8 (1936).
(*12*) Young and Siegel, *J. Am. Chem. Soc.*, *66*, 354–8 (1944).
(*13*) L. G. Davey, as cited by: Johnson, *J. Am. Chem. Soc.*, *55*, 3029–32 (1933).
(*14*) Burtle and Shriner, *J. Am. Chem. Soc.*, *69*, 2059–60 (1947).
(*15*) Whitmore and Sloat, *J. Am. Chem. Soc.*, *64*, 2968–70 (1942).
(*16*) Sherman and Amstutz, *J. Am. Chem. Soc.*, *72*, 2195–9 (1950).
(*17*) Gaertner, *J. Am. Chem. Soc.*, *72*, 4326–7 (1950).
(*18*) Gaertner, *J. Am. Chem. Soc.*, *73*, 3934–7 (1951).
(*19*) Campaigne and LeSuer, *J. Am. Chem. Soc.*, *70*, 1555–8 (1948).
(*20*) Gilman and Towle, *Rec. trav. chim.*, *69*, 428–32 (1950).
(*21*) Lecocq and Buu-Hoï, *Compt. rend.*, *224*, 658–9 (1947); *Chem. Abstr.*, *41*, 4791 (1947).
(*22*) Newman, *J. Am. Chem. Soc.*, *62*, 2295–300 (1940).
(*23*) Siegel, Boyer, and Joy, *J. Am. Chem. Soc.*, *73*, 3237–40 (1951).
(*24*) Malm and Summers, *J. Am. Chem. Soc.*, *73*, 362–3 (1951).
(*25*) Siegel, Coburn, and Levering, *J. Am. Chem. Soc.*, *73*, 3163–5 (1951).
(*26*) Rupe, *Ann.*, *402*, 149–86 (1913).
(*27*) Gilman and Schulz, *J. Am. Chem. Soc.*, *52*, 3588–90 (1930).
(*28*) Mousseron and Du, *Bull. soc. chim.*, [5], *15*, 91–6 (1948).
(*29*) Carré, *Bull. soc. chim.*, [4], *5*, 486–9 (1909).
(*30*) Carré, *Bull. soc. chim.*, [4], *7*, 841–6 (1910).
(*31*) Moser and Sause, *J. Org. Chem.*, *15*, 631–3 (1950).
(*32*) Gaertner, *J. Am. Chem. Soc.*, *74*, 766–7 (1952).
(*33*) Gaertner, *J. Am. Chem. Soc.*, *74*, 2185–8 (1952).
(*34*) Sontag, *Ann. chim.*, [11], *1*, 359–438 (1934).

has been made to include all reported "normal" reactions, for it is felt that isolation of the expected product when no special search is made for "abnormal" products is without critical significance.

It will be noted that all the reagents that are reported as reacting "abnormally" with benzylmagnesium chloride belong to classes of compounds which when suitably catalyzed condense with more or less activated benzene nuclei under relatively mild experimental conditions. The substituents that may be regarded as activating in this sense are those which are sometimes described as capable of donating electrons to the aromatic nucleus. The phenolate ion represents an extreme case of activation of this kind; it may be regarded as a resonant structure to which the following canonical forms contribute.

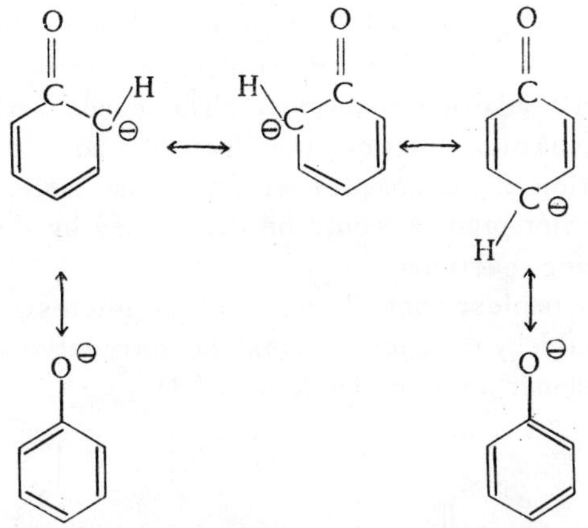

Phenol is in general an excellent Friedel-Crafts reactant; it condenses readily with aldehydes (notably formaldehyde) under a variety of conditions, and the ion, at somewhat elevated temperatures (120–140°), even condenses with carbon dioxide (Kolbe synthesis).

The analogy between the phenolate and benzyl ions is obvious.

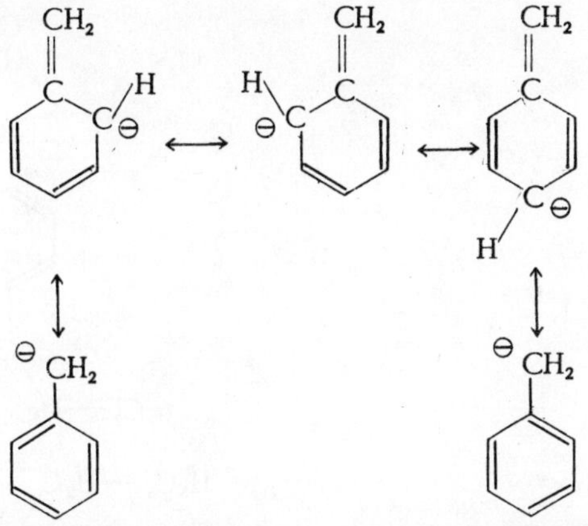

As a benzylmagnesium chloride co-reactant, formaldehyde is unique in that it is highly reactive with respect to both "normal" Grignard reagent addition and benzenoid condensation, and in that steric inhibition is at a minimum with respect to both Grignard reagent addition and *ortho* benzenoid condensation.

If, as there would seem to be every reason to believe, the "normal" addition of a Grignard reagent to an aldehyde has the same mechanism as the "normal" addition of a Grignard reagent to a ketone, the first step in the reaction is almost certainly the formation of a Werner complex of Grignard reagent and aldehyde. Presumably this would also be the first step in an *ortho* condensation reaction. The formation of such a complex undoubtedly facilitates the polarization or ionization* of the Grignard

*Ionization does not necessarily imply ionic dissociation. The Werner complex may well exist in the form of an ion-pair.

reagent (which would favor condensation by activating the benzene ring) and probably activates the aldehyde with respect to both the condensation and "normal" addition reactions. The condensation reaction is probably an intracomplex reaction; the "normal" addition probably consists in the reaction of the complex with a second molecule of Grignard reagent.* The major product would be determined by the relative rates of the two competing reactions.

Reduced to its simplest possible terms in the interests of clarity,† the case of the formaldehyde reaction might be formulated as follows (essentially in the manner proposed by Johnson[4,5]):

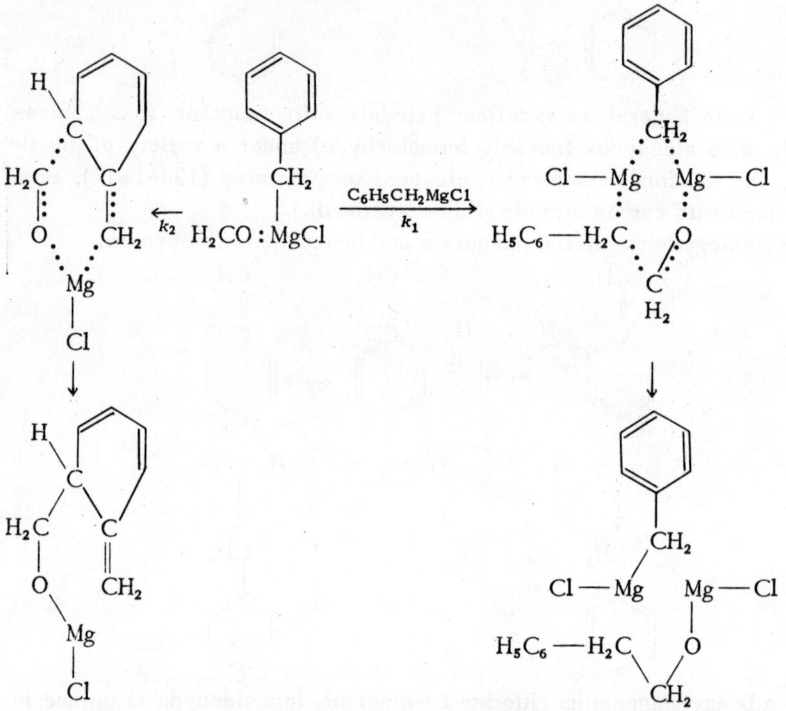

H, C, H_2C, C, O, CH_2, Mg, Cl $\xleftarrow{k_2}$ $C_6H_5CH_2$ | $H_2CO:MgCl$ $\xrightarrow[k_1]{C_6H_5CH_2MgCl}$ CH_2, Cl—Mg, Mg—Cl, H_5C_6—H_2C, O, C, H_2

↓ ↓

H, C, H_2C, C, O, CH_2, Mg, Cl CH_2, Cl—Mg, Mg—Cl, H_5C_6—H_2C, O, CH_2

The fate of the hydrogen atom attached to the carbon atom at which *ortho* condensation takes place has been determined in part by tritium tracer experiments performed by A. R. Van Dyken[6] of the Argonne National Laboratory. Among others, the following series of reactions was carried out. The tritium content of the product in each case is indicated parenthetically in terms of μcuries per mmole.

I $2\text{-}CH_3C_6H_4MgBr \xrightarrow{HTO} 1\text{-}T\text{-}2\text{-}CH_3C_6H_4$ (48.9)

*See Chapter VI, The "Normal" Addition Reactions.

†See Chapter IV, Constitution and Dissociation of Grignard Reagents.

[5] Johnson, Chapter 25 of Gilman's "Organic Chemistry," John Wiley & Sons, Inc., New York, 2nd ed., *1943*, Vol. II, pp. 1879–82.

[6] Van Dyken, Report to the Organochemical Seminar of the University of Chicago, March 7, 1951.

$$II \quad \text{1-T-2-}CH_3C_6H_4 \xrightarrow{SO_2Cl_2} \text{1-T-2-}ClCH_2C_6H_4 \quad (48.5)$$

$$IIIa \quad \text{1-T-}C_6H_4\text{-2-}CH_2MgCl \xrightarrow{(HCHO)_x} \text{1-}CH_3\text{-2-}HOCH_2C_6H_4(T)$$

$$IIIb \quad \text{1-}CH_3\text{-2-}HCCH_2C_6H_4(T) \xrightarrow{C_6H_5NCO} \text{1-}CH_3\text{-2-}C_6H_5NHCO_2C_6H_4(T) \, (37.5)$$

$$IV \quad \text{1-}CH_3\text{-2-}HOCH_2C_6H_4(T) \xrightarrow[25^\circ]{\text{alk. } KMnO_4} \text{2-}CH_3C_6H_4CO_2H(T) \quad (37.4)$$

$$V \quad \text{1-}CH_3\text{-2-}HOCH_2C_6H_4(T) \xrightarrow[\text{reflux}]{\text{alk. } KMnO_4} \text{1,2-}HO_2CC_6H_4(T) \quad (24.3)$$

In addition, it was found that the toluene formed in the reaction had a tritium content corresponding to 53.0 μcuries per mmole.

From these data it is evident that, as might be expected, approximately half the *ortho* condensation takes place at the tritium-substituted carbon atom. It is further apparent that the initial condensation product is an "active" hydrogen (or tritium) compound that reacts fairly readily with excess Grignard reagent. This reaction might well take place in such manner as to lead directly to the formation of a rearranged Grignard reagent.

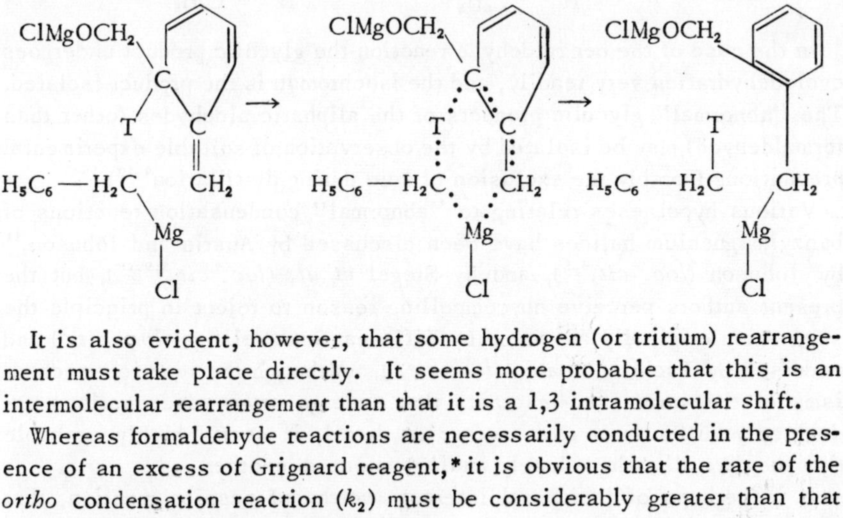

ClMgOCH₂ — C(T) — C(=CH₂) ... H_5C_6—H_2C — Mg — Cl → ClMgOCH₂ — C···T···H_5C_6—H_2C ··· Mg — Cl ··· CH_2 → ClMgOCH₂-C₆H₄-CH₂—Mg—Cl + H_5C_6—H_2C—T

It is also evident, however, that some hydrogen (or tritium) rearrangement must take place directly. It seems more probable that this is an intermolecular rearrangement than that it is a 1,3 intramolecular shift.

Whereas formaldehyde reactions are necessarily conducted in the presence of an excess of Grignard reagent,* it is obvious that the rate of the *ortho* condensation reaction (k_2) must be considerably greater than that of the "normal" addition reaction (k_1).

Benzaldehyde and the higher aliphatic aldehydes undergo the *ortho* condensation with benzylmagnesium chloride to the greatest extent when the aldehyde is present in excess, and then two molecules of aldehyde condense with one of Grignard reagent. For example, when the "normal" order of addition of benzaldehyde to benzylmagnesium chloride is employed (*i.e.*, when the Grignard reagent is present in excess) the "nor-

*Even the pure liquid formaldehyde of Walker, *J. Am. Chem. Soc.*, *55*, 2821–6 (1935), (relatively stable at −80°) polymerizes rapidly in ethereal solution at 0°, so that under no ordinary experimental conditions is it possible to introduce an excess of monomeric formaldehyde into a homogeneous Grignard reaction system.

mal'' addition product (1,2-diphenylethanol) is obtained in *ca.* 90 percent yield; when the order of addition is reversed the yield of "normal" addition product is materially lowered, and that of the product resulting from *ortho* condensation (1,3-diphenylisochroman) may exceed it.[7,8]

It seems probable that the first step in isochroman formation is *ortho* condensation, and that the second molecule of benzaldehyde then reacts either directly with the "active" hydrogen compound initially formed or with the Grignard reagent derived from it.

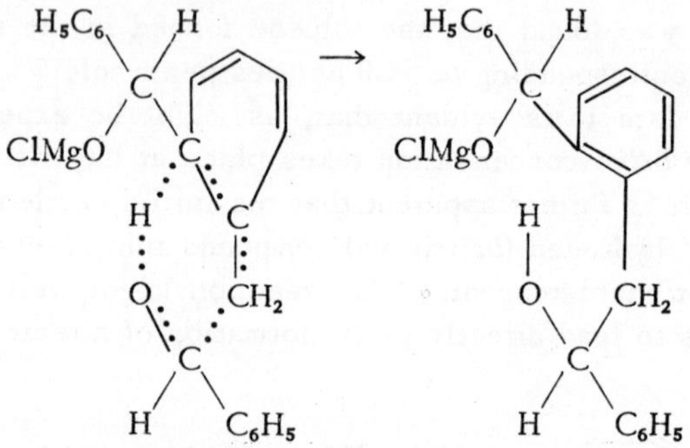

H_5C_6 H → H_5C_6 H
C C
ClMgO C ClMgO
H C H
O CH_2 O CH_2
C C
H C_6H_5 H C_6H_5

In the case of the benzaldehyde reaction the glycolic product undergoes cyclodehydration very readily, and the isochroman is the product isolated. The "abnormal" glycolic products of the aliphatic aldehydes (other than formaldehyde) may be isolated by the observation of suitable experimental precautions (notably the exclusion of acid during distillation[9,10]).

Various hypotheses relating to "abnormal" condensation reactions of benzylmagnesium halides have been discussed by Austin and Johnson,[11] by Johnson (*loc. cit.*[4,5]), and by Siegel *et al.* (*loc. cit.*[8,9,10]), but the present authors perceive no compelling reason to reject in principle the suggestion originally advanced by Tiffeneau and Delange (*loc. cit.*[2]) and endorsed by Tschitschibabin (*loc. cit.*[3]). Although the reaction mechanisms of the various co-reactants that undergo *ortho* condensations undoubtedly differ from one another in detail, it seems highly probable that they are all rather closely analogous one to another.

It is perhaps of incidental interest, worthy of passing mention, that carbon dioxide, which reacts "normally" with benzylmagnesium chloride to yield phenylacetic acid, and which had therefore been regarded by some organic chemists as a typically "normal" co-reactant has been found to undergo *ortho* condensation readily with some of the benzyl ana-

---

[7] Schmidlin and García-Banús, *Ber.*, *45*, 3193–203 (1912). See also: García-Banús and Medrano, *Anales. soc. españ. fís. quím.*, *21*, 436–63; *Chem. Abstr.*, *18*, 2144 (1924); García-Banús, *Anales soc. españ. fís. quím.*, *26*, 372–98 (1928); *Chem. Abstr.*, *23*, 2178 (1929).

[8] Siegel, Coburn, and Levering, *J. Am. Chem. Soc.*, *73*, 3163–5 (1951).

[9] Young and Siegel, *J. Am. Chem. Soc.*, *66*, 354–8 (1944).

[10] Siegel, Boyer, and Joy, *J. Am. Chem. Soc.*, *73*, 3237–40 (1951).

[11] Austin and Johnson, *J. Am. Chem. Soc.*, *54*, 647–60 (1932).

logs (see Table XVII-I). Even the phenyl ring of the benzyl group, when activated by the introduction of a *meta* methyl substituent, is able to participate to some degree in *ortho* condensation with carbon dioxide. The "abnormal" product in this case had been reported by Mousseron and Du[12] as 2,6-dimethylbenzoic acid, but has been found by Moser and Sause[13] to be in fact 2,4-dimethylbenzoic acid. *A priori* this would appear more probable on the grounds (*a*) that the *ortho* position *para* to the substituent methyl group should be the more highly activated of the two, and (*b*) that this position should be less subject to steric inhibition.

Schmidlin[14] supposed that he had succeeded in preparing the Grignard reagent of triphenylmethyl chloride in two isomeric forms: namely, an unstable *alpha* quinonoid form, and a stable *beta* form of the expected configuration. He believed that the *alpha* form could be converted into the *beta* form by heating, and that the two forms could be distinguished by their behavior toward benzaldehyde or cinnamaldehyde. Toward these reagents the *beta* form was supposed to be unreactive, whereas the *alpha* form was supposed to undergo *para*-condensation.

As Tschitschibabin[15] showed, Schmidlin's conclusions were based in part upon faulty observation and in part upon gratuitous assumption. Schmidlin's *alpha* form, which supposedly reacted with water to form "triphenylmethyl," was in reality a mixture of a little triphenylmethylmagnesium chloride with a considerable amount of hexaphenylethane. Tschitschibabin found that the Grignard reagent reacts "normally" with benzoic ester to give an 80 percent yield of crude benzopinacolin, and with carbon dioxide to give a 90 percent yield of triphenylacetic acid. As he pointed out, there is no reason to suppose that the *para* condensation of benzaldehyde with this reagent differs fundamentally from the similar *ortho* condensation of formaldehyde with benzylmagnesium chloride.

In the case of triphenylmethylmagnesium chloride it is obvious that steric hindrance to *ortho* condensation is prohibitive. If the "normal" aldehyde addition is indeed trimolecular (as seems most probable), steric inhibition of this reaction must also be considerable. Tschitschibabin, however, did detect small quantities of the "normal" addition product with benzaldehyde in addition to the major *para* condensation product. As in the case of the benzylmagnesium halides, *para* condensation probably results from interaction of two Werner-complex aggregates.

"ABNORMAL" REACTIONS OF SUBSTITUTED ALLYLMAGNESIUM HALIDES

The earliest reported allylic rearrangement (involving the Grignard reagent) of which the present authors have knowledge is a hybrid reaction

[12] Mousseron and Du, *Bull. soc. chim.*, [5], *15*, 91–6 (1948).

[13] Moser and Sause, *J. Org. Chem.*, *15*, 631–3 (1950).

[14] Schmidlin, *Ber.*, *39*, 4183–98 (1906); *40*, 2316–29 (1907); *41*, 426–30 (1908); Schmidlin and Hodgson, *ibid.*, *41*, 430–7 (1908).

[15] Tschitschibabin, *Ber.*, *40*, 3965–70 (1907); *42*, 3469–72 (1909).

in the sense that both Grignard reagent and co-reactant are allylic; namely, that of magnesium with cinnamyl chloride (Rupe and Bürgin[16]). The reaction was conducted under conditions which might be expected to lead chiefly to a "Wurtz product." Doubtless some of the product formed is attributable to a Wurtz reaction, analogous to that whereby biphenyl is formed in the reaction of magnesium with bromobenzene. Probably the major portion of the product, however, is attributable to reaction of the cinnamyl halide with its own Grignard reagent. According to Rupe and Bürgin, only about 25–30 percent of the product obtained consisted of bicinnamyl (1,6-diphenyl-1,5-hexadiene); the remainder, which they described as 1,4-diphenyl-1-hexene, must in reality have been chiefly 1,4-diphenyl-1,5-hexadiene.[17] The respective yields reported are not quantitatively significant, for they total somewhat more than 100 percent, but the ratio between products is probably approximately correct for the conditions imposed.

von Braun and Köhler[18] have claimed that bicinnamyl is obtainable in better yield from cinnamyl bromide than from cinnamyl chloride, but this claim is not confirmed by the reports of Kuhn and Winterstein[19] or Koch.[20] On the basis of ultraviolet absorption spectrum measurements, Koch estimates that the product he obtained by treating 111 g. of cinnamyl chloride with 9 g. of metallic magnesium consisted of 3–5 percent *meso*-α,α′-divinylbibenzyl (**I**), 20 percent *trans*-bicinnamyl (**II**), and 75 percent isobicinnamyl (1,4-diphenyl-1,5-hexadiene) (**III**). An experiment conducted similarly with cinnamyl bromide yielded 1 percent **I**, 10 percent **II** and eighty-nine percent **III**. When distilled under reduced pressure or when heated to 150°, **I** rearranges to yield approximately three parts of **II** and two parts of **III**.

Similar reactions have been studied by other investigators. For example, Prévost and Richard[21] report that 1-bromo-2-pentene, when treated with magnesium, yields 3,7-decadiene, 3-ethyl-1,5-octadiene, and 3,4-diethyl-1,5-hexadiene in the approximate proportions 0.295 : 0.652 : 0.052, together with a small amount of unidentified material. The aggregate yield of identified material is about 90 percent. According to Lespieau and Heitzmann,[22] "crotyl bromide" reacts with magnesium to form a mixture of isomeric "dicrotyls." There is reasonable doubt that the bromides used in these studies were pure isomers.[23]

---

[16] Rupe and Bürgin, *Ber.*, *43*, 172–8 (1910).

[17] *Cf.* Prévost, *Bull. soc. chim.*, [4], *49*, 1372–81 (1931); Gilman and Harris, *J. Am. Chem. Soc.*, *54*, 2072–5 (1932); Harris, *Iowa State Coll. J. Sci.*, *6*, 425–8 (1932); *Chem. Abstr.*, *27*, 279 (1933).

[18] von Braun and Köhler, *Ber.*, *51*, 79–96 (1918).

[19] Kuhn and Winterstein, *Helv. Chim. Acta*, *11*, 87–116 (1928).

[20] Koch, *J. Chem. Soc.*, *1948*, 1111–7.

[21] Prévost and Richard, *Bull. soc. chim.*, [4], *49*, 1368–72 (1931).

[22] Lespieau and Heitzmann, *Compt. rend.*, *200*, 1077–80 (1935); *Chem. Abstr.*, *29*, 4325 (1935); *Bull. soc. chim.*, [5], 3, 273–7 (1936).

[23] See: Young, Richards, and Azorlosa, *J. Am. Chem. Soc.*, *61*, 3070–4 (1939).

Henne *et al.*[24] have studied the reactions of magnesium with "isomeric crotyl chlorides." From "secondary crotyl chloride" (3-chloro-1-butene) they obtained an aggregate yield of about 67 percent of identified products in the proportions indicated: 2,6-octadiene (0.045); 3-methyl-1,5-heptadiene (0.850); 3,4-dimethyl-1,5-hexadiene (0.104). From "primary crotyl chloride" (1-chloro-2-butene) they obtained an aggregate yield of about 54 percent of two isomers plus "a little" of the third. Assuming that "a little" signifies something of the order of 1 percent, the reported distribution would be approximately: 2,6-octadiene (0.018); 3-methyl-1,5-heptadiene (0.909); 3,4-dimethyl-1,5-hexadiene (0.073). From a crude mixture of the isomeric chlorides they obtained an aggregate yield of 67 percent of identified products in the proportions indicated: 2,6-octadiene (0.060); 3-methyl-1,5-heptadiene (0.895); 3,4-dimethyl-1,5-hexadiene (0.045). In view of the experimental difficulties attendant upon quantitative separation of isomeric product mixtures of this kind, it is difficult to decide whether or not the apparent differences in product distributions are in fact real.

As might be expected, the reactions of magnesium with allyl chloride and with β-methallyl chloride (2-methyl-3-chloro-1-propene) gave the respective "normal" products: 1,5-hexadiene (60 percent) and 2,5-dimethyl-1,5-hexadiene (65 percent) (Henne *et al.*, *loc. cit.*[24]).

Entirely aside from the possibility of such complications as functional exchange, experiments like those just described offer no basis for decision as to whether the "abnormalities" of the reactions are attributable to the allylic Grignard reagents or the allylic co-reactants. However, thanks in large part to the studies of Young and co-workers, there is considerable available evidence on both points.

According to Gilman *et al.*,[25] the Grignard reagent derived from cinnamyl chloride reacts with carbon dioxide, with phenyl isocyanate, or with ethyl chloroformate as though it had the constitution $C_6H_5CH(MgCl)CH{=}CH_2$. However, the yields of the isocyanate and chloroformate products are not stated, and those claimed for β-methylatropic acid* are 11.4–27.1 percent. It is also reported by Ou Kuin-Houo[26] that "cinnamylmagnesium bromide" reacts similarly with acetaldehyde, though yields are not stated.

---

[24] Henne, Chanan, and Turk, *J. Am. Chem. Soc.*, *63*, 3474–6 (1941).

[25] Gilman and Harris, *J. Am. Chem. Soc.*, *49*, 1825–8 (1927); *53*, 3541–6 (1931); Gilman, Kirby, Fothergill, and Harris, *Proc. Iowa Acad. Sci.*, *34*, 221–2 (1927); *Chem. Abstr.*, *22*, 4504 (1928); Harris, *Iowa State Coll. J. Sci.*, *6*, 425–8 (1932); *Chem. Abstr.*, *27*, 279 (1933).

* Actually, the product initially formed is the labile phenylvinylacetic acid, $C_6H_5CH(CO_2H)CH{=}CH_2$ (m.p. 23–24°), which is easily converted by heating, or by warming with acids or alkalies, to the stable β-methylatropic acid, $C_6H_5C(CO_2H){=}CHCH_3$ (m.p. 135–136°).

[26] Ou Kuin-Houo, *Ann. chim.*, [11], *13*, 175–241 (1940).

On the other hand, Coleman and Forrester[27] report a 14 percent yield of cinnamylamine from the reaction of this Grignard reagent with chloroamine.

On the basis of the assumptions (1) that the Grignard reagent is an equilibrium mixture of isomeric forms, and (2) that the products of hydrolysis may be expected to reflect reliably the composition of the isomeric mixture, Young *et al.*[28] conclude that "cinnamylmagnesium chloride" comprises approximately 75 percent of the secondary reagent and 25 percent of the primary reagent. These assumptions will be considered in connection with the following discussion of the analogous butenylmagnesium halides for which more extensive data are available.

Reported data concerning the reactions of butenyl Grignard reagents are summarized in Table XVII-II. The first four items of Table XVII-II are included, with somewhat more detail, in Table XVII-III, which records reactions of butenyl Grignard reagents with "active hydrogen" compounds.

As a preliminary to consideration of the reactions of butenyl Grignard reagents it may be well to take note of a few experimental observations which supply something in the way of general background. Winstein and Young[29] claim to have effected the first isolation of pure crotyl and α-methallyl (methylvinylcarbinyl) bromides. They find that both bromides approach equilibrium (*ca.* 85.5 percent primary, 14.5 percent secondary) very rapidly (<5 minutes) at 100°, and more slowly (*ca.* 10 days) at room temperature. This, taken in conjunction with the fact that Young and Lane[30] have found that all investigated methods of converting crotyl or α-methallyl alcohols to bromides are productive of isomeric mixtures, makes it seem highly probable that all early literature reports of reactions of butenylmagnesium halides, whatever their designations, relate to reagents prepared from halide mixtures.[31] This point, however, is not so significant as it might at first appear, for, according to Young, Winstein, and Prater,[32] butenylmagnesium bromides, whether prepared from one of the pure isomers or from an isomeric mixture, always yield on acid hydrolysis the same mixture of 1-butene (56.4 ± 2.0 percent), *cis*-2-butene (26.5 ± 1.4 percent), and *trans*-2-butene (17.2 ± 3.0 percent). Actually, the relative proportions of butenes vary somewhat with the conditions of the hydrolysis, as is shown in a subsequent study by Wilson, Roberts, and Young[33] (Table XVII-III).

[27] Coleman and Forrester, *J. Am. Chem. Soc.*, *58*, 27–8 (1936).

[28] Young, Ballou, and Nozacki, *J. Am. Chem. Soc.*, *61*, 12–15 (1939); Campbell and Young, *ibid.*, *69*, 688–90 (1947).

[29] Winstein and Young, *J. Am. Chem. Soc.*, *58*, 104–7 (1936).

[30] Young and Lane, *J. Am. Chem. Soc.*, *59*, 2051–6 (1937).

[31] See also: Young, Richards, and Azorlosa, *J. Am. Chem. Soc.*, *61*, 3070–4 (1939).

[32] Young, Winstein, and Prater, *J. Am. Chem. Soc.*, *58*, 289–91 (1936).

[33] Wilson, Roberts, and Young, *J. Am. Chem. Soc.*, *72*, 215–7 (1950).

Table XVII-II

SOME REACTIONS OF BUTENYL GRIGNARD REAGENTS

Reagent	Co-reactant*	Product(s) (% yield)		Ref.
		Crotyl	α-Methallyl	
C_4H_7MgBr	H^+	43.6	56.4	*1*
C_4H_7MgCl	H^+	45.8	54.2	*2*
C_4H_7MgBr	H^+	49.7–7.8	50.3–92.2	*3*
$(C_4H_7)_2Mg$	H^+	55.5	44.5	*4*
C_4H_7MgBr	O_2	*ca.* 45 †	*ca.* 55 †	*5*
C_4H_7MgCl	CO_2 ‡	...	70.0	*6*
C_4H_7MgBr	CO_2 ‡	...	75.0	*7*
C_4H_7MgBr	CO_2 §	...	63.0 ¶	*7*
$(C_4H_7)_2Mg$	CO_2 ‡	...	37.0	*6*
C_4H_7MgBr	HCHO	none	50.0	*6*
C_4H_7MgBr	$(HCHO)_x$	...	38.0	*15*
C_4H_7MgBr	CH_3CHO	...	+	*8*
C_4H_7MgBr	CH_3CHO	...	84.0	*6*
C_4H_7MgBr	$H_2C{=}CHCHO$	...	+	*8*
C_4H_7MgBr	$H_2C{=}CHCH_2Br$	*ca.* 45 †	*ca.* 55 †	*9*
C_4H_7MgBr	C_2H_5CHO	...	25.0	*8*
C_4H_7MgBr	$(CH_3)_2CO$	...	81.0	*6*
C_4H_7MgBr	HCO_2C_2H	...	+	*10*
C_4H_7MgBr	$ClCH_2O$-*n*-C_4H_9	...	+	*11*

* For the first four items in this table, designation of the co-reactant as the hydrogen ion probably presents too simple a picture (see Table XVII-III).

† The statement published is to the effect that "...reaction of the Grignard reagent with oxygen to form alcohols, or with allyl bromide to form heptadienes, leads to the same mixture of primary and secondary radicals as that produced by the action of water (*1,2*)."

‡ By the method of Fieser, Holmes, and Newman, *J. Am. Chem. Soc.*, *58*, 1055 (1936), *i.e.*, method IV, Table XIII-I.

§ By the method of Arnold, Bank, and Liggett, *J. Am. Chem. Soc.*, *63*, 3444–6 (1941), *i.e.*, method VI, Table XIII-I.

¶ In addition to the acid, an unidentified dibutenyl ketone was obtained in 13 percent yield.

Table XVII-II (Continued)

Reagent	Co-reactant	Product(s) (% yield)		Ref.
		Crotyl	α-Methallyl	
C_4H_7MgBr	C_6H_5NCO	...	+	*10*
C_4H_7MgBr	C_6H_5CHO	...	+	*8*
C_4H_7MgBr	$(i\text{-}C_3H_7)_2CO$	13.4	75.6	*12*
C_4H_7MgCl	$(i\text{-}C_3H_8)_2CO$	5.1	79.9	*12*
C_4H_7MgBr	$HC(OC_2H_5)_3$	...	+	*10*
C_4H_7MgBr	$HC(OC_2H_5)_3$	...	73.0	*15*
C_4H_7MgBr	$i\text{-}C_3H_7CO\text{-}t\text{-}C_4H_9$	...	74.0	*13*
C_4H_7MgBr	$(t\text{-}C_4H_9)_2CO$	69.0	...	*13*
C_4H_7MgBr	$CH_3COC_6H_2\text{-}2,4,6\text{-}(CH_3)_3$	...	76.0	*14*
C_4H_7MgBr	$(C_6H_5)_2CO$	...	+*	*13*
C_4H_7MgBr	$i\text{-}C_3H_7COC_6H_2\text{-}2,4,6\text{-}(CH_3)_3$	+ (?)†	+†	*13*

* On heating, the addition product yields 77 percent *trans*-2-butene and 23 percent *cis*-2-butene; presumably the product is therefore the α-methallyl derivative.

† Thermal decomposition of the product is reported as yielding 6 ± 5 percent 1-butene, 24 ± 5 percent *trans*-2-butene, and 70 ± 5 percent *cis*-2-butene; presumably the product is therefore substantially the α-methallyl derivative.

REFERENCES FOR TABLE XVII-II

(*1*) Young, Winstein, and Prater, *J. Am. Chem. Soc.*, *58*, 289–91 (1936).
(*2*) Young and Eisner, *J. Am. Chem. Soc.*, *63*, 2113–5 (1941).
(*3*) Wilson, Roberts, and Young, *J. Am. Chem. Soc.*, *72*, 215–7 (1950).
(*4*) Young and Pokras, *J. Org. Chem.*, *7*, 233–40 (1942).
(*5*) Siegal, M. A. Dissertation, University of California, L. A., 1939, as cited by Young and Pokras (*4*) and Young and Roberts (*14b*).
(*6*) Roberts and Young, *J. Am. Chem. Soc.*, *67*, 148–50 (1945).
(*7*) Lane, Roberts, and Young, *J. Am. Chem. Soc.*, *66*, 543–5 (1944).
(*8*) Ou Kuin-Houo, *Ann. chim.*, [11], *13*, 175–241 (1940).
(*9*) Wax, M. A. Dissertation, University of California, L. A., 1940, as cited by Young and Pokras (*4*).
(*10*) Young and Roberts, *J. Am. Chem. Soc.*, *68*, 649–52 (1946).
(*11*) Young, Roberts, and Wax, *J. Am. Chem. Soc.*, *67*, 841–3 (1945).
(*12*) Young and Roberts, *J. Am. Chem. Soc.*, *67*, 319–21 (1945).
(*13*) Wilson, Roberts, and Young, *J. Am. Chem. Soc.*, *72*, 218–9 (1950).
(*14*) Young and Roberts, *J. Am. Chem. Soc.*, (*a*) *66*, 2131 (1944); (*b*) *68*, 1472–5 (1946).
(*15*) Inhoffen, Bohlman, and Reinefeld, *Chem. Ber.*, *82*, 313–6 (1949).

TABLE XVII-III

BUTENES FROM THE REACTION OF BUTENYLMAGNESIUM BROMIDE WITH "ACTIVE HYDROGEN" COMPOUNDS *

Reagent	Solvent	*trans*-2-Butene (%)	*cis*-2-Butene (%)	1-Butene (%)
(2 *N* H_2SO_4)†	(None)†	(20.4)†	(25.4)†	(54.2)†
(2 *N* H_2SO_4)‡	(None)‡	(23.2 ± 0.4)‡	(32.2 ± 0.3)‡	(44.5 ± 0.3)‡
2 *N* H_2SO_4§	None§	17.2 ± 3.0§	26.5 ± 1.4§	56.4 ± 2.0§
2 *N* H_2SO_4	None	21.1 ± 0.7	28.6 ± 0.7	50.3 ± 1.6
2 *N* H_2SO_4	Ethyl ether	13.5 ± 0.5	16.6 ± 0.1	69.9 ± 0.4
2 *N* H_2SO_4	Butyl ether	13.1 ± 1.4	14.3 ± 0.8	72.9 ± 2.1
2 *N* H_2SO_4	Benzene	13.6	10.0	76.4
2 *N* H_2SO_4	Heptane	12.4 ± 0.7	11.0 ± 0.9	76.5 ± 1.5
HCl	Ethyl ether	10.1 ± 2.4	6.5 ± 1.9	83.4 ± 4.1
NH_4I	Ethyl ether	28.4 ± 0.6	30.1 ± 0.1	41.5 ± 0.5
CH_3CO_2H	None	15.2	19.1	65.7
CH_3CO_2H	Ethyl ether	10.0 ± 0.9	10.1 ± 1.1	80.0 ± 0.5
$ClCH_2CO_2H$	Ethyl ether	3.3 ± 0.8	4.8 ± 2.6	92.2 ± 1.6
Cl_3CCO_2H	Ethyl ether	7.7 ± 0.6	6.2 ± 0.1	86.3 ± 0.7
C_2H_5OH	None	19.8 ± 0.4	25.4 ± 0.2	54.8 ± 0.6
$C_6H_5C{\equiv}CH$¶	Ethyl ether¶	1.0¶	5.4¶	93.6¶

* Except as otherwise specified, the data in this table are taken from the paper of Wilson, Roberts, and Young, *J. Am. Chem. Soc.*, 72, 215–7 (1950). Butene analysis by infra-red absorption. Average deviations from the mean of several (2–6) experiments are given.

† These data are for butenylmagnesium chloride, Young and Eisner, *J. Am. Chem. Soc.*, 63, 2113–5 (1941). Butene analysis by bromination, and fractionation of dibromides.

‡ These data are for dibutenylmagnesium, Young and Pokras, *J. Org. Chem.*, 7, 233–40 (1942). Butene analysis by bromination, and fractionation of dibromides.

§ These data are for butenylmagnesium bromide, Young, Winstein, and Prater, *J. Am. Chem. Soc.*, 58, 289–91 (1936). Butene analysis by bromination, and fractionation of dibromides.

¶ These data are taken from the paper of Young and Roberts, *J. Am. Chem. Soc.*, 68, 1472–5 (1946). Butene analysis by infra-red absorption.

TABLE XVII-III (Continued)

Reagent	Solvent	*trans*-2-Butene (%)	*cis*-2-Butene (%)	1-Butene (%)
s-$C_4H_9(i$-$C_3H_7)_2COH$	Ethyl ether	17.8 ± 0.6	13.7 ± 1.0	68.5 ± 1.6
2,4,6-$(CH_3)_3C_6H_2COCH(C_6H_5)_2$	Ethyl ether + benzene	2.7 ± 2.8	35.9 ± 7.2	61.4 ± 4.4
$(C_6H_5SO_2)_2CH_2$	Ethyl ether	x*	32–x*	68*

* Butene analysis by bromination, and fractionation of dibromides.

In some of the earlier papers of their series on allylic rearrangements Young and co-workers[34] marshalled arguments in support of the hypothesis that a butenyl Grignard reagent is an equilibrium mixture of isomeric forms, and assumed, sometimes implicitly, occasionally explicitly, that the composition of the butene mixture obtained upon acid hydrolysis of the reagent is indicative of the equilibrium composition.

The reason why the latter assumption is untenable is precisely the same as the reason why the hydrogen chloride cleavage of unsymmetrical organomercurials cannot be expected to assign allylic radicals to their proper places in the "electronegativity series," and has been stated by Kharasch and Swartz.[35] It has now been recognized by Young *et al.*[36] Briefly, it is that olefinic compounds in general, and allylic organometallics in particular, are bases in the Brønsted sense. Hence allylic organometallic compounds are capable of undergoing acidic cleavage by a mechanism (1a, 2a) other than the "normal" one (1b, 2b) which may be regarded as general for organometallics.

$$\text{(1a)} \quad H_3CCH{=}CHCH_2MgX + HB \longrightarrow [H_3CCH_2CHCH_2MgX]^+ + B$$
$$\longrightarrow H_3CCH_2CH{=}CH_2 + B + MgX^+$$

$$\text{(1b)} \quad H_3CCH{=}CHCH_2MgX + HB \longrightarrow H_3CCH{=}CHCH_3 + B + MgX^+$$

$$\text{(2a)} \quad H_3C(H_2C{=}CH)CHMgX + HB \longrightarrow [H_3C(H_3CCH)CHMgX]^+ + B$$
$$\longrightarrow H_3CCH{=}CHCH_3 + B + MgX^+$$

$$\text{(2b)} \quad H_3C(H_2C{=}CH)CHMgX + HB \longrightarrow H_3CCH_2CH{=}CH_2 + B + MgX^+$$

In more recent papers Young *et al.*[37] have abandoned the equilibrium mixture hypothesis, and have concluded that the available experimental data are consistent with the supposition that butenyl Grignard reagents are essentially crotylmagnesium halides. In order to minimize tiresome expansion of an unprofitable discussion, it is here categorically asserted that the problem of the constitution of allylic Grignard reagents is but one of many structural problems incapable of purely chemical solution. Detailed explicit substantiation of this assertion should be unnecessary; the following examination of possibilities is sufficiently illustrative.

A. The butenyl Grignard reagent is essentially a crotylmagnesium halide.

1. For the reason already stated acid hydrolysis of the reagent yields inconclusive results.

2. To account for the products obtained upon reaction with carbonyl compounds, among which carbon dioxide may be included, it is assumed

---

[34] See, especially: Young and Winstein, *J. Am. Chem. Soc.*, 58, 441–3 (1936); Young, Kaufman, Loshokoff, and Pressman, *ibid.*, 60, 900–3 (1938); Young and Pokras, *J. Org. Chem.*, 7, 233–40 (1942).

[35] Kharasch and Swartz, *J. Org. Chem.*, 3, 405–8 (1938).

[36] Wilson, Roberts, and Young, *J. Am. Chem. Soc.*, 72, 215–7 (1950).

[37] See, *e.g.*: Young and Roberts, *J. Am. Chem. Soc.*, 68, 649–52 (1946); *ibid.*, 68, 1472–5 (1946); Wilson, Roberts, and Young, *loc. cit.*[36]

that allylic Grignard reagents are capable of reacting by a mechanism other than any that may be reasonably postulated for the "normal" reactions of the general run of Grignard reagents. A reaction in which a single molecule of Grignard reagent serves both as activator of the carbonyl group and as co-reactant has been suggested by Young and Roberts (*loc. cit.*[37]); it appears to embody nothing inherently improbable.

```
    H   CH3              H   CH3              H   CH3
     \ /                  \ /                  \ /
R     C                R   C               R    C
 \     \\               \ : \\:               \ / \
  C     CH               C     CH               C    CH
R'||    |       →      R'|:    |:       →     R'|    ||
  O     CH2              O.   .CH2              O    CH2
   .   /                  .  .                   \
    Mg                     Mg                     Mg
    |                      |                      |
    X                      X                      X
```

3. To account for the mixture of alcohols obtained upon oxygenation of the reagent it is assumed that reduction of the peroxy compound presumably formed in the initial stage of the reaction (see Chapter XX, Oxygen) takes place by a mechanism other than the usual one.

```
CH3CH=CHCH2—O···O—MgX
          .      .
     X—Mg         CH—CH3   →
          .      /
       H2C···CH

                         CH3CH=CHCH2—O   O—MgX
                                     /     \
                                X—Mg        CH—CH3
                                           /
                                   H2C=CH
```

B. The butenyl Grignard reagent is essentially an α-methallylmagnesium halide.

1. For the reason already stated the acid hydrolysis of the reagent yields inconclusive results.

2. It is assumed that reaction with carbonyl compounds takes place by the "normal" mechanism (see Chapter VI, The "Normal" Addition Reactions).

3. It is assumed that in the oxygenation reaction the reduction of the peroxy intermediate compound takes place by a mechanism other than the usual one.

C. The butenyl Grignard reagent is an equilibrium mixture of isomeric forms.

1. For the reason already stated the acid hydrolysis of the reagent yields inconclusive results.

2. It is assumed that reaction with carbonyl compounds takes place by the "normal" mechanism, but that the secondary form of the Grignard reagent is considerably more reactive than the primary form. This is in

accord with the findings of Kharasch and Weinhouse[38] concerning the relative reactivities of Grignard reagents toward ketones. Judged on the basis of the probable electronegativities of the respective organic radicals, a crotyl-magnesium halide should have a potential reactivity approximating that of the corresponding benzyl reagent; an α-methallylmagnesium halide should have a potential reactivity somewhat greater than that of the corresponding *t*-butyl reagent. In both cases the unsaturated reagent should be subject to somewhat less steric inhibition than the saturated reagent to which it is compared.

Interconversion of forms would be effected rapidly through an exchange process of the sort responsible for establishment of the Schlenk equilibrium (see Chapter IV, The Schlenk Equilibrium).

If, on the other hand, it be assumed that reaction follows the mechanism proposed for crotylmagnesium bromide, it must be assumed that the primary form of the reagent is considerably more reactive than the secondary form. There would appear to be no *a priori* reason for such an assumption other than the invocation of a rather dubious steric effect.

3. Whether the oxygenation reaction is assumed to follow the "normal" or a special mechanism, mixtures of alcohols would be expected. In the "normal" reaction the secondary form of the reagent might be expected to be the more effective in the reduction stage (Wuyts[39] and Kharasch and Reynolds[40]; see Chapter XX, Oxygen).

Recapitulation. Underlying all the foregoing discussion relating to structure is the implicit assumption that the Grignard reagent may be regarded as an essentially covalent compound. To the extent that the reagent is ionized, however, it cannot be said to have any structure in the classical sense, for the butenyl ion is a resonant aggregate to which the following forms undoubtedly make the principal contributions.

$$CH_3-CH=CH-\overset{\ominus}{C}H_2 \longleftrightarrow CH_3-\overset{\ominus}{C}H-CH=CH_2$$

This point was appreciated by Prévost,[41] who, as early as 1927 coined the term "synionie" to designate the phenomenon.

Although it must be reiterated that this type of constitutional problem does not admit of purely chemical solution, the present authors are inclined to believe that, to the extent that the Grignard reagent may be regarded as a covalent compound, or that ion-pairs may be regarded as having definite points of mutual attachment, the following hypotheses seem reasonable and are consistent (though not uniquely so) with the known chemical facts.

(1) The butenyl Grignard reagents (and probably most analogous allylic Grignard reagents) are equilibrium mixtures of isomeric forms. (2) Under

[38] Kharasch and Weinhouse, *J. Org. Chem.*, *1*, 209–30 (1936).

[39] Wuyts, *Bull. soc. chim. Belg.*, *36*, 222–38 (1927).

[40] Kharasch and Reynolds, *J. Am. Chem. Soc.*, *65*, 501–4 (1943).

[41] Prévost, *Compt. rend.*, *185*, 132–4 (1927).

ordinary reaction conditions equilibrium is rapidly established by exchange of the Schlenk type. (3) In many reactions either form of the Grignard reagent is potentially capable of reacting simultaneously by (*a*) the "normal" mechanism and (*b*) a special allylic mechanism. Although it is possible that in some instances one mechanism may be preferred to the virtual exclusion of the others, it is also conceivable that in other instances as many as four (or more) mechanisms may operate simultaneously. (4) The preferred mechanism (or mechanisms) will be determined in part by the nature of the co-reactant, but may, in some cases, be materially affected by the reaction conditions. (For example bimolecular mechanisms would be favored over trimolecular mechanisms by operation in the presence of an excess of co-reactant, and *vice versa*.)

It may be remarked in passing that, in general, the formation of a so-called "abnormal" product in the reaction of an allylic Grignard reagent need not necessarily involve any "rearrangement" at all in the ordinary sense of the term.

REACTIONS OF GRIGNARD REAGENTS WITH ALLYLIC CO-REACTANTS

Allylic Halides. Although they are, in the opinion of the present authors, devoid of critical theoretical significance, reported data on the reactions of Grignard reagents with allylic halides are assembled for the convenience of the reader in Table XVII-IV. In some instances there is reasonable doubt of the purity of the isomer reported. Even when a pure and relatively stable isomer is employed, however, it seems highly probable that rearrangement would take place readily in the presence of magnesium halide.

As has been pointed out in Chapter XVI the reaction of a Grignard reagent with an organic halide may be regarded as a special type of solvolysis. To the extent that such a solvolysis might proceed by an S_N1 mechanism allylic isomers would lose their individuality, for either isomer of a pair would give rise to the same resonant cation. For example, the butenyl ion may be represented as follows.

$$H_3C-CH=CH-\overset{\oplus}{C}H_2 \longleftrightarrow H_3C-\overset{\oplus}{C}H-CH=CH_2$$

To the extent that reaction might take place through a bimolecular mechanism involving a cyclic intermediate, isomer individuality would be preserved, but, for the reasons outlined, the existent data are scarcely a reliable guide to what actually does take place.

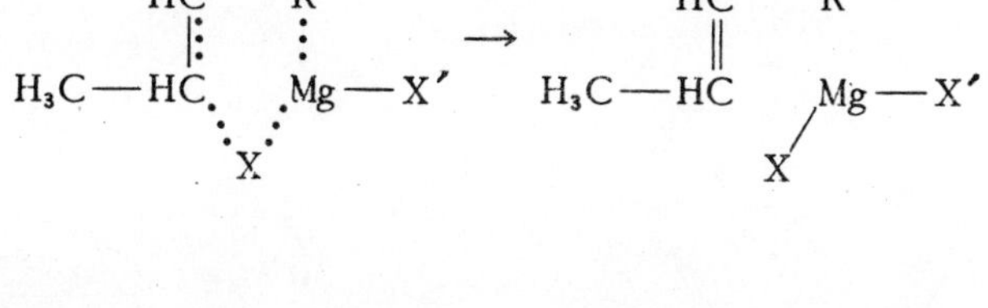

$$\begin{array}{c} \text{[cyclic intermediate: } H_3C-HC\!\!\stackrel{\vdots}{=}\!\!CH\cdots CH_2\cdots R\cdots Mg-X'\text{, with } X \text{ bridging HC and Mg]} \end{array} \longrightarrow \begin{array}{c} H_3C-HC=CH-CH_2-R \;\; + \;\; X-Mg-X' \end{array}$$

```
        CH3                      CH3
        |                        |
       .CH                       CH
      /:  :                     /  \
    HC     R                  HC    R
     :     :        →          ||
    H2C.   .Mg—X'             H2C   Mg—X'
       ·  ·                         /
        X                          X
```

On the whole it seems probable that two or more mechanisms may operate simultaneously in such reactions.

Butenyl esters. The suggestion of a special mechanism has also been advanced to account for the behavior of crotyl and α-methallyl mesitoates when treated with phenylmagnesium bromide.[42] Crotyl mesitoate undergoes cleavage to yield crotylbenzene only, whereas α-methallyl mesitoate yields crotylbenzene and α-methallylbenzene in approximately the same proportions as either of the isomeric butenyl chlorides. These reactions are discussed in more detail in Chapter VIII, Ester Cleavages.

---

[42] (*a*) Arnold and Liggett, *J. Am. Chem. Soc.*, *67*, 337–8 (1945). (*b*) Arnold and Searles, *ibid.*, *71*, 2021–3 (1949). (*c*) Wilson, Roberts, and Young, *ibid.*, *71*, 2019–20 (1949).

TABLE XVII-IV

REACTIONS OF GRIGNARD REAGENTS WITH ALLYLIC HALIDES

Halide	RMgX	Product(s)	Ref.
$C_3H_4Cl_2$			
$H_2C{=}CHCHCl_2$	CH_3MgBr	$CH_4 + C_2H_6 + C_2H_5CH{=}CHCl + C_2H_5CH{=}CHCH_3 + H_2C{=}CHCH(CH_3)_2 + CH_3(H_2CCH{=}CH)_2CH_3$ + high-boiling hydrocarbons	*1*
$H_2C{=}CHCHCl_2$	n-C_3H_7MgBr	C_6H_{14} + n-$C_4H_9CH{=}CHCl$ (*ca.* 25%) + n-$C_3H_7CH{=}CH$-n-C_4H_9 + $C_{12}H_{22}$ (30%)	*2*
$H_2C{=}CHCHCl_2$	i-C_3H_7MgBr	$C_3H_8 + C_6H_{14}$ + i-$C_4H_9CH{=}CHCl$ + i-$C_4H_9CH{=}CH$-i-C_3H_7 + $H_2C{=}CHCH(i\text{-}C_3H_7)_2$ + i-$C_3H_7(H_2CCH{=}CH)_2$-i-C_3H_7 + high-boiling hydrocarbons	*1*
$H_2C{=}CHCHCl_2$	n-C_4H_9MgBr	$C_4H_{10} + C_8H_8$ + n-$C_5H_{11}CH{=}CHCl$ + n-$C_5H_{11}CH{=}CH$-n-C_4H_9 + $H_2C{=}CHCH(n\text{-}C_4H_9)_2$ + n-$C_4H_9(H_2CCH{=}CH)_2$-n-C_4H_9 + high-boiling hydrocarbons	*1*
$H_2C{=}CHCHCl_2$	C_6H_5MgBr	$C_6H_5CH_2CH{=}CHCl$ ("poor yield") + tar	*3*
$ClCH{=}CHCH_2Cl$	CH_3MgBr	$CH_4 + C_2H_6 + C_2H_5CH{=}CHCl + C_2H_5CH{=}CHCH_3 + H_2C{=}CHCH(CH_3)_2 + CH_3(H_2CCH{=}CH)_2CH_3$ + high-boiling hydrocarbons	*1*
$ClCH{=}CHCH_2Cl$	n-C_3H_7MgBr	C_6H_{14} + n-$C_4H_9CH{=}CHCl$ ("very little") + n-$C_3H_7CH{=}CH$-n-C_4H_9 + $C_{12}H_{22}$ (>30%)	*2*
$ClCH{=}CHCH_2Cl$	i-C_3H_7MgBr	$C_3H_8 + C_6H_{14}$ + i-$C_4H_9CH{=}CHCl$ + i-$C_4H_9CH{=}CH$-i-C_3H_7 + $H_2C{=}CHCH(i\text{-}C_3H_7)_2$ + i-$C_3H_7(H_2CCH{=}CH)_2$-i-C_3H_7 + high-boiling hydrocarbons	*1*
$ClCH{=}CHCH_2Cl$	n-C_4H_9MgBr	$C_4H_{10} + C_8H_{18}$ + n-$C_5H_{11}CH{=}CHCl$ + n-$C_5H_{11}CH{=}CH$-n-C_4H_9 + $H_2C{=}CHCH(n\text{-}C_4H_9)_2$ + n-$C_4H_9(H_2CCH{=}CH)_2$-n-C_4H_9 + high-boiling hydrocarbons	*1*
$ClCH{=}CHCH_2Cl$	4-BrC_6H_4MgBr	4-$BrC_6H_4CH_2CH{=}CHCl$ ("high yield")	*4*
$ClCH{=}CHCH_2Cl$	C_6H_5MgBr	$C_6H_5CH_2CH{=}CHCl$ (*ca.* quant.)	*4*

TABLE XVII-IV (Continued)

Halide	RMgX	Product(s)	Ref.
$C_3H_4Cl_2$ (*cont.*)			
$ClCH{=}CHCH_2Cl$	$2\text{-}CH_3C_6H_4MgBr$	$2\text{-}CH_3C_6H_4CH_2CH{=}CHCl$ ("high yield")	4
$ClCH{=}CHCH_2Cl$	$4\text{-}CH_3C_6H_4MgBr$	$4\text{-}CH_3C_6H_4CH_2CH{=}CHCl$ ("high yield")	4
$ClCH{=}CHCH_2Cl$	$4\text{-}CH_3OC_6H_4MgBr$	$4\text{-}CH_3OC_6H_4CH_2CH{=}CHCl$ ("high yield")	4
$ClCH{=}CHCH_2Cl$	$4\text{-}i\text{-}C_3H_7C_6H_4MgBr$	$4\text{-}i\text{-}C_3H_7C_6H_4CH_2CH{=}CHCl$ ("high yield")	4
$ClCH{=}CHCH_2Cl$	$2\text{-}CH_3\text{-}5\text{-}i\text{-}C_3H_7C_6H_3MgBr$	$2\text{-}CH_3\text{-}5\text{-}i\text{-}C_3H_7C_6H_3CH_2CH{=}CHCl$ ("high yield")	4
$C_3H_4Br_2$			
$BrCH{=}CHCH_2Br$	CH_3MgBr	$CH_4 + C_2H_6 + C_4H_7Br + (H_2C{=}CH{-})_2$ (5%) $+ C_8H_{14} + C_{10}H_{18}$ or $C_{10}H_{16}$	2,5
$BrCH{=}CHCH_2Br$	C_2H_5MgBr	$BrCH{=}CH\text{-}n\text{-}C_3H_7 + C_7H_{14}$ (30%)	2,5
$BrCH{=}CHCH_2Br$	$n\text{-}C_3H_7MgBr$	C_6H_{14} (5%) $+ n\text{-}C_3H_7CH{=}CH\text{-}n\text{-}C_4H_9$ (47%) $+ C_{12}H_{22}$ + high-boiling unsaturates	2,5
$BrCH{=}CHCH_2Br$	C_6H_5MgBr	$BrCH{=}CHCH_2C_6H_5$ (50%)	2,6
C_3H_4ICl			
$ClCH{=}CHCH_2I$	$n\text{-}C_3H_7MgBr$	$n\text{-}C_4H_9CH{=}CHCl$ (?)* + unidentified products	3
C_4H_5Cl			
$H_2C{=}C{=}CHCH_2Cl$	CH_3MgCl	$H_2C{=}C(CH_3)CH{=}CH_2$ (14.7%)	7,8
$H_2C{=}C{=}CHCH_2Cl$	CH_3MgI	$H_2C{=}C(CH_3)CH{=}CH_2$ (23.5%)	7,8
$H_2C{=}C{=}CHCH_2Cl$	$n\text{-}C_4H_9MgBr$	$H_2C{=}C(n\text{-}C_4H_9)CH{=}CH_2$ (13.1%)	7,8
$H_2C{=}C{=}CHCH_2Cl$	C_6H_5MgBr	$H_2C{=}C{=}CHCH_2C_6H_5$ (4.0–7.2%) $+ H_2C{=}$	7,8
		$C(C_6H_5)CH{=}CH_2$ (8.4–9.2%) $+ [H_2C{=}C(C_6H_5)CH{=}CH_2]_2$ (25.3–26.7%)	7,8
$H_2C{=}C{=}CHCH_2Cl$	$C_6H_5CH_2MgCl$	$H_2C{=}C{=}CHCH_2CH_2C_6H_5$	8
$H_2C{=}C{=}CHCH_2Cl$	$n\text{-}C_7H_{15}MgCl$	$H_2C{=}C(n\text{-}C_7H_{15})CH{=}CH_2$ (21.0%)	7,8

* Not positively identified; small yield if any.

TABLE XVII-IV (Continued)

Halide	RMgX	Product(s)	Ref.
$C_4H_5Cl_3$			
$Cl_2C{=}C(CH_3)CH_2Cl$	CH_3MgBr	$C_2H_6 + [(CH_3)_2C{=}C(CH_3)CH_2{-}]_2 + Cl_2C{=}C(CH_3)CH_2C(CH_3)_2C(CH_3){=}CH_2 + Cl_2C{=}C(CH_3)CH_2CH_2C(CH_3){=}C(CH_3)_2$	*9*
$C_4H_6Br_2$			
$BrCH{=}C(CH_3)CH_2Br$	C_2H_5MgBr	C_8H_{16} (30%) + $C_6H_{11}Br$ + $C_{10}H_{17}Br$	*2*
C_4H_7Cl			
$CH_3CH{=}CHCH_2Cl$	$H_2C{=}CHCH_2MgCl$	$(H_2C{=}CHCH_2)_2CH_2$ (>50.8%) + $H_2C{=}CHCH(CH_3)CH_2CH{=}CH_2$ (<3.2%)	*10*
$CH_3CH{=}CHCH_2Cl$	$H_2C{=}CHCH_2MgBr$	$CH_3CH{=}CHCH_2CH_2CH{=}CH_2$ (53.5%)	*11*
$CH_3CH{=}CHCH_2Cl$	Butenyl-MgBr	$(CH_3CH{=}CHCH_2{-})_2$ (8.6%) + $H_2C{=}CHCH(CH_3)CH_2CH{=}CHCH_3$ (59.0%) + $[H_2C{=}CHCH(CH_3){-}]_2$ (5.0%)	*10*
$CH_3CH{=}CHCH_2Cl$	$n\text{-}C_4H_9MgCl$	$CH_3CH{=}CH\text{-}n\text{-}C_5H_{11}$ (60%) + $H_2C{=}CHCH(CH_3)\text{-}n\text{-}C_4H_9$ (10%)	*12*
$CH_3CH{=}CHCH_2Cl$	C_6H_5MgBr	$CH_3CH{=}CHCH_2C_6H_5$ (46 ± 3%) + $H_2C{=}CHCH(CH_3)C_6H_5$ (14 ± 2%)	*13*
$CH_3CH{=}CHCH_2Cl$ + $CH_3(H_2C{=}CH)CHCl$	$n\text{-}C_4H_9MgCl$	$H_2C{=}CHCH(CH_3)CH_2CH{=}CHCH_3$ (6x%) + $H_2C{=}CHCH(CH_3)\text{-}n\text{-}C_4H_9$ (9x%) + $CH_3CH{=}CH\text{-}n\text{-}C_5H_{11}$ (85x%)	*14*
$CH_3CH{=}CHCH_2Cl$ (41%) + $CH_3(H_2C{=}CH)CHCl$ (59%)	C_6H_5MgBr	$CH_3CH{=}CHCH_2C_6H_5$ (81 ± 3x%) + $H_2C{=}CHCH(CH_3)C_6H_5$ (19 ± 2x%)	*13*
$CH_3(H_2C{=}CH)CHCl$	$H_2C{=}CHCH_2MgCl$	$(H_2C{=}CHCH_2)_2CH_2$ (42.4%) + $H_2C{=}CHCH(CH_3)CH_2CH{=}CH_2$ (13.2%)	*10*
$CH_3(H_2C{=}CH)CHCl$	Butenyl-MgBr	$(CH_3CH{=}CHCH_2{-})_2$ (2.3%) + $H_2C{=}CHCH(CH_3)CH_2CH_2CH{=}CH_2$ (65.4%) + $[H_2C{=}CHCH(CH_3){-}]_2$ (8.4%)	*10*

TABLE XVII-IV (Continued)

Halide	RMgX	Product(s)	Ref.
C_4H_7Cl (*cont.*)			
$CH_3(H_2C{=}CH)CHCl$	C_6H_5MgBr	$CH_3CH{=}CHCH_2C_6H_5$ (52 ± 4%) + $CH_3(H_2C{=}CH)CHC_6H_5$ (14 ± 2%)	*13*
C_4H_7Br			
$CH_3CH{=}CHCH_2Br$	C_6H_5MgBr	$CH_3CH{=}CHCH_2C_6H_5$ (34%)	*15*
$CH_3CH{=}CHCH_2Br$	$C_6H_5CH_2CH_2MgBr$	$H_2C{=}CHCH(CH_3)CH_2CH_2C_6H_5$	*15*
$CH_3CH{=}CHCH_2Br$ (87%) + $CH_3(H_2C{=}CH)CHBr$ (13%)	Butenyl-MgBr	$(CH_3CH{=}CHCH_2{-})_2$ (5.8%) + $H_2C{=}CHCH(CH_3)CH_2CH{=}CHCH_3$ (51.0%) + $[H_2C{=}CHCH(CH_3){-}]_2$ (1.2%)	*10*
$CH_3CH{=}CHCH_2Br$ + $CH_3(H_2C{=}CH)CHBr$*	$(CH_2)_4CHMgCl$	$CH_3(H_2C{=}CH)CHCH(CH_2)_4$ + *cis*- and *trans*-$CH_3CH{=}CHCH_2CH(CH_2)_4$	*16*
$CH_3(H_2C{=}CH)CHBr$	Butenyl-MgBr	$(CH_3CH{=}CHCH_2{-})_2$ (37.5%) + $H_2C{=}CHCH(CH_3)CH_2CH{=}CHCH_3$ (26.3%) + $[H_2C{=}CHCH(CH_3){-}]_2$ (11.3%)	*10*
$CH_3(H_2C{=}CH)CHBr$	$C_6H_5CH_2CH_2MgBr$	$CH_3CH{=}CH(CH_2)_3C_6H_5$	*15*
C_5H_9Cl			
$CH_3(CH_3CH{=}CH)CHCl$	n-C_3H_7MgCl	$CH_3(CH_3CH{=}CH)CH$-n-C_3H_7	*14*
C_5H_9Br			
$C_2H_5CH{=}CHCH_2Br$	C_2H_5MgBr	$C_2H_5CH{=}CH$-n-C_3H_7 (16–20%) + $(C_2H_5)_2CHCH{=}CH_2$ (60–64%)	*18,17*
$C_2H_5CH{=}CHCH_2Br$	C_6H_5MgBr	$C_2H_5CH{=}CHCH_2C_6H_5$ (25–33x%) + $C_2H_5(C_6H_5)CHCH{=}CH_2$ (66–75x%)	*18*
$CH_3(CH_3CH{=}CH)CHBr$	CH_3MgBr	$CH_3CH{=}CH(CH_3)_2CH$ (57%)	*19*
$CH_3(CH_3CH{=}CH)CHBr$	n-C_3H_7MgBr	$CH_3(CH_3CH{=}CH)CH$-n-C_3H_7 (27%)	*19*

* From the addition of hydrogen bromide to 1,3-butadiene.

TABLE XVII-IV (Continued)

Halide	RMgX	Product(s)	Ref.
C_5H_9Br (*cont.*)			
$CH_3(CH_3CH{=}CH)CHBr$	n-C_4H_9MgBr	$CH_3(CH_3CH{=}CH)CH$-n-C_4H_9 (28%)	*19*
$CH_3(CH_3CH{=}CH)CHBr$	i-C_4H_9MgBr	$CH_3(CH_3CH{=}CH)CH$-i-C_4H_9 (36%)	*19*
$CH_3(CH_3CH{=}CH)CHBr$	s-C_4H_9MgBr	$CH_3(CH_3CH{=}CH)CH$-s-C_4H_9 (8%)	*19*
$CH_3(CH_3CH{=}CH)CHBr$	t-C_4H_9MgBr	$CH_3(CH_3CH{=}CH)CH$-t-C_4H_9 (5%)	*19*
$CH_3(CH_3CH{=}CH)CHBr$	$(CH_2)_4CHMgBr$	$CH_3(CH_3CH{=}CH)CHCH(CH_2)_4$ (15%)	*19*
$C_6H_8Br_2$			
$(-HC{=}CHCH_2Br)_2$	C_2H_5MgBr	n-$C_3H_7CH{=}CHCH(C_2H_5)CH{=}CH_2$ + (n-$C_3H_7CH{=}CH-)_2$ + $[H_2C{=}CH(C_2H_5)CH-]_2$ + C_2H_5(n-$C_3H_7)CHCH{=}CHCH{=}CH_2$ (?) + $BrCH_2(C_2H_5)CHCH{=}CHCH{=}CH_2$ (?) + unidentified products	*20*
$C_7H_{13}ClO$			
$C_2H_5OCH_2CH_2CH{=}CHCH_2Cl$	C_2H_5MgBr	Rec. $C_7H_{13}ClO$ (18.5%) + $C_2H_5OCH_2CH_2CH{=}CH$-n-C_3H_7 (43.8%) + $H_2C{=}CH(C_2H_5OCH_2CH_2)(C_2H_5OCH_2CH_2CH{=}CHCH_2)CH$ (16.1%)	*22*
$C_2H_5OCH_2CH_2CH{=}CHCH_2Cl$	n-C_4H_9MgCl	Rec. $C_7H_{13}ClO$ (12.0%) + $C_2H_5OCH_2CH_2CH{=}CH$-n-C_5H_{11} (54.3%) + $H_2C{=}CH(C_2H_5OCH_2CH_2)(C_2H_5OCH_2CH_2CH{=}CHCH_2)CH$ (16.7%)	*22*
$H_2C{=}CH(C_2H_5OCH_2CH_2)CHCl$	C_2H_5MgBr	Rec. $C_7H_{13}ClO$ (5.0%) + $C_2H_5OCH_2CH_2CH{=}CH$-n-C_3H_7 (49.3%) + $H_2C{=}CH(C_2H_5OCH_2CH_2)(C_2H_5OCH_2CH_2CH{=}CHCH_2)CH$ (18.6%)	*22*
$H_2C{=}CH(C_2H_5OCH_2CH_2)CHCl$	n-C_4H_9MgBr	Rec. $C_7H_{13}ClO$ (11.3%) + $C_2H_5OCH_2CH_2CH{=}CH$-n-C_5H_{11} (53.1%) + $H_2C{=}CH(C_2H_5OCH_2CH_2)(C_2H_5OCH_2CH_2CH{=}CHCH_2)CH$ (19.1%)	*22*

TABLE XVII-IV (Continued)

Halide	RMgX	Product(s)	Ref.
C_9H_9Cl			
$C_6H_5CH{=}CHCH_2Cl$	CH_3MgBr	$C_6H_5CH{=}CHC_2H_5$ (89%) + $(C_6H_5CH{=}CHCH_2{-})_2$ (1%) + $C_6H_5CH{=}CHCH_2CH(C_6H_5)CH{=}CH_2$ (5%)	*21*
C_9H_9Br			
$C_6H_5CH{=}CHCH_2Br$	C_2H_5MgBr	$C_6H_5CH{=}CH$-n-C_3H_7 (*ca.* 50%) + $C_2H_5(C_6H_5)CHCH{=}CH_2$ (*ca.* 25%)*	*18*
$C_6H_5CH{=}CHCH_2Br$	C_2H_5MgBr	C_2H_5Br (14.0%) + $C_6H_5CH{=}CHCH_3$ (2.5%) + $C_6H_5CH_2CH{=}CH_2$ (2.5%) + $(C_6H_5CH{=}CHCH_2{-})_2$ (4.5%) + $C_2H_5(C_6H_5)CHCH{=}CH_2$ (23.0%) + $C_6H_5CH{=}CH$-n-C_3H_7 (50.0%) + C_2H_6 (10.0%) + cond'n products†	*20*
$C_9H_{17}Cl$			
i-$C_4H_9CH{=}CH(CH_3)_2CCl$ + i-$C_3H_7[(CH_3)_2C{=}CH]CHCl$	CH_3MgCl	i-$C_4H_9CH{=}CH$-t-C_4H_9 (16.7x%) + i-$C_3H_7[(CH_3)_2C{=}CH]CHCH_3$ (83.3x%)	*14*
$C_9H_{17}ClO$			
n-$C_4H_9OCH_2CH_2CH{=}CHCH_2Cl$	n-C_4H_9MgBr	Rec. $C_9H_{17}ClO$ (13.0%) + n-$C_4H_9OCH_2CH_2CH{=}CH$-n-C_5H_{11} (43.7%) + $H_2C{=}CH(n$-$C_4H_9OCH_2CH_2)(n$-$C_4H_9OCH_2CH_2CH{=}CHCH_2)CH$ (23.2%)	22
n-$C_4H_9OCH_2CH_2CH{=}CHCH_2Cl$	C_6H_5MgBr	Rec. $C_9H_{17}ClO$ (12.5%) + n-$C_4H_9OCH_2CH_2CH{=}CHCH_2C_6H_5$ (66.0%) + C_6H_6	22
$H_2C{=}CH(n$-$C_4H_9OCH_2CH_2)CHCl$	n-C_4H_9MgBr	Rec. $C_9H_{17}ClO$ (13.8%) + n-$C_4H_9OCH_2CH_2CH{=}CH$-n-C_5H_{11} (44.1%) + $H_2C{=}CH(n$-$C_4H_9OCH_2CH_2)(n$-$C_4H_9OCH_2CH_2CH{=}CHCH_2)CH$ (23.2%)	22
$H_2C{=}CH(n$-$C_4H_9OCH_2CH_2)CHCl$	C_6H_5MgBr	Rec. $C_9H_{17}ClO$ (14.5%) + n-$C_4H_9OCH_2CH_2CH{=}CHCH_2C_6H_5$ (67.0%) + C_6H_6	22

* Slow addition of Et_2O-bromide solution to Grignard reagent solution; several hours reflux.

† Addition of bromide to Grignard reagent solution; twelve hours at room temperature.

REFERENCES FOR TABLE XVII-IV

(*1*) Pourrat, *Compt. rend.*, *228*, 1031–3 (1949).
(*2*) Kirrmann, *Bull. soc. chim.*, [4], *47*, 834–47 (1930).
(*3*) Kirrmann, Pacaud, and Dosque, *Bull. soc. chim.*, [5], *1*, 860–71 (1934).
(*4*) Bert, *Compt. rend.*, *180*, 1504–6 (1925).
(*5*) Kirrmann, *Compt. rend.*, *182*, 1629–31 (1926); *Chem. Abstr.*, *20*, 3155 (1926).
(*6*) von Braun and Kühn, *Ber.*, *58B*, 2168–73 (1925).
(*7*) Carothers and Berchet, *J. Am. Chem. Soc.*, *55*, 1094–6 (1933).
(*8*) Carothers, U. S. Patent 2,072,867, March 9, 1937; *Chem. Abstr.*, *31*, P3335 (1937).
(*9*) Kirrmann and Jacob, *Bull. soc. chim.*, [5], 7, 586–93 (1940).
(*10*) Young, Roberts, and Wax, *J. Am. Chem. Soc.*, *67*, 841–3 (1945).
(*11*) Levy and Cope, *J. Am. Chem. Soc.*, *66*, 1684–8 (1944).
(*12*) Cleveland, *J. Chem. Phys.*, *11*, 1–6 (1943).
(*13*) Wilson, Roberts, and Young, *J. Am. Chem. Soc.*, *71*, 2019–20 (1949).
(*14*) Henne, Chanan, and Turk, *J. Am. Chem. Soc.*, *63*, 3474–6 (1941).
(*15*) Lawrence and Shelton, *Ind. Eng. Chem.*, *42*, 136–40 (1950).
(*16*) Plate, Sterligov, and Bazhulin, *J. Gen. Chem.* (U.S.S.R), *14*, 955–9 (1944); *Chem. Abstr.*, *39*, 4594 (1945).
(*17*) Prévost, *Compt. rend.*, *187*, 946–8 (1928); *Chem. Abstr.*, *23*, 2149 (1929).
(*18*) Prévost and Daujat, *Bull. soc. chim.*, [4], *47*, 588–94 (1930).
(*19*) Mulliken, Wakeman, and Gerry, *J. Am. Chem. Soc.*, *57*, 1605–7 (1935).
(*20*) Prévost, *Bull. soc. chim.*, [4], *49*, 1372–81 (1931).
(*21*) Kharasch, Lambert, and Urry, *J. Org. Chem.*, *10*, 298–306 (1945).
(*22*) Pudovik and Vinokurova, *J. Gen. Chem.* (U.S.S.R.), *19*, 1882–90 (1949); *Chem. Abstr.*, *44*, 1896 (1950).

CHAPTER XVIII

The Tschugaeff-Zerewitinoff Method for the Determination of "Active" Hydrogen

On the basis of the observation of Tissier and Grignard[1] that organomagnesium halides react with alcohols and phenols according to the equation

$$RMgX + R'OH \rightarrow RH + R'OMgX,$$

Tschugaeff[2] suggested the use of Grignard reagents for (1) the detection of hydroxylic compounds and (2) the separation of hydroxylic compounds from hydrocarbons, ethers, and other "indifferent" substances. He further suggested, that with the aid of a suitable gas-measuring device, such as a Knop nitrometer, ethereal methylmagnesium iodide might be employed for the quantitative estimation of dry hydroxylic substances. Tschugaeff published no experimental data, and apparently made no further contribution to the subject; the continued linkage of his name with the method subsequently developed by others is probably attributable to Zerewitinoff's[3] insistence on crediting him with the original idea.

Quantitative data were first published by Hibbert and Sudborough,[4] who, however, in the interests of greater accuracy, found it desirable to modify somewhat the method as originally suggested by Tschugaeff. To avoid the gradual permeation by water of the india-rubber connections of a Knop nitrometer, they substituted a mercury-filled Lunge nitrometer or Hempel burette. To avoid the slow absorption of oxygen by the Grignard reagent, they displaced the air from their apparatus with dry nitrogen. The uncertainty inherent in correction for the highly variable (with temperature) vapor pressure of ethyl ether was minimized by employing the relatively non-volatile amyl ether as solvent. Their data are included in the accompanying tabulation (references *1*, *4*, and *8*).

Zerewitinoff, whose systematic investigations have resulted in the attachment of his name to this method, also adopted the Lunge nitrometer as a measuring instrument, and employed amyl ether as the Grignard reagent solvent. He added the refinement of using dry pyridine, a much more

---

[1]Tissier and Grignard, *Compt. rend.*, *132*, 835–7 (1901); *J. Chem. Soc.*, *80,I*, 316 (1901).

[2]Tschugaeff, *Ber.*, *35*, 3912–4 (1902).

[3]Zerewitinoff, *Ber.*, *47*, 1659 (1914).

[4]Hibbert and Sudborough, *Proc. Chem. Soc.*, *19*, 285–6 (1903); *J. Chem. Soc.*, *85*, 933–8 (1904).

nearly universal solvent than amyl ether, to dissolve the substances to be tested. Because his reaction chamber was small, and there was opportunity for oxygen absorption before mixture of the reactants, he regarded the use of an inert atmosphere as unnecessary. He did, however, make provision for careful temperature control. His apparatus and method are described in detail (with drawings) in the *Berichte*[5] and in the *Zeitschrift für analytische Chemie*.[6] The apparatus and method (with slight modifications) are also described in detail in the twenty-second edition of Gatterman-Wieland.[7] In this form the method is well adapted to samples of the order of magnitude of 0.1 to 0.2 g.

Arnold and Rondestvedt[8] (Table XVIII-I, reference *38*) used a semimicro modification of the Zerewitinoff apparatus, devised by Lauer and Zaugg, for samples of the order of magnitude of 80–100 mg., and stated that a description thereof was then "in press." Search of the *Chemical Abstracts* indices for 1946–51, however, fails to reveal any reference thereto. A micro apparatus suitable for use with samples of the order of magnitude of 3–10 mg. is described (with drawing) by Flaschenträger.[9]

In a modification of the method not described in great detail, Moureu and Mignonac[10] used ethyl ether as solvent for both Grignard reagent and substance tested. Similar determinations have been made by Ciusa[11] and by Gilman and Fothergill.[12] A method of this kind, employing an atmosphere of nitrogen, and adapted to samples of the order of magnitude of 50–200 mg., is described (with drawing) by Braude and Stern.[13] It is said to be accurate to ±1–2 percent, but is applicable only to relatively non-volatile compounds with functional groups reacting completely at room temperature. Correction for ether vapor is made from the vapor-pressure data of Taylor and Smith.[14]

Fuchs *et al.*[15] describe (with diagram) a modified Zerewitinoff apparatus including a dibutyl phthalate manometer, and a procedure employing a *n*-butyl ether solution of methylmagnesium iodide under an atmosphere of nitrogen. After nitrogen flushing at 70°, the system is cooled to the vicinity of room temperature and maintained by means of a bath within a temperature range of 1° while reaction takes place. Results are calculated on the basis of the density of methane and the vapor pressure of *n*-butyl

[5] Zerewitinoff, *Ber.*, *40*, 2023–31 (1907).

[6] Zerewitinoff, *Z. anal. Chem.*, *50*, 680–91 (1911).

[7] English translation by W. McCartney, "Laboratory Methods of Organic Chemistry," The Macmillan Company, New York, *1934*, pp. 72–4.

[8] Arnold and Rondestvedt, *J. Am. Chem. Soc.*, *68*, 2176–8 (1946).

[9] Flaschenträger, *Z. physiol. Chem.*, *146*, 219–26 (1925); *Chem. Abstr.*, *19*, 3230 (1925).

[10] Moureu and Mignonac, *Compt. rend.*, *158*, 1624–31 (1914).

[11] Ciusa, *Gazz. chim. ital.*, *50,II*, 53–5 (1920); *Chem. Abstr.*, *15*, 837 (1921).

[12] Gilman and Fothergill, *J. Am. Chem. Soc.*, *49*, 2815–8 (1927).

[13] Braude and Stern, *J. Chem. Soc.*, *1946*, 404–6.

[14] Taylor and Smith, *J. Am. Chem. Soc.*, *44*, 2450–63 (1922).

[15] Fuchs, Ishler, and Sandhoff, *Ind. Eng. Chem.*, *Anal. Ed.*, *12*, 507–9 (1940).

ether at the temperature employed. The use of isoamyl ether is said to give results of equal precision but to require longer reaction times.

A somewhat similar apparatus in which, however, the reaction chamber and the gas burette are water-jacketed, is described (with diagram) by Lehman and Basch.[16] Modification of the procedure to employ a pyridine suspension of methylmagnesium iodide-pyridine complex as the reagent, and methane saturated with pyridine vapor as the inert atmosphere, together with provision for the application of heat during the reaction period, leads to theoretical "active" hydrogen values for some compounds (such as picric acid and hydroquinone) that give negative results by the method of Fuchs *et al.*

Various other minor modifications of apparatus and method have been suggested or used from time to time (see, *e.g.*, Schmitz-Dumont and Hamann[17]; Oddo[18]). One of the more radical, though not necessarily more meritorious, innovations consists in operation under an atmosphere of carbon dioxide (Terent'ev *et al.*[19]). "The carbon dioxide enters the reaction vessel (after complete air replacement) under a layer of ethereal solution of the substance to be analyzed, to eliminate any initial reaction between carbon dioxide and methylmagnesium iodide. The stream of carbon dioxide is now broken. The methane formed replaces the carbon dioxide from the vessel and the reaction is completed in an atmosphere of methane. Dry carbon dioxide, which is now passed through, carries over the methane into the azotometer and reacts with excess of methylmagnesium iodide. By transferring the gas from the azotometer into the eudiometer it is measured, as is often done in Duma's nitrogen determination."

Although methylmagnesium iodide was used by Zerewitinoff and most of his followers, the bromide and chloride are equally applicable. For substances containing only "active" hydrogen groups the ethylmagnesium halides are just as satisfactory, but when reducible carbonyl groups are present the results may be complicated by ethylene evolution.

The substance to be analyzed may be treated as such, but more satisfactory results are usually obtained when it is dissolved in the Grignard reagent solvent, in pyridine, or in an aromatic hydrocarbon such as benzene, toluene, or xylene. Anisole and phenetole are also applicable as solvents, but necessitate a correction for the solubility of methane (Sudborough and Hibbert[20]).

---

[16]Lehman and Basch, *Ind. Eng. Chem., Anal. Ed.*, *17*, 428–9 (1945).

[17]Schmitz-Dumont and Hamann, *Ber.*, *66B*, 71–6 (1933); *J. prakt. Chem.*, [2], *139*, 162–6, 167–79 (1934).

[18]Oddo, *Ber.*, *44*, 2048–52 (1911).

[19]Terent'ev and Shcherbakova, *J. Gen. Chem.* (U.S.S.R.), *10*, 2041–6 (1940); *15*, 86–9 (1945); *16*, 855–8 (1946); Terent'ev, Shcherbakova, and Kremenskaya, *ibid.*, *17*, 100–4 (1947); *Chem. Abstr.*, *35*, 4308 (1941); *40*, 1420 (1946); *41*, 1575 (1947); *42*, 109 (1948).

[20]Sudborough and Hibbert, *J. Chem. Soc.*, *95*, 477–80 (1909).

THE "GRIGNARD MACHINE"

For simultaneous estimations of the "active" hydrogen and the additive capacity of bifunctional compounds, Kohler[21] devised an apparatus commonly known as the "Grignard machine." It and the method of operation are described in detail (with drawings) in the papers cited. Kohler operated under an atmosphere of nitrogen, purified by passage through a Fieser[22] train. According to Hollyday and Cottle,[23] who describe (with drawing) a modified "Grignard machine," tank nitrogen constitutes an altogether satisfactory atmosphere for determinations of this kind.

By Kohler's method a measured volume of standardized methylmagnesium iodide-isoamyl ether solution (in considerable excess) is added to a 0.2-g. sample of the substance investigated (or to a xylene solution thereof). Reaction is facilitated by brief warming of the reaction mixture. The volume of evolved methane is then measured. The amount of unused Grignard reagent is then determined by the addition of a measured volume of water (in excess), and measurement of the volume of methane consequently evolved.

Substantially the original apparatus and method of Kohler have been employed by Smith and Guss,[24] by Whitmore *et al.*,[25] and by Kadesch[26] to study the competitive enolization and addition reactions of enolizable ketones. Their data are summarized in Table VI-IX of the section on enolization of Chapter VI.

A modification of the Grignard machine suitable for use with samples of the order of 2-20 mg., and a procedure employing amyl ether as solvent under an atmosphere of nitrogen, are described by Soltys.[27]

"ACTIVE" HYDROGEN GROUPS

Generally speaking, compounds of the following types may be expected to react more or less rapidly with methylmagnesium halides at room temperature to give approximately quantitative yields of methane: water of hydration (two equivalents); the mineral acid salts of nitrogen bases; carboxylic, sulfonic, sulfinic, and sulfenic acids; phenols, alcohols, and glycols; hydroperoxides; mercaptans; phosphines; primary amines (one equivalent); secondary aromatic amines; amides (one equivalent); imides; cyclic amines of the pyrrole and indole types*; monosubstituted acetylenes*;

---

[21]Kohler, Stone, and Fuson, *J. Am. Chem. Soc.*, *49*, 3181–8 (1927); Kohler and Richtmyer, *ibid.*, *52*, 3736–8 (1930).

[22]Fieser, *J. Am. Chem. Soc.*, *46*, 2639–47 (1924).

[23]Hollyday and Cottle, *Ind. Eng. Chem., Anal. Ed.*, *14*, 774–6 (1942).

[24]Smith and Guss, *J. Am. Chem. Soc.*, *59*, 804–6 (1937).

[25]Whitmore and Randall, *J. Am. Chem. Soc.*, *64*, 1242–6 (1942); Whitmore and Block, *ibid.*, *64*, 1619–21 (1942); Whitmore and Lewis, *ibid.*, *64*, 2964–6 (1942).

[26]Kadesch, *J. Am. Chem. Soc.*, *66*, 1207–13 (1944).

[27]Soltys, *Mikrochem.*, *20*, 107–25 (1936); *Chem. Abstr.*, *30*, 5146 (1936).

*Concerning these and acetylene see section on Hydrogen Displacement Methods, Chapter II, pp. 66–86.

monosubstituted hydrazines (2 equivalents); α,α-disubstituted hydrazines (one equivalent); α,β-disubstituted hydrazines (two equivalents); oximes; phenylhydrazones (one equivalent); semicarbazones (two equivalents).

Secondary aliphatic amines, although they react very slowly at room temperature (Hibbert[28]), yield one equivalent of methane on heating (70–125°). As a rule primary amines yield one equivalent of methane at room temperature and a second on heating, (Sudborough and Hibbert[29]), as do amides* (Zerewitinoff[30]). Some polyfunctional compounds do not yield the quantity of methane corresponding to all the supposedly "active" hydrogen atoms present even when heated, presumably because of the insolubility (and consequent unreactivity) of the products of partial reaction. This is true, for example, of urea and thiourea, each of which liberates two equivalents of methane in the cold, and three on heating (Zerewitinoff, *loc. cit.*[30]). In general, diamines also yield two equivalents of methane in the cold, and three on heating (Zerewitinoff[31]).

A few hydrocarbons, such as fluorene and its derivatives, indene (Zerewitinoff, *loc. cit.*[31]), pentadeca-6,9-diyne (Tchao Yin Lai[32]), 1,5-diphenyl-1,4-pentadiyne, and 1-phenylpent-4-en-1-yne (Grignard and Lepayre[33]), liberate methane when heated with methyl Grignard reagents.

The reactions of Grignard reagents with enolizable ketones are discussed in the section on enolization of Chapter VI, and the "Grignard machine" data of several investigators are recorded in Table VI-IX. When the ketone is strongly "hindered" so that the competitive addition reaction is completely circumvented, as in the case of acetomesitylene, the liberation of methane is approximately quantitative (Kohler *et al.*[34]). According to Schlenk *et al.*,[35] the second "active" hydrogen of phenylacetic acid should also be attributed to enolization. Malonic ester (Zerewitinoff[36]) undoubtedly falls in the same class.

Other "pseudo-acidic" substances react with methyl Grignard reagents to liberate methane in varying quantities. By way of example may be cited the nitriles with labile *alpha* hydrogen atoms, discussed in the section on Keteniminate Formation, Chapter X.

Ishikawa and Kojima[37] report a considerable degree of keteniminization of benzyl cyanide, and state further that, in pyridine solution, any anhydride,

[28] Hibbert, *J. Chem. Soc.*, *101*, 328–41 (1912).

[29] Sudborough and Hibbert, *J. Chem. Soc.*, *95*, 477–80 (1909).

*Trichloroacetamide is an exception, yielding two equivalents of methane in the cold.

[30] Zerewitinoff, *Ber.*, *41*, 2233–43 (1908).

[31] Zerewitinoff, *Ber.*, *45*, 2384–9 (1912).

[32] Tchao Yin Lai, *Bull. soc. chim.*, [4], *53*, 1537–43 (1933).

[33] Grignard and Lepayre, *Compt. rend.*, *192*, 250–3 (1931); *Chem. Abstr.*, *25*, 2421 (1931); *Bull. soc. chim.*, [4], *43*, 930–1 (1928).

[34] Kohler, Stone, and Fuson, *J. Am. Chem. Soc.*, *49*, 3181–8 (1927).

[35] Schlenk, Hilleman, and Rodloff, *Ann.*, *487*, 135–54 (1931).

[36] Zerewitinoff, *Ber.*, *41*, 2233–43 (1908).

[37] Ishikawa and Kojima, *Science Repts. Tokyo Bunsika Daigaku*, *1*, 289–96 (1934); *Chem. Abstr.*, *28*, 2697 (1934).

such as acetic, butyric, isovaleric, succinic, or phenylacetic, which contains neighboring carboxyl, methyl, or methylene groups invariably has an "active" hydrogen content varying from 1.21 for phenylacetic to 0.14 for isovaleric.

It has sometimes been assumed[38] that the reactions of aliphatic nitro compounds with Grignard reagents are essentially reactions of the *aci* forms. That this can scarcely be taken for granted, however, is indicated by the gas-forming reactions with methyl Grignard reagents of aromatic nitro compounds[39] and such non-hydrogenous aliphatic nitro compounds as tribromo- and trichloronitromethane[40] and tetranitromethane.[41]

Sulfones with labile *alpha* hydrogen atoms also undergo a reaction analogous to enolate formation.[41.1] For example, phenethyl *p*-tolyl sulfone and β,β-diphenylethyl *p*-tolyl sulfone each liberate at least one molecular equivalent of methane when treated with methylmagnesium iodide at 50–75°. Methyl *p*-tolyl sulfone (with methylmagnesium iodide) liberates methane slowly at room temperature; when heated it appears to have two "active" hydrogen atoms.

SOURCES OF ERROR, AND LIMITATIONS OF THE METHOD

Aside from the foregoing discussion, the reader's general knowledge of the properties of Grignard reagents would suggest the advisability of precautions to exclude moisture and oxygen. As has already been mentioned, the use of anisole or phenetole as solvents necessitates correction for the solubility of methane (Sudborough and Hibbert[42]). Some investigators have encountered errors in the use of pyridine as a sample solvent. Schmitz-Dumont and Hamann,[43] for example, found it desirable to introduce into their determinations corrections based on blank runs. Tanberg[44] reported considerable gas evolution upon the addition of various samples of pyridine to methylmagnesium iodide solution, and concluded that pyridine is not a suitable solvent for "active" hydrogen determinations.

Zerewitinoff[45] suggested that one source of gas evolution in Tanberg's experiments might be the presence in the Grignard reagent of excess

[38] See, *e.g.*, Zerewitinoff, *Ber.*, *43*, 3590–5 (1910).

[39] Gilman and Fothergill, *J. Am. Chem. Soc.*, *49*, 2815–8 (1927); see also the section on Nitro Compounds, Chapter XIX.

[40] Gilman and Fothergill, *Bull. soc. chim.*, [4], *45*, 1132–6 (1929).

[41] Gilman, Fothergill, and Towne, *J. Am. Chem. Soc.*, *52*, 405–7 (1930).

[41.1] Kohler and Potter, *J. Am. Chem. Soc.*, *57*, 1316–21 (1935); *ibid.*, *58*, 2166–70 (1936); Gilman and Webb, *ibid.*, *71*, 4062–6 (1949); Field, *ibid.*, *74*, 3919–21 (1952).

[42] Sudborough and Hibbert, *J. Chem. Soc.*, *95*, 477–80 (1907).

[43] Schmitz-Dumont and Hamann, *J. prakt. Chem.*, [2], *139*, 162–6 (1934).

[44] Tanberg, *J. Am. Chem. Soc.*, *36*, 335–7 (1914).

[45] Zerewitinoff, *Ber.*, *47*, 2417–23 (1914).

methyl iodide, giving rise to the reaction sequence

$$C_5H_5N \xrightarrow{CH_3I} \left[C_5H_5N\text{—}CH_3\right]^{+}I^{-} \xrightarrow{CH_3MgI} C_2H_6 + C_5H_5N + MgI_2$$

(See section on Quaternary Salts, Chapter XIX.) He further called attention to the fact that Tanberg's pyridine was dried by twenty-four hour reflux with barium oxide, and showed experimentally that pyridine undergoes reduction upon prolonged heating with barium hydroxide.

Jurecek[46] also calls attention to precautions to be observed in the use of pyridine as a sample solvent. When pyridine is used as a suspending medium for the Grignard reagent-pyridine complex as well as for a sample solvent, the solubility of methane in pyridine must also be taken into account (Lehman and Basch[47]).

Hibbert[48] reported that primary aliphatic alcohols, especially the lower members of the series, give results materially lower than the theoretical when measured for "active" hydrogen by his variation of Tschugaeff's method. Zerewitinoff's[49] determinations reveal no such error. Hollyday and Cottle[50] have discovered one source of this discrepancy in the respective concentrations employed by the two investigators. Check experiments showed that methanol at a concentration of 0.245 mole per liter of the reaction mixture liberated 89 percent of the theoretical quantity of methane; at 0.100 molar, 94 percent; and at 0.0647 molar, 99.9 percent. Apparently the methoxide precipitate formed at relatively high concentrations carries with it some methanol of solvation. Another probable source of error in Hibbert's determinations is the loss of relatively volatile test material in the course of sweeping the apparatus with nitrogen.

Variations in apparent "active" hydrogen values with solvent employed have been investigated by Lieff *et al.*[51] Their data are included in Table XVIII-I (reference 27). In general, the discrepancies between values obtained in the solvents commonly used (provided the media are truly *solvents* for the materials tested) are relatively trivial; dioxane, however, is an exception insofar as samples containing enolizable carbonyl groups are concerned. Wright[52] has related this phenomenon to the relative reactivities of dimethylmagnesium and the ordinary methyl Grignard reagent with respect to carbonyl-group addition. Dimethylmagnesium being the less reactive with respect to carbonyl-group addition tends to give some-

[46] Jureček, *Chem. Listy*, *40*, 239–45 (1946); *Chem. Abstr.*, *44*, 9220 (1950).
[47] Lehman and Basch, *Ind. Eng. Chem.*, *Anal. Ed.*, *17*, 428–9 (1945).
[48] Hibbert, *J. Chem. Soc.*, *101*, 328–41 (1912).
[49] Zerewitinoff, *Ber.*, *40*, 2023–31 (1907); *45*, 2384–9 (1912).
[50] Hollyday and Cottle, *Ind. Eng. Chem.*, *Anal. Ed.*, *14*, 774–6 (1942).
[51] Lieff, Wright, and Hibbert, *J. Am. Chem. Soc.*, *61*, 865–7 (1939).
[52] Wright, *J. Am. Chem. Soc.*, *61*, 1152–6 (1939).

what higher "active" hydrogen values when compounds containing enolizable carbonyl groups are tested in dioxane.

It has been found by Fuchs *et al.*[53] that certain polyfunctional phenols (*e.g.*, hydroquinone, toluhydroquinone, phloroglucinol) and certain polyfunctional aromatic acids (*e.g.*, phthalic, isophthalic, terephthalic, trimesic, pyromellitic) do not react with methylmagnesium iodide in *n*-butyl ether solution at or near room temperature. As has been suggested by Lehman and Basch,[54] this is probably a consequence of the relative insolubilities of these compounds and of their initial reaction products in the medium chosen. In warm pyridine these compounds all react with methylmagnesium iodide, and most of them liberate methane equivalent to the calculated number of "active" hydrogen atoms present.

Other sources of error are to be found chiefly in gas-forming reactions of "interfering" groups. Readily reducible carbonyl groups, for example, may react with aliphatic Grignard reagents other than the methyl to liberate olefins (see section on Grignard Reductions in Chapter VI). The reactions of nitro groups, already mentioned in the foregoing discussion, have been investigated, albeit not very exhaustively, by Gilman *et al.*[55] Nitroso, azoxy, and azo compounds also undergo gas-forming reactions with methyl Grignard reagents (see sections on these various types of compounds in Chapter XIX on Miscellaneous Nitrogen Compounds).

APPLICATIONS OF THE METHOD

Applications of the method to the study of simultaneous addition, enolization, and reduction reactions of ketones have already been mentioned, and are discussed in Chapter VI. Zerewitinoff has used it for the estimation of water in anthracite[56] and of free fatty acids in natural oils.[57] Allen *et al.*,[58] have employed it to distinguish between lactols and open-chain ketonic acids. Greenwood and Gortner[59] have investigated the supposed "protection" of amino groups by hydrochloride formation, using a procedure that is essentially a modified Zerewitinoff determination. Wright[60] has studied the relative reactivities of methylmagnesium chloride and dimethylmagnesium with respect to "active" hydrogen groups and carbonyl-group addition. By a special adaptation of the Zerewitinoff method, Ivanoff *et al.* have studied the rates of gas evolution in the reac-

---

[53] Fuchs, Ishler and Sandhoff, *Ind. Eng. Chem., Anal. Ed.*, *12*, 507–9 (1940).

[54] Lehman and Basch, *Ind. Eng. Chem., Anal. Ed.*, *17*, 428–9 (1945).

[55] Gilman and Fothergill, *J. Am. Chem. Soc.*, *49*, 2815–8 (1927); *Bull. soc. chim.*, [4], *45*, 1132–6 (1929); Gilman, Fothergill, and Towne, *J. Am. Chem. Soc.*, *52*, 405–7 (1930).

[56] Zerewitinoff, *Z. anal. Chem.*, *50*, 680–91 (1911).

[57] Zerewitinoff, *Z. anal. Chem.*, *52*, 729–37 (1914).

[58] Allen, Normington, and Wilson, *Can. J. Research*, *11*, 382–94 (1934); *Chem. Abstr.*, *29*, 135 (1935).

[59] Greenwood and Gortner, *J. Org. Chem.*, 6, 401–9 (1941).

[60] Wright, *J. Am. Chem. Soc.*, *61*, 1152–6 (1939).

tions of various aliphatic Grignard reagents with chloromagnesium phenylacetate[61] and indene[62] in the erroneous belief that they could thus establish a relative order of bond forces in a series of molecules of the type R—MgX. Innumerable investigators have, of course, used the method in attempts to arrive at satisfactory constitutional assignments for substances of unknown structure.

Hibbert[63] has used the amounts of methane evolved in reactions of methylmagnesium iodide with a series of α-naphthol-ketone mixtures to estimate roughly the relative reactivities of the ketones. Lewis and Wright[64] have adopted essentially the same method to compare the reactivity of benzophenone with those of various *para*-substituted benzophenones.

A representative, though not exhaustive collection of data is presented in Table XVIII-I. Data relating to substances of indefinite, uncertain, or unknown constitution are purposely omitted, as are studies of substances of highly complicated structure, such as that of Fischer and Rothemund[65] on hæmin and pyrrole derivatives.

---

[61] Ivanoff and Spassoff, *Bull. soc. chim.*, [4], *51*, 619–22 (1932).

[62] Ivanoff and Abdouloff, *Compt. rend.*, *196*, 491–3 (1933); *Chem. Abstr.*, *27*, 2421 (1933); Ivanov and Ibdulov, *Ann. univ. Sofia II, Faculté phys.-math.*, *30*, 53–8 (1934); *Chem. Abstr.*, *29*, 2951 (1935).

[63] Hibbert, *J. Chem. Soc.*, *101*, 341–5 (1912).

[64] Lewis and Wright, *J. Am. Chem. Soc.*, *74*, 1257–9 (1952).

[65] Fischer and Rothemund, *Ber.*, *61B*, 1268–76 (1928).

TABLE XVIII-I

RESULTS OF DETERMINATIONS OF APPARENT "ACTIVE" HYDROGEN CONTENT BY THE TSCHUGAEFF-ZEREWITINOFF METHOD

Grignard reagents used (G.R.) are indicated as follows: (Me), CH_3MgI; (Me*), CH_3MgBr; (Me†), CH_3MgCl; (Me‡), $(CH_3)_2Mg$; (Et), C_2H_5MgI; (Et*), C_2H_5MgBr, (Et†), C_2H_5MgCl; (Pr*), n-C_3H_7MgBr; (Bu*), n-C_4H_9MgBr.

Sample (G.R.)	G. R. Solvent	Sample Solvent	Apparent "Active" H		Ref.
			Cold	Heated	
C_1					
Br_3CNO_2 (Me)	Bu_2O	Bu_2O	—	0.95	*21*
Cl_3CNO_2 (Me)	*i*-Am_2O	*i*-Am_2O	—	0.43	*21*
$(O_2N)_4C$ (Me)	Bu_2O	Bu_2O	—	0.99	*22*
CH_3NO_2 (Me)	Am_2O	Am_2O	0.83	0.93	*6*
CH_3NO_2 (Me)	Am_2O	C_5H_5N	0.97	—	*6*
CH_3NO_2 (Et*)	Et_2O	Et_2O	0.87	—	*13*
$(H_2N)_2CS$ (Me)	Am_2O	C_5H_5N	2.14	2.77	*3*
CH_3OH (Me)	EtOPh	EtOPh	0.44	—	*8*
CH_3OH (Me)	Am_2O	C_5H_5N	0.96	—	*9*
CH_3OH (Me)	*i*-Am_2O	*i*-Am_2O	0.82–0.97	0.89–1.03	*41*
CH_3OH (Et*)	Et_2O	Et_2O	1.07	—	*13*
$(H_2N)_2CO$ (Me)	Am_2O	C_5H_5N	2.15	3.09	*3*
C_2					
Cl_3CCONH_2 (Me)	Am_2O	C_5H_5N	2.05	—	*3*
$Cl_3CCHO \cdot H_2O$ (Me)	Am_2O	Am_2O	2.04	—	*1*
CH_3COSH (Et)	*i*-Am_2O	C_5H_5N	0.77	—	*7*
CH_3CO_2H (Et)	*i*-Am_2O	C_5H_5N	0.81	—	*7*
CH_3CSNH_2 (Me)	Am_2O	C_5H_5N	1.26	2.08	*3*
CH_3CONH_2 (Me)	Am_2O	C_5H_5N	1.04	2.11	*3*
$C_2H_5NO_2$ (Me)	Am_2O	Am_2O	0.65	0.79	*6*
$C_2H_5NO_2$ (Et*)	Et_2O	Et_2O	0.95	—	*13*
C_2H_5OH (Me)	EtOPh	EtOPh	0.72	—	*8*

TABLE XVIII-I (Continued)

Sample (G.R.)	G. R. Solvent	Sample Solvent	Apparent "Active" H		Ref.
			Cold	Heated	
C_2 (*cont.*)					
C_2H_5OH (Me)	Am_2O	C_5H_5N	1.03	—	*9*
C_2H_5OH (Me)	*i*-Am_2O	*i*-Am_2O	—	0.99–1.02	*41*
C_2H_5OH (Et)	*i*-Am_2O	C_5H_5N	1.03	—	*7*
$(—CH_2OH)_2$ (Me)	Am_2O	C_5H_5N	2.04	—	*2*
$(—CH_2OH)_2$ (Et)	*i*-Am_2O	C_5H_5N	2.02	—	*7*
$CH_3CH(NH_2)OH$ (Me)	Am_2O	C_5H_5N	2.10	3.08	*3*
$(—CH_2NH_2)_2$ (Me)	Am_2O	C_5H_5N	1.80	2.77	*9*
C_3					
C_3HCl_7 (Me)	Et_2O	Et_2O	*ca.* 1	—	*47*
$H_2C(CO_2H)_2$ (Me)	Am_2O	C_5H_5N	2.86	—	*3*
$H_2C{=}CHCH_2OH$ (Me)	*i*-Am_2O	*i*-Am_2O	—	1.00	*41*
$H_2C{=}CHCH_2OH$ (Et)	*i*-Am_2O	C_5H_5N	0.91	—	*7*
$H_2C(CONH_2)_2$ (Me)	Am_2O	C_5H_5N	2.25	4.23	*3*
$(CH_3)_2C{=}NOH$ (Me)	Am_2O	Am_2O	0.99	—	*1*
n-$C_3H_7NO_2$ (Me)	Am_2O	Am_2O	0.68	0.71	*6*
i-$C_3H_7NO_2$ (Me)	Am_2O	Am_2O	0.69	0.81	*6*
$H_2NCO_2C_2H_5$ (Me)	Am_2O	C_5H_5N	2.04	—	*10*
$H_2NCO_2C_2H_5$ (Me)	Am_2O	C_5H_5N	1.19	1.89	*3*
$H_2NCO_2C_2H_5$ (Me)	Am_2O	Am_2O	1.22	2.00	*3*
n-C_3H_7SH (Me)	Am_2O	C_5H_5N	0.93	—	*3*
n-C_3H_7OH (Me)	EtOPh	EtOPh	0.83	—	*8*
n-C_3H_7OH (Me)	Am_2O	C_5H_5N	1.05	—	*9*
n-C_3H_7OH (Me)	*i*-Am_2O	*i*-Am_2O	—	1.00	*41*
n-C_3H_7OH (Et)	*i*-Am_2O	C_5H_5N	0.98	—	*7*
$CH_3CH(OH)CH_2OH$ (Me)	Am_2O	C_5H_5N	1.96	—	*2*
$CH_3CH(OH)CH_2OH$ (Et)	*i*-Am_2O	C_5H_5N	2.01	—	*7*

TABLE XVIII-I (Continued)

Sample (G.R.)	G. R. Solvent	Sample Solvent	Apparent "Active" H		Ref.
			Cold	Heated	
C_3 (*cont.*)					
n-$C_3H_7NH_2$ (Et*)	Et_2O	Et_2O	1.04	—	*11*
C_4					
Pyrrole (Et)	i-Am_2O	C_5H_5N	0.99	—	7
Pyrrole (Et*)	Et_2O	Et_2O	1.00	—	*13*
Succinimide (Me)	Am_2O	C_5H_5N	1.14	—	3
Succinimide (Et)	i-Am_2O	C_5H_5N	0.95	—	7
$(HO_2CCH_2—)_2$ (Me)	Am_2O	C_5H_5N	2.04	—	2
$[HO_2CCH(OH)—]_2$ (Me)	Am_2O	C_5H_5N	4.02	—	2
$H_5C_2O_2CCONH_2$ (Me)	Am_2O	C_5H_5N	1.24	1.93	3
n-$C_3H_7CO_2H$ (Me)	Am_2O	C_5H_5N	1.02	—	*12*
n-$C_3H_7CO_2H$ (Et)	i-Am_2O	C_5H_5N	0.94	—	7
α-$[HON{=}C(CH_3)—]_2$	Am_2O	C_5H_5N	2.04	—	2
4-Hydroxymethyl-1,3-dioxolane (Me)	i-Am_2O	C_5H_5N	—	1.09	27
4-Hydroxymethyl-1,3-dioxolane (Me)	i-Am_2O	Dioxane	—	1.06	27
i-C_4H_9SH (Me)	Am_2O	C_5H_5N	0.98	—	3
i-C_4H_9OH (Me)	Am_2O	C_5H_5N	1.00	—	9
t-C_4H_9OH (Me)	i-Am_2O	i-Am_2O	—	1.01	*41*
$HOCH_2(CHOH)_2CH_2OH$ (Me)	Am_2O	C_5H_5N	4.06	—	2
$HOCH_2(CHOH)_2CH_2OH$ (Et)	i-Am_2O	C_5H_5N	3.81	—	7
$(C_2H_5)_2NH$ (Et)	i-Am_2O	C_5H_5N	0.98	—	7
$(C_2H_5)_2NH$ (Et*)	Et_2O	Et_2O	1.05	—	*11*
n-$C_4H_9NH_2$ (Et*)	Et_2O	Et_2O	1.03	—	*11*
C_5					
1-Methylpyrrole (Et*)	Et_2O	Et_2O	0.00	—	*13*
Glutarimide (Me)	Am_2O	C_5H_5N	1.03	—	3

TABLE XVIII-I (Continued)

Sample (G.R.)	G. R. Solvent	Sample Solvent	Apparent "Active" H		Ref.
			Cold	Heated	
C_5 *(cont.)*					
$(CH_3CO)_2CH_2$ (Me)	Am_2O	Am_2O	0.82	1.00	*3*
$(CH_3)_2C(CO_2H)_2$ (Me)	Am_2O	C_5H_5N	2.02	—	*2*
$CH_3CH(OH)CO_2C_2H_5$ (Me)	Am_2O	C_5H_5N	1.06	—	*2*
Arabinose (Me)	Am_2O	C_5H_5N	4.01	—	*2*
$(CH_2)_5NH$ (Et*)	Et_2O	Et_2O	1.05	—	*11*
3-Methylpyrrolidine (Et*)	Et_2O	Et_2O	1.07	—	*11*
i-$C_5H_{11}SH$ (Me)	Am_2O	C_5H_5N	0.99	—	*3*
i-$C_5H_{11}OH$ (Me)	Am_2O	C_5H_5N	0.97	—	*2*
i-$C_5H_{11}OH$ (Et)	*i*-Am_2O	C_5H_5N	0.93	—	*7*
t-$C_5H_{11}OH$ (Me)	Am_2O	C_5H_5N	1.03	—	*2*
$C(CH_2OH)_4$ (Me)	Am_2O	C_5H_5N	4.09	—	*2*
C_6					
$Br_5C_6NO_2$ (Me)	Bu_2O	Bu_2O	—	1.43	*22*
1,3,4,5-$Cl_4C_6(NO_2)_2$ (Me)	Bu_2O	Bu_2O	—	1.96[a]	*21*
1,3,4,5-$Cl_4C_6(NO_2)_2$ (Me†)	Bu_2O	Bu_2O	—	2.24[b]	*21*
2,4,6-$Br_3C_6H_2OH$ (Me)	EtOPh	EtOPh	0.91	—	*8*
2,4,6-$Br_3C_6H_2OH$ (Me)	Bu_2O	—	1.06	—	*43*
1,3,5-$(O_2N)_3C_6H_3$ (Me)	Bu_2O	Xylene	2.51	3.47	*20*
1,3,5-$(O_2N)_3C_6H_3$ (Et*)	Et_2O	Et_2O	0.00	—	*13*
1,3,5-$(O_2N)_3C_6H_3$ (Et*)	Et_2O	Et_2O	—	1.49	*16*
2,4,6-$(O_2N)_3C_6H_2OH$ (Me)	Bu_2O	—	0.00	—	*43*
2,4,6-$(O_2N)_3C_6H_2OH$ (Me)	C_5H_5N	—	—	1.00	*44*
C_6H_5NO (Et*)	Et_2O	Et_2O	—	1.09	*16*

[a] Heated at 70° for 1.50 hour.
[b] Heated at 70° for 1.00 hour.

TABLE XVIII-I (Continued)

Sample (G.R.)	G. R. Solvent	Sample Solvent	Apparent "Active" H		Ref.
			Cold	Heated	
C_6 (*cont.*)					
$C_6H_5NO_2$ (Me)	Bu_2O	C_5H_5N	—	1.49	*21*
$C_6H_5NO_2$ (Me)	Bu_2O	Bu_2O	—	1.13–1.57	*21*
$C_6H_5NO_2$ (Me)	Et_2O	Et_2O	—	0.97	*16*
$C_6H_5NO_2$ (Me)	Bu_2O	Bu_2O	0.98	1.03	*16*
$C_6H_5NO_2$ (Et*)	Et_2O	Et_2O	—	1.53	*16*
$C_6H_5NO_2$ (*n*-Pr*)	Et_2O	Et_2O	—	1.90	*16*
$C_6H_5NO_2$ (*n*-Bu*)	Et_2O	Et_2O	—	1.68	*16*
2-$O_2NC_6H_4OH$ (Me)	Am_2O	Am_2O	1.15	—	*1*
4-$O_2NC_6H_4OH$ (Me)	Am_2O	MeOPh	0.89	—	*6*
4-$ClC_6H_4NH_2$ (Me)	EtOPh	EtOPh	0.89	—	*8*
4-$ClC_6H_4NH_2$ (Me)	EtOPh	EtOPh	0.99	1.95	*4*
C_6H_5SH (Me)	Am_2O	C_5H_5N	1.04	—	*3*
C_6H_5OH (Et)	*i*-Am_2O	C_5H_5N	1.13	—	*7*
C_6H_5OH (Et*)	Et_2O	Et_2O	1.04	—	*13*
$OC<(CH{=}CH)_2>CHOH$ (Me)	Am_2O	Am_2O	—	1.03	*1*
1,2-$(HO)_2C_6H_4$ (Me)	Am_2O	C_5H_5N	1.93	—	*2*
1,2-$(HO)_2C_6H_4$ (Me)	Bu_2O	—	1.99	—	*43*
1,3-$(HO)_2C_6H_4$ (Me)	Am_2O	Am_2O	2.00	—	*1*
1,3-$(HO)_2C_6H_4$ (Me)	Bu_2O	—	0.98	—	*43*
1,3-$(HO)_2C_6H_4$ (Me)	C_5H_5N	—	—	0.96	*44*
1,3-$(HO)_2C_6H_4$ (Et*)	Et_2O	Et_2O	2.01	—	*13*
1,3-$(HO)_2C_6H_4$ (Et)	*i*-Am_2O	C_5H_5N	2.15	—	*7*
1,4-$(HO)_2C_6H_4$ (Me)	Am_2O	C_5H_5N	2.02	—	*2*
1,4-$(HO)_2C_6H_4$ (Me)	Bu_2O	—	0.00	—	*43*
1,4-$(HO)_2C_6H_4$ (Me)	C_5H_5N	—	—	2.01	*44*
1,4-$(HO)_2C_6H_4$ (Me†)	Et_2O	Et_2O	1.60	—	*40*
3-$O_2NC_6H_4NH_2$ (Me)	Am_2O	MeOPh	1.02	1.80	*6*

TABLE XVIII-I (Continued)

Sample (G.R.)	G. R. Solvent	Sample Solvent	Apparent "Active" H		Ref.
			Cold	Heated	
C_6 (*cont.*)					
3-$O_2NC_6H_4NH_2$ (Me)	Am_2O	Mesitylene	1.01	1.85	*6*
$C_6H_5SO_2H$ (Me)	Am_2O	C_5H_5N	0.97	—	*2*
$C_6H_5SO_2H$ (Et)	*i*-Am_2O	C_5H_5N	0.95	—	*7*
1,2,3-$(HO)_2C_6H_3$ (Me)	Am_2O	Am_2O	3.00	—	*1*
1,2,3-$(HO)_3C_6H_3$ (Me)	Bu_2O	—	3.02	—	*43*
1,2,3-$(HO)_3C_6H_3$ (Me)	C_5H_5N	—	—	2.80	*44*
1,3,5-$(HO)_3C_6H_3$ (Me)	Bu_2O	—	0.00	—	*43*
1,3,5-$(HO)_3C_6H_3$ (Me)	C_5H_5N	—	—	1.00	*44*
$C_6H_5NH_2$ (Me†)	Et_2O	Et_2O	1.94	—	*40*
$C_6H_5NH_2$ (Me†)	Et_2O	C_6H_6	1.00	—	*40*
$C_6H_5NH_2$ (Et*)	Et_2O	Et_2O	1.03	—	*11*
$C_6H_5PH_2$ (Et*)	Et_2O	Et_2O-C_6H_6	—	*ca.* 2	*18*
$C_6H_5NHNH_2$ (Et*)	Et_2O	Et_2O	1.96	—	*11*
1,2-$(H_2N)_2C_6H_4$ (Me)	Am_2O	C_5H_5N	1.89	2.81	*9*
1,2-$(H_2N)_2C_6H_4$ (Me)	Am_2O	MeOPh	2.24	3.09	*9*
1,3-$(H_2N)_2C_6H_4$ (Me)	Am_2O	C_5H_5N	1.93	2.82	*9*
1,3-$(H_2N)_2C_6H_4$ (Et*)	Et_2O	Et_2O	1.91	—	*11*
1,4-$(H_2N)_2C_6H_4$ (Me)	Am_2O	C_5H_5N	1.90	2.91	*9*
$CH_3COCH_2CO_2C_2H_5$ (Me)	Am_2O	C_5H_5N	0.87	—	*3*
$CH_3COCH_2CO_2C_2H_5$ (Me)	Am_2O	Am_2O	0.95	1.14	*3*
$CH_3COCH_2CO_2C_2H_5$ (Me)	Am_2O	Am_2O	0.93	—	*1*
$CH_3COCH_2COC_2H_5$ (Me†)	Et_2O	Et_2O	1.01	—	*40*
$CH_3COCH_2CO_2C_2H_5$ (Et*)	Et_2O	Et_2O	1.05	—	*13*
Cyclohexene hydroperoxide (Me)	Am_2O	C_5H_5N	0.91	—	*33*
$CH_3COCH_2CO_2C_2H_5$ (Me)	*i*-Am_2O	—	1.00	—	*43*
1,3,5-$(HO)_3C_6H_3 \cdot 2H_2O$ (Me)	Am_2O	C_5H_5N	7.13	—	*2*
n-$C_5H_{11}CO_2H$ (Me)	Am_2O	C_5H_5N	0.98	—	*12*

TABLE XVIII-I (Continued)

Sample (G.R.)	G. R. Solvent	Sample Solvent	Apparent "Active" H		Ref.
			Cold	Heated	
C_6 (*cont.*)					
$(—CONHC_2H_5)_2$ (Me)	Am_2O	C_5H_5N	2.19	—	*3*
Glucose (Me)	Am_2O	C_5H_5N	—	4.58	*27*
Glucose (Me)	Am_2O	Dioxane	—	1.10	*27*
$(CH_2)_5CHNH_2$ (Et*)	Et_2O	Et_2O	1.05	—	*11*
$CH_3COCH_2CH_2NR_2$ (Me) ($R = CH_3$, C_2H_5, n-C_4H_9)	i-Am_2O	—	0.90–0.95	—	*35*
Glucose (Me) ($C_6H_{12}O_6 \cdot H_2O$)	Am_2O	C_5H_5N	6.69	—	*2*
Mannitol (Me)	Am_2O	C_5H_5N	6.02	—	*2*
Mannitol (Et)	i-Am_2O	C_5H_5N	5.82	—	*7*
i-$C_6H_{13}NH_2$ (Et*)	Et_2O	Et_2O	1.00	—	*11*
Rhamnose (Me) ($C_6H_{16}O_5 \cdot H_2O$)	Am_2O	C_5H_5N	5.93	—	*2*
C_7					
2-$O_2NC_6H_4CHO$ (Me)	Am_2O	C_5H_5N	1.00	—	*15*
2-$O_2NC_6H_4CHO$ (Et*)	Et_2O	Et_2O	—	1.67	*16*
3-$O_2NC_6H_4CHO$ (Me)	Am_2O	C_5H_5N	0.21	—	*15*
3-$O_2NC_6H_4CHO$ (Et*)	Et_2O	Et_2O	—	1.43	*16*
4-$O_2NC_6H_4CHO$ (Me)	Am_2O	C_5H_5N	0.29	—	*15*
2,4-$(O_2N)_2C_6H_4CHO$ (Me)	Am_2O	C_5H_5N	1.03	—	*15*
$C_6H_5CO_2H$ (Me)	Et_2O	Et_2O	—	0.96	*16*
$C_6H_5CO_2H$ (Me)	i-Am_2O	C_5H_5N	—	1.18	*27*
$C_6H_5CO_2H$ (Me)	i-Am_2O	Dioxane	—	1.06	*27*
$C_6H_5CO_2H$ (Me)	Bu_2O	—	1.02	—	*43*
$C_6H_5CO_2H$ (Me)	Bu_2O	Xylene	1.03	1.15	*20*
$C_6H_5CO_2H$ (Et*)	Et_2O	Et_2O	—	1.01	*16*
2-$HOC_6H_4CO_2H$ (Me)	Am_2O	C_5H_5N	2.04	—	*2*
2-$HOC_6H_4CO_2H$ (Me†)	Et_2O	C_6H_6	2.00	—	*40*
2-$HOC_6H_4CO_2H$ (Et)	i-Am_2O	C_5H_5N	1.94	—	*7*

TABLE XVIII-I (Continued)

Sample (G.R.)	G. R. Solvent	Sample Solvent	Apparent "Active" H		Ref.
			Cold	Heated	
C_7 (*cont.*)					
$C_6H_5CONH_2$ (Me)	Am_2O	C_5H_5N	0.97	2.16	3
$C_6H_5CH_2NO_2$ (Me)	Am_2O	C_5H_5N	0.75	—	6
2-$CH_3C_6H_4NO_2$ (Me)	Bu_2O	Bu_2O	—	1.20–1.36[c]	21
2-$H_2NC_6H_4CO_2H$ (Me)	Bu_2O	Xylene	2.50	3.54	20
$C_6H_5CH_2SH$ (Me)	Am_2O	C_5H_5N	0.95	—	3
$C_6H_5NHCSNH_2$ (Me)	Am_2O	C_5H_5N	1.93	2.21	3
$C_6H_5CH_2OH$ (Me)	EtOPh	EtOPh	0.84	—	8
$C_6H_5CH_2OH$ (Et)	*i*-Am_2O	C_5H_5N	1.00	—	7
$C_6H_5NHCONH_2$ (Me)	Am_2O	C_5H_5N	1.85	2.02	3
2-$CH_3OC_6H_4OH$ (Me)	Am_2O	C_5H_5N	1.05	—	2
2-$CH_3OC_6H_4OH$ (Me)	Am_2O	C_5H_5N	1.04	—	14
1,4-$(HO)_2$-2-$CH_3C_6H_3$ (Me)	Bu_2O	—	0.00	—	43
2-$CH_3C_6H_5NO_2$ (Et*)	Et_2O	Et_2O	—	1.69	16
4-$CH_3C_6H_5NO_2$ (Et*)	Et_2O	Et_2O	—	1.65	16
"Methoxyresorcinol" (Me)	Bu_2O	—	2.07	—	43
$CH_3NHC_6H_5$ (Me)	EtOPh	EtOPh	1.00	—	4
$CH_3NHC_6H_5$ (Et*)	Et_2O	Et_2O	1.03	—	11
2-$CH_3C_6H_4NH_2$ (Me)	Am_2O	C_5H_5N	1.89	2.93	9
4-$CH_3C_6H_4NH_2$ (Me)	Am_2O	Am_2O	0.98	1.95	4
$C_6H_5CH_2NH_2$ (Et*)	Et_2O	Et_2O	0.96	—	11
4-$CH_3OC_6H_4NH_2$ (Et*)	Et_2O	Et_2O	1.07	—	11
Methylketol (Et)	*i*-Am_2O	C_5H_5N	0.97	—	7
$H_2C(CO_2C_2H_5)_2$ (Me)	Bu_2O	—	1.00	—	43
$H_2C(CO_2C_2H_5)_2$ (Me)	Am_2O	C_5H_5N	1.03	—	3
α-Methylglucoside (Me)	Am_2O	C_5H_5N	4.09	—	2

[c] Heated at 70° for 0.50 to 1.50 hour.

TABLE XVIII-I (Continued)

Sample (G.R.)	G. R. Solvent	Sample Solvent	Apparent "Active" H Cold	Apparent "Active" H Heated	Ref.
C_7 *(cont.)*					
i-$C_3H_7COCHRCH_2NH_2$ (Me) (R = CH_3, C_2H_5, n-C_3H_7)	Am_2O	Am_2O	*ca.* 2	—	*26*
C_8					
Phthalimide (Me)	Am_2O	C_5H_5N	1.13	—	*3*
Phthalimide (Me)	C_5H_5N	—	—	0.98	*44*
C_6H_4-1,2-$(CO_2H)_2$ (Me)	Bu_2O	—	0.00	—	*43*
C_6H_4-1,3-$(CO_2H)_2$ (Me)	Bu_2O	—	0.00	—	*43*
C_6H_4-1,4-$(CO_2H)_2$ (Me)	Bu_2O	—	0.00	—	*43*
Indole (Et)	i-Am_2O	C_5H_5N	0.81	—	*7*
Indole (Me)	Am_2O	Xylene	1.02	1.04	*24*
2-Methylbenzoselenazole (Et*)	Et_2O	Et_2O	*ca.* 1	—	*36*
$CH_3COC_6H_5$ (Me)	i-Am_2O	—	—	0.15	*17*
$CH_3COC_6H_5$ (Me)	i-Am_2O	—	—	0.12	*27*
$CH_3COC_6H_5$ (Me)	i-Am_2O	C_5H_5N	—	0.78	*27*
$CH_3COC_6H_5$ (Me)	i-Am_2O	Dioxane	—	0.78	*27*
$CH_3COC_6H_5$ (Me)	i-Am_2O	Xylene	—	0.03	*27*
$CH_3COC_6H_5$ (Me‡)	Dioxane	Dioxane	—	0.60	*42*
2-$CH_3C_6H_4CO_2H$ (Me)	Bu_2O	—	1.05	—	*43*
3-$CH_3C_6H_4CO_2H$ (Me)	Bu_2O	—	1.05	—	*43*
4-$CH_3C_6H_4CO_2H$ (Me)	Bu_2O	—	1.05	—	*43*
4-$CH_3OC_6H_4CO_2H$ (Me)	i-Am_2O	—	1.00	—	*43*
3-HO-4-$CH_3OC_6H_3CHO$ (Me)	i-Am_2O	C_5H_5N	—	1.02	*27*
3-HO-4-$CH_3OC_6H_3CHO$ (Me)	i-Am_2O	Dioxane	—	0.92	*27*
3-HO-4-$CH_3OC_6H_3CHO$ (Me)	i-Am_2O	Xylene	—	0.89	*27*
3-CH_3O-4-HOC_6H_3CHO (Me)	Am_2O	C_5H_5N	2.03	—	*2*
3-CH_3O-4-HOC_6H_3CHO (Me)	Am_2O	C_5H_5N	0.93	—	*14*
3-CH_3O-4-HOC_6H_3CHO (Me)	i-Am_2O	—	—	0.65	*27*

TABLE XVIII-I (Continued)

Sample (G.R.)	G. R. Solvent	Sample Solvent	Apparent "Active" H		Ref.
			Cold	Heated	
C_8 (*cont.*)					
3-CH_3O-4-HOC_6H_3CHO (Me)	*i*-Am_2O	C_5H_5N	—	0.99	*27*
3-CH_3O-4-HOC_6H_3CHO (Me)	*i*-Am_2O	Dioxane	—	0.99	*27*
$CH_3CONHC_6H_5$ (Me)	*i*-Am_2O	—	—	1.01	*17*
$CH_3(C_6H_5)CHOH$ (Et)	*i*-Am_2O	C_5H_5N	0.93	—	*7*
1,2-$(CH_3O)_2C_6H_4$ (Me)	*i*-Am_2O	—	—	0.01	*27*
1,2-$(CH_3O)_2C_6H_4$ (Me)	*i*-Am_2O	C_5H_5N	—	0.00	*27*
4-$CH_3C_6H_4SO_2CH_3$ (Me)	*i*-Am_2O	Xylene (?)	+	2	*54*
$C_2H_5NHC_6H_5$ (Me)	EtOPh	EtOPh	1.01	—	*4*
$C_2H_5NHC_6H_5$ (Me)	EtOPh	EtOPh	0.91	—	*8*
$C_2H_5NHC_6H_5$ (Me)	Am_2O	Am_2O	0.99	—	*8*
$CH_3COCH(C_2H_5)CO_2C_2H_5$ (Et*)	Et_2O	Et_2O	1.04	—	*13*
$(CH_2)_5N(CH_2)_3NH_2$ (Me*)	Et_2O	Et_2O	1.80	—	*40*
C_9					
C_6H_3-1,3,5-$(CO_2H)_3$ (Me)	Bu_2O	—	0.00	—	*43*
Indene (Me)	Am_2O	C_5H_5N	0.00	0.92	*9*
$C_6H_5CH{=}CHCO_2H$ (Me)	*i*-Am_2O	C_5H_5N	—	1.15	*27*
$C_6H_5CH{=}CHCO_2H$ (Me)	*i*-Am_2O	Dioxane	—	0.98	*27*
$C_6H_5CH{=}CHCO_2H$ (Me)	*i*-Am_2O	Xylene	—	1.08	*27*
1-Methylindole (Et*)	Et_2O	Et_2O	0.00	—	*13*
2-Methylindole (Et*)	Et_2O	Et_2O	1.07	—	*13*
Skatole (Me)	Am_2O	Xylene	1.01	1.05	*24*
Skatole (Et)	*i*-Am_2O	C_5H_5N	0.97	—	*7*
7-Methylindole (Me)	Am_2O	Xylene	1.01	1.03	*24*
2-*o*-Nitrophenyl-1,3-dioxolane (Me)	Am_2O	C_5H_5N	0.99	—	*15*
$C_6H_5CH_2CH_2O_2CH$ (Me)	*i*-Am_2O	C_5H_5N	—	0.08	*27*
$C_6H_5CH_2CH_2O_2CH$ (Me)	*i*-Am_2O	Dioxane	—	0.51	*27*

TABLE XVIII-I (Continued)

Sample (G.R.)	G. R. Solvent	Sample Solvent	Apparent "Active" H		Ref.
			Cold	Heated	
C_9 (*cont.*)					
$C_6H_5CH_2CH_2O_2CH$ (Me)	*i*-Am_2O	Xylene	—	0.04	*27*
2-$HOC_6H_4CO_2C_2H_5$ (Me)	Am_2O	Am_2O	0.99	—	*1*
3,4-$(CH_3O)_2C_6H_3CHO$ (Me)	*i*-Am_2O	—	—	0.05	*27*
3,4-$(CH_3O)_2C_6H_3CHO$ (Me)	*i*-Am_2O	C_5H_5N	—	0.36	*27*
3,4-$(CH_3O)_2C_6H_3CHO$ (Me)	*i*-Am_2O	Dioxane	—	0.44	*27*
3,4-$(CH_3O)_2C_6H_3CHO$ (Me)	*i*-Am_2O	Xylene	—	0.03	*27*
3-CH_3O-4-$HOC_6H_4COCH_3$ (Me)	*i*-Am_2O	C_5H_5N	—	1.25	*27*
3-CH_3O-4-$HOC_6H_4COCH_3$ (Me)	*i*-Am_2O	Dioxane	—	0.91	*27*
3-CH_3O-4-$HOC_6H_4COCH_3$ (Me)	*i*-Am_2O	Xylene	—	0.97	*27*
$C_2H_5(C_6H_5)CHOH$ (Me*)	Et_2O	Et_2O	1.11	—	*40*
1,2,3-$(CH_3O)_3C_6H_3$ (Me)	*i*-Am_2O	C_5H_5N	—	0.03	*27*
1,2,3-$(CH_3O)_3C_6H_3$ (Me)	*i*-Am_2O	Dioxane	—	0.03	*27*
1,2,3-$(CH_3O)_3C_6H_3$ (Me)	*i*-Am_2O	Xylene	—	0.03	*27*
5-*n*-Hexylisoxazole (Et*)	Et_2O	Et_2O	*ca.* 1	—	*11*
$CH_3COC(CH_3)(C_2H_5)$-*n*-C_3H_7 (Me*)	Et_2O	Et_2O	0.99	—	*53*
C_{10}					
C_6H_2-1,2,4,5-$(CO_2H)_4$ (Me)	Bu_2O	—	0.00	—	*43*
1-$C_{10}H_7OH$ (Me)	Am_2O	C_5H_5N	1.02	—	*10*
1-$C_{10}H_7OH$ (Me)	EtOPh	MeOPh	0.93	—	*8*
1-$C_{10}H_7OH$ (Me)	Am_2O	Am_2O	0.98	—	*1*
1-$C_{10}H_7OH$ (Me)	*i*-Am_2O	—	1.01	—	*43*
1-$C_{10}H_7OH$ (Et*)	Et_2O	Et_2O	1.11	—	*13*
2-$C_{10}H_7OH$ (Me)	Bu_2O	—	1.01	—	*43*
2-$C_{10}H_7OH$ (Me)	Am_2O	C_5H_5N	1.01	—	*2*
2-$C_{10}H_7OH$ (Me)	Am_2O	Am_2O	0.99	—	*1*
2-$C_{10}H_7OH$ (Et)	*i*-Am_2O	C_5H_5N	0.93	—	*7*

TABLE XVIII-I (Continued)

Sample (G.R.)	G. R. Solvent	Sample Solvent	Apparent "Active" H		Ref.
			Cold	Heated	
C_{10} (*cont.*)					
1-$C_{10}H_7NH_2$ (Et*)	Et_2O	Et_2O	1.01	—	*11*
2-$C_{10}H_7NH_2$ (Me)	Am_2O	Am_2O	1.00	1.97	*4*
2-$C_{10}H_7NH_2$ (Me†)	Et_2O	Et_2O	—	0.99	*40*
2-$C_{10}H_7NH_2$ (Me†)	—	—	—	1.98	*40*
2-$C_{10}H_7NH_2$ (Et*)	Et_2O	Et_2O	1.01	—	*11*
1,2-$(H_2N)_2C_{10}H_6$ (Me)	Am_2O	C_5H_5N	2.05	2.91	*9*
$CH_3COCH_2COC_6H_5$ (Me)	Am_2O	Am_2O	0.88	1.00	*3*
$CH_3COCH_2COC_6H_5$ (Me)	Am_2O	Am_2O	0.66	—	*5*
1,2-$(CH_3CO_2)_2C_6H_4$ (Me)	*i*-Am_2O	C_5H_5N	—	0.24	*27*
1,2-$(CH_3CO_2)_2C_6H_4$ (Me)	*i*-Am_2O	Dioxane	—	0.73	*27*
1,2-$(CH_3CO_2)_2C_6H_4$ (Me)	*i*-Am_2O	Xylene	—	0.06	*27*
2-CH_3O-4-$H_2C{=}CHCH_2C_6H_3OH$ (Me)	Am_2O	C_5H_5N	1.08	—	*14*
Tetralin hydroperoxide (Me)	Am_2O	C_5H_5N	0.98	—	*33*
2-CH_3-6-*i*-$C_3H_7C_6H_3OH$ (Me)	Am_2O	C_5H_5N	1.03	—	*14*
2-*i*-C_3H_7-5-$CH_3C_6H_3OH$ (Me)	Am_2O	C_5H_5N	1.00	—	*14*
2-*i*-C_3H_7-5-$CH_3C_6H_3OH$ (Me†)	Et_2O	C_6H_6	1.03	—	*40*
4-$(C_2H_5)_2NC_6H_4NO$ (Et*)	Et_2O	Et_2O	—	0.74	*16*
n-$C_5H_{11}C{\equiv}CCH_2CH{=}CH_2$ (Et*)	C_6H_6	C_6H_6	—	*ca.* 1	*45,46*
n-$C_4H_9C{\equiv}CC(CH_3){=}CHCH_2OH$ (Me)	?	?	1.05	—	*49*
Ascaridole (Me)	Am_2O	—	—	0.98	*33*
Ascaridole (Me)	Am_2O	C_5H_5N	0.38–0.60[d]	—	*33*
Camphor oxime (Me)	Am_2O	C_5H_5N	1.01	—	*2*
Camphor oxime (Et)	*i*-Am_2O	C_5H_5N	1.17	—	*7*
Borneol (Me)	Am_2O	C_5H_5N	0.99	—	*2*
Borneol (Me)	Am_2O	C_5H_5N	0.99	—	*14*
Geraniol (Me)	Am_2O	C_5H_5N	1.04	—	*14*

[d] Apparent active H: 0.38 at 15°; 0.60 at 25°.

TABLE XVIII-I (Continued)

Sample (G.R.)	G. R. Solvent	Sample Solvent	Apparent "Active" H		Ref.
			Cold	Heated	
C_{10} (*cont.*)					
Geraniol (Et)	*i*-Am_2O	C_5H_5N	1.01	—	*7*
Terpineol (Me)	Am_2O	C_5H_5N	1.01	—	*14*
Linaloöl (Me)	Am_2O	C_5H_5N	1.01	—	*14*
Menthene-3 hydroperoxide (Me)	Am_2O	C_5H_5N	0.91	—	*33*
Menthol (Me)	Am_2O	C_5H_5N	1.01	—	*2,14*
Menthol (Me)	Am_2O	MeOPh	0.98	—	*6*
Menthol (Me)	Am_2O	Xylene	0.99	—	*6*
Menthol (Me)	Am_2O	Mesitylene	1.01	—	*6*
Menthol (Et)	*i*-Am_2O	C_5H_5N	0.99	—	*7*
Citronellol (Me)	Am_2O	C_5H_5N	1.06	—	*14*
i-$C_3H_7COC(CH_3)_2CH(OH)C_2H_5$ (Me)	Am_2O	C_5H_5N	1.01	—	*34*
C_{11}					
$C_6H(CO_2H)_5$ (Me)	Bu_2O	—	0.00	—	*43*
$C_6H_5C{\equiv}CCH_2CH{=}CH_2$ (Et*)	C_6H_6	C_6H_6	—	*ca.* 1	*45,46*
3-Ethyl-5-phenylpyrazole (Et*)	Et_2O	Et_2O	1.06	—	*11*
3,4-$(CH_3O)_2C_6H_3CH{=}CHCH_3$ (Me)	*i*-Am_2O	C_5H_5N	—	0.04	*27*
3,4-$(CH_3O)_2C_6H_3CH{=}CHCH_3$ (Me)	*i*-Am_2O	Dioxane	—	0.06	*27*
$CH_3COC_6H_4$-2,4,6-$(CH_3)_3$ (Me)	*i*-Am_2O	Xylene	—	0.99	*17*
n-$C_4H_9C{\equiv}C{-}C(CH_3){=}CHCH(CH_3)OH$ (Me)	?	?	1.00	—	*49*
Menthone semicarbazone (Me)	*i*-Am_2O	C_5H_5N	1.96	2.00	*3*
n-$C_6H_{13}CH(CH_3)CH_2CH(CH_3)OH$ (Me)	?	?	1.05	—	*49*
Methyl 2,3,4,6-tetramethyl-α-D-glucoside (Me)	*i*-Am_2O	C_5H_5N	—	0.33	*27*
Methyl 2,3,4,6-tetramethyl-α-D-glucoside (Me)	*i*-Am_2O	Dioxane	—	0.35	*27*
Methyl 2,3,4,6-tetramethyl-α-D-glucoside (Me)	*i*-Am_2O	Xylene	—	0.24	*27*
Methyl 2,3,4,6-tetramethyl-β-D-glucoside (Me)	*i*-Am_2O	C_5H_5N	—	0.18	*27*
Methyl 2,3,4,6-tetramethyl-β-D-glucoside (Me)	*i*-Am_2O	Dioxane	—	0.09	*27*

TABLE XVIII-I (Continued)

Sample (G.R.)	G. R. Solvent	Sample Solvent	Apparent "Active" H		Ref.
			Cold	Heated	
C_{12}					
2,4,6-$(O_2N)_3C_6H_2N_2C_6H_4$-4-NH_2 (Me)	Bu_2O	Xylene	2.03	3.32	*20*
2,4,6-$(O_2N)_3C_6H_2N_2C_6H_4$-4-NH_2 (Me)	*i*-Am_2O	Xylene	2.09	3.62	*20*
Carbazole (Et)	*i*-Am_2O	C_5H_5N	0.99	—	*7*
Carbazole (Et*)	Et_2O	Et_2O	1.03	—	*11*
$(C_6H_5N=)_2$ (Me)	Bu_2O	Bu_2O	0.24	0.29	*20*
$(C_6H_5)_2NH$ (Me)	EtOPh	EtOPh	0.84	—	*8*
$(C_6H_5)_2NH$ (Me)	*i*-Am_2O	—	—	1.07	*17*
$(C_6H_5)_2NH$ (Me)	EtOPh	EtOPh	0.98	—	*4*
$(C_6H_5)_2NH$ (Et)	*i*-Am_2O	C_5H_5N	1.01	—	*7*
$(C_6H_5)_2NH$ (Et*)	Et_2O	Et_2O	0.94	—	*11*
4-$H_2NC_6H_4N_2C_6H_5$ (Me)	Bu_2O	Bu_2O	1.69	2.18	*20*
4-$H_2NC_6H_4N=NC_6H_5$ (Me)	Am_2O	C_5H_5N	1.07	2.08	*6*
4-$H_2NC_6H_4N=NC_6H_5$ (Me)	Am_2O	Xylene	0.99	2.05	*6*
(4-$H_2NC_6H_4$—$)_2$ (Me)	Am_2O	C_5H_5N	1.92	3.11	*9*
(4-$H_2NC_6H_4$—$)_2$ (Me†)	Et_2O	Et_2O	2.00	—	*40*
(4-$H_2NC_6H_4$—$)_2$ (Me)	Am_2O	MeOPh	1.99	3.14	*9*
(4-$H_2NC_6H_4$—$)_2$ (Me†)	—	—	—	2.00	*40*
(4-$H_2NC_6H_4$—$)_2$ (Et*)	Et_2O	Et_2O	2.04	—	*11*
$(C_6H_5NH—)_2$ (Et*)	Et_2O	Et_2O	2.04	—	*11*
$(C_6H_5)_2NNH_2$ (Et*)	Et_2O	Et_2O	1.05	—	*11*
2,4,5,6-$(CH_3)_4C_6HCH_2(OH)CN$ (Me)	*i*-Am_2O	—	*ca.* 1	—	*31*
n-$C_4H_9C\equiv CC(CH_3)=CHC(CH_3)_2OH$ (Me)	?	?	0.95	—	*49*
$CH_3(CH_2)_{10}CO_2H$ (Me)	Am_2O	C_5H_5N	0.99	—	*12*
C_{13}					
Euxanthone (Me)	Am_2O	C_5H_5N	1.99	—	*3*
2-$O_2NC_6H_4CO_2H\cdot C_6H_3(NO_2)_3$ (Me)	Am_2O	C_5H_5N	2.15	2.81	*6*

TABLE XVIII-I (Continued)

Sample (G.R.)	G. R. Solvent	Sample Solvent	Apparent "Active" H		Ref.
			Cold	Heated	
C_{13} *(cont.)*					
$2\text{-}O_2NC_6H_4CO_2H \cdot C_6H_3(NO_2)_3$ (Me)	Am_2O	Xylene	2.03	3.11	*6*
Fluorene (Me)	Am_2O	C_5H_5N	0.00	1.04	*9*
$(C_6H_5)_2CO$ (Me)	*i*-Am_2O	—	—	0.02	*17*
$4\text{-}H_2NC_6H_4COC_6H_5$ (Et*)	Et_2O	Et_2O	*ca.* 1	—	*28*
$C_6H_5CH{=}NNHC_6H_5$ (Et*)	Et_2O	Et_2O	1.16	—	*13*
$(C_6H_5)_2CHOH$ (Me)	Am_2O	C_5H_5N	0.95	—	*2*
$(C_6H_5)_2CHOH$ (Me)	Am_2O	MeOPh	0.94	—	*6*
$(C_6H_5)_2CHOH$ (Me)	Am_2O	Xylene	0.90	—	*6*
$(C_6H_5)_2CHOH$ (Me)	Am_2O	Mesitylene	1.14	—	*6*
$(C_6H_5)_2CHOH$ (Me)	*i*-Am_2O	—	—	1.02	*17*
$(C_6H_5NH)_2CO$ (Me)	Am_2O	C_5H_5N	2.13	—	*3*
$C_6H_5(C_6H_5CH_2)NNH_2$ (Et*)	Et_2O	Et_2O	1.12	—	*11*
C_{14}					
Alizarin (Me)	Am_2O	C_5H_5N	2.03	—	*2*
Quinizarin (Me)	Am_2O	C_5H_5N	1.98	—	*2*
$(C_6H_5CO{-})_2$ (Me)	*i*-Am_2O	—	—	0.09	*17*
$(2\text{-}H_2NC_6H_4CH{=})_2$ (Me)	Am_2O	C_5H_5N	2.21	2.90	*9*
$C_6H_5COCH_2C_6H_5$ (Me)	Am_2O	Am_2O	0.12	—	*1*
$C_6H_5COCH_2C_6H_5$ (Me)	*i*-Am_2O	—	—	0.06	*17*
$C_6H_5COCH_2C_6H_5$ (Me‡)	Dioxane	Dioxane	—	0.24	*42*
$C_6H_5COCH(OH)C_6H_5$ (Me)	*i*-Am_2O	—	—	1.04	*27*
$C_6H_5COCH(OH)C_6H_5$ (Me)	*i*-Am_2O	—	—	1.00	*42*
$C_6H_5COCH(OH)C_6H_5$ (Me)	Am_2O	C_5H_5N	1.07	—	*2*
$C_6H_5COCH(OH)C_6H_5$ (Me)	*i*-Am_2O	C_5H_5N	—	1.25	*27*
$C_6H_5COCH(OH)C_6H_5$ (Me)	*i*-Am_2O	Dioxane	—	1.35	*27*
$C_6H_5COCH(OH)C_6H_5$ (Me)	Am_2O	Am_2O	—	1.03	*1*

TABLE XVIII-I (Continued)

Sample (G.R.)	G. R. Solvent	Sample Solvent	Apparent "Active" H		Ref.
			Cold	Heated	
C_{14} (*cont.*)					
$C_6H_5COCH(OH)C_6H_5$ (Me†)	Dioxane	Dioxane	—	1.2–1.3	*42*
$(—CONHC_6H_5)_2$ (Me)	Am_2O	C_5H_5N	2.20	—	*3*
α-$[HON{=}C(C_6H_5)—]_2$	Am_2O	C_5H_5N	2.03	—	*2*
$C_6H_5CONHC_6H_4$-2-CH_3 (Me)	Am_2O	C_5H_5N	1.09	—	*3*
$C_6H_5CONHCH_2C_6H_5$ (Me)	*i*-Am_2O	—	—	1.01	*17*
$C_6H_5COCH(OH)C_6H_5$ (Me)	*i*-Am_2O	—	—	1.02	*17*
$C_6H_5COCH(OH)C_6H_5$ (Et)	*i*-Am_2O	C_5H_5N	1.03	—	*7*
4-$(CH_3)_2NC_6H_4N_2C_6H_5$ (Me)	Bu_2O	Bu_2O	0.33	0.42	*20*
4-Acetyl-*s*-hydrindacene (Me)	?	?	0.30	—	*38*
C_{15}					
Chrysin (Me)	Am_2O	C_5H_5N	2.05	—	*3*
Fisetin (Me)	Am_2O	C_5H_5N	3.98	—	*3*
Morin (Me)	Am_2O	C_5H_5N	5.00	—	*3*
$(C_6H_5CO)_2CHBr$ (Me)	*i*-Am_2O	Xylene	—	0.06	*17*
3,4-Diphenylisoxazolone (Me)	*i*-Am_2O	*i*-Am_2O	—	*ca.* 1	*19*
$(C_6H_5CO)_2CH_2$ (Me)	Am_2O	Am_2O	0.95	—	*5*
$(C_6H_5CO)_2CH_2$ (Me)	*i*-Am_2O	Xylene	—	1.06	*17*
$C_6H_5COCH(O_2CH)C_6H_5$ (Me)	*i*-Am_2O	Dioxane	—	0.86	*27*
$C_6H_5COCH(O_2CH)C_6H_5$ (Me)	*i*-Am_2O	Xylene	—	0.05	*27*
$C_6H_5COCH(OCH_3)C_6H_5$ (Me)	*i*-Am_2O	C_5H_5N	—	0.07	*27*
$C_6H_5COCH(OCH_3)C_6H_5$ (Me)	*i*-Am_2O	Xylene	—	0.13	*27*
4-$CH_3C_6H_4SO_2CH_2CH_2C_6H_5$ (Me)	*i*-Am_2O	Xylene (?)	—	$\geqq 1$	*54*
$C_2H_5(C_6H_5)_2CHOH$ (Me*)	Et_2O	Et_2O	1.25	—	*40*
9-Acetyl-5,6,7,8-tetrahydrobenz[*f*]indan (Me)	?	?	0.62	—	*38*
2,4,6-$(CH_3)_3C_6H_2CH_2CO$-*t*-C_4H_9 (Me)	Am_2O	C_5H_5N	*ca.* 0	—	*32*
$[CH_3(CH_2)_4C{\equiv}C]_2CH_2$ (Et)	Et_2O	Et_2O	0.00	0.57	*23*
$[CH_3(CH_2)_4C{\equiv}C]_2CH_2$ (Et)	Et_2O-C_6H_6	Et_2O-C_6H_6	—	1.32	*23*

TABLE XVIII-I (Continued)

Sample (G.R.)	G. R. Solvent	Sample Solvent	Apparent "Active" H		Ref.
			Cold	Heated	
C_{16}					
"Di-indole" (Me)	Am_2O	Xylene	2.04	2.04	*24*
Hematein (Me)	Am_2O	C_5H_5N	4.07	—	*3*
1-$C_6H_5NHC_{10}H_7$ (Me)	EtOPh	EtOPh	1.00	—	*4*
2-$C_6H_5NHC_{10}H_7$ (Me)	EtOPh	EtOPh	1.06	—	*4*
$(C_6H_5CO)_2CHCH_3$ (Me)	*i*-Am_2O	Xylene	—	0.16	*17*
$C_6H_5COCH(O_2CCH_3)C_6H_5$ (Me)	*i*-Am_2O	C_5H_5N	—	0.58	*27*
$C_6H_5COCH(O_2CCH_3)C_6H_5$ (Me)	*i*-Am_2O	Dioxane	—	0.42	*27*
$C_6H_5COCH(O_2CCH_3)C_6H_5$ (Me)	*i*-Am_2O	Xylene	—	0.10	*27*
$C_6H_5COCH(NHCOCH_3)C_6H_5$ (Me)	*i*-Am_2O	—	*ca.* 1	—	*31*
Brazilin ($C_{16}H_{14}O_5 \cdot 1.5H_2O$) (Me)	Am_2O	C_5H_5N	3.97	—	*3*
9-Acetyl-1,2,3,4,5,6,7,8-octahydroänthracene (Me)	?	?	0.95	—	*38*
Hematoxylin ($C_{16}H_{14}O_6 \cdot 3H_2O$) (Me)	Am_2O	C_5H_5N	5.01	—	*3*
Glucose pentaäcetate (Me)	*i*-Am_2O	C_5H_5N	—	1.6	*27*
Glucose pentaäcetate (Me)	*i*-Am_2O	Dioxane	—	1.9	*27*
2,4,6-$(CH_3)_3C_6H_2C(OH)(CH_3)CO$-*t*-$C_4H_9$ (Me)	Am_2O	C_5H_5N	*ca.* 1	—	*32*
2,4,6-$(CH_3)_3C_6H_2COC(OH)(CH_3)$-*t*-$C_4H_9$ (Me)	Am_2O	C_5H_5N	*ca.* 1	—	*32*
$CH_3(CH_2)_{14}CO_2H$ (Me)	Am_2O	C_5H_5N	0.97	—	*12*
n-$C_{16}H_{33}OH$ (Et)	*i*-Am_2O	C_5H_5N	0.79	—	*7*
C_{17}					
$(C_6H_5C\equiv C)_2CH_2$ (Et*)	Et_2O	Et_2O	—	0.95	*46,45*
$(C_6H_5C\equiv C)_2CH_2$ (Et*)	C_6H_5	C_6H_5	—	1.84	*46,45*
$C_6H_5C(=NH)$-1-$C_{10}H_7$ (Et*)	Et_2O	Et_2O	1.08	—	*11*
$(CH_3)_2C(COC_6H_5)_2$ (Me)	Am_2O	Am_2O	0.00	—	*5*
Morphine ($C_{17}H_{19}NO_3$) (Me)	Am_2O	C_5H_5N	1.95	1.96	*6*
Morphine ($C_{17}H_{19}NO_3 \cdot H_2O$) (Me)	Am_2O	C_5H_5N	3.96	3.96	*6*
Cocaine ($C_{17}H_{21}NO_4 \cdot HCl$) (Me)	Am_2O	C_5H_5N	1.21	1.19	*6*

TABLE XVIII-I (Continued)

Sample (G.R.)	G. R. Solvent	Sample Solvent	Apparent "Active" H		Ref.
			Cold	Heated	
C_{17} (*cont.*)					
4-$(CH_3)_2NC_6H_4C(=NH)C_6H_4$-4-$N(CH_3)_2$ (Et*)	Et_2O	Et_2O	1.04	—	*11*
Atropine (Me)	Am_2O	C_5H_5N	1.12	1.20	*6*
C_{18}					
4-$H_2NC_6H_4N=NC_6H_5 \cdot C_6H_3(NO_2)_3$ (Me)	Am_2O	Xylene	1.03	2.02	*6*
4-$C_6H_5NHC_6H_4N_2C_6H_5$ (Me)	Bu_2O	Bu_2O	1.26	1.42	*20*
"Di-skatole" (Me)	Am_2O	Xylene	2.05	2.00	*24*
"Di-7-methylindole" (Me)	Am_2O	Xylene	1.95	1.90	*24*
2,2′-Bis-(*o*-nitrophenyl)-4,4′-bi-1,3-dioxolanyl (Me)	Am_2O	C_5H_5N	1.28	—	*15*
3,4-$(CH_3O)_2C_6H_3COCH=CHC_6H_3$-2-OH-4-$OCH_3$ (Me)	Am_2O	C_5H_5N	1.05	—	*3*
2,4,5,6-$(CH_3)_4C_6HCOCH(NH_2 \cdot HCl)C_6H_5$ (Me)	*i*-Am_2O	—	*ca.* 3	*ca.* 4	*31*
n-$C_8H_{17}CH=CH(CH_2)_7CO_2H$ (Me)	Am_2O	C_5H_5N	0.97	—	*12*
n-$C_6H_{13}CH(OH)CH_2CH=CH(CH_2)_7CO_2H$ (Me)	Am_2O	C_5H_5N	1.98	—	*12*
$CH_3(CH_2)_{16}CO_2H$ (Me)	Am_2O	C_5H_5N	1.06	—	*12*
"Dihydroxystearic acid" (Me)	Am_2O	C_5H_5N	2.95	—	*12*
$[(t\text{-}C_4H_9)_2C(OH)—]_2$ (Me)	Am_2O	C_5H_5N	1.90	—	*29*
C_{19}					
9-Phenylfluorene (Me)	Am_2O	C_5H_5N	0.00	1.10	*9*
9-Phenyl-9-fluorenol (Me)	Am_2O	C_5H_5N	0.36–0.41	1.02–1.17	*9*
9-Phenyl-9-fluorenol (Me)	Am_2O	MeOPh	—	1.02	*9*
Aurin (Me)	C_5H_5N	—	—	1.97	*44*
2-$O_2NC_6H_4(C_6H_5)_2CH$ (Me)	Am_2O	C_5H_5N	1.01	—	*15*
$(C_6H_5)_3COH$ (Me)	Am_2O	C_5H_5N	1.00	—	*2*
$(C_6H_5)_3COH$ (Et)	*i*-Am_2O	C_5H_5N	1.05	—	*7*
3,9-Bis-(*o*-nitrophenyl)-2,4,8,10-tetroxaspiro[5.5]-hendecane (Me)	Am_2O	C_5H_5N	1.27	—	*15*

TABLE XVIII-I (Continued)

Sample (G.R.)	G. R. Solvent	Sample Solvent	Apparent "Active" H		Ref.
			Cold	Heated	
C_{19} *(cont.)*					
Cinchonine (Me)	Am_2O	C_5H_5N	1.22	1.25	*6*
Cinchonidine (Me)	Am_2O	C_5H_5N	1.11	1.08	*6*
C_{20}					
Fluorescein (Me)	Am_2O	C_5H_5N	—	2.11	*2*
p-Hydroxydiphenylphthalide (Me)	Am_2O	Am_2O	—	1.04	*51*
K salt of phenolphthalein (Et)	Et_2O	Et_2O	*ca.* 1	—	*48*
Phenolphthalein (Et)	Et_2O	Et_2O	0.00	—	*48*
Phenolphthalein (Me)	Am_2O	Am_2O	—	0.15	*51*
Phenolphthalein (Me)	Am_2O	C_5H_5N	—	1.95	*51*
Phenolphthalein (Me)	C_5H_5N	—	—	2.07	*44*
Benzenehydroquinonephthalein (Me)	Am_2O	C_5H_5N	—	2.14	*51*
Phenolresorcinolphthalein (Me)	Am_2O	Am_2O	—	0.35	*51*
Phenolresorcinolphthalein (Me)	Am_2O	C_5H_5N	—	3.24	*51*
$(2\text{-}C_{10}H_7)_2NH$ (Me)	EtOPh	EtOPh	1.08	—	*4*
$C_6H_5COCH(C_6H_5)_2$ (Me)	*i*-Am_2O	—	—	0.14	*17*
$C_6H_5COCH(C_6H_5)_2$ (Me)	*i*-Am_2O	—	—	0.02	*27*
$C_6H_5COCH(C_6H_5)_2$ (Me)	*i*-Am_2O	C_5H_5N	—	0.11	*27*
$C_6H_5COCH(C_6H_5)_2$ (Me)	*i*-Am_2O	Dioxane	—	0.48	*27*
$C_6H_5COCH(C_6H_5)_2$ (Me†)	Dioxane	Dioxane	—	0.11	*42*
Benzenepyrocatecholphthalein (Me)	Am_2O	Am_2O	—	0.22	*51*
Benzenepyrocatecholphthalein (Me)	Am_2O	C_5H_5N	—	2.26	*51*
$2,4,5,6\text{-}(CH_3)_4C_6HCOCH(NHCOCH_3)C_6H_5$ (Me)	*i*-Am_2O	—	*ca.* 2	—	*31*
Quinidine (Me)	Am_2O	C_5H_5N	0.86	0.86	*6*
Quinine (Me)	Am_2O	C_5H_5N	0.97	1.18	*6*
Quinine hydrate ($C_{20}H_{24}N_2O_2\cdot 3H_2O$) (Me)	Am_2O	C_5H_5N	7.08	—	*6*
$(4\text{-}CH_3OC_6H_4)_2CHC(C_2H_5)_2OH$ (Me)	?	?	0.80–0.85	—	*50*

TABLE XVIII-I (Continued)

Sample (G.R.)	G. R. Solvent	Sample Solvent	Apparent "Active" H		Ref.
			Cold	Heated	
C_{21}					
13-Dibenzo[*a,i*]fluorene (Me)	Am_2O	C_5H_5N	0.00	1.14	9
$4\text{-}CH_3C_6H_4SO_2CH_2CH(C_6H_5)_2$ (Me)	*i*-Am_2O	Xylene (?)	—	≧1	54
Phenolphthaleïn monomethyl ether (Me)	Am_2O	Am_2O	—	1.08	51
Strychnine (Me)	Am_2O	C_5H_5N	0.70	—	25
Strychnine (Me)	Am_2O	MeOPh	1.31	1.63	25
Dihydrostrychnine (Me)	Am_2O	MeOPh	1.15	1.24	25
Tetrahydrostrychnine (Me)	Am_2O	MeOPh	1.58	1.77	25
C_{22}					
3,6-Dimethyl-4,5-diphenylphthalic anhydride (Me)	?	?	0.80	—	30
3,3′,3″-Trimethoxy-4,4′-dihydroxyfuchsone (Me)	C_5H_5N	—	—	2.06	44
Narcotine (Me)	Am_2O	C_5H_5N	0.00	—	6
Desoxyvomicine (Me)	Am_2O	MeOPh	1.35	1.66	25
Vomicine (Me)	Am_2O	C_5H_5N	1.04	—	25
Vomicine (Me)	Am_2O	MeOPh	2.06	2.13	25
Vomicine (Me)	Am_2O	Xylene	1.71	2.09	25
Vomicidine (Me)	Am_2O	MeOPh	1.03	0.98	25
Dihydrovomicine (Me)	Am_2O	MeOPh	1.43	1.72	25
C_{23}					
Brucine (Me)	Am_2O	C_5H_5N	0.09	—	6
Brucine (Me)	Am_2O	C_5H_5N	0.81	—	25
Brucine (Me)	Am_2O	MeOPh	0.88	0.93	25
Dihydrobrucine (Me)	Am_2O	MeOPh	0.81	0.99	25
$2,4,5,6\text{-}(CH_3)_4C_6HC(O_2CCH_3)_2CH(NHCOCH_3)C_6H_5$ (Me)	*i*-Am_2O	—	*ca.* 0	—	31

TABLE XVIII-I (Continued)

Sample (G.R.)	G. R. Solvent	Sample Solvent	Apparent "Active" H		Ref.
			Cold	Heated	
C_{24}					
"Tri-indole" (Me)	Am_2O	Xylene	3.04	3.10	*24*
Phenolthymolphthaleïn (Me)	Am_2O	Am_2O	—	0.23	*51*
Phenolthymolphthaleïn (Me)	Am_2O	C_5H_5N	—	2.17	*51*
Thymolpyrocatecholphthaleïn (Me)	Am_2O	C_5H_5N	—	3.37	*51*
Thymolresorcinolphthaleïn (Me)	Am_2O	Am_2O	—	0.15	*51*
Thymolresorcinolphthaleïn (Me)	Am_2O	C_5H_5N	—	3.32	*51*
C_{25}					
Phenol(methyl-4-thymol)phthaleïn	Am_2O	Am_2O	—	1.02	*51*
(Methyl-4-thymol)pyrocatecolphthaleïn	Am_2O	C_5H_5N	—	2.21	*51*
(Methyl-4-thymol)resorcinolphthaleïn (Me)	Am_2O	Am_2O	—	2.03	*51*
(Methyl-4-thymol)resorcinolphthaleïn (Me)	Am_2O	C_5H_5N	—	2.19	*51*
C_{26}					
1-Methyl-2,5,6-triphenyl-7-oxo-1,4-methano-1,2,3,4-tetrahydrobenzene (Me)	?	?	*ca.* 0	—	*30*
$CH_3(CH_2)_{24}CO_2H$ (Me)	Am_2O	C_5H_5N	1.00	—	*12*
C_{27}					
1,4-Dimethyl-3-benzoyl-5,6-diphenyl-7-oxo-1,4-methano-1,2,3,4-tetrahydrobenzene (Me)	?	?	0.80	—	*30*
1-Methyl-3,5,6-triphenyl-7-hydroxy-7-R-1,4-methano-1,2,3,4-tetrahydrobenzene (Me) (R = CH_3, C_6H_5, 1-$C_{10}H_7$)	?	?	*ca.* 1	—	*30*
C_{31}					
13-α-Naphthyl-13-dibenzo[*a*,*i*]fluorene (Me)	Am_2O	C_5H_5N	0.00	1.02	9
13-α-Naphthyl-13-dibenzo[*a*,*i*]fluorenol (Me)	Am_2O	C_5H_5N	0.16	0.90	9

TABLE XVIII-I (Continued)

Sample (G.R.)	G. R. Solvent	Sample Solvent	Apparent "Active" H		Ref.
			Cold	Heated	
C_{31} (*cont.*)					
1,2,5,6-Tetraphenyl-7-oxo-1,4-methano-1,2,3,4-tetrahydrobenzene (Me)	?	?	*ca.* 0	—	39
MesCOCH(Mes)CH_2COMes[e] (Me)	*i*-Am_2O	*i*-Am_2O	*ca.* 1	*ca.* 1.5	52
C_{32}					
Etioporphyrin II (Me)	Bu_2O	C_6H_6	2.06	—	37
C_{33}					
N-Methyletioporphyrin II (Me)	Bu_2O	C_6H_5	1.04	—	37
C_{34}					
3,3a,5,6-Tetraphenyl-3a,4,7,7a-tetrahydro-1-indenone (Me)	?	?	*ca.* 1	—	30

[e] Mes = mesityl = 2,4,6-$(CH_3)_3C_6H_2$—.

REFERENCES FOR TABLE XVIII-I

(*1*) Hibbert and Sudborough, *Proc. Chem. Soc.*, *19*, 285–6 (1903); *J. Chem. Soc.*, *85*, 933–8 (1904).
(*2*) Zerewitinoff, *Ber.*, *40*, 2023–31 (1907).
(*3*) Zerewitinoff, *Ber.*, *41*, 2233–43 (1908).
(*4*) Sudborough and Hibbert, *J. Chem. Soc.*, *95*, 477–80 (1909).
(*5*) Smedley, *J. Chem. Soc.*, 97, 1484–94 (1910).
(*6*) Zerewitinoff, *Ber.*, *43*, 3590–5 (1910).
(*7*) Oddo, *Ber.*, *44*, 2048–52 (1911).
(*8*) Hibbert, *J. Chem. Soc.*, *101*, 328–41 (1912).
(*9*) Zerewitinoff, *Ber.*, *45*, 2384–9 (1912).
(*10*) Zerewitinoff, *Ber.*, *47*, 2417–23 (1914).
(*11*) Moureu and Mignonac, *Compt. rend.*, *158*, 1624–31 (1914).
(*12*) Zerewitinoff, *Z. anal. Chem.*, *52*, 729–37 (1914).
(*13*) Ciusa, *Gazz. chim. ital.*, *50,II*, 53–5 (1920); *Chem. Abstr.*, *15*, 837 (1921).
(*14*) Zerewitinoff, *Z. anal. Chem.*, *68*, 321–7 (1926).
(*15*) Tanasescu, *Bull. soc. chim.*, [4], *39*, 1443–55 (1926).
(*16*) Gilman and Fothergill, *J. Am. Chem. Soc.*, *49*, 2815–8 (1927).
(*17*) Kohler, Stone, and Fuson, *J. Am. Chem. Soc.*, *49*, 3181–8 (1927).
(*18*) Job and Dusollier, *Compt. rend.*, *184*, 1454–6 (1927); *Chem. Zentr.*, *1927,II*, 920; *Chem. Abstr.*, *21*, 3049 (1927).
(*19*) Kohler and Blatt, *J. Am. Chem. Soc.*, *50*, 504–15 (1928).
(*20*) Gilman and Fothergill, *J. Am. Chem. Soc.*, *50*, 867–9 (1928).
(*21*) Gilman and Fothergill, *Bull. soc. chim.*, [4], *45*, 1132–6 (1929).
(*22*) Gilman, Fothergill, and Towne, *J. Am. Chem. Soc.*, *52*, 405–7 (1930).
(*23*) Tchao Yin Lai, *Bull. soc. chim.*, [4], *53*, 1537–43 (1933).
(*24*) Schmitz-Dumont and Hamann, *Ber.*, *66B*, 71–6 (1933).
(*25*) Wieland and Holscher, *Ann.*, *500*, 70–91 (1933).
(*26*) Wiley and Adkins, *J. Am. Chem. Soc.*, *60*, 914–8 (1938).
(*27*) Lieff, Wright, and Hibbert, *J. Am. Chem. Soc.*, *61*, 865–7 (1939).
(*28*) Nesmeyanov and Sazonova, *Bull. acad. sci. U.R.S.S.*, *Classe sci. chim.*, *1941*, 499–519; *Chem. Abstr.*, *37*, 2724 (1943).
(*29*) Stevens and Mowat, *J. Am. Chem. Soc.*, *64*, 554–6 (1942).
(*30*) Allen and Van Allan, *J. Am. Chem. Soc.*, *64*, 1260–7 (1942).
(*31*) Weissberger and Glass, *J. Am. Chem. Soc.*, *64*, 1724–7 (1942).
(*32*) Fuson and Robertson, *J. Org. Chem.*, 7, 466–71 (1942).
(*33*) Freibs, *Ber.*, *75B*, 953–7 (1942).
(*34*) Erickson and Kitchens, *J. Am. Chem. Soc.*, *68*, 492–6 (1946).
(*35*) Spaeth, Geissman, and Jacobs, *J. Org. Chem.*, *11*, 399–404 (1946).
(*36*) Courtot and Devalotte, *Compt. rend.*, *223*, 64–7 (1946); *Chem. Abstr.*, *41*, 446 (1947).
(*37*) Ellingson and Corwin, *J. Am. Chem. Soc.*, *68*, 1112–5 (1946).
(*38*) Arnold and Rondestvedt, *J. Am. Chem. Soc.*, *68*, 2176–8 (1946).
(*39*) Allen and Van Allan, *J. Am. Chem. Soc.*, *68*, 2387–90 (1946).
(*40*) Terent'ev, Shcherbakova, and Kremenskaya, *J. Gen. Chem.* (U.S.S.R.), *17*, 100–4 (1947); *Chem. Abstr.*, *42*, 109 (1948).
(*41*) Hollyday and Cottle, *Ind. Eng. Chem.*, *Anal. Ed.*, *14*, 774–6 (1942).
(*42*) Wright, *J. Am. Chem. Soc.*, *61*, 1152–6 (1939).
(*43*) Fuchs, Ishler, and Sandhoff, *Ind. Eng. Chem.*, *Anal. Ed.*, *12*, 507–9 (1940).
(*44*) Lehman and Basch, *Ind. Eng. Chem.*, *Anal. Ed.*, *17*, 428–9 (1945).
(*45*) Grignard and Lepayre, *Compt. rend.*, *192*, 250–3 (1931); *Chem. Abstr.*, *25*, 2421 (1931).
(*46*) Grignard and Lepayre, *Bull. soc. chim.*, [4], *43*, 930–1 (1928).

(47) Rebek and Mandrino, *Österr. Chem.-Ztg.*, *41*, 49–52 (1938); *Chem. Zentr.*, *1938,II*, 1204; *Chem. Abstr.*, *32*, 3755 (1938).
(48) Oddo and Vassallo, *Gazz. chim. ital.*, *42,II*, 204–36 (1912); *Chem. Abstr.*, 7, 341 (1913).
(49) Cymerman, Heilbron, and Jones, *J. Chem. Soc.*, *1944*, 144–7.
(50) Földi and Demjén, *Ber.*, *74B*, 930–4 (1941).
(51) Lin Che Kin, *Ann. chim.*, [11], *13*, 317–99 (1940).
(52) Lutz and Kibler, *J. Am. Chem. Soc.*, *62*, 360–72 (1940).
(53) Lester and Proffitt, *J. Am. Chem. Soc.*, *71*, 1877–8 (1949).
(54) Kohler and Potter, *J. Am. Chem. Soc.*, *57*, 1316–21 (1935).

CHAPTER XIX

Reactions of Grignard Reagents with Miscellaneous Nitrogen Compounds*

ISOCYANATES AND ISOTHIOCYANATES

It was reported by Blaise[1] that phenyl isocyanate ($C_6H_5—N{=}C{=}O$) reacts with organomagnesium iodides (RMgI) to form products which, upon hydrolysis, yield anilides ($RCONHC_6H_5$).

Nothing is certainly known concerning the mechanism, or even the order, of the reaction. However, the studies of Gilman *et al.*[2,3] make it appear probable that the condensation of phenyl isocyanate with one molecule of Grignard reagent is essentially an ionic addition at the terminal (C=O) double bond.

$$C_6H_5—N{=}C{=}O + RMgX \rightarrow C_6H_5—N{=}CR—OMgX \xrightarrow{H_2O}$$
$$[RC(OH){=}NC_6H_5] + MgXOH \rightarrow RCONHC_6H_5 + MgXOH$$

Thus far the reaction proceeds smoothly at or below the boiling point of ethyl ether, usually with very good (80-90 percent) yields. Even in the presence of a large excess of Grignard reagent further reaction does not take place at an appreciable rate in ether solution (Gilman *et al.*, *loc. cit.*[2,3]).

*The present authors have found the preparation of this (frankly compilative) chapter one of the least enjoyable tasks of the project undertaken. In so far as the essentially ionic addition reactions discussed are concerned, the facts may generally be taken to be substantially as reported. In oxidation-reduction reactions (especially those involving "non-reducing" Grignard reagents), however, it is felt that the present "factual" foundation affords far too slippery a footing for confident theorization or profitable speculation. In some individual cases, specific reasons for this general dysphoria are stated in the following text, and lines of investigation are suggested. Without intended criticism of earlier investigators who (having no reason to suspect the profound influence on some reactions of traces of metallic impurities in reagent magnesium) honestly reported their observations of the results of technically admirable work, it is suggested that the interested reader may here find many subjects worthy of re-examination.

[1] Blaise, *Compt. rend.*, *132*, 38-41 (1901); *Chem. Zentr.*, *1901,I*, 298.

[2] Gilman and Kinney, *J. Am. Chem. Soc.*, *46*, 493-7 (1924).

[3] Gilman, Kirby, and Kinney, *J. Am. Chem. Soc.*, *51*, 2252-61 (1929).

Because of the tractability of the reaction, and the ready isolability of the well-characterized products, the condensation of an aryl isocyanate with a Grignard reagent has been recommended as a means for the identification of alkyl halides or of alcohols readily convertible to halides.[4,5] However, it should be noted in this connection that the reaction sometimes involves rearrangement. Thus, Schwartz and Johnson[6] found that 2-chloro-2-methylbutane, neopentyl chloride, and allyl bromide all give rearranged products.

$$CH_3(i\text{-}C_3H_7)CHCl \xrightarrow{Mg} C_5H_{11}MgCl \xrightarrow{C_6H_5NCO} C_2H_5(CH_3)_2CCONHC_6H_5$$

$$t\text{-}C_4H_9CH_2Cl \xrightarrow{Mg} C_5H_{11}MgCl \xrightarrow{C_6H_5NCO} C_2H_5(CH_3)_2CCONHC_6H_5$$

$$H_2C{=}CHCH_2Br \xrightarrow{Mg} C_3H_5MgBr \xrightarrow{C_6H_5NCO} CH_3CH{=}CHCONHC_6H_5$$

Young and Roberts[7] also report that the only product isolated by them (in 74 percent yield) from the reaction of butenylmagnesium bromide with phenyl isocyanate was the anilide of the terminally double-bonded acid.

$$\text{Butenyl-MgBr} \xrightarrow{C_6H_5NCO} H_2C{=}CHCH(CH_3)CONHC_6H_5$$

So far as one may judge from the available data the reactions of Grignard reagents with aryl isothiocyanates appear to be similar in all respects to those with aryl isocyanates. According to Sachs and Loevy,[8] methyl isothiocyanate and allyl isothiocyanate also react similarly. Reactions which are reported as proceeding "normally" are recorded in Table XIX-I.

Gilman *et al.* (*loc. cit.*[3]) found that, under "forced reaction" conditions (*i.e.*, six to eight hours reflux in ether-toluene at 70–80°), phenyl isocyanate reacts with three molecules of phenylmagnesium bromide to yield (44 percent) a product which they identified as phenyl-o-biphenylylmethylaniline. Under the same conditions the same product was obtained in about the same yields from phenyl isothiocyanate and from benzophenone anil. They formulate the reaction as follows:

$$C_6H_5{-}N{=}C{=}O \xrightarrow{C_6H_5MgBr} C_6H_5{-}N{=}C(C_6H_5)OMgBr \xrightarrow{C_6H_5MgBr} C_6H_5{-}N{=}C(C_6H_5)_2 + (BrMg)_2O$$

$$C_6H_5{-}N{=}C(C_6H_5)_2 \xrightarrow{C_6H_5MgBr} BrMg(C_6H_5)N{-}CH(C_6H_5)C_6H_4\text{-}2\text{-}C_6H_5 \xrightarrow{H_2O} C_6H_5NHCH(C_6H_5)C_6H_4\text{-}2\text{-}C_6H_5 + MgBrOH$$

This reaction is discussed further in the section on Anils, Schiff Bases, etc. (*q.v.*).

---

[4] Gilman and Furry, *J. Am. Chem. Soc.*, *50*, 1214–6 (1928).
[5] Underwood and Gale, *J. Am. Chem. Soc.*, *56*, 2117–20 (1934).
[6] Schwartz and Johnson, *J. Am. Chem. Soc.*, *53*, 1063–8 (1931).
[7] Young and Roberts, *J. Am. Chem. Soc.*, *68*, 649–52 (1946).
[8] Sachs and Loevy, *Ber.*, *37*, 874–8 (1904).

TABLE XIX-I

"NORMAL" REACTIONS OF GRIGNARD REAGENTS WITH ISOCYANATES AND ISOTHIOCYANATES

RMgX	R′NCO or R′NCS	M. P. RCONHR′ or RCSNHR′	Ref.
CH_3MgCl	C_6H_5NCO	112–113°	*10*
CH_3MgI	$H_2C{=}CHCH_2NCS$	b. 135–136°/17 mm.	*2*
CH_3MgI	$4\text{-}ClC_6H_4NCS$	143°	*2*
CH_3MgI	C_6H_5NCS	75°	*1*
CH_3MgI	$4\text{-}C_2H_5OC_6H_4NCS$	99–100°	*2*
CH_3MgI	$1\text{-}C_{10}H_7NCO$	160°	*4*
C_2H_5MgCl	C_6H_5NCO	104.0–104.5°	*10*
C_2H_5MgBr	$H_2C{=}CHCH_2NCS$	b. 136°/12 mm.	*2*
C_2H_5MgBr	$4\text{-}C_2H_5OC_6H_4NCS$	74–75°	*2*
C_2H_5MgBr	$1\text{-}C_{10}H_7NCO$	126°	*4*
C_2H_5MgBr	$[-C_6H_4\text{-}4\text{-}NCS]_2$	228–229°	*2*
C_2H_5MgI	C_6H_5NCS	67.0–67.5°	*1*
n-C_3H_7MgCl	C_6H_5NCO	91–92°	*10*
n-C_3H_7MgBr	C_6H_5NCO	92°	*8*
n-C_3H_7MgBr	C_6H_5NCS	32–33°	*1*
n-C_3H_7MgBr	$1\text{-}C_{10}H_7NCO$	121°	*4*
i-C_3H_7MgCl	C_6H_5NCO	104.0–104.5°	*10*
i-C_3H_7MgBr	C_6H_5NCO	103°	*8*
α-Furyl-MgBr	C_6H_5NCO	121–122°	*6*
n-C_4H_9MgCl	C_6H_5NCO	62–63°	*10*
n-C_4H_9MgCl	$4\text{-}CH_3C_6H_4NCO$	72–73°	*10*
n-C_4H_9MgCl	$1\text{-}C_{10}H_7NCO$	109–110°	*10*
n-C_4H_9MgBr	C_6H_5NCO	63°	*8*
n-C_4H_9MgBr	$1\text{-}C_{10}H_7NCO$	112°	*4*
i-C_4H_9MgCl	C_6H_5NCO	109–110°	*10*
i-C_4H_9MgCl	$4\text{-}CH_3C_6H_4NCO$	106–107°	*10*
i-C_4H_9MgCl	$1\text{-}C_{10}H_7NCO$	125–126°	*10*
i-C_4H_9MgBr	C_6H_5CNO	109.5°	*8*

TABLE XIX-I (Continued)

RMgX	R′NCO or R′NCS	M. P. RCONHR′ or RCSNHR′	Ref.
i-C_4H_9MgBr	C_6H_5CNS	—	*1*
s-C_4H_9MgCl	C_6H_5NCO	105.5–106.5°	*10*
s-C_4H_9MgCl	4-$CH_3C_6H_4NCO$	92.5–93.0°	*10*
s-C_4H_9MgCl	1-$C_{10}H_7NCO$	128–129°	*10*
s-C_4H_9MgBr	C_6H_5NCO	108°	*8*
t-C_4H_9MgCl	C_6H_5NCO	128°	*8*
t-C_4H_9MgCl	C_6H_5NCO	132–133°	*10*
t-C_4H_9MgCl	4-$CH_3C_6H_4NCO$	119–120°	*10*
t-C_4H_9MgCl	1-$C_{10}H_7NCO$	146–147°	*10*
n-$C_5H_{11}MgCl$	C_6H_5NCO	94–95°	*10*
n-$C_5H_{11}MgCl$	4-$CH_3C_6H_4NCO$	74–75°	*10*
n-$C_5H_{11}MgBr$	C_6H_5NCO	96°	*8*
i-$C_5H_{11}MgCl$	C_6H_5NCO	110.0–110.5°	*10*
i-$C_5H_{11}MgCl$	4-$CH_3C_6H_4NCO$	61.5–62.5°	*10*
i-$C_5H_{11}MgCl$	1-$C_{10}H_7NCO$	110–111°	*10*
i-$C_5H_{11}MgBr$	C_6H_5NCO	108.5°	*8*
i-$C_5H_{11}MgBr$	C_6H_5NCS	63°	*1*
$CH_3(C_2H_5)CHCH_2MgBr$	C_6H_5NCO	88°	*8*
$CH_3(n$-$C_3H_7)CHMgCl$	C_6H_5NCO	86–87°	*10*
$CH_3(n$-$C_3H_7)CHMgCl$	4-$CH_3C_6H_4NCO$	107.5–108.5°	*10*
$CH_3(n$-$C_3H_7)CHMgCl$	1-$C_{10}H_7NCO$	117–118°	*10*
$CH_3(n$-$C_3H_7)CHMgBr$	C_6H_5NCO	88°	*8*
$(C_2H_5)_2CHMgCl$	C_6H_5NCO	126–127°	*10*
$(C_2H_5)_2CHMgCl$	4-$CH_3C_6H_4NCO$	90–91°	*10*
$(C_2H_5)_2CHMgCl$	1-$C_{10}H_7NCO$	102.5–103.5°	*10*
$(C_2H_5)_2CHMgBr$	C_6H_5NCO	123–124°	*8*
t-$C_5H_{11}MgCl$	C_6H_5NCO	92°	*8*
t-$C_5H_{11}MgCl$	C_6H_5NCO	90–91°	*10*
t-$C_5H_{11}MgCl$	4-$CH_3C_6H_4NCO$	83.0–83.5°	*10*
t-$C_5H_{11}MgCl$	1-$C_{10}H_7NCO$	137–138°	*10*

TABLE XIX-I (Continued)

RMgX	R′NCO or R′NCS	M. P. RCONHR′ or RCSNHR′	Ref.
C_6H_5MgBr	CH_3NCS	79°	2
C_6H_5MgBr	$H_2C{=}CHCH_2NCS$	b. 135–136°/17 mm.	2
C_6H_5MgBr	$4\text{-}C_2H_5OC_6H_4NCS$	127°	2
C_6H_5MgBr	$1\text{-}C_{10}H_7NCO$	161°	4
$C_2H_5CH{=}CH(CH_2)_2MgBr$	C_6H_5NCO	87°	11
$(CH_2)_5CHMgCl$	C_6H_5NCO	143–144°	10
$(CH_2)_5CHMgBr$	C_6H_5NCO	146°	8
$(CH_2)_5CHMgBr$	$1\text{-}C_{10}H_7NCO$	188°	4
$n\text{-}C_6H_{13}MgBr$	C_6H_5NCO	69°	8
$CH_3(n\text{-}C_4H_9)CHMgCl$	C_6H_5NCO	91–92°	10
$4\text{-}ClC_6H_4CH_2MgCl$	C_6H_5NCO	165–166°	10
$C_6H_5CH_2MgCl$	C_6H_5NCO	117°	8
$C_6H_5CH_2MgCl$	C_6H_5NCO	115–116°	10
$C_6H_5CH_2MgCl$	$1\text{-}C_{10}H_7NCO$	166°	4
$C_6H_5CH_2MgBr$	C_6H_5NCS	87°	2
$4\text{-}CH_3C_6H_4MgBr$	$1\text{-}C_{10}H_7NCO$	173°	4
$n\text{-}C_3H_7CH{=}CH(CH_2)_2MgBr$	C_6H_5NCO	100°	11
$n\text{-}C_7H_{15}MgBr$	C_6H_5NCO	57°	8
$C_6H_5C{\equiv}CMgBr$	C_6H_5NCO	126–127°	3
$C_6H_5CH{=}CHMgBr$	$1\text{-}C_{10}H_7NCO$	217°	4
$C_6H_5(CH_2)_2MgCl$	C_6H_5NCO	96°	10
$CH_3[\alpha\text{-furyl-}(CH_2)_2]CHMgBr$	$1\text{-}C_{10}H_7MgBr$	109.5–110.0°	7
$n\text{-}C_4H_9CH{=}CH(CH_2)_2MgBr$	C_6H_5NCO	95°	11
3,3-Dimethylcyclohexyl-MgBr	$1\text{-}C_{10}H_7NCO$	204.0–204.5°	12
DL-$CH_3(n\text{-}C_6H_{13})CHMgBr$*	C_6H_5NCO	72–73°	8
D-$CH_3(n\text{-}C_6H_{13})CHMgBr$†	C_6H_5NCO	72–73°	8
$1\text{-}C_{10}H_7MgBr$	$1\text{-}C_{10}H_7NCO$	236°	4
$1\text{-}C_{10}H_7CH_2MgCl$	C_6H_5NCO	155°	5
$(C_6H_5)_3CMgBr$	C_6H_5NCS		9

* From DL-$CH_3(n\text{-}C_6H_{13})CHBr$.

† From D-$CH_3(n\text{-}C_6H_{13})CHBr$.

REFERENCES FOR TABLE XIX-I

(*1*) Sachs and Loevy, *Ber.*, *36*, 585–8 (1903).
(*2*) Sachs and Loevy, *Ber.*, *37*, 874–8 (1904).
(*3*) Johnson and McEwen, *J. Am. Chem. Soc.*, *48*, 469–76 (1926).
(*4*) Gilman and Furry, *J. Am. Chem. Soc.*, *50*, 1214–6 (1928).
(*5*) Gilman and Kirby, *J. Am. Chem. Soc.*, *51*, 3475–8 (1929).
(*6*) Shepard, Winslow, and Johnson, *J. Am. Chem. Soc.*, *52*, 2083–90 (1930).
(*7*) Gilman and Hickey, *J. Am. Chem. Soc.*, *52*, 2144–7 (1930).
(*8*) Schwartz and Johnson, *J. Am. Chem. Soc.*, *53*, 1063–8 (1931).
(*9*) Bachmann and Cockerill, *J. Am. Chem. Soc.*, *55*, 2932–4 (1933).
(*10*) Underwood and Gale, *J. Am. Chem. Soc.*, *56*, 2117–20 (1934).
(*11*) Normant, *Compt. rend.*, *226*, 1734–6 (1948); *Chem. Abstr.*, *42*, 7237 (1948).
(*12*) von Doering and Beringer, *J. Am. Chem. Soc.*, *71*, 2221–6 (1949).

COMPOUNDS CONTAINING THE GROUPING —N=C<

Aldimines. Busch[9] reported that Grignard reagents react additively with benzylideneaniline, and studied the reaction further with Rinck,[10] extending it to other methyleneimines with Leefhelm.[11]

In general, addition to methyleneimines of the type R′N=CHR″ takes place under relatively mild conditions (*i.e.*, at or below the boiling point of ethyl ether) to give fairly good yields of products which, upon hydrolysis, liberate secondary amines.

$$\mathrm{RMgX + R'N{=}CHR'' \longrightarrow R'N(MgX)CHRR'' \xrightarrow{H_2O} R'NHCHRR'' + MgXOH}$$

A representative preparation is described by Campbell *et al.*[12] "To one mole of *n*-propylmagnesium bromide in 250 ml. of dry ether was added a solution of 66.5 g. (0.5 mole) of benzylideneëthylamine in 50 ml. of dry ether, over a period of one and one-half to two hours; the reaction mixture was refluxed for several hours and allowed to stand overnight. It was hydrolyzed by pouring onto ice and hydrochloric acid."

The authors observe, as a matter of practical interest, that consistently good (60 to 90 percent) yields are obtained when Grignard reagent and base are used in one-to-one molecular ratio only in cases of the more reactive Grignard reagents (*e.g.*, methylmagnesium bromide) and the simplest aldimines (*e.g.*, benzylidenemethylamine). In other cases a twofold excess of Grignard reagent is recommended. The yields reported in Table XIX-II (reference *11*) are for one-to-one reactant ratio, and hence are not in most cases the maximum attainable.

Of the mechanism, or order, of the reaction nothing is known, but it seems probable that additions of this kind are essentially ionic.

---

[9] Busch, *Ber.*, *37*, 2691–4 (1904).
[10] Busch and Rinck, *Ber.*, *38*, 1761–72 (1905).
[11] Busch and Leefhelm, *J. prakt. Chem.*, [2], 77, 20–5 (1907).
[12] Campbell, Helbing, Florkowski, and Campbell, *J. Am. Chem. Soc.*, *70*, 3868–70 (1948).

TABLE XIX-II

REACTIONS OF GRIGNARD REAGENTS WITH METHYLENEIMINES OF THE TYPE $R'N{=}CHR''$ (ALDIMINES)

R'	R''	RMgX	Yield (%) $R'NHCHRR''$	Ref.
CH_3	H	$C_6H_5CH_2MgCl$	—	*10*
CH_3	CH_3	$C_6H_5CH_2MgCl$	—	*10*
CH_3	C_6H_5	CH_3MgI	*ca.* quant.	*3*
CH_3	C_6H_5	C_2H_5MgBr	75	*11*
CH_3	C_6H_5	C_2H_5MgI	—	*3*
CH_3	C_6H_5	n-C_3H_7MgBr	66	*11*
CH_3	C_6H_5	i-C_3H_7MgBr	60	*11*
CH_3	C_6H_5	C_6H_5MgBr	—	*3*
CH_3	C_6H_5	$C_6H_5CH_2MgCl$	95	*9*
CH_3	2-HOC_6H_4	$C_6H_5CH_2MgCl$	72	*9*
CH_3	3-HOC_6H_4	$C_6H_5CH_2MgCl$	30	*9*
CH_3	4-HOC_6H_4	$C_6H_5CH_2MgCl$	13	*9*
CH_3	3,4-$CH_2O_2C_6H_3$	$C_6H_5CH_2MgCl$	66	*9*
CH_3	2-$CH_3OC_6H_4$	$C_6H_5CH_2MgCl$	78	*9*
CH_3	3-$CH_3OC_6H_4$	$C_6H_5CH_2MgCl$	78	*9*
CH_3	2-HO-3-$CH_3OC_6H_3$	$C_6H_5CH_2MgCl$	53	*9*
CH_3	3-CH_3O-4-HOC_6H_3	$C_6H_5CH_2MgCl$	38	*9*
CH_3	3-$C_2H_5OC_6H_4$	$C_6H_5CH_2MgCl$	74	*9*
CH_3	2,3-$(CH_3O)_2C_6H_3$	$C_6H_5CH_2MgCl$	79	*9*
CH_3	3,4-$(CH_3O)_2C_6H_3$	$C_6H_5CH_2MgCl$	52	*9*
CH_3	4-$(CH_3)_2NC_6H_4$	$C_6H_5CH_2MgCl$	75	*9*
C_2H_5	C_6H_5	CH_3MgI	*ca.* quant.	*3*
C_2H_5	C_6H_5	C_2H_5MgBr	39	*11*
C_2H_5	C_6H_5	C_2H_5MgI	—	*3*
C_2H_5	C_6H_5	n-C_3H_7MgBr	40	*11*
C_2H_5	C_6H_5	n-C_4H_9MgBr	37	*11*
C_2H_5	C_6H_5	C_6H_5MgBr	—	*3*
C_2H_5	C_6H_5	n-$C_4H_9C{\equiv}CMgBr$	0	*11*

TABLE XIX-II (Continued)

R′	R″	RMgX	Yield (%) R′NHCHRR″	Ref.
C_2H_5	C_6H_5	$C_6H_5CH_2MgCl$	74	*11*
C_2H_5	$4\text{-}CH_3OC_6H_4$	$C_6H_5CH_2MgCl$	79	*9*
$HOCH_2CH_2$	$4\text{-}CH_3OC_6H_4$	$C_6H_5CH_2MgCl$	79	*9*
$H_2C{=}CHCH_2$	C_6H_5	$C_6H_5CH_2MgCl$	78	*9*
$H_2C{=}CHCH_2$	$4\text{-}CH_3OC_6H_4$	$C_6H_5CH_2MgCl$	86	*9*
$n\text{-}C_3H_7$	C_6H_5	C_2H_5MgBr	27	*11*
$n\text{-}C_3H_7$	C_6H_5	C_6H_5MgBr	25	*11*
$n\text{-}C_4H_9$	C_6H_5	C_2H_5MgBr	30	*11*
$n\text{-}C_4H_9$	C_6H_5	C_6H_5MgBr	27	*11*
C_6H_5	C_2H_5O	$2\text{-}CH_3C_6H_4MgBr$	55	*5*
C_6H_5	C_6H_5	CH_3MgI	79	*1*
C_6H_5	C_6H_5	C_2H_5MgI	—	*2*
C_6H_5	C_6H_5	$n\text{-}C_3H_7MgI$	—	*2*
C_6H_5	C_6H_5	$i\text{-}C_5H_{11}MgI$	—	*2*
C_6H_5	C_6H_5	C_6H_5MgBr	—	*2*
C_6H_5	C_6H_5	C_6H_5MgI	—	*1*
C_6H_5	C_6H_5	$C_6H_5CH_2MgCl$	—	*2*
C_6H_5	C_6H_5	$1\text{-}C_{10}H_7MgBr$	—	*2*
C_6H_5	$2\text{-}CH_3OC_6H_4$	CH_3MgI	—	*4*
C_6H_5	$2\text{-HO-}5\text{-}CH_3C_6H_3$	CH_3MgI	—	*4*
C_6H_5	$2\text{-}CH_3O\text{-}5\text{-}CH_3C_6H_3$	CH_3MgI	—	*4*
C_6H_5	$4\text{-}i\text{-}C_3H_7C_6H_4$	CH_3MgI	—	*2*
$(CH_2)_5CH$	C_6H_5	$C_6H_5CH_2MgCl$	40	*9*
$C_6H_5CH_2$	C_6H_5	C_2H_5MgX	—	*8*
$C_6H_5CH_2$	C_6H_5	C_6H_5MgX	—	*8*
$C_6H_5CH_2$	C_6H_5	$C_6H_5CH_2MgCl$	53	*9*
$C_6H_5CH_2$	$4\text{-}HOC_6H_4$	$C_6H_5CH_2MgCl$	52	*9*
$C_6H_5CH_2$	$4\text{-}CH_3C_6H_4$	C_2H_5MgX	—	*8*
$C_6H_5CH_2$	$4\text{-}CH_3OC_6H_4$	C_2H_5MgX	—	*8*

TABLE XIX-II (Continued)

R′	R″	RMgX	Yield (%) R′NHCHRR″	Ref.
2-$CH_3C_6H_4$	C_6H_5	C_6H_5MgBr	—	*2*
4-$CH_3C_6H_4$	C_6H_5	C_6H_5MgBr	—	*2*
2-$CH_3OC_6H_4$	C_6H_5	C_6H_5MgBr	—	*2*
4-$CH_3OC_6H_4$	C_6H_5	C_6H_5MgBr	—	*2*
2-$C_{10}H_7$	C_6H_5	2-$C_6H_5C_6H_4MgI$	7	*12*
$C_6H_5(C_6H_5CO)C{=}C(C_6H_5)$	H	CH_3MgI	—	*7*
$C_6H_5(C_6H_5CO)C{=}C(C_6H_5)$	H	C_6H_5MgBr	—	*6*
$C_6H_5(C_6H_5CO)C{=}C(C_6H_5)$	CH_3	CH_3MgI	—	*7*

REFERENCES FOR TABLE XIX-II

(1) Busch, *Ber.*, 37, 2691–4 (1904).
(2) Busch and Rinck, *Ber.*, 38, 1761–72 (1905).
(3) Leefhelm, *J. prakt. Chem.*, [2], 77, 20–5 (1907).
(4) Anselmino, *Ber.*, 40, 3465–74 (1907).
(5) Gatterman, *Ann.*, 393, 215–34 (1912).
(6) Kohler and Blatt, *J. Am. Chem. Soc.*, 50, 1217–26 (1928).
(7) Kohler and Richtmyer, *J. Am. Chem. Soc.*, 50, 3092–106 (1928).
(8) Grammaticakis, *Compt. rend.*, 207, 1224–5 (1938); *Chem. Abstr.*, 33, 2494 (1939).
(9) Moffett and Hoehn, *J. Am. Chem. Soc.*, 69, 1792–4 (1947).
(10) Evdokimoff, *Gazz. chim. ital.*, 77, 318–26 (1947); *Chem. Abstr.*, 42, 2586 (1948).
(11) Campbell, Helbing, Florkowski, and Campbell, *J. Am. Chem. Soc.*, 70, 3868–70 (1948).
(12) Gilman and Morton, *J. Am. Chem. Soc.*, 70, 2514–5 (1948).

The relatively unreactive *n*-butylethynylmagnesium bromide did not undergo addition; the only product isolated appeared to be a dimer ($C_{18}H_{22}N_2$) of the original base (benzylideneëthylamine). Knowledge of the constitution of this "dimer" might throw some light on the reaction mechanism.

Ketimines. When the hydrogen atom of $R'N{=}CHR''$ is replaced by an alkyl or aryl group the "normal" addition reaction does not take place.[13] Aliphatic or aliphatic-aromatic ketoanils react as though they existed in the tautomeric enamic form.[14]

$$[R'N{=}CR''{-}CH_2R''' \rightleftharpoons R'NH{-}CR''{=}CHR'''] \xrightarrow{RMgX} R'N(MgX)CR''{=}CHR''' + RH$$

This statement should not be interpreted as necessarily implying that only the enamic form reacts. There may well be a Grignard reagent enaminization of ketimines similar to the analogous Grignard reagent enolization of ketones (*q.v.*, Chapter VI). There is, however, spectroscopic evidence to indicate that some ketoanils, at least, exist largely in the enamic form.[15]

Plancher and Ravenna[16] had obtained from the interaction of acetophenone anil and phenylmagnesium bromide a product (admittedly impure) which they believed to have the empirical formula $C_{20}H_{19}N$, corresponding to that of an addition product, $CH_3(C_6H_5)_2CNHC_6H_5$. Operating under the conditions described by Plancher and Ravenna, however, Short and Watt (*loc. cit.*[14a]) isolated, together with a little aniline, a product of the em-

[13] See, *e.g.*, Grammaticakis, *Compt. rend.*, 223, 804–6 (1946); *Chem. Abstr.*, 41, 1602 (1947).

[14] See, *e.g.*, (*a*) Short and Watt, *J. Chem. Soc.*, 1930, 2293–7; (*b*) Montagne, *Compt. rend.*, 199, 671–3 (1934); *Chem. Abstr.*, 29, 465 (1934).

[15] von Auwers and Susemihl, *Ber.*, 63B, 1072–86 (1930).

[16] Plancher and Ravenna, *Atti accad. Lincei*, [5], 15,II, 555–61 (1906); *Chem. Zentr.*, 1907,I, 111.

pirical formula $C_{22}H_{19}N$ which they satisfactorily identified as dypnone anil. The reaction, therefore, has the appearance of a cleavage-condensation which may be represented stoichiometrically (without prejudice regarding mechanism) as follows:

$$C_6H_5N(MgBr)C(C_6H_5){=}CH_2 + C_6H_5NHC(C_6H_5){=}CH_2 \rightarrow C_6H_5NHMgBr + CH_3(C_6H_5)C{=}CHC(C_6H_5){=}NC_6H_5$$

When the complicating presence of benzene in the hydrolysis product was avoided by the use of ethylmagnesium bromide, dypnone anil was isolated in 81 percent yield.

Short and Watt (*loc. cit.*[14a]) also investigated some of the Grignard reactions of acetone anil. With excess methylmagnesium bromide in amyl ether they observed methane evolution corresponding to 0.94 equivalent of "active" hydrogen.

When the anil was treated successively with ethylmagnesium bromide and methyl sulfate, *N*-methyl-*N*-isopropenylaniline was obtained in fairly good yield (9 g. of amine from 13 g. of anil).

$$(CH_3)_2C{=}NC_6H_5 \xrightarrow{C_2H_5MgBr} C_2H_6 + H_2C{=}C(CH_3)N(MgBr)C_6H_5$$

$$\xrightarrow{(CH_3)_2SO_4} H_2C{=}C(CH_3)N(CH_3)C_6H_5 + CH_3SO_4MgBr$$

When phenylmagnesium bromide was employed, benzene, together with some aniline, was isolated. The presence of aniline among the reaction products indicates that acetone anil, like acetophenone anil, undergoes some cleavage. If cleavage is indeed concomitant to condensation, and if the reaction involves one molecule (or ion-pair) of enaminate and one molecule of anil (or enamine), as heretofore suggested, it would appear that chances of isolating the condensation product would be best when one equivalent of Grignard reagent is added to two equivalents of anil, and when the Grignard reagent selected is such as to yield a gaseous or easily volatile product in the initial enaminization step.

Although benzophenone anil appears to react vigorously with methylmagnesium bromide in ethyl ether (heat effect), practically quantitative recovery of the anil can be achieved upon hydrolysis of the resultant precipitate (Short and Watt, *loc. cit.*[14a]). Whereas there is here no possibility of enaminization, and no gas evolution is observed, the interaction must consist in Werner complex formation analogous to that observed with dimethylaniline, for example.

When benzophenone anil is refluxed with phenylmagnesium bromide in ether-toluene solution at 70–80° for six to eight hours, the major isolable product (42 percent yield) is the result of an addition, but is not the triphenylmethylaniline which would be expected to result from "normal" addition of the Grignard reagent at the carbon-nitrogen double bond.[17] Formally, at least, the reaction is a 1,4-addition.

---

[17] Gilman, Kirby, and Kinney, *J. Am. Chem. Soc.*, *51*, 2252–61 (1929).

$$C_6H_5-C(C_6H_5)=NC_6H_5 \xrightarrow{C_6H_5MgBr} C_6H_5-C(=C\text{-ring}\cdot CH(C_6H_5))-N(MgBr)C_6H_5 \xrightarrow{H_2O}$$

$$C_6H_5-CH(C_6H_4\text{-}2\text{-}C_6H_5)-NHC_6H_5 + MgBrOH$$

A similar 1,4-addition has been observed in the case of the corresponding *N*-2-naphthyl compound.[18]

$$2\text{-}C_{10}H_7N=C(C_6H_5)_2 \xrightarrow{C_6H_5MgBr} \xrightarrow{H_2O}$$
$$2\text{-}C_{10}H_7NHCH(C_6H_4\text{-}2\text{-}C_6H_5)C_6H_5 \quad (51\text{–}71\%)$$

It is reported[19] that the monoanil of benzil, on prolonged heating with a large excess of methylmagnesium iodide, gives α-methylbenzoïn in good yield. This has the appearance of a normal addition at the carbonyl double bond, (followed by hydrolysis), but may be more complicated.

$$C_6H_5COC(=NC_6H_5)C_6H_5 \xrightarrow{CH_3MgI}$$
$$CH_3(C_6H_5)C(OMgI)C(=NC_6H_5)C_6H_5 \xrightarrow{2\ H_2O}$$
$$CH_3(C_6H_5)C(OH)COC_6H_5 + C_6H_5NH_2 + MgIOH$$

With ethylmagnesium bromide or iodide or with phenylmagnesium bromide a similar reaction does not occur; the products are benzanilide, benzoic acid, aniline, and benzil (Montagne and Garry, *loc. cit.*[19]).

The dianil of biacetyl is said to undergo "normal" addition with one equivalent of methylmagnesium iodide, ethylmagnesium bromide, *n*-butylmagnesium bromide,[20] or benzylmagnesium chloride[21] in ether solution.

$$CH_3C(=NC_6H_5)C(=NC_6H_5)CH_3 \xrightarrow{RMgX}$$
$$R(CH_3)C[N(MgX)C_6H_5]C(=NC_6H_5)CH_3 \xrightarrow{H_2O}$$
$$R(CH_3)C(NHC_6H_5)C(=NC_6H_5)CH_3 + MgXOH$$

The reaction with *t*-butylmagnesium chloride yields a product of empirical formula $C_{20}H_{26}N_2$ also believed to have the structure resulting from "normal" addition.[22] In contradiction of an earlier report, it is stated that

[18] Gilman and Morton, *J. Am. Chem. Soc.*, *70*, 2514–5 (1948).

[19] Montagne and Garry, *Compt. rend.*, *204*, 1659–61 (1937); *Chem. Abstr.*, *31*, 6223 (1937).

[20] Garry, *Ann. chim.*, [11], *17*, 5–99 (1942).

[21] Montagne and Garry, *Compt. rend.*, *208*, 1734–7 (1939); *Chem. Zentr.*, *1940*,*I*, 859.

[22] Roch-Garry, *Bull. soc. chim.*, [5], *14*, 450–3 (1947).

the dianil of benzil also undergoes "normal" addition with one equivalent of methylmagnesium iodide, as well as with ethylmagnesium iodide (Garry, *loc. cit.*[20]).

When reactions of biacetyl dianil with methylmagnesium iodide, ethylmagnesium bromide, or *n*-butylmagnesium bromide are conducted in boiling benzene, "normal" additions of two equivalents of Grignard reagent take place (Garry, *loc. cit.*[20]).

Ketimines of the type R′R″C=NH apparently suffer no inhibition of the "normal" addition. At any rate it is reported by Rehberg and Henze[23] that methyl- and ethylphenacylcarbinimines add allylmagnesium halides to form the corresponding alkylallylphenacylcarbinamines in 85 and 89 percent yields respectively.

$$R(C_6H_5CO)C{=}NH \xrightarrow{H_2C{=}CHCH_2MgX} R(C_6H_5CO)C{=}NMgX + C_3H_6$$

$$\xrightarrow{H_2C{=}CHCH_2MgX} R(H_2C{=}CHCH_2)(C_6H_5CO)CN(MgBr)_2$$

$$\xrightarrow{H_2O} R(H_2C{=}CHCH_2)(C_6H_5CO)CNH_2 + 2\ MgBrOH$$

Aldazines. Franzen and Deibel[24] report that, when treated with two equivalents of ethylmagnesium bromide, benzaldazine $[(C_6H_5CH{=}N{-})_2]$ is reduced to benzylbenzylidenehydrazine $(C_6H_5CH_2NHN{=}CHC_6H_5)$. This observation has been confirmed by Busch and Fleischman,[25] who observed further that when a considerable excess (*ca.* four equivalents) of Grignard reagent is used, 3,4-diphenylhexane is isolable (in addition to the reduced base). The hydrocarbon is regarded as resulting from decomposition of the presumably unstable monoaddition product.

$$C_2H_5(C_6H_5)CHNHN{=}CHC_6H_5 \rightarrow C_2H_5(C_6H_5)CHN{=}NCH_2C_6H_5$$

$$\rightarrow C_2H_5(C_6H_5)CH\cdot + N_2 + \cdot CH_2C_6H_5$$

$$2\ C_2H_5(C_6H_5)CH\cdot \rightarrow [C_2H_5(C_6H_5)CH{-}]_2$$

When benzaldazine was treated with phenylmagnesium bromide the products isolated were benzylbenzylidenehydrazine, benzhydrylbenzylidenehydrazine, and benzhydrylhydrazine (possibly a hydrolysis fragment of the "normal" monoaddition product).

Benzylmagnesium chloride, with benzaldazine, formed the "normal" addition product $[C_6H_5(C_6H_5CH_2)CHNHN{=}CHC_6H_5]$ and *sym.*-dibenzylhydrazine.

From the reaction of anisaldazine with benzylmagnesium chloride the "normal" addition product $[4\text{-}CH_3OC_6H_4(C_6H_5CH_2)CHNHN{=}CHC_6H_4\text{-}4\text{-}OCH_3]$ was isolated in two (presumably stereoisomeric) forms.

According to Bretschneider *et al.*,[26] anisaldazine, treated with an excess of ethylmagnesium bromide yields a nitrogenous intermediate (m. 76–78°), characterized as $[C_2H_5(4\text{-}CH_3OC_6H_4)CHNH{-}]_2$, which upon

[23] Rehberg and Henze, *J. Am. Chem. Soc.*, 63, 2785–9 (1941).
[24] Franzen and Deibel, *Ber.*, 38, 2716–8 (1905).
[25] Busch and Fleischman, *Ber.*, 43, 740–50 (1910).
[26] Bretschneider, Jonge-Bretschneider, and Ajtai, *Ber.*, 74B, 571–88 (1941).

thermal decomposition loses nitrogen to form a mixture (m. 144°) of the meso (m. 186–187°) and racemic (m. 126–128°) forms of the dimethyl ether of hexestrol.*

The nature of the incidental reduction reactions reported is not clear. A reduction of an aldazine by ethylmagnesium bromide analogous to the ketonic reductions by alkyl Grignard reagents (*q.v.*, Chapter VI) is, of course, conceivable, but such a reduction could not be effected by a benzylmagnesium halide. A reduction analogous to that of the azo compounds (*q.v.*) seems improbable. A magnesious halide reduction brought about by the presence of excess metallic magnesium also appears improbable, and in any case could not occur when the halide employed is a chloride. The reaction invites further study, with note taken of the presence or absence of stilbene and/or bibenzyl, and of the effect of metallic impurities.

Hydramides. According to Busch and Leefhelm,[27] hydrobenzamide [$(C_6H_5CH{=}N)_2CHC_6H_5$], when treated with an excess of alkyl or aralkyl Grignard reagent (CH_3MgI, C_2H_5MgI, n-C_3H_7MgI, $C_6H_5CH_2MgCl$), and then, after ether distillation, heated on a water-bath to frothing, yields a product from which, upon hydrolysis, benzaldehyde, primary amine, and secondary amine may be recovered in various proportions, depending upon the details of experimental procedure. Comparative studies with ethylmagnesium iodide indicate that excess Grignard reagent, together with vigorous (oil-bath) and prolonged heat-treatment, favors the production of secondary amine at the expense of benzaldehyde and primary amine. The reaction is visualized by Busch and Leefhelm as follows:

$$(C_6H_5CH{=}N)_2CHC_6H_5 \xrightarrow{2\ RMgX} [R(C_6H_5)CHN(MgX)]_2CHC_6H_5$$

$$[R(C_6H_5)CHN(MgX)]_2CHC_6H_5 \xrightarrow{RMgX} R(C_6H_5)CHN(MgX)_2 + [R(C_6H_5)CH]_2NMgX$$

$$[R(C_6H_5)CHN(MgX)]_2CHC_6H_5 \xrightarrow{3\ H_2O} C_6H_5CHO + 2\ R(C_6H_5)CHNH_2 + 2\ MgXOH$$

$$R(C_6H_5)CHN(MgX)_2 + [R(C_6H_5)CH]_2NMgX \xrightarrow{3\ H_2O} 3\ MgXOH + R(C_6H_5)CHNH_2 + [R(C_6H_5)CH]_2NH$$

When α-naphthylmagnesium bromide is used the products are primary amine [$C_6H_5(1\text{-}C_{10}H_7)CHNH_2$] and isoämarine (2-phenyl-4,5-*trans*-diphenyl-4,5-dihydroimidazole). The formation of isoämarine is interesting, for it suggests a type of reduction similar to that undergone by the azo compounds (*q.v.*), in which case bi-α-naphthyl would be a probable reaction product.

---

*Undoubtedly a preliminary atmospheric oxidation of the hydrazo to the azo compound is here involved.

[27] Busch and Leefhelm, *J. prakt. Chem.*, [2], 77, 1–20 (1907).

Anishydramide [$(4\text{-}CH_3OC_6H_4CH{=}N)_2CHC_6H_5$], with methyl- and ethylmagnesium iodides and phenylmagnesium bromide, yielded primary amines [$R(4\text{-}CH_3OC_6H_4)CHNH_2$].

Carbodiimides. According to Busch and Hobein,[28] carbodiphenylimide [$(C_6H_5N{=})_2C$] undergoes "normal" monoaddition with Grignard reagents.

$$(C_6H_5N{=})_2C \xrightarrow{RMgX} C_6H_5N{=}CRN(MgX)C_6H_5 \xrightarrow{H_2O} C_6H_5N{=}CRNHC_6H_5 + MgXOH$$

The following Grignard reagents are reported to give the addition product in the percentage yields indicated: methylmagnesium iodide (*ca.* 65), phenylmagnesium bromide (>70), benzylmagnesium chloride (40), α-naphthylmagnesium bromide (60).

Phenylhydrazones and osazones. Busch and Rinck[29] report that the phenylhydrazone of benzaldehyde forms an addition product with methylmagnesium iodide.

$$C_6H_5CH{=}NNHC_6H_5 \xrightarrow{CH_3MgI} \xrightarrow{H_2O} CH_3(C_6H_5)CHNHNHC_6H_5$$

It would appear that the "normal" addition at the carbon-nitrogen double bond is characteristic of the simple phenylhydrazones of aldehydes.[30] Although the present authors have encountered in the literature no statement pro or con, it seems probable that the initial reaction is the replacement of "active" hydrogen, which is then followed by addition.

$$R'CH{=}NNHC_6H_5 \xrightarrow{RMgX} R'CH{=}NN(MgX)C_6H_5 + RH$$

$$\xrightarrow{RMgX} RR'CHN(MgX)N(MgX)C_6H_5$$

$$\xrightarrow{H_2O} RR'CHNHNHC_6H_5 + 2\ MgXOH$$

In addition to a "good yield" of the "normal" product, the reaction between benzaldehyde phenylhydrazone and ethylmagnesium bromide is reported to produce aniline, α-phenylpropylamine, and propiophenone (Grammaticakis, *loc. cit.*[30a]). Symmetrically substituted phenylhydrazines of the type produced by "normal" addition are highly susceptible to "autoxidation" (*cf.* Grammaticakis, *loc. cit.*[30b]).

$$RR'CHNHNHC_6H_5 \xrightarrow{O_2} RR'C{=}NNHC_6H_5 + H_2O$$

and it seems highly probable that the corresponding halomagnesium intermediates would be similarly oxygen-sensitive. Propiophenone is therefore readily accounted for as a hydrolysis fragment of a secondary oxidation product. Aniline and α-phenylpropylamine obviously result from reductive cleavage of the addition product, but whether this is a true Grignard reagent reduction or the consequence of hydrolysis in the presence of residual magnesium is not apparent from the available data.

---

[28] Busch and Hobein, *Ber.*, *40*, 4296–8 (1907).

[29] Busch and Rinck, *Ber.*, *38*, 1761–72 (1905).

[30] Grammaticakis, (*a*) *Compt. rend.*, *202*, 1289–91 (1936); *Chem. Abstr.*, *30*, 4156 (1936); (*b*) *Compt. rend.*, *204*, 1262–3 (1937); *Chem. Abstr.*, *31*, 4954 (1937); (*c*) *Compt. rend.*, *208*, 287–9 (1939); *Chem. Abstr.*, 33, 3778 (1939).

Other secondary products of similar reactions (*cf.* Grammaticakis, *loc. cit.*[30c]) are imines, which are presumed to result from decomposition of the primary addition products.

$$RR'CHNHC_6H_5 \longrightarrow RR'C{=}NH + H_2NC_6H_5$$

The principal reactions of Grignard reagents with *N*-acylphenylhydrazones of benzaldehyde are said to be:

$$\text{(A)}\quad C_6H_5CH{=}NN(COR')C_6H_5 \xrightarrow{RMgX} R(C_6H_5)CHNHN(COR')C_6H_5$$

$$\text{(B)}\quad C_6H_5CH{=}NN(COR')C_6H_5 \xrightarrow{RMgX} C_6H_5CH{=}NNHC_6H_5 + RCOR'$$ [31]

The *N*-acetyl derivative reacts chiefly according to **A** with ethylmagnesium bromide, but almost exclusively according to **B** with methylmagnesium iodide. With phenylmagnesium bromide the primary reaction is B, and in the presence of excess Grignard reagent *sym.*-phenylbenzhydrylhydrazine, benzophenone phenylhydrazone, benzophenone anil, benzophenone imine, aniline, and *sym.*-tetraphenylethane are formed as secondary products.

The *N*-benzoyl and *N*-phenylcarbamyl derivatives undergo chiefly the "normal" addition reaction (**A**) with methylmagnesium iodide and ethyl- and phenylmagnesium bromides.

According to Wuyts and Lacourt,[32] thioacylated hydrazones also react additively.

$$RCSN(CH_3)N{=}CHR \xrightarrow{2\ CH_3MgI} RC(CH_3)(SMgI)N(CH_3)N(MgI)CH(CH_3)R$$

$$\xrightarrow{H_2O} R(CH_3)C(SH)N(CH_3)NHCH(CH_3)R$$

$$(R = C_6H_5,\ 2\text{-}CH_3C_6H_4,\ 4\text{-}CH_3C_6H_4)$$

The *S*-methylated thiohydrazides probably react additively in propyl ether also although the overall reaction has the appearance of a metathetical exchange.[33]

$$RC(SCH_3){=}NN(CH_3)R \xrightarrow{C_2H_5MgBr} R(C_2H_5)C(SCH_3)N(MgBr)N(CH_3)R$$

$$\xrightarrow{H_2O} R(C_2H_5)C{=}NN(CH_3)R + CH_3SH + MgXOH$$

$$(R = C_6H_5,\ 2\text{-}CH_3C_6H_4,\ 4\text{-}CH_3C_6H_4)$$

Diels *et al.*[34] report carbonyl double-bond addition (in preference to N=C double-bond addition) to N-methyl biacetyl phenylhydrazone to the extent of 65–80 percent.

$$CH_3COC(CH_3){=}NN(CH_3)C_6H_5 \xrightarrow{RMgX} HO(CH_3)CRC(CH_3){=}NN(CH_3)C_6H_5$$

$$[RMgX = CH_3MgI\ (75\text{–}80\%);\ C_2H_5MgI\ (65\%);\ C_6H_5MgBr\ (76\%)]$$

---

[31] Grammaticakis, *Compt. rend.*, *208*, 1910–2 (1939); *Chem. Zentr.*, *1940,II*, 335; *Chem. Abstr.*, *33*, 7287 (1939).

[32] Wuyts and Lacourt, *Bull. soc. chim. Belg.*, *45*, 445–53 (1936).

[33] Wuyts and Lacourt, *Bull. soc. chim. Belg.*, *44*, 395–410 (1935).

[34] Diels and ter Meer, *Ber.*, *42*, 1940–5 (1909); Diels and Johlin, *ibid.*, *44*, 403–10 (1911).

The phenylhydrazones of ketones appear to be more or less sterically inhibited so far as "normal" addition of a Grignard reagent at the carbon-nitrogen double bond is concerned.[35] That active hydrogen is replaced was shown by Gilman *et al.*,[36] who treated benzophenone phenylhydrazone successively with phenylmagnesium bromide and diphenylcarbamyl chloride, thus obtaining the corresponding semicarbazide.

$$(C_6H_5)_2C{=}NNHC_6H_5 \xrightarrow{C_6H_5MgBr} (C_6H_5)_2C{=}NN(MgBr)C_6H_5$$
$$\xrightarrow{(C_6H_5)_2NCOCl} (C_6H_5)_2C{=}NN(C_6H_5)CON(C_6H_5)_2$$

Grammaticakis[37] reports benzophenone anil, together with a little benzophenone, aniline, and ammonia, as the principle product of reaction (presumably "forced") between benzophenone phenylhydrazone and ethylmagnesium bromide. Under similar treatment acetophenone and acetone phenylhydrazones yield α-phenyl- and α-methylindoles respectively. To account for the products observed, Grammaticakis proposes an equilibrium between isomeric forms of the hydrazone.

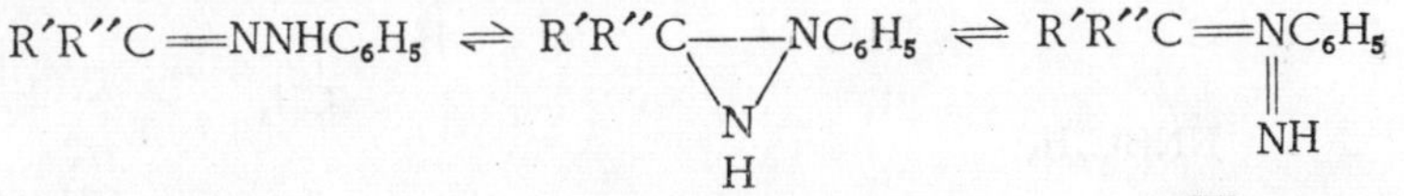
R′R″C=NNHC₆H₅
R′R″C——NC₆H₅
N
H
R′R″C=NC₆H₅
NH

(I) (II) (III)

It is then postulated that form **III** (after "active" hydrogen replacement) undergoes an unusual series of reactions which does some violence to the ordinary concepts of valence.

Other cyclization reactions of phenylhydrazones reported by Grammaticakis[38] are as follows.

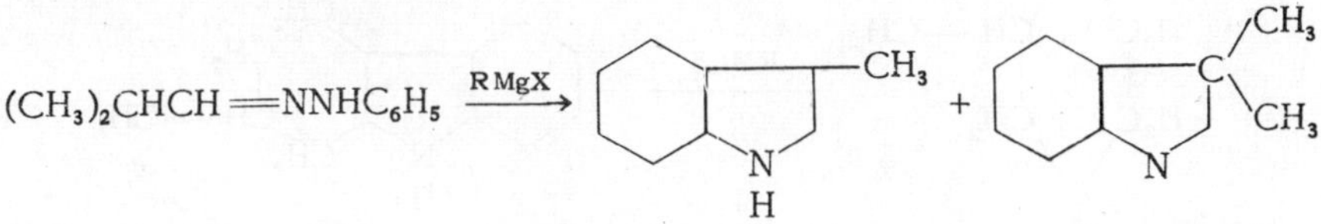
(CH₃)₂CHCH=NNHC₆H₅
RMgX
CH₃
N
H
+
CH₃
C
CH₃
N

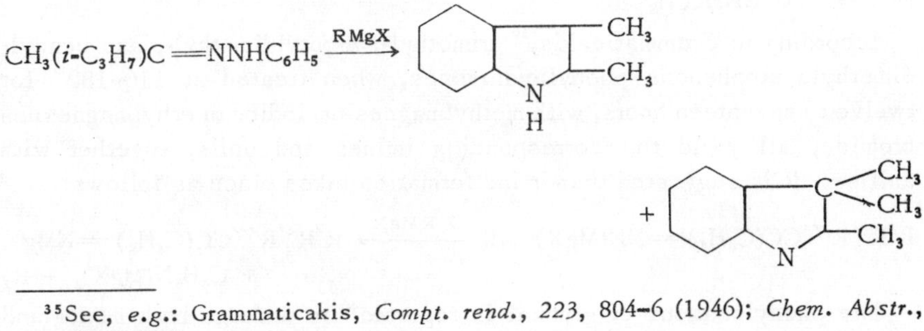
CH₃(i-C₃H₇)C=NNHC₆H₅
RMgX
CH₃
CH₃
N
H
+
CH₃
C
CH₃
CH₃
N

[35] See, *e.g.*: Grammaticakis, *Compt. rend.*, *223*, 804–6 (1946); *Chem. Abstr.*, *41*, 1602 (1947).

[36] Coleman, Gilman, Adams, and Pratt, *J. Org. Chem.*, 3, 99–107 (1938).

[37] Grammaticakis, *Compt. rend.*, *204*, 502–4 (1937); *Chem. Abstr.*, *31*, 3460 (1937).

[38] Grammaticakis, (*a*) *Compt. rend.*, *209*, 317–9 (1939); *Chem. Abstr.*, *34*, 100 (1940); (*b*) *Compt. rend.*, *210*, 569–72 (1940); *Chem. Abstr.*, *34*, 3986 (1940).

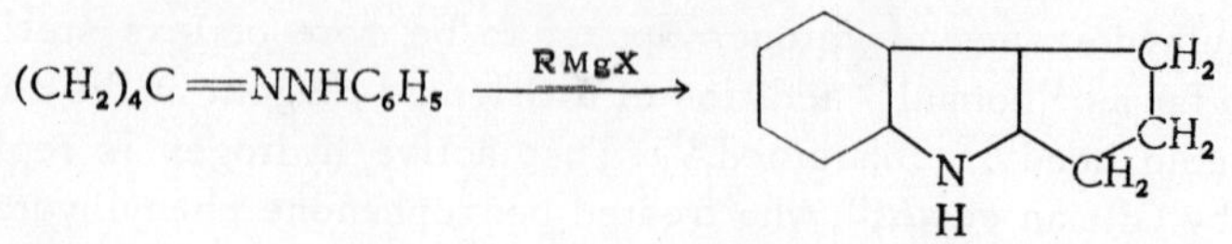

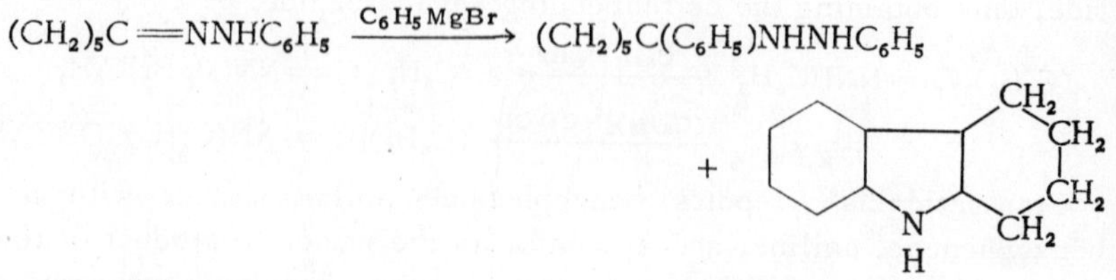

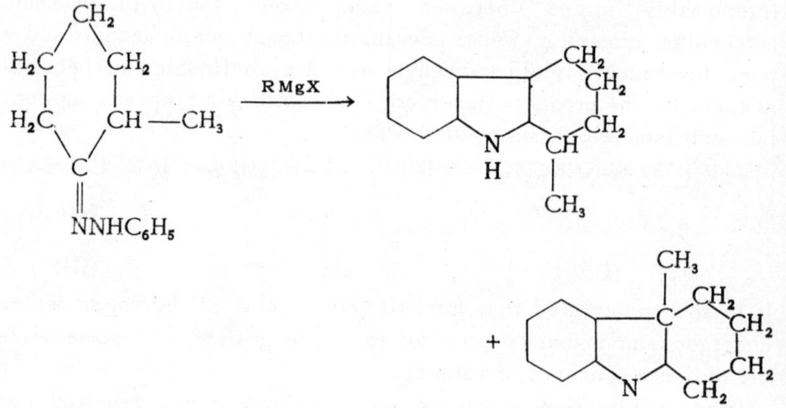

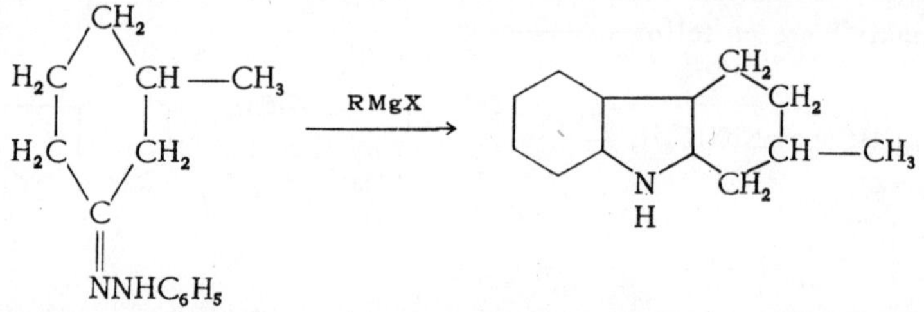

$$(CH_2)_4C{=}NNHC_6H_5 \xrightarrow{RMgX}$$ [tetrahydrocarbazole structure: CH_2, CH_2, CH_2, N–H]

$$(CH_2)_5C{=}NNHC_6H_5 \xrightarrow{C_6H_5MgBr} (CH_2)_5C(C_6H_5)NHNHC_6H_5$$

+ [indole fused to seven-membered ring: CH_2, CH_2, CH_2, CH_2, N–H]

[2-methylcyclohexanone phenylhydrazone: CH_2, H_2C, CH_2, H_2C, $CH{-}CH_3$, $C{=}NNHC_6H_5$] $\xrightarrow{RMgX}$ [tetrahydrocarbazole: CH_2, CH_2, CH_2, $CH{-}CH_3$, N–H]

+ [CH_3, C, CH_2, CH_2, CH_2, CH_2, N]

[3-methylcyclohexanone phenylhydrazone: CH_2, H_2C, $CH{-}CH_3$, H_2C, CH_2, $C{=}NNHC_6H_5$] $\xrightarrow{RMgX}$ [tetrahydrocarbazole: CH_2, CH_2, $CH{-}CH_3$, CH_2, N–H]

According to Grammaticakis,[39] trimethyl-, *n*-butyldimethyl-, and benzyldimethylacetophenone phenylhydrazones, when treated at 116–180° for twelve to seventeen hours, with methylmagnesium iodide or ethylmagnesium bromide, all yield the corresponding imines and anils, together with aniline. It is suggested that imine formation takes place as follows:

$$R'R''R'''CC(C_6H_5){=}NN(MgX)C_6H_5 \xrightarrow{2\ RMgX} R'R''R'''CC(C_6H_5){=}NMgX + C_6H_5N(MgX)_2 + R_2$$

The phenylosazone of glyoxal is reported[40] to undergo both mono- and di-addition with phenylmagnesium bromide.

[39] Grammaticakis, *Compt. rend.*, *206*, 1307–9 (1938); *Chem. Abstr.*, *32*, 5798 (1938).

[40] Grammaticakis, *Compt. rend.*, *208*, 1998–2000 (1939); *Chem. Abstr.*, 33, 7285 (1939).

$$\begin{array}{l} HC{=}NNHC_6H_5 \\ | \\ HC{=}NNHC_6H_5 \end{array} \xrightarrow{C_6H_5MgBr} \underset{(I)}{\begin{array}{l} C_6H_5C{=}NNHC_6H_5 \\ | \\ HC{=}NNHC_6H_5 \end{array}} + \underset{(II)}{\begin{array}{l} C_6H_5C{=}NNHC_6H_5 \\ | \\ C_6H_5CHNHNHC_6H_5 \end{array}}$$

$$+ \underset{(III)}{\begin{array}{l} C_6H_5C{=}NNHC_6H_5 \\ | \\ C_6H_5C{=}NNHC_6H_5 \end{array}} + \underset{(IV)}{C_6H_5CH{=}NNHC_6H_5}$$

Compounds **I**, **II**, and **III** must all result from autoxidation of the addition products, which are highly oxygen-sensitive. *sym.*-Benzylidenephenylhydrazine (**IV**) may be a cleavage-rearrangement fragment of the mono-addition product.

$$\begin{array}{l} C_6H_5CHNHNHC_6H_5 \\ | \\ HC{=}NNHC_6H_5 \end{array} \rightarrow C_6H_5CH{=}NNHC_6H_5 + H_2C{=}NNHC_6H_5$$

Strangely enough it is said that the phenylosazone of phenylglyoxal does not react with methylmagnesium iodide, although it is reported to yield mono-addition products with both ethyl- and phenylmagnesium bromides (Grammaticakis, *loc. cit.*[40]).

$$\begin{array}{l} C_6H_5C{=}NNHC_6H_5 \\ | \\ HC{=}NNHC_6H_5 \end{array} \xrightarrow{C_2H_5MgBr} \begin{array}{l} C_6H_5C{=}NNHC_6H_5 \\ | \\ C_6H_5CHNHNHC_6H_5 \end{array}$$

$$\begin{array}{l} C_6H_5C{=}NNHC_6H_5 \\ | \\ HC{=}NNHC_6H_5 \end{array} \xrightarrow{C_6H_5MgBr} \begin{array}{l} C_6H_5C{=}NNHC_6H_5 \\ | \\ C_6H_5CHNHNHC_6H_5 \end{array} + \begin{array}{l} C_6H_5C{=}NNHC_6H_5 \\ | \\ C_6H_5C{=}NNHC_6H_5 \end{array} \quad (V)$$

The phenylosazone of diphenylglyoxal (**V**) does not condense with methylmagnesium iodide or ethyl- or phenylmagnesium bromides, even when the reaction mixtures are heated for as long as fourteen hours (Grammaticakis, *loc. cit.*[40]).

Oximes and isonitroso compounds. The oximes do not react readily (except as "active hydrogen" compounds) with Grignard reagents in ether solution. All other reactions reported have been carried out under more or less "forced" conditions. For example, Busch and Hobein[41] distilled most of the ether from a solution of phenylmagnesium bromide, and then made portionwise addition of α-benzaldoxime to the warm residual paste. The heat of "active" hydrogen replacement was then sufficient to effect condensation, with the production of *N*-benzhydrylaniline. When the methyl or benzyl ethers of α-benzaldoxime were used, condensation was effected by oil-bath heating, with formation of the same product.

When α-benzaldoxime and its methyl ether were treated analogously with α-naphthylmagnesium bromide, the product isolated was α-naphthylamine.

[41] Busch and Hobein, *Ber.*, *40*, 2096–9 (1907).

Grammaticakis[42] treated benzaldoxime with a large excess (6–10 equiv.) of ethylmagnesium bromide and obtained *N*-3-pentylaniline, together with 1-imino-1-phenylpropane and aniline. Analogous products were obtained when anisaldoxime was treated with excess ethylmagnesium bromide, or with phenylmagnesium bromide.

$$C_6H_5CH{=}NOH \xrightarrow{C_2H_5MgBr} (C_2H_5)_2CHNHC_6H_5 + C_2H_5(C_6H_5)C{=}NH + C_6H_5NH_2$$

$$4\text{-}CH_3OC_6H_4CH{=}NOH \xrightarrow{C_6H_5MgBr} (C_6H_5)_2CHNHC_6H_4\text{-}4\text{-}OCH_3 + C_6H_5(4\text{-}CH_3OC_6H_4)C{=}NH + 4\text{-}CH_3OC_6H_4NH_2$$

Grammaticakis (*loc. cit.*[42]) proposes that aryl aldoximes react with Grignard reagents in the following ways:

$$(1) \quad ArCH{=}NOH \xrightarrow{RMgX} ArNHCHO$$

$$(1a) \quad ArNHCOH \xrightarrow{RMgX} ArNH_2 + RCHO \quad \text{or}$$

$$(1b) \quad ArNHCHO \xrightarrow{2\ RMgX} ArNHCHR_2$$

$$(2) \quad ArCH{=}NOH \xrightarrow{RMgX} ArCN$$

$$(2a) \quad ArCN \xrightarrow{RMgX} ArRCH{=}NH$$

It scarcely seems necessary to postulate an *N*-arylated formamide as an intermediate, although some rearrangement of the Beckmann type is indicated by the major product of the reaction of benzaldoxime with ethylmagnesium bromide, for instance. Following a scheme suggested to account for the acid-catalyzed Beckmann rearrangement of oximes,[43] one might substitute for the first series of reactions above proposed:

$$(1) \quad ArCH{=}NOMgX \xrightarrow{RMgX} [ArCH{=}\underset{MgX}{\ddot{N}}OMgX]^+R^- \xrightarrow{-(XMg)_2O} [ArCH{=}N:]^+R^- \rightarrow RCH{=}NAr$$

$$(1a) \quad RCH{=}NAr \xrightarrow{H_2O} RCHO + ArNH_2$$

$$(1b) \quad RCH{=}NAr \xrightarrow{RMgX} R_2CHN(MgX)Ar \xrightarrow{H_2O} R_2CHNHAr + MgXOH$$

Stieglitz and Maver[44] attempted the preparation of a hydroxylamine derivative by treating acetophenone oxime with phenylmagnesium bromide in the hope of effecting a "normal" addition at the carbon-nitrogen double bond, and at first believed that they had succeeded. It was subsequently found (Stieglitz and Cole[45]), however, that the product of this reaction is

---

[42] Grammaticakis, *Compt. rend.*, *210*, 716–8 (1940); *Chem. Abstr.*, *34*, 5062 (1940).

[43] See, *e.g.*: Wallis, Gilman's "Organic Chemistry," John Wiley and Sons, Inc., New York, 2nd edition, *1943*, p. 984.

[44] Maver, Dissertation, University of Chicago, *1926*.

[45] Cole, Dissertation, University of Chicago, *1929*.

in fact 1,1-diphenyl-2-aminoëthanol. The similar reactions of propiophenone and desoxybenzoïn oximes were studied (under Stieglitz) by Sturgeon[46] and Campbell,[47] respectively, and analogous products were obtained. Similar results are reported by Campbell *et al.*[48]

$$Ar(RCH_2)C{=}NOH \xrightarrow{C_6H_5MgBr} Ar(C_6H_5)C(OH)CH(NH_2)R$$

Campbell (*loc. cit.*[47]) had suggested, without at the time being able to offer proof, that the rather unusual nitrogen rearrangement involved takes place through ethyleneimine formation. Hoch,[49] however, isolated both 1,1-diphenyl-1,2-iminopropane and 1,1-diphenyl-2-aminopropanol as products of the reaction of propiophenone oxime with phenylmagnesium bromide. When ethylmagnesium bromide was used, the ethyleneimine (2,3-imino-3-phenylpentane) was the sole product. Campbell *et al.*[50] subsequently showed that the product obtained depends principally on the method of isolation. When the reaction mixture is hydrolyzed at low temperature (*ca.* 0°) with dilute hydrochloric acid, or, better still, iced ammonium chloride solution, the ethyleneimine is obtained; when hydrolysis is carried out at higher temperatures with strongly acidic solutions the amino alcohol is obtained.

$$Ar(R'CH_2)C{=}NOMgX \xrightarrow{RMgX} ArC(R)(-N(MgX)(OMgX))-CH(H)R' \xrightarrow{-MgXOH} RArC\overset{N-MgX}{—}CHR'$$

$$\xrightarrow{H_2O} RArC\overset{N-H}{—}CHR' \xrightarrow{H_2O} RArC(OH)CH(NH_2)R'$$

Campbell[51] has also shown that the aliphatic Grignard reagents are similar in their behavior to the aryl reagents.

When $R'CH_2$ is replaced by an aryl or tertiary alkyl group this type of reaction is, of course, impossible. According to Hoch[52] the principal reaction in such cases is usually a reduction of the oxime to the imine, which may be isolated as such or as the corresponding ketone, depending upon experimental conditions. The mechanism of the reduction is unknown, but the stoichiometric requirements would be met by some such scheme as the following:

---

[46] Sturgeon, Dissertation, University of Chicago, *1929*.

[47] Campbell, Dissertation, University of Chicago, *1932*.

[48] (*a*) Campbell and McKenna, *J. Org. Chem.*, 4, 198–205 (1939); (*b*) Campbell, Campbell, and Chaput, *ibid.*, 8, 99–102 (1943).

[49] Hoch, *Compt. rend.*, *198*, 1865–8 (1934); *Chem. Abstr.*, *28*, 4711 (1934).

[50] Campbell, Campbell, McKenna, and Chaput, *J. Org. Chem.*, 8, 103–9 (1943).

[51] Campbell, Campbell, Hess, and Schaffner, *J. Org. Chem.*, 9, 184–6 (1944).

[52] Hoch (*a*) *Compt. rend.*, *203*, 799–801 (1936); *Chem. Abstr.*, *31*, 1786 (1937); (*b*) *Compt. rend.*, *204*, 358–60 (1937); *Chem. Abstr.*, *31*, 3026 (1937).

$$R'(CH_3)_2CC(C_6H_5){=}N{-}OMgX \xrightarrow{RMgX} R'(CH_3)_2CC(C_6H_5){=}\overset{\cdot\cdot}{N}{-}OMgX \quad (\text{N coordinated to } Mg \text{ bearing } X \text{ and } R)$$

$$\xrightarrow{RMgX} R'(CH_3)_2CC(C_6H_5){=}NMgX + (XMg)_2O + R_2 \ [\text{or } R_{(+H)} + R_{(-H)}]$$

($R' = t\text{-}C_4H_9$; $RMgX = C_2H_5MgBr$, C_6H_5MgBr, $4\text{-}CH_3C_6H_4MgBr$: $R' = C_6H_5CH_2$; $RMgX = CH_3MgI$, C_6H_5MgBr Hoch, *loc. cit.*[52b])

From the products of a similar reduction of diphenylhydroxylamine by phenylmagnesium bromide, Gilman and McCracken[53] were able to isolate 71 percent of the theoretical yield of biphenyl. The amount of phenol detectable did not exceed that in a blank control experiment.

Products isolated in some other experiments indicate that a rearrangement of the Beckman type may compete with the simple reduction. However, it is scarcely necessary to assume, as Hoch (*loc. cit.*[52a]) has done, that benzanilide is an intermediate in the reaction of benzophenone oxime with methylmagnesium iodide. A scheme similar to that suggested for the benzaldoxime rearrangement would suffice to account for the acetophenone and aniline isolated after hydrolysis. The trace of benzophenone anil detected might well result from exchange of the imine with acetophenone anil rather than from reaction with the free aniline which would result from reaction of benzanilide with the Grignard reagent. Moreover, it is difficult to see how acetophenone could survive as such in the presence of excess Grignard reagent.

Revised in accordance with the foregoing comments, Hoch's reaction scheme becomes:

$$(1)\quad (C_6H_5)_2C{=}NOMgI \xrightarrow{CH_3MgI} CH_3(C_6H_5)C{=}NC_6H_5 \xrightarrow{H_2O} CH_3COC_6H_5{}^* + C_6H_5NH_2{}^*$$

$$(2)\quad (C_6H_5)_2C{=}NOMgI \xrightarrow{2\,CH_3MgI} (C_6H_5)_2C{=}NMgI \xrightarrow{CH_3(C_6H_5)C{=}NC_6H_5}$$

$$(C_6H_5)_2C{=}NC_6H_5{}^* + CH_3(C_6H_5)C{=}NMg \xrightarrow{H_2O}$$

$$(C_6H_5)_2CO^* + C_6H_5NH_2{}^* + CH_3COC_6H_5{}^* + NH_3$$

The products starred were isolated by Hoch. In addition he obtained an unidentified base to which he assigned the empirical formula $(C_{14}H_{11}N)_2$.

A similar Beckmann-type rearrangement would make benzophenone anil an intermediate in the reaction of phenylmagnesium bromide with benzophenone oxime, and would thus account for the *o*-phenylbenzhydrylaniline isolated by Hoch (*loc. cit.*[52a]). (*Cf.* Gilman *et al.*, *loc. cit.*[53]) It is perhaps unfortunate that no one has seen fit to carry out this reaction with an aryl Grignard reagent other than phenylmagnesium bromide. With *p*-tolylmagnesium bromide, for example, the product should be

[53] Gilman and McCracken, *J. Am. Chem. Soc.*, *49*, 1052–61 (1927).

$C_6H_5NH—CH—C_6H_5$ (cyclohexyl ring bearing C_6H_4-4-CH_3 and CH_3) or $C_6H_5NH—CH—C_6H_4$-4-CH_3 (cyclohexyl ring bearing C_6H_4-4-CH_3)

or a mixture of the two.

As might be expected, under mild reaction conditions the isonitroso compounds react as ketones (as well as "active" hydrogen compounds). Some typical reactions reported are as follows.

$$CH_3COC(=NOR)CH_3 \xrightarrow{CH_3MgI} \xrightarrow{H_2O} (CH_3)_2C(OH)C(=NOR)CH_3$$

($R = CH_3$, $C_6H_5CH_2$; yields 60, 75%; Diels[54])

$$C_6H_5COCH=NOH \xrightarrow{2\ C_6H_5MgBr} \xrightarrow{H_2O} (C_6H_5)_2C(OH)CH=NOH$$

(75%, Orékhoff,[55] Chang[56])

$$\beta\text{-}C_6H_5COC(=NOH)C_6H_5 \xrightarrow{2\ C_6H_5MgBr} \xrightarrow{H_2O} (C_6H_5)_2C(OH)C(=NOH)C_6H_5$$

(65%, Orékhoff[55])

$$CH_3COCH=NOH \xrightarrow{2\ n\text{-}C_4H_9MgX} \xrightarrow{H_2O} CH_3(n\text{-}C_4H_9)C(OH)CH=NOH$$

(Freon[57])

$$CH_3COC(=NOH)CH_3 \xrightarrow{2\ RMgX} \xrightarrow{H_2O} R(CH_3)C(OH)C(=NOH)CH_3$$

($R = CH_3$, n-C_4H_9; Freon[57])

Isonitrosocamphor is reported (Forster[58]) to yield with methylmagnesium iodide a compound of the empirical formula $C_{11}H_{19}O_2N$ (m. 180°), and isonitrosothiocamphor with the same Grignard reagent (Sen[59]), an orange liquid of empirical formula $C_{11}H_{17}NS$.

Under mild conditions dioximes react as "active" hydrogen compounds (Longo[60]).

$$RC(=NOH)C(=NOH)R' \xrightarrow{2\ R''MgX} RC(=NOMgX)C(=NOMgX)R' + 2\ R''H$$

$$\alpha\text{- or } \beta\text{-}C_6H_5C(=NOH)C(=NOH)NH_2 \xrightarrow{3\ CH_3MgI} 3\ CH_4 + \alpha\text{- or } \beta\text{-}C_6H_5C(=NOMgI)C(=NOMgI)NHMgI$$

---

[54] Diels and ter Meer, *Ber.*, *42*, 1940–5 (1909).

[55] Orékhoff and Tiffeneau, *Bull. soc. chim.*, [4], *41*, 839–43 (1927).

[56] Chang and Tseng, *Trans. Sci. Soc. China*, 7, 225–32 (1932); *Chem. Abstr.*, *26*, 5555 (1932).

[57] Freon, *Compt. rend.*, *200*, 464–6 (1935); *Chem. Abstr.*, *29*, 2918 (1935).

[58] Forster, *Proc. Chem. Soc.*, *20*, 207 (1904).

[59] Sen, *J. Indian Chem. Soc.*, *15*, 537–42 (1938); *Chem. Abstr.*, 33, 2506 (1939).

[60] Longo, *Gazz. chim. ital.*, *65*, 84–8 (1935); *Chem. Abstr.*, *29*, 3983 (1935).

$$\alpha\text{- or } \beta\text{-4-}CH_3C_6H_4C(=NOH)C(=NOH)NH_2 \xrightarrow{3\ CH_3MgI}$$
$$3\ CH_4 + \alpha\text{- or } \beta\text{-4-}CH_3C_6H_4C(=NOMgI)C(=NOMgI)NHMgI$$

It is of some interest that ethylmagnesium bromide is reported to effect a partial conversion of the *syn* to the *anti* form of 4-$BrC_6H_4C(=NOH)CH=CHC_6H_5$.[61]

Semicarbazones. According to Biquard[62] the semicarbazone of acetophenone, when treated with an excess (ten molecular equivalents) of ethylmagnesium bromide undergoes replacement of three "active" hydrogen atoms in the cold, and of a fourth upon heating. The product obtained in 60 to 70 percent yield is assigned the structure of 6-phenyl-1,4-dihydro-1,2,4-triazine. It is postulated that the semicarbazone reacts in a form isomeric with that of the conventional formulation, as follows:

$$H_2C=C(C_6H_5)NHNHC(OH)=NH \xrightarrow{4\ C_2H_5MgBr}$$
$$H_2C=C(C_6H_5)N(MgBr)N(MgBr)C(OMgBr)=NMgBr \xrightarrow{-\ (BrMg)_2O}$$

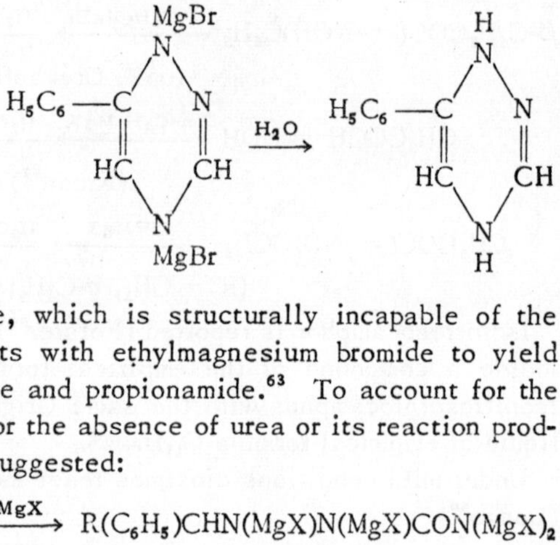

```
          MgBr                              H
           N                                N
          / \                              / \
H5C6 —C     N          H2O     H5C6 —C     N
       ||    ||        ——→            ||    ||
      HC     CH                      HC     CH
         \  /                           \  /
          N                               N
         MgBr                             H
```

Benzaldehyde semicarbazone, which is structurally incapable of the same type of isomerism, reacts with ethylmagnesium bromide to yield (after hydrolysis) propiophenone and propionamide.[63] To account for the products isolated, as well as for the absence of urea or its reaction products, the following scheme is suggested:

$$C_6H_5CH=NNHCON(MgX)_2 \xrightarrow{2\ RMgX} R(C_6H_5)CHN(MgX)N(MgX)CON(MgX)_2$$
$$\xrightarrow{RMgX} R(C_6H_5)C=NMgX + HN(MgX)_2 + RCON(MgX)_2$$

Biquard found that although both urea and phenylurea react with Grignard reagents, in no case is an amide among the products of the reaction.

This study was further extended to the semicarbazone of *n*-butyldimethylacetophenone.[64] From the reaction with ethylmagnesium bromide were obtained 4,4-dimethyl-3-octanone (40 percent), benzene, and a small quantity of propiophenone. The reaction scheme proposed is:

---

[61] Blatt and Stone, *J. Am. Chem. Soc.*, 53, 4134–49 (1931).
[62] Biquard, *Bull. soc. chim.*, [5], 3, 656–65 (1936).
[63] Biquard, *Bull. soc. chim.*, [5], 3, 666–8 (1936).
[64] Biquard, *Bull. soc. chim.*, [5], 5, 207–15 (1938).

$$n\text{-}C_4H_9(CH_3)_2CC(C_6H_5)=NNHCONH_2 \xrightarrow{4\ C_2H_5MgBr}$$
$$n\text{-}C_4H_9(CH_3)_2CC(C_2H_5)(C_6H_5)N(MgBr)N(MgBr)CON(MgBr)_2 \quad (A)$$

$$A \rightarrow C_6H_5MgBr + n\text{-}C_4H_9(CH_3)_2CC(C_2H_5)=NN(MgBr)CON(MgBr)_2 \quad (B)$$

$$A \rightarrow n\text{-}C_4H_9(CH_3)_2CMgBr + C_2H_5(C_6H_5)C=NN(MgBr)CON(MgBr)_2 \quad (C)$$

$$B \xrightarrow{2\ C_2H_5MgBr} n\text{-}C_4H_9(CH_3)_2C(C_2H_5)=NMgBr + C_2H_5N(MgBr)_2 + C_2H_5CON(MgBr)_2$$

$$C \xrightarrow{2\ C_2H_5MgBr} C_2H_5(C_6H_5)C=NMgBr + C_2H_5N(MgBr)_2 + C_2H_5CON(MgBr)_2$$

According to Gilman *et al.*[65] benzophenone 4,4-diphenylsemicarbazone reacts with phenylmagnesium bromide, undergoing replacement of one "active" hydrogen atom, and forming an intermediate which can be benzylated with benzyl chloride to yield benzophenone 2-benzyl-4,4-diphenylsemicarbazone.

$$(C_6H_5)_2C=NNHCON(C_6H_5)_2 \xrightarrow{C_6H_5MgBr} (C_6H_5)_2C=NN(MgBr)CON(C_6H_5)_2$$
$$\xrightarrow{C_6H_5CH_2Cl} (C_6H_5)_2C=NN(CH_2C_6H_5)CON(C_6H_5)_2$$

"Normal" N=C double-bond additions of Grignard reagents to the phenylsemicarbazones of aldehydes to give better than 90 percent yields of addition products are reported by Grammaticakis.[66]

$$C_6H_5CH=NNHCONHC_6H_5 \xrightarrow{C_2H_5MgBr} C_2H_5(C_6H_5)CHNHNHCONHC_6H_5$$

$$C_2H_5CH=NNHCONHC_6H_5 \xrightarrow{C_6H_5MgBr} C_2H_5(C_6H_5)CHNHNHCONHC_6H_5$$

$$C_6H_5CH=NNHCONHC_6H_5 \xrightarrow{C_6H_5MgBr} (C_6H_5)_2CHNHNHCONHC_6H_5$$

$$4\text{-}CH_3OC_6H_4CH=NNHCONHC_6H_5 \xrightarrow{C_2H_5MgBr} C_2H_5(4\text{-}CH_3OC_6H_4)CHNHNHCONHC_6H_5$$

$$C_2H_5CH=NNHCONHC_6H_5 \xrightarrow{4\text{-}CH_3OC_6H_4MgBr} C_2H_5(4\text{-}CH_3OC_6H_4)CHNHNHCONHC_6H_5$$

$$4\text{-}CH_3OC_6H_4CH=NNHCONHC_6H_5 \xrightarrow{C_6H_5MgBr} C_6H_5(4\text{-}CH_3OC_6H_4)CHNHNHCONHC_6H_5$$

DIAZO COMPOUNDS

Forster and Cardwell[67] reported that diazocamphor, when treated with methylmagnesium iodide, yields camphorquinone α-methylhydrazone.

[65] Coleman, Gilman, Adams, and Pratt, *J. Org. Chem.*, *3*, 99–107 (1938).

[66] Grammaticakis, *Compt. rend.*, *228*, 323–4 (1949); *Chem. Abstr.*, *43*, 3901 (1949).

[67] Forster and Cardwell, *J. Chem. Soc.*, *103*, 861–70 (1913).

Phenylmagnesium bromide treatment yields the corresponding phenylhydrazone. Diazodeoxybenzoin undergoes comparable reactions to yield the respective benzil hydrazones.

$$C_8H_{14}\left\langle\begin{matrix}CN_2\\ |\\ CO\end{matrix}\right. \xrightarrow{RMgX} \xrightarrow{H_2O} C_8H_{14}\left\langle\begin{matrix}C{=}NNHR\\ |\\ CO\end{matrix}\right.$$

$$\begin{matrix}C_6H_5{-}CN_2\\ |\\ C_6H_5{-}CO\end{matrix} \xrightarrow{RMgX} \xrightarrow{H_2O} \begin{matrix}C_6H_5{-}C{=}NNHR\\ |\\ C_6H_5{-}CO\end{matrix}$$

Zerner,[68] approximately simultaneously, investigated the reactions of several Grignard reagents with diazoacetic ester and diazomethane.

$$H_5C_2O_2CCHN_2 \xrightarrow{CH_3MgI} \xrightarrow{H_2O} H_5C_2O_2CCH{=}NNHCH_3 \ (ca.\ 30\%)$$

$$H_5C_2O_2CCHN_2\ (10\ g.) \xrightarrow{C_6H_5MgBr} \xrightarrow{H_2O} (C_6H_5)_2C(OH)CH{=}NNHC_6H_5\ (2\ g.)$$

$$H_2CN_2 \xrightarrow{C_6H_5CH_2MgCl} \xrightarrow{H_2O} C_8H_{10}N_2\ (\text{consistent with } H_2C{=}NNHCH_2C_6H_5)$$

$$H_2CN_2 \xrightarrow[(19\ g.\ C_6H_5Br)]{C_6H_5MgBr} \xrightarrow{H_2O} C_6H_5CH{=}NNHC_6H_5\ (1.4\text{–}1.6\ g.)$$

The series of reactions proposed to account for the production of benzaldehyde phenylhydrazone is consistent with the known reactions of diazo compounds and hydrazones (*q.v.*), although, as has been pointed out previously, autoxidation might very well take place prior to, as well as subsequent to, hydrolysis.

$$H_2CN_2 \xrightarrow{C_6H_5MgBr} H_2C{=}NN(MgBr)C_6H_5 \xrightarrow{C_6H_5MgBr}$$

$$C_6H_5CH_2N(MgBr)N(MgBr)C_6H_5 \xrightarrow{H_2O}$$

$$C_6H_5CH_2NHNHC_6H_5 \xrightarrow{O_2} C_6H_5CH{=}NNHC_6H_5$$

Maury[69] obtained benzaldehyde phenyl- and benzylhydrazones in "good yields" by treatment of phenyldiazomethane with phenylmagnesium bromide and benzylmagnesium chloride, respectively.

Analogous reactions of diphenyldiazomethane are reported by Gilman *et al.*[70]

$$(C_6H_5)_2CN_2\ (13.2\ g.) \xrightarrow{CH_3MgI} (C_6H_5)_2C{=}NNHCH_3\ (12\ g.,\ crude)$$

$$(C_6H_5)_2CN_2 \xrightarrow{C_6H_5MgBr} (C_6H_5)_2C{=}NNHC_6H_5\ (70\%)$$

$$(C_6H_5)_2CN_2\ (16\ g.) \xrightarrow{C_6H_5CH_2MgCl} (C_6H_5)_2C{=}NNHCH_2C_6H_5\ (18.2\ g.,\ crude)$$

With diazomethane and methylmagnesium iodide or bromide, or with ethylmagnesium iodide, the same investigators obtained only unidentified

[68] Zerner, *Monatsh.*, *34*, 1609–30, 1631–7 (1913); *Chem. Zentr.*, *1914,I*, 522, 524.

[69] Maury, as cited by Coleman, Gilman, Adams, and Pratt, *J. Org. Chem.*, 3, ftnote, p. 103 (1938).

[70] Coleman, Gilman, Adams, and Pratt, *J. Org. Chem.*, 3, 99–107 (1938).

gaseous products. From the reaction of phenylmagnesium bromide with diazomethane they were able to isolate a 48 percent yield of the 1-phenyl-2-benzylhydrazine which was presumably the predecessor of Zerner's phenylhydrazone. *n*-Butylmagnesium bromide and benzylmagnesium chloride both gave reduction as well as condensation.

$$H_2CN_2 \xrightarrow{n\text{-}C_4H_9MgBr} H_3CNHNH\text{-}n\text{-}C_4H_9\ (53\%)$$

$$H_2CN_2 \xrightarrow{C_6H_5CH_2MgCl} H_3CNHNHCH_2C_6H_5$$

The nature of the reduction reactions is undetermined, but in the case of benzylmagnesium chloride at least it must obviously be of a type different from that of the Grignard reagent reduction of ketones (*q.v.*).

The choice between the classical cyclic formulation for diazomethane and any alternative can scarcely be made on purely chemical grounds. The results of electron-diffraction studies, however, are strongly indicative of a linear configuration, and Boersch[71] has suggested a resonance hybrid of canonical forms **A** and **B**, to which might perhaps be added the further form **C**.

$$H_2C{=}\overset{\oplus}{N}{=}\overset{\ominus}{\underset{\cdot\cdot}{N}}: \leftrightarrow H_2\overset{\ominus}{C}{-}\overset{\oplus}{N}{\equiv}N: \leftrightarrow H_2C{=}\underset{\cdot\cdot}{N}{-}\underset{\cdot\cdot}{N}:$$

(A) (B) (C)

Whatever the relative contributions of the respective resonance forms to the hybrid structure, there is on the terminal nitrogen atom at least one electron-pair available for complex formation with the Grignard reagent. The simplest possibility that suggests itself with regard to mechanism is that a complex of this kind rearranges (as is probably the case with the nitrile-Grignard reagent complexes, *q.v.*).

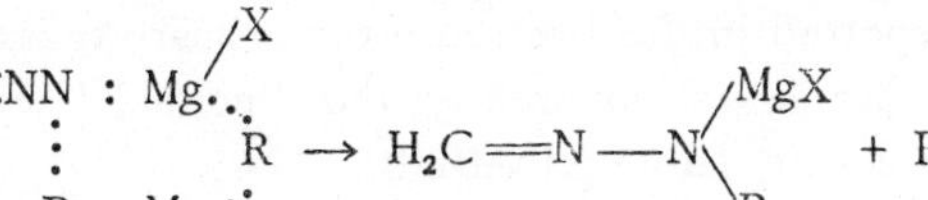

$$H_2CNN:Mg\langle^{X}_{R} \rightarrow H_2C{=}N{-}\dot{N}\langle^{MgX}_{R}$$

There is also the possibility that the complex originally formed reacts with a second molecule of Grignard reagent (as is probably the case in the ketone additions, *q.v.*).

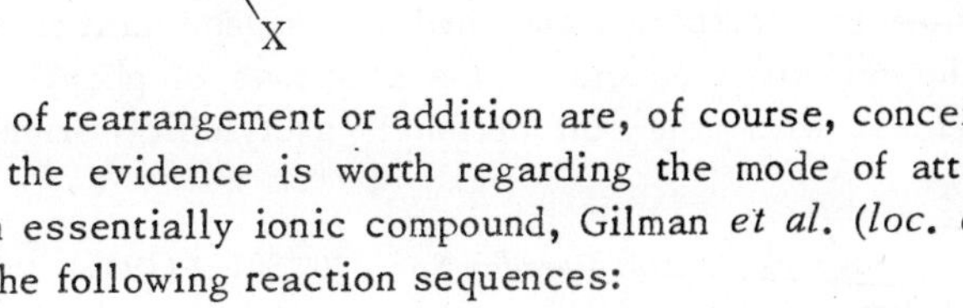

$$\begin{matrix} H_2CNN : Mg^{/X}\cdot. & \\ \vdots \qquad\qquad R & \rightarrow H_2C{=}N{-}N\langle^{MgX}_{R} \quad + RMgX \\ R\cdots Mg\cdot\cdot_{\backslash X} & \end{matrix}$$

Other modes of rearrangement or addition are, of course, conceivable.

For what the evidence is worth regarding the mode of attachment of groups in an essentially ionic compound, Gilman *et al.* (*loc. cit.*[70]) have carried out the following reaction sequences:

[71] Boersch, *Monatsh.*, 65, 311–37 (1935). See also: Ramsay, *J. Chem. Phys.*, 17, 666–7 (1949).

$$(C_6H_5)_2CN_2 \xrightarrow{C_6H_5MgBr} \xrightarrow{(C_6H_5)_2NCOCl} (C_6H_5)_2C{=}NN(C_6H_5)CON(C_6H_5)_2$$

$$(C_6H_5)_2C{=}NNHC_6H_5 \xrightarrow{C_6H_5MgBr} \xrightarrow{(C_6H_5)_2NCOCl} (C_6H_5)_2C{=}NN(C_6H_5)CON(C_6H_5)_2$$

AZIDES

Despite chemical and other arguments to the contrary, the organic azides probably have a linear structure,[72] which may be regarded as a resonance hybrid:

$$R{-}\ddot{N}{=}\overset{\oplus}{N}{=}\overset{\ominus}{\ddot{N}}: \leftrightarrow R{-}\overset{\ominus}{\ddot{N}}{-}\overset{\oplus}{N}{\equiv}N: \leftrightarrow R{-}\ddot{N}{=}\ddot{N}{-}\ddot{N}:$$

When the cyclic azide formula was in vogue it was the custom to formulate the reaction of an azide with a Grignard reagent as a ring-opening process:

$$\begin{matrix} & & N \\ R{-}N & \diagup & \| \\ \vdots & & N \\ X{-}Mg & \vdots & \\ & & R' \end{matrix} \rightarrow RN(MgX)N{=}NR' \xrightarrow{H_2O} RNHN{=}NR'$$

Since it is well-known, however, that the resultant triazenes are tautomeric, there would seem to be no valid *a priori* objection to regarding these reactions as similar in all essential respects to the corresponding reactions of diazo compounds (*q.v.*)

$$RN_3 \xrightarrow{R'MgX} RN{=}NN(MgX)R' \xrightarrow{H_2O} RN{=}NNHR' \rightleftharpoons RNHN{=}NR'$$

In fact it had been early observed by Dimroth[73] that the triazene obtained from the reaction of phenyl azide with benzylmagnesium chloride is identical with that obtained from the reaction of benzyl azide with phenylmagnesium bromide.

$$C_6H_5N_3 \xrightarrow{C_6H_5CH_2MgCl} \xrightarrow{H_2O} C_6H_5N{=}NNHCH_2C_6H_5$$

$$\rightleftharpoons$$

$$C_6H_5CH_2N_3 \xrightarrow{C_6H_5MgBr} \xrightarrow{H_2O} C_6H_5CH_2N{=}NNHC_6H_5$$

In all cases reported in the literature the primary reaction of a Grignard reagent with an azide is apparently the "normal" triazene formation. Data are summarized in Table XIX-III.

Kleinfeller[74] reports some interesting secondary products apparently resulting from the rearrangement, hydrolysis, and further reaction with azide of the primary products of the reactions of phenyl and *p*-bromophenyl azides with the bifunctional acetylenic Grignard reagent, $(\equiv CMgBr)_2$.

---

[72] See, *e.g.*, Sidgwick, *Trans. Faraday Soc.*, *30*, 801–4 (1945).

[73] Dimroth, *Ber.*, *38*, 670–88 (1905).

[74] (*a*) Kleinfeller, *J. prakt. Chem.*, [2], *119*, 61–73 (1929); (*b*) Kleinfeller and Bonig, *ibid.*, [2], *132*, 175–99 (1932).

TABLE XIX-III

TRIAZENE (RN_3HR') FORMATION BY REACTION OF AZIDES (RN_3) WITH GRIGNARD REAGENTS ($R'MgX$)

RN_3	$R'MgX$	Yield (%) RN_3HR'	Ref.
CH_3N_3	CH_3MgI	22*	3
4-$BrC_6H_4N_3$	CH_3MgI	—	4
4-$BrC_6H_4N_3$	$(\equiv CMgBr)_2$	—	5,6
C_6H_4-1,3-$(N_3)_2$	$(\equiv CMgBr)_2$	—	5
C_6H_4-1,3-$(N_3)_2$	C_2H_5MgBr	58	5
C_6H_4-1,3-$(N_3)_2$	C_6H_5MgBr	—	5
$C_6H_5N_3$	CH_3MgI	75	1,2
$C_6H_5N_3$	$(\equiv CMgBr)_2$	—	5,6
$C_6H_5N_3$	C_2H_5MgI	55	2
$C_6H_5N_3$	$H_2C{=}CHCH_2MgBr$	100 (crude)	7
$C_6H_5N_3$	C_6H_5MgBr	71	1
$C_6H_5N_3$	$C_6H_5CH_2MgCl$	"Good"	2
$C_6H_5N_3$	4-$CH_3C_6H_4MgBr$	—	4
$C_6H_5N_3$	4-$C_2H_5OC_6H_4MgBr$	—	4
$C_6H_5N_3$	1-$C_{10}H_7MgBr$	—	4
$C_6H_5CH_2N_3$	CH_3MgI	88†	2
$C_6H_5CH_2N_3$	C_6H_5MgBr	"Good"	2
4-$CH_3C_6H_4N_3$	CH_3MgI	—	4
4-$C_2H_5OC_6H_4N_3$	CH_3MgI	—	4
4-$C_2H_5OC_6H_4N_3$	C_6H_5MgBr	—	4
1-$C_{10}H_7N_3$	C_6H_5MgBr	—	4

* Isolated as cuprous salt, $Cu^+(CH_3N_3CH_3)^-$, for which stated yield is reported.
† Isolated as silver salt, $Ag^+(C_6H_5N_3CH_3)^-$, for which stated yield is reported.

REFERENCES FOR TABLE XIX-III

(*1*) Dimroth, *Ber.*, *36*, 909–13 (1903).
(*2*) Dimroth, *Ber.*, *38*, 670–88 (1905).
(*3*) Dimroth, *Ber.*, *39*, 3905–12 (1905).
(*4*) Dimroth, Eble, and Gruhl, *Ber.*, *40*, 2390–401 (1907).
(*5*) Kleinfeller, *J. prakt. Chem.*, [2], *119*, 61–73 (1929).
(*6*) Kleinfeller and Bönig, *J. prakt. Chem.*, [2], *132*, 175–99 (1932).
(*7*) Pochinok, *J. Gen. Chem.* (U.S.S.R.), *16*, 1303–5 (1946); *Chem. Abstr.*, *41*, 3066 (1947).

Berthot[74.1] reports reactions of phenylmagnesium bromide with various acyl and carbalkoxy azides as follows:

$$C_6H_5CON_3 + C_6H_5MgBr \rightarrow C_6H_5CONHN{=}NC_6H_5$$

$$\underset{(8.6\ g.)}{H_2NCON_3} + \underset{(15.7\ g.\ C_6H_5Br)}{C_6H_5MgBr} \rightarrow \underset{(2.5\text{–}3.0\ g.)}{H_2NCONHN{=}NC_6H_5}$$

$$C_6H_5NHCON_3 + C_6H_5MgBr \rightarrow C_6H_5NHCOC_6H_5 + MgBrN_3$$

$$H_2CONHNHCON_3 + C_6H_5MgBr \rightarrow (C_6H_5CON{=}NNHCONH{-})_2$$

$$\underset{(10.1\ g.)}{CH_3OCON_3} + \underset{(15.7\ C_6H_5Br)}{C_6H_5MgBr} \rightarrow \underset{(2.0\text{–}2.5\ g.)}{CH_3OCONHN{=}NC_6H_5}$$

$$C_2H_5OCON_3 + C_6H_5MgBr \rightarrow C_2H_5OCONHN{=}NC_6H_5$$

[74.1] Bertho, *J. prakt. Chem.*, [2], *116*, 101–17 (1927).

NITROSO COMPOUNDS

The reactions that have been more thoroughly studied are those of aromatic nitroso compounds with arylmagnesium halides. That which may reasonably be regarded as the "normal" reaction consists in the addition of the Grignard reagent to the nitrogen-oxygen double bond of the nitroso compound to form a diarylhydroxylamine derivative.[75]

$$\text{ArNO} + \text{Ar}'\text{MgX} \rightarrow \text{ArAr}'\text{NOMgX} \xrightarrow{H_2O} \text{ArAr}'\text{NOH}$$

The principal secondary reactions are reductive. One, which is discussed in more detail in the section on hydroxylamines (*q.v.*), consists in the reduction of the "normal" addition product to the corresponding diarylamine derivative:

$$2\ \text{ArAr}'\text{NOMgX} + 2\ \text{Ar}'\text{MgX} \rightarrow 2\ \text{ArAr}'\text{NMgX} + \text{Ar}'_2 + 2\ (\text{XMg})_2\text{O}$$

The other, competitive with the "normal" addition, consists in reduction of the nitroso compound to the corresponding azo or hydrazo compound.

$$\text{ArNO} \xrightarrow{\text{Ar}'\text{MgX}} (\text{ArN}{=})_2 \quad \text{or} \quad (\text{ArNH}{-})_2$$

Although it has not been specifically demonstrated for this reduction, as it has for the hydroxylamine reduction,[76] that biaryl (rather than a phenol) is a co-product, the fact that it is effected in excellent yields by a magnesium-magnesium iodide mixture[77,78] is strongly indicative of the general reaction type.

Bachmann (*loc. cit.*[78]) has shown that use of the reducing reagent in excess leads to production of the hydrazo product, whereas the use of smaller proportions leads to the corresponding azo compound. He has further shown that the complete reduction intermediate reacts with nitroso compound to form azo compound.

$$2\ C_6H_5N(MgI)N(MgI)C_6H_5 + 2\ C_6H_5NO \rightarrow 3\ C_6H_5N{=}NC_6H_5 + 2\ (IMg)_2O$$

The following reaction scheme (which should not be interpreted too literally in a mechanistic sense) is therefore offered as consistent with the known facts.

$$C_6H_5{-}\ddot{N}{=}\ddot{O}: \xrightarrow{2\ C_6H_5MgBr} C_6H_5{-}\underset{\underset{Br\diagup\ \diagdown C_6H_5}{Mg}}{\ddot{N}}{=}\ddot{O}:Mg\begin{matrix}\diagup Br \\ \diagdown C_6H_5\end{matrix} \rightarrow$$

$$C_6H_5{-}\underset{\underset{MgBr}{|}}{\ddot{N}}{-}OMgBr + C_6H_5{-}C_6H_5$$

---

[75] See Ingold, *J. Chem. Soc.*, *127*, 513-8 (1925).

[76] Gilman and McCracken, *J. Am. Chem. Soc.*, *49*, 1052-61 (1927).

[77] Gilman and Heck, *Rec. trav. chim.*, *50*, 522-4 (1931).

[78] Bachmann, *J. Am. Chem. Soc.*, *53*, 1524-31 (1931).

$$C_6H_5-\ddot{N}(MgBr)-OMgBr \xrightarrow{C_6H_5MgBr} C_6H_5-\ddot{N}(MgBr)(\leftarrow Mg(Br)C_6H_5)-OMgBr$$

$$2\ C_6H_5-\ddot{N}(MgBr)(\leftarrow Mg(Br)C_6H_5)-OMgBr \rightarrow C_6H_5-N(MgBr)-N(MgBr)-C_6H_5 + C_6H_5-C_6H_5 + 2\ (BrMg)_2O$$

$$2\ C_6H_5N(MgBr)N(MgBr)C_6H_5 + 2\ C_6H_5NO \rightarrow 3\ C_6H_5N{=}NC_6H_5 + 2\ (BrMg)_2O$$

On the basis of the scanty evidence available it would appear that low-temperature ($<-10°$) operation favors the hydrazo reduction over the "normal" addition. Data are summarized in Table XIX-IV. When reported, percentage yields are stated; otherwise a plus sign in the appropriate column indicates the product isolated. No significance need be attached to the fact that a product is not reported as present in any given instance.

No reactions of simple *t*-alkyl nitroso compounds have been reported. Tilden *et al.*[79] have reported reactions of methylmagnesium iodide with pinene and α- and β-limonene nitrosochlorides, but in view of the probable uncertainties regarding the structures of both starting materials and products, no theoretical conclusions can be drawn from their work.

Aston and Menard[80] report a variety of dehydrohalogenation, reduction, and condensation reactions of 2-bromo- and 2-chloro-2-nitrosopropane, but no generalizations can be based on this study.

N-NITROSOAMINES

From the meagre data available it would appear that the "normal" primary reaction of a nitrosoamine with a Grignard reagent consists in addition at the nitrogen-oxygen double bond.

According to Wieland and Fressel,[81] ethylmagnesium iodide reacts with *N*-nitrosodiethylamine to form the diethylhydrazone of acetaldehyde. The reaction with *N*-nitrosodiphenylamine is similar. These reactions are accompanied by the evolution of a gas "recognized as ethane."

---

[79] (*a*) Tilden and Stokes, *J. Chem. Soc.*, 87, 836–40 (1905); (*b*) Tilden and Shepheard, *ibid.*, 89, 920–3 (1906).

[80] Aston and Menard, *J. Am. Chem. Soc.*, 57, 1920–4 (1935).

[81] Wieland and Fressel, *Ber.*, 44, 898–904 (1911).

TABLE XIX-IV

REACTIONS OF NITROSO COMPOUNDS WITH GRIGNARD REAGENTS

RNO	R′MgX	RR′NOH	RR′NH	(RN=)$_2$	(RNH—)$_2$	Ref.
C_6H_5NO	AlkMgX	...	...	(?)*	...	*1*
C_6H_5NO	C_6H_5MgBr	*ca.* 50%	+	+	...	*2,3,5*
C_6H_5NO	C_6H_5MgBr	...	33.1%	+	...	*7*
C_6H_5NO	Mg + MgI_2	...	...	...	+	*8*
C_6H_5NO	Mg + 2 MgI_2	...	...	71%	...	*9*
C_6H_5NO	Mg + 4 MgI_2	...	...	...	66%	*9*
4-$CH_3C_6H_4NO$	C_6H_5MgBr	*ca.* 40%	...	...	...	*6*
4-$CH_3C_6H_4NO$	4-$CH_3C_6H_4MgBr$	40–50%	...	...	...	*4,5*
4-$CH_3OC_6H_4NO$	C_6H_5MgBr	...	...	+	...	*6*
4-$(CH_3)_2NC_6H_4NO$	C_2H_5MgBr	...	...	+	...	*6*
4-$(CH_3)_2NC_6H_4NO$	C_6H_5MgBr	...	...	+	...	*6*
4-$(CH_3)_2NC_6H_4NO$	C_6H_5MgBr	...	26.4%	...	...	*7*
4-$(CH_3)_2NC_6H_4NO$	4-$CH_3OC_6H_4MgBr$	...	...	+	...	*6*

* Actually, the product is reported as "a crystalline yellow base."

REFERENCES FOR TABLE XIX-IV

(*1*) Wieland, *Ber.*, *36*, 2315–9 (1903).
(*2*) Wieland and Roseeu, *Ber.*, *45*, 494–9 (1912).
(*3*) Wieland and Offenbächer, *Ber.*, *47*, 2111–5 (1914).
(*4*) Wieland and Roseeu, *Ber.*, *48*, 1117–21 (1915).
(*5*) Wieland and Roth, *Ber.*, *53B*, 210–30 (1920).
(*6*) Wieland and Kögl, *Ber.*, *55B*, 1798–803 (1922).
(*7*) Gilman and McCracken, *J. Am. Chem. Soc.*, *49*, 1052–61 (1927).
(*8*) Gilman and Heck, *Rec. trav. chim.*, *50*, 522–4 (1931).
(*9*) Bachmann, *J. Am. Chem. Soc.*, *53*, 1524–31 (1931).

This has the appearance of a "normal" addition, followed by the equivalent of a dehydration.*

$$R_2NNO \xrightarrow{C_2H_5MgI} R_2NN(OMgI)CH_2CH_3 \xrightarrow{-MgIOH} R_2NN{=}CHCH_3$$

When phenylmagnesium bromide reacts with *N*-nitrosodiethylamine the reported[81] products are phenyldiethylhydrazine (an addition-reduction product) and 1-ethyl-1-α-phenylethyl-2-phenylhydrazine (possibly an addition-"dehydration"-addition product). A reaction scheme which might conceivably account for the formation of the latter product is as follows:

$$(C_2H_5)_2NNO \xrightarrow{C_6H_5MgBr} (C_2H_5)_2NN(OMgBr)C_6H_5 \xrightarrow{-MgBrOH}$$

$$C_2H_5N\underset{\underset{CH_3}{|}}{\overset{}{\diagdown CH \diagup}}NC_6H_5 \xrightarrow{C_6H_5MgBr} C_2H_5[CH_3(C_6H_5)CH]NN(MgBr)C_6H_5$$

The reported[82] products of the reactions of *N*-nitrosodiarylamines with arylmagnesium halides are the triarylhydrazines.

$$(C_6H_5)_2NNO \xrightarrow{C_6H_5MgBr} (C_6H_5)_2NNHC_6H_5 + C_6H_5OH\ (?)$$

$$(4\text{-}CH_3C_6H_4)_2NNO\ (10\ g.) \xrightarrow{C_6H_5MgBr} (4\text{-}CH_3C_6H_4)_2NNHC_6H_5\ (3\text{–}4\ g.,\ crude)$$

The nature of the reduction has not been established. Although Wieland[82b] has detected phenol in one such reaction mixture, this in itself is irrelevant. The present authors have found that when no special precautions are taken to exclude oxygen it is often possible to isolate 8–10 percent of phenol from phenylmagnesium bromide reaction mixtures. By analogy with the corresponding hydroxylamine reductions (*q.v.*), the co-product of this reduction should be biphenyl.

$$(C_6H_5)_2NN(OMgBr)C_6H_5 \xrightarrow{2\ C_6H_5MgBr} (C_6H_5)NN(MgBr)C_6H_5 + (C_6H_5-)_2 + (BrMg)_2O$$

Gilman and Heck[83] state, without detailed specification of experimental conditions, that attempted reduction of *N*-nitrosodiphenylamine with magnesium-magnesium iodide led chiefly to recovery of unchanged material (together with a little tar formation). They also remark in passing that preliminary experiments with the *N*-nitrosodiphenylamine-phenylmagnesium bromide reaction have led to the isolation of a product which is "apparently *o*-anilinotriphenylamine or an isomer."

---

*It is, of course, conceivable that the sequence is addition, reduction, and autoxidation, but the corresponding phenylmagnesium bromide reaction makes the hypothesis stated seem more attractive on the ground that autoxidation prior to hydrolysis would probably be insufficient. No critical conclusions can be drawn until such experiments are performed quantitatively with careful oxygen exclusion, and all the products are isolated and positively identified.

[82] (*a*) Wieland and Reverdy, *Ber.*, *48*, 1112–6 (1915); (*b*) Wieland and Roseeu, *ibid.*, *48*, 1117–21 (1915).

[83] Gilman and Heck, *Rec. trav. chim.*, *50*, 522–4 (1931).

Other reported reactions (Wieland, *loc. cit.*[82b]) unsupported by data sufficient to warrant discussion are:

$$\text{(diphenylene)NNO} \xrightarrow{C_6H_5MgBr} \text{(diphenylene)NH} + (C_6H_5)_2NH$$

$$C_6H_5N(NO)COCH_3 \xrightarrow{C_6H_5MgBr} C_6H_5NHCOCH_3 + (C_6H_5)_2NH$$

Insofar as the Grignard reactions of nitrosoamines are of any theoretical interest whatsoever, they invite the expenditure of about one first-class doctoral dissertation.

AZOXY COMPOUNDS, FUROXANS, AMINE OXIDES, AND NITRILE OXIDES

Gilman and Heck[83] report an "excellent yield" of azobenzene upon reduction of azoxybenzene with magnesium-magnesium iodide. Using one equivalent of this reducing agent with azoxybenzene Bachmann[84] obtained a 94 percent yield of azobenzene; with two equivalents he obtained hydrazobenzene in 92 percent yield. Bachmann also found that the reduction product of azobenzene reduces an equivalent of azoxybenzene, being simultaneously oxidized to azobenzene; the overall yield of azobenzene was *ca.* 93 percent.

According to Kursanov *et al.*[85] azoxybenzene and *p,p′*-azoxytoluene are both reduced by Grignard reagents to the corresponding azo compounds. The reduction is evidently of the same type as that of the hydroxylamines (*q.v.*).

$$(ArN)_2O + 2\ RMgX \longrightarrow (ArN{=})_2 + (XMg)_2O + R_2$$

Kursanov's data are summarized in Table XIX-V.

TABLE XIX-V

REDUCTION OF AZOXY COMPOUNDS BY GRIGNARD REAGENTS

$(ArN)_2O$	RMgX	$(ArN{=})_2$ (%)	R_2 (%)
$(C_6H_5N)_2O$	C_6H_5MgBr	95.8	64.4
$(C_6H_5N)_2O$	$4\text{-}CH_3C_6H_4MgCl$	+	+
$(C_6H_5N)_2O$	$1\text{-}C_{10}H_7MgBr$	+	56.3
$(C_6H_5N)_2O$	$(C_6H_5)_2CHMgBr$	66.3	71.7
$(4\text{-}CH_3C_6H_4N)_2O$	C_6H_5MgBr	60.1	83.5
$(4\text{-}CH_3C_6H_4N)_2O$	$C_6H_5CH_2MgCl$	73.8	36.3

The question of the proper formulation of the so-called "glyoxime peroxides," or furoxans, has been the subject of some disagreement.

[84] Bachmann, *J. Am. Chem. Soc.*, 53, 1524–31 (1931).

[85] Kursanov, Kursanova, and Blokhina, *J. Gen. Chem.* (U.S.S.R.), 8, 1786–90 (1938); *Chem. Abstr.*, 33, 4979 (1939).

According to present-day valence concepts the preferable formulation is probably that of a 1,2,5-isoxadiazole oxide.[86] In the case of the unsymmetrically substituted derivatives, however,

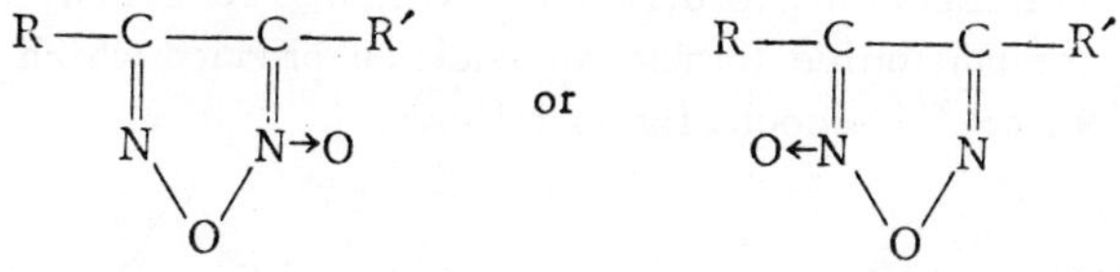

$$\begin{array}{c} R-C=\!=C-R' \text{ (ring: } C=N-O-N(\rightarrow O)=C) \end{array} \quad \text{or} \quad \begin{array}{c} R-C=\!=C-R' \text{ (ring: } C=N(\rightarrow O)-O-N=C) \end{array}$$

this poses a more or less arbitrary choice as to the point of attachment of the oxide oxygen. Probably no static formula does justice to the facts.

Wieland and Semper[87] report that "methylanisylglyoxime peroxide" forms with ethereal methylmagnesium iodide a yellow, insoluble complex, which, upon hydrolysis, regenerates the original compound.

According to Bigiavi,[88] Angeli (no reference cited) effected the cleavage of "methyl-3,4-methylenedioxyphenylglyoxime peroxide" with phenylmagnesium bromide and obtained as products piperonylonitrile and acetophenone. Bigiavi (*loc. cit.*[88]) refluxed the same furoxan with methylmagnesium iodide in benzene for six hours and recovered piperonylonitrile and 3,4-methylenedioxyacetophenone. Similar treatment of the methylanisyl derivative with phenylmagnesium bromide yielded anisonitrile and an unstable product, designated as 1-nitroso-1-phenylethanol, which decomposes to yield acetophenone.

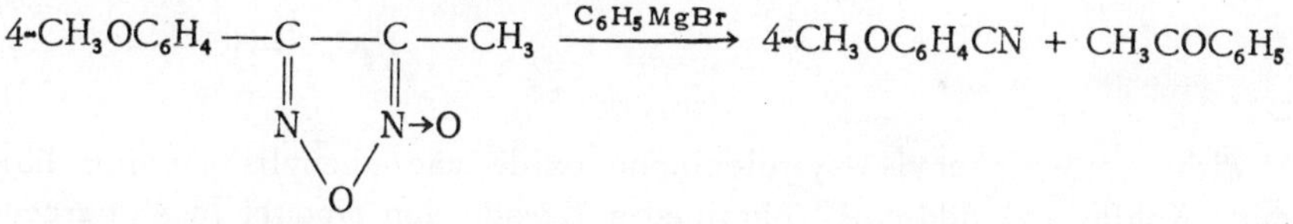

$$4\text{-}CH_3OC_6H_4-C(=N-O-N(\rightarrow O)=)C-CH_3 \xrightarrow{C_6H_5MgBr} 4\text{-}CH_3OC_6H_4CN + CH_3COC_6H_5$$

Kohler and Barrett[89] treated 3,4,5-triphenylisoxazoline oxide with six equivalents of ethylmagnesium bromide and obtained, in 50 percent yield, a reduction product which they formulated as the *N*-hydroxyisoxazolidine. This characterization was subsequently abandoned in favor of an open-chain oxime formulation.[90]

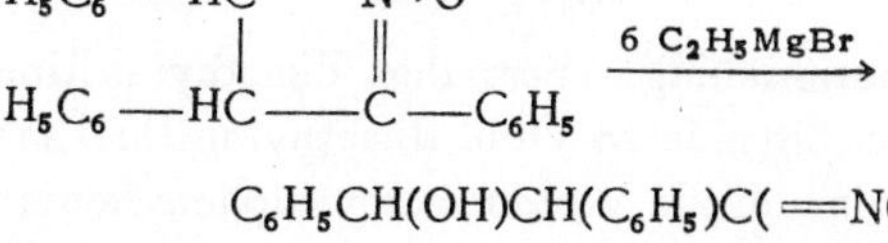

$$\begin{array}{l} H_5C_6-HC-O-N\rightarrow O \\ \quad\ | \qquad\qquad \| \\ H_5C_6-HC-C-C_6H_5 \end{array} \xrightarrow{6\ C_2H_5MgBr}$$

$$C_6H_5CH(OH)CH(C_6H_5)C(=NOH)C_6H_5\ (50\%) + C_{23}H_{23}O_2N + \text{gas}$$

---

[86] See, *e.g.*, Smith, *Chem. Revs.*, *23*, 193–285 (1938).

[87] Wieland and Semper, *Ann.*, *358*, 36–70 (1908).

[88] Bigiavi, *Gazz. chim. ital.*, *51,II*, 324–9 (1922); *Chem. Abstr.*, *16*, 1394 (1922).

[89] Kohler and Barrett, *J. Am. Chem. Soc.*, *46*, 2105–13 (1924).

[90] Kohler and Richtmyer, *J. Am. Chem. Soc.*, *52*, 2038–46 (1930).

Upon treatment of the same isoxazoline oxide (0.06 mole) with excess benzylmagnesium chloride Kohler and Richtmyer (*loc. cit.*[90]) obtained the same oxime in *ca.* 65 percent yield (0.039 mole), together with bibenzyl (0.053 mole, corresponding to 0.107 mole Grignard reagent).*

Methylmagnesium iodide formed an addition product which Kohler and Richtmyer (*loc. cit.*[90]) account for as follows:

$$\begin{array}{c} H_5C_6\text{—}HC\overset{O}{\frown}N\rightarrow O \\ H_5C_6\text{—}HC\text{—}C\text{—}C_6H_5 \end{array} \xrightarrow{3\ CH_3MgI} \begin{array}{c} H_5C_6\text{—}HC\overset{O}{\frown}N\text{—}OMgI \\ H_5C_6\text{—}HC\text{—}C(CH_3)(C_6H_5) \end{array} \rightarrow$$

$$C_6H_5COCH(C_6H_5)C(CH_3)(C_6H_5)NHOMgI \rightarrow CH_3(C_6H_5)C(OH)CH(C_6H_5)C(CH_3)(C_6H_5)NHOH$$

Phenylmagnesium bromide gave a nitrogen-free product which Kohler and Richtmyer (*loc. cit.*[90]) formulate as an oxetane.

$$\begin{array}{c} H_5C_6\text{—}HC\overset{O}{\frown}N\rightarrow O \\ H_5C_6\text{—}HC\text{—}C\text{—}C_6H_5 \end{array} \xrightarrow{C_6H_5MgBr} \begin{array}{c} H_5C_6\text{—}HC\overset{O}{\frown}N\text{—}OH \\ H_5C_6\text{—}HC\text{—}C(C_6H_5)_2 \end{array} \rightarrow \begin{array}{c} H_5C_6\text{—}HC\text{—}O \\ H_5C_6\text{—}HC\text{—}C(C_6H_5)_2 \end{array}$$

With 2,4,5-triphenyl-3-pyrroleninone oxide and phenylmagnesium bromide Kohler and Addinall[91] obtained a 1,3-addition product in 85 percent yield. The corresponding 2-*p*-bromophenyl-4-*p*-chlorophenyl-5-phenyl compound reacted similarly.

$$\begin{array}{c} O \\ \uparrow \\ N \\ H_5C_6\text{—}C \qquad C\text{—}C_6H_4\text{-4-Br} \\ 4\text{-ClH}_4C_6\text{—}C\text{—}C{=}O \end{array} \xrightarrow{C_6H_5MgBr} \begin{array}{c} OH \\ | \\ N \\ H_5C_6\text{—}C \qquad C(C_6H_4\text{-4-Br})(C_6H_5) \\ 4\text{-ClH}_4C_6\text{—}C\text{—}C{=}O \end{array}$$

Belov and Savich[92] make the astonishing report that dimethylaniline oxide reacts with phenylmagnesium bromide to yield dimethylaniline and phenol, whereas methyldiphenylamine oxide yields methyldiphenylamine and biphenyl:

---

* Part of the bibenzyl was undoubtedly formed during the preparation of the Grignard reagent.

[91] Kohler and Addinall, *J. Am. Chem. Soc.*, *52*, 1590–604 (1930).

[92] Belov and Savich, *J. Gen. Chem.* (U.S.S.R.), *17*, 262–8 (1947); *Chem. Abstr.*, *42*, 530 (1948).

$$C_6H_5(CH_3)_2NO + C_6H_5MgBr \xrightarrow[\text{in } C_7H_8]{\text{reflux}} C_6H_5OH\ (90\%) + C_6H_5(CH_3)_2N\ (66\%)$$

$$CH_3(C_6H_5)_2NO + 2\ C_6H_5MgBr \xrightarrow[\text{in } Et_2O]{\text{5 hrs. reflux}} (C_6H_5-)_2\ (ca.\ 100\%) + CH_3(C_6H_5)_2N\ (96\%)$$

These experiments should be repeated with Grignard reagents prepared from sublimed magnesium.

From the reaction of benzonitrile oxide with methylmagnesium iodide Wieland[93] obtained acetophenone oxime, acetophenone, and a little benzonitrile. By a similar reaction with phenylethynylmagnesium iodide Palazzo[94] succeeded in preparing 3,5-diphenylisoxazole.

$$C_6H_5CNO \xrightarrow{C_6H_5C\equiv CMgI} \begin{matrix} HC & \text{---} & C\text{---}C_6H_5 \\ \| & & \| \\ H_5C_6\text{---}C & & N \\ & \diagdown O \diagup & \end{matrix}$$

Ponzio[95] reports that a compound to which he assigns the constitution of the oxide of benzoyl cyanide oxime is converted by methylmagnesium iodide to methylphenylglyoxime.

According to Angeli *et al.*[96] "*N*-phenylbenzaldoxime" reacts additively with ethylmagnesium iodide and phenylmagnesium bromide. The *N*-benzyl derivative reacts similarly with phenylmagnesium bromide.

$$C_6H_5CH{=}\underset{\displaystyle R}{\underset{|}{N}}{\rightarrow}O \xrightarrow{R'MgX} \xrightarrow{H_2O} R'(C_6H_5)CHNROH$$

HYDROXYLAMINES AND ALKOXYAMINES

The possibility of preparing primary amines by the reaction of Grignard reagents with hydroxylamine was investigated by Weissberger *et al.*[97] In a typical experiment, performed under nitrogen, a phenylmagnesium bromide-hydroxylamine reaction mixture was allowed to stand at 0° for one hour, and then for another hour at room temperature. The yield of aniline was 2.4 percent, based on the bromobenzene employed, or 8.5 percent, based on the hydroxylamine used. Other products isolated were: benzene (66.9 percent); biphenyl (15.3 percent); phenol (2.2 percent); and ammonia (22.3 percent).

Paolini and Paolini[98] have found that by the Zerewitinoff method (*q.v.*), hydroxylamine, *N*-benzoylhydroxylamine, and *N*-phenylsulfonylhydroxyl-

---

[93] Wieland, *Ber.*, *40*, 1667–76 (1907).

[94] Palazzo, *Gazz. chim. ital.*, *77*, 214–21 (1947); *Chem. Abstr.*, *42*, 904 (1948).

[95] Ponzio, *Gazz. chim. ital.*, *53*, 507–13 (1923); *Chem. Abstr.*, *17*, 3876 (1923).

[96] Angeli, Alessandri, and Aiazzi-Mancini, *Atti accad. Lincei*, *20,I*, 546–55 (1911); *Chem. Abstr.*, *5*, 3403 (1911).

[97] Weissberger, Fasold, Bach, *J. prakt. Chem.*, [2], *124*, 29–32 (1929).

[98] Paolini and Paolini, *Gazz. chim. ital.*, *62*, 1059–65 (1932); *Chem. Abstr.*, *27*, 2672 (1933).

amine all reveal the presence of two "active" hydrogen atoms per molecule. Benzoylation of the halomagnesium hydroxylamine derivative (with benzoyl chloride) yields *N*-benzoxybenzamide ($C_6H_5CONHO_2CC_6H_5$).

Heated at 100° for several hours with ethylmagnesium bromide, *N*-phenylsulfonylhydroxylamine is reduced to benzenesulfonamide. *N*-*p*-Tolylsulfonylhydroxylamine undergoes similar reduction.

Busch and Hobein[99] reported a 20 percent yield of triphenylhydrazine from the reaction of phenylhydrazine with phenylmagnesium bromide. With *p*-chlorophenylhydrazine they obtained *p*,*p*′-dichloroazobenzene.

With magnesium-magnesium iodide reducing mixture Gilman and Heck[100] obtained azobenzene and aniline from phenylhydroxylamine.

Wieland and Roseeu[101] had correctly assumed that a diphenylhydroxylamine derivative is the primary product of the reaction of nitrosobenzene with phenylmagnesium bromide, but mistakenly postulated that the further reduction to diphenylamine takes place through the reaction:

$$(C_6H_5)_2NOMgBr + C_6H_5MgBr \longrightarrow (C_6H_5)_2NMgBr + C_6H_5OMgBr$$

TABLE XIX-VI

REACTIONS OF ALKOXYAMINES WITH GRIGNARD REAGENTS

$RONH_2$	$R'MgX$	$R'NH_2$ (%)	Authors
CH_3ONH_2	C_2H_5MgBr	67	S. & K.[103a]
CH_3ONH_2	*n*-C_4H_9MgCl	58	B. & J.[104]
CH_3ONH_2	*n*-C_4H_9MgBr	63	B. & J.[104]
CH_3ONH_2	*i*-C_4H_9MgBr	90	B. & J.[104]
CH_3ONH_2	*s*-C_4H_9MgCl	73	S. & K.[103a]
CH_3ONH_2	*t*-C_4H_9MgCl	74	S. & K.[103a]
CH_3ONH_2	*t*-C_4H_9MgCl	70	B. & J.[104]
CH_3ONH_2	$BrMg(CH_2)_5MgBr$	68	B. & J.[104]
CH_3ONH_2	*i*-$C_5H_{11}MgCl$	80	S. & K.[103a]
CH_3ONH_2	*i*-$C_5H_{11}MgBr$	71	S. & K.[103a,b]
CH_3ONH_2	*i*-$C_5H_{11}MgI$	5	S. & K.[103a]
CH_3ONH_2	4-BrC_6H_4MgBr	73	S. & K.[103a]
CH_3ONH_2	C_6H_5MgBr	65	S. & K.[103a,b]
CH_3ONH_2	C_6H_5MgI	<1	S. & K.[103a]
CH_3ONH_2	$BrMg(CH_2)_6MgBr$	51	B. & J.[104]
CH_3ONH_2	$BrMg(CH_2)_{10}MgBr$	53	B. & J.[104]
$C_6H_5CH_2ONH_2$	C_2H_5MgBr	46	S. & K.[103b]
$C_6H_5CH_2ONH_2$	*i*-$C_5H_{11}MgBr$	67	S. & K.[103b]
$C_6H_5CH_2ONH_2$	4-BrC_6H_4MgBr	58	S. & K.[103b]
$C_6H_5CH_2ONH_2$	C_5H_5MgBr	57	S. & K.[103b]
$C_6H_5CH_2ONH_2$	C_6H_5MgI	7	S. & K.[103b]
$C_6H_5CH_2ONH_2$	$(CH_2)_5CHMgBr$	62	S. & K.[103b]
$C_6H_5CH_2ONH_2$	$C_6H_5CH_2MgCl$	79	S. & K.[103b]
$C_6H_5CH_2ONH_2$	2,4,6-$(CH_3)_3C_6H_2MgBr$	25	S. & K.[103b]
$C_6H_5CH_2ONH_2$	1-$C_{10}H_7MgBr$	38	S. & K.[103b]

[99] Busch and Hobein, *Ber.*, *40*, 2099–102 (1907).
[100] Gilman and Heck, *Rec. trav. chim.*, *50*, 522–4 (1931).
[101] Wieland and Roseeu, *Ber.*, *48*, 1117–21 (1915).

It was shown by Gilman and McCracken[102] that this reduction requires two equivalents, rather than one, of the Grignard reagent, and that the co-product is biphenyl rather than phenol.

$$(C_6H_5)_2NOMgBr + 2\ C_6H_5MgBr \longrightarrow (C_6H_5)_2NMgBr + (C_6H_5 —)_2 + (BrMg)_2O$$

Primary amines may be prepared in rather satisfactory yields by the reactions of alkoxyamines with organomagnesium chlorides or bromides (but not iodides) at -10 to $-15°$. Preparations reported by Sheverdina and Kocheshkov[103] and by Brown and Jones[104] are summarized in Table XIX-VI.

NITRO COMPOUNDS

The reaction of a nitro compound with a Grignard reagent was first investigated by Moureu,[105] who announced the preparation, in unspecified yield, of *N,N*-diethylhydroxylamine from nitroethane and ethylmagnesium iodide. Other early reports of such reactions are as follows:

$$C_6H_5NO_2 \xrightarrow{C_6H_5C\equiv CMgBr} C_{10}H_{16} \quad \text{(Iotsitch[106])}$$

$$C_6H_5NO_2 \xrightarrow{C_2H_5MgI} C_2H_5(C_6H_5)NH + 2 \text{ unidentified distillation fractions,}$$
$$b_{10-12}\ 165\text{–}170° \text{ and } b_{10-12}\ 170\text{–}200° \quad \text{(Oddo[107]);}$$

$$\text{Nitrocamphor} \xrightarrow{CH_3MgI} C_{11}H_{19}O_3N, \quad \text{m. } 83° \quad \text{(Forster[108]);}$$

$$4\text{-}CH_3C_6H_4NO_2 \longrightarrow 4\text{-}CH_3C_6H_4NO + 4\text{-}CH_3C_6H_5NHOH$$
$$+ 4\text{-}CH_3C_6H_4NH_2 + (4\text{-}CH_3C_6H_4N)_2O \quad \text{(Pickard and Kenyon[109]);}$$

$$C_2H_5NO_2 \xrightarrow{C_2H_5MgI} (C_2H_5)_2NOH + C_2H_5NH_2 + (C_2H_5)_2NH$$
$$+ C_2H_5(s\text{-}C_4H_9)NOH + C_2H_6 + C_2H_4 \quad \text{(Bewad[110]);}$$

$$C_2H_5NO_2 \xrightarrow{n\text{-}C_3H_7MgI} C_2H_5(n\text{-}C_3H_7)NOH + n\text{-}C_3H_7(s\text{-}C_5H_{11})NOH$$
$$+ C_3H_8 + C_3H_6 \quad \text{(Bewad[110]);}$$

$$n\text{-}C_3H_7NO_2 \xrightarrow{C_2H_5MgI} C_2H_5(n\text{-}C_3H_7)NOH + C_2H_5(s\text{-}C_5H_{11})NOH$$
$$+ C_2H_6 + C_2H_4 \quad \text{(Bewad[110]).}$$

---

[102] Gilman and McCracken, *J. Am. Chem. Soc.*, *49*, 1052–61 (1927).

[103] Sheverdina and Kocheshkov, (*a*) *J. Gen. Chem.* (U.S.S.R.), 8, 1825–30 (1938); *Chem. Abstr.*, 33, 5804 (1939); (*b*) *Bull. acad. sci. U.R.S.S., Classe sci. chim.*, *1941*, 75–8; *Chem. Zentr.*, *1942,I*, 1872; *Chem. Abstr.*, 37, 3066 (1943).

[104] Brown and Jones, *J. Chem. Soc.*, *1946*, 781–2.

[105] Moureu, *Compt. rend.*, *132*, 837–9 (1901); *Chem. Zentr.*, *1901,I*, 1000.

[106] Iotsitch, *J. Russ. Phys.-Chem. Soc.*, *35*, 555 (1903); *Bull. soc. chim.*, [3], *32*, 719 (1904).

[107] Oddo, *Atti accad. Lincei*, [5], *13,II*, 220–4 (1904); *Chem. Zentr.*, *1904,II*, 1113.

[108] Forster, *Proc. Chem. Soc.*, *20*, 207 (1904).

[109] Pickard and Kenyon, *Proc. Chem. Soc.*, *23*, 153 (1907).

[110] Bewad, *Ber.*, *40*, 3065–83 (1907).

The earlier literature has been reviewed and discussed by Hepworth[111] who also carried out some Barbier-type reactions with aryl nitro compounds and alkyl halides.

$$ArNO_2 \xrightarrow{Mg + AlkX} (ArN=\!=)_2 + AlkArNH$$

$$(ArNO_2 = C_6H_5NO_2,\ 2\text{-}CH_3C_6H_4NO_2,\ 4\text{-}CH_3C_6H_4NO_2,\ 1\text{-}C_{10}H_7NO_2;\quad AlkX = CH_3I,\ C_2H_5Br)$$

From the reaction mixture of 123 g. of nitrobenzene, 42 g. of magnesium, and 175 g. of ethyl bromide, he isolated 27 g. (*ca.* 30 percent) of azobenzene and 25 g. (*ca.* 21 percent) of *N*-ethylaniline.

Gilman and Heck[112] found the reaction of magnesium-magnesium iodide with nitrobenzene "slow and limited in extent." Under the not very precisely defined conditions employed they effected a 65 percent recovery of nitrobenzene, and were able to isolate only a little aniline as a reduction product.

Wang[113] has undertaken a summarization of the facts concerning the interactions of nitro compounds and Grignard reagents as follows: (1) aliphatic nitro compounds give β,β-disubstituted hydroxylamines; (2) aromatic nitro compounds and alkylmagnesium halides give *s*-tetrasubstituted hydrazines; and (3) aromatic nitro compounds and arylmagnesium halides give secondary amines. As will be seen from the data cited, this presents rather too simple a picture.

According to Buckley,[114] when ethyl nitrate is combined with one equivalent of ethylmagnesium bromide solution at 0° a vigorous exothermic reaction takes place, and a solid complex $[(C_2H_5)_2N(\rightarrow O)OMgBr]$ separates from the solution. No gas is evolved in this phase of the reaction. When an additional two equivalents of Grignard reagent is added, the complex for the most part dissolves, and one equivalent of gas is evolved. The chief liquid product is *N,N*-diethylhydroxylamine; one equivalent of Grignard reagent remains unchanged.

When the intermediate $(C_2H_5)_2N(\rightarrow O)OMgBr$ is reduced with zinc and hydrochloric acid, a 60 percent yield of diethylamine is obtained. The analogous intermediate from methyl nitrate and ethylmagnesium bromide yields 63 percent methylethylamine. Similar intermediates are obtained from isopropyl and *t*-butyl nitrates, but attempts to reduce them with zinc and hydrochloric acid fail because of their instability.

Kursanov and Solodkov[115] have investigated some reactions of aromatic nitro compounds with arylmagnesium halides, and have characterized the

---

[111] Hepworth, *J. Chem. Soc.*, *117*, 1004–12 (1920). See also: Oddo, *Gazz. chim. ital.*, *41,I*, 273–94 (1911); *Chem. Abstr.*, *5*, 2639 (1911).

[112] Gilman and Heck, *Rec. trav. chim.*, *50*, 522–4 (1931).

[113] Wang, *Trans. Sci. Soc. China*, 7, 253–63 (1932); *Chem. Abstr.*, *26*, 5545 (1932).

[114] Buckley, *J. Chem. Soc.*, *1947*, 1492–4.

[115] Kursanov and Solodkov, *J. Gen. Chem.* (U.S.S.R.), 5, 1487–93 (1935); *Chem. Abstr.*, *30*, 2181 (1936).

overall reaction as follows:

$$RNO_2 + 4\,R'MgX \rightarrow RR'NMgX + R'OMgX + R'_2 + (XMg)_2O$$

Their data are summarized in Table XIX-VII. The formation of biaryls is strongly suggestive of a radical process.

TABLE XIX-VII

REACTIONS OF ARYL NITRO COMPOUNDS WITH ARYLMAGNESIUM HALIDES

RNO_2	$R'MgX$	RR'NH (%)	R'OH (%)	R'_2 (%)
$C_6H_5NO_2$	C_6H_5MgBr	62	63	50
$C_6H_5NO_2$	$4\text{-}CH_3C_6H_4MgBr$	60	55	69
$C_6H_5NO_2$	$1\text{-}C_{10}H_7MgBr$	—	44	—
$1\text{-}C_{10}H_7NO_2$	C_6H_5MgBr	49	64	62

Assuming, as Kursanov and Solodkov (*loc. cit.*[115]) do, that the initial reaction of an aryl nitro compound with an arylmagnesium halide consists in an addition followed by a reduction to a diarylhydroxylamine derivative, the further reduction to a diarylamine derivative is readily accounted for by the study of Gilman and McCracken.[116]

$$RNO_2 \xrightarrow{R'MgX} RR'(XMgO)N{\rightarrow}O \xrightarrow{R'MgX} RR'NOMgX + R'OMgX$$

$$RR'NOMgX \xrightarrow{2\,R'MgX} RR'NMgX + R'_2 + (XMg)_2O$$

However, it is conceivable that the initial reduction may precede addition, and that nitrosobenzene is the primary intermediate, or at least one of the possible intermediates, of the reaction. That reduction may take place without addition is indicated by the "preliminary study" of Pickard and Kenyon (*loc. cit.*[109]), although in this case it is not stated whether the Grignard reagent was alkyl or aryl.

Apparently a similar gross reaction sequence (though not necessarily with the same reaction mechanisms) may take place, at least in part, with aryl nitro compounds and alkylmagnesium halides, as witness the products of Hepworth's (*loc. cit.*[111]) reactions.

The formation of an azo compound might be attributed to interaction between nitroso compound and the corresponding amine (or between their respective halomagnesium derivatives). An alternative scheme has been suggested in the discussion of the reactions of nitroso compounds (*q.v.*). An azoxy compound might result similarly from interaction between a nitroso compound and the corresponding hydroxylamine (or their respective halomagnesium derivatives).

Bewad's study (*loc. cit.*[110]) suggests that an isoöxime (nitrone) may be one of the intermediates of the reaction of an aliphatic nitro compound with a Grignard reagent. Such an intermediate might arise through initial reaction of the nitro compound in the aci form (or its conversion to the salt of the aci form by the Grignard reagent).

---

[116] Gilman and McCracken, *J. Am. Chem. Soc.*, *49*, 1052–61 (1927).

$$C_2H_5NO_2 \xrightarrow{C_2H_5MgI} CH_3CH{=}N(\rightarrow O)OMgI + C_2H_6$$

The only direct evidence bearing on this point is the statement (without supporting specifications) in an abstract of a paper by Wang[117] to the effect that the initial product of the reaction of nitromethane with phenylmagnesium bromide is the nitronic salt [$H_2C{=}N(\rightarrow O)OMgBr$].

Assuming such an initial product, the formation of an isoöxime might take place as follows:

$$CH_3CH{=}N(\rightarrow O)OMgI \xrightarrow{C_2H_5MgI} CH_3CH{=}\underset{OMgI}{\overset{C_2H_5}{N}}{-}OMgI \rightarrow$$

$$CH_3CH{=}N(\rightarrow O)C_2H_5 + (IMg)_2O$$

It is reasonable to suppose that an isoöxime might react with more Grignard reagent to form a hydroxylamine derivative.

$$CH_3CH{=}N(\rightarrow O)C_2H_5 \xrightarrow{C_2H_5MgI} CH_3CH(C_2H_5)N(OMgI)C_2H_5$$

For direct evidence on this point there is the statement of Angeli *et al.*[118] that *N*-phenylisobenzaldoxime reacts with ethylmagnesium iodide to produce a compound of empirical formula $C_{15}H_{17}ON$, believed to be a hydroxylamine.

$$C_6H_5CH{=}N(\rightarrow O)C_6H_5 \xrightarrow{C_2H_5MgI} \xrightarrow{H_2O} C_2H_5(C_6H_5)CHN(C_6H_5)OH$$

Similarly,

$$C_6H_5CH{=}N(\rightarrow O)C_6H_5 \xrightarrow{C_6H_5MgBr} \xrightarrow{H_2O} (C_6H_5)_2CHN(C_6H_5)OH + C_{19}H_{15}ON;$$

$$C_6H_5CH{=}N(\rightarrow O)CH_2C_6H_5 \xrightarrow{C_6H_5MgBr} \xrightarrow{H_2O}$$

$$C_{20}H_{19}ON \text{ [consistent with } (C_6H_5)_2CHN(CH_2C_6H_5)OH]$$

All these reactions would repay more detailed quantitative study with special precautions for the exclusion of oxygen and for the collection, definite identification, and measurement of evolved gases.

Kohler and Stone[119] have reported the 1,4-addition of phenylmagnesium bromide to β-nitrostyrene to form an intermediate that is readily converted to a 90 percent yield of the sodium salt of the isonitro compound. Boiling in dilute aqueous solution converts the isonitro salt to the true nitro compound.

$$(C_6H_5)_2CHC(C_6H_5){=}N({=}O)ONa \xrightarrow[H_2O]{\Delta} (C_6H_5)_2CHCH(C_6H_5)NO_2$$

A similar experiment with methylmagnesium iodide yielded no well-defined product.

---

[117] Wang, *Trans. Sci. Soc. China*, 7, 265–70 (1932); *Chem. Abstr.*, 26, 5545 (1932).

[118] Angeli, Alessandri, and Mancini, *Atti accad. Lincei.*, [5], 20,*I*, 546–55 (1911); *Chem. Zentr.*, *1911,II*, 606.

[119] Kohler and Stone, *J. Am. Chem. Soc.*, 52, 761–8 (1930).

TABLE XIX-VIII

SOME REACTIONS OF GRIGNARD REAGENTS WITH α-NITRO OLEFINS

α-Nitro Olefin	RMgX	Product(s)
$H_2C{=}CHNO_2$ (11.2 g.)	C_2H_5MgBr (50.0 g. C_2H_5Br)	n-$C_4H_9NO_2$ (3.2 g.); $C_2H_5(n$-$C_3H_7)C{=}NOH$ (4.7 g.); basic oil (4.8 g.); gas (4.4 l.)
$H_2C{=}CHNO_2$	n-C_4H_9MgBr (excess)	n-$C_6H_{13}NO_2$ (43%); n-$C_4H_9(n$-$C_5H_{11})C{=}NOH$ (27.5%)
$H_2C{=}CHNO_2$	n-C_4H_9MgBr (*ca.* 1 equiv., 0°)	n-$C_6H_{13}NO_2$ (65%)
$CH_3CH{=}CHNO_2$	$(CH_2)_5CHMgBr$	$CH_3[(CH_2)_5CH]CHCH_2NO_2$
$H_2C{=}C(CH_3)NO_2$	C_2H_5MgBr	$CH_3(n$-$C_3H_7)CHNO_2$
$(CH_3)_2C{=}CHNO_2$ (34.0 g.)	CH_3MgI (71.0 g. CH_3I)	t-$C_4H_9CH_2NO_2$ (16.2 g., 42%)
$(CH_3)_2C{=}CHNO_2$ (40.0 g.)	C_2H_5MgBr (48.0 g. C_2H_5Br)	$C_2H_5(CH_3)_2CCH_2NO_2$ (60%)
$(CH_3)_2C{=}CHNO_2$ (34.0 g.)	C_2H_5MgI	$C_2H_5(CH_3)_2CCH_2NO_2$ (57.5%); $C_8H_{14}O_3N_2$ (0.4 g.)
$(CH_3)_2C{=}CHNO_2$ (20.0 g.)	$H_2C{=}CHCH_2MgBr$	$H_2C{=}CHCH_2(CH_3)_2CCH_2NO_2$ (6.5 g.)
$(CH_3)_2C{=}CHNO_2$ (10.0 g.)	t-$C_5H_{11}MgCl$	t-$C_5H_{11}(CH_3)_2CCH_2NO_2$ (6.5 g.)
$CH_3CH{=}C(CH_3)NO_2$ (20.0 g.)	C_6H_5MgBr	$CH_3(C_6H_5)CHCH(CH_3)NO_2$ (22.5 g., crude)
$CH_3CH{=}C(CH_3)NO_2$ (30.0 g.)	n-$C_{12}H_{25}MgBr$	$CH_3(n$-$C_{12}H_{25})CHCH(CH_3)NO_2$ (20.0 g.)
$(\alpha$-$C_4H_3O)CH{=}CHNO_2$* (14.0 g.)	n-C_4H_9MgBr	n-$C_4H_9(\alpha$-$C_4H_3O)CHCH_2NO_2$* (6.5 g.)
1-Nitrocyclohexene (32.0 g.)	$C_6H_5CH_2MgBr$	1-Nitro-2-benzylcyclohexane (23.5 g., crude)
$C_6H_5CH{=}C(CH_3)NO_2$ (32.0 g.)	n-C_4H_9MgBr	n-$C_4H_9(C_6H_5)CHCH(CH_3)NO_2$ (29.0 g.)

* α-C_4H_3O = 2-furyl.

Methyl-, ethyl-, and benzylmagnesium iodides reacted with nitrostilbene to give 85–88 percent yields of the isonitro derivatives, which were converted to the nitro compounds in 95 percent yields.

$$C_6H_5CH{=}C(C_6H_5)NO_2 \xrightarrow{RMgI} R(C_6H_5)CHC(C_6H_5){=}N({\to}O)OMgI \xrightarrow{NaOH}$$
$$R(C_6H_5)CHC(C_6H_5){=}N({\to}O)ONa \xrightarrow[H_2O]{\Delta} R(C_6H_5)CHCH(C_6H_5)NO_2$$

According to Buckley,[120] the initial step in the reaction of an alkyl Grignard reagent with an α-nitro olefin is rapid 1,4-addition to the conjugated system C=CN=O to form a complex which may be decomposed with water to yield a nitro paraffin, or which may react with more Grignard reagent to form a complex which, upon hydrolysis, yields an oxime. Simultaneously, some 1,2-addition to the nitro olefin occurs, to give a complex which, upon hydrolysis, yields basic products, "probably dialkylhydroxylamines." In many, though not in all, cases, inverse addition (*i.e.*, addition of the Grignard reagent to the nitro olefin) results in polymerization of the nitro olefin. The results of several experiments by Buckley (*loc. cit.*[120]) and Buckley and Ellery[121] are summarized in Table XIX-VIII.

Lambert *et al.*[122] have also described the formation of a saturated nitro compound by the 1,4-addition of phenylmagnesium bromide to α-nitroisobutylene.

$$\underset{(40.0\ g.)}{(CH_3)_2C{=}CHNO_2} + \underset{(9.6\ g.\ Mg)}{C_6H_5MgBr} \longrightarrow \underset{(13.0\ g.)}{C_6H_5(CH_3)_2CCH_2NO_2}$$

NITRITES AND NITRATES

The reactions of organic nitrites and nitrates with Grignard reagents appear to have been but little studied. Moureu[123] reported obtaining *N,N*-diethylhydroxylamine, in unspecified yield from the reaction of isobutyl nitrite with ethylmagnesium iodide. Sudborough *et al.*[124] state that organic nitrites, among other types of compounds, appear to be capable of forming additive complexes with Grignard reagents. Bewad[125] obtained *N,N*-di-*n*-propylhydroxylamine (in 25 percent yield) from the reaction of *n*-propylmagnesium iodide with isopropyl nitrite.

Alessandri[126] claims to have obtained a very small yield of 2-methyl-3-nitroindole from the reaction of 2-methylindolylmagnesium iodide and ethyl nitrate. Hepworth[127] investigated the reactions of methylmagnesium iodide and ethylmagnesium bromide with the nitric esters of ethanol,

[120] Buckley, *J. Chem. Soc.*, *1947*, 1494–7.
[121] Buckley and Ellery, *J. Chem. Soc.*, *1947*, 1497–500.
[122] Lambert, Rose, and Weedon, *J. Chem. Soc.*, *1949*, 42–6.
[123] Moureu, *Compt. rend.*, *132*, 837–9 (1901); *Chem. Zentr.*, *1901,I*, 1000.
[124] Sudborough, Hibbert, and Beard, *Proc. Chem. Soc.*, *20*, 165 (1904).
[125] Bewad, *Ber.*, *40*, 3065–83 (1907).
[126] Alessandri, *Atti accad. Lincei*, [5], *24,II*, 194–9 (1915); *Chem. Zentr.*, *1916,I*, 1072.
[127] Hepworth, *J. Chem. Soc.*, *119*, 251–60 (1921).

ethylene glycol, glycerol, and pentaërythritol. Although yields are not stated, the reactions are said to take the course:

$$RONO_2 \xrightarrow{R'MgX} \xrightarrow{H_2O} R'_2NOH + ROH$$

In the case of ethyl nitrate and ethylmagnesium bromide a trace of diethylamine was also detected.

OXIDES AND HALO OXIDES OF NITROGEN

These reactants, also, have received but little attention; the recorded data follow.

$NO_2 \xrightarrow{C_2H_5MgI} (C_2H_5)_2NOH$ (Wieland[128])

$NO_2 \xrightarrow{n\text{-}C_4H_9MgBr} (n\text{-}C_4H_9)_2NOH$ (Dermer and Dermer[129])

$N_2O \xrightarrow{CH_3MgI}$ No reaction on long warming. (Zerner[130])

$N_2O_2 \xrightarrow{CH_3MgI} CH_3N(OH)NO$ (Sand and Singer[131])

$N_2O_2 \xrightarrow{C_6H_5MgBr} C_6H_5N(OH)NO$ (*ca.* 29%) (Sand and Singer[131])

$N_2O_3 \xrightarrow{C_6H_5MgBr} C_6H_5N_2NO_3$ (15%) (Makarova and Nesmeyanov[132])

$NOCl \xrightarrow{C_6H_5MgBr} C_6H_5NO$ (56%) + $MgBrCl$ (Oddo[133])

NO_2Cl (or NO_2Br) $\xrightarrow{C_6H_5MgBr} (C_6H_5—)_2 + C_6H_5X$ (Zuskine[134])

$NO_2Cl \xrightarrow{RMgX} RCl$ (Steinkopf and Kühnel[135])
($R = CH_3, C_2H_5, C_6H_5$; $X = Br, I$).

N-HALOAMINES AND *N*-HALOIMINES

Buylla[136] reported that when *N*-iododiethylamine is subjected to the action of ethylmagnesium bromide the iodide is recovered quantitatively.

Strecker[137] recovered only ammonium salts from the reactions of nitrogen trichloride with ethylmagnesium bromide and iodide, respectively.

---

128 Wieland, *Ber.*, *36*, 2315–9 (1903).

129 Dermer and Dermer, *J. Am. Chem. Soc.*, *64*, 3056–7 (1942).

130 Zerner, *Monatsh.*, *34*, 1609–30 (1913).

131 Sand and Singer, *Ann.*, *329*, 190–4 (1903).

132 Makarova and Nesmeyanov, *J. Gen. Chem.* (U.S.S.R.), *9*, 771–9 (1939); *Chem. Abstr.*, *34*, 391 (1940).

133 Oddo, *Gazz. chim. ital.*, *39,I*, 659–61 (1909); *Chem. Zentr.*, *1909,II*, 694.

134 Zuskine, *Bull. soc. chim.*, [4], *37*, 187 (1925).

135 Steinkopf and Kühnel, *Ber.*, *75B*, 1323–30 (1942).

136 Buylla, *Rev. real. acad. cien.*, *Madrid*, *9*, 635–53, 718–34 (1910); *Chem. Abstr.*, *5*, 3802 (1911).

137 Strecker, *Ber.*, *43*, 1131–6 (1910).

TABLE XIX-IX

REACTIONS OF MONOCHLORAMINE WITH GRIGNARD REAGENTS

R (in RMgX)	X = Cl		X = Br		X = I	
	RNH_2(%)	NH_3(%)	RNH_2(%)	NH_3(%)	RNH_2(%)	NH_3(%)
CH_3	...	...	26.3	68.4	7.6	87.5
C_2H_5	57.2	39.6	27.7	65.7	16.2	81.4
n-C_3H_7	58.2	36.9	27.0	63.8	13.9	69.8
i-C_3H_7	65.5	29.5	37.2	54.7	9.0	79.0
n-C_4H_9	58.9	38.5	27.2	65.2	15.3	84.7
s-C_4H_9	70.0	20.0	51.1	38.9	15.8	74.1
t-C_4H_9	60.2	39.0	20.2	79.7	4.8	81.4
i-C_5H_{11}	55.2	41.2	26.8	71.7	10.9	83.9
$(C_2H_5)_2CH$	71.7	19.0	31.6	61.9	13.7	79.1
t-C_5H_{11}	66.2	30.9	14.3	79.2	2.0	80.2
C_6H_5	26.7	68.0	14.5	83.9	0.8	95.6
$C_6H_5CH_2$	85.0	3.7	54.7	38.7	49.4	45.8
$C_6H_5CH_2CH_2$	74.0	18.4	42.3	52.6	15.0	73.7

Le Févre[138] found that *N*-chloropiperidine reacts violently with phenylmagnesium bromide, but recovered only biphenyl from the reaction products. Upon reëxamination of this reaction, Le Févre[139] isolated 21 g. of crude chlorobenzene and 2.5 g. of biphenyl from the reaction (at 0°) of 42 ml. of *N*-chloropiperidine with a moderate excess of phenylmagnesium bromide solution. (The amount of biphenyl is, of course, within the probable limits of Wurtz byproduct in the Grignard reagent preparation.) Extending his exploration to other *N*-chloro compounds, Le Févre was able to isolate chlorobenzene as a product of the reaction of phenylmagnesium bromide with: monochloroamine, nitrogen trichloride, *N*-chlorodimethylamine, *N*-chlorodiethylamine, chloramine-T (*N*-chloro-*p*-toluenesulfonamide), and dichloramine-T.

A rather extensive investigation of the reactions of monochloroämine with Grignard reagents has been conducted by Coleman *et al.*[140] Their data are summarized in Table XIX-IX.

Coleman and Blomquist[141] have assumed as a working hypothesis that the organomagnesium halide and the diorganomagnesium, with which it is presumably in Schlenk[142] equilibrium, react differently with monochloroamine:

$$R_2Mg + H_2NCl \rightarrow RNHMgCl + RH;$$

$$RMgX + H_2NCl \rightarrow RCl + H_2NMgX.$$

It is assumed that if any primary amine is formed directly from the organomagnesium halide, it is formed by some process stoichiometrically representable by:

$$2\ RMgX + H_2NCl \rightarrow RNHMgX + RH + MgXCl$$

As a test of this hypothesis they treated monochloroämine with the various *n*-butylmagnesium halides and with di-*n*-butylmagnesium under identical conditions in ethereal solution at 0°. Their data are summarized in Table XIX-X. When an equivalent of magnesium iodide was added to the di-*n*-butylmagnesium solution the yields of amine and ammonia were approximately the same as for *n*-butylmagnesium iodide. In ether-dioxane solution at −60° di-*n*-butylmagnesium gave a 97 percent yield of amine, with no ammonia detectable.

TABLE XIX-X

REACTIONS OF MONOCHLOROAMINE WITH RMgX AND R_2Mg

Grignard reagent	RNH_2 (%)	NH_3 (%)
n-C_4H_9MgCl	57	43
n-C_4H_9MgBr	29	70
n-C_4H_9MgI	12	70
$(n$-$C_4H_9)_2Mg$	82	14

[138] Le Févre, *J. Chem. Soc.*, *1932*, 1376–9.

[139] Le Févre, *J. Chem. Soc.*, *1932*, 1745–7.

[140] (*a*) Coleman and Hauser, *J. Am. Chem. Soc.*, *50*, 1193–6 (1928); (*b*) Coleman and Yager, *ibid.*, *51*, 567–9 (1929).

[141] Coleman and Blomquist, *J. Am. Chem. Soc.*, *63*, 1692–4 (1941).

[142] Schlenk and Schlenk, *Ber.*, *62B*, 920–4 (1929). (See Chapter IV.)

TABLE XIX-XI

REACTIONS OF VARIOUS *N*-MONOCHLORO- AND *N,N*-DICHLOROALKYLAMINES WITH GRIGNARD REAGENTS

Haloamine ($RNHCl$, R_2NCl, $RNCl_2$)	Grignard Reagent ($R'MgCl$)	Prim. Amine (%) (RNH_2)	Sec. Amine (%) ($RR'NH$, R_2NH)	Tert. Amine (%) ($R'R_2N$, RR'_2N)
CH_3NHCl	n-C_4H_9MgCl	72	14	—
CH_3NHCl	$C_6H_5CH_2MgCl$	70	14	—
C_2H_5NHCl	$C_6H_5CH_2MgCl$	75	12	—
$(CH_3)_2NCl$ (5°)	$C_6H_5CH_2MgCl$	—	95	5
$(C_2H_5)_2NCl$ (−10°)	$C_6H_5CH_2MgCl$	—	90	5
$(C_2H_5)_2NCl$ (5°)	$C_6H_5CH_2MgCl$	—	89	5
$(C_2H_5)_2NCl$ (40°)	$C_6H_5CH_2MgCl$	—	83	5
$(C_2H_5)_2NCl$ (70°)	$C_6H_5CH_2MgCl$	—	76	7
$(n$-$C_3H_7)_2NCl$ (5°)	$C_6H_5CH_2MgCl$	—	78	5
$(n$-$C_4H_9)_2NCl$	n-C_4H_9MgCl	—	85	4
CH_3NCl_2	n-C_3H_7MgCl	52	12	8
CH_3NCl_2	n-C_4H_9MgCl	36	11	9
CH_3NCl_2	n-$C_5H_{11}MgCl$	34	12	8
CH_3NCl_2	$C_6H_5CH_2MgCl$	28	19	6
$C_2H_5NCl_2$	n-C_4H_9MgCl	43	22	5
$C_2H_5NCl_2$	$C_6H_5CH_2MgCl$	43	25	3

Coleman and Forrester[143] investigated the possibility of allylic rearrangement during the reaction of Grignard reagents with monochloroämine with negative results for the reagents tested. Their reported yields of "normal" primary amines for the respective Grignard reagents are: benzylmagnesium chloride, 92 percent; 1-naphthylmethylmagnesium chloride, 47 percent; cinnamylmagnesium chloride, 14 percent. These authors believe that if the isomeric amine was present in any case it was present as less than 1 percent of the reaction product.

Coleman[144] has also studied the reactions of Grignard reagents with *N*-chloroälkylamines, *N*-chlorodialkylamines, and *N,N*-dichloroälkylamines. His data are summarized in Table XIX-XI.

Similar data for nitrogen trichloride are presented in Table XIX-XII.[145]

TABLE XIX-XII

REACTIONS OF NITROGEN TRICHLORIDE WITH GRIGNARD REAGENTS

RMgX	RNH_2 (%)	R_2NH (%)	NH_3 (%)
C_2H_5MgCl	29	6	22
C_2H_5MgBr	16	2	30
C_2H_5MgI	3	1	26
i-C_3H_7MgCl	23	2	23
n-C_4H_9MgCl	37	5	15
n-C_4H_9MgBr	21	2	20
n-C_4H_9MgI	4	1	31
s-C_4H_9MgCl	23	3	26
s-C_4H_9MgBr	10	1	31
s-C_4H_9MgI	3	1	26
t-C_4H_9MgCl	30	2	15
n-$C_5H_{11}MgCl$	21	5	21
C_6H_5MgCl	4	1	38
$C_6H_5CH_2MgCl$*	32	7	8
$C_6H_5CH_2CH_2MgCl$	20	2	27

* A trace of $(C_6H_5CH_2)_3N$ was also detected in this reaction.

In the reactions of monochloroämine with Grignard reagents the evolution of nitrogen is negligible. With monobromoämine, however, there is appreciable nitrogen evolution.

The data of Coleman *et al.*[146] are summarized in Table XIX-XIII.

Like monobromoämine, dibromoämine evolves nitrogen in its reactions with Grignard reagents. Table XIX-XIV records the data of Coleman *et al.*[147]

---

[143] Coleman and Forrester, *J. Am. Chem. Soc.*, *58*, 27–8 (1936).

[144] Coleman, *J. Am. Chem. Soc.*, *55*, 3001–5 (1933).

[145] Coleman, Buchanan, and Paxson, *J. Am. Chem. Soc.*, *55*, 3669–72 (1933). See also: Coleman and Buchanan, *Proc. Iowa Acad. Sci.*, *38*, 168 (1931); *Chem. Abstr.*, *27*, 1862 (1933).

[146] Coleman, Soroos, and Yager, *J. Am. Chem. Soc.*, *55*, 2075–80 (1933).

[147] Coleman, Yager, and Soroos, *J. Am. Chem. Soc.*, *56*, 965–6 (1934). See also: Coleman, Yager, and Soroos, *Proc. Iowa Acad. Sci.*, *40*, 112 (1933).

TABLE XIX-XIII

REACTIONS OF MONOBROMOAMINE WITH GRIGNARD REAGENTS

RMgX	RNH_2 (%)	NH_3 (%)	N_2 (%)
n-C_4H_9MgCl	29	64	15
n-C_4H_9MgBr	9	78	7
n-C_4H_9MgI	3	89	8
s-C_4H_9MgCl	46	42	15
t-C_4H_9MgCl	45	22	5
t-C_4H_9MgBr	8	78	12
t-C_4H_9MgI	5	85	3
C_6H_5MgCl	4	85	11
$C_6H_5CH_2MgCl$	63	30	12
$C_6H_5CH_2CH_2MgCl$	34	51	6

TABLE XIX-XIV

REACTIONS OF DIBROMOAMINE WITH GRIGNARD REAGENTS

RMgX	RNH_2 (%)	R_2NH (%)	NH_3 (%)	N_2 (%)
n-C_4H_9MgCl	15	5	70	7
n-C_4H_9MgBr	5	1	89	—
n-C_4H_9MgI	2	0.4	95	1
s-C_4H_9MgCl	21	5	62	8
t-C_4H_9MgCl	24	5	53	9
t-C_4H_9MgBr	16	5	67	4
t-C_4H_9MgI	3	1	89	7
$C_6H_5CH_2MgCl$	34	6	41	4
$C_6H_5CH_2CH_2MgCl$	18	3	73	1

According to Le Maistre *et al.*,[148] the principal reaction of an *N*-chloroïmine with a Grignard reagent is a metathetical exchange:

$$RCH{=}NCl + R'MgX \rightarrow RCH{=}NMgX + R'Cl$$

A competing, but relatively slow, reaction leads to nitrile formation.

$$RCH{=}NCl + R'MgX \rightarrow RCN + R'H + MgXCl$$

Data are summarized in Table XIX-XV.

TABLE XIX-XV

REACTIONS OF *N*-CHLOROIMINES WITH GRIGNARD REAGENTS

RCH=NCl	R'MgX	Temp. (°C)	RCH=NH (%)	RCN (%)
2-$ClC_6H_4CH{=}NCl$	C_2H_5MgBr	−45	43	13
4-$ClC_6H_4CH{=}NCl$	C_2H_5MgBr	0	45	20
4-$ClC_6H_4CH{=}NCl$	C_2H_5MgBr	23–28	45	34
4-$ClC_6H_4CH{=}NCl$	4-ClC_6H_4MgBr*	0	18	5
4-$ClC_6H_4CH{=}NCl$	C_6H_5MgBr	0	61	10
2-$CH_3OC_6H_4CH{=}NCl$	C_2H_5MgBr	0	50	17

* A 25 percent yield of *p*-dichlorobenzene was obtained in this reaction.

[148] Le Maistre, Rainsford, and Hauser, *J. Org. Chem.*, 4, 106–10 (1939).

AZO COMPOUNDS

It was observed by Franzen and Deibel[149] that azobenzene reacts with two equivalents of ethylmagnesium bromide to yield hydrazobenzene and a gas which they assumed to be butane. Azo-*p*-toluene behaved similarly.

Gilman and Pickens[150] studied the reactions of azobenzene with various Grignard reagents. Gaseous products were not identified, but several Grignard reagent coupling products (*n*-octane, bicyclohexyl, biphenyl, and bi-*p*-tolyl) were isolated. Attempts to alkylate or acylate the dihalomagnesium derivative suggested by the reaction scheme

$$(C_6H_5N{=\!=})_2 + 2\,RMgX \rightarrow [C_6H_5(XMg)N{-\!-}]_2 + R_2$$

were partially successful in that some *sym.*-diphenyldibenzoylhydrazine was isolated when benzoyl chloride was used.

$$[C_6H_5(XMg)N{-\!-}]_2 + 2\,C_6H_5COCl \rightarrow [C_6H_5(C_6H_5CO)N{-\!-}]_2 + 2\,MgXCl$$

Busch and Hobein[151] had suggested that azobenzene might be an intermediate in the conversion of phenylhydroxylamine to triphenylhydrazine by phenylmagnesium bromide, and that azobenzene might react additively with the Grignard reagent,

$$(C_6H_5N{=\!=})_2 + C_6H_5MgBr \rightarrow (C_6H_5)_2NN(MgBr)C_6H_5$$

which would imply that the reduction of azobenzene by excess phenylmagnesium bromide should involve the improbable reaction:

$$(C_6H_5)_2NN(MgBr)C_6H_5 + C_6H_5MgBr \rightarrow (C_6H_5{-\!-})_2 + [C_6H_5(BrMg)N{-\!-}]_2$$

Gilman and Adams[152] went to the trouble to show that such a reaction does not, in fact, take place. When they treated triphenylhydrazine with excess phenylmagnesium bromide (or ethylmagnesium bromide), and hydrolyzed the resultant reaction mixture, the hydrazine was recovered almost quantitatively.

In a quantitative study Rheinboldt and Kirkberg[153] resolved any remaining doubts as to the course of such reduction reactions, and showed that the nature of the hydrocarbon product depends upon the nature of the reducing Grignard reagent. When the organic radical of the Grignard reagent is of a type that disproportionates readily, disproportion products are formed; when the radical is incapable of disproportionation, the coupling product is formed.

$$(C_6H_5N{=\!=})_2 \xrightarrow{2\,CH_3MgI} \xrightarrow{H_2O} C_2H_6\ (78\%) + (C_6H_5NH{-\!-})_2\ (46\%)$$

$$\xrightarrow{C_2H_5MgBr} \xrightarrow{H_2O} C_2H_6\ (73\%) + C_2H_4\ (66\%) + (C_6H_5NH{-\!-})_2\ (65\%)$$

---

[149] Franzen and Deibel, *Ber.*, *38*, 2716–8 (1905).
[150] Gilman and Pickens, *J. Am. Chem. Soc.*, *47*, 2406–16 (1925).
[151] Busch and Hobein, *Ber.*, *40*, 2099–102 (1907).
[152] Gilman and Adams, *J. Am. Chem. Soc.*, *48*, 2004–5 (1926).
[153] Rheinboldt and Kirkberg, *J. prakt. Chem.*, [2], *118*, 1–13 (1928).

$$\xrightarrow{n\text{-}C_3H_7MgBr} \xrightarrow{H_2O} C_3H_8\ (67\%) + C_3H_6\ (63\%) + (C_6H_5NH—)_2\ (67\%)$$

$$\xrightarrow{i\text{-}C_4H_9MgBr} \xrightarrow{H_2O} C_4H_8\ (20\%) + C_8H_{18} + (C_6H_5NH—)_2\ (51\%)$$

$$\xrightarrow{C_6H_5MgBr} \xrightarrow{H_2O} (C_6H_5—)_2 + (C_6H_5NH—)_2\ (21\%)$$

It has been shown by Gilman and Heck[154] and by Bachmann[155] that the same reduction is effected by magnesium-magnesium iodide. The latter obtained hydrazobenzene in 85–90 percent yields, together with a little aniline.

The relative rates of reaction of various Grignard reagents with azobenzene have been investigated by Gilman *et al.*,[156] who found that, in general: the aliphatic Grignard reagents (other than methyl) react most rapidly; the methyl reagents are intermediate in reaction rate; and the aryl reagents react slowly.

That the initial interaction of azo compound and Grignard reagent is complex formation is suggested by the visual observations (precipitation) of several authors. The initial precipitates formed by the combination of Grignard reagents with several hydroxylated azo compounds in ethereal solution have been investigated by Taurins.[157] Complexes of the following types (in which RMgX = CH_3MgI, C_2H_5MgBr, C_6H_5MgBr, C_6H_5MgI, $C_6H_5CH_2MgCl$) are reported: $RMgX \cdot C_6H_5N{=}NC_6H_4\text{-4-OH} \cdot (Et_2O)_2$; $(RMgX)_2 \cdot C_6H_5N{=}NC_{10}H_7\text{-1-OH} \cdot (Et_2O)_n$; $RMgX \cdot (4\text{-}HOC_6H_4N{=})_2 \cdot (Et_2O)_2$. Also described are: $(C_6H_5)_2Mg \cdot (C_6H_5N{=}NC_6H_4\text{-4-OH})_2 \cdot (Et_2O)_n$; $(C_6H_5)_2Mg \cdot C_6H_5N{=}NC_6H_4\text{-4-OH} \cdot (Et_2O)_n$; $(MgBr_2)_2 \cdot (C_6H_5N{=}NC_6H_4\text{-4-OH})_3$; $MgI_2 \cdot (C_6H_5N{=}NC_6H_4\text{-4-OH})_2$.

The earlier literature has been reviewed by Gilman and Bailie,[158] who also contribute the following quantitative data:

$$(C_6H_5N{=})_2\ (4\text{ g.}, 0.022\text{ mole}) + C_2H_5MgBr\ (0.055\text{ mole}) \xrightarrow[\text{reflux}]{\text{6 hrs.}} \text{recovered } (C_6H_5N{=})_2\ (1.4\text{ g.}) + (C_6H_5NH—)_2\ (2.35\text{ g.})$$

$$(C_6H_5N{=})_2\ (18.2\text{ g.}, 0.1\text{ mole}) + C_6H_5MgBr\ (0.22\text{ mole}) \xrightarrow[\text{reflux}]{\text{8 hrs.}} \text{recovered } (C_6H_5N{=})_2\ (4.5\text{ g.}) + (C_6H_5NH—)_2\ (11.5\text{ g.}) + (C_6H_5—)_2\ (6.1\text{ g.}) + \text{tar}$$

A more recent study at the University of Chicago[158.1] has shown that the interaction of pure azobenzene with ethereal phenylmagnesium bromide

[154] Gilman and Heck, *Rec. trav. chim.*, 50, 522–4 (1931).

[155] Bachmann, *J. Am. Chem. Soc.*, 53, 1524–31 (1931).

[156] Gilman, Heck, and St. John, *Rec. trav. chim.*, 49, 212–5 (1930).

[157] Taurins, *Acta, Univ. Latviensis Kim. Fakult Serija*, 2, 321–8 (1934); *Chem. Abstr.*, 29, 1400 (1935).

[158] Gilman and Bailie, *J. Org. Chem.*, 2, 84–94 (1937).

[158.1] Kharasch, Matthews, and Nudenberg, unpublished work.

prepared from sublimed magnesium produces no biphenyl beyond that incidental to Grignard reagent preparation (4–6 percent). Under the same conditions phenylmagnesium bromide from ordinary magnesium turnings gave rise to 50–60 percent yields of biphenyl. Methylmagnesium bromide from either metallic source yielded ethane readily upon gentle warming of the ethereal reaction mixture.

Acyl azo compounds are reported to yield both the "normal" reduction products and addition products (Stollé and Reichert[159])

$$(C_6H_5CON{=})_2 \xrightarrow{C_2H_5MgBr} C_6H_5CONHN(C_2H_5)COC_6H_5$$

$$(C_6H_5CON{=})_2 \xrightarrow{n\text{-}C_3H_7MgBr} (C_6H_5CONH{-})_2 + C_6H_5CONHN(n\text{-}C_3H_7)COC_6H_5 \text{ (30\%)}$$

$$(C_6H_5CON{=})_2 \xrightarrow{i\text{-}C_3H_7MgBr} (C_6H_5CONH{-})_2 \text{ (chiefly)} + C_6H_5CONHN(i\text{-}C_3H_7)COC_6H_5 \text{ (little)}$$

$$(C_6H_5CON{=})_2 \xrightarrow{i\text{-}C_4H_9MgBr} C_6H_5CONHN(i\text{-}C_4H_9)COC_6H_5$$

$$(C_6H_5CON{=})_2 \xrightarrow{i\text{-}C_5H_{11}MgBr} C_6H_5CONHN(i\text{-}C_5H_{11})COC_6H_5 \text{ (40\%)}$$

$$(C_6H_5CON{=})_2 \xrightarrow{C_6H_5MgBr} C_6H_5CONHN(C_6H_5)COC_6H_5 \text{ (30\%)}$$

$$(C_6H_5CON{=})_2 \xrightarrow{C_6H_5CH_2MgCl} (C_6H_5CONH{-})_2 + C_6H_5CONHN(CH_2C_6H_5)COC_6H_5 \text{ (30\%)}$$

$$C_6H_5N{=}NCOC_6H_5 \xrightarrow{C_2H_5MgBr} C_6H_5(C_2H_5)NNHCOC_6H_5 \text{ (25\%)}$$

$$C_6H_5N{=}NCOC_6H_5 \xrightarrow{C_6H_5MgBr} (C_6H_5)_2NNHCOC_6H_5 \text{ (50\%)}$$

Also reported by Stollé and Reichert (*loc. cit.*[159]):

$$(H_3CO_2CN{=})_2 \xrightarrow{C_6H_5MgBr} H_3CO_2C(C_6H_5)NNHCO_2CH_3 \text{ ("poor yield")}$$

QUATERNARY SALTS

The reactions of quaternary salts with Grignard reagents were first investigated by Freund,[160] who reported on 1-methylquinolinium and 9-phenyl-10-methylacridinium iodides. These are in general metathetical reactions in which the positive halomagnesium ion of the Grignard reagent combines with the negative ion of the quaternary salt (or base) and the negative organic ion of the Grignard reagent attaches to some atom other than the quaternized nitrogen atom of the positive ion of the salt (or base), forming a covalent molecule.

For quinolinium salts the "normal" reaction appears to be that described by the general equation:

---

[159] Stollé and Reichert, *J. prakt. Chem.*, [2], *122*, 344–9 (1929).

[160] Freund, *Ber.*, 37, 4666–72 (1904).

$$\left[\text{(N-R quinolinium, 2-R')}\right]^+ X^- + R''MgX' \rightarrow \text{(1-R-2-R'-2-R''-1,2-dihydroquinoline)} + MgXX'$$

Such reactions are reported by: Freund (*loc. cit.*[160]); Freund and Richard;[161] and Craig.[162]

Isoquinolinium salt reactions, as reported by Freund and Bode[163] and by Bergmann and Rosenthal,[164] are similar.

$$\left[\text{(N-R isoquinolinium)}\right]^+ X^- + R'MgX' \rightarrow \text{(1-H-1-R'-2-R-1,2-dihydroisoquinoline)} + MgXX'$$

In the acridinium salt reactions bond formation takes place at the 9 position (Freund, *loc. cit.*;[160] Freund and Bode, *loc. cit.*;[163] Semon and Craig[165]).

$$\left[\text{(9-R'-10-R acridinium)}\right]^+ X^- + R''MgX' \rightarrow \text{(9-R'-9-R''-10-R-9,10-dihydroacridine)} + MgXX'$$

The benz[*a*]acridinium salt reactions are similar, bond formation taking place at the 12 position (Freund and Bode, *loc. cit.*[163]).

2,4-Dihydropyrazinium salts (and bases) have been found by Aston *et al.*[166] to form 6-substituted 1,2,4,6-tetrahydropyrazines.

$$\left[\text{(R,R'-substituted dihydropyrazinium)}\right]^+ X^- + R''MgX' \rightarrow \text{(R,R',R''-substituted tetrahydropyrazine)} + MgXX'$$

The quinoxalinium salt reactions appear to be similar (Freund and Richard, *loc. cit.*[161]).

---

[161] Freund and Richard, *Ber.*, *42*, 1101–21 (1909).
[162] Craig, *J. Am. Chem. Soc.*, *60*, 1458–65 (1938).
[163] Freund and Bode, *Ber.*, *42*, 1746–66 (1909).
[164] Bergmann and Rosenthal, *J. prakt. Chem.*, [2], *135*, 267–81 (1932).
[165] Semon and Craig, *J. Am. Chem. Soc.*, *58*, 1278–82 (1936).
[166] Aston, Ailman, Scheuermann, and Koch, *J. Am. Chem. Soc.*, *56*, 1163–6 (1934).

$$[\text{quinoxalinium (1-R, 2,3-R}'_2)]^+ X^- + R''MgX' \rightarrow \text{(1-R, 2-R}''\text{, 2,3-R}'_2\text{-dihydroquinoxaline)} + MgXX'$$

Phenazinium salts undergo 10-addition (Hilleman;[167] McIlwain[168]).

$$[\text{10-R-phenazinium}]^+ X^- + R'MgX' \rightarrow \text{5-R}'\text{-10-R-5,10-dihydrophenazine} + MgXX'$$

Dibenzo[*ac*]phenazinium salts (specifically, flavinduline bromide) are reported to undergo α- (*i.e.*, 8b-) substitution with alkyl Grignard reagents, *N*- (*i.e.*, 14-) substitution with aryl Grignard reagents, and a combination of the two with benzylmagnesium chloride (Freund and Richard, *loc. cit.*[161]).

$$[\text{N-}C_6H_5\text{-dibenzo[}ac\text{]phenazinium}]^+ Br^- + AlkMgX \rightarrow \text{(8b-Alk, N-}C_6H_5\text{ adduct)} + MgXBr$$

$$(AlkMgX = CH_3MgI,\ C_2H_5MgBr)$$

$$[\text{N-}C_6H_5\text{-dibenzo[}ac\text{]phenazinium}]^+ Br^- + C_6H_5MgBr \rightarrow \text{(N,N'-di-}C_6H_5\text{-dihydro compound)} + MgBr_2$$

[167] Hilleman, *Ber.*, *71B*, 42–6 (1938).
[168] McIlwain, *J. Chem. Soc.*, *1937*, 1704–11.

With benzylmagnesium chloride, berberine hydrochloride reacts to give a nearly quantitative yield of 2,3-methylenedioxy-8-benzyl-11,12-dimethoxy-5,6-dihydrodibenzo[*ag*]quinolazine (Freund and Beck[169]). The reactions with methylmagnesium iodide and phenylmagnesium bromide are similar.

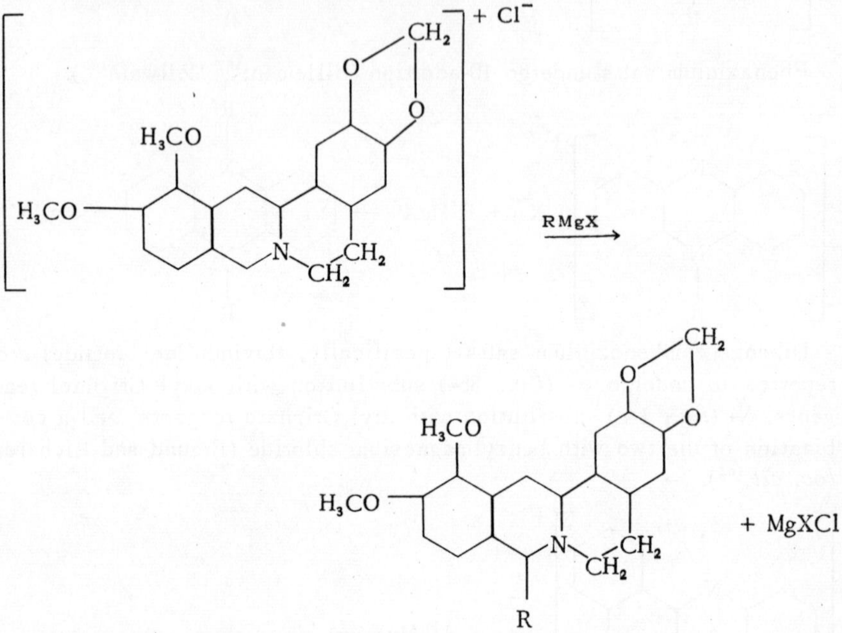

[berberinium structure: H_3CO, H_3CO, O–CH_2–O, N, CH_2, CH_2] $+ Cl^-$ $\xrightarrow{RMgX}$ [product structure: H_3CO, H_3CO, O–CH_2–O, N, CH_2, CH_2, R] $+ MgXCl$

Salts of the "triphenylmethane dye" type (crystal violet, brilliant green) undergo addition at the methane carbon atom (Freund and Richard, *loc. cit.*;[161] Freund and Beck[170]).

$$[ArAr'C{=}C_6H_4{=}N(CH_3)_2]^+Cl^- + RMgX \rightarrow RArAr'CC_6H_4\text{-}4\text{-}N(CH_3)_2 + MgXCl$$

According to Reiber and Stewart,[171] tetraalkylmethyleneimmonium salts react with Grignard reagents to form tertiary amines.

$$[(CH_3)_2C{=}N(C_2H_5)_2]^+I^- + CH_3MgI \rightarrow t\text{-}C_4H_9(C_2H_5)_2N + MgI_2$$

The foregoing reactions bear a marked resemblance to the pyrrilium salt reactions described by Löwenbein and Rosenbaum.[172]

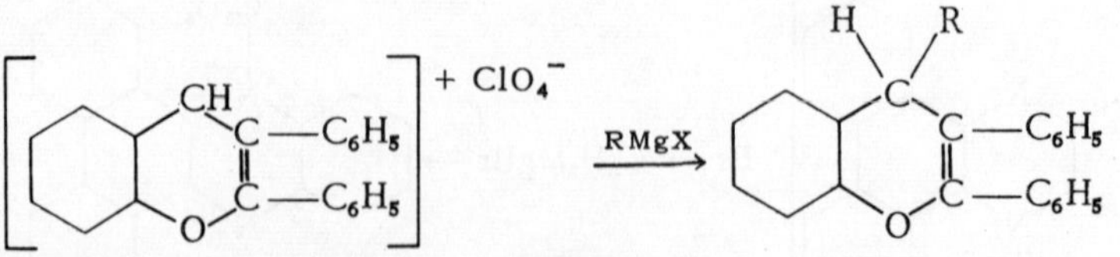

[benzopyrylium structure: CH, C–C_6H_5, C–C_6H_5, O] $+ ClO_4^-$ $\xrightarrow{RMgX}$ [product: C(H)(R), C–C_6H_5, C–C_6H_5, O]

[169] Freund and Beck, *Ber.*, 37, 4673–9 (1904).
[170] Freund and Beck, *Ber.*, 37, 3679–80 (1904).
[171] Reiber and Stewart, *J. Am. Chem. Soc.*, 62, 3026–30 (1940).
[172] Löwenbein and Rosenbaum, *Ann.*, 448, 223–48 (1926).

$$\left[\text{2,3,4-triphenylbenzopyrylium (4-}C_6H_5\text{, 2,3-di-}C_6H_5\text{)}\right]^+ + ClO_4^- \xrightarrow{C_6H_5MgBr} \text{2,2,3,4-tetraphenyl-2H-benzopyran}$$

A reductive isoxazolinium salt reaction is described by Kohler and Richtmyer.[173]

$$\left[\begin{array}{l} C_6H_5-C=C\diagdown -C_6H_5 \\ \quad | \qquad \quad \rangle O \\ C_6H_5-C=N\diagup -C_2H_5 \end{array}\right] + FeCl_4^- \xrightarrow[\text{or } C_6H_5MgBr]{CH_3MgI} \begin{array}{l} C_6H_5-C-COC_6H_5 \\ \qquad \| \\ C_6H_5-C-NHC_2H_5 \end{array}$$

The corresponding chloride reacts very slowly with methylmagnesium iodide and not at all with phenylmagnesium bromide.

The corresponding pseudobase undergoes a similar reduction (Kohler and Richtmyer, *loc. cit.*[173]).

$$\begin{array}{l} C_6H_5-C-C(C_6H_5)OH \\ \qquad \| \qquad \quad \rangle O \\ C_6H_5-C-NC_2H_5 \end{array} \xrightarrow{3\ CH_3MgI} \begin{array}{l} C_6H_5-C-COC_6H_5 \\ \qquad \| \\ C_6H_5-C-NHC_2H_5 \end{array} + \text{gas (2 equiv.)}$$

Proof addendum. Work still in progress at The University of Chicago[173.1] at this writing suggests that the gramine methiodide-Grignard reagent reactions of Snyder *et al.*[173.2] are special cases of a general allylic phenomenon that invites further study.

Apparently the presence of an allylic grouping among the quaternary nitrogen substituents is a necessary, but not always a sufficient, predisposing factor in reactions of this type. For example, phenylmagnesium bromide prepared from sublimed magnesium cleaves allylphenyldimethylammonium bromide under relatively mild experimental conditions in the manner indicated by the following equation:

$$[H_2C=CHCH_2N(CH_3)_2C_6H_5]^+Br^- + C_6H_5MgBr \rightarrow$$
$$H_2C=CHCH_2C_6H_5 + N(CH_3)_2C_6H_5 + MgBr_2$$

Under the same conditions allyltrimethylammonium bromide is unaffected by phenylmagnesium bromide prepared from sublimed magnesium, but undergoes cleavage when "catalytic" quantities of cobalt, nickel, or iron salts are added to the reaction system.

AMMONIA, AMINES, HYDRAZINES, AND TRIAZENES

For the most part, ammonia and the simple primary and secondary amines behave toward Grignard reagents as "active hydrogen" compounds

---

[173] Kohler and Richtmyer, *J. Am. Chem. Soc.*, 50, 3092–106 (1928).

[173.1] Kharasch, Williams, and Nudenberg, unpublished work.

[173.2] Snyder, Eliel, and Carnahan, *J. Am. Chem. Soc.*, 73, 970–3 (1951). *Cf.* Geissmann and Armen, *ibid.*, 74, 3916–9 (1952).

(*q.v.*, Chapter XVIII), and form so-called "nitrogen Grignard reagents." According to Hennion and Wolf,[174] ammonia decomposes *n*-butylethynylmagnesium bromide or chloride and forms complex amorphous precipitates to which they attribute the composition

$$n\text{-}C_4H_9C{\equiv}CMgNH_2{\cdot}(MgX_2)_2{\cdot}Mg(NH_2)_2{\cdot}(NH_3)_6$$

For reactions of Grignard reagents with cyclic secondary amines (such as pyrrole, indole, etc.), which form compounds that behave for the most part like "true" Grignard reagents, consult Chapter II on Preparation of Grignard Reagents. Concerning Grignard reagent complex formation with tertiary amines see the same chapter.

The special case of the alkoxymethyl tertiary amines (R_2NCH_2OR') is discussed in Chapter XV on Ethers, etc. (*q.v.*).

Puxeddu[175] reports that 3-amino-*p*-cresol and "amino-β-naphthol" evolve no gas when treated with ethylmagnesium iodide, but form yellowish-brown precipitates of the general composition $R(OH)NH_2{\cdot}(R'MgX)_2$. The precipitates so formed, when treated with acetyl chloride, evolve ethane and form acetyl derivatives.

According to Gilman and Adams,[176] triphenylhydrazine, treated with ethyl- or phenylmagnesium bromide, yields an intermediate from which, upon hydrolysis, most of the hydrazine may be recovered unchanged.

Meunier[177] observed evolution of ethane and formation of iodomagnesyl derivatives when hydrazobenzene and α,γ-diphenyltriazene, respectively, were treated with ethylmagnesium iodide.

Bachmann[178] reports that treatment of hydrazobenzene with ethylmagnesium iodide yields a di(iodomagnesyl) derivative identical with that formed by the addition of magnesious iodide ($Mg + MgI_2$) to azobenzene.

Grammaticakis[179] found, however, that α-acyl-β-phenylhydrazines do not react with Grignard reagents in ethereal solution. Treatment of α-acetyl-β-phenylhydrazines with phenylmagnesium bromide at 116–120° for seven to twelve hours yielded 2-phenylindole, together with a little acetophenone and acetophenone phenylhydrazone. α-Formyl-β-phenylhydrazine, similarly treated, yields benzophenone, together with a little benzophenone anil and benzophenone phenylhydrazone. α-Benzoyl-β-phenylhydrazine yields benzophenone phenylhydrazone, benzophenone anil, benzophenone imine, and benzophenone. In all cases traces of aniline and phenylhydrazine were detected.

According to Wuyts and Lacourt,[180] 1-methyl-1-thiobenzoyl-2-phenylhydrazine is reduced by ethylmagnesium bromide.

---

[174] Hennion and Wolf, *Proc. Indiana Acad. Sci.*, *48*, 98–101 (1939); *Chem. Abstr.*, *33*, 6794 (1939).

[175] Puxeddu, *Gazz. chim. ital.*, *53*, 99–105 (1923); *Chem. Zentr.*, *1924,I*, 1923.

[176] Gilman and Adams, *J. Am. Chem. Soc.*, *48*, 2004–5 (1926).

[177] Meunier, *Compt. rend.*, *136*, 758–9 (1903); *Chem. Zentr.*, *1903,I*, 1024.

[178] Bachmann, *J. Am. Chem. Soc.*, *53*, 1524–31 (1931).

[179] Grammaticakis, *Compt. rend.*, *207*, 239–41 (1938); *Chem. Abstr.*, *34*, 2808 (1940).

[180] Wuyts and Lacourt, *Bull. soc. chim. Belg.*, *44*, 395–410 (1935).

$$C_6H_5CSN(CH_3)NHC_6H_5 \xrightarrow{2\ C_2H_5MgBr} C_6H_5CH_2N(CH_3)NHC_6H_5 + (BrMg)_2S + 2\ C_2H_4$$

The arylation or alkylation of cyclic amines by Grignard reagents has been reported by various authors. The reactions appear to consist in complex formation, with subsequent rearrangement to form an addition compound. (For discussions of reaction mechanism see: Bergstrom and McAllister[181] and Tchéoufaki and Kwang-liang.[182]) Generally speaking, dihydro derivatives of the type formed upon hydrolysis lose hydrogen very readily (probably by autoxidation), but in a few cases the isolation of the dihydro derivatives has been reported.

Oddo[183] found that 2-phenylquinoline is formed (apparently in small yield) either when (*a*) a mixture of magnesium (6 g.), quinoline (32 g.), bromobenzene (40 g.), and toluene (50 ml.) is heated in an oil-bath at 140°, or when (*b*) a mixture of phenylmagnesium bromide (18 g.), quinoline (12.9 g.), and pyridine (8.9 g.) is refluxed for two hours. Bergstrom and McAllister (*loc. cit.*[181]) autoclaved quinoline in ethereal phenylmagnesium bromide at 150–160° for three hours and obtained a 66 percent yield of crude 2-phenylquinoline.

According to Gilman and Gainer,[184] the room-temperature reaction of diphenylmagnesium with quinoline is materially faster than the corresponding reaction of phenylmagnesium bromide.

Quinoline + $(C_6H_5)_2Mg$ $\xrightarrow{\text{48 hrs.}}$ 2-H,2-C_6H_5-1,2-dihydroquinoline, N–MgC_6H_5 $\xrightarrow{C_6H_5NO_2}$ 2-C_6H_5-quinoline (44%)

Quinoline + C_6H_5MgBr $\xrightarrow{\text{48 hrs.}}$ 2-H,2-C_6H_5-1,2-dihydroquinoline, N–MgBr $\xrightarrow{C_6H_5NO_2}$ 2-C_6H_5-quinoline (5%)

---

[181] Bergstrom and McAllister, *J. Am. Chem. Soc.*, *52*, 2845–9 (1930).

[182] Tchéoufaki and Kwang-liang, *Sci. Record* (China), *2*, 70–4 (1947); *Chem. Abstr.*, *42*, 2605 (1948).

[183] Oddo, *Atti accad. Lincei*, [5], *16,I*, 413–8 (1907); *Chem. Zentr.*, *1907,I*, 1543; *Atti accad. Lincei*, [5], *16,I*, 538–45 (1907); *Chem. Zentr.*, *1907,II*, 73; *Gazz. chim. ital.*, *37,I*, 568–76 (1907); *Chem. Zentr.*, *1907,II*, 612.

[184] Gilman and Gainer, *J. Am. Chem. Soc.*, *71*, 2327–8 (1949).

It is conceivable that the apparent difference in the behavior of the two reagents is not altogether what it appears. If this is essentially a reaction of the radical type, peroxidic materials introduced in the dioxane involved in diphenylmagnesium preparation might play a significant part.

Fuson *et al.*[184.1] have found that reaction of benzylmagnesium chloride with 2-methoxyquinoline leads, not to replacement of the methoxyl group, as might have been expected, but to formation of the 4-benzyl derivative of 2-methoxy-1,4-(or 3,4-)dihydroquinoline.

$$\text{2-methoxyquinoline } (\text{N}, -\text{OCH}_3) \xrightarrow{C_6H_5CH_2MgCl}$$

$$\text{1,4-dihydro: } \text{H}, \text{CH}_2\text{C}_6\text{H}_5 \text{ at C-4}; -\text{OCH}_3; \text{N-H} \quad \text{or} \quad \text{3,4-dihydro: } \text{H}, \text{CH}_2\text{C}_6\text{H}_5 \text{ at C-4}; \text{CH}_2; -\text{OCH}_3; \text{N}$$

1,4-Addition to α-benzylidenequinaldines is reported by Hoffman *et al.*[185]

$$\text{quinolyl-}CH{=}CHC_6H_4\text{-4-Cl} \xrightarrow{C_6H_5MgBr} \text{quinolyl-}CH_2CH(C_6H_5)C_6H_4\text{-4-Cl} \ (64\%)$$

$$\text{quinolyl-}CH{=}CHC_6H_5 \xrightarrow{C_6H_5MgBr} \text{quinolyl-}CH_2CH(C_6H_5)_2 \ (70\%)$$

Autoclave treatment of pyridine with ethyl- and phenylmagnesium bromides gave 2-ethyl- and 2-phenylpyridine in 45 and 44 percent yields, respectively (Bergstrom and McAllister, *loc. cit.*[181]). By shaking pyridine with benzylmagnesium chloride in ethereal solution containing a little dioxane for twenty-four hours, Bergmann and Rosenthal[186] obtained a small (*ca.* 7.5 percent) yield of a derivative which they designated as 2-benzylpyridine. Their identification has been questioned by Veer and

[184.1] Fuson, Jackson, and Grieshaber, *J. Org. Chem.*, *16*, 1529–35 (1951).
[185] Hoffman, Farlow, and Fuson, *J. Am. Chem. Soc.*, *55*, 2000–4 (1933).
[186] Bergmann and Rosenthal, *J. prakt. Chem.*, [2], *135*, 267–81 (1932).

St. Goldschmidt,[187] who, after twenty-four hours refluxing of an ethereal solution of pyridine and benzylmagnesium chloride, isolated an 8.5 percent yield of a derivative which they identified as 4-benzylpyridine.

By shaking quinoline (10.3 g.) for two days with ethereal benzylmagnesium chloride containing dioxane (15 ml.), Bergmann and Rosenthal (*loc. cit.*[186]) obtained a mixture of 2-phenylquinoline (6.5 g.), 4-phenylquinoline (0.8 g.), and 2,4-diphenylquinoline (1.4 g.).

Similar treatment of isoquinoline (10.3 g.) yielded 1-benzyl-1,2-dihydroïsoquinoline (11.0 g.) (Bergmann and Rosenthal, *loc. cit.*[186]). By autoclaving isoquinoline with ethereal ethylmagnesium bromide at 150–160° for three hours, Bergstrom and McAllister (*loc. cit.*[181]) obtained 1-ethylisoquinoline in 66 percent yield.

Acridine (15.6 g.) shaken with ethereal benzylmagnesium chloride and dioxane for two days yielded 9-benzyl-9,10-dihydroacridine (4.0 g.) and 9-benzylacridine (Bergmann and Rosenthal, *loc. cit.*[186]). By treatment of acridine with methylmagnesium iodide in a manner not specifically described, Bergmann and Haskelberg[188] obtained 5,10-dimethyl-5,10-dihydroacridine.

Etienne[189] observed no reaction of 1-azanthracene (benzo[g]quinoline) in cold ethereal solution, but in benzene obtained 9-phenyl-1-azanthracene. The 9-chloro derivative behaved similarly. When the bromomagnesyl intermediate obtained from the latter was treated with acetyl chloride, however, an acetyl derivative of 2-phenyl-9-chloro-1,2-dihydro-1-azanthracene was isolated.

Ethylmagnesium bromide is reported as reacting (presumably in autoclave) with nicotine, cinchonine, 2-picoline, quinaldine, and 4,4′-bipyridyl, but the products were not identified (Bergstrom and McAllister, *loc. cit.*[181]).

Lukeš[190] added *N*-methylpyrrolidine (50 g.) dropwise to an ethereal solution of methylmagnesium bromide (from 36 g. magnesium) and allowed the mixture to stand for twenty-four hours. During the reaction 8.4 l. of gas (90 percent methane) was evolved. 1,2-Dimethyl-Δ^2-pyrroline and 1,2,3-trimethylpyrrolidine were isolated. In similar reactions ethylmagnesium and *n*-propylmagnesium bromides yielded 1-methyl-2-alkyl-Δ^2-pyrrolines and 1-methyl-2,2-dialkylpyrrolidines. From a reaction with phenylmagnesium bromide only 1-methyl-2-phenyl-Δ^2-pyrroline was isolated.

According to Hoshino[191] 3-(β-aminoethyl)indole, treated with four equivalents of methylmagnesium iodide forms "dinordesoxyeseroline" in 30 percent yield. The corresponding 2-methyl derivative, similarly treated, yields "dinordesoxy-9-methyleseroline."

---

[187] Veer and St. Goldschmidt, *Rec. trav. chim.*, *65*, 793–5 (1946).

[188] Bergmann and Haskelberg, *J. Chem. Soc.*, *1939*, 1–5.

[189] Étienne, *Compt. rend.*, *219*, 622–4 (1944); *Chem. Abstr.*, *40*, 1513 (1946).

[190] Lukeš, *Chem. Listy*, *27*, 97–100, 121–5 (1933); *Chem. Abstr.*, *27*, 5323 (1933).

[191] Hoshino, *Abstracts of Japan Chem. Lit.*, *6*, 390–1 (1932); *Chem. Abstr.*, *27*, 291 (1933).

CYANAMIDES

So far as the available evidence extends the cyanamides appear to undergo, for the most part, the "normal" addition reactions of cyano compounds (*q.v.*, Chapter X).

$$R_2NCN \xrightarrow{R'MgX} \xrightarrow{H_2O} R_2NC(=NH)R'$$

From phenylcyanamide and phenylmagnesium bromide Busch and Hobein[192] obtained somewhat less than a 20 percent yield of *N*-phenylbenzamidine. α-Napthylmagnesium bromide yielded only a trace of *N*-phenylnaphthoamidine.

Adams and Beebe[193] treated 12 g. of dibenzylcyanamide with ethylmagnesium bromide, and isolated 15 g. of crude *N,N*-dibenzylpropionamidine hydrochloride. Phenyl- and *p*-tolylmagnesium bromides reacted similarly to form the respective amidines in 70 percent, or better, yields.

Vuylsteke[194] reports the reaction of dimethylcyanamide with phenylmagnesium bromide to form *N,N*-dimethylbenzamidine. In a similar reaction benzylmagnesium chloride reacted to produce not only the amidine, but the cleavage products, benzyl cyanide and dimethylamine, as well. Vuylsteke did not succeed in separating the products of the ethylmagnesium bromide reaction.

ISONITRILES (CARBYLAMINES)

The formation of benzaldehyde by the action of phenylmagnesium bromide on methylcarbylamine (methyl isocyanide) was reported by Sachs and Loevy.[195] Gilman and Heckert,[196] however, were able to isolate only traces of benzaldehyde from the same reaction. From ethylcarbylamine they obtained no identifiable product. *t*-Butylcarbylamine yielded a little benzamide, a little benzophenone, and triphenylcarbinol (23.7 percent). *p*-Tolylcarbylamine gave a tarry reaction product in which only small amounts of *p*-toluidine were identified.

MISCELLANEOUS UNCLASSIFIED NITROGEN COMPOUNDS

Tarbell and Fukushima[197] treated 1,1-dimethylethyleneimine successively with a Grignard reagent and methyl *p*-chloromethylbenzoate in an attempt to alkylate the nitrogen atom, but without success. Treatment of 1,1-dimethyl-2-β-cyanoethylethyleneimine with methyl or phenyl Grignard reagents led only to the formation of polymeric material.

---

[192] Busch and Hobein, *Ber.*, *40*, 4296–9 (1907).

[193] Adams and Beebe, *J. Am. Chem. Soc.*, *38*, 2768–72 (1916).

[194] Vuylsteke, *Bull. sci. acad. roy. Belg.*, [5], *12*, 535–44 (1926); *Chem. Abstr.*, *21*, 1108 (1927).

[195] Sachs and Loevy, *Ber.*, *37*, 874–8 (1904).

[196] Gilman and Heckert, *Bull. soc. chim.*, [4], *43*, 224–30 (1928).

[197] Tarbell and Fukushima, *J. Am. Chem. Soc.*, *68*, 2499–502 (1946).

According to Busch and Fleischmann[198] α-chlorobenzylideneaniline behaves toward Grignard reagents like an alkyl halide, although the reaction mechanism is doubtless quite different.

$$Cl(C_6H_5)C{=}NC_6H_5 + RMgX \rightarrow R(C_6H_5)C{=}NC_6H_5 + MgXCl$$
$$(RMgX = CH_3MgI,\ C_2H_5MgBr,\ C_6H_5MgBr)$$

Mousseron and Winternitz[199] fused α-chlorocyclohexylamine with ethylmagnesium bromide and obtained cyclohexanone. The *N*-methyl, *N*-ethyl, and *N*-*n*-butyl derivatives behaved similarly, but the *N*,*N*-dimethyl compound did not react.

The reactions of several diazonium salts with ethereal Grignard reagents have been investigated by Hodgson and Marsden.[200]

$$(RN_2)_2ZnCl_4 \xrightarrow{R'MgX} RX + R_2 + R'N{=}NR\ (15\%)$$
$$(R = C_6H_5,\ 4\text{-}CH_3C_6H_4;\ R'MgX = CH_3MgI,\ C_2H_5MgBr,\ C_2H_5MgI)$$

$$(C_6H_5N_2)_2ZnCl_4 \xrightarrow{C_6H_5MgBr} (C_6H_5{-})_2 + (C_6H_5N{=})_2\ (21\%)$$

$$(4\text{-}CH_3C_6H_4N_2)_2ZnCl_4 \xrightarrow{C_6H_5MgBr} 4\text{-}CH_3C_6H_4Br + C_6H_5N{=}NC_6H_4\text{-}4\text{-}CH_3\ (21\%)$$

$$(1\text{-}C_{10}H_7N_2)_2ZnCl_4 \xrightarrow{CH_3MgI} C_{10}H_8 + 1\text{-}C_{10}H_7I + (1\text{-}C_{10}H_7{-})_2 + CH_3N{=}N\text{-}1\text{-}C_{10}H_7\ (7\%)$$

$$(1\text{-}C_{10}H_7N_2)_2ZnCl_4 \xrightarrow{C_2H_5MgBr} 1\text{-}C_{10}H_7Br + (1\text{-}C_{10}H_7{-})_2 + C_2H_5N{=}N\text{-}1\text{-}C_{10}H_7\ (5\%)$$

$$(1\text{-}C_{10}H_7N_2)_2ZnCl_4 \xrightarrow{C_6H_5MgBr} (C_6H_5{-})_2 + 1\text{-}C_{10}H_7Br + (1\text{-}C_{10}H_7{-})_2 + C_6H_5N{=}N\text{-}1\text{-}C_{10}H_7\ (6\%) + (1\text{-}C_{10}H_7N{=})_2\ (23\%)$$

According to Backhouse and Dwyer[201] the pyridine-coördinated iodine salt of *m*,*p*′-dinitro-1,3-diphenyltriazene reacts with methylmagnesium iodide to form the metallic salt of the triazene.

Wuyts and Lacourt[202] treated the following 2,3-dihydro-1,3,4-thiodiazoles with five molecular equivalents of methylmagnesium iodide and recovered them completely unchanged: 3,5-diphenyl-, 2-methyl-3,5-diphenyl-, 2,5-dimethyl-3-phenyl-, 2-methyl-3-*p*-tolyl-5-*o*-tolyl-. The 2,3,5-triphenyl-derivative was similarly unaffected by ethylmagnesium bromide.

Sonn and Schmidt[203] report that thionylaniline reacts additively with Grignard reagents to form sulfinanilides.

$$C_6H_5N{=}S{=}O \xrightarrow{RMgX} \xrightarrow{H_2O} RSONHC_6H_5\ (36\text{–}52\%)$$
$$(RMgX = C_2H_5MgBr,\ C_6H_5MgBr,\ C_6H_5CH_2MgCl)$$

---

198 Busch and Fleischmann, *Ber.*, *43*, 2553–6 (1910).

199 Mousseron and Winternitz, *Compt. rend.*, *221*, 701–3 (1945).

200 Hodgson and Marsden, *J. Chem. Soc.*, *1945*, 274–6.

201 Backhouse and Dwyer, *J. Proc. Roy. Soc., N. S. Wales*, *80*, 220–3 (1947); *Chem. Abstr.*, *42*, 1902 (1948).

202 Wuyts and Lacourt, *Bull. soc. chim. Belg.*, *45*, 445–53 (1936).

203 Sonn and Schmidt, *Ber.*, *57B*, 1355–6 (1924).

Similar reactions have been studied by Gilman and Morris,[204] who prepared benzenesulfinanilide (80 percent yield), *p*-toluenesulfinanilide, and phenylmethanesulfinanilide (61.6 percent). The derivatives prepared with *n*-butylmagnesium bromide and cyclohexylmagnesium bromide are susceptible to hydrolysis and spontaneous oxidation, and were recovered as the sulfonates in 80 and 75 percent yields respectively.

Meyer and Näbe[205] treated cyanuric bromide with ethylmagnesium bromide and obtained a product which upon hydrolysis with hydrochloric acid, yielded propionic acid.

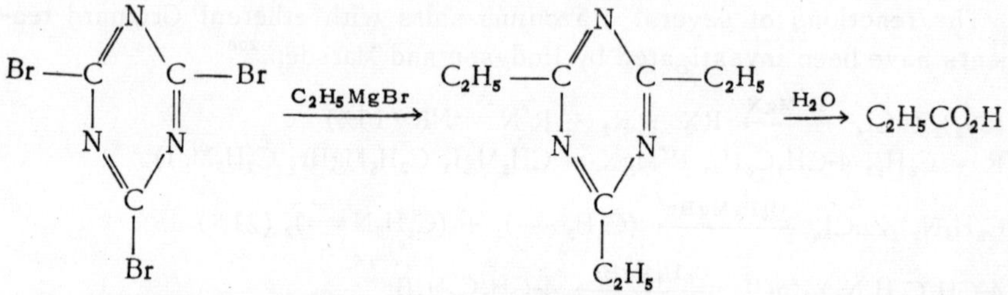

$$\text{(2,4,6-tribromo-1,3,5-triazine)} \xrightarrow{C_2H_5MgBr} \text{(2,4,6-}C_2H_5\text{-1,3,5-triazine)} \xrightarrow{H_2O} C_2H_5CO_2H$$

From cyanuric chloride and phenylmagnesium bromide Ostragovich[206] obtained a mixture of the dichloromonophenyl- and monochlorodiphenyl-1,3,5-triazines.

According to Kohler[207] 3,4-diphenyl-5-benzoylisoxazole reacts as a ketone with one equivalent of Grignard reagent. With excess reagent, however, the reaction proceeds farther; the product isolated is a furanone.

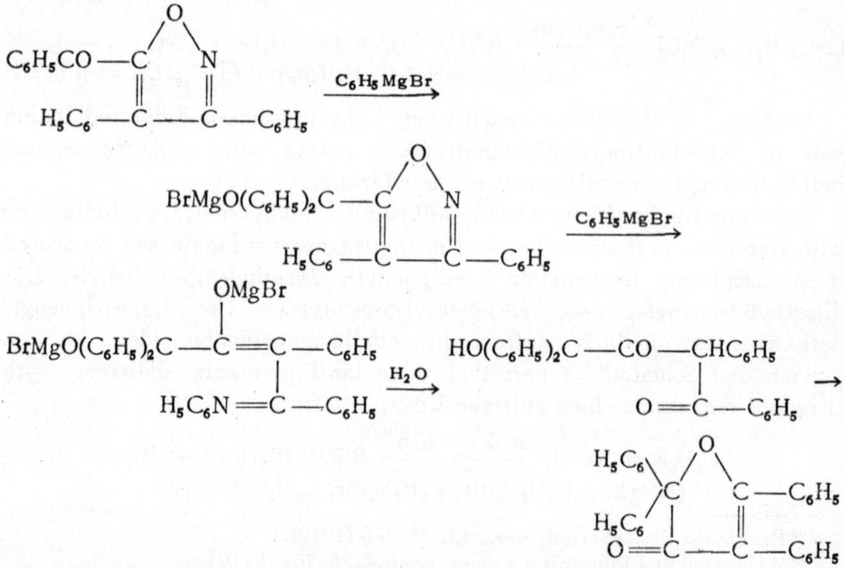

$$C_6H_5CO{-}C{=}C(C_6H_5){-}C(C_6H_5){=}N{-}O \text{ (ring)} \xrightarrow{C_6H_5MgBr} BrMgO(C_6H_5)_2C{-}C{=}C(C_6H_5){-}C(C_6H_5){=}N{-}O \text{ (ring)} \xrightarrow{C_6H_5MgBr}$$

$$BrMgO(C_6H_5)_2C{-}C(OMgBr){=}C(C_6H_5){-}C(C_6H_5){=}NC_6H_5 \xrightarrow{H_2O} HO(C_6H_5)_2C{-}CO{-}CH(C_6H_5){-}C(C_6H_5){=}O \rightarrow$$

$$(H_5C_6)_2C{<}\text{(ring: O, C(}C_6H_5\text{)=C(}C_6H_5\text{), C=O)}$$

[204] Gilman and Morris, *J. Am. Chem. Soc.*, *48*, 2399–404 (1926).
[205] Meyer and Näbe, *J. prakt. Chem.*, [2], *82*, 521–38 (1910).
[206] Ostragovich, *Chem.-Ztg.*, *36*, 738–9 (1912); *Chem. Zentr.*, *1912,II*, 607.
[207] Kohler, (*a*) *J. Am. Chem. Soc.*, *46*, 1733–47 (1924); (*b*) *47*, 3030–6 (1925).

2-Methyl-3,4-diphenyl-Δ^3-isoxazolinone forms two products with phenylmagnesium bromide. Kohler and Blatt[208] described the reactions involved as follows:

(I) 2-methyl-3,4-diphenyl-Δ^3-isoxazolinone $\xrightarrow{C_6H_5MgBr}$ 5-(BrMgO)-5-C_6H_5 adduct (ring O–N–CH_3; H_5C_6—C=C—C_6H_5)

$\xrightarrow[FeCl_3]{HCl}$ [3,4,5-triphenyl-2-methylisoxazolium]$^+$ + $FeCl_4^-$

(II) 2-methyl-3,4-diphenyl-Δ^3-isoxazolinone $\xrightarrow{2\ C_6H_5MgBr}$

$$BrMgO(C_6H_5)_2CC(C_6H_5){=}C(C_6H_5)N(CH_3)OMgBr$$
$$\rightarrow HO(C_6H_5)_2CCH(C_6H_5)COC_6H_5 \rightarrow (C_6H_5)_2C{=}C(C_6H_5)COC_6H_5$$

According to Adams *et al.*[209] alkyl thiocyanates appear to react with Grignard reagents in a manner reminiscent of that of cyanogen bromide (*q.v.*, Chapter X).

(I) $RSCN + R'MgX \rightarrow RSR' + MgXCN$

(II) $RSCN + R'MgX \rightarrow RSMgX + R'CN$

When isobutyl thiocyanate and ethylmagnesium bromide are the reactants, reaction **II** predominates when the normal order of addition is employed, and reaction **I** when the order of addition is reversed.

Evidence for the formation of R′CN is seen in the products of the reactions of phenylmagnesium bromide with isobutyl thiocyanate and with benzyl thiocyanate, among which benzophenone anil and benzophenone are prominent.

Other reactions reported are those of ethylmagnesium bromide with isobutyl, *n*-heptyl, and benzyl isocyanates, and that of isobutylmagnesium bromide with benzyl isocyanate.

---

[208] Kohler and Blatt, *J. Am. Chem. Soc.*, *50*, 1217–26 (1928).

[209] Adams, Bramlet, and Tendick, *J. Am. Chem. Soc.*, *42*, 2369–74 (1920).

CHAPTER XX

Reactions of Grignard Reagents with Oxygen, Sulfur, Selenium, and Tellurium

OXYGEN

The oxygen-oxidation of aromatic Grignard reagents was first reported by Bodroux,[1] who thereby obtained several phenols in 5–10 percent yields. In a subsequent paper[2] somewhat higher yields (10–22 percent) were claimed for these and several naphthols.

Bouveault[3] isolated about 20 percent of cyclohexanol from the cyclohexanecarboxylic acid obtained by the carbonation of cyclohexylmagnesium chloride, and correctly attributed the byproduct to an oxidation reaction analogous to that reported by Bodroux (arising from oxygen contamination of the carbon dioxide used). Having only a limited supply of cyclohexyl chloride available, he checked his conclusion by oxidation of benzylmagnesium chloride, from which he obtained an 80 percent yield of benzyl alcohol. The oxidation of cyclohexylmagnesium chloride to form cyclohexanol was later confirmed by Sabatier and Mailhe.[4] Similar oxidation of phenethylmagnesium bromide to form phenethyl alcohol in 60 percent yield was reported by Grignard.[5]

Schmidlin[6] observed the atmospheric oxidation of triphenylmethyl Grignard reagents, which he formulated as follows:

$$2\,(C_6H_5)_3CMgCl \xrightarrow{3\,O} [(C_6H_5)_3CO—]_2 + O(MgCl)_2$$

although triphenylcarbinol was obtained upon hydrolysis of the reaction mixture. Schmidlin's report is contradicted by Bachmann and Cockerill,[7] who maintain that the principal oxygenation product of triphenylmethylmagnesium bromide is the carbinolate.

Wuyts[8] studied the oxidation of phenylmagnesium bromide in ethereal solution in some detail, and isolated from the reaction mixture: phenol, other unidentified phenolic substances, benzene, biphenyl, *p*-terphenyl,

---

[1] Bodroux, *Compt. rend.*, *136*, 158–9 (1903); *Chem. Zentr.*, *1903,I*, 508.
[2] Bodroux, *Bull. soc. chim.*, [3], *31*, 33–6 (1904).
[3] Bouveault, *Bull. soc. chim.*, [3], *29*, 1051–4 (1903).
[4] Sabatier and Mailhe, *Ann. chim.*, [8], *10*, 527–71 (1907).
[5] Grignard, *Compt. rend.*, *138*, 1048–50 (1904); *J. Chem. Soc.*, *86,I*, 494 (1904).
[6] Schmidlin, *Ber.*, *39*, 628–36, 4183–98 (1906); *41*, 423–5 (1908).
[7] Bachmann and Cockerill, *J. Am. Chem. Soc.*, *55*, 2932–4 (1933).
[8] Wuyts, *Compt. rend.*, *148*, 930–1 (1909); *Chem. Zentr.*, *1909,I*, 1855.

α-phenylethanol, and ethanol. He proposed that the formation of the phenolate takes place in two steps, of which the first is the peroxidation of the Grignard reagent.

$$C_6H_5MgBr \xrightarrow{O_2} C_6H_5O_2MgBr \xrightarrow{C_6H_5MgBr}$$
$$2\ C_6H_5OMgBr \xrightarrow{2\ H_2O} 2\ C_6H_5OH + Mg(OH_2) + MgBr_2$$

The ethanol and α-phenylethanol were ascribed to a side-reaction of the Grignard peroxide with ethyl ether, yielding, with other products, ethanol and acetaldehyde. Wuyts showed that oxygenated ethereal phenylmagnesium bromide solutions give positive peroxide tests with hydroquinone, diphenylamine, and *p*-dimethylaminophenyl sulfide.

The effect of temperature on the yields of phenol obtainable by the oxidation of phenylmagnesium bromide was studied by Porter and Steele,[9] who found that over the range from 0° to 32° the yield steadily decreased from 22.9 to 16.8 percent. Among the byproducts of the reaction they identified terphenyl, quinone, and 4,4′-dihydroxybiphenyl. According to them, biphenyl is a product solely of the Wurtz side-reaction in the preparation of the Grignard reagent, and does not increase in amount during the oxidation.

Ivanoff[10] found that there is little difference in the yields of phenol obtainable by oxidation of phenylmagnesium bromide at −20° (28.8 percent) and at −55 to −50° (27.8 percent). Adopting −20° as the probable optimum temperature of operation, he investigated the oxidation of several arylmagnesium bromides, alone and in the presence of equimolecular quantities of alkylmagnesium halides. In all cases the yields of phenolic products obtainable by the oxidation of arylmagnesium bromides alone were nearly doubled in the presence of a molecular equivalent of alkylmagnesium halide. (Gilman[11] has made use of Ivanoff's method in the preparation of dibenzofuranols without discussion of its theoretical implications.) Ivanoff also showed that the increased yield of phenol obtainable by the oxidation of phenylmagnesium bromide in the presence of one equivalent of benzylmagnesium chloride (47.5 percent) is further enhanced when the oxidation is carried out in the presence of two equivalents of the alkyl reagent (53.3 percent).

Strangely enough, Ivanoff (*loc. cit.*[10]) concluded that in the "mixed" reaction the alkyl Grignard reagent is first peroxidized, and the peroxide is then reduced by the aryl Grignard reagent. Wuyts,[12] however, offered the more probable interpretation that alkyl Grignard reagents are in general better reducing agents than aryl Grignard reagents, and hence effect more readily the second step of the postulated reaction sequence.

---

[9] Porter and Steele, *J. Am. Chem. Soc.*, *42*, 2650–4 (1920).

[10] Ivanoff, *Bull. soc. chim.*, [4], 39, 47–55 (1926).

[11] Gilman, Bywater, and Parker, *J. Am. Chem. Soc.*, *57*, 885–7 (1935); Gilman and Van Ess, *ibid.*, *61*, 1365–71 (1939).

[12] Wuyts, *Bull. soc. chim. Belg.*, 36, 222–38 (1927).

$$ArO_2MgX + AlkMgX' \longrightarrow ArOMgX + AlkOMgX'$$

This view would explain not only the enhanced yields of phenols obtainable by oxidation of aryl Grignard reagents in the presence of alkyl Grignard reagents but the relatively high yields of alcohols generally obtainable by oxidation of alkyl Grignard reagents as compared with the relatively poor yields of phenols obtainable by the oxidation of aryl Grignard reagents (see Table XX-II).

Kharasch and Reynolds[13] have extended Ivanoff's study on the oxidation of aryl-alkyl Grignard reagent mixtures, and have reached conclusions similar to those of Wuyts. They have further shown that the addition of cobaltous chloride ($CoCl_2$) to the reaction system has relatively little effect on the course of the reaction in the oxidation of an alkyl Grignard reagent, but that in the oxidation of an aryl Grignard reagent it materially decreases the yield of phenolic product and increases the yield of coupling product (*e.g.*, biphenyl from phenylmagnesium bromide). Incidentally, it would appear that Porter and Steele (*loc. cit.*[9]) are probably wrong in their contention that no biphenyl is formed during the oxidation of phenylmagnesium bromide. Under experimental conditions commonly employed the amount of Wurtz byproduct arising from the preparation of the Grignard reagent should not exceed 10–12 percent; with reasonable care it can undoubtedly be held to considerably less. Significantly larger amounts of biphenyl have been isolated from phenylmagnesium bromide oxidation reaction mixtures by Wuyts (*loc. cit.*[8]) (15.4–20.6 percent), by Gilman and Wood[14] (18 percent), and by Kharasch and Reynolds (*loc. cit.*[13]) (28 percent). Wuyts believed that biphenyl is formed by the reaction:

$$2\ C_6H_5MgX + O \longrightarrow (C_6H_5 -)_2 + O(MgX)_2$$

but it is at least equally probable that it results in other ways from the decomposition, or side-reaction with the solvent, of the peroxidized Grignard reagent.

Further direct experimental evidence regarding the first step of the oxygen-oxidation of Grignard reagents has been supplied by Walling and Buckler[14.1], who, by operating at low temperature (−71°), succeeded in preparing several alkyl hydroperoxides from the corresponding Grignard reagents. Their data are summarized in Table XX-I.

Concerning the mechanism of the reaction, the hypothesis that appears to accord best with the known facts may be outlined as follows. (1) The formation of alcoholates or phenolates by the oxygen-oxidation of Grignard reagents takes place, as suggested by Wuyts, in two steps: (*a*) the peroxidation of the Grignard reagent, and (*b*) the reduction of the peroxide by a second molecule of Grignard reagent. (2) Whereas both aryl and alkyl Grignard reagents are readily peroxidized by molecular oxygen

---

[13] Kharasch and Reynolds, *J. Am. Chem. Soc.*, 65, 501–4 (1943).
[14] Gilman and Wood, *J. Am. Chem. Soc.*, 48, 806–10 (1926).
[14.1] Walling and Buckler, *J. Am. Chem. Soc.*, 75, 4372–3 (1953).

TABLE XX-1

PREPARATION OF ALKYL HYDROPEROXIDES BY SLOW ADDITION OF ETHEREAL RMgX SOLUTION (50 ml.) TO O_2-SATURATED Et_2O (50 ml.)

RMgX (*N*)	Temp. (°C)	Time (min.)	Yield (%)
t-C_4H_9MgCl (0.53)	− 7	80	27.9
t-C_4H_9MgCl (0.53)	−74	80	91.4
t-C_4H_9MgCl (1.62)	−65	40	34.4
t-C_4H_9MgCl (1.62)	−71	120	78.4
t-C_4H_9MgCl (1.74)	−69	70	45.9
t-C_4H_9MgCl (0.56)	−71	40	85.7
C_2H_5MgCl (0.48)	−71	40	57.0
C_2H_5MgBr (0.54)	−71	40	28.2
t-$C_5H_{11}MgCl$ (0.35)	−71	40	91.9
$(CH_2)_5CHMgCl$ (0.52)	−71	40	66.2
$(CH_2)_5CHMgBr$ (0.69)	−71	40	30.0
$C_6H_5CH_2MgCl$ (0.50)	−71	40	30.0
CH_3(*n*-C_6H_{13})CHMgCl (0.50)	−71	40	91.4

in the first step of the reaction, alkyl reagents are greatly superior to aryl reagents as reducing agents in the second step of the reaction. (3) In the absence of sufficiently effective Grignard reducing agents, the aryl peroxides react with ethyl ether or decompose or both. (4) Temperatures as low as −20° inhibit the reaction of aryl peroxides with ethyl ether or their decomposition or both, but little or no advantage accrues to operation at still lower temperatures.

Insofar as there is loss of intermediate peroxide by reaction with the solvent, it should be possible to effect improvement in the yield of phenolic product by operation in solvents less susceptible to peroxide attack than ethyl ether. Ivanoff (*loc. cit.*[10]), operating at −20° has reported an average yield of 34.8 percent of phenol in benzene (as compared with an average yield of 28.8 percent in ethyl ether). Gilman and Wood (*loc. cit.*[14]) have reported a 45 percent yield of phenol in phenetole (as compared with a 29 percent yield in ethyl ether at −5°).

When employed as a preparative method, the oxidation of most alkylmagnesium bromides and chlorides with dry, carbon dioxide-free air or oxygen may be expected to give good to excellent yields of the corresponding alcohols. The best chance of obtaining fair to good yields of phenolic products by the analogous oxidation of arylmagnesium bromides of chlorides is insured by operating in relatively inert solvents (*e.g.*, benzene, toluene, anisole, phenetole) at reasonably low temperatures (*ca.* 0°) in the presence of one and a half to two molecular equivalents of an alkylmagnesium chloride or bromide. The use of iodides is to be avoided, for Meisenheimer and Schlichenmayer[15] have shown that considerable quantities of iodides (corresponding to the desired alcohols or phenols) are formed in such reactions.

[15]Meisenheimer and Schlichenmayer, *Ber.*, *61B*, 2029–43 (1928); *Chem. Abstr.*, 14, 172 (1920); *Atti accad. Lincei*, *27,II*, 300–4 (1918); *J. Chem. Soc.*, *116,I*, 134; *Chem. Abstr.*, *13*, 3324 (1919).

Among the Grignard reagents which do not yield hydroxy compounds upon oxygenation are the pyrrylmagnesium halides, which form "pyrrole blacks."[16] This, however, is scarcely surprising in view of the facility with which pyrrole itself undergoes "autoxidation."

TABLE XX-II

THE OXYGEN-OXIDATION OF GRIGNARD REAGENTS

RMgX	Product(s)	Ref.
CH_3		
CH_3MgI	CH_3I; CH_3OH	*34*
C_2		
$(\equiv CMgBr)_2$	No isolable product	*20*
C_2H		
$HC\equiv CMgBr$	CH_3CO_2H (23%)	*21*
C_2H_5		
C_2H_5MgBr	C_2H_5OH (88.5%)	*52*
C_2H_5MgI	C_2H_5I; C_2H_5OH	*34*
$C_3H_4F_3$		
$F_3CCH_2CH_2MgCl$ (0.8 mole $C_3H_4ClF_3$)	$F_3CCH_2CH_2OH$ (36 g.)	*33*
C_4H_4N		
Pyrryl-MgI	"Pyrrole black"	*1*
C_4H_9		
i-C_4H_9MgBr	*i*-C_4H_9OH (74%)	*50*
t-C_4H_9MgCl	*t*-C_4H_9OH (80%)	*50*
C_6H_5		
C_6H_5MgBr	C_6H_5OH (5–10%; 18%)	*6,7*
C_6H_5MgBr	C_6H_6 (10.6–23.1%); $CH_3(C_6H_5)CHOH$ (11.8–20.3%); $(C_6H_5)_2O$; $(C_6H_5-)_2$ (15.4–20.6%); $(C_6H_5)_2C_6H_4$; C_6H_5OH (27.8%); C_2H_5OH	*52,49*
C_6H_5MgBr	C_6H_5OH (22.9–16.8% at 0–32°); $(C_6H_5)_2C_6H_4$; $(4\text{-}HOC_6H_4-)_2$; quinone	*36,17*
C_6H_5MgBr	C_6H_5OH (av'ge 28.8% at −20°; 27.8% at −55 to −50°)	*24*
C_6H_5MgBr + 1 equiv. C_2H_5MgBr	C_6H_5OH (av'ge 38.3% at −20°)	*24*
C_6H_5MgBr + 1 equiv. *n*-C_3H_7MgBr	C_6H_5OH (av'ge 41.6% at −20°)	*24*
C_6H_5MgBr + 1 equiv. *i*-$C_5H_{11}MgBr$	C_6H_5OH (av'ge 46.7% at −20°; av'ge 42.7% at 0° and at room temp.)	*24*
C_6H_5MgBr + 1 equiv. $C_6H_5CH_2MgCl$	C_6H_5OH (av'ge 47.5% at −20°)	*24*

[16] Angeli and Pieroni, *Gazz. chim. ital.*, *49,I*, 154–8 (1919).

TABLE XX-II (Continued)

RMgX	Product(s)	Ref.
C_6H_5 (*cont.*)		
C_6H_5MgBr + 2 equiv. $C_6H_5CH_2MgCl$	C_6H_5OH (av'ge 53.3% at −20°)	*24*
C_6H_5MgBr	C_6H_5OH (28%)	*27*
C_6H_5MgBr + 1.1 equiv. *i*-C_3H_7MgBr	C_6H_5OH (43%)	*27*
C_6H_5MgBr + 1.5 equiv. *i*-C_3H_7MgBr	C_6H_5OH (64%)	*27*
C_6H_5MgBr + 1.5 equiv. *n*-C_4H_9MgBr	C_6H_5OH (47%)	*27*
C_6H_5MgBr + 1.2 equiv. $(CH_2)_5CHMgBr$	C_6H_5OH (74%)	*27*
C_6H_5MgI	C_6H_5I; C_6H_5OH; $CH_3(C_6H_5)CHOH$; C_6H_6	*34*
C_6H_{11}		
$(CH_2)_5CHMgCl$	$(CH_2)_5CHOH$ (80.7%); $[(CH_2)_5CH]_2O$	*49,39,4*
C_6H_{13}		
CH_3(*i*-C_4H_9)$CHMgCl$	CH_3(*i*-C_4H_9)$CHOH$ (62%)	*48*
n-$C_3H_7(CH_3)_2CMgCl$	*n*-$C_3H_7(CH_3)_2COH$ (48%); C_6H_{12}	*48*
C_7H_7		
$C_6H_5CH_2MgCl$	$C_6H_5CH_2OH$ (80%)	*9*
2-$CH_3C_6H_4MgBr$	2-$CH_3C_6H_4OH$ (5–10%; 20%)	*6,7*
2-$CH_3C_6H_4MgBr$	2-$CH_3C_6H_4OH$ (27.2% at −20°)	*24*
2-$CH_3C_6H_4MgBr$ + 1 equiv. $C_6H_5CH_2MgCl$	2-$CH_3C_6H_4OH$ (av'ge 40.8% at −20°)	*24*
3-$CH_3C_6H_4MgBr$	3-$CH_3C_6H_4OH$ (25.1% at −20°)	*24*
4-$CH_3C_6H_4MgBr$	4-$CH_3C_6H_4OH$ (5–10%; 15%)	*6,7*
4-$CH_3C_6H_4Mg$	4-$CH_3C_6H_4OH$ (15.3%); $(4\text{-}CH_3C_6H_4—)_2$ (16.0%); $CH_3C_6H_5$ (11.0%); $CH_3(4\text{-}CH_3C_6H_4)CHOH$ (11.0%)	*17*
4-$CH_3C_6H_4MgBr$	4-$CH_3C_6H_4OH$ (28.5% at −20°)	*24*
4-$CH_3C_6H_4MgBr$ + 1 equiv. $C_6H_5CH_2MgCl$	4-$CH_3C_6H_4OH$ (av'ge 54.1% at −20°	*24*
C_6H_9		
n-$C_4H_9C{\equiv}CMgBr$	"Relatively inert" (-31°, 8 hrs.)	*28*
C_7H_7O		
4-$CH_3OC_6H_4MgBr$	4-$CH_3OC_6H_4MgBr$ (5–10%; 12%)	*6,7*
C_7H_{15}		
i-$C_3H_7CH(CH_3)CH_2CH_2MgCl$ (0.11 mole $C_7H_{15}Cl$)	*i*-$C_3H_7CH(CH_3)CH_2CH_2OH$ (8 g.)	*40*
CH_3(*i*-C_5H_{11})$CHMgCl$	CH_3(*i*-C_5H_{11})$CHOH$ (60%)	*48*
CH_3(*t*-$C_4H_9CH_2$)$CHMgCl$	CH_3(*t*-$C_4H_9CH_2$)$CHOH$ (65.4%)	*35,48*
n-$C_4H_9(CH_3)_2CMgCl$	*n*-$C_4H_9(CH_3)_2COH$ (42%); C_7H_{14}	*48*
i-$C_4H_9(CH_3)_2CMgCl$	*i*-$C_4H_9(CH_3)_2COH$ (32%); C_7H_{14}	*48*
t-$C_4H_9(CH_3)_2CMgCl$	*t*-$C_4H_9(CH_3)_2COH$	*46*
$CH_3(C_2H_5)$(*i*-C_3H_7)$CMgCl$	$CH_3(C_2H_5)$(*i*-C_3H_7)COH (31.7%)	*35*

TABLE XX-II (Continued)

RMgX	Product(s)	Ref.
C_8H_5		
$C_6H_5C\equiv CMgBr$	$C_6H_5CH=CO$	*20*
$C_8H_6NaO_2$		
$C_6H_5CH(CO_2Na)MgX$	$C_6H_5CH(OH)CO_2H$ (38%); $[HO_2C(C_6H_5)CH-]_2$ (8%)	*25*
C_8H_9		
$C_6H_5CH_2CH_2MgBr$	$C_6H_5CH_2CH_2OH$ (60%)	*19*
C_8H_9O		
4-$C_2H_5OC_6H_4MgBr$	4-$C_2H_5OC_6H_4OH$ (5–10%)	*6,7*
$C_8H_{12}N$		
Cryptopyrryl-MgBr	(3,5-Dimethyl-4-ethyl-2-pyrryl)(3,5-dimethyl-4-ethyl-2-pyrrylidene)methane; $C_{16}H_{24}ON_2$ (8–10%)	*13*
C_8H_{17}		
n-$C_8H_{17}MgBr$	*n*-$C_8H_{17}OH$ (80%)	*18*
t-$C_4H_9(CH_3)_2CCH_2MgCl$ (36 g. $C_8H_{17}Cl$)	*t*-$C_4H_9(CH_3)_2CCH_2OH$ (17 g., 53%)	*51*
C_9H_9		
4-$H_2C=CHCH_2C_6H_4MgBr$ (40 g. C_9H_9Br	4-$H_2C=CHCH_2C_6H_4OH$ (5 g.)	*37*
4-$CH_3CH=CHC_6H_4MgBr$	4-$CH_3CH=CHC_6H_4OH$ (30%)	*37*
C_9H_{11}		
4-*i*-$C_3H_7C_6H_4MgCl$	4-*i*-$C_3H_7C_6H_4OH$ (71–80% on basis of G. r. consumed)	*5*
4-*i*-$C_3H_7C_6H_4MgBr$	4-*i*-$C_3H_7C_6H_4OH$ (25 g., 18%); *i*-$C_3H_7C_6H_5$ (66 g.)	*4*
$C_{10}H_6Br$		
4-$BrC_{10}H_6$-1-MgBr	4-$BrC_{10}H_6$-1-OH (22%)	*7*
5-$BrC_{10}H_6$-2-MgBr	5-$BrC_{10}H_6$-2-OH	*12*
$C_{10}H_6Cl$		
4-$ClC_{10}H_6$-1-MgBr	4-$ClC_{10}H_6$-1-OH (21%)	*7*
$C_{10}H_7$		
1-$C_{10}H_7MgBr$	1-$C_{10}H_7OH$ (12%)	*7*
1-$C_{10}H_7MgBr$ + 1.7 equiv. *i*-C_3H_7MgBr	1-$C_{10}H_7OH$ (70%)	*27*
$C_{10}H_{17}$		
$C_{10}H_{17}MgCl$*	Borneol and isoborneol in approx. 1 : 1 ratio	*38,3,22,23*

* From pinene hydrochloride, bornyl chloride, or isobornyl chloride.

TABLE XX-II (Continued)

RMgX	Product(s)	Ref.
$C_{10}H_{17}$ (*cont.*)		
$C_{10}H_{17}MgCl$[†]	*trans*-2-Decalol, m. 75° (5/6 of product); *trans*-2-decalol, m. 53° (1/6 of product)	*11,10*
$C_{10}H_{17}MgCl$[‡]	*cis*-2-Decalol, m. 19° (2/5 of product); *cis*-2-decalol, m. 105° (3/5 of product)	*11*
$C_{10}H_{17}MgCl$[§]	2-Decalol, m. 75°	*10*
$C_{10}H_{17}MgCl$[¶]	*cis*-2-Decalol, m. 19°	*10*
$C_{11}H_9O$		
6-$CH_3OC_{10}H_6$-2-MgBr (118.5 g. $C_{11}H_9BrO$) + *i*-C_3H_7MgBr (123.0 g. C_3H_7Br)	6-$CH_3OC_{10}H_6$-2-OH (40-42%)	*14*
$C_{11}H_{15}O$		
$C_6H_5O(CH_2)_5MgI$	$C_6H_5O(CH_2)_5OH$	*47*
$C_{12}H_7O$		
1-Dibenzofuryl-MgBr	1-Dibenzofuranol	*26*
2-Dibenzofuryl-MgBr (36.5 g. $C_{12}H_7BrO$) + *n*-C_4H_9MgBr (19.1 g. C_4H_9Br)	2-Dibenzofuranol (36.7%, crude)	*15*
$C_{12}H_9$		
4-$C_6H_5C_6H_4MgX$	4-$C_6H_5C_6H_4OH$	*44*
$C_{12}H_9O$		
4-$C_6H_5OC_6H_4MgCl$	4-$C_6H_5OC_6H_4OH$	*29*
$C_{13}H_9O_2$		
2-Methoxy-3-dibenzofuranyl-MgBr (0.15 mole $C_{13}H_9BrO_2$) + *n*-C_4H_9MgBr (0.15 mole C_4H_9Br)	2-Methoxy-3-dibenzofuranol (71%)	*16*
$C_{13}H_{17}$		
4-$(CH_2)_5CHC_6H_4CH_2MgCl$	4-$(CH_2)_5CHC_6H_4CH_2OH$ (34%)	*8*
$C_{14}H_9$		
9-Phenanthryl-MgBr	9-Phenanthrol (23%)	*2*

[†] From chlorinated *trans*-decalin.
[‡] From chlorinated *cis*-decalin.
[§] From *trans*-2-chlorodecalin.
[¶] From chlorinated *cis*-β-decalin.

TABLE XX-II (Continued)

RMgX	Product(s)	Ref.
$C_{14}H_9O$		
2,2,5,7,8-Pentamethyl-6-chromanyl-MgBr (4 g. $C_{14}H_9BrO$)	2,2,5,7,8-Pentamethyl-6-chromanol (250 mg.)	*45*
$C_{16}H_{33}$		
n-$C_{16}H_{33}MgBr$	n-$C_{16}H_{33}OH$ (59%)	*18*
$C_{19}H_{15}$		
$(C_6H_5)_3CMgCl$	$(C_6H_5)_3COH$	*41,42,43*
$C_{27}H_{45}$		
Cholesteryl-MgCl	*epi*-Cholesterol and cholesterol in approx. 1 : 1 ratio	*32,31,30*

REFERENCES FOR TABLE XX-II

(*1*) Angeli and Pieroni, *Gazz. chim. ital.*, *49,I*, 154–8 (1919); *Chem. Abstr.*, *14*, 172 (1920); *Atti accad. Lincei*, *27,II*, 300–4 (1918); *J. Chem. Soc.*, *116,I*, 134; *Chem. Abstr.*, *13*, 3324 (1919).
(*2*) Bachmann, *J. Am. Chem. Soc.*, *56*, 1363–7 (1934).
(*3*) Barbier and Grignard, *Bull. soc. chim.*, [3], *31*, 840 (1904).
(*4*) Bert, *Bull. soc. chim.*, [4], *37*, 1397–410 (1925).
(*5*) Bert, *Bull. soc. chim.*, [4], *37*, 1577–91 (1925).
(*6*) Bodroux, *Compt. rend.*, *136*, 158–9 (1903); *Chem. Zentr.*, *1903,I*, 508.
(*7*) Bodroux, *Bull. soc. chim.*, [3], *31*, 33–6 (1904).
(*8*) Bodroux and Thomassin, *Bull. soc. chim.*, [5], *6*, 1411–6 (1939).
(*9*) Bouveault, *Bull. soc. chim.*, [3], *29*, 1051–4 (1903).
(*10*) Cauquil and Inamura, *Bull. soc. chim.*, [5], *7*, 660–1 (1940).
(*11*) Cauquil and Tsatsas, *Compt. rend.*, *218*, 463–4 (1944); *Chem. Abstr.*, *39*, 2501 (1945).
(*12*) Fieser and Riegel, *J. Am. Chem. Soc.*, *59*, 2561–5 (1937).
(*13*) Fischer, Baumgartner, and Plötz, *Ann.*, *493*, 1–19 (1932).
(*14*) French and Sears, *J. Am. Chem. Soc.*, *70*, 1279–80 (1948).
(*15*) Gilman, Bywater, and Parker, *J. Am. Chem. Soc.*, *57*, 885–7 (1935).
(*16*) Gilman and Van Ess, *J. Am. Chem. Soc.*, *61*, 1365–71 (1939).
(*17*) Gilman and Wood, *J. Am. Chem. Soc.*, *48*, 806–10 (1926).
(*18*) Goebel and Marvel, *J. Am. Chem. Soc.*, *55*, 1693–6 (1933).
(*19*) Grignard, *Compt. rend.*, *138*, 1048–50 (1904); *J. Chem. Soc.*, *86,I*, 494 (1904); *Chem. Zentr.*, *1904,I*, 1493.
(*20*) Grignard and Lepayre, *Bull. soc. chim.*, [4], *43*, 141–2 (1928).
(*21*) Grignard and Lepayre, *Bull. soc. chim.*, [4], *43*, 930–1 (1928).
(*22*) Hesse, *Ber.*, *39*, 1127–55 (1906).
(*23*) Houben, *Ber.*, *39*, 1700–2 (1906).
(*24*) Ivanoff, *Bull. soc. chim.*, [4], *39*, 47–55 (1926).
(*25*) Ivanov and Spasov, *Arhiv. Hem. Farm.*, *8*, 8–10 (1934); *Chem. Abstr.*, *28*, 6711 (1934).
(*26*) Jacoby, Hayes, and Van Ess, *Proc. Iowa Acad. Sci.*, *43*, 204–5 (1936); *Chem. Abstr.*, *32*, 4160 (1938).
(*27*) Kharasch and Reynolds, *J. Am. Chem. Soc.*, *65*, 501–4 (1943).
(*28*) Kroeger and Nieuwland, *J. Am. Chem. Soc.*, *58*, 1861–3 (1936).

(29) Mailhe and Murat, *Bull. soc. chim.*, [4], *11*, 228–32 (1912).
(30) Marker, U. S. Patent 2,255,074, Sept. 9, 1941; *Chem. Abstr.*, *35*, P8216 (1941).
(31) Marker, Kamm, Oakwood, and Laucius, *J. Am. Chem. Soc.*, *58*, 1948–50 (1936).
(32) Marker, Oakwood, and Crooks, *J. Am. Chem. Soc.*, *58*, 481–3 (1936).
(33) McBee and Truchan, *J. Am. Chem. Soc.*, *70*, 2910–1 (1948).
(34) Meisenheimer and Schlichenmayer, *Ber.*, *61B*, 2029–43 (1928).
(35) Miller, *J. Am. Chem. Soc.*, *69*, 1764–8 (1947).
(36) Porter and Steele, *J. Am. Chem. Soc.*, *42*, 2650–4 (1920).
(37) Quelet, *Bull. soc. chim.*, [4], *45*, 255–74 (1929).
(38) Rivière, *Ann. chim.*, [12], *1*, 157–231 (1946).
(39) Sabatier and Mailhe, *Ann. chim.*, [8], *10*, 527–74 (1907).
(40) Schmerling, *J. Am. Chem. Soc.*, *67*, 1438–41 (1945).
(41) Schmidlin, *Ber.*, *39*, 628–36 (1906).
(42) Schmidlin, *Ber.*, *39*, 4183–98 (1906).
(43) Schmidlin, *Ber.*, *41*, 423–5 (1908).
(44) Schmidlin, *Ber.*, *45*, 3171–82 (1912).
(45) Smith, U. S. Patent 2,397,212, Jan. 7, 1943; *Chem. Abstr.*, *40*, P3573 (1946).
(46) Stevens and McCoubrey, *J. Am. Chem. Soc.*, *63*, 2847–8 (1941).
(47) von Braun, Deutsch, and Schmatloch, *Ber.*, *45*, 1246–63 (1912).
(48) Whitmore and Johnston, *J. Am. Chem. Soc.*, *60*, 2265–7 (1938).
(49) Wuyts, *Bull. soc. chim. Belg.*, *36*, 222–38 (1927).
(50) Whitmore and Lux, *J. Am. Chem. Soc.*, *54*, 3448–54 (1932).
(51) Whitmore, Marker, and Plambeck, *J. Am. Chem. Soc.*, *64*, 1626–30 (1941).
(52) Wuyts, *Compt. rend.*, *148*, 930–1 (1909); *Chem. Zentr.*, *1909,I*, 1855.

The implication that many preparative, and all investigative Grignard reactions should be protected from oxygen is obvious. Gilman *et al.*[17] have repeatedly warned that oxidation losses during prolonged Grignard reagent refluxes are likely to be considerable, and Gilman and Zoellner[18] caution against similar losses in carbonation reactions. Goebel and Marvel[19] have pointed out that, at 0° or below, oxidation of exposed Grignard reagent solutions is very rapid because at such low temperatures ether vapor affords practically no protection of the solution.

CHEMILUMINESCENCE

Procedure for a lecture-demonstration of the chemiluminescent effect arising from the treatment of ethereal phenylmagnesium bromide with moist air was described by Heczko,[20] who, however, erroneously attributed the effect to moisture. Among others who have observed chemiluminescence accompanying the oxygenation of Grignard reagents are

[17] Gilman, Beaber, and Myers, *J. Am. Chem. Soc.*, *47*, 2047–52 (1925); Gilman and Wood, *ibid.*, *48*, 806–10 (1926); Gilman and St. John, *Bull. soc. chim.*, [4], *45*, 1091–5 (1929); Gilman and Hewlett, *Rec. trav. chim.*, *48*, 1124–8 (1929).

[18] Gilman and Zoellner, *J. Am. Chem. Soc.*, *53*, 1945–8 (1931).

[19] Goebel and Marvel, *J. Am. Chem. Soc.*, *55*, 1693–6 (1933).

[20] Heczko, *Chem.-Ztg.*, *35*, 199–200 (1911); *Chem. Zentr.*, *1911,I*, 1032; *Chem. Abstr.*, *5*, 1706 (1911).

Schmidlin,[21] Späth,[22] and Bachmann.[23] The effect has been studied by Möller,[24] by Lifschitz,[25] and by Evans, Dufford, and co-workers.[26]

Despite some apparently conflicting reports the following summary may be accepted as probably factual. (1) The intensity and apparent color of the chemiluminescence vary with the individual Grignard reagent and with the concentration of the solution. (2) In general the aryl Grignard reagents are more intensely luminescent than the alkyl reagents. (3) The maximum effect for aryl reagents is observable at concentrations approximating one molar; for alkyl reagents at higher dilutions (*ca.* one-eighth molar). (4) In general the aryl organomagnesium chlorides emit light of greatest intensity and longest wave-lengths, the iodides of least intensity and shortest wavelengths. (5) Although the intensity and apparent color of the luminescence vary with the organic radical of the Grignard reagent, there is no readily discernible simple relationship between structure and nature of the luminescent effect; molecular weight is not the controlling factor. (6) The presence of ether is not essential; the effect is observable in essentially ether-free solutions. (7) Temperature has little effect on the intensity or apparent color of the luminescence. (8) In general the rate of the oxidation reaction does not determine the intensity or color of the luminescence; for a given Grignard reagent the intensity is higher at higher oxidation rates. (9) The intensity and color of the luminescence are neither directly nor inversely relatable to the heat of the reaction.

On the whole, it would appear that no chemically significant generalizations may be based upon the existent data.

SULFUR

It was found by Wuyts and Cosyns[27] that sulfur (flowers) reacts vigorously upon gradual addition to an ethereal Grignard reagent. The products recovered upon hydrolysis were the thiols, the disulfides, and, in the case of phenylmagnesium bromide, the sulfide.

---

[21] Schmidlin, *Ber.*, *45*, 3171–82 (1912).

[22] Späth, *Monatsh.*, *36*, 4–12 (1915).

[23] Bachmann, *J. Am. Chem. Soc.*, *56*, 1363–7 (1934).

[24] Möller, *Arch. Pharm. Chim.*, *21*, 449 (1914); *Chem. Abstr.*, *9*, 623 (1915).

[25] Lifschitz, *Helv. Chim. Acta*, *1*, 472–4 (1918); Lifschitz and Kalberer, *Z. physik. Chem.*, *102*, 393–45 (1922).

[26] Evans and Dufford, *J. Am. Chem. Soc.*, *45*, 278–85 (1923); Dufford, Calvert, and Nightingale, *ibid.*, *45*, 2058–72 (1923); *47*, 95–102 (1925); Evans and Diepenhorst, *ibid.*, *48*, 715–23 (1926); Dufford, Nightingale, and Gaddum, *ibid.*, *49*, 858–64 (1927); Dufford, *ibid.*, *50*, 1822–4 (1928); Dufford, Nightingale, and Calvert, *J. Optical Soc. Am.*, *9*, 405–9 (1924); *Chem. Abstr.*, *19*, 608 (1925); *Phys. Rev.*, [2], *21*, 203–4 (1923); Thomas and Dufford, *J. Optical Soc. Am.*, *23*, 251–5 (1933); *Chem. Abstr.*, *27*, 4737 (1933).

[27] Wuyts and Cosyns, *Bull. soc. chim.*, [3], *29*, 689–93 (1903).

$$\underset{(32.0\text{ g. }C_2H_5I)}{C_2H_5MgI} + \underset{(7.0\text{ g.})}{S_x} \longrightarrow \underset{(4.0\text{ g.})}{C_2H_5SH} + \underset{(2.5\text{ g.})}{(C_2H_5S—)_2}$$

$$\underset{(60.0\text{ g. }C_6H_5Br)}{C_6H_5MgBr} + \underset{(12.0\text{ g.})}{S_x} \longrightarrow \underset{(4.8\text{ g.})}{C_6H_5SH} + \underset{(24.0\text{ g.})}{(C_6H_5S—)_2} + \underset{(0.5\text{ g.})}{(C_6H_5)_2S}$$

Taboury[28] treated some dozen arylmagnesium halides with octahedral sulfur which had been repeatedly crystallized from carbon disulfide and then pulverized, and obtained the corresponding thiols and disulfides.

Wuyts[29] attributed the phenyl sulfide detected in his study with Cosyns (*loc. cit.*[27]) to a secondary reaction, and showed that phenylmagnesium bromide reacts with phenyl disulfide to form phenyl sulfide and bromomagnesium thiophenolate.

$$(RS—)_2 + RMgX \longrightarrow R_2S + RSMgX$$

In a subsequent study[30] he showed that bromomagnesium thiophenolate reacts with sulfur to form phenyl disulfide and bromomagnesium sulfide.

$$2\ RSMgX + S_x \longrightarrow (RS—)_2 + S(MgX)_2$$

The latter is the source of the hydrogen sulfide often liberated in the hydrolysis of sulfur reaction mixtures.

In his earlier paper[29] Wuyts suggested that the sulfur reaction might follow a course analogous to that of the oxygenation, but later[30] inclined to the opinion that the halomagnesium thiolate (RSMgX) is the initial reaction product. By avoiding, as far as possible, the presence of an excess of sulfur he was able to prepare thiophenol from phenylmagnesium bromide in 80 percent yield.

A good (70 percent) yield of thiol was obtained by Bachmann and Cockerill[31] upon treatment of triphenylmethylmagnesium bromide with sulfur.

Mousseron *et al.*[32] report (without specifying yields) the preparation of thiols from cyclopentylmethylmagnesium chloride, 3-methylcyclopentylmethylmagnesium chloride, 3-methylcyclohexylmagnesium chloride, 3-methylcyclohexylmethylmagnesium chloride, 2-cyclohexenyl-1-magnesium chloride, and 2-decalylmagnesium chloride.

Grignard and Lepayre[33] refluxed sulfur with an ethyl ethereal solution of ethynylidenemagnesium bromide [$(\equiv CMgBr)_2$] for fifty hours, and obtained a black powder of unknown constitution containing 66–72 percent sulfur.

---

[28] Taboury, *Compt. rend.*, *138*, 982–3 (1904); *Chem. Zentr.*, *1904*,*I*, 1413; *Bull. soc. chim.*, [3], *29*, 761–5 (1903); *Ann. chim.*, [8], *15*, 5–66 (1908).

[29] Wuyts, *Bull. soc. chim.*, [3], *35*, 166 (1906).

[30] Wuyts, *Bull. soc. chim.*, [4], *5*, 405–12 (1909).

[31] Bachmann and Cockerill, *J. Am. Chem. Soc.*, *55*, 2932–4 (1933).

[32] Mousseron, Bousquet, and Marret, *Bull. soc. chim.*, [5], *15*, 84–90 (1948).

[33] Grignard and Lepayre, *Bull. soc. chim.*, [4], *43*, 930–1 (1928).

Sulfurization of pyrrylmagnesium iodide like oxygenation, leads to the formation of "pyrrole blacks."[34,35]

The β-indolylmagnesium bromides, upon treatment with sulfur, yield the sulfides (R_2S).[34,35] Upon successive treatment with sulfur and an acyl halide, however, they yield the thiol esters ($RSOCR'$),[34,35] together with disulfides [$(RS—)_2$].[36]

According to Oddo and Raffa (*loc. cit.*[36]), the reaction of β-methyl-α-indolylmagnesium bromide with sulfur proceeds in a different way, probably through a dithio intermediate (RS_2MgBr). The product isolated is a trisulfide (R_2S_3).

SELENIUM

Taboury[37] treated seven arylmagnesium halides with selenium in a manner similar to that employed for sulfur, obtaining the selenols, the diselenides, and, in three cases, the selenides. By operating with a deficiency of selenium (0.8 equivalent), Wuyts[38] obtained selenophenol from phenylmagnesium bromide in 81.2 percent yield. According to Giua and Cherchi,[39] selenium, like oxygen and sulfur, yields "pyrrole black" with pyrrylmagnesium bromide.

TELLURIUM

Giua and Cherchi (*loc. cit.*[39]) treated phenylmagnesium bromide with tellurium and obtained tellurophenol and phenyl telluride. Pyrrylmagnesium bromide, similarly treated, yielded "pyrrole black."

---

[34] Guia and Cherchi, *Gazz. chim. ital.*, *50,I*, 362–77 (1920); *Chem. Abstr.*, *15*, 521 (1921).

[35] Oddo and Mingoia, *Gazz. chim. ital.*, *62*, 299–317 (1932); *Chem. Abstr.*, *26*, 4603 (1932).

[36] Oddo and Raffa, *Gazz. chim. ital.*, *71*, 242–53 (1941); *Chem. Abstr.*, *36*, 2854 (1942).

[37] Taboury, *Compt. rend.*, *138*, 982–3 (1904); *Chem. Zentr.*, *1904,I*, 1413; *Bull. soc. chim.*, [3], *29*, 761–5 (1903); *Ann. chim.*, [8], *15*, 5–66 (1908).

[38] Wuyts, *Bull. soc. chim.*, [4], *5*, 405–12 (1909).

[39] Giua and Cherchi, *Gazz. chim. ital.*, *50,I*, 362–77 (1920); *Chem. Abstr.*, *15*, 521 (1921).

CHAPTER XXI

Reactions of Grignard Reagents with Miscellaneous Sulfur, Selenium, and Tellurium Compounds

ALKYL SULFATES

The idea of employing the reactions of alkyl sulfates (rather than of alkyl halides) with Grignard reagents for the preparation of hydrocarbons apparently occurred to Werner and Zilkens[1] and to Houben[2] nearly simultaneously.[3] The reaction which they regarded as "normal," and which they reported, is described stoichiometrically as follows:

(I) $$R_2SO_4 + R'MgX \longrightarrow RR' + RSO_4MgX$$

Upon more detailed investigation Suter and Gerhart[4] found that there is in addition a reaction of the type:

(IIA) $$R_2SO_4 + R'MgX \longrightarrow RX + RSO_4MgR'$$

(IIB) $$2\ RSO_4MgR' \longrightarrow R'_2Mg + (RSO_4)_2Mg$$

When, for example, ethereal *n*-butylmagnesium bromide was treated with slightly more than one equivalent of ethyl sulfate the resultant solution contained nearly pure di-*n*-butylmagnesium, and there was an 86 percent yield of ethyl bromide (as estimated by bromide ion disappearance). The subject was sufficiently investigated to show that the mutual reactivities of various reactant pairs (with respect to reactions I and II) vary over a considerable range.

For obvious reasons it is recommended that, in general, a ratio of two moles of ester per mole of Grignard reagent be employed in preparative work. Suter and Gerhart (*loc. cit.*[4]) found that when phenylmagnesium bromide and *n*-butyl sulfate are combined in one-to-one ratio the yield of *n*-butylbenzene is about 16 percent, whereas doubling the proportion of ester increases the yield to 42 percent.

Bert[5] has studied the reactions of phenylmagnesium bromide with methyl ethyl sulfate, ethyl *n*-propyl sulfate, and ethyl *n*-butyl sulfate, and reports that the hydrocarbon product in each case contains the smaller of the alkyl radicals originally present in the unsymmetrical ester. It ap-

---

[1] Werner and Zilkens, *Ber.*, *36*, 2116–8 (1903).

[2] Houben, *Ber.*, *36*, 3083–6 (1903).

[3] If interested in priority polemics see: Werner and Zilkens, *Ber.*, *36*, 3618–9 (1903); Houben, *Ber.*, *37*, 488–9 (1904).

[4] Suter and Gerhart, *J. Am. Chem. Soc.*, *57*, 107–9 (1935). See also: Cope, *ibid.*, *56*, 1578–81 (1934).

[5] Bert, *Compt. rend.*, *178*, 1182–4 (1924); *Chem. Zentr.*, *1924,II*, 170.

pears probable that more extensive quantitative studies would lead to some qualification of this generalization.

Using especially prepared benzyl chloride, and employing the method of Gilman and Catlin,[6] Burtle and Shriner[7] treated benzylmagnesium chloride with ethyl sulfate, obtaining a product which, upon oxidation, yielded about 5 percent of terephthalic acid. This implies a rather unusual, though by no means unique, type of "allylic rearrangement" (*q.v.*, Chapter XVII), for most rearrangement products of benzylmagnesium halides are *o*-tolyl compounds.

$$(C_2H_5)_2SO_4 \xrightarrow{C_6H_5CH_2MgCl} \xrightarrow{H_2O} n\text{-}C_3H_7C_6H_5 + 4\text{-}CH_3C_6H_4C_2H_5$$

Gilman and Kirby[8] report a reaction in which methyl sulfate apparently acts as a coupling reagent:

$$(CH_3)_2SO_4 + (C_6H_5)_2CHMgCl \longrightarrow [(C_6H_5)_2CH—]_2\ (95.5\%) + (C_6H_5)_2CHCH_3\ (2.3\%)$$

However, the tendency of benzhydryl chloride to yield Wurtz product during attempted Grignardization, as well as the tendency of the Grignard reagent toward homolytic dissociation, invites further study of this reaction with magnesium of high purity.

SULFONIC ESTERS

Like the alkyl sulfates, the alkyl esters of the aryl sulfonic acids react with Grignard reagents in two ways:[9]

$$\text{(I)} \quad ArSO_2OR + R'MgX \longrightarrow ArSO_2OMgX + RR'$$

$$\text{(II)} \quad ArSO_2OR + R'MgX \longrightarrow ArSO_2OMgR' + RX$$

Reaction I, first reported by Ferns and Lapworth,[10] is usually regarded as "normal," and is most commonly employed for preparative purposes.

Kenyon *et al.*[11] have shown that when R is optically active reaction II takes place with retention of most of the optical activity, and presumably with inversion.

$$(a) \quad \text{D}(+)\text{-}4\text{-}CH_3C_6H_4SO_2OCH(CH_3)R \xrightarrow{R'MgBr} (-)\text{-}R(CH_3)CHBr$$

$$(R = C_2H_5,\ n\text{-}C_6H_{13},\ C_6H_5CH_2;\ R' = C_2H_5,\ C_6H_5)$$

$$(b) \quad (-)\text{-}4\text{-}CH_3C_6H_4SO_2OCH(CH_3)CO_2C_2H_5 \xrightarrow{RMgX} (+)\text{-}CH_3CHXCO_2C_2H_5$$

$$(RMgX = C_2H_5MgBr,\ C_6H_5MgBr,\ C_2H_5OMgI)$$

---

[6] Gilman and Catlin, *Organic Syntheses*, Coll. Vol. I, 2nd ed., 471–3 (1941).

[7] Burtle and Shriner, *J. Am. Chem. Soc.*, *69*, 2059–60 (1947).

[8] Gilman and Kirby, *J. Am. Chem. Soc.*, *48*, 1733–6 (1926).

[9] Suter and Gerhart, *J. Am. Chem. Soc.*, *57*, 107–9 (1935).

[10] Ferns and Lapworth, *Proc. Chem. Soc.*, *28*, 18–9 (1912); *J. Chem. Soc.*, *101*, 273–87 (1912).

[11] (*a*) Kenyon, Phillips, and Turley, *J. Chem. Soc.*, *127*, 399–417 (1925); (*b*) Kenyon, Phillips and Pittman, *ibid.*, *1935*, 1072–84.

TABLE XXI-I

REACTIONS OF GRIGNARD REAGENTS WITH SYMMETRICAL ALKYL SULFATES

R_2SO_4	$R'MgX$	RR'	Ref.
$[(CH_3)_2SO_4]$	$(MgBr_2)$	$[CH_3Br$ (93%)]	*24*
$[(CH_3)_2SO_4]$	(MgI_2)	$[CH_3I$ (97%)]	*24*
$(CH_3)_2SO_4$	5-Iodo-2-furyl-MgI	[2-Iodofuran (72%)]	*23*
$(CH_3)_2SO_4$	t-C_4H_9MgI	$(CH_3)_4C$ (75%)	*3*
$(CH_3)_2SO_4$	C_6H_5MgBr	$CH_3C_6H_5$ (31%)	*1*
$(CH_3)_2SO_4$	C_6H_5MgBr	$CH_3C_6H_5$ (41%)	*2*
2 $(CH_3)_2SO_4$	C_6H_5MgBr	$CH_3C_6H_5$ (62%)	*11*
$(CH_3)_2SO_4$	C_6H_5MgBr	$CH_3C_6H_5$ (37%)	*24*
$(CH_3)_2SO_4$	C_6H_5MgI	$CH_3C_6H_5$ (22%)	*24*
$(CH_3)_2SO_4$	n-$C_4H_9C{\equiv}CMgBr$	n-$C_4H_9C{\equiv}CCH_3$ (*ca.* 70%)	*19*
$(CH_3)_2SO_4$	3-$F_3CC_6H_4MgBr$	1-CH_3-3-$F_3CC_6H_4$ (9%)	*12*
$(CH_3)_2SO_4$	$C_6H_5CH_2MgCl$	$C_2H_5C_6H_5$ (21%)	*2*
$(CH_3)_2SO_4$	4-$CH_3C_6H_4MgBr$	1,4-$(CH_3)_2C_6H_4$ (74%)	*1*
$(CH_3)_2SO_4$	4-$CH_3C_6H_4MgBr$	1,4-$(CH_3)_2C_6H_4$ (68%)	*2*
$(CH_3)_2SO_4$	2,4-$(CH_3)_2C_6H_3MgBr$	1,2,4-$(CH_3)_3C_6H_3$ (52%)	*24*
$(CH_3)_2SO_4$	2,4-$(CH_3)_2C_6H_3MgBr$	1,2,4-$(CH_3)_3C_6H_3$ (50–60%)	*22*
$(CH_3)_2SO_4$	2,4-$(CH_3)_2C_6H_3MgI$	1,2,4-$(CH_3)_3C_6H_3$ (29%)	*24*
2 $(CH_3)_2SO_4$	2,4-$(CH_3)_2C_6H_3MgI$	1,2,4-$(CH_3)_3C_6H_3$ (37%)	*9*
$(CH_3)_2SO_4$	n-$C_6H_{13}C{\equiv}CMgBr$	n-$C_6H_{13}C{\equiv}CCH_3$ (*ca.* 70%)	*19*
2 $(CH_3)_2SO_4$	2,4,6-$(CH_3)_3C_6H_2MgBr$	1,2,4,6-$(CH_3)_4C_6H_2$ (52–60%)	*8,18*
$(CH_3)_2SO_4$	2,4,6-$(CH_3)_3C_6H_2MgBr$	1,2,4,6-$(CH_3)_4C_6H_2$ (49%)	*24*
$(CH_3)_2SO_4$	1-$C_{10}H_7CH_2MgCl$	1-$C_{10}H_7C_2H_5$ (55%)	*21*
$(CH_3)_2SO_4$	5-$CH_3C_{10}H_6$-1-MgBr	1,5-$(CH_3)_2C_{10}H_6$ (34%)	*10*
$(CH_3)_2SO_4$	8-$CH_3C_{10}H_6$-1-MgBr	1,8-$(CH_3)_2C_{10}H_6$ (36%)	*10*
$(CH_3)_2SO_4$	2,7-$(CH_3)_2C_{10}H_5$-1-MgBr	1,2,7-$(CH_3)_3C_{10}H_5$	*14*
3 $(CH_3)_2SO_4$	2,6-$(CH_3)_2$-4-t-$C_4H_9C_6H_2MgBr$	1,2,6-$(CH_3)_3$-4-t-$C_4H_9C_6H_2$ (33%)	*15*
$(CH_3)_2SO_4$	4-i-$C_3H_7C_6H_4(CH_2)_3MgCl$	1-i-C_3H_7-4-n-$C_4H_9C_6H_4$	*16*
$(CH_3)_2SO_4$	$(C_6H_5)_2CHMgCl$	$(C_6H_5)_2CHCH_3$ (2%)	*7*

TABLE XXI-I (Continued)

R_2SO_4	$R'MgX$	RR'	Ref.
$(C_2H_5)_2SO_4$	$H_2C{=}CHC{\equiv}CMgBr$	$H_2C{=}CHC{\equiv}CC_2H_5$ (*ca.* 70%)	*19*
$(C_2H_5)_2SO_4$	n-C_4H_9MgBr	n-C_6H_{14} (69%)	*4*
$(C_2H_5)_2SO_4$	4-BrC_6H_4MgBr	4-$BrC_6H_4C_2H_5$ (45%)	*4,17*
$(C_2H_5)_2SO_4$	C_6H_5MgBr	$C_6H_5C_2H_5$ (33%)	*4*
$(C_2H_5)_2SO_4$	n-$C_4H_9C{\equiv}CMgBr$	n-$C_4H_9C{\equiv}CC_2H_5$ (*ca.* 70%)	*19*
$(C_2H_5)_2SO_4$	$(CH_2)_5CHMgBr$	$(CH_2)_5CHC_2H_5$ (80%)	*4*
2 $(C_2H_5)_2SO_4$	$C_6H_5CH_2MgCl$	C_6H_5-n-C_3H_7 (70–75%)	*6,4*
2 $(C_2H_5)_2SO_4$	$C_6H_5CH_2MgCl$	C_6H_5-n-C_3H_7 (chiefly); 4-$C_2H_5C_6H_4CH_3$ (0.4–5.0%)	*20*
$(C_2H_5)_2SO_4$	4-$CH_3OC_6H_4MgBr$	4-$CH_3OC_6H_4C_2H_5$ (89%)	*4*
$(C_2H_5)_2SO_4$	$C_6H_5C{\equiv}CMgBr$	$C_6H_5C{\equiv}CC_2H_5$ (70%)	*4*
$(C_2H_5)_2SO_4$	2-$C_2H_5C_6H_4MgBr$	1,2-$(C_2H_5)_2C_6H_4$ (49%)	*13*
$(C_2H_5)_2SO_4$	4-$C_2H_5C_6H_4MgBr$	1,4-$(C_2H_5)_2C_6H_4$ (58%)	*13*
$(C_2H_5)_2SO_4$	2,6-$(CH_3)_2C_6H_3MgI$	1,3-$(CH_3)_2$-2-$C_2H_5C_6H_3$	*18*
$(C_2H_5)_2SO_4$	n-$C_6H_{13}C{\equiv}CMgBr$	n-$C_6H_{13}C{\equiv}CC_2H_5$ (*ca.* 70%)	*19*
$(C_2H_5)_2SO_4$	1-$C_{10}H_7MgBr$	1-$C_2H_5C_{10}H_7$ (71%)	*4*
$(C_2H_5)_2SO_4$	4-i-$C_3H_7C_6H_4(CH_2)_3MgCl$	1-i-C_3H_7-4-n-$C_5H_{11}C_6H_4$	*16*
$(i$-$C_3H_7)_2SO_4$	C_6H_5MgBr	C_6H_5-i-C_3H_7 (10%)	*5*
$(i$-$C_3H_7)_2SO_4$	4-$CH_3C_6H_4MgBr$	1-CH_3-4-i-$C_3H_7C_6H_4$ (10%)	*5*
$(i$-$C_3H_7)_2SO_4$	4-i-$C_3H_7C_6H_4(CH_2)_3MgCl$	1-i-C_3H_7-4-i-$C_6H_{13}C_6H_4$	*16*
$(n$-$C_4H_9)_2SO_4$	C_6H_5MgBr	C_6H_5-n-C_4H_9 (16%)	*11*
2 $(n$-$C_4H_9)_2SO_4$	C_6H_5MgBr	C_6H_5-n-C_4H_9 (42%)	*11*

REFERENCES FOR TABLE XXI-I

(*1*) Werner and Zilkens, *Ber.*, *36*, 2116–8 (1903).
(*2*) Houben, *Ber.*, *36*, 3083–6 (1903).
(*3*) Ferrario and Fagetti, *Gazz. chim. ital.*, *38,II*, 630–4 (1908); *Chem. Zentr.*, *1909,I*, 463.
(*4*) Gilman and Hoyle, *J. Am. Chem. Soc.*, *44*, 2621–6 (1922).
(*5*) Bert, *Compt. rend.*, *176*, 840–7 (1923); *Chem. Abstr.*, *17*, 1957 (1923).
(*6*) Gilman and Catlin, *Organic Syntheses*, Coll. Vol. I, 2nd ed., 471–3 (1941); Gilman and Meyers, *Organic Syntheses*, *4*, 59–61 (1925).
(*7*) Gilman and Kirby, *J. Am. Chem. Soc.*, *48*, 1733–6 (1926).
(*8*) Smith, *Organic Syntheses*, Coll. Vol. II, 360–2 (1943); *Organic Syntheses*, *11*, 66–9 (1931); Smith and MacDougall, *J. Am. Chem. Soc.*, *51*, 3001–8 (1929).
(*9*) Smith and Lund, *J. Am. Chem. Soc.*, *52*, 4144–50 (1930).
(*10*) Vesely and Stursa, *Collection Czechoslov. Chem. Comm.*, *3*, 430–1 (1931); *Chem. Abstr.*, *25*, 4877 (1931).
(*11*) Suter and Gerhart, *J. Am. Chem. Soc.*, *57*, 107–9 (1935).
(*12*) Simons and Ramler, *J. Am. Chem. Soc.*, *65*, 389–92 (1943).
(*13*) Karabinos, Serijan, and Gibbons, *J. Am. Chem. Soc.*, *68*, 2107–8 (1946).
(*14*) Buu-Hoï and Lecocq, *J. Chem. Soc.*, *1946*, 830–2.
(*15*) Fuson, Mills, Klose, and Carpenter, *J. Org. Chem.*, *12*, 587–95 (1947).
(*16*) Bert, *Compt. rend.*, *186*, 373–5 (1928); *Chem. Zentr.*, *1928,I*, 1758.
(*17*) Roy and Marvel, *J. Am. Chem. Soc.*, *57*, 1311–4 (1935).
(*18*) Birch, Dean, Fidler, and Lowry, *J. Am. Chem. Soc.*, *71*, 1362–9 (1949).
(*19*) Thorne, Hennion, and Nieuwland, *J. Am. Chem. Soc.*, *58*, 796–7 (1936).
(*20*) Burtle and Shriner, *J. Am. Chem. Soc.*, *69*, 2059–60 (1947).
(*21*) Gilman and Kirby, *J. Am. Chem. Soc.*, *51*, 3475–8 (1929).
(*22*) Maxwell and Adams, *J. Am. Chem. Soc.*, *52*, 2959–72 (1930).
(*23*) Gilman and Wright, *J. Am. Chem. Soc.*, *55*, 3302–4 (1933).
(*24*) Cope, *J. Am. Chem. Soc.*, *56*, 1578–81 (1934).

Other than this nothing bearing on the mechanisms of the reactions has been established.

Gilman and Heck[12] have shown by direct experiment, and Rossander and Marvel[13] by inference, that the sulfonates formed in reactions I and II are capable of further reaction with the sulfonic ester.

$$\text{(III)} \qquad ArSO_2OMgX + ArSO_2OR \longrightarrow RX + (ArSO_2O)_2Mg$$

$$\text{(IV)} \qquad ArSO_2OMgR' + ArSO_2OR \longrightarrow RR' + (ArSO_2O)_2Mg$$

Gilman and Heck (*loc. cit.*[12]) confirmed equation III by carrying out the following reaction sequence:

$$2\text{-}C_{10}H_7SO_2OH \xrightarrow{CH_3MgI} 2\text{-}C_{10}H_7SO_2OMgI \xrightarrow{4\text{-}CH_3C_6H_4SO_2O\text{-}n\text{-}C_4H_9} n\text{-}C_4H_9I$$

Rossander and Marvel (*loc. cit.*[13]) confirmed, for several reactant pairs (see Table XXI-II), the implication of equation IV that a two-to-one ester-Grignard reagent ratio should result in higher RR′ yields than a one-to-one ratio.

Data reported for reactions I and II, presumably including the contributions of reactions III and IV, are summarized in Table XXI-II.

---

[12] Gilman and Heck, *J. Am. Chem. Soc.*, *50*, 2223–30 (1928).
[13] Rossander and Marvel, *J. Am. Chem. Soc.*, *50*, 1491–6 (1928).

TABLE XXI-II

REACTIONS OF GRIGNARD REAGENTS WITH ALKYL ESTERS OF ARYL SULFONIC ACIDS

(α-C_4H_3S = 2-thienyl; C_7H_7 = *p*-tolyl)

$ArSO_2OR$	$R'MgX$	% RR'*	% RX*	Ref.
$C_6H_5SO_3(CH_2)_2Cl$	$R'MgX$	+	...	*13*
$C_7H_7SO_3CH_3$	C_6H_5MgBr	38	...	*3*
$C_7H_7SO_3CH_3$	$C_6H_5CH_2MgBr$	41	...	*3*
$C_7H_7SO_3CH_3$	C_7H_7MgBr	29	...	*3*
2 $C_7H_7SO_3(CH_2)_2Cl$	$(\alpha$-$C_4H_3S)MgBr$	71	...	*14,16*
$C_7H_7SO_3(CH_2)_2Cl$	n-$C_3H_7C{\equiv}CMgBr$	38	...	*17*
$C_7H_7SO_3(CH_2)_2Cl$	C_6H_5MgBr	36†	...	*2,6*
$C_7H_7SO_3(CH_2)_2Cl$	$C_6H_5CO_2MgBr$	5	...	*2*
$C_7H_7SO_3(CH_2)_2Cl$	$C_6H_5CH_2MgCl$	59†	...	*2,6*
$C_7H_7SO_3(CH_2)_2Cl$	2-$CH_3C_6H_4MgBr$	+†	...	*6*
$C_7H_7SO_3(CH_2)_2Cl$	C_7H_7MgBr	+†	...	*6*
$C_7H_7SO_3(CH_2)_2Cl$	$C_6H_5C{\equiv}CMgBr$	75	...	*2*
$C_7H_7SO_3(CH_2)_2Cl$	$C_6H_5C{\equiv}CMgBr$	46	86	*18*
$C_7H_7SO_3(CH_2)_2Cl$	$C_6H_5CH{=}CHMgBr$	0‡	0‡	*12*
$C_7H_7SO_3(CH_2)_2Cl$	$C_7H_7CH_2MgCl$	+†	...	*6*
$C_7H_7SO_3(CH_2)_2Cl$	2,4-$(CH_3)_2C_6H_3MgBr$	+†	...	*6*
$C_7H_7SO_3(CH_2)_2Cl$	2,5-$(CH_3)_2C_6H_3MgBr$	+†	...	*6*
$C_7H_7SO_3(CH_2)_2Cl$	4-i-$C_3H_7C_6H_4MgBr$	+†	...	*6*
$C_7H_7SO_3(CH_2)_2Cl$	2-CH_3-4-i-$C_3H_7C_6H_3MgBr$	+†	...	*6*
$C_7H_7SO_3(CH_2)_2Cl$	4-n-$C_7H_{15}C_6H_4MgBr$	30	...	*15*
$C_7H_7SO_3C_2H_5$	C_2H_5MgI	...	32	*5*
$C_7H_7SO_3C_2H_5$	C_6H_5MgBr	30	...	*3,1*
$C_7H_7SO_3C_2H_5$	$(CH_2)_5CHMgBr$	9	...	*3*
$C_7H_7SO_3C_2H_5$	$C_6H_5CH_2MgCl$	38	...	*3*
$C_7H_7SO_3C_2H_5$	C_7H_7MgBr	37	...	*3*
$C_7H_7SO_3C_2H_5$	$C_6H_5OC{\equiv}CMgBr$	15	...	*11*
$C_7H_7SO_3C_2H_5$	$C_6H_5(CH_2)_3MgCl$	40	...	*3*
$C_7H_7SO_3C_2H_5$	1-$C_{10}H_7MgBr$	19	...	*3*
$C_7H_7SO_3C_2H_5$	n-$C_{12}H_{25}MgBr$	27	...	*3*
$C_7H_7SO_3CH_2CH{=}CH_2$	$C_6H_5CH_2MgCl$	47	...	*3*
2 $C_7H_7SO_3(CH_2)_3Cl$	C_2H_5MgBr	23	+	*9*
$C_7H_7SO_3(CH_2)_3Cl$	$(\alpha$-$C_4H_3S)MgBr$	61	...	*16*
$C_7H_7SO_3(CH_2)_3Cl$	n-C_4H_9MgCl	...	+	*9*
$C_7H_7SO_3(CH_2)_3Cl$	n-C_4H_9MgBr	...	+	*9*
$C_7H_7SO_3(CH_2)_3Cl$	n-C_4H_9MgI	...	+	*9*
2-$C_7H_7SO_3(CH_2)_3Cl$	C_6H_5MgBr	62	+	*9*
$C_7H_7SO_3(CH_2)_3Cl$	$(CH_2)_5CHMgBr$	14	+	*9*
2 $C_7H_7SO_3(CH_2)_3Cl$	$(CH_2)_5CHMgBr$	62	+	*9*

* Where a product is reported but the yield is not specifically stated, that fact is indicated by a plus sign in the appropriate column; where a product may have been present but apparently was not sought by the investigators cited, that fact is indicated by triple dots in the appropriate column.

† The yields of RR' product obtained by Bert (*6*) are reported as ranging from 30 to 80 percent and are said to have been "mostly high."

‡ Khitrik (*12*) reports "no reaction."

TABLE XXI-II (Continued)

$ArSO_2OR$	R'MgX	% RR'*	% RX*	Ref.
2 $C_7H_7SO_3(CH_2)_3Cl$	n-$C_6H_{13}MgBr$	52	+	*9*
$C_7H_7SO_3(CH_2)_3Cl$	$C_6H_5CH_2MgCl$	42	+	*9*
2 $C_7H_7SO_3(CH_2)_3Cl$	$C_6H_5CH_2MgCl$	50	+	*9*
$C_7H_7SO_3(CH_2)_3Cl$	n-$C_7H_{15}MgBr$	11	+	*9*
2 $C_7H_7SO_3(CH_2)_3Cl$	n-$C_7H_{15}MgBr$	50	+	*9*
$C_7H_7SO_3(CH_2)_3Cl$	$C_6H_5C \equiv CMgBr$	75	...	*18*
$C_7H_7SO_3(CH_2)_3Cl$	$C_6H_5(CH_2)_4MgCl$	25	+	*9*
2 $C_7H_7SO_3(CH_2)_3Cl$	$C_6H_5(CH_2)_4MgCl$	44	+	*9*
2 $C_7H_7SO_3(CH_2)_3Cl$	n-$C_{12}H_{25}MgBr$	30	+	*9*
2 $C_7H_7SO_3$-n-C_3H_7	4-BrC_6H_4MgBr	43	...	*7*
$C_7H_7SO_3$-n-C_3H_7	$C_6H_5CH_2MgCl$	36	...	*3*
$C_7H_7SO_3$-n-C_4H_9	n-C_3H_7MgI	...	67	*5*
2 $C_7H_7SO_3$-n-C_4H_9	4-BrC_6H_4MgBr	42	...	*7*
$C_7H_7SO_3$-n-C_4H_9	C_6H_5MgBr	64§	67§	*5*
$C_7H_7SO_3$-n-C_4H_9	$C_6H_5CH_2MgCl$	25	...	*3*
$C_7H_7SO_3$-n-C_4H_9	$C_6H_5CH_2MgCl$	67	+	*5*
2 $C_7H_7SO_3$-n-C_4H_9	$C_6H_5CH_2MgCl$	26	...	*10*
$C_7H_7SO_3$-n-C_4H_9	n-$C_7H_{15}MgBr$	14	...	*3*
$C_7H_7SO_3$-n-C_4H_9	$C_6H_5OC \equiv CMgBr$	52	...	*11*
$C_7H_7SO_3$-i-C_4H_9	$C_6H_5CH_2MgCl$	33	...	*3*
$C_7H_7SO_3$-s-C_4H_9	$C_6H_5CH_2MgCl$	30	...	*3*
D(+)-$C_7H_7SO_3CH(CH_3)C_2H_5$	C_2H_5MgBr	...	+¶	*8*
(−)-$C_7H_7SO_3CH(CH_3)CO_2C_2H_5$	C_2H_5MgBr	...	+¶	*4*
(−)-$C_7H_7SO_3CH(CH_3)CO_2C_2H_5$	C_6H_5MgBr	...	+¶	*4*
$C_7H_7SO_3CH(CH_3)CO_2C_2H_5$	C_6H_5MgBr	...	55	*5*
$C_7H_7SO_3$-n-C_5H_{11}	4-BrC_6H_5MgBr	41	...	*7*
$C_7H_7SO_3$-n-C_5H_{11}	$C_6H_5CH_2MgCl$	45	...	*3*
$C_7H_7SO_3CH_2C_6H_4$-4-Br	$C_6H_5C \equiv CMgBr$	50	...	*19*
$C_7H_7SO_3CH_2C_6H_5$	$C_6H_5CH_2MgCl$	55‖	...	*3*
$C_7H_7SO_3CH_2C_6H_5$	4-$BrC_6H_4C \equiv CMgBr$	26	...	*19*
D(+)-$C_7H_7SO_3CH(CH_3)CH_2C_6H_5$	C_6H_5MgBr	...	+¶	*8*
D(+)-$C_7H_7SO_3CH(CH_3)$$n$-$C_6H_{13}$	C_6H_5MgBr	...	+¶	*8*

§In addition to the products here indicated, this reaction also yielded a small amount of phenyl p-tolyl sulfone.

¶The product reported retains optical activity, presumably with inversion of configuration.

‖The yield reported is probably high by reason of inclusion of the Wurtz by-product formed in preparation of the Grignard reagent.

REFERENCES FOR TABLE XXI-II

(*1*) Ferns and Lapworth, *Proc. Chem. Soc.*, *28*, 18–9 (1912); *J. Chem. Soc.*, *101*, 273–87 (1912).
(*2*) Gilman and Beaber, *J. Am. Chem. Soc.*, *45*, 839–42 (1923).
(*3*) Gilman and Beaber, *J. Am. Chem. Soc.*, *47*, 518–25 (1925).
(*4*) Kenyon, Phillips, and Turley, *J. Chem. Soc.*, *127*, 399–417 (1925).
(*5*) Gilman and Heck, *J. Am. Chem. Soc.*, *50*, 2223–30 (1928).
(*6*) Bert, *Compt. rend.*, *186*, 373–5 (1928); *Chem. Zentr.*, *1928,I*, 1758.
(*7*) Roy and Marvel, *J. Am. Chem. Soc.*, *57*, 1311–4 (1935).
(*8*) Kenyon, Phillips, and Pittman, *J. Chem. Soc.*, *1935*, 1072–84.
(*9*) Rossander and Marvel, *J. Am. Chem. Soc.*, *50*, 1491–6 (1928).

(10) Gilman and Robinson, *Organic Syntheses*, 10, 4–5 (1930).
(11) Jacobs, Cramer, and Weiss, *J. Am. Chem. Soc.*, 62, 1849–54 (1940).
(12) Khitrik, *J. Gen. Chem.* (U.S.S.R.), 10, 2098–100 (1940); *Chem. Abstr.*, 35, 3961 (1941).
(13) Bert, *Compt. rend.*, 213, 1015–6 (1941); *Chem. Abstr.*, 37, 4049 (1943).
(14) Blicke and Leonard, *J. Am. Chem. Soc.*, 68, 1934–6 (1946).
(15) Sulzbacher and Bergmann, *J. Org. Chem.*, 13, 303–8 (1948).
(16) Blicke and Burckhalter, *J. Am. Chem. Soc.*, 64, 477–80 (1942).
(17) Newman and Wotiz, *J. Am. Chem. Soc.*, 71, 1292–7 (1949).
(18) Johnson, Schwartz, and Jacobs, *J. Am. Chem. Soc.*, 60, 1882–4 (1938).
(19) Johnson, Jacobs, and Schwartz, *J. Am. Chem. Soc.*, 60, 1885–9 (1938).

In addition to the reactions already discussed, sulfonic esters are capable of undergoing sulfone formation with Grignard reagents.

$$RSO_2OR' + R''MgX \longrightarrow RSO_2R'' + R'OMgX$$

Although this tendency appears to be intensified in the esters of the alkanesulfonic acids and in the aryl esters of the aryl sulfonic acids, it is not exclusively confined to them, for Gilman and Heck (*loc. cit.*[12]) report the formation of small quantities of phenyl *p*-tolyl sulfone in the reaction of phenylmagnesium bromide with *n*-butyl *p*-toluenesulfonate. Data are summarized in Table XXI-III.

TABLE XXI-III

REACTIONS OF GRIGNARD REAGENTS WITH ALKANESULFONIC ESTERS AND ARYL *p*-TOLUENESULFONATES

(C_7H_7 = *p*-tolyl.)

RSO_2OR'	$R''MgX$	% $R'R''$	% RSO_2R''	Ref.
$C_2H_5SO_3CH_3$	C_6H_5MgBr	21	14	3
$C_2H_5SO_3C_2H_5$	C_6H_5MgBr	+*	+†	1,5
$C_2H_5SO_3C_6H_5$	C_6H_5MgBr	6–11‡	74	3
$(CH_2)_5CHSO_3C_2H_5$	C_6H_5MgBr	18	...	4
$C_7H_7SO_3C_6H_5$	C_6H_5MgBr	...	44	2
$C_7H_7SO_3C_6H_5$	C_7H_7MgBr	...	45	2
$C_7H_7SO_3C_6H_5$	$4\text{-}CH_3OC_6H_4MgBr$	...	82	2
$C_7H_7SO_3C_6H_5$	$1\text{-}C_{10}H_7MgBr$	...	71	2
$C_7H_7SO_3C_6H_4\text{-}2\text{-}CH_3$	C_6H_5MgBr	...	43	2
$(C_7H_7SO_3C_6H_4\text{-}4-)_2$	C_6H_5MgBr	...	61	2

* Present in small amount only.
† Principal product.
‡ The yield of biphenyl reported (1–2 g. from 25 g. ester) is attributable in large part, and perhaps altogether, to Wurtz byproduct formation in preparation of the Grignard reagent.

REFERENCES FOR TABLE XXI-III

(1) Ferns and Lapworth, *Proc. Chem. Soc.*, 28, 18–9 (1912); *J. Chem. Soc.*, 101, 273–87 (1912).
(2) Gilman, Beaber, and Myers, *J. Am. Chem. Soc.*, 47, 2047–52 (1925).
(3) Gilman and Robinson, *Bull. soc. chim.*, [4], 45, 636–41 (1929).
(4) Gilman and Heck, *J. Am. Chem. Soc.*, 50, 2223–30 (1928).
(5) Strecker, *Ber.*, 43, 1131–6 (1910).

Other papers bearing on the reactions of Grignard reagents with sulfonic esters, but containing little specific information, have been published by Wedekind and Schenk[14] and by Mine.[15]

ESTERS OF OTHER SULFUR ACIDS

Sulfites. Strecker[16] reported reactions of phenylmagnesium bromide and benzylmagnesium chloride with ethyl sulfite to yield sulfoxides.

$$(C_2H_5O)_2SO \xrightarrow{RMgX} R_2SO$$

Bert[17] recommended *n*-butyl sulfite as preferable to thionyl chloride for the Grignard preparation of sulfoxides, and reported having effected such sulfoxide preparations with *n*-butyl-, phenyl-, and *p*-cumylmagnesium bromides and with *p*-isopropylbenzylmagnesium chloride.

Gilman *et al.*[18] have shown that the alcohols (or phenols) which might be expected as byproducts of such reactions are also formed.

$$(n\text{-}C_4H_9O)_2SO \xrightarrow{C_6H_5MgBr} (C_6H_5)_2SO\ (40\%) + n\text{-}C_4H_9OH\ (44\%)$$

$$(C_6H_5O)_2SO \xrightarrow{C_6H_5MgBr} (C_6H_5)_2SO\ (67\text{–}74\%) + C_6H_5OH\ (85\text{–}88\%)$$

$$(C_6H_5O)_2SO \xrightarrow{C_6H_5CH_2MgCl} (C_6H_5CH_2)_2SO\ (52\%) + C_6H_5OH\ (53\%)$$

Sulfinates. Gilman *et al.*[18,19] have further shown that the sulfinates also react with Grignard reagents to form sulfoxides and alcohols.

$$4\text{-}CH_3C_6H_4SO\text{—}OCH_2CH_2Cl \xrightarrow{C_6H_5MgBr} 4\text{-}CH_3C_6H_4SOC_6H_5\ (31\%)$$

$$4\text{-}CH_3C_6H_4SO\text{—}OC_2H_5 \xrightarrow{C_6H_5CH_2MgCl} 4\text{-}CH_3C_6H_4SOCH_2C_6H_5\ (57\%)$$

$$4\text{-}CH_3C_6H_4SO\text{—}O\text{-}n\text{-}C_4H_9 \xrightarrow{C_6H_5MgBr} 4\text{-}CH_3C_6H_4SOC_6H_5\ (46\%) + n\text{-}C_4H_9OH\ (67\%)$$

$$C_6H_5SO\text{—}OCH_3 \xrightarrow{C_6H_5MgBr} (C_6H_5)_2SO\ (65\%) + CH_3OH$$

Sulfenates. Methyl benzenesulfenate reacts similarly with phenylmagnesium bromide to form phenyl sulfide and methyl alcohol (Gilman and Robinson, *loc. cit.*[19b]).

$$C_6H_5S\text{—}OCH_3 \xrightarrow{C_6H_5MgBr} (C_6H_5)_2S\ (63\%) + CH_3OH$$

Gilman, Robinson, and Beaber (*loc. cit.*[18]) report the isolation of some sulfoxide from this reaction mixture.

$$C_6H_5S\text{—}OCH_3 \xrightarrow{C_6H_5MgBr} (C_6H_5)_2S\ (48\%) + (C_6H_5)_2SO$$

---

[14] Wedekind and Schenk, *Ber.*, *54B*, 1604–12 (1921).

[15] Mine, *J. Chem. Soc. Japan*, *55*, 905–9, 1087–90 (1934); *56*, 200–9, 1112–7 (1935); *Chem. Abstr.*, *29*, 753, 5427, 7940 (1935); *30*, 441 (1936).

[16] Strecker, *Ber.*, *43*, 1131–6 (1910).

[17] Bert, *Compt. rend.*, *178*, 1826–8 (1924); *Chem. Abstr.*, *18*, 2496 (1924).

[18] Gilman, Robinson, and Beaber, *J. Am. Chem. Soc.*, *48*, 2715–8 (1926).

[19] (*a*) Gilman and Beaber, *J. Am. Chem. Soc.*, *45*, 839–42 (1923); (*b*) Gilman and Robinson, *Bull. soc. chim.*, [4], *45*, 636–41 (1929).

Thiolsulfonates. The so-called "disulfoxides," actually thiolsulfonates, react with Grignard reagents to form sulfides and sulfinic acids (Gilman *et al.*[20]).

$$4\text{-}CH_3C_6H_4SO_2—SC_6H_4\text{-}p\text{-}CH_3 \xrightarrow{C_6H_5CH_2MgCl} 4\text{-}CH_3C_6H_4SCH_2C_6H_5\ (23\%) + 4\text{-}CH_3C_6H_4SO_2H\ (100\%)$$

$$4\text{-}CH_3C_6H_4SO_2—SC_6H_4\text{-}p\text{-}CH_3 \xrightarrow{4\text{-}CH_3C_6H_4MgBr} (4\text{-}CH_3C_6H_4)_2S\ (65\%) + 4\text{-}CH_3C_6H_4SO_2H\ (51\%)$$

$$4\text{-}CH_3C_6H_4SO_2—SC_6H_4\text{-}p\text{-}CH_3 \xrightarrow{C_6H_5MgBr} 4\text{-}CH_3C_6H_4SC_6H_5\ (69\%) + 4\text{-}CH_3C_6H_4SO_2H\ (54\%)$$

$$4\text{-}CH_3C_6H_4SO_2—SC_6H_4\text{-}p\text{-}CH_3 \xrightarrow{CH_3MgI} 4\text{-}CH_3C_6H_4SCH_3\ (87\%)$$

$$4\text{-}CH_3C_6H_4SO_2—SC_2H_5 \xrightarrow{C_6H_5MgBr} C_2H_5SC_6H_5\ (29\%)$$

Thiocarboxylates. Hepworth and Clapham[21] found that alkyl thiocarboxylic esters react with Grignard reagents to yield mercaptans and tertiary alcohols, an observation which has been confirmed by Gilman, Robinson, and Beaber (*loc. cit.*[18]).

$$R'CO—SR'' \xrightarrow{RMgX} R'R_2COH + R''SH$$

According to the latter authors, ethyl thionebenzoate, upon treatment with excess phenylmagnesium bromide, forms a sulfur-containing intermediate which, upon standing under hydrolytic conditions, liberates benzophenone.

$$C_6H_5CS—OC_2H_5 \xrightarrow{4\ C_6H_5MgBr} \xrightarrow{H_2O} (C_6H_5)_2CO\ (28\%)$$

The corresponding dithiobenzoate, however, is said to yield triphenylmethyl mercaptan (Gilman, Robinson, and Beaber, *loc. cit.*[18]).

$$C_6H_5CS_2C_2H_5 \xrightarrow{C_6H_5MgBr} (C_6H_5)_3CSH$$

CARBON DISULFIDE AND CARBONYL SULFIDE

Insofar as they have been studied the reactions of carbon disulfide with Grignard reagents appear to be altogether analogous to the corresponding reactions of carbon dioxide (*q.v.*, Chapter XIII).

$$CS_2 + RMgX \longrightarrow RCS_2MgX$$

Undoubtedly the initial product of reaction is, like its oxygen analog, capable of further reaction with excess Grignard reagent. Moreover, the dithiocarboxylic acids are both sensitive to atmospheric oxidation and susceptible to thermal decomposition. It is not surprising therefore that early investigators, who employed the "normal" order of addition, and who took no special precautions for cooling or oxygen exclusion, either

[20] Gilman, Smith, and Parker, *J. Am. Chem. Soc.*, *47*, 851–60 (1925).
[21] Hepworth and Clapham, *J. Chem. Soc.*, *119*, 1188–99 (1921).

reported very low yields of dithiocarboxylic acids or were reticent on the subjects of yields.

Wuyts *et al.*[22] found that aromatic dithiocarboxylic acids could be converted to derivatives of aromatic aldehydes by treatment with phenylhydrazine, semicarbazide, or hydroxylamine, thus providing a means for the conversion of an aryl halide to the corresponding aldehyde.

$$ArX \xrightarrow{Mg} ArMgX \xrightarrow{CS_2} ArCS_2Mg \xrightarrow{C_6H_5NHNH_2}$$

$$ArCH{=}NNHC_6H_5 + S + H_2S \xrightarrow{H_2O} ArCHO$$

They employed a well-conceived experimental technique, operating under nitrogen, and adding the Grignard reagent slowly to an excess of carbon disulfide with moderative cooling. They report yields of 46 and 53 per-cent for *p*-bromo- and *p*-chlorodithiobenzoic acids, respectively.

Available data are summarized in Table XXI-IV.

TABLE XXI-IV

REACTIONS OF GRIGNARD REAGENTS WITH CARBON DISULFIDE

RMgX	RCS_2H	Ref.
CH_3MgI	CH_3CS_2H (17.9%)	*4a,5,9*
C_2H_5MgBr	$C_2H_5CS_2H$ (11.9%)	*4b,5*
n-C_3H_7MgBr	*n*-$C_3H_7CS_2H$ (5.0%)	*4b*
i-C_4H_9MgBr	*i*-$C_4H_9CS_2H$ (4.4%)	*4b*
i-$C_5H_{11}MgBr$	*i*-$C_5H_{11}CS_2H$ (4.4%)	*4b*
4-BrC_6H_4MgBr	4-$BrC_6H_4CS_2H$ (46.0%)	*10,2*
4-ClC_6H_4MgBr	4-$ClC_6H_4CS_2H$ (53.0%)	*11*
C_6H_5MgBr	$C_6H_5CS_2H$ (>9.0%)*	*6,2,8,9,10,11*
$(CH_2)_5CHMgX$	$(CH_2)_5CHCS_2H$	*9*
$C_6H_5CH_2MgCl$	$C_6H_5CH_2CS_2H$ (>3.0%)†	*5,1,2,9*
2-$CH_3C_6H_4MgBr$	2-$CH_3C_6H_4CS_2H$ (>59.6%)‡	*12,8,9,10,11*
4-$CH_3C_6H_4MgBr$	4-$CH_3C_6H_4CS_2H$ (>23.3%)‡	*12,9,10,11*
2,4,5-$(CH_3)_3C_6H_2MgBr$	2,4,5-$(CH_3)_3C_6H_2CS_2H$ (>43.9%)‡	*12*
2,4,6-$(CH_3)_3C_6H_2MgBr$	2,4,6-$(CH_3)_3C_6H_2CS_2H$ (>2.2%)‡	*12*
1-$C_{10}H_7MgBr$	1-$C_{10}H_7CS_2H$	*2,8,9,10,11*
2-$C_{10}H_7MgBr$	2-$C_{10}H_7CS_2H$	*10,11*
2-CH_3-5-*i*-$C_3H_7C_6H_3MgBr$	2-CH_3-5-*i*-$C_3H_7C_6H_3CS_2H$	*7*
2,3,5,6-$(CH_3)_4C_6HMgBr$	?§	*12*
$C_{10}H_{17}MgCl$¶	$C_{10}H_7CS_2H$	*3*
$(CH_3)_5C_6MgBr$	?§	*12*
$(C_6H_5)_2C{=}C(C_6H_5)MgBr$	$(C_6H_5)_2C{=}C(C_6H_5)CS_2H$	*13*

*The recorded yield is that of the ester obtained upon treatment of the Grignard reaction product with ethyl sulfate.

†The recorded yield is that of the ester obtained upon treatment of the Grignard reaction product with methyl sulfate.

‡The recorded yield is that of the aldehyde obtained by the method of Wuyts (*8,9,10,11*).

§No aldehyde was obtained by the method of Wuyts (*8,9,10,11*).

¶From pinene hydrochloride.

[22] Wuyts, *Bull. soc. chim. Belg.*, *38*, 194–204 (1929); *39*, 58–66 (1930); Wuyts, Berman, and Lacourt, *ibid.*, *40*, 665–72 (1931); Wuyts and Koeck, *ibid.*, *41*, 196–201 (1932).

REFERENCES FOR TABLE XXI-IV

(*1*) Houben and Kesselkaul, *Ber.*, *35*, 3695–6 (1902).
(*2*) Houben, *Ber.*, *39*, 3219–33 (1906).
(*3*) Houben and Doescher, *Ber.*, *39*, 3503–9 (1906).
(*4*) Houben and Pohl (*a*) *Ber.*, *40*, 1303–7 (1907); (*b*) *ibid.*, *40*, 1725–30 (1907).
(*5*) Houben and Schulze, *Ber.*, *43*, 2481–5 (1910).
(*6*) Gilman, Robinson, and Beaber, *J. Am. Chem. Soc.*, *48*, 2715–8 (1926).
(*7*) Wheeler and Thomas, *J. Am. Chem. Soc.*, *50*, 3106–9 (1928).
(*8*) Wuyts, *Bull. soc. chim. Belg.*, *38*, 195–204 (1929).
(*9*) Wuyts, *Bull. soc. chim. Belg.*, *39*, 58–66 (1930).
(*10*) Wuyts, Berman, and Lacourt, *Bull. soc. chim. Belg.*, *40*, 665–72 (1931).
(*11*) Wuyts and Koeck, *Bull. soc. chim. Belg.*, *41*, 196–201 (1932).
(*12*) Smith and Nichols, *J. Org. Chem.*, *6*, 489–506 (1941).
(*13*) Koelsch, *J. Am. Chem. Soc.*, *54*, 2045–8 (1932).

As products of the reactions of carbonyl sulfide with several Grignard reagents, Weigert[23] isolated tertiary alcohols and thiocarboxylic acids.

$$C_2H_5MgBr \xrightarrow{COS} (C_2H_5)_3COH\ (38\%) + C_2H_5COSH\ (9\%)$$

$$C_6H_5MgBr \xrightarrow{COS} (C_6H_5)_3COH\ (52\%) + C_6H_5COSH\ (40\%)$$

$$2\text{-}CH_3C_6H_4MgBr \xrightarrow{COS} 2\text{-}CH_3C_6H_4COSH\ (73\%)$$

$$4\text{-}CH_3C_6H_4MgBr \xrightarrow{COS} (4\text{-}CH_3C_6H_4\text{—})_2\ (22\%) + 4\text{-}CH_3C_6H_4COSH\ (50\%)$$

SULFUR DIOXIDE

In his classical paper describing early work on the preparations and reactions of organomagnesium halides, Grignard[24] expressed the intention of investigating "the action on organomagnesium compounds of a certain number of other gases [than carbon dioxide], and in particular that of sulfurous anhydride." Apparently more engrossing problems intervened.

Rosenheim and Singer,[25] reasoning that, by analogy with the behavior of carbon dioxide, sulfur dioxide should react with Grignard reagents to form salts of sulfinic acids, investigated several such reactions and obtained the expected products in 50–60 percent yields. Other reports of similar reactions are recorded in Table XXI-V.

The sulfinates so formed are capable of further reaction with excess Grignard reagent, as was shown by Oddo.[26]

$$C_6H_5MgBr \xrightarrow{SO_2} C_6H_5SO_2MgBr \xrightarrow{C_6H_5MgBr} (C_6H_5)_2S\ \text{(chiefly)} + (C_6H_5)_2SO$$

[23] Weigert, *Ber.*, *36*, 1007–13 (1903).
[24] Grignard, *Ann. chim.*, [7], *24*, 433–90 (1901).
[25] Rosenheim and Singer, *Ber.*, *37*, 2152–4 (1904).
[26] Oddo, *Gazz. chim. ital.*, *41,I*, 11–6 (1911); *Chem. Zentr.*, *1911,I*, 1116; *Chem. Abstr.*, *5*, 2635 (1911).

TABLE XXI-V

REACTIONS OF GRIGNARD REAGENTS WITH SULFUR DIOXIDE

RMgX	RSO_2H	Ref.
C_2H_5MgX	$C_2H_5SO_2H$ (50–60%)	*1*
RMgBr*	RSO_2H*	*9*
n-C_3H_7MgBr	n-$C_3H_7SO_2H$ (50–60%)	*1*
n-C_4H_9MgBr	n-$C_4H_9SO_2H$ (69%)	*10,5*
i-$C_5H_{11}MgBr$	i-$C_5H_{11}SO_2H$	*5*
C_6H_5MgBr	$C_6H_5SO_2H$ (50–60%)	*1,4*
$(CH_2)_5CHMgCl$	$(CH_2)_5CHSO_2H$	*2*
$(CH_2)_5CHMgCl$	$(CH_2)_5CHSO_2H$	*5,7*
$C_6H_5CH_2MgCl$	$C_6H_5CH_2SO_2H$	*8*
2-$CH_3C_6H_4CH_2MgBr$	2-$CH_3C_6H_4CH_2SO_2H$	*8*
3-$CH_3C_6H_4CH_2MgBr$	3-$CH_3C_6H_4CH_2SO_2H$ + 2,6-$(CH_3)_2C_6H_3SO_2H$	*8*
4-$CH_3C_6H_4CH_2MgBr$	4-$CH_3C_6H_4CH_2SO_2H$	*8*
3,3-Dimethylcyclohexyl-MgBr (10.25 g. $C_8H_{15}Br$)	$C_8H_{15}SO_2H$ (yielding 4.55 g. $C_8H_{15}SO_3Na$)	*12*
n-$C_8H_{17}MgBr$	n-$C_8H_{17}SO_2H$ (41.6%)	*10*
n-$C_9H_{19}MgBr$	n-$C_9H_{19}SO_2H$ (37.6%)	*10*
$C_{10}H_{17}MgCl$†	$C_{10}H_{17}SO_2H$	*3*
n-$C_{10}H_{21}MgBr$	n-$C_{10}H_{23}SO_2H$ (34.5%)	*10*
4-$CH_3C_6H_4(CH_3)_2CCH_2MgCl$	4-$CH_3C_6H_4(CH_3)_2CCH_2SO_2H$ (>52%)‡	*6*
n-$C_{11}H_{23}MgBr$	n-$C_{11}H_{23}SO_2H$ (49.8%)	*10*
n-$C_{12}H_{25}MgBr$	n-$C_{12}H_{25}SO_2H$ (56.5%)	*10*
n-$C_{12}H_{25}MgBr$	$(n\text{-}C_{12}H_{25}SO_2)_2Mg \cdot 2\ H_2O$ (80%)§	*11*
n-$C_{12}H_{25}MgBr$	n-$C_{12}H_{25}SO_2S$-n-$C_{12}H_{25}$ ¶	*11*
n-$C_{13}H_{27}MgBr$	n-$C_{13}H_{27}SO_2H$ (38.7%)	*10*
n-$C_{14}H_{29}MgBr$	n-$C_{14}H_{29}SO_2H$ (39.2%)	*10*
n-$C_{15}H_{31}MgBr$	n-$C_{15}H_{31}SO_2H$ (43.0%)	*10*
n-$C_{16}H_{33}MgBr$	n-$C_{16}H_{33}SO_2H$ (57.2%)	*10*

* R = C_2H_5, n-C_3H_7, n-C_4H_9, n-C_5H_{11}.

† From pinene hydrochloride.

‡ The figure recorded represents the yield of the sulfonic acid obtained upon oxidation of the Grignard product.

§ By treatment of the Grignard reagent from 125 g. n-$C_{12}H_{25}Br$ with 32 g. SO_2 at −40 to −35°, and addition of the reaction mixture to cold aqueous NH_4Cl.

¶ By treatment of the Grignard reagent from 200 g. n-$C_{12}H_{25}Br$ with a threefold excess of SO_2 at −35°. According to Marvel and Johnson (*11*), 1-dodecanesulfinic acid is slowly converted, on standing, to 1-dodecyl 1-dodecanethiolsulfonate. They attribute the conversion to the disproportionation reaction:

$$3\ n\text{-}C_{12}H_{25}SO_2H \longrightarrow n\text{-}C_{12}H_{25}SO_2S\text{-}n\text{-}C_{12}H_{25} + n\text{-}C_{12}H_{25}SO_3H + H_2O.$$

REFERENCES FOR TABLE XXI-V

(*1*) Rosenheim and Singer, *Ber.*, 37, 2152–4 (1904).
(*2*) Borsche and Lang, *Ber.*, 38, 2766–9 (1905).
(*3*) Houben and Doescher, *Ber.*, 39, 3503–9 (1906).
(*4*) Oddo, *Gazz. chim. ital.*, *41,I*, 11–6 (1911); *Chem. Zentr.*, *1911,I*, 1116; *Chem. Abstr.*, 5, 2635 (1911).
(*5*) von Braun and Weissbach, *Ber.*, *63B*, 2836–47 (1930).
(*6*) Archer, Malkemus, and Suter, *J. Am. Chem. Soc.*, 67, 43–5 (1945).

(7) Mousseron and Granger, *Bull. soc. chim. France*, *1946*, 251–6; *Chem. Abstr.*, *40*, 6430 (1946).
(8) Mousseron and Nguyen-Phuoc-Du, *Bull. soc. chim. France*, *1948*, 91–6; *Chem. Abstr.*, *42*, 4551 (1948).
(9) Houlton and Tartar, *J. Am. Chem. Soc.*, *60*, 544–8 (1938).
(10) Allen, *J. Org. Chem.*, 7, 23–30 (1942).
(11) Marvel and Johnson, *J. Org. Chem.*, *13*, 822–9 (1948).
(12) von Doering and Beringer, *J. Am. Chem. Soc.*, *71*, 2221–6 (1949).

Truchet[27] obtained a mixture of ethyl phenyl sulfoxide and ethyl phenyl sulfide upon treatment of benzenesulfinic acid with an excess of ethylmagnesium bromide. Burton and Davy[28] have reported a 51 percent yield of sulfoxide resulting from the treatment of *p*-toluenesulfinic acid with excess cold ethereal phenylmagnesium bromide. Similarly, Gilman *et al.*[29] report a 23 percent yield of benzyl *p*-tolyl sulfoxide (with 57 percent sulfinic acid recovery) upon treatment of *p*-toluenesulfinic acid with benzylmagnesium chloride.

Schmidt-Nickels[30] treated triphenylmethoxymagnesium bromide and the corresponding bromomagnesium derivative of 9-phenyl-9-fluorenol with sulfur dioxide and obtained the ester salts of sulfurous acid.

$$ROMgBr \xrightarrow{SO_2} ROSO_2MgBr \xrightarrow{H_2O} (ROSO_2)_2Mg + MgBr_2$$

However, when α,α-diphenylethoxymagnesium bromide was similarly treated a condensation product was obtained.

$$CH_3(C_6H_5)_2COMgBr \xrightarrow{SO_2} \xrightarrow{H_2O} CH_3(C_6H_5)_2CCH{=}C(C_6H_5)_2$$

ACID HALIDES

Sulfonyl halides. The products commonly reported as resulting from the reactions of Grignard reagents with sulfonyl chlorides are sulfones, sulfoxides, and sulfides. Wedekind and Schenk[31] and Hepworth and Clapham[32] sought to account for the secondary products as resulting from further reaction of the Grignard reagents with the highly stable sulfones presumed to be the primary products of reaction. This despite the fact that the latter investigators observed no reaction when phenyl sulfone was refluxed with methylmagnesium iodide in toluene for eighteen hours, and found phenyl benzyl sulfone and trimethylenetrisulfone similarly inert.

It was subsequently shown by Gilman and Fothergill[33] that sulfonyl chlorides, like the corresponding sulfonic esters (*q.v.*), are capable of

[27] Truchet, *Compt. rend.*, *191*, 296–9 (1930); *Chem. Zentr.*, *1930,II*, 3019; *Chem. Abstr.*, *25*, 501 (1931).
[28] Burton and Davy, *J. Chem. Soc.*, *1948*, 528–9.
[29] Gilman, Smith, and Parker, *J. Am. Chem. Soc.*, *47*, 851–60 (1925).
[30] Schmidt-Nickels, *Ber.*, *62B*, 917–9 (1929).
[31] Wedekind and Schenk, *Ber.*, *54B*, 1604–12 (1921).
[32] Hepworth and Clapham, *J. Chem. Soc.*, *119*, 188–98 (1921).
[33] Gilman and Fothergill, *J. Am. Chem. Soc.*, *51*, 3501–8 (1929).

reacting with Grignard reagents in more than one way:

$$RSO_2Cl + R'MgX \longrightarrow RSO_2R' + MgXCl$$

$$RSO_2Cl + R'MgX \longrightarrow RSO_2MgX + R'Cl$$

They suggested that sulfoxide formation might be attributed to the reaction:

$$RSO_2MgX + R'MgX \longrightarrow RSOR' + (XMg)_2O$$

Burton and Davy[34] report that the principal product of the reaction of thiophene-2-sulfonyl chloride with phenylmagnesium bromide (twenty-two hours reflux in benzene) is phenyl sulfoxide (possibly admixed with a little 2-thienyl phenyl sulfoxide). To account for this product they propose a reaction scheme similar to that of Gilman and Fothergill (*loc. cit.*[33]), but including an exchange step (presumably an equilibrium).

$$(\alpha\text{-}C_4H_3S)SO_2Cl + C_6H_5MgBr \longrightarrow (\alpha\text{-}C_4H_3S)SO_2MgBr + C_6H_5Cl$$

$$(\alpha\text{-}C_4H_3S)SO_2MgBr + C_6H_5MgBr \rightleftharpoons (\alpha\text{-}C_4H_3S)MgBr + C_6H_5SO_2MgBr$$

$$C_6H_5SO_2MgBr + C_6H_5MgBr \longrightarrow (C_6H_5)_2SO + (BrMg)_2O$$

Whether or not Grignard reagents prepared from sublimed magnesium would react similarly apparently has not been determined.

Burton and Hu[35] reasoned that if such an exchange does in fact take place it should be possible to demonstrate the presence of the resultant 2-thienyl Grignard reagent by carbonation of the reaction mixture. When they passed carbon dioxide (for twenty hours) into such a reaction mixture which had previously been refluxed for twenty hours they were indeed able to recover a 30 percent yield of thiophene-2-carboxylic acid.

The concept of such an exchange might also be invoked to account for the small amount of *p*-tolyl sulfoxide which Wedekind and Schenk[36] detected among the products of the reaction of *p*-toluenesulfonyl chloride with ethylmagnesium bromide.

$$4\text{-}CH_3C_6H_4SO_2Cl + 4\text{-}CH_3C_6H_4MgBr \longrightarrow (4\text{-}CH_3C_6H_4)_2SO + MgBrCl$$

and/or

$$4\text{-}CH_3C_6H_4SO_2MgBr + 4\text{-}CH_3C_6H_4MgBr \longrightarrow (4\text{-}CH_3C_6H_4)_2SO + (BrMg)_2O$$

The occurrence of sulfides among the products of reaction of Grignard reagents with sulfinates (Oddo,[26] Truchet[27]—see preceding section) and with thionyl chloride (Oddo,[26] Grignard and Zorn[37]) is strongly suggestive that sulfoxides are capable of undergoing Grignard reduction. This possibility is discussed in the section on Sulfoxides p. 1296.

A summary of reported reactions of Grignard reagents with sulfonyl halides is recorded in Table XXI-VI. Steinkopf and Jaeger[38] report that

[34] Burton and Davy, *J. Chem. Soc.*, *1948*, 528–9.

[35] Burton and Hu, *J. Chem. Soc.*, *1949*, 258.

[36] Wedekind and Schenk, *Ber.*, *54B*, 1604–12 (1921).

[37] Grignard and Zorn, *Compt. rend.*, *150*, 1177–9 (1910); *Chem. Zentr.*, *1910,II*, 143.

[38] Steinkopf and Jaeger, *J. prakt. Chem.*, [2], *128*, 63–88 (1930).

TABLE XXI-VI

REACTIONS OF GRIGNARD REAGENTS WITH SULFONYL HALIDES

RSO_2X	$R'MgX'$	RSO_2R'(%)*	RSO_2H(%)*	$R'X$(%)*	$RSOR'$(%)*	RSR'(%)*	Ref.
$(\alpha\text{-}C_4H_3S)SO_2Cl$	C_6H_5MgBr	...	...	...	+(?)†	...	7,8
$C_6H_5SO_2F$	CH_3MgI	+	...	...	...	...	5
$C_6H_5SO_2Cl$	CH_3MgI	...	53.0	27.0	...	...	6
$C_6H_5SO_2Cl$	C_2H_5MgBr	...	32.0	33.0	...	...	6
$C_6H_5SO_2Cl$	C_2H_5MgBr	+	...	...	+	+	3
$C_6H_5SO_2Cl$	C_6H_5MgBr	...	+	+	...	...	1
$C_6H_5SO_2Cl$	C_6H_5MgBr	...	...	...	+	+	2
$C_6H_5SO_2Cl$	C_6H_5MgBr	+	...	...	+	...	3
$C_6H_5SO_2Cl$	C_6H_5MgBr	35.0	0.5	16.3	...	...	4
$C_6H_5SO_2Cl$	$C_6H_5CH_2MgCl$	+	...	...	41.7	+	3
$C_6H_5SO_2Cl$	$C_6H_5CH_2MgCl$	2.9	...	60.0	...	...	4
$C_6H_5SO_2Cl$	$4\text{-}CH_3C_6H_4MgBr$	...	+	...	...	...	7
$C_6H_5SO_2Cl$	$4\text{-}CH_3C_6H_4MgBr$	17.5	46.4	27.0	...	...	4
$C_6H_5SO_2Cl$	$n\text{-}C_5H_{11}C\equiv CMgBr$	...	20.0	37.0	...	...	6
$C_6H_5SO_2Cl$	$C_6H_5C\equiv CMgBr$	...	1.2	13.7	...	...	4
$C_6H_5SO_2Cl$	$C_6H_5C\equiv CMgBr$	...	25.0	35.0	...	...	6
$C_6H_5SO_2Cl$	$C_6H_5CH{=}CHMgBr$	...	39.6	40.4	...	...	4
$C_6H_5SO_2Cl$	$1\text{-}C_{10}H_7MgBr$	...	...	39.7	...	...	4
$4\text{-}CH_3C_6H_3\text{-}1,3\text{-}(SO_2F)_2$	C_6H_5MgBr	+	...	...	...	...	5
$4\text{-}CH_3C_6H_4SO_2Cl$	CH_3MgI	...	...	...	+	+	2
$4\text{-}CH_3C_6H_4SO_2Cl$	C_2H_5MgBr	...	+	...	+‡	+	2
$4\text{-}CH_3C_6H_4SO_2Cl$	C_2H_5MgBr	...	37.0	22.0	...	...	6
$4\text{-}CH_3C_6H_4SO_2Cl$	$n\text{-}C_4H_9MgBr$	...	60.6	8.7	...	...	4

* A plus sign indicates that the product has been reported without statement of yield.

† It is reported by Burton and Davy (7) that the principal product of this reaction is phenyl sulfoxide (R'_2SO), possibly admixed with a little 2-thienyl phenyl sulfoxide ($RSOR'$).

‡ Wedekind and Schenk (2) also detected a small amount of *p*-tolyl sulfoxide (R_2SO) among the products of this reaction.

TABLE XXI-VI (Continued)

RSO_2X	$R'MgX'$	RSO_2R'(%)*	RSO_2H(%)*	$R'X$(%)*	$RSOR'$(%)*	RSR'(%)*	Ref.
$4\text{-}CH_3C_6H_4SO_2Cl$	C_6H_5MgBr	32.9	10.7	11.0	...	...	4
$4\text{-}CH_3C_6H_4SO_2Cl$	C_6H_5MgBr	+	...	...	+	...	2
$4\text{-}CH_3C_6H_4SO_2Cl$	C_6H_5MgBr	...	...	19.8†	62.0†	...	7
$4\text{-}CH_3C_6H_4SO_2Cl$	C_6H_5MgBr	...	...	...	40.0‡	38.0‡	7
$4\text{-}CH_3C_6H_4SO_2Cl$	C_6H_5MgBr	27.5§	...	24.2§	...	...	7
$4\text{-}CH_3C_6H_4SO_2Cl$	$(CH_2)_5CHMgBr$	...	67.1	66.3	...	...	4
$4\text{-}CH_3C_6H_4SO_2Cl$	$C_6H_5C\equiv CMgBr$	...	27.0	33.0	...	...	6
$4\text{-}CH_3C_6H_4SO_2Br$	C_6H_5MgBr	...	30.2	53.8	...	...	4
$4\text{-}CH_3C_6H_4SO_2I$	C_6H_5MgBr	...	11.8	65.1	...	...	4
$1\text{-}C_{10}H_7SO_2Cl$	C_6H_5MgBr	13.0	...	24.5	...	...	4

* A plus sign indicates that the product has been reported without statement of yield.
† Twenty-two hours reflux in benzene.
‡ Eighteen hours reflux in benzene.
§ Reaction at $-5°$ in ether.

REFERENCES FOR TABLE XXI-VI

(1) Oddo, *Atti accad. Lincei*, [5], *14,I*, 169–74 (1905); *Chem. Zentr.*, *1905,I*, 1145.
(2) Wedekind and Schenk, *Ber.*, *54B*, 1604–12 (1921).
(3) Hepworth and Clapham, *J. Chem. Soc.*, *119*, 1188–98 (1921).
(4) Gilman and Fothergill, *J. Am. Chem. Soc.*, *51*, 3501–8 (1929).
(5) Steinkopf and Jaeger, *J. prakt. Chem.*, [2], *128*, 63–88 (1930).
(6) Truchet, *Ann. chim.*, [10], *16*, 309–419 (1931).
(7) Burton and Davy, *J. Chem. Soc.*, *1948*, 528–9.
(8) Burton and Hu, *J. Chem. Soc.*, *1949*, 258.

the reaction of methylmagnesium iodide with benzenesulfonyl fluoride produces, in addition to the sulfone, an unidentified acidic substance of the empirical formula $C_{13}H_{14}O_4S_2$. The reaction of phenylmagnesium bromide with toluene-2,4-disulfonyl fluoride yields a similar byproduct ($C_{25}H_{22}O_4S$).

Thionyl and sulfuryl chlorides. Grignard and Zorn[39] investigated the reactions of several organomagnesium halides with thionyl chloride and found the products to be sulfoxides and sulfides.

$$SOCl_2 \xrightarrow{C_2H_5MgBr} (C_2H_5)_2S + C_2H_4$$

$$SOCl_2 \xrightarrow{i\text{-}C_5H_{11}MgBr} (i\text{-}C_5H_{11})_2SO\ (50\%) + (i\text{-}C_5H_{11})_2S\ (14\%) + i\text{-}C_5H_{11}OH$$

$$SOCl_2 \xrightarrow{4\text{-}CH_3C_6H_4MgBr} (4\text{-}CH_3OC_6H_4)_2SO$$

$$SOCl_2 \xrightarrow{2,4\text{-}(CH_3O)_2C_6H_3MgBr} [2,4\text{-}(CH_3O)_2C_6H_3]_2SO$$

Sulfide formation was attributed to further reaction of the Grignard reagent with the sulfoxide initially formed. It was postulated that the hypothetical sulfonium hydroxide derivative so formed may decompose in either of two ways:

$$\text{(I)} \qquad R_3SOMgX \longrightarrow R_2S + ROMgX$$

$$\text{(II)} \qquad (C_nH_{2n+1})_3SOMgX \longrightarrow (C_nH_{2n+1})_2S + C_nH_{2n} + MgXOH$$

Strecker[40] obtained sulfoxides by treatment of thionyl chloride with phenylmagnesium bromide and benzylmagnesium chloride. With ethylmagnesium iodide, Oddo[41] obtained ethyl sulfide, and with phenylmagnesium bromide, a mixture of sulfide and sulfoxide, chiefly the former.

Oddo[42] has also investigated reactions of sulfuryl chloride.

$$SO_2Cl_2 \xrightarrow{C_6H_5MgBr} C_6H_5SO_2Cl + MgBrCl$$

$$SO_2Cl_2 \xrightarrow{C_2H_5MgI} \xrightarrow{H_2O} C_2H_5SO_2H\ (55\text{–}60\%)$$

---

[39] Grignard and Zorn, *Compt. rend.*, *150*, 1177–9 (1910); *Chem. Zentr.*, *1910,II*, 143.

[40] Strecker, *Ber.*, *43*, 1131–6 (1910).

[41] Oddo, *Gazz. chim. ital.*, *41,I*, 11–6 (1911); *Chem. Zentr.*, *1911,I*, 1116; *Chem. Abstr.*, *5*, 2635 (1911).

[42] Oddo, *Atti accad. Lincei*, [5], *14,I*, 169–74 (1905); *Chem. Zentr.*, *1905,I*, 1145.

Cherbuliez and Schnauder[43] have found that when the Grignard reagent is a bromide there is a considerable exchange of halogen between the initial products of reaction. Apparently this is not so when the Grignard reagent is an iodide. Their data are summarized in Table XXI-VII. Phenylmagnesium iodide is said to react very feebly with sulfuryl chloride (no figures are given).

TABLE XXI-VII

REACTIONS OF GRIGNARD REAGENTS WITH SULFURYL CHLORIDE

RMgX	RSO_2X (%)
CH_3MgBr	CH_3SO_2Br (21)
CH_3MgI	CH_3SO_2Cl (26)
C_2H_5MgCl	$C_2H_5SO_2Cl$ (31)
C_2H_5MgBr	$C_2H_5SO_2Br$ (35)
C_2H_5MgI	$C_2H_5SO_2Cl$ (32)
C_6H_5MgBr	$C_6H_5SO_2X$ (5)*
$C_6H_5CH_2MgCl$	$C_6H_5CH_2SO_2Cl$ (34)

* The product was a mixture of bromide and chloride in the ratio 0.78:0.22.

Chlorosulfonates. Hepworth and Clapham[44] report that the reaction of ethylmagnesium bromide with ethyl chlorosulfonate yields ethyl sulfoxide and ethyl sulfide.

SULFUR CHLORIDES

Strecker[45] treated sulfur monochloride with phenylmagnesium bromide and isolated phenyl disulfide. Ferrario[46] investigated this and other reactions of sulfur monochloride in somewhat more detail, as well as reactions of sulfur dichloride and tetrachloride. His findings are summarized in the following equations.

$$S_2Cl_2 \xrightarrow{CH_3MgI} CH_3Cl + (CH_3)_2S + (CH_3S—)_2 + \text{trisulfide}$$

$$S_2Cl_2 \xrightarrow{C_2H_5MgBr} C_2H_6 + C_2H_5Cl + (C_2H_5)_2S + (C_2H_5S—)_2$$

$$S_2Cl_2\ (40\ g.) \xrightarrow[(91\ g.\ C_6H_5Br)]{C_6H_5MgBr} C_6H_5Cl\ (4\ g.) + (C_6H_5—)_2\ (30\ g.)$$
$$+ (C_6H_5)_2S\ (6\ g.) + (C_6H_5S—)_2\ (25\ g.) + \text{trisulfide} + \text{tetrasulfide}$$

$$SCl_2 \xrightarrow{C_6H_5MgBr} C_6H_5Cl + (C_6H_5—)_2 + (C_6H_5)_2S + (C_6H_5S—)_2 + \text{trisulfide} + \text{tetrasulfide}$$

$$SCl_4 \xrightarrow{C_6H_5MgBr} \text{Same products as for } SCl_2\text{, but with more } C_6H_5Cl$$

[43] Cherbuliez and Schnauder, *Helv. Chim. Acta*, 6, 249–57 (1923).
[44] Hepworth and Clapham, *J. Chem. Soc.*, *119*, 1188–98 (1921).
[45] Strecker, *Ber.*, *43*, 1131–6 (1910).
[46] Ferrario, *Bull. soc. chim.*, [4], 7, 518–27 (1910).

SULFOXIDES

From the results of his work with Zorn on the reactions of organomagnesium halides with thionyl chloride (*q.v.*), Grignard[47] drew the conclusion that, whereas aryl sulfoxides are inert as regards further reaction with the Grignard reagent, alkyl sulfoxides may react additively. He accounted for the isoamyl sulfide and isoamyl alcohol formed in the isoamylmagnesium bromide reaction by postulating the formation of an intermediate sulfonium hydroxide derivative capable of decomposing in the manner indicated below:

$$(i\text{-}C_5H_{11})_2SO \xrightarrow{i\text{-}C_5H_{11}MgBr} [(i\text{-}C_5H_{11})_3S]^+[OMgBr]^-$$
$$\longrightarrow (i\text{-}C_5H_{11})_2S + i\text{-}C_5H_{11}OMgBr$$

It was subsequently shown by Hepworth and Clapham[48] that operation at sufficiently elevated temperatures (as in boiling toluene solution) brings about reaction of the aryl sulfoxides also. Their results are summarized in the following equations:

$$(i\text{-}C_5H_{11})_2SO\ (5.0\ g.) + CH_3MgI\ (19.0\ g.\ CH_3I) \xrightarrow[(b.\ C_7H_8)]{15\ hrs.} (i\text{-}C_5H_{11})_2S\ (3.0\ g.)$$

$$(C_6H_5)_2SO\ (5.0\ g.) + CH_3MgI\ (14.0\ g.\ CH_3I) \xrightarrow[(b.\ C_7H_8)]{12\ hrs.}$$
$$(C_6H_5)_2S\ (2.5\ g.) + \text{rec.}\ (C_6H_5)_2SO\ (2.2\ g.)$$

$$(C_6H_5)_2SO\ (5.0\ g.) + C_6H_5MgBr \xrightarrow[(b.\ C_7H_8)]{15\ hrs.} (C_6H_5)_2S\ (1.5\ g.)$$

$$C_6H_5(C_6H_5CH_2)SO\ (5.0\ g.) + CH_3MgI\ (14.0\ g.\ CH_3I) \xrightarrow[(b.\ C_7H_8)]{}$$
$$C_6H_5SCH_2C_6H_5\ (2.0\ g.) + \text{rec.}\ C_6H_5(C_6H_5CH_2)SO\ (2.5\ g.)$$

The evident stability of the sulfides under the reaction conditions imposed is sufficient evidence of their inertia toward Grignard reagents (however, see also the section on Thio and Seleno Ethers, Chapter XV). When 5.5 g. of phenyl sulfone was refluxed in toluene solution with methylmagnesium iodide for eighteen hours it was possible to recover 4.0 g. of sulfone, and no traces of sulfide or sulfonium base could be detected.

Unfortunately Hepworth and Clapham established no material balance between reactants and products, so that their experiments constitute no commentary on Grignard's hypothesis concerning the course of the reaction. More recently, however, Wildi *et al.*[49] have demonstrated that arylmagnesium halides are capable of combining with phenyl sulfoxide to form triarylsulfonium bases. They refluxed the reactants in benzene so-

---

[47] Grignard and Zorn, *Compt. rend.*, *150*, 1177–9 (1910); *Chem. Zentr.*, *1910,II*, 143.

[48] Hepworth and Clapham, *J. Chem. Soc.*, *119*, 1188–98 (1921).

[49] Wildi, Taylor, and Potratz, *J. Am. Chem. Soc.*, *73*, 1965–7 (1951).

lution under an atmosphere of nitrogen for periods of the order of twenty-four hours and then treated the reaction mixtures with relatively concentrated hydrobromic acid. The following crystalline triarylsulfonium bromides were isolated in the indicated percentage yields: $[(C_6H_5)_3S]^+Br^-$ (49.4); $[3\text{-}CH_3C_6H_4(C_6H_5)_2S]^+Br^-$ (23.4); $[4\text{-}CH_3C_6H_4(C_6H_5)_2S]^+Br^-$ (34.1); $[2,5\text{-}(CH_3)_2C_6H_3(C_6H_5)_2S]^+Br^-$ (12.1).

Apparently the α,β-unsaturated sulfoxides exhibit some characteristic peculiarities, for Kohler and Potter[49.1] report that styryl *p*-tolyl sulfoxide, when treated with ethylmagnesium bromide, yields, in addition to ethyl *p*-tolyl sulfide, 80 percent of 1,4-diphenyl-1,3-butadiene. The same sulfoxide, treated with phenylmagnesium bromide, is said to yield, in addition to phenyl *p*-tolyl sulfide, β,β,β-triphenylethyl *p*-tolyl sulfide.

SULFONES

When Hepworth and Clapham (*loc. cit.*[48]) refluxed 5.5 g. of phenyl sulfone with methylmagnesium iodide in toluene solution for eighteen hours they were able to recover 4.0 g. of the sulfone. No phenyl sulfide or sulfonium base was detected.

Because phenyl benzyl sulfone was also recovered, apparently unchanged, after high-temperature treatment with methylmagnesium iodide and hydrolysis of the reaction mixture, Hepworth and Clapham concluded that this sulfone also is unreactive toward Grignard reagents. Unfortunately the reaction was not investigated in the Zerewitinoff apparatus.

Kohler and Potter (*loc. cit.*[49.1]) found that phenethyl *p*-tolyl sulphone and β,β-diphenylethyl *p*-tolyl sulfone liberate at least one molecular equivalent each of methane when treated with isoamyl ethereal methylmagnesium iodide at 50–75°. Methyl *p*-tolyl sulfone liberates methane from methylmagnesium iodide slowly at room temperature. In the latter case it would appear that there are two replaceable hydrogen atoms, for, when the resultant organometallic intermediate is treated with benzoyl chloride, the product is dibenzoylmethyl *p*-tolyl sulfone.

Kohler and Potter[49.2] also obtained from bis-(*p*-tolylsulfonyl)methane a bromomagnesium derivative which, when treated with benzoyl chloride, yielded α,α-bis-(*p*-tolylsulfonyl)acetophenone.

$$(4\text{-}CH_3C_6H_4SO_2)_2CHMgBr \xrightarrow{C_6H_5COCl} (4\text{-}CH_3C_6H_4SO_2)_2CHCOC_6H_5 \ (81\%)$$

Gilman and Webb[49.3] report that ethyl phenyl sulfone, treated successively with ethylmagnesium bromide and carbon dioxide, yields an acidic gum. Field,[49.4] treating methyl phenyl sulfone successively with ethyl-

[49.1] Kohler and Potter, *J. Am. Chem. Soc.*, 57, 1316–21 (1935).
[49.2] Kohler and Potter, *J. Am. Chem. Soc.*, 58, 2166–30 (1936).
[49.3] Gilman and Webb, *J. Am. Chem. Soc.*, 71, 4062–6 (1949).
[49.4] Field, *J. Am. Chem. Soc.*, 74, 3919–21 (1952).

magnesium bromide and benzaldehyde, obtained 1-phenyl-2-phenylsulfonylethanol in good yield.

$$\underset{(15.0\text{ g.})}{CH_3SO_2C_6H_5} \xrightarrow[(14.5\text{ g. }C_2H_5Br)]{C_2H_5MgBr} \xrightarrow[(12.7\text{ g.})]{C_6H_5CHO} \underset{(22.7\text{ g., 90\% crude; 18.5 g., 73\% pure})}{C_6H_5SO_2CH_2CH(OH)C_6H_5}$$

These hydrogen displacements are strikingly similar to ketone-enolate conversions (*q.v.*), and should probably be formulated similarly.

$$\begin{array}{l} \qquad\quad O \\ \qquad\quad \uparrow \\ H_2C—S—C_6H_4\text{-}4\text{-}CH_3 \\ /\qquad \searrow \\ H \qquad\quad O \\ \qquad\quad \vdots \\ H_3C—Mg \\ \qquad\quad | \\ \qquad\quad X \end{array} \longrightarrow CH_4 + [4\text{-}CH_3C_6H_4SO_2CH_2]^-MgX^+$$

The analogy is emphasized by the fact that, by a process similar to the reductive enolization of an α-halo ketone (*q.v.*), an α-halo sulfone may be converted to a halomagnesium derivative that behaves like a Grignard reagent. According to Kohler and Tishler,[49.5] bis(phenylsulfonyl)dibromomethane, treated with ethylmagnesium bromide, yields a di(bromomagnesium) derivative which, however, is only monobenzoylated by benzoyl chloride.

$$(C_6H_5SO_2)_2CBr_2 \xrightarrow{C_2H_5MgBr} (C_6H_5SO_2)_2C(MgBr)_2 \xrightarrow{C_6H_5COCl \quad (H_3O^+)} (C_6H_5SO_2)_2CHCOC_6H_5$$

Ziegler and Connor[49.6] report that when 34.8 g. of *p*-tolylsulfonylmethyl bromide was treated with 0.15 mole of phenylmagnesium bromide they were able to recover from the reaction mixture, after acid hydrolysis, 15.5 g. (59 percent) of methyl *p*-tolyl sulfone and 18.2 g. (77 percent) of bromobenzene.

α,β-Unsaturated sulfones also undergo 1,4-additions of Grignard reagents, analogous to those of α,β-unsaturated ketones (*q.v.*), to yield enol-like halomagnesium derivatives which behave like Grignard reagents. According to Kohler and Potter (*loc. cit.*[49.1]), benzylidenemethyl *p*-tolyl sulfone reacts with phenylmagnesium bromide to yield the same bromomagnesium derivative that is obtained upon treatment of β,β-diphenylethyl *p*-tolyl sulfone with ethyl- or phenylmagnesium bromide. Perhaps the absolute identity of the two halomagnesium derivatives should not be taken for granted, however, for analogous pairs of ketonic enolates have been found to yield stereoisomeric derivatives upon acylation[49.7] or halogenation[49.8] [see Chapter VI, α-Halo Ketones, Probable Mechanism of

---

[49.5] Kohler and Tishler, *J. Am. Chem. Soc.*, 57, 217–24 (1935).
[49.6] Ziegler and Connor, *J. Am. Chem. Soc.*, 62, 2596–9 (1940).
[49.7] Kohler, Tishler, and Potter, *J. Am. Chem. Soc.*, 57, 2517–21 (1935).
[49.8] Lutz and Kibler, *J. Am. Chem. Soc.*, 62, 360–72 (1940).

α-Halo Ketone Dehalogenation; Chapter VI, Grignard Reagent Addition to Conjugated Carbonyl Systems, Probable Mechanism of 1,4-Addition].

THIOKETONES (THIONES)

Schönberg, *et al.*[50] have studied a few thioketone-Grignard reagent reactions. In general the products are ethylene sulfides (thioëpoxides) or the corresponding ethylene derivatives, which are probably formed by loss of sulfur by the thermolabile sulfides.

$$(4\text{-}CH_3OC_6H_4)_2CS\ (5.5\ g.) \xrightarrow[(5\ g.\ C_6H_5Br)]{C_6H_5MgBr} (4\text{-}CH_3OC_6H_4)_2C\overset{\ S\ }{—}C(C_6H_4\text{-}4\text{-}OCH_3)_2\ (3.9\ g.)$$

With the same thioketone, "good yields" of sulfide were obtained with $2\text{-}CH_3OC_6H_4MgBr$, $1\text{-}C_{10}H_7MgBr$, and C_6H_5MgI; a poor yield with C_2H_5MgBr. Other reactions reported are:

$$(4\text{-}C_2H_5OC_6H_4)_2CS \xrightarrow{C_6H_5MgBr} (4\text{-}C_2H_5OC_6H_4)_2C\overset{\ S\ }{—}C(C_6H_4\text{-}4\text{-}OC_2H_5)_2$$

$$(3\text{-}CH_3\text{-}4\text{-}C_2H_5OC_6H_3)_2CS \xrightarrow{C_6H_5MgBr} (3\text{-}CH_3\text{-}4\text{-}C_2H_5OC_6H_3)_2C\overset{\ S\ }{—}C(C_6H_4\text{-}3\text{-}CH_3\text{-}4\text{-}OC_2H_5)_2$$

$$\text{(xanthione) } C{=}S \xrightarrow{C_6H_5MgBr} [\text{(xanthylidene) } C{=}]_2$$

Apparently these are essentially radical reactions, for Schönberg and Schütz[51] have found that treatment of a thioketone with magnesium-magnesium iodide yields the same products as treatment with a Grignard reagent. They explain the reaction as follows:

$$2\ R_2CS + Mg + MgI_2 \longrightarrow R_2C(SMgI)C(SMgI)R_2 \longrightarrow R_2C\overset{\ S\ }{—}CR_2 + (IMg)_2S$$

$$R_2C\overset{\ S\ }{—}CR_2 \longrightarrow (R_2C{=})_2 + S$$

The desirability of the prosecution of analogous studies with *filtered* Grignard reagents prepared from sublimed magnesium is indicated.

---

[50] Schönberg, *Ber.*, *58B*, 1793–1801 (1925); Schönberg, Rosenbach, and Schütz, *Ann.*, *454*, 37–46 (1927).

[51] Schönberg and Schütz, *Ber.*, *60B*, 2351–3 (1927).

MISCELLANEOUS UNCLASSIFIED SULFUR COMPOUNDS

Delepine[52] has investigated the reactions of several Grignard reagents with several thiochloroformic esters. According to his reports such reactions take the course:

$$ClCSOR + R'MgX \longrightarrow R'CSOR + MgXCl$$

Cobb[53] has reported on the reactions of phenylmagnesium bromide with o-sulfobenzoic anhydride and the corresponding high- and low-melting acid chlorides as follows:

$$C_6H_4(CO)(SO_2)O \xrightarrow{2\ C_6H_5MgBr} C_6H_4[C(C_6H_5)_2OH](SO_3H) + C_6H_4[C(C_6H_5)_2-O-SO_2]$$

(*ca.* 10% of total)

$$C_6H_4(COCl)(SO_2Cl) \xrightarrow{3\ C_6H_5MgBr} C_6H_4[C(C_6H_5)_2OH](SO_2C_6H_5)$$

(h.-m. chloride)

$$C_6H_4(CCl_2)(SO_2)O \xrightarrow{2\ C_6H_5MgBr} C_6H_4[C(C_6H_5)_2-O-SO_2]$$

(l.-m. chloride)

According to Wuyts and Lacourt,[54] when *S*-methylated thiohydrazides are treated with ethylmagnesium bromide, the methylmercapto group is replaced by an ethyl group.

$$RC(SCH_3){=}NNCH_3R \xrightarrow{C_2H_5MgBr} R(C_2H_5)C{=}NN(CH_3)R + MgBrSCH_3$$

$$(R = C_6H_5,\ 2\text{-}CH_3C_6H_5,\ 4\text{-}CH_3C_6H_5)$$

The corresponding *N*-methylated thiohydrazides are reduced by ethylmagnesium bromide.

$$C_6H_5CSN(CH_3)NHC_6H_5 \xrightarrow{C_2H_5MgBr} C_6H_5CH_2N(CH_3)NHC_6H_5 + (BrMg)_2S + C_2H_4$$

Gilman and Vernon[55] observed no reaction (other than "active" hydrogen replacement) of *p*-toluenesulfonamide with excess phenylmagnesium

[52] Delepine, *Compt. rend.*, *150*, 1607–8 (1910); *153*, 279–82 (1911); *Chem. Zentr.*, *1910,II*, 794; *1911,II*, 1213.

[53] Cobb, *Am. Chem. J.*, *35*, 486–508 (1906); Cobb and Fuller, *ibid.*, *45*, 605–11 (1911).

[54] Wuyts and Lacourt, *Bull. soc. chim. Belg.*, *44*, 395–410 (1935).

[55] Gilman and Vernon, *Rec. trav. chim.*, *48*, 745–7 (1929).

bromide in boiling ether. In boiling anisole some tar was formed, but 62.5 percent of the amide was recovered. The corresponding imide [$(4\text{-}CH_3C_6H_4SO_2)_2NH$] is similarly inert toward phenylmagnesium bromide in boiling ether or toluene, as is benzenesulfinanilide. *N,N*-Diethylbenzenesulfenamide slowly undergoes cleavage when refluxed at 70° with phenylmagnesium bromide in ether-toluene solution.

$$C_6H_5SN(C_2H_5)_2 \xrightarrow{C_6H_5MgBr} (C_6H_5)_2S + (C_2H_5)_2NH$$

The reactions of saccharin and *N*-alkylated saccharins are reported in Chapter XII on Amides, etc. (*q.v.*).

Wuyts[56] reports that disulfides undergo Grignard reagent cleavage.

$$(C_6H_5S—)_2 \text{ (21.8 g.)} \xrightarrow[(32.7\text{ g. }C_2H_5Br)]{C_2H_5MgBr} C_6H_5SH \text{ (10.3 g.)} + C_2H_5SC_6H_5 \text{ (12.3 g.)}$$

$$(C_6H_5S—)_2 \text{ (21.8 g.)} \xrightarrow[(41.4\text{ g. }1\text{-}C_{10}H_7Br)]{1\text{-}C_{10}H_5MgBr} C_6H_5SH \text{ (9.3 g.)} + C_6H_5S\text{-}1\text{-}C_{10}H_7 \text{ (18 g., crude)}$$

$$(C_2H_5S—)_2 \text{ (12.2 g.)} \xrightarrow[(27.8\text{ g. }i\text{-}C_4H_9Cl)]{i\text{-}C_4H_9MgCl} C_2H_5SH \text{ (13 g. Hg salt)} + C_2H_5S\text{-}i\text{-}C_4H_9 \text{ (6 g.)}$$

Other examples of disulfide cleavage are reported by Burton and Davy.[57]

$$(\alpha\text{-}C_4H_3S)_2S_2 \text{ (7.1 g.)} \xrightarrow[(0.1\text{ mole})]{C_6H_5MgBr} (\alpha\text{-}C_4H_3S)SC_6H_5 \text{ (3.9 g.)}$$

$$(4\text{-}CH_3C_6H_4S—)_2 \text{ (12.3 g.)} \xrightarrow[(0.15\text{ mole})]{C_6H_5MgBr} 4\text{-}CH_3C_6H_4SH \text{ (1.5 g.)} + 4\text{-}CH_3C_6H_4SC_6H_5 \text{ (6.5 g.)}$$

Reactions of thionylaniline are reported in Chapter XIX on Miscellaneous Nitrogen Compounds (*q.v.*).

4,4,5,5-Tetraphenyltrimethylene-1,3-disulfide is inert toward phenylmagnesium bromide, according to Schönberg *et al.*[58]

According to Mustafa and Gad,[59] naphthasultone reacts with phenyl- and 1-naphthylmagnesium bromides in boiling ether-benzene solution to form hydroxylated sulfones.

O — SO₂ (naphthalene) $\xrightarrow{ArMgBr}$ HO SO₂Ar (naphthalene)

[56] Wuyts, *Bull. soc. chim.*, [3], 35, 166–9 (1906).
[57] Burton and Davy, *J. Chem. Soc.*, *1948*, 325–7, 528–9.
[58] Schönberg, Kaltschmitt, and Schulten, *Ber.*, *66B*, 245–50 (1933).
[59] Mustafa and Gad, *J. Chem. Soc.*, *1949*, 384–7.

The sulfonylidene ring is similarly opened by phenylmagnesium bromide (Mustafa and Gad, *loc. cit.*[59]).

$$\text{H}_3\text{C-C}_6\text{H}_3(\text{SO}_2\text{-O})(\text{O-SO}_2)\text{C}_6\text{H}_3\text{-CH}_3 \xrightarrow{2\ C_6H_5MgBr} 2\ \text{H}_3\text{C-C}_6\text{H}_3(\text{OH})\text{-SO}_2\text{C}_6\text{H}_5$$

The reactions of various thioacylated hydrazines with methylmagnesium iodide are reported by Wuyts and Lacourt[60] to take the following course:

$$ArCSN(CH_3)N{=}CHAr \xrightarrow{2\ CH_3MgI} Ar(CH_3)C(SH)N(CH_3)NHCH(CH_3)Ar$$

$$(Ar = C_6H_4,\ 2\text{-}CH_3C_6H_4,\ 4\text{-}CH_3C_6H_4)$$

According to the same authors,[60] several derivatives of 2,3-dihydro-1,3,4-thiodiazole were recovered completely unchanged after treatment with five molecular equivalents of methylmagnesium iodide.

SELENIUM COMPOUNDS

Pieroni and Coli[61] conducted a Barbier-type reaction with magnesium, ethyl bromide and selenium monobromide. Their description of the reaction is as follows:

$$Se_2Br_2 \xrightarrow{2\ C_2H_5MgBr} (C_2H_5Se{-})_2 + 2\ MgBr_2$$

$$(C_2H_5Se{-})_2 \xrightarrow{C_2H_5Br} C_2H_5SeSe(C_2H_5)_2Br$$

$$C_2H_5SeSe(C_2H_5)_2Br \xrightarrow{C_2H_5MgBr} \xrightarrow{H_2O} HSeSe(C_2H_5)_3 + MgBr_2 + C_2H_5OH$$

They also treated selenium bromide with the dihalomagnesium derivative of acetylene:

$$4\ Se_2Br_2 \xrightarrow{(\equiv CMgBr)_2} \xrightarrow{H_2O} (\equiv C{-}Se{-}C{\equiv}C{-}SeOH)_2 + 6\ MgBr_2 + 4\ Se + 2\ HBr$$

Pieroni and Balduzzi[62] treated phenylmagnesium bromide with selenium monobromide and obtained phenyl diselenide which, upon heating, readily loses selenium to form the selenide. They also report that *m*-

[60] Wuyts and Lacourt, *Bull. soc. chim. Belg.*, *45*, 445–53 (1936).

[61] Pieroni and Coli, *Gazz. chim. ital.*, *44,II*, 349–53 (1914); *Chem. Zentr.*, *1915,I*, 730.

[62] Pieroni and Balduzzi, *Gazz. chim. ital.*, *45,II*, 106–11 (1915); *Chem. Zentr.*, *1915,II*, 1134.

aminophenylmagnesium bromide [*sic*] reacts with selenium monobromide to form the selenide.

Strecker and Willing[63] have reported reactions of Grignard reagents with selenium monobromide, selenium monochloride, selenium tetrachloride, and selenyl chloride, as follows:

$$Se_2Br_2 \xrightarrow{C_6H_5CH_2MgCl} (C_6H_5CH_2)_2SeBr_2 + (C_6H_5CH_2Se—)_2$$

$$Se_2Cl_2 \xrightarrow{C_6H_5MgBr} (C_6H_5Se—)_2 + (C_6H_5)_2Se$$

$$Se_2Cl_2 \xrightarrow{C_6H_5CH_2MgCl} (C_6H_5CH_2Se—)_2 + (C_6H_5CH_2)_2SeCl_2$$

$$SeCl_4 \xrightarrow{C_6H_5CH_2MgCl} (C_6H_5CH_2)_2SeCl_2$$

$$SeOCl_2 \xrightarrow{C_6H_5MgBr} (C_6H_5)_2Se$$

$$SeOCl_2 \xrightarrow{C_6H_5CH_2MgCl} (C_6H_5CH_2)_2SeCl_2$$

Mingoia[64] has prepared selenocarboxylic acids by treating hydrogen selenide successively with a Grignard reagent and a carbonyl chloride.

$$H_2Se \xrightarrow{C_2H_5MgBr} HSeMgBr \xrightarrow{C_6H_5COCl} C_6H_5COSeH$$

$$H_2Se \xrightarrow{C_2H_5MgBr} HSeMgBr \xrightarrow{CH_3COCl} CH_3COSeH$$

The selenium of such acids is said to be readily replaceable by atmospheric oxygen.

Other reactions of bromomagnesium hydrogen selenide reported by Mingoia (*loc. cit.*[64b]) are:

$$HSeMgBr + ClCO_2C_2H_5 \longrightarrow C_2H_5OCOSeH \longrightarrow CO + Se + C_2H_5OH$$

$$HSeMgBr + C_2H_5MgI \longrightarrow C_2H_5SeH$$

$$HSeMgBr + CH_3CHO \longrightarrow CH_3CHSe$$

$$HSeMgBr + C_6H_5CHO \longrightarrow C_6H_5CHSe$$

TELLURIUM COMPOUNDS

Tellurium compounds have been investigated chiefly by Lederer. A summary of available data is recorded in Table XXI-VIII. The reactions suggested by Lederer to account for the observed products of the tetrahalides are:

$$TeCl_4 + 4\ RMgBr \longrightarrow Te + 4\ MgBrCl + R_2$$

$$TeCl_4 + 3\ RMgBr \longrightarrow R_3TeCl + 3\ MgBrCl$$

$$R_3TeCl + RMgBr \longrightarrow R_2Te + MgBrCl + R_2$$

---

[63] Strecker and Willing, *Ber.*, *48*, 196–206 (1915).

[64] Mingoia, (*a*) *Gazz. chim. ital.*, *56*, 835–9 (1926); *Chem. Zentr.*, *1927*,*I*, 1953; (*b*) *Gazz. chim. ital.*, *58*, 667–73 (1928); *Chem. Zentr.*, *1929*,*I*, 634.

TABLE XXI-VIII

REACTIONS OF GRIGNARD REAGENTS WITH TELLURIUM COMPOUNDS

Te Comp'd	RMgX	Product(s)	Ref.
$TeCl_4$	C_6H_5MgBr (5 equiv.)	$C_6H_5Cl + (C_6H_5—)_2 + (C_6H_5)_2Te + (C_6H_5)_3TeX$*	*1,2*
$TeCl_4$	$2\text{-}CH_3C_6H_4MgBr$	$(2\text{-}CH_3C_6H_4)_3TeX$*	*2*
$TeCl_4$	$3\text{-}CH_3C_6H_4MgBr$	$(3\text{-}CH_3C_6H_4)_3TeX$* (*ca.* 26%)	*7*
$TeCl_4$	$4\text{-}CH_3C_6H_4MgBr$	$(4\text{-}CH_3C_6H_4)_3TeX$*	*2*
$TeCl_4$	$2\text{-}CH_3OC_6H_4MgBr$	$(2\text{-}CH_3OC_6H_4)_3TeX$* (*ca.* 15–25%)	*18*
$TeCl_4$	$4\text{-}CH_3OC_6H_4MgBr$	$(4\text{-}CH_3OC_6H_4)_3TeX$*	*7*
$TeCl_4$	$2,4\text{-}(CH_3)_2C_6H_3MgBr$	$[2,4\text{-}(CH_3)_2C_6H_3]_3TeX$*	*7*
$TeCl_4$	$2,5\text{-}(CH_3)_2C_6H_3MgBr$	$[2,5\text{-}(CH_3)_2C_6H_3]_3TeX$*	*7*
$TeCl_4$	$2\text{-}C_2H_5OC_6H_4MgBr$	$(2\text{-}C_2H_5OC_6H_4)_3TeX$* (*ca.* 28%)	*10*
$TeCl_4$	$4\text{-}C_2H_5OC_6H_4MgBr$	$(4\text{-}C_2H_5OC_6H_4)_3TeX$* (*ca.* 29%)	*10*
$TeBr_2$	2-Thienyl-MgBr	$(2\text{-}C_4H_3S)_2Te$† (*ca.* 62%)	*15*
$TeBr_2$	$4\text{-}BrC_6H_4MgBr$	$(4\text{-}BrC_6H_4)_2Te$† (*ca.* 27%) + $4\text{-}BrC_6H_4TeC_6H_4C_6H_4\text{-}4Br$¶ (*ca.* 24%)	*9*
$TeBr_2$	$4\text{-}ClC_6H_4MgBr$	$(4\text{-}ClC_6H_4)_2Te$† (*ca.* 54%)	*9*
$TeBr_2$	$3\text{-}CH_3C_6H_4MgBr$	$(3\text{-}CH_3C_6H_4Te—)_2$	*5*
$TeBr_2$	$3\text{-}CH_3OC_6H_4MgI$	$(3\text{-}CH_3OC_6H_4)_2Te$† (*ca.* 48%)	*14*
$TeBr_2$	$4\text{-}CH_3OC_6H_4MgBr$	$(4\text{-}CH_3OC_6H_4)_2Te$† (*ca.* 62%)	*6*
$TeBr_2$	$2,4\text{-}(CH_3)_2C_6H_3MgBr$	$[2,4\text{-}(CH_3)_2C_6H_3]_2Te$† (*ca.* 53%)	*3*
$TeBr_2$	$2,5\text{-}(CH_3)_2C_6H_3MgBr$	$[2,5\text{-}(CH_3)_2C_6H_3]_2Te$ (*ca.* 52%)	*3*
$TeBr_2$	$4\text{-}C_2H_5OC_6H_4MgBr$	$(4\text{-}C_2H_5OC_6H_4)_2Te$‡ (*ca.* 39%)	*13*
$TeBr_2$	$2,4,6\text{-}(CH_3)_3C_6H_2MgBr$	$[2,4,6\text{-}(CH_3)_3C_6H_4]_2Te$	*4*
$TeBr_2$	$1\text{-}C_{10}H_7MgBr$	$(1\text{-}C_{10}H_7)_2Te$† (*ca.* 62%)	*12*
$TeBr_2$	$2\text{-}C_2H_5OC_6H_4MgBr$	$(2\text{-}C_2H_5OC_6H_4)_2Te$† (*ca.* 34%)	*11*
$(2\text{-Thienyl})_2TeBr_2$	2-Thienyl-MgBr	$(2\text{-}C_4H_3S)_3TeBr$	*15*
$(C_6H_5)_2TeCl$	$R'MgBr$	$R'(C_6H_5)_2TeX$§	*16*
$(C_6H_5)_2TeBr_2$	$2\text{-}CH_3C_6H_4MgBr$	$C_6H_5(2\text{-}CH_3C_6H_4)Te$¶ (*ca.* 18%)	*17*

* Product isolated after treatment with KI, as R_3TeI.

† Product isolated, after treatment with Br_2, as R_2TeBr_2.

‡ Product isolated, after treatment with I_2, as R_2TeI_2.

§ Product isolated, after treatment with KI, as $R'R_2TeI$; $R' = C_6H_5$, $2\text{-}CH_3C_6H_4$, $3\text{-}CH_3C_6H_4$, $4\text{-}CH_3C_6H_4$, $4\text{-}CH_3OC_6H_4$, $2,4\text{-}(CH_3)_2C_6H_3$, $2,5\text{-}(CH_3)C_6H_3$, $3,4\text{-}(CH_3)_2C_6H_3$, $2,4,6\text{-}(CH_3)_3C_6H_2$, $1\text{-}C_{10}H_7$.

¶ Product isolated, after treatment with Br_2, as $RR'TeBr_2$.

TABLE XXI-VIII (Continued)

Te Comp'd	RMgX	Product(s)	Ref.
$C_6H_5(2\text{-}CH_3C_6H_4)TeBr$	CH_3MgI	$C_6H_5(2\text{-}CH_3C_6H_4)Te$ (77%)	*17*
$(3\text{-}CH_3C_6H_4)_2TeBr_2$	CH_3MgI	$(3\text{-}CH_3C_6H_4)_2Te$ (90%)	*5*
$(4\text{-}CH_3C_6H_4)_2TeCl_2$	C_6H_5MgBr	$C_6H_5(4\text{-}CH_3C_6H_4)_2TeX$* (75%)	*8*
$(4\text{-}CH_3C_6H_4)_2TeBr_2$	C_6H_5MgBr	$C_6H_5(4\text{-}CH_3C_6H_4)Te$† (*ca.* 78%)	*8*
$[2,4\text{-}(CH_3)_2C_6H_4]_2TeBr_2$	CH_3MgI	$[2,4\text{-}(CH_3)_2C_6H_4]_2Te$ (65%)	*3*
$(4\text{-}C_2H_5OC_6H_4)_2TeI_2$	CH_3MgI	$(4\text{-}C_2H_5OC_6H_4)_2Te$	*13*
$(1\text{-}C_{10}H_7)_2TeBr_2$	C_2H_5MgI	$(1\text{-}C_{10}H_7)_2Te$	*12*

*Product isolated, after treatment with KI, as $R'R_2TeI$.
†Product isolated, after treatment with Br_2, as $RR'TeBr_2$.

REFERENCES FOR TABLE XXI-VIII

(*1*) Lederer, *Compt. rend.*, *151*, 611–2 (1911).
(*2*) Lederer, *Ber.*, *44*, 2287–92 (1911).
(*3*) Lederer, *Ber.*, *49*, 334–44 (1916).
(*4*) Lederer, *Ber.*, *49*, 345–9 (1916).
(*5*) Lederer, *Ber.*, *49*, 1071–6 (1916).
(*6*) Lederer, *Ber.*, *49*, 1076–82 (1916).
(*7*) Lederer, *Ber.*, *49*, 1385–9 (1916).
(*8*) Lederer, *Ber.*, *49*, 1615–22 (1916).
(*9*) Lederer, *Ber.*, *49*, 2002–5 (1916).
(*10*) Lederer, *Ber.*, *49*, 2529–31 (1916).
(*11*) Lederer, *Ber.*, *49*, 2532–8 (1916).
(*12*) Lederer, *Ber.*, *49*, 2663–6 (1916).
(*13*) Lederer, *Ber.*, *50*, 238–43 (1917).
(*14*) Lederer, *Ber.*, *52B*, 1989–92 (1919).
(*15*) Krause and Renwanz, *Ber.*, *62B*, 1710–6 (1929).
(*16*) Lederer, *Ber.*, *53B*, 1430–45 (1920).
(*17*) Lederer, *Ber.*, *53B*, 1674–80 (1920).
(*18*) Lederer, *Ber.*, *53B*, 2342–6 (1920).

CHAPTER XXII

Reactions of Grignard Reagents with Silicon Compounds

There have been numerous general reviews of the chemistry of organosilicon compounds, most of which include some discussion of the Grignard reactions. Two of the more comprehensive and more readily accessible surveys are those of Rochow[1] and of Burkhard *et al.*[2] Both contain references to earlier reviews.

The Grignard reactions of silicon compounds reported are chiefly those of the halides and esters. It is now generally recognized that the silicon analogs of the ketones do not exist and that the silicone reactions reported by Kipping and Hackford[3] must be those of compounds of the type $[—RR'SiO—]_x$. Similarly the supposed orthosiliconic acids are now known to be non-isolable; if they exist at all they immediately undergo dehydration-condensation to form "polymers." The dihydroxydialkylsilicanes behave similarly, but the dihydroxydiarylsilicanes appear to be reasonably stable.

SILICON HALIDES

Unlike carbon tetrachloride, silicon tetrachloride is capable of reacting successively with four molecules of Grignard reagent. However, the relative reactivities of the four halides ($SiCl_4$, $RSiCl_3$, R_2SiCl_2, R_3SiCl) do not correspond to the relative amounts of chlorine present. Fouss[4] has subjected the problem of successive substitution in compounds of the type AX_4 to mathematical analysis. On the basis of Kipping's[5] figures for the products of the reaction of one molecular equivalent of silicon tetrachloride with two and a quarter molecular equivalents of phenylmagnesium bromide (trichlorophenylsilicane, 14 percent; dichlorodiphenylsilicane, 44 percent; chlorotriphenylsilicane, 5 percent), Fuoss concludes that trichlorophenylsilicane is materially more reactive than either silicon tetrachloride or dichlorodiphenylsilicane. Whether for steric or other reasons, the fourth halogen atom appears to be the most difficultly

[1]Rochow, "An Introduction to the Chemistry of the Silicones," John Wiley & Sons, Inc., New York, x + 137 pp, *1946*.

[2]Burkhard, Rochow, Booth, and Hartt, *Chem. Revs.*, *41*, 97–149 (1947).

[3]Kipping and Hackford, *J. Chem. Soc.*, *99*, 138–45 (1911).

[4]Fuoss, *J. Am. Chem. Soc.*, *65*, 2406–8 (1943).

[5]Kipping, *J. Chem. Soc.*, *101*, 2108–25 (1912).

replaceable of all. Indeed, Medoks and Kotelkov[6] report that, even in the presence of an excess of Grignard reagent, the reaction of silicon tetrafluoride with phenylmagnesium bromide does not proceed at room temperature beyond the formation of fluorotriphenylsilicane.

Qualitative examination of the available data indicates that in general the silicon halides are more reactive toward alkyl than toward aryl Grignard reagents, which would suggest that the order of reactivity for Grignard reagents is the same as that established by Kharasch and Weinhouse[7] for the ketones (in which reactivity increases as the "electronegativity" of the organic radical of the Grignard reagent decreases). If this be true, however, steric factors must also play a significant, and sometimes a critical, part, for Sommer *et al.*[8] report that when chlorotriethylsilicane is treated with an equimolecular mixture of methyl- and ethylmagnesium bromides the only condensation product detectable is methyltriethylsilicane.[9]

Like silicon tetrachloride, silicochloroform is subject to successive chlorine replacements upon reaction with Grignard reagents.

According to Schumb and Saffer[10] hexachlorodisilicoethane reacts with alkyl or aryl Grignard reagents to form hexaälkyl- or hexaäryldisilicoethanes, respectively. Silicon-to-silicon bond cleavage is also reported (Schumb and Saffer, *loc. cit.*;[10] Schwarz and Sexauer[11]). Octachlorotrisilicopropane apparently yields cleavage products only with phenylmagnesium bromide (Schumb and Saffer, *loc. cit.*[10]).

Hexachlorosilicyl oxide is reported as reacting similarly to hexachlorodisilicoethane (Schumb and Saffer, *loc. cit.*;[10] Emeléus and Payne[12].)

SILICON ESTERS

Tetraëthoxysilicane and the orthosiliconates react with Grignard reagents in a manner similar to that of the corresponding halides, though somewhat less readily.

Data concerning representative reactions are assembled in Table XXII-I. No attempt has been made to include an exhaustive resumé of the patent literature. Reactions leading to product mixtures of unknown composition have been, for the most part, intentionally omitted.

---

[6]Medoks and Kotelkov, *J. Gen. Chem.* (U.S.S.R.), 7, 2007-8 (1937); *Chem. Abstr.*, 32, 531 (1938).

[7]Kharasch and Weinhouse, *J. Org. Chem.*, 1, 209-30 (1936).

[8]Sommer, Kerr, and Whitmore, *J. Am. Chem. Soc.*, 70, 434-5 (1948).

[9]The methyl radical is somewhat more "electronegative" than the ethyl radical. For a discussion of the relative "electronegativities" of organic radicals see: Kharasch and Reinmuth, *J. Chem. Education*, 5, 404-18; 8, 1703-48 (1931); Kharasch, Reinmuth, and Mayo, *ibid.*, 11, 82-96 (1934); 13, 7-19 (1936).

[10]Schumb and Saffer, *J. Am. Chem. Soc.*, 61, 363-6 (1939).

[11]Schwarz and Sexauer, *Ber.*, 59B, 333-7 (1926).

[12]Emeléus and Payne, *J. Chem. Soc.*, 1947, 1590-2.

SOME ILLUSTRATIVE PREPARATIONS

Ethyltrichlorosilane from silicon tetrachloride (*Andrianov*[13]).—Magnesium (12 g.) was treated with several drops of tetraëthoxysilane and then dropwise with 40 g. of ethyl bromide, after which an additional 22 g. of ethyl bromide in benzene solution was added, and the mixture was re-refluxed for an hour and a half (yield 93.3% C_2H_5MgBr). To the Grignard solution was slowly added 85 g. of silicon tetrachloride in 100 ml. of benzene, and the mixture was refluxed for three to four hours (yield 65 g., 80%, $C_2H_5SiCl_3$).

Dichlorodiethylsilane from silicon tetrachloride (*Andrianov*[13]).—The preparation of the dialkyl derivative was carried out in the manner described for the monoalkyl derivative save that the quantity of silicon tetrachloride was halved [yield 70.3%, $(C_2H_5)_2SiCl_2$].

Fluorotri-n-amylsilane from silicon tetrafluoride (*Gierut et al.*[14]).—One mole of *n*-amylmagnesium chloride was prepared in a 2-liter, three-necked flask equipped with a reflux condenser, a stirrer, and an inlet tube extending to the bottom of the flask. Silicon tetrafluoride was passed into the well-stirred Grignard solution until a short time after the system had separated into a clear upper layer and a gray, turbid lower layer. The layers were separated; the lower, ether-insoluble layer was thoroughly washed with ether, and the washings were added to the upper layer. Ether was distilled from the ethereal layer and the residue was fractionally distilled. The principal fraction (b.p. 267°/745 mm.) was fluorotri-*n*-amylsilane (50 g., 57.6%).

Tetraëthylsilane from silicon tetrachloride (*Sugden and Wilkins*[15]).—To 128 g. of magnesium in 690 ml. of dry ether, 10 g. of ethyl bromide and a crystal of iodine were added. When vigorous reaction set in the remainder of the ethyl bromide (440 g. in all), diluted with 200 ml. of benzene, was added slowly. Finally a further 500 ml. of benzene, warmed to 40°, was added, and the Grignard solution was decanted from excess magnesium. To this Grignard solution was added 68 g. of silicon tetrachloride, and the mixture was heated on the water-bath for twelve to fifteen hours. After decomposition with dilute acid and removal of the solvents from the benzene-ether layer, 45 g. of crude product was obtained. From this the silicols were removed by repeated shaking with concentrated sulfuric acid. The residue (20 g.) proved upon distillation to be nearly pure tetraëthylsilane.

Tetraphenylsilane from silicon tetrachloride (*Schumb and Saffer*[16]).—In an experiment employing the Barbier modification of the Grignard reac-

---

[13] Andrianov, *J. Gen. Chem.*, (U.S.S.R.), *16*, 487–92 (1946); *Chem. Abstr.*, *41*, 701 (1947).

[14] Gierut, Sowa, and Nieuwland, *J. Am. Chem. Soc.*, 58, 897–8 (1936).

[15] Sugden and Wilkins, *J. Chem. Soc.*, *1931*, 126–8.

[16] Schumb and Saffer, *J. Am. Chem. Soc.*, *61*, 363–6 (1939).

tion, 6 g. of silicon tetrachloride and 30 g. of bromobenzene in 100 ml. of anhydrous ether were allowed to drop on magnesium turnings activated with a crystal of iodine. The vigorous ensuing reaction ultimately yielded 8.8 g. (75%) of tetraphenylsilane.

Triethylsilane from trichlorosilane (*Whitmore et al.*[17]).—Ethylmagnesium bromide (12.6 moles) was prepared in a 5-liter three-necked flask, fitted with an efficient stirrer, a dropping funnel, and a large bulb condenser, each connected with a Dry Ice-acetone trap. A cold solution of 406.5 g. (3 moles) of trichlorosilane in 1200 ml. of anhydrous ethyl ether was added, with cooling and vigorous stirring during a period of six hours. The mixture was stirred at room temperature for eight hours and then heated to reflux for five hours. Ether was removed from the reaction mixture through a 20-plate column, and the residue was heated on a steam-bath for ten hours. With cooling, the solid residue was hydrolyzed with 180 ml. of water, followed by 372 ml. of concentrated hydrochloric acid. The aqueous layer was separated and extracted twice with 500-ml. portions of ether. The ether extracts and product were combined, washed with water, and then dried over 150 g. of anhydrous potassium carbonate. Fractional distillation of the product through a 20-plate column yielded 270.3 g. (77.5%) of triethylsilane.

Hexaëthyldisiloxane from ethyl orthosilicate (*Di Giorgio* et al.[18]).—In a 12-liter three-necked flask, fitted with a mercury-sealed stirrer, reflux condenser, and dropping funnel, there was prepared 22 equivalents of ethylmagnesium bromide in 10 liters of ether. The flask was cooled with tap water, and 1450 g. (7.0 moles) of ethyl orthosilicate was added during one hour. After one hour stirring at room temperature the ether was distilled, and the residue was heated on a steam-bath for twelve hours. The ether was then returned to the flask, and hydrolysis was effected with ice, water, and acid. After separation of the ether layer, the ether was distilled from the product; a small amount of ethanol was also removed by distillation. The product was dissolved, with cooling, in 1.5 liter of concentrated sulfuric acid. This was then added to 6 liters of cold water, and the organic layer was separated, dried with calcium chloride, and fractionated. Hexaëthyldisiloxane (573 g., 2.3 moles) was thus obtained in 66% yield.

---

[17]Whitmore, Pietrusza, and Sommer, *J. Am. Chem. Soc.*, 69, 2108–10 (1947).
[18]Di Giorgio, Strong, Sommer, and Whitmore, *J. Am. Chem. Soc.*, 68, 1380 (1946).

TABLE XXII-I

REACTIONS OF GRIGNARD REAGENTS WITH SILICON COMPOUNDS

(Polymers are listed under the empirical formulae of the monomers.)

Si Comp'd	RMgX	Product(s)	Ref.
SiF_4			
SiF_4	C_2H_5MgBr	$(C_2H_5)_3SiF$ (45%); $(C_2H_5)_4Si$ (*ca.* 45%)	53,54
SiF_4	n-C_3H_7MgBr	$(n\text{-}C_3H_7)_3SiF$ (62%)	53
SiF_4	n-C_4H_9MgCl (1 mole)	$(n\text{-}C_4H_9)_3SiF$ (51 g., 70%)	53
SiF_4	n-C_4H_9MgBr (1 mole)	$(n\text{-}C_4H_9)_3SiF$ (46 g., 63.2%)	53
SiF_4	n-$C_5H_{11}MgCl$ (1 mole)	$(n\text{-}C_5H_{11})_3SiF$ (50 g., 57.6%)	53
SiF_4	C_6H_5MgBr (excess)	$(C_6H_5)_3SiF$	55
SiF_4	$C_6H_5CH_2MgCl$	$(C_6H_5CH_2)_3SiF$; $(C_6H_5CH_2)_4Si$	56
SiF_6Na_2			
Na_2SiF_6 (30 g.)	C_2H_5MgBr (144 g. C_2H_5Br)	$(C_2H_5)_4Si$ (23%)	57
Na_2SiF_6 (3.8 g.)	C_6H_5MgBr (26 g. C_6H_5Br)	$(C_6H_5)_4Si$ (33.9%)	42
Na_2SiF_6 (3.76 g.)	$C_6H_5CH_2MgCl$ (10.22 g. $C_6H_5CH_2Cl$)	$(C_6H_5CH_2)_4Si$ (20.7%)	58,42
$SiCl_4$			
$SiCl_4$ (3.97 moles)	CH_3MgCl (1.6 l., 3.1 *M*)	CH_3SiCl_3 (115 g. crude; 60 g. pure)	2
$SiCl_4$ (212 ml.)	CH_3MgCl (2.05 l., 2.3 *M*)	$(CH_3)_2SiCl_2$ (26.5 g.)	2
$SiCl_4$	CH_3MgBr (9.9 moles)	CH_3SiCl_3 (564 g., 38%)	3
$SiCl_4$ (1 l.)	CH_3MgX (2 moles)	CH_3SiCl_3; $(CH_3)_2SiCl_2$	4,5
$SiCl_4$ (1 mole)	CH_3MgBr (3 moles)	$(CH_3)_2SiCl_2$; $(CH_3)_3SiCl$	6,7
$SiCl_4$ (50 g.)	CH_3MgBr (30 g. Mg)	$(CH_3)_4Si$ (*ca.* 13.2 g.)	8
$SiCl_4$ (4.4 moles)	CH_3MgBr (19.1 moles)	$(CH_3)_4Si$ (63%)	9
$SiCl_4$	CH_3MgBr	$(CH_3)_4Si$	10,10.1
$SiCl_4$	CH_3MgI	$(CH_3)_4Si$	11
$SiCl_4$ (30 g.)	$HC{\equiv}CMgBr$	After hydrolysis: $[(HC{\equiv}C)_3Si]_2O$ (3–5 g.)	12

TABLE XXII-I (Continued)

Si Comp'd	RMgX	Product(s)	Ref.
$SiCl_4$ (*cont.*)			
$SiCl_4$ (1.0 equiv.)	C_2H_5MgCl (2.25 equiv.)	$(C_2H_5)_4Si$ (0.0 part); $(C_2H_5)_3SiCl$ (0.26 part); $(C_2H_5)_2SiCl_2$ (0.1 part); $C_2H_5SiCl_3$ (0.5 part)*	*126*
$SiCl_4$ (1.0 equiv.)	C_2H_5MgCl (3.6 equiv.)	$(C_2H_5)_4Si$ (0.24 part); $(C_2H_5)_3SiCl$ (1.00 part); $(C_2H_5)_2SiCl_2$ (0.89 part); $C_2H_5SiCl_3$ (0.19 part)†	*126*
$SiCl_4$	C_2H_5MgCl	$(C_2H_5)_4Si$ (70–80%)	*17*
$SiCl_4$ (50 g.)	C_2H_5MgBr (1.2 equiv.)	$C_2H_5SiCl_3$ (30–35 g., crude)	*13,3,8,14*
$SiCl_4$ (1 equiv.)	C_2H_5MgBr (2 equiv. Mg)	$C_2H_5SiCl_3$; $(C_2H_5)_2SiCl_2$ ("poor yields")	*15*
$SiCl_4$ (85 g.)	C_2H_5MgBr (*ca.* 1 equiv.)	$C_2H_5SiCl_3$ (65 g.)	*16*
$SiCl_4$	C_2H_5MgBr (*ca.* 2 equiv.)	$(C_2H_5)_2SiCl_2$ (70.3%)	*16,64*
$SiCl_4$ (160 g.)	C_2H_5MgBr (2.5 equiv.)	$C_2H_5SiCl_3$; $(C_2H_5)_2SiCl_2$ (*ca.* 18 g.); $(C_2H_5)_3SiCl$	*15,8,18*
$SiCl_4$ (68 g.)	C_2H_5MgBr (440 g. C_2H_5Br)	$(C_2H_5)_4Si$ (*ca.* 20 g.)	*19,8,17, 20*
$SiCl_4$	C_2H_5MgI	$C_2H_5SiCl_3$; $(C_2H_5)_2SiCl_2$; $(C_2H_5)_3SiCl$; $(C_2H_5)_4Si$	*13a*
$SiCl_4$	$H_2C{=}CHCH_2Cl$ + Mg	$(H_2C{=}CHCH_2)_4Si$ (*ca.* 90%)	*21*
$SiCl_4$ (100 g.)	n-C_3H_7MgBr (1.25 equiv. Mg)	n-$C_3H_7SiCl_3$ (*ca.* 30 g.)	*22,8,23, 24,25*
$SiCl_4$	n-C_3H_7MgX	$(n$-$C_3H_7)_4Si$	*19*
$SiCl_4$ (4 moles)	i-C_3H_7MgCl	i-$C_3H_7SiCl_3$ (30–50%)	*26*
$SiCl_4$ (0.8 g.)	2-Thienyl-MgI (10 g. C_4H_3SI)	$(\alpha$-$C_4H_3S)_4Si$ (50%)	*27*
$SiCl_4$ (125 g.)	n-C_4H_9MgBr (20.5 g. Mg)	n-$C_4H_9SiCl_3$ (86.5 g., crude)	*8,28*
$SiCl_4$	n-C_4H_9MgX	$(n$-$C_4H_9)_2SiCl_2$	*7*

* The aggregate product contained 34% Si, as compared with 17.9% Si for $(C_2H_5)_2SiCl_2$.

† The aggregate product contained 24% Si, as compared with 18.6% Si for $(C_2H_5)_3SiCl$.

TABLE XXII-I (Continued)

Si Comp'd	RMgX	Product(s)	Ref.
$SiCl_4$ (*cont.*)			
$SiCl_4$ (0.103 mole)	n-C_4H_9MgBr (1.05 mole C_4H_9Br)	$(n\text{-}C_4H_9)_4Si$ (44.5%)	*20*
$SiCl_4$ (116 g.)	i-C_4H_9MgBr (16.6 g. C_4H_9Br)	i-$C_4H_9SiCl_3$ (*ca.* 79.5 g.)	*8*
$SiCl_4$	i-C_4H_9MgCl (*ca.* 1 equiv.)	i-$C_4H_9SiCl_3$	*16*
$SiCl_4$	i-C_4H_9MgCl (*ca.* 2 equiv.)	$(i\text{-}C_4H_9)_2SiCl_2$	*16*
$SiCl_4$ (20 g.)	$H_2C(CH_2CH_2MgBr)_2$ (30 g. $C_4H_8Br_2$)	$(CH_2)_5SiCl_2$ (*ca.* 59%)	*29*
$SiCl_4$	n-$C_5H_{11}MgBr$	n-$C_5H_{11}SiCl_3$ (52%)	*31*
$SiCl_4$ (113.5 g.)	i-$C_5H_{11}MgBr$ (100.7 g. $C_5H_{11}Br$)	i-$C_5H_{11}SiCl_3$	*23,8,16, 30*
$SiCl_4$ (330 g.)	$4\text{-}BrC_6H_4MgBr$ (420 g. $C_6H_4Br_2$)	$4\text{-}BrC_6H_4SiCl_3$ (140 g.); $(4\text{-}BrC_6H_4)_2SiCl_2$ (60 g.)	*32*
$SiCl_4$ (400 g.)	$4\text{-}ClC_6H_4MgBr$ (382 g. C_6H_4BrCl)	$4\text{-}ClC_6H_4SiCl_3$ (180 g.)	*32*
$SiCl_4$ (150 g.)	C_6H_5MgBr (1 equiv.)	$C_6H_5SiCl_3$ (83 g., crude)	*30,33,34, 35,36*
$SiCl_4$ (170 g.)	C_6H_5MgBr (0.75 equiv.)	$C_6H_5SiCl_3$ (*ca.* 100 g.)	*37,38*
$SiCl_4$ (170 g.)	C_6H_5MgBr (2.25 equiv.)	$C_6H_5SiCl_3$ (30 g.); $(C_6H_5)_2SiCl_2$ (110 g.); $(C_6H_5)_3SiCl$ (15 g.)	*39,40*
$SiCl_4$ (8 g.)	C_6H_5MgBr (17 g.)	After hydrolysis: $(C_6H_5)_2Si(OH)_2$ (25–30%)	*41*
$SiCl_4$ (1 mole)	C_6H_5MgBr (8 moles)	After hydrolysis: $(C_6H_5)_3SiOH$	*41*
$SiCl_4$ (10 g.)	C_6H_5MgBr (93 g. C_6H_5Br)	$(C_6H_5)_4Si$ (48%)	*42*
$SiCl_4$ (6 g.)	C_6H_5Br (30 g.) + Mg	$(C_6H_5)_4Si$ (8.8 g., 75%)	*1*
$SiCl_4$ (35 g.)	$(CH_2)_5CHMgBr$ (2 equiv.)	$(CH_2)_5CHSiCl_3$; $[(CH_2)_5CH]_2SiCl_2$; conden'n products	*49*
$SiCl_4$ (1.5 mole)	n-$C_6H_{13}MgBr$ (1.5 mole)	n-$C_6H_{13}SiCl_3$ (50%)	*31,16,50*
$SiCl_4$	n-$C_6H_{13}MgCl$ (93 g., *ca.* 2 equiv.)	$(n\text{-}C_6H_{13})_2SiCl_2$ (38.5 g.)	*16*
$SiCl_4$ (113.5 g.)	$C_6H_5CH_2MgCl$ (84.2 g. C_7H_7Cl)	$C_6H_5CH_2SiCl_3$	*23,3,16, 30,43*
$SiCl_4$	$C_6H_5CH_2Cl$ + Mg	$C_6H_5CH_2SiCl_3$; $(C_6H_5CH_2)_2SiCl_2$; $(C_6H_5CH_2)_3SiCl$	*15*

TABLE XXII-I (Continued)

Si Comp'd	RMgX	Product(s)	Ref.
$SiCl_4$ (*cont.*)			
$SiCl_4$	$C_6H_5CH_2MgCl$ (2.4 equiv.)	$(C_6H_5CH_2)_2SiCl_2$	*44,45*
$SiCl_4$ (1 mole)	$C_6H_5CH_2MgCl$ (3 moles)	After hydrolysis: $(C_6H_5CH_2)_2Si(OH)_2$ ("poor yield"); $(C_6H_5CH_2)_3SiOH$	*46*
$SiCl_4$ (1 mole)	$C_6H_5CH_2MgCl$ (4 moles)	After hydrolysis: $(C_6H_5CH_2)_3SiOH$ ("good yield")	*46*
$SiCl_4$ (12 g.)	$C_6H_5CH_2MgCl$ (70.8 g. C_7H_7Cl)	$(C_6H_5CH_2)_4Si$ (45.1%)	*42*
$SiCl_4$ (10 g.)	2-$CH_3C_6H_4MgBr$ (55 g. C_7H_7Br)	Brown tar	*1*
$SiCl_4$ (10 g.)	3-$CH_3C_6H_4MgBr$ (55 g. C_7H_7Br)	(3-$CH_3C_6H_4)_4Si$ (1.8 g., 8%)	*1*
$SiCl_4$ (10 g.)	4-$CH_3C_6H_4MgBr$ (50 g. C_7H_7Br)	(4-$CH_3C_6H_4)_4Si$ (7 g., 30%)	*1,47,48*
$SiCl_4$	*n*-$C_8H_{17}MgBr$	*n*-$C_8H_{17}SiCl_3$	*31*
$SiCl_4$ (113.5 g.)	1-$C_{10}H_7MgBr$ (138 g. $C_{10}H_7Br$)	1-$C_{10}H_7SiCl_3$	*23,36*
$SiCl_4$ (113.4 g.)	1-$C_{10}H_7MgBr$ (138 g. $C_{10}H_7Br$)	1-$C_{10}H_7SiCl_3$ (53.2%)	*16*
$SiCl_4$	*n*-$C_{10}H_{21}MgBr$	*n*-$C_{10}H_{21}SiCl_3$ (54%)	*31*
$SiCl_4$ (100 g.)	4-$(C_2H_5)_3SiC_6H_4MgBr$ (117 g. $C_{12}H_{19}BrSi$)	4-$(C_2H_5)_3SiC_6H_4SiCl_3$ (39 g., crude)	*51*
$SiCl_4$ (140 parts)	*n*-$C_{12}H_{25}MgCl$ (95 parts $C_{12}H_{25}Cl$)	*n*-$C_{12}H_{25}SiCl_3$ (67%)	*52*
$SiCl_4$	*n*-$C_{12}H_{25}MgBr$	*n*-$C_{12}H_{25}SiCl_3$ (29%)	*31*
$SiCl_4$	*n*-$C_{14}H_{29}MgCl$	*n*-$C_{14}H_{29}SiCl_3$ (50%)	*52*
$SiCl_4$	*n*-$C_{14}H_{29}MgBr$	*n*-$C_{14}H_{29}SiCl_3$ (48%)	*31*
$SiCl_4$	*n*-$C_{18}H_{37}MgCl$	*n*-$C_{18}H_{37}SiCl_3$	*52*
$SiBr_4$			
$SiBr_4$ (18 g.)	C_6H_5MgBr (45 g. C_6H_5Br)	$(C_6H_5)_4Si$ (10 g., 60%)	*1*
Si_2Cl_6			
Si_2Cl_6 (20 g.)	CH_3MgBr (11.2 g. Mg)	$[(CH_3)_3Si—]_2$ (0.9 g.)	*30,59*
Si_2Cl_6 (20 g.)	C_2H_5MgBr (55 g. C_2H_5Br)	$[(C_2H_5)_3Si—]_2$ (9.0 g., 50%); $(C_2H_5)_4Si$	*1*

TABLE XXII-I (Continued)

Si Comp'd	RMgX	Product(s)	Ref.
Si_2Cl_6 (*cont.*)			
Si_2Cl_6 (15 g.)	n-C_3H_7MgCl (50 g. C_3H_7Cl)	$[(n\text{-}C_3H_7)_3Si-]_2$ ("large yield"); $(n\text{-}C_3H_7)_4Si$ ("very little")	*1*
Si_2Cl_6	C_6H_5MgBr	$(C_6H_5)_2SiCl_2$ and "other monosilane derivatives	*60*
Si_2Cl_6 (10 g.)	C_6H_5MgBr (55 g. C_6H_5Br)	$[(C_6H_5)_3Si-]_2$ (7 g., 40%); $(C_6H_5)_4Si$ (trace)	*1*
Si_2Cl_6 (12 g.)	$C_6H_5CH_2Cl$ (100 g.) + Mg (15 g.)	$[(C_6H_5CH_2)_3Si-]_2$	*61*
Si_2Cl_6 (13 g.)	4-$CH_3C_6H_4MgBr$ (70 g. C_7H_7Br)	$[(4\text{-}CH_3C_6H_4)_3Si-]_2$ (7 g., 35%)	*1*
Si_2Br_6			
Si_2Br_6 (35 g.)	C_6H_5MgBr (85 g. C_6H_5Br)	$[(C_6H_5)_3Si-]_2$ (1 g.); $(C_6H_5)_4Si$ (15 g.)	*1*
Si_2Br_6O			
$O(SiBr_3)_2$ (25 g.)	C_6H_5MgBr (60 g. C_6H_5Br)	$(C_6H_5)_3SiOH$	*1*
Si_2Cl_6O			
$O(SiCl_3)_2$ (1 mole)	CH_3MgCl (2.4 moles) + CH_3MgI (0.1 mole)	$Si_2OCl_4(CH_3)_2$ (0.56 mole, 56%)	62
$O(SiCl_3)_2$ (0.7 mole)	C_2H_5MgBr (0.875 mole)	$Cl_3SiOSiCl_2C_2H_5$ (40%, crude; 24%, pure)	62
$O(SiCl_3)_2$ (1 mole)	C_2H_5MgBr (2.5 moles)	$Si_2OCl_4(C_2H_5)_2$ (87%, crude; 28%, pure)	62
$O(SiCl_3)_2$ (1 mole)	C_2H_5MgBr (3.75 moles)	$Si_2OCl_3(C_2H_5)_3$ (85%, crude; 29.5%, pure)	62
$O(SiCl_3)_2$ (1 mole)	C_2H_5MgBr (6.25 moles)	$Si_2OCl_2(C_2H_5)_4$ (78%, crude; 11%, pure); $Si_2OCl(C_2H_5)_5$ (12 g., crude)	62
$O(SiCl_3)_2$ (6 g.)	C_6H_5MgBr (30 g. C_6H_5Br)	$O[Si(C_6H_5)_3]_2$ (45%); $(C_6H_5)_3SiOH$	*1*
$O(SiCl_3)_2$ (1 mole)	C_6H_5MgBr (2.85 moles)	$Si_2OCl_4(C_6H_5)_2$ (0.175 mole, 17.5%)	62
Si_3Cl_8			
Si_3Cl_8 (18 g.)	C_6H_5MgBr (80 g. C_6H_5Br)	$[(C_6H_5)_3Si-]_2$; $(C_6H_5)_4Si$ (2 g.)	*1*

TABLE XXII-I (Continued)

Si Comp'd	RMgX	Product(s)	Ref.
$HSiCl_3$			
$HSiCl_3$	CH_3MgCl	$HSiCl_2CH_3$	*63*
$HSiCl_3$ (60 g.)	CH_3MgBr (175 g.)	$HSi(CH_3)_3$ ("poor yield")	*65*
$HSiCl_3$ (0.86 mole)	CH_3MgBr (1.75 mole CH_3Br) + n-C_3H_7MgBr (0.86 mole C_3H_7Br)	$HSi(CH_3)_2$-n-C_3H_7 (10 g., 12%)	*66*
$HSiCl_3$ (0.1 mole)	C_2H_5MgCl (0.3 mole)	$HSi(C_2H_5)_3$ (10 ml.)	*67*
$HSiCl_3$ (135.5 g.)	C_2H_5MgBr (1.25 mole)	$HSiCl_2C_2H_5$; $HSiCl(C_2H_5)_2$ (19%)	*63*
$HSiCl_3$ (3.0 moles)	C_2H_5MgBr (12.6 moles)	$HSi(C_2H_5)_3$ (70–78%)	*68,43,66, 69,115*
$HSiCl_3$ (0.1 mole)	$H_2C{=}CHCH_2MgBr$ (1 mole)	$HSi(CH_2CH{=}CH_2)_3$	*67*
$HSiCl_3$ (0.65 mole)	n-C_3H_7MgBr (1.51 mole C_3H_7Br)	$HSi(n$-$C_3H_7)_3$ (45 g., 43%)	*66*
$HSiCl_3$ (0.86 mole)	n-C_3H_7MgBr (0.86 mole C_3H_7Br) + CH_3MgBr (1.75 mole CH_3Br)	$HSi(CH_3)_2$-n-C_3H_7 (10 g., 12%)	*66*
$HSiCl_3$ (0.34 mole)	i-C_3H_7MgCl (1.5 mole)	After hydrolysis at −10 to −5° with dil. H_2SO_4: $(i$-$C_3H_7)_2SiHOH$ (?) (5.6 g., 11%); $[(i$-$C_3H_7)_2SiH]_2O$ (?) (15.8 g., 42%). After similar hydrolysis with dil. HCl, $[i$-$C_3H_7)_2SiH]_2O$ (?) (67 g., 85%)	*70*
$HSiCl_3$ (0.38 mole)	n-C_4H_9MgCl (0.35 mole)	n-$C_4H_9SiHCl_2$ (4.0%)	*115*
$HSiCl_3$ (0.20 mole)	n-C_4H_9MgCl (0.40 mole)	$(n$-$C_4H_9)_2SiHCl$	*115*
$HSiCl_3$ (0.10 mole)	n-C_4H_9MgCl (0.50 mole)	$(n$-$C_4H_9)_3SiH$ (5.0%)	*115*
$HSiCl_3$ (0.30 mole)	i-C_4H_9MgCl (0.25 mole)	i-$C_4H_9SiHCl_2$ (3.5%)	*115*
$HSiCl_3$ (0.15 mole)	i-C_4H_9MgCl (0.30 mole)	$(i$-$C_4H_9)_2SiHCl$ (2.0%)	*115*
$HSiCl_3$ (0.40 mole)	i-$C_5H_{11}MgCl$ (0.35 mole)	i-$C_5H_{11}SiHCl_2$	*115*
$HSiCl_3$ (0.15 mole)	i-$C_5H_{11}MgCl$ (0.30 mole)	$(i$-$C_5H_{11})_2SiHCl$ (1.5%)	*115*
$HSiCl_3$ (813 g.)	4-ClC_6H_4MgBr (1.97 mole)	$HSiCl_2C_6H_4$-4-Cl	*72*
$HSiCl_3$ (6 moles)	C_6H_5MgCl (6 moles)	$HSiCl_2C_6H_5$ (188 g.)	*72*
$HSiCl_3$ (0.8 mole)	C_6H_5MgBr (0.37 mole C_6H_5Br)	$HSiCl_2C_6H_5$ (26%, crude)	*71*
$HSiCl_3$	C_6H_5MgBr	$HSiCl_2C_6H_5$; $HSiCl(C_6H_5)_2$	*63*

TABLE XXII-I (Continued)

Si Comp'd	RMgX	Product(s)	Ref.
$HSiCl_3$ (*cont.*)			
$HSiCl_3$	C_6H_5MgBr	$HSiCl(C_6H_5)_2$	*73*
$HSiCl_3$ (36.2 g.)	C_6H_5MgBr (185 g. C_6H_5Br)	$HSi(C_6H_5)_3$ (52 g., 73%)	*74*
$HSiCl_3$ (0.20 mole)	$(CH_2)_5CHMgCl$ (0.80 mole)	$[(CH_2)_5CH]_3SiH$ (4.4%)	*115*
$HSiCl_3$	$C_6H_5CH_2MgCl$ (1 equiv.)	$HSiCl_2CH_2C_6H_5$; $HSiCl(CH_2C_6H_5)_2$; $HSi(CH_2C_6H_5)_3$	*67,63*
$HSiCl_3$	$C_6H_5CH_2MgCl$	$HSiCl(CH_2C_6H_5)_2$	*73*
$HSiCl_3$ (0.3 mole)	$C_6H_5CH_2MgCl$ (0.6 mole)	$HSiCl(CH_2C_6H_5)_2$ (26 ml.); $HSi(CH_2C_6H_5)_3$	*67*
$HSiCl_3$ (0.1 mole)	$C_6H_5CH_2MgCl$ (0.6 mole)	$HSi(CH_2C_6H_5)_3$ (67%)	*67,115*
$HSiCl_3$ (0.50 mole)	$C_6H_5CH_2MgCl$ (0.50 mole) + CH_3MgCl (0.50 mole)*	$CH_3(C_6H_5CH_2)SiHCl$ (2.4%)	*115*
$HSiCl_3$ (0.80 mole)	$C_6H_5CH_2MgCl$ (0.80 mole) + CH_3MgCl (1.60 mole)*	$C_6H_5CH_2(CH_3)_2SiH$ (16.5%)	*115*
$HSiCl_3$ (0.45 mole)	$C_6H_5CH_2MgCl$ (0.90 mole) + CH_3MgCl (0.50 mole)*	$CH_3(C_6H_5CH_2)_2SiH$ (22.1%)	*115*
$HSiCl_3$ (1220 g.)	4-$CH_3C_6H_4MgBr$ (144 g. Mg)	$HSiCl_2C_6H_4$-4-CH_3 (219.7 g.)	*72*
$HSiCl_3$ (478 g.)	4-$CH_3C_6H_4MgBr$ (1450 g.)	$HSiCl(C_6H_4$-4-$CH_3)_2$ (41%)	*73*
$HSiCl_3$ (1080 g.)	1-$C_{10}H_7MgBr$ (2.36 moles)	$HSiCl_2$-1-$C_{10}H_7$	*72*
CH_3SiCl_3			
CH_3SiCl_3 (0.5 mole) + $(CH_3)_2SiCl_2$ (3.75 moles)	CH_3MgCl (500 ml., 4.1 *M*)	$(CH_3)_3SiCl$ (38.7 g., 0.35 mole); $(CH_3)_2SiCl_2$ (159.2 g., 1.23 mole); intermediate fraction (30.8 g.)	*81*
CH_4SiCl_2			
$HSiCl_2CH_3$ (0.74 mole)	C_2H_5MgBr (1.56 mole C_2H_5Br)	$HSi(C_2H_5)_2CH_3$ (15 g., 20%)	*66*
$HSiCl_2CH_3$ (0.39 mole)	*n*-C_3H_7MgBr (0.82 mole C_3H_7Br)	$HSi(n\text{-}C_3H_7)_2CH_3$ (25 g., 49%)	*66*
$HSiCl_2CH_3$	C_6H_5MgBr	$HSiCl(CH_3)C_6H_5$	*73*

* The Grignard reagents were added successively to the ethereal halide in the order implied.

TABLE XXII-I (Continued)

Si Comp'd	RMgX	Product(s)	Ref.
$C_2H_4SiCl_4$			
$ClCH_2CH_2SiCl_3$ (0.5 mole)	CH_3MgBr (3 moles)	$(CH_3)_4Si$ (24 g., 55%); C_2H_4 (equiv. 11.9 g. $C_2H_4Br_2$)	75
$ClCH_2CH_2SiCl_3$ (1.5 mole)	C_2H_5MgBr (7.6 moles)	$(C_2H_5)_4Si$ (0.75 mole, 50%); C_2H_4 (equiv. 12.5 g. $C_2H_4Br_2$)	75
$CH_3CHClSiCl_3$ (1.0 mole)	CH_3MgBr (3.5 equiv.)	$CH_3CHClSi(CH_3)_3$ (72.3 g., 53%)	3
$C_2H_5SiCl_3$			
$ClCH_2(CH_3)SiCl_2$ + $ClCH_2(CH_3)_2SiCl$	CH_3MgBr	$ClCH_2Si(CH_3)_3$	86
$C_2H_5SiCl_3$ (53 g.)	CH_3MgBr (26 g. Mg)	$C_2H_5Si(CH_3)_3$ (14.5 g., crude; 8.3 g., pure)	8,31
$C_2H_5SiCl_3$	CH_3MgI	$C_2H_5Si(CH_3)_3$	76
$C_2H_5SiCl_3$ (55 g.)	i-C_4H_9MgBr (10 g. Mg)	$C_2H_5(i\text{-}C_4H_9)SiCl_2$ (13.2 g., crude)	8
$C_2H_5SiCl_3$ (100 g.)	C_6H_5MgBr (1.1 equiv.)	$C_2H_5SiCl_3$ (5–10 g.); $C_2H_5(C_6H_5)SiCl_2$ (40–50 g., crude)	13,30,70
$C_2H_5SiCl_3$	$C_6H_5CH_2MgCl$ (1 equiv.)	$C_2H_5(C_6H_5CH_2)SiCl_2$ (60–80%)*	77,78
$C_2H_5SiCl_3$	$C_6H_5CH_2Cl$ (1 equiv.) + Mg (1 equiv.)	$C_2H_5(C_6H_5CH_2)SiCl_2$ (60–70%)†	79
$C_2H_5SiCl_3$ (150 g.)	$C_6H_5CH_2Cl$ (2 equiv.) + Mg (1 equiv.)	$C_2H_5(C_6H_5CH_2)_2SiCl$ (40–50%)‡	80
$C_2H_6SiCl_2$			
$(CH_3)_2SiCl_2$ (3.75 moles) + CH_3SiCl_3 (0.5 mole)	CH_3MgCl (500 ml., 4.1 *M*)	$(CH_3)_3SiCl$ (38.7 g., 0.35 mole); $(CH_3)_2SiCl_2$ (159.2 g., 1.23 mole); intermediate fraction (30.8 g.)	81
$(CH_3)_2SiCl_2$ (24 moles)	C_2H_5MgBr (18.35 moles C_2H_5Br)	$C_2H_5(CH_3)_2SiCl$ (8.33 moles); $C_2H_5(CH_3)_2SiBr$ (1.506 mole); $(CH_3)_2(C_2H_5)_2Si$ (0.723 mole)§	71

* Dropwise addition of Grignard solution to cooled, stirred Et_2O-halide solution; twelve to twenty-four hours at room temperature.

† Gradual addition of benzyl chloride to cooled, stirred suspension of magnesium in Et_2O-halide solution.

‡ Slow (two and one-half hours) dropwise addition of benzyl chloride to cooled, stirred suspension of magnesium in Et_2O-halide solution; three to four hours reflux.

§ Accidental loss of some material during course of reaction.

TABLE XXII-I (Continued)

Si Comp'd	RMgX	Product(s)	Ref.
$C_2H_6SiCl_2$ (*cont.*)			
$(CH_3)_2SiCl_2$ (0.39 mole)	$(CH_3)_3SiCH_2MgCl$ (0.8 mole chloride)	$(CH_3)_2Si[CH_2Si(CH_3)_3]_2$ (0.25 mole, 65%)	*82*
$(CH_3)_2SiCl_2$ (5.5 moles)	$(CH_3)_3SiOSi(CH_3)_2CH_2MgCl$ (5 moles chloride)	After hydrolysis and hydrofluorination: $H_2C[Si(CH_3)_2F]_2$ (532 g., 63%)	*83*
$(CH_3)_2SiCl_2$ (1.2 mole)	$(CH_3)_3SiOSi(CH_3)_2CH_2MgCl$ (2.5 moles chloride)	After hydrolysis: $(CH_3)_3SiOSi(CH_3)_2CH_2Si(CH_3)_3$ (7%); $H_2C[(CH_3)_2SiOSi(CH_3)_3]_2$ (22%); $[(CH_3)_3SiOSi(CH_3)_2CH_2]_2Si(CH_3)_2$ (10%). Residue, after hydrofluorination, yielded $H_2C[Si(CH_3)_2F]_2$ (48%)	*83*
$HSiCl_2C_2H_5$	C_2H_5MgCl (excess)	$HSi(C_2H_5)_3$ (50–55%)	*84*
$HSiCl_2C_2H_5$	C_6H_5MgBr	$HSiCl(C_2H_5)C_6H_5$	*73*
$HSiCl_2C_2H_5$	$C_6H_5CH_2MgCl$	$HSiCl(C_2H_5)CH_2C_6H_5$	*73*
C_2H_6SiO			
$[(CH_3)_2SiO]_x$ (66 g., 0.89 equiv.)	CH_3MgI (0.92 mole)	$(CH_3)_3SiOH$ (3.3 g.)	*88*
$C_3H_5SiCl_3$			
$H_2C{=}CHCH_2SiCl_3$	CH_3MgBr	$CH_3(H_2C{=}CHCH_2)SiCl_2$	*89*
$C_3H_7SiCl_3$			
n-$C_3H_7SiCl_3$ (50 g.)	CH_3MgBr (22.6 g. Mg)	n-$C_3H_7(CH_3)_3Si$ (25.5 g., crude; 13.5 g., pure)	*8,31*
n-$C_3H_7SiCl_3$ (56 g.)	C_2H_5MgBr (9.2 g. Mg)	$C_2H_5(n$-$C_3H_7)SiCl_2$ (*ca.* 26 g., crude)	*8*
n-$C_3H_7SiCl_3$ (18 g.)	C_2H_5MgBr (12.5 g. Mg)	n-$C_3H_7(C_2H_5)_3Si$ (4.5 g.)	*30,76*
n-$C_3H_7SiCl_3$	C_2H_5MgBr	n-$C_3H_7(C_2H_5)_3Si$ (71%)	*31*
$CH_3(ClCH_2)_2SiCl$	CH_3MgBr (sl. excess)	$(ClCH_2)_2(CH_3)_2Si$ (63%)	*90*
$Cl_2CH(CH_3)_2SiCl$	CH_3MgBr (sl. excess)	$Cl_2CH(CH_3)_3Si$ (70%)	*90*

TABLE XXII-I (Continued)

Si Comp'd	RMgX	Product(s)	Ref.
$C_3H_8SiCl_2$			
$HSiCl_2$-*i*-C_3H_7	4-ClC_6H_4MgBr	$HSiCl$(*i*-C_3H_7)C_6H_4-4-Cl	*73*
$ClCH_2(CH_3)_2SiCl$	CH_3MgBr	$ClCH_2(CH_3)_3Si$ (90%)	*85,86*
$ClCH_2(CH_3)_2SiCl$ + $ClCH(CH_3)SiCl_2$	CH_3MgBr	$ClCH_2(CH_3)_3Si$	*86*
$ClCH_2(CH_3)_2SiCl$	$(CH_3)_3SiCH_2MgCl$	$ClCH_2(CH_3)_2SiCH_2Si(CH_3)_3$ (32%)	*82*
$ClCH_2(CH_3)_2SiCl$	C_6H_5MgBr	$ClCH_2(CH_3)_2SiC_6H_5$ (72%)	*110*
C_3H_9SiCl			
$(CH_3)_3SiCl$ (0.5 mole) + $(C_2H_5)_3SiCl$ (0.5 mole)	C_2H_5MgBr (0.5 mole)	After hydrolysis: $C_2H_5(CH_3)_3Si$ (0.18 mole); $(C_2H_5)_4Si$ (0.095 mole, crude); $(CH_3)_3SiOSi(C_2H_5)_3$ (0.091 mole); $[(C_2H_5)_3Si]_2O$ (0.101 mole)	*91*
$(CH_3)_3SiCl$ (5 moles)	$H_2C{=}CHCH_2MgBr$ (5.8 equiv.)	$H_2C{=}CHCH_2(CH_3)_3Si$ (51%)	*95*
$(CH_3)_3SiCl$ (0.5 mole) + $(C_2H_5)_3SiCl$ (0.5 mole)	*n*-C_3H_7MgBr (0.5 mole)	After hydrolysis: *n*-$C_3H_7(CH_3)_3Si$ (0.287 mole); $[(C_2H_5)_3Si]_2O$ (0.13 mole); $(CH_3)_3SiOSi(C_2H_5)_3$ (0.045 mole)	*91*
$(CH_3)_3SiCl$ (0.5 mole)	$(CH_3)_3SiCH_2MgCl$ (0.5 mole $C_3H_{11}ClSi$)	$[(CH_3)_3Si]_2CH_2$ (0.31 mole, 63%)	*82,87*
$(CH_3)_3SiCl$ (81 g.)	4-BrC_6H_4MgBr (177 g. $C_6H_4Br_2$)	4-$BrC_6H_4(CH_3)_3Si$ (90.5 g., 53%)	*92*
$(CH_3)_3SiCl$ (220 g.)	4-ClC_6H_4MgBr (382 g. C_6H_4BrCl)	4-$ClC_6H_4(CH_3)_3Si$ (305 g., 83%)	*92*
$(CH_3)_3SiCl$ (100 g.)	$(CH_3)_3SiOSi(CH_3)_2CH_2MgCl$ (200 g. $C_5H_{17}ClOSi_2$)	$(CH_3)_3SiOSi(CH_3)_2CH_2Si(CH_3)_3$ (150 ml.)	*93,94*
$(CH_3)_3SiCl$	$C_6H_5CH_2MgCl$	$C_6H_5CH_2(CH_3)_3Si$ (74%)	*96*
$(CH_3)_3SiCl$	*n*-$C_7H_{15}MgBr$	*n*-$C_7H_{15}(CH_3)_3Si$ (46%)	*31*
$(CH_3)_3SiCl$ (0.37 mole)	*n*-$C_{12}H_{25}MgBr$ (0.6 mole)	*n*-$C_{12}H_{25}(CH_3)_3Si$ (56%)	*31*
$C_4H_9SiCl_3$			
n-$C_4H_9SiCl_3$ (30 g.)	CH_3MgBr (12.4 g. Mg)	*n*-$C_4H_9(CH_3)_3Si$ (11.4 g.)	*8,31*

TABLE XXII-I (Continued)

Si Comp'd	RMgX	Product(s)	Ref.
$C_4H_9SiCl_3$ (*cont.*)			
n-$C_4H_9SiCl_3$ (25.5 g.)	C_2H_5MgBr (14 g. Mg)	*n*-$C_4H_9(C_2H_5)_3Si$ (6.4 g.)	30
i-$C_4H_9SiCl_3$ (50 g.)	C_2H_5MgBr (7.8 g. Mg)	C_2H_5(*i*-C_4H_9)$SiCl_2$ (16 g., crude)	8
i-$C_4H_9SiCl_3$ (29 g.)	C_2H_5MgBr (17 g. Mg)	*i*-$C_4H_9(C_2H_5)_3Si$ (6.2 g.)	30,76
t-$C_4H_9SiCl_3$ (0.1 mole)	CH_3MgBr (0.5 mole)	*t*-$C_4H_9(CH_3)_3Si$ (61%)	97,98
$C_4H_{10}SiCl_2$			
$(C_2H_5)_2SiCl_2$ (24.5 g.)	CH_3MgI (9.8 g. Mg)	$(CH_3)_2(C_2H_5)_2Si$ (*ca.* 6 g.)	8
$(C_2H_5)_2SiCl_2$ (10 g.)	$H_2C{=}CHCH_2MgBr$ (37 g. C_3H_5Br)	$(C_2H_5)_2(H_2C{=}CHCH_2)_2Si$ (55–60%)	99
$(C_2H_5)_2SiCl_2$ (11 g.)	$H_2C(CH_2CH_2MgBr)_2$ (24 g. $C_5H_{10}Br_2$)	$(CH_2)_5Si(C_2H_5)_2$ (*ca.* 2 g.)	29
$C_5H_{10}SiCl_2$			
$(CH_2)_5SiCl_2$ (23.2 g.)	CH_3MgBr (8.3 g. Mg)	$(CH_2)_5Si(CH_3)_2$	29
$C_5H_{11}SiCl_3$			
i-$C_5H_{11}SiCl_3$ (30 g.)	CH_3MgBr (11.5 g. Mg)	*i*-$C_5H_{11}(CH_3)_3Si$ (19 g., crude)	8,31
i-$C_5H_{11}SiCl_3$ (37.5 g.)	C_2H_5MgBr (20 g. Mg)	*i*-$C_5H_{11}(C_2H_5)_3Si$ (12.5 g.)	30,76
$C_5H_{12}SiCl_2$			
C_2H_5(*n*-C_3H_7)$SiCl_2$ (21.3 g.)	CH_3MgBr (7.2 g. Mg)	C_2H_5(*i*-C_3H_7)$(CH_3)_2Si$ (13.3 g., crude)	8
$C_6H_4SiCl_3Br$			
4-$BrC_6H_4SiCl_3$ (40 g.)	C_2H_5MgBr (70 g. C_2H_5Br)	4-$BrC_6H_4(C_2H_5)_3Si$ (34 g., 91%)	32,51
$C_6H_4SiCl_4$			
4-$ClC_6H_4SiCl_3$	C_2H_5MgBr	4-$ClC_6H_4(C_2H_5)_3Si$ (88%)	32
$C_6H_5SiCl_3$			
$C_6H_5SiCl_3$ (67 g.)	CH_3MgBr (26 g. Mg)	$C_6H_5(CH_3)_3Si$ (37.5 g.)	30,76

TABLE XXII-I (Continued)

Si Comp'd	RMgX	Product(s)	Ref.
$C_6H_5SiCl_3$ (*cont.*)			
$C_6H_5SiCl_3$ (30 g.)	C_2H_5MgBr (14.5 g. Mg)	$C_6H_5(C_2H_5)_3Si$ (17.5 g.)	*30,33,43*
$C_6H_5SiCl_3$ (220 g.)	4-BrC_6H_4MgBr (265 g. $C_6H_4Br_2$)	4-$BrC_6H_4(C_6H_5)SiCl_2$	*51*
$C_6H_5SiCl_3$ (211 g.)	$(CH_2)_5CHMgBr$ (480 g. $C_6H_{11}Br$)	$C_6H_5[(CH_2)_5CH]_2SiCl$ (5–20 g.); $(CH_2)_5CH(C_6H_5)SiCl_2$ (15–20 g., crude)	*100*
$C_6H_5SiCl_3$ (10 g.)	$(CH_2)_5CHMgBr$ (100 g. $C_6H_{11}Br$)	$C_6H_5[(CH_2)_5CH]_2SiOCH(CH_2)_5$ (15 g., crude)	*101*
$C_6H_5SiCl_3$* (50 g.)	$(CH_2)_5CHMgBr$ (large excess)	$HSi[CH(CH_2)_5]_2C_6H_5$ (40 g.); $C_6H_5[(CH_2)_5CH]_2SiOCH(CH_2)_5$ (20 g.); $C_6H_5[(CH_2)_5CH]_2SiOH$ and conden'n products of $C_6H_5[(CH_2)_5CH]Si(OH)_2$ (10 g.)	*101*
$C_6H_5SiCl_3$	$C_6H_5CH_2MgCl$	$C_6H_5(C_6H_5CH_2)SiCl_2$	*102*
$C_6H_8SiO_3$			
$C_6H_5Si(OH)_3$ (10 g.)	C_6H_5MgBr (large excess)	$(C_6H_5)_3SiOH$ (5 g.)	*103*
$C_6H_{13}SiCl_3$			
n-$C_6H_{13}SiCl_3$ (0.5 mole)	CH_3MgBr (1.7 mole)	*n*-$C_6H_{13}(CH_3)_3Si$ (79%)	*31*
$C_6H_{14}SiFCl$			
$ClCH_2CH_2(C_2H_5)_2SiF$ (0.27 mole)	CH_3MgBr (0.64 equiv.)	$(CH_3)_2(C_2H_5)_2Si$ (0.16 mole, 59%); C_2H_4 (36%)	*105*
$C_6H_{14}SiCl_2$			
$(n\text{-}C_3H_7)_2SiCl_2$ (crude)	CH_3MgBr	$(CH_3)_2(n\text{-}C_3H_7)_2Si$ (impure)	8
$C_2H_5(i\text{-}C_4H_9)SiCl_2$ (23 g.)	CH_3MgBr (6.9 g. Mg)	$C_2H_5(i\text{-}C_4H_9)(CH_3)_2Si$ (6 g.)	8

* This reaction was conducted under an atmosphere of nitrogen.

TABLE XXII-I (Continued)

Si Comp'd	RMgX	Product(s)	Ref.
$C_6H_{14}SiCl_2$ (*cont.*)			
$ClCH_2CH_2(C_2H_5)_2SiCl$ (0.33 mole)	CH_3MgBr (0.93 equiv.)	$(CH_3)_2(C_2H_5)_2Si$ (0.19 mole, 57.5%); C_2H_4 (25%)	*105*
$CH_3CHCl(C_2H_5)_2SiCl$ (0.33 mole)	CH_3MgBr (0.5 mole)	$CH_3(CH_3CHCl)(C_2H_5)_2Si$ (0.29 mole, 87%)	*104*
$CH_3CHCl(C_2H_5)_2SiCl$ (0.38 mole)	C_6H_5MgBr (0.67 mole)	$CH_3CHCl(C_6H_5)(C_2H_5)_2Si$ (0.20 mole, 57%)	*104*
$C_6H_{15}SiBr$			
$(C_2H_5)_3SiBr$	C_6H_5MgBr	"Unsuccessful"	*43*
$(C_2H_5)_3SiBr$ (10 g.)	$C_6H_5CH_2MgCl$ (12.6 g. C_7H_7Cl)	$C_6H_5CH_2(C_2H_5)_3Si$ (5.5 g., 50%)	*43*
$C_6H_{15}SiCl$			
$(C_2H_5)_3SiCl$	CH_3MgBr	$CH_3(C_2H_5)_3Si$ (60%)	*31*
$(C_2H_5)_3SiCl$ (0.42 mole)	CH_3MgBr (0.42 mole) + C_2H_5MgBr (0.42 mole)	$CH_3(C_2H_5)_3Si$ (0.28 mole); *no* $(C_2H_5)_4Si$	*91*
$(C_2H_5)_3SiCl$ (0.5 mole) + $(CH_3)_3SiCl$ (0.5 mole)	C_2H_5MgBr (0.5 mole)	After hydrolysis: $C_2H_5(CH_3)_3Si$ (0.18 mole); $(C_2H_5)_4Si$ (0.095 mole, crude; $(CH_3)_3SiOSi(C_2H_5)_3$ (0.091 mole); $[(C_2H_5)_3Si]_2O$ (0.101 mole)	*91*
$(C_2H_5)_3SiCl$ (0.5 mole) + $(CH_3)_3SiCl$ (0.5 mole)	n-C_3H_7MgBr (0.5 mole)	After hydrolysis: n-$C_3H_7(CH_3)_3Si$ (0.287 mole); $[(C_2H_5)_3Si]_2O$ (0.13 mole); $(CH_3)_3SiOSi(C_2H_5)_3$ (0.045 mole)	*91*
$(C_2H_5)_3SiCl$	n-C_4H_9MgBr	n-$C_4H_9(C_2H_5)_3Si$ (50%)	*31*
$(C_2H_5)_3SiCl$	n-$C_5H_{11}MgBr$	n-$C_5H_{11}(C_2H_5)_3Si$ (75%)	*31*
$(C_2H_5)_3SiCl$	$CH_3CH{=}C(CH_3)C{\equiv}CMgX$	$CH_3CH{=}C(CH_3)C{\equiv}C(C_2H_5)_3Si$	*106*
$(C_2H_5)_3SiCl$	n-$C_6H_{13}MgBr$	n-$C_6H_{13}(C_2H_5)_3Si$ (60%)	*31*
$(C_2H_5)_3SiCl$	n-$C_7H_{15}MgBr$	n-$C_7H_{15}(C_2H_5)_3Si$ (68%)	*31*
$C_6H_{15}SiClO_3$			
$(C_2H_5O)_3SiCl$	C_2H_5MgBr	$C_2H_5(C_2H_5O)_3Si$	*107*

TABLE XXII-I (Continued)

Si Comp'd	RMgX	Product(s)	Ref.
$C_6H_{15}SiClO_3$ (*cont.*)			
$(C_2H_5O)_3SiCl$	C_6H_5MgBr	$C_6H_5(C_2H_5O)_3Si$	*107*
$C_6H_{15}Si_2Cl_3O$			
$Si_2OCl_3(C_2H_5)_3$ (293 g., crude)	C_2H_5MgBr (*ca.* 2.5 equiv.)	$Si_2OCl(C_2H_5)_5$ (12.5%, pure)	*62*
$C_6H_{16}SiO_2$			
$(CH_3)_2Si(OC_2H_5)_2$	CH_3Cl + Mg	$(CH_3)_3SiOC_2H_5$ (73%)	*108*
$C_6H_{17}Si_2Cl$			
$(CH_3)_3SiCH_2Si(CH_3)_2Cl$	CH_3MgBr	$[(CH_3)_3Si]_2CH_2$	*111*
$C_6H_{18}Si_2O_4S$			
$[(CH_3)_3Si]_2SO_4$ (0.33 mole)	C_2H_5MgBr (0.9 mole)	$C_2H_5(CH_3)_3Si$ (0.55 mole, 83.5%)	*109*
$[(CH_3)_3Si]_2SO_4$ (0.3 mole)	*n*-C_3H_7MgBr (0.8 mole)	*n*-$C_3H_7(CH_3)_3Si$ (55%); $(CH_3)_3SiBr$	*109*
$[(CH_3)_3Si]_2SO_4$* (0.3 mole)	*i*-C_3H_7MgBr (0.7 mole)	$(CH_3)_3SiBr$ (0.31 mole, 51.5%)	*109*
$[(CH_3)_3Si]_2SO_4$† (0.3 mole)	*i*-C_3H_7MgBr (0.7 mole)	*i*-$C_3H_7(CH_3)_3Si$ (0.155 mole, 34%)	*109*
$C_7H_7SiCl_3$			
$C_6H_5CH_2SiCl_3$ (41 g.)	CH_3MgBr (14 g. Mg)	$C_6H_5CH_2(CH_3)_3Si$ (20 g., crude; 11.5 g., pure)	*8*
$C_6H_5CH_2SiCl_3$	C_2H_5MgBr	$C_6H_5CH_2(C_2H_5)_3Si$ (40%)	*43*

* Addition of Et_2O-sulfate solution to Grignard solution; one hour stirring at room temperature; distillation of volatile material on steam-bath (six hours).

† Addition of Et_2O-sulfate solution to Grignard solution; eight days reflux with stirring; distillation of volatile material on steam-bath (six hours).

TABLE XXII-I (Continued)

Si Comp'd	RMgX	Product(s)	Ref.
$C_7H_{10}SiO_3$			
$C_6H_5CH_2Si(OH)_3$*	$C_6H_5CH_2MgCl$ (large excess)	$(C_6H_5CH_2)_3SiOH$	*103*
$C_8H_{10}SiCl_2$			
$C_2H_5(C_6H_5)SiCl_2$ (10.5 g.)	CH_3MgBr (6 g. Mg)	$C_2H_5(C_6H_5)(CH_3)_2Si$ (7.4 g.)	*8*
$C_2H_5(C_6H_5)SiCl_2$	CH_3MgI	$CH_3(C_2H_5)(C_6H_5)SiCl$	*77*
$C_2H_5(C_6H_5)SiCl_2$	n-C_3H_7MgBr (1 equiv.)	$C_2H_5(n$-$C_3H_7)(C_6H_5)SiCl$; $C_2H_5(C_6H_5)(n$-$C_3H_7)_2Si$	*13a,77,78*
$C_8H_{10}SiO$			
$[C_2H_5(C_6H_5)SiO]_x$	CH_3MgI	$CH_3(C_2H_5)(C_6H_5)SiOH$	*103*
$[C_2H_5(C_6H_5)SiO]_x$	C_2H_5MgBr	$C_6H_5(C_2H_5)_2SiOH$	*103*
$C_8H_{17}SiCl_3$			
n-$C_8H_{17}SiCl_3$	CH_3MgBr	n-$C_8H_{17}(CH_3)_3Si$ (89%)	*31*
n-$C_8H_{17}SiCl$	C_2H_5MgBr	n-$C_8H_{17}(C_2H_5)_3Si$ (77%)	*31*
$C_8H_{20}SiO_4$			
$Si(OC_2H_5)_4$	CH_3Cl + Mg	$(CH_3)_2Si(OC_2H_5)_2$; $CH_3Si(OC_2H_5)_3$	*118,112*
$Si(OC_2H_5)_4$ (1.5 mole)	CH_3MgI (2.5 moles CH_3I)	$CH_3Si(OC_2H_5)_3$; $(CH_3)_2Si(OC_2H_5)_2$; $CH_3SiO_2C_2H_5$ (?)	*113*
$Si(OC_2H_5)_4$	C_2H_5Cl + Mg	Products not separable by fractional distillation	*118*
$Si(OC_2H_5)_4$ (7 moles)	C_2H_5MgBr (22 moles)	$(C_2H_5)_3SiOC_2H_5$, yielding, upon hydrolysis, $[(C_2H_5)_3Si]_2O$ (2.3 moles, 66%)	*114*
$Si(OC_2H_5)_4$ (104 g.)	C_2H_5MgBr (1 equiv.) + Mg (12 g.)	$C_2H_5Si(OC_2H_5)_3$ (61%)	*50,35*

* It is now generally agreed that triplicate silicanetriols are not isolable; if they exist at all they immediately undergo dehydration-condensation to form "polymers".

TABLE XXII-I (Continued)

Si Comp'd	RMgX	Product(s)	Ref.
$C_8H_{20}SiO_4$ (*cont.*)			
$Si(OC_2H_5)_4$ (220 ml.)	C_2H_5MgBr (170 ml.) + Mg (55 g.)	After hydrolysis: "resinous diethyl silicanol"	*116*
$Si(OC_2H_5)_4$	$H_2C{=}CHCH_2Cl$ + Mg	$H_2C{=}CHCH_2Si(OC_2H_5)_3$ (50%)	*117*
$Si(OC_2H_5)_4$	$H_2C{=}CHCH_2Br$ + Mg	$H_2C{=}CHCH_2Si(OC_2H_5)_3$ (55.1%)	*117*
$Si(OC_2H_5)_4$	n-C_3H_7MgBr + Mg	n-$C_3H_7Si(OC_2H_5)_3$	*35*
$Si(OC_2H_5)_4$	i-C_3H_7MgBr + Mg	i-$C_3H_7Si(OC_2H_5)_3$ (20.2%)	*50*
$Si(OC_2H_5)_4$ (2080 g.)	n-C_4H_9MgCl (360 g. Mg)	n-$C_4H_9Si(OC_2H_5)_3$ (215 g.); $(n$-$C_4H_9)_2Si(OC_2H_5)_2$ (595 g.)	*118*
$Si(OC_2H_5)_4$ (1 mole)	n-C_4H_9MgBr (1 mole)	n-$C_4H_9Si(OC_2H_5)_3$ (27%)	*113*
$Si(OC_2H_5)_4$ (0.825 mole)	n-C_4H_9MgBr (4 moles)	$(n$-$C_4H_9)_4Si$ (56%)	*113*
$Si(OC_2H_5)_4$	RCl + Mg (R = n-C_4H_9, n-C_5H_{11})	$RSi(OC_2H_5)_3$; $R_2Si(OC_2H_5)_2$; $R_3SiOC_2H_5$	*119*
$Si(OC_2H_5)_4$	i-C_4H_9X + Mg	i-$C_4H_9Si(OC_2H_5)_3$ (71%)	*50*
$Si(OC_2H_5)_4$	i-$C_5H_{11}X$ + Mg	i-$C_5H_{11}Si(OC_2H_5)_3$ (48%)	*50*
$Si(OC_2H_5)_4$ (10 g.)	C_6H_5MgBr (7.6 g. C_6H_5Br)	$C_6H_5Si(OC_2H_5)_3$	*120*
$Si(OC_2H_5)_4$	C_6H_5Br + Mg	$C_6H_5Si(OC_2H_5)_3$	*35*
$Si(OC_2H_5)_4$	n-$C_6H_{13}X$ + Mg	n-$C_6H_{13}Si(OC_2H_5)_3$ (50.3%)	*50*
$Si(OC_2H_5)_4$ (220 ml.)	4-$CH_3C_6H_4MgBr$ (275 ml.) + Mg (55 g.)	$(4$-$CH_3C_6H_4)_2Si(OC_2H_5)_2$	*116*
$Si(OC_2H_5)_4$ (330 g.)	$C_6H_5C{\equiv}CMgBr$ (152 g. $C_6H_5C{\equiv}CH$)	$C_6H_5C{\equiv}CSi(OC_2H_5)_3$ (75%)	*12*
$Si(OC_2H_5)_4$	2,4-$(CH_3)_2C_6H_3MgI$	2,4-$(CH_3)_2C_6H_3Si(OC_2H_5)_3$	*120*
$Si(OC_2H_5)_4$ (10 g.)	1-$C_{10}H_7MgBr$ (10 g. $C_{10}H_7Br$)	1-$C_{10}H_7Si(OC_2H_5)_3$	*120*
$Si(OC_2H_5)_4$ (10 g.)	2-$C_{10}H_7MgI$ (12 g. $C_{10}H_7I$)	2-$C_{10}H_7Si(OC_2H_5)_3$	*120*
$C_8H_{22}Si_2O$			
$(CH_3)_3SiCH_2Si(CH_3)_2OC_2H_5$	CH_3MgBr	$[(CH_3)_2Si]_2CH_2$	*111*
$C_9H_{12}SiCl_2$			
$C_2H_5(C_6H_5CH_2)SiCl_2$	n-C_3H_7MgBr (1 equiv.)	$C_2H_5(n$-$C_3H_7)C_6H_5CH_2SiCl$ (50–60%); $C_2H_5(C_6H_5CH_2)(n$-$C_3H_7)_2Si$	77,78

TABLE XXII-I (Continued)

Si Comp'd	RMgX	Product(s)	Ref.
$C_9H_{12}SiCl_2$ (*cont.*)			
$C_2H_5(C_6H_5CH_2)SiCl_2$	n-C_3H_7MgBr (excess)	$C_2H_5(C_6H_5CH_2)(n\text{-}C_3H_7)_2Si$	*121*
$C_2H_5(C_6H_5CH_2)SiCl_2$	i-C_4H_9MgBr (1 equiv.)	$C_2H_5(i\text{-}C_4H_9)(C_6H_5CH_2)SiCl$ (*ca.* 40%)	*79*
$C_9H_{12}SiO$			
$[C_2H_5(C_6H_5CH_2)SiO]_x$	C_2H_5MgBr (1.5 equiv.)	$C_6H_5CH_2(C_2H_5)_2SiOH$	*103*
$[C_2H_5(C_6H_5CH_2)SiO]_x$	n-C_3H_7MgBr (1.5 equiv.)	$C_2H_5(n\text{-}C_3H_7)(C_6H_5CH_2)SiOH$	*103*
$C_9H_{25}Si_3Cl$			
$(CH_3)_3Si[CH_2Si(CH_3)_2]_2Cl$	CH_3MgBr	$(CH_3)_2Si[CH_2Si(CH_3)_3]_2$	*111*
$C_{10}H_{21}SiCl_3$			
n-$C_{10}H_{21}SiCl_3$	CH_3MgBr	n-$C_{10}H_{21}(CH_3)_3Si$ (80%)	*31*
n-$C_{10}H_{21}SiCl_3$	C_2H_5MgBr	n-$C_{10}H_{21}(C_2H_5)_3Si$ (78%)	*31*
$C_{11}H_{17}SiCl$			
$C_2H_5(n\text{-}C_3H_7)(C_6H_5)SiCl$	CH_3MgI (excess)	$CH_3(C_2H_5)(n\text{-}C_3H_7)(C_6H_5)Si$	*13b*
$C_2H_5(n\text{-}C_3H_7)(C_6H_5)SiCl$	$C_6H_5CH_2MgCl$	$C_2H_5(n\text{-}C_3H_7)(C_6H_5)(C_6H_5CH_2)Si$ (50–60%)	*121*
$C_{11}H_{30}Si_3O$			
$(CH_3)_3Si[CH_2Si(CH_3)_2]_2OC_2H_5$	CH_3MgBr	$(CH_3)_2Si[CH_2Si(CH_3)_3]_2$	*111*
$C_{12}H_9SiCl_2Br$			
$4\text{-}BrC_6H_4(C_6H_5)SiCl_2$ (82 g.)	C_2H_5MgBr (5 equiv.)	$4\text{-}BrC_6H_4(C_6H_5)(C_2H_5)_2Si$; $4\text{-}C_2H_5C_6H_4(C_6H_5)(C_2H_5)_2Si$	*51*
$C_{12}H_{10}SiCl_2$			
$(C_6H_5)_2SiCl_2$	CH_3MgI (excess)	$(CH_3)_2(C_6H_5)_2Si$	*122*

TABLE XXII-I (Continued)

Si Comp'd	RMgX	Product(s)	Ref.
$C_{12}H_{10}SiCl_2O_2$			
$(C_6H_5O)_2SiCl_2$	C_2H_5MgBr	$(C_2H_5)_2Si(OC_2H_5)_2$	*45*
$(C_6H_5O)_2SiCl_2$	C_6H_5MgBr (2 equiv.)	After hydrolysis: $(C_6H_5)_2Si(OH)_2$	*123*
$C_{12}H_{19}SiCl$			
$C_2H_5(n\text{-}C_3H_7)(C_6H_5CH_2)SiCl$	CH_3MgI	$CH_3(C_2H_5)(n\text{-}C_3H_7)(C_6H_5CH_2)Si$ (*ca.* 60%)	*77,78*
$C_2H_5(n\text{-}C_3H_7)(C_6H_5CH_2)SiCl$	$i\text{-}C_3H_7MgBr$	$C_2H_5(n\text{-}C_3H_7)(i\text{-}C_3H_7)(C_6H_5CH_2)Si$ (60%)	*125*
$C_{12}H_{19}Si_2Cl_3$			
4-$[(C_2H_5)_3Si]C_6H_4SiCl_3$ (40 g.)	C_2H_5MgBr (97 g. C_2H_5Br)	1,4-$[(C_2H_5)_3Si]_2C_6H_4$ (*ca.* 15.5 g.)	*51*
$C_{12}H_{27}SiClO_3$			
$(i\text{-}C_4H_9O)_3SiCl$	C_2H_5MgBr	$C_2H_5Si(O\text{-}i\text{-}C_4H_9)_3$	*107*
$(i\text{-}C_4H_9O)_3SiCl$	C_6H_5MgBr	$C_6H_5Si(O\text{-}i\text{-}C_4H_9)_3$	*107*
$C_{14}H_{14}SiO$			
$[(C_6H_5CH_2)_2SiO]_3$	CH_3MgI	$CH_3(C_6H_5CH_2)_2SiOH$	*103*
$C_{14}H_{16}SiO_2$			
$(C_6H_5CH_2)_2Si(OH)_2$	CH_3MgI (large excess)	$CH_3(C_6H_5CH_2)_2SiOH$	*103*
$C_{14}H_{29}SiCl_3$			
$n\text{-}C_{14}H_{29}SiCl_3$	CH_3MgBr	$n\text{-}C_{14}H_{29}(CH_3)_3Si$ (50%)	*31*
$C_{14}H_{38}SiO_4$			
$(CH_3)_3Si[CH_2Si(CH_3)_2]_3OC_2H_5$	CH_3MgBr	$[(CH_3)_3SiCH_2Si(CH_3)_2]_2CH_2$	*111*
$C_{15}H_{33}SiClO_3$			
$(i\text{-}C_5H_{11}O)_3SiCl$	C_2H_5MgBr	$C_2H_5Si(O\text{-}i\text{-}C_5H_{11})_3$	*107*

TABLE XXII-I (Continued)

Si Comp'd	RMgX	Product(s)	Ref.
$C_{15}H_{33}SiClO_3$ (*cont.*)			
$(i\text{-}C_5H_{11}O)_3SiCl$	C_6H_5MgBr	$C_6H_5Si(O\text{-}i\text{-}C_5H_{11})_3$	*107*
$C_{18}H_{15}SiCl$			
$(C_6H_5)_3SiCl$	CH_3MgI (excess)	$CH_3(C_6H_5)_3Si$	*121*
$(C_6H_5)_3SiCl$	C_2H_5MgBr (excess)	$C_2H_5(C_6H_5)_3Si$	*121,76*
$C_{18}H_{15}SiClO_3$			
$(C_6H_5O)_3SiCl$	C_6H_5MgBr	$C_6H_5Si(OC_6H_5)_3$	*123*
$C_{18}H_{27}SiBr$			
$C_6H_5[(CH_2)_5CH]_2SiBr$	C_2H_5MgBr	$C_2H_5(C_6H_5)[(CH_2)_5CH]_2Si$	*101*
$C_{48}H_{40}Si_4I_2$			
$[(C_6H_5)_2Si]_4I_2$	C_2H_5MgBr (large excess)	$[(C_6H_5)_2Si]_4(C_2H_5)_2$	*124*
$[(C_6H_5)_2Si]_4I_2$	C_6H_5MgBr (large excess)	No reaction	*124*

REFERENCES FOR TABLE XXII-I

(*1*) Schumb and Saffer, *J. Am. Chem. Soc.*, *61*, 363–6 (1939).
(*2*) Gilliam, Liebhafsky, and Winslow, *J. Am. Chem. Soc.*, *63*, 801–3 (1941).
(*3*) Sommer and Whitmore, *J. Am. Chem. Soc.*, *68*, 485–7 (1946).
(*4*) Booth and Martin, *J. Am. Chem. Soc.*, *68*, 2655–7 (1946).
(*5*) Hyde, U. S. Patent 2,413,049, Dec. 24, 1946; *Chem. Abstr.*, *41*, P2069 (1947).
(*6*) Booth and Suttle, *J. Am. Chem. Soc.*, *68*, 2658–60 (1946).
(*7*) Pearlson, Brice, and Simons, *J. Am. Chem. Soc.*, *67*, 1769–70 (1945).
(*8*) Bygdén, *Ber.*, *44*, 2640–52 (1911).
(*9*) Whitmore and Sommer, *J. Am. Chem. Soc.*, *68*, 481–4 (1946).
(*10*) Helm and Mack, *J. Am. Chem. Soc.*, *59*, 60–2 (1937).
(*10.1*) Dennis and Hance, *J. Phys. Chem.*, *30*, 1055–9 (1926).
(*11*) Aston, Kennedy, and Messerly, *J. Am. Chem. Soc.*, *63*, 2343–8 (1941).
(*12*) Vol'nov and Reutt, *J. Gen. Chem.* (U.S.S.R.), *10*, 1600–4 (1940); *Chem. Abstr.*, *35*, 2853 (1941).
(*13*) Kipping, (*a*) *Proc. Chem. Soc.*, *20*, 15–6 (1904); (*b*) *J. Chem. Soc.*, *91*, 209–40 (1907).
(*14*) Booth and Cornell, *J. Am. Chem. Soc.*, *68*, 2650–2 (1946).
(*15*) Martin and Kipping, *J. Chem. Soc.*, *95*, 302–14 (1909).
(*16*) Andrianov, *J. Gen. Chem.* (U.S.S.R.), *41*, 487–92 (1946); *Chem. Abstr.*, *41*, 701 (1947).
(*17*) Larsson, *Trans. Chalmers Univ. Technol., Gothenberg, Swed.*, No. 79, 3–6 (1948); *Chem. Abstr.*, *43*, 2928 (1949).
(*18*) Alfrey, Honn, and Mark, *J. Polymer Sci.*, *1*, 102–20 (1946); *Chem. Abstr.*, *40*, 3396 (1946).
(*19*) Sugden and Wilkins, *J. Chem. Soc.*, *1931*, 126–8.
(*20*) Tseng and Chao, *Science Repts. Natl. Univ. Peking*, *1*, No. 4, 21–37 (1936); *Chem. Abstr.*, *31*, 655 (1937).
(*21*) Kropa, U. S. Patent 2,388,161, Oct. 30, 1945; *Chem. Abstr.*, *40*, P592 (1946).
(*22*) Meads and Kipping, *J. Chem. Soc.*, *107*, 459–68 (1915).
(*23*) Melzer, *Ber.*, *41*, 3390–5 (1908).
(*24*) Sommer, Dorfman, Goldberg, and Whitmore, *J. Am. Chem. Soc.*, *68*, 488–9 (1946).
(*25*) Booth and Halbedel, *J. Am. Chem. Soc.*, *68*, 2652–4 (1946).
(*26*) Booth and Spessard, *J. Am. Chem. Soc.*, *68*, 2660–2 (1946).
(*27*) Krause and Renwanz, *Ber.*, *62B*, 1710–6 (1929).
(*28*) Booth and Schwarz, *J. Am. Chem. Soc.*, *68*, 2662–5 (1946).
(*29*) Bygdén, *Ber.*, *48*, 1236–42 (1915).
(*30*) Bygdén, *Ber.*, *45*, 707–13 (1912).
(*31*) Whitmore, Sommer, Di Giorgio, Van Strien, Bailey, Hall, Pietrusza, and Kerr, *J. Am. Chem. Soc.*, *68*, 475–81 (1946).
(*32*) Grüttner and Krause, *Ber.*, *50*, 1559–68 (1917).
(*33*) Ipatiew and Dolgow, *Ber.*, *62B*, 1220–6 (1929).
(*34*) Kipping, *J. Chem. Soc.*, *105*, 679–90 (1914).
(*35*) Post and Hofrichter, *J. Org. Chem.*, *4*, 363–4 (1938).
(*36*) Koton, *J. Applied Chem.* (U.S.S.R.), *12*, 1435–9 (1939); *Chem. Abstr.*, *34*, 6242 (1940).
(*37*) Kipping, Murray, and Maltby, *J. Chem. Soc.*, *1929*, 1180–91.
(*38*) Meads and Kipping, *J. Chem. Soc.*, *105*, 679–90 (1914).
(*39*) Kipping, *J. Chem. Soc.*, *101*, 2108–25 (1912).
(*40*) Kipping and Murray, *J. Chem. Soc.*, *1927*, 2734–7.
(*41*) Dilthey and Eduardoff, *Ber.*, 37, 1139–42 (1904).

(42) Manulkin and Yakubova, *J. Gen. Chem.* (U.S.S.R.), *10*, 1300–2 (1940); *Chem. Abstr.*, 35, 3240 (1941).
(43) Kraus and Nelson, *J. Am. Chem. Soc.*, *56*, 195–202 (1934).
(44) Robison and Kipping, *J. Chem. Soc.*, *93*, 439–56 (1908).
(45) Hanford, U. S. Patent 2,386,793, Oct. 16, 1945; *Chem. Abstr.*, *40*, P604 (1946).
(46) Dilthey, *Ber.*, *38*, 4132–6 (1905).
(47) Pink and Kipping, *J. Chem. Soc.*, *123*, 2830–7 (1923).
(48) Steele and Kipping, *J. Chem. Soc.*, *1929*, 2545–50.
(49) Palmer and Kipping, *J. Chem. Soc.*, *1930*, 1020–8.
(50) Andrianov and Gribanova, *J. Gen. Chem.* (U.S.S.R.), 8, 552–6 (1938); *Chem. Abstr.*, 32, 7892 (1938).
(51) Grüttner and Cauer, *Ber.*, *51*, 1283–92 (1918).
(52) Hyde, U. S. Patent 2,413,050, Dec. 24, 1946; *Chem. Abstr.*, *41*, P2069 (1947).
(53) Gierut, Sowa, and Nieuwland, *J. Am. Chem. Soc.*, *58*, 897–8 (1936).
(54) Jaeger and Dijkstra, *Z. anorg. Chem.*, *143*, 233–58 (1935).
(55) Medoks and Kotelkov, *J. Gen. Chem.* (U.S.S.R.), 7, 2007–8 (1937); *Chem. Abstr.*, 32, 531 (1938).
(56) Medoks, *J. Gen. Chem.* (U.S.S.R.), 8, 291–3 (1938); *Chem. Abstr.*, 32, 5392 (1938).
(57) Manulkin, *J. Gen. Chem.* (U.S.S.R.), *16*, 235–42 (1946); *Chem. Abstr.*, *41*, 90 (1947).
(58) Soshestvenskaya, *J. Gen. Chem.* (U.S.S.R.), 8, 294–6 (1938); *Chem. Abstr.*, 32, 5392 (1938).
(59) Martin, *Ber.*, *46*, 2442–7 (1913).
(60) Schwarz and Sexauer, *Ber.*, *59B*, 333–7 (1926).
(61) Schumb and Saffer, *J. Am. Chem. Soc.*, *63*, 93–5 (1941).
(62) Emeléus and Payne, *J. Chem. Soc.*, *1947*, 1590–2.
(63) Emeléus and Robinson, *J. Chem. Soc.*, *1947*, 1592–4.
(64) de Man, van Steenis, and Waterman, *Rec. trav. chim.*, *67*, 864–8 (1948).
(65) Taylor and Walden, *J. Am. Chem. Soc.*, *66*, 842–3 (1944).
(66) Price, *J. Am. Chem. Soc.*, *69*, 2600–4 (1947).
(67) Jenkins, Lavery, Guenther, and Post, *J. Org. Chem.*, *13*, 862–6 (1948).
(68) Whitmore, Pietrusza, and Sommer, *J. Am. Chem. Soc.*, *69*, 2108–10 (1947).
(69) Meals, *J. Am. Chem. Soc.*, *68*, 1880–1 (1946).
(70) Gilman and Clark, *J. Am. Chem. Soc.*, *69*, 1499–500 (1947).
(71) Lewis, *J. Am. Chem. Soc.*, *69*, 717 (1947).
(72) Barry, British Patent 618,403, Feb. 21, 1949; *Chem. Abstr.*, *43*, P5801 (1949).
(73) Barry, British Patent 622,970, May 10, 1949; *Chem. Abstr.*, *44*, P658 (1950).
(74) Reynolds, Bigelow, and Kraus, *J. Am. Chem. Soc.*, *51*, 3067–72 (1929).
(75) Sommer, Goldberg, Dorfman, and Whitmore, *J. Am. Chem. Soc.*, *68*, 1083–5 (1946).
(76) Dolgov and Volnov, *Zhur. Obshcheĭ Khim.*, Khim. Ser., *I*, 91–104 (1931); *Chem. Abstr.*, *25*, 4535 (1931).
(77) Kipping, *Proc. Chem. Soc.*, *21*, 65–6 (1905).
(78) Kipping, *J. Chem. Soc.*, *91*, 717–47 (1907).
(79) Luff and Kipping, *J. Chem. Soc.*, *93*, 2004–16 (1908).
(80) Challenger and Kipping, *J. Chem. Soc.*, *97*, 142–54 (1910).
(81) Gilliam and Sauer, *J. Am. Chem. Soc.*, *66*, 1793 (1944).
(82) Sommer, Goldberg, Gold, and Whitmore, *J. Am. Chem. Soc.*, *69*, 980 (1947).
(83) Bluestein, *J. Am. Chem. Soc.*, *70*, 3068–71 (1948).
(84) Meals, *J. Am. Chem. Soc.*, *68*, 1880–1 (1946).
(85) Whitmore, Sommer, and Gold, *J. Am. Chem. Soc.*, *69*, 1976–7 (1947).

(86) Roedel, *J. Am. Chem. Soc.*, *71*, 269–72 (1949).
(87) Sommer, Mitch, and Goldberg, *J. Am. Chem. Soc.*, *71*, 2746–50 (1949).
(88) Sauer, *J. Am. Chem. Soc.*, *66*, 1707–10 (1944).
(89) Hurd, U. S. Patent 2,420,912, May 20, 1947; *Chem. Abstr.*, *41*, P5145 (1947).
(90) Speier and Daubert, *J. Am. Chem. Soc.*, *70*, 1400–1 (1948).
(91) Sommer, Kerr, and Whitmore, *J. Am. Chem. Soc.*, *70*, 434–5 (1948).
(92) Burkhard, *J. Am. Chem. Soc.*, *68*, 2103 (1946).
(93) Speier, U. S. Patent 2,444,858, July 6, 1948; *Chem. Abstr.*, *42*, P7317 (1948).
(94) Corning Glass Works, British Patent 621,009, Apr. 1, 1949; *Chem. Abstr.*, *43*, P7500 (1949).
(95) Sommer, Tyler, and Whitmore, *J. Am. Chem. Soc.*, *70*, 2872–4 (1948).
(96) Gilman and Marshall, *J. Am. Chem. Soc.*, *71*, 2066–9 (1949).
(97) Tyler, Sommer, and Whitmore, *J. Am. Chem. Soc.*, *69*, 981 (1947).
(98) Tyler, Sommer, and Whitmore, *J. Am. Chem. Soc.*, *70*, 2876–8 (1948).
(99) Yakovlev, *J. Gen. Chem.* (U.S.S.R.), *19*, 1969–70 (1949); *Chem. Abstr.*, *44*, 1016 (1950).
(100) Cusa and Kipping, *J. Chem. Soc.*, *1932*, 2205–9.
(101) Cusa and Kipping, *J. Chem. Soc.*, *1933*, 1040–3.
(102) Robison and Kipping, *J. Chem. Soc.*, *101*, 2156–66 (1912).
(103) Kipping and Hackford, *J. Chem. soc.*, *99*, 138–45 (1911).
(104) Sommer, Bailey, Strong, and Whitmore, *J. Am. Chem. Soc.*, *68*, 1881–3 (1946).
(105) Gold, Sommer, and Whitmore, *J. Am. Chem. Soc.*, *70*, 2874–6 (1948).
(106) Bowden, Braude, and Jones, *J. Chem. Soc.*, *1946*, 948–52.
(107) Kalinin, *Compt. rend. acad. Sci. U.R.S.S.*, *26*, 365–9 (1940); *Chem. Abstr.*, *35*, 2470 (1941).
(108) Daudt, U. S. Patent 2,390,518, Dec. 11, 1945; *Chem. Abstr.*, *40*, P1866 (1946).
(109) Sommer, Kerr, and Whitmore, *J. Am. Chem. Soc.*, *70*, 445–7 (1948).
(110) Sommer, Gold, Goldberg, and Marans, *J. Am. Chem. Soc.*, *71*, 1509 (1949).
(111) Goodwin, British Patent 631,619, Nov. 7, 1949; *Chem. Abstr.*, *44*, 4491 (1950).
(112) McGregor and Warrick, U. S. Patent 2,384,384, Sept. 4, 1945; *Chem. Abstr.*, *40*, P730 (1946).
(113) Post and Hofrichter, *J. Org. Chem.*, *5*, 572–8 (1940).
(114) Di Giorgio, Strong, Sommer, and Whitmore, *J. Am. Chem. Soc.*, *68*, 1380 (1946).
(115) Jenkins and Post, *J. Org. Chem.*, *15*, 552–5 (1950).
(116) Hackford, Shaw, and Smith, British Patent 591,149, Aug. 8, 1947; *Chem. Abstr.*, *42*, P586 (1948).
(117) Andrianov and Kamenskaya, *J. Gen. Chem.* (U.S.S.R.), *8*, 969–71 (1938); *Chem. Abstr.*, *33*, 1266 (1939).
(118) McGregor and Warrick, U. S. Patent 2,442,053, May 25, 1948; *Chem. Abstr.*, *42*, P7786 (1948).
(119) McGregor and Warrick, U. S. Patent 2,380,057, July 10, 1945; *Chem. Abstr.*, *40*, P88 (1946).
(120) Khotinsky and Seregenkoff, *Ber.*, *41*, 2946–53 (1908).
(121) Marsden and Kipping, *Proc. Chem. Soc.*, *24*, 12 (1908); *J. Chem. Soc.*, *93*, 198–210 (1908).
(122) Kipping, *J. Chem. Soc.*, *1927*, 104–7.
(123) Jörg and Stetter, *J. prakt. Chem.*, [2], *117*, 305–10 (1927).
(124) Kipping, *J. Chem. Soc.*, *123*, 2598–603 (1923).
(125) Davies and Kipping, *J. Chem. Soc.*, *95*, 69–80 (1909).
(126) Kohlschütter, Scheele, and Jaekel, Unpublished work, as cited by: Kohlschütter, *Fortschritte chem. Forschung*, *1*, 1–60 (1949).

CHAPTER XXIII

Reactions of Grignard Reagents with Miscellaneous Non-metallic Substances

HALOGENS

It is probable that the first halogenation of a Grignard reagent was unwittingly effected by Fleck.[1] In one of several attempts to prepare the then unknown organomagnesium halides, he treated diphenylmagnesium with bromine. Unfortunately, he used an excess of bromine and arrived at the conclusions that the reaction takes the course

$$(C_6H_5)_2Mg + 2\ Br_2 \rightarrow 2\ C_6H_5Br + MgBr_2$$

and that no stable intermediate of the formula C_6H_5MgBr is formed. Gilman and Brown[2] have since shown that in all probability the reaction occurs stepwise:

$$(C_6H_5)_2Mg + Br_2 \rightarrow C_6H_5MgBr + C_6H_5Br$$

$$C_6H_5MgBr + Br_2 \rightarrow C_6H_5Br + MgBr_2$$

The iódination of Grignard reagents and attempts by Jolibois,[3] Leroide,[4] and Job and Reich[5] to use iodine titration as a method for quantitative estimation of organomagnesium compounds, as well as a critique of the method by Gilman *et al.*[6] are discussed in Chapter III on Estimation and Detection of Grignard Reagents (*q.v.*).

More recently, calorimetric measurements of the reactions of methylmagnesium iodide with iodine have been used by Mackle and Ubbelohde[7] as a basis for the estimation of the heats of dissociation: $D_{(CH_3—I)}$ and $D_{(CH_3—Mg)}$.

Published data on other halogenations of Grignard reagents are summarized in Table XXIII-I.

In general it would appear that the better yields of halides (RX′) might be expected when the Grignard reagent (RMgX) solution is added to an excess of a cold halogen (X'_2) solution.[8] When "coupling" is possible

[1] Fleck, *Ann.*, *276*, 129–47 (1893).
[2] Gilman and Brown, *J. Am. Chem. Soc.*, *52*, 1181–5 (1930).
[3] Jolibois, *Compt. rend.*, *155*, 213–5 (1912); *Chem. Abstr.*, 6, 2740 (1912).
[4] Leroide, *Ann. chim.*, [9], *16*, 354–410 (1921).
[5] Job and Reich, *Bull. soc. chim.*, [4], 33, 1414–33 (1923).
[6] Gilman, Wilkinson, Fishel, and Meyers, *J. Am. Chem. Soc.*, *45*, 150–8 (1923).
[7] Mackle and Ubbelohde, *J. Chem. Soc.*, *1948*, 1161–70
[8] *Cf.*, *e.g.*, Gilman and Vernon, *J. Am. Chem. Soc.*, 48, 1063–6 (1926).

TABLE XXIII-I

REACTIONS OF GRIGNARD REAGENTS WITH HALOGENS

RMgX	X'_2	RX'	2 R*	Ref.
$(\equiv CMgBr)_2$	Br_2	$(=CBr_2)_2$; $(\equiv CBr)_2$ (?)	...	2
$(\equiv CMgBr)_2$	I_2	$(\equiv CI)_2$	...	2,*cf.* 19
C_2H_5MgBr	I_2	C_2H_5I (<20%)	...	6
C_2H_5MgI	Br_2	C_2H_5Br	...	6
n-C_3H_7MgBr	I_2	n-C_3H_7I (80%)	...	1a
i-C_3H_7MgI	Br_2	i-C_3H_7Br (30–40%)	...	6
n-$C_3H_7C\equiv CMgBr$	I_2	n-$C_3H_7C\equiv CI$ (69–76%)†	...	7
n-$C_3H_7C\equiv CMgBr$	I_2	n-$C_3H_7C\equiv CI$ (77%)	...	10
n-$C_3H_7C\equiv CMgX$ (2 equiv.)	I_2	...	$(n$-$C_3H_7C\equiv C—)_2$	19
i-$C_3H_7C\equiv CMgBr$	I_2	i-$C_3H_7C\equiv CI$ (33%)	...	3
i-$C_5H_{11}MgCl$	I_2	i-$C_5H_{11}I$ (80%)	...	1a
t-$C_4H_9CH_2MgCl$	Br_2	t-$C_4H_9CH_2Br$ (82%)	...	15
t-$C_4H_9CH_2MgCl$	I_2	t-$C_4H_9CH_2I$ (88%, crude)	...	15
4-BrC_6H_4MgBr	I_2	4-BrC_6H_4I	...	1b
C_6H_5MgBr	Cl_2	?‡	...	6
C_6H_5MgBr	Br_2	C_6H_5Br (30–40%)	$(C_6H_5—)_2$	6
C_6H_5MgBr§	I_2	C_6H_5I (25–30%)	$(C_6H_5—)_2$	6,1a
C_6H_5MgBr¶	I_2	C_6H_5I (90%)	...	6
C_6H_5MgI	Cl_2	C_6H_5Cl (20–25%)	...	6
C_6H_5MgI	Br_2	C_6H_5Br (30–40%)	$(C_6H_5—)_2$	6
C_6H_5MgI	I_2	C_6H_5I	$(C_6H_5—)_2$ (chief product)	6
2-$CH_3C_6H_4MgBr$¶	I_2	2-$CH_3C_6H_4I$ (80%)	...	6
3-$CH_3C_6H_4MgBr$¶	I_2	3-$CH_3C_6H_4I$ (76%)	...	6
4-$CH_3C_6H_4MgBr$	Cl_2	4-$CH_3C_6H_4Cl$ (18–20%)	...	6
4-$CH_3C_6H_4MgBr$	I_2	4-$CH_3C_6H_4I$	...	1a
4-$CH_3C_6H_4MgBr$¶	I_2	4-$CH_3C_6H_4I$ (74%)	...	6
n-$C_5H_{11}C\equiv CMgBr$	I_2	n-$C_5H_{11}C\equiv CI$ (69–76%)†	...	7
n-$C_5H_{11}C\equiv CMgX$ (2 equiv.)	I_2	...	$(n$-$C_5H_{11}C\equiv C—)_2$	19
$(C_2H_5O)_2CHC\equiv CMgBr$	I_2	$(C_2H_5O)_2CHC\equiv CI$	...	8,18
$C_6H_5C\equiv CMgBr$	Br_2	$C_6H_5C\equiv CBr$	...	2
$C_6H_5C\equiv CMgBr$	I_2	(?), m.p. 99–100°	...	2
$C_6H_5C\equiv CMgX$	I_2	...	$(C_6H_5C\equiv C—)_2$	19
$C_6H_5OC\equiv CMgBr$	I_2	$C_6H_5OCI=CI_2$ (60%)	...	16
$[C_6H_5CH(CO_2Na)]^-MgX^+$	Br_2	$C_6H_5CHBrCO_2H$	...	12
$(CH_2)_5CHC\equiv CMgBr$	I_2	$(CH_2)_5CHC\equiv CI$ (69–76%)†	...	7

* The symbol 2 R is intended to include both coupling products (R_2) and disproportionation products $[R_{(+H)} + R_{(-H)}]$.

† This is the range of yields reported for $RC\equiv CI$ when R is aliphatic.

‡ Reaction explosive.

§ Normal order of addition (I_2 to C_6H_5MgBr).

¶ Reversed order of addition (RMgX solution to I_2 solution).

TABLE XXIII-I (Continued)

RMgX	X'_2	RX′	2 R*	Ref.
n-$C_6H_{13}C{\equiv}CMgBr$	I_2	n-$C_6H_{13}C{\equiv}CI$ (88%)	...	11
$C_6H_5CH_2C{\equiv}CMgBr$ (1 equiv.)	I_2	$C_6H_5CH_2C{\equiv}CI$	...	7
$C_6H_5CH_2C{\equiv}CMgX$ (2 equiv.)	I_2	...	$(C_6H_5CH_2C{\equiv}C-)_2$	19
1-Indenyl-MgBr	Br_2	1,2,3-Tribromoindane + 1-bromoindene (?)	...	4
1-Indenyl-MgBr	I_2	...	1,1′-Biindenyl (82%)	4
2-HO-5-$CH_3C_6H_3C{\equiv}CMgBr$	I_2	2-HO-5-$CH_3C_6H_4C{\equiv}CI$ (66–68%)‡	...	
$C_6H_5CH_2CH_2C{\equiv}CMgBr$ (1 equiv.)	I_2	$C_6H_5CH_2CH_2C{\equiv}CI$	...	7
$C_6H_5CH_2CH_2C{\equiv}CMgBr$ (2 equiv.)	I_2	...	$(C_6H_5CH_2CH_2C{\equiv}C-)_2$	19
2,4-$(CH_3)_2C_6H_3C{\equiv}CMgBr$ (1 equiv.)	I_2	2,4-$(CH_3)_2C_6H_3C{\equiv}CI$ (66–68%)‡	...	7
2,4-$(CH_3)_2C_6H_3C{\equiv}CMgBr$ (2 equiv.)	I_2	...	[2,4-$(CH_3)_2C_6H_3C{\equiv}C-]_2$ (80%)	7,19
n-$C_8H_{17}C{\equiv}CMgBr$	I_2	n-$C_8H_{17}C{\equiv}CI$ (70%)	...	11
n-$C_9H_{19}C{\equiv}CMgBr$	I_2	n-$C_9H_{19}C{\equiv}CI$ (69–76%)†	...	7
1-$C_{10}H_7C{\equiv}CMgBr$ (1 equiv.)	I_2	n-$C_{10}H_7C{\equiv}CI$	...	7
1-$C_{10}H_7C{\equiv}CMgBr$ (2 equiv.)	I_2	...	$(1\text{-}C_{10}H_7C{\equiv}C-)_2$ (82%)	7
4-$(C_2H_5)_3SiC_6H_4MgBr$	I_2	4-$(C_2H_5)_3SiC_6H_4I$ (82%)	...	5
n-$C_{10}H_{21}C{\equiv}CMgBr$	I_2	n-$C_{10}H_{21}C{\equiv}CI$ (95%)	...	11
n-$C_{12}H_{25}MgCl$	I_2	n-$C_{12}H_{25}I$ (71.0%) + n-$C_{12}H_{25}Cl$ (16.4%)	n-$C_{24}H_{50}$ (5.1%) + $C_{12}H_{26}$ + $C_{12}H_{24}$ (4.3%)	14
9-Anthryl-MgBr	I_2	9-Iodoanthracene (53%)	...	17
10-Phenyl-9-anthryl-MgBr	I_2	9-Iodo-10-phenyl-anthracene (50–55%)	...	13
$(C_6H_5)_2C{=}C(C_6H_5)MgBr$	I_2	$(C_6H_5)_2C{=}C(C_6H_5)I$ (52%)	...	9

*The symbol 2 R is intended to include both coupling products (R_2) and disproportionation products $[R_{(+H)} + R_{(-H)}]$.

†This is the range of yields reported for RC≡CI when R is aliphatic.

‡This is the range of yields reported for RC≡CI when R is aromatic.

REFERENCES FOR TABLE XXIII-I

(1) Bodroux, (*a*) *Compt. rend.*, *135*, 1350–1 (1902); *J. Chem. Soc.*, *84,I*, 221 (1903); (*b*) *Compt. rend.*, *136*, 1138–9 (1903); *J. Chem. Soc.*, *84,I*, 592 (1903).

(2) Iotsitch, *J. Russ. Phys.-Chem. Soc.*, 35, 1269–75 (1903); *Bull. soc. chim.*, [3], *181* (1905).

(3) Kalinine, *J. Russ. Phys.-Chem. Soc.*, 38, 1042–6 (1907); *Chem. Abstr.*, *1*, 1271 (1907).

(4) Grignard and Courtot, *Compt. rend.*, *154*, 361–4 (1912); *Chem. Abstr.*, 6, 1132 (1912).

(5) Grüttner and Krause, *Ber.*, *50*, 1559–68 (1917).
(6) Datta and Mitter, *J. Am. Chem. Soc.*, *41*, 287–92 (1919).
(7) Grignard and Perrichon, *Ann. chim.*, [10], *5*, 5–36 (1926).
(8) Grard, *Compt. rend.*, *189*, 541–3 (1929).
(9) Koelsch, *J. Am. Chem. Soc.*, *54*, 2045–8 (1932).
(10) Vaughn, *J. Am. Chem. Soc.*, *55*, 1293 (1933).
(11) Vaughn, *J. Am. Chem. Soc.*, *55*, 3453–8 (1933).
(12) Ivanov and Spasov, *Arhiv. Hem. Farm.*, *8*, 8–10 (1934); *Chem. Abstr.*, *28*, 6711 (1934).
(13) Dufraisse, Velluz, and Velluz, *Bull. soc. chim.*, [5], *4*, 1260–4 (1937).
(14) Oldham and Ubbelohde, *J. Chem. Soc.*, *1938*, 201–6.
(15) Whitmore, Wittle, and Harriman, *J. Am. Chem. Soc.*, *61*, 1585–6 (1939).
(16) Jacobs and Whitcher, *J. Am. Chem. Soc.*, *64*, 2635–8 (1942).
(17) Bachmann and Kloetzel, *J. Org. Chem.*, 3, 55–61 (1938).
(18) Grard, *Ann. chim.*, [10], *13*, 336–81 (1930).
(19) Grignard and Tchéoufaki, *Compt. rend.*, *188*, 357–61 (1929); *British Chem. Abstr.*, *1929A*, 290.

(*i.e.*, when the Grignard reagent is capable of condensing with the corresponding halide) the better yields of "coupling product" (R_2) might be expected when the halogen solution is added slowly to the hot Grignard reagent solution.[9]

BORON COMPOUNDS

Reported reactions of boron compounds have been confined to those of the boric esters and boron trihalides. Apparently both the alkoxy groups of the esters and the halogen atoms of the trihalides are capable of successive replacement. However, the esters have been commonly employed for the preparation of organoboronic acids [$RB(OH)_2$], and the trihalides for the preparation of trialkyl- or triarylborines (R_3B). Data are summarized in Table XXIII-II. The products reported are those obtained upon hydrolysis of the intermediates originally formed.

PHOSPHORUS COMPOUNDS

Phosphines. The phosphines, like their nitrogen analogs, react with Grignard reagents as "active hydrogen" compounds (Job and Desollier[10]).

$$PH_3 \xrightarrow{C_2H_5MgBr} HP(MgBr)_2 + 2\ C_2H_6$$

$$C_6H_5PH_2 \xrightarrow{C_2H_5MgBr} C_6H_5P(MgBr)_2 + 2\ C_2H_6$$

$$(C_6H_5)_2PH \xrightarrow{C_2H_5MgBr} (C_6H_5)_2PMgBr + C_2H_6$$

Phosphorus trichloride. In one of several attempts to convert diphenylmagnesium to a phenylmagnesium halide Fleck[11] investigated the action

[9] *Cf.*, *e.g.*, (*a*) Grignard and Perrichon, *Ann. chim.*, [10], *5*, 5–36 (1926); (*b*) Grignard and Tchéoufaki, *Compt. rend.*, *188*, 357–61 (1929); *British Chem. Abstr.*, *1929A*, 290.

[10] Job and Desollier, *Compt. rend.*, *184*, 1454–6 (1927); *Chem. Abstr.*, *21*, 3049 (1927).

[11] Fleck, *Ann.*, *276*, 129–47 (1893).

TABLE XXIII-II

REACTIONS OF GRIGNARD REAGENTS WITH BORON COMPOUNDS

B Compound	RMgX	Product(s)	Ref.
BF_3	CH_3MgBr	$(CH_3)_3B$ (87%)	*11*
BF_3	C_2H_5MgBr	$(C_2H_5)_3B$ (74%, crude)	*11*
BF_3	n-C_3H_7MgCl	$(n$-$C_3H_7)_3B$ (60%)*	*3*
BF_3	i-C_4H_9MgCl	$(i$-$C_4H_9)_3B$ (*ca.* quant.)	*3*
BF_3	i-$C_5H_{11}MgCl$	$(i$-$C_5H_{11})_3B$ (60%)*	*3*
BF_3	C_6H_5MgBr	$(C_6H_5)_3B$ (50%)	*4,5*
BF_3	$(CH_2)_5CHMgBr$	$[(CH_2)_5CH]_3B$ (54%, crude)	*7*
BF_3	$C_6H_5CH_2MgCl$	$(C_6H_5CH_2)_3B$	*8*
BF_3	4-$CH_3C_6H_4MgBr$	$(4$-$CH_3C_6H_4)_3B$ (50%, crude)	*7*
BF_3	$2,5$-$(CH_3)_2C_6H_3MgBr$	$[2,5$-$(CH_3)_2C_6H_3]_3B$ (45%)	*8*
BF_3	1-$C_{10}H_7MgBr$	$(1$-$C_{10}H_7)_3B$	*8*
BCl_3	C_6H_5MgBr	$C_6H_5B(OH)_2$	*2*
$B(OCH_3)_3$	n-C_3H_7MgBr	n-$C_3H_7B(OH)_2$ (54%, crude)	*10*
$B(OCH_3)_3$	n-C_4H_9MgBr	n-$C_4H_9B(OH)_2$ (60–70%, crude)	*10*
$B(OCH_3)_3$	i-C_4H_9MgBr	i-$C_4H_9B(OH)_2$ (57%, crude)	*10*
$B(OCH_3)_3$	n-$C_5H_{11}MgBr$	n-$C_5H_{11}B(OH)_2$ (70%, crude)	*10*
$B(OCH_3)_3$	C_6H_5MgBr	$C_6H_5B(OH)_2 + CH_3OH + CH_3C_6H_5$	*1*
$B(OCH_3)_3$	C_6H_5MgBr	$C_6H_5B(OH)_2$ (86%) + CH_3OH	*6*
$B(OCH_3)_3$	n-$C_6H_{13}MgBr$	n-$C_6H_{13}B(OH)_2$ (70%, crude)	*10*
$B(OC_2H_5)_3$	C_6H_5MgBr	$C_6H_5B(OH)_2$	*1*
$B(O$-n-$C_3H_7)_3$	C_6H_5MgBr	$C_6H_5B(OH)_2$	*1*
$B(O$-n-$C_4H_9)_3$	n-$C_{14}H_{29}MgBr$	n-$C_{14}H_{29}B(OH)_2$	*10*
$B(O$-i-$C_4H_9)_3$	CH_3MgI	$CH_3B(OH)_2$	*1*
$B(O$-i-$C_4H_9)_3$	RMgX†	$RB(OH)_2$	*1*
$B(O$-i-$C_4H_9)_3$	4-BrC_6H_4MgBr	4-$BrC_6H_4B(OH)_2$	*9*
$B(O$-i-$C_4H_9)_3$	2-ClC_6H_4MgBr	2-$ClC_6H_4B(OH)_2$	*9*
$B(O$-i-$C_4H_9)_3$	C_6H_5MgBr	$C_6H_5B(O$-i-$C_4H_9)_2$ (50%)	*1*
$B(O$-i-$C_4H_9)_3$	$C_6H_5CH_2MgCl$	$C_6H_5CH_2B(OH)_2$	*1*
$B(O$-i-$C_4H_9)_3$	2-$CH_3C_6H_4MgBr$	2-$CH_3C_6H_4B(OH)_2$	*9*
$B(O$-i-$C_4H_9)_3$	3-$CH_3C_6H_4MgBr$	3-$CH_3C_6H_4B(OH)_2$	*1,9*
$B(O$-i-$C_4H_9)_3$	4-$CH_3C_6H_4MgBr$	4-$CH_3C_6H_4B(OH)_2$	*9*
$B(O$-i-$C_4H_9)_3$	2-$CH_3OC_6H_4MgBr$	2-$CH_3OC_6H_4B(OH)_2$	*9*
$B(O$-i-$C_4H_9)_3$	3-$CH_3OC_6H_4MgBr$	3-$CH_3OC_6H_4B(OH)_2$	*9*
$B(O$-i-$C_4H_9)_3$	4-$CH_3OC_6H_4MgBr$	4-$CH_3OC_6H_4B(OH)_2$	*9*
$B(O$-i-$C_5H_{11})_3$	C_6H_5MgBr	$C_6H_5B(OH)_2$	*1*
$B(OC_6H_5)_3$	n-C_3H_7MgBr	$B(n$-$C_3H_7)_3$ (7%) + C_6H_5OH (56%)	*6*
$B(OC_6H_5)_3$	n-C_4H_9MgBr	$B(n$-$C_4H_9)_3$ (?) + C_6H_5OH (80%)	*6*
$B(OC_6H_5)_3$	C_6H_5MgBr	$C_6H_5B(OH)_2$ (16.5%) + C_6H_5OH (40%)	*6*

*On basis of RX.

†R = C_2H_5, n-C_3H_7, i-C_4H_9, i-C_5H_{11}.

REFERENCES FOR TABLE XXIII-II

(*1*) Khotinsky and Melamed, *Ber.*, *42*, 3090–6 (1909).

(*2*) Strecker, *Ber.*, *43*, 1131–6 (1910).

(*3*) Krause and Nitsche, *Ber.*, *54B*, 2784–9 (1921).

(*4*) Krause and Nitsche, *Ber.*, *55B*, 1261–5 (1922).

(*5*) Krause and Polack, *Ber.*, *59B*, 777–85 (1926).

(*6*) Gilman and Vernon, *J. Am. Chem. Soc.*, *48*, 1063–6 (1926).

(7) Krause and Polack, *Ber.*, *61B*, 271–6 (1928).
(8) Krause and Nobbe, *Ber.*, *63B*, 934–42 (1930).
(9) König and Scharnbeck, *J. prakt. Chem.*, [2], *128*, 153–70 (1930).
(10) Snyder, Kuck, and Johnson, *J. Am. Chem. Soc.*, *60*, 105–11 (1938).
(11) Brown, *J. Am. Chem. Soc.*, *67*, 374–8 (1945).

on the magnesium compound of phosphorus trichloride. According to him the reaction apparently took the course:

$$PCl_3 + (C_6H_5)_2Mg \rightarrow (C_6H_5)_2PCl + MgCl_2$$

In general, phosphorus trichloride reacts with Grignard reagents to form trialkyl- or triarylphosphines. The trisubstituted phosphines are, however, readily oxidized to phosphine oxides by atmospheric oxygen. When this takes place, either accidentally or by design, in the presence of excess Grignard reagent, a phosphonium base, readily convertible by strong acid to a phosphonium salt, may be formed.

$$PCl_3 \xrightarrow{RMgX} R_3P \xrightarrow{O_2} R_3PO \xrightarrow{RMgX} [R_4P]^+OMgX^- \xrightarrow{HX} [R_4P]^+X^-$$

Thus, Augur and Billy[12] reported the products of reaction of phosphorus trichloride with excess methylmagnesium iodide as tetramethylphosphonium chloride and phosphorus diiodide (P_2I_4). Dodonov and Medox[13] report a 73 percent yield of tetraphenylphosphonium bromide from treatment of a mixture of triphenylphosphine and phenylmagnesium bromide successively with oxygen, water, and hydrobromic acid. Willard *et al.*[14] have prepared tetraphenylphosphonium bromide in 91 percent yield by adding phosphorus trichloride to an excess of phenylmagnesium bromide, and then treating the reaction mixture successively with atmospheric oxygen and aqueous hydrochloric acid.

When methylmagnesium iodide was slowly added to phosphorus trichloride, and the reaction mixture was then successively oxygenated and hydrolyzed, the products were dimethylphosphinic acid (principally), methylphosphoric acid, and trimethylphosphine oxide (Augur and Billy, *loc. cit.*[12]).

Monochloro and dichloro phosphine derivatives. The monochloro and dichloro phosphine derivatives, when added to an excess of Grignard reagent react in a manner analogous to that of phosphorus trichloride.

$$RR'PCl + R''MgX \rightarrow RR'R''P + MgXCl$$

$$RPCl_2 + 2\,R'MgX \rightarrow RR'_2P + 2\,MgXCl$$

(For specific reactions and references see Table XXIII-III.) According to Grüttner and Wiernik,[15] aryldichlorophosphines react with pentamethyl-

[12] Augur and Billy, *Compt. rend.*, *139*, 597–9 (1904); *Chem. Zentr.*, *1904,II*, 1451.
[13] Dodonov and Medox, *Ber.*, *61B*, 907–11 (1928).
[14] Willard, Perkins, and Blicke, *J. Am. Chem. Soc.*, *70*, 737–8 (1948).
[15] Grüttner and Wiernik, *Ber.*, *48*, 1473–86 (1915).

enemagnesium bromide to give yields of the order of 36 percent of arylpentamethylene phosphines.

$$C_6H_5PCl_2 \xrightarrow{BrMg(CH_2)_5MgBr} (CH_2)_5PC_6H_5 \ (36.2\%)$$

$$4\text{-}CH_3C_6H_4PCl_2 \xrightarrow{BrMg(CH_2)_5MgBr} (CH_2)_5PC_6H_4\text{-}4\text{-}CH_3 \ (35.7\%)$$

A similar reaction with tetramethylene magnesium bromide has been reported by Grüttner and Krause.[16]

Phosphorus pentachloride. Apparently three of the chlorine atoms of phosphorus pentachloride are more reactive toward Grignard reagents than the other two, for Grignard and Savard[17] report triphenylphosphine chloride [$(C_6H_5)_3PCl_2$] as the product of reaction with phenylmagnesium bromide. According to Kolitowska,[18] triphenylphosphine and tetraphenylphosphonium bromide are byproducts of this reaction.

Grignard and Savard (*loc. cit.*[17]) report that triphenylphosphine chloride behaves as a chlorinating agent.

$$(C_6H_5)_3PCl_2 + 2\ RMgX \rightarrow 2\ RCl + (C_6H_5)_3P(MgX)_2$$

$$(RMgX = CH_3MgI,\ C_2H_5MgI,\ C_2H_5MgBr)$$

Phosphoryl chloride ($POCl_3$). When phosphoryl chloride is treated with three or more equivalents of Grignard reagent it yields a trisubstituted phosphine oxide. The reaction is probably stepwise, for Sauvage[19] reports dibenzylphosphinic acid and di-α-naphthylphosphinic acid as byproducts of the preparations of tribenzylphosphine oxide and tri-α-naphthylphosphine oxide, respectively. By employing the reversed order of addition (so that phosphoryl chloride should always be present in excess), Kosolapoff[20] was able to prepare diphenylphosphinic and bis-*p*-chlorophenylphosphinic acids (in this article mis-named phosphonic acids) in 55 and 51 percent yields, respectively.

$$POCl_3 \xrightarrow{2\ RMgX} R_2POCl \xrightarrow{H_2O} R_2PO_2H$$

The possibility of "blocking" one of the chlorine atoms of phosphoryl chloride (*i.e.*, of replacing it by a readily hydrolyzable group) was investigated by Michaelis and Wegner.[21] They found that substitution of a phenoxy group for a chlorine atom still permitted triple replacement by the Grignard reagent.

$$C_6H_5OPOCl_2 \xrightarrow{C_6H_5MgBr} (C_6H_5)_3PO$$

When, however, the piperidinamide corresponding to this phenyl ester was employed, satisfactory, though unspecified, yields of phosphinic acids

[16] Grüttner and Krause, *Ber.*, *49*, 437–44 (1916).

[17] Grignard and Savard, *Compt. rend.*, *192*, 592–5 (1931); *Chem. Abstr.*, *25*, 2702 (1931).

[18] Kolitowska, *Roczniki Chem.*, 8, 568–75 (1928); *Chem. Abstr.*, *23*, 2158 (1929).

[19] Sauvage, *Compt. rend.*, *139*, 674–6 (1904); *Chem. Zentr.*, *1904,II*, 1638.

[20] Kosolapoff, *J. Am. Chem. Soc.*, *64*, 2982–3 (1942).

[21] Michaelis and Wegner, *Ber.*, *48*, 316–8 (1915).

were obtained, presumably through the reaction sequence:

$$(CH_2)_5NPOCl_2 \xrightarrow{RMgX} (CH_2)_5NPOR_2 \xrightarrow{H_2O} R_2PO_2H$$

$$(R = C_6H_5,\ C_6H_5CH_2,\ 2\text{-}CH_3C_6H_4,\ 4\text{-}CH_3C_6H_4,\ \text{"naphthyl"})$$

Kosolapoff[22] has shown that the amide derived from the cheaper and more readily available diethylamine serves the purpose at least as well. His reported percentage yields of phosphinic acids from several Grignard reagents are as indicated: n-C_4H_9MgBr (82); 4-$CH_3C_6H_4MgBr$ (75); 2-$CH_3OC_6H_4MgBr$ (74); 4-$CH_3OC_6H_4MgBr$ (79).

Kosolapoff[23] has found it possible, by operating at relatively low temperature (5–10°), to achieve a partial replacement of the chlorine of the diethylamide to obtain a phosphonic acid.

$$\underset{(95.0\text{ g., }0.5\text{ mole})}{(C_2H_5)_2NPOCl_2} \xrightarrow{n\text{-}C_4H_9MgBr} \xrightarrow{H_2O} \underset{(53.2\text{ g., }67\%)}{n\text{-}C_4H_9PO_3H_2} + \underset{(<1.0\text{ g.})}{(n\text{-}C_4H_9)_2PO_2H}$$

The feasibility of "blocking" a chlorine atom by quaternization with a tertiary base (specifically, pyridine) has also been investigated by Kosolapoff (*loc. cit.*[23]). This expedient proved most effective when reversed addition was employed, but the yields obtained from the pyridine complex of phosphoryl chloride were inferior to those obtained from the diethylamide.

$$POCl_3 \cdot C_5H_5N \xrightarrow{n\text{-}C_4H_9MgBr} \xrightarrow{H_2O} (n\text{-}C_4H_9)_2PO_2H\ (47.5\%)$$

$$POCl_3 \cdot C_5H_5N \xrightarrow{n\text{-}C_6H_{13}MgBr} \xrightarrow{H_2O} (n\text{-}C_6H_{13})_2PO_2H\ (40.5\%)$$

Similar "blocking" of a second chlorine atom, however, is apparently impossible, for the use of a second equivalent of pyridine led to the production of phosphinic acids only.

Kosolapoff's pyridine experiments suggest a more plausible explanation of the behavior of the *N*-methylacridone-phosphoryl chloride complex of Gleu and Schubert[24] than that embodied in the rather fantastic scheme proposed by those investigators:

$$POCl_3 \cdot C_{13}H_{11}NO \xrightarrow{C_6H_5MgBr} \xrightarrow{H_2O} (C_6H_5)_2PO_2H\ (85.0\%)$$

or (in view of the biacrydilidene byproduct),

$$POCl_3 \cdot C_{13}H_{11}NCl_2 \xrightarrow{C_6H_5MgBr} \xrightarrow{H_2O} (C_6H_5)_2PO_2H$$

Phosphoric and phosphorous esters. According to Gilman *et al.*,[25] phosphoric and phosphorous esters behave toward aryl Grignard reagents very much like the corresponding chlorides (see Table XXIII-III). No trialkylphosphine oxide was isolated, however, when triphenyl phosphate was treated with n-propylmagnesium bromide nor when tri-p-tolyl phosphate was treated with benzylmagnesium chloride.

---

[22] Kosolapoff, *J. Am. Chem. Soc.*, *71*, 369–70 (1949).

[23] Kosolapoff, *J. Am. Chem. Soc.*, *72*, 5508–9 (1950).

[24] Gleu and Schubert, *Ber.*, *73B*, 805–11 (1940).

[25] (*a*) Gilman and Vernon, *J. Am. Chem. Soc.*, *48*, 1063–6 (1926); (*b*) Gilman and Robinson, *Rec. trav. chim.*, *48*, 328–31 (1929).

Phosphorus sulfides. According to Malatesta,[26] phosphorus pentasulfide reacts with excess (*ca.* 4 equiv.) Grignard reagent to yield dithiophosphonic acid, and trisubstituted phosphine sulfide. Some mercaptan (attributed to free sulfur) is also found. Malatesta and Pizzoti (*loc. cit.*[26a]) believe that two principal reactions take place, as follows:

$$P_2S_5 + 6\ RMgX \rightarrow 2\ R_3PS + 3\ MgX_2 + 3\ MgS$$

$$P_2S_5 + 2\ RMgX \rightarrow [RP({=}S)SMgX]_2S \xrightarrow[2\ HCl]{2\ H_2O} 2\ RP({=}S)(OH)SH + MgCl_2 + H_2S + MgX_2$$

Other reactions of phosphorus sulfides are recorded in Table XXIII-III, as are reactions of various miscellaneous phosphorus compounds.

TABLE XXIII-III

REACTIONS OF GRIGNARD REAGENTS WITH PHOSPHORUS COMPOUNDS

P Compound	RMgX	Product(s)*	Ref.
PCl_3	4 CH_3MgI	$[(CH_3)_4P]^+Cl^-$ + P_2I_4	2
PCl_3 (excess)	CH_3MgBr (+ O_2)	$(CH_3)_2PO(OH)$ (chief product) + $(CH_3)_3PO$ + $CH_3PO(OH)_2$	2
PCl_3	C_2H_5MgBr	$(C_2H_5)_3P$ (70%)	4
PCl_3	$H_2C{=}CHCH_2MgBr$	$(H_2C{=}CHCH_2)_3P$	29
PCl_3	n-C_3H_7MgBr	$(n$-$C_3H_7)_3P$ (58%)	16
PCl_3	n-C_4H_9MgBr	$(n$-$C_4H_9)_3P$ (54%)	15
PCl_3	i-C_4H_9MgBr	$(i$-$C_4H_9)_3P$ (47%)	16
PCl_3	2-Pyridyl-MgBr	$(\alpha$-$C_5H_4N)_3P$	24, 30
PCl_3	n-$C_5H_{11}MgBr$	$(n$-$C_5H_{11})_3P$ (39%)	16
PCl_3	i-$C_5H_{11}MgBr$	$(i$-$C_5H_{11})_3P$ (39%)	16
PCl_3	$CH_3(C_2H_5)CHCH_2MgBr$	$[CH_3(C_2H_5)CHCH_2]_3P$ ("poor yield")	16
PCl_3	C_6H_5MgBr	$(C_6H_5)_3P$ (19–22%)	1,3
PCl_3	C_6H_5MgBr	$(C_6H_5)_3P$ (90%, crude; 76%, pure)	12
PCl_3	C_6H_5MgBr (+ O_2)	$[(C_6H_5)_4P]^+Br^-$ (91%)	26
PCl_3	Indolyl-MgBr	$(\beta$-$C_8H_6N)_3P$ + $(N$-$C_8H_6N)_3P$	18
PCl_3	α-Methylindolyl-MgBr	$(\beta$-$C_9H_8N)_3P$ + $(N$-$C_9H_8N)_3P$	18
4-$BrC_6H_4PCl_2$	$H_2C{=}CHCH_2MgBr$	4-$BrC_6H_4P(CH_2CH{=}CH_2)_2$ (56%)	29
$C_6H_5PCl_2$	CH_3MgI	$C_6H_5P(CH_3)_2$ (35%)	13, 11
$C_6H_5PCl_2$	C_2H_5MgBr	$C_6H_5P(C_2H_5)_2$	11

* The products reported are those obtained after hydrolysis of the reaction mixture.

[26] (*a*) Malatesta and Pizzoti, *Gazz. chim. ital.*, 76, 167–81 (1946); *Chem. Abstr.*, *41*, 2012 (1947); (*b*) Malatesta, *Gazz. chim. ital.*, 77, 509–17 (1947); *Chem. Abstr.*, *42*, 5411 (1948).

TABLE XXIII-III (Continued)

P Compound	RMgX	Product(s)*	Ref.
$C_6H_5PCl_2$	$H_2C{=}CHCH_2MgBr$	$C_6H_5P(CH_2CH{=}CH_2)_2$ (34%)	29
$C_6H_5PCl_2$	n-C_3H_7MgBr	$C_6H_5P(n$-$C_3H_7)_2$ (58%)	16
C_6H_5PCl	$H_2C{=}C(CH_3)CH_2MgBr$	$C_6H_5P[CH_2CH(CH_3){=}CH_2]_2$ (56%)	29
$C_6H_5PCl_2$	$BrMg(CH_2)_4MgBr$	$C_6H_5P(CH_2)_4$ (31–35%)	9
$C_6H_5PCl_2$	n-C_4H_9MgBr	$C_6H_5P(n$-$C_4H_9)_2$ (52%)	15
$C_6H_5PCl_2$	i-C_4H_9MgBr	$C_6H_5P(i$-$C_4H_9)_2$ (56%)	16
$C_6H_5PCl_2$	2-Pyridyl-MgBr	$C_6H_5P(\alpha$-$C_5H_4N)_2$	30
$C_6H_5PCl_2$	$BrMg(CH_2)_5MgBr$	$C_6H_5P(CH_2)_5$ (36%)	7
$C_6H_5PCl_2$	n-$C_5H_{11}MgBr$	$C_6H_5P(n$-$C_5H_{11})_2$ (57%)	16
$C_6H_5PCl_2$	i-$C_5H_{11}MgBr$	$C_6H_5P(i$-$C_5H_{11})_2$ (47%)	16
$C_6H_5PCl_2$	$CH_3(C_2H_5)CHCH_2MgBr$	$C_6H_5P[CH_2CH(CH_3)C_2H_5]_2$ (31%)	16
$C_6H_5PCl_2$	i-$C_6H_{13}MgBr$	$C_6H_5P(i$-$C_6H_{13})_2$ (27%)	16
4-$CH_3C_6H_4PCl_2$	C_2H_5MgBr	4-$CH_3C_6H_4P(C_2H_5)_2$	24
4-$CH_3C_6H_4PCl_2$	$H_2C{=}CHCH_2MgBr$	4-$CH_3C_6H_4P(CH_2CH{=}CH_2)_2$ (27%)	29
4-$CH_3C_6H_4PCl_2$	n-C_3H_7MgBr	4-$CH_3C_6H_4P(n$-$C_3H_7)_2$ (50%)	16
4-$CH_3C_6H_4PCl_2$	n-C_4H_9MgBr	4-$CH_3C_6H_4P(n$-$C_4H_9)_2$ (47%)	15
4-$CH_3C_6H_4PCl_2$	i-C_4H_9MgBr	4-$CH_3C_6H_4P(i$-$C_4H_9)_2$ (25%)	16
4-$CH_3C_6H_4PCl_2$	$BrMg(CH_2)_5MgBr$	4-$CH_3C_6H_4P(CH_2)_5$ (36%)	7
4-$CH_3C_6H_4PCl_2$	n-$C_5H_{11}MgBr$	4-$CH_3C_6H_4P(n$-$C_5H_{11})_2$ (56%)	16
4-$CH_3C_6H_4PCl_2$	i-$C_5H_{11}MgBr$	4-$CH_3C_6H_4P(i$-$C_5H_{11})_2$	16
4-$CH_3C_6H_4PCl_2$	$CH_3(C_2H_5)CHCH_2MgBr$	4-$CH_3C_6H_4P[CH_2CH(CH_3)$-$C_2H_5]_2$ (34%)	16
4-$CH_3C_6H_4PCl_2$	i-$C_6H_{13}MgBr$	4-$CH_3C_6H_4P(i$-$C_6H_{13})_2$	16
4-$CH_3OC_6H_4PCl_2$	$H_2C{=}CHCH_2MgBr$	4-$CH_3OC_6H_4P(CH_2CH{=}CH_2)_2$ (43%)	29
4-$CH_3OC_6H_4PCl_2$	n-C_3H_7MgBr	4-$CH_3OC_6H_4P(n$-$C_3H_7)_2$ (47%)	19
4-$CH_3OC_6H_4PCl_2$	n-C_4H_9MgBr	4-$CH_3OC_6H_4P(n$-$C_4H_9)_2$ (38%)	19
4-$CH_3OC_6H_4PCl_2$	n-$C_5H_{11}MgBr$	4-$CH_3OC_6H_4P(n$-$C_5H_{11})_2$ (34%)	19
4-$C_2H_5C_6H_4PCl_2$	$H_2C{=}CHCH_2MgBr$	4-$C_2H_5C_6H_4P(CH_2CH{=}CH_2)_2$ (56%)	29
4-$C_2H_5C_6H_4PCl_2$	n-C_3H_7MgBr	4-$C_2H_5C_6H_4P(n$-$C_3H_7)_2$ (44%)	19
4-$C_2H_5C_6H_4PCl_2$	n-C_4H_9MgBr	4-$C_2H_5C_6H_4P(n$-$C_4H_9)_2$ (36%)	19
4-$C_2H_5C_6H_4PCl_2$	n-$C_5H_{11}MgBr$	4-$C_2H_5C_6H_4P(n$-$C_5H_{11})_2$ (35%)	19
2,5-$(CH_3)_2C_6H_3PCl_2$	CH_3MgI	2,5-$(CH_3)_2C_6H_3P(CH_3)_2$ (*ca.* 64%)	20

* The products reported are those obtained after hydrolysis of the reaction mixture.

TABLE XXIII-III (Continued)

P Compound	RMgX	Product(s)*	Ref.
2,5-$(CH_3)_2C_6H_3PCl_2$	C_2H_5MgBr	2,5-$(CH_3)_2C_6H_3P(C_2H_5)_2$ (74%)	20
2,5-$(CH_3)_2C_6H_3PCl_2$	n-C_3H_7MgBr	2,5-$(CH_3)_2C_6H_3P(n\text{-}C_3H_7)_2$ (64%)	20
2,5-$(CH_3)_2C_6H_3PCl_2$	n-C_4H_9MgBr	2,5-$(CH_3)_2C_6H_3P(n\text{-}C_4H_9)_2$ (64%)	20
2,5-$(CH_3)_2C_6H_3PCl_2$	i-C_4H_9MgBr	2,5-$(CH_3)_2C_6H_3P(i\text{-}C_4H_9)_2$	20
2,5-$(CH_3)_2C_6H_3PCl_2$	n-$C_5H_{11}MgBr$	2,5-$(CH_3)_2C_6H_3P(n\text{-}C_5H_{11})_2$	20
$H_2C{=}C(CH_3)C_6H_4PCl_2$	$H_2C{=}CHCH_2MgBr$	$H_2C{=}C(CH_3)C_6H_4P(CH_2C{=}CH_2)_2$ (53%)	29
4-$C_6H_5OC_6H_4PCl_2$	$H_2C{=}CHCH_2MgBr$	4-$C_6H_5OC_6H_4P(CH_2CH{=}CH_2)_2$ (*ca.* 28%)	29
$(C_2H_5)_2PCl$	2-$CH_3OCH_2C_6H_4CH_2CH_2MgCl$	$(C_2H_5)_2PCH_2CH_2C_6H_4$-2-$CH_2OCH_3$ (74%)	32
$(C_2H_5)_2PCl$	2-$CH_3O(CH_2)_3C_6H_4MgBr$	$(C_2H_5)_2PC_6H_4$-2-$(CH_2)_3OCH_3$ (73%)	32
4-$BrC_6H_4(C_6H_5)PCl$	C_2H_5MgBr	4-$BrC_6H_4(C_6H_5)PC_2H_5$	24
4-$BrC_6H_4(C_6H_5)PCl$	2-Pyridyl-MgBr	4-$BrC_6H_4(C_6H_5)P(\alpha\text{-}C_5H_4N)$	24
4-$BrC_6H_4(C_6H_5)PCl$	3-Pyridyl-MgBr	4-$BrC_6H_5(C_6H_5)P(\beta\text{-}C_5H_4N)$	24
4-$BrC_6H_4(C_6H_5)PCl$	4-$CH_3OC_6H_4MgBr$	4-$BrC_6H_4(C_6H_5)PC_6H_4$-4-OCH_3	24
4-$BrC_6H_4(C_6H_5)PCl$	4-$(CH_3)_2NC_6H_4MgBr$	4-$BrC_6H_4(C_6H_5)PC_6H_4$-4-$N(CH_3)_2$ (37%)	24
$(C_6H_5)_2PCl$	CH_3MgX	$(C_6H_5)_2PCH_3$ (70%)	11
$(C_6H_5)_2PCl$	C_2H_5MgBr	$(C_6H_5)_2PC_2H_5$ (70%)	11
$(C_6H_5)_2PCl$	2-Pyridyl-MgBr	$(C_6H_5)_2P(\alpha\text{-}C_5H_4N)$ (20%)	30
$(C_6H_5)_2PCl$	$C_6H_5CH_2MgCl$	$(C_6H_5)_2PCH_2C_6H_5$	11
C_6H_5(4-$CH_3OC_6H_4$)PCl	C_2H_5MgBr	C_6H_5(4-$CH_3OC_6H_4$)PC_2H_5	24
C_6H_5(4-$CH_3OC_6H_4$)PCl	n-C_3H_7MgBr	C_6H_5(4-$CH_3OC_6H_4$)P-n-C_3H_7	24
C_6H_5(4-$CH_3OC_6H_4$)PCl	n-C_4H_9MgBr	C_6H_5(4-$CH_3OC_6H_4$)P-n-C_4H_9 (70%)	24
C_6H_5(4-$CH_3OC_6H_4$)PCl	4-$CH_3C_6H_4MgBr$	C_6H_5(4-$CH_3OC_6H_4$)PC_6H_4-4-CH_3	24
PCl_5	C_6H_5MgBr	$(C_6H_5)_3P$ + $(C_6H_5)_3PCl_2$ + $[(C_6H_5)_4P]^+Br^-$	14
PCl_5	C_6H_5MgBr	$(C_6H_5)_3PCl_2$	21
$POCl_3$	RMgX[†]	R_3PO	5
$POCl_3$	$H_2C{=}C(CH_3)CH_2MgBr$	$[H_2C{=}C(CH_3)CH_2]_3PO$	29
$POCl_3$	4-ClC_6H_4MgBr[‡]	(4-ClC_6H_4)$_2$PO(OH) (51%) + (4-ClC_6H_4)$_3$PO (7%)	23
$POCl_3$	C_6H_5MgBr	$(C_6H_5)_3PO$	3,5, 21

* The products reported are those obtained after hydrolysis of the reaction mixture.

[†] R = CH_3, C_2H_5, n-C_3H_7, C_6H_5, $C_6H_5CH_2$.

[‡] Reversed order of addition.

TABLE XXIII-III (Continued)

P Compound	RMgX	Product(s)*	Ref.
$POCl_3$	C_6H_5MgBr†	$(C_6H_5)_2PO(OH)$ 55% + $(C_6H_5)_3PO$ (7%)	23
$POCl_3$	$C_6H_5CH_2MgCl$	$(C_6H_5CH_2)_3PO$ + $(C_6H_5CH_2)_2PO(OH)$	3
$POCl_3$	1-$C_{10}H_7MgBr$	(1-$C_{10}H_7)_3PO$ + (1-$C_{10}H_7)_2PO(OH)$	3
$PSCl_3$	CH_3MgI	$[(CH_3)_2PS]_2$ (?)	33
$PSCl_3$	C_2H_5MgBr (excess)	$(C_2H_5)_2PS(OH)$	8
$PSCl_3$	C_6H_5MgBr	$(C_6H_5)_3PS$	8
$PSCl_3$	$C_6H_5CH_2MgCl$	$(C_6H_5CH_2)_3PS$ + $(C_6H_5CH_2)_2PS(OH)$	8
$C_6H_{13}NO \cdot POCl_3$‡	C_6H_5MgBr	$(C_6H_5)_2PO(OH)$ (85%)	22
$C_5H_5N \cdot POCl_3$§	n-C_4H_9MgBr	$(n$-$C_4H_9)_2PO(OH)$ (47.5%)	34
$C_5H_5N \cdot POCl_3$§	n-$C_6H_{13}MgBr$	$(n$-$C_6H_{13})_2PO(OH)$ (40.5%)	34
$C_6H_5OPOCl_2$	C_6H_5MgBr	$(C_6H_5)_3PO$	6
$(C_2H_5)_2NPOCl_2$	n-C_4H_9MgBr	$(n$-$C_4H_9)_2PO(OH)$ (82%)	31
$(C_2H_5)_2NPOCl_2$	n-C_4H_9MgBr	n-$C_4H_9PO(OH)_2$ (67%) + $(n$-$C_4H_9)_2PO(OH)$ (trace)¶	34
$(C_2H_5)_2NPOCl_2$	4-$CH_3C_6H_4MgBr$	(4-$CH_3C_6H_4)_2PO(OH)$ (75%)	31
$(C_2H_5)_2NPOCl_2$	2-$CH_3OC_6H_4MgBr$	(2-$CH_3OC_6H_4)_2PO(OH)$ (74%)	31
$(C_2H_5)_2NPOCl_2$	4-$CH_3OC_6H_4MgBr$	(4-$CH_3OC_6H_4)_2PO(OH)$ (79%)	31
$(CH_2)_5NPOCl_2$	RMgX‖	$R_2PO(OH)$	6
$P(OCH_3)_3$	C_6H_5MgBr (excess)	$CH_3O(C_6H_5)_2PO$ (42%)	17
$P(OC_2H_5)_3$	C_6H_5MgBr (excess)	$(C_6H_5)_3PO$ (10%)	17
$P(OC_6H_5)_3$	C_6H_5MgBr	$(C_6H_5)_3P$ (60%) + C_6H_5OH (68%)	10
$PO(OCH_3)_3$	C_6H_5MgBr	"No toluene"	17
$PO(OC_2H_5)_3$	C_6H_5MgBr	$C_6H_5PO(OC_2H_5)_2$ (16%) + $(C_6H_5)_2PO(OH)$ (17%)	17
$PO(OC_6H_5)_3$	n-C_3H_7MgBr	C_6H_5OH (49%) + unidentified product	10
$PO(OC_6H_5)_3$	4 C_6H_5MgBr	$(C_6H_5)_3PO$ (17%) + C_6H_5OH (49%)	10
$PO(OC_6H_4$-4-$CH_3)_3$	C_6H_5MgBr	$(C_6H_5)_3PO$ (50%) + 4-$CH_3C_6H_4OH$ (54%)	10
$PO(OC_6H_4$-4-$CH_3)_3$	$C_6H_5CH_2MgCl$	4-$CH_3C_6H_4OH$ (28%) + unidentified product	10
$C_6H_5PO(OC_2H_5)_3$	C_6H_5MgBr	$(C_6H_5)_2PO(OH)$ (32.5%)	34
P_2I_4	CH_3MgI	$[(CH_3)_4P]^+I^-$	2

* The products reported are those obtained after hydrolysis of the reaction mixture.

† Reversed order of addition.

‡ The complex from *N*-methylacridone and phosphoryl chloride; possibly $C_6H_{13}NCl_2 \cdot POCl_3$; probably a quaternary salt.

§ The complex from pyridine and phosphoryl chloride; probably a quaternary salt.

¶ Low-temperature (5–10°) reaction.

‖ R = C_6H_5, $C_6H_5CH_2$, 2-$CH_3C_6H_4$, 4-$CH_3C_6H_4$, 1-$C_{10}H_7$.

TABLE XXIII-III (Continued)

P Compound	RMgX	Product(s)*	Ref.
P_2S_5	CH_3MgI	$(CH_3)_3PS + (CH_3)_2PS(SH) + CH_3PS(OH)SH$ (?)	27
P_2S_5	RMgBr†	RPS(OH)SH + RPS(SH) + R_3PS + RSH	25
P_2S_5	i-C_4H_9MgBr	$(i\text{-}C_4H_9)_3P + (i\text{-}C_4H_9)_2PS(SH)$	27
P_2S_5	$(CH_2)CHMgBr$	$[(CH_2)_5CH]_3P$ (?) + $[(CH_2)_5CH]_2PS(SH)$ + $(CH_2)_5CHPS(OH)SH$	27
P_3S_6	C_2H_5MgBr	$(C_2H_5)_3P + (C_2H_5)_3PS$	28
P_3S_6	C_6H_5MgBr	$(C_6H_5)_3P + (C_6H_5)_3PS$ + phenylthiophosphonic acids	28
P_4S_3	C_2H_5MgBr	$(C_2H_5)_2PH$ (21%) + $(C_2H_5)_3P$ (6%)	28
P_4S_3	C_6H_5MgBr	$(C_6H_5)_2PH$ (24%)	28
P_4S_7	C_2H_5MgBr	$(C_2H_5)_3P$ (*ca.* 40%) + ethylthiophosphinic acids	28

*The products reported are those obtained after hydrolysis of the reaction mixture.

†R = C_2H_5, i-C_3H_7, C_6H_5.

REFERENCES FOR TABLE XXIII-III

(*1*) Pfeiffer, Heller, and Pietsch, *Ber.*, *37*, 4620-3 (1904).
(*2*) Auger and Billy, *Compt. rend.*, *139*, 597-9 (1904); *Chem. Zentr.*, *1904,II*, 1451.
(*3*) Sauvage, *Compt. rend.*, *139*, 674-6 (1904); *Chem. Zentr.*, *1904,II*, 1638.
(*4*) Hibbert, *Ber.*, *39*, 160-2 (1906).
(*5*) Pickard and Kenyon, *J. Chem. Soc.*, *89*, 262-73 (1906).
(*6*) Michaelis and Wagner, *Ber.*, *48*, 316-8 (1915).
(*7*) Grüttner and Wiernik, *Ber.*, *48*, 1473-86 (1915).
(*8*) Strecker and Grossmann, *Ber.*, *49*, 63-87 (1916).
(*9*) Grüttner and Krause, *Ber.*, *49*, 437-44 (1916).
(*10*) Gilman and Vernon, *J. Am. Chem. Soc.*, *48*, 1063-6 (1926).
(*11*) Meisenheimer, Casper, Horing, Lauter, Lichtenstadt, and Samuel, *Ann.*, *449*, 213-48 (1926).
(*12*) Dodonov and Medox, *Ber.*, *61B*, 907-11 (1928).
(*13*) Ingold, Shaw, and Wilson, *J. Chem. Soc.*, *1928*, 1280-6.
(*14*) Kolitowska, *Roczniki Chem.*, *8*, 568-75 (1928); *Chem. Abstr.*, *23*, 2158 (1929).
(*15*) Davies and Jones, *J. Chem. Soc.*, *1929*, 33-5.
(*16*) Davies, Pearse, and Jones, *J. Chem. Soc.*, *1929*, 1262-8.
(*17*) Gilman and Robinson, *Rec. trav. chim.*, *48*, 328-31 (1929).
(*18*) Mingoia, *Gazz. chim. ital.*, *60*, 144-9 (1930); *Chem. Zentr.*, *1930,I*, 3473; *Chem. Abstr.*, *24*, 3783 (1930).
(*19*) Jackson, Davies, and Jones, *J. Chem. Soc.*, *1930*, 2298-301.
(*20*) Jackson and Jones, *J. Chem. Soc.*, *1931*, 575-8.
(*21*) Grignard and Savard, *Compt. rend.*, *192*, 592-5 (1931); *Chem. Abstr.*, *25*, 2702 (1931).

(22) Gleu and Schubert, *Ber.*, *73B*, 805–11 (1940).
(23) Kosolapoff, *J. Am. Chem. Soc.*, *64*, 2982–3 (1942).
(24) Davies and Mann, *J. Chem. Soc.*, *1944*, 276–83.
(25) Malatesta and Pizzoti, *Gazz. chim. ital.*, *76*, 167–81 (1946); *Chem. Abstr.*, *41*, 2012 (1947).
(26) Willard, Perkins, and Blicke, *J. Am. Chem. Soc.*, *70*, 737–8 (1948).
(27) Malatesta, *Gazz. chim. ital.*, *77*, 509–17 (1947); *Chem. Abstr.*, *42*, 5411 (1948).
(28) Malatesta, *Gazz. chim. ital.*, *77*, 518–25 (1927); *Chem. Abstr.*, *42*, 5413 (1948).
(29) Jones, Davies, Bowden, Edwards, Davis, and Thomas, *J. Chem. Soc.*, *1947*, 1446–50.
(30) Mann and Watson, *J. Org. Chem.*, *13*, 502–31 (1948).
(31) Kosolapoff, *J. Am. Chem. Soc.*, *71*, 369–70 (1949).
(32) Beeby and Mann, *J. Chem. Soc.*, *1951*, 411–5.
(33) Kabachnik and Shepeleva, *Izvest. Akad. Nauk S.S.S.R., Otdel. Khim. Nauk*, *1949*, No. 1, 56–9; *Chem. Abstr.*, *43*, 5739 (1949).
(34) Kosolapoff, *J. Am. Chem. Soc.*, *72*, 5508–9 (1950).

Index of Grignard Reagents

As is obvious upon inspection, the following index is self-ordered on the basis of empirical formulae. It is designed to answer for the referent questions that fall into four general categories.

1. Is there a published claim that a given Grignard reagent has been prepared or must have been present in a Barbier-type synthesis? [Presence in the index constitutes an affirmative answer. Where the evidence supporting the claim appears insufficient or questionable, or where reports of other investigators cast doubt upon the claim, the present authors have appended a question mark (?). Where the original investigator's designation of a Grignard reagent leaves doubt as to its precise identity, that designation is placed in quotation marks. Where the constitution of a Grignard reagent is uncertain or indeterminate, an explanatory footnote is appended. More or less arbitrary conventional representations of structural units in formulae that might prove unintelligible or ambiguous to the average referent are also explained in footnotes. Absence of a given Grignard reagent from the index *may* be the result of oversight, or an inevitable consequence of post-publication-deadline report.]

2. Is there in the present text a description of, or reference to a published description of, the preparation of an indexed Grignard reagent? [Affirmative answers are indicated by page-number references in Arabic numerals set in *italic* type. Incidentally, not all preparations described constitute good preparative methods.]

3. Is there in the present text discussion or mention of: (a) unique or special properties, or (b) unique or special uses, or (c) uses in significant experiments, of an indexed Grignard reagent? [Affirmative answers are indicated by page-number references in Arabic numerals set in Roman type. Mentions of nonspecific uses of individual Grignard reagents are not, in general, indexed.]

4. Are there published reports of reactions of an indexed Grignard reagent with the one or more of the more generally-used Grignard-reagent coreactants? [Affirmative answers are indicated by appropriate table-number references in Roman numerals set in Roman type. Absence of tabular record *may* be due to oversight, or to recency of report.]

*From "heptafluorobromopropane."
†From "heptafluoroïodopropane."

*From $CH_3CH{=}CHCH_2Cl$ and/or $CH_3(H_2C{=}CH)CHCl$; concerning the constitution of the butenyl Grignard reagents, see pp. 60, 1145–1157.

†From $CH_3CH{=}CHCH_2Br$ and/or $CH_3(H_2C{=}CH)CHBr$; concerning the constitution of the butenyl Grignard reagents, see pp. 60, 1145–1157.

*5-Cyclopentadienylmagnesium bromide.

†From D(+)-s-$C_4H_9CH_2Cl$.
‡From D(+)-s-$C_4H_9CH_2Br$.

*Orientation uncertain.
†From 2-$ClHgC_6H_4OH$ + C_2H_5MgBr.

---

*This compound is undoubtedly analogous to the enolates that behave as true Grignard reagents.

*From 2-ethyl-4-methylpyrrole.

*In the opinion of Schlenk, Hilleman, and Rodloff, *Ann.*, *487*, 135–54 (1951), this "Grignard reagent" should be formulated as an enolate.

†From "opsopyrrolecarboxylic acid."

---

*From 2,3-dimethyl-4-ethylpyrrole.
†From 2,4-dimethyl-3-ethylpyrrole.
‡From a mixture of $CH_3(CH_2)_4CH=CHCH_2Br$ and $H_2C=CH[CH_3(CH_2)_4]CHBr$.
§From "diisobutylene hydrochloride"; the acid obtained upon carbonation is $t\text{-}C_4H_9CH_2(CH_3)_2CCO_2H$.

*From $C_6H_5CH=CHCH_2Cl$; concerning the constitution of the cinnamyl Grignard reagents, see pp. 60, 1147–1148.

†It is possible that the supposed Grignard reagent has not been prepared. From the attempted reaction with oxalic ester only bi-α-cumyl (the Wurtz product) was isolated. Brown, Mighton, and Senkus, *J. Org. Chem.*, 3, 62–75 (1938), report an unsuccessful attempt to prepare $C_6H_5(CH_3)_2CMgCl$.

‡From "hemopyrrolecarboxylic acid."

*From 2-chloro-1,2,3,4-tetrahydronaphthalene.

†From 1-bromo-(4-methyl-3-cyclohexen-1-yl)propane.

*From 2-chlorodecalin—either stereoisomer.

†From *trans*-2-chlorodecalin.

‡From chlorinated *trans*-decalin.

§From chlorinated *cis*-decalin.

¶From chlorinated *cis*-β-decalin.

‖From pinene hydrochloride.

**From bornyl chloride.

††From (+)-α-pinene hydrochloride; Rivière, *Ann. chim.*, [12], *1*, 157–231 (1946), concludes that this reagent is an equimolecular mixture of bornyl- and isobornylmagnesium chlorides.

‡‡Prepared by refluxing in xylene for three hours at *ca.* 140° the Grignard reagent from (+)-α-pinene hydrochloride.

§§Prepared by partial (*ca.* 66%) carbonation of the Grignard reagent from (+)-α-pinene hydrochloride.

¶¶From bornyl iodide.

‖‖From 1,8-dichloro-*p*-menthane.

***R = 4-methyl-3-cyclohexen-1-yl.

†††From 5-bromo-*p*-menthane.

‡‡‡In the opinion of Schlenk, Hilleman, and Rodloff, *Ann.*, *487*, 135–54 (1931), this "Grignard reagent" should be formulated as an enolate.

*This compound is undoubtedly analogous to the enolates that behave as true Grignard reagents.

*This compound is undoubtedly analogous to the enolates that behave as true Grignard reagents.

†R = β-(2, 6, 6-trimethyl-1-cyclohexenyl)vinyl.

‡R = 2,2,6-trimethylcyclohexyl.

§$C_{12}H_8{=}$ = o-biphenylene; X = Br,I.

*From 9,10-bis-*p*-bromophenylanthracene.
†$C_{12}H_8$== = *o*-biphenylene.

‡$C_{12}H_8$=== *o*-biphenylene.

General Index

in cleavage of oxirane ring, 964–965